BERGEY'S MANUAL

OF

DETERMINATIVE BACTERIOLOGY

BERGEY'S MANUAL
OF
DETERMINATIVE
BACTERIOLOGY

BY

ROBERT S. BREED
Late Professor Emeritus, Cornell University, Geneva, New York

E. G. D. MURRAY
Research Professor, University of Western Ontario,
London, Ontario, Canada

NATHAN R. SMITH
Senior Bacteriologist, Retired, Plant Industry Station,
U. S. Department of Agriculture, Beltsville, Maryland

and

Ninety-four Contributors

Whose Names Appear on the Immediately Following Pages

SEVENTH EDITION

BALTIMORE

THE WILLIAMS & WILKINS COMPANY

1957

First Edition, August, 1923
Second Edition, December, 1925
Third Edition, January, 1930
Fourth Edition, March, 1934
Preprint of pages ix + 79 of Fifth Edition, October, 1938
Fifth Edition, April, 1939
Sixth Edition, January, 1948
Seventh Edition, October, 1957
Reprinted September, 1959
Reprinted March, 1962
Reprinted June, 1964

Made in United States of America

Library of Congress
Catalog Card Number
57-11183

COMPOSED AND PRINTED AT THE
WAVERLY PRESS, INC.
Mt. Royal and Guilford Aves.
Baltimore 2, Md., U. S. A.

LIST OF CONTRIBUTORS

† Deceased.

† Deceased.

† Deceased.

† Deceased.

PREFACE TO SEVENTH EDITION

The general format of the seventh edition of BERGEY's MANUAL OF DETERMINATIVE BACTERIOLOGY differs but little from that of the sixth edition. However, examination will reveal many changes in the content as the result of a thoroughgoing revision. Among these the following seem to be worthy of special comment.

The most obvious change is that of the separation into two volumes of the material comparable to that which appeared in the sixth edition. The present volume is entitled the seventh edition of BERGEY's MANUAL OF DETERMINATIVE BACTERIOLOGY. This MANUAL contains an outlined classification of the bacteria and the descriptions of the taxa from Class to Species and Subspecies, together with the appropriate keys. Nearly all species regarded as having been inadequately described or that could not be definitely placed have been excluded, together with many of the less important synonyms of the accepted species. These, together with the index to all the literature of both accepted and poorly described organisms have been transferred to a volume to be known as the INDEX BERGEYANA. The latter volume will include all descriptions and citations to species formerly found as appendices or indefinitely placed as *species incertae sedis*. The host and habitat index will also be found in the INDEX BERGEYANA. The net result is that the MANUAL itself contains descriptions of many more species with more adequate descriptions than have former editions; the transfer of much material to the INDEX BERGEYANA has meant a reduction in the number of pages and a book of more convenient size and greater usefulness. The INDEX BERGEYANA should prove to be an invaluable tool for the research microbiologist, containing, as it will, references to the whole field of systematic bacteriology and an index to the names of described species, both valid and invalid.

Much material of historical value and interest in the sixth and earlier editions of the MANUAL has been excluded, not because it is lacking in real value to the student, but because repetition of its publication is now unnecessary.

This edition of the MANUAL represents the coordinated results of the work of one hundred contributors, about thirty-five more than assisted in preparing the sixth edition. The contributors to the MANUAL are to be regarded in all nomenclatural matters as strictly the authors of their sections. All new names of taxa and the names of all new combinations are to be ascribed to these authors, and not to the editors of the MANUAL. Contributors from countries other than the United States are more numerous than in the earlier editions. In other words, the MANUAL is rapidly assuming the character of an international publication. To all of these contributors the sincere thanks of the Board of Editors, and particularly of the Editor-in-Chief, are due. The seventh edition is a tribute to the patience, care and scientific acumen of these individuals. Special note should be taken of the assistance rendered in the office of the Editor-in-Chief by Mr. Erwin Lessel, Miss Maude Hogan, Mrs. Eleanore Heist Clise and Mrs. Margaret Edson Breed.

The keys to the several categories of taxa (orders, families, tribes, genera and species) have been revised with a view to making them more reliable and useful. There is included also an artificial key to the species prepared by Professor V. B. D. Skerman, which key should prove helpful.

The Section on Nomenclature, including a synopsis of the Botanical Code of Nomenclature, has been eliminated. At the time of preparation of the sixth edition, the International Code of Bacteriological Nomenclature had not been finally approved, and emphasis was properly laid upon the rules used in Botany. This is no longer pertinent. The Bacteriological Code appeared in 1948 too late for use in making appropriate revisions in the 6th Edition of the MANUAL. The revised International Code of Nomenclature of the Bacteria and Viruses is about to be published. This contains annotations that should prove of value to the student, and should be regarded as a helpful aid in the understanding of the nomenclature used in the 7th Edition of the MANUAL.

The naming and classification of the viruses, as published in the sixth edition of the MANUAL, was regarded by some eminent virologists as perhaps inadvisable because it was premature. They felt strongly that the problems of morphology, physiology, pathogenesis and inter-relationships of the viruses were not as yet sufficiently resolved to make satisfactory taxonomy and classification practicable. After consultation with the International Subcommittee on Viruses it was decided that the Virus Section should not be included in the seventh edition. This deletion has been made with the full expectation that sufficient international agreement will be reached to make possible adequate treatment in the eighth edition. The Editorial Committee recognizes that a satisfactory system of nomenclature and taxonomy for the viruses is imperative.

The Editors wish to repeat and emphasize a statement made in the Preface of the first edition of the MANUAL:

"The assistance of all bacteriologists is earnestly solicited in the correction of possible errors in the text."

Among the tasks of the several editions of the MANUAL has been the codification of an increasingly satisfactory classification of the bacteria and the correction of the nomenclature of the past. The present volume undoubtedly has many errors that were not caught notwithstanding a most earnest effort. There are also many unresolved questions. Inasmuch as this volume appears at almost the same time as the Revised International Bacteriological Code, there are doubtless still some inconsistencies.

E. G. D. MURRAY
N. R. SMITH
R. S. BREED, *Chairman*
Editorial Committee

NOTE

The Board of Trustees of BERGEY's MANUAL wish to record their profound sorrow at the death on February 10, 1956, of Dr. Robert S. Breed, Chairman of the Board of Trustees and Editor-in-Chief of the MANUAL. Most regrettable is the fact that he did not live to see in printed form the results of his untiring and devoted labor. At the time of his death, most of the manuscript for the seventh edition had been placed in the hands of the publisher; the remainder was in such shape that it could be promptly submitted. The Board of Trustees of the Bergey Trust, including the Board of Editors, wish to pay tribute to the devotion, energy and skill of Dr. Breed over a period of many years, as shown in the organization of better bacterial nomenclature and classification. The science of microbiology is his debtor.

Reconciliation of the nomenclature used in the seventh edition of the MANUAL with the provisions of the revised International Code of Nomenclature of the Bacteria and Viruses had not been entirely completed by Dr. Breed. As far as possible, these discrepancies have been corrected before publication.

The death of Dr. Breed leaves the Editorial Committee without a chairman and editor-in-chief. The Board of Trustees is unanimous in the belief that a successor to Dr. Breed should be found outside its present membership. Dr. Breed was also Chairman of the Board of Trustees. Following his death, reorganization of the Board was undertaken by Dr. Conn, as Treasurer, and Dr. Buchanan was designated as Chairman. The latter has agreed to serve until publication of the seventh edition of BERGEY's MANUAL and of the first edition of the companion volume, planned by Dr. Breed and christened by him the INDEX BERGEYANA. It is recognized to be a matter of urgency and difficulty to replace Dr. Breed with an editor-in-chief for the eighth edition and to find a means of making this onerous responsibility something more than the labor of love it always was to him.

E. G. D. MURRAY
N. R. SMITH
H. J. CONN
R. E. BUCHANAN, *Chairman*
Board of Trustees

PREFACE OF FIRST EDITION

The elaborate system of classification of the bacteria into families, tribes and genera by a Committee on Characterization and Classification of the Society of American Bacteriologists (1917, 1920) has made it very desirable to be able to place in the hands of students a more detailed key for the identification of species than any that is available at present. The valuable book on "Determinative Bacteriology" by Professor F. D. Chester, published in 1901, is now of very little assistance to the student, and all previous classifications are of still less value, especially as earlier systems of classification were based entirely on morphologic characters.

It is hoped that this manual will serve to stimulate efforts to perfect the classification of bacteria, especially by emphasizing the valuable features as well as the weaker points in the new system which the Committee of the Society of American Bacteriologists has promulgated. The Committee does not regard the classification of species offered here as in any sense final, but merely a progress report leading to more satisfactory classification in the future.

The Committee desires to express its appreciation and thanks to those members of the society who gave valuable aid in the compilation of material and the classification of certain species. . . .

The assistance of all bacteriologists is earnestly solicited in the correction of possible errors in the text; in the collection of descriptions of all bacteria that may have been omitted from the text; in supplying more detailed descriptions of such organisms as are described incompletely; and in furnishing complete descriptions of new organisms that may be discovered, or in directing the attention of the Committee to publications of such newly described bacteria.

> DAVID H. BERGEY, *Chairman*
> FRANCIS C. HARRISON
> ROBERT S. BREED
> BERNARD W. HAMMER
> FRANK M. HUNTOON
> *Committee on Manual.*

August, 1923.

CONTENTS

xiii

* Erratum: Due to a clerical error the orders *Caryophanales* and *Actinomycetales* of the class *Schizomycetes* appear in the wrong sequence in numerous places throughout the MANUAL: correctly, *Caryophanales* is Order V and should appear before Order VI, *Actinomycetales* (see pages 12, 33, and 34 for reasons why *Caryophanales* precedes *Actinomycetales* in the classification scheme).

INTRODUCTION

Suggestions for the Use of the Manual In Classifying Unknown Organisms

No organism can be classified before its morphological, cultural, physiological and pathogenic characters have been determined through a detailed study.

The characters used in the keys to orders, families and genera may ordinarily be determined by the use of a dozen or more of the procedures described in the Manual of Microbiological Methods issued by the Committee on Bacteriological Technic of the Society of American Bacteriologists. More complete examinations are required in special cases to identify and to describe individual species necessitating resort to the original literature. When those prevailing are inadequate, new criteria are desirable. This desideratum extends to some higher taxa to achieve more exact and distinctive definitions.

It is urged that beginning students be taught all of the techniques necessary for the identification of species in the hope that the taxonomic work of the future may be placed on a satisfactory basis.

After a complete study of the characters of the organism has been made, either of two courses may be followed. (1) Use the Keys in the body of the text as explained below. These follow what are believed to be the natural relationships that exist between various groups of bacteria. (2) The beginning student may, however, find the artificial key at the back of the MANUAL to be more helpful than the natural keys in determining the identity of an unknown culture.

In all cases it should be kept in mind that many descriptions of species of bacteria are not mentioned in this MANUAL. Failure to find agreement between an unknown culture and any of the descriptions given in this MANUAL does not prove that the unknown culture represents a species that has never been studied and described.

If the student wishes to follow through the natural keys he should turn to page 33 and ascertain first in which order the organism belongs. When the order has been ascertained, turn to the page of the MANUAL on which the key to that order is given. In this key ascertain the family or sub-family to which the organism belongs.

When the family has been determined, again refer to the page of the MANUAL on which the key to that family is given. In this key ascertain the tribe to which the organism belongs.

When the tribe has been determined, again find the page of the MANUAL on which the key to the tribe is given. In this key ascertain the genus to which the organism belongs.

When the genus has been determined, again refer to the page of the MANUAL on which the key to that genus is given. In this key trace out the species under investigation.

For example, if one wishes to identify a short, peritrichous, Gram-negative, non-spore-forming, non-chromogenic rod that grows well on ordinary culture media at 37°C., fermenting glucose and lactose with the production of acid and gas, not liquefying gelatin, with negative reaction for acetylmethylcarbinol, citrate-negative, alginate-negative, pectinase-negative, producing indole and reducing nitrates, consult the key to the orders on page 33.

In this key examine I: *Cells rigid. Motile by means of polar flagella or non-motile.* This does not indicate our organism, which is peritrichous. We turn next to II: *Not as above.* Under A: *Cells rigid. Spherical or straight, rod-shaped cells. Occur singly, in chains or in trichomes. Motile by means of peritrichous flagella or non-motile.* These characters agree with those of the organism in question.

We turn now to 1, in the same key: *Cells spherical or rod-shaped. No trichomes, though chains of cells may occur.* This indicates that the organism in question belongs in Order IV, *Eubacteriales.*

In the key to the families of Order *Eubacteriales*, p. 281, examine I: *Cells rod-shaped. Gram-negative.* This indicates the organism in question, so we turn next to A: *Aerobic or facultatively anaerobic*, which again indicates the organism in question.

The next entry, 1: *Large, ovoid to rod-shaped cells, sometimes yeast-like in appearance. Free-living in soil. Fix free nitrogen*, does not indicate the culture under study so we turn to 2: *Not as above.*

The heading, 2: *Heterotrophic rods which may not require organic nitrogen for growth. Usually motile, with one to six flagella. Frequently form nodules or tubercles on roots of plants or show violet chromogenesis. Colonies usually large and slimy, especially on mannitol agar*, does not indicate the organism in question. We then turn to aa: *Not as above.*

Heading b: *Straight rods which grow readily on ordinary peptone media. May of may not ferment sugars anaerobically with the production of organic acids* again indicates the culture under study.

The heading c: *Glucose usually attacked oxidatively or not at all* does not indicate the organism in question as it is an active fermenter of glucose and lactose. cc: *Ferment glucose anaerobically, frequently producing visible gas from glucose, and sometimes lactose* indicates that the culture under study belongs in the Family IV, *Enterobacteriaceae.*

We now turn to the key to the tribes of family *Enterobacteriaceae*, page 334. In this key we examine I: *Lactose fermented anaerobically, usually within 48 hours.* This indicates the culture under study.

The entry A: *Prodigiosin not produced* also indicates the non-chromogenic organism in question. Likewise, 1: *Do not produce protopectinase. Not parasitic on plants* also applies to our culture, so we turn to the key to the genera of Tribe I, *Escherichieae*, page 335.

We turn now to I: *Alginic acid is not decomposed with the production of acid and gas.* This likewise indicates the organism is question. Under this, A: *Lactose is fermented within 48 hours* also indicates the culture under study, as does 1:

Acetylmethylcarbinol not produced. Methyl red test positive. Salts of citric acid may or may not be used as a sole source of carbon. This places the organism in Genus J *Escherichia.*

We turn now to the key to the species of Genus I, *Escherichia,* page 335. On tracing our organism in this key we find that its characters correspond with those of *Escherichia coli* and turn to the description of this species for a final confirmation of this identification.

It is self evident that where the characters of the original culture have not been determined accurately or completely, the identity of the unknown cannot be determined positively.

A second difficulty in the use of a key comes from inexperience in the use of technical terms; that is, the student may not thoroughly understand the meaning of the statement in the key and so cannot follow a route through the key with certainty. For example in the keys used here, the student must know the difference between (1) chains of cells which are composed of dividing cells which do not separate at once, and (2) trichomes which are composed of dividing cells which remain more permanently together and are normally flattened against each other on adjacent sides. The trichomes may show some differentiation into holdfast cells and reproductive cells (conidia). Both chains of cells and trichomes are to be distinguished from the mycelial threads found in *Actinomycetaceae*: the latter are unseptate and show true branching.

The student should be warned not to take descriptions in the Manual too literally or too rigidly. Descriptions are usually drawn to represent average findings. Especially among bacteria, characters such as sugar fermentations, gelatin liquefaction, presence or absence of flagella and other things may vary within a species. Sometimes these variations are due to slight, possibly unrecognized variations in the techniques used in determining these characters. Real knowledge of the characteristics of species may also be very incomplete. This is true not only with respect to the physiological activities of these microorganisms but also to such detectable structural features as the number and position of flagella. Dark-field movies of motile cells and photographs taken with the electron microscope are revealing new and heretofore unsuspected facts regarding structural features.

Source and habitat data are frequently helpful in aiding the student to recognize species of bacteria and may indicate that the pathogenicity of the culture in question may need to be tried on some specific animal or plant. By habitat is meant the kind of a place in which the organism normally grows; by source, the particular material and place from which the culture was obtained. This source may or may not indicate the natural habitat. The source of cultures is invariably more limited in scope than the habitat, as bacteria normally occur wherever their particular habitat may be found in a world-wide distribution.

CONSIDERATIONS INFLUENCING THE CLASSIFICATION USED IN THIS EDITION OF THE MANUAL

Robert S. Breed

Cornell University, Geneva, New York

The development of the classification systems used in the various editions of BERGEY'S MANUAL has caused those of us responsible for this work to give considerable thought to the probable evolutionary development of the living things that are included under the general terms bacteria and, more recently, viruses.

For those who are not familiar with the principles of evolution, it might be well to bear in mind that all living things, including bacteria and viruses, do but represent the present form of a long line of ancestral forms. Customarily these lines of development are thought of as being not lineal but like the twigs and branches of a tree which trace their origin back to the trunk of the tree, living species being regarded as the separate and distinct tips of the twigs.

Bacteria and viruses, endowed as they are with a simple morphology, are naturally thought of as being primordial or primitive in nature. This concept is fundamental in all systems of classification that have been developed for these organisms. Nevertheless it should not be forgotten that the different species or kinds of these morphologically simple living things now extant may have undergone many types of changes during the course of their evolutionary development. However, because bacteria and viruses do not have hard parts that fossilize, there is little that can be learned about their evolution directly from historical geology (paleontology).

It is difficult to picture the environment under which the undifferentiated, unicellular organisms lived when they first appeared on the earth, but it is certain that this environment was quite different from the environment in which similar organisms live today. One important feature of the present-day environment that would have been lacking in the earliest periods would be the association of unicellular organisms with more highly developed types of living plants and animals and with the resultant accumulation of organic materials that must take place as the natural processes of life and death go forward. Organisms which are saprophytic and, still less, those which are parasitic would not have had conditions favorable for their existence in the earliest periods in which life developed on this planet. This makes it necessary to assume that the earliest living things must have existed on comparatively simple, largely inorganic food materials. With this thought in mind, some students of the systematic relationships of living things have thought of the chemoautotrophic bacteria that still exist as being more like primordial living things than are other types of bacteria.

It is true that the chemoautotrophic organisms are able to live on simple inorganic foods that were, in all probability, available to living things under early conditions in the development of the earth. However, it does not necessarily follow that chemoautotrophic forms are the only ones that could have existed in the beginning. It seems even more reasonable to assume that early living forms developed a pigment like chlorophyll that enabled primordial bacteria to utilize the sun's energy in synthesizing organic matter. Such photosynthetic pigments are found in purple or green bacteria. These photoautotrophic forms could have existed on the simple foods available when life began as readily as could chemoautotrophic forms.

In either case, it is necessary to assume that living protoplasm, with its complex enzymatic systems, existed before primordial bacteria, which utilized inorganic materials as food. In other words, complex proteins had to be in existence before either chemoautotrophic or photoautotrophic bacteria of the types now found on the earth could exist.

Even if it is granted that photoautotrophic living things were primordial, it must also be granted that when the existence of such organisms is postulated we are not starting with the beginning of life itself. So little is known about the possibility of living proteins (protoplasm) developing out of inorganic compounds that speculation regarding this development has brought but very little information that is factual.

In the present edition of BERGEY'S MANUAL, the classification used has been rearranged on the assumption that the photoautotrophic bacteria extant today presumably are the living organisms that are most nearly like the primordial types of bacteria.

In support of this thought it should be kept in mind that the earliest living forms must necessarily have been free-living forms, not saprophytes nor parasites. This being the case, forms such as viruses that are very tiny in size and therefore necessarily of a simple structure ought not to be regarded as primitive just because of a comparatively simple structure. The viruses are adapted to life within living protoplasm, and they represent an extreme degree of specialization to a parasitic existence. They are known as organisms that invade the living cells of higher plants and animals, including man. The latter are the living things that were latest in development in geological time. Viruses could not have existed before their host plants and animals were developed.

The term "viruses" ought not to be used for the hypothetical, very tiny, free-living primordial organisms that must have existed before primordial bacteria. Some investigators feel that such organisms may still exist in some as yet unrecognized form.

It is not surprising that a great development has taken place in outline classifications since bacteriologists first tried to develop such classifications to express the possible relationships of the organisms with which they have worked. While O. F. Mueller (Animalcula infusoria et Marina. Hauniae. 1786) and C. G. Ehrenberg (Die Infusionsthierchen als vollkommende Organismen. Leipzig, 1838) made simple beginnings along this line, their knowledge of bacteria as they are known today was very limited indeed. Even in 1838, when Ehrenberg published his description of the types of organisms found in infusions, microscopes had not yet been developed to a place where even large bacteria could be studied with any satisfaction.

By 1872, Ferdinand Cohn (Untersuchungen über Bacterien. I. Beitr. z. Biol. d. Pflanzen., *1*, Heft 2, 1872, 187–222), the botanist, began to understand that a great variety of types of bacteria were in existence, and he was able to arrange an outline classification on which later classifications of bacteria have been built. However, his first outline classification of bacteria was scarcely published before he felt that he should have expressed the relationships of the bacteria to the simplest types of algae in a more intimate way. He therefore, in 1875 (Untersuchungen über Bacterien., II. *ibid.*, *1*, Heft 3, 1875, 141–207), drew up a second classification in which he integrated the known groups of bacteria with known groups of blue-green algae in a class, the *Schizophyta*. This arrangement assumed that the bacteria had a much more intimate relationship to the blue-green algae than the true fungi have to the green, red and brown algae.

It should be noted that early classifications of bacteria were based primarily upon structural characters, particularly the shape of the cells. This was a natural development, as morphological characters had been found to be useful in drawing up natural classifications of higher plants and animals. It is also quite natural that workers who drew up these classifications should have regarded the spherical organisms that they found as being primitive in nature. Little was known at that time of the distribution of bacteria in nature. It was not until later that it came to be realized that the bacteria that are spherical in shape are normally found on the skin or in secretions of skin glands (milk and other dairy products, etc.) of vertebrates. Few cocci exist as free-living forms in water or soil. Likewise, when physiological studies were made, it was found that the cocci require comparatively complex foods for their existence. Few modern classifications retain the arrangement in which cocci are placed first as suggested by Cohn in 1872.

Others have developed the early classifications* drawn up by Cohn, with many individuals contributing to the development of a better and better understanding of the evolutionary development of the bacteria. In the 1890's, two groups of individuals undertook the publication of manuals describing the known species of bacteria. These two groups exercised a great influence on the development of systematic bacteriology.

Migula (Arb. Bact. Inst., Karlsruhe, *1*, 1894, 235–238; in Engler and Prantl, Natürlichen Pflanzenfamilien, Schizophyta, 1 Teil, *1a*, 1895, 1–44) and his students began their work at Karlsruhe, Germany, in the early part of the 1890's, publishing various papers and books, the last of which was Migula's

---

* For a more detailed discussion of outline classifications developed by bacteriologists, see MANUAL, 3rd ed., 1930, 1–23; and MANUAL, 6th ed., 1948, 5–38.

System der Bakterien (Bd. 1, 1897, 368 pp.; Bd. 2, 1900, 1068 pp., Jena). Only one edition was published.

During the same period K. B. Lehmann and R. E. Neumann of Würzburg, Germany, began the publication of their Bakteriologische Diagnostik, the first edition of which was published, as were later editions, in two volumes (J. F. Lehmann Verlag, München). The first edition was soon followed by a second and later editions, the work being seriously interrupted by the first World War after the publication of the 5th edition. Following the war they republished the 5th edition with a supplement as the 6 edition and later carried through a complete revision of this text which appeared as the 7th edition in 1927. No further editions have been issued.

In the meantime, interest in taxonomic work had crystallized in the newly organized (1899) Society of American Bacteriologists, led at first by F. D. Chester. His Manual of Determinative Bacteriology, published in 1901 (The MacMillan Co., New York), had great influence in guiding the thought of American bacteriologists, but it never has been widely known outside of North America.

As the Society developed, others took an active interest in this work, among them R. E. Buchanan (Jour. Bact., *1*, 1916, 591–596; *2*, 1917, 155–164, 347–350, 603–617; *3*, 1918, 27–61, 175–181, 301–306, 403–406, 461–474, 541–545), who organized an outline classification of all bacteria as then known. This was published just as another member of the Society, C.-E. A. Winslow, who had, with his wife, completed a monographic study of the *Coccaceae* (Winslow, C. -E. A., and Winslow, A. R. Systematic relationships of the Coccaceae, 300 pp., 1908, John Wiley & Sons, New York), urged the Society to form a Committee to organize a better classification for bacteria. The Society of American Bacteriologists' Committee, of which Winslow was made Chairman, combined forces with Buchanan and published first a preliminary (Jour. Bact., *2*, 1917, 505–566) and then a final report (Jour. Bact., *5*, 1920, 191–229) on the classification of bacteria. The report of this Committee was accepted with the thought that further revisions of this outline classification were to be expected as knowledge developed.

Meanwhile in Europe, Orla-Jensen (Cent. f. Bakt., II Abt., *22*, 1909, 305–346) had made notable contributions to knowledge in this field. Still later A. J. Kluyver and C. B. van Niel (Zent. f. Bakt., II Abt., *34*, 1936, 369–403) and others continued the development of classifications of bacteria, but European workers have been badly handicapped in their work because of the chaotic conditions that have existed during two world wars fought largely in Europe.

Developments in the field of systematic bacteriology led to the publication by D. H. Bergey of a manuscript on which he had been working for a long time, his thought being that a new edition of Chester's Manual of Determinative Bacteriology was badly needed, as indeed it was. In order to aid Bergey in securing publication of his manuscript, the Society of American Bacteriologists appointed a Committee to assist him, Dr. F. C. Harrison, Chairman. The first edition of

BERGEY'S MANUAL appeared in 1923 (The Williams & Wilkins Co., Baltimore). Successive editions of this MANUAL were issued in 1925, 1930 and 1936. Before his death in 1937, Bergey requested that an Editorial Board take over future editions of BERGEY'S MANUAL.

At the same time, Bergey used the accumulated royalties that had previously been placed in the custody of the Society of American Bacteriologists to organize the so-called BERGEY'S MANUAL Trust. The publication of the 5th and 6th editions of BERGEY'S MANUAL has been carried out by the Trustees of this Trust, who, by the provisions of the Deed of Trust, must always be men trained as bacteriologists. The Board of Trustees consisted at first of Dr. D. H. Bergey, Professor R. S. Breed and Professor E. G. D. Murray. Dr. A. Parker Hitchens was elected to this Board after Dr. Bergey's death, when Professor Breed was made Chairman of the Board.

Because of the truly enormous development of our knowledge of bacteria, viruses and related organisms, the Editorial Board asked students of special groups to assist in the revisions of the groups in which they were interested. Thus more than 40 specialists assisted in the preparation of the 5th edition, and more than 60 individuals in the preparation of the 6th edition of the Manual. Canadian bacteriologists as well as bacteriologists from the U. S. A. have participated in the MANUAL work from the beginning. This participation by Canadian workers has increased during the preparation of the manuscript for the 7th edition, as has the participation from other countries. Fourteen countries are represented among the more than 100 specialists who have contributed to the 7th edition of the MANUAL.

After the death of Dr. A. Parker Hitchens, Dr. N. R. Smith was appointed to the Board of Trustees and to the Editorial Board of the Manual, and shortly thereafter the Board of Trustees was made a board of five members by the election of Dr. R. E. Buchanan and Dr. Harold J. Conn to this Board.

In preparing manuscripts for the present edition of BERGEY'S MANUAL, specialists have found many places where the relationships of described species of bacteria have not been well presented in the literature. Consequently, they have been stimulated to publish many papers reporting their findings. The individual specialists have normally been persons who have actively worked with cultures of the organisms that belong to the group for which they have prepared the manuscript. Thus the development of the present edition of the MANUAL has stimulated much research in the field of systematic bacteriology that would never have been accomplished under other conditions. It is hoped that in the future the BERGEY'S MANUAL Trust can become a center for research in the field of systematic bacteriology and virology. The work thus far accomplished has been carried out largely by volunteer workers. If adequate funds were available for the support of such work its value could be greatly increased.

Out of studies by specialists of the accumulated knowledge of the systematic relationships of the microorganisms considered in BERGEY'S MANUAL OF DETER-MINATIVE BACTERIOLOGY, the three of us chiefly responsible for organizing this work (Professor R. S. Breed, Professor E. G. D. Murray and Dr. N. R. Smith) have developed an outline classification which expresses our ideas of the relationships of the simplest types of living things. These are represented by such common terms as true bacteria, filamentous bacteria, actinomycetes, slime bacteria, spirochetes, rickettsias and related larger viruses and the filterable viruses. This general classification also expresses our ideas of the relationships of these undifferentiated types of living things to higher plants.

This outline may not express the views of other special students of this subject adequately, as all such outlines represent compromises between differing viewpoints. One such difference of viewpoint that has been discussed among the three of us chiefly responsible for the outline given here has been the question whether a third kingdom, the *Protophyta* as defined below, ought not to be recognized in addition to the Plant and Animal Kingdoms. Prof. E. G. D. Murray has been the one in our group who has felt most strongly that the bacteria and related organisms are so different from plants and animals that they should be grouped in a kingdom equal in rank with these kingdoms. It is quite probable that support for this viewpoint would be stronger if early biologists had known how different these important and widely diversified microorganisms are from plants and animals. Even today it must be recognized that our knowledge of the number of kinds of bacteria is growing rapidly as habitats not previously adequately explored are studied. The human body is, as a matter of fact, practically the only habitat that has been comprehensively studied as a source of bacteria. Even in this case it is the bacteria that cause diseases that are best known.

Our knowledge of the still smaller types of parasitic and pathogenic organisms such as the numerous kinds of organisms found in the *Rickettsiales* and *Virales* is still more inadequate than our knowledge of the true bacteria. In fact our present-day knowledge of the filterable viruses could perhaps best be compared with Cohn's knowledge of the bacteria when he first drew up a system of classification for bacteria in 1872.

Three groups are included in the outline presented here: (a) the blue-green algae, (b) bacteria and related forms, and (c) the rickettsias and viruses. These are placed in a single division of the plant kingdom for which the term *Protophyta* has been used. This name was suggested by a botanist, Sachs (Lehrbuch der Botanik, 4 Aufl., 926 pp., Wilhelm Engelmann, Leipzig). Recently Sachs' concept of this group has been developed further by a Russian systematist, N. A. Krassilnikov (Guide to the Bacteria and Actinomycetes (Russian), Izd. Akad. Nauk, Moskau, U.S.S.R., 1949, 830 pp.), and it is developed still further in the present edition of the MANUAL.

Of the three names used for the different classes of *Protophyta*, *Schizomycetes* was suggested by von Naegeli (Bericht über der Verhandlungen der bot. Section der 33 Versammlung deutscher Naturforscher und Ärzter. Bot. Ztng., *15*, 1857, 760) and *Schizophyceae* by Cohn (Jahresber. Schles. Ges. f. vaterl. Cultur f. 1879, 279-289), and these have been generally used. The development of our knowledge of the rickettsias and viruses is so recent that no truly satisfactory class name has previously been suggested for this entire group. This has caused Dr. C. B. Philip, who has acted as editor of the section covering rickettsias and related species in the present (7th) edition of the MANUAL, to suggest the name *Microtatobiotes* for Class III. The latter is a more appropriate name for the entire group of organisms included in the orders *Rickettsiales* and *Virales* than any that has previously been suggested. Dr. Philip has discussed the new developments in the classification of the order *Rickettsiales* in a recent paper (Canadian Jour. Microbiol., *2*, 1956, 261). Therefore the present discussion is limited to an explanation of the reasons for increasing the number of orders recognized in Class II, *Schizomycetes* von Naegeli, from five to ten.

The organisms placed in Class II, *Schizomycetes* von Naegeli, in the 6th edition were arranged in five orders as follows:

Division I. *Schizophyta* Cohn, 1875. (Fission plants.)
    Class   I. *Schizophyceae* Cohn, 1879. (Fission algae. Blue-green algae.)
    Class II. *Schizomycetes* von Naegeli, 1857. (Fission fungi, bacteria.)
       Order   I. *Eubacteriales* Buchanan, 1917 (The true bacteria.)
       Order II. *Actinomycetales* Buchanan, 1917. (The mycobacteria, actinomyces, streptomyces and related forms.)
       Order III. *Chlamydobacteriales* Buchanan, 1917. (The alga-like, filamentous bacteria.)
       Order IV. *Myxobacteriales* Jahn, 1911. (The slime bacteria.)
       Order V. *Spirochaetales* Buchanan, 1918. (The spirochetes and related forms.)

Supplements: Groups whose relationships were regarded as uncertain.
    Group   I. Order *Rickettsiales* Buchanan and Buchanan, 1938, *emend.* Gieszczykiewicz, 1939. (Rickettsias and related organisms.)
    Group II. Order *Virales* Breed, Murray and Hitchens, 1944. (Filterable viruses.)
    Group III. Family *Borrelomycetaceae* Turner, 1935. (Pleuro-pneumonia-like organisms.)

This outline as given above is similar to the outline followed in earlier editions of the MANUAL and is based upon the outline classification developed by Buchanan (*op. cit.*) in 1916–18. It is expanded in the present edition of the MANUAL as follows:

Division I. *Protophyta* Sachs, 1874, *emend.* Krassilnikov, 1949.* (Primitive plants.)
    Class I. *Schizophyceae* Cohn, 1879. (Blue-green algae.)
    Class II. *Schizomycetes* von Naegeli, 1857. (Bacteria and related forms.)
       Order   I. *Pseudomonadales* Orla-Jensen, 1921.
       Order   II. *Chlamydobacteriales* Buchanan, 1917.
       Order III. *Hyphomicrobiales* Douglas, 1956.
       Order IV. *Eubacteriales* Buchanan, 1917.

---

* *Protophyta* was previously used by Endlicher, S. (Genera Plantarum, Vindobonae, 1836, p. 1) in two different senses: (1) for Sectio I, Algae and Lichens of his Regio I *Thallophyta*, (2) for Cohors II of his Sectio III, *Acrobrya*, to include horse tails, ferns, etc. This use may be disregarded under Article 26 of the International Code of Botanical Nomenclature. This reads: "The rules of priority and typification do not apply to names of taxa above the rank of orders.".

Order   V. *Actinomycetales* Buchanan, 1917.
Order   VI. *Caryophanales* Peshkoff, 1940.
Order VII. *Beggiatoales* Buchanan, 1956.
Order VIII. *Myxobacterales* Jahn, 1911.
Order   IX. *Spirochaetales* Buchanan, 1918.
Order   X. *Mycoplasmatales* Freundt, 1955.
Class III. *Microtatobiotes* Philip, 1955.
    Order I. *Rickettsiales* Buchanan and Buchanan, 1938, *emend.* Gieszczy-
    kiewicz, 1939.
    Order II. *Virales* Breed, Murray and Hitchens, 1944.
Division II. *Thallophyta* Endlicher, 1836.
Division III. *Bryophyta* Haeckel, 1866.
Division IV. *Pteridophyta* Haeckel, 1866.
Division V. *Spermatophyta* Goebel, 1882.*

It has been felt desirable to subdivide the Order *Eubacteriales*, as defined in the 6th edition of the MANUAL, into Order I, *Pseudomonadales*, which includes all of the polar-flagellate types of true bacteria, and Order IV, *Eubacteriales*, which includes the peritrichous types of true bacteria. As in the 6th edition, the photosynthetic purple and green bacteria that are polar flagellate have been included in the order with the colorless polar-flagellate bacteria. This arrangement emphasizes a concept first introduced into the classification of bacteria by Migula (Arb. Bact. Inst. Karlsruhe, *1*, 1894, 235–238). This concept is analogous to the concept used by protozoologists who recognize the orders *Flagellata* and *Infusoria* in *Protozoa*.

Bacteriologists have recognized differences between polar flagellate and peritrichous bacteria ever since Migula emphasized them, but there has always been a residual protest against drawing a sharp line between the two groups of bacteria. While there is good reason to draw a sharp line between the ordinary polar flagellate types of bacteria and the peritrichous types, there are certain groups such as legume nodule bacteria (*Rhizobium*), the violet bacteria (*Chromobacterium*), the agrobacteria (*Agrobacterium*) and certain motile forms placed in the family *Corynebacteriaceae* that present a type of peritrichous flagellation that, when studied superficially, is misleading. Some cultures of these organisms are found to show only a single flagellum, while others closely related to these monotrichous species show several flagella peritrichously arranged. On casual examination these conditions appear to form a transition between the two types of flagellation. However, this clearly is not the case. This apparently intermediate type of flagellation seems to be a comparatively recent development in which the flagella of certain peritrichously flagellated species have undergone a retrogressive specialization. In this the organisms have become primarily dependent on one flagellum as their chief organ of locomotion. They therefore are included in Order IV, *Eubacteriales*, with other peritrichous bacteria.

---

* Goebel, K., in his edition of Sach's Grundzüge der Systematik und speciellen Pflanzenmorphologie, p. 334, 1882, was apparently the first author to use this name, although he used the incorrect spelling *Spermaphyta*.

Eubacteriales is defined to include not only the bacteria that are peritrichously flagellated but also such non-motile forms as seem by their physiology to be closely related to these peritrichous species.

The placing of non-motile species of bacteria in systems of classification has always caused difficulty. Some students think that lack of motility is a character which should be used as a basis for separation of groups. However, evidence is continually accumulating that indicates that separation of larger groups among the bacteria solely by means of motility or lack of motility leads to a violent disarrangement of natural groupings. Some non-motile bacteria present fundamental physiologies and other characters that show that they are much like certain polar flagellate organisms. Such non-motile species are placed in the classification used here in Order I, *Pseudomonadales*. However, where non-motile species show fundamental physiologies and other characters more like those of peritrichous species, then they have been placed in Order IV, *Eubacteriales*. Organisms living in habitats where they are unable to use organs of locomotion are usually found to be non-motile. This is very natural from the standpoint of evolution.

Some bacteria develop into trichomes, which may be defined as chains (filaments) of bacteria where the relationship between the cells in the chain have become so intimate that the cells rarely live a separate, independent existence. Sometimes the cells in the chain show a differentiation into hold-fast cells and/or reproductive cells distinct from the usual vegetative cells. This differentiation resembles that found among the simpler algae. Because the cells in these trichomes sometimes develop flagella that are placed singly or in a tuft near or at the pole of the cell, while others develop cells with peritrichous flagella, it has been felt desirable to recognize two orders among these bacteria that occur in trichomes: Order II, *Chlamydobacteriales*, for the polar flagellate types and Order VI, *Caryophanales*, for the peritrichous types. Some non-motile species occur in these orders also.

Little is known about the relationships of certain species of bacteria which show a budding form of reproduction that is different from the simple cell division (fission) that takes place in the four orders previously discussed. Only a few of these species that reproduce by budding are well known, though some of them occur abundantly in suitable habitats. Because the indications are that many species of these organisms exist in nature, Prof. H. C. Douglas has set these apart in a new order, *Hyphomicrobiales*, p. 276. Where flagellation has been observed among these budding forms, it is of the polar type so that Order III has been associated with Order I, *Pseudomonadales*, and Order II, *Chlamydobacteriales*, in the arrangement of the 10 orders as given above.

Until recently everyone has thought of Order V, *Actinomycetales*, as including species all of which were non-motile.* However Couch, in a series of papers, the latest published in 1955 (Jour. Elisha Mitchell Sci. Soc., *71*, 1955, 148–155),

---

* Also see footnote p. 713 for a discussion of motility in species of *Nocardia* by H. L. Jensen.

has shown that microorganisms that belong in this order sometimes exist in water rather than as pathogens affecting animals or plants or in soil. These water-inhabiting, saprophytic types of *Actinomycetes* have developed sporangia in which motile or non-motile spores may develop. In a way they are analogous to the so-called water molds. The structure of the vegetative cells and mycelia of these water-inhabiting *Actinomycetes* is like that of the aerobic *Actinomycetes*.

Order VII, *Beggiatoales*, has been organized by Dr. R. E. Buchanan, page 837, to include a group of bacteria, primarily ocurring in trichomes, that are motile but which lack flagella. In spite of this lack they have the power to glide, roll or oscillate as do certain species of blue-green algae. While none of these bacterial types develop photosynthetic pigments, they are frequently and apparently quite properly regarded as colorless, saprophytic forms of blue-green algae. Certain species oxidize sulfur compounds with the liberation of free sulfur granules. Some specialists prefer to transfer this group to Class I, *Schizophyceae*, as colorless species of blue-green algae rather than to include them with Class II, *Schizomycetes*. As bacteriologists have been primarily responsible for developing our knowledge of the species in this order, they are retained here in Class II, *Schizomycetes*.

Our knowledge of Order VIII, *Myxobacterales*, the so-called slime bacteria, was first developed by botanists rather than bacteriologists. These organisms occur in leaf mold and on the dung of animals. Recently species causing diseases of fish have been found. The cells of these species move with a flexuous motion in a slime which normally grows up into fruiting bodies large enough to be visible to the naked eye.

The organisms placed in Order IX, *Spirochaetales*, have always been set off by themselves though certain species are known that are so much like other species of bacteria placed in the genus *Spirillum* in Order I, *Pseudomonadales*, that they may be regarded as transitional forms. Sometimes, without sufficient justification, these spirally twisted organisms have been placed among the *Protozoa*.

The tenth order of Class II, *Schizomycetes*, is the newly organized Order X, *Mycoplasmatales* Freundt. Because a review of the nomenclature of the pleuropneumonia-like organisms (Buchanan, Cowan and Wikén, Internat. Bull. Bact. Nomen. and Taxon., *5*, 1955, 13–20) has shown that the first generic name applied to these organisms that has a legitimate standing is *Mycoplasma* Nowak (Ann. Inst. Past., *43*, 1929, 1330–1352), this name has been adopted for use in the classification of the pleuropneumonia-like organisms that has been prepared by Freundt (Internat. Bull. Bact. Nomen. and Taxon., *5*, 1955, 67–78). This generic name has also been used by Edward (Internat. Bull. Bact. Nomen. and Taxon., *5*, 1955, 85–93). While other order names, such as *Borrelomycetales* Turner (Jour. Path. and Bact., *41*, 1935, 1–32), have been suggested, the generic name *Borrelomyces* Turner on which the order name is founded has never come into general use, and *Borrelomyces* is in fact an illegitimate homonym of *Mycoplasma* Nowak. Acceptance of the order name *Mycoplasmatales* is in accordance with the principles of the Bacteriological Code of Nomenclature, and it should tend to stabilize the nomenclature of this group.

In closing this discussion of the revised classification, it should again be emphasized that it has been developed as a result of a study of the ideas which previous workers have expressed in preparing the outlines that they have suggested. Previous workers have laid what appears, with our present knowledge, to be a satisfactory foundation on which to build. The introduction of new ideas has come about largely as a result of continuous study of the literature and conferences with our colleagues, including the specialists who have contributed and are contributing so much to the knowledge that has accumulated in past years. A generous share of the credit for the things that constitute a real advance in our knowledge should go to these specialists. Where the classification here presented has defects, it is to be hoped that they will be discovered promptly and eliminated.

HOW BACTERIA ARE NAMED AND IDENTIFIED

Prof. R. E. Buchanan

Dean of Graduate School (Emeritus) and Director of Experiment Station (Emeritus), Iowa State College, Ames, Iowa

A manual of determinative bacteriology, such as the present volume, has several important functions. These should be recognized and understood by the student if he is to use the volume with satisfaction.

First, the manual should list and describe all the kinds (species) of bacteria and viruses known through adequate publication in bacteriology or virology. Obviously, however, only those organisms that have usable published descriptions can be included.

Second, the manual should arrange the descriptions of the kinds (species) in smaller or larger groups (*taxa*, singular, *taxon*) on the basis of resemblances and differences in an effort to show inter-relationships.

Third, the manual should indicate for each species its correct name, likewise the correct name for each group (taxon) of related species.

That branch of biology which has for its purpose the orderly arrangement of the descriptions of species and other taxa, together with the application of the correct names, is termed *taxonomy*.

The manual, through its *indices*, should enable the student who knows the correct name of an organism (or even a synonym of such name) to discover the description of the organism and its characteristics, as well as something of its relationships. If, on the other hand, he has an organism whose characteristics and description he has determined or recorded, but whose name and relationships he does not know, a satisfactory manual, through its *keys*, should enable him to determine the correct name, its probable relationships and its position in a classification.

Nomenclature. The necessity for applying names to species or kinds of bacteria and to groups of inter-related organisms is self-evident. A name given by one person should be understood by others, and as far as practicable all individuals should use the same name for the same kind of organism. It is helpful, therefore, if there can be agreement regarding the method of naming bacteria and agreement as to the correct name for each kind or species. *Nomenclature* includes all discussions as to methods of naming and of the correctness of particular names.

What kinds of names are used. Two kinds of names are commonly given to the different species of plants and animals, (1) the common, provincial, vernacular or *casual* names and (2), the international or *scientific* names. These should be carefully differentiated, and their respective advantages and disadvantages noted.

It is inevitable, and on the whole probably desirable, that for each kind of

15

familiar animal or plant in each language there will be coined a name. Usually the name for the same organism will be different in each language. For example, we have in English *Oak*, in German *Eiche*, in Latin *Quercus*, etc. For many less common kinds, however, there may be no such vernacular names developed. There have been, of course, many casual or vernacular names given to kinds of bacteria. In English we speak of the tubercle bacillus, the typhoid germ, the gonococcus, the Welch bacillus, the golden pus coccus, and many others. Similarly, we find in German Typhusbazillus and in French bacille typhique, enterocoque, etc. Not infrequently scientific names may be adopted into a modern language and converted into vernacular names. For example, the English name *aster* and the scientific generic name *Aster* are applied to the same group. This is frequently a convenience, and in general this practice is to be commended. For example, many of the "scientific" generic names used in bacteriology are also used as names in English and other languages. This adaptation is particularly convenient when the organisms in the group under discussion are of importance and are frequently referred to in the literature. Custom and nomenclatural rules suggest certain discretion and appropriateness in the use of these casual or vernacular names. The following suggestions, based upon nomenclatural precedent and custom, should prove useful to the student.

1. The name of a genus is a noun in the singular. It is not a collective noun and should never be used with a plural verb. Do not use such an expression as "The *Salmonella* are abundant."

2. However, custom since the beginning of binomial nomenclature has sanctioned the use of the plural of generic names. One may say "The *Salmonellae* (*Corynebacteria, Rhizobia, Sarcinae, Bacilli*) are." These Latin plurals are used with the meaning "The species of the genus *Salmonella* (etc.) are." They do not connote the existence of more than one genus *Salmonella*.

3. Custom has also sanctioned the use of the generic name in the singular in an expression such as "This *Sarcina* is yellow" with the meaning "This species of *Sarcina* is yellow."

4. The Latin plural of a generic name should be employed whenever the name is used as indicated in 2 above. "The *Salmonellas* or *Sarcinas* are . . ." should be avoided because of the use of the English plural endings.

5. An English (vernacular) name may be coined from any generic name. This is done usually only for genera that are under lengthy discussion or of considerable economic significance.

6. An English, or vernacular, name of a genus may be used also in the plural, as in "the corynebacteria are . . ." with the meaning "The species of corynebacterium under consideration." When a Latin generic name is converted into the English vernacular, either the English or the Latin plural may be used. Perhaps the Latin plural is the better choice, but one finds "The salmonellas are . . . ." Note that when used as a vernacular (English) word the generic name is never regarded as a proper noun and is not capitalized or italicized.

More than one form of a name may be derived in English (vernacular) from a generic name. A member of the genus *Spironema* may be termed a spironema or a spironeme, a member of the genus *Streptomyces* a streptomyces or a streptomycete.

7. A genus includes usually several to many species; it is the name of a group of species. The expression "The genus *Salmonella* is . . ." or "*Salmonella* is . . ." should always be preferred to such ambiguous phrases as "The *Salmonella* group is."

In contrast to common, vernacular or casual names, the scientific name for each kind of organism is planned to be the same in all countries and in all languages. When a correct scientific name is used, no question should arise in any language as to what organism is intended. The names thus applied are supposed to conform to certain general rules.

International codes of nomenclature. In order that there be correct scientific names, it is essential that there be international agreement as to the rules governing their creation. Botanists and zoologists have met in numerous international congresses in which delegates were accredited from the great botanical and zoological societies, museums and educational institutions of the world. Codes of nomenclature, designed to tell how names of taxa should be published and to list the criteria of correctness, have been developed. These codes or lists of rules and recommendations are quite similar in essentials for botany and zoology, although they differ in some details.

The question arose in bacteriology: Are either or both of these codes satisfactory or adaptable to the use of microbiologists? Three views have been expressed by various writers. Some few suggested that the naming of bacteria cannot well conform to the approved international rules as their classification involves considerations not familiar to botanists and zoologists generally. The second group insisted that unicellular forms of life are neither plants nor animals, but *Protista*, and that taxonomic rules, etc., should be distinct for this group and coordinate with the corresponding rules for plants and for animals. The third view, more commonly expressed, was that the bacteria are sufficiently closely related to the plants and animals so that (in so far as they apply) the international agreements of the botanists (or zoologists) should be used as a basis for naming them.

International opinion on this topic was finally crystallized by resolutions adopted by the First International Congress of the International Society for Microbiology held in Paris in 1930. These resolutions, approved also by the plenary session of the International Society for Microbiology, were in part as follows:

"It is clearly recognized that the living forms with which the microbiologists concern themselves are in part plants, in part animals, and in part primitive. It is further recognized that *in so far as they may be applicable and appropriate* the nomenclatural codes agreed upon by International Congresses of Botany and Zoology should be followed in the naming of micro-organisms. Bearing in mind, however, the peculiarly independent course of development that bacteriology has taken in the past fifty years, and the elaboration of special descriptive criteria which bacteriologists have of necessity developed, it is the opinion of the International Society for Microbiology that the bacteria constitute a group for which special arrangements are necessary. Therefore the International Society for Microbiology has decided to consider the subject of bacterial nomenclature as a part of its permanent program."

The International Society established a permanent Nomenclature Committee to pass upon suggestions and to make recommendations. This committee is composed of members (about 100 in all) from the participating nations. Two permanent secretaries were named, one to represent primarily medical and veterinary bacteriology, and one to represent other phases of bacteriology.*

It soon became apparent that the botanical and zoological codes of nomenclature included many items having no significance in bacteriology and virology and that bacterial and viral nomenclature required special consideration.

In 1936, at the London International Microbiological Congress, it was decided that an independent, but closely integrated, Code of Bacteriological Nomenclature be developed. In 1939, at the next International Congress, a Judicial Commission of fourteen was appointed and directed to prepare a code for consideration at the next Congress. The International Code of Bacteriological Nomenclature prepared by the Commission was approved in 1947 by the International Committee and by the plenary session of the Copenhagen Congress. These rules were published in English in March, 1948,† and later in French, Spanish, German and Japanese.

The Code was amended at Rio de Janeiro in 1950 and at Rome in 1953. The present code should be accessible to all bacteriologists and virologists. It has been edited and annotated by the Editorial Board of the Judicial Commission.‡ It should be consulted by all who wish to determine the correctness of names used in the literature and by those who describe new species or other taxa.

Some general principles of nomenclature. Every student of bacteriology should be familiar with certain rules of nomenclature if he is to use names intelligently. If he wishes to correct names improperly used or if he desires to name new species, some additional rules should be observed:

1. Each distinct kind of bacterium is called a species.

2. To each distinct species a name is given consisting usually of two Latin words, as *Bacillus subtilis.*

3. The first word is the name of the genus or group to which the organism belongs. It is *always* written with a capital letter. It is a Latin or latinized Greek

---

* The permanent secretary for medical and veterinary bacteriology at the present time is Dr. S. T. Cowan, National Collection of Type Cultures, Central Public Health Laboratory, Colindale Avenue, London, N.W. 9, England. The permanent secretary for general bacteriology at the present time is Dr. T. Wikén, Laboratory for Microbiology, Technical University, Delft, Holland.

† International Bacteriological Code of Nomenclature. Edited by R. E. Buchanan, R. St. John-Brooks and R. S. Breed. Jour. Bact., *55*, 1948, 287–306.

‡ In press, 1956.

word, or a new word compounded from Latin or Greek stems, or it may be derived from some other language; but whatever its origin, *when used as a generic name, it must be regarded as a Latin noun.* If it is a word not found in classic Latin, it is still to be treated as Latin. Some examples of generic names in bacteriology which are Latin or which are formed from Latin roots are: *Bacillus* (masculine) a small rod; *Cristispira* (feminine) a crested spiral; *Lactobacillus* (masculine) a milk small rod; *Sarcina* (feminine) a packet or bundle. Many others are words from the Greek or are compounded from Greek roots, the words transliterated into Latin letters and with endings modified in conformity with Latin usage; some words of Greek origin are *Micrococcus* (masculine) a small grain (sphere); *Bacterium* (neuter) a small rod; *Clostridium* (neuter) a small spindle; *Corynebacterium* (neuter) clubbed small rod; *Actinomyces* (masculine) ray fungus. Other generic names have been given in honor of persons or places as *Beggiatoa* (feminine), *Borrelia* (feminine), *Eberthella* (feminine), *Pasteurella* (feminine), *Erwinia* (feminine), *Zopfius* (masculine).

4. The second word in the scientific name of a species is a *specific epithet.* It is *not* capitalized (some authors capitalize species names derived from proper nouns). The specific epithet may be:

(a) An adjective modifying the noun and indicating by its ending agreement with the generic name in gender, as *Bacterium album* (white *Bacterium*), *Bacillus albus* (white *Bacillus*), *Sarcina alba* (white *Sarcina*), *Eberthella dispar* (different *Eberthella*), *Bacterium variabile* (variable *Bacterium*), *Brucella melitensis* (maltese *Brucella*), *Bacillus teres* (rounded *Bacillus*), *Bacillus graveolens* (sweet-smelling *Bacillus*).

Typical adjectives

	Masculine	Feminine	Neuter
white	*albus*	*alba*	*album*
black	*niger*	*nigra*	*nigrum*
delicate	*tener*	*tenera*	*tenerum*
sharp	*acer*	*acris*	*acre*
variable	*variabilis*	*variabilis*	*variabile*
different	*dispar*	*dispar*	*dispar*
like a berry	*coccoides*	*coccoides*	*coccoides*
gas-forming	*aerogenes*	*aerogenes*	*aerogenes*

(b) An adjective in the form of the present participle of a verb, as *Clostridium dissolvens* (the dissolving *Clostridium*, in the sense of the *Clostridium* which is able to dissolve), *Bacillus adhaerens* (the adhering *Bacillus*), *Acetobacter ascendens* (the climbing *Acetobacter*), *Bacillus esterificans* (the ester-producing *Bacillus*). The endings for present participles used as adjectives are the same for all genders. The past participle is used occasionally, as in *Pseudomonas aptata* (the adapted *Pseudomonas*), *Spirillum attenuatum* (the attenuated *Spirillum*).

(c) A noun in the genitive (possessive) modifying the generic name. There is no necessary agreement in gender or number. Examples, *Clostridium welchii*

(Welch's *Clostridium*), *Salmonella pullorum* (the *Salmonella* of chicks), *Streptococcus lactis* (the *Streptococcus* of milk), *Brucella abortus* (the *Brucella* of abortion), *Clostridium tetani* (the *Clostridium* of tetanus), *Diplococcus pneumoniae* (the *Diplococcus* of pneumonia), *Salmonella anatum* (the *Salmonella* of ducks).

(d) A noun in apposition, that is, an explanatory noun. This does not agree necessarily with the generic name in gender. This method of naming is relatively uncommon in bacteriology. Examples are *Actinomyces scabies* (the scurf or scab *Actinomyces*), *Bacillus lacticola* (the milk-dweller *Bacillus*), *Rhizobium radicicola* (the root-dweller *Rhizobium*), *Salmonella london* (The London *Salmonella*).

5. The author of the name of a taxon is often cited by having his name follow that of the species, as *Bacillus subtilis* Cohn. Sometimes the name of another author is indicated also in parentheses, as *Micrococcus luteus* (Schroeter) Cohn. This means that Schroeter first named the species, giving it the specific epithet *luteum*, (placing it in the genus *Bacteridium*). Cohn transferred it to the genus *Micrococcus*. It should be noted that the name of a person following that of an organism frequently is not that of the individual who first discovered or described it, but of the person who first gave it the accepted name. For example, *Clostridium welchii* (Migula) Holland was first described by Dr. Wm. H. Welch, but not named by him. It was named by Migula in honor of Dr. Welch and later placed in the genus *Clostridium* by Holland.

6. Sometimes species of bacteria are subdivided into subspecies or varieties. These are likewise given Latin designations, and the entire name written, as: *Streptococcus lactis* subspecies (var.) *maltigenes* (the *Streptococcus* of milk producing malt flavor), or merely *Streptococcus lactis maltigenes*.

Some principles of taxonomy. The student of bacteriology should recognize the meaning of certain terms used regularly in classifications.

(1) **Species** (plural **species**). A species of plant (or animal) is assumed above to be one kind of plant. But how much difference must exist between two cultures of bacteria before one is justified in regarding the organisms in them as being of distinct kinds or species? No rule can be laid down. It depends largely upon convenience and upon more or less arbitrary but considered decision. As stated by Hitchcock (Descriptive Systematic Botany, New York, 1925, p. 8): "The unit of classification is a coherent group of like individuals, called a species. The term is difficult to define with precision because a species is not a definite entity, but a taxonomic concept." Hucker and Pederson (New York Agric. Exper. Sta. Tech. Bull. 167, 1930, p. 39) state: "The difficulty met with among these lower forms in dividing them into well-defined groups has led many to question whether these small groups of 'species' are natural groups and whether such groups can be considered to be similar to 'species' among higher forms. However this may be, it is necessary to arrange bacteria as well as possible into groups or so-called 'species' for convenience in classification," and again (Hucker, New York Agric. Exper. Sta. Tech. Bull. 100, 1924, p. 29), "characters applicable to the differentiation of species must evidence a certain amount of constancy when studied over a large series of tests. Furthermore, characters adapted

to the differentiation of larger natural groups or genera should, in addition to constancy, show some correlation with other constant characteristics. The presence of this relationship or correlation between characters for the division of genera indicates that the groupings are being made along natural rather than artificial lines."

Type culture. It is quite evident that when a new species of bacterium is described, it must include the particular culture from which the species description was made. This original culture is termed the *type culture.* One may develop a definition as follows: A species of bacterium *is* the type culture or specimen together with all other cultures or specimens regarded by an investigator as sufficiently like the type (or sufficiently closely related to it) to be grouped with it. It is self-evident that different investigators may not draw the same boundaries for a given species. There are some practical difficulties, but no better definition has been evolved.

(2) **Genus** (plural **genera**). A genus is a group of related species. In some cases a genus may include only a single species (is said to be monotypic); in most cases several to many species are included in a genus. The quite pertinent question should be asked: How close must be the resemblances (how close the relationships) among the species of a group to entitle them to inclusion in the same genus? In other words, how is it possible to delimit accurately the boundaries of a genus? This is a matter on which there is no agreement, and probably can be none. Much of the confusion in modern bacteriological terminology is to be attributed to this fact. Nevertheless, in the course of time experience tends to delimit many genera with reasonable accuracy. As stated by Hitchcock (Descriptive Systematic Botany, New York, 1925, p. 9): "Convenience may play a role in determining generic lines. Extremely large groups may be broken up on the basis of differences of smaller degree not common to a group of closely allied species, than if the group consisted of a few species. In general, the botanist, in delimiting genera, keeps in mind two important requirements, that of showing natural affinities and that of aiding correct identification."

However, a genus may be defined helpfully in another way. One of the species described as belonging to a genus is designated as the *type* species; a genus may therefore be defined as including this type species together with such other species as the investigator (or taxonomist) regards as sufficiently closely related. It is apparent that some authors may draw the lines narrowly, others broadly. Some early authors, for example, recognize only two genera of rod-shaped bacteria, one for those without endospores (*Bacterium*), and one for those producing endospores (*Bacillus*). These genera thus defined are very large, each containing hundreds, perhaps thousands, of species. Other students break up these large genera into many smaller ones. There is not much point to the question as to which is right and which is wrong. A better question is, which is the more convenient, better represents relationships, better facilitates diagnosis, and proves most useful.

(3) **Family.** A family in taxonomy is a group of related genera one of which

is designated as the type genus. In general the name of the family is formed from the name of the type genus by affixing the suffix -aceae to the stem of the generic name. The word is plural. Among bacterial families commonly recognized are *Bacillaceae*, named from its type genus, *Bacillus, Pseudomonadaceae* from *Pseudomonas, Spirochaetaceae* from *Spirochaeta, Actinomycetaceae* from *Actinomyces* and *Spirillaceae* from *Spirillum*.

(4) **Order.** An order is a group of related families. It is usually named by substituting the suffix -ales for -aceae in the name of the type family. Among ordinal names that have been used in bacteriology are *Actinomycetales, Spirochaetales, Myxobacterales.*

(5) **Class.** A class is a group of related orders. In this treatise the bacteria are treated as constituting the class *Schizomycetes* in Division I., *Protophyta*, of the plant kingdom.

(6) **Other categories.** Other *categories* or *ranks* of names are used for higher groups. Sometimes families are divided into sub-families, these into tribes, these into subtribes, and these finally into genera.

How to identify an organism by name. One of the purposes of this MANUAL OF DETERMINATIVE BACTERIOLOGY, as noted previously, is to facilitate the finding of the correct scientific name of a bacterium. It is well, however, to note some of the reasons why this result, the identification of an unknown culture, may not eventuate. Among these the following may be listed:

(1) The unknown organism awaiting identification by the investigator may possibly be one which has never been named; or, if named, perhaps was inadequately described. Of course it will not be listed in the MANUAL. Little effort on the part of bacteriologists has been devoted to describing or naming bacteria except as they have been found to have some economic significance or to possess some striking or unusual characteristics. There are quite probably many times as many species of unknown bacteria as have been described and named. Such unknown species are all about us. It is not surprising, therefore, if one sometimes encounters undescribed species. When such unnamed species are found, particularly if they are of economic importance or are related to such forms, it is highly desirable that they should be adequately described and named, and the results published and made accessible.

(2) The unknown organism may have been described and named in some publication, but the description and name have been overlooked in the preparation of the MANUAL. Perhaps the description has been so inadequate or incomplete that it has not been possible to place it in a satisfactory classification. It should be noted that the number of species that have been described is so great that no one individual can know them all. Progress in classification comes about largely as the result of the work of specialists in particular groups. Unfortunately most groups of bacteria have not been adequately monographed. It is evidently the function of a MANUAL such as this to draw largely upon the work of those who have published monographs covering special groups of bacteria and to supplement their achievements as far as possible by a necessarily less satisfactory consideration of the unmonographed groups. It is clear that the fact that an

organism cannot be identified from this text is no proof that it has not been described and named.

(3) It is possible, of course, that an error has been made in the selection of the correct name in this MANUAL. Bacteriological literature has, in recent years, been engaged in the herculean task of rectifying the nomenclatural blunders of the past. It is desirable, therefore, that users of the keys and descriptions of this MANUAL should be familiar with the rules governing the correct choice of names, and themselves propose suitable corrections where needed.

Some general rules governing nomenclature that should be known to students of bacteriology. In summary, some of the more important rules and recommendations of the Bacteriological Code may be briefly paraphrased. In case of doubt, the Annotated Code itself should be consulted.

1. Every individual microorganism belongs to a species, every species to a genus, every genus to a family, every family to an order, every order to a class. Each one of these ranks is called a *taxon* (plural *taxa*) (Principle 7).

2. Each taxonomic group (taxon) with a given definition (circumscription), position, and rank can bear only one correct name, the earliest name given to it that is in accordance with the rules of nomenclature (Principle 9).

3. The name of a species is made up of two words consisting of the name of the genus followed by the specific epithet. The term "epithet" means a single descriptive word or a single descriptive phrase. If the latter, the component words are to be united or joined by a hyphen. Within the same genus, no two species names may bear the same specific epithet (Rule 6).

4. Each taxon (species, genus, family, order) should have designated a nomenclatural type. The type of a bacterial species is *preferably* a designated culture preferably maintained in a national type culture collection. When a new species is described and named, a culture should be deposited by the author with such type culture collection where it will be available as a standard and useful in identification of other cultures believed to be related.

The nomenclatural type of a genus is a species of the genus selected in accordance with the rules.

The nomenclatural type of a family is a genus contained within the family. The family name is formed by adding the ending *-aceae* to the stem of the name of the type genus. The nomenclatural type of the family *Pseudomonadaceae* is the genus *Pseudomonas* (Rule 9).

5. **Correct names.** For the name of a taxon (species, genus, family, etc.) to be correct it must meet certain requirements. The most important of these are as follows:

a. The name must be the oldest that conforms to the rules.

b. The name must have been validly published. This means that the name must have been distributed in printed matter (periodicals, books, other publications) together with a description or clear reference to a previously published description. The name must be accepted by the author. It is not validly published if merely cited as a synonym. A name that has not been validly published is without standing in nomenclature.

c. A legitimate name is one that conforms to all the nomenclatural rules.

d. A correct name of a taxon is that legitimate name which for a given taxon takes into consideration the boundaries or circumscription of the taxon. For example, if one author recognizes two species in a genus, each species will have a correct name determined by the application of the rules. Another author may unite the two into a single species, which will have a correct name under the rules.

6. **Citation of authors and names.**

a. It is customary in formal use of the name of a species to cite the name of the author, usually with the year of publication. This means exactly what it says, one cites the author of the name of the taxon being used. This is not necessarily the name of the author who first described the organism. For example, one cites *Bacillus subtilis* Cohn, 1872.

b. When a named species is transferred to another genus, the name of the author who proposed the specific epithet is inserted in parentheses between the new species name and the name of the author of the new combination. For example, Neisser and Kuschbert in 1883 named an organism *Bacillus xerosis*. Lehmann and Neumann in 1899 transferred this organism to their newly created genus *Corynebacterium*, correctly retaining the original specific epithet (as *xerose* to agree in gender with *Corynebacterium*), and the new combination is cited as *Corynebacterium xerose* (Neisser and Kuschbert, 1883) Lehmann and Neumann, 1899. Obviously citation of author and date with the name of an organism is necessary only when the organism is first mentioned in a publication.

7. **Changes in names required by union or segregation of taxa.**

a. When a genus is divided into two or more genera, the generic name must be retained for one of them. The generic name must be retained for the genus containing the type species.

b. When a species is divided into two or more species, the specific epithet must be retained for one of them. The specific epithet of the species containing the type must be retained for this species.

c. When a species is transferred from one genus to another, the specific epithet is retained unless the resulting species name is a later homonym or a tautonym or unless there is available an earlier validly published specific epithet.

8. **Rejection and replacement of names.**

a. A name or epithet must not be rejected, changed or modified merely because it is badly chosen or disagreeable, or because another is preferable or better known. Exceptions can be made only by international action through the Judicial Commission of the International Committee.

b. A name must be rejected if it is illegitimate, that is, if it is contrary to a rule. There are numerous defects which may make a name illegitimate, for example, it may have been superfluous when proposed. Exceptions can be made by international approval through action of the Judicial Commission.

9. **Spelling and gender of names of taxa.**

a. The original spelling of a name or epithet must be retained, except in the case of a typographical error or of a clearly unintentional orthographic error. It may be difficult to determine when a typographical or orthographic error has occurred. In cases where there is doubt it is advisable to ask the Judicial Commission to consider the matter and to render an OPINION which will be authoritative.

b. The gender of generic names is determined as follows:

(1) A Greek or Latin word adopted as a generic name retains the gender of the Greek or Latin.

(2) Generic names which are modern compounds formed from two or more Greek or Latin words take the gender of the last component. If the ending is changed from that of the original Greek or Latin word, the gender is determined by the rules of gender of the Greek or Latin respectively.

(3) Arbitrarily formed generic names, i.e., those not formed from Latin or Greek, take the gender assigned to them by their authors. Where the original author did not indicate the gender, the next subsequent author has the right of choice.

10. **Provisions for exceptions to the rules or for their interpretation.** Whenever, in the opinion of any microbiologist, an interpretation of any rule or recommendation of nomenclature is desirable because the correct application of such rule or recommendation is doubtful, or the stability of nomenclature could be increased by the conservation or by the rejection of some name which is a source of confusion or error, it is recommended that he prepare a résumé outlining the problem, citing pertinent references, and indicating reasons for and against specific interpretations. This résumé should be submitted to the Chairman of the Judicial Commission; if desired, through one of the Permanent Secretaries. An OPINION will be formulated, which may not be issued until it has been approved by at least eight members of the Commission.

Before the preparation of an OPINION, a preliminary statement is usually published in the International Bulletin of Bacteriological Nomenclature and Taxonomy, the official organ of the International Committee on Bacteriological Nomenclature, Iowa State College Press, Ames, Iowa, U. S. A.

Those who are interested in the solution of special nomenclatural problems have open to them as an avenue of communication and publication the columns of the International Bulletin. The Board of Editors includes the chairman of the Judicial Commission and the two permanent secretaries. Requests for assistance in the solution of bacteriological nomenclatural problems may be sent to any member of the Editorial Board at the following addresses:

Prof. R. E. Buchanan, Chairman of Judicial Commission and of the Editorial Board. Room 316 Curtiss Hall, Iowa State College, Ames, Iowa, U. S. A.

Dr. S. T. Cowan, Permanent Secretary of the International Committee and of the Judicial Commission. National Collection of Type Cultures, Central Public Health Laboratory, Colindale Avenue, London, N.W. 9, England.

Prof. Dr. Torsten Wikén, Permanent Secretary of the International Committee and of the Judicial Commission. Laboratory for Microbiology, Technical University, Delft, Holland.

Derivation, accentuation and pronunciation of names of taxa and of specific epithets. A serious attempt has been made in this MANUAL to give the derivation of the words used as names of taxa (genera, families, etc.) and of the specific epithets of the species names of the microorganisms described. Some guide to pronunciation is given by designation of the principal accent. The rules clearly state that all names of taxa are to be treated as Latin. But in modern times the pronunciation of Latin words shows little uniformity. However, the principal accent can be properly placed. Syllabication of the words may also be helpful.

1. No Latin word consisting of two or more syllables is accented on the last syllable.

2. A Latin word consisting of two or more syllables is accented either on the next to the last syllable (the penult) or on the second to the last syllable (antepenult).

How may one determine which of the two syllables is to be accented? The rule is easily stated. If the next to the last syllable (penult) is long, it should be accented; if short, the preceding syllable (antepenult) is to be accented.

When is a syllable said to be long? There are several criteria; those most readily recognized are as follows:

1. If a syllable has a single *long* vowel, the syllable is long. A standard Latin dictionary will indicate whether the vowel is long. In words derived from Greek those syllables containing *omega* (ω) or *eta* (η) are long, those with *omicron* (o) or *epsilon* (ε) are short. In a Greek lexicon the other vowels are usually marked to indicate length.

2. If a syllable contains a diphthong, it is long.

3. If there is a double consonant or two consonants following a vowel, the syllable is long. For example:

Ba.cil′lus. The accent is on the next to the last syllable (penult) because of the double *l*.

Bac.te′ri.um. The accent is on the antepenult because the vowel in the penult is short.

Ba.cil.la′ce.ae. The accent is on the antepenult because the vowel of the penult is short.

Spi.ro.ne′ma. The accent is on the penult because the vowel of the penult is long; it is the Greek *eta* (η).

Mic.ros.pi′ra. The Greek *epsilon iota* (ει) is a diphthong; when translated into Latin, it becomes a long *i*, and the accent is on the penult.

Use of Greek and Latin in naming taxa. The Greek and Latin alphabets are not identical. Greek words to be used as stems for the Latin names of taxa must be transliterated into Latin (not translated); the Greek letters must be changed to the Latin equivalents. The Latins developed well-recognized rules for doing this. With most letters the shift is simple, in other cases, the changes are more complicated. Before a Latin name of a taxon is formed, the Greek word needs to be spelled with Latin letters, and the whole word placed, when possible, in the corresponding Latin declension with appropriate gender ending. How can the Greek derivations be indicated without confusion to the student who knows little or nothing of Greek? In this MANUAL the following procedure has been adopted as standard and as probably the most readily understood. The student must remember that the change is from Greek to Latin (not to English) orthography. The system used here is not that usually found in giving derivations in medical or general English dictionaries. Some illustrations may be helpful.

The Greek word for sulfur is θεῖον. The first letter, *theta* (θ), has no Latin equivalent; the Latins used *th*. The second letter, *epsilon* (ε), is the equivalent of short *e* in Latin. The third letter, *iota* (ι), is equivalent to *i*, the fourth, *omicron* (ο), is short *o*, and the last, *nu* (ν), is *n*. One may transliterate as *theion*. But the ει of the Greek, a diphthong, was transliterated by the Latins as a long *i*. The ending ον of the Greek indicates that the noun is neuter. The corresponding neuter ending in Latin is *um*. In final form we may write θεῖον = *theion* = *thium*. In the MANUAL the statement given is simply Gr. neut. n. (Greek neuter noun) *thium* sulfur. *Thi* is the stem from which a great number of new Latin names of taxa have been constructed, as *Thioploca*, *Thioderma*, *Thiocystis*.

Some awkward transliterations are to be found in the literature. The Greek diphthong αι = *ai* was usually transliterated as *ae* by the Latins. The Greek αἷμα = *haima* = *haema*. *Haemophilus* is correctly spelled; *Hemophilus* is not a "simplified spelling" but an incorrectly spelled modern Latin word.

One finds many errors of transliteration in bacteriological nomenclature. If corrected, the words should be regarded as alternative spellings (variants) of the same word and not as two different words.

Sometimes there are incongruities in transliteration of Greek into Latin form in a single word. For example, the specific epithet of the species *Micrococcus lysodeikticus* is an interesting mixture. The second component of the word is the Greek δεικτικόσ. The first letter, *delta* (δ), is *d*; the second, *epsilon* (ε), is short *e*; the third (and sixth), *iota* (ι), is short *i*; the fourth (and seventh) is *kappa* (κ), the Latin *c*; the eighth, *omicron* (ο), is short *o*; and the final, *sigma* (σ), is *s*. The Latins used *i* for the diphthong ει. There is no *k* in the Latin alphabet. The masculine ending *os* in Greek becomes *us* in Latin. Hence, δεικτικόσ = *deicticos* = *dicticus*. Correct transliteration would have given *lysodicticus* instead of the current *lysodeikticus*.

However, in general, it is well to observe the rule that the original spelling of the word be conserved, unless it can be regarded definitely as a slip of the pen.

A few generic names have been so commonly incorrectly accented as to constitute accepted exceptions. Several examples may be cited.

Many generic names in bacteriology and protozoology have as the final component *-monas*, as *Pseudomonas* and *Xanthomonas*. The Greek word is μονάς. The first vowel is short. Correct accentuation would give *Pseu.do′mo.nas*, *Xan.-tho′mo.nas*, etc. with the accent on the antepenult. There is a tendency to regard the *o* as long and to place the accent on the penult, giving *Pseu.do.mo′nas*, the pronunciation accepted by such dictionaries as Century and Dorland.

Again, many Modern Latin names of taxa have -*myces* as the last component. The Greek is μύκης = *myces* in which the first vowel is definitely short. In these generic names the accent would seem properly to be on the antepenult, as *Ac.- ti.no'my.ces* and *Strep.to'my.ces*. The commonly accepted accentuation is *Ac.ti.no.my' ces* and *Strep.to.my'ces*.

There is also some confusion relative to syllabication and accentuation in Modern Latin names of taxa ending in -*oides*. The derivation of the ending makes it evident that the *oi* is not a diphthong, and the *o* and *i* should be differentiated and separately pronounced. For example, the generic name *Bacteroides* should be syllabicated and accented *Bac.te.ro.i'des*. There has been confusion with the English diphthong *oi*, and pronunciation with one less syllable, *Bac.te.roi'des*, has been recognized.

Abbreviations. The following abbreviations are used in the MANUAL in giving derivations.

Gr. = Greek. The original Greek spelling is not given in the MANUAL. As noted above, the word is transliterated into the Latin alphabet; the gender endings of the Greek are changed usually to the Latin gender endings of the corresponding Latin declension. This makes evident the stems* that may be used in construction of the Modern Latin names. Gr. means latinized Greek.

L. = Latin. Usually this indicates that the word is one used in classic Latin (or in some cases post-classic Latin) and found in an unabridged Latin dictionary.

M.L. = Modern Latin. A word used as the name of a taxon or as a specific epithet, to be treated and used as a Latin word, of various derivations but not classic Latin.

Med. L. = Medieval (sometimes pharmaceutical) Latin. Many words derived from languages other than Latin were Latinized during the middle ages and utilized in fields such as pharmacy, alchemy and biology. Some Modern Latin names are derived from these.

fem. = feminine gender.	n. = noun.
mas. = masculine gender.	part. adj. = participial adjective.
neut. = neuter gender.	v. = verb.
part. = participle.	nom. = nominative.
adj. = adjective.	gen. = genitive.

pl. = plural. Note that the names of all taxa higher than the genus are plural and have plural endings, as *Bacillaceae, Actinomycetales.*

---

* The stem to be used in making compounds is not always complete in the nominative. It is found by dropping the genitive ending. For example, the generic name *Actinomyces* has as the genitive, *Actinomycetis;* the stem used in compounds is *Actinomycet-,* hence the family name derived from *Actinomyces* is *Actinomycetaceae,* not *Actinomycaceae.* Note should be taken of the fact that all Greek words that end in -*ma* are neuter and have as genitive -*matis.* The stem (combining form) always ends in *mat.* For example *Treponema,* gen. *Treponematis,* has as its stem *Treponemat-* from which one may derive a family name *Treponemataceae* (not *Treponemaceae*).

DIVISION I. PROTOPHYTA* SACHS, 1874, EMEND. KRASSILNIKOV, 1949.

(Sachs, Lehrbuch der Botanik, 4 Aufl., 1874, 249; *Schizophyta* Cohn, Beitr. z. Biol. d. Pflanzen, *1*, Heft 3, 1875, 202; Krassilnikov, Guide to the Bacteria and Actinomycetes, Izd. Akad. Nauk, U.S.S.R., Moskau, 1949, 41.)

Pro.to.phy'ta. Gr. combining form *protos* first (in time), primordial; Gr. noun *phytum* plant; M.L. pl.noun *Protophyta* primordial plants.

Unicellular organisms and organisms which occur in trichomes. Generally these forms are too small to be distinguishable to the naked eye. Ordinarily no differentiation of cells is evident, although those forms that occur in trichomes may show some differentiation into vegetative and specialized cells of various types (heterocysts, holdfast cells and reproductive cells). Increase in number of individual cells is normally effected by simple cell division (fission), rarely by budding; however among the most highly advanced forms, spores of various types may be developed (endospores, conidia or gonidia). In the highly specialized parasites such as the viruses, the processes of reproduction have become so intimately associated with the living protoplasm of the host cells, and the virus particles are so minute (less than 200 millimicrons in diameter) that the exact method of reproduction has not yet been determined with certainty. For many years it was believed that these organisms do not possess nuclei; however, in recent years simple types of nuclear bodies have been demonstrated in many of these organisms, and a nucleus, or at least definite nuclear material (chromatin), has been found to be present in all cases. Do not contain chloroplastids, which are found in the cells of the green portions of higher plants. Ubiquitous, occurring in the air, everywhere on the surface of the earth, in and on plants and animals and even far below the surface of the earth in mine waters.

Key to the classes of division **Protophyta.**

I. Organisms which possess the photosynthetic **pigment** phycocyanin in addition to chlorophyll.

Class I. *Schizophyceae*, p. 30.

II. Organisms which usually do not contain photosynthetic pigments. None contain phycocyanin.

A. Reproduction by fission. Cells not normally filterable, though filterable stages are known in some species.

Class II. *Schizomycetes*, p. 33.

B. Cells so minute that the exact form of reproduction is not clearly understood as yet. All possess filterable stages.

Class III. *Microtatobiotes*, p. 931.

---

* The sections which characterize the Division *Protophyta*, the classes, the orders and in some cases the families have been prepared by Prof. Robert S. Breed, Cornell University, Geneva, New York.

CLASS I. SCHIZOPHYCEAE COHN, 1879.

(*Myxophyceae* Stizenberger, 1860; *Phycochromophyceae* Rabenhorst, 1863; *Cyanophyceen* Sachs, Lehrbuch der Botanik, 4 Aufl., 1874, 249; Cohn, Jahresber. Schles. Ges. f. vaterl. Cultur, f. 1879, 279–289.)

Schi.zo.phy′ce.ae. Gr. noun *schizo* cleft, fission; Gr. noun *phycus* seaweed, alga; M.L. pl. noun *Schizophyceae* fission algae.

The organisms in this class are usually designated as the blue-green algae and are studied in connection with other types of algae (green, brown and red) and the higher fungi in courses in Cryptogamic Botany. However, the blue-green algae differ structurally from all other types of *Thallophyta*. On the other hand they resemble the bacteria so that the blue-green algae and the bacteria are commonly classed in the same Division of the Plant Kingdom.

In order to identify the species of blue-green algae, consult any of the following books: O. Kirchner, *Schizophyceae*, in Engler and Prantl, Die Natürlichen Pflanzenfamilien, I Teil, Abt. la, 1900, 45–92; Gilbert H. Smith, Cryptogamic Botany, 2nd ed., Vol. 1, Algae and Fungi, New York, 1955, 526 pp.; Gilbert H. Smith, Freshwater Algae of the United States, New York, 1950, 719 pp.

The *Schizophyceae* are not described further in the present MANUAL.

CLASS II

SCHIZOMYCETES VON NAEGELI

By

ROBERT S. BREED
Late Professor Emeritus, Cornell University, Geneva, New York

E. G. D. MURRAY
*Research Professor, University of Western Ontario,
London, Ontario, Canada*

NATHAN R. SMITH
*Senior Bacteriologist, Retired, Plant Industry Station, U. S. Department
of Agriculture, Beltsville, Maryland*

and

Specialists whose names appear on the following pages
in connection with the sections prepared by them

CLASS II. SCHIZOMYCETES VON NAEGELI, 1857.

(Von Naegeli, Bericht Verhandl. d. bot. Section d. 33 Versammling deutsch. Naturforsch. u. Arzt. Bot. Ztg., 1857, 760; Bacterien, Cohn, Beitr. z. Biol. d. Pflanzen, *1*, Heft 2, 1872, 127; *Bacteriaceae* Cohn, Arch. f. path. Anat., *55*, 1872, 237; *Schizomycetaceae* DeToni and Trevisan, in Saccardo, Sylloge Fungorum, *8*, 1889, 923; *Bacteriales* Clements (as an ordinal name), The Genera of Fungi, Minneapolis, 1909, 8; *Schizomycetacea* Castellani and Chalmers, Manual of Tropical Medicine, 3rd ed., 1919, 924; *Mychota* Enderlein, Bakterien-Cyclogenie, 1924, 236; *Schizomycetae* Stanier and van Niel, Jour. Bact., *42*, 1941, 458).

Schi.zo.my.ce′tes. Gr. noun *schiza* cleft, fission; Gr. noun *myces, mycetis* fungus; M.L. mas.pl.n. *Schizomycetes* the class of fission fungi.

Typically unicellular plants. Cells usually small, sometimes ultramicroscopic. Frequently motile. For many years it was thought that the cells of *Schizomycetes* and of the related *Schizophyceae* did not possess the nucleus invariably found in the cells of other plants. However, using modern cytological techniques, investigators have now demonstrated a true nucleus in bacterial cells. Individual cells may be spherical or straight, curved or spiral rods. These cells may occur in regular or irregular masses, or even in cysts. Where they remain attached to each other after cell division, they may form chains or even definite trichomes. The latter may show some differentiation into holdfast cells and into motile or non-motile reproductive cells. Some grow as branching mycelial threads whose diameter is not greater than that of ordinary bacterial cells, i.e., about one micron. Some species produce pigments. The true purple and green bacteria possess pigments much like or related to the true chlorophylls of higher plants. These pigments have photosynthetic properties. The phycocyanin found in the blue-green algae does not occur in the *Schizomycetes*. Multiplication is typically by cell division. Endospores are formed by some species included in *Eubacteriales*. Sporocysts are found in *Myxobacterales*. Ultramicroscopic reproductive bodies are found in *Mycoplasmatales*. The bacteria are free-living, saprophytic, parasitic or even pathogenic. The latter types cause diseases of either plants or animals. Ten orders are recognized.

Key to the orders of class **Schizomycetes**.

I. Cells rigid. Spherical, rod-shaped (straight or curved) or spiral in form. Sometimes in trichomes. Motile by means of polar flagella or non-motile.

A. Cells coccoid, straight or curved rods, or spiral in form. Sometimes occur as chains of cells. Cells may contain photosynthetic purple or green pigments. Not in trichromes. Usually motile by means of polar flagella. Occasionally non-motile.

Order I. *Pseudomonadales*, p. 35.

B. Not as above.

1. Cells in trichomes that are frequently in a sheath. Occasionally motile (swarm spores) or non-motile conidia are developed. The sheaths may contain a deposit of ferric hydroxide, and the trichomes may be attached to a substrate.

Order II. *Chlamydobacteriales*, p. 262.

2. Cells reproduce by a process of budding rather than by ordinary cell division (fission). May be attached to a substrate by a stalk. One genus contains species with photosynthetic pigments (*Rhodomicrobium*).

Order III. *Hyphomicrobiales*, p. 276.

II. Not as above.

A. Cells rigid. Spherical or straight rod-shaped cells. Occur singly, in chains or in trichomes. Motile by means of peritrichous flagella or non-motile. Not acid-fast.

1. Cells spherical or rod-shaped; no trichomes though chains of cells may occur.

Order IV. *Eubacteriales*, p. 281.

    2. Cells in trichomes.

Order VI. Caryophanales, p. 830.

B. Not as above.

    1. Cells rigid and may grow out into a branching mycelium-like structure which may even develop chains of aerial conidia giving colonies a superficial resemblance to mold colonies. In two genera spores develop within sporangia (sporangiospores), and in one of these genera the spores are motile. Where cells occur singly or in simple branched forms, they are frequently acid-fast.

Order V. Actinomycetales, p. 694.

    2. Not as above.

        a. Cells rigid, usually large and may occur as coccoid cells or trichomes. Sulfur granules may occur on the surface or within the cells. Move by a gliding, oscillating or rolling, jerky motion like that of some blue-green algae. No flagella present.

Order VII. Beggiatoales, p. 837.

        aa. Not as above.

            b. Longer or shorter flexuous cells.

                c. Cells flexuous, creeping on a substrate. Frequently pointed at both ends. Fruiting bodies are usually developed from a thin spreading colony (pseudoplasmodium). Slime bacteria.

Order VIII. Myxobacterales, p. 854.

                cc. Cells in the form of longer or shorter spirals. Swim freely by flexion of cells.

Order IX. Spirochaetales, p. 892.

            bb. Non-motile, highly pleomorphic organisms of a very delicate character. Possess filterable stages.

Order X. Mycoplasmatales, p. 914.

ORDER I. PSEUDOMONADALES ORLA-JENSEN, 1921.

(Jour. Bact., *6*, 1921, 270.)

Pseu.do.mo.na.da'les. M.L. fem.pl.n. *Pseudomonadaceae* type family of the order; *-ales* ending to denote an order; M.L. fem.pl.n. *Pseudomonadales* the *Pseudomonadaceae* order.

Straight, curved or spiral, rigid, rod-shaped bacteria. Rarely occur in pairs or chains. The cells in a few species are ellipsoidal and are frequently spoken of as being coccoid or even spherical in form. They are usually about 1.0 micron in diameter, but in a few species the individual cell is larger than is normal for bacterial cells, reaching a size of 3.0 to 14.0 microns in diameter and as much as 100 microns in length. The cells are usually polar flagellate. When motile they sometimes bear a single flagellum, in other cases a tuft of flagella. The flagella are normally found at one or both ends of the cell, but in one genus the curved cells bear a tuft of flagella that is attached in the middle of the concave side (*Selenomonas*). Non-motile species whose characteristics indicate that they belong in this order with closely related, motile species occasionally occur. Cells are Gram-negative so far as known. The cells in one sub-order contain pigments that have the power of photosynthesis. The cells in the second sub-order lack such pigments, as do all other groups of bacteria. The cells in the first sub-order are photo-autotrophic, while chemo-autotrophic species occur in the second sub-order. Energy is frequently secured by oxidative processes though there are also many species that show a fermentative physiology. Cells quite frequently occur in zoogloeal masses. No endospores are found, and reproduction is by means of fission. Many species occur in coastal, swamp and pond waters and in soil. Some are parasitic and some are even pathogenic, causing diseases of fishes and other cold-blooded vertebrates. There are a few species (cholera, blue pus, etc.) that cause diseases of warm-blooded mammals, including man.

Key to the sub-orders of order **Pseudomonadales.**

I. Cells contain red, purple, brown or green photosynthetic pigments. Sometimes also enclose granules of free sulfur.
> Sub-order I. *Rhodobacteriineae*, p. 35.

II. Cells do not contain photosynthetic pigments, although they may produce greenish, brownish, rose or yellow, diffusible, water-soluble pigments or yellow or red non-water-soluble pigments. Free sulfur granules may occur within or without the cells (*Thiobacteriaceae*). Ferric hydroxide may be deposited (*Caulobacteriaceae*).
> Sub-order II. *Pseudomonadineae*, p. 67.

SUBORDER I. **Rhodobacteriineae** BREED, MURRAY AND HITCHENS, 1944.*

(Family *Rhodobacteriaceae* Migula, Syst. d. Bakt., *2*, 1900, 1042; Breed, Murray and Hitchens, Bact. Rev., *8*, 1944, 257.)

Rho.do.bac.te.ri.i'ne.ae. M.L. neut.n. *Rhodobacterium* a genus of bacteria; *-ineae* ending to denote a suborder; M.L. fem.pl.n. *Rhodobacteriineae* the *Rhodobacterium* suborder.

---

* Rearranged and revised by Prof. C. B. van Niel, Hopkins Marine Station, Pacific Grove, California, July, 1953.

Cells spherical, rod-, vibrio- or spiral-shaped. Diameter of individual cells from less than 1.0 to over 10 microns. Red, purple, brown or green bacteria which contain bacteriochlorophyll or other chlorophyll-like green pigments, and which usually also possess one or more carotenoid pigments. Capable of carrying out a photosynthetic metabolism which differs from that of green plants in that it does not proceed with the evolution of oxygen, and depends upon the presence of extraneous oxidizable compounds which are dehydrogenated with the simultaneous reduction of carbon dioxide. As oxidizable substrates, a variety of simple substances can be used, such as sulfide, or other reduced sulfur compounds, molecular hydrogen, alcohols, fatty acids, hydroxy- and keto-acids, etc. All can be grown in strictly anaerobic cultures when illuminated. Those members which can grow in the presence of air can also be cultured in the dark under aerobic conditions. Color depends markedly on environmental conditions; small individuals appear colorless unless observed in masses. May contain sulfur globules. Described species have largely been found in freshwater habitats. Some species occur in marine habitats.

Key to the families of suborder Rhodobacteriineae.

I. Purple bacteria whose pigment system consists of bacteriochlorophyll and various carotenoids capable of carrying out a photosynthetic metabolism.
   A. Contain sulfur globules in the presence of hydrogen sulfide. The sulfur purple bacteria.
               Family I. *Thiorhodaceae*, p. 38.
   B. Do not contain sulfur globules even in the presence of hydrogen sulfide. All require organic growth factors. The non-sulfur purple and brown bacteria.
               Family II. *Athiorhodaceae*, p. 53.
II. Green sulfur bacteria containing a pigment system which has the characteristics of a chlorophyllous compound although it differs from the chlorophyll of green plants and from the bacteriochlorophyll of the purple bacteria.
               Family III. *Chlorobacteriaceae*, p. 61.

The organisms previously included in the order *Thiobacteriales* Buchanan do not constitute a taxonomic entity; they represent rather a physiological-ecological community. In this sense, however, a special treatment of this group as a unit has decided advantages from a determinative point of view.

When first proposed as a systematic assemblage, the order *Thiobacteria* Migula (Syst. d. Bakt., *2*, 1900, 1039) was intended to include the morphologically conspicuous organisms which, in their natural habitat, contain globules of sulfur as cell inclusions. Since Winogradsky (Beitr. z. Morph. u. Physiol. d. Bact., I, Schwefelbacterien, 1888) had elucidated the function of hydrogen sulfide and of sulfur in their metabolism, the characteristic inclusions appeared linked with a hitherto unrecognized type of physiology, *viz.* the oxidation of an inorganic substance instead of the decomposition of organic materials. From this oxidation the sulfur bacteria derive their energy for maintenance and growth.

Two groups of sulfur bacteria could be distinguished, one consisting of colorless, the other of red or purple organisms. The members of both groups presented an unusual morphology apart from the sulfur droplets: in all cases the individual cells were considerably larger than those of the common bacteria, while many species grew as distinctive colonial aggregates. Migula separated these sulfur bacteria into two families, *Beggiatoaceae* and *Rhodobacteriaceae*. Even at that time, however, some difficulties existed as to just what organisms should properly be considered as sulfur bacteria. Miyoshi (Jour. Coll. Sci., Imp. Univ., Tokyo, *10*, 1897, 143) had discovered a bacterium which forms strands, incrusted with sulfur, in sulfur springs but which does not store sulfur globules in its cells. Although physiologically this organism appeared to comply with Winogradsky's concept of a sulfur bacterium, the absence of the typical cell inclusions made Miyoshi decide it could not be considered as such. The problem was aggravated when Nathansohn, Beijerinck and Jacobsen published their studies on small, colorless, *Pseudomonas*-like bacteria capable of oxidizing hydrogen sulfide, sulfur and thiosulfate, and evidently dependent upon this oxidation process for their development. Morphologically these organisms have little in common with the *Beggiatoaceae*; they were designated by Beijerinck as species of *Thiobacillus* and have since been rightly considered as members of the order *Pseudomonadales* (see p. 35). Nevertheless, these organisms are physiologically in no way different from the *Beggiatoaceae*, so that if physiology only is considered, a good case could be made out for their incorporation in the *Thiobacteriales*.

Furthermore, Molisch (Die Purpurbakterien, Jena, 1907, 95 pp.) described in some detail a number of bacterial species which, in view of their characteristic pigment system, appeared closely related to the *Rhodobacteriaceae*, but which develop only in organic media and are, therefore, not sulfur bacteria in the sense of Winogradsky or Migula. In stressing the importance of pigmentation, Molisch combined the red sulfur bacteria and the newly-discovered purple bacteria into an order *Rhodobacteria* with the two families *Thiorhodaceae* and *Athiorhodaceae*. It is this grouping that has been followed in the present edition of the MANUAL.

Among the non-sulfur purple bacteria, or *Athiorhodaceae*, is included an organism which, on the basis of its morphology and manner of growth, does not conform to the criteria of the order *Pseudomonadales*. This is *Rhodomicrobium vannielii* Duchow and Douglas (Jour. Bact., *58*, 1949, 409). Physiologically it is a typical non-sulfur purple bacterium in that it is capable of development in strictly anaerobic media supplied with an appropriate oxidizable substrate only when the cultures are illuminated and carries out a photosynthetic metabolism without oxygen evolution. Multiplication is not, however, by transverse fission but by bud formation at the end of a thin filament growing out of a pole of the mother cell followed by the formation of a cross wall in the connecting filament. This mode of development is similar to that encountered in the non-photosynthetic bacterium *Hyphomicrobium vulgare*.

It should also be emphasized here that some of the sulfur purple bacteria (*Thiopedia*, for example) and all of the green sulfur bacteria appear at present to be permanently immotile.

Only a very small number of typical sulfur bacteria have been studied in pure cultures. As a result the descriptions of genera and species rest mainly on observations made with collections from natural sources or crude cultures. Most investigators have implicitly accepted differences in cell size or in colonial appearance as a sufficient justification for establishing independent species. Evidently this procedure presupposes a considerable degree of constancy of such characteristics in the organisms in question. It is true that Winogradsky's investigations have provided a reasonable basis for this belief, but later studies with pure cultures of certain purple bacteria have established beyond a doubt that environmental conditions, such as composition of the medium and temperature, may exert a profound influence on the general morphology of these organisms. By this it is not intended to infer that the previously proposed genera and species of sulfur bacteria should be abandoned, but it does follow that a cautious evaluation of the distinguishing features is necessary. In the absence of carefully conducted investigations on morphological constancy and variability of most of the previously recognized species of sulfur bacteria with pure cultures grown under a variety of external conditions, the best approach appears to be a tentative arrangement of these organisms based upon those characteristics which are readily ascertainable. Experience with this group over the past twenty-five years has shown that, while Winogradsky's fundamental work must remain the foundation of present taxonomic efforts, it is advisable to simplify the much more elaborate classification developed by Buchanan which was followed in previous editions of this MANUAL.

Certain genera of sulfur purple bacteria, created by Winogradsky, will very probably be consolidated when detailed information concerning the morphology of the organisms is available. Until such time it seems, however, best to retain most of them, even though the distinguishing characteristics are not always very clear. For the benefit of those who are familiar with previous methods of classification, it will be indicated where deviations have been adopted.

The non-sulfur purple bacteria (*Athiorhodaceae* Molisch; *Rhodobacterioideae* Buchanan) have been subjected to a comparative morphological and physiological study comprising more than 150 strains, among which all previously proposed genera and species are represented (van Niel, Bact. Rev., *8*, 1944, 1–118). It has been found that the characteristics upon which Molisch based the seven genera of this group are inadequate, and a new classification with only two distinguishable genera has been proposed. This system will be followed here.

Nadson (Bull. Jard. Imper. Bot., St. Petersburg, *12*, 1912, 64) described a new type of small, green bacteria not containing sulfur globules in the presence of hydrogen sulfide but excreting elemental sulfur. They are photosynthetic and are capable of growing in anaerobic culture when illuminated. The green pigment differs from the green plant chlorophylls and from the bacteriochlorophyll of the purple bacteria but has the characteristics of a chlorophyllous compound. These are grouped in the family *Chlorobacteriaceae*.

FAMILY I. THIORHODACEAE MOLISCH, 1907.

(Die Purpurbakterien, Jena, 1907, 27.)

Thi.o.rho.da′ce.ae. Gr. noun *thium* sulfur; Gr. noun *rhodum* the rose; -*aceae* ending to denote a family; M.L. fem.pl.n. *Thiorhodaceae* (probably intended to mean) the family of sulfur red bacteria.

Unicellular organisms, often developing as cell aggregates or families of variable size and shape. Single cells have the form of spheres, ovoids, short rods, vibrios, spirals, long rods or, occasionally, chains. They occur in nature in environments containing sulfides and require light for their development; infra-red irradiation of a wave-length extending to about 900 millimicrons is effective. They produce a pigment system composed of green bacteriochlorophyll and yellow and red carotenoids. As a result they appear as bluish violet, pale purple, brownish to deep red cell masses. Single cells, unless they are of considerable size, usually appear to be unpigmented. These are anaerobic or microaerophilic organisms with a photosynthetic metabolism in which carbon dioxide is reduced with the aid of special hydrogen donors without the liberation of molecular oxygen. Where these organisms are found in nature, hydrogen sulfide acts as a hydrogen donor, and sulfur, the first intermediate oxidation product, accumulates as sulfur droplets in the cells. Probably all members of the group can utilize a number of organic substances in place of hydrogen sulfide as hydrogen donors for photosynthesis. Thus they are potentially mixotrophic.

Characterization of the genera in this group has, since Winogradsky's studies (Beiträge zur Morphologie und Physiologie der Schwefelbacterien, Leipzig, 1888), been based upon the mode of development of the cell aggregates. Pure-culture studies (Bavendamm, Die farblosen und roten Bakterien, I. Schwefelbakterien, Pflanzenforschung, Heft 2, 1924, 74 pp.; van Niel, Arch. f. Mikrobiol., *3*, 1931, 1–112; Manten, Antonie van Leeuwenhoek, *8*, 1942, 164 pp.) have shown, however, that not only the sequence of events in the formation of the aggregates but also the appearance and form of the latter, even including the size and shape of the component cells, are influenced to a considerable extent by environmental conditions. This obviously casts doubt upon the usefulness of the previously used diagnostic criteria for genera and species. On the other hand, the scope of pure-culture studies has not yet attained sufficient breadth to warrant the use of a different approach. As a provisional measure, Winogradsky's genera are therefore maintained. Even the larger taxonomic units must be regarded as being of tentative value only.

Key to the genera of family **Thiorhodaceae.**

I. Cells usually combined into aggregates.
  A. Cells grouped as regular sarcina packets.
  Genus I. *Thiosarcina,* p. 39.
  B. Cells not in sarcina packets.
    1. Aggregates in the form of a flat sheet.
      a. Cells in regular arrangement, with tetrads as the common structural unit.
      Genus II. *Thiopedia,* p. 40.
      aa. Cells in irregular aggregates.
      Genus III. *Thiocapsa,* p. 41.
    2. Aggregates in the form of three-dimensional masses.
      a. Cells distinctly rod-shaped and arranged in a net-like structure.
      Genus IV. *Thiodictyon,* p. 41.
      aa. Cells not so arranged.
        b. Cells in a common capsule, individuals rather scattered and loosely grouped.
        Genus V. *Thiothece,* p. 42.
        bb. Cells in rather dense clumps.
          c. Aggregates embedded in conspicuous common slime capsule.
            d. Aggregates small, compact, often several of them enclosed together in a common capsule.
            Genus VI. *Thiocystis,* p. 42.
          dd. Aggregates large and solid, later break up into small clusters.
          Genus VII. *Lamprocystis,* p. 43.
          cc. Common capsule lacking or very transient.
            d. Aggregates as a whole exhibit amoeboid movements.
            Genus VIII. *Amoebobacter,* p. 44.
          dd. Aggregates devoid of amoeboid movements.
          Genus IX. *Thiopolycoccus,* p. 45.
II. Cells usually occurring singly.
  A. Cells clearly spiral-shaped.
  Genus X. *Thiospirillum,* p. 46.
  B. Cells not spiral-shaped.
    1. Cells irregular, often swollen, distorted, or composed of long, crooked and bent rods to filaments.
    Genus XI. *Rhabdomonas,* p. 48.
    2. Cells regular, spherical to short rods or bean-shaped.
      a. Cells spherical, as a rule non-motile, and each one surrounded by a rather wide capsule.
      Genus XII. *Rhodothece,* p. 50.
      aa. Cells ellipsoidal, ovoid, short rods or vibrios, actively motile.
      Genus XIII. *Chromatium,* p. 50.

Genus I. **Thiosarcina** *Winogradsky, 1888.*

(Zur Morphologie und Physiologie der Bacterien, I. Schwefelbacterien, Leipzig, 1888 104.)

Thi.o.sar.ci′na. Gr. noun *thium* sulfur; M.L. fem.n. *Sarcina* a genus of bacteria; M.L fem.n. *Thiosarcina* sulfur *Sarcina.*

Individual cells spherical, forming regular cubical packets of sarcina-shape, resulting from consecutive division in three perpendicular planes. Packets commonly containing 8 to 64 cells. Infrequently motile. Non-spore-forming. Contain bacteriochlorophyll and carotenoid pigments, hence, pigmented purplish to red. Capable of carrying out a photosynthetic metabolism in the presence of hydrogen sulfide, cells then storing sulfur globules. Anaerobic.

The type species is *Thiosarcina rosea* (Schroeter) Winogradsky.

1. **Thiosarcina rosea** (Schroeter, 1886) Winogradsky, 1888. (*Sarcina rosea* Schroeter, Kryptog.-Flora von Schlesien, *3*, 1, 1886, 154; Winogradsky, Zur Morphologie und Physiologie der Schwefelbacterien, Leipzig, 1888, 104.)

ro'se.a. L. adj. *roseus* rosy, rose-colored.

Cells spherical, 2 to 3 microns in diameter, occurring in packets containing 8 to 64 cells. Infrequently motile. Color ranging from purplish rose to nearly black.

Anaerobic.

Habitat: Occur less frequently than other sulfur purple bacteria; probably widely distributed in mud and stagnant bodies of water containing hydrogen sulfide and exposed to light; sulfur springs.

Illustration: Issatchenko, Recherches sur les microbes de l'océan glacial arctique, Petrograd, 1914, Plate II, fig. 5.

Genus II. **Thiopedia** *Winogradsky, 1888.*

(Zur Morphologie und Physiologie der Bacterien, I. Schwefelbacterien, Leipzig, 1888, 85.) Thi.o.pe'di.a. Gr.n. *thium* sulfur; Gr.n. *pedium* a plain, a flat area; M.L. fem.n. *Thiopedia* a sulfur plain.

Individual cells spherical to short rod-shaped, the latter shortly before cell division. Arranged in flat sheets with typical tetrads as the structural units. These arise from divisions of the cells in two perpendicular directions. Cell aggregates of various sizes, ranging from single tetrads to large sheets composed of thousands of cells. Non-motile. Non-spore-forming. Contain bacteriochlorophyll and carotenoid pigments. Capable of photosynthesis in the presence of hydrogen sulfide, then storing sulfur globules. Anaerobic.

The type species is *Thiopedia rosea* Winogradsky.

1. **Thiopedia rosea** Winogradsky, 1888. (*Erythroconis littoralis* Oersted, Naturhist. Tidsskrift, *3*, 1840–1841, 555; Winogradsky, Zur Morphologie und Physiologie der Schwefelbacterien, Leipzig, 1888, 85.)

ro'se.a. L. adj. *roseus* rosy, rose-colored.

Cells 1 to 2 microns, often appearing as slightly elongated cocci regularly arranged in platelets.

Color, pale red to nearly black, depending upon the amount of sulfur stored. Red color visible only with large cell masses, not in individuals.

According to Winogradsky, the cells are often embedded in a common slime capsule; the extensive studies of Utermöhl (Archiv f. Hydrobiol., Suppl. Vol. *5*, 1925, 251–276) make the regular occurrence of such capsules extremely doubtful. On the other hand, Utermöhl emphasizes as quite charac-

teristic the common presence of a relatively large pseudovacuole, or aerosome, in the cells of this species encountered in plankton samples. Winogradsky does not mention this; nevertheless, it appears to be a regular and valuable distinguishing feature.

Anaerobic.

Habitat: Widely distributed in mud and stagnant bodies of fresh, brackish and salt water containing hydrogen sulfide and exposed to light; sulfur springs. Common, frequently giving rise to very extensive mass developments.

Illustrations: Warming, Videnskab. Meddel. naturhist. Forening, Kjöbenhavn, 1876, Plate VIII, fig. 2; Winogradsky, *op. cit.*, 1888, 85, Plate III, fig. 18; Pringsheim, Naturwissensch., *20*, 1932, 481, the last one a truly excellent photomicrograph.

Genus III. **Thiocapsa** *Winogradsky, 1888.*

(Schwefelbacterien, Leipzig, 1888, 84.)

Thi.o.ca'psa. Gr.n. *thium* sulfur; L.n. *capsa* a box; M.L. fem.n. *Thiocapsa* sulfur box.

Cells spherical, occurring in families of irregularly arranged individuals held together in a common slime capsule. The aggregates are spread out flat on the substrate. Motility not observed. As the colony grows, the capsule bursts, and the cells are spread apart. General morphology and development thus appear similar to that in the genus *Aphanocapsa* among the blue-green algae. Contain bacteriochlorophyll and carotenoid pigments; capable of photosynthesis in the presence of hydrogen sulfide. Under such conditions sulfur is stored in the form of globules in the cells. This genus is so much like *Thiothece* that it is doubtful whether a distinction can be maintained.

The type species is *Thiocapsa roseopersicina* Winogradsky.

Key to the species of genus **Thiocapsa.**

I. Individual cells about 3 microns in diameter.
      1. *Thiocapsa roseopersicina.*
II. Individual cells about 1.5 microns in diameter.
      2. *Thiocapsa floridana.*

1. **Thiocapsa roseopersicina** Winogradsky, 1888. (Schwefelbacterien, Leipzig, 1888, 84).

ro.se.o.per.si.ci'na. L. adj. *roseus* rosy; Gr. noun *persicus* the peach, Persian apple, Persian; M.L. adj. *roseopersicinus* rosy-peach (colored).

Cells spherical, 2.5 to 3 microns in diameter, occurring in families of irregularly arranged individuals held together in a common slime capsule. Motility not observed. Usually a distinct rose-red. Stored sulfur droplets may attain a considerable size.

Habitat: Mud and stagnant bodies of water containing hydrogen sulfide and exposed to light; sulfur springs.

Illustration: Winogradsky, *loc. cit.*, Plate IV, fig. 15.

2. **Thiocapsa floridana** Uphof, 1927. (Arch. f. Hydrobiol., *18*, 1927, 84.)

flo.ri.da'na. M.L. adj. *floridanus* pertaining to Florida.

Cells spherical, about 1.5 microns in diameter. In groups of irregular colonies, each surrounded by a common capsule, several colonies being stuck together. Motility not observed.

Source: Palm Springs, Florida and Lake Sakskoje, near Eupatoria, Crimea.

Habitat: Mud and stagnant water containing hydrogen sulfide and exposed to light; sulfur springs. Probably ubiquitous.

Illustration: Uphof, *ibid.*, 83, fig. VI.

Genus IV. **Thiodictyon** *Winogradsky, 1888.*

(Winogradsky, Schwefelbacterien, Leipzig, 1888, 80; *Rhododictyon* Orla-Jensen, Cent. f. Bakt., II Abt., *22*, 1909, 334.)

Thi.o.dic'ty.on. Gr. noun *thium* sulfur; Gr. noun *dictyum* or *dictyon* net; M.L. neut.n. *Thiodictyon* sulfur net.

Cells rod-shaped, frequently with pointed ends, somewhat resembling spindles. Form aggregates in which the cells become arranged end to end in a net-like structure, somewhat reminiscent of the shape of the green alga *Hydrodictyon.* The shape is not constant; cells may also form more compact masses. Sometimes groups of cells separate from the main aggregate by active movements. Common gelatinous capsule not observed. Contain bacteriochlorophyll and carotenoid pigments; cells usually very faintly colored. Capable of photosynthesis in the presence of hydrogen sulfide, the cells then storing sulfur as small globules.

The type species is *Thiodictyon elegans* Winogradsky.

1. Thiodictyon elegans Winogradsky, 1888. (Schwefelbacterien, Leipzig, 1888, 80.) e'le.gans. L. adj. *elegans* choice, elegant. Rods 1.5 to 1.7 by 2.5 to 5 microns; or longer just prior to cell division. Usually contain a large pseudovacuole (aerosome), leaving a rather thin protoplasmic sheath along the cell wall.

Sulfur droplets generally quite small; deposited exclusively in the thin protoplasmic layer.

Issatchenko (Études microbiologiques des Lacs de Boue, Leningrad, 1927, 113–114) recognizes a forma *minus* and a forma *magna*, differentiated mainly by the size of the individual rods.

Habitat: Mud and stagnant water containing hydrogen sulfide and exposed to light; sulfur springs.

Illustrations: Winogradsky, *loc. cit.*, Plate III, fig. 13–17.

Genus V. **Thiothece** *Winogradsky, 1888.*

(Schwefelbacterien, Leipzig, 1888, 82.)

Thi.o.the'ce Gr. noun *thium* sulfur; Gr. noun *thece* a box, chest; M.L. fem.n. *Thiothece* sulfur box.

Sulfur purple bacteria which, in their growth characteristics, resemble the blue-green alga *Aphanothece*. Cells spherical to relatively long cylindrical-ellipsoidal, embedded in a gelatinous capsule of considerable dimensions. Following cell division the daughter cells continue to secrete mucus which causes the individual bacteria to remain clearly separated by an appreciable distance; the common capsule thus appears only loosely filled. The cells may become actively motile and separate themselves from the colony. Such swarmers closely resemble the cells of certain species of *Chromatium*. Contain bacteriochlorphyll and carotenoid pigments. Capable of photosynthesis in the presence of hydrogen sulfide, producing elemental sulfur as an intermediate oxidation product which is stored as sulfur globules inside the cells.

The type species is *Thiothece gelatinosa* Winogradsky.

1. Thiothece gelatinosa Winogradsky, 1888. (Schwefelbacterien, Leipzig, 1888, 82.) ge.la.ti.no'sa. L. part. adj. *gelatus* frozen, stiffened; M.L. noun *gelatinum* gelatin, that which stiffens; M.L. adj. *gelatinosus* gelatinous.

Cells 4 to 6 by 4 to 7 microns, spherical to cylindrical. Color of individual cells, faint, often grayish violet or even dirty yellowish. Sulfur globules usually deposited

in outermost layers of protoplasm and generally small.

Habitat: Mud and stagnant water containing hydrogen sulfide and exposed to light; sulfur springs.

Illustrations: Winogradsky, *loc. cit.*, Pl. III, fig. 9–12; Miyoshi, Jour. Coll. Sci., Imp. Univ. Tokyo, Japan, *10*, 1897, 170, Pl. XIV, fig. 25.

Genus VI. **Thiocystis** *Winogradsky, 1888.*

(Schwefelbacterien, Leipzig, 1888, 60.)

Thi.o.cys'tis. Gr. noun *thium* sulfur; Gr. noun *cystis* the bladder, a bag; M.L. fem.n. *Thiocystis* sulfur bag.

Sulfur purple bacteria which form compact colonies, many of which may be loosely embedded in a common gelatinous capsule. Individual cells spherical to ovoid, often diplococcus-shaped. Colonies may emerge as more or less large units from out of the common capsule and break up afterwards, sometimes into single swarmers; or the aggregates may split up inside the original capsule and release small motile units or single swarmers. In pure cultures frequently develop as single cells and diplococci. Produce bacteriochlorophyll and carotenoid pigments, coloring the cell masses purplish to red. Capable of photosynthesis, in the presence of hydrogen sulfide, whereby elemental sulfur is formed as an intermediate oxidation product which is deposited as droplets inside the cells.

The type species is *Thiocystis violacea* Winogradsky.

Key to the species of genus **Thiocystis.**

I. Individual cells more than 2 microns in width.
>   1. *Thiocystis violacea.*

II. Individual cells about 1 micron or less in width.
>   2. *Thiocystis rufa.*

1. **Thiocystis violacea** Winogradsky, 1888. (Schwefelbacterien, Leipzig, 1888, 65.) vi.o.la′ce.a. L. adj. *violaceus* violet-colored.

Cells about 2.5 to 5.5 microns in diameter, spherical to ovoid. Swarmers actively motile by means of polar flagella.

Colonies: Small, inside a common capsule, containing not over 30 cells. Several such colonies form loosely arranged aggregates, most characteristically composed of about 10 to 20 colonies in a single capsule. The result is a nearly spherical zoogloea. In small colonies, the cells appear as rather distinct tetrads; in larger colonies, the cells become somewhat compressed and the tetrad-like arrangement may be lost.

In pure cultures, the species often fails to produce the characteristic capsules; the organisms then occur as actively motile single cells or diplococci, with little or no slime formation. No pseudocapsules are formed.

Habitat: Mud and stagnant water containing hydrogen sulfide and exposed to light; sulfur springs.

Illustrations: Zopf, Zur Morphologie der Spaltpflanzen, Leipzig, 1882, Pl. V, fig. 12; Winogradsky, *op. cit.*, 1888, 65, Pl. II, Fig. 1–7.

2. **Thiocystis rufa** Winogradsky, 1888. (Schwefelbacterien, Leipzig, 1888, 65.) ru′fa. L. adj. *rufus* red, reddish.

Cells less than 1 micron in diameter. Color red, usually darker than in the type species. When the cells are stuffed with sulfur globules, the aggregates appear almost black.

The common gelatinous capsule usually contains a far greater number of closely packed individual colonies than is the case in *Thiocystis violacea.*

Habitat: Mud and stagnant water containing hydrogen sulfide and exposed to light; sulfur springs.

Illustration: Winogradsky, *loc. cit.*, Pl. II, fig. 8.

Genus VII. **Lamprocystis** *Schroeter, 1886.*

(In part, *Clathrocystis* Cohn, Beitr. Biol. Pfl., *1*, Heft 3, 1875, 156; in part, *Cohnia* Winter, in Rabenhorst, Kryptogamen-Flora, 2 Aufl., 1884, 48; not *Cohnia* Kunth, Enumeratio plantarum, *5*, 1850, 35; Schroeter, Die Pilze Schlesiens, in Cohn, Kryptogamen-Flora von Schlesien, *3*, 1, 1886, 151.)

Lam.pro.cys′tis. Gr. adj. *lamprus* bright, brilliant; Gr. noun *cystis* the bladder, a bag; M.L. fem.n. *Lamprocystis* a brilliant bag.

Sulfur purple bacteria which form more or less large aggregates of cells enclosed in a common gelatinous capsule. Individual cells spherical to ovoid. Small aggregates closely resemble those of *Thiocystis*, even to the extent of the tetrad-like arrangement of cells in the small colonies. Behavior of the large aggregates during development appears to be different; the small individual cell groups or colonies do not emerge from the slime capsule until the initially relatively compact cell mass becomes broken up into smaller clusters, these eventually forming a somewhat net-like structure. This behavior has been ascribed to a change in the mode of cell division which at first appears to take place in three perpendicular planes and later presumably changes to a division in only two directions. Cells when free are motile by means of polar flagella. In pure culture also this type rarely, if ever, produces large aggregates with the development here mentioned as characteristic for the genus (Bavendamm, Die farblosen und roten Schwefelbakterien, Pflanzenforschung, Heft 2, 1924, 76). This, along with the other similarities, makes it doubtful whether future studies will result in the retention of the genera *Lamprocystis* and *Thiocystis* side by side. Produce bacteriochlorophyll and carotenoid pigments, coloring the cell masses purplish pink to red. Capable of photosynthesis in the presence of hydrogen sulfide, storing elemental sulfur as globules inside the cells.

The type species is *Lamprocystis roseopersicina* (Kützing) Schroeter.

1. **Lamprocystis roseopersicina** (Kützing, 1849) Schroeter, 1886. (*Protococcus roseopersicinus* Kützing, Species Algarum, Leipzig, 1849, 196; Schroeter, in Cohn, Kryptogamen-Flora von Schlesien, *3*, 1, 1886, 151.)

ro.se.o.per.si.ci'na. L. adj. *roseus* rosy; Gr. noun *persicus* the peach (Persian apple); M.L. adj. *roseopersicinus* rosy peach (-colored).

Cells spherical to ovoid, 2 to 2.5 microns in diameter, up to 5 microns long before cell division. Motile by means of polar flagella.

Winogradsky reports that the cells frequently contain pseudovacuoles.

Habitat: Mud and stagnant water containing hydrogen sulfide and exposed to light; sulfur springs.

Illustrations: Warming, Videnskab. Meddel. naturhistor. Foren., Kjöbenhavn, 1876, Pl. VIII, fig. 3 g; Zopf, Z. Morphol. d. Spaltpflanzen, Leipzig, 1882, Pl. V, fig. 8, 13; Winogradsky, Schwefelbacterien, Leipzig, 1888, Pl. II, fig. 9–15; Bavendamm, Die farblosen und roten Schwefelbakterien, Jena, 1924, Pl. II, fig. 3.

Genus VIII. **Amoebobacter** *Winogradsky, 1888.*

(Schwefelbacterien, Leipzig, 1888, 71.)

A.moe.bo.bac'ter. M.L. noun *Amoeba* a protozoan genus; Gr. noun *amoebe* change, transformation; M.L. noun *bacter* a rod; M.L. mas.n. *Amoebobacter* changeable rod.

Sulfur purple bacteria, usually occurring in aggregates composed of many individuals without a characteristic common capsule. Slime formation can, nevertheless, be observed with very small colonies. With growth of the individual cells, the capsule bursts and the cell mass slowly moves out while the bacteria remain united. The colonies change their shape during growth and in response to environmental influences; the individual cells appear motile and cause the movements of the entire colony. Winogradsky ascribes the coherence of the cell masses to the existence of interconnecting protoplasmic filaments between cells, but these have never been observed, and their occurrence is extremely doubtful. It is much more probable that the bacteria are held together by mucus, though not so much of the latter is produced as to form a clearly discernible capsule. Produce bacteriochlorophyll and carotenoid pigments. Capable of photosynthesis in the presence of hydrogen sulfide, then storing sulfur as droplets inside the cells.

The type species is *Amoebobacter roseus* Winogradsky.

The characterizations of the genera *Amoebobacter*, *Lamprocystis*, *Thiocystis*, *Thiocapsa* and *Thiothece* are based upon the arrangement of individual bacteria in a common capsule. However, from Winogradsky's descriptions of *Amoebobacter* and from pure-culture studies with *Thiocystis* and *Lamprocystis*, the capsules have been shown to vary considerably, depending upon developmental stages and environmental conditions. Therefore it is quite possible that future investigations will show the desirability of restricting the number of genera.

Key to the species of genus **Amoebobacter**.

I. Cells spherical to ovoid, about 2.5 to 3.5 microns in diameter and up to 6 microns in length prior to cell division.

1. *Amoebobacter roseus.*

II. Cells distinctly rod-shaped, about 1.5 to 2 microns in width by 2 to 4 microns in length.
2. *Amoebobacter bacillosus.*
III. Cells spherical, quite small, about 0.5 to 1 micron in diameter.
3. *Amoebobacter granula.*

1. **Amoebobacter roseus** Winogradsky, 1888. (Schwefelbacterien, Leipzig, 1888, 77.) ro'se.us. L. adj. *roseus* rosy.

Cells spherical to ovoid, 2.5 to 3.5 microns in width and up to 6 microns in length. Motile. Often contain pseudovacuoles. Cell aggregates often form transitory hollow spheres or sacks with the bacteria occupying the periphery as a shallow layer. These are reminiscent of stages in the development of *Lamprocystis*.

Habitat: Mud and stagnant water containing hydrogen sulfide and exposed to light; sulfur springs.

Illustrations: Winogradsky, *loc. cit.*, Pl. III, fig. 1–6.

2. **Amoebobacter bacillosus** Winogradsky, 1888. (Winogradsky, Schwefelbacterien, Leipzig, 1888, 78; *Thioderma roseum* Miyoshi, Jour. Coll. Sci., Imp. Univ. Tokyo, Japan, *10*, 1897, 158.)

ba.cil.lo'sus. L. dim.noun *bacillus* a small staff or rod; M.L. adj. *bacillosus* full of (made up of) small rods.

Cells rod-shaped, about 1.5 to 2 microns by 2 to 4 microns. Cells contain pseudovacuoles (aerosomes). Sulfur globules deposited exclusively in peripheral protoplasmic layer, usually quite small.

Miyoshi's incomplete description of *Thioderma roseum* (*loc. cit.*), type species of genus *Thioderma*, is sufficient to make practically certain that it is identical with *Amoebobacter bacillosus*. The description of *Thiodictyon elegans* Winogradsky (*op. cit.*, 1888, 80) suggests that it cannot be distinguished from this species.

Habitat: Mud and stagnant water containing hydrogen sulfide and exposed to light; sulfur springs.

Illustrations: Zopf, Z. Morphol. d. Spaltpfl., Leipzig, 1882, Pl. V, fig. 26–27; Winogradsky, *op. cit.*, 1888, Pl. III, fig. 7.

3. **Amoebobacter granula** Winogradsky, 1888. (Schwefelbacterien, Leipzig, 1888, 78.)

gra'nu.la. L. dim.noun *granulum* a small grain; M.L. fem.n. *granula* a small grain.

Cells spherical, small, about 0.5 to 1.0 micron in diameter. Faint pigmentation; the sulfur inclusions give the cell masses a black appearance. Aggregates are apt to consist of closely-knit masses which are difficult to separate.

When sulfur is stored, a single droplet usually fills most of the cell. Because of the high refractive index of this globule, it becomes difficult if not impossible to make accurate observations of the cell shape.

Habitat: Mud and stagnant water containing hydrogen sulfide and exposed to light; sulfur springs.

Illustration: Winogradsky, *loc. cit.*, Pl. III, fig. 8.

Genus IX. **Thiopolycoccus** *Winogradsky, 1888.*

(Schwefelbacterien, Leipzig, 1888, 79.)

Thi.o.po.ly.coc'cus. Gr. noun *thium* sulfur; Gr. adj. *poly* many; Gr. noun *coccus* a berry; M.L. noun *coccus*; M.L. mas.n. *Thiopolycoccus* with many sulfur cocci.

Sulfur purple bacteria which form dense aggregates of rather solid construction and irregular shape. The colonies appear, in contrast with those of *Amoebobacter*, non-motile and do not tend to form hollow zoogloeal structures by which they are differentiated from *Lamprocystis*. Cell masses held together by mucus which does not, however, appear as a regular capsule. Large clumps may fissure with the formation of irregular shreds and lobes which continue to break up into smaller groups of cells. Individual bacteria spherical, motility not observed. Contain bacteriochlorophyll and carotenoid pigments, so that the aggregates, in accord with the dense packing with individual cells, appear distinctly red.

Capable of photosynthesis in the presence of hydrogen sulfide, when the cells store elemental sulfur as droplets inside the cells.

The type species is *Thiopolycoccus ruber* Winogradsky.

1. **Thiopolycoccus ruber** Winogradsky, 1888. (Schwefelbacterien, Leipzig, 1888, 79.) ru'ber. L. adj. *ruber* red.

Cells spherical, about 1.2 microns in diameter. No motility observed.

Habitat: Mud and stagnant water containing hydrogen sulfide and exposed to light; sulfur springs.

Illustrations: Winogradsky, *loc. cit.*, Pl. IV, fig. 16–18; Issatchenko, Recherches sur les microbes de l'océan glacial arctique, Petrograd, 1914, Pl. II, fig. 7.

Genus X. **Thiospirillum** *Winogradsky, 1888.*

(*Ophidomonas* Ehrenberg, Die Infusionstierchen, Leipzig, 1838, 43; Winogradsky, Schwefelbacterien, Leipzig, 1888, 104.)

Thi.o.spi.ril'lum. Gr. noun *thium* sulfur; M.L. dim.neut.n. *Spirillum* a bacterial genus; Gr. noun *spira* a spiral; M.L. neut.n. *Thiospirillum* sulfur *Spirillum*.

Sulfur purple bacteria, occurring singly as spirally wound cells, motile by means of polar flagella. Contain bacteriochlorophyll and carotenoid pigments, coloring the cells brownish to purplish red. Capable of photosynthesis in the presence of hydrogen sulfide, during which they produce and store, as an intermediate oxidation product, elemental sulfur in the form of droplets inside the cells.

The differentiation of species in this group has been based exclusively on observations with material from natural collections and from laboratory mass cultures. The criteria used are the size and shape of the spirals and the color of the organisms. Not a single representative has so far been obtained and studied in pure culture, so that no information is available concerning the constancy or variability of these characteristics. It is likely, however, that such properties may be greatly influenced by environmental factors. Hence, the following key and descriptions of species are apt to be modified when more extensive studies have been made. The published descriptions of some species make it seem probable that they should not even be incorporated in *Thiospirillum*.

The type species is *Thiospirillum jenense* (Ehrenberg) Winogradsky.

Key to the species of genus **Thiospirillum.**

I. Width of cells 2.5 microns or more.
   A. Color of cells, especially in masses, yellowish brown to orange-brown.
   1. Thiospirillum jenense.
   B. Color of cells deep red or violet.
      1. Cells long, typical spirals; clearly red.
   2. Thiospirillum sanguineum.
      2. Cells short, slightly curved, vibrio-shaped; color purple to violet-red.
   3. Thiospirillum violaceum.
II. Width of cells less than 2.5 microns.
   A. Width of cells 1.5 to 2.5 microns.
   4. Thiospirillum rosenbergii.
   B. Width of cells about 1 micron.
   5. Thiospirillum rufum.

1. **Thiospirillum jenense** (Ehrenberg, 1838) Winogradsky, 1888. (*Ophidomonas jenensis* Ehrenberg, Die Infusionstierchen, Leipzig, 1838, 44; Winogradsky, Schwefel-bacterien, Leipzig, 1888, 104; *Thiospirillum crassum* Hama, Jour. Sci. Hiroshima Univ., Ser. B, Div. 2, Bot., *1*, 1933, 157.)

je.nen'se. M.L. adj. *jenensis* pertaining to

Jena; named for the city of Jena, Germany, where Ehrenberg discovered this organism.

Cells 2.5 to 4.0 microns thick, cylindrical, sometimes pointed at the ends; coiled as spirals, generally 30 to 40 microns in length, but may be as long as 100 microns. Complete turns may measure from 15 to 40 microns with a wave depth of 3 to 7 microns. Polar flagellate. Tufted at both ends. Olive-brown, sepia-brown and reddish brown.

This coloring appears to be the only recognizable difference from *Thiospirillum sanguineum*. *Thiospirillum crassum* Hama (*loc. cit.*), reported to be 3.7 to 4 by 12 to 40 microns and yellowish brown in color, thus becomes indistinguishable from *Thiospirillum jenense*; the 80-microns-long *Thiospirillum jenense* forma *maxima* Szafer (Bull. Acad. Sci. Cracovie, Sér. B, 1910, 162) does not, at present, justify recognition as a special taxonomic entity.

It is even doubtful whether the observed color difference between *Thiospirillum jenense* and *Thiospirillum sanguineum* constitutes a valid criterion for their maintenance as two distinct species (Buder, Jahrb. wiss. Bot., *56*, 1915, 534; Bavendamm, Die farblosen und roten Schwefelbakterien, Pflanzenforschung, Heft 2, 1924, 131).

Habitat: Mud and stagnant water containing hydrogen sulfide and exposed to light; more rarely in sulfur springs.

Illustrations: Zettnow, Ztschr. f. Hyg., *24*, 1897, Pl. II, fig. 49–52; Buder, *op. cit.*, 1915, 534, fig. 1; Szafer, *op. cit.*, 1910, Pl. IV, fig. 4; Hama, *op. cit.*, 1933, Pl. 18, fig. 1, 8a; Pl. 19, fig. 1.

2. **Thiospirillum sanguineum** (Ehrenberg, 1840) Winogradsky, 1888. (*Ophidomonas sanguinea* Ehrenberg, Verhandl. Akad. Wiss. Berlin, 1840, 201; *Spirillum sanguineum* Cohn, Beitr. Biol. Pfl., *1*, Heft 3, 1875, 169; Winogradsky, Schwefelbacterien, Leipzig, 1888, 104.)

san.gui′ne.um. L. adj. *sanguineus* blood-colored, blood-red.

Cells cylindrical, sometimes attenuated at ends, spirally coiled; 2.5 to 4.0 microns in width, commonly about 40 microns long with a range of from 10 to 100 microns. Size and shape of coils variable, complete turns measuring from 15 to 40 microns in length and from ½ to ⅟₁₀ of the length in width. Polar flagellate, usually tufted at both ends. Individual cells rose-red with a grayish hue, groups of cells deep red. Sulfur droplets numerous under appropriate conditions.

Habitat: Mud and stagnant water containing hydrogen sulfide and exposed to light; rarely in sulfur springs.

Illustrations: Cohn, *op. cit.*, 1875, Pl. VI, fig. 15; Warming, Vidensk. Meddel. naturhist. Foren., Kjöbenhavn, 1876, Pl. VII, fig. 8; Buder, Jahrb. wiss. Bot., *56*, 1915, 534, fig. 2.

3. **Thiospirillum violaceum** (Warming, 1876) Winogradsky, 1888. (*Spirillum violaceum* Warming, Vidensk. Meddel. naturhist. Foren., Kjöbenhavn, 1876, 395; Winogradsky, Schwefelbacterien, Leipzig, 1888, 104.)

vi.o.la′ce.um. L. adj. *violaceus* violet-colored.

Cells short and fat, 3 to 4 by 8 to 10 microns, ends smoothly rounded. Slightly curved, bean- or vibrio-shaped. Only rarely are they twisted suggesting a spirillum. Polar flagellate.

The shape of cell seems to fit the genus *Chromatium* rather than *Thiospirillum*, and Warming (*op. cit.*, 1876, 395) emphasizes the resemblance to *Chromatium okenii*.

Color: Bluish violet; this color may be related to a scarcity of sulfur droplets in the cells.

Habitat: Mud and stagnant water.

Illustration: Warming, *op. cit.*, 1876, Pl. VII, fig. 3.

4. **Thiospirillum rosenbergii** (Warming, 1875) Winogradsky, 1888. (*Spirillum rosenbergii* Warming, Vidensk. Meddel. naturhist. Foren., Kjöbenhavn, *7*, 1875, 346; Winogradsky, Schwefelbacterien, Leipzig, 1888, 104.)

ro.sen.ber′gi.i. M.L. gen.noun *rosenbergii* of Rosenberg; named for Rosenberg, a Danish algologist.

Cells 1.5 to 2.5 by 4 to 12 microns; coiled, with turns of about 6 to 7.5 microns in length and variable width up to 3 or 4 microns. Color very dark, due to numerous sulfur globules. Color of protoplasm not recorded.

Habitat: Mud and stagnant water containing hydrogen sulfide and exposed to light. Probably widely distributed, but less frequently recorded as the organism is not so spectacular as the large *Thiospirillum jenense* and *Thiospirillum sanguineum.*

Illustration: Warming, *op. cit.*, 1876, Pl. X, fig. 12.

5. Thiospirillum rufum (Perty, 1852) Migula, 1900. (*Spirillum rufum* Perty, Bern, 1852, 179; Migula, Syst. d. Bakt. *2*, 1900, 1050.)

ru'fum. L. adj. *rufus* red, reddish.

General characteristics presumably those of the genus, although it does not appear either from Perty's description or from that of Migula (*loc. cit.*), Bavendamm (Die farb-losen und roten Schwefelbakterien Jena, 1924, 132) or Huber-Pestalozzi (Die Binnengewässer, *16*, Heft 1, Das Phytoplankton des Süsswassers, Stuttgart, 1938, 304) that the cells ever contain sulfur globules. Only the red color is emphasized. Consequently, it is quite possible that this organism belongs in the genus *Rhodospirillum.*

Cells 1.0 by 8 to 18 microns; coiled to occupy $1\frac{1}{2}$ to 4 turns, the latter commonly 4 microns wide by 4 microns long. These dimensions agree with those of *Rhodospirillum rubrum* (Esmarch) Molisch, and it seems probable that the two organisms are identical.

Habitat: Found in red slime spots on the side of a well. Mud and stagnant bodies of water.

Illustration: Migula, Syst. d. Bakt., *1*, 1897, Pl. III, fig. 7.

Genus XI. Rhabdomonas Cohn, 1875.

(Cohn, Beitr. Biol. Pfl., *1*, Heft 3, 1875, 167; *Rhabdochromatium* Winogradsky, Schwefelbacterien, Leipzig, 1888, 100.)

Rhab.do.mo'nas. Gr. noun *rhabdus* a rod; Gr. noun *monas* a unit, monad; M.L. noun *Monas* a protozoan genus; M.L. fem.n. *Rhabdomonas* the rod monad.

Sulfur purple bacteria, as a rule occurring singly in the form of rather irregular, long rods to filaments, exhibiting more or less pronounced swellings, or club and spindle shapes. Filamentous structures, sometimes with constrictions, giving the filament the appearance of a string of beads. These may be surrounded by a relatively inconspicuous slime capsule which can be rendered visible by India ink. The less distorted cell types are frequently motile by means of polar flagella. Produce bacteriochlorophyll and carotenoid pigments, coloring the cells pinkish to purplish red. Capable of photosynthesis in the presence of hydrogen sulfide and then storing sulfur globules as an intermediate oxidation product inside the cells.

The status of this genus is doubtful. Winogradsky (*loc. cit.*) recognized the similarity of its members to species of *Chromatium* and the occurrence of many intermediate forms which make a sharp distinction between the two genera impossible. He preferred the designation of *Rhabdochromatium* as a sub-genus. Warming (Videnskab. Meddel. naturhist. Foren., Kjöbenhavn, 1876, 320 ff.), Nadson (Bull. Jard. Impér. Bot. St. Pétersb., *3*, 1903, 116), van Niel (Arch. f. Mikrobiol., *3*, 1931, 61) and Ellis (Sulphur Bacteria, London and New York, 1932, 151) considered the species of *Rhabdochromatium* as abnormal growth forms (involution forms) of corresponding species of *Chromatium*, while Lauterborn (Verhandl. naturhistor.-medizin. Vereins, Heidelberg, N.F., *13*, 1915, 424), Buder (Jahrb. wiss. Bot., *58*, 1919, 534) and Bavendamm (Die farblosen und roten Schwefelbakterien, Pflanzenforschung, Heft 2, 1924, 129) favor generic rank.

The type species is *Rhabdomonas rosea* Cohn.

Key to the species of genus Rhabdomonas.

I. Cells not containing calcium carbonate inclusions in addition to sulfur globules.
  A. Cells more than 3 microns in width.
  1. *Rhabdomonas rosea.*

B. Cells less than 3 microns in width.
2. *Rhabdomonas gracilis.*
II. Cells containing calcium carbonate inclusions in addition to sulfur globules.
3. *Rhabdomonas linsbaueri.*

1. **Rhabdomonas rosea** Cohn, 1875. (Cohn, Beitr. Biol. Pfl., *1*, Heft 3, 1875, 167; *Beggiatoa roseo-persicina* Zopf, Z. Morphol. d. Spaltpflanzen, Leipzig, 1882, 30; *Rhabdochromatium roseum* Winogradsky, Schwefelbacterien, Leipzig, 1888, 100; *Rhabdochromatium fusiforme* Winogradsky, *ibid.*, 102.) ro'se.a. L. adj. *roseus* rosy, rose-red.

Cells uneven in width and length, often swollen to spindle-shaped, sometimes tending towards filamentous growth. The greatest width of a spindle-shaped or fusiform cell may be close to 10 microns; in the more filamentous structures it is usually around 5 microns. The length varies between 10 and 30 microns for single cells; filamentous forms, frequently showing bulges and constrictions suggestive of compound structures in which cell division has been incomplete, may attain considerably greater lengths, up to 100 microns. The ends of spindle-shaped cells often taper to very fine points or attenuated fibers; also, filaments are generally thinner toward the extremities. Single individuals and short filaments are motile by means of polar flagella, long filaments rarely motile. The ends of a filament may become pinched off and swim away.

Color rose-red; cells are usually filled with sulfur globules.

There is no good reason for maintaining *Rhabdomonas fusiformis* (*Rhabdochromatium fusiforme* Winogradsky) as a separate species; the variations in size and shape bring this form well within the range of *Rhabdomonas rosea*. Present indications strongly suggest that the latter species should be regarded as a peculiar developmental form of *Chromatium okenii*.

Habitat: Mud and stagnant water containing hydrogen sulfide and exposed to light; sulfur springs.

Illustrations: Cohn, *op. cit.*, 1875, Pl. VI, fig. 14; Warming, Vidensk. Meddel. naturhistor. Foren., Kjöbenhavn, 1876, Pl. VII, fig. 1c-e; Zopf, *op. cit.*, 1882, Pl. V, fig. 2b; Winogradsky, *op. cit.*, 1888, Pl. IV, fig. 9–11, 13–14.

2. **Rhabdomonas gracilis** (Warming, 1876) Bergey et al., 1923. (*Monas gracilis* Warming, Vidensk. Meddel. naturhist. Foren., Kjöbenhavn, 1876, 331; *Rhabdochromatium minus* Winogradsky, Schwefelbacterien, Leipzig, 1888, 102; *Rhodocapsa suspensa* Molisch, Die Purpurbakterien, Jena, 1907, 17; Bergey et al., Manual, 1st ed., 1923, 402.) gra'ci.lis. L. adj. *gracilis* thin, slender.

Cells much smaller than those of *Rhabdomonas rosea* and with less tendency to form fusiform cells. Usually filamentous, more or less cylindrical, often with constrictions, but found up to 60 microns in length. Shorter filaments motile. Polar flagellate. Slime formation may occur under special conditions. Rose-red. Sulfur globules. Probably an abnormal growth form of *Chromatium virosum*.

Habitat: Mud and stagnant water containing hydrogen sulfide and exposed to light; sulfur springs.

Illustrations: Warming, *op. cit.*, 1876, Pl. VII, fig. 5; Winogradsky, *op. cit.*, 1888, Pl. IV, fig. 12; Molisch, *op. cit.*, 1907, Pl. II, fig. 11–12.

3. **Rhabdomonas linsbaueri** (Gicklhorn, 1921) van Niel, 1948. (*Rhabdochromatium linsbaueri* Gicklhorn, Ber. d. deut. bot. Ges., *39*, 1921, 312; van Niel, in Manual, 6th ed., 1948, 855.) lins.bau'er.i. M.L. gen.noun *linsbaueri* of Linsbauer; named for K. Linsbauer, an Austrian botanist.

Cells resemble those of *Rhabdomonas rosea*, irregular, rod-shaped, 3 to 5 microns wide, up to 30 microns in length.

The characteristic feature of the species, and the chief means of differentiation, is the occurrence of calcium carbonate inclusions in addition to the sulfur globules in the cells. Whether this is strictly an environmentally conditioned characteristic, due to the photosynthetic development of the bacteria in a medium rich in calcium ions, so that calcium carbonate is precipitated as the alkalinity increases, has not yet been established but seems possible. In that case the identity of this species with *Rhabdomonas rosea* would become evident.

Source: From a pond near Graz, Austria.

Habitat: Fresh water.

Genus XII. **Rhodothece** *Molisch, 1907*.

(Die Purpurbakterien, Jena, 1907, 19.)

Rho.do.the'ce. Gr. noun *rhodum* the rose; Gr. noun *thece* box (capsule); *Rhodothece* the rose capsule.

Sulfur purple bacteria, occurring singly, not aggregated in families. Cells spherical, each surrounded by a rather wide capsule which is, however, rarely visible without special staining. Motility not observed. Contain bacteriochlorophyll and carotenoid pigments, coloring the cells reddish. Capable of photosynthesis in the presence of hydrogen sulfide; the cells then store sulfur globules, arising as an intermediate oxidation product of the sulfide.

In view of the experiences of Bavendamm and others that a number of representatives of the sulfur purple bacteria, characterized by typical colonial aggregates when found in nature, may develop as single cells in pure culture, it is quite conceivable that the genus *Rhodothece* is identical with some other genus, e.g., *Thiopedia* or *Lamprocystis*, and that these genera represent different growth forms induced by environmental conditions.

The type species is *Rhodothece pendens* Molisch.

1. **Rhodothece pendens** Molisch, 1907. (Die Purpurbakterien, Jena, 1907, 19.)

pen'dens. L. part.adj. *pendens* hanging.

Cells spherical, frequently occurring as diplococci, occasionally as very short chains or clumps of 3 to 5 individuals. 1.8 to 2.5 microns in diameter. Produce rather abundant slime. Cells embedded in individual capsules which are rarely visible without staining (India ink). Characteristic is the regular occurrence of pseudovacuoles (aerosomes) which are supposed to keep the cells suspended in liquid media. Refractive phenomena due to the pseudovacuoles and to the sulfur globules distort the cell shape under ordinary illumination so that bacteria appear as polygons rather than round cells. Usually 2 aerosomes and 2 sulfur globules per cell. Color not observable in individual bacteria. Cell groups are rose-red. Motility not observed.

Habitat: Mud and stagnant water containing hydrogen sulfide and exposed to light. Not reported from sulfur springs.

Illustrations: Molisch, Die Purpurbakterien, Jena, 1907, Pl. II, fig. 13–14.

Genus XIII. **Chromatium** *Perty, 1852*.

(Zur Kenntniss kleinster Lebensformen, Bern, 1852, 174.)

Chro.ma'ti.um. Gr. noun *chromatium* color, paint.

Cells occur singly, more or less ovoid, bean- or vibrio-shaped or short rods. The last-mentioned are often thick-cylindrical with rounded ends. Motile by means of polar flagella. Contain bacteriochlorophyll and carotenoid pigments, coloring the cells various shades of red. Capable of photosynthesis in the presence of hydrogen sulfide and storing elemental sulfur as an incomplete oxidation product in the form of globules inside the cells.

At present the genus contains twelve described species. Differentiation of these species has, in the past, been based almost entirely upon size and shape of individual cells, often with complete disregard for the variability of these criteria. The unsatisfactory and arbitrary nature of such a classification has occasionally been pointed out, and with much justification. Winogradsky (Schwefelbacterien, Leipzig, 1888, 98) mentions the many transitional stages that can be observed between *Chromatium okenii* and *Chromatium weissei*; Strzeszewski (Bullet. Acad. Sci., Cracovie, Sér. B, 1913, 321) holds that it is impossible to distinguish, on the basis of sizes or otherwise, between *Chromatium weissei* and *Chromatium minus*. Such contentions, derived from observations on material from natural collections or crude cultures, have been greatly strengthened by studies with pure cultures of species of *Chromatium*. Thus van Niel (Arch. f. Mikrobiol., *3*, 1931, 59) reported variations in width from 1 to 4 microns, and in length from 2 to 10 microns or even up to 50 microns; Manten (Antonie van Leeuwenhoek, *8*, 1942, 164 ff.) found size differences of 1 to 14 microns with a pure culture of an organism that he identified as *Chromatium okenii*. Often the differences in size of a pure culture can be related to special environmental conditions. On account of such results a designation of species on the basis of size relations alone is manifestly unsatisfactory. Moreover, the available data do not suggest that differences in shape, color or arrangement of sulfur globules can be used more effectively. Lack of adequate experimental results with a sufficiently large number and variety of pure cultures prevents a more rational classification at present.

The previously proposed species have been listed below with their respective characteristics and arranged as far as possible in the order of decreasing width.

Two *Chromatium* species have been described as containing inclusions of calcium carbonate in addition to sulfur globules. As in the case of *Rhabdomonas linsbaueri*, it is not known whether this feature may be a direct consequence of the calcium ion content and pH of the environment and thus fail to have taxonomic significance.

The type species is *Chromatium okenii* Perty.

1. Chromatium gobii Issatchenko, 1914. (Recherches sur les microbes de l'océan glacial arctique, Petrograd, 1914, 253.)

go'bi.i. M.L. gen.noun *gobii* of Gobi; named for Prof. X. Gobi.

Cells 10 microns by 20 to 25 microns.

Source: From sea water of the Arctic Ocean.

Habitat: Presumably ubiquitous in the colder portions of the Ocean at least.

Illustration: Issatchenko, *loc. cit.*, Pl. II, fig. 12.

2. Chromatium warmingii (Cohn, 1875) Migula, 1900. (*Monas warmingii* Cohn, Beitr. Biol. Pfl., *1*, Heft 3, 1875, 167; Migula, Syst. d. Bakt., *2*, 1900, 1048.)

war.min'gi.i. Named for Eugene Warming, a Danish botanist; M.L. gen.noun *warmingii* of Warming.

Cells 8 by 15 to 20 microns, also smaller (Cohn).

Illustration: Cohn, *op. cit.*, 1875. Pl. VI, fig. 11.

3. Chromatium linsbaueri Gicklhorn, 1921. (Ber. d. deut. botan. Ges., *39*, 1921, 312.)

lins.bau'er.i. Named for K. Linsbauer, an Austrian botanist; M.L. gen.noun *linsbaueri* of Linsbauer.

Cells 6 by up to 15 microns (Gicklhorn); 6 to 8 microns in width (Ellis, Sulphur Bacteria, London and New York, 1932,

147). Special characteristic is the occurrence of calcium carbonate inclusions. Otherwise resembles *Chromatium okenii*.

Source: From a pool in the Stiftingtal, near Graz, Austria.

Habitat: Fresh water.

Illustrations: Gicklhorn, *op. cit.*, 1921, 314, fig. 1; Ellis, *op. cit.*, 1932, 148, fig. 31.

4. Chromatium okenii (Ehrenberg, 1838) Perty, 1852. (*Monas okenii* Ehrenberg, Infusionsthierchen, Leipzig, 1838; Perty, Zur Kenntniss kleinster Lebensformen, Bern, 1852, 174.) This is the type species of genus *Chromatium*.

o.ke'ni.i. Named for L. Oken, a German naturalist; M.L. gen.noun *okenii* of Oken.

Cells 5.6 to 6.3 by 7.5 to 15 microns (Cohn); minimum width 4.5 microns (Issatchenko, Borodin Jubilee Vol., 1929?, 8); with many transitions to *Chromatium weissei* (Winogradsky, Schwefelbacterien, Leipzig, 1888, 92). Also: 3.5 by 8 to 12 microns and varying in size from 1 to 15 microns (Manten, Antonie van Leeuwenhoek, *8*, 1942, 164).

Illustrations: Cohn, Beitr. Biol. Pfl., *1*, Heft 3, 1875, Pl. VI, fig. 12; Winogradsky, *op. cit.*, 1888, Pl. IV, fig. 3–4; Issatchenko, Recherches sur les microbes de l'océan glacial arctique, Petrograd, 1914, Pl. II, fig. 9.

5. Chromatium weissei Perty, 1852.

(Zur Kenntniss kleinster Lebensformen, Bern, 1852, 174.)

weis'se.i. Named for J. F. Weisse, a zoologist; M.L. gen.noun *weissei* of Weisse.

Cells 4.2 by 5.7 to 11.5 microns (Perty); also 3 to 4 by 7 to 9 microns (Issatchenko, Borodin Jubilee Volume, 1929?, 8); transitions to *Chromatium okenii* (Winogradsky, Schwefelbacterien, Leipzig, 1888, 92); transitions to *Chromatium minus* (Strzeszewski, Bull. Acad. Sci., Cracovie, Sér. B, 1913, 321).

Illustrations: Winogradsky, *op. cit.*, 1888, Pl. IV, fig. 1-2, Miyoshi, Jour. Coll. Sci., Imp. Univ. Tokyo, Japan, *10*, 1897, Pl. XIV, fig. 15.

6. Chromatium cuculliferum Gicklhorn, 1920. (Cent. f. Bakt., II Abt., *50*, 1920, 419.)

cu.cul.li'fe.rum. L. noun *cucullus* hood, cap; L. v. *fero* to bear; M.L. adj. *cucullifer* cap-bearing.

Cells 4 by 6 to 8 microns (Gicklhorn); according to Bavendamm (Schwefelbakterien, Jena, 1924, 127), identical with *Chromatium warmingii* forma *minus*. Gicklhorn claims this organism to be colorless, which appears very doubtful.

Source: From the pond in the Annen Castle Park, Graz, Austria.

Habitat: Fresh-water ponds.

Illustration: Gicklhorn, *op. cit.*, 1920, 419, fig. 2.

7. Chromatium minus Winogradsky, 1888. (Schwefelbacterien, Leipzig, 1888, 99.)

mi'nus. L. comp.adj. *minor* (neut. *minus*) less, smaller.

Cells 3 by 3.5 to 7 microns (Winogradsky); also 1.7 to 3 microns in width and up to 8.5 microns in length (Issatchenko, Borodin Jubilee Volume, 1929?, 9); all transitions to *Chromatium weissei* from which it cannot be distinguished (Strzeszewski, Bull. Acad. Sci., Cracovie, Sér. B, 1913, 321).

Illustrations: Winogradsky, *op. cit.*, 1888, Pl. IV, fig. 5; Miyoshi, Jour. Coll. Sci., Imp. Univ., Tokyo, Japan, *10*, 1897, Pl. XIV, fig. 16; Issatchenko, Recherches sur les microbes de l'océan glacial arctique, Petrograd, 1914, Pl. II, fig. 10-11.

8. Chromatium vinosum (Ehrenberg, 1838). Winogradsky, 1888. (*Monas vinosa* Ehrenberg, Die Infusionstierchen, Leipzig, 1838, 11; Winogradsky, Schwefelbacterien, Leipzig, 1888, 99.)

vi.no'sum. L. adj. *vinosus* full of wine.

Cells 2 by 2.5 to 5 microns; also 1.4 to 3 by 1.5 to 5 microns (Jimbo, Botan. Magaz. Tokyo, *51*, 1937, 872); 1.7 to 2 by 2 to 9 microns (Issatchenko, Borodin Jubilee Volume, 1929?, 9); or 1 to 1.3 microns by 2.5 to 3 microns (Schrammeck, Beitr. Biol. d. Pflanzen, *22*, 1935, 317). Jimbo considers *Thioderma roseum* Miyoshi to be identical with *Chromatium vinosum*.

Illustrations: Winogradsky, *op. cit.*, 1888, Pl. IV, 6-7; Miyoshi, Jour. Coll. Sci., Imp. Univ. Tokyo, Japan, *10*, 1897, Pl. XIV, fig. 17; Nadson, Bull. Jard. Imp. Botan., St. Pétersbourg, *12*, 1912, Pl. III, fig. 1-2.

9. Chromatium violaceum Perty, 1852. (Zur Kenntniss kleinster Lebensformen, Bern, 1852, 174.)

vi.o.la'ce.um. L. adj. *violaceus* violet-colored.

Cells about 2 by 2 to 3 microns. According to Cohn (Beitr. Biol. Pfl., *1*, Heft 3, 1875, 166), probably identical with *Chromatium vinosum*. Apparently includes various sizes.

10. Chromatium molischii (Bersa, 1926) van Niel, 1948. (*Pseudomonas molischii* Bersa, Planta, *2*, 1926, 375; van Niel, in Manual, 6th ed., 1948, 858.)

mo.li'schi.i. Named for H. Molisch, an Austrian botanist; M.L. gen.noun *molischii* of Molisch.

Cells about 2 by 2.5 to 8 microns. Supposedly contain calcium carbonate as inclusions.

Illustration: Bersa, *op. cit.*, 1926, 376, fig. 3.

11. Chromatium gracile Strzeszewski, 1913. (Bull. Acad. Sci., Cracovie, Sér. B, 1913, 321.)

gra'ci.le. L. adj. *gracilis* thin, slender.

Cells 1 to 1.3 by 2 to 6 microns; also to 1.5 microns in width (Issatchenko, Études microbiologiques des Lacs de Boue, Leningrad, 1927, 114).

Illustration: Strzeszewski, *op. cit.*, 1913,

Pl. XXXIX, fig. 1–2; Tokuda, Botan. Magaz., Tokyo, *50*, 1936, 339, fig. 1–23.

12. Chromatium minutissimum Winogradsky, 1888. (Schwefelbacterien, Leipzig, 1888, 100.)

mi.nu.tis'si.mum. L. sup.adj. *minutissimus* very small.

Cells about 1 to 1.2 by 2 microns. Also from 0.5 to 0.7 by 0.6 to 1 micron (Issatchenko, Recherches sur les microbes de l'océan glacial arctique, Petrograd, 1914, 253), and 1 to 3 by 2 to 5 microns (Issatchenko, Borodin Jubilee Volume, 1929?, 9).

Illustrations: Winogradsky, *op. cit.*, 1888, Pl. IV, fig. 8; Miyoshi, Jour. Coll. Sci., Imp. Univ., Tokyo, Japan, *10*, 1897, Pl. XIV, fig. 18.

FAMILY II. ATHIORHODACEAE MOLISCH, 1907.

(Die Purpurbakterien, Jena, 1907, 28.)

A.thi.o.rho.da'ce.ae. Gr. pref. *a* without; Gr. noun *thium* sulfur; Gr. noun *rhodum* the rose; *-aceae* ending to denote a family; M.L. fem.pl.n. *Athiorhodaceae* (probably intended to mean) the family of the non-sulfur red bacteria.

Unicellular bacteria, of relatively small size, occurring as spheres, short rods, vibrios, long rods and spirals. Motility is due to the presence of polar flagella. Gram-negative. They produce a pigment system composed of bacteriochlorophyll and one or more carotenoids, coloring the cells yellowish brown, olive-brown, dark brown or various shades of red. Color usually not observable with single cells but only with cell masses. Generally microaerophilic, although many representatives may grow at full atmospheric oxygen tension. Capable of development under strictly anaerobic conditions, but only in illuminated cultures by virtue of a photosynthetic metabolism. The latter is dependent upon the presence of extraneous hydrogen donors, such as alcohols, fatty acids, hydroxy- and keto-acids, and does not proceed with the evolution of molecular oxygen. Those members which can grow in the presence of air can also be cultivated in darkness, but only under aerobic conditions.

The growth requirements of some of the species in this family have been reported by Hutner (Arch. Biochem., *3*, 1944, 439; Jour. Bact., *52*, 1946, 217; Jour. Gen. Microbiol., *4*, 1950, 286); his findings are incorporated in the descriptions which follow.

Key to the genera of family **Athiorhodaceae.**

I. Cells rod-shaped or spherical, not spiral-shaped.

Genus I. *Rhodopseudomonas*, p. 53.

II. Cells spiral-shaped.

Genus II. *Rhodospirillum*, p. 58.

Genus I. **Rhodopseudomonas** *Kluyver and van Niel, 1937, emend. van Niel, 1944.*

(Includes *Rhodobacillus* Molisch, Die Purpurbakterien, Jena, 1907, 14; *Rhodobacterium* Molisch, *ibid.*, 16; *Rhodococcus* Molisch, *ibid.*, 20; *Rhodovibrio* Molisch, *ibid.*, 21; *Rhodocystis* Molisch, *ibid.*, 22; *Rhodonostoc* Molisch, *ibid.*, 23; *Rhodosphaera* Buchanan, Jour. Bact., *3*, 1918, 472; *Rhodorhagus* (sic) Bergey et al., Manual, 2nd ed., 1925, 414; *Rhodomonas* Kluyver and van Niel, Zent. f. Bakt., II Abt., *94*, 1936, 397; not *Rhodomonas* Orla-Jensen, Cent. f. Bakt., II Abt., *22*, 1909, 331; Kluyver and van Niel, in Czurda and Maresch, Arch. f. Mikrobiol., *8*, 1937, 119; *Rhodorrhagus* Bergey et al., Manual, 5th ed., 1939, 905; van Niel, Bact. Rev., *8*, 1944, 86.)

Rho.do.pseu.do.mo'nas. Gr. noun *rhodum* the rose; Gr. adj. *pseudes* false; Gr. noun *monas* monad, unit; M.L. fem.n. *Pseudomonas* a bacterial genus; M.L. fem.n. *Rhodopseudomonas* the rose *Pseudomonas*.

Spherical and rod-shaped bacteria, motile by means of polar flagella. Gram-negative.

Contain bacteriochlorophyll which enables them to carry out a photosynthetic metabolism. The latter is dependent upon the presence of extraneous oxidizable substances and proceeds without the evolution of molecular oxygen. Though some members can oxidize inorganic substrates, none appears to be strictly autotrophic due to the need for special organic growth factors. Produce accessory pigments causing the cultures, especially when kept in light, to appear in various shades of brownish yellow to deep red.

The type species is *Rhodopseudomonas palustris* (Molisch) van Niel.

Keys to the species of genus **Rhodopseudomonas**.

I. Based upon morphological characters.
  A. Cells clearly rod-shaped in all media.
  1. Cells short, somewhat curved, to long branched rods, size of young and short cells 0.6 to 0.8 by 1.2 to 2 microns; in older cultures up to 10 microns long; do not form slime; liquid cultures, when young, or after shaking, evenly turbid. Color red to dark brown-red.
  1. *Rhodopseudomonas palustris.*
  2. Cells slender rods, 0.5 by 1.2 microns, usually clumped together in extensive slime masses. Cultures pale brown to peach-colored.
  2. *Rhodopseudomonas gelatinosa.*
  B. Cells more or less spherical in media at pH below 7.
  1. In media at pH about 7 clearly rod-shaped, 1 by 1 to 2.5 microns. Chains of cells frequent and in characteristic zigzag arrangement.
  3. *Rhodopseudomonas capsulata.*
  2. In media at pH above 7 cells still predominantly spherical, 0.7 to 4 microns in diameter. Mostly single, little tendency to chain formation.
  4. *Rhodopseudomonas spheroides.*
II. Based chiefly on physiological properties.
  A. Gelatin liquefied.
  2. *Rhodopseudomonas gelatinosa.*
  B. Gelatin not liquefied.
  1. Does not produce mucus in media at pH above 8. Color the same under aerobic and anaerobic conditions of growth.
  1. *Rhodopseudomonas palustris.*
  2. Produce mucus in media at pH above 8. Color brown in anaerobic, red in aerobic culture.
    a. Develops readily in media with 0.2 per cent propionate as the chief oxidation substrate. Mucus production marked at pH above 8, but very limited between 7 and 8.
  3. *Rhodopseudomonas capsulata.*
    aa. Does not develop in media with 0.2 per cent propionate as the main oxidation substrate. Slime formation extensive at pH above 7.
  4. *Rhodopseudomonas spheroides.*
III. Based principally upon biochemical characters.
  A. Thiosulfate used as main oxidation substrate.
  1. *Rhodopseudomonas palustris.*
  B. Thiosulfate not used.
  1. Propionate (0.2 per cent) used.
  3. *Rhodopseudomonas capsulata.*
  2. Propionate not used.
    a. Mannitol and sorbitol (0.2 per cent) used.
  4. *Rhodopseudomonas spheroides.*
    aa. Mannitol and sorbitol not used.
  2. *Rhodopseudomonas gelatinosa.*

1. **Rhodopseudomonas palustris** (Molisch, 1907) van Niel, 1944. (*Rhodobacillus palustris* Molisch, *Rhodobacterium capsulatum* Molisch and *Rhodovibrio parvus* Molisch, Die Purpurbakterien, Jena, 1907, 14, 18 and 21; van Niel, Bact. Rev., 8, 1944, 89.) pa.lus′tris. L. adj. *paluster* marshy, swampy.

Cells usually distinctly rod-shaped, though in young cultures very short, lightly curved rods may often predominate. Size variable, even for the same strain, and strongly influenced by age of culture and composition of medium. Rather consistently short cells in young cultures in yeast extract, especially when incubated anaerobically in the light or in anaerobic cultures with substrates, such as malonate, which permit only a slow and scant development. Dimensions in such cultures 0.6 to 0.8 by 1.2 to 2 microns. More often, especially in older cultures, cells are much longer, up to 10 microns. Highly characteristic is the pronounced tendency to the formation of irregularly shaped, bent and crooked long rods, occasionally swollen at one or both extremities, and frequently suggesting branching. Such cells usually form clusters reminiscent of *Corynebacterium* and *Mycobacterium* cultures.

Cells in young cultures actively motile by means of polar flagella; irregular and long cells as a rule non-motile. Gram-negative.

Growth in liquid media never mucoid; sediment in older cultures homogeneous and smooth, readily redispersible.

Color varies considerably, depending upon the medium, and especially in anaerobic illuminated cultures. Where development is slight (as in malonate, thiosulfate and, usually, glycerol media), the color is a light pink; in media containing fatty acids, more nearly dark reddish brown. Color due to bacteriochlorophyll and a number of different carotenoid pigments; most strains produce, in addition, a water-soluble, noncarotenoid, bluish red pigment which diffuses into the culture medium.

In yeast extract cultures growth is possible over the range pH 6 to 8.5. With certain substrates, especially fatty acids, the combined effect of low pH and a substrate concentration of 0.1 to 0.2 per cent may prevent growth. No characteristic odors save that old cultures may develop a distinct ionone-like fragrance. Gelatin is not liquefied; leucine is generally utilized as a substrate.

Most strains are able to grow on the surface of agar plates or slants; a few, especially when first isolated, appear more sensitive to oxygen and develop only in stabs in which the upper region may remain free of growth. Generally such strains can be adapted to grow at full atmospheric oxygen tension.

Most fatty acids and hydroxy acids are adequate oxidation substrates. All cultures can grow at the expense of thiosulfate and produce rapid and profuse growth in glutarate and ethanol media. No development in media containing, as the chief oxidation substrate, 0.2 per cent sorbitol, glucose or mannose, even though these substances are not inhibitory. Molecular hydrogen can be oxidized.

All cultures can develop anaerobically in illuminated cultures by photosynthesis.

p-amino-benzoic acid is required for growth (Hutner).

Optimum temperature generally rather high, good development being possible up to 37° C. However, certain strains exhibit a lower optimum temperature.

Distinctive characters: Morphological resemblance to species of *Mycobacterium* in old cultures, ability to grow with thiosulfate as the chief oxidizable substrate, and failure to develop in media which contain carbohydrates or sugar alcohols in a concentration of 0.2 per cent as the main oxidizable compounds.

Habitat: Regularly found in mud and stagnant bodies of water.

Illustrations: Molisch, *op. cit.*, 1907, Plate I, fig. 1, 2; Plate II, fig. 10; van Niel, *op. cit.*, 1944, fig. 1–3, p. 18, and fig. 18–26, p. 90.

2. **Rhodopseudomonas gelatinosa** (Molisch, 1907) van Niel, 1944. (*Rhodocystis gelatinosa* Molisch, Die Purpurbakterien, Jena, 1907, 22; van Niel, Bact. Rev., 8, 1944, 98.)

ge.la.ti.no′sa. L. part.adj. *gelatus* frozen, stiffened; M.L. *gelatinum* gelatin, that which stiffens; M.L. adj. *gelatinosus* full of gelatin, gelatinous.

Cells in young cultures short and small rods, approximately 0.5 by 1 to 2 microns. In old cultures much longer, up to 15 microns, and then irregularly curved rods, often swollen and gnarled in places up to 1 micron in width. In this stage the cells bear some resemblance to those found in old cultures of *Rhodopseudomonas palustris*, but the characteristic *Mycobacterium*-like clusters of the latter are absent. Single cells infrequent due to a copious mucus production in all media which causes the cells to clump together. While young cells are actively motile by means of polar flagella, motility is often difficult to ascertain as a result of the pronounced tendency to conglomerate; the individuals in the clumps appear to be non-motile. Gram-negative. Gelatin is liquefied; of the single amino acids alanine, asparagine, aspartic and glutamic acids appear generally satisfactory substrates.

Color quite distinctive in most anaerobic cultures as a pale, delicate, pinkish shade, rather peach-colored. Only in the presence of rather high concentrations of yeast extract (when a much heavier growth is obtained than with low concentrations supplemented with 0.2 per cent of various single oxidation substrates) do the slimy cell masses appear a dirty, faded brown. Color is due to bacteriochlorophyll and carotenoid pigments. Occasionally a water-soluble, non-carotenoid, bluish red pigment is produced which diffuses into the culture medium.

In yeast extract, growth occurs over a pH range extending from at least 6.0 to 8.5.

Cultures produce a characteristic acrid odor.

More sensitive to fatty acids than are other species of *Rhodopseudomonas*; with 0.2 per cent propionate no growth occurs. The best single oxidizable substrates appear to be ethanol, glucose, fructose and mannose, as well as a variety of amino acids. Citrate also permits good growth; not, on the other hand, glycerol, mannitol, sorbitol or tartrate in the usual concentration of 0.2 per cent.

Thiosulfate is not oxidized; behavior towards molecular hydrogen unknown.

More pronouncedly microaerophilic than the other *Rhodopseudomonas* species; most cultures cannot develop on aerobically incubated slants or agar plates.

Capable of strictly anaerobic development in illuminated cultures by virtue of a photosynthetic metabolism.

Thiamin plus biotin is required for growth (Hutner).

Temperature relations so far unknown.

Distinctive characters: The small size of the individual cells and the pronounced clumping which causes the cultures to be exceptionally stringy; the unusual color of the cell masses; the ability to liquefy gelatin, to utilize citrate and a number of amino acids. Correlated with these is the failure to grow in media with 0.2 per cent propionate, tartrate and glycerol.

Habitat: Regularly present in stagnant bodies of water and in mud.

Illustrations: Molisch, *op. cit.*, 1907, Plate I, fig. 8; van Niel, *op. cit.*, 1944, fig. 55–60, p. 99; fig. 61–66, p. 100.

3. **Rhodopseudomonas capsulata** (Molisch, 1907) van Niel, 1944. (*Rhodonostoc capsulatum* Molisch, Die Purpurbakterien, Jena, 1907, 23; *Rhodopseudomonas capsulatus* (sic) van Niel, Bact. Rev., *8*, 1944, 92.)

cap.su.la'ta. L. dim.noun *capsula* a small chest, capsule; M.L. adj. *capsulatus* capsulated.

Depending upon the pH of the medium, cells nearly spherical, or as distinct rods, often devoid of motility. Motility due to polar flagella. The spherical cells are found in media with a pH below 7; they are usually arranged in chains resembling streptococci. Rod-shaped cells are characteristic for media with pH above 7; the higher the pH, the longer the rods. Individual cells slightly less than 1 micron wide, although attenuated rods (about 0.5 micron in width) are frequent at pH above 8, and slightly swollen cells (to 1.2 microns) are found in media containing sugars. Length varies from 1 to 6 microns; most common dimensions in approximately neutral media, 2 to 2.5 microns. At pH above 8, abnormal growth in the form of irregular filaments. Outstandingly characteristic is the zigzag arrangement of the cells in chains. Gram-negative.

Cultures in media of pH 8 or above are distinctly mucoid.

Color: Anaerobic cultures develop with a brown color, the shade ranging from a light yellowish brown to a deep mahogany-brown. When grown in the presence of oxygen, the cultures are dark red. Even the pigmentation of the brown-colored organisms from an anaerobic culture can be changed into a distinct red by shaking a suspension with air for some hours; light enhances the rate of this color change. Color due to bacteriochlorophyll and carotenoid pigments. No diffusible water-soluble pigment is produced.

Growth possible over a pH range from at least 6 to 8.5, morphology becoming abnormal in the alkaline media.

Most cultures are odorless, although occasionally a faint peach-like odor can be detected.

Growth is not inhibited by the presence of oxygen, although the pigmentation is thereby affected.

Fatty acids and most substituted acids are satisfactory substrates. Rapid and abundant growth with propionate at a concentration of 0.2 per cent. At this same concentration glutaric acid leads, at best, to very meager cultures, while tartrate, citrate and gluconate fail to induce growth, as do also ethanol, glycerol, mannitol and sorbitol. In media with 0.2 per cent glucose or fructose good growth is obtained. No growth with mannose. Thiosulfate is not, but molecular hydrogen can be, oxidized by this species.

Gelatin is not liquefied; of the amino acids, alanine and glutamic acid are satisfactory substrates while leucine is not utilized.

Distinctive characters: Cell shape and arrangement in chains; brown color of anaerobic, red pigmentation of aerobic cultures; ability to grow in media with 0.2 per cent propionate, glucose, fructose, alanine and glutamic acid; failure to develop with leucine, as well as with ethanol, glycerol, mannitol and sorbitol in the above-mentioned concentration.

All cultures can develop anaerobically in illuminated cultures by a photosynthetic metabolism.

Thiamin is required for growth; a few strains require biotin and nicotinic acid in addition (Hutner).

Optimum temperature distinctly lower than for *Rhodopseudomonas palustris*, and, as a rule, around 25° C.

Habitat: Regularly found in stagnant bodies of water and in mud.

Illustrations: Molisch, *op. cit.*, 1907, Plate II, fig. 9; van Niel, *op. cit.*, 1944, fig. 4–6, p. 19; fig. 27–32, p. 92; and fig. 33–38, p. 93.

4. **Rhodopseudomonas spheroides** van Niel, 1944. (*Rhodococcus capsulatus* Molisch, Die Purpurbakterien, Jena, 1907, 20; *Rhodococcus minor* Molisch, *ibid.*, 21; van Niel, Bact. Rev., **8**, 1944, 95.)

sphe.ro.i'des or sphe.roi'des. Gr. adj. *sphaeroides* globular.

Cells generally single, nearly spherical, diameter without slime capsule variable, depending upon medium, ranging from 0.7 to 4 microns. In young cultures actively motile by means of polar flagella; motility soon ceases in media which are or become alkaline. Copious slime production in media at pH above 7. In strongly alkaline cultures abnormal cell-shapes occur in the form of irregular, swollen and distorted rods, often having the appearance of spore-bearing cells, simulated by the production of fat bodies. In sugar-containing media egg-shaped cells, measuring as a rule 2.0 to 2.5 by 2.5 to 3.5 microns, are frequently found. Gram-negative.

Color: Anaerobic cultures develop with brown color, ranging in shade from a light, dirty greenish brown to a dark brown. Cultures grown in the presence of oxygen are distinctly red. As in the case of *Rhodopseudomonas capsulata*, the brown color of an anaerobic culture can be changed to red by shaking with air, light stimulating the color change. Color due to bacteriochlorophyll and carotenoid pigments. The large majority of cultures of this species produce, in addition, a water-soluble, non-carotenoid, bluish red pigment which diffuses into the culture medium.

Gelatin is not liquefied, and growth with single amino acids appears somewhat erratic. No definite correlations have been observed.

Development is possible over a wide pH range, extending from at least 6.0 to 8.5.

All cultures exhibit an unpleasant putrid odor.

Requires for optimal development higher concentrations of yeast extract as a supply of growth factors than either *Rhodopseudomonas palustris* or *Rhodopseudomonas capsulata* and is more sensitive to low fatty acid concentrations. With 0.2 per cent propionate in a neutral medium, no growth occurs; caproic and pelargonic acids are toxic in concentrations below 0.1 per cent. On the other hand, tartrate and gluconate can serve as oxidation substrates, as can also ethanol, glycerol, mannitol, sorbitol, glucose, fructose and mannose in 0.2 per cent concentrations.

In sugar-containing media, acid is produced; the pH may drop to below 4.0 before development ceases. Acid production from glucose occurs both in presence and absence of air, and in illuminated as well as in non-illuminated cultures. In cultures exposed to light, the acid usually disappears later on.

Thiosulfate is not oxidized; hydrogen oxidation has not been observed.

Oxygen does not prevent growth; colonies develop on the surface of agar plates exposed to air, with a red pigmentation. Capable of strictly anaerobic development in illuminated cultures by photosynthesis.

Thiamin, biotin and nicotinic acid are required for growth (Hutner).

Optimum temperature, below 30° C.

Distinctive characters: Spherical cell-shape in most media; brown color of anaerobic and red pigmentation of aerobic cultures; growth with 0.2 per cent tartrate, gluconate, ethanol, glycerol, mannitol, sorbitol, glucose, fructose and mannose; failure to grow with 0.2 per cent propionate.

Habitat: Regularly found in stagnant bodies of water and in mud.

Illustrations: Molisch, *op. cit.*, 1907, Plate II, fig. 15; van Niel, *op. cit.*, 1944, fig. 7–8, p. 19; fig. 39–45, p. 96; fig. 46–54, p. 97.

Genus II. **Rhodospirillum** *Molisch, 1907, emend. van Niel, 1944.*

(Molisch, Die Purpurbakterien, Jena, 1907, 24; van Niel, Bact. Rev., *8*, 1944, 86; the genus now includes the genus *Phaeospirillum* Kluyver and van Niel, Zent. f. Bakt., II Abt., *94*, 1936, 396.)

Rho.do.spi.ril′lum. Gr. noun *rhodum* the rose; Gr. noun *spira* a coil, a spiral; M.L. dim.neut.n. *Spirillum* a bacterial genus; M.L. neut.n. *Rhodospirillum* the rose *Spirillum*.

Spiral-shaped bacteria, motile by means of polar flagella. Gram-negative. Contain bacteriochlorophyll and are potentially photosynthetic in the presence of extraneous oxidizable substances. Molecular oxygen is not produced. Unable to grow in strictly mineral media, even when possessed of the ability to utilize hydrogen as oxidizable substrate, due to the need for organic nutrilites. Produce accessory pigments causing the cultures, especially when grown in the light, to appear in various shades of red to brown.

The type species is *Rhodospirillum rubrum* (Esmarch) Molisch.

Key to the species of genus **Rhodospirillum.**

I. Cultures deep red without brownish tinge; characteristic absorption band around 550 millimicrons.

1. *Rhodospirillum rubrum.*

II. Cultures reddish brown to orange; characteristic absorption maximum around 520, not 550, millimicrons.

A. Cells 0.5 or less micron in width.

2. *Rhodospirillum fulvum.*

B. Cells more than 0.5 micron wide.

1. Size of cells 0.7 to 0.9 by 5 to 10 microns.

3. *Rhodospirillum molischianum.*

2. Size 1.2 to 1.5 by 14 to 30 microns.

4. *Rhodospirillum photometricum.*

1. **Rhodospirillum rubrum** (von Esmarch, 1887) Molisch, 1907. (*Spirillum rubrum* von Esmarch, Cent. f. Bakt., *1*, 1887, 225; *Rhodospirillum giganteum* Molisch, Die Purpurbakterien, Jena, 1907, 24; Molisch, *ibid.*, 25.)

rub'rum. L. adj. *ruber* red.

Cells characteristically spiral-shaped, but size of elements variable within wide limits, depending upon environmental conditions during growth. Width of cells from 0.5 to 1.5 microns; length from 2 to 50 microns, and over; even in a single culture such differences may be found. Also the shape and size of the spiral coil varies much; it usually ranges between 1 to 4 microns in width, and from 1.5 to 7 microns in length. In alanine media the majority of the cells occur in the form of half-circles to complete rings; malate media tend to produce much flattened spirals. In old cultures involution forms appear, straightened spirals and irregularly swollen cells, the latter common in media with higher fatty acids. Such cells stain irregularly, contain fatty inclusions, and are occasionally branched. Young cultures show active motility, due to polar flagella. Gram-negative.

Mucus is not produced. In calcium-deficient media the growth is flocculent, as if agglutinated. With an adequate calcium supply the growth in liquid media is homogeneous, suspended and consists of single cells.

Gelatin is not liquefied; the amino acids alanine, asparagine, aspartic and glutamic acids are satisfactory oxidizable compounds.

Color: Ordinarily deep and dark red, without any brownish tinge. In ethanol media lighter, and a characteristic pink. Pigment production markedly influenced by oxygen and light. Slants incubated in darkness present a pale grayish surface growth with a faint reddish hue, while often showing deep-red cell masses in the region between glass wall and agar surface where development proceeds at low oxygen tension. The color is due to bacteriochlorophyll and carotenoid pigments. Among the latter, spirilloxanthin is quantitatively predominant and is responsible for the characteristic absorption band at 550 millimicrons. Water-soluble, diffusible pigments are not produced.

Development possible over a pH range of at least 6 to 8.5, although, as in other cases, the combination of an acid reaction and the presence of fatty acids may prevent growth.

Cultures produce a distinctive odor, reminiscent of slightly putrid yeast.

In general, grow well with fatty acids as the chief oxidizable substrate; however, are prevented from growing by 0.2 per cent propionate in a neutral medium. Most substituted acids are equally satisfactory, with the exception of tartrate, gluconate and citrate. In a concentration of 0.2 per cent, ethanol is a suitable substrate, whereas the carbohydrates and their corresponding polyalcohols are not utilized.

Thiosulfate is not oxidized; molecular hydrogen can be used by some strains.

Rather microaerophilic; many strains, upon initial isolation, incapable of growth at atmospheric oxygen tension. Subsequent adaptation can be induced, but even such adapted cultures exhibit negative chemotaxis to air.

Capable of strictly anaerobic development in illuminated cultures on the basis of a photosynthetic metabolism.

Biotin is required for growth (Hutner).

Optimum temperature generally between 30° and 37° C.

Distinctive characters: The most important characteristics of the species are the spiral shape, combined with the ability to produce a red pigment with a definite absorption maximum at 550 millimicrons in the intact cells. Diagnostically useful are the good growth in media with 0.2 per cent ethanol, alanine, asparagine, aspartate or glutamate and the inadequacy of similar concentrations of carbohydrates and thiosulfate as substrates.

Habitat: Regularly present in stagnant bodies of water and in mud.

Illustrations: Molisch, *ibid.*, Plate I, fig. 5–7; van Niel, Bact. Rev., *8*, 1944, fig. 9–10, p. 19; fig. 11–16, p. 24; fig. 67–75, p. 103; fig. 76–84, p. 104; fig. 85–90, p. 106; fig. 91–96, p. 107.

2. **Rhodospirillum fulvum** van Niel, 1944. (Bact. Rev., *8*, 1944, 108.)

ful'vum. L. adj. *fulvus* deep or reddish yellow, tawny.

Characteristic for the species is the very

small size of the individual cells. These are not over 0.5 micron wide and generally not longer than 2.5 microns. The most common shape consists of a complete turn of about 1 by 1.5 microns. In media with fatty acids as a substrate the spirals appear somewhat steeper than in fumarate, succinate or malate cultures. Swollen individuals resembling vibrios are encountered in cultures which do not appear quite healthy. Formation of mucus or clumping has not been observed.

Gelatin is not liquefied; aspartate has been the only amino acid capable of inducing growth. Thiosulfate is not oxidized.

Color: Quite distinct from that of *Rhodospirillum rubrum*; colonies and stab cultures are a reddish brown while liquid cultures often appear brownish orange. The color is due to bacteriochlorophyll and carotenoid pigments; among the latter spirilloxanthin, as evidenced by the absence of an absorption maximum at 550 millimicrons, is not represented as a major constituent. Does not produce water-soluble, diffusible pigments.

Capable of strictly anaerobic development in illuminated cultures, due to photosynthetic metabolism.

Fatty acids and the four-carbon dicarboxylic acids are uniformly good substrates; glutarate is not used. Ethanol and glucose, in a concentration of 0.2 per cent, have yielded satisfactory cultures; other carbohydrates, as well as the corresponding polyalcohols, have given negative results.

Little information available concerning pH and temperature relations. Behaves generally as a strict anaerobe; adaptation to microaerophilic conditions has not been achieved. Negative aerotaxis very pronounced.

Distinctive characters: The small size and the color of the cultures serve as adequate criteria for its differentiation from *Rhodospirillum rubrum*. The strictly anaerobic nature and the failure to grow with glutarate and various amino acids except aspartate can probably be used as supplementary specific properties.

Habitat: Bodies of stagnant water and mud.

Illustrations: Van Niel, *ibid.*, fig. 97–102, p. 109; Giesberger, Jour. Microb. and Serol., *13*, 1947, fig. 1–2, p. 141.

3. **Rhodospirillum molischianum** Giesberger, 1947. (Jour. Microbiol. and Serol., *13*, 1947, 137.)

mo.li.schi.an'um. M.L. adj. *molischianus* pertaining to Molisch.

Cells characteristically spiral-shaped, moderately large, 0.7 to 0.9 by 5 to 10 microns. Mostly with one or two complete turns which vary in width from 1.3 to 2 microns and in length from 4 to 6 microns; this depends upon environmental conditions.

Color: Distinctly reddish brown due to the presence of bacteriochlorophyll and carotenoids, the latter responsible for the absorption maxima at 520 and 485 millimicrons. Spirilloxanthin absent.

Capable of development under strictly anaerobic conditions in media containing ethanol or fatty- or hydroxy-acids as oxidizable substrates. Citrate can also be utilized in this manner, but not glycerol, glucose, hydrogen sulfide or thiosulfates. Tends to be strictly anaerobic, and hence capable of development only in illuminated cultures.

Does not liquefy gelatin.

Distinctive characters: The absence of an absorption band at 550 millimicrons and the ability to utilize citrate serve to distinguish this type from *Rhodospirillum rubrum*, which it closely resembles in size and shape. The individual cell size differentiates this species from *R. fulvum* and *R. photometricum*.

Habitat: Widely distributed. Regularly present in stagnant water and mud; can be found in abundance in anaerobic cultures of hay extract inoculated with such materials and incubated in light.

Illustrations: Giesberger, *ibid.*, fig. 3–5, p. 141.

4. **Rhodospirillum photometricum** Molisch, 1907. (Die Purpurbakterien, Jena, 1907, 24.)

pho.to.me'tri.cum. Gr. noun *phōs* light; Gr. adj. *metricus* measured; M.L. adj. *photometricus* light-measured.

Cells large, stout, spiral-shaped. Mostly with one or two complete turns whose wave length varies in width from 4 to 6 microns and in length from 7 to 10 microns; this is dependent upon environmental conditions. Actively motile by means of a single polar flagellum.

Color: Distinctly reddish brown due to the presence of bacteriochlorophyll and carotenoids, the latter responsible for the absorption maxima at 520 and 485 millimicrons. Spirilloxanthin not formed.

Capable of development under strictly anaerobic conditions in media containing ethanol, fatty acids or hydroxy acids as oxidizable substrates. Citrate can also be utilized in this manner, but not glycerol,

glucose, hydrogen sulfide or thiosulfates. Strongly microaerophilic; tends to be strictly anaerobic, and hence capable of development only in illuminated cultures.

Does not liquefy gelatin.

Distinctive characters: Readily distinguishable from *Rhodospirillum rubrum* by the absence of an absorption band at 550 millimicrons and from *R. fulvum* and *R. molischianum* by the greater size of its cells.

Habitat: Stagnant water and mud; widely distributed.

Illustrations: Molisch, *ibid.*, Plate 1, fig. 5–6; Giesberger, Jour. Microbiol. and Serol., *13*, 1947, fig. 6–9, p. 141.

FAMILY III. CHLOROBACTERIACEAE LAUTERBORN, 1913.

(*Chlorobakteriaceae* (sic) Lauterborn, Alg. Bot. Ztschr., *19*, 1913, 99.)

Chlo.ro.bac.te.ri.a′ce.ae. M.L. neut.n. *Chlorobacterium* type genus of the family; -*aceae* ending to denote a family; M.L. fem.pl.n. *Chlorobacteriaceae* the *Chlorobacterium* family.

Green bacteria, usually of small size, occurring singly or in cell masses of various shapes and sizes, developing in environments containing rather high concentrations of hydrogen sulfide and exposed to light. As a rule not containing sulfur globules but frequently depositing elemental sulfur outside the cells. Contain green pigments of a chlorophyllous nature, though not identical with the common green plant chlorophylls nor with bacteriochlorophyll. Capable of photosynthesis in the presence of hydrogen sulfide; do not liberate oxygen.

A number of genera have been proposed; some are characterized by special colonial growth forms while others are characterized on the basis of a supposed symbiotic habitus where the green bacteria grow in more or less characteristic aggregates together with other microorganisms. In view of the variations in size and shape exhibited by the only member of this group which has so far been obtained and studied in pure culture (van Niel, Arch. f. Mikrobiol., *3*, 1931, 65ff.), the validity of many of these genera is doubtful. The following keys and descriptions, therefore, bear a strictly provisional character. Here, as in the case of the sulfur purple bacteria, significant advances can only be expected from pure-culture studies under controlled environmental conditions.

Key to the genera of family **Chlorobacteriaceae.**

I. Free-living bacteria not intimately associated with other microbes.
  A. Bacteria not united into well defined colonies.
               Genus I. *Chlorobium*, p. 62.
  B. Bacteria united into characteristic aggregates.
    1. Bacteria without intracellular sulfur globules.
               Genus II. *Pelodictyon*, p. 63.
    2. Bacteria with intracellular sulfur globules.
               Genus III. *Clathrochloris*, p. 64.
II. Green bacteria found as symbiotic aggregates with other organisms.
  A. Aggregates composed of green bacteria and protozoa.
               Genus IV. *Chlorobacterium*, p. 65.

B. Aggregates composed of two different types of bacteria.
  1. Aggregates small, barrel-shaped, actively motile and consisting of a central, polar flagellate, rod-shaped bacterium with a covering of sulfur green bacteria.
          Genus V. *Chlorochromatium*, p. 65.
  2. Aggregates large, cylindrical, non-motile and composed of a central filamentous bacterium with a more or less extensive covering of sulfur green bacteria.
          Genus VI. *Cylindrogloea*, p. 66.

Genus I. Chlorobium *Nadson, 1912.*

(Bull. Jard. Impér. Botan., St. Pétersb., *12*, 1912, 64 (Russian), 83 (German).)

Chlo.ro'bi.um. Gr. adj. *chlorus* greenish yellow, green; Gr. noun *bios* life; M.L. neut.n. *Chlorobium* green life.

Sulfur green bacteria, occurring singly or in chains, individual cells of various sizes and shapes, from spherical to relatively long rod-shaped, the latter sometimes coiled into tight spirals; often united in chains and generally embedded in a slime capsule. Non-motile. Gram-negative. Contain a chlorophyllous pigment different from the common green plant chlorophylls and from bacteriochlorophyll. Capable of photosynthesis in the presence of hydrogen sulfide, during which they produce elemental sulfur which is excreted outside the cells. Do not form spores.

The type species is *Chlorobium limicola* Nadson.

Key to the species of genus Chlorobium.

I. Does not utilize thiosulfates as oxidizable substrate.
          1. *Chlorobium limicola.*
II. Utilizes thiosulfates as oxidizable substrate.
          2. *Chlorobium thiosulfatophilum.*

1. Chlorobium limicola Nadson, 1912. (Bull. Jard. Impér. Botan., St. Pétersb., *12*, 1912, 64 (Russian), 83 (German).)

li.mi'co.la. L. noun *limus* mud; L. v. *colo* to dwell; M.L. fem.n. *limicola* the mud dweller.

Cells occur in various sizes and shapes which are markedly dependent upon environmental conditions. In young and healthy cultures, predominantly small, ovoid to short rods, 0.7 by 0.9 to 1.5 microns, frequently united in chains resembling streptococci. Greatly elongated and irregularly bent and curved rods also occur as involution forms; these rods may likewise remain united in chains. Club-shaped and spirally wound to tightly coiled involution forms have been described, but the conditions for their formation are not understood, and in recent pure-culture studies these have never been encountered (Larsen, Jour. Bact., *64*, 1952, 187). Regularly produce mucus; in media of inadequate composition this may lead to the formation of cell conglomerates of different sizes and shapes and a stringy appearance of the cultures. In healthy cultures the bacteria remain evenly dispersed and settle very slowly. Non-motile.

Color: Intensely green in healthy cultures; poor pigmentation and then yellowish green in media deficient in iron.

Strictly anaerobic, obligatory photosynthetic bacteria whose occurrence in nature is dependent upon the presence of hydrogen sulfide. They utilize this substance, as well as elemental sulfur and molecular hydrogen, as oxidizable substrates; produce sulfur from sulfides but do not store sulfur globules inside the cells. Oxidation of sulfide may yield sulfur as an end product, but under optimal conditions the sulfur is further oxidized to sulfate. Unable to use thiosulfate and tetrathionate as oxidizable substrates. Development in organic media free of sulfide has not been obtained.

Source: Isolated from mud and stagnant water, containing hydrogen sulfide, from the St. Petersburg Botanical Garden. Also found by Bicknell (Lloydia, *12*, 1949, 183) in Sodon Lake, Bloomfield Hills, Michigan.

Habitat: Widely distributed in mud and stagnant water. Mass development under conditions of relatively high sulfide concentrations and low pH in environments exposed to light.

Illustrations: Nadson, *op. cit.*, 1912, Pl. III, fig. 3–12; van Niel, Arch. f. Mikrobiol., *3*, 1931, fig. 8, p. 66.

2. Chlorobium thiosulfatophilum Larsen, 1952. (Jour. Bact., *64*, 1952, 187.)

thi.o.sul.fa.to'phi.lum. M.L. noun *thiosulfatum* thiosulfate; Gr.adj. *philus* loving; M.L. adj. *thiosulfatophilus* thiosulfateloving.

Cells indistinguishable from those of *Chlorobium limicola*.

Color: As in *Chlorobium limicola*.

Strictly anaerobic, obligatory photosynthetic bacteria. Utilize sulfides, sulfur, thiosulfate, tetrathionate and molecular hydrogen as oxidizable substrates; produce sulfate from inorganic sulfur compounds. Unable to grow in organic media free of oxidizable, inorganic sulfur compounds.

Distinctive characters: Differs from *Chlorobium limicola* in its ability to oxidize thiosulfate and tetrathionate.

Source: Isolated from marine and freshwater mud.

Habitat: Same as for *Chlorobium limicola*.

Genus II. **Pelodictyon** Lauterborn, 1913.

(Allgem. botan. Ztschr., *19*, 1913, 98; Verhandl. naturhistor.-medizin. Vereins, Heidelberg, N.F. *13*, 1915, 431.)

Pe.lo.dic'ty.on. Gr. adj. *pělos* dark-colored; Gr. noun *dictyon* net; M.L. neut.n. *Pelodictyon* a dark-colored net.

Sulfur green bacteria, individual cells ovoid to distinctly rod-shaped, producing rather extensive mucoid capsules and generally united into large colonies of characteristic shapes. Non-motile. Contain chlorophyllous pigments different from the common green plant chlorophylls and from bacteriochlorophyll. Capable of photosynthesis in the presence of hydrogen sulfide, but do not store sulfur globules inside the cells.

The type species is *Pelodictyon clathratiforme* (Szafer) Lauterborn.

Key to the species of genus **Pelodictyon.**

I. Cells united in colonies in a net-like fashion.
                        1. *Pelodictyon clathratiforme.*

II. Cells arranged in tightly packed colonies without net-like structure.
    A. Colonies composed of irregularly arranged cell-masses, extending in three dimensions.
                        2. *Pelodictyon aggregatum.*
    B. Colonies consisting of parallel strands and extending in two dimensions.
                        3. *Pelodictyon parallelum.*

1. Pelodictyon clathratiforme (Szafer, 1910) Lauterborn, 1913. (*Aphanothece clathratiforme* Szafer, Bull. Acad. Sci., Cracovie, Sér. B, *3*, 1910, 162; Lauterborn, Allgem. botan. Ztschr., *19*, 1913, 98; also see Verhandl. naturhist.-medizin. Vereins, Heidelberg, N.F. *13*, 1915, 430.)

clath.ra.ti.for'me. L. part.adj. *clathratus* latticed; L. noun *forma* shape, form; M.L. adj. *clathratiformis* lattice-like.

Cells generally rod-shaped, ranging from slightly elongated ovoids to distinct rods, often vacuolated, about 0.5 to 1.5 by 2 to 4 microns, producing rather wide slime capsules. Characteristically united into three-dimensional colonies which present a net-like appearance with mazes of about 10 to 50 microns. Non-motile.

Color: Yellowish green.

Abnormal cell forms (involution forms) not uncommon, consisting of elongated and curved, forked, or club-shaped and swollen rods, occasionally suggesting rudimentary branching at the extremities. Such cells may be found as elements in chains for the greater part composed of normal individuals.

Habitat: Mud and stagnant water containing rather high concentrations of hydrogen sulfide and exposed to light; sulfur springs.

Illustrations: Szafer, *op. cit.*, 1910, Pl. VI, fig. 5; Perfiliev, Jour. Microbiol. (Russian), *1*, 1914, Pl. II, fig. 1, 5–12; Lauterborn, *op. cit.*, 1915, Pl. III, fig. 33.

2. Pelodictyon aggregatum Perfiliev, 1914. (*Aphanothece luteola* Schmidle, Beihefte Botan. Cent., *10*, 1901, 179; Perfiliev, Jour. Microbiol. (Russian), *1*, 1914, 197.)

ag.gre.ga'tum. L. part.adj. *aggregatus* added to a flock, aggregated, clumped.

Cells usually rod-shaped, about 1 to 1.5 by 2 to 4 microns, often vacuolated, producing slime capsules and united into irregularly shaped, three-dimensional colonies in which the cells are more or less tightly packed without orderly arrangement. Colonies may attain a size of up to 1 mm; frequently they are not fully compact but contain less dense areas or appear perforated, thus forming transition stages to *Pelodictyon clathratiforme*. Non-motile.

Color: Yellowish green.

Abnormal cell forms (involution forms) usually in the shape of elongated and curved, forked or club-shaped and swollen rods, occasionally suggesting branching at extremities.

Source: Isolated from sulfureted water in Europe; also reported by Dutton and Juday (Ecology, *25*, 1944, 277) from Scaffold Lake, Wisconsin.

Habitat: Mud and stagnant water containing rather high concentrations of hydrogen sulfide and exposed to light; sulfur springs.

Illustrations: Perfiliev, *ibid.*, Pl. II, fig. 2; Lauterborn, Verhandl. naturhistor.-medizin. Vereins, Heidelberg, N.F. *13*, 1915, Pl. III, fig. 29–31.

3. Pelodictyon parallelum (Szafer, 1910) Perfiliev, 1914. (*Aphanothece parallela* Szafer, Bull. Acad. Sci., Cracovie, Sér. B, *3*, 1910, 163; Perfiliev, Jour. Microbiol. (Russian), *1*, 1914, 198.)

pa.ral.le'lum. Gr. adj. *parallēlus* parallel.

Cells rather small, spherical to ovoid, or even rod-shaped; about 0.5 to 1 by 1 to 3 microns, occurring in chains and forming flat, plate-like, two-dimensional aggregates in which the chains are arranged as parallel strands. Non-motile.

Color: Yellowish green.

Abnormal cell forms not specifically mentioned, but likely to occur and to resemble those of other species.

This species may well be a special growth-form of *Chlorobium limicola*.

Habitat: Mud and stagnant water containing rather high concentrations of hydrogen sulfide and exposed to light; sulfur springs.

Illustrations: Szafer, *op. cit.*, 1910, Pl. VI, fig. 7; Perfiliev, *op. cit.*, 1914, Pl. II, fig. 2.

Genus III. **Clathrochloris** *Geitler, 1925.*

(Geitler, in Pascher, Die Süsswasserflora Deutschlands, Österreichs und der Schweiz, Jena, *12*, 1925, 457.)

Clath.ro.chlo'ris. L. pl.noun *clathri* lattice; Gr. adj. *chlorus* green; M.L. fem.n. *Clathrochloris* green lattice.

Sulfur green bacteria of small size, generally spherical and arranged in chains which are united into loose, trellis-shaped aggregates, somewhat similar to those of *Pelodictyon clathratiforme* and *Pelodictyon aggregatum*. Cells usually contain sulfur globules. Color is yellowish green. Non-motile.

The type species is *Clathrochloris sulphurica* (Szafer) Geitler.

1. Clathrochloris sulphurica (Szafer, 1910) Geitler, 1925. (*Aphanothece sulphurica* Szafer, Bull. Acad. Sci., Cracovie, Sér. B, *3*, 1910, 162; Geitler, Die Süsswasserflora Deutschlands, Österreichs und der Schweiz, Jena, *12*, 1925, 457.)

sul.phur'i.ca. L. noun *sulfur* (sometimes *sulphur*) sulfur; M.L. adj. *sulphuricus* sulfuric.

Cells spherical, about 0.5 to 0.7 micron in diameter, usually containing sulfur globules. Non-motile.

Color: Yellowish green.

The reported occurrence of sulfur globules in the cells of this very small species is surprising; it is the only one among the sulfur green bacteria in which these inclusions have been encountered. The published descriptions are even more fragmentary than those of other members of the group.

Source: Reported only from sulfur springs in Lubién Wielki, near Lwow, Poland.

Habitat: Mud and stagnant water containing rather high concentrations of hydrogen sulfide and exposed to light; sulfur springs.

Illustration: Szafer, *op. cit.*, 1910, Pl. VI, fig. 6.

Genus IV. **Chlorobacterium** *Lauterborn, 1915*.

(Lauterborn, Verhandl, naturhist.-medizin. Vereins, Heidelberg, N.F., *13*, 1915, 429; not *Chlorobacterium** Guillebeau, Landw. Jahrb. d. Schweiz, *4*, 1890, 32.)

Chlo.ro.bac.te'ri.um. Gr. adj. *chlorus* green; L. noun *bacterium* a small rod; M.L. neut.n. *Chlorobacterium* a green rodlet.

Sulfur green bacteria(?) which grow symbiotically as an outside covering on cells of protozoa, such as amoeba and flagellates. Cells rod-shaped, often slightly curved, greenish. Non-motile.

The type species is *Chlorobacterium symbioticum* Lauterborn.

1. **Chlorobacterium symbioticum** Lauterborn, 1915. (Verhandl. naturhist.-medizin. Vereins, Heidelberg, N.F., *13*, 1915, 429.)

sym.bi.o'ti.cum. Gr. adj. *symbioticus* of companionship, symbiotic.

Cells rod-shaped, about 0.5 by 2 to 5 microns, often slightly curved. Non-motile.

Occur as a peripheral covering of certain protozoa with which they may form a symbiotic unit.

It is not certain that this is a sulfur green bacterium: the descriptions of localities where it was found fail to mention the presence of hydrogen sulfide in the environment; this should be a prerequisite for a member of this group.

Source: Reported from a number of pools in Germany.

Habitat: Stagnant water.

Illustrations: Lauterborn, *loc. cit.*, Pl. III, fig. 34–36; Pascher, Die Süsswasserflora Deutschlands, Österreichs und der Schweiz, Jena, *12*, 1925, fig. 149.

Genus V. **Chlorochromatium** *Lauterborn, 1906*.

(Allgem. botan. Ztschr., *19*, 1906, 196.)

Chlo.ro.chro.ma'ti.um. Gr. adj. *chlorus* green; Gr. noun *chromatium* color, paint; M.L. neut.n. *Chromatium* a bacterial genus; M.L. neut.n. *Chlorochromatium* a green *Chromatium*.

Sulfur green bacteria, ovoid to rod-shaped with rounded ends. Occur as barrel-shaped aggregates consisting of a rather large, colorless, polar flagellate bacterium as the center which is surrounded by green bacteria, arranged in 4 to 6 rows, ordinarily from 2 to 4 cells high. The entire conglomerate behaves like a unit, is motile, and multiplies by the more or less simultaneous fission of its components.

The green constituents contain a chlorophyllous pigment which is not identical with the common green plant chlorophylls or with bacteriochlorophyll. Capable of photosynthesis in the presence of hydrogen sulfide but do not store sulfur globules in the cells.

The type species is *Chlorochromatium aggregatum* Lauterborn.

---

* It has been proposed that *Chlorobacterium* Guillebeau be rejected as a generic name in bacteriology and placed in the list of *nomina generica rejicienda* (Internat. Bull. Bact. Nomen. and Tax., *1*, 1951, 43 and *2*, 1952, 110).

1. **Chlorochromatium aggregatum** Lauterborn, 1906. (Allgem. botan. Ztschr., *19*, 1906, 196.)

ag.gre.ga'tum. L. part.adj. *aggregatus* flocked together, clumped.

Cells of the green component 0.5 to 1.0 by 1.0 to 2.5 microns, mostly from 8 to 16 individuals surrounding the central bacterium. Size of the total barrel-shaped unit variable, generally 2.5 to 5 by 7 to 12 microns. Occasionally a group of the complex colonies may remain attached in a chain.

Anaerobic.

Habitat: Mud and stagnant water containing rather high concentrations of hydrogen sulfide and exposed to light.

There is at present no good reason for distinguishing 2 varieties (forma *typica* and forma *minor*) or even species, on the basis of size differences of the colony, as Geitler proposed (Die Süsswasserflora Deutschlands, Österreichs und der Schweiz, Jena, *12*, 1925, 460). The reported and personally observed sizes of such units show that the extreme limits are linked by a complete series of transitions.

Illustrations: Buder, Ber. deut. botan. Ges., *31*, 1914, Generalversam., Pl. XXIV, fig. 1–5; Perfiliev, Jour. Microbiol. (Russian), *1*, 1914, fig. 1–5, p. 213.

Genus VI. **Cylindrogloea** *Perfiliev, 1914.*

(Jour. Microbiol. (Russian), *1*, 1914, 223.)

Cy.lin.dro.gloe'a. Gr. noun *cylindrus* cylinder; Gr. noun *gloea* gum; M.L. fem.n. *Cylindrogloea* cylindrical gum.

Sulfur green bacteria consisting of small ovoid to rod-shaped cells growing in association with a filamentous, colorless, central bacterium, thus forming colonies of a cylindrical shape. Non-motile. The green component contains a chlorophyllous pigment different from the common chlorophylls of green plants and from bacteriochlorophyll. Capable of photosynthesis in the presence of hydrogen sulfide without depositing sulfur globules in the cells.

The type species is *Cylindrogloea bacterifera* Perfiliev.

1. **Cylindrogloea bacterifera** Perfiliev, 1914. (Jour. Microbiol. (Russian), *1*, 1914, 223.)

bac.te.ri'fe.ra. Gr. neut.n. *bactrum* a rod; M.L. mas.n. *bacter* rod (a combining form); L. verbal suf. *fer* bearing; M.L. adj. *bacterifera* rod-bearing.

Individual green components ovoid to rod-shaped, about 0.5 to 1 by 2 to 4 microns, very similar to those of the complex *Chlorobacterium symbioticum* and *Chlorochromatium aggregatum* with which they may well be identical. The central filamentous bacterium is embedded in a slime capsule of considerable dimensions. This, in turn, is surrounded by a layer of green bacteria, usually one cell thick. The green organisms may form a very dense outer covering, or they may be more sparsely distributed over the slime capsule. The entire unit is again surrounded by a sizeable slime zone. Aggregates measure about 7 to 8 microns in width and up to 50 microns in length; they are non-

motile. Both components appear to be non-spore-forming.

Habitat: Mud and stagnant water containing rather high concentrations of hydrogen sulfide and exposed to light.

Illustration: Perfiliev, *ibid.*, fig. 6–11, p. 213.

Perfiliev rightly emphasizes, as Buder had done for *Chloronium mirabile*, the provisional nature of thus using a generic designation for an apparently stable complex composed of two different organisms. It remains possible that the last three genera of symbiotic entities represent fortuitous combinations whose occurrence is conditioned by environmental factors. If so, the generic terminology would be devoid of any taxonomic significance, and the green bacteria should be relegated to more appropriate genera. Indications suggestive of this state of affairs can be found in the literature; for example in Utermöhl's observation (Archiv

f. Hydrobiol., Suppl. *5*, 1925, 279) that the complex *Chlorochromatium aggregatum* may, especially in the presence of oxygen, disintegrate, whereupon the green constituents appear as small *Pelodictyon aggregatum* (*Schmidlea luteola*) colonies.

SUBORDER II. **Pseudomonadineae** BREED, MURRAY AND SMITH, SUB-ORDO NOV.

Pseu.do.mo.na.di'ne.ae. M.L. fem.n. *Pseudomonas, -adis* a genus of bacteria; *-ineae* ending to denote a suborder; M.L. fem.pl.n. *Pseudomonadineae* the *Pseudomonas* suborder.

Cells normally about 1 micron in diameter, but among the colorless sulfur bacteria they may be as much as 14 microns in diameter. The cells do not contain photosynthetic pigments, but diffusible, water-soluble pigments of a type not found elsewhere among bacteria occur in many species. Also, non-water-soluble yellow or red pigments occur in some genera. The motile species are invariably polar flagellate. Some groups are strictly autotrophic, oxidizing simple inorganic compounds; others are also oxidative but are facultatively heterotrophic or heterotrophic in their physiology. A few genera include species that ferment simple sugars, even producing H_2 and CO_2 as do the common acid- and gas-producing coliform bacteria. The organisms in one genus (*Zymomonas*) even carry out an alcoholic fermentation similar to that of yeasts. The majority of the species grow well and fairly rapidly on the surfaces of ordinary culture media. Some species that attack agar or cellulose or that show other unusual types of physiology are more fastidious in their requirements. Only a few species are strictly anaerobic as in *Vibrio* and *Desulfovibrio*. The species in this suborder are largely found in salt- or fresh-water or in soil. Some are parasitic and a few are pathogenic to vertebrates including man.

Key to the families of suborder **Pseudomonadineae.**

I. Coccoid to rod-shaped cells. Occasionally individual rods may be curved although the majority of the cells are straight.
   A. Cells not attached to a substrate.
      1. Cells have the power to oxidize simple compounds such as ammonia, nitrites, methane, hydrogen, carbon monoxide, sulfur or sulfur compounds. Chemo-auto-trophic or facultatively chemo-autotrophic.
         a. Do not secure their energy from the oxidation of sulfur compounds.
            b. Oxidize ammonia to nitrites or nitrites to nitrates. Autotrophic.
               Family I. *Nitrobacteraceae*, p. 68.
            bb. Oxidize methane, hydrogen or carbon monoxide. Autotrophic.
               Family II. *Methanomonadaceae*, p. 74.
         aa. Oxidize sulfur compounds, frequently with a deposit of free sulfur granules or crystals within or without the cells.
               Family III. *Thiobacteriaceae*, p. 78.
      2. Cells frequently oxidative, although they are sometimes fermentative in their physiology. Usually heterotrophic. Rarely facultatively autotrophic
               Family IV. *Pseudomonadaceae*, p. 88.
   B. Cells in free-floating films or attached to a substrate.
      a. Cells attached to the substrate by means of a stalk, usually with a holdfast.
               Family V. *Caulobacteraceae*, p. 212.
      aa. Cells in free-floating films or attached to the substrate by means of capsular material.
               Family VI. *Siderocapsaceae*, p. 217.
II. Curved, vibrio-like to spiral-shaped cells.
               Family VII. *Spirillaceae*, p. 228.

FAMILY I. NITROBACTERACEAE BUCHANAN, 1917.*

(Jour. Bact., *2*, 1917, 349 and Jour. Bact., *3*, 1918, 179.)

Ni.tro.bac.te.ra'ce.ae. M.L. *Nitrobacter* name of type genus of the family; *-aceae* ending to denote a family; M.L. plural noun *Nitrobacteraceae* the *Nitrobacter* family.

Cells without endospores; rod-shaped, ellipsoidal or even spherical (*Nitrosococcus*) or spirillar in shape (*Nitrosospira*). Flagella polar, occasionally absent. Gram-negative. Organisms which derive energy from the oxidation of ammonia to nitrite or from the oxidation of nitrite to nitrate; these bacteria depend on this oxidation for growth and fail to grow on media containing organic matter in the absence of the specific inorganic materials used as sources of energy. Many organic compounds commonly used in standard culture media are toxic to these bacteria. Not parasitic. Commonly found in soil and fresh water.

The type genus for the family is *Nitrobacter* Winogradsky.

As it appears to be a more logical arrangement, the genera that include the species that oxidize ammonia are discussed first although the type genus does not belong in this group.

Key to the genera of family **Nitrobacteraceae.**

I. Ammonia oxidized to nitrite.
  A. Zoogloeae not formed. Cells occur separately, free or in dense aggregates.
    1. Cells not spiral-shaped.
      a. Cells ellipsoidal.

      Genus I. *Nitrosomonas*, p. 68.

      aa. Cells spherical.

      Genus II. *Nitrosococcus*, p. 69.

    2. Cells spiral.

      Genus III. *Nitrosospira*, p. 70.

  B. Zoogloeae formed.
    1. Zoogloea surrounded by a common membrane forming a cyst.

      Genus IV. *Nitrosocystis*, p. 70.

    2. No common membrane surrounds the cells. The massed cells are embedded in slime.

      Genus V. *Nitrosogloea*, p. 71.

II. Nitrite oxidized to nitrate.
  A. Zoogloeae not formed.

      Genus VI. *Nitrobacter*, p. 72.

  B. Zoogloeae formed.

      Genus VII. *Nitrocystis*, p. 73.

Genus I. **Nitrosomonas** *Winogradsky, 1890.*

(*Nitromonas* Winogradsky, Ann. Inst. Past., *4*, 1890, 257; not *Nitromonas* Orla-Jensen, Cent. f. Bakt., II Abt., *22*, 1909, 334; Arch. Sci. biol., St. Petersburg, *1*, 1892, 127; *emend.* S. and H. Winogradsky, Ann. Inst. Past., *50*, 1933, 393.)

Ni.tro.so.mo'nas. M.L. *nitrosus* nitrous; Gr. *monas, monadis* a unit, monad; M.L. fem.n. *Nitrosomonas* nitrous monad, *i.e.*, the monad producing nitrite.

Cells ellipsoidal, non-motile or with a single polar flagellum, occurring singly, in pairs, short chains or irregular masses which are not enclosed in a common membrane. Oxidize ammonia to nitrite more rapidly than the other genera of this family.

The type species is *Nitrosomonas europaea* Winogradsky.

---

* Completely revised by Dr. R. L. Starkey, New Jersey Agricultural Experiment Station, New Brunswick, N. J., March, 1943; minor revisions, November, 1953.

1. Nitrosomonas europaea Winogradsky, 1892. (Arch. Sci. biol., St. Petersburg, *1*, 1892, 127.)

eu.ro.pae'a. Gr. adj. *europaeus* of Europe, European.

Rods, 0.9 to 1.0 by 1.1 to 1.8 microns, occurring singly, rarely in chains of three to four. Possess a single polar flagellum 3 to 4 times the length of the rods, or rarely one at either end.

Grow readily in aqueous media without organic matter and containing ammonium sulfate, potassium phosphate and magnesium carbonate. The cells accumulate in soft masses around the particles of magnesium carbonate at the bottom of the flask. The liquid is occasionally turbid through development of motile swarm cells or monads.

Small, compact, sharply defined colonies brownish in color on silica gel

Aerobic.

Strictly autotrophic.

Source: Soils of Zurich, Switzerland; of Gennevilliers, France; and Kazan, Russia.

Habitat: Presumably widely distributed in soil.

2. Nitrosomonas monocella Nelson, 1931. (Zent. f. Bakt., II Abt., *83*, 1931, 287.)

mon.o.cel'la. Gr. *monus* single; L. *cella* room, cell; M.L. adj. *monocellus* one-celled.

Ovoid rods, 0.6 to 0.9 micron, often occurring in pairs. Young cells nearly spherical. Motile by means of a single polar flagellum 3 to 5 times as long as the rod. Gram-positive (Nelson). Found negative by H. J. Conn (personal communication).

No growth in nutrient broth, nutrient agar, nutrient or plain gelatin, plain or litmus milk, glucose or plain yeast water, or on potato.

Silica gel or agar plates of inorganic medium: No typical colonies, but yellowish brown masses of growth around particles of $CaCO_3$ in the medium.

Inorganic liquid medium containing ammonium salts: Uniform development throughout the liquid as well as in the carbonate sediment.

Even low concentrations of organic matter retard or completely inhibit the initiation of growth. Plant extracts are toxic.

Free CO_2 and O_2 necessary for growth.

Optimum pH, 8.0 to 9.0. Poor growth below pH 7.0. Some growth above pH 9.0.

Optimum temperature for growth and oxidation, 28° C.

Aerobic.

Strictly autotrophic.

Source: Isolated from field soil.

Habitat: Presumably widely distributed in soil.

Genus II. Nitrosococcus *Winogradsky, 1892.*

(Arch. Sci. biol., St. Petersburg, *1*, 1892, 127.)

Ni.tro.so.coc'cus. M.L. *nitrosus* nitrous; Gr. *coccus* grain, berry; M.L. mas.n. *Nitrosococcus* nitrous sphere.

Cells large spheres, non-motile, not producing zoogloeae. Oxidize ammonia to nitrite.

The type species is *Nitrosococcus nitrosus* (Migula) Buchanan.

1. Nitrosococcus nitrosus (Migula, 1900) Buchanan, 1925. (*Nitrosococcus* Winogradsky, Ann. Inst. Past., *5*, 1891, 577; Arch. Sci. biol., St. Petersburg, *1*, 1892, 127; *Micrococcus nitrosus* Migula. Syst. d. Bakt., *2*, 1900, 194; Buchanan, Gen. Syst. Bact., 1925, 402.)

ni.tro'sus. M.L. adj. *nitrosus* nitrous.

Large spheres, 1.5 to 1.7 microns in size, with thick cell membranes. Motility could not be demonstrated. Stain readily with aniline dyes. Zoogloea formation not observed. Gram-positive (Omelianski, Cent. f. Bakt., II Abt., *19*, 1907, 263).

Liquid medium: Turbid.

Silica gel: Both dark and light colonies. Surface colonies look like small drops of a turbid yellowish liquid.

Aerobic.

Optimum temperature, between 20° and 25° C.

Source: Isolated from soil from Quito,

Ecuador; Campinas, Brazil; and Melbourne, Australia.

Habitat: Presumably widely distributed in soil.

Genus III. Nitrosospira Winogradsky, 1931.

(S. Winogradsky, Compt. rend. Acad. Sci., Paris, *192*, 1931, 1004; S. Winogradsky and H. Winogradsky, Ann. Inst. Past., *50*, 1933, 394 and 406.)

Ni.tro.so.spi'ra. M.L. *nitrosus* nitrous; Gr. *spira* a coil, spiral; M.L. fem.n. *Nitrosospira* nitrous spiral.

Cells spiral-shaped. Oxidize ammonia to nitrite very slowly.

The type species is *Nitrosospira briensis* S. Winogradsky and H. Winogradsky.

1. **Nitrosospira briensis** S. Winogradsky and H. Winogradsky, 1933. (Ann. Inst. Pasteur, *50*, 1933, 407.)

bri.en'sis. French Brie, place name; M.L. adj. *briensis* of Brie.

Spirals wound tightly to form very small cylinders as long as 15 to 20 microns. Short spirals have the appearance of short rods and ellipsoidal cells. Small pseudo-cocci observed in old cultures.

Colonies on silica gel: Small, occasionally containing cyst-like aggregates of cells. The cysts are more poorly developed than in *Nitrosocystis*.

Aerobic.

Optimum pH, between 7.0 and 7.2.

Source: Uncultivated pasture soil of Brie, France.

Habitat: Presumably widely distributed in soil.

2. **Nitrosospira antarctica** S. Winogradsky and H. Winogradsky, 1933. (Ann. Inst. Past., *50*, 1933, 407.)

ant.arc'tic.a. Gr. *anti* opposite; Gr. *arctus* a bear; Gr. adj. *antarcticus* opposite the bear, antarctic.

Cells and colonies similar to those of *N. briensis* except that the cells are generally wound together to form more compact spirals.

Aerobic.

Optimum pH, between 7.0 and 7.2.

Source: Soil from the Antarctic.

Habitat: Presumably widely distributed in soil.

Genus IV. Nitrosocystis Winogradsky, 1931.

(S. Winogradsky, Compt. rend. Acad. Sci., Paris, *192*, 1931, 1003; also see S. Winogradsky and H. Winogradsky, Ann. Inst. Past., *50*, 1933, 394 and 399.)

Ni.tro.so.cyst'is. M.L. adj. *nitrosus* nitrous; Gr. noun *cystis* bladder, cyst; M.L. fem.n. *Nitrosocystis* nitrous cyst.

Cells ellipsoidal or elongated, uniting in compact, rounded aggregates surrounded by a common membrane to form cysts. The cysts disintegrate to free the cells, particularly when transferred to fresh media. Within the cyst the cells are embedded in slime. Ammonia is oxidized to nitrite at a rate intermediate between that of *Nitrosomonas* and that of *Nitrosospira*.

Winogradsky and Winogradsky (*ibid.*, 393) differentiated between *Nitrosomonas* and *Nitrosocystis* in that the former produced soft (or clear) colonies and the latter produced hard (or dark) colonies on silica gel. However, Kingma Boltjes (Arch. Mikrobiol., *6*, 1935, 79) was able to obtain both hard and soft colonies in cultures of *Nitrosomonas* derived from single-cell isolates. Meiklejohn (Nature, *168*, 1951, 561; also see Jour. Soil Sci., *4*, 1953, 62), furthermore, states that the appearance of hard or soft colonies is dependent upon the density of the silica gel and upon whether the colonies are in the gel or on the surface; consequently she regards *Nitrosocystis* as probably identical with *Nitrosomonas*. Some observers (Imšenecki, Nature, *157*, 1946, 877; and Grace, Nature, *168*, 1951, 117; also see Riassunti d. Comunicazione, VI Cong. Internaz. d. Microbiol., Roma, *1*, 1953, 53) have suggested that the organisms described in this genus are myxobacters or that the cultures were contaminated with myxobacters; however, this does not seem probable.

The type species is *Nitrosocystis javanensis* (Winogradsky) Starkey.

1. Nitrosocystis javanensis (Winogradsky, 1892) Starkey, 1948. (*Nitrosomonas javanensis* Winogradsky, Arch. Sci. biol., St. Petersburg, *1*, 1892, 127; Starkey, in Manual, 6th ed., 1948, 72.)

jav.a.nen'sis. Java, a place name; M.L. adj. *javanensis* of Java, Javanese.

Small ellipsoidal cells having a diameter of 0.5 to 0.6 micron. Possess a polar flagellum 20 times as long as the rods.

In liquid medium produces very compact zoogloeal masses of cells and motile swarmers. The large zoogloeae are themselves composed of smaller compact aggregates of cells.

On silica gel the colonies are circular to elliptical becoming clear or light brown.

Aerobic.

Strictly autotrophic.

Source: Soil of Buitenzorg, Java; Tokyo, Japan; and La Reghaia, Tunisia.

Habitat: Presumably widely distributed in soil.

2. Nitrosocystis coccoides Starkey, 1948. (*Nitrosocystis a*, S. Winogradsky and H. Winogradsky, Ann. Inst. Past., *50*, 1933, 401; Starkey, in Manual, 6th ed., 1948, 72.)

coc.co.i'des. Gr. *coccus* grain, berry; Gr. *idus* form, shape; M.L. adj. *coccoides* coccus-shaped.

Ellipsoidal cells about 1.5 microns in diameter. Occur as compact aggregates of cells imbedded in mucus and surrounded by a thickened capsule to form cyst-like bodies. Cells rarely solitary but more often in pairs and in small groups of four or more. Probably motile. The mucus which surrounds the cells is not readily stained whereas the outside coating stains more easily.

Colonies on silica gel: As colonies develop, the coating of $CaCO_3$ on the gel becomes yellowish and dissolves, and the colony appears as a bulbous, angular, brown body which may become 0.5 mm in diameter. The cells are held firmly together in these irregularly shaped bulbous aggregates.

Aerobic.

Source: Poor soils of Brie and elsewhere in France.

Habitat: Presumably widely distributed in forest and manured soils.

Genus V. **Nitrosogloea** *H. Winogradsky, 1935.*

(Compt. rend. Acad. Sci., Paris, *200*, 1935, 1887; Ann. Inst. Pasteur, *58*, 1937, 335.)

Ni.tro.so.gloe'a. M.L. *nitrosus* nitrous; Gr. *gloea* glue, jelly; M.L. fem.n. *Nitrosogloea* nitrous jelly.

Cells ellipsoidal or rod-shaped. Embedded in slime to form zoogloeae. No common membrane surrounds the cell aggregates. Oxidize ammonia to nitrite.

It has been suggested that these organisms were contaminated with myxobacters. See note under *Nitrosocystis* for references.

The type species is *Nitrosogloea merismoides* H. Winogradsky.

1. Nitrosogloea merismoides H. Winogradsky, 1935. (*Nitrosocystis "I"*, H. Winogradsky, Trans. Third Intern. Cong. Soil Sci., Oxford, *1*, 1935, 139; H. Winogradsky, Compt. rend. Acad. Sci., Paris, *200*, 1935, 1887; also see Ann. Inst. Past., *58*, 1937, 333.)

mer.is.mo.i'des. Gr. *merismus* a division; Gr. *idus* form, shape; M.L. adj. *merismoides* resembling a division.

Ellipsoidal cells 0.5 by 1.5 microns. Oval cells or short rods forming tetards or chains, each group with its own sheath. The groups vary in shape producing branched chains, irregular or compact aggregates.

Colonies on silica gel: Cells encased in a pale yellow mucilage giving the colony a dull appearance. Colony surface studded with little humps.

Aerobic.

Source: Activated sludge.
Habitat: Unknown.

2. Nitrosogloea schizobacteroides H. Winogradsky, 1935.

(*Nitrosocystis "II"*, H. Winogradsky, Trans. Third Intern. Cong. Soil Sci., Oxford, *1*, 1935, 139; H. Winogradsky, Compt. rend. Acad. Sci., Paris, *200*, 1935, 1887; Ann. Inst. Past., *58*, 1937, 333.)

schiz.o.bac.te.ro.i'des. Gr. *schiza* cleft, fission; Gr. noun *bactrum* a rod; Gr. noun *idus* form, shape; M.L. adj. *schizobacteroides* shaped like a fission rod.

Elongated rods or short filaments 3 to 4 microns long.

Colonies on silica gel: Flat groups of cells are produced which are united in a common sheath. The aggregates form a pseudo-tissue of interwoven filaments suggestive of a fungus pad. The pad can be removed as a unit from the medium.

Aerobic.

Source: Activated sludge.
Habitat: Unknown.

3. Nitrosogloea membranacea H. Winogradsky, 1935.

(*Nitrosocystis "III"*, H. Winogradsky, Trans. Third Intern. Cong. Soil Sci., Oxford, *1*, 1935, 139; Compt. rend. Acad. Sci., Paris, *200*, 1935, 1887; Ann. Inst. Past., *58*, 1937, 333.)

mem.bran.a'ce.a. L. adj. *membranaceus* membranaceous.

Ellipsoidal cells commonly in pairs and also solitary.

Colonies on silica gel: Appear as dull mucoid material with a pale straw color. The cells are held firmly together so that the entire colony is easily picked up with the transfer needle. No structural units within the colony.

Aerobic.

Source: Activated sludge.
Habitat: Unknown.

Genus VI. Nitrobacter *Winogradsky, 1892.*

(Arch. Sci. biol., St. Petersburg, *1*, 1892, 127.)

Ni.tro.bac'ter. Gr. noun *nitrum* nitre, M.L. nitrate; M.L. noun *bacter* the masculine form of the Gr. neut.n. *bactrum* a rod; M.L. mas.n. *Nitrobacter* nitrate rod.

Cells rod-shaped. Oxidize nitrites to nitrates.

The type species is *Nitrobacter winogradskyi* Winslow et al.

1. Nitrobacter winogradskyi Winslow et al., 1917.

(*Nitrobacter* Winogradsky, Arch. Sci. biol., St. Petersburg, *1*, 1892, 127; *Bacterium nitrobacter* Lehmann and Neumann, Bakt. Diag., 2 Aufl., *2*, 1899, 187; Winslow et al., Jour. Bact., *2*, 1917, 552.)

wi.no.grad'sky.i. Named for S. Winogradsky, the microbiologist who first isolated these bacteria; M.L. mas.gen.n. *winogradskyi* of Winogradsky.

Description taken from Gibbs (Soil Sci., *8*, 1919, 448).

Short, non-motile rods with gelatinous membrane, 0.6 to 0.8 by 1.0 to 1.2 microns. Do not stain readily. Gram-negative (Omelianski, Cent. f. Bakt., II Abt., *19*, 1907, 263).

Can be cultivated on media free of organic matter. Sensitive to certain organic compounds.

Washed agar colonies: In 7 to 10 days very small, light brown, circular to irregular colonies, becoming darker.

Silica gel: Colonies smaller but more dense than those on washed agar.

Washed agar slant: In 7 to 10 days scant, grayish streak.

Inorganic solution medium: After 10 days flocculent sediment. Sensitive to ammonium salts under alkaline conditions.

Nitrite is oxidized to nitrate.

Aerobic.

Strictly autotrophic.

Optimum temperature, between 25° and 28° C.

Source: Soil.

Habitat: Presumably widely distributed in soil.

2. Nitrobacter agilis Nelson, 1931.

(Zent. f. Bakt., II Abt., *83*, 1931, 287.)

ag'il.is. L. adj. *agilis* agile, quick.

Rods, 0.5 by 0.8 to 0.9 micron, occurring singly, sometimes in pairs or larger aggregates. Rapidly motile with a long, thin, polar flagellum often 7 to 10 times as long as the rod. (Non-motile culture obtained by Kingma Boltjes, Arch. f. Mikrobiol., *6*, 1935, 79.) Gram-negative.

No growth in nutrient broth, nutrient agar, nutrient or plain gelatin, litmus or plain milk, glucose or plain yeast water, or on potato.

Nitrite agar: After two weeks, produces semi-spherical, minute, nearly transparent colonies. Oxidation usually complete in 10 to 14 days.

Inorganic liquid medium containing nitrite: Produces uniformly dispersed growth.

Optimum pH, between 7.6 and 8.6. Limits of growth, 6.6 to 10.0.

Temperature relations: Optimum for growth, between 25° and 30° C. Optimum for oxidation, 28° C. No oxidation at 37° C. Thermal death point, 60° C. for five minutes.

Strictly autotrophic.

Aerobic.

Source: Isolated from greenhouse soils and from sewage effluents in Madison, Wisconsin.

Habitat: Presumably widely distributed in soil.

Genus *VII*. Nitrocystis *H. Winogradsky, 1935.*

(Trans. Third Intern. Cong. Soil Sci., Oxford, *1*, 1935, 139.)

Ni.tro.cyst'is. Gr. noun *nitrum* nitre, M.L. nitrate; Gr. noun *cystis* bladder, cyst; M.L. fem.n. *Nitrocystis* nitrate cyst.

Cells ellipsoidal or rod-shaped. Embedded in slime and united into compact zoogloeal aggregates. Oxidize nitrites to nitrates.

It has been suggested that these organisms were really myxobacters. See note under *Nitrosocystis* for references.

The type species is *Nitrocystis sarcinoides* H. Winogradsky.

1. **Nitrocystis sarcinoides** H. Winogradsky, 1937. (*Nitrocystis B. A.*, H. Winogradsky, Compt. rend. Acad. Sci., Paris, *200*, 1935, 1888; also see Ann. Inst. Past., *58*, 1937, 336.)

sar.cin.o.i'des. L. *sarcina* a packet; Gr. *idus* form, shape; M.L. adj. *sarcinoides* resembling *Sarcina*, a genus of bacteria.

Small rods 0.5 by 1.0 micron. Cells ellipsoidal or wedge-shaped and grouped in sarcina-like packets.

Colonies on silica gel: On the surface of gel coated with kaolin the colonies appear as small, raised, amber warts. The colonies grow up to 5 mm in diameter. The colonies are viscous and sticky when young, and they become brown with age, shrink, and look like scales and become hard like grains of sand. Each colony is enveloped in several layers of a thick slime which holds the cells together so that the entire colony can be removed with a transfer needle.

Aerobic.

Source: Activated sludge.

Habitat: Unknown.

2. **Nitrocystis micropunctata** (H. Winogradsky, 1935) H. Winogradsky, 1937. (*Nitrocystis "III"*, H. Winogradsky, Trans. Third Intern. Cong. Soil Sci., Oxford, *1*, 1935, 139; *Nitrogloea micropunctata* H. Winogradsky, Compt. rend. Acad. Sci., Paris, *200*, 1935, 1888; H. Winogradsky, Ann. Inst. Past., *58*, 1937, 326.)

mi.cro.punc.ta'ta. Gr. *micrus* small; L. *punctatus* spotted; M.L. adj. *micropunctatus* full of small spots.

Cells are ellipsoidal rods, about 0.5 micron in diameter, which stain poorly except at the ends. Encased in a viscous slime.

Colonies on silica gel: Like those of *N. sarcinoides* except that they are clearer and have a more plastic consistency. The cells are not held together by the slime in the colony as with *N. sarcinoides*. The capsule is more readily differentiated in old colonies.

Aerobic.

Source: Activated sludge.

Habitat: Unknown.

FAMILY II. METHANOMONADACEAE BREED Fam. Nov.*

(*Oxydobacteriaceae* Orla-Jensen, *pro parte*, Cent. f Bakt., II Abt., *22*, 1909, 329; *Protobacterieae* Rahn, Cent. f. Bakt., II Abt., *96*, 1937, 273.)

Me.tha.no.mo.na.da′ce.ae. M.L. noun *Methanomonas, -adis* a genus of bacteria; *-aceae* ending to denote a family; M.L. fem.pl.n. *Methanomonadaceae* the *Methanomonas* family.

Rod-shaped organisms deriving their life energy from the oxidation of simple compounds of hydrogen or carbon. Polar flagellate when motile. Gram-negative. Found in soil and water.

It is clear that the species placed in the genera in this family belong with other polar flagellate bacteria (the group of pseudomonads in the broad sense). Their method of deriving energy from oxidative processes is in accord with that of many other polar-flagellate bacteria. As a matter of convenience and as a means of emphasizing the fact that the species included here secure their energy from the oxidation of simple hydrogen and carbon compounds, the genera that have been proposed to include these species are grouped into a family separate from those of the species that secure their energy from the oxidation of simple nitrogen or sulfur compounds on the one hand, and those that normally secure their energy from the oxidation of glucose or other organic compounds on the other hand. Further studies of the differences in physiology found among the **polar** flagellate bacteria are badly needed.

Key to the genera of the family **Methanomonadaceae.**

I. Organisms deriving their life energy from the oxidation of simple compounds of hydrogen.
   A. Cells capable of securing growth energy by the oxidation of methane.
      Genus I. *Methanomonas*, p. 74.
   B. Cells capable of securing growth energy by the oxidation of hydrogen.
      Genus II. *Hydrogenomonas*, p. 75.
II. Organisms deriving their life energy from the oxidation of carbon monoxide.
      Genus III. *Carboxydomonas*, p. 77.

Genus I. **Methanomonas** *Orla-Jensen, 1909.*

(Cent. f. Bakt., II Abt., *22*, 1909, 311.)

Me.tha.no.mo′nas. Gr. *methy* wine; Gr. *methe* strong drink; M.L. *methanum* methane; Gr. *monas* a unit, monad; M.L. fem.n. *Methanomonas* methane monad.

Cells monotrichous, capable of obtaining energy from oxidation of methane to CO_2 and water.

The type species is *Methanomonas methanica* (Söhngen) Orla-Jensen.

1. **Methanomonas methanica** (Söhngen, 1906) Orla-Jensen, 1909. (*Bacillus methanicus* Söhngen, Cent. f. Bakt., II Abt., *15*, 1906, 513; Orla-Jensen, Cent. f. Bakt., II Abt., *22*, 1909, 311.)

me.tha′ni.ca. M.L. noun *methanum* methane; M.L. adj. *methanicus* relating to methane.

Short rods, 0.5 to 0.8 by 2.0 to 3.0 microns, motile in young cultures by means of a single flagellum. In older cultures nearly spherical. Can be cultivated in an atmosphere composed of one part CH_4 and two parts air on washed agar containing the necessary inorganic salts. The growth is membranous.

At the end of two weeks, the organisms changed an atmosphere containing 225 ml

---

* Revised by Prof. Robert S. Breed, Cornell University, Geneva, New York, January, 1954.

CH_4 and 321 ml O_2 to the following:

CH$_4$......................... 0 ml
CO$_2$......................... 78 ml
O$_2$......................... 172 ml

In addition, 21 ml CO_2 were dissolved in the liquid.

Habitat: Presumably widely distributed in soil.

Genus II. **Hydrogenomonas** *Orla-Jensen, 1909.*

(Cent. f. Bakt., II Abt., *22*, 1909, 311.)

Hy.dro.ge.no.mo'nas. Gr. *hydro* water; Gr. *genus* race, offspring; whence, M.L. *hydrogenum* hydrogen, that which produces water; Gr. *monas* a unit, monad; M.L. fem. noun *Hydrogenomonas* hydrogen monad.

Short rods that are polar flagellate when motile. Cells capable of deriving energy from the oxidation of hydrogen. They may grow well on organic media without hydrogen although this has not been shown to be true in all cases. Gram-negative. Found in soil and water.

This group of bacteria is characterized by the ability to grow in substrates containing no organic matter and to use elemental hydrogen as the source of energy for growth. Under these conditions CO_2 is used as the source of carbon. Bacteria with similar physiological characteristics but differing in morphology are placed in the genera *Bacillus* and *Clostridium*. Although other bacteria and even certain algae have enzyme systems which can activate hydrogen and reduce CO_2 in the process, there is no evidence that these organisms are able to grow in inorganic media with hydrogen as the exclusive source of energy (see Stephenson and Strickland, Biochem. Jour., *25*, 1931, 205–215; Woods, Biochem. Jour., *30*, 1936, 515; Lee and Umbreit, Zent. f. Bakt., II Abt., *101*, 1940, 354; Gaffron, Amer. Jour. Bot., *27*, 1940, 273).

The type species is *Hydrogenomonas pantotropha* (Kaserer) Orla-Jensen.

Key to the species of genus **Hydrogenomonas.**

I. Not sensitive to high concentrations of O_2 .
   A. When growing autotrophically, no pellicle on liquid media.
                       1. *Hydrogenomonas pantotropha.*
   B. When growing autotrophically, pellicle formed on liquid media.
                       2. *Hydrogenomonas facilis.*
II. Sensitive to high concentrations of O_2 .
   A. When growing autotrophically, no pellicle on liquid media.
                       3. *Hydrogenomonas flava.*
   B. When growing autotrophically, pellicle formed on liquid media.
                       4. *Hydrogenomonas vitrea.*

1. **Hydrogenomonas pantotropha** (Kaserer, 1906) Orla-Jensen, 1909. (*Bacillus pantotrophus* Kaserer, Cent. f. Bakt., II Abt., *16*, 1906, 688; Orla-Jensen, Cent. f. Bakt., II Abt., *22*, 1909, 311.)

pan.to'troph.a. Gr. prefix *panto* all; Gr. *trophus* feeder; M.L. adj. *pantotrophus* omnivorous.

Rods, 0.4 to 0.5 by 1.2 to 1.5 microns, with rounded ends. Occur singly, in pairs and in chains. Encapsulated. Actively motile by means of a single, long, polar flagellum. Gram stain not recorded. Bipolar staining in old cultures.

Inorganic solution: When cultivated under an atmosphere of O_2 , CO_2 and H_2 , the liquid becomes turbid without pellicle formation.

Inorganic solid media: When cultivated under an atmosphere of O_2 , CO_2 and H_2 , the colonies are yellow and slimy, and the agar plates have an odor resembling hot, soapy water.

Gelatin colonies: Yellow, smooth, rarely concentrically ringed or greenish.

Gelatin stab: Growth only at surface. As a rule no liquefaction.

Agar colonies: Same as on gelatin, greenish, often slimy.

Broth: Turbid, somewhat slimy; pellicle occasionally produced.

Milk: No coagulation. A yellow pellicle forms. Medium becomes slimy and assumes a dirty flesh color.

Potato: Moist, yellow, glistening.

Indole not produced.

Hydrogen sulfide not produced.

Nitrites not produced from nitrates.

Carbohydrates not utilized.

Aerobic.

Optimum temperature, between 28° and 30° C.

Facultatively autotrophic.

Distinctive characters: Develops autotrophically in inorganic medium under an atmosphere of H_2, O_2 and CO_2. Oxidizes hydrogen to water and uses CO_2 as the source of carbon for growth.

Source: Isolated from soil near Vienna.

Habitat: Probably widely distributed in soil.

2. Hydrogenomonas facilis Schatz and Bovell, 1952.* (An undescribed *Hydrogenomonas*, Schatz, Proc. Soc. Amer. Bact., Baltimore Meeting, 1950, 124; Schatz and Bovell, Jour. Bact., 63, 1952, 87.)

fa'ci.lis. L. adj. *facilis* ready, quick.

Rods 0.3 by 2.0 microns in autotrophic and 0.4 by 2.5 microns in heterotrophic cultures. Occur singly, in pairs and in short chains. Motile by means of one or two polar flagella. Gram-negative.

Gelatin stab: Rapidly liquefied.

Agar colonies: Round, raised, glistening, translucent, non-fluorescent and non-mucoid. No distinctive odor developed.

Autotrophic media: Cultures readily maintained in media of this type.

Autotrophic gas uptake: The same overall reaction is effected as that carried out by certain anaerobically adapted green algae $(6H_2 + 2O_2 + CO_2 \rightarrow CH_2O + 5H_2O)$. In an atmosphere of CO_2 and H_2, no CO_2 fixation accompanies the quantitative reduction of nitrate to nitrite by molecular H_2; nor is there any change in concentration of bicarbonate or in total gas pressure (Warburg apparatus) when acetone, pyruvate or α-ke-

toglutarate are added (Schatz, Jour. Gen. Microbiol., 6, 1952, 329).

Broth: Turbid with pellicle.

Milk: Slowly digested with alkalinization.

Potato: Abundant, spreading, non-pigmented growth.

Indole not produced.

Hydrogen sulfide not produced.

Acetylmethylcarbinol not produced.

Nitrites produced from nitrates.

Aerobic, obligate.

Non-hemolytic.

Optimum temperature, 28° C.

Source: Isolated from soil.

Habitat: Presumably widely distributed in soil.

3. Hydrogenomonas flava Niklewski, 1910. (Jahrb. f. wissensch. Botanik, 48, 1910, 113; emend. Kluyver and Manten, Antonie v. Leeuwenhoek, 8, 1942, 71.)

fla'va. L. *flavus* yellow.

Rods 1.5 microns in length. Motile by means of polar flagella. Gram-negative.

Agar colonies on inorganic medium in presence of H_2, O_2 and CO_2: Small, smooth, yellow, shining, adhering to medium. Develop well below surface of medium, but growth is paler.

Gelatin not liquefied.

Inorganic liquid medium in presence of H_2, O_2 and CO_2: No pellicle formation. Good development when there is from 2 to 8 per cent oxygen in the gas. At higher O_2 concentrations good growth occurs only in association with *H. vitrea* or other bacteria.

Oxidizes hydrogen to water.

Microaerophilic, growing in an atmosphere of low oxygen tension, not exceeding 8 per cent.

Facultatively autotrophic.

Distinctive characters: Found singly on slides whereas the rod-shaped cells of *Hydrogenomonas vitrea* tend to cling together in masses. Colonies on agar opaque, not transparent.

Source: Isolated from mud, garden soil, pasture land, vegetable mold and peat.

Habitat: Presumably widely distributed in soil.

---

* Prepared by Prof. Albert Schatz, National Agricultural College, Farm School P.O., Bucks Co., Pennsylvania, December, 1953.

4. **Hydrogenomonas vitrea** Niklewski, 1910. (Jahrb. f. wissensch. Botanik, *48*, 1910, 113.)

vit're.a. L. *vitreus* of glass.

Rods 2.0 microns in length, cells adhering to each other as by slime. Motility not observed.

Agar colonies on inorganic medium in presence of H_2, O_2 and CO_2 : Delicate, transparent, with slight fluorescence and yellow center. Surface folded. Do not develop readily beneath the surface of medium.

Agar streak on inorganic substrate: Same as agar colonies except that growth is spreading.

Inorganic liquid medium in presence of H_2, O_2 and CO_2 : Pellicle, adherent to wall of tube. Good development when there is from 2 to 8 per cent oxygen in the gas. At higher O_2 concentrations good growth occurs only in association with *H. flava* or other bacteria.

Oxidizes hydrogen to water.

Microaerophilic, growing in an atmosphere of low oxygen tension, not exceeding 8 per cent.

Facultatively autotrophic.

Distinctive characters: Grows in substrates containing no organic matter and produces a pellicle.

Source: Isolated from mud, garden soil, pasture land, vegetable mold and peat.

Habitat: Presumably widely distributed in soil.

Genus III. **Carboxydomonas** *Orla-Jensen, 1909.*

(Cent. f. Bakt., II Abt., *22*, 1909, 311.)

Car.box.y.do.mo'nas. L. noun *carbo* charcoal, carbon; Gr. adj. *oxys* sharp; Gr. noun *monas* a unit, monad; M.L. fem.n. *Carboxydomonas* the carbon-oxidizing monad.

Autotrophic, rod-shaped cells capable of securing growth energy by the oxidation of CO, forming CO_2 .

The type species is *Carboxydomonas oligocarbophila* (Beijerinck and van Delden) Orla-Jensen.

1. **Carboxydomonas oligocarbophila** (Beijerinck and van Delden, 1903) Orla-Jensen, 1909. (*Bacillus oligocarbophilus* Beijerinck and van Delden, Cent. f. Bakt., II Abt., *10*, 1903, 33; Orla-Jensen, Cent. f. Bakt., II Abt., *22*, 1909, 311.)*

o.li.go.car.bo'phi.la. Gr. adj. *oligus* little, scanty; L. noun *carbo* charcoal, car-ɔon; Gr. adj. *philus* loving; M.L. adj. *oligo-:arbophilus* loving little carbon.

Rods very small, 0.5 by 1.0 micron, color-ıess, united into irregular masses by a slimy substance. Non-motile. There is little cytoplasm within the slimy, cellulose-like wall of the cells.

Growth occurs in culture fluids free from organic matter and on washed agar containing the necessary inorganic salts.

Media containing carbonaceous materials: No growth.

Liquid media: A thick, slimy film is produced.

CO is utilized as food and as such is oxidized to CO_2 . In symbiosis with other bacteria, hydrogen in water is oxidized by the catalytic reduction of CO_2 to CO. The CO is then metabolized, again forming CO_2 (Kaserer, Cent. f. Bakt., II Abt., *16*, 1906, 681).

Growth best in the dark.

Optimum temperature, 25° C.

* Kistner (Proc. Kon. Nederl. Akad. van Wetenschappen, Amsterdam, Series C, *56*, 1953, 443), in a paper received after the section covering *Carboxydomonas* was prepared, questions the data gathered by Beijerinck, Kaserer, Lantzsch and others. He concluded that their reports were based on doubtful and imperfect observations. Using a carefully controlled technique, he was able to isolate an organism which oxidized CO to CO_2 and which had the characters of a pseudomonad (polar flagellate, straight rod). On further testing, however, because it also oxidized H_2 , he concluded that it belonged in the genus *Hydrogenomonas*. Further studies on the species are promised.

Discussion: In spite of the fact that several able bacteriologists have studied this species and the actinomycete that has a similar physiology, several important points are left in doubt; the most important of these is whether Beijerinck was right in thinking the actinomycete something distinct from his *Bacillus oligocarbophilus*, or whether Lantzsch (Cent. f. Bakt., II Abt., *57*, 1922, 309) was right in thinking of them as but stages in the growth cycle of a single species. Definite data in regard to the Gram reaction would be helpful in clarifying this situation. If the species is to be accepted as non-motile but related to polar-flagellate bacteria, it must be Gram-negative. If an actinomycete, it would be Gram-positive. Lantzsch reports the organism he studied (which was an actinomycete) to be Gram-positive.

Source: Isolated from garden soil.

Habitat: Presumably widely distributed in soil.

FAMILY III. THIOBACTERIACEAE JANKE, 1924.*

(Allgem. Tech. Mikrobiol., Dresden and Leipzig, I Teil, 1924, 68.)

Thi.o.bac.te.ri.a'ce.ae. M.L. neut.n. *Thiobacterium* type genus of the family; *-aceae* ending to denote a family; M.L. fem.pl.n. *Thiobacteriaceae* the *Thiobacterium* family.

Coccoid, straight or curved rod-shaped bacteria. Oxidize sulfur compounds, usually depositing free sulfur granules within or without the cells. Never filamentous. Colorless sulfur bacteria that are sometimes embedded in gelatinous pellicles or in gelatinous bladder-like colonies. Polar flagellate when motile. Presumably Gram-negative. Found in places where hydrogen sulfide occurs or may oxidize free sulfur, thiosulfates or related compounds.

While all of the species placed in this family have been described as colorless sulfur bacteria, they are still inadequately known and may not all deserve to be designated as sulfur bacteria. It is hoped that placing them together in one family will cause comparative studies to be made.

The type genus is *Thiobacterium* Janke.

Key to the genera of family **Thiobacteriaceae.**

I. Free sulfur granules deposited within or without the cells. Usually found in sulfurous waters or soil.
  A. Cells coccoid or straight rods.
    1. Non-motile so far as known.
      Genus I. *Thiobacterium*, p. 79.
    2. Motile by means of polar flagella so far as known.
      a. Cells rod-shaped, very large.
      Genus II. *Macromonas*, p. 80.
      aa. Cells round to ovoid, large.
      Genus III. *Thiovulum*, p. 81.
  B. Cells large, curved rods, somewhat pointed.
      Genus IV. *Thiospira*, p. 82.
II. Oxidize free sulfur, thiosulfates and related sulfur compounds to sulfates. Autotrophic or facultatively autotrophic.
      Genus V. *Thiobacillus*, p. 83.

---

* Revision of *Thiobacteriaceae* Janke prepared by Prof. Dr. Alexander Janke, Technische Hochschule, Vienna, Austria, December, 1954, with the assistance of Prof. Robert S. Breed, Cornell University, Geneva, New York.

Genus I. **Thiobacterium** *Janke, 1924.**

(Janke, Allgem. Tech. Mikrobiol., I Teil, 1924, 68; not *Thiobacterium* Issatchenko and Salimowskaja, Zur Morphologie u. Physiol. der Thionsäurebakterien (Russian), Izyiestia Gosud. Gidrobiol. Inst. (Memoirs State Hydrobiol. Inst. Leningrad), No. 21, 1928, 61.)

Thi.o.bac.te'ri.um. Gr. noun *thium* sulfur; Gr. dim. noun *bacterium* a small rod; M.L. neut.n. *Thiobacterium* small sulfur rod.

Rod-shaped, sulfur bacteria found in fresh or salt water or soil. Cells 1.0 micron or less in diameter. Motility not observed. Sulfur granules sometimes found inside, sometimes outside the cells. These cells may or may not be embedded in pellicles or in spherical, bladder-like colonies.

The type species is *Thiobacterium bovista* Janke.

Key to the species in genus **Thiobacterium.**

I. Sulfur grains are found within the cells. Forms colonies in bladder-like masses which resemble puff balls.

> 1. *Thiobacterium bovista.*

II. Sulfur grains are found outside of the cells.

    A. Produces colonies on the surface of water containing proper nutrients. Sulfur crystals are found among the cells.

> 2. *Thiobacterium cristalliferum.*

    B. Produces a surface film in the form of a network on water. Sulfur globules are found among the cells.

> 3. *Thiobacterium retiformans.*

1. **Thiobacterium bovista** (Molisch, 1912) Janke, 1924. (*Bacterium bovista* Molisch, Cent. f. Bakt., II Abt., *33*, 1912, 59; Janke, Allgem. Tech. Mikrobiol., I Teil, 1924, 68.)

bo.vis'ta. M.L. noun *Bovista* a genus of puff balls; from German *bovist* puff ball; M.L. fem.n. *bovista* puff ball.

Rod-shaped bacteria embedded in the wall of bladder-like gelatinous colonies, the interiors of which are filled with a clear liquid. The cells are 0.6 to 1.5 by 2.0 to 5.0 microns, occurring by the thousands in each colony. Each cell contains from one to four sulfur granules. No motility observed. The cells stain well with gentian violet while the gelatinous matrix stains poorly, if at all.

The spherical colonies increase in number by a kind of budding process that produces smaller colonies. The colonies are white by reflected light, black or bluish black by transmitted light. Groups of these colonies have the appearance of groups of puff balls of variable sizes. They occur near the surface of the water.

These organisms have not been cultivated in pure culture.

Source: Found commonly in sulfurous sea-water in the harbor at Trieste.

Habitat: Presumably widely distributed in coastal waters containing hydrogen sulfide.

2. **Thiobacterium cristalliferum** (Gicklhorn, 1920) Janke, 1924. (*Bacterium cristalliferum* Gicklhorn, Cent. f. Bakt., II Abt., *50*, 1920, 420; Janke, Allgem. Tech. Mikrobiol., I Teil, 1924, 68.)

cris.tal.li'fe.rum. Gr. noun *crystallus* a crystal; L. v. *fero* to bear; M.L. adj. *cristalliferus* crystal-bearing.

Straight to curved, rod-shaped bacteria. 0.3 to 0.5 by 1.0 to 2.4 microns. Deposit sulfur crystals outside of the cells. Non-motile. Stain readily in gentian violet.

Colonies developed on the surface of water

---

* Prepared by Prof. Dr. Alexander Janke, Technische Hochschule, Vienna, Austria, December, 1954.

containing potassium sulfide (K₂S) which was inoculated with a handful of garden soil from Graz, Austria. At the end of three weeks, numerous, snow-white colonies developed on the surface of the water. Colonies which at first are of microscopic size may become 0.8 to 1.5 mm in diameter. Sulfur crystals appear by transmitted light as a black mass in the center of the smaller colonies, but these crystals extend to the margin in older colonies.

Habitat: Garden soil.

3. **Thiobacterium retiformans** (Gicklhorn, 1920) Janke, 1924. (*Bacterium retiformans* Gicklhorn, Cent. f. Bakt., II Abt., *50*, 1920, 421; Janke, Allgem. Tech. Mikrobiol., I Teil., 1924, 68.)

re.ti.for'mans. L. noun *rete* a net; L. v. *formo* to form; M.L. part.adj. *retiformans* net-forming.

Rod-shaped bacteria, 0.5 to 1.0 by 2.0 to 4.5 microns. Globular sulfur granules found among the cells. Non-motile. Forms pellicles and zoogloeal masses.

Developed in water containing potassium sulfide (K₂S) which was inoculated with the decaying roots of nettle plants. This species developed a delicate pellicle in the form of a network on the surface of the water. It also formed zoogloeal masses attached to the wall of the culture flask.

Source: Soil containing decaying roots, Graz, Austria.

Habitat: Presumably widely distributed.

Genus II. **Macromonas** *Utermöhl and Koppe, 1923.**

(Utermöhl and Koppe, Verhandl. Intern. Ver. f. Theoret. u. angew. Limnologie, 1923, 86; *Thiovibrio* Janke, Allgem. Tech. Mikrobiol., I Teil, 1924, 68.)

Mac.ro.mo'nas. Gr. adj. *macrus* large; Gr. noun *monas* a unit, monad; M.L. fem.n. *Macromonas* a large monad.

Colorless, cylindrical to bean-shaped bacteria, actively motile by means of a single polar flagellum. Cells large, 3.0 to 14.0 microns in diameter. Multiplication by constriction (fission). Chiefly characterized by the occurrence of calcium carbonate inclusions in the form of large spherules. In their natural habitat they may also contain small sulfur globules.

Two species have been distinguished, primarily on the basis of cell size. Whether this is sufficiently constant to serve as a specific character has not been definitely established. From studies on the organisms in their natural habitat, which are still limited in scope and extent, it appears at present that the two species should be maintained, at least provisionally. It is possible, however, that further observations, especially with cultures under different environmental conditions, will show the occurrence of intermediate types and of a greater range of variation in size of pure cultures than has previously been reported.

The type species is *Macromonas mobilis* (Lauterborn) Utermöhl and Koppe.

Key to the species of genus **Macromonas.**

I. Cells measure 12 microns or more in length and 8 microns or more in width.
1. *Macromonas mobilis.*
II. Cells measure less than 12 microns in length and 5 microns or less in width.
2. *Macromonas bipunctata.*

1. **Macromonas mobilis** (Lauterborn, 1915) Utermöhl and Koppe, 1923. (*Achromatium mobile* Lauterborn, Verhandl. Naturhist.-medizin. Vereins, Heidelberg, N. F., *13*, 1915, 413; Utermöhl and Koppe,

Verhandl. Intern. Ver. f. theoret. u. angew. Limnologie, 1923, 86 and Utermöhl and Koppe, Arch. f. Hydrobiol., Suppl. Bd. *5*, 1925, 234.)

mo'bi.lis. L. adj. *mobilis* movable, motile.

---

* Prepared by Prof. Dr. Alexander Janke, Technische Hochschule, Vienna, Austria, December, 1954.

Colorless sulfur bacteria always occurring singly; slightly curved, elongated ellipsoids or cylinders with broad, hemispherical ends. Width varies from 8 to 14 microns, length from 12 to 30 microns; most common size, 9 by 20 microns. Multiplication by constriction in the middle.

Cells actively motile by means of a single polar flagellum distinctly visible without special staining. It is 20 to 40 microns long, and, with respect to the direction of motion, always posteriorly placed. Rate of movement somewhat sluggish, about 800 microns per minute, probably on account of the high specific gravity of the cells.

Normally contain small sulfur droplets and, in addition, large, roughly spherical inclusions of calcium carbonate. Two to four such crystal masses almost fill a single cell. Under unfavorable conditions the calcium carbonate crystals may disappear before the sulfur globules.

Microaerophilic; apparently require hydrogen sulfide.

Habitat: Found in fresh-water environments containing sulfide and calcium ions, as in shallow basins and streams in the upper layers of the mud.

2. **Macromonas bipunctata** (Gicklhorn, 1920) Utermöhl and Koppe, 1925. (*Pseudomonas bipunctata* Gicklhorn, Cent. f. Bakt., II Abt., *50*, 1920, 425; Utermöhl and Koppe, Arch. f. Hydrobiol., Suppl. Bd. *5*, 1925, 235.)

bi.punc.ta'ta. L. *bis* twice; L. part.adj. *punctatus* punctate, dotted; M.L. adj. *bipunctatus* twice punctate.

Cells colorless, occurring singly; cylindrical with hemispherical ends, after cell division often temporarily pear-shaped. 3 to 5 by 8 to 12 microns. Multiplication by constriction in the middle.

Actively motile by means of a single polar flagellum, about 10 to 15 microns long, always posteriorly placed with respect to the direction of movement. Flagellum delicate, not visible without staining. Rate of movement sluggish, about 600 microns per minute. Probably this slow motion is due to the high specific gravity of the cells.

Normally contain calcium carbonate crystals as inclusions. These are in the form of large spherules, one or two of which nearly fill the individual cells. Sulfur globules have not been demonstrated with certainty as yet.

Microaerophilic, but it is uncertain whether hydrogen sulfide is required.

A second species that is like *Macromonas bipunctata*, except that the cells are smaller in size, has been named by Gicklhorn (*op. cit.*, *50*, 1920, 425). Pure-culture studies may show the two species to be identical as difference in size of cells has not been found to be significant elsewhere among sulfur bacteria.

Source: From stems, leaves, etc. of fresh-water plants in ponds near Graz, Austria.

Habitat: Found in fresh-water environments containing calcium ions; but it has been found in sulfide-containing as well as in sulfide-free water. Also found in shallow basins and streams in upper layers of the mud.

Genus III. **Thiovulum** *Hinze, 1913.** *

(Ber. d. deutsch. bot. Ges., *31*, 1913, 195.)

Thi.o'vu.lum. Gr. noun *thium* sulfur; L. noun *ovum* egg; M.L. neut.dim.n. *Thiovulum* small sulfur egg.

Unicellular organisms, round to ovoid, 5.0 to 20.0 microns in diameter. Cytoplasm often concentrated at one end of the cell, the remaining space being occupied by a large vacuole. Multiplication by constriction which, in late stages, merges into fission. Actively motile; movements accompanied by rapid rotation. Flagellation not definitely demonstrated, but type of locomotion suggests polar flagellation. Normally contain sulfur globules in the cytoplasm; hence, these are frequently concentrated at one end of the cell.

It is difficult to establish distinct species. Those that have been described differ only in

* Prepared by Prof. Dr. Alexander Janke, Technische Hochschule, Vienna, Austria, December, 1954.

size, and the differences appear to be far from constant. The ovoid cells of *Thiovulum majus* are noted as being 11 to 18 microns long and 9 to 17 microns wide, while *Thiovulum minus* comprises the smaller forms from 9.6 to 11.0 microns long by 7.2 to 9.0 microns wide. In view of the regular occurrence of all intermediate sizes, it seems best to recognize only a single species at present.

The type species is *Thiovulum majus* Hinze.

1. Thiovulum majus Hinze, 1913. (Hinze, Ber. d. deutsch. bot. Ges., *31*, 1913, 195; including *Thiovulum minus* Hinze, *loc. cit.*; *Thiovulum mulleri* Lauterborn, Verhandl. Naturhist.-medizin. Vereins, Heidelberg, N. F., *13*, 1915, 414.)

ma'jus. L. comp.adj. *major* larger.

Unicellular organisms, spherical to ovoid. Cytoplasm often concentrated at one end of the cell, the remainder being occupied by a vacuole. Multiplication by constriction which, in late stages, merges into fission. Size of cells, 5 to 20 microns in diameter.

The most characteristic feature is its motility; it is the only one of the spherical to ovoid, colorless sulfur bacteria capable of rapid movement. Flagellation has not been definitely demonstrated, but the type of locomotion suggests the presence of polar flagella.

Normally contains sulfur droplets in cytoplasm, frequently concentrated at one end of cell.

Microaerophilic; apparently requires hydrogen sulfide.

Habitat: Found in sulfide-containing water, usually accumulating near the surface. Often found in cultures of decaying algae and in both fresh-water and marine environments.

Genus IV. **Thiospira** *Vislouch, 1914.**

(Vislouch, Jour. de Microbiologie, *1*, 1914, 50; *Sulfospirillum* Kluyver and van Niel, Zent. f. Bakt., II Abt., *94*, 1936, 396; *Thiospirillum* Janke, Allgem. Tech. Mikrobiol., I Teil, 1924, 68; not *Thiospirillum* Winogradsky, Schwefelbakterien, Leipzig, 1888, 104.)

Thi.o.spi'ra. Gr. noun *thium* sulfur; Gr. noun *spira* a coil; M.L. fem.n. *Thiospira* sulfur coil or spiral.

Colorless, motile, slightly bent, large rods, somewhat pointed at the ends, with granules of sulfur within the cells and a small number of flagella at the ends.

The type species is *Thiospira winogradskyi* (Omelianski) Vislouch.

Key to the species of genus **Thiospira.**

I. Large spirilla containing numerous sulfur granules.

1. *Thiospira winogradskyi.*

II. Clear center of spirilla cells contains two, occasionally one or three, sulfur granules.

2. *Thiospira bipunctata.*

1. Thiospira winogradskyi (Omelianski, 1905) Vislouch, 1914. (*Thiospirillum winogradskyi* Omelianski, Cent. f. Bakt., II Abt., *14*, 1905, 769; Vislouch, Jour. de Microbiologie (Russian), *1*, 1914, 50.)

wi.no.grad'sky.i. M.L. gen.noun *winogradskyi* of Winogradsky; named for S. N. Winogradsky, a Russian bacteriologist.

Large sulfur spirilla, somewhat pointed at the ends, 2.0 to 2.5 by 50 microns. Numerous granules of sulfur. Very motile, with one to two polar flagella.

The large, very active sulfur spirillum found by Gicklhorn (Cent. f. Bakt., II Abt., *50*, 1920, 418) may have belonged to this species.

Habitat: Curative mud.

2. Thiospira bipunctata (Molisch, 1912) Vislouch, 1914. (*Spirillum bipunctatum*

---

* Prepared by Prof. Dr. Alexander Janke, Technische Hochschule, Vienna, Austria, December, 1954.

Molisch, Cent. f. Bakt., II Abt., *33*, 1912, 55; Vislouch, Jour. de Microbiologie (Russian), *1*, 1914, 50.)

bi.punc.ta'ta. L. *bis* twice; L. noun *punctum* a point, spot; M.L. adj. *bipunctatus* two-spotted.

Small, slightly bent sulfur spirilla, markedly pointed at the ends; 6.6 to 14 microns long, 1.7 to 2.4 microns wide (in the center of the cell). Both ends are more or less filled with large volutin (metachromatic) granules. Several minute granules of sulfur are present in the clear center and sometimes at the ends. Old cells possess one flagellum at each end; young cells have a flagellum at one end.

Habitat: Sea and salt waters.

Genus V. Thiobacillus *Beijerinck, 1904.*[*]

(Beijerinck, Cent. f. Bakt., II Abt., *11*, 1904, 593; not *Thiobacillus* Ellis, Sulphur Bacteria, London, 1932, 130; *Sulfomonas* Orla-Jensen, Cent. f. Bakt., II Abt., *22*, 1909, 314.)

Thi.o.ba.cil'lus. Gr. noun *thium* sulfur; L. noun *bacillus* a small rod; M.L. mas.n. *Thiobacillus* a sulfur rodlet.

Small, Gram-negative, rod-shaped cells. Non-motile or motile, usually by means of a single polar flagellum. Energy derived from the oxidation of incompletely oxidized sulfur compounds, principally from elemental sulfur and thiosulfate but in some cases also from sulfide, sulfite and polythionates. The principal product of oxidation is sulfate, but sulfur is sometimes formed. Grow under acid or alkaline conditions and derive carbon from carbon dioxide or from bicarbonates in solution; some are obligate and some facultatively autotrophic. Some species are anaerobic in the presence of nitrate. Found in soil, mine wastewaters, sewage, effluents and related sources.

The type species of this genus is strictly autotrophic as are the majority of the species in the genus. It has been suggested that *Thiobacillus* should be restricted to these autotrophic species and that the facultatively autotrophic species be placed in the genus *Pseudomonas*. Some heterotrophic species now placed in *Pseudomonas* are known to have the ability to oxidize thiosulfates (Starkey, Soil Sci., *39*, 1935, 325).

The type species is *Thiobacillus thioparus* Beijerinck.

Key to the species of genus Thiobacillus.

I. Thiosulfate oxidized with increased acidity.
  A. Tetrathionate not formed as an intermediate product.
    1. Strictly autotrophic.
      a. Does not oxidize ferrous salts.
                    1. *Thiobacillus thioparus.*
      aa. Oxidizes ferrous salts.
                    2. *Thiobacillus ferrooxidans.*
    2. Facultatively autotrophic.
      a. Aerobic.
        b. Does not oxidize free sulfur.
                    3. *Thiobacillus novellus.*
        bb. Oxidizes free sulfur to sulfate.
                    4. *Thiobacillus coproliticus.*
      aa. Facultatively anaerobic in presence of nitrate.
                    5. *Thiobacillus denitrificans.*
  B. Tetrathionate formed as intermediate product.
    1. Final pH, 3.0.
                    6. *Thiobacillus neopolitanus.*

---

[*] Revised by Dr. C. D. Parker, South Melbourne, Australia, with the assistance of Dr. Kenneth L. Temple, Morgantown, West Virginia, June, 1954.

2. Final pH, 1.0 or less.
   a. Nitrate utilized.
      7. *Thiobacillus concretivorus.*
   aa. Nitrate not utilized.
      8. *Thiobacillus thiooxidans.*
II. Thiosulfate oxidized with increased alkalinity.
      9. *Thiobacillus trautweinii.*

1. **Thiobacillus thioparus** Beijerinck, 1904. (Arch. d. Sci. Exact. et Nat. Haarlem, Sér. 2, 9, 1904, 153; also see Cent. f. Bakt., II Abt., *11*, 1904, 593.)

thi.o'par.us. Gr. noun *thium* sulfur; L.v. *paro* to produce; M.L. adj. *thioparus* sulfur-producing.

Thin, short rods, 0.5 by 1.0 to 3.0 microns, averaging 0.5 by 1.7 microns. Motile. Starkey (Soil Sci., *39*, 1935, 209) reports the isolation of cultures (C) that he regards as practically identical with this species though they were non-motile and of coccoid form. Gram-negative.

Thiosulfate liquid medium: Pellicle consists of cells and free sulfur. Medium becomes turbid. pH drops to 4.5.

Thiosulfate agar colonies: Small (1 to 2 mm in diameter) circular, whitish yellow due to precipitated sulfur. Turn brown in old cultures.

No growth on organic media.

Optimum reaction, close to neutrality. Growth occurs between pH 7.8 and 4.5.

Strictly autotrophic. Derives its energy by the oxidation of thiosulfate to sulfate and sulfur without the intermediate formation of tetrathionate. Also oxidizes elemental sulfur. Does not oxidize hydrogen sulfide or sulfides.

Utilizes nitrate and ammonium salts as sources of nitrogen.

Aerobic.

Source: Canal water, mud and soil.

Habitat: Presumably widely distributed.

2. **Thiobacillus ferrooxidans** Temple and Colmer, 1951. (Iron oxidizing bacterium, Colmer, Temple and Hinkle, Jour. Bact., *59*, 1950, 317; Temple and Colmer, Jour. Bact., *62*, 1951, 605.)

fer.ro.o'xi.dans. L. noun *ferrum* iron; Gr. adj. *oxys* sharp, acid; M.L. v. *oxido* to oxidize or make acid; M.L. part.adj. *ferrooxidans* iron-oxidizing.

Description prepared by Dr. Kenneth L. Temple, Morgantown, West Virginia.

Short rods, 0.5 by 1.0 micron, with rounded ends. Occur singly or in pairs, rarely in chains. Motile, presumably polar flagellate. Gram-negative.

Thiosulfate agar colonies: Very thin and small with irregular margins, becoming whitish in center upon aging.

Thiosulfate liquid medium: Uniform turbidity; delicate pellicle in two or three weeks.

Ferrous agar: Colonial appearance varies with ferrous-iron content of agar: on low to moderate iron concentration, an amber zone reveals the presence of microscopic colonies which become lobed and coated with hydrated ferric oxide; on high ferrous iron concentration, growth is abundant becoming heavily encrusted with hydrated ferric oxide.

Ferrous liquid medium: Clear, rapidly turning amber to reddish brown due to production of ferric iron; ferric hydrate precipitated. Pellicle composed of cells and ferric hydrate.

Nitrogen sources: Utilizes ammonia; nitrate to a lesser extent.

Aerobic.

Optimum pH, between 2.5 and 5.8. No growth above pH 6.0. There is some stepwise adaptation to a lower pH than 2.5.

Strictly autotrophic, deriving its energy from the oxidation of thiosulfates or inorganic ferrous iron. Sulfur not appreciably utilized.

Distinctive characters: The pH range approaches that of *Thiobacillus thiooxidans* but does not extend below pH 2.0, and elemental sulfur is not appreciably used. Thiosulfate is oxidized rapidly but both liquid and agar cultures differ in appearance from *Thiobacillus thioparus*. Ferrous iron serves as a sufficient energy source with the concomitant formation of enormous quantities of ferric ions in acid media where ferric iron is not otherwise produced in quantity. The lobed, iron-encrusted colony formed on ferrous agar is unique. Cultures maintained on ferrous media lose the ability to oxidize thiosulfate, but colonies maintained on thiosulfate media retain their iron-oxidizing capacity.

Source: Isolated from bituminous coal mine drainage waters which were strongly acid and high in ferrous iron. Found in West Virginia and Pennsylvania.

Habitat: Acid waters of high iron content including drainage from several types of mines and soils containing pyrite or marcasite.

3. **Thiobacillus novellus** Starkey, 1934. (Jour. Bact., *28*, 1934, 365; Jour. Gen. Physiol., *18*, 1935, 325; Soil Sci., *39*, 1935, 207, 210.)

no.vel'lus. L. dim.adj. *novellus* new.

Short rods or ellipsoidal cells 0.4 to 0.8 by 0.6 to 1.8 microns. Non-motile. Gramnegative.

Gelatin stab: Mucoid growth at point of inoculation. Sub-surface growth meager. slow liquefaction.

Agar plate: Growth slow, colorless, moist, raised, circular, 1 mm in diameter. Deep colonies tiny, lens-shaped.

Thiosulfate agar plate: Growth slow, becoming white from precipitated sulfur. Surface colonies small, circular, moist. Crystals of $CaSO_4$ appear throughout the agar.

Agar slant: Growth fairly abundant, soft, somewhat ropy, raised, shining, moderately spreading; whitish in reflected light, brownish opalescence in transmitted light.

Thiosulfate agar slant: Growth very thin, practically colorless. No sub-surface growth. Sulfur usually precipitated as white, frosty film on the surface.

Agar stab: White to cream-colored growth confined close to point of inoculation; penetrates to bottom of tube.

Thiosulfate agar stab: No appreciable surface growth.

Broth: Slightly turbid. Gelatinous pellicle. Forms long, streamer-like network extending from surface to the bottom. Some sediment.

Thiosulfate broth: Uniform turbidity. No pellicle. Whitish sediment with thin, incomplete membrane on the bottom of the flask. Reaction acid in a few days, changes pH 7.8 to 5.8 with decomposition of a small quantity of thiosulfate.

Sulfur solution medium of slightly alkaline reaction: No growth.

Potato slant: Growth limited, cream-colored, moist, shining, slightly brown.

Litmus milk: Slow development of slight alkalinity.

Facultatively autotrophic.

Optimum reaction: Close to neutrality (limiting reactions, pH 5.0 to 9.0).

Aerobic.

Distinctive characters: Oxidizes thiosulfate to sulfate and sulfuric acid. Does not oxidize free sulfur.

Source: Isolated from soils.

Habitat: Soils.

4. **Thiobacillus coproliticus** Lipman and McLees, 1940. (Soil Sci., *50*, 1940, 432.)

co.pro.lit'i.cus. Gr. noun *coprus* dung; Gr. noun *lithus* a stone; whence coprolite, a fossil dung; M.L. adj. *coproliticus* of a coprolite.

Long, thin rods 0.1 to 0.2 by 6 to 8 (may measure 3 to 40) microns. Straight, S-shaped and curved cells. Motile by means of a single polar flagellum.

Peptone soil extract agar: Slight growth.

Nutrient broth: Little or no growth.

Thiosulfate agar: Slow development. Produces small, watery colonies raised above the agar surface. Colonies have been noted which were white from precipitated sulfur.

Thiosulfate broth: Thiosulfate is oxidized. Little or no turbidity. No pellicle. No sediment. Change in reaction from pH 7.6 to 6.1.

Sulfur broth: Sulfur is oxidized. No turbidity.

Facultatively autotrophic.

Aerobic.

Distinctive characters: Develops in inorganic media and oxidizes thiosulfate and sulfur to sulfate. Media with slightly alkaline reactions most favorable for growth.

Source: Isolated from coprolite rock material from Triassic period (Arizona).

Habitat: Unknown.

5. **Thiobacillus denitrificans** Beijerinck, 1904. (Beijerinck, Cent. f. Bakt., II Abt., *11*, 1904, 597; *Sulfomonas denitrificans* Orla-Jensen, Cent. f. Bakt., II Abt., *22*, 1909, 314.)

de.ni.tri'fi.cans. L. pref. *de* off, removed; M.L. noun *niter* saltpeter, nitrate; M.L. v. *nitrifico* to make nitrate, to nitrify; M.L. *denitrifico* to denitrify; M.L. part.adj. *denitrificans* denitrifying.

Short rods, 0.5 by 1 to 3 microns. Motile by means of a single polar flagellum (Tjulpanova-Mossevitch, Arch. d. Sci. Biol., U.S.S.R., *30*, 1930, 203).

Inorganic broth: Growth with production of gas, predominantly nitrogen.

Thiosulfate agar colonies: Thin; clear or weakly opalescent.

Optimum reaction: Neutral or slightly alkaline.

Autotrophic, utilizing carbon from CO_2, carbonates and bicarbonates. Considered to be strictly autotrophic by Lieske (Ber. d. deutsch. botan. Gesell., *30*, 1912, 12) and facultatively by Tjulpanova-Mossevitch (*op. cit.*, *30*, 1930, 203). Beijerinck stated (Kon. Akad. v. Wetenschappen Amsterdam, *42*, 1920, 899) that whereas the organism developed initially in an inorganic medium, it lost the autotrophic habit by cultivation in an organic medium.

Facultatively anaerobic. Can live in the absence of free O_2 in the presence of nitrate.

Distinctive characters: Oxidizes thiosulfate to sulfate under anaerobic conditions using nitrate as the hydrogen acceptor which is reduced to N_2. Also oxidizes sulfide, elemental sulfur and dithionate.

Habitat: Canal and river water, salt water, soil, peat, composts and mud.

6. **Thiobacillus neapolitanus** Parker, *nom. nov.* (Neue Gruppe von Schwefelbakterium, Nathansohn, Mitt. Zool. Sta., Neapel, *15*, 1902, 655; *Thiobacillus X*, Parker, Jour. Gen. Microbiol., *8*, 1953, 344.)

ne.a.po.li.ta'nus. L. adj. *neapolitanus* pertaining to Naples.

Short rods, 0.5 by 1.0 to 1.5 microns. Nonmotile. Gram-negative.

Thiosulfate agar colonies: Small (1 to 2 mm in diam.) circular, convex; whitish yellow due to precipitated sulfur.

Thiosulfate liquid medium; Uniform turbidity with pellicle which contains free sulfur. pH drops to 3.0.

Sulfur liquid medium: Very slight, uniform turbidity.

Optimum pH, about 6.0; growth occurs between pH 8.5 to 3.0.

Temperature relations: Optimum, 28° C.; slow growth at 10° and 37° C.; death occurs at 55° C.

Strictly autotrophic. Derives energy by the oxidation of thiosulfate, tetrathionate, elemental sulfur and hydrogen sulfide. Thiosulfate is oxidized to tetrathionate, sulfate and sulfuric acid; tetrathionate is oxidized to sulfate and sulfuric acid while free sulfuric acid only is formed from elemental sulfur and hydrogen sulfide. Utilizes atmospheric CO_2 as a source of carbon.

Nitrogen sources: Ammonium; nitrate- and nitrite-nitrogen.

Aerobic.

Comments: It has not been clear until recently (Parker, Jour. Gen. Microbiol., *8*, 1953, 344) that this organism is a species separate from *Thiobacillus thioparus* Beijerinck. The isolation and detailed study of an organism from concrete identical in most respects with Nathansohn's description of his isolate but different from Beijerinck's and Starkey's description of *Thiobacillus thioparus* makes it clear that two separate species are involved. *Thiobacillus neapolitanus* produces tetrathionate and sulfate from thiosulfate and oxidizes H_2S and tetrathionate whereas *Thiobacillus thioparus* produces sulfur and sulfate from thiosulfate and does not oxidize H_2S or tetrathionate.

Source: Originally isolated by Nathansohn from sea water at Naples, Italy. Isolated by Parker from early stages of the corrosion of concrete sewers and other concrete structures.

Habitat: Presumably widely distributed in soil and water, including sea water.

7. **Thiobacillus concretivorus** Parker,

1945. (Austral. Jour. Exper. Biol. and Med. Sci., *23*, 1945, 81; also see Jour. Gen. Microbiol., *8*, 1953, 344.)

con.cre.ti'vo.rus. L. noun *concretum* firm or solid matter; L. v. *voro* to devour or destroy; M.L. part.adj. *concretivorus* concrete-destroying.

Short, straight rods 0.5 by 1.5 to 2.0 microns with square ends. Stain irregularly, showing deeply stained granules in poorly stained slender rods. Motile, presumably polar flagellate. Motility lost in older cultures. Single polar flagellum, two to three times the length of the organism (unpublished data). Gram-negative.

Thiosulfate agar colonies: Minute, water-clear, whitish yellow on prolonged incubation. No confluent growth.

Thiosulfate liquid medium: Uniform turbidity, slight deposit of sulfur. No pellicle.

Sulfur liquid medium: Uniform turbidity; floating sulfur granules fall to the bottom.

Strictly aerobic.

Temperature relations: Optimum, 28° C.; slow growth at 10° and 37° C.; death occurs at 55° C.

Strictly autotrophic, utilizing atmospheric CO_2 as the source of carbon; growth inhibited by higher concentrations of glucose, glycerol and lactate. Derives energy from its oxidation of elemental sulfur, thiosulfate and hydrogen sulfide, oxidizing them ultimately to sulfate and sulfuric acid. Thiosulfate is oxidized with the intermediate production of tetrathionate.

Nitrogen sources: Utilizes ammonium- and nitrate-nitrogen equally well. Nitrate is not toxic whereas nitrite is.

Optimum reaction: Growth occurs between pH 6.0 and acid concentrations up to 10 per cent. Sulfuric acid optimum is between pH 2.0 and 4.0.

Distinctive characters: Responsible for the rapid corrosion of concrete sewers and other concrete structures where the sewer air contains hydrogen sulfide.

Habitat: Corroding concrete in sewers; also found in sewage and presumably in soil and fresh water.

8. **Thiobacillus thiooxidans** Waksman and Joffe, 1922. (Jour. Bact., 7, 1922, 239.)

thi.o.ox'i.dans. Gr. noun *thium* sulfur; Gr. adj. *oxys* sharp, acid; M.L. v. *oxido* to make acid, to oxidize; M.L. part.adj. *thiooxidans* oxidizing sulfur.

Short rods: 0.5 by 1.0 micron with rounded ends. Occur singly, in pairs or in chains. Motile by means of a single polar flagellum. Gram-negative (Starkey, Soil Sci., *39*, 1935, 210).

Thiosulfate agar: Scant growth. Nearly transparent colonies.

Sulfur broth: Uniform turbidity. No sediment or surface growth. Medium becomes very acid (below pH 1.0).

Thiosulfate broth: Uniform turbidity. Medium becomes acid, and sulfur is precipitated.

Nitrogen sources: Utilizes ammonia-nitrogen but not nitrate-nitrogen, which is toxic. Asparagin, urea and peptone not utilized.

Temperature relations: Optimum, between 28° and 30° C. Slow growth at 18° and 37° C. Death occurs between 55° and 60° C.

Optimum reaction, between pH 2.0 and 3.5. (Limiting reactions, pH 6.0 to less than pH 0.5.)

Strictly autotrophic, deriving its energy from the oxidation of elemental sulfur and thiosulfate, oxidizing these to sulfuric acid. It utilizes the CO_2 of the atmosphere as a source of carbon.

Strictly aerobic.

Distinctive characters: This species produces more acid, from oxidation of sulfur, and continues to live in a more acid medium, than any other living organism yet reported, the hydrogen-ion concentration of the medium increasing to a pH 0.6 and less.

Source: Isolated from composts of soil, sulfur and rock phosphate, and soils containing incompletely oxidized sulfur compounds.

Habitat: Soil.

9. **Thiobacillus trautweinii** Bergey et al., 1925. (Thionsäurebakterium, Trautwein, Cent. f. Bakt., II Abt., *53*, 1921, 513; also see *ibid.*, *61*, 1924, 1; Bergey et al., Manual, 2nd ed., 1925, 39; *Bacterium thiogenes* Lehmann, in Lehmann and Neumann, Bakt. Diag., 7 Aufl., *2*, 1927, 516.)

traut.wein'i.i. M.L. gen.noun *trautweinii* of Trautwein; named for K. Trautwein, who first isolated and studied this species.

Short rods, 0.5 by 1.0 to 2.0 microns. Motile by means of six to eight long flagella. Gram-negative.

Gelatin stab: Slow liquefaction. No chromogenesis.

Thiosulfate agar: Colonies small, white, 1 mm in diameter.

Thiosulfate liquid medium: Very little visible turbidity, no sulfur precipitated. Produces sulfate and tetrathionate with increase in pH. Rate of thiosulfate oxidation increased by presence of organic compounds.

No acid or gas from sugars.

Nitrites and gas produced from nitrate-peptone broth; no ammonia produced. May live anaerobically in the presence of nitrates.

Indole not produced.

Hydrogen sulfide not produced.

Starch is hydrolyzed.

Lipolytic.

Catalase-positive.

Non-hemolytic.

Temperature relations: Optimum, 27° C. Minimum, 6.9° C. Maximum, between 36.5° and 40° C. Death occurs in 2 to 5 minutes at 55° C.

Optimum pH, between 7.9 and 8.5. pH limits, 6.0 and 10.0.

Comments: Trautwein (Cent. f. Bakt., II Abt., *61*, 1924, 5) regards his bacterium as being closely related to the fluorescent group and to the denitrifying bacteria of Burri and Stutzer. Starkey (Jour. Gen. Physiol., *18*, 1935, 346) reports this species to be heterotrophic. However, Lehmann (in Lehmann and Neumann, Bakt. Diag., 7 Aufl., *2*, 1927, 516), under whom Trautwein did his work, reports that this species is a facultative autotroph as does Parker also (Jour. Gen. Microbiol., *3*, 1953, 344). As facultatively autotrophic species are included in *Thiobacillus* as defined, this species has again been included in *Thiobacillus* (see Manual, 2nd ed., 1925, 39). Starkey's culture B and Parker's M cultures appear to be identical with *Thiobacillus trautweinii*.

Source: Isolated from soil and water (Trautwein) and from purified sewage from Würzburg (Lehmann).

Habitat: Widely distributed in polluted waters and soil.

FAMILY IV. PSEUDOMONADACEAE WINSLOW ET AL., 1917.

(Winslow, Broadhurst, Buchanan, Krumwiede, Rogers and Smith, Jour. Bact., *2*, 1917, 555.)

Pseu.do.mo.na.da′ce.ae. M.L. fem.n. *Pseudomonas* type genus of the family; -aceae ending to denote a family; M.L. fem.pl.n. *Pseudomonadaceae* the *Pseudomonas* family.

Cells elongate, straight rods, occasionally coccoid. Motile by means of polar flagella which are either single or in small or large tufts. A few species are non-motile. Gram-negative. May possess either water-soluble pigments that diffuse through the medium or non-water-soluble pigments. Usually grow well and fairly rapidly on the surface of culture media. Aerobic. Frequently oxidative in their physiology but may be fermentative. Usually found in soil or water, including sea water or even heavy brines. Many plant and a few animal pathogens.

Key to the genera of family **Pseudomonadaceae.**

I. Attack glucose and other sugars either oxidatively or fermentatively.

    A. Genera in which the species are either known or are thought to attack glucose oxidatively.

        1. Bacteria which do not produce readily detectable acetic acid though they may oxidize ethanol. May produce a water-soluble pigment which diffuses through the medium.

            a. Cultures may or may not produce a water-soluble pigment which is bluish, greenish or brownish in color. Rose, lilac- and yellow-colored, diffusible pigments occasionally occur.

Genus I. *Pseudomonas*, p. 89.

aa. Cultures develop a yellow, non-water-soluble pigment. Cells normally mono-trichous. Mostly plant pathogens which cause a necrosis.

Genus II. *Xanthomonas*, p. 152.

2. Bacteria which produce readily detectable amounts of acetic acid by the oxidation of ethanol. The vinegar bacteria.

Genus III. *Acetobacter*, p. 183.

B. Genera in which the species ferment glucose, usually with the production of H_2 and CO_2.

1. Cells carry out a fermentation like that of the coliform bacteria. Usually produce acid and gas from glucose.

a. Cells not known to fix free atmospheric nitrogen.

b. Water organisms. Common species cause diseases of fishes. Also found in leeches. Not luminescent.

Genus IV. *Aeromonas*, p. 189.

bb. Luminescent bacteria commonly found on dead fishes and crustacea on salt-water beaches.

Genus V. *Photobacterium*, p. 193.

aa. Cells fix free atmospheric nitrogen.

Genus VI. *Azotomonas*, p. 198.

2. Cells carry out an alcoholic fermentation similar to that of yeasts.

Genus VII. *Zymomonas*, p. 199.

II. Do not attack carbohydrates or, if so, produce only slight amounts of acid from glucose and similar sugars. Includes certain species which require at least 12 per cent salt for growth.

A. Do not require salt in excess of 12 per cent for growth.

1. Cells not embedded in a gelatinous matrix.

a. Cells rod-shaped.

b. Soil and water bacteria that are known to dissimilate alkylamines.

Genus VIII. *Protaminobacter*, p. 200.

bb. Soil and water bacteria that are known to dissimilate alginic acid.

Genus IX. *Alginomonas*, p. 202.

aa. Soil bacteria that are known to utilize phenol and similar aromatic compounds. Cells may be branched.

Genus X. *Mycoplana*, p. 204.

2. Cells embedded in a gelatinous matrix; this matrix may be of a branching form.

Genus XI. *Zoogloea*, p. 206.

B. Requires at least 12 per cent salt before growth will take place.

Genus XII. *Halobacterium*, p. 207.

Genus I. **Pseudomonas** *Migula, 1894.** *

(*Chlorobacterium* Guillebeau†, Landw. Jahrb. d. Schweiz, *4*, 1890, 32; Migula, Arb. bakt. Inst. Karlsruhe, *1*, 1894, 237.)

Pseu.do′mo.nas or Pseu.do.mo′nas‡. Gr. *pseudes* false; Gr. *monas* a unit, monad; M.L. fem.n. *Pseudomonas* false monad.

Cells monotrichous, lophotrichous or non-motile. Gram-negative. Frequently develop

---

* Completely revised by Dr. Wm. C. Haynes, Northern Utilization Research Branch, U.S.D.A., Peoria, Illinois (Species Nos. 1–58) and by Prof. Walter H. Burkholder, Cornell University, Ithaca, New York (Species Nos. 59–149), September, 1953.

† See Footnote, p. 65. Also see Internat. Bull. Bact. Nomen. and Tax., *2*, 1952, 121, for a proposal to conserve *Pseudomonas* Migula.

‡ The former accords with the Latin rules of accentuation; the latter is commonly used.

fluorescent, diffusible pigments of a greenish, bluish, violet, lilac, rose, yellow or other color. Sometimes the pigments are bright red or yellow and non-diffusible; there are many species that fail to develop any pigmentation. The majority of species oxidize glucose to gluconic acid, 2-ketogluconic acid or other intermediates. Usually inactive in the oxidation of lactose. Nitrates are frequently reduced either to nitrites, ammonia or to free nitrogen. Some species split fat and/or attack hydrocarbons. Many species are found in soil and water, including sea water or even heavy brines. Many are plant pathogens; very few are animal pathogens.

The borderline between the straight rods found in *Pseudomonas* and the curved rods found in *Vibrio* is not sharp: occasionally curved rods may occur in species that normally are composed of straight rods, this variation sometimes being dependent upon the medium used. Recently, however, Shewan, Hodgkiss and Liston (Nature, *173*, 1954, 208) have described a method employing antibiotics and a vibriostatic agent whereby a sharper differentiation between pseudomonads and vibrios may possibly be effected. Future studies of this nature may show that some of the species in the genus *Pseudomonas* should be transferred to the genus *Vibrio*, and vice versa.

The type species is *Pseudomonas aeruginosa* (Schroeter) Migula.

Key to the species of genus **Pseudomonas.**

I. Soil and water forms. A few species are pathogenic to warm- and cold-blooded vertebrates.
  A. Soil and fresh-water forms (a few are pathogenic).
    1. Produce diffusible pigments, usually of a yellow, green or blue color; may be fluorescent. (Soluble pigments are not formed in all media. Furthermore, the ability to produce such pigments may be lost. Therefore, failure to observe soluble-pigment formation does not preclude identity with species listed in this category.)
      a. Grow in gelatin.
        b. Gelatin liquefied.
          c. Polar flagellate.
            d. Grows readily at 42°C. on ordinary media.
              e. Milk becomes alkaline.
                1. *Pseudomonas aeruginosa.*
              ee. Milk acidified.
                2. *Pseudomonas pseudomallei.*
            dd. Grow poorly or not at all at 42° C.
              e. Grow readily at 37° C.
                f. Not known to attack cellulose.
                  g. Milk becomes alkaline, indole not produced.
                    3. *Pseudomonas reptilivora.*
                  gg. Milk acidified, indole produced.
                    4. *Pseudomonas caviae.*
                  ggg. Action on milk and indole production unrecorded.
                    5. *Pseudomonas boreopolis.*
                ff. Attack cellulose.
                  g. Milk becomes alkaline, coagulated and peptonized, and litmus is reduced.
                    6. *Pseudomonas effusa.*
                  gg. No growth in milk.
                    7. *Pseudomonas ephemerocyanea.*

ee. Grow poorly or not at all at 37°C.
    f. Reaction in milk becomes acid or alkaline.
       g. Acid reaction produced in milk.
            8. *Pseudomonas fairmontensis.*
       gg. Alkaline reaction produced in milk.
         h. Produces crystals of chlororaphine.
             9. *Pseudomonas chlororaphis.*
         hh. Chlororaphine not produced.
           i. Indole produced.
              10. *Pseudomonas myxogenes.*
              11. *Pseudomonas schuylkilliensis.*
           ii. Indole not produced.
             j. Produces an intense, diffusible, yellow to orange pigment in cream or in cream layer of milk.
                12. *Pseudomonas synxantha.*
             jj. Fail to produce diffusible, yellow pigment in cream or in cream layer of milk.
               k. Nitrites produced from nitrates.
                13. *Pseudomonas fluorescens.*
               kk. Nitrites not produced from nitrates.
                14. *Pseudomonas pavonacea.*
                15. *Pseudomonas geniculata.*
                16. *Pseudomonas septica.*
    ff. Reaction in milk unchanged. Becomes blue in association with lactic-acid bacteria.
           17. *Pseudomonas syncyanea.*
cc. Non-motile.
    d. Produces iodinin.
          18. *Pseudomonas iodinum.*
    dd. Iodinin not produced.
       e. Grows poorly or not at all at 37° C.
            13. *Pseudomonas fluorescens* (non-motile variety).
       ee. Grows readily at 37° C.
            19. *Pseudomonas smaragdina.*
bb. Gelatin not liquefied.
    c. Polar flagellate.
       d. Grow readily at 37° C.
          e. Reaction in milk unchanged.
             20. *Pseudomonas putida.*
         ee. Alkaline reaction in milk.
            f. Litmus reduced.
              21. *Pseudomonas striata.*
           ff. Litmus not reduced.
              22. *Pseudomonas ovalis.*
       dd. Grow poorly or not at all at 37° C.
          e. Reaction in milk acid.
            f. Musty odor produced in culture media.
              23. *Pseudomonas taetrolens.*

           ff. Musty odor not produced in culture media.
               24. *Pseudomonas incognita.*
               25. *Pseudomonas rugosa.*
        ee. Reaction in milk alkaline.
               26. *Pseudomonas mildenbergii.*
               27. *Pseudomonas convexa.*
    cc. Non-motile.
               28. *Pseudomonas eisenbergii.*
  aa. No growth in gelatin.
               29. *Pseudomonas erythra.*
2. Soluble pigments not produced or not reported.
  a. Gelatin liquefied.
    b. Polar flagellate.
      c. Grow readily at 42° C.
        d. Alkaline reaction in milk.
               1. *Pseudomonas aeruginosa* (achro-
                  mogenic variety).
        dd. Acid reaction in milk.
               2. *Pseudomonas pseudomallei*
                  (achromogenic variety).
      cc. Grow readily at 25° C. but poorly or not at all at 37° C.
        d. Acid reaction in milk.
          e. May-apple odor produced in milk. Nitrites not produced
            from nitrates.
               30. *Pseudomonas fragi.*
          ee. Musty odor produced from all media. Nitrites and am-
            monia produced from nitrates.
               31. *Pseudomonas perolens.*
        dd. Alkaline reaction in milk.
               32. *Pseudomonas mephitica.*
               33. *Pseudomonas putrefaciens.*
               34. *Pseudomonas cohaerens.*
  aa. Gelatin not liquefied.
    b. Polar flagellate.
      c. Grow readily at 37° C.
        d. Action on cellulose not known or not reported.
          e. Acid produced in milk.
               35. *Pseudomonas ambigua.*
          ee. Milk unchanged.
               36. *Pseudomonas oleovorans.*
        eee. Action on milk unknown or unreported.
          f. Utilize hydrocarbons.
               37. *Pseudomonas arvilla.*
               38. *Pseudomonas dacunhae.*
               39. *Pseudomonas desmolytica.*
               40. *Pseudomonas rathonis.*
               41. *Pseudomonas salopia.*
        ff. Ability to utilize hydrocarbons unreported.
          g. Nitrites not produced from nitrates.
               42. *Pseudomonas cruciviae.*
         gg. Nitrates, nitrites, nitramids and N₂O reduced
            to elemental nitrogen.
               43. *Pseudomonas stutzeri.*

dd. Attack cellulose
  e. Acid produced in milk.
    44. *Pseudomonas tralucida.*
  ee. Milk unchanged.
    45. *Pseudomonas lasia.*
cc. Grow readily at 25° C. but poorly or not at all at 37°C.
  d. Action on cellulose unknown or unreported.
    e. Alkaline reaction in milk. Attacks riboflavin converting it to lumichrome.
      46. *Pseudomonas riboflavina.*
    ee. Reaction in milk unknown or unreported.
      f. Nitrates reduced to elemental nitrogen.
        47. *Pseudomonas denitrificans.*
      ff. Nitrates reduced to nitrites. Indole decomposed with formation of blue crystals of indigotin.
        48. *Pseudomonas indoloxidans.*
  dd. Attacks cellulose.
    49. *Pseudomonas mira.*
B. Sea-water and brine forms (a few are pathogenic).
  1. Produces pigments which are soluble in culture media. Gelatin liquefied.
    50. *Pseudomonas nigrifaciens.*
  2. Pigments soluble in culture media not produced.
    a. Gelatin liquefied.
      b. Polar flagellate.
        c. No growth in milk.
          d. Indole produced; nitrites produced from nitrates.
            51. *Pseudomonas ichthyodermis.*
          dd. Indole not produced; nitrites not produced from nitrates.
            e. Produces hydrogen sulfide and ammonia from tryptone; no acid from glucose.
              52. *Pseudomonas marinoglutinosa.*
            ee. Hydrogen sulfide not produced; glucose acidified.
              53. *Pseudomonas membranoformis.*
        cc. Action in milk unknown or unreported.
          d. Digests agar.
            54. *Pseudomonas gelatica.*
          dd. Do not digest agar.
            e Deposit CaCO₃ in sea-water gelatin and in agar media in old cultures. Do not grow in 12 to 30 per cent salt solutions.
              55. *Pseudomonas calcis.*
              56. *Pseudomonas calciprecipitans.*
            ee. Does not deposit CaCO₃ in sea-water gelatin or in agar media. Grows well in 12 to 30 per cent salt solutions.
              56a. *Pseudomonas halestorga.*
    bb. Non-motile. Cellulose attacked. Insoluble yellow pigment produced.
      57. *Pseudomonas iridescens* (gelatin-liquefying variety).
  aa. Gelatin not liquefied.
    b. Polar flagellate.
      c. Does not attack cellulose. Produces an insoluble purple pigment in vegetable extracts.
        58. *Pseudomonas beijerinckii.*

bb. Non-motile.
 c. Cellulose attacked. Produces an insoluble yellow pigment.
   57. *Pseudomonas iridescens* (non-gelatin-liquefying variety).
II. Plant pathogens, causing leaf spot, leaf stripe and similar diseases. (Also see Host Plant Key, p. 96.)
 A. Green fluorescent pigment produced.
  1. Gelatin liquefied.
   a. Acid from sucrose.
    b. Growth in 5 per cent salt.
      59. *Pseudomonas aceris.*
      60. *Pseudomonas angulata.*
      61. *Pseudomonas aptata.*
      62. *Pseudomonas primulae.*
      63. *Pseudomonas viridilivida.*
    bb. No growth in 5 per cent salt.
     c. Beef peptone agar turns deep brown.
       64. *Pseudomonas delphinii.*
     cc. Beef peptone agar uncolored.
      d. Colonies yellow.
       65. *Pseudomonas cepacia.*
      dd. Colonies white to cream.
       66. *Pseudomonas apii.*
       67. *Pseudomonas asplenii.*
       68. *Pseudomonas berberidis.*
       69. *Pseudomonas coronafaciens.*
       70. *Pseudomonas lachrymans.*
       71. *Pseudomonas maculicola.*
       72. *Pseudomonas mangiferaeindicae.*
       73. *Pseudomonas marginata.*
       74. *Pseudomonas medicaginis.*
       75. *Pseudomonas phaseolicola.*
       76. *Pseudomonas pisi.*
       77. *Pseudomonas syringae.*
       78. *Pseudomonas tomato.*
    bbb. Growth in salt solution not recorded.
      79. *Pseudomonas atrofaciens.*
      80. *Pseudomonas cumini.*
      81. *Pseudomonas desaiana.*
      82. *Pseudomonas erodii.*
      83. *Pseudomonas lapsa.*
      84. *Pseudomonas martyniae.*
      85. *Pseudomonas matthiolae.*
      86. *Pseudomonas morsprunorum.*
      87. *Pseudomonas papulans.*
      88. *Pseudomonas pseudozoogloeae.*
      89. *Pseudomonas rimaefaciens.*
      90. *Pseudomonas striafaciens.*
      91. *Pseudomonas tabaci.*
  aa. No acid from sucrose.
   b. Lipolytic.
      92. *Pseudomonas polycolor.*

bb. Not lipolytic.

93. *Pseudomonas viridiflava.*

bbb. Lipolytic action not reported.

94. *Pseudomonas ananas.*
95. *Pseudomonas bowlesiae.*
96. *Pseudomonas ligustri.*
97. *Pseudomonas marginalis.*
98. *Pseudomonas sesami.*
99. *Pseudomonas setariae.*
100. *Pseudomonas tolaasii.*
101. *Pseudomonas washingtoniae.*

aaa. Acid from sucrose not reported.

102. *Pseudomonas barkeri.*
103. *Pseudomonas betle.*
104. *Pseudomonas gladioli.*
105. *Pseudomonas mellea.*
106. *Pseudomonas panacis.*
107. *Pseudomonas ribicola.*
108. *Pseudomonas xanthochlora.*

2. Gelatin not liquefied.
    a. Acid from sucrose.

109. *Pseudomonas aleuritidis.*
110. *Pseudomonas glycinea.*
111. *Pseudomonas savastanoi.*
112. *Pseudomonas tonelliana.*

    aa. No acid from sucrose.
      b. Non-motile.

113. *Pseudomonas cissicola.*

      bb. Motile.

114. *Pseudomonas calendulae.*
115. *Pseudomonas cichorii.*
116. *Pseudomonas nectarophila.*
117. *Pseudomonas viburni.*

aaa. Acid from sucrose not reported.

118. *Pseudomonas mori.*
119. *Pseudomonas stizolobii.*
120. *Pseudomonas viciae.*

B. Green fluorescent pigment not produced or not reported.
  1. Gelatin liquefied.
    a. Acid from sucrose.
      b. Beef-peptone agar turns dark brown.

121. *Pseudomonas alliicola.*
122. *Pseudomonas gardeniae.*

      bb. Beef-peptone agar uncolored or only slightly so.
        c. Colonies tan to brown.

123. *Pseudomonas caryophylli.*
124. *Pseudomonas solanacearum.*

      cc. Colonies white or colorless.

125. *Pseudomonas castaneae.*
126. *Pseudomonas passiflorae.*
127. *Pseudomonas seminum.*
128. *Pseudomonas vitiswoodrowii.*

aa. No acid from sucrose.

129. *Pseudomonas fabae.*

aaa. Acid from sucrose not reported.

130. *Pseudomonas astragali.*
131. *Pseudomonas colurnae.*
132. *Pseudomonas iridicola.*
133. *Pseudomonas levistici.*
134. *Pseudomonas maublancii.*
135. *Pseudomonas polygoni.*
136. *Pseudomonas radiciperda.*

2. Gelatin not liquefied.
  a. Acid from sucrose.

137. *Pseudomonas cattleyae.*
138. *Pseudomonas dysoxyli.*
139. *Pseudomonas helianthi.*
140. *Pseudomonas melophthora.*

  aa. No acid from sucrose.

141. *Pseudomonas alboprecipitans.*
142. *Pseudomonas andropogonis.*
143. *Pseudomonas lignicola.*
144. *Pseudomonas petasitis.*
145. *Pseudomonas woodsii.*

  aaa. Acid from sucrose not reported.

146. *Pseudomonas eriobotryae.*
147. *Pseudomonas panicimiliacei.*
148. *Pseudomonas saliciperda.*

3. Gelatin liquefaction not reported.

149. *Pseudomonas wieringae.*

HOST PLANT KEY

Where the host plant is known, the following key will be found useful.
I. Cause of necrotic spots on mushrooms.

100. *Pseudomonas tolaasii.*

II. Cause of spots on ferns, *Asplenium nidus.*

67. *Pseudomonas asplenii.*

III. Cause of leaf blights and streaks on monocotyledonous plants.
  A. Attack members of the family *Amaryllidaceae.*

121. *Pseudomonas alliicola.*
65. *Pseudomonas cepacia.*

  B. Attacks members of the family *Bromeliaceae.*

94. *Pseudomonas ananas.*

  C. Attack members of the family *Gramineae.*

141. *Pseudomonas alboprecipitans.*
142. *Pseudomonas andropogonis.*
79. *Pseudomonas atrofaciens.*
69. *Pseudomonas coronafaciens.*
81. *Pseudomonas desaiana.*
83. *Pseudomonas lapsa.*
147. *Pseudomonas panicimiliacei.*
99. *Pseudomonas setariae.*
90. *Pseudomonas striafaciens.*

D. Attack members of the family *Iridaceae*.
    104. *Pseudomonas gladioli*.
    132. *Pseudomonas iridicola*.
    73. *Pseudomonas marginata*.
E. Attacks members of the family *Musaceae*.
    134. *Pseudomonas maublancii*.
F. Attacks members of the family *Orchidaceae*.
    137. *Pseudomonas cattleyae*.
G. Attacks members of the family *Palmaceae*.
    101. *Pseudomonas washingtoniae*.
IV. Cause of leaf, stem and fruit spots on dicotyledonous plants.
A. Attacks members of the family *Aceraceae*.
    59. *Pseudomonas aceris*.
B. Attacks members of the family *Anacardiaceae*.
    72. *Pseudomonas mangiferaeindicae*.
C. Attacks members of the family *Apocynaceae*.
    112. *Pseudomonas tonelliana*.
D. Attacks members of the family *Araliaceae*.
    106. *Pseudomonas panacis*.
E. Attacks members of the family *Berberidaceae*.
    68. *Pseudomonas berberidis*.
F. Attacks members of the family *Betulaceae*.
    131. *Pseudomonas colurnae*.
G. Attacks members of the family *Caprifoliaceae*.
    117. *Pseudomonas viburni*.
H. Attack members of the family *Caryophyllaceae*.
    123. *Pseudomonas caryophylli*.
    145. *Pseudomonas woodsii*.
I. Attacks members of the family *Chenopodiaceae*.
    149. *Pseudomonas wieringae*.
J. Attack members of the family *Compositae*.
    114. *Pseudomonas calendulae*.
    115. *Pseudomonas cichorii*.
    139. *Pseudomonas helianthi*.
    97. *Pseudomonas marginalis*.
    144. *Pseudomonas petasitis*.
    63. *Pseudomonas viridilivida*.
K. Attack members of the family *Cruciferae*.
    71. *Pseudomonas maculicola*.
    85. *Pseudomonas matthiolae*.
L. Attacks members of the family *Cucurbitaceae*.
    70. *Pseudomonas lachrymans*.
M. Attacks members of the family *Euphorbiaceae*.
    109. *Pseudomonas aleuritidis*.
N. Attacks members of the family *Fagaceae*.
    125. *Pseudomonas castaneae*.
O. Attacks members of the family *Geraniaceae*.
    82. *Pseudomonas erodii*.
P. Attack members of the family *Leguminosae*.
    130. *Pseudomonas astragali*.
    129. *Pseudomonas fabae*.
    110. *Pseudomonas glycinea*.

       74. *Pseudomonas medicaginis.*
       75. *Pseudomonas phaseolicola.*
       76. *Pseudomonas pisi.*
      136. *Pseudomonas radiciperda.*
      127. *Pseudomonas seminum.*
      119. *Pseudomonas stizolobii.*
      110. *Pseudomonas viciae.*
       93. *Pseudomonas viridiflava.*

Q. Attacks members of the family *Martyniaceae.*
       84. *Pseudomonas martyniae.*

R. Attacks members of the family *Meliaceae.*
      138. *Pseudomonas dysoxyli.*

S. Attacks members of the family *Moraceae.*
      118. *Pseudomonas mori.*

T. Attack members of the family *Oleaceae.*
       96. *Pseudomonas ligustri.*
      111. *Pseudomonas savastanoi.*

U. Attacks members of the family *Passifloraceae.*
      126. *Pseudomonas passiflorae.*

V. Attacks members of the family *Pedaliaceae.*
       98. *Pseudomonas sesami.*

W. Attacks members of the family *Piperaceae.*
      103. *Pseudomonas betle.*

X. Attacks members of the family *Polygonaceae.*
      135. *Pseudomonas polygoni.*

Y. Attacks members of the family *Primulaceae.*
       62. *Pseudomonas primulae.*

Z. Attacks members of the family *Ranunculaceae.*
       64. *Pseudomonas delphinii.*

AA. Attack members of the family *Rosaceae.*
      102. *Pseudomonas barkeri.*
      146. *Pseudomonas eriobotryae.*
      140. *Pseudomonas melophthora.*
       86. *Pseudomonas morsprunorum.*
      116. *Pseudomonas nectarophila.*
       87. *Pseudomonas papulans.*

BB. Attacks members of the family *Rubiaceae.*
      122. *Pseudomonas gardeniae.*

CC. Attacks members of the family *Salicaceae.*
      148. *Pseudomonas saliciperda.*

DD. Attacks members of the family *Saxifragaceae.*
      107. *Pseudomonas ribicola.*

EE. Attack members of the family *Solanaceae*
       60. *Pseudomonas angulata.*
      105. *Pseudomonas mellea.*
       92. *Pseudomonas polycolor.*
       88. *Pseudomonas pseudozoogloeae.*
       91. *Pseudomonas tabaci.*
       78. *Pseudomonas tomato.*

FF. Attacks members of the family *Ulmaceae.*
      143. *Pseudomonas lignicola.*

GG. Attack members of the family *Umbelliferae.*
       66. *Pseudomonas apii.*

95. *Pseudomonas bowlesiae.*
80. *Pseudomonas cumini.*
133. *Pseudomonas levistici.*
HH. Attacks members of the family *Vitaceae.*
113. *Pseudomonas cissicola.*
II. Attack members of numerous families.
61. *Pseudomonas aptata.*
124. *Pseudomonas solanacearum.*
77. *Pseudomonas syringae.*
108. *Pseudomonas xanthochlora.*

1. **Pseudomonas aeruginosa** (Schroeter, 1872) Migula, 1900. (*Bacterium aeruginosum* Schroeter, in Cohn, Beitrage z. Biologie, *1*, Heft 2, 1872, 126; *Bacillus pyocyaneus* Gessard, Compt. rend. Acad. Sci., Paris, *94*, 1882, 536; *Pseudomonas pyocyanea* Migula, in Engler and Prantl, Die natürl. Pflanzenfam., *1*, 1a, 1895, 29; Migula, Syst. d. Bakt., *2*, 1900, 884.)

ae.ru.gi.no'sa. L. adj. *aeruginosus* full of copper rust or verdigris, hence green.

Common name: Blue pus organism.

Rods, 0.5 to 0.6 by 1.5 microns, occurring singly, in pairs and short chains. Motile, possessing one to three polar flagella. (Monotrichous according to Reid, Naghski, Farrell and Haley, Penn. Agr. Exp. Sta., Bull. 422, 1942, 6.) Gram-negative.

Gelatin colonies: Yellowish or greenish yellow, fringed, irregular, skein-like, granular, rapidly liquefying.

Gelatin stab: Rapid liquefaction. The fluid assumes a yellowish green or bluish green color.

Agar colonies: Large, spreading, grayish with dark center and translucent edge, irregular. Medium greenish.

Agar slant: Abundant, thin, white, glistening, the medium turning green to dark brown or black, fluorescent.

Broth: Marked turbidity with thick pellicle and heavy sediment. Medium yellowish green to blue, with fluorescence, later brownish. Often produces pyocyanine, fluorescein and pyrorubrin (Meader, Robinson and Leonard, Am. Jour. Hyg., *5*, 1925, 682).

Litmus milk: A soft coagulum is formed, with rapid peptonization and reduction of litmus. Reaction alkaline.

Potato: Luxuriant, dirty brown, the medium becoming dark green.

Indole usually not produced (Sandiford, Jour. Path. and Bact., *44*, 1937, 567).

Nitrates reduced to nitrites and nitrogen.

Glucose, fructose, galactose, arabinose, maltose, lactose, sucrose, dextrin, inulin, glycerol, mannitol and dulcitol are not fermented. Glucose oxidized to gluconic acid, 2-ketogluconic acid and other intermediates (Lockwood, Tabenkin and Ward, Jour. Bact., *42*, 1941, 51; Haynes, Jour. Gen. Microbiol., *5*, 1951, 939).

Blood serum: Liquefied. Yellow liquid, greenish on surface.

Blood hemolyzed.

Cultures have marked odor of trimethylamine.

Aerobic, facultative.

Optimum temperature, 37° C. Good growth at 42° C.

Pathogenic for rabbits, guinea pigs, rats and mice.

Distinctive characters: Some strains produce pyocyanine, a phenazine derivative which is extractable from alkaline media with chloroform as a deep blue pigment. Upon addition of acid, the color is transformed to red and becomes insoluble in chloroform. The ability to grow well at 42° C., to oxidize gluconic acid to 2-ketogluconic acid and to produce a slime in potassium gluconate media permits identification even though pyocyanine is not formed (Haynes, *loc. cit.*).

Source: Pus from wounds. Regarded as identical with one of the plant pathogens (*Pseudomonas polycolor*) by Elrod and Braun (Jour. Bact., *44*, 1942, 633).

Habitat: Cause of various human and animal lesions. Found in polluted water and sewage.

2. **Pseudomonas pseudomallei** (Whitmore, 1913) Haynes, *comb. nov.* (*Bacillus pseudomallei* Whitmore, Jour. Hyg., *13*, 1913, 1; *Bacillus whitmori* Stanton and Fletcher, Trans. 4th Cong. Far East Assn. Trop. Med., *2*, 1921, 196; also see Jour. Hyg., *23*, 1925, 347; *Malleomyces pseudomallei* Breed, in Manual, 5th ed., 1939, 300; *Loefflerella pseudomallei* Brindle and Cowan, Jour. Path. and Bact., *63*, 1951, 574.)

pseu.do.mal'le.i. Gr. adj. *pseudes* false; L. noun *malleus* the disease glanders; M.L. noun *pseudomalleus* false glanders; M.L. gen.noun *pseudomallei* of false glanders.

Short rods, with rounded ends, occurring singly and in short chains. Motile. Possess 1 to 4 polar flagella (Brindle and Cowan, *ibid.*, 571); this was confirmed by de Lajudie, Fournier and Chambon (Ann. Inst. Past., *85*, 1953, 112). Show bipolar staining. Gram-negative.

Gelatin stab: Moderate, crateriform liquefaction.

Agar colonies: Circular, slightly raised, thick, opaque, cream-colored with irregular margin.

Glycerol agar slant: Wrinkled, thick, rugose, cream-colored growth.

Broth: Turbid with pellicle.

Litmus milk: Curdling with slowly developed acidity; pink sediment; may be digested.

Potato: Vigorous, cream-colored growth. Indole not produced.

Acid from glucose, maltose, lactose, sucrose and mannitol.

Grows in simple, chemically defined media containing single amino acids or the ammonium salt of certain organic acids as the sole carbon, nitrogen and energy source in a mineral salt base (Levine, Dowling, Evenson and Lien, Jour. Bact., *67*, 1954, 350).

Blood serum slowly liquefied.

Aerobic, facultative.

Optimum temperature, 37° C.; but will grow readily at 42° C. (Cowan, personal communication, March, 1955).

Distinctive character: Brygoo and Richard (Ann. Inst. Past., *83*, 1952, 822) report that a large number of strains, isolated in Saigon, produce a yellow pigment which is extractable in 2 per cent boiling HCl; a few of these strains become non-pigmented when cultured on glycerol agar media. While this pigment has sometimes been described as water-soluble, Brindle and Cowan (*op. cit.*, 1951, 574) suggest that this species may be more closely related to the species placed in *Xanthomonas* than to those placed in *Pseudomonas*. The xanthomonads develop yellow, non-diffusible, carotenoid pigments.

Source: Isolated from lesions and blood in rats, guinea pigs, rabbits and man; also isolated once from a transient nasal discharge in a horse, once from a splenic abscess in a cow and once from a fatal case of an infected sheep. Virulent and avirulent strains can also be readily isolated from water at Saigon, Indochina, if appropriate media are used (Fournier and Chambon, personal communication, 1955).

Habitat: Glanders-like infections (melioidosis) in rats, guinea pigs, rabbits and man in India, Federated Malay States and Indo-China.

3. **Pseudomonas reptilivora** Caldwell and Ryerson, 1940. (*Pseudomonas reptilivorous* (sic) Caldwell and Ryerson, Jour. Bact., *39*, 1940, 335.)

rep.ti.li'vo.ra. L. n. *reptile* a reptile; L. v. *voro* to devour; M.L. adj. *reptilivorus* reptile-destroying.

Rods, 0.5 by 1.5 to 2.0 microns, occurring singly, in pairs and in short chains. Actively motile with two to six polar flagella. Gram-negative.

Gelatin colonies: After 24 hours, small, circular, smooth, entire. Liquefaction. Medium becomes yellowish green fluorescent.

Gelatin stab: Infundibuliform liquefaction becoming stratiform. Putrid odor present.

Serum slant: Liquefied.

Agar cultures: Circular, smooth, glistening, slightly raised, butyrous, translucent, 2 mm in diameter.

Agar slant: Growth abundant, smooth, filiform, glistening, butyrous and translucent.

Broth: Turbid with pellicle and sediment. Putrid odor.

Litmus milk: Alkaline, peptonization, complete reduction. Disagreeable odor.

Potato: Growth moderate, spreading,

glistening, yellowish gray to creamy. Disagreeable odor. Medium becomes brownish gray.

Indole not produced.

Nitrites not produced from nitrates.

Acetylmethylcarbinol not produced.

Hydrogen sulfide not produced.

Slightly acid, becoming alkaline in glucose. No acid from arabinose, xylose, lactose, sucrose, maltose, trehalose, raffinose, mannitol, dulcitol, inositol or salicin.

Starch not hydrolyzed.

Pathogenic for guinea pigs and rabbits, horned lizards, Gila monsters and chuckwallas. Marked hemolysis of rabbit cells and slight hemolysis of Gila monster cells suspended in agar.

Temperature relations: Optimum, 20° to 25° C. Maximum, 37° C. A retest of several strains of this organism by Haynes shows that it grows well at 37° C. and is closely related to, though not identical with, *Pseudomonas aeruginosa* Migula.

Distinctive characters: Yellowish green fluorescence present only in meat infusion media. The pigment is water-soluble, but insoluble in chloroform. Pathogenic for guinea pigs, rabbits, horned lizards and chuckwallas.

Source: Isolated from a bacterial disease of horned lizards and Gila monsters.

Habitat: Pathogenic for lizards.

4. **Pseudomonas caviae** Scherago, 1936. (Jour. Bact., *31*, 1936, 83; also see Jour. Inf. Dis., *60*, 1937, 245.)

ca'vi.ae. M.L. fem.noun *Cavia* generic name of the guinea pig; from So. American Indian, "cabiai", a guinea pig; *caviae* of *Cavia*.

Rods, 0.6 to 1.0 by 1.5 to 3.0 microns, occurring singly and in pairs; rounded ends. Motile by means of 1 to 3 polar flagella. Encapsulated. Gram-negative.

Gelatin stab: Infundibuliform liquefaction.

Agar colonies: Circular, convex, smooth, iridescent and translucent, finely granular, entire.

Agar slant: Growth abundant, grayish white, butyrous, filiform, glistening, translucent, markedly iridescent. Medium even-tually tinged greenish yellow, becoming brownish yellow.

Broth: Cloudy, pellicle, abundant light yellow granular sediment, becoming brown. Medium becomes yellow.

Litmus milk: Acidified, coagulated, peptonized, litmus partially reduced.

Potato: Growth scant, filiform, glistening, light yellow to light orange, becoming light brown.

Hydrogen sulfide not produced.

Indole produced.

Nitrites produced from nitrates.

Blood serum not liquefied.

Blood not hemolyzed.

Sodium formate decomposed.

Catalase-negative.

Methyl red positive; acetylmethylcarbinol not produced.

Citrate broth: No growth.

Methylene blue reduced.

Acid but no gas from glucose, fructose, galactose, maltose, cellobiose, mannitol, lactose, arabinose, sucrose, trehalose, sorbitol, mannose, dextrin, salicin, glycerol, aesculin, amygdalin and starch. No acid from xylose, dulcitol, rhamnose, inulin, adonitol, raffinose, erythritol or inositol.

Aerobic, facultative.

Optimum temperature, 37° C. Grows at 25° C.

Source: Isolated from guinea pigs dead from epizootic septicemia.

Habitat: From infected guinea pigs so far as known.

5. **Pseudomonas boreopolis** Gray and Thornton, 1928. (Cent. f. Bakt., II Abt., *73*, 1928, 92.)

bo.re.o'po.lis. Gr. *boreas* north; Gr. *polis* a city; M.L. fem.gen.n. *boreopolis* of North City.

Rods, 0.5 to 1.0 by 2.0 to 3.0 microns, occurring singly and in pairs. Motile with one to five polar flagella. Gram-negative.

Gelatin colonies: Liquefied.

Gelatin stab: Liquefied. Medium reddened by some strains.

Agar colonies: Circular or amoeboid, white to buff, flat to convex, smooth, glistening, translucent border.

Agar slant: Filiform, whitish, raised, smooth, glistening, fluorescent.

Broth: Turbid.

Nitrates reduced to nitrites by some strains.

Starch not hydrolyzed.

Acid produced from glucose by most strains.

Attacks naphthalene.

Aerobic, facultative.

Grows at 35° to 37° C.

Source: Isolated from soil.

Habitat: Soil.

6. Pseudomonas effusa Kellerman et al., 1913. (Kellerman, McBeth, Scales and Smith, Cent. f. Bakt., II Abt., *39*, 1913, 515; also see Soil Science, *1*, 1916, 472.)

ef.fu'sa. L. adj. *effusus* spread out.

Rods 0.4 by 1.7 microns. Motile by means of one to three polar flagella. Gram-negative.

Gelatin stab: Liquefied. A non-liquefying variety is also found.

Agar slant: Luxuriant, glistening, moist, creamy, spreading growth. Medium becomes greenish fluorescent.

Peptone starch agar slant: Abundant, flat, moist, rich creamy growth. Medium shows greenish fluorescence.

Broth: Turbid; viscid sediment. Medium becomes greenish fluorescent.

Litmus milk: Alkaline. Coagulation and digestion. Litmus reduced. A variety that acts more slowly on litmus milk is also found.

Potato: Abundant, creamy, glistening, brownish flesh-colored growth.

Indole not produced.

Nitrites produced from nitrates.

Ammonia is produced.

No acid from glucose, starch, lactose, sucrose, maltose, glycerol or mannitol.

Starch hydrolysis weak.

Cellulose is attacked.

Aerobic, facultative.

Temperature relations: Optimum, 37° C. Survives 60° C., but not 70° C., for 15 minutes.

Source: Isolated from soils in Utah.

Habitat: Soil.

7. Pseudomonas ephemerocyanea Fuller and Norman, 1943. (Jour. Bact., *46*, 1943, 274.)

e.phe.me.ro.cy.a'ne.a. Gr. adj. *epheme-rus* short-lived; Gr. adj. *cyaneus* blue; M.L. adj. *ephemerocyaneus* ephemeral blue.

Rods, 0.3 to 0.4 by 2.2 to 2.8 microns, straight to slightly bent with rounded ends, arranged singly. Motile by means of 1 to 3 polar flagella. Gram-negative.

Gelatin stab: Liquefied.

Starch agar colonies: Pinpoint colonies in three days, 1 to 2 mm in 5 days. White becoming tan, raised, glistening, smooth, entire.

Water-insoluble dextrin colonies: Pinpoint colonies show an enzymic zone, white, convex, entire.

Starch agar slant: Heavy gelatinous, light brown becoming deeper brown.

Litmus milk: No visible growth.

Indole not produced.

Nitrites produced from nitrates.

Starch hydrolyzed.

Attacks glucose, lactose, maltose, galactose, arabinose and xylose. Utilizes cellulose, cellulosan, water-soluble and water-insoluble cellulose dextrins and pectin. Slow utilization of gum arabic and calcium gluconate.

In mineral nutrient media, filter paper strips are disintegrated at the air-liquid interface with the formation of a transitory violet or blue color which becomes light brown.

Peptone, yeast extract, nitrate and ammonia serve as nitrogen sources.

Aerobic.

Optimum temperature, 22° to 35° C.

Distinctive characters: In media containing cellulose a transitory intense blue or violet color develops. In aerated cultures the entire medium becomes blue. The pigment appears to be water-soluble. After a few hours the color becomes light brown.

Source: Isolated from soil.

Habitat: Soil.

8. Pseudomonas fairmontensis (Wright, 1895) Chester, 1901. (*Bacillus Fairmontensis* (sic) Wright, Memoirs Nat. Acad. Sci., *7*, 1895, 458; Chester, Man. Determ. Bact., 1901, 311.)

fair.mon.ten'sis. Fairmount Park (Philadelphia) place name; M.L. adj. *fairmontensis* pertaining to Fairmount.

Medium-sized rods, occurring singly, in

pairs and in chains. Motile, possessing a single polar flagellum. Gram-negative.

Gelatin colonies: Circular, white, translucent. Dark centers with a greenish shimmer, thinner edges and faint radial lines.

Gelatin stab: Crateriform liquefaction.

Agar slant: Grayish white, glistening. Agar becomes green.

Broth: Turbid; delicate pellicle; white sediment. Becomes green.

Litmus milk: Acid, coagulated; litmus reduced.

Potato: Raised, granular, spreading, viscid. Becomes brownish.

Indole produced.

Action on nitrates unknown.

Aerobic, facultative.

Optimum temperature, 20° to 25° C. Fails to grow at 35° C.

Source: From water from the Schuylkill River.

Habitat: Water.

9. **Pseudomonas chlororaphis** (Guignard and Sauvageau, 1894) Bergey et al., 1930. (*Bacillus chlororaphis* Guignard and Sauvageau, Compt. rend. Soc. Biol., Paris, *1*, 10 sér., 1894, 841; Bergey et al., Manual, 3rd ed., 1930, 166.)

chlo.ro′ra.phis. Gr. *chlorus* green; Gr. noun *rhaphis* a needle; M.L. fem.n. *chlororaphis* a green needle.

Description taken from Lasseur (Ann. de la Sci. Agron., Sér. 4, 2ᵉ Année, *2*, 1913, 165). While Guignard and Sauvageau (*op. cit.*, 1894, 841) found spores in this species, Gessard, on reisolation, could find no spores (Ann. de la Sci. Agron., Sér. 3, 6ᵉ Année, *2*, 1911, 374). The identification of the reisolated culture was confirmed by Guignard. The original description is brief and inadequate and is probably based on a contaminated culture.

Rods, 0.8 by 1.5 microns, with rounded ends, occurring singly and in pairs. Motile with one to six polar flagella. Gram-negative. After continued cultivation some cells decolorize slowly.

Gelatin colonies: Circular, viscid, transparent, glistening, lobate margin with fluorescent corona. Dissociates readily (Lasseur and Dupaix-Lasseur, Trav. Lab.

Microbiol. Fac. Pharm. Nancy, Fasc. 9, 1936, 35).

Gelatin stab: Rapid liquefaction. Fluorescent. Chlororaphine crystals may form.

Broth: Turbid, greenish, fluorescent. Crystals of green chlororaphine may form. Broth becomes viscous.

Litmus milk: Alkaline; coagulated. Becomes viscous. Chlororaphine crystals may form in the central part of the culture. Odor of coumarin.

Potato: Citron-yellow layer. Crystals of chlororaphine are formed.

Nitrites produced from nitrates.

Indole not produced.

Pigment formation: Asparagine, potassium phosphate, glycerol, sulfate of magnesium and sulfate of iron are indispensable to the formation of crystals of chlororaphine. Green crystals develop slowly and poorly in peptone solutions, best in synthetic media.

Aerobic, facultative.

Optimum temperature, between 25° and 30° C. Cultures killed in ten minutes at 63° C.

Pathogenic for mice, guinea pigs, frogs, fresh-water fishes and crayfishes. An exotoxin is formed.

Distinctive character: Produces a beautiful emerald-green pigment which crystallizes in cultures as fine needles in bundles or as needles radiating from a center. The crystals form slowly and are not always present. Other species of pseudomonads, e.g. *Pseudomonas iodinum*, form crystals. As this power is readily lost, it raises the question whether other species of green, fluorescent pseudomonads may not form crystals under proper conditions.

Source: Isolated from dead larvae of the cockchafer. Later reisolated by various French bacteriologists from contaminated water supplies.

Habitat: Decomposing organic matter and fresh water so far as known.

10. **Pseudomonas myxogenes** Fuhrmann, 1907. (Cent. f. Bakt., II Abt., *17*, 1907, 356.)

myx.o′ge.nes. Gr. *myxa* slime; Gr. *gennao* to produce, beget; M.L. adj. *myxogenes* slime-producing.

Rods, 0.4 to 0.5 by 1.0 to 1.5 microns, occurring singly and in pairs. Motile, possessing a bundle of five to seven polar flagella. Gram-negative.

Gelatin colonies: Smooth, soft, flat, spreading, brownish yellow, entire. Medium becomes yellowish green fluorescent.

Gelatin stab: Growth along stab. Liquefaction with yellowish white sediment.

Agar colonies: Circular, raised, smooth, amorphous, entire.

Agar slant: Lemon-yellow, moist, mucoid, gistening, becoming light green-fluorescent.

Broth: Turbid, with slimy white sediment. No pellicle.

Litmus milk: Flocculent precipitation. Slow peptonization with yellow serum. Alkaline.

Potato: Dirty yellow, moist, glistening, entire.

Indole produced.

Nitrates reduced to nitrites and ammonia. No gas formed.

Acid from glucose. No acid from lactose or sucrose.

Aerobic, facultative.

Optimum temperature, 22° C. Scant growth at 35° C.

Distinctive character: Grows in broth containing up to 6 per cent by volume of alcohol.

Source: Isolated from beer.

Habitat: Found in materials undergoing alcoholic fermentation, but probably also occurs elsewhere.

11. Pseudomonas schuylkilliensis Chester, 1901. (*Bacillus fluorescens schuylkilliensis* Wright, Memoirs Natl. Acad. Sci., *7*, 1895, 448; Chester, Man. Determ. Bact., 1901, 320.)

schuyl.kil.li.en′sis. Schuylkill, name of a river; M.L. adj. *schuylkilliensis* of the Schuylkill.

Short rods, with rounded ends, occurring singly, in pairs and in chains. Motile, possessing a polar flagellum. Gram-negative.

Gelatin colonies: Grayish white, translucent. Medium becomes bluish green fluorescent.

Gelatin stab: Slow crateriform liquefaction, with blue-green fluorescence.

Agar slant: Grayish, translucent growth. Medium shows greenish fluorescence.

Broth: Turbid, with delicate pellicle and blue-green fluorescence. Stringy sediment.

Litmus milk: Alkaline. Coagulated, with slow reduction of litmus; peptonized.

Potato: Brownish, spreading, viscid, thick.

Indole produced (trace).

Aerobic, facultative.

Does not grow at 35° to 36° C.

Source: Isolated from Schuylkill River water.

Habitat: Water.

12. Pseudomonas synxantha (Ehrenberg, 1840) Holland, 1920. (*Vibrio synxanthus* Ehrenberg, Verhandl. d. Berl. Akad., 1840, 202; Holland, Jour. Bact., *5*, 1920, 220.)

syn.xan′tha. Gr. pref. *syn-* along with, together; Gr. adj. *xanthus* yellow; M.L. adj. *synxanthus* with yellow.

Description from Hammer (Res. Bull. 20, Iowa Agr. Exp. Sta., 1915); also see Zimmermann (Bakt. unserer Trink- und Nutzwässer, Chemnitz, *2*, 1890, 44).

Rods, 0.5 to 0.6 by 1.3 to 2.2 microns, occurring singly and in pairs. Motile with polar flagella (Hammer, personal communication, 1944). Gram-negative.

Gelatin stab: Liquefied; a greenish tinge, a heavy, flocculent sediment and a partial membrane and ring appear in two weeks.

Agar colonies: After 72 hours, large, spreading, transparent; bluish cast by reflected light. Colonies may show flesh color (Zimmermann).

Agar slant: Growth raised, shiny, white, becoming brown and heavy.

Agar stab: Growth heaviest near the surface, becoming light brown, heavy, spreading.

Broth: Turbid, becoming alkaline and green; pellicle and brittle membrane form in older cultures. With the addition of glucose or galactose, black granules form on the membranes of older cultures.

Uschinsky's and Dunham's solutions: Turbid, occasionally becoming green.

Litmus milk: Coagulated; casein digested in older cultures. Litmus reduced.

Potato: Growth spreading, brown with greenish edges.

Indole not produced.

Acid but no gas from glucose, fructose, galactose and glycerol. No acid or gas from salicin or raffinose.

Aerobic.

Grows well at 20° C.

Distinctive character: Produces an intense, diffusible, yellow to orange color in cream or in the cream layer of milk.

Source: Isolated from bitter milk.

Habitat: Milk and cream so far as is known.

13. Pseudomonas fluorescens Migula, 1895. (*Bacillus fluorescens liquefaciens* Flügge, Die Mikroorganismen, 1886, 289; Migula, in Engler and Prantl, Die natürl. Pflanzenfamilien, 1, 1a, 1895, 29.)

flu.o.res′cens. L. *fluor* a flux; M.L. *fluoresco* to fluoresce; fluor-spar, a fluxing mineral which is fluorescent; M.L. part. adj. *fluorescens* fluorescing.

Rods, 0.3 to 0.5 by 1.0 to 1.8 microns, occurring singly and in pairs. Motile, possessing a polar flagellum; occasionally nonmotile. Gram-negative.

Gelatin colonies: Circular, with greenish center, lobular, liquefying quickly; occasionally viscid.

Gelatin stab: Infundibuliform liquefaction, with whitish to reddish gray sediment.

Agar slant: Abundant, reddish layer, becoming reddish gray. The medium shows greenish to olive-brown coloration.

Broth: Turbid, flocculent, with yellowish green pellicle and grayish sediment.

Litmus milk: No coagulation; becoming alkaline.

Potato: Thick, grayish yellow, spreading, becoming light sepia-brown in color; occasionally viscid.

Indole not produced.

Nitrates reduced to nitrites and ammonia.

Acid from glucose.

Blood serum liquefied.

Aerobic.

Optimum temperature, between 20° and 25° C.

Not pathogenic.

Source: Water, sewage, feces.

Habitat: Soil, water and occasionally

foodstuffs that have become contaminated from these sources.

14. Pseudomonas pavonacea Levine and Soppeland, 1926. (Bull. No. 77, Iowa State Agr. College, 1926, 41.)

pa.vo.na′ce.a. L. adj. *pavonaceus* like a peacock's tail, variegated.

Rods, 0.5 by 4.5 microns, with truncate ends, occurring singly and in chains. Old cells develop 2 to 4 knob-like processes. Sluggishly motile. Gram-negative.

Gelatin stab: Crateriform liquefaction. Medium becoming brown.

Agar colonies: Circular, raised, becoming green, amorphous, entire.

Agar slant: Green, smooth, glistening, viscid, medium becoming dark brown.

Broth: Turbid, with viscid sediment. Medium turned brown.

Litmus milk: Slightly alkaline. Litmus reduced. Peptonized after 10 days.

Potato: No growth.

Hydrogen sulfide produced.

Indole not produced.

Neither nitrites nor gas produced from nitrates.

Blood serum liquefied in 5 days.

No acid or gas from glucose, lactose, sucrose or glycerol.

Aerobic, facultative.

Optimum temperature, 22° C. Scant growth at 37° C.

Distinctive characters: Growth on solid media distinctly green. Not fluorescent. Medium becomes brown.

Source: Isolated from activated sludge.

15. Pseudomonas geniculata (Wright, 1895) Chester, 1901. (*Bacillus geniculatus* Wright, Memoirs Nat. Acad. Sci., 7, 1895, 459; Chester, Man. Determ. Bact., 1901, 313.)

ge.ni.cu.la′ta. L. adj. *geniculatus* jointed.

Medium-sized rods, occurring singly, in pairs and in chains. Motile, possessing 1 to 4 polar flagella. Gram-negative.

Gelatin colonies: Circular, whitish, assume a greenish shimmer, translucent. Deep colonies yellowish.

Gelatin stab: Infundibuliform liquefaction. Sediment light pink.

Agar slant: Grayish, glistening, translucent, limited. Agar becomes brownish green.
Broth: Turbid, with slight gray pellicle and sediment. Broth becomes green.
Litmus milk: Alkaline; reduction of litmus; slight coagulation. Serum becomes green.
Potato: Thin, brownish, moist, glistening, viscid.
Indole not produced.
Aerobic, facultative.
Optimum temperature, between 20° and 25° C. No growth at 35° C.
Source: From water from the Schuylkill River.
Habitat: Water.

16. **Pseudomonas septica** Bergey et al., 1930. (*Bacillus fluorescens septicus* Stutzer and Wsorow, Cent. f. Bakt., II Abt., *71*, 1927, 113; Bergey et al., Manual, 3rd ed., 1930, 169.)
sep'ti.ca. Gr. adj. *septicus* putrefactive, septic.
Rods, 0.6 to 0.8 by 0.8 to 2.0 microns, occurring singly. Motile with a polar flagellum. Gram-negative.
Gelatin stab: Infundibuliform liquefaction.
Agar colonies: Circular with opalescent center and transparent periphery.
Agar slant: Moderate, undulate margin.
Broth: Turbid with fragile pellicle, greenish in upper portion.
Litmus milk: Alkaline, coagulated.
Blood serum not liquefied.
Acid from glucose.
Aerobic, facultative.
Optimum temperature, 20° C.
Source: Isolated from diseased caterpillars.
Habitat: From infected caterpillars so far as known.

17. **Pseudomonas syncyanea** (Ehrenberg, 1840). Migula, 1895. (*Vibrio syncyaneus* Ehrenberg, Berichte ü.d. Verh. d. k. Preuss. Akad. d. Wissensch. z. Berlin, *5*, 1840, 202; Migula, in Engler and Prantl, Die natürl. Pflanzenfam., *1*, 1a, 1895, 29.)
syn.cy.a'ne.a. Gr. *syn-* along with, entirely; Gr. *cyaneus* dark blue, dark; M.L. adj. *syncyaneus* entirely blue.

Rods with rounded ends, occurring singly, occasionally in chains, 0.7 by 2.0 to 4.0 microns. Motile with two to four polar flagella. Gram-negative.
Gelatin colonies: Flat, bluish, translucent.
Gelatin stab: Surface growth shiny, grayish blue. The medium is colored steel-blue with greenish fluorescence. Gelatin is liquefied. Some strains do not liquefy.
Agar slant: Grayish white streak. The medium takes on a bluish gray color with slight fluorescence.
Broth: Turbid with marked fluorescence.
Litmus milk: Unchanged. In association with lactic-acid bacteria the milk takes on a deep blue color.
Potato: Yellowish gray, shiny layer, becoming bluish gray. The tissue becomes bluish gray.
Indole not produced.
Nitrites not produced from nitrates.
Aerobic, facultative.
Optimum temperature, 25° C.
Source: From milk that was bluish in color.
Habitat: The cause of blue milk.

18. **Pseudomonas iodinum** (Davis, 1939) Tobie, 1939. (*Chromobacterium iodinum* Davis, Zent. f. Bakt., II Abt., *100*, 1939, 273; Tobie, Bull. Assoc. Diplômés Microbiol. Fac., Nancy, No. 18, 1939, 16.)
i.o.di'num. M.L. neut.noun *iodinum* iodine.
Rods, 0.5 by 1.0 to 2.0 microns, occurring singly. Non-motile. Gram-negative.
Gelatin stab: Stratiform liquefaction. Crystals of iodinin form.
Agar colonies: Round, smooth, gray-white, moist, glistening. Dark purple crystals having the appearance of iodine crystals form in the growth and in the adjacent medium. This pigment is actually a phenazine di-N-oxide, there being no iodine present (Clemo and McIlwain, Jour. Chem. Soc., Pt. 1, 1938, 479; Clemo and Daglish, Jour. Chem. Soc., Pt. 1, 1950, 1481).
Broth: Turbid. Crystals of iodinin form on bottom of tube.
Litmus milk: Alkaline; slow reduction of litmus.

Potato: Viscous, creamy, spreading, becoming dark.

Catalase-positive.

Indole not produced.

Nitrites produced from nitrates.

No acid from carbohydrates.

Acetylmethylcarbinol not produced.

Aerobic.

Optimum temperature, 28° C. Grows at 37° C.

Distinguishing character: The pigment, iodinin, is readily formed in any medium containing soluble nitrogenous compounds. Potassium and sodium citrates markedly stimulate pigment production. Yeast extract is inhibitory to formation of iodinin, which is soluble in benzene, toluene, xylene, chloroform, carbon disulfide and ethyl acetate. Such solutions are ruby red. The pigment, like pyocyanin and chlororaphine, is a phenazine derivative.

Source: Isolated from milk.

Habitat: Unknown.

19. **Pseudomonas smaragdina** (Mez, 1898) Migula, 1900. (*Bacillus smaragdinus foetidus* Reiman, Inaug. Dissertation, Würzburg, 1887; *Bacterium smaragdinum* Mez, Mikroskopische Wasseranalyse, Berlin, 1898, 49; Migula, Syst. d. Bakt., *2*, 1900, 890.)

sma.rag'di.na. Gr. adj. *smaragdinus* of smaragdus, emerald-green.

Small rods, occurring singly. Non-motile. Gram-negative.

Gelatin colonies: Small, convex, irregular, whitish with greenish shimmer.

Gelatin stab: Slight surface growth. Infundibuliform liquefaction. The liquefied medium becomes light emerald-green in color.

Agar colonies: Small, brownish yellow, convex.

Agar slant: Abundant growth with greenish fluorescence.

Broth: Turbid.

Litmus milk: Not coagulated.

Potato: Dark brown, becoming chocolate-brown.

Indole not produced.

Nitrates not reduced.

The cultures give off an odor resembling jasmine.

Aerobic, facultative.

Optimum temperature, 37° C.

Subcutaneous and intravenous inoculations into rabbits cause death in 36 to 48 hours.

Source: Isolated from nasal secretions in ozena.

Habitat: Unknown.

20. **Pseudomonas putida** (Trevisan, 1889) Migula, 1895. (*Bacillus fluorescens putidus* Flügge, Die Mikroorganismen, 2 Aufl., 1886, 288; *Bacillus putidus* Trevisan, I gen. e le specie d. Batteriacee, 1889, 18; Migula, in Engler and Prantl, Die natür. Pflanzenfam., *1*, 1a, 1895, 29.)

pu'ti.da. L. adj. *putidus* stinking, fetid.

Rods with rounded ends. Motile, possessing polar flagella. Gram-negative.

Gelatin colonies: Small, finely granular, fluorescent with dark center, surrounded by a yellow zone, with pale gray margin.

Gelatin stab: Dirty white surface growth, becoming greenish, fluorescent. No liquefaction.

Agar colonies: Circular, raised, smooth, amorphous, entire, with fluorescent zone around the periphery.

Agar slant: Yellowish green layer, becoming fluorescent.

Broth: Turbid, fluorescent.

Litmus milk: Unchanged.

Potato: Thin, gray to brownish, slimy layer.

Cultures give off odor of trimethylamine.

Indole not produced.

Nitrites produced from nitrates.

Aerobic, facultative.

Temperature relations: Optimum, 25° C. Will grow at 37° C. (Reid et al., Penn. Agr. Exp. Sta., Bull. 422, 1942, 9).

Relationship to other species: Identical with *Pseudomonas fluorescens* Migula according to Lehmann and Neumann (Bact. Diag., 1, Aufl., *2*, 1896, 271) except that it does not liquefy gelatin. See *Pseudomonas eisenbergii* Migula.

Source: Isolated from putrid materials.

Habitat: Putrefying materials; water.

21. **Pseudomonas striata** Chester, 1901. (*Bacillus striatus viridis* Ravenel, Memoirs

Nat. Acad. Sci., *8*, 1896, 22; Chester, Man. Determ. Bact., 1901, 325.)

stri.a'ta. L. v. *strio* to groove; L. part.adj. *striatus* grooved.

Slender rods, of variable lengths, staining irregularly, occurring singly and in pairs. Motile, possessing polar flagella. Gram-negative.

Gelatin colonies: Circular, yellowish, with filamentous border.

Gelatin stab: No liquefaction.

Agar slant: Smooth, glistening, irregular, spreading. Agar becomes yellowish green.

Broth: Turbid, becoming slightly greenish.

Litmus milk: No coagulation; becoming alkaline; litmus reduced.

Potato: Moist, glistening, spreading, becoming chocolate-brown.

Indole not produced.

Aerobic.

Grows well at 25° and 36° C.

Source: Isolated from soil.

Habitat: Soil.

22. Pseudomonas ovalis Chester, 1901. (*Bacillus fluorescens ovalis* Ravenel, Memoirs Nat. Acad. Sci., *8*, 1896, 9; Chester, Man. Determ. Bact., 1901, 325.)

o.va'lis. L. n. *ovum* an egg; M.L. adj. *ovalis* oval.

Rods, short with rounded ends, occurring singly. Motile, possessing polar flagella. Gram-negative.

Gelatin colonies: Irregular, lobate, slightly granular, translucent, grayish becoming bluish.

Gelatin stab: No liquefaction. Faintly green near surface.

Agar colonies: Circular, opaque, entire, greenish fluorescence.

Agar slant: Thin, spreading, greenish white. Agar becomes yellowish.

Broth: Turbid, with pellicle and white sediment; faintly green.

Potato: Scant, yellowish brown growth.

Indole not produced.

Aerobic, facultative.

Grows well at 25° and 36° C.

Source: Isolated from soil.

Habitat: Soil.

23. Pseudomonas taetrolens Haynes, *nom. nov.* (*Pseudomonas graveolens* Levine and Anderson, Jour. Bact., *23*, 1932, 343; not *Pseudomonas graveolens* Migula, Syst. d. Bakt., *2*, 1900, 934.)

taet'ro.lens. L. adj. *taeter* offensive; L. part. *olens* having an odor; M.L. part.adj. *taetrolens* foul-smelling.

Short rods with rounded ends, occurring singly, in pairs and in short chains. Motile (Levine and Anderson). One to five polar flagella (found on retest of cultures by Haynes, 1953). Gram-negative.

Gelatin stab: Not liquefied.

Agar colonies: Circular, slightly raised, smooth, entire, amorphous internal structure.

Agar slant: Growth abundant and tan-colored; medium darkened. Penetrating odor of must.

Broth: Turbid; thin, oily pellicle and sediment. Odor of must.

Litmus milk: Acid, coagulated; litmus reduced.

Indole not produced.

Nitrites not produced from nitrates.

Hydrogen sulfide produced.

Starch not hydrolyzed.

Acid but no gas produced from glucose, lactose, galactose, mannose, fructose, rhamnose and xylose. Slight acidity in glycerol and mannitol. No acid or gas from aesculin, amygdalin, arabitol, dextrin, dulcitol, glycogen, inulin, maltose, melizitose, pectin, raffinose, salicin, sorbitol, starch, sucrose, xylan, arabinose, erythritol or trehalose.

Aerobic.

Catalase-positive.

Optimum temperature, between 23° and 25° C. Scant growth at 33° and 10° C.

Distinctive character: A strong musty odor develops in media in which this organism grows. In this respect it resembles *P. perolens* which, however, liquefies gelatin and reduces nitrates.

Source: Isolated from musty eggs; also from milk by Olsen and Hammer (Iowa State College Jour. Sci., *9*, 1934, 125).

Habitat: Found in various foods that have a musty odor; presumably widely distributed.

24. Pseudomonas incognita Chester, 1901. (*Bacillus fluorescens incognitus* Wright,

Memoirs Nat. Acad. Sci., 7, 1895, 436; Chester, Man. Determ. Bact., 1901, 323.)

in.cog'ni.ta. L. adj. *incognitus* not examined, unknown.

Short rods, with rounded ends, occurring singly, in pairs and in chains. Motile, possessing a polar flagellum. Gram-negative.

Gelatin colonies: Thin, translucent, slightly granular, becoming greenish. Margin undulate. The medium assumes a blue-green fluorescence.

Gelatin stab: No liquefaction.

Agar slant: Thin, moist, translucent. Agar becomes greenish.

Broth: Turbid, becoming greenish. Pellicle and whitish sediment form.

Litmus milk: Slightly acid in a month. Litmus slowly reduced.

Potato: Moist, glistening, spreading, brown.

Indole is produced (trace).

Aerobic, facultative.

No growth at 35° to 36° C.

Comment: Wright (*op. cit.*, 1895, 441) described an organism that is very similar to this species except that it may produce a faint brownish green coloration in a gelatin stab; Wright named the organism *Bacillus nexibilis* (*Bacterium nexibilis* Chester, Ann. Rept. Del. Col. Agr. Exp. Sta., 9, 1897, 74; *Pseudomonas nexibilis* Chester, *op. cit.*, 1901, 309).

Source: Isolated from water from the Schuylkill River.

Habitat: Water.

25. Pseudomonas rugosa (Wright, 1895) Chester, 1901. (*Bacillus rugosus* Wright, Memoirs Nat. Acad. Sci., 7, 1895, 438; Chester, Man. Determ. Bact., 1901, 323.)

ru.go'sa. L. adj. *rugosus* full of wrinkles.

Small rods, with rounded ends, occurring singly, in pairs and in chains. Motile, possessing 1 to 4 polar flagella. Gram-negative.

Gelatin colonies: Grayish, translucent, slightly raised, irregular, sinuous, radiately erose to entire.

Gelatin stab: Dense grayish green, limited, wrinkled, reticulate surface growth. No liquefaction. Medium becomes green.

Agar slant: Grayish white, limited, slightly wrinkled, translucent. Agar becomes green.

Broth: Turbid, with thin whitish pellicle and sediment.

Litmus milk: Acid, coagulated, partly reduced.

Potato: Moist, glistening, brown, spreading.

Indole is produced (trace).

Aerobic.

Optimum temperature, 30° C. Does not grow at 35° C.

Source: From water from the Schuylkill River.

Habitat: Water.

26. Pseudomonas mildenbergii Bergey et al., 1930. (Der Blaubacillus, Mildenberg, Cent. f. Bakt., II Abt., *56*, 1922, 309; Bergey et al., Manual, 3rd ed., 1930, 172.)

mil.den.ber'gi.i. Mildenberg, a patronymic; M.L. gen.noun *mildenbergii* of Mildenberg.

Rods, 0.3 to 0.5 by 1.0 to 3.5 microns, with rounded ends, occurring singly. Motile, possessing polar flagella. Gram-negative.

Gelatin colonies: Circular, lobed, smooth, glistening, slightly raised, steel-blue, entire.

Gelatin stab: No liquefaction.

Agar colonies: Small, circular, yellowish or reddish yellow, entire, becoming lobed, grayish green, iridescent. The medium becomes dirty grayish green.

Agar slant: Smooth, spreading, slimy, glistening, grayish green to dark green, fluorescent.

Broth: Turbid green, iridescent to opalescent with slimy sediment.

Litmus milk: Not coagulated, blue ring.

Potato: Slimy, glistening, spreading, steel blue.

Indole not produced.

Nitrites not produced from nitrates.

Aerobic, facultative.

Optimum temperature, 25° C.

Source: Isolated from air.

27. Pseudomonas convexa Chester, 1901. (*Bacillus fluorescens convexus* Wright, Memoirs Nat. Acad. Sci., 7, 1895, 438; Chester, Man. Determ. Bact., 1901, 325.)

con.vex'a. L. adj. *convexus* vaulted, convex.

Short, thick rods, with rounded ends.

Motile, possessing a polar flagellum. Gram-negative.

Gelatin colonies: Circular, convex, glistening, greenish, translucent. The medium becomes blue-green, fluorescent.

Gelatin stab: Light green, raised, glistening surface growth. No liquefaction. Medium becomes blue-green fluorescent.

Agar slant: Moist, translucent, glistening, light greenish. The medium assumes a greenish color.

Broth: Turbid, becoming greenish.

Litmus milk: No coagulation; alkaline.

Potato: Pale brown, spreading.

Indole not produced.

Aerobic, facultative.

Little or no growth at 35° to 36° C.

Source: From water from the Schuylkill River.

Habitat: Water.

28. **Pseudomonas eisenbergii** Migula, 1900. (Fluorescirender Bacillus No. 18, Eisenberg, Bakt. Diag., 1 Aufl., 1886, Taf. 7; *Bacillus fluorescens non liquefaciens* Eisenberg, Bakt. Diag., 3 Aufl., 1891, 145; Migula, Syst. d. Bakt., *2*, 1900, 913; *Pseudomonas non-liquefaciens* Bergey et al., Manual, 1st ed., 1923, 132.)

eis.en.ber′gi.i. Named for James Eisenberg, the bacteriologist who first described this species; M.L. gen.n. *eisenbergii* of Eisenberg.

Short, slender rods with rounded ends. Non-motile. Gram-negative.

Gelatin colonies: Fern-like surface colonies. Medium around colonies has a pearly luster.

Gelatin stab: Surface growth has fluorescent shimmer. Scant growth along stab. No liquefaction.

Agar slant: Greenish growth.

Broth: Turbid, fluorescent.

Litmus milk: Unchanged.

Potato: Diffuse, brownish layer. The surface acquires a grayish blue color.

Indole not produced.

Nitrites produced from nitrates.

Acid from glucose.

Blood serum liquefied.

Aerobic.

Optimum temperature, 25° C.

Not pathogenic.

Habitat: Water.

29. **Pseudomonas erythra** Fuller and Norman, 1943. (Jour. Bact., *46*, 1943, 276.)

e′ry.thra. Gr. adj. *erythrus* red.

Rods, 0.2 to 0.4 by 1.2 to 1.5 microns, with rounded ends, usually arranged singly. Motile with a single polar flagellum. Encapsulated. Gram-negative.

Gelatin stab: No growth.

Starch agar: No growth.

Water-insoluble dextrin agar: Scant growth. Subsurface colonies appear after 8 to 10 days. Colonies are angular, small, surrounded by a clear zone 2 to 5 mm in diameter. Buff or reddish brown.

Litmus milk: No growth.

Indole not produced.

Nitrites not produced from nitrates.

Starch not hydrolyzed.

No growth in media containing the usual carbohydrates. Cellulose and water-insoluble dextrins are utilized. Filter paper strips in mineral solution develop reddish brown spots above the surface of the liquid. Solution becomes cloudy. Colonies enlarge and become viscous, and the paper becomes reddish. The filter paper does not break with moderate shaking but may be wound up in a slimy mass. In cellulose media a reddish, water-soluble pigment is produced.

Yeast extract and nitrate are suitable nitrogen sources.

Aerobic.

Grows in a range from 22° to 35° C.

Source: Isolated from soil.

Habitat: Soil.

30. **Pseudomonas fragi** (Eichholz, 1902) Huss, 1907, *emend.* Hussong et al., 1937. (*Bacterium fragi* Eichholz, Cent. f. Bakt., II Abt., *9*, 1902, 425; Huss, Cent. f. Bakt., II Abt., *19*, 1907, 661; Hussong, Long and Hammer, Iowa Agr. Exp. Sta. Res. Bull. 225, 1937, 122.)

fra′gi. L. neut.n. *fragum* strawberry; L. gen.n. *fragi* of the strawberry.

Description from Hussong, Long and Hammer (*loc. cit.*).

Rods, 0.5 to 1.0 by 0.75 to 4.0 microns, occurring singly, in pairs and in chains.

Motile with a polar flagellum. Gram-negative.

Gelatin: Crateriform to stratiform liquefaction in 3 to 4 days.

Agar colonies: Convex, glistening, generally butyrous, occasionally viscid. Rough, smooth and intermediate forms are recognized in the description quoted. The rough forms are less proteolytic and less active in the hydrolysis of fats.

Agar slant: Growth abundant, spreading, raised, white, shiny, generally butyrous. Sweet ester-like odor resembling that of the flower of the May apple.

Broth: Turbidity and sediment with a thin pellicle.

Litmus milk: Acid ring followed by acid coagulum at surface. Complete coagulation in 2 to 3 weeks, some digestion. Characteristic May-apple or strawberry odor.

Potato: Growth echinulate to arborescent, raised, glistening, white, becoming brownish.

Indole not produced.

Nitrites not produced from nitrates.

Ammonia produced from peptone.

Hydrogen sulfide not produced.

Acid from glucose and galactose, sometimes arabinose. No acid from glycerol, inulin, lactose, fructose, maltose, mannitol, raffinose, salicin or sucrose.

No acetylmethylcarbinol produced.

Fat is generally hydrolyzed (Nashif and Nelson, Jour. Dairy Sci., *36*, 1953, 459–488).

Aerobic.

Grows from 10° to 30° C. No growth at 37° C. Very sensitive to heat.

Comment: Various names have been given this species. Hussong (Thesis, Iowa State College, 1932) thinks that these varieties are the result of dissociative action.

Source: Isolated from milk and other dairy products, dairy utensils, water, etc.

Habitat: Soil and water. Widely distributed (Morrison and Hammer, Jour. Dairy Sci., *24*, 1941, 9).

31. **Pseudomonas perolens** (Turner, 1927) Szybalski, 1950. (*Achromobacter perolens* Turner, Austral. Jour. Exp. Biol. and Med. Sci., *4*, 1927, 57; Szybalski, Nature, *165*, 1950, 733.)

pe.ro′lens. L. v. *perolere* to emit a penetrating odor; L. part.adj. *perolens* emitting an odor.

Small, imperfect spheres and coccoid rods; occasionally longer rods with rounded ends; occur singly and in short chains. 0.3 by 0.4 to 2.55 microns. Motile with a single polar flagellum. Gram-negative.

Gelatin: Liquefied.

Agar slants: Growth moderate, glistening, raised, butyrous, spreading, with undulate border; whitish by reflected and semi-translucent by transmitted light.

Broth: Turbid, with a flocculent sediment and a slight pellicle.

Litmus milk: Acid, gradually decolorized, partial clotting.

Blood serum: Liquefied.

Potato: Growth thick, glistening, raised, brownish.

Nitrites and ammonia produced from nitrates.

Indole not produced.

Acid but no gas from glucose, fructose, galactose, glycerol, mannitol and arabinose. Sucrose, maltose, lactose, raffinose, dulcitol, salicin and inulin not utilized.

Aerobic, facultative.

Grows well at room temperature. No growth at 37° C.

Distinctive characters: Produces a musty odor in eggs. Other varieties and species of *Pseudomonas* that produce the same odor have been described (Szybalski, *loc. cit.*). Resembles *Pseudomonas fragi* but produces a musty rather than a May-apple odor in media.

Source: Isolated from eggs with a musty odor.

Habitat: Musty eggs.

32. **Pseudomonas mephitica** Claydon and Hammer, 1939. (Jour. Bact., *37*, 1939, 254.)

me.phi′ti.ca. L. adj. *mephiticus* pestilential (skunk-like) odor.

Rods, 0.5 to 1.0 by 1.5 to 14.0 microns, occurring singly, in pairs and in chains. Actively motile with a polar flagellum. Gram-negative.

Gelatin: Slow liquefaction.

Agar colonies: Convex, circular, about 3

mm in diameter, shiny, grayish white, entire, of the consistency of bread dough.

Agar slant: Growth grayish white,
wrinkled, echinulate. After 1 or 2 days a
skunk-like odor develops.

Broth: Turbid. Sediment. White pellicle.

Potato: Growth echinulate, shiny, brownish.

Litmus milk: A skunk-like odor develops
in 1 to 2 days. Grayish blue surface ring in
about 3 days. Alkaline in 7 to 10 days. In
two weeks complete reduction. Slight proteolysis and viscosity.

Hydrogen sulfide not produced.

Indole not produced.

Nitrites produced from nitrates.

Acid but no gas produced slowly from
glucose, fructose, maltose and sucrose. No
acid from arabinose, dextrin, galactose,
glycerol, lactose, mannitol, raffinose or
salicin.

Aerobic, facultative.

Optimum temperature, 21° C. Growth
slight at 5° and 30°C. No growth at 37° C.

Source: Several cultures isolated from
butter having a skunk-like odor.

Habitat: Presumably derived from the
rinse water.

33. **Pseudomonas putrefaciens** (Derby
and Hammer, 1931) Long and Hammer,
1941. (*Achromobacter putrefaciens* Derby
and Hammer, Iowa Agr. Exp. Sta., Res.
Bull. 145, 1931, 401; Long and Hammer,
Jour. Bact., *41*, 1941, 100.)

pu.tre.fa'ci.ens. L. v. *putrefacio* to make
rotten; L. part.adj. *putrefaciens* making
rotten.

Rods, 0.5 to 1.0 by 1.1 to 4.0 microns,
occurring singly and in pairs. Motile with
a single flagellum. Gram-negative.

Gelatin stab: Rapid, saccate to stratiform liquefaction, with reddish brown sediment in the liquefied portion.

Agar colony: Circular, smooth, glistening, slightly raised, somewhat transparent,
with brownish tinge.

Agar slant: Echinulate, slightly reddish
brown, viscous.

Broth: Turbid, with thin, gray pellicle
and reddish brown sediment.

Litmus milk: Rapid reduction and proteolysis with odor of putrefaction.

Potato: Echinulate, smooth, glistening,
viscous, reddish brown.

Indole not produced.

Nitrites are produced from nitrates.

Acid from maltose and sucrose. No action
on glucose, fructose, galactose, arabinose,
lactose, raffinose, dextrin, inulin, salicin,
amygdalin, glycerol, mannitol or sorbitol.

Ammonia is formed.

Aerobic, facultative.

Optimum temperature, 21° C. No growth
at 37° C.

Source: Isolated from tainted butter.

Habitat: Milk, cream, butter, water, soil
and creamery equipment (Long and Hammer, *loc. cit.*; Claydon and Hammer, *op.
cit.*, Res. Bull. 267, 1939).

34. **Pseudomonas cohaerens** (Wright,
1895) Chester, 1901. (*Bacillus cohaerens*
Wright, Mem. Nat. Acad. Sci., *7*, 1895, 464;
Pseudomonas cohaerea (sic) Chester, Man.
Determ. Bact., 1901, 312.)

co.hae'rens. L. part.adj. *cohaerens* co-
hering, uniting together.

Rods, occurring singly and in pairs, sometimes in chains. Motile, possessing a polar
flagellum. Gram-negative.

Gelatin colonies: Circular, elevated, grayish, translucent, entire. Become white with
an elevated, brownish, central nodule.

Gelatin stab: Slow liquefaction.

Agar slant: Elevated, grayish white,
translucent, glistening, with irregular margins.

Broth: Turbid; coherent, wrinkled pellicle which adheres to the walls of the container.

Litmus milk: Alkaline, coagulated, slowly
peptonized, litmus reduced.

Potato: Thick, granular, translucent,
spreading.

Indole not produced.

Grows at 25° C.

Aerobic.

Source: Isolated from water from the
Schuylkill River.

Habitat: Water.

35. **Pseudomonas ambigua** (Wright,
1895) Chester, 1901. (*Bacillus ambiguus*
Wright, Memoirs Nat. Acad. Sci., *7*, 1895,

439; Chester, Man. Determ. Bact., 1901, 308.)

am.bi'gu.a. L. adj. *ambiguus* going about, hence uncertain.

Small rods, with rounded ends, occurring singly, in pairs and in chains. Motile, possessing a polar flagellum. Gram-negative.

Gelatin colonies: Gray, translucent, slightly raised, irregular, radiate, with transparent margin.

Gelatin stab: No liquefaction.

Agar slant: Gray, limited, entire.

Broth: Turbid, with gray sediment.

Litmus milk: Acid, slowly coagulated. Litmus reduced.

Potato: Gray to creamy, viscid, spreading.

Indole produced.

Aerobic, facultative.

Optimum temperature, between 30° and 35° C.

Source: Isolated from water from the Schuylkill River.

Habitat: Water.

36. **Pseudomonas oleovorans** Lee and Chandler, 1941. (Jour. Bact., *41*, 1941, 378.)

o.le.o'vor.ans. L. *oleum* oil; L. v. *voro* to destroy, consume; M.L. part.adj. *oleovorans* oil-consuming.

Short rods, 0.5 by 0.8 to 1.5 microns, occurring singly and in pairs. Motile. Gram-negative.

Gelatin stab: No liquefaction after 6 weeks.

Gelatin colonies: Up to 1 mm in diameter, fluorescent; similar to agar colonies.

Surface agar colonies: After 24 hours 1 to 2 mm in diameter, smooth, convex, shiny, opaque, creamy, fluorescent by transmitted light. Edge entire in young colonies.

Deep agar colonies: 0.5 by 1.0 to 1.5 mm, lens-shaped, buff-colored, not fluorescent.

Agar slant: Growth raised, smooth, fluorescent, edge erose.

Broth: After 24 hours, moderate turbidity with slight yellowish, viscid sediment. No pellicle or ring. No soluble pigment produced.

Litmus milk: No change.

Indole not produced.

Potato: Good growth.

Nitrites are produced from nitrates.

Starch is hydrolyzed.

No acid from glucose, lactose, sucrose, galactose, xylose, mannitol, salicin or glycerol.

Equally good growth at 25° and 37° C.

Aerobic.

Distinctive character: The fluorescent quality of the colonies is not imparted to any of the artificial media used.

Source: Isolated from cutting compound (oil-water emulsion) circulating in a machine shop. The oil in this compound may be utilized as a sole source of energy.

Habitat: Probably oil-soaked soils. Abundant in cutting compounds.

37. **Pseudomonas arvilla** Gray and Thornton, 1928. (Cent. f. Bakt., II Abt., *73*, 1928, 90.)

ar.vil'.la. L. *arvum* a field; M.L. dim.noun *arvilla* a small field.

Rods, 0.5 to 0.7 by 2.0 to 3.0 microns. Motile with one to five polar flagella. Gram-negative.

Gelatin colonies: Circular, whitish, convex, smooth, glistening, lobate.

Gelatin stab: No liquefaction.

Agar colonies: Circular or amoeboid, white to buff, flat to convex, smooth, glistening, opaque, entire.

Agar slant: Filiform, whitish, convex, smooth, ringed, entire.

Broth: Turbid.

Nitrites not produced from nitrates.

Starch not hydrolyzed.

Acid from glucose.

Attacks naphthalene.

Aerobic, facultative.

Grows at 37° C.

Source: Isolated from soil.

Habitat: Soil.

38. **Pseudomonas dacunhae** Gray and Thornton, 1928. (Cent. f. Bakt., II Abt., *73*, 1928, 90.)

da.cun'hae. d'Acunha, place name, Island; M.L. gen.noun *dacunhae* of d'Acunha.

Rods 0.5 to 0.8 by 1.5 to 3.0 microns. Motile with one to six polar flagella. Gram-negative.

Gelatin colonies: Circular, whitish, raised, smooth, glistening, entire.

Gelatin stab: No liquefaction.

Agar colonies: Circular to amoeboid, white, flat, glistening, opaque, entire.

Agar slant: Filiform, pale buff, raised, smooth, glistening, undulate.

Broth: Turbid.

Nitrites not produced from nitrates.

Starch not hydrolyzed.

No acid from carbohydrate media.

Attacks phenol.

Aerobic, facultative.

Grows at 37° C.

Source: Isolated from soil.

Habitat: Soil.

39. Pseudomonas desmolytica Gray and Thornton, 1928. (Cent. f. Bakt., II Abt., *73*, 1928, 90.)

des.mo.ly'ti.ca. Gr. *desmus* bond; Gr. *lyticus* able to loose; M.L. adj. *desmolyticus* bond-loosening.

Rods, 0.7 to 0.8 by 2.0 to 3.0 microns, occurring singly and in pairs. Motile, with one to five polar flagella. Gram-negative.

Gelatin colonies: Circular, gray to buff, raised or umbonate. Smooth, glistening, entire.

Gelatin stab: No liquefaction.

Agar colonies: Circular or amoeboid, whitish, flat or convex, smooth, translucent to opaque, entire.

Agar slant: Filiform, pale buff, raised, smooth, undulate.

Broth: Turbid.

Nitrites often produced from nitrates.

Starch not hydrolyzed.

Acid usually produced from glucose.

Attacks naphthalene.

Aerobic, facultative.

Grows at 35° C.

Source: Isolated from soil.

Habitat: Soil.

40. Pseudomonas rathonis Gray and Thornton, 1928. (Cent. f. Bakt., II Abt., *73*, 1928, 90.)

ra.tho'nis. Ratho Park, place name; M.L. gen.noun *rathonis* of Ratho.

Small rods, 0.5 to 1.0 by 1.0 to 3.0 microns, occurring singly and in pairs. Motile, with polar flagella. Gram-negative.

Gelatin colonies: Circular, white, raised, smooth, glistening, undulate.

Gelatin stab: No liquefaction.

Agar colonies: Circular, buff, flat, smooth, glistening, entire.

Agar slant: Filiform, pale buff, convex, smooth, glistening, undulate.

Broth: Turbid; pellicle may form.

Nitrites may be produced from nitrates.

Starch may be hydrolyzed.

Acid may be produced from glucose and glycerol.

Attacks phenol and cresol at times, also naphthalene.

Aerobic, facultative.

Grows at 35° C.

Source: Isolated from manure and soil.

Habitat: Manure and soil.

41. Pseudomonas salopia Gray and Thornton, 1928. (*Pseudomonas salopium* (sic) Gray and Thornton, Cent. f. Bakt., II Abt., *73*, 1928, 91.)

sa.lo'pi.a. Med.L. *Salop* Shropshire; M.L. adj. *salopius* of Shropshire.

Rods, 0.7 to 1.0 by 1.0 to 3.0 microns, occurring singly and in pairs. Motile with one to six polar flagella. Gram-negative.

Gelatin colonies: Circular, grayish buff, flat, rugose or ringed, translucent border.

Gelatin stab: No liquefaction.

Agar colonies: Circular or amoeboid, white to buff, flat to convex, smooth, glistening, translucent border, entire.

Agar slant: Filiform, whitish, raised, smooth, glistening, lobate.

Broth: Turbid with pellicle.

Nitrites not produced from nitrates.

Starch not hydrolyzed.

Acid from glucose and sucrose.

Attacks naphthalene.

Aerobic, facultative.

Grows at 35° C.

Source: Isolated from soil.

Habitat: Soil.

42. Pseudomonas cruciviae Gray and Thornton, 1928. (Cent. f. Bakt., II Abt., *73*, 1928, 91.)

cru.ci'vi.ae. L. *crux, crucis* a cross; L. *via* a way; M.L. *Crucivia* Waycross, a place name.

Rods, 1.0 by 1.0 to 3.0 microns, occurring singly and in pairs. Motile with one to five polar flagella. Gram-negative.

Gelatin colonies: Circular, white, convex, smooth, undulate.

Gelatin stab: No liquefaction.

Agar colonies: Circular or amoeboid, white to buff, flat to convex, smooth, entire.

Agar slant: Filiform, pale buff, raised, smooth, undulate.

Broth: Turbid.

Nitrites not produced from nitrates.

Starch not hydrolyzed.

No acid in carbohydrate media.

Attacks phenol and *m*-cresol.

Aerobic, facultative.

Optimum temperature, between 30° and 35° C.

Source: Isolated from soil.

Habitat: Soil.

43. Pseudomonas stutzeri (Lehmann and Neumann, 1896) Kluyver, 1942. (*Bacillus denitrificans II* Burri and Stutzer, Cent. f. Bakt., II Abt., *1*, 1895, 392; *Bacterium stutzeri* Lehmann and Neumann, Bakt. Diag., 1 Aufl., *2*, 1896, 237; *Bacillus nitrogenes* Migula, Syst. d. Bakt., *2*, 1900, 793; *Pseudomonas stutzeri* Kluyver, in Koningsberger, Leerb. d. algem. Plantkunde, Scheltema and Holkema, Amsterdam, *2*, 1942, 198; not *Pseudomonas stutzeri* Migula, Syst. d. Bakt., *2*, 1900, 929.)

stut'ze.ri. Named for Dr. A. Stutzer, one of the bacteriologists who originally described this species; M.L. gen.noun *stutzeri* of Stutzer.

Description taken from van Niel and Allen (Jour. Bact., *64*, 1952, 421).

Rods, 0.5 to 0.8 by 1.0 to 3.0 microns. Motile, possessing a single polar flagellum. Gram-negative.

Gelatin and agar colonies: Strongly coherent to media, dry consistency later becoming mucoid, resemble craters with elevated ridges which often branch and merge, concentric zones, polygonal elements, granular.

Gelatin: No liquefaction.

Peptone and yeast agar: Good growth.

Broth: Surface film on nitrate- or nitrite-free media which readily breaks up and precipitates.

Potato: Luxuriant, wrinkled, slimy, flesh-to peach-colored growth.

Nitrates, nitrites, nitramines and N₂O reduced to elemental nitrogen.

Carbohydrates: No growth when used as a carbon source in mineral media.

Aerobic, facultative.

Optimum pH, 7.0; growth even at pH 9.0.

Optimum temperature, 35° C.

Distinctive characters: Colony shape and consistency, mode and color of potato growth, ability to grow anaerobically in media with nitrate, nitrite, nitramine or N₂O, producing foam.

Source: Isolated from soil.

Habitat: Found widely distributed in soil, manure, mud and stagnant water.

44. Pseudomonas tralucida Kellerman et al., 1913. (Kellerman, McBeth, Scales and Smith, Cent. f. Bakt.. II Abt., *39*, 1913, 37.)

tra.lu'ci.da. L. adj. *tralucidus* transparent.

Rods 0.6 by 1.2 microns. Motile with one or two polar flagella. Gram-negative.

Gelatin stab: No liquefaction.

Agar slant: Moderate, flat, glistening, grayish growth.

Broth: Turbid; granular sediment.

Litmus milk: Acid, no coagulation.

Potato: No growth.

Indole not produced.

Nitrites produced from nitrates.

Ammonia not produced.

Starch hydrolysis slight.

Acid from glucose, maltose, lactose, sucrose, starch, glycerol and mannitol.

Attacks cellulose.

Aerobic, facultative.

Optimum temperature, 37° C. Grows also at 20° C.

Habitat: Soil.

45. Pseudomonas lasia Fuller and Norman, 1943. (Jour. Bact., *46*, 1943, 275.)

la'si.a. Gr. adj. *lasius* hairy, rough, shaggy, woolly.

Rods, 0.5 to 0.6 by 1.2 to 2.0 microns, usually occurring singly but sometimes in chains. Motile with a single polar flagellum. Gram-negative.

Gelatin stab: No liquefaction.

Starch agar colonies: Convex, pale yellow, becoming cream color, entire, round. Subsurface colonies look like small, woolly balls.

Water-insoluble dextrin colonies: Colonies grow below the surface and have a woolly appearance. Colonies are surrounded by clear zones. Become cream to pale yellow in color.

Litmus milk: Unchanged except for reduction of litmus at bottom of the tube.

Indole not produced.

Nitrites produced from nitrates.

Starch hydrolyzed.

Glucose, xylose, maltose and starch readily utilized. Arabinose, galactose and gum arabic feebly attacked. No acid formed in any of the above-mentioned substrates. Cellulose, cellulosan, water-soluble and water-insoluble cellulose, dextrins, hemicellulose and pectin readily attacked. Filter paper strips become pale yellowish in the area attacked.

Peptone, yeast extract, nitrate and ammonia are suitable nitrogen sources.

Aerobic.

Grows between 22° and 35° C.

Source: Isolated from soil.

Habitat: Soil.

46. Pseudomonas riboflavina Foster, 1944. (*Pseudomonas riboflavinus* (sic) Foster, Jour. Bact., *47*, 1944, 27; also see Jour. Bact., *48*, 1944, 97.)

ri.bo.fla'vi.na. M.L. adj. *riboflavinus* pertaining to riboflavin.

Thin rods of variable length. Motile. Gram-negative.

Gelatin stab: No liquefaction.

Yeast-extract agar colonies: Small, convex, smooth, transparent; slightly dentate edges. If glucose is added to the agar, copious quantities of polysaccharides are formed. Presence of fructose, mannitol, sucrose, maltose, lactose, xylose and galactose also lead to polysaccharide formation.

Yeast-extract glucose broth: Becomes so viscid that it scarcely flows.

Milk: Soft curd forms. Slowly peptonized.

Nitrites produced from nitrates.

No acid or gas from fructose, mannitol, sucrose, maltose, lactose, xylose or galactose. Acetic acid oxidized.

Acetylmethylcarbinol not produced.

Urea, glycine, ammonium chloride or sodium nitrate cannot be used as substitutes for organic-nitrogen sources. Neither could 20 water-soluble accessory factors substitute for yeast extract in a synthetic mineral salts-glucose medium.

No pigment produced in any medium.

Starch not hydrolyzed.

Optimum temperature, between 30° and 33° C.

Distinctive characters: In organic media containing a small amount of organic matter such as yeast extract or peptone and 0.05 to 0.2 per cent riboflavin, the riboflavin is attacked and converted to lumichrome, which accumulates in the culture as lemon-yellow crystals. If riboflavin is not provided in the medium, appreciable quantities of it are synthesized by this organism.

Source: Isolated from soil rich in riboflavin.

Habitat: Unknown.

47. Pseudomonas denitrificans Bergey et al., 1923. (*Bacillus denitrificans fluorescens* Christensen, Cent. f. Bakt., II Abt., *11*, 1903, 190; Bergey et al., Manual, 1st ed., 1923, 131.)

de.ni.tri'fi.cans. L. *de* away, from; L. *nitrum* soda; M.L. nitrate, niter; M.L. *denitrifico* to denitrify; M.L. part.adj. *denitrificans* denitrifying.

Rods, 0.5 to 0.7 by 0.5 to 1.25 microns, occurring singly and in pairs in large, slimy masses. Motile. Gram-negative.

Gelatin colonies: Small, circular, contoured, raised, moist, pearly gray, glistening.

Gelatin stab: Whitish, lobed surface growth. Yellowish green growth in stab. No liquefaction.

Agar colonies: Pearly white, circular, entire.

Agar slant: Broad, whitish, contoured, moist, entire.

Broth: Turbid, with thick, wrinkled pellicle.

Litmus milk: Not coagulated.

Potato: Reddish gray layer.

Indole not produced.

Nitrates reduced with production of nitrogen.

Aerobic, facultative.

Optimum temperature, 25° C.

Source: Isolated from soil.
Habitat: Soil.

48. Pseudomonas indoloxidans Gray, 1928. (Proc. Roy. Soc. London, B, *102*, 1928, 263.)

in.dol.o'xi.dans. M.L. neut.n. *indolum* indole; M.L. part.adj. *oxidans* oxidizing; from Gr. adj. *oxys* sharp, acid; M.L. part. adj. *indoloxidans* indole-oxidizing.

Rods 1.0 by 3.0 microns. Motile with one to four polar flagella. Gram-negative.

Gelatin colonies: Round, convex, buff, smooth, glistening, erose.

Gelatin stab: No liquefaction.

Agar colonies: Round, convex, white, watery; transparent border, erose.

Agar slant: Filiform, convex, whitish, smooth, glistening, undulate.

Broth: Cloudy.

Indole not produced.

Nitrites produced from nitrates. No gas.

No acid or gas from glucose, sucrose, lactose, maltose or glycerol.

Starch not hydrolyzed.

Phenol and *m*-cresol not attacked.

Distinctive character: Indole decomposed in mineral salts agar medium with the formation of blue crystals of indigotin.

Aerobic.

Optimum temperature, between 25° and 28° C.

Source: Isolated from soil from Italian Tyrol.

Habitat: Soil.

49. Pseudomonas mira McBeth, 1916. (Soil Science, *1*, 1916, 467.)

mi'ra. L. adj. *mirus* extraordinary.

Rods 0.4 by 1.6 microns. Motile with a single polar flagellum. Gram-negative.

Gelatin stab: Good growth. No liquefaction.

Agar colonies: Circular, convex, grayish white, granular, lacerate.

Agar slant: Moderate, flat, grayish white, somewhat iridescent.

Broth: Turbid.

Litmus milk: Alkaline.

Potato: Moderate, grayish white, leathery growth.

Indole not produced.

Nitrites produced from nitrates.

Ammonia is produced.

No acid from glucose, maltose, lactose, sucrose, starch, glycerol or mannitol.

Cellulose decomposed. Filter paper strips disintegrated at surface of liquid medium.

Aerobic, facultative.

Optimum temperature, 20° C.

Source: Isolated from soil.

Habitat: Soil.

50. Pseudomonas nigrifaciens White, 1940. (Scientific Agriculture, *20*, 1940, 643.)

ni.gri.fa'ci.ens. L. *niger* black; L. v. *facio* to make; M.L. part.adj. *nigrofaciens* blackening.

Rods, 0.5 by 1.5 to 2.0 microns, occurring singly or in pairs and having rounded ends. Actively motile with a single polar flagellum. Gram-negative.

Gelatin stab: Pigmented surface growth after 24 hours. Slight crateriform liquefaction changing to saccate.

Agar colonies: Circular, convex, smooth, glistening, entire, 2 to 4 mm in diameter. Slight fluorescence in early stages. The medium assumes a brownish color.

Agar slant: Growth filiform, smooth, moist, glistening, with blackish pigmentation at 4° and 15° C. in 48 hours, the medium turning brownish. Slight fluorescence in early stages.

Broth: Turbid after 24 hours. After 5 to 6 days a black ring and then a pellicle forms, later a black sediment. Medium turns brown.

Litmus milk: A black ring appears after 3 days at 15° C. followed by a pellicle. Litmus is reduced. Alkaline reaction. No coagulation. Digested with a putrid odor.

Potato: No growth, even in presence of 1.5 per cent salt.

Nitrites not produced from nitrates in 7 days. No gas produced.

Starch is hydrolyzed. Natural fats not hydrolyzed.

Alkaline reaction produced in sucrose, maltose, lactose, glucose, mannitol and raffinose broth (pH 8.2). No gas produced.

Ammonia produced in peptone broth.

Aerobic.

Optimum pH, 6.8 to 8.4.

Temperature relations: Minimum, 4° C. Optimum, 25° C. Maximum, 33° to 35° C.

Distinctive characters: No or slow growth in culture media in the absence of salt. Maximum growth and pigmentation appears with 1.5 and 2.5 per cent salt. Optimum pigmentation occurs at 4° and 15° C. Pigment insoluble in chloroform.

Source: Several cultures isolated from samples of discolored butter.

Habitat: Causes a black to reddish brown discoloration of print butter. Evidently widely distributed in nature.

51. Pseudomonas ichthyodermis (Wells and ZoBell, 1934) ZoBell and Upham, 1944. (*Achromobacter ichthyodermis* (sic) Wells and ZoBell, Proc. Nat. Acad. Sci., *20*, 1934, 123; ZoBell and Upham, Bull. Scripps Inst. Oceanography, *5*, 1944, 246 and 253.)

ich.thy.o.der'mis. Gr. *ichthys* fish; Gr. *derma* skin; M.L. *ichthyodermis* fish skin.

Small rods, 0.9 to 1.3 by 3.0 to 5.0 microns, occurring singly and in pairs. Motile, with a tuft of polar flagella. Pleomorphic forms predominate in old cultures. Encapsulated. Gram-negative.

Requires sea water following initial isolation. The following differential media are prepared with sea water:

Agar colonies: Glistening, colorless, convex, circular, 2 to 4 mm in diameter.

Agar slants: Abundant, filiform, raised, smooth, opalescent growth.

Gelatin tube: Rapid crateriform liquefaction complete in 5 days at 18° C.

Sea-water broth: Turbidity, with pellicle, little granular sediment and no odor.

Milk: No growth.

Potato: No growth unless dialyzed in sea water. Then fair growth with no pigment.

Acid from glucose, sucrose and mannitol but not from lactose or glycerol.

Starch hydrolyzed.

Ammonia liberated from peptone, but no hydrogen sulfide produced.

Indole formed in tryptophane sea-water broth.

Nitrites produced from nitrates.

Optimum temperature, between 25° and 30° C.; 37° C. incubation will kill recently isolated organisms.

Aerobic, facultative.

Source: Isolated from diseased kilifish (*Fundulus parvipinnis*).

Habitat: Skin lesions and muscle tissue of infected marine fish.

52. Pseudomonas marinoglutinosa (ZoBell and Allen, 1935) ZoBell, 1943. (*Achromobacter marinoglutinosus* (sic) ZoBell and Allen, Jour. Bact., *29*, 1935, 246; ZoBell, Jour. Bact., *46*, 1943, 45.)

ma.ri.no.glu.ti.no'sa. L. *marinus* marine; L. *glutinosus* full of glue, viscous; M.L. adj. *marinoglutinosus*. Meaning obscure.

Short rods, 0.7 to 1.0 by 1.8 to 2.4 microns, with rounded ends, occurring singly, in pairs and in clumps. Motile with polar flagella. Staining granular. Encapsulated. Gram-negative.

Gelatin stab: Moderate filiform growth with slight napiform liquefaction. No pigment.

Agar colonies: Round with concentric circles and crinkled radial lines, 1.5 to 5.0 mm in diameter. No pigment.

Agar slant: Moderate, filiform, flat. Butyrous consistency.

Broth: Moderate clouding, marked ring, adherent film of growth on test tube wall, flaky sediment.

Milk: No growth.

Potato: No growth.

Indole not produced.

Nitrites not produced from nitrates.

Hydrogen sulfide and ammonia produced from Bacto-tryptone.

Acid but no gas from xylose and dextrin. No acid from glucose, lactose, sucrose or mannitol.

Starch is hydrolyzed.

Optimum temperature, between 20° and 25° C.

Aerobic, facultative.

Source: Isolated from sea water.

Habitat: Sea water.

53. Pseudomonas membranoformis (ZoBell and Allen, 1935) ZoBell, 1943. (*Achromobacter membranoformis* ZoBell and Allen, Jour. Bact., *29*, 1935, 246; ZoBell, Jour. Bact., *46*, 1943, 45.)

mem.bra.no.for'mis. L. *membrana* a membrane; L. *forma* appearance; M.L. adj. *membranoformis* membranous.

Rods, 0.9 to 1.2 by 3.5 to 4.8 microns, occurring singly and in pairs. Motile with lophotrichous flagella. Encapsulated. Gram-negative.

Gelatin stab: Growth filiform, best at top, with slow crateriform liquefaction.

Agar colonies: Circular, 1.0 to 2.5 mm, with crinkled surface.

Agar slant: Moderate, beaded, raised growth. Membranous consistency. Becomes browned with age.

Broth: Slight turbidity, flocculent sediment, film of growth on walls of test tube.

Milk: No growth.

Potato: No growth.

Indole not produced.

Nitrites not produced from nitrates.

Hydrogen sulfide not produced.

Acid but no gas from glucose, sucrose, dextrin and mannitol. No acid from lactose or xylose.

Starch not hydrolyzed.

Optimum temperature, between 20° and 25° C.

Aerobic.

Source: Isolated from sea water.

Habitat: Sea water.

54. Pseudomonas gelatica (Gran, 1902) Bergey et al., 1930. (*Bacillus gelaticus* Gran, Bergens Museums Aarbog., 1902, 14; Bergey et al., Manual, 3rd ed., 1930, 175.)

ge.la'ti.ca. L. part.adj. *gelatus* frozen, congealed, jellied; M.L. adj. *gelaticus* resembling hardened gelatin.

Rods, with rounded ends, 0.6 to 1.2 by 1.2 to 2.6 microns, occurring singly, in pairs, and sometimes in short chains. Motile, type of flagellation not recorded. Gram-negative. All media prepared with 3 per cent salt.

Fish-gelatin colonies: Circular, transparent, glistening, becoming brownish in color.

Fish-gelatin stab: Liquefaction infundibuliform. Two varieties are recognized: one produces a green fluorescence; the other does not produce a water-soluble pigment.

Sea-weed agar colonies: Circular, flat, entire, glistening, grayish blue center with reddish brown periphery. Liquefied.

Fish-agar slant: Flat, transparent streak, with undulate margin, reddish brown to grayish white.

Broth: Turbid with flocculent pellicle and grayish yellow sediment, viscid.

Indole not produced.

Nitrites not produced from nitrates.

Starch hydrolyzed.

No action on sugars.

Aerobic, facultative.

Temperature relations: Optimum temperature, between 20° and 25° C. Maximum, between 30° and 32° C. Minimum, 0° C.

Distinctive character: Requires 3 to 4 per cent salt for growth.

Source: Isolated from sea water from the Norwegian coast.

Habitat: Probably associated with the decomposition of algae in coastal waters.

55. Pseudomonas calcis (Drew, 1912) Kellerman and Smith, 1914. (*Bacterium calcis* Drew, Yearbook Carnegie Inst. Wash., *11*, 1912, 136; Kellerman and Smith, Jour. Wash. Acad. Sci., *4*, 1914, 400.)

cal'cis. L. fem.noun *calx, calcis* limestone, chalk; L. *calcis* of limestone.

Rods, 1.1 by 1.5 to 3.0 microns, usually single but may form long chains. Actively motile with one polar flagellum. Gram-negative.

Grows best in sea water or 3 per cent salt media. Deposits $CaCO_3$.

Agar colonies: Circular, with finely irregular outline, granular appearance, elevated, spreading; old colonies having brownish tinge in center.

Gelatin stab: Infundibuliform liquefaction.

Gelatin colonies: Small, with liquefaction.

Broth: Good growth especially in presence of potassium nitrate, peptone or calcium malate.

Acid from glucose, mannitol and sucrose but not from lactose.

Nitrates reduced to nitrites and ammonia.

Aerobic, facultative.

Optimum temperature, between 20° and 28° C.

Habitat: Sea water and marine mud.

56. Pseudomonas calciprecipitans Molisch, 1925. (Cent. f. Bakt., II Abt., *65*, 1925, 130.)

cal.ci.pre.ci'pi.tans. L. *calx, calcis* lime; L. *praecipito* to throw down; M.L. part.adj. *calciprecipitans* lime-precipitating.

Thin rods, 0.5 to 0.8 by 1.5 to 3.6 microns, with rounded ends, often staining irregularly. Motile, with one polar flagellum. Gram-negative.

Gelatin colonies: Circular, light brown in color (large colonies show $CaCO_3$ crystals).

Gelatin stab: Surface growth with filiform growth in depth. Liquefaction starts at bottom.

Agar colonies (sea water); Grayish white, glistening. In two to three weeks crystals of calcium carbonate form in the agar.

Agar slant: Slight, whitish surface growth becoming thick, spreading, glistening, with abundant $CaCO_3$ crystals in medium.

Ammonia formed.

Aerobic, facultative.

Optimum temperature, 20° C.

Source: Isolated from sea water.

Habitat: Sea water.

56a. **Pseudomonas halestorga** Elazari-Volcani, 1940. (*Pseudomonas halestorgus* (sic) Elazari-Volcani, Studies on the Microflora of the Dead Sea. Thesis, Hebrew University, Jerusalem, 1940, VIII and 82.)

hal.e'stor.ga. Gr. noun *hale* salt water; Gr. adj. *storgus* loving; M.L. adj. *halestorgus* salt-water-loving.

Rods, the length of which varies greatly depending on the concentrations of salt: at 3 to 24 per cent, they are usually 0.5 by 1.3 to 4.0 microns, occurring singly and in pairs; in 0.5 and 30 per cent salt and in Dead Sea water, the rods are usually very long, twisted threads. Motile by means of a single, polar flagellum. Gram-negative.

Gelatin stab (12 per cent salt, 1 per cent proteose peptone, 15 per cent gelatin): Filiform, very slight infundibuliform liquefaction after six weeks.

Agar colonies (12 per cent salt, 1 per cent proteose peptone, 2 per cent KNO_3): Circular, smooth, entire, slightly convex, glistening, slightly transparent, grayish.

Agar slant (12 per cent salt, 1 per cent proteose peptone, 2 per cent KNO_3): Moderate, filiform, raised, smooth, slightly transparent, grayish growth.

Broth (12 per cent salt, 1 per cent peptone): Very turbid; whitish pellicle is formed.

Indole not produced.

No acid or gas from glucose, fructose, galactose, mannose, lactose, sucrose, maltose, arabinose, xylose, raffinose, inulin, dextrin, glycerol, mannitol or salicin.

Starch not hydrolyzed.

Nitrites are produced from nitrates; no gas is produced.

Aerobic.

Optimum temperature, 30° C.

Salt tolerance: Halotolerant, growing slightly in 0.5 per cent salt, strongly in 3 to 30 per cent salt and moderately in Dead Sea water.

Source: Isolated from the water of the Dead Sea.

Habitat: Found in places where the salt content of water is high.

57. **Pseudomonas iridescens** Stanier, 1941. (Jour. Bact., *43*, 1941, 542.)

ir.id.es'cens. Gr. fem.noun *iris, -idis* the rainbow; M.L. part.adj. *iridescens* showing colors of the rainbow.

Rods, 0.2 to 0.3 by 1.5 to 7.0 microns, average length 5.0 to 6.0 microns, occurring singly. Non-motile. Gram-negative.

Sea water gelatin stab: Filiform growth. Liquefaction by some strains.

Sea water agar colonies: Concave, 2 to 3 mm in diameter, smooth, glistening, translucent, pale yellow, edge irregular. After 2 to 3 days a marked iridescence. Later colonies rough, opaque, bright yellow, sunken central portion with translucent periphery.

Sea water agar slant: Growth spreading, smooth, glistening, translucent, pale yellow, iridescent, butyrous.

Sea water broth: Turbid, light yellow, granular pellicle.

Indole not produced.

Nitrites not produced from nitrates.

Hydrogen sulfide not produced.

Catalase-positive.

Urease-negative.

Acid from xylose, glucose, galactose, lactose, maltose, sucrose and cellobiose. No acid from arabinose. Starch and cellulose are attacked.

Aerobic.

Temperature relations: Optimum, 23° C. Minimum, 5° C. Maximum, 30° C.

Salt range: 0.25 to 6.0 per cent. Optimum, 1.0 to 4.0 per cent.

Source: Sea water.

Habitat: Common along the coast of the North Pacific.

58. Pseudomonas beijerinckii Hof, 1935. (Travaux botaniques néerlandais, *32*, 1935, 152.)

bei.jer.inck'i.i. M.L. gen.noun *beijerinckii* of Beijerinck; named for Prof. M. W. Beijerinck of Delft, Holland.

Small rods. Motile with polar flagella.

Gelatin: No liquefaction.

Indole not produced.

Nitrites produced from nitrates by four out of six strains.

Cellulose not decomposed.

Acid from glucose. In yeast-water with 2 per cent glucose and 12 per cent NaCl, no gas is produced.

Pigment production: Insoluble purple pigment produced but not in all media; is localized markedly; reduced oxygen tension necessary; optimum pH, 8.0; not produced in yeast-water or in peptone-water; produced only when grown in extracts of beans or some other vegetable.

Aerobic.

Source: Six strains isolated from beans preserved with salt.

Habitat: Causes purple discoloration of salted beans.

59. Pseudomonas aceris (Ark, 1939) Starr and Burkholder, 1942. (*Phytomonas aceris* Ark, Phytopath., *29*, 1939, 969; Starr and Burkholder, Phytopath., *32*, 1942, 601.)

a'ce.ris. L. *acer* the maple; L. neut. gen.noun *aceris* of the maple.

Rods 0.3 to 0.8 by 0.8 to 2.5 microns. Motile, with 1 to 2 polar flagella. Gram-negative.

Green fluorescent pigment produced.

Gelatin: Liquefied.

Beef-extract-peptone agar: Colonies are grayish white, appearing in 24 hours.

Broth: Turbid.

Milk: Clearing with no coagulation.

Nitrites produced from nitrates (Burkholder and Starr, Phytopath., *38*, 1948, 498).

Indole not produced.

Hydrogen sulfide not produced.

Acid from glucose, fructose, galactose, arabinose, xylose, sucrose, maltose, lactose, raffinose, mannitol, glycerol and dulcitol.

Slight growth in broth plus 6 per cent salt (Burkholder).

Optimum temperature, between 13° and 31° C.

Source: From diseased leaves of the large leaf maple, *Acer macrophyllum*.

Habitat: Causes a disease of *Acer spp.*

60. Pseudomonas angulata (Fromme and Murray, 1919) Holland, 1920. (*Bacterium angulatum* Fromme and Murray, Jour. Agr. Res., *16*, 1919, 219; Holland, Jour. Bact., *5*, 1920, 224.)

ang.u.la'ta. L. part.adj. *angulatus* with angles, angular.

Description from Clara (Cornell Agr. Exp. Sta. Mem. 159, 1934, 24).

Rods 0.75 to 1.5 by 1.5 to 3.0 microns. Motile, with 1 to 6 polar flagella. Gram-negative.

Gelatin: Liquefied.

Green fluorescent pigment produced.

Beef-extract agar colonies: Dull white, circular, raised, smooth and glistening.

Broth: Turbid and greenish in 36 hours.

Milk: Alkaline.

Nitrites produced from nitrates (Burkholder and Starr, Phytopath., *38*, 1948, 498).

Indole not produced.

Hydrogen sulfide not produced.

Lipolytic action negative (Starr and Burkholder, Phytopath., *32*, 1942, 601).

Acid but no gas from glucose, galactose, fructose, mannose, arabinose, xylose, sucrose and mannitol. Alkaline reaction from salts of citric, malic, succinic and tartaric acids. Rhamnose, maltose, lactose, raffinose, glycerol, salicin, and acetic, lactic and formic acids are not fermented.

Starch not hydrolyzed.

Slight growth in broth plus 5 to 6 per cent salt (Burkholder).

Aerobic, facultative.

Relationship to other species: Braun (Phytopath., *27*, 1937, 283) considers this species to be identical in culture with *Pseudomonas tabaci*, but they differ in the type of disease they produce.

Source: Isolated by Fromme and Murray from small angular leaf spots on tobacco.

Habitat: Causes the angular leaf spot of tobacco (*Nicotiana tabacum*).

61. Pseudomonas aptata (Brown and Jamieson, 1913) Stevens, 1925. (*Bacterium aptatum* Brown and Jamieson, Jour. Agr. Res., *1*, 1913, 206; Stevens, Plant Disease Fungi, New York, 1925, 22.)

ap.ta'ta. L. part.adj. *aptatus* adapted.

Rods 0.6 by 1.2 microns. Motile, with bipolar flagella. Gram-negative.

Green fluorescent pigment produced in culture.

Gelatin: Liquefied.

Agar slants: Moderate growth along streak, filiform, whitish, glistening.

Broth: Turbid, with formation of a pellicle.

Milk: Becomes alkaline and clears.

Nitrites not produced from nitrates.

Indole not produced in 10 days. Slight amount found later.

Hydrogen sulfide not produced.

Acid from glucose, galactose and sucrose. No acid from lactose, maltose or mannitol (Paine and Banfoot, Ann. Appl. Biol., *11*, 1924, 312).

Starch not hydrolyzed.

Slight growth in broth plus 7 per cent salt (Burkholder).

Temperature relations: Optimum, between 27° and 28° C. Minimum, below 1° C. Maximum, between 34° and 35° C.

Aerobic.

Source: Isolated from diseased nasturtium leaves from Virginia and diseased beet leaves from Utah.

Habitat: Pathogenic on sugar beets, nasturtiums and lettuce.

62. Pseudomonas primulae (Ark and Gardner, 1936) Starr and Burkholder, 1942. (*Phytomonas primulae* Ark and Gardner, Phytopath., *26*, 1936, 1053; Starr and Burkholder, Phytopath., *32*, 1942, 601.)

pri'mu.lae. L. dim.adj. *primulus* the first; M.L. fem.noun *Primula* generic name; M.L. gen.noun *primulae* of *Primula*.

Rods 0.51 to 0.73 by 1.0 to 3.16 microns. Motile, with a polar flagellum. Gram-negative.

Green fluorescent pigment produced in culture.

Gelatin: Liquefied.

Agar colonies: Round, convex, smooth, glistening, yellowish.

Milk: Coagulated.

Nitrites not produced from nitrates.

Indole not produced.

Hydrogen sulfide not produced.

Not lipolytic (Starr and Burkholder, Phytopath., *32*, 1942, 601).

Acid but no gas from glucose, lactose, sucrose, maltose, galactose, arabinose, glycerol, dulcitol and mannitol. Starch not hydrolyzed.

Growth in broth plus 5 per cent salt.

Temperature relations: Optimum between 19° and 22° C. Minimum, 10° C. Maximum, 34° C.

Optimum pH between 6.8 and 7.0. Minimum, between 4.5 and 5.0.

Aerobic, facultative.

Source: Isolated from leaf-spot of *Primula polyantha*.

Habitat: Pathogenic on *Primula spp*.

63. Pseudomonas viridilivida (Brown, 1915) Holland, 1920. (*Bacterium viridilividum* Brown, Jour. Agr. Res., *4*, 1915, 475; Holland, Jour. Bact., *5*, 1920, 225.)

vi.ri.di.li'vi.da. L. *viridis* green; L. *lividus* blue; M.L. adj. *viridilividus* greenish blue.

Rods 1.0 to 1.25 by 1.25 to 3.0 microns. Motile, with 1 to 3 polar flagella. Gram-negative.

Green fluorescent pigment produced in culture.

Gelatin: Slow liquefaction.

Beef agar colonies: Cream-white, round, smooth, translucent, edges entire.

Broth: Turbid, becomes lime-green.

Milk: Alkaline and clears.

Nitrites produced from nitrates (Burkholder and Starr, Phytopath., *38*, 1948, 498).

Indole produced.

Not lipolytic (Starr and Burkholder, Phytopath., *32*, 1942, 601).

Acid from glucose and sucrose (Burkholder).

Grows well in 4.5 per cent salt. Grows in 7 per cent salt (Burkholder).

Temperature relations: Minimum, 1.5° C. Maximum, 34.5° C.

Aerobic.

Source: Isolated from diseased lettuce from Louisiana.

Habitat: Pathogenic on lettuce, *Lactuca sativa*.

64. Pseudomonas delphinii (Smith, 1904) Stapp, 1928. (*Bacillus delphinii* Smith, Science, *19*, 1904, 417; Stapp, in Sorauer, Handbuch der Pflanzenkrankheiten, *2*, 5 Aufl., 1928, 106.)

del.phi′ni.i. Gr. *delphinium* the larkspur; M.L. dim.neut.noun *Delphinium* generic name; M.L. gen.noun *delphinii* of larkspur.

Rods 0.6 to 0.8 by 1.5 to 2.0 microns. Chains present. Motile, with 1 to 6 polar flagella. Encapsulated. Gram-negative.

Green fluorescent pigment produced in culture.

Gelatin: Liquefied.

Beef agar slants: Growth thin, smooth, shining, transparent, margins entire, crystals. Agar becomes dark brown.

Broth: Turbid in 24 hours with delicate pellicle.

Milk: Becomes alkaline and clears.

Nitrites produced from nitrates (Burkholder and Starr, Phytopath., *38*, 1948, 498).

Indole not produced.

Hydrogen sulfide not produced.

Lipolytic action negative (Starr and Burkholder, Phytopath., *32*, 1942, 601).

Acid from glucose, galactose and fructose; slight acid from sucrose. No acid from lactose, maltose, glycerol or mannitol.

Starch: Hydrolysis feeble.

Weak growth in broth plus 4 per cent salt.

Optimum pH, 6.7 to 7.1. pH range, 5.6 to 8.6.

Temperature relations: Optimum, 25° C. Minimum, 1° C. or less. Maximum, 30° C.

Source: Isolated from black spot of delphinium.

Habitat: Pathogenic on delphinium causing a black spot in the leaves.

65. Pseudomonas cepacia Burkholder, 1950. (Phytopath., *40*, 1950, 116.)

ce.pa′ci.a. L. fem.noun *caepa* or *cepa* onion; M.L. adj. *cepacius* of or like onion.

Rods, 0.8 by 1.0 to 2.8 microns, occurring singly or in pairs. Motile, with 1 to 3 polar flagella. Gram-negative.

Gelatin: Slow liquefaction.

Beef-extract-peptone agar: Slants sulfur-yellow, filiform, butyrous to slightly viscid. Most cultures appear rough. Yellow to yellow-green pigment diffuses into medium about the colony.

Potato dextrose agar: Pale yellow. No change in medium.

Broth: Turbid in 24 hours; yellow pellicle.

Milk: Litmus reduced. Medium clears and becomes tan with a yellow pellicle.

Krumwiede's Triple sugar agar: Growth very abundant, yellow-green and extremely wrinkled; medium becomes red.

Nitrites produced from nitrates.

Indole not produced.

Hydrogen sulfide not produced.

Acid but no gas from glucose, fructose, lactose, maltose, sucrose, arabinose, xylose, glycerol, mannitol and salicin; alkaline reaction from sodium salts of citric, hippuric, malonic and tartaric acids. Growth is slight in rhamnose. 2 per cent ethyl alcohol not utilized.

Starch not hydrolyzed.

Sodium ammonium pectate medium not liquefied.

Methyl red test negative; acetylmethylcarbinol not produced.

Growth in 3 per cent but not in 5 per cent salt.

Temperature relations: Optimum, 30° C. Minimum, between 6° and 9° C. Maximum, 42° C.

Aerobic.

Source: Seven isolates from different onion bulbs collected in New York State.

Habitat: Pathogenic on onions, *Allium cepa*.

66. Pseudomonas apii Jagger, 1921. (Jour. Agr. Res., *21*, 1921, 186.)

a′pi.i. L. *apium* celery; M.L. neut.noun *Apium* generic name of celery; M.L. neut. gen.noun *apii* of celery.

Description from Clara (Cornell Agr. Exp. Sta. Mem. 159, 1934, 24).

Rods 0.75 to 1.5 by 1.5 to 3.0 microns. Motile with a polar flagellum. Gram-negative.

Green fluorescent pigment produced in various media.

Gelatin: Liquefied.

Beef-extract agar colonies: Circular,

glistening, smooth, edges entire. Grayish white with bluish tinge.

Broth: Turbid in 36 hours. Pellicle formed.

Milk: Becomes alkaline. No curd.

Nitrites produced from nitrates (Burkholder and Starr, Phytopath., *38*, 1948, 498).

Indole not produced.

Hydrogen sulfide not produced.

Acid but no gas from glucose, galactose, fructose, mannose, arabinose, xylose, sucrose, mannitol and glycerol. Alkaline reaction from salts of acetic, citric, malic and succinic acids. Rhamnose, maltose, lactose, raffinose salicin, and formic, lactic and artaric acids are not utilized.

Starch not hydrolyzed.

Aerobic, facultative.

Distinctive character: Pathogenicity appears limited to celery.

Source: Jagger isolated this repeatedly from diseased celery leaves.

Habitat: Pathogenic on celery, *Apium graveolens*.

67. Pseudomonas asplenii (Ark and Tompkins, 1946) Săvulescu, 1947. (*Phytomonas asplenii* Ark and Tompkins, Phytopath., *36*, 1946, 760; Săvulescu, Anal. Acad. Romane, III, *22*, 1947, 11.)

a.sple′ni.i. Gr. neut.noun *asplenum* spleenwort; M.L. neut.noun *Asplenium* generic name; M.L. gen.noun *asplenii* of *Asplenium*.

Rods 0.3 to 0.5 by 1.2 to 2.4 microns. Motile, with 1 to 3 polar flagella. Gram-negative.

Gelatin: Liquefied.

Beef-extract-peptone agar slants: Grayish white with fluorescence in the medium.

Potato-dextrose-peptone agar: Growth rapid, heavy, strongly grayish white, butyrous; medium darkens with age.

Nutrient broth: Turbid in 24 hours; no pellicle.

Milk: No curd.

Indole not produced.

Nitrites not produced from nitrates.

Hydrogen sulfide not produced.

Acid but no gas from glucose, galactose, fructose, arabinose, xylose, maltose and sucrose. Slight acidity in lactose after long incubation; no acid in raffinose.

Starch not hydrolyzed.

Growth good in Fermi's, Cohn's and Uschinsky's solutions.

Temperature relations: Optimum between 22° and 30° C. Minimum, 1° C. Maximum, 34° C.

Source: Six isolates and 3 reisolates from lesions on the bird's nest fern.

Habitat: Pathogenic on the fern, *Asplenium nidus*.

68. Pseudomonas berberidis (Thornberry and Anderson, 1931) Stapp, 1935. (*Phytomonas berberidis* Thornberry and Anderson, Jour. Agr. Res., *43*, 1931, 36; Stapp, Bot. Rev., *1*, 1935, 407.)

ber.be′ri.dis. M.L. *Berberis* generic name of barberry; M.L. fem.gen.noun *berberidis* of barberry.

Rods, 0.5 to 1.0 by 1.5 to 2.5 microns, occurring singly or in pairs. Motile with 2 to 4 polar flagella. Encapsulated. Gram-negative (Burkholder); not Gram-positive as stated in original description.

Green fluorescent pigment produced in culture (Burkholder).

Gelatin: Not liquefied.

Glucose agar slants: Growth moderate, filiform at first, later beaded, raised, smooth, white. Butyrous in consistency.

Milk: Becomes alkaline. No other change.

Nitrites produced from nitrates (Burkholder and Starr, Phytopath., *38*, 1948, 498).

Indole not produced.

Hydrogen sulfide not produced.

Not lipolytic (Starr and Burkholder, Phytopath., *32*, 1942, 601).

Acid from glucose, galactose and sucrose. Maltose and rhamnose not utilized (Burkholder).

No gas from carbohydrates.

Starch not hydrolyzed.

Temperature relations: Optimum, 18° C. Minimum, 7° C. Maximum, 30° C.

Aerobic.

Source: Repeated isolations from leaves and twigs of barberry.

Habitat: Pathogenic on barberry, *Berberis thunbergerii* and *B. vulgaris*.

69. Pseudomonas coronafaciens (Elliott, 1920) Stevens, 1925. (*Bacterium corona-*

faciens Elliott, Jour. Agr. Res., *19*, 1920, 153; Stevens, Plant Disease Fungi, 1925, 27.)

co.ro.na.fa'ci.ens. L. *corona* crown; L. *facio* to make; M.L. part.adj. *coronafaciens* halo-producing.

Rods, 0.65 by 2.3 microns, occurring in chains. Motile with polar flagella. Encapsulated. Gram-negative.

Green fluorescent pigment produced in culture.

Gelatin: Slow liquefaction.

Nutrient agar colonies: White, becoming irregularly circular, flat with raised margins.

Broth: Slight turbidity in 24 hours. Heavy pellicle formed.

Milk: Alkaline. A soft curd formed followed by clearing. Curd sometimes absent.

Test for nitrites produced in nitrate broth negative or faint (Burkholder and Starr, Phytopath., *38*, 1948, 498).

Indole not produced.

Hydrogen sulfide not produced.

Not lipolytic (Starr and Burkholder, Phytopath., *32*, 1942, 601).

Acid but no gas from glucose and sucrose. Starch hydrolysis slight.

Slight growth in broth plus 2 per cent salt.

Temperature relations: Optimum between 24° and 25° C. Minimum, 1° C. Maximum, 31° C.

Comment: A variety pathogenic on brome-grass, *Bromus inermis*, has been described by Reddy and Godkin (Phytopath., *13*, 1923, 81). Produces water-soaked spots which are dark purple in color. Has been artificially inoculated on oats (*Avena sativa*). Also pathogenic on *Agropyron repens*.

Source: Numerous isolations from blighted blades of oats.

Habitat: Causes a halo spot on oats (*Avena sativa*). Artificial inoculations show barley (*Hordeum vulgare*), rye (*Secale cereale*) and wheat (*Triticum aestivum*) to be susceptible.

70. **Pseudomonas lachrymans** (Smith and Bryan, 1915) Carsner, 1918. (*Bacterium lachrymans* Smith and Bryan, Jour. Agr. Res., *5*, 1915, 466; Carsner, Jour. Agr. Res., *15*, 1918, 201.)

lach'ry.mans. L. *lacrimo* to shed tears; M.L. part.adj. *lachrymans* shedding tears.

Description from Smith and Bryan (*op. cit.*, 1915, 466) and Clara (Cornell Agr. Exp. Sta. Mem. 159, 1934, 26).

Rods 0.8 by 1.0 to 2.0 microns. Motile with 1 to 5 polar flagella. Encapsulated. Gram-negative.

Green fluorescent pigment produced in culture.

Gelatin: Liquefied.

Beef-peptone agar colonies: Circular, smooth, glistening, transparent, whitish, entire margins.

Broth: Turbid in 24 hours. White precipitate with crystals.

Milk: Turns alkaline and clears.

Nitrites not produced from nitrates.

Indole reaction weak.

Hydrogen sulfide not produced.

Not lipolytic (Starr and Burkholder, Phytopath., *32*, 1942, 601).

Acid but no gas from glucose, fructose, mannose, arabinose, xylose, sucrose and mannitol. Alkaline reaction from salts of citric, malic and succinic acids. Maltose, rhamnose, lactose, raffinose, glycerol and salicin not fermented (Clara, *op. cit.*, 1934, 26).

Starch partially digested. Not digested (Clara, *loc. cit.*).

Growth in 3 per cent salt after 12 days. No growth in 4 per cent salt.

Temperature relations: Optimum between 25° and 27° C. Minimum, 1° C. Maximum, 35° C.

Aerobic, facultative (Clara, *loc. cit.*).

Source: Isolated from diseased cucumber leaves collected in New York, Wisconsin, Indiana and in Ontario, Canada.

Habitat: Pathogenic on cucumber, *Cucumis sativus*, and related plants.

71. **Pseudomonas maculicola** (McCulloch, 1911) Stevens, 1913. (*Bacterium maculicolum* McCulloch, U. S. Dept. Agr., Bur. Plant Ind. Bul., *225*, 1911, 14; Stevens, The Fungi which cause Plant Diseases, 1913, 28.)

ma.cu.li'co.la. L. *macula* spot; L. *-cola* a dweller; M.L. noun *maculicola* spot dweller.

Rods 0.9 by 1.5 to 3.0 microns. Filaments present. Motile with 1 to 5 polar flagella. Gram-negative.

Green fluorescent pigment produced in culture.

Gelatin: Liquefied.

Beef-peptone agar colonies: Whitish, circular, shining, translucent, edges entire.

Broth: Turbid. No ring or pellicle.

Milk: Becomes alkaline and clears.

Nitrites not produced from nitrates.

Indole production feeble.

Hydrogen sulfide not produced.

Not lipolytic (Starr and Burkholder, Phytopath., *32*, 1942, 601).

Acid from glucose, galactose, xylose, sucrose, glycerol and mannitol. Alkaline reaction from salts of citric, malic, malonic and succinic acids. Salicin, maltose and salts of hippuric and tartaric acids not utilized (Burkholder).

Slight growth in broth plus 4 per cent salt (Erw. Smith, Bact. Plant Diseases, 1920, 306).

Aerobic.

Temperature relations: Optimum between 24° and 25° C. Minimum, 0° C. Maximum, 29° C.

Source: Isolated from diseased cauliflower leaves from Virginia.

Habitat: Pathogenic on cauliflower and cabbage.

72. **Pseudomonas mangiferaeindicae** Patel et al., 1948. (*Pseudomonas mangiferaeindicae* (sic) Patel, Moniz and Kulkarni, Curr. Sci., *17*, 1948, 189; Indian Phytopath., *1*, 1948, 147.)

man.gi'fe.rae.in''di.cae. M.L. fem.noun *Mangifera* mango bearer; L. adj. *indicus* of India; *mangiferaeindicae* of *Mangifera indica*.

Rods, 0.36 to 0.54 by 0.45 to 1.44 microns, occurring singly or in chains of 2 to 4. Motile with 1 or 2 polar flagella. Gram-negative.

Gelatin: Liquefied.

Nutrient agar colonies: Flat, smooth, glistening, round with entire margins, white to creamy, border deeper in color.

Potato glucose agar slants: Growth copious, raised, smooth, glistening, filiform, opalescent, butyrous, white.

Broth: Turbid with pellicle in 7 days. Slight sediment.

Milk: Litmus reduced in 7 days. Cleared with gelatinous sediment. Casein digested.

Loeffler's blood serum: Liquefied.

Uschinsky's solution: Good growth.

Nitrites not produced from nitrates.

Indole not produced.

Hydrogen sulfide produced.

Acid but no gas from glucose, lactose and sucrose. Slight growth and acid in mannitol. L-arabinose, maltose, fructose, inulin, glycerol, salicin, sodium tartrate and asparagine not utilized.

Starch hydrolyzed.

Lipase not produced.

Growth in 2 per cent salt.

Temperature relations: Optimum between 20° and 25° C. Minimum, 5° C. Maximum, 35° C.

Aerobic.

Source: Isolated from diseased leaves of mangoes.

Habitat: Pathogenic on *Mangifera indica*, *Spondias mangiferae* and *Anacardium occidentale*.

73. **Pseudomonas marginata** (McCulloch, 1921) Stapp, 1928. (*Bacterium marginatum* McCulloch, Science, *54*, 1921, 115; Jour. Agr. Res., *29*, 1924, 174; Stapp, in Sorauer, Handbuch der Pflanzenkrankheiten, *2*, 5 Aufl., 1928, 56.)

mar.gi.na'ta. L. *margino* to furnish with a border; L. part.adj. *marginatus* margined.

Rods 0.5 to 0.6 by 0.8 to 1.8 microns. Motile with 1 to 4 bipolar flagella. Encapsulated. Gram-negative.

Green fluorescent pigment produced in Uschinsky's and Fermi's solutions.

Gelatin: Liquefied.

Agar colonies: White, circular, smooth, translucent, viscid, with definite margins at first thin but later thick and contoured. Surface wrinkled.

Milk: At first slightly acid, then alkaline. Casein digested.

Nitrites not produced from nitrates.

Indole production slight.

Hydrogen sulfide production slight.

Lipolytic (Starr and Burkholder, Phytopath., *32*, 1942, 601).

Acid but no gas from glucose, lactose, sucrose and glycerol.

Starch hydrolysis feeble.

Growth in 3.5 per cent salt. No growth in 4 per cent salt.

Temperature relations: Optimum between

30° and 32° C. Minimum between 8° and 9° C. Maximum, 40° C.

pH range, 4.6 to 9.1.

Source: Repeatedly isolated from diseased gladiolus.

Habitat: Pathogenic on *Gladiolus spp.* and *Iris spp.*

74. Pseudomonas medicaginis Sackett, 1910. (Science, *31*, 1910, 553; also Colorado Agr. Exp. Sta., Bull. 158, 1910, 11.)

me.di.ca'gi.nis. Gr. *mēdice* the Median grass, alfalfa, lucerne, medic; M.L. fem. noun *Medicago* generic name of alfalfa; M.L. fem.gen.noun *medicaginis* of lucerne or alfalfa.

Rods 0.7 by 1.2 microns. Motile with 1 to 4 flagella. Filaments present. Gram-negative.

Green fluorescent pigment produced in culture.

Gelatin: Not liquefied.

Nutrient agar colonies: Growth in 24 hours whitish, glistening.

Broth: Turbid in 24 hours. Pellicle formed. Viscid sediment.

Milk: Becomes alkaline. No change.

Nitrites not produced from nitrates.

Indole not produced.

Hydrogen sulfide not produced.

Not lipolytic (Starr and Burkholder, Phytopath., *32*, 1942, 601).

Starch not hydrolyzed.

No gas from carbohydrates. Acid from sucrose.

Slight growth in broth plus 3.75 per cent salt.

Temperature relations: Optimum between 28° and 30° C. Maximum, 37.5°C.

Aerobic.

Source: Isolated from brown lesions on leaves and stems of alfalfa.

Habitat: Pathogenic on alfalfa, *Medicago sp.*

75. Pseudomonas phaseolicola (Burkholder, 1926) Dowson, 1943. (*Phytomonas medicaginis* var. *phaseolicola* Burkholder, Phytopath., *16*, 1926, 915; Dowson, Trans. Brit. Mycol. Soc., *26*, 1943, 10.)

pha.se.o.li'co.la. Gr. *phaseolus* the kidney bean; L. dim.mas.noun *phaseolus* the kidney bean; L.mas.gen.noun *phaseoli* of the bean; L. *cola* dweller; M.L. fem.noun *phaseolicola* the bean dweller.

Description from Burkholder and Zaleski (Phytopath., *22*, 1932, 85).

Rods 1.0 by 2.0 microns, sometimes slightly curved; filaments present. Motile with a polar flagellum. Gram-negative.

Green fluorescent pigment produced in culture.

Gelatin stab: Slow liquefaction.

Beef extract agar: Whitish, circular colonies, 2 mm in diameter. Edges entire.

Broth: Turbid.

Milk: Alkaline.

Nitrites not produced from nitrates.

Indole not produced.

Hydrogen sulfide not produced.

Not lipolytic (Starr and Burkholder, Phytopath., *32*, 1942, 601).

Acid but no gas from glucose, fructose, mannose, arabinose, xylose, sucrose and glycerol. No acid from rhamnose, lactose, maltose, mannitol or salicin. Alkali from salts of citric and malic acids, but not from acetic, formic, lactic or tartaric acids. Starch and cellulose not hydrolyzed.

Slight growth in broth plus 4 per cent salt.

Temperature relations: Optimum between 20° and 23° C. Minimum, 2.5° C. Maximum, 33° C. (Hedges, Jour. Agr. Res., *36*, 1928, 428).

Chemical tolerance: Optimum pH between 6.7 and 7.3. Minimum between 5.0 and 5.3. Maximum between 8.8 and 9.2 (Kotte, Phyt. Zeitsch., *2*, 1930 453).

Microaerophilic.

Source: Isolated from leaves, pod and stem of beans showing halo blight.

Habitat: Pathogenic on beans (*Phaseolus vulgaris*), the kudzu vine (*Pueraria hirsuta*) and related plants.

76. Pseudomonas pisi Sackett, 1916. (Colorado Agr. Exp. Sta., Bull. 218, 1916, 19.)

pi'si. Gr. *pisus* or *pisum* the pea; M.L. neut.noun *Pisum* generic name of the pea; M.L. neut.gen.noun *pisi* of the pea.

Rods 0.68 to 2.26 microns. Motile with a polar flagellum. Gram-negative.

Green fluorescent pigment produced in culture.

Gelatin: Liquefied.

Agar slants: Moderate growth in 24 hours, filiform, glistening, grayish white.

Broth: Turbid with a scum in 5 days.

Milk: Alkaline, soft curd, clears.

Nitrites not produced from nitrates.

Indole not produced.

Hydrogen sulfide not produced.

Not lipolytic (Starr and Burkholder, Phytopath., *32*, 1942, 601).

Acid but no gas from glucose, galactose and sucrose.

Starch not hydrolyzed.

Temperature relations: Optimum between 27° and 28° C. Minimum, 7° C. Maximum, 37.5° C.

Aerobic.

Source: Ten cultures isolated from 5 collections of diseased peas showing water-soaked lesions on stems and petioles.

Habitat: Pathogenic on garden peas, *Pisum sativum*, and field peas, *P. sativum* var. *arvense*.

77. Pseudomonas syringae van Hall, 1902. (Kennis der Bakt. Pflanzenziekte, Inaug. Diss., Amsterdam, 1902, 191.)

sy.rin'gae. Gr. *syrinx, syringis* a pipe or tube; M.L. fem.noun *Syringa* generic name of syringa or lilac; M.L. fem.gen.noun. *syringae* of the lilac.

Description from Clara (Cornell Agr. Exp. Sta. Mem. 159, 1934, 29).

Rods 0.75 to 1.5 by 1.5 to 3.0 microns. Motile with 1 or 2 polar flagella. Gram-negative.

Green fluorescent pigment produced in culture.

Gelatin: Liquefied.

Beef-extract agar colonies: Circular, grayish white with bluish tinge. Surface smooth. Edges entire or irregular.

Broth: Turbid in 36 hours. No pellicle.

Milk: Alkaline.

Nitrites not produced from nitrates.

Indole not produced.

Hydrogen sulfide not produced.

Not lipolytic (Starr and Burkholder, Phytopath., *32*, 1942, 601).

Slight growth in broth plus 4 per cent salt.

Acid but no gas from glucose, galactose, mannose, arabinose, xylose, sucrose, mannitol and glycerol. Alkaline reaction from salts of citric, malic, succinic and lactic acids. Rhamnose, maltose, lactose, raffinose, salicin, and acetic, formic and tartaric acids not fermented.

Starch not hydrolyzed.

Aerobic, facultative.

Comment: Orsini (Int .n. Bull. Plant Protect., *33*, 1942, 33) reports that a variety of this species is pathogenic on the pepper plant (*Capsicum*).

Source: Van Hall originally isolated this pathogen from lilac.

Habitat: Pathogenic on lilac, citrus, cow peas, beans, lemons, cherries and many unrelated plants.

78. Pseudomonas tomato (Okabe, 1933) Alstatt, 1944. (*Bacterium tomato* Okabe, Jour. Soc. Trop. Agr. Formosa, *5*, 1933, 32; Alstatt, U. S. Dept. Agr., Plant Dis. Rept., *28*, 1944, 530.)

to.ma'to. Am.Ind. *tomatl*; Sp. *tomate*; Eng. *tomato*; M.L. noun *tomato*.

Rods 0.69 to 0.97 by 1.8 to 6.8 microns. Motile with 1 to 3 polar flagella. Gram-negative.

Green fluorescent pigment produced in culture.

Gelatin: Slow liquefaction.

Beef-extract agar colonies: White, circular, flat and glistening.

Broth: Turbid in 24 hours. Pellicle.

Milk: Becomes alkaline and clears.

Nitrites are usually produced from nitrates.

Indole not produced.

Hydrogen sulfide not produced.

Acid but no gas from glucose, sucrose and lactose. No acid from maltose or glycerol.

Starch hydrolysis feeble.

Slight growth in 3 per cent salt.

Temperature relations: Optimum between 20° and 25° C. Maximum, 33° C.

Aerobic.

Source: Isolated from diseased tomato leaves.

Habitat: Pathogenic on tomato, *Lycopersicon esculentum*.

79. Pseudomonas atrofaciens (McCulloch, 1920) Stevens, 1925. (*Bacterium atrofaciens* McCulloch, Jour. Agr. Res., *18*, 1920, 549; Stevens, Plant Disease Fungi, New York, 1925, 22.)

at.ro.fa'ci.ens. L. *ater* black; L. *facio* to make; M.L. part.adj. *atrofaciens* blackening.
Rods 0.6 by 1.0 to 2.7 microns. Long chains formed in culture. Encapsulated. Motile with 1 to 4 polar or bipolar flagella. Gram-negative
Green fluorescent pigment produced in culture.
Gelatin: Liquefied.
Beef-peptone-agar colonies: Circular, shining, translucent, white.
Broth: Growth never heavy, slight rim, and a delicate pellicle.
Milk: Becomes alkaline and clears.
Nitrites produced from nitrates (Burkholder and Starr, Phytopath., *38*, 1948, 498).
Indole: Slight production.
Hydrogen sulfide: Slight production.
Acid but no gas from glucose, galactose and sucrose.
Starch is slightly hydrolyzed.
Temperature relations: Optimum between 25° and 28° C. Minimum below 2° C. Maximum between 36° and 37° C.
Aerobic.
Source: Isolated from diseased wheat grains collected throughout the United States and Canada.
Habitat: Causes a basal glume-rot of wheat.

80. **Pseudomonas cumini** (Kovachevski, 1936) Dowson, 1943. (*Phytomonas cumini* Kovachevski, Bull. Soc. Bot. Bulgarie, *7*, 1936, 27; Dowson, Trans. Brit. Mycol. Soc., *26*, 1943, 10.)
cu'mi.ni. Gr. *cuminum* cumin; M.L. neut.noun *Cuminum* generic name of cumin; M.L. neut.gen.noun *cumini* of cumin.
Rods, 0.5 to 0.7 by 1.0 to 3.0 microns, occurring in chains and filaments. Motile with 1 to 3 polar flagella. Gram-negative.
Green fluorescent pigment formed in culture.
Gelatin: Rapidly liquefied.
Potato agar colonies: Grayish white, circular, glistening, smooth, butyrous.
Broth: Moderate turbidity. Pseudozoogloea.
Milk: Not coagulated. Casein peptonized.
Nitrites not produced from nitrates.
Indole not produced.
Hydrogen sulfide not produced.

Acid but no gas from glucose and sucrose. No acid from lactose or glycerol. Starch not hydrolyzed.
Temperature range, 5° to 31° C.
Aerobic.
Source: Isolated from blighted cumin (*Cuminum*).
Habitat: Pathogenic on cumin and dill.

81. **Pseudomonas desaiana** (Burkholder, 1939) Săvulescu, 1947. (*B. pyocyaneus saccharum* Desai, Ind. Jour. Agr. Sci., *5*, 1935, 391; *Phytomonas desaiana* Burkholder, in Bergey et al., Manual, 5th ed., 1939, 174; Săvulescu, Anal. Acad. Romane, III, *22*, 1947 11.)
de.sai.a'na. M.L. adj. *desaianus*. Named for Prof. Desai of India.
Rods 0.6 to 1.2 by 1.2 to 2.2 microns. Motile with a polar flagellum. Gram-negative.
Green fluorescent pigment produced in culture.
Gelatin: Liquefied.
Agar colonies: Grayish blue. Raised.
Broth: Light clouding. Pellicle.
Milk: Peptonized without coagulation.
Nitrites not produced from nitrates.
Indole not produced.
Glucose, sucrose, lactose and glycerol fermented without gas.
Starch: Hydrolysis present.
Optimum temperature, 30° C.
Aerobic.
Source: Isolated from stinking rot of sugar cane in India and associated with a white non-pathogenic bacterium.
Habitat: Pathogenic on sugar cane, *Saccharum officinarum*.

82. **Pseudomonas erodii** Lewis, 1914. (Phytopath., *4*, 1914, 231.)
e.ro'di.i. Gr. *erodius* the heron; M.L. neut.noun *Erodium* generic name of heronbill; M.L. neut.gen.noun *erodii* of *Erodium*.
Rods 0.6 to 0.8 by 1.2 to 1.8 microns. Motile with 1 to 3 polar flagella. Gram-negative.
Green fluorescent pigment produced in culture.
Gelatin: Liquefied.
Agar streak: Heavy, smooth, cream-colored growth in 24 hours.
Broth: Dense clouding in 24 hours.

Milk: Turns alkaline and clears, litmus reduced.

Nitrites not produced from nitrates.

Indole produced in 14 days.

Hydrogen sulfide not produced.

Acid but no gas from glucose, sucrose, lactose and glycerol.

Temperature: No growth at 35° C.

Aerobic, obligate.

Source: Isolated from *Erodium texanum* and 4 varieties of *Pelargonium*.

Habitat: Causes a leaf spot of *Erodium texanum* and *Pelargonium spp.*

83. Pseudomonas lapsa (Ark, 1940) Starr and Burkholder, 1942. (*Phytomonas lapsa* Ark, Phytopath., *30*, 1940, 1; Starr and Burkholder, Phytopath., *32*, 1942, 601.)

lap'sa. L. v. *labor* to fall down, slip; L. part.adj. *lapsus* fallen down.

Rods 0.56 by 1.55 microns. Motile, with 1 to 4 polar flagella. Gram reaction not reported; presumably Gram-negative.

Produces fluorescence in Uschinsky's, Fermi's and Cohn's solutions.

Gelatin: Liquefied (Burkholder).

Nitrites produced from nitrates (Burkholder and Starr, Phytopath., *38*, 1948, 498).

Acid but no gas from glucose, sucrose, maltose, lactose, glycerol, arabinose, xylose, galactose, raffinose and mannitol.

Slight growth in broth plus 5 per cent salt (Burkholder).

Relationship to other species: Resembles *Pseudomonas desaiana*.

Source: Isolated from stalk rot of field corn in California; also from *Diabrotica* beetles.

Habitat: Pathogenic on corn and sugar cane.

84. Pseudomonas martyniae (Elliott, 1924) Stapp, 1928. (*Bacterium martyniae* Elliott, Jour. Agr. Res., *29*, 1924, 490; Stapp, in Sorauer, Handbuch der Pflanzenkrankheiten, *2*, 5 Aufl., 1928, 278.)

mar.tyn'i.ae. M.L. *Martynia* genus of flowering plants; M.L. gen.fem. *martyniae* of *Martynia*.

Rods, 0.59 to 1.68 microns, occurring in chains. Encapsulated. Motile with one to several bipolar flagella. Gram-negative.

Green fluorescent pigment produced.

Gelatin: Liquefied.

Beef agar colonies: White, round, smooth, glistening, raised.

Broth: Clouding in bands. Thin pellicle. Small crystals.

Milk: Soft acid curd with peptonization.

Nitrites produced from nitrates after 2 weeks.

Indole not produced.

Hydrogen sulfide production slight.

Acid but no gas from glucose, galactose, arabinose and sucrose. No acid from rhamnose, lactose, maltose, raffinose, mannitol or glycerol.

Starch hydrolysis none or feeble.

Temperature relations: Optimum, 26° C. Minimum, 1.5° C. Maximum, 37° C.

Chemical tolerance: Optimum pH, 6.0 to 6.7. pH range, 5.4 to 8.9.

Aerobic.

Source: Isolated from diseased leaves of the unicorn plant from Kansas.

Habitat: Pathogenic on *Martynia louisiana*.

85. Pseudomonas matthiolae (Briosi and Pavarino, 1912) Dowson, 1943. (*Bacterium matthiolae* Briosi and Pavarino, Atti della Reale Accad. dei Lincei Rend., *21*, 1912, 216; Dowson, Trans. Brit. Mycol. Soc., *26*, 1943, 10.)

mat.thi'o.lae. Mattioli patronymic; M.L. fem.noun *Matthiola* generic name of stock; M.L. fem.gen.noun *matthiolae* of *Matthiola*.

Rods 0.4 to 0.6 by 2.0 to 4.0 microns. Gram-positive. Gram-negative (Mushin, Proc. Roy. Soc. Victoria, *53*, 1941, 201).

Green fluorescent pigment produced in culture.

Gelatin: Liquefied.

Beef agar colonies: White, circular, slightly elevated, margins smooth.

Broth: Slightly turbid. Becomes pale green.

Milk: Coagulation with acid reaction.

Nitrites produced from nitrates (Mushin, Proc. Trans. Brit. Mycol. Soc., *26*, 1943, 10).

Hydrogen sulfide not produced.

Acid from glucose, galactose, fructose, mannose, rhamnose, glycerol, mannitol, acetic acid, citric acid, formic acid, lactic acid, malic acid and succinic acid. Feeble acid from maltose. No acid or gas from lactose, sucrose, raffinose, starch, salicin or tartaric acid (Mushin).

Temperature relations: Optimum, between 20° and 24° C. Minimum, below 0° C. Maximum, 38.5° C. (Mushin).

Limits of growth in broth are pH 4.4 to pH 9.5 (Mushin).

Aerobic.

Source: Isolated from vascular and parenchymatic disease of stocks, *Matthiola incana* var. *annua*.

Habitat: Pathogenic on stocks.

86. **Pseudomonas morsprunorum** Wormald, 1931. (*Pseudomonas mors-prunorum* (sic) Wormald, Jour. Pom. and Hort. Sci., *9*, 1931, 251.)

mors'pru.no.rum. L. *mors* death; L. *prunus* plum; M.L. fem.noun *morsprunorum* plum death.

Rods. Motile with a polar flagellum. Gram-positive (1931). Gram-negative (1932).

Gelatin: Liquefied.

Agar colonies: White.

Broth plus 5 per cent sucrose: White and cloudy.

Nitrites not produced from nitrates.

Acid but no gas from glucose, lactose, sucrose and glycerol.

Starch not hydrolyzed.

Strict aerobe.

Comment: Possibly a green fluorescent organism since it produces a faint yellow color in Uschinsky's solution.

Distinctive characters: Differs from *Pseudomonas prunicola* (*Pseudomonas syringae*) in that it produces a white cloudy growth in broth plus 5 per cent sucrose, a rapid acid production in nutrient agar plus 5 per cent sucrose, and a faint yellow or no color in Uschinsky's solution.

Source: Isolated from cankers on plum trees in England.

Habitat: Pathogenic on *Prunus spp.*

87. **Pseudomonas papulans** Rose, 1917. (Phytopath., *7*, 1917, 198.)

pa'pu.lans. L. v. *papulo* to produce pustules; L. part.adj. *papulans* producing pustules.

Rods 0.8 by 0.8 to 2.5 microns. Motile with 1 to 6 polar flagella. Gram-negative.

Green, fluorescent pigment produced in various media.

Gelatin: Liquefied.

Broth: Turbid with pellicle.

Fermi's and Uschinsky's solutions: Good growth.

Milk: Litmus reduced; no acid.

Nitrites not produced from nitrates. Nitrites produced from nitrates (Burkholder and Starr, Phytopath., *88*, 1948, 498).

Indole not produced.

Hydrogen sulfide not produced.

Acid but no gas from glucose, fructose, galactose, mannose, arabinose, xylose, sucrose, glycerol, mannitol, sorbitol, salicin and esculin.

No acid or gas from rhamnose, lactose, maltose, raffinose, trehalose, melizitose, starch, inulin, dextrin, dulcitol or arbutin.

Alkaline reaction produced in glycogen and in acetic, citric, formic, lactic, malic and succinic acids.

Temperature relations: Optimum, 27° C. Minimum, 3.5° C. Maximum, 34.5° C.

Chemical tolerance: Optimum pH, 7.0. Minimum, 5.0. Maximum, 9.4.

Source: Twenty-five cultures isolated from blisters on apples and from rough bark.

Habitat: Pathogenic on apple trees.

88. **Pseudomonas pseudozoogloeae** (Honing, 1914) Stapp, 1928. (*Bacterium pseudozoogloeae* Honing, Bull. van Het. Deli Proefstation, Medan, *1*, 1914, 7; Stapp, in Sorauer, Handbuch der Pflanzenkrankheiten, *2*, 5 Aufl., 1928, 274.)

pseu.do.zo.o.gloe'ae. Gr. *pseudes* false; Gr. *zoum* animal; Gr. *gloea* glue; M.L. fem.noun *Zoogloea* bacterial generic name; M.L. fem.gen.noun *pseudozoogloeae* of a false zoogloea.

Rods 0.7 to 1.5 by 0.9 to 2.5 microns. Chains. Motile with 1 or 2 polar flagella. Gram-negative.

Green fluorescent pigment produced in culture.

Gelatin: Liquefied.

Agar colonies: Round, flat, yellow-gray.

Broth: Moderate turbidity with pseudozoogloeae in the pellicle.

Milk: Coagulation. No clearing.

Nitrites not produced from nitrates.

Indole not produced.

Hydrogen sulfide produced.

Acid but no gas from glucose, lactose, maltose, sucrose and mannitol.

Aerobic, facultative.

Source: Isolated from the black rust of tobacco.

Habitat: Pathogenic on tobacco, *Nicotiana tabacum*.

89. **Pseudomonas rimaefaciens** Koning, 1938. (Chron. Bot., *4*, 1938, 11; Meded. Phytop. Labor, Willie Comm. Scholt., *14*, 1938, 24.)

ri.mae.fa'ci.ens. L. *rima* a crack; L. v. *facio* to make; M.L. part.adj. *rimaefaciens* making cracks.

Rods 0.6 to 2.4 microns in length. Motile with 1 to 3 flagella. Gram-negative.

Yellow-green, fluorescent, water-soluble pigment produced in culture.

Gelatin: Liquefied.

Agar colonies: Round, convex, smooth, somewhat granular with hyaline edge.

Broth: Turbid. Surface growth with a sediment in a few days.

Milk: Alkaline and clears.

Nitrites not produced from nitrates. Peptone, asparagin, urea, gelatin, nitrates and ammonium salts are sources of nitrogen.

Hydrogen sulfide not produced.

Indole production slight.

Growth with the following carbon sources plus NO_3 : glucose, sucrose, glycerol, succinates, malates, citrates and oxalates. Less growth with mannitol, fructose, galactose, lactose and salicylate. Acid is produced rom the sugars. No growth with dextrin, nulin, maltose, lactose, rhamnose, salicin, tartrates, acetates or formates.

Starch not hydrolyzed.

Aerobic.

Temperature relations: Optimum, 25° C. Very slow growth at 14° C. Maximum, about 37° C. Thermal death point between 42° and 48° C.

Relationship to other species: This may be *Pseudomonas syringae* since the characters are the same and both organisms can infect *Impatiens sp. Pseudomonas syringae* infects poplars (Elliott, Bacterial Plant Pathogens, 1930, 218).

Source: Strains of the pathogen isolated from poplar cankers in France and in the Netherlands.

Habitat: Pathogenic on *Populus brabantica, P. trichocarpa* and *P. candicans*.

90. **Pseudomonas striafaciens** (Elliott, 1927) Starr and Burkholder, 1942. (*Bacterium striafaciens* Elliott, Jour. Agr. Res., *35*, 1927, 823; Starr and Burkholder, Phytopath., *32*, 1942, 601.)

stri.a.fa'ci.ens. L. *stria* a furrow; M.L. part.adj. *striafaciens* furrowing.

Rods 0.66 by 1.76 microns. Motile with one to several flagella. Encapsulated. Gram-negative.

Green fluorescent pigment produced.

Gelatin: Liquefied.

Beef-peptone agar colonies: White, raised, margins entire or slightly undulating.

Broth: Clouding in layers. Ring and slight pellicle.

Milk: Alkaline, sometimes a soft curd which digests or clears.

Slight production of nitrites from nitrates.

Indole not produced.

Acid but no gas from glucose, fructose and sucrose. No acid from lactose, maltose, glycerol or mannitol.

Starch: Hydrolysis slight.

Optimum temperature, 22° C.

Optimum pH, between 6.5 and 7.0.

Aerobic.

Distinctive characters: Differs from *Pseudomonas coronafaciens* in that the cells are somewhat smaller and the pathogen produces a streak on oat blades instead of a halo spot.

Source: Forty cultures isolated from oats gathered in various parts of America.

Habitat: Pathogenic on cultivated oats and, to a slight degree, on barley.

91. **Pseudomonas tabaci** (Wolf and Foster, 1917) Stevens, 1925. (*Bacterium tabacum* (sic) Wolf and Foster, Science, *46*, 1917, 362; also Jour. Agr. Res., *12*, 1918, 449; Stevens, Plant Disease Fungi, New York, 1925, 36.)

ta.ba'ci. M.L. noun *tabacum* tobacco; M.L. gen.noun *tabaci* of tobacco.

Rods 1.2 by 3.3 microns. Motile with a polar flagellum. Gram-negative.

Gelatin: Liquefied.

Potato agar colonies: Grayish white, circular, raised, wet-shining, smooth.

Milk: Alkaline; clears.

Nitrites produced from nitrates (Burkholder and Starr, Phytopath., *38*, 1948, 498).

Indole not produced.

Acid from glucose, galactose, fructose, l-arabinose, xylose, sucrose, pectin, mannitol and glycerol (Braun, Phytopath., *27*, 1937, 289).

Ammonium sulfate, potassium nitrate, cystine, glutamic acid, glycine, succinimide, oxamide, acetamide and urea can be used as nitrogen sources (Braun).

Starch not hydrolyzed.

Aerobic.

Relationship to other species: Braun (*loc. cit.*) states that *Pseudomonas tabaci* and *Pseudomonas angulata* are identical in culture.

Source: Isolated from wildfire lesions and tobacco leaves in North Carolina.

Habitat: Pathogenic on tobacco, *Nicotiana tabacum*.

92. **Pseudomonas polycolor** Clara, 1930. (Phytopath., *20*, 1930, 704.)

po.ly'co.lor. Gr. *poly-* many; L. *color* color; M.L. adj. *polycolor* many colored.

Description taken from Clara (Cornell Agr. Exp. Sta. Mem. 159, 1934, 28).

Rods 0.75 to 1.2 by 1.05 to 3.0 microns. Motile with 1 or 2 polar flagella. Gram-negative.

Green fluorescent pigment produced in culture.

Gelatin: Liquefied.

Beef-extract agar colonies: Grayish white, circular, raised; thin, transparent margins.

Broth: Turbid in 36 hours with thin pellicle.

Milk: Alkaline; no curd.

Nitrites not produced from nitrates.

Indole not produced.

Hydrogen sulfide not produced.

Lipolytic (Starr and Burkholder, Phytopath., *32*, 1942, 601).

Acid but no gas from glucose, galactose,

fructose, mannose, arabinose, xylose, mannitol and glycerol. Alkaline reaction from salts of acetic, citric, malic, lactic and formic acids. Rhamnose, sucrose, maltose, lactose, raffinose and salicin not fermented.

Starch not hydrolyzed.

Aerobic, facultative.

Good growth in broth plus 7 per cent salt.

Temperature relations: Optimum between 25° and 30° C. Maximum between 37° and 39° C.

Distinctive characters: Differs from *Pseudomonas mellea* in type of lesion produced; does not digest starch nor reduce nitrates and does not form acid from lactose nor sucrose. Pathogenic for laboratory animals (Elrod and Braun, Sci., *94*, 1941, 520). Cultural characters differ from those of *Pseudomonas aeruginosa* Migula.

Source: Repeatedly isolated from leaf spot of tobacco in the Philippines.

Habitat: Pathogenic on tobacco.

93. **Pseudomonas viridiflava** (Burkholder, 1930) Clara, 1934. (*Phytomonas viridiflava* Burkholder, Cornell Agr. Exp. Sta. Mem. 127, 1930, 63; Clara, Science, *75*, 1934, 111.)

vi.ri.di.fla'va. L. *viridis* green; L. *flavus* yellow; M.L. adj. *viridiflavus* greenish yellow.

Description from Clara (Cornell Agr Exp. Sta. Mem. 139, 1934, 30).

Rods 0.75 to 1.5 by 1.5 to 3.15 microns. Motile with 1 or 2 polar flagella. Gram-negative.

Green fluorescent pigment produced in culture.

Gelatin: Liquefied.

Beef-extract agar colonies: Grayish white, margins corrugated, edges irregular.

Broth: Turbid in 36 hours.

Milk: Becomes alkaline and clears.

Nitrites not produced from nitrates.

Indole not produced.

Hydrogen sulfide not produced.

Not lipolytic (Starr and Burkholder, Phytopath., *32*, 1942, 601).

Acid but no gas from glucose, fructose, mannose, arabinose, xylose, mannitol and glycerol. Alkaline reaction from salts of acetic, citric, malic, lactic and succinic acids. Sucrose, lactose, maltose, raffinose, salicin, and salts of formic and tartaric acids not fermented.

Starch: No hydrolysis.

Growth in broth plus 5 per cent NaCl.

Aerobic, facultative.

Comment: A variety that does not grow in Uschinsky's solution and that produces colonies of an unusual shape has been isolated from the stems and leaves of blighted beans in Denmark. See Petersen (Tidsskr. f. Planteavl., *38*, 1932, 851).

Source: Two cultures isolated from spotted beans, one from England and one from Switzerland.

Habitat: Pathogenic on bean, *Phaseolus vulgaris*.

94. **Pseudomonas ananas** Serrano, 1934. (Philipp. Jour. Sci., *55*, 1934, 355.)

a'na.nas. Braz.Ind. *ananas* pineapple; M.L. indecl.neut.noun *ananas*.

Rods 0.6 by 1.8 microns. Motile with 1 to 4 polar flagella. Gram-negative.

Green fluorescent pigment produced in certain media.

Gelatin: Liquefied.

Beef-extract glucose agar colonies: White, with undulating edges, smooth to rugose, glistening to dull.

Beef-extract agar: Growth scant.

Broth: Feeble growth.

Milk: Becomes alkaline with curd.

Nitrites not produced from nitrates.

Indole not produced.

Hydrogen sulfide not produced.

Acid but no gas from glucose, xylose and mannitol. Feeble with lactose. No acid from sucrose.

Starch not hydrolyzed.

Temperature relations: Optimum between 30° and 31° C. Minimum between 7° and 10° C. Maximum, 45° C.

Aerobic.

Source: Isolated from rotted pineapples.

Habitat: Causes a rot of pineapples, *Ananas comosus*.

95. **Pseudomonas bowlesiae** (Lewis and

Watson, 1927) Dowson, 1943.* (*Phytomonas bowlesii* (sic) Lewis and Watson, Phytopath., *17*, 1927, 511; *Pseudomonas bowlesiae* Dowson, Trans. Brit. Mycol. Soc., *26*, 1943, 9.)

bow.le'si.ae. M.L. fem.n. *Bowlesia* generic name; M.L. gen.noun *bowlesiae* of *Bowlesia*.

Rods, 0.5 to 0.7 by 1.2 to 1.6 microns, occurring singly, in pairs or in short chains. Motile with bipolar flagella. Gram-negative.

Green fluorescent pigment produced in culture.

Gelatin: Liquefied.

Agar slants: Yellowish, moist, glistening and viscid.

Broth: Uniform turbidity throughout. Heavy viscous sediment in old cultures.

Milk: Alkaline; coagulation with a slow peptonization.

Nitrites produced from nitrates.

Indole produced.

Hydrogen sulfide produced.

Acid from glucose, maltose and xylose. No acid from sucrose.

Temperature relations: Optimum, 27° C. Minimum, −1° C. Maximum, 37° C.

Chemical tolerance: Optimum pH, 7.2. pH range, 4.5 to 8.6.

Aerobic.

Source: Isolated from diseased, water-soaked spots of bowlesia.

Habitat: Pathogenic on *Bowlesia septentrionalis*.

96. **Pseudomonas ligustri** (d'Oliveira, 1936) Săvulescu, 1947. (*Bacterium ligustri* d'Oliveira, Revista Agron., *24*, 1936, 434; Săvulescu, Anal. Acad. Romane, III, *22*, 1947, 11.)

li.gus'tri. L. *ligustrum* the privet; M.L. neut.noun *Ligustrum* generic name of privet; *ligustri* of the privet.

Rods 0.5 to 0.7 by 1.3 to 3.0 microns. No chains. Not encapsulated. Motile with 2 to 5 polar flagella. Gram-negative.

Green pigment produced on Dox agar and in broth.

Gelatin: Liquefied.

---

* The authors of this binomial report (personal communication) that the original spelling *bowlesii* used for the specific epithet is an orthographic error. The correct spelling is "*bowlesiae*".

Beef-extract agar colonies: Growth moderate. Milky white, circular, convex.

Broth: Turbid in 24 hours. No pellicle.

Milk: Coagulated in 6 days and later digested. Litmus slightly acid.

Nitrites not produced from nitrates.

Indole not produced.

Ammonia not produced.

No gas from carbohydrates. Acid from glucose, galactose, arabinose and mannose. No acid from sucrose, maltose, lactose, raffinose, mannitol or salicin.

Source: From diseased Japanese privet in Lisbon, Portugal.

Habitat: Pathogenic on privet, *Ligustrum japonicum*.

97. Pseudomonas marginalis (Brown, 1918) Stevens, 1925. (*Bacterium marginale* Brown, Jour. Agr. Res., *13*, 1918, 386; Stevens, Plant Disease Fungi, New York, 1925, 30; *Phytomonas intybi* Swingle, Phytopath., *15*, 1925, 730.)

mar.gi.na'lis. L. *margo, marginis* edge, margin; M.L. adj. *marginalis* marginal.

Description from Brown (*op. cit.*, 1918, 386) and Clara (Cornell Agr. Exp. Sta. Mem. 159, 1934, 27).

Rods. Motile with 1 to 3 polar flagella. Gram-negative.

Green fluorescent pigment produced in culture.

Gelatin: Liquefied.

Agar colonies: Cream-colored to yellowish.

Broth: Turbid, with pellicle.

Milk: Alkaline. Soft curd at times.

Nitrites are produced from nitrates. Not produced (Clara).

Indole not produced.

Hydrogen sulfide not produced.

Acid but no gas from glucose, galactose, fructose, mannose, arabinose, xylose, rhamnose, mannitol and glycerol. Alkali from salts of acetic, citric, malic, formic, lactic, succinic and tartaric acids. Sucrose, maltose, lactose, raffinose and salicin not fermented (Clara).

Starch hydrolysis feeble. None (Clara).

Temperature relations: Optimum between 25° and 26° C. Minimum, 0° C. Maximum, 38° C.

Aerobic.

Source: Isolated from marginal lesion on lettuce from Kansas.

Habitat: Pathogenic on lettuce and related plants.

98. Pseudomonas sesami Malkoff, 1906. (Cent. f. Bakt., II Abt., *16*, 1906, 665.)

se'sa.mi. Gr. *sesamum* sesame; M.L. neut.noun *Sesamum* generic name of sesame; *sesami* of sesame.

Description from Nakata (Ann. Phyt. Soc. Japan, *2*, 1930, 242).

Rods 0.6 to 0.8 by 1.2 to 3.8 microns. Motile with 2 to 5 polar flagella. Gram-negative.

Green fluorescent pigment produced in culture.

Gelatin: Liquefaction rapid.

Beef-agar colonies: Circular, flat, striate, smooth, entire margins, white.

Broth: Growth rapid. No pellicle.

Milk: Alkaline. No coagulation.

Nitrites not produced from nitrates.

Indole not produced.

Hydrogen sulfide not produced.

Acid but no gas from glucose. No acid from lactose, sucrose or glycerol.

Starch not hydrolyzed.

Temperature relations: Optimum, 30° C. Minimum, 0° C. Maximum, 35° C.

Aerobic, facultative.

Source: Isolated from brown spots on leaves and stems of sesame.

Habitat: Pathogenic on sesame.

99. Pseudomonas setariae (Okabe, 1934) Săvulescu, 1947. (*Bacterium setariae* Okabe, Jour. Soc. Trop. Agr. Formosa, *6*, 1934, 63; Săvulescu, Anal. Acad. Romane, III, *22*, 1947, 11.)

se.ta'ri.ae. L. *saeta* a bristle; M.L. *saetarius* bristle-like; M.L. fem.noun *Setaria* generic name of foxtail; *setariae* of *Setaria*.

Rods 0.4 to 0.8 by 1.8 to 4.4 microns. Motile with a polar, seldom bipolar, flagellum. Gram-negative.

Yellowish, water-soluble pigment produced in culture.

Gelatin: Slow liquefaction.

Beef-extract agar colonies: Circular, white, opalescent, smooth, glistening.

Broth: Turbid after 18 hours. Pellicle.

Milk: Alkaline; clears.

Nitrites produced from nitrates.

Indole produced.

Hydrogen sulfide not produced.

Acid but no gas from glucose, galactose and glycerol. No acid from lactose, maltose or sucrose.

Starch: Feeble hydrolysis.

Grows in 3 per cent salt.

Temperature relations: Optimum between 31° and 34° C. Maximum, 42° C.

Aerobic.

Source: Isolated from brown stripe of Italian millet.

Habitat: Pathogenic on Italian millet, *Setaria italica*.

100. Pseudomonas tolaasii Paine, 1919. (Ann. Appl. Biol., *5*, 1919, 210.)

to.laa'si.i. Tolaas patronymic; *tolaasii* of Tolaas.

Rods 0.4 to 0.5 by 0.9 to 1.7 microns. Motile with 1 to 5 polar flagella. Gram-negative.

Green fluorescent pigment produced in culture.

Gelatin: Liquefied.

Bouillon agar: Streak develops in 24 hours, dirty bluish white, wet-shining and slightly raised.

Broth: Turbid in 24 hours. Pellicle.

Milk: Becomes alkaline and clears.

Nitrites not produced from nitrates.

Indole production slight.

Acid but no gas from glucose. No acid from lactose or sucrose.

Starch hydrolysis feeble.

Optimum temperature, 25° C.

Source: Isolated in England from brown-spot of cultivated mushrooms.

Habitat: Pathogenic on cultivated mushrooms.

101. Pseudomonas washingtoniae (Pine 1943) Elliott 1951. (*Phytomonas washingtoniae* Pine, Phytopath., *33*, 1943, 1203; Elliott, Man. Bact. Plant Path., 2nd ed., 1951, 100.)

wash.ing.to'ni.ae. M.L. fem.noun *Washingtonia* a generic name; *washingtoniae* of *Washingtonia*.

Rods, 0.69 by 1.61 microns, occurring singly or in short chains. Motile with 1 to 3 polar flagella. Gram-negative.

Green pigment in certain media.

Gelatin: Liquefied.

Potato dextrose agar colonies: Circular, smooth, convex, glistening, white to cream, butyrous, edges entire.

Milk: No curd; peptonization with a green color in 7 days.

Indole not produced.

Nitrites not produced from nitrates.

Hydrogen sulfide produced in minute amounts.

Acid but no gas from glucose, fructose and L-arabinose in 24 hours; from galactose and xylose in 48 hours. No acid from sucrose, lactose, cellobiose, maltose, mannitol, D-sorbitol, glycerol, salicin or raffinose.

Starch not hydrolyzed.

Aerobic.

Thermal death point between 47° and 48° C.

Source: Isolated from spots on the leaves of the palm, *Washingtonia filifera*.

Habitat: Pathogenic on the Washington palm.

102. Pseudomonas barkeri (Berridge, 1924) Clara, 1934. (Bacillus of pear blossom disease, Barker and Grove, Ann. Appl. Biol., *1*, 1914, 94; Barker and Grove's organism, Doidge, Ann. Appl. Biol., *4*, 1917, 50; *B. barkeri* Berridge, Ann. Appl. Biol., *11*, 1924, 73; Clara, Science, *75*, 1934, 11.)

bar'ker.i. M.L. gen.noun *barkeri* of Barker; named for B. T. P. Barker, one of the two men who first described this organism.

Description from Doidge (*op. cit.*, 1917, 50).

Rods 0.5 to 0.8 by 2.0 to 4.0 microns. Motile with 1 to 4 polar flagella. Gram-negative (Burkholder), not Gram-positive.

Green fluorescent pigment produced in culture.

Gelatin: Liquefied.

Agar: Growth is white, feeble, flat, glistening, smooth-edged.

Broth: Slightly turbid in 24 hours.

Milk: Slowly cleared.

Nitrites not produced from nitrates.

Indole not produced unless culture warmed.

Starch slowly digested.

Source: Barker made many cultures from blighted pear blossoms. Doidge received a culture from Barker.

Habitat: Causes a blossom blight of pear.

103. Pseudomonas betle (Ragunathan, 1928) Burkholder, 1948. (*Bacterium betle* Ragunathan, Ann. Roy. Gard., Peradeniya, Ceylon, *11*, 1928, 51; Burkholder, in Manual, 6th ed., 1948, 130.)

bet'le. Malayan noun *betle* betel; M.L. indeclin.noun *betle*.

Rods, 0.5 by 1.5 to 2.5 microns, occurring singly or in short chains. Non-motile. Gram-negative.

Green pigment formed in nutrient gelatin and in broth.

Gelatin: Liquefied.

Bovril agar colonies: Honey-yellow, circular at first, later echinulate. Raised, smooth and shiny.

Broth: Surface becomes cloudy in 2 days. Pellicle.

No gas from lactose, maltose or sucrose.

Starch is reduced.

Aerobic.

Source: Five cultures isolated from leaf spots on the betel vine.

Habitat: Pathogenic on the betel vine, *Piper belle.*

104. Pseudomonas gladioli Severini, 1913. (Annali d. Bot., Rome, *11*, 1913, 420.)

gla.di'o.li. L. *gladiolus* a small sword lily; M.L. mas.n. *Gladiolus* generic name of gladiolus; M.L. gen.noun *gladioli* of gladiolus.

Rods 0.6 by 2.3 to 2.8 microns. Motile with one or more polar flagella. Gram-negative.

A pale yellow, water-soluble pigment found, later orange.

Gelatin colonies: Cream-colored, wartlike. Rapid liquefaction.

Milk: Coagulated and slowly peptonized.

Nitrites not produced from nitrates.

Indole not produced.

No gas.

Aerobic.

Optimum temperature between 28° and 30° C.

Habitat: Causes a corm rot of gladiolus and other tubers.

105. Pseudomonas mellea Johnson, 1923. (Jour. Agr. Res., *23*, 1923, 489.)

mel'le.a. L. adj. *melleus* pertaining to honey.

Rods 0.6 by 1.8 microns. Encapsulated. Motile with 1 to 7 polar flagella. Gram-negative.

Green fluorescent pigment produced in culture.

Gelatin: Liquefied.

Potato-glucose agar: Growth abundant, smooth, glistening, viscid, honey-colored.

Broth: Turbid in 24 hours. Pellicle.

Milk: Alkaline; clears.

Nitrites not produced from nitrates.

Indole not produced.

Hydrogen sulfide not produced.

Starch hydrolysis feeble.

Growth inhibited by 4 per cent salt.

Temperature relations: Optimum between 26° and 28° C. Maximum, 36° C.

Aerobic, facultative.

Distinctive character: Differs from *Pseudomonas pseudozoogloeae* in that it produces on tobacco a brown instead of a black spot with a halo, is orange-yellow in culture, and turns milk alkaline.

Source: Isolated from brown rusty spots on tobacco in Wisconsin.

Habitat: Pathogenic on leaves of tobacco, *Nicotiana tobacum.*

106. Pseudomonas panacis (Nakata and Takimoto, 1922) Dowson, 1943. (*Bacterium panaxi* Nakata and Takimoto, Bull. Agr. Sta. Chosen, *5*, 1922, 1; Dowson, Trans. Brit. Mycol. Soc., *26*, 1943, 10.)

pa'na.cis. Gr. *panax* the plant heal-all; M.L. neut.noun *Panax* a generic name; M.L. gen.noun *panacis* of *Panax*.

Description from Elliott (Bact. Plant Pathogens, 1930, 173).

Rods 0.5 by 1.3 to 1.5 microns. Chains. Motile with 4 to 6 polar flagella. Gram-negative.

Green fluorescent pigment produced in culture.

Gelatin: Slight liquefaction.

Agar colonies: White.

Milk: Coagulated.

No gas from sugars.

Habitat: Causes a root rot of ginseng, *Panax quinquefolium.*

107. Pseudomonas ribicola Bohn and Maloit, 1946. (Jour. Agr. Res., *73*, 1946, 288.) ri.bi'co.la. M.L. noun *Ribes* generic name of currant; L. *colo* to dwell; M.L. fem.n. *ribicola* the currant dweller.

Rods, 0.4 to 0.9 by 0.9 to 1.7 microns, occurring singly, in pairs and in hypha-like chains. Motile by 1 or more polar flagella. Gram-negative.

Gelatin: Very slow liquefaction.

Beef-extract agar colonies: Punctiform, smooth, translucent, white; edges entire.

Beef-extract agar slant: Growth scant, filiform, glistening, translucent, white, slightly viscid.

Broth: Slightly turbid; no ring or pellicle.

Potato dextrose slants: Growth moderate, filiform, glistening, butyrous to viscid. Medium slightly yellow. Dirty pink pigment in old cultures.

Milk: Slightly darkened, becoming alkaline.

Nitrites produced from nitrates.

Growth good in Uschinsky's and Fermi's solutions; yellow-green pigment produced. No growth in Cohn's and Ashby's mannitol solutions.

Indole not produced.

Hydrogen sulfide not produced.

Acid from glucose, galactose, fructose, xylose and mannitol.

Starch not hydrolyzed.

Asparagine utilized as a carbon-nitrogen source. Tyrosine oxidized.

Not lipolytic.

Temperature relations: Optimum, between 20° and 25° C. Minimum, less than 3.5° C. Maximum, between 30° and 32° C.

Source: Six single-cell isolates from leaf spot of golden currant in Wyoming.

Habitat: Pathogenic on *Ribes aureum.*

108. Pseudomonas xanthochlora (Schuster, 1912) Stapp, 1928. (*Bacterium xanthochlorum* Schuster, Arbeit. a. d. Kaiserl. Biolog. Anstalt. f. Land. u. Forstw., *8*, 1912, 452; Stapp, in Sorauer, Handbuch der Pflanzenkrankheiten, *2*, 5 Aufl., 1928, 213.) xan.tho.chlō'ra. Gr. *xanthus* yellow; Gr.

chlorus green; M.L. adj. *xanthochlorus* yellowish green.

Description from Erw. Smith (Bacteria in Rel. to Plant Dis., *3*, 1914, 272).

Rods 0.75 to 1.5 by 3.0 microns. Motile with 1 to 3 polar flagella. Gram-negative.

Green fluorescent pigment produced in culture.

Gelatin: Slow liquefaction.

Agar colonies: Circular, slightly raised, yellow-white.

Broth: Strong clouding in 24 hours. A white pellicle.

Milk: Slow coagulation and clearing.

Nitrites produced from nitrates.

Indole produced after 10 days.

Hydrogen sulfide produced slowly.

Acid but no gas from glucose and galactose.

Temperature relations: Optimum, 27° C. Minimum, 2° C. Maximum, 44° C.

Source: Isolated from rotting potato tubers in Germany.

Habitat: Pathogenic on potato tubers and a number of unrelated plants.

109. Pseudomonas aleuritidis (McCulloch and Demaree, 1932) Stapp, 1935. (*Bacterium aleuritidis* McCulloch and Demaree, Jour. Agr. Res., *45*, 1932, 339; Stapp, Bot. Rev., *1*, 1935, 408.) a.leu.ri'ti.dis. Gr. *aleurites* of wheaten flour; M.L. fem.noun *Aleurites* generic name; M.L. gen.noun *aleuritidis* of *Aleurites.*

Rods 0.6 to 0.7 by 1.1 to 3.0 microns. Motile with 1 to 5 polar, rarely bipolar, flagella. Encapsulated. Gram-negative.

Green fluorescent pigment produced in certain media.

Gelatin: Not liquefied.

Beef agar slants: Growth is thin, white and viscid.

Broth: A heavy white surface growth in 24 hours. Sediment.

Milk: Becomes alkaline, but no separation.

Nitrites produced from nitrates.

Indole test feebly positive.

Hydrogen sulfide test feebly positive.

Acid but no gas from glucose, galactose and glycerol. Slow acid production from sucrose, maltose and lactose.

Starch hydrolysis feeble.

Temperature relations: Optimum between 27° and 28° C. Maximum, 37° C.

Chemical tolerance: Optimum pH between 6.2 and 6.8. pH range, 5.4 to 8.9.

Source: Isolations from naturally infected tung oil trees in Georgia.

Habitat: Pathogenic on the tung oil tree (*Aleurites fordi*), on the bean (*Phaseolus vulgaris*) and the castor bean (*Ricinus communis*).

110. Pseudomonas glycinea Coerper, 1919. (Jour. Agr. Res., *18*, 1919, 188.)

gly.ci'ne.a. Gr. *glycys* sweet; M.L. fem.noun *Glycine* generic name of a legume; M.L. adj. *glycinea* of the soybean.

Rods 1.2 to 1.5 by 2.3 to 3.0 microns. Motile with polar flagella. Gram-negative.

Green fluorescent pigment produced in culture.

Gelatin: Not liquefied.

Beef-peptone agar colonies: Appear in 24 hours. Circular, creamy white, smooth, shining and convex. Margins entire. Butyrous in consistency.

Milk: Litmus turns blue and later a separation of the milk occurs. Casein not digested.

Nitrites produced from nitrates (Burkholder and Starr, Phytopath., *38*, 1948, 498).

Indole test feebly positive.

Not lipolytic (Starr and Burkholder, Phytopath., *32*, 1942, 601).

Acid from glucose and sucrose.

Starch not hydrolyzed.

Temperature relations: Optimum between 24° and 26° C. Minimum, 2° C. Maximum, 35° C.

Aerobic, facultative.

Comment: A variety of this species that differs slightly in morphology, action in milk and in chromogenesis has been described by Takimoto (Jour. Plant Prot., Tokyo, *14*, 1927 556). It was isolated from leaf spots on soy bean in Formosa.

Source: A number of cultures isolated from soybeans in Wisconsin.

Habitat: Pathogenic on soybean, *Glycine max* (*Soja max*).

111. Pseudomonas savastanoi (Erw. Smith. 1908) Stevens, 1913. (*Bacterium savastanoi* Erw. Smith, U. S. Dept. Agr. Plant Ind. Bull. 131, 1908, 31; Stevens, The Fungi which Cause Plant Diseases, 1913, 33.)

sa.vas.ta'no.i. Savastano patronymic; *savastanoi* of Savastano.

Description from Brown (Jour. Agr. Res., *44*, 1932, 711).

Rods 0.4 to 0.8 by 1.2 to 3.3 microns. Motile with 1 to 4 polar flagella. Gram-negative.

Green fluorescent pigment found in culture.

Gelatin: No liquefaction.

Beef agar colonies: White, smooth, flat, glistening, margins erose or entire.

Broth: Turbid on the second day. No pellicle or ring.

Milk: Becomes alkaline.

Nitrites not produced from nitrates.

Hydrogen sulfide not produced.

Acid but no gas from glucose, galactose and sucrose.

Starch hydrolyzed.

Temperature relations: Optimum between 23° and 24° C. Minimum, 1° C. Maximum, 32° C.

Chemical tolerance: Optimum between 6.8 and 7.0. Minimum, 5.6. Maximum, 8.5.

Aerobic.

Comment: A variety that differs but slightly from this species is described as pathogenic on ash, *Fraxinus excelsior* and *F. americana*, but not on olive. Produces a canker on ash. See Brown (Jour. Agr. Res., *44*, 1932, 721).

Source: Smith isolated his cultures from olive galls collected in California.

Habitat: Pathogenic on olive.

112. Pseudomonas tonelliana (Ferraris, 1926) Burkholder, 1948. (*Bacterium tonellianum* Ferraris, Trattato di Patologia e Terapia Vegetale, 3rd ed., *1*, 1926, 104; Burkholder, in Manual, 6th ed., 1948, 132.)

to.nel.li.a'na. M.L. adj. *tonellianus* pertaining to Tonelli; named for A. Tonelli.

Description from C. O. Smith (Phytopath., *18*, 1928, 503) unless otherwise noted.

Rods 0.5 to 0.6 by 1.5 to 2.5 microns. Motile with 1 to 3 polar flagella. Gram-negative (Adam and Pugsley, Jour. Dept. Agr. Victoria, *32*, 1934, 304).

Gelatin: No liquefaction.

Potato glucose agar colonies: Flat, circular, shining; margins somewhat undulated.

Broth: Dense clouding with partial pellicle.

Milk: Alkaline. No separation.

Nitrites not produced from nitrates (Adam and Pugsley).

Indole produced. Not produced (Adam and Pugsley).

Acid but no gas from glucose and sucrose. No acid from lactose (Adam and Pugsley).

Starch not hydrolyzed (Adam and Pugsley).

Comment: *Pseudomonas savastanoi* is similar in culture but is not pathogenic on oleanders.

Source: Both Ferraris and C. O. Smith isolated the pathogen from galls on oleander.

Habitat: Pathogenic on oleander, *Nerium oleander*.

113. Pseudomonas cissicola (Takimoto, 1939) Burkholder, 1948. (*Aplanobacter cissicola* Takimoto, Ann. Phytopath. Soc. Japan, *9*, 1939, 43; Burkholder, in Manual, 6th ed., 1948, 134.)

cis.si′co.la. Gr. *cissus* ivy; M.L. fem.noun *Cissus* generic name of flowering plant; L. *-cola* dweller; M.L. fem.noun *cissicola* *Cissus* dweller.

Rods 0.5 to 0.9 by 1.0 to 2.0 microns. Non-motile. Encapsulated. Gram-negative.

Green fluorescent pigment formed in Uschinsky's solution.

Gelatin: No liquefaction.

Potato-extract agar colonies: Circular, convex, smooth, dirty white.

Broth: Feeble clouding followed by precipitation of pellicle and rim.

Nitrites not produced from nitrates.

Indole not produced.

Hydrogen sulfide not produced.

No acid nor gas from sucrose, glucose, lactose or glycerol.

Starch not hydrolyzed.

Salt toleration, 3 per cent.

Temperature relations: Optimum, 30° C. Minimum, 10° C. Maximum, 35° C. Thermal death point between 49° and 50° C.

Source: Isolated from black spots on leaves of Japanese ivy, *Cissus japonica*, in Japan.

Habitat: Pathogenic only on *Cissus japonica*.

114. Pseudomonas calendulae (Takimoto, 1936) Dowson, 1943. (*Bacterium calendulae* Takimoto, Ann. Phytopath. Soc. Japan, *5*, 1936, 341; Dowson, Trans. Brit. Mycol. Soc., *26*, 1943, 9.)

ca.len′du.lae. L. fem.pl.noun *calendae* (*Kalendae*) The Calends, first day of month; M.L. fem.dim.noun *Calendula* generic name of a flowering plant; M.L. gen.noun *calendulae* of *Calendula*.

Rods 0.5 by 1.0 to 2.0 microns. Motile with 1 to 3 polar flagella. Gram-negative.

Green fluorescent pigment produced in Uschinsky's and in Cohn's solutions.

Gelatin: Not liquefied.

Agar colonies: Circular, smooth, flat, dirty white.

Broth: Turbid.

Milk: No coagulation.

Nitrites not produced from nitrates.

Indole produced in small amount.

Hydrogen sulfide not produced.

Acid but no gas from glucose and glycerol. No acid from lactose or sucrose.

Starch not hydrolyzed.

Temperature relations: Optimum between 27° and 30° C. Minimum between 0° and 7° C. Maximum, 37° C.

Habitat: Pathogenic on marigolds, *Calendula officinalis*.

115. Pseudomonas cichorii (Swingle, 1925) Stapp, 1928. (*Phytomonas cichorii* Swingle, Phytopath., *15*, 1925, 730; Stapp, in Sorauer, Handbuch der Pflanzenkrankheiten, *2*, 5 Aufl., 1928, 291; *Pseudomonas endiviae* Kotte, Phyt. Ztschr., *1*, 1930, 609; *Bacterium formosanum* Okabe, Jour. Soc. Trop. Agr., Formosa, *7*, 1935, 65.)

ci.cho′ri.i. Gr. *cichora* (pl.) succory, chicory; L. *cichorium* chicory; M.L. neut.noun *Cichorium* generic name of flowering plant; M.L. gen.noun *cichorii* of chicory.

Description from Clara (Cornell Agr. Exp. Sta. Mem. 159, 1934, 26) which is a description of a culture of *Pseudomonas endiviae* from Kotte. Swingle's description is very meager.

Rods 0.75 to 1.5 by 1.5 to 3.75 microns. Motile with 1 or 2 polar flagella. Gram negative.

Green fluorescent pigment produced in culture.

Gelatin: No liquefaction.

Beef-extract agar colonies: Circular, grayish white with bluish tinge, raised with slightly irregular edges.

Broth: Turbid in 36 hours with a smooth, viscous pellicle.

Milk: Alkaline.

Nitrites not produced from nitrates.

Indole not produced.

Hydrogen sulfide not produced.

Not lipolytic (Starr and Burkholder, Phytopath., *32*, 1942, 601).

Acid but no gas from glucose, galactose fructose, mannose, arabinose, xylose, mannitol and glycerol. Alkaline production from salts of acetic, citric, lactic, malic, succinic and tartaric acids. Rhamnose, maltose, sucrose, lactose, raffinose and salicin not utilized.

Starch not hydrolyzed.

Slight growth in broth plus 6 per cent NaCl.

Chemical tolerance: Optimum pH, between 6.8 and 7.1. Minimum, between 5.0 and 5.3. Maximum, between 9.2 and 9.4. (Kotte, *op. cit.*, *2*, 1930, 453).

Aerobic, facultative.

Source: Isolated from rot of French endive, *Cichorium intybus*, by Swingle and by Okabe, and from *C. endivia* by Kotte.

Habitat: Pathogenic on endive, lettuce and larkspur.

116. **Pseudomonas nectarophila** (Doidge, 1917) Rosen and Bleeker, 1933. (*Bacterium nectarophilum* Doidge, Ann. Appl. Biol., *4*, 1917, 73; Rosen and Bleeker, Jour. Agr. Res., *46*, 1933, 98.)

nec.ta.ro'phi.la. Gr. *nectar* nectar; Gr. adj. *philus* loving; M.L. adj. *nectarophilus* nectar-loving.

Rods 0.5 to 0.7 by 0.6 to 1.5 microns. Motile with 1 to 5 polar flagella. Encapsulated. Gram-negative.

Green fluorescent pigment produced in culture.

Gelatin: No liquefaction.

Nutrient agar colonies: Yellowish white, wet-shining, smooth; margins irregular.

Broth: Heavy turbidity in 24 hours. Sediment.

Milk: Cleared.

Nitrites not produced from nitrates.

Indole not produced.

Acid from glucose and galactose. No acid from sucrose.

Starch hydrolysis feeble.

Optimum temperature between 25° and 30° C.

Aerobic, facultative.

Distinctive character: Differs from *Pseudomonas barkeri* in that it does not liquefy gelatin nor produce indole. Produces capsules.

Source: Isolated from blighted pear blossoms in South Africa.

Habitat: Pathogenic on pear blossoms.

117. **Pseudomonas viburni** (Thornberry and Anderson, 1931) Stapp, 1935. (*Phytomonas viburni* Thornberry and Anderson, Phytopath., *21*, 1931, 912; Stapp, Bot. Rev. *1*, 1935, 407.)

vi.bur'ni. L. *viburnum* way-faring tree; M.L. neut.noun *Viburnum* name of a genus of flowering plants; M.L. gen.noun *viburni* of *Viburnum*.

Rods 0.5 to 1.0 by 1.0 to 2.0 microns. Encapsulated. Motile with 2 to 4 polar flagella. Gram-negative (Burkholder); not Gram-positive as stated in original.

Green fluorescent pigment produced in culture (Burkholder).

Gelatin: No liquefaction.

Glucose beef-extract colonies: Dull gray, circular, edges entire.

Broth: Turbid with pellicle.

Milk: Alkaline.

Nitrites not produced from nitrates.

Indole not produced.

Hydrogen sulfide not produced.

Not lipolytic (Starr and Burkholder, Phytopath., *32*, 1942, 601).

Acid from glucose and galactose but not sucrose (Burkholder).

Starch: No hydrolysis.

Slight growth in 3.5 per cent salt (Burkholder).

Temperature relations: Optimum, 25° C. Minimum, 12° C. Maximum, 35° C.

Aerobic.

Source: Isolated from angular leaf spots and stem lesions on arrow-wood, *Viburnum opulus*, etc.

Habitat: Pathogenic on *Viburnum spp.*

118. Pseudomonas mori (Boyer and Lambert, 1893) Stevens, 1913. (*Bacterium mori* Boyer and Lambert, Compt. rend. Acad. Sci., Paris, *117*, 1893, 342; *Bacterium mori* Boyer and Lambert *emend.* Erw. Smith, Science, *31*, 1910, 792; Stevens, The Fungi which Cause Plant Diseases, 1913, 30.)

mo'ri. Gr. *morum* the black mulberry; M.L. fem.noun *Morus* the generic name of mulberry; M.L. gen.noun *mori* of the mulberry.

Description from Smith (*op. cit.*, 1910, 792).

Rods 0.9 to 1.3 by 1.8 to 4.5 microns. Motile with a polar flagellum. Gram-negative.

Green fluorescent pigment produced in culture.

Gelatin: Not liquefied.

Agar colonies: White, slow-growing, smooth, flat; edges entire, becoming undulate.

Milk: Becomes alkaline and clears.

Nitrites not produced from nitrates.

Indole test negative or feebly positive.

Hydrogen sulfide not produced (Okabe, Jour. Soc. Trop. Agr., *5*, 1933, 166).

No growth in broth plus 4 per cent salt (Okabe, *loc. cit.*).

No gas from carbohydrates.

Temperature range, 1° C. to 35° C.

Source: Smith isolated the pathogen from blighted shoots of mulberry from Georgia. Also received cultures from Arkansas and the Pacific Coast.

Habitat: Pathogenic on mulberry, *Morus*.

119. Pseudomonas stizolobii (Wolf, 1920) Stapp, 1935. (*Aplanobacter stizolobii* Wolf, Phytopath., *10*, 1920, 79; Stapp, Bot. Rev., *1*, 1935, 405.)

sti.zo.lo'bi.i. Gr. *stizo* to prick, tattoo; Gr. dim. *lobium* a small lobe; M.L. neut.noun *Stizolobium* plant generic name; M.L. gen.noun *stizolobii* of *Stizolobium*.

Rods 0.6 to 0.7 by 1.0 to 1.6 microns. Non-motile (Wolf, *op. cit.*, 1920, 79). Motile

with a short polar flagellum (McCulloch, Phytopath., *18*, 1928, 460). Encapsulated. Gram-negative.

Gelatin: No liquefaction.

Agar colonies: Circular, smooth, white, raised and opaque. Margins entire to slightly undulate.

Broth: Slightly turbid throughout. No pellicle or ring.

Milk: Alkaline.

Nitrites not produced from nitrates.

Indole not produced.

No acid or gas in peptone broth plus sugars.

Starch not hydrolyzed.

Optimum temperature between 25° and 28° C.

Distinctive characters: Differs from *Pseudomonas sojae* (*Pseudomonas glycinea*) in the smaller size of cell, the absence of a pellicle and dense clouding of broth. The pathogen does not infect soybean.

Source: Isolated from the leaf spot of velvet bean.

Habitat: Pathogenic on velvet bean, *Stizolobium deeringianium*.

120. Pseudomonas viciae Uyeda, 1915. (Uyeda, in Takimoto, Jour. Plant Protect., Japan, *2*, 1915, 845.)

vi'ci.ae. L. *vicia* vetch; M.L. fem.noun *Vicia* generic name of vetch; M.L. gen.noun *viciae* of vetch.

Rods 0.5 to 0.8 by 1.2 to 2.0 microns. Motile with 2 to 4 polar flagella. Reported as Gram-positive; however, probably in error. No cultures are available for a retest of this character.

Green fluorescent pigment produced in culture.

Gelatin colonies: Pale white, glistening, finally turning brown. No liquefaction.

Milk: Coagulates and clears.

Nitrites not produced from nitrates.

Hydrogen sulfide not produced.

Aerobic, facultative.

Habitat: Pathogenic on the broad bean (*Vicia faba*), the turnip (*Brassica rapa*), the carrot (*Daucus carota*) and the sweet potato (*Ipomoea batatas*).

121. Pseudomonas alliicola (Burkholder, 1942) Starr and Burkholder, 1942.

(*Phytomonas alliicola* Burkholder, Phytopath., *32*, 1942, 146; Starr and Burkholder, Phytopath., *ibid.*, 601.)

al.li.i′co.la. L. *allium* onion; L. -*cola* dweller; M.L. fem.noun *alliicola* onion dweller.

Rods 0.7 to 1.4 by 1.05 to 2.8 microns. Motile with 1 to several polar flagella, at times bipolar. Gram-negative.

Gelatin: Liquefied.

Beef-extract peptone agar streaks: Moderate in growth, white at first, later dirty in appearance, edges wavy, consistency viscid. Medium deep brown.

Potato-glucose agar frequently becomes greenish.

Broth: Turbid with light pellicle. Brown.

Milk: Cleared and litmus reduced. Neutral.

Nitrites produced from nitrates.

Indole not produced.

Hydrogen sulfide not produced.

Lipolytic action very strong.

Acid but no gas from l-arabinose, d-xylose, rhamnose, glucose, d-galactose, fructose, d-lactose, maltose, sucrose, glycerol, mannitol and salicin. Alkali from salts of acetic, citric, formic, hippuric, lactic, malic, succinic and tartaric acids.

Starch not hydrolyzed.

Slight growth in broth plus 4 per cent salt.

Aerobic.

Temperature relations: Optimum, 30° C. Minimum, 5° C. Maximum, 41° C.

Source: Seven isolates from storage rot of onion bulbs.

Habitat: Pathogenic on onion bulbs, *Allium cepa*.

122. **Pseudomonas gardeniae** Burkholder and Pirone, 1941. (Phytopath., *31*, 1941, 194.)

gar.de′ni.ae. L. Garden patronymic; M.L. fem.noun *Gardenia* plant generic name; M.L. gen.noun *gardeniae* of *Gardenia*.

Rods 0.75 by 2.4 microns. Motile with 1 to 2 polar flagella. Gram-negative.

Gelatin: Liquefied.

Beef-extract peptone agar colonies: Growth fair, white to dirty gray and viscid. Medium becoming dark brown.

Potato-glucose agar: No brown color.

Broth: Turbid with pellicle. Dark brown.

Milk: Soft curd with pellicle. Clears in zones. Litmus reduced.

Nitrites produced from nitrates.

Hydrogen sulfide not produced.

Indole not produced.

Acid from glucose, galactose, xylose, rhamnose, sucrose, maltose, mannitol, glycerol and salicin. Alkali produced from the salts of citric, malic, malonic, succinic, tartaric and hippuric acids. Good growth in tyrosine and in asparagine broth.

Starch not hydrolyzed.

Aerobic.

Source: Eight isolates from leaf spots of gardenias in New Jersey.

Habitat: Pathogenic on leaves of *Gardenia jasminoides*.

123. **Pseudomonas caryophylli** (Burkholder, 1942) Starr and Burkholder, 1942. (*Phytomonas caryophylli* Burkholder, Phytopath., *32*, 1942, 143; Starr and Burkholder, *ibid.*, 601.)

ca.ry.o′phyl.li. Gr. *caryophyllum* nut leaf, the clover tree; M.L. mas.noun *caryophyllus* specific epithet in *Dianthus caryophyllus*, the clove-pink or carnation; M.L. gen.noun *caryophylli* of the carnation.

Rods 0.35 to 0.95 by 1.05 to 3.18 microns. At times slightly curved. Motile with 1 to several polar flagella. Frequently bipolar. Gram-negative.

Gelatin: Liquefaction after 3 to 4 weeks.

Potato glucose agar colonies: 3 to 4 mm in diameter, circular, smooth, glistening, edges entire. Color is tan to gray-mauve. Old culture dark brown. Consistency butyrous.

Broth: Turbid with a white sediment.

Milk: Litmus slowly becomes blue. Slight reduction at bottom of tube. No clearing.

Nitrites produced from nitrates. Also ammonia and gas are produced in a synthetic nitrate medium. Asparagine, KNO_3 and $NH_4H_2PO_4$ can be utilized.

Indole not produced.

Hydrogen sulfide not produced.

Lipolytic action slight to moderate.

Acid from l-arabinose, d-xylose, rhamnose, glucose, d-galactose, fructose, d-lactose, maltose, sucrose, glycerol, mannitol and salicin. Alkali with sodium salts of acetic, citric, formic, hippuric, lactic, malic, maleic, succinic and tartaric acids.

Starch not hydrolyzed.

Aerobic.

Temperature relations: Optimum between 30° and 33° C. Minimum, 5° C. or less. Maximum, 46° C.

Slight growth in broth plus 3.5 per cent salt.

Source: Isolated first by L. K. Jones and later by W. H. Burkholder from dying carnation plants from Spokane, Washington. Twelve isolates used in description.

Habitat: Pathogenic on roots and stalks of the carnation, *Dianthus caryophyllus*.

124. Pseudomonas solanacearum (Erw. Smith, 1896) Erw. Smith, 1914. (*Bacillus solanacearum* Erw. Smith, U. S. Dept. Agr., Div. Veg. Phys. and Path., Bull. 12, 1896, 10; Erw. Smith, Bacteria in Relation to Plant Diseases, *3*, 1914, 178.)

so.la.na.ce.a'rum. L. *solanum* the nightshade; -*aceae* familial ending; M.L. fem.pl. noun *Solanaceae* the nightshade family; M.L. fem.pl.gen.n. *solanacearum* of the *Solanaceae*.

Rods 0.5 to 1.5 microns. Motile with a polar flagellum. Gram-negative.

Gelatin: Nakata (Jour. Sci. Agr. Soc. Tokyo, *294*, 1927, 216) states there are two forms, one of which shows slight liquefaction. The other shows no liquefaction.

Agar colonies: Small, irregular, roundish, smooth, wet-shining, opalescent, becoming brown.

Broth: Slight pellicle. Broth turns brown.

Milk: Cleared without precipitation of casein.

Nitrites produced from nitrates.

Indole not produced.

Hydrogen sulfide not produced (Burkholder).

Glucose, sucrose, glycerol, sodium citrate, peptone, tyrosine, asparagine and glutamic acid are utilized (Mushin, Austral. Jour. Expt. Biol. and Med., *16*, 1938, 325).

Nitrogen sources utilized are ammonia, nitrates (KNO₃), asparagine, tyrosine, peptone and glutamic acid, but not potassium nitrite (Mushin, *loc. cit.*).

Starch not hydrolyzed.

Temperature relations: Optimum between 35° and 37° C. Minimum, 10° C. Maximum, 41° C.

Pathogenicity readily lost in culture.

Comment: A variety that turns litmus milk and cream red has been described by Erw. Smith (Bact. in Relation to Plant Diseases, *3*, 1914, 282). It was isolated by J. A. Honing from diseased tobacco plants in Medan, Sumatra.

Source: Isolated from brown-rot of solanaceous plants.

Habitat: Soil pathogen in warm, moist climates attacking numerous species of plants, especially potato, tobacco and tomato.

125. Pseudomonas castaneae (Kawamura, 1934) Săvulescu, 1947. (*Bacterium castaneae* Kawamura, Ann. Phytopath. Soc. Japan, *3*, 1934, 15; Săvulescu, Anal. Acad. Romane, III, *22*, 1947, 11.)

cas.ta'ne.ae. Gr. *castanum* the chestnut tree; L. *castanea* the chestnut; M.L. fem.noun *Castanea* generic name of chestnut; M.L. gen.noun *castaneae* of the chestnut.

Rods 0.8 to 1.2 by 1.0 to 1.8 microns. Motile with 1 to 5 polar flagella. Gram-negative.

Gelatin: Liquefied.

Beef agar colonies: White, circular, edges slightly undulate, viscid.

Milk: No coagulation. Peptonized.

Acid but no gas from glucose, sucrose and glycerol. No acid from lactose.

Temperature relations: Optimum between 25° and 27° C. Minimum, 3° C. Maximum, 35° C.

Aerobic, facultative.

Habitat: Causes water-soaked spotting on leaves and shoots of chestnut, *Castanea*.

126. Pseudomonas passiflorae (Reid, 1939) Burkholder, 1948. (*Phytomonas passiflorae* Reid, New Zealand Jour. Sci. and Tech., *22*, 1939, 264a; Burkholder, in Manual, 6th ed., 1948, 138.)

pas.si.flo'rae. L. *passio* passion; L. *flos, floris* a flower; M.L. fem.noun *Passiflora* generic name of passion flower; M.L. gen.noun *passiflorae* of the passion flower.

Rods 0.2 to 0.5 by 1.2 to 3.2 microns.

Motile with 1 to 5 polar flagella. Encapsulated. Gram-negative.

Gelatin: Liquefied.

Beef-peptone agar colonies: Small, flat, smooth, dry, shining, translucent, grayish and butyrous.

Broth: Turbid in 4 days. Transient pellicle.

Milk: Slightly alkaline. No coagulation nor clearing.

Nitrites not produced from nitrates. No growth on synthetic nitrate agar.

Indole not produced.

Hydrogen sulfide not produced.

Acid reaction occurs in galactose, starch and sucrose. No gas.

Starch not hydrolyzed.

Source: From diseased leaves and fruit of the passion fruit in New Zealand.

Habitat: Pathogenic on *Passiflora edulis*.

127. Pseudomonas seminum Cayley, 1917. (Jour. Agr. Sci., *8*, 1917, 461.)

se'mi.num. L. *semen, seminis* seed; L. gen.pl. *seminum* of seeds.

Rods 1.0 by 4.0 to 5.0 microns. Spore-like bodies present. Encapsulated. Motile with a single flagellum. Reported as Gram-positive; however, probably in error. No cultures are available for a retest of this character.

Gelatin: Rapid liquefaction.

Agar colonies: White, more or less circular, transparent, spreading.

Broth: Turbid. Pellicle.

Litmus milk: Milk becomes clear and apricot color.

Nitrites produced from nitrates.

Acid but no gas from glucose and sucrose. No acid from lactose.

Starch: No hydrolysis.

Optimum temperature, 25° C.

Aerobic, facultative.

Source: Isolated from seeds, stems and pods of diseased peas in England.

128. Pseudomonas vitiswoodrowii Patel and Kulkarni, 1951. (*Pseudomonas vitiswoodrowii* (sic) Patel and Kulkarni, Curr. Sci., *20*, 1951, 132.)

vi.tis.wood.ro'wi.i. L. fem.noun *vitis* a vine; M.L. fem.noun *Vitis* a generic name;

Woodrow patronymic; M.L. gen.noun *woodrowii* of Woodrow.

Rods 0.8 by 1.5 microns. Motile with a single polar flagellum. Gram-negative.

Gelatin: Liquefied.

Potato dextrose agar colonies: Circular, capitate with margins entire. Pale, dull gray. 1.2 cm in diameter in 7 days.

Broth: Turbid.

Potato cylinders: Scant growth. Medium dark gray.

Milk: Litmus reduced and casein digested.

Hydrogen sulfide produced.

Loeffler's blood serum: Liquefied.

Indole not produced.

Synthetic asparagine medium. No growth.

Methyl red test negative; acetylmethylcarbinol not produced.

Nitrites not produced from nitrates.

Acid but no gas from glucose, lactose and sucrose, but no growth in salicin.

Salt tolerance: Up to 1 per cent.

Optimum temperature between 25° and 28° C.

Aerobic.

Source: Isolated from leaves of *Vitis woodrowii* in India.

Habitat: Pathogenic on *V. woodrowii* but not on *V. vinifera*.

129. Pseudomonas fabae (Yu, 1936) Burkholder, 1948. (*Phytomonas fabae* Yu, Bull. of the Chinese Bot. Soc., *2*, 1936, 34; Burkholder, in Manual, 6th ed., 1948, 139.)

fa'bae. L. *faba* the horse bean; M.L. gen.noun *fabae* of the horse bean.

Rods 0.8 to 1.1 by 1.1 to 2.8 microns. Motile with 1 to 4 polar flagella. Gram-negative.

Gelatin: Liquefied.

Nutrient agar colonies: Circular, entire, viscid, glistening, raised, smooth to wrinkled, white to salmon. Medium amber.

Broth: Turbid after 12 hours. Pellicle.

Milk: Growth slow. Clears.

Nitrites produced from nitrates.

Indole production slight.

Hydrogen sulfide not produced.

Acid but no gas from glucose. No acid nor gas developed from arabinose, xylose, fructose, galactose, sucrose, lactose, maltose, raffinose, dextrin, inulin, mannitol or adonitol in a 1 per cent Bacto-peptone broth.

Starch: Very weak diastatic action.

Temperature relations: Optimum, 35° C. Minimum, 4° C. Maximum between 37° and 38° C. Thermal death point between 52° and 53° C.

Aerobic.

Growth retarded in 2 per cent salt. Very slight growth in 3 per cent salt.

Source: From diseased broad beans at Nanking, China.

Habitat: Pathogenic on broad or Windsor bean, *Vicia faba*.

130. **Pseudomonas astragali** (Takimoto, 1930) Săvulescu, 1947. (*Bacterium astragali* Takimoto, Jour. Plant Protect., *17*, 1930, 732; Săvulescu, Anal. Acad. Romane, III, *22*, 1947, 11.)

as.tra′ga.li. Gr. *astragalus* a vertebra, also a leguminous plant; M.L. mas.noun *Astragalus* a generic name; M.L. gen.noun *astragali* of *Astragalus*.

Description translated by Dr. K. Togashi.

Rods 0.7 to 0.8 by 1.2 to 2.2 microns. Motile, with 1 or 2 flagella. Gram-negative.

Gelatin: Liquefied.

Agar plates: Growth somewhat slow, colorless or grayish white, entire margins, more or less aqueous, butyrous.

Uschinsky's medium: Growth vigorous, turbid, not viscid; ring and sediment.

Milk: No coagulation of casein, slow digestion. Alkaline.

Nitrites not produced from nitrates.

Indole not produced.

Hydrogen sulfide produced in small amount.

No acid or gas from glucose, sucrose, lactose or glycerol in broth.

Starch not hydrolyzed.

Temperature relations: Minimum, below 5° C. Maximum, 33° C. Thermal death point between 50° and 51° C.

Aerobic.

Source: Species isolated from *Astragalus sp.*

Habitat: Causes a black leaf-spot of *Astragalus sp.*

131. **Pseudomonas colurnae** (Thorn-

berry and Anderson, 1937) Burkholder, 1948. (*Phytomonas colurnae* Thornberry and Anderson, Phytopath., *27*, 1937, 948; Burkholder, in Manual, 6th ed., 1948, 139.)

co.lur′nae. L. fem.noun *corylus* the hazel or filbert; L. adj. *colurnus* (transposition of *corulnus*) pertaining to hazel.

Rods 0.8 to 1.0 by 1.0 to 1.8 microns. Single, in pairs or chains. Encapsulated. Motile with 1 to 2 polar flagella. Gram-negative.

Gelatin: Liquefied.

Glucose agar slants: Growth filiform, raised, dull, smooth, opaque and viscid.

Broth: Moderate turbidity. Ring.

Milk: Peptonization complete with acid production. No reduction of litmus nor coagulation.

Nitrites not produced from nitrates.

Indole not produced.

Hydrogen sulfide not produced.

No appreciable amount of gas from xylose, glucose, sucrose or glycerol.

Starch hydrolyzed.

Temperature relations: Optimum, 21° C. Minimum, 5° C. Maximum, 35° C. Thermal death point, 50° C.

Aerobic.

Source: From leaves and young stems of the Turkish hazelnut in Illinois.

Habitat: Pathogenic on the Turkish hazelnut, *Corylus colurna*.

132. **Pseudomonas iridicola** (Takimoto, 1931) Stapp, 1935. (*Bacterium iridicola* Takimoto, Fungi, Nippon Fungological Soc., *1*, 1931, 24; Stapp, Bot. Rev., *1*, 1935, 408.)

i.ri.di′co.la. Gr. *iris, iridis* the rainbow, the plant iris; M.L. fem.noun *Iris* generic name; L. -*cola* dweller; M.L. fem.noun *iridicola* iris dweller.

Rods 0.7 to 0.8 by 1.2 to 2 microns. Motile with 1 to 3 polar flagella. Gram-negative.

Gelatin: Liquefied.

Beef agar colonies: White, circular, raised or convex.

Milk: Clears without coagulation.

No acid or gas from carbohydrates.

Starch digested.

Temperature relations: Optimum, 38° C. Minimum, 4° C.

Source: Isolated from a brown leaf spot of iris.

Habitat: Pathogenic on *Iris tectorum* and *Iris japonica*.

133. Pseudomonas levistici Osterwalder, 1909. (Cent. f. Bakt., II Abt., *25*, 1909, 260.)

le.vis'ti.ci. L. neut.noun *ligusticum* a Ligurian plant, lovage; L. neut.noun *levisticum* a corruption of *ligusticum*; M.L. neut.noun *Levisticum* generic name of lovage; M.L. gen.noun *levistici* of *Levisticum*.

Rods 0.5 to 0.7 by 1.1 to 1.5 microns. Motile with a polar flagellum. Gram-negative.

Gelatin: Colonies greenish white. Liquefied.

Nutrient agar: Good growth at room temperature. Yellowish white.

Broth: Pellicle.

Indole produced.

Hydrogen sulfide not produced.

Source: Isolated from spots on the leaves of lovage.

Habitat: Pathogenic on lovage, *Levisticum officinale*.

134. Pseudomonas maublancii (Foex and Lansade, 1936) Săvulescu, 1947. (*Bacterium maublancii* Foex and Lansade, Compt. rend. Acad. Sci., Paris, *202*, 1936, 2174; Săvulescu, Anal. Acad. Romane, III, *22*, 1947, 11.)

mau.blan'ci.i. Maublanc, patronymic; M.L. gen.noun *maublancii* of Maublanc.

Rods 0.4 by 1.3 microns. Motile with 1 to 3 polar flagella. Gram-negative.

Gelatin: Liquefied.

Gelatin colonies: Round, translucent, margins entire.

Broth: Thin pellicle.

Milk: Not coagulated; clears.

Nitrites not produced from nitrates.

Indole not produced.

Hydrogen sulfide not produced.

Carbohydrates not fermented.

Ammonia produced.

Growth in Fermi's solution, not in Uschinsky's solution.

Source: Isolated from rotting vascular and parenchymatic tissue of banana stalks.

Habitat: Causes a disease of the banana plant.

135. Pseudomonas polygoni (Thornberry and Anderson, 1937) Burkholder, 1948. (*Phytomonas polygoni* Thornberry and Anderson, Phytopath., *27*, 1937, 947; Burkholder, in Manual, 6th ed., 1948, 140.)

po.ly'go.ni. Gr. *polygonum* knot weed; M.L. neut.noun *Polygonum* generic name; M.L. gen.noun *polygoni* of *Polygonum*.

Rods 0.5 to 1.5 by 1.5 to 2.5 microns. Motile with 2 to 8 bipolar flagella. Encapsulated. Gram-positive (?). Other species reported by these investigators as Gram-positive have proved to be Gram-negative on a retest (Burkholder).

Gelatin: Liquefied. Brown.

Glucose agar slant: Abundant, filiform, flat, dull, smooth, pale olive-gray, butyrous. Medium turns brown.

Broth: Turbid. Pellicle.

Milk: Alkaline and clears. Litmus not reduced.

Nitrites not produced from nitrates.

Indole not produced.

Hydrogen sulfide not produced.

No appreciable amount of gas from carbohydrates.

Starch: No hydrolysis.

Temperature relations: Optimum, 18° C. Minimum, 7° C. Maximum, 35° C.

Aerobic.

Source: From diseased leaves of *Polygonum convolvulus* in Illinois.

Habitat: Pathogenic on black bindweed, *Polygonum convolvulus*.

136. Pseudomonas radiciperda (Javoronkova, 1932) Săvulescu, 1947. (*Bacterium radiciperda* Javoronkova, Bull. Plant Protect., Leningrad, Ser. II, *5*, no. 1, 1932, 161; Săvulescu, Anal. Acad. Romane, III, *22*, 1947, 11.)

ra.di.ci.per'da. L. *radix, radicis* root; L. *perdo* to destroy; M.L. fem.noun *radiciperda* the root destroyer.

Description from Javoronkova (Rev. App. Myc., *11*, 1932, 652).

Rods 0.8 by 1.0 to 2.0 microns. Encapsulated. Motile by means of 1 or 2 polar flagella. Gram-negative.

Gelatin: Liquefied.

Beef-peptone agar colonies: Round, smooth, shining, white to pale yellow.

Milk: Peptonized.

Indole not produced.

Hydrogen sulfide not produced.

Acid but no gas from carbohydrates.

Optimum temperature between 23° and 25° C.

Aerobic.

Habitat: Causes a root rot of red clover (*Trifolium pratense*), lentils (*Lens esculenta*) and lucerne.

137. **Pseudomonas cattleyae** (Pavarino, 1911) Săvulescu, 1947. (*Bacterium cattleyae* Pavarino, Atti R. Acad. Naz. Lincei Rend. Cl. Sci. Fis., Mat. e Nat., *20*, 1911, 233; Săvulescu, Anal. Acad. Romane, III, *22*, 1947, 11.)

catt'ley.ae. M.L.fem.noun *Cattleya* a generic name; M.L. gen.noun *cattleyae* of *Cattleya*.

Description from Ark and Thomas (Phytopath., *36*, 1946, 697).

Rods, 0.4 to 0.6 by 2.4 microns, occurring singly or in pairs. Motile by means of 1 or 2 bipolar flagella. Gram-negative.

Gelatin: No liquefaction.

Beef-extract peptone agar colonies: Large, entire, smooth, with criss-cross markings. Grayish white and butyrous.

Broth: Turbid in 24 hours with very delicate pellicle.

Fermi's, Cohn's, and Uschinsky's solutions: Good growth.

Hydrogen sulfide not produced.

Indole not produced.

Nitrites produced from nitrates.

Litmus milk: Unchanged after 2 weeks.

Acid but no gas from glucose, galactose, fructose, arabinose, xylose, lactose, sucrose, dulcitol, glycerol and mannitol. No acid or gas from raffinose.

Starch: Slight hydrolysis.

Optimum temperature between 25° and 35° C.

Source: Four isolates and 4 reisolates from leaf spots of orchids by Ark and Thomas.

Habitat: Pathogenic on *Cattleya sp.* and *Phalaenopsis sp.*

138. **Pseudomonas dysoxyli** Hutchinson, 1949. (New Zealand Jour. Sci. and Tech., Sec. B, *30*, 1949, 275.)

dy.so'xy.li. M.L. neut.noun *Dysoxylum* generic name of a forest tree; M.L. gen.noun *dysoxyli* of *Dysoxylum*.

Rods 0.4 to 0.6 by 0.6 to 1.0 micron. Motile with 1 to 2 polar flagella. Gram-negative.

Gelatin: No liquefaction.

Beef-peptone agar colonies: Circular, punctiform to 8 mm in diameter, gray, translucent. Surface smooth and edges entire to undulate. Medium brown in 1 week.

Nutrient broth: Dense flocculent pellicle at surface. Strong clouding in 3 days.

Litmus milk: No change in 4 days. After 12 days amber whey at top and 1 inch of pink precipitate at base.

Indole not produced.

Hydrogen sulfide not produced.

Methyl red test negative; acetylmethylcarbinol not produced.

Nitrites not produced from nitrates.

Synthetic medium: Acid but no gas from glucose, fructose, lactose, sucrose, raffinose and mannitol within 3 weeks. No acid from arabinose, maltose, melizitose, starch, inulin, dextrin, glycerol or salicin.

Starch hydrolyzed.

Temperature relations: Optimum, 25° C. Minimum, 4° C. Maximum, 36° C.

Source: Many cultures isolated from diseased leaves of *Dysoxylum spectabile* in New Zealand.

Habitat: Pathogenic on leaves of the forest tree *Dysoxylum spectabile*.

139. **Pseudomonas helianthi** (Kawamura, 1934) Săvulescu, 1947. (*Bacterium helianthi* Kawamura, Ann. Phyt. Soc. Japan, *4*, 1934, 27; Săvulescu, Anal. Acad. Romane, III, *22*, 1947, 11.)

he.li.an'thi. Gr. *helius* the sun; Gr. *anthus* a flower; M.L. mas.noun *Helianthus* generic name of sunflower; M.L. gen.noun *helianthi* of the sunflower.

Rods 1.0 to 1.4 by 1.6 to 2.4 microns. Motile with a single polar flagellum. Gram-negative.

Gelatin: No liquefaction.

Beef agar colonies: White, circular, edges entire.

Broth: Turbid. Pellicle.

Milk: Peptonized. Litmus reduced.

Nitrates: Gas production.

Indole not produced.
Hydrogen sulfide not produced.
Acid but no gas from sucrose and glycerol.
No acid from lactose and maltose.
Starch hydrolyzed.
Temperature relations: Optimum between 27° and 28° C. Minimum, 12° C. Maximum, 35.5° C.
Chemical tolerance: Good growth at pH 6.4. No growth at pH 5.4 and pH 8.8
Habitat: Pathogenic on sunflower, *Helianthus debilis.*

140. Pseudomonas melophthora Allen and Riker, 1932. (Phytopath., *22*, 1932, 557.)
me.loph'tho.ra. Gr. *melum* apple; Gr. *phthora* decay, destruction; M.L. adj. *melophthorus* apple-destroying.

Rods 0.68 by 1.32 microns. Motile with 2 polar flagella. Gram-negative; Gram-positive cells appear in old cultures.
Gelatin: No liquefaction.
Nutrient agar plus 2 per cent glucose: Colonies appear in 36 hours. After 3 days colonies circular, smooth, glistening, convex; edges entire; light pink, but not constant.
Broth: Good growth. Pellicle and sediment.
Milk: Little change, if any.
Nitrites not produced from nitrates.
Indole not produced.
Hydrogen sulfide not produced.
Acid from arabinose, glucose, galactose, fructose, sucrose and glycerol. No acid from lactose, maltose, dextrin or inulin.
Starch not hydrolyzed.
Optimum temperature between 21° and 25° C.
Source: Description based on 7 cultures isolated from rotting apples and from apple maggots.
Habitat: Pathogenic on apples and found with the apple maggot, *Rhagoletis pomonella.*

141. Pseudomonas alboprecipitans Rosen, 1922. (Ann. Missouri Bot. Garden, *9*, 1922, 383.)
al.bo.pre.ci'pi.tans. L. *album* the color white; L. v. *praecipito* to precipitate; M.L. part.adj. *alboprecipitans* forming a white sediment.
Description revised in accordance with

Johnson, Roberts and Cash (Jour. Agr. Res., *78*, 1949, 723).
Rods, 0.6 by 1.8 microns, occurring singly or in pairs. Encapsulated. Motile with a polar flagellum. Gram-negative.
Gelatin: Liquefied
Nutrient agar colonies: White, circular, raised, smooth, sticky, with margins entire. Whitish discoloration of the medium.
Broth: Turbid in 24 hours. Heavy sediment in old cultures.
Uschinsky's solution: Turbid in 24 hours; pellicle formed.
Cohn's and Fermi's solutions: No growth.
Milk: Becomes alkaline and slowly clears.
Nitrites produced from nitrates.
Indole not produced.
Hydrogen sulfide production slight.
Acid but no gas from glucose, galactose, fructose, sucrose, lactose, raffinose, glycerol and mannitol. No acid from maltose.
Starch hydrolyzed.
Temperature relations: Optimum between 30° and 35° C. Minimum, 0° C. Maximum, 40° C.
Aerobic.
Distinctive character: White precipitate in culture media.
Source: Isolated a number of times from foxtail grass.
Habitat: Pathogenic on foxtail, *Chactochloa lutescens*, and other grasses.

142. Pseudomonas andropogonis (Erw. Smith, 1911) Stapp, 1928. (*Bacterium andropogoni* (sic) Erw. Smith, Bacteria in Relation to Plant Diseases, *2*, 1911, 63; Elliott and Smith, Jour. Agr. Res., *38*, 1929, 4; *Pseudomonas andropogoni* (sic) Stapp, in Sorauer, Handbuch der Pflanzenkrankheiten, *2*, 5 Aufl., 1928, 27.)
an.dro.po.go'nis. Gr. *anēr, andris* a man; Gr. mas.noun *pōgōn, pōgōnis* beard; M.L. mas.noun *Andrōpōgon, -ōnis* man's beard, generic name; M.L. gen.noun *andropogonis* of *Andropogon.*
Description from Elliott and Smith (*op. cit.*, 1929, 4).
Rods 0.64 by 1.76 microns. Motile with one to several bipolar flagella. Encapsulated. Gram-negative.
Gelatin: Feeble liquefaction or none.
Beef-extract agar colonies: Slow growing, round, smooth, glistening, viscid, white.

Broth: Growth slow with moderate turbidity in 48 hours. A thin pellicle.
Milk: Alkaline and clears.
Nitrites not produced from nitrates.
Indole not produced.
Hydrogen sulfide not produced.
Not lipolytic (Starr and Burkholder, Phytopath., *32*, 1942, 601).
Acid but no gas from glucose, arabinose, fructose and xylose. No acid from sucrose, maltose, lactose, raffinose, glycerol or mannitol.
Starch partially digested.
Temperature relations: Optimum between 22° and 30° C. Minimum, 1.5° C. Maximum between 37° and 38° C.
Chemical tolerance: Optimum pH between 6.0 and 6.6. Minimum, 5.0. Maximum between 8.3 and 8.6.
Source: Elliott used for her description 4 cultures isolated from lesions on sorgo, sorghum and broom-corn.
Habitat: Pathogenic on sorghum, *Holcus sorghum*.

143. Pseudomonas lignicola Westerdijk and Buisman, 1929. (De Iepenziekte, Arnhem, 1929, 51.)
lig.ni′co.la. L. *lignum* wood; L. *-cola* dweller; M.L. fem.noun *lignicola* wood dweller or inhabitant.
Rods. Single or short chains. Motile with 1 to several polar flagella. Gram-negative.
Gelatin: No liquefaction.
Malt agar streaks: Milk-white with a colorless edge.
Broth: Turbid with light pellicle.
Milk: No coagulation. No acid.
Nitrites not produced from nitrates.
Indole not produced.
Starch hydrolysis slight.
Optimum temperature, ±25° C.
Source: From vessels of elm wood showing dark discoloration, in Holland.
Habitat: Pathogenic on elm wood.

144. Pseudomonas petasitis (Takimoto, 1927) Săvulescu, 1947. (*Bacterium petasitis* (sic) Takimoto, Ann. Phyt. Soc. Japan, *2*, 1927, 55; Săvulescu, Anal. Acad. Romane, III, *22*, 1947, 11.)
pe.ta′si.tis. Gr. mas.noun *petasus* a sombrero, a broad-brimmed felt hat; Gr.

mas.noun *petasites* a broad-leafed plant, colt's foot; M.L. mas.noun *Petasites* generic name; M.L. gen.noun *petasitis* of *Petasites*.
Rods 0.8 to 1.1 by 1.1 to 1.7 microns. Motile with a polar flagellum. Gram-negative.
Gelatin: No liquefaction.
Beef agar colonies: White, circular or amoeboid, butyrous.
Broth: Strong turbidity. Pellicle.
Milk: Coagulated in 30 days.
Nitrites produced from nitrates with gas formation.
Indole not produced.
Hydrogen sulfide not produced.
No evident acid in peptone broth, but gas from glucose, lactose and sucrose. Acid but no gas from glycerol.
Weak growth in broth plus 6 per cent salt.
Temperature relations: Optimum between 27° and 30° C. Minimum, approximately 5° C. Maximum, 47° C.
Source: Isolated from brown to black lesions on *Petasites japonicus* in Japan.
Habitat: Pathogenic on leaves of *Petasites japonicus*.

145. Pseudomonas woodsii (Erw. Smith, 1911) Stevens, 1925. (*Bacterium woodsii* Erw. Smith, Bacteria in Relation to Plant Diseases, *2*, 1911, 62; Stevens, Plant Disease Fungi, New York, 1925, 39.)
wood′si.i. Named for A. F. Woods, an American plant pathologist; M.L. gen.noun *woodsii* of Woods.
Description from Burkholder and Guterman (Phytopath., *25*, 1935, 118).
Rods 0.67 by 1.56 microns. Motile with a polar flagellum. Gram-negative.
Gelatin: No liquefaction.
Beef-extract agar slants: Growth slow and scant, filiform, creamy, butyrous.
Broth: Turbid.
Milk: Becomes alkaline but otherwise little changed.
Nitrites not produced from nitrates.
Indole not produced.
Hydrogen sulfide not produced.
Not lipolytic (Starr and Burkholder, Phytopath., *32*, 1942, 601).
Acid but no gas from glucose, fructose, galactose, arabinose, xylose, rhamnose, lactose, glycerol and mannitol. Alkaline reac-

tion from salts of acetic, citric, malic and succinic acids. Sucrose, maltose, salicin, and lactic and formic acids not fermented.

Starch not hydrolyzed.

Slight growth in broth plus 3 per cent salt. Aerobic.

Source: Isolated from water-soaked lesions on carnation leaves.

Habitat: Pathogenic on carnation, *Dianthus caryophyllus*.

146. **Pseudomonas eriobotryae** (Takimoto, 1931) Dowson, 1943. (*Bacterium eriobotryae* Takimoto, Jour. Plant Protect., *18*, 1931, 354; Dowson, Trans. Brit. Mycol. Soc., *26*, 1943, 10.)

e.ri.o.bo'try.ae. Gr. *erium* wool; Gr. *botrys* grape cluster; M.L. fem.noun *Eriobotrya* woolly grape, a generic name; M.L. gen.noun *eriobotryae* of *Eriobotrya*.

Translated by Dr. K. Togashi.

Rods 0.7 to 0.9 by 2.2 to 3.0 microns. Motile, with 1 or 2 flagella. Gram-negative.

Gelatin: Not liquefied.

Agar-plates: Colonies appear after 3 days, white or hyaline, butyrous, margins entire.

Broth: Moderately turbid; pellicle powdery; ring formed.

Milk: No coagulation, peptonized slowly. Alkaline.

Nitrites not produced from nitrates.

Indole not produced.

Hydrogen sulfide not produced.

No acid or gas from glucose, sucrose, lactose or glycerol in broth.

Starch not hydrolyzed.

Temperature relations: Optimum between 25° and 26° C. Minimum, below 4° C. Maximum, 32° C. Thermal death point, 51° C.

Aerobic.

Source: Species isolated from loquat, *Eriobotrya japonica*.

Habitat: Causes a bud rot of *Eriobotrya japonica*.

147. **Pseudomonas panicimiliacei** (Ikata and Yamauchi, 1931) Săvulescu, 1947. (*Bacterium panici-miliacei* Ikata and Yamauchi, Jour. Plant Protect., *18*, 1931, 35; *Pseudomonas panici-miliacei* (sic) Săvulescu, Anal. Acad. Romane, III, *22*, 1947, 11.)

pa.ni.ci.mi.li.a'ce.i. L. *panicum* panic

grass; L. adj. *miliaceus* pertaining to millet; *Panicum miliaceum* millet.

Description translated by Dr. K. Togashi.

Rods 0.8 to 1.1 by 1.8 to 2.6 microns. Motile, with a single flagellum. Gram-negative.

Gelatin: Not liquefied.

Potato-agar plates: Growth moderate, whitish, then tinged with light orange, undulating margins.

Broth: Turbid; white pellicle formed.

Milk: No coagulation and slow digestion. Alkaline.

Nitrites produced from nitrates.

Indole not produced.

Hydrogen sulfide not produced.

No acid and no gas from sucrose, glucose, lactose, glycerol or sodium nitrate.

Starch not hydrolyzed.

Optimum temperature between 30° and 35° C.

Aerobic, facultative.

Source: Species first isolated from millet, *Panicum miliaceum*.

Habitat: Causes a leaf stripe of *Panicum miliaceum*.

148. **Pseudomonas saliciperda** Lindeijer, 1932. (Inaug. Diss., Univ. Amsterdam, 1932; Phytopath. Ztschr., *6*, 1933, 373.)

sa.li.ci.per'da. L. *salix, salicis* willow; L. *perdo* to destroy; M.L. fem.noun *saliciperda* willow destroyer.

Rods 1.2 to 2.1 microns in length. Motile with a polar flagellum. Gram-negative.

Gelatin: No liquefaction.

Beef wort agar colonies: Gray-white.

Milk: No acid nor coagulation.

Nitrites produced (small amount) from nitrates.

Indole production slight.

No gas from carbohydrates.

Starch not hydrolyzed.

Aerobic, facultative.

Source: Isolated from wilted branches of willow.

Habitat: Pathogenic on willow, *Salix spp.*

149. **Pseudomonas wieringae** (Elliott, 1930) Săvulescu, 1947. (*Phytomonas betae* Wieringa, Nederl. Tijdschr. Hyg., Microbiol. en Serol., Leiden, *2*, 1927, 148; *Bac-*

terium wieringae Elliott, Man. Bact. Plant Pathogens, 1930, 264; Săvulescu, Anal. Acad. Romane, III, *22*, 1947, 11.)

wie'ring.ae. Named for Dr. K. T. Wieringa, the bacteriologist who first described the species; M.L. gen.noun *wieringae* of Wieringa.

Because *Bacterium betae* Chester (Ann. Rept. Del. Col. Agr. Exp. Sta., *9*, 1897, 53) may be a pseudomonad, the more distinctive species name proposed by Elliott has been retained.

Description from Elliott (*op. cit.*, 1930, 264).

Rods 0.5 by 2.0 microns. Motile with 1 to 5 polar flagella. Gram-negative.

Beef-agar colonies: Smooth, round, white to grayish, fluorescent.

Milk: Cleared in 5 days. Not coagulated.

Nitrites not produced from nitrates.

No gas from sugars.

Temperature relations: Optimum between 28° and 30° C. Minimum, 4° C. Maximum, 37° C.

Source: Isolated from vascular rot of beets in Holland.

Habitat: Pathogenic on beets, *Beta vulgaris*.

Genus II. **Xanthomonas** *Dowson, 1939.**

(*Phytomonas* Bergey et al., Manual, 1st ed., 1923, 174; not *Phytomonas* Donovan, Lancet, *177*, 1909, 1495 (type species (monotypy) *Phytomonas davidi* Donovan, a flagellate); Dowson, Zent. f. Bakt., II Abt., *100*, 1939, 187.)

Xan.tho'mo.nas or Xan.tho.mo'nas†. Gr. adj. *xanthus* yellow; Gr. fem.n. *monas* unit, monad; M.L. fem.n. *Xanthomonas* yellow monad.

Cells usually monotrichous. A yellow, non-water-soluble pigment is produced on agar. A diffusible, brown color infrequently occurs in beef extract agar. Proteins are usually readily digested. Milk usually becomes alkaline. Hydrogen sulfide is produced. Asparagine is not sufficient as an only source of carbon and nitrogen. Acid (and also gas in one species, No. 19) produced from mono- and disaccharides. Some species liquefy a pectin medium, others do not (Burkholder and Starr, Phytopath., *38*, 1948, 500). Mostly plant pathogens causing necroses.

The type species is *Xanthomonas hyacinthi* (Wakker) Dowson.

Key to the species of genus **Xanthomonas.**

I. Colonies yellow; pigment non-water-soluble.
    A. Gelatin liquefied.
        1. Starch hydrolysis feeble.
            a. Nitrites not produced from nitrates.
                1. *Xanthomonas hyacinthi*.
                2. *Xanthomonas pruni*.
                3. *Xanthomonas vitians*.
            aa. Nitrites produced from nitrates.
                4. *Xanthomonas beticola*.
                5. *Xanthomonas rubrilineans*.
        2. Starch hydrolysis strong.
            a. Nitrites not produced from nitrates.
                b. No brown pigment in beef-extract agar.
                6. *Xanthomonas barbareae*.
                 7. *Xanthomonas begoniae*.
                 8. *Xanthomonas betlicola*.
                 9. *Xanthomonas campestris*.

---

* Prepared by Prof. Walter H. Burkholder, Cornell University, Ithaca, N. Y., June, 1943; revised November, 1953.

† The former accords with the Latin rules of accentuation; the latter is in common usage.

10. *Xanthomonas cassiae.*
11. *Xanthomonas cajani.*
12. *Xanthomonas citri.*
13. *Xanthomonas clerodendri.*
14. *Xanthomonas corylina.*
15. *Xanthomonas cucurbitae.*
16. *Xanthomonas desmodii.*
17. *Xanthomonas desmodiigangeticii.*
18. *Xanthomonas dieffenbachiae.*
19. *Xanthomonas hemmiana.*
20. *Xanthomonas holcicola.*
21. *Xanthomonas incanae.*
22. *Xanthomonas juglandis.*
23. *Xanthomonas lespedezae.*
24. *Xanthomonas maculifoliigardeniae.*
25. *Xanthomonas malvacearum.*
26. *Xanthomonas pelargonii.*
27. *Xanthomonas phaseoli.*
28. *Xanthomonas plantaginis.*
29. *Xanthomonas ricinicola.*
30. *Xanthomonas sesbaniae.*
31. *Xanthomonas stizolobiicola.*
32. *Xanthomonas taraxaci.*
33. *Xanthomonas translucens.*
34. *Xanthomonas uppalii.*
35. *Xanthomonas vasculorum.*
36. *Xanthomonas vesicatoria.*
37. *Xanthomonas vignicola.*
bb. Brown pigment produced in beef-extract media.
38. *Xanthomonas nakatae.*
27. *Xanthomonas phaseoli.*
aa. Nitrites produced from nitrates.
39. *Xanthomonas papavericola.*
aaa. Ammonia produced from nitrates.
40. *Xanthomonas alfalfae.*
3. Starch not hydrolyzed.
a. Nitrites produced from nitrates.
41. *Xanthomonas acernea.*
aa. Nitrites not produced from nitrates.
42. *Xanthomonas carotae.*
43. *Xanthomonas hederae.*
44. *Xanthomonas phormicola.*
36. *Xanthomonas vesicatoria.*
aaa. Ammonia produced in nitrate media.
45. *Xanthomonas geranii.*
4. Starch hydrolysis not reported.
a. Nitrites produced from nitrates.
46. *Xanthomonas antirrhini.*
47. *Xanthomonas heterocea.*
aa. Nitrites not produced from nitrates.
48. *Xanthomonas badrii.*
49. *Xanthomonas gummisudans.*
50. *Xanthomonas nigromaculans.*

B. Gelatin not liquefied.
  1. Starch hydrolyzed.
         51. *Xanthomonas axonopodis.*
  2. Starch not hydrolyzed.
         52. *Xanthomonas oryzae.*
C. Gelatin not reported.
  1. Starch hydrolyzed.
         53. *Xanthomonas celebensis.*
II. Colonies whitish to cream; pigment non-water-soluble.
  A. Gelatin liquefied.
    1. Starch hydrolyzed.
      a. Nitrites produced from nitrates.
         54. *Xanthomonas panici.*
         55. *Xanthomonas proteamaculans.*
         56. *Xanthomonas manihotis.*
      aa. Nitrites not reported.
         57. *Xanthomonas rubrisubalbicans.*
    2. Starch not reported.
         58. *Xanthomonas cannae.*
         59. *Xanthomonas conjac.*
         60. *Xanthomonas zingiberi.*

HOST PLANT KEY

The following key will be found useful for purposes of identification where the bacterium
is isolated from a known host plant.

I. Cause of leaf, stem and fruit spots and occasional blights of monocotyledonous plants.
  A. Attack members of the family *Araceae.*
         59. *Xanthomonas conjac.*
         18. *Xanthomonas dieffenbachiae.*
  B. Attacks members of the family *Cannaceae.*
         58. *Xanthomonas cannae.*
  C. Attack members of the family *Gramineae.*
         51. *Xanthomonas axonopodis.*
         20. *Xanthomonas holcicola.*
         52. *Xanthomonas oryzae.*
         53. *Xanthomonas panici.*
          5. *Xanthomonas rubrilineans.*
         57. *Xanthomonas rubrisubalbicans.*
         33. *Xanthomonas translucens.*
         35. *Xanthomonas vasculorum.*
  D. Attacks members of the family *Iridaceae.*
         49. *Xanthomonas gummisudans.*
  E. Attack members of the family *Liliaceae.*
          1. *Xanthomonas hyacinthi.*
         44. *Xanthomonas phormicola.*
  F. Attacks members of the family *Musaceae.*
         52. *Xanthomonas celebensis.*
  G. Attacks members of the family *Zingiberaceae.*
         60. *Xanthomonas zingiberi.*
II. Cause of leaf, stem and fruit spots and occasional blights of dicotyledonous plants.
  A. Attacks members of the family *Aceraceae.*
         41. *Xanthomonas acernea.*

B. Attacks members of the family *Araliaceae*.
>43. *Xanthomonas hederae*.

C. Attacks members of the family *Begoniaceae*.
>7. *Xanthomonas begoniae*.

D. Attacks members of the family *Betulaceae*.
>14. *Xanthomonas corylina*.

E. Attacks members of the family *Chenopodiaceae*.
>4. *Xanthomonas beticola*.

F. Attack members of the family *Compositae*.
>48. *Xanthomonas badrii*.
>50. *Xanthomonas nigromaculans*.
>32. *Xanthomonas taraxaci*.
>3. *Xanthomonas vitians*.

G. Attacks members of the family *Convolvulaceae*.
>34. *Xanthomonas uppalii*.

H. Attack members of the family *Cruciferae*.
>6. *Xanthomonas barbareae*.
>9. *Xanthomonas campestris*.
>21. *Xanthomonas incanae*.
>36. *Xanthomonas vesicatoria*.

I. Attacks members of the family *Cucurbitaceae*.
>15. *Xanthomonas cucurbitae*.

J. Attack members of the family *Euphorbiaceae*.
>56. *Xanthomonas manihotis*.
>29. *Xanthomonas ricinicola*.

K. Attack members of the family *Geraniaceae*.
>45. *Xanthomonas geranii*.
>26. *Xanthomonas pelargonii*.

L. Attacks members of the family *Juglandaceae*.
>22. *Xanthomonas juglandis*.

M. Attack members of the family *Leguminosae*.
>40. *Xanthomonas alfalfae*.
>11. *Xanthomonas cajani*.
>10. *Xanthomonas cassiae*.
>16. *Xanthomonas desmodii*.
>17. *Xanthomonas desmodiigangeticii*.
>23. *Xanthomonas lespedezae*.
>27. *Xanthomonas phaseoli*.
>30. *Xanthomonas sesbaniae*.
>31. *Xanthomonas stizolobiicola*.
>37. *Xanthomonas vignicola*.

N. Attacks members of the family *Malvaceae*.
>25. *Xanthomonas malvacearum*.

O. Attacks members of the family *Papaveraceae*.
>39. *Xanthomonas papavericola*.

P. Attacks members of the family *Piperaceae*.
>8. *Xanthomonas betlicola*.

Q. Attacks members of the family *Plantaginaceae*.
>28. *Xanthomonas plantaginis*.

R. Attacks members of the family *Proteaceae*.
>55. *Xanthomonas proteamaculans*.

S. Attacks members of the family *Rosaceae*.
>2. *Xanthomonas pruni*.

T. Attacks members of the family *Rubiaceae*.
   24. *Xanthomonas maculifoliigardeniae*.
U. Attacks members of the family *Rutaceae*.
   12. *Xanthomonas citri*.
V. Attacks members of the family *Scrophulariaceae*.
   46. *Xanthomonas antirrhini*.
W. Attack members of the family *Solanaceae*.
   19. *Xanthomonas hemmiana*.
   47. *Xanthomonas heterocea*.
   36. *Xanthomonas vesicatoria*.
X. Attacks members of the family *Tiliaceae*.
   38. *Xanthomonas nakatae*.
Y. Attacks members of the family *Umbelliferae*.
   42. *Xanthomonas carotae*.
Z. Attacks members of the family *Verbenaceae*.
   13. *Xanthomonas clerodendri*.

---

1. Xanthomonas hyacinthi (Wakker, 1883) Dowson, 1939. (*Bacterium hyacinthi* Wakker, Botan. Centralblatt, *14*, 1883, 315; Dowson, Zent. f. Bakt., II Abt., *100*, 1939, 188.)

hy.a.cin′thi. Gr. *hyacinthus* the hyacinth; M.L. mas.n. *Hyacinthus* generic name; M. L. gen.noun *hyacinthi* of hyacinth.

Description from Smith (Div. Veg. Phys. and Path., U. S. D. A. Bul. *26*, 1901, 40); additional characters determined by Burkholder.

Rods 0.4 to 0.6 by 0.8 to 2.0 microns. Motile with a polar flagellum. Filaments present. Gram-negative.

Gelatin: Slow liquefaction.

Agar colonies: Circular, flat, moist, shining, bright yellow. Media stained brown.

Milk: Casein is precipitated and digested. Tyrosine crystals produced.

Nitrites not produced from nitrates.

Indole: Slight production.

Hydrogen sulfide produced.

Acid but no gas from glucose, fructose, lactose, sucrose, galactose, maltose, salicin and ethyl alcohol. Slight acid from xylose. Alkaline reaction in citrate. Mannitol, dulcitol and malonate not utilized.

Starch: Hydrolysis slight.

Pectate medium not liquefied.

Temperature relations: Optimum, between 28° and 30° C. Minimum, 4° C. Maximum, between 34° and 35° C.

Aerobic, with the exception of maltose, where it is facultatively anaerobic.

Habitat: Produces a yellow rot of hyacinth bulbs, *Hyacinthus orientalis*.

2. Xanthomonas pruni (Erw. Smith, 1903) Dowson, 1939. (*Pseudomonas pruni* Erw. Smith, Science, N. S. *17*, 1903, 456; Dowson, Zent. f. Bakt., II Abt., *100*, 1939, 190.)

pru′ni. L. *prunus* plum; M.L. fem.n. *Prunus* generic name; M.L. gen.noun *pruni* of *Prunus*.

Description from Dunegan (U. S. Dept. Agr., Tech. Bull. 273, 1932, 23).

Rods 0.2 to 0.4 by 0.8 to 1.0 micron. Encapsulated. Motile with a polar flagellum. Gram-negative.

Gelatin: Liquefied.

Beef-extract agar colonies: Yellow, circular, smooth, convex, edges entire.

Broth: Turbid becoming viscid.

Milk: Precipitation of casein; digestion.

Nitrites not produced from nitrates.

Indole not produced.

Hydrogen sulfide not produced. Hydrogen sulfide produced (Burkholder).

Lipolytic (Starr and Burkholder, Phytopath., *32*, 1942, 600).

Acid from arabinose, xylose, glucose, fructose, galactose, mannose, maltose, lactose, sucrose, raffinose and melezitose.

Starch is hydrolyzed (slight).

Pectate medium not liquefied.

Aerobic.

Temperature relations: Optimum, between 24° and 29° C. Maximum, 37° C.

Source: Smith isolated this pathogen from Japanese plums.

Habitat: Pathogenic on plum (*Prunus salicina*), peach (*P. persica*), apricot (*P. armeniaca*), etc.

3. Xanthomonas vitians (Brown, 1918) Dowson, 1943. (*Bacterium vitians* Brown, Jour. Agr. Res., *13*, 1918, 379; Dowson, Trans. Brit. Mycol. Soc., *26*, 1943, 13.)

vi'ti.ans. L. *vitio* to injure; L. part.adj. *vitians* injuring.

Rods. Motile with bipolar flagella. Gram-negative.

Gelatin: Slow liquefaction.

Beef-extract agar colonies: Circular, smooth, thin, cream to cream-yellow.

Broth: Turbid with yellow ring.

Milk: Clears and turns alkaline.

Nitrites not produced from nitrates.

Indole: Feeble production.

Hydrogen sulfide: Feeble production.

Acid but no gas from glucose.

Starch: Feeble hydrolysis.

Pectate medium not liquefied.

Temperature relations: Optimum, between 26° and 28° C. Minimum, 0° C. Maximum, 35° C.

Aerobic.

Source: Isolated from the stem of diseased lettuce plants from South Carolina.

Habitat: Pathogenic on lettuce, *Lactuca sativa*.

4. Xanthomonas beticola (Smith et al., 1911) Săvulescu, 1947. (*Bacterium beticolum* Smith, Brown and Townsend, U. S. Dept. Agr., Bur. Plant Ind., Bul. 213, 1911, 194; Săvulescu, Anal. Acad. Romane, III, *22*, 1947, 12).

be.ti'co.la. L. *beta* the beet; L. v. *colo* to inhabit; M.L. noun *beticola* the beet dweller.

Description from Brown, Jour. Agr. Res., *37*, 1928, 167, where the species is referred to as *Bacterium beticola* (Smith, Brown and Townsend) Potebnia.

Rods 0.4 to 0.8 by 0.6 to 2.0 microns. Motile with 1 to 4 polar flagella. Encapsulated. Presumably Gram-negative although originally reported as Gram-variable.

Gelatin: Liquefied.

Beef-agar slants: Growth moderate, filiform, flat, glistening, yellow.

Broth: Turbid, yellow ring, abundant sediment.

Milk: Coagulation and peptonization.

Indole not produced.

Hydrogen sulfide produced.

Nitrites produced from nitrates.

Acid from glucose, sucrose, maltose and mannitol. No acid from lactose.

Starch hydrolysis feeble.

Temperature relations: Optimum, 29° C. Minimum, 1.5° C. Maximum, 39° C.

Chemical tolerance: Optimum pH, 6.5. Minimum, between 4.5 and 4.8. Maximum, between 9.0 and 9.5.

Tolerates salt up to 9 per cent.

Aerobic.

Comment: It is doubtful whether this species belongs in this genus.

Source: Isolated from galls on sugar beets collected in Colorado, Kansas and Virginia.

Habitat: Produces galls on sugar beets and on garden beets.

5. Xanthomonas rubrilineans (Lee et al., 1925) Starr and Burkholder, 1942. (*Phytomonas rubrilineans* Lee, Purdy, Barnum and Martin, Hawaiian Sugar Planters' Assoc. Bul., 1925, 25; Starr and Burkholder, Phytopath., *32*, 1942, 600.)

ru.bri.li'ne.ans. L. *ruber* red; *lineo* to make a straight line; *rubrilineans* making red stripes.

Rods 0.7 by 1.67 microns. Motile with 1 or seldom more polar flagella. Gram-negative.

Gelatin: Liquefied.

Agar (Beef-extract + glucose) colonies: Small, smooth, glistening, buff to yellow.

Broth: Turbid with pellicle. Sediment.

Milk: Casein precipitated and digested.

Nitrites produced from nitrates.

Indole not produced.

Hydrogen sulfide not produced.

Not lipolytic (Starr and Burkholder, Phytopath., *32*, 1942, 600).

Acid from glucose, fructose, arabinose, xylose, lactose, sucrose, raffinose and mannitol.

Starch: Slight hydrolysis.

Pectate medium not liquefied.

Growth range, pH 5.4 to pH 7.3.

Aerobic, facultative.

Source: Isolated from red stripe lesions in sugar cane.

Habitat: Pathogenic on sugar cane.

6. Xanthomonas barbareae Burkholder, 1941. (Phytopath., *31*, 1941, 348.)

bar.ba're.ae. M.L. fem.n. *Barbarea* generic name of cress; M.L. gen.noun *barbareae* of *Barbarea*.

Rods 0.4 to 0.95 by 1.0 to 3.15 microns. Motile with a single polar flagellum. Gram-negative.

Gelatin: Liquefied.

Beef-extract peptone colonies: Circular, yellow, smooth, butyrous, growth moderate.

Potato glucose agar: Growth abundant, pale yellow. Mucoid.

Broth: Turbid, yellow granular ring.

Milk: Soft curd, with clearing and production of tyrosine crystals. Litmus reduced.

Nitrates utilized but no nitrites produced. Asparagine and nitrites not utilized.

Hydrogen sulfide produced.

Indole not produced.

Lipolytic (Starr and Burkholder, Phytopath., *32*, 1942, 600).

Acid from glucose, galactose, xylose, maltose, sucrose and glycerol. Alkali produced from salts of malonic, citric, malic and succinic acids. Rhamnose, salicin and hippuric acid salts not utilized.

Starch hydrolyzed.

Pectate medium liquefied.

Aerobic.

Distinctive characters: Similar to *Xanthomonas campestris* but does not infect cabbage, cauliflower or horseradish.

Source: From black rot of winter cress, *Barbarea vulgaris*.

Habitat: Pathogenic on leaves and stems of *Barbarea vulgaris*.

7. Xanthomonas begoniae (Takimoto, 1934) Dowson, 1939. (*Bacterium begoniae* Takimoto, Jour. Plant Protect., *21*, 1934, 262; Dowson, Zent. f. Bakt., II Abt., *100*, 1939, 190.)

be.go'ni.ae. Named for Bégon; M.L. fem.n. *Begonia* generic name; M.L. gen. noun *begoniae* of *Begonia*.

Translated by Dr. K. Togashi.

Rods 0.5 to 0.6 by 1.2 to 2.0 microns.

Motile with a polar flagellum. Gram-negative.

Gelatin: No liquefaction. Liquefaction (Wieringa, Tidschr. Plantziekt., *41*, 1935, 312; McCulloch, Jour. Agr. Res., *54*, 1937, 859; Dowson, *op. cit.*, 1939, 190; Stapp, Arbeiten Biol. Reichsanst. f. Land- u. Forstw., *22*, 1938, 392).

Potato agar colonies: Circular, convex, smooth, moist, shining, yellow.

Broth: Turbid. Yellow pellicle and precipitation.

Milk: No coagulation. Casein digested. Alkaline.

Nitrites not produced from nitrates.

Indole not produced.

Hydrogen sulfide produced.

Lipolytic (Starr and Burkholder, Phytopath., *32*, 1942, 600).

No acid or gas in peptone broth from glucose, sucrose, lactose or glycerol. Acid from glucose, sucrose, lactose, mannitol and glycerol in peptone-free medium (McCulloch, *op. cit.*, 1937, 859).

Starch hydrolyzed (Dowson, Jour. Roy. Hort. Soc., *63*, 1938, 289).

Pectate medium not liquefied.

Temperature relations: Optimum, 27°C. Minimum, between 1° and 3° C. Maximum, 37° C.

Source: Isolated from leaf spot of tuberous begonia.

Habitat: Pathogenic on *Begonia spp.*

8. Xanthomonas betlicola Patel et al., 1951. (Patel, Kulkarni and Dhande, Curr. Sci., *20*, 1951, 106.)

bet.li'co.la. East Indian betle, the name of the betel, a shrubby vine; L. v. *colo* to dwell; M.L. fem.n. *betlicola* the betel-dweller.

Rods slender, occurring singly or in pairs. Motile. Encapsulated. Gram-negative.

Gelatin: Liquefied.

Potato-glucose agar colonies: 11 mm in diameter in 7 days, baryta-yellow, lobate, striations at periphery.

Broth: Turbid; yellow growth.

Milk: Litmus reduced. Casein digested.

Loeffler's blood serum liquefied.

Indole not produced.

Hydrogen sulfide produced.

Nitrites not produced from nitrates.
Methyl red negative: acetylmethylcarbinol not produced.
Synthetic asparagine medium: No growth.
Acid but no gas from glucose, lactose and sucrose. Salicin not attacked.
Starch hydrolyzed.
Salt tolerance: Up to 3 per cent.
Optimum temperature, between 25° and 28° C.
Aerobic.
Source: Isolated from leaves, stems and petioles of *Piper betle* in India.
Habitat: Pathogenic on *Piper betle*.

9. **Xanthomonas campestris** (Pammel, 1895) Dowson, 1939. (*Bacillus campestris* Pammel, Iowa Agr. Exp. Sta. Bull. 27, 1895, 130; Dowson, Zent. f. Bakt., II Abt., *100*, 1939, 190.)
cam.pes'tris. L. *campestris* of a level field this specific epithet is also that of *Brassica campestris*, a host.
Description from McCulloch (Jour. Agr. Res., *38*, 1929, 278). Species is probably composed of several varieties. See descriptions by Mekta, Ann. Appl. Biol., *12*, 1925, 330; Paine and Nirula, Ann. Appl. Biol., *15*, 1928, 46; Wormald and Frampton, Ann. Rept. East. Mall. Res. Sta., 1926 and 1927, II Supplement, 1928, 108; and others.
Rods 0.3 to 0.5 by 0.7 to 2.0 microns. Motile with a polar flagellum. Encapsulated. Gram-negative.
Gelatin: Liquefied.
Beef agar colonies: Wax-yellow, round, smooth, shining, translucent, margins entire.
Broth: Turbid with yellow rim and sometimes a pellicle.
Milk: Casein digested with the formation of tyrosine crystals. Alkaline.
Nitrites not produced from nitrates.
Indole production weak.
Hydrogen sulfide produced.
Lipolytic (Starr and Burkholder, Phytopath., *32*, 1942, 600).
Acid but no gas from glucose, sucrose, lactose, glycerol and mannitol.
Starch hydrolyzed.
Pectate medium liquefied.
Temperature relations: Optimum, between 28° and 30° C. Maximum, 36° C.

Aerobic.
Distinctive characters: Causes a vascular infection in cabbage, cauliflower and rutabagas.
Comment: A variety pathogenic on horseradish and related species has been described by McCulloch (Jour. Agr. Res., *38*, 1929, 269). Causes a leaf spot. Does not liquefy pectate medium.
Source: Pammel (*op. cit.*, 1895, 130) first isolated the pathogen from diseased rutabagas.
Habitat: Pathogenic on cabbage, cauliflower and other related species.

10. **Xanthomonas cassiae** Kulkarni et al., 1951. (Kulkarni, Patel and Dhande, Curr. Sci., *20*, 1951, 47.)
cas'si.ae. M.L. fem.n. *Cassia* generic name of host; M.L. gen.noun *cassiae* of *Cassia*.
Rods 0.8 to 1.0 by 1.2 to 2.1 microns. Motile with a single polar flagellum. Gram-negative.
Gelatin: Liquefied.
Potato-glucose agar colonies: 1.2 cm in diameter after 7 days, smooth, circular, lobate, glistening, convex, butyrous, pinard-yellow.
Milk: Litmus reduced. Medium peptonized.
Hydrogen sulfide produced.
Nitrites not produced from nitrates.
Loeffler's blood serum: Liquefied.
Methyl red negative; acetylmethylcarbinol not produced.
Acid but no gas from glucose, lactose and sucrose. Arabinose, glycerol and salicin not attacked.
Starch hydrolyzed.
Koser's citrate medium: Growth.
Synthetic asparagine medium: Slight growth.
Non-lipolytic.
Salt tolerance: Up to 3 per cent.
Optimum temperature, 27° C.
Aerobic.
Source: Isolated from leaves, stems and petioles of *Cassia tora* in India.
Habitat: Pathogenic on *Cassia tora*.

11. **Xanthomonas cajani** Kulkarni et al., 1950. (Kulkarni, Patel and Abhyankar, Curr. Sci., *19*, 1950, 384.)

ca'ja.ni. M.L. mas.n. *Cajanus* generic name of host; M.L. gen.noun *cajani* of *Cajanus*.

Rods 0.9 to 1.4 by 1.3 to 2.2 microns. Encapsulated. Motile with a single polar flagellum. Gram-negative.

Gelatin: Liquefied.

Potato-glucose agar colonies: 1.5 cm in diameter after 7 days, smooth, glistening, entire, pulvinate, naphthalene-yellow.

Milk: Litmus reduced. Casein digested.

Loeffler's blood serum: Liquefied in 10 days.

Hydrogen sulfide produced.

Nitrites not produced from nitrates.

Acid but no gas from glucose, lactose and sucrose. Salicin not attacked. Citrates utilized.

Starch hydrolyzed.

Methyl red negative; acetylmethylcarbinol not produced.

Synthetic asparagine medium: No growth.

Salt tolerance: Up to 3 per cent.

Optimum temperature, 30° C.

Aerobic.

Relationship to other species: Similar to *Xanthomonas phaseoli*, which also infects various legumes.

Source: Isolated from the pigeon pea, *Cajanus cajan*, in India.

Habitat: Pathogenic on *Cajanus cajan*.

12. **Xanthomonas citri** (Hasse, 1915) Dowson, 1939. (*Pseudomonas citri* Hasse, Jour. Agr. Res., *4*, 1915, 97; Dowson, Zent. f. Bakt., II Abt., *100*, 1939, 190.)

cit'ri. L. *citrus* the citrus; M.L. fem.n. *Citrus* generic name; M.L. gen.noun *citri* of *Citrus*.

Rods, 0.5 to 0.75 by 1.5 to 2.0 microns, occurring in chains. Motile with a single polar flagellum. Gram-negative.

Gelatin: Liquefied.

Beef agar colonies: Appear in 36 to 48 hours; circular, smooth, raised, dull yellow.

Broth: Turbid in 24 hours. A yellow ring forms.

Milk: Casein is precipitated.

Nitrites not produced from nitrates.

Hydrogen sulfide produced (Reid, New Zealand Jour. Sci. and Tech., *22*, 1938, 60).

Indole not produced.

No gas from glucose, lactose or mannitol.

Starch hydrolyzed (Reid, *loc. cit.*).

Aerobic.

Temperature relations: Optimum, between 25° and 34° C. Minimum, 10° C. Maximum, 38° C. (Okabe, Jour. Soc. Trop. Agr., *4*, 1932, 476).

Source: Isolated from canker on orange.

Habitat: Produces a canker on many species of *Citrus* and related plants.

13. **Xanthomonas clerodendri** Patel et al., 1952. (*Xanthomonas clerodendroni* (sic) Patel, Kulkarni and Dhande, Curr. Sci., *21*, 1952, 74.)

cle.ro.den'dri. M.L. neut.n. *Clerodendron* generic name of the plant host; M.L. gen. noun *clerodendri* of *Clerodendron*.

Rods, 0.5 by 1.1 microns, occurring singly or in chains. Encapsulated. Gram-negative.

Gelatin: Liquefied.

Potato-glucose agar colonies: Circular, 1.8 cm in diameter in 7 days, margins entire. Pale lemon-yellow.

Litmus milk: Casein digested. Litmus reduced and milk peptonized.

Hydrogen sulfide produced.

Nitrites not produced from nitrates.

Acid but no gas from glucose, sucrose and lactose. No growth in salicin.

Starch hydrolyzed.

Optimum temperature, about 31° C. Thermal death point, 51° C.

Source: From a leaf spot on *Clerodendron phlomoides*.

Habitat: Pathogenic on *Clerodendron phlomoides*.

14. **Xanthomonas corylina** (Miller et al., 1940) Starr and Burkholder, 1942. (Miller, Bollen, Simmons, Gross and Barss, Phytopath., *30*, 1940, 731; Starr and Burkholder, Phytopath., *32*, 1942, 598.)

co.ry.li'na. Gr. *corylus* the hazel; M.L. adj. *corylinus* pertaining to hazel.

Rods 0.5 to 0.7 by 1.1 to 3.8 microns.

Motile with a polar flagellum. Encapsulated. Gram-negative.

Gelatin: Liquefied.

Nutrient glucose-agar streaks: Growth abundant, filiform, convex, glistening, smooth, opaque, pale lemon-yellow, viscid.

Broth: Turbid. Ring formed in 2 to 5 days.

Milk: Enzymatic curd that is slowly digested. Litmus reduced. Crystal formation (Burkholder).

Nitrites not produced from nitrates.

Nitrogen sources utilized are peptone, aspartic acid, alanine, leucine, sodium ammonium phosphate, allantoin, tyrosine, uric acid and brucine.

Indole not produced.

Hydrogen sulfide not produced on lead acetate agar. H_2S produced after ZoBell and Feltham's method (Burkholder).

Selenium dioxide reduced.

Lipolytic (Starr and Burkholder, *ibid.*, 600).

Acid but no gas from glucose, fructose, galactose, lactose, sucrose, maltose, xylose, raffinose, mannitol, glycerol and starch. Alkali from salts of citric, lactic, malic and succinic acids. Arabinose, rhamnose, dulcitol, salicin, inulin and cellulose not utilized.

Starch hydrolyzed.

Pectate medium not liquefied.

Temperature relations: Optimum, between 28° and 32° C. Minimum, between 5° and 7° C. Maximum, 37° C. Thermal death point between 53° and 55° C.

pH range for growth: pH 5.2 to 10.5. Optimum pH, between 6 and 8.

Strict aerobe.

Distinctive characters: Cultural characters the same or similar to those of *Xanthomonas juglandis*. The two species do not cross-infect.

Source: 26 isolates from widely scattered filbert orchards in Oregon and Washington.

Habitat: Pathogenic on filberts (*Corylus avellana and C. maxima*).

15. Xanthomonas cucurbitae (Bryan, 1926) Dowson, 1939. (*Bacterium cucurbitae* Bryan, Science, *63*, 1926, 165; Bryan, Jour. Agr. Res., *40*, 1930, 389; Dowson, Zent. f. Bakt., II Abt., *100*, 1939, 190.)

cu.cur'bi.tae. L. *cucurbita* a gourd; M.L. fem.n. *Cucurbita* generic name; M.L. gen. noun *cucurbitae* of *Cucurbita*.

Rods 0.45 to 0.6 by 0.5 to 1.3 microns. Motile, usually with a single polar flagellum. Gram-negative.

Gelatin: Liquefied.

Beef-agar slants: Growth moderate, mustard-yellow, undulating margins, viscid to butyrous.

Broth: Moderately turbid. Ring and yellow sediment.

Milk: Precipitation of casein; digestion. Alkaline.

Nitrites not produced from nitrates.

Indole not produced.

Hydrogen sulfide produced.

Acid from glucose, galactose, fructose, lactose, maltose, sucrose and glycerol. No acid from mannitol.

Starch hydrolyzed.

Pectate medium not liquefied.

Temperature relations: Optimum, between 25° and 30° C. Maximum, 35° C.

pH range for growth: pH 5.8 to 9.0. Optimum pH, between 6.5 and 7.0.

Slight growth in 5 per cent salt.

Aerobic.

Source: Species first isolated from squash.

Habitat: Causes a leaf spot of squash and related plants.

16. Xanthomonas desmodii Uppal and Patel, 1949. (Uppal and Patel, in Patel, Curr. Sci., *18*, 1949, 213; also see Patel, Indian Phytopath., *2*, 1949, 5.)

des.mo'di.i. M.L. neut.n. *Desmodium* generic name of host; M.L. gen.noun *desmodii* of *Desmodium*.

Rods, 0.4 to 0.8 by 1.6 to 2.4 microns, occurring singly or in pairs. Motile with a single polar flagellum. Gram-negative.

Gelatin: Liquefied.

Nutrient agar slants: Growth fair, filiform, flat, dull, smooth, opaque and pinard-yellow.

Potato-glucose agar (neutral) colonies: Yellowish amber with colorless margins, circular, viscid, smooth and wet.

Beef broth: Growth slow. Moderate in 48 hours and good in 4 days.

Milk: Litmus turns red in 10 days. Reduction slow.

Indole not produced.

Hydrogen sulfide production fair.

Nitrites not produced from nitrates.

No growth in Cohn's, Uschinsky's or Fermi's solution.

Acid but no gas from glucose, galactose, lactose, mannitol, maltose and sucrose in synthetic medium. Poor growth in salicin, raffinose, fructose, arabinose, xylose, dulcitol and glycerol, and no growth in tartaric, citric, acetic or formic acids. No growth when asparagine is used as carbon-nitrogen source.

Starch hydrolyzed.

Temperature relations: Optimum, between 25° and 30° C. Slight growth at 11° C. No growth at 38° C.

Chemical tolerance: Optimum pH, between 6.8 and 7.3. No growth at pH 8.5; slight growth at pH 3.2.

Aerobic.

Source: From diseased *Desmodium diffusum* in India.

Habitat: Pathogenic on *Desmodium diffusum*, not on *D. gangeticum*.

17. Xanthomonas desmodiigangeticii
Uppal et al., 1948. (*Xanthomonas desmodiigangeticii* (sic) Uppal, Patel and Moniz, in Patel and Moniz, Indian Phytopath., *1*, 1948, 140; also see Patel and Moniz, Curr. Sci., *17*, 1948, 268.)

des.mo'di.i.gan.ge'ti.ci.i. M.L. neut.n. *Desmodium gangeticum* name of host species; M.L. gen.noun *desmodiigangeticii* of *Desmodium gangeticum*.

Rods 0.7 to 1.4 by 1.5 to 2.5 microns. Motile with a single flagellum. Gram-negative.

Gelatin: Liquefied.

Nutrient agar slants: Growth fair, dull, flat, opalescent, lemon-chrome.

Nutrient broth: Moderately turbid. No pellicle.

Milk: Litmus reduced. No tyrosine.

Nitrites not produced from nitrates.

Hydrogen sulfide produced.

Indole not produced.

Non-lipolytic.

Uschinsky's solution: Growth.

Acetylmethylcarbinol not produced.

Arabinose, xylose, glucose, galactose, fructose, maltose, sucrose, raffinose, mannitol, salicin and sodium citrate are utilized. Asparagine utilized as carbon-nitrogen source.

Starch hydrolyzed.

Salt tolerance: Growth retarded by 3 per cent salt; inhibited by 4 per cent salt.

Temperature relations: Optimum, between 20° and 25° C. Minimum, 5°C. Maximum, 35° C.

Aerobic.

Source: From a disease of *Desmodium gangeticum* found in India.

Habitat: Pathogenic on *Desmodium gangeticum* but not on *D. diffusum*.

18. Xanthomonas dieffenbachiae
(McCulloch and Pirone, 1939) Dowson, 1943. (*Phytomonas dieffenbachiae* McCulloch and Pirone, Phytopath., *29*, 1939, 962; Dowson, Trans. Brit. Mycol. Soc., *26*, 1943, 12.)

dief.fen.bach'i.ae. Dieffenbach patronymic; M.L. fem.n. *Dieffenbachia* generic name; M.L. gen.noun *dieffenbachiae* of *Dieffenbachia*.

Rods 0.3 to 0.4 by 1.0 to 1.5 microns. Encapsulated. Motile with a single polar flagellum. Gram-negative.

Gelatin: Liquefied.

Beef-infusion peptone agar colonies: Slow growing, circular, flat, smooth, translucent, butyrous, massicot- to Naples-yellow.

Broth: Turbid. Yellow rim or slight pellicle.

Milk: Slow peptonization and formation of tyrosine crystals. Litmus reduced.

Nitrites not produced from nitrates.

Indole not produced.

Hydrogen sulfide produced.

Acid from glucose, sucrose, lactose, galactose, fructose and glycerol. Growth but no acid in maltose and mannitol.

Starch moderately hydrolyzed.

Temperature relations: Optimum, between 30° and 31° C. Minimum, 5° C. Maximum, between 37° and 38° C.

Aerobic.

Source: Seven isolates from diseased leaves of *Dieffenbachia picta*.

Habitat: Pathogenic on *Dieffenbachia picta*. Artificial infection of *Dracaena fragrans*.

19. Xanthomonas hemmiana
(Yamamoto, 1951) Burkholder, *comb. nov.* (*Phytomonas hemmianus* (sic) Yamamoto, Forsch. auf dem Gebiet d. Pflanzenkr., *4*, 1951, 163.)

hem.mi.a'na. Named for T. Hemmi, a Japanese plant pathologist; M.L. adj. *hemmianus* of Hemmi.

Rods, 0.3 to 0.7 by 1.3 to 2.2 microns, occurring singly or in pairs. Motile with 1 to 3 polar flagella. Gram-negative.

Gelatin: Liquefied.

Beef extract agar colonies: Small, circular, smooth, flat or raised with regular margins, white to pale yellow.

Beef broth: Moderate clouding.

Milk: Clearing after coagulation. Litmus red.

Uschinsky's solution: Good growth.

Cohn's solution: Poor growth.

Potato: Growth smooth, copious and olive-buff.

Nitrites produced from nitrates.

Indole produced.

Hydrogen sulfide produced.

Acid and gas from glucose, sucrose and glycerol. Acid from lactose.

Starch hydrolyzed.

Temperature relations: Optimum, 32° C. Growth above 36° C. and below 2° to 8° C.

Optimum pH, between 6 and 7; no growth below pH 3.

Aerobic.

Relationship to other species: This species closely resembles the species placed in *Aeromonas* Kluyver and van Niel.

Source: Isolated from leaf spot of Jimson weed, *Datura spp.*

Habitat: Pathogenic on *Datura metel, D. meteloides, D. inermis*, tomato and petunia.

20. **Xanthomonas holcicola** (Elliott, 1930) Starr and Burkholder, 1942. (*Bacterium holcicola* Elliott, Jour. Agr. Res., *40*, 1930, 972; Starr and Burkholder, Phytopath. *32*, 1942, 600.)

hol.ci′co.la. Gr. *holcus* kind of grass; M.L. mas.n. *Holcus* generic name of velvet grass and sorghum; L. v. *colo* to dwell; M.L. fem.n. *holcicola, Holcus* dweller.

Rods 0.75 by 1.58 microns. Motile with 1 or 2 polar flagella. Encapsulated. Gram-negative.

Gelatin: Liquefied.

Beef-infusion peptone agar colonies: Round, umbonate, glistening, smooth, translucent to opaque, wax-yellow, butyrous.

Broth: Trace of growth in 24 hours. Later turbid with a slight ring.

Milk: Casein precipitated and peptonized. Alkaline.

Nitrite production doubtful.

Indole not produced.

Hydrogen sulfide produced.

Lipolytic (Starr and Burkholder, *loc. cit.*).

Acid but no gas from sucrose.

Starch hydrolyzed.

Temperature relations: Optimum, between 28° and 30° C. Minimum, 4° C. Maximum, between 36° and 37° C.

pH range for growth: pH 5.5 to 9.0. Optimum pH, between 7.0 and 7.5.

Source: Isolated from many collections of sorghum leaves showing a streak disease.

Habitat: Pathogenic on leaves of *Holcus sorghum* and *H. halepensis*.

21. **Xanthomonas incanae** (Kendrick and Baker, 1942) Starr and Weiss, 1943. (*Phytomonas incanae* Kendrick and Baker, California Bull. 665, 1942, 10; Starr and Weiss, Phytopath., *33*, 1943, 316.)

in.ca′nae. L. adj. *incanus* hoary, gray; from host *Matthiola incana*.

Rods 0.4 to 0.8 by 0.6 to 2.5 microns. Motile with a polar flagellum. Gram-negative.

Gelatin: Liquefied.

Beef extract agar colonies: Round, smooth, convex or pulvinate, glistening, margin entire, picric-yellow to amber color.

Broth: Turbid.

Milk: No coagulation. A clearing of the medium.

Nitrites not produced from nitrates.

Indole not produced.

Lipolytic (Starr and Burkholder, Phytopath., *32*, 1942, 600).

Acid but no gas from glucose, lactose, sucrose, mannitol, d-galactose, xylose, d-mannose, raffinose, trehalose and glycerol. No acid from maltose, l-arabinose or rhamnose.

Starch not hydrolyzed. Starch hydrolyzed (Burkholder).

Pectate medium liquefied.

Tolerates 3 per cent salt.

Growth in beef broth at pH 4.4.

Aerobic.

Distinctive characters: Causes a disease of flowering stock but not of cabbage. Differs from *Xanthomonas campestris* in that it does not utilize l-arabinose or maltose.

Source: Four isolates from diseased plants of *Matthiola incana*.

Habitat: Pathogenic on flowering stocks.

22. Xanthomonas juglandis (Pierce, 1901) Dowson, 1939. (*Pseudomonas juglandis* Pierce, Bot. Gaz., *31*, 1901, 272; Dowson, Zent. f. Bakt., II Abt., *100*, 1939, 190.)

jug.lan′dis. L. *juglans, juglandis* the walnut; M.L. fem.n. *Juglans* generic name of walnut; M.L. gen.noun *juglandis* of the walnut.

Description from Miller, Bollen, Simmons, Gross and Barss (Phytopath., *30*, 1940, 731).

Rods 0.5 to 0.7 by 1.1 to 3.8 microns. Motile with a polar flagellum. Encapsulated. Gram-negative.

Gelatin: Liquefied.

Nutrient glucose-agar streaks: Growth abundant, filiform, convex, glistening, smooth, opaque, pale lemon-yellow, viscid.

Broth: Turbid. Ring formed in 2 to 5 days.

Milk: Enzymatic curd that is slowly digested. Litmus reduced. Crystal formation (Burkholder).

Nitrites not produced from nitrates.

Nitrogen sources utilized are peptone, aspartic acid, alanine, leucine, sodium ammonium phosphate, allantoin, tyrosine, uric acid and brucine.

Indole not produced.

Hydrogen sulfide not produced on lead acetate agar. H_2S produced after ZoBell and Feltham's method (Burkholder).

Selenium dioxide reduced.

Lipolytic (Starr and Burkholder, Phytopath., *32*, 1942, 600).

Acid but no gas from glucose, fructose, galactose, lactose, sucrose, maltose, xylose, raffinose, mannitol, glycerol and starch. Alkali from salts of citric, lactic, malic and succinic acids. Arabinose, rhamnose, dulcitol, salicin, inulin and cellulose not utilized.

Starch hydrolyzed.

Pectate medium not liquefied.

Temperature relations: Optimum, between 28° and 32° C. Minimum, between 5° and 7° C. Maximum, 37° C. Thermal death point, between 53° and 55° C.

pH range for growth, 5.2 to 10.5. Optimum pH, between 6 and 8.

Source: Isolated from black spots on the leaves and nuts of English walnuts, *Juglans regia*.

Habitat: Pathogenic on the walnut, *Juglans spp.*

23. Xanthomonas lespedezae (Ayers et al., 1939) Starr, 1946. (*Phytomonas lespedezae* Ayers, Lefebvre and Johnson, U. S. Dept. Agr. Tech. Bull. 704, 1939, 19; Starr, Jour. Bact., *51*, 1946, 136.)

les.pe.de′zae. Named after Lespedez; M.L. fem.n. *Lespedeza* generic name; M.L. gen.noun *lespedezae* of *Lespedeza*.

Rods, 0.56 by 1.62 microns, occurring singly, in pairs, or occasionally in short chains. Encapsulated. Motile with a single polar flagellum. Gram-negative.

Gelatin: Liquefied.

Nutrient agar colonies: Circular, raised, glistening, translucent, viscid, yellow.

Broth: Turbid in 48 hours.

Milk: Peptonized; becomes alkaline.

Blood serum and egg albumin: Liquefied.

Nitrites not produced from nitrates.

Indole produced after 11 days.

Hydrogen sulfide produced.

No gas from carbohydrates.

Starch hydrolyzed.

Pectate medium liquefied.

Aerobic.

Temperature relations: Optimum, near 35°C. No growth at 5°C. or at 40°C.

Source: Isolated from diseased *Lespedeza spp.* collected in Virginia, New York and Illinois.

Habitat: Pathogenic on *Lespedeza spp.*

24. Xanthomonas maculifoliigardeniae (Ark, 1946) Elrod and Braun, 1947. (*Phytomonas maculifolium-gardeniae* (sic) Ark, Phytopath., *36*, 1946, 867; *Xanthomonas maculafoliumgardeniae* (sic) Elrod and Braun, Jour. Bact., *53*, 1947, 515.)

ma.cu.li.fo′li.i.gar.de′ni.ae. L. fem.n. *macula* a spot; L. neut.n. *folium* a leaf; M.L. neut.n. *maculifolium* a leaf spot; M.L. fem.n. *Gardenia* the generic name of the host; *gardeniae* of gardenia; M.L. gen.noun *maculifoliigardeniae* of leaf spot of gardenia.

Rods 0.3 to 0.5 by 1.6 to 2.0 microns. Encapsulated. Motile with 1 to 2 polar flagella. Gram-negative.

Gelatin: Slow liquefaction.

Beef-peptone agar colonies: Growth

rapid. Slightly raised, yellow, butyrous in young cultures, difficult to pick up in old cultures.

Broth: Turbid in 24 hours.

Milk: White curd in bottom. Litmus a dirty wine color in supernatant liquid.

Uschinsky's medium: Good growth.

Fermi's solution: Scant growth.

Indole not produced.

Hydrogen sulfide not produced.

Nitrites not produced from nitrates. Ammonia produced from peptone.

Acid but no gas from arabinose, glucose, fructose, galactose, lactose, maltose, mannitol, raffinose, sucrose and xylose. Glycerol not attacked. Tartrate utilized.

Starch hydrolyzed.

Temperature relations: Optimum, between 22° and 28° C. Minimum, 10° C. Maximum, 37° C. Thermal death point, 50° C.

Source: Six isolates from gardenia leaf spots.

Habitat: Causes a spot on young leaves of gardenias.

25. **Xanthomonas malvacearum** (Erw. Smith, 1901) Dowson, 1939. (*Pseudomonas malvacearum* Erw. Smith, U. S. Dept. Agr., Div. Veg. Phys. and Path., Bull. 28, 1901, 153; Dowson, Zent. f. Bakt., II Abt., *100*, 1939, 190.)

mal.va.ce.a′rum. L. *malva* the mallow; M.L. fem.pl.n. *Malvaceae* the mallow family; M.L. fem.pl.gen.n. *malvacearum* of the mallows.

Description from Elliott (Man. Bact. Plant Pathogens, 1930, 153) and Lewis (Phytopath., *20*, 1930, 723).

Rods. Motile with a single polar flagellum. Gram-negative.

Gelatin: Liquefied.

Agar slants: Growth moderate, convex, smooth, glistening, pale yellow, wavy to irregular margins.

Broth: Slight to moderate turbidity. Sediment.

Milk: Casein precipitated and slowly digested.

Nitrites not produced from nitrates.

Hydrogen sulfide produced (Burkholder).

Not lipolytic (Starr and Burkholder, Phytopath., *32*, 1942, 600).

Acid but no gas from glucose, galactose, fructose, xylose, lactose, maltose, sucrose, raffinose, glycerol, inulin and glycogen. Alkaline reaction from salts of acetic, citric, lactic and succinic acids. No fermentation of arabinose, mannitol, dulcitol, salicin, and salts of formic, oxalic and tartaric acids (Lewis).

Starch hydrolyzed (Lewis).

Pectate medium not liquefied.

Temperature relations: Optimum, between 25° and 30° C. Maximum, between 36° and 38° C. (Elliott).

Source: Isolated from angular leaf spot of cotton.

Habitat: Pathogenic on cotton, wherever it is grown, causing a leaf spot, a stem lesion and a boll lesion.

26. **Xanthomonas pelargonii** (Brown, 1923) Starr and Burkholder, 1942. (*Bacterium pelargoni* (sic) Brown, Jour. Agr. Res., *23*, 1923, 372; Starr and Burkholder, Phytopath., *32*, 1942, 600.)

pe.lar.go′ni.i. Gr. *pelargus* the stork: M.L. neut.n. *pelargonium* generic name of stork's bill; M.L. gen.noun *pelargonii* of *Pelargonium*.

Rods 0.67 by 1.02 microns. Encapsulated. Motile with a single polar flagellum. Gram-negative.

Gelatin: Slow liquefaction.

Beef-agar colonies: Cream-colored, glistening, round, with delicate internal markings.

Broth: Turbid in 24 hours. Incomplete pellicle.

Milk: Alkaline. Clearing in bands.

Nitrites not produced from nitrates.

Indole production slight.

Hydrogen sulfide produced.

Lipolytic (Starr and Burkholder, Phytopath., *32*, 1942, 600).

Slight acid but no gas from glucose, sucrose and glycerol.

Starch hydrolysis feebly positive.

Pectate medium liquefied.

Temperature relations: Optimum, 27° C. Maximum, 35° C.

No growth in broth plus 3.5 per cent salt.

Aerobic.

Source: Isolated from spots on leaves of *Pelargonium* from District of Columbia, Maryland and New Jersey.

Habitat: Pathogenic on *Pelargonium spp.* and *Geranium spp.*

27. Xanthomonas phaseoli (Erw. Smith, 1897) Dowson, 1939. (*Bacillus phaseoli* Erw. Smith, Bot. Gaz., *24*, 1897, 192; A. A. A. S. Proc., *46* 1898, 288; Dowson, Zent. f. Bakt., II Abt., *100*, 1939, 190.)

pha.se'o.li. Gr. *phaselus* the kidney bean; L. *phaseolus* kidney bean; M.L. mas.n. *Phaseolus* generic name of bean; M.L. gen. noun *phaseoli* of the bean.

Description from Burkholder (Cornell Agr. Exp. Sta. Mem. 127, 1930, 18; Phytopath., *22*, 1932, 609).

Rods 0.87 by 1.9 microns. Motile with a single polar flagellum. Gram-negative.

Gelatin: Liquefied.

Beef-extract agar colonies: Circular, amber-yellow, smooth, butyrous, edges entire.

Broth: Turbid in 24 hours. Yellow ring.

Milk: Casein precipitated and digested. Alkaline. Tyrosine crystals formed.

Nitrites not produced from nitrates.

Indole not produced.

Hydrogen sulfide produced.

Lipolytic (Starr and Burkholder, Phytopath., *32*, 1942, 600).

Acid but no gas from glucose, galactose, fructose, arabinose, xylose, maltose, lactose, sucrose, raffinose and glycerol. Alkaline reaction from salts of acetic, malic, citric and succinic acids. Mannitol, dulcitol, salicin and formic and tartaric acids not fermented.

Starch hydrolyzed.

Pectate medium not liquefied.

Aerobic.

Very slight growth in beef broth plus 4 per cent salt (Hedges, Jour. Agr. Res., *29*, 1924, 243).

Distinctive character: Similar in culture to *Xanthomonas campestris*, *X. juglandis*, *X. vesicatoria*, etc., but they do not cross infect.

Comments: A variety that produces pustules on the leaves and pod of soy bean, *Glycine max*, both in America and Japan, has been described by Hedges (Science, *56*, 1922, 11). Liquefies pectate medium.

Two additional varieties have been described which produce a dark brown color

in a beef extract peptone medium and also in tyrosine medium. The first of these is pathogenic on beans (*Phaseolus vulgaris*) and related plants. The second was isolated from white kidney beans in India and is pathogenic on *Phaseolus vulgaris*, *P. lunatus*, *P. coccineus* and *Dolichos lablab*.

Habitat: Pathogenic on the bean (*Phaseolus vulgaris*), the hyacinth bean (*Dolichos lablab*), the lupine (*Lupinus polyphyllus*), etc. Not pathogenic on the soy bean (*Glycine sp.*) nor cowpea (*Vigna sp.*).

28. Xanthomonas plantaginis (Thornberry and Anderson, 1937) Burkholder, 1948. (*Phytomonas plantaginis* Thornberry and Anderson, Phytopath., *27*, 1937, 947; Burkholder, in Manual, 6th ed., 1948, 161.)

plan.ta'gi.nis. L. *plantago*, *plantaginis* the plantain; M.L. fem.n. *Plantago* generic name of plantain; M.L. gen.noun *plantaginis* of plantain.

Rods, 0.6 to 1.0 by 1.0 to 1.8 microns, occurring singly or in chains. Encapsulated. Motile with 1 to 2 polar flagella. Gram-negative.

Gelatin: Slight liquefaction.

Glucose agar slant: Growth moderate, filiform, raised, opaque, yellow and viscid.

Broth: Moderately turbid with ring.

Milk: Slight acidity, no reduction of litmus. Peptonization.

Nitrites not produced from nitrates.

Indole not produced.

Hydrogen sulfide not produced.

No appreciable amount of gas from carbohydrates.

Starch hydrolyzed.

Temperature relations: Optimum, 25° C. Minimum, 12° C. Maximum, 35° C. Thermal death point, 50° C.

Aerobic.

Source: From diseased leaves of *Plantago lanceolata* in Illinois.

Habitat: Pathogenic on *Plantago spp.*

29. Xanthomonas ricinicola (Elliott, 1930) Dowson, 1939. (*Bacterium ricini* Yoshi and Takimoto, Jour. Plant Protect., Tokyo, *15*, 1928, 12; *Bacterium ricinicola* Elliott, Man. Bact. Plant Path., 1930, 193; Dowson, Zent. f. Bakt., II Abt., *100*, 1939, 190.)

ri.ci.ni'co.la. L. *ricinus* the castor oil

plant; M.L. mas.n. *Ricinus* generic name of the castor bean; L. v. *colo* to dwell; M.L. fem.n. *ricinicola, Ricinus* dweller.

Rods, 0.4 to 0.9 by 1.3 to 2.6 microns, occurring in short chains. Encapsulated. Motile with polar flagella. Gram-negative.

Gelatin: Liquefied.

Nutrient agar colonies: Lemon-yellow, changing to brown.

Milk: Slightly acid. No coagulation. Peptonization.

Nitrites not produced from nitrates.

Acid but no gas from lactose.

Starch hydrolyzed.

Temperature relations: Optimum, between 29° and 30° C. Minimum, 2.5° C. Maximum, 39° C.

Aerobic.

Comment: Elliott (*loc. cit.*) renamed this species to avoid confusion with *Phytomonas ricini* Archibald.

Source: Isolated from leaf-spot of castor bean.

Habitat: Pathogenic on *Ricinus communis*.

30. **Xanthomonas sesbaniae** Patel et al., 1952. (Patel, Kulkarni and Dhande, Curr. Sci., *21*, 1952, 74.)

ses.ba'ni.ae. M.L. fem.n. *Sesbania* generic name of the plant host; M.L. gen.noun *sesbaniae* of *Sesbania*.

Rods, 0.7 by 1.3 microns, occurring singly or in chains. Encapsulated. Gram-negative.

Gelatin: Liquefied.

Potato-glucose agar colonies: Circular, 2 cm in diameter in 7 days, with striations starting 5 mm away from the center up to the periphery. Barium-yellow.

Litmus milk: Slightly peptonized with casein digested. Litmus slowly reduced.

Hydrogen sulfide produced.

Nitrites not produced from nitrates.

Acid but no gas from glucose, sucrose and lactose. Salicin not attacked.

Starch hydrolyzed.

Temperature relations: Optimum, 31° C. Thermal death point, 51° C.

Source: Isolated from leaf spots on *Sesbania aegyptiaca*.

Habitat: Pathogenic on *Sesbania aegyptiaca*.

31. **Xanthomonas stizolobiicola** Patel et al., 1951. (Patel, Kulkarni and Dhande, Curr. Sci., *20*, 1951, 106.)

sti.zo.lo.bi.i'co.la. M. L. neut.n. *Stizolobium* generic name of host; L. v. *colo* to inhabit; M.L. fem.n. *stizolobiicola* the *Stizolobium* dweller.

Rods. Mostly single. Encapsulated. Motile. Gram-negative.

Gelatin: Liquefied.

Nutrient agar colonies: 8 mm in diameter in 4 days, flat, entire, glistening, creamy to pinard-yellow.

Broth: Good growth.

Synthetic asparagine medium: No growth.

Loeffler's blood serum: Liquefied in 10 days.

Hydrogen sulfide produced.

Nitrites not produced from nitrates.

Methyl red negative; acetylmethylcarbinol not produced.

Indole not produced.

Acid but no gas from glucose, lactose and sucrose. Salicin not attacked.

Starch and casein hydrolyzed.

Lipolytic.

Salt tolerance: Up to 3 per cent.

Optimum temperature, between 28° and 30° C.

Aerobic.

Relationship to other species: Elliott (Man. Bact. Plant Path., 2nd ed., 1951, 129) lists *Xanthomonas phaseoli* on *Stizolobium deeringianum*. The two pathogens appear similar.

Source: Isolated from leaves, stems and petioles of *Stizolobium deeringianum* in India.

Habitat: Pathogenic on *Stizolobium deeringianum*.

32. **Xanthomonas taraxaci** Niederhauser, 1943. (Phytopath., *33*, 1943, 961.)

ta.rax'a.ci. M.L. neut.n. *Taraxacum* generic name of host; M.L. gen.noun *taraxaci* of *Taraxacum*.

Rods, 0.7 to 1.2 by 1.4 to 3.3 microns, occurring singly or in pairs. Motile with a single polar flagellum. Gram-negative.

Gelatin: Rapid liquefaction.

Beef-extract peptone agar colonies: Circular, smooth, bright yellow. Growth moderate.

Broth: Turbid with thin ring.

Milk: Litmus reduced. Soft curd precipitated and slowly digested. Liquid gradually clears. Tyrosine crystals produced.

Nitrites not produced from nitrates.

Indole not produced.

Hydrogen sulfide produced.

Lipase produced.

Acid from glucose, xylose, galactose, fructose, lactose, sucrose and glycerol. Arabinose, maltose, raffinose, inulin, mannitol, ethanol and salicin not attacked. Salts of acetic, citric, lactic, malic and succinic acids utilized with an increase in pH. Salts of tartaric, formic, salicylic and benzoic acids not utilized.

Starch hydrolyzed.

Pectate medium liquefied.

Salt tolerance: 3.25 to 3.5 per cent.

Temperature relations: Optimum, 30° C. Minimum, between 0° and 3° C. Maximum, 38° C.

Aerobic.

Source: Seven isolates from diseased Russian dandelions grown at Ithaca, New York.

Habitat: Pathogenic on *Taraxacum koksaghyz*, Russian dandelion.

33. **Xanthomonas translucens** (Jones et al., 1917) Dowson, 1939. (*Bacterium translucens* Jones, Johnson and Reddy, Jour. Agr. Res., *11*, 1917, 637; Dowson, Zent. f. Bakt., II Abt., *100*, 1939, 190.)

trans.lu'cens. L. *transluceo* to be translucent; L. part. *translucens* being translucent.

Rods 0.5 to 0.8 by 1.0 to 2.5 microns. Motile with a single polar flagellum. Gram-negative.

Gelatin: Liquefied.

Beef-peptone agar colonies: Round, smooth, shining, amorphous except for inconspicuous, somewhat irregular concentric striations within, wax-yellow tinged with old gold; margin entire.

Broth: Turbidity becomes rather strong. Pellicle.

Milk: Soft coagulum and digestion. Milk clears. Tyrosine crystals produced.

Nitrites not produced from nitrates.

Indole: Slight production.

Hydrogen sulfide produced.

Lipolytic (Starr and Burkholder, Phytopath., *32*, 1942, 600).

Ammonia from peptone.

Acid but no gas from glucose, d-fructose, d-mannose, d-galactose, sucrose, lactose and sometimes salicin. No utilization of l-rhamnose, inositol, maltose, raffinose, inulin, d-mannitol or dulcitol.

Starch hydrolyzed.

Pectate medium not liquefied.

Temperature relations: Optimum, 26° C. Minimum, 6° C. Maximum, 36° C.

Aerobic.

Distinctive characters: Many forms of *Xanthomonas translucens* have been described, all of which have the same cultural characters; they differ mainly in pathogenicity.

Comment: Various varieties, *formae speciales* and races of this species have been described. See Elliott (Man. Bact. Plant Path., 2nd ed., 1951, 142–146) for details.

Source: Originally isolated from bacterial blight of barley.

Habitat: Causes water-soaked stripes, streaks or other lesions on leaves, culms or glumes of grain and related plants. Occurs naturally on *Triticum spp., Hordeum spp., Bromus spp., Secale cereale, Phleum pratense* and, by inoculation, on *Avena spp.*

34. **Xanthomonas uppalii** Patel, 1948. (Indian Phytopath., *1*, 1948, 67.)

up.pa'li.i. Named for B. N. Uppal, an Indian plant pathologist; M.L. gen.noun *uppalii* of Uppal.

Rods, 0.7 to 1.0 by 2.0 to 2.4 microns, mostly single. Motile with a single polar flagellum. Gram-negative.

Gelatin: Rapid liquefaction.

Nutrient agar slants: Growth smooth, slightly raised, dull, filiform, opalescent, lemon-chrome.

Potato-glucose agar colonies: Growth copious, glistening, butyrous, empire-yellow.

Broth: Turbid. No pellicle. Sediment and floccules in 4 days.

Milk: Growth good. Litmus reduced.

Indole not produced.

Hydrogen sulfide produced.

Nitrites and ammonia not produced. Acetylmethylcarbinol not produced. No growth in Uschinsky's, Cohn's or Koser's uric acid medium.

Acid but no gas from glucose, lactose, sucrose, mannitol, raffinose, salicin and xylose. Fructose, arabinose and rhamnose not attacked.

Starch hydrolyzed.

Temperature relations: Optimum, 30°C. Minimum, 10°C. Maximum, 40°C.

pH range for growth, pH 5.3 to 9.2. Optimum pH, 7.0.

Source: Isolated from *Ipomoea muricata* in India.

Habitat: Pathogenic on *Ipomoea muricata*.

35. Xanthomonas vasculorum (Cobb, 1893) Dowson, 1939. (*Bacillus vascularum* (sic) Cobb, Agr. Gaz. of New South Wales, *4*, 1893, 777; abst. in Cent. f. Bakt., II Abt., *1*, 1895, 41; *Xanthomonas vascularum* (sic) Dowson, Zent. f. Bakt., II Abt., *100*, 1939, 190.)

vas.cu.lo'rum. L. *vasculum* a small vessel; M.L. neut.pl.gen.n. *vasculorum* of small vessels.

Description from Erw. Smith (Bact. in Rel. to Plant Dis., *3*, 1914, 54).

Rods 0.4 by 1.0 micron. Motile with a single polar flagellum. Originally reported as Gram-variable but later found to be Gram-negative (Elliott, Man. Bact. Plant Path., 2nd ed., 1951, 147).

Gelatin: Liquefaction feeble. Liquefaction good (Burkholder).

Beef-extract agar colonies: Pale yellow, smooth, glistening, not noticeably viscid.

Broth: Good growth.

Milk: Alkaline.

Nitrites not produced from nitrates.

Lipolytic (Starr and Burkholder, Phytopath., *32*, 1942, 600).

Acid but no gas from glucose, fructose and glycerol. No acid from lactose.

Starch hydrolyzed (Burkholder).

Pectate medium lipuefied.

Temperature relations: Optimum, 28° C. Thermal death point, about 50° C. (Elliott, *op. cit.*, 1951, 147).

Source: Isolated from diseased sugar cane.

Habitat: Pathogenic on sugar cane, *Saccharum officinarum*, causing a bacterial gummosis.

36. Xanthomonas vesicatoria (Doidge, 1920) Dowson, 1939. (*Bacterium vesicatorium* Doidge, Jour. Dept. Agr., S. Africa, *1*, 1920, 718; also Ann. Appl. Biol., *7*, 1921, 428; Dowson, Zent. f. Bakt., II Abt., *100*, 1939, 190.)

ve.si.ca.to'ri.a. L. *vesica* a blister; M.L. adj. *vesicatorius* causing a blister.

Rods 0.6 to 0.7 by 1.0 to 1.5 microns. Encapsulated. Motile with a single polar flagellum. Originally reported as Gram-positive but later found to be Gram-negative by Gardner and Kendrick (Phytopath., *13*, 1923, 307) and Higgins (Phytopath., *12*, 1922, 513).

Gelatin: Liquefied.

Nutrient agar colonies: Good growth. Circular, wet-shining, Naples-yellow, edges entire.

Milk: Casein precipitated and slowly digested. Tyrosine crystals.

Nitrites not produced from nitrates.

Indole not produced.

Hydrogen sulfide produced (Burkholder).

Lipolytic (Starr and Burkholder, Phytopath., *32*, 1942, 600).

Acid but no gas from glucose, fructose, sucrose, lactose, galactose, glycerol and dextrin.

Certain strains hydrolyze starch, others do not (Burkholder and Li, Phytopath., *31*, 1941, 753).

Pectate medium liquefied.

Optimum temperature, 30° C.

Distinctive character: *Xanthomonas vesicatoria* is reported as pathogenic on tomatoes and peppers. However Burkholder and Li (*loc. cit.*) report that there are sufficient cultural and pathogenic differences between the organism infecting tomatoes and the organism infecting peppers to warrant their separation into distinct species.

Comment: A variety pathogenic on radishes, turnips and other crucifers, and on tomato and peppers, has been described by White (Phytopath., *20*, 1930, 653). Differs from *Xanthomonas campestris* in that it does not cause a vascular disease. Unlike a variety of the latter species, it is not pathogenic on horseradish. Originally isolated from leaf spots of radishes and turnips in Indiana.

Source: Isolated from spotted tomato fruits in South Africa.

Habitat: Pathogenic on tomatoes, *Lycopersicon esculentum*, and peppers, *Capsicum annuum*.

37. Xanthomonas vignicola Burkholder, 1944. (Phytopath., *34*, 1944, 431.)

vig.ni'co.la. M.L. fem.n. *Vigna* generic name of host; L. v. *colo* to dwell; M.L. fem.n. *vignicola* the *Vigna* dweller.

Rods 0.7 (0.46 to 0.92) by 1.76 (1.0 to 2.8) microns. Motile with a single polar flagellum. Gram-negative.

Gelatin: Liquefied.

Beef-extract peptone agar slant: Filiform, glistening, edges entire, primuline-yellow, butyrous.

Broth: Turbid in 48 hours; heavy ring; no pellicle.

Litmus milk: Light curd becoming solid. Slow peptonization with crystal formation. Litmus reduced. Brownish syrup at end of 6 weeks.

Hydrogen sulfide produced.

Indole not produced.

Nitrites not produced from nitrates.

Asparagine and tyrosine not utilized as carbon-nitrogen sources. Tyrosine broken down to a brownish pigment in other media.

Lipolytic.

Salt tolerance: 2 per cent retards and 3 per cent inhibits growth.

Acid but no gas from glucose, galactose, lactose, maltose, sucrose and raffinose. Alkaline reactions with salts of citric and malic acids. Fructose, l-arabinose, xylose, rhamnose, glycerol, salicin and the sodium salts of lactic, formic, succinic, tartaric and hippuric acids not attacked.

Starch hydrolyzed.

Pectate medium liquefied.

Aerobic.

Temperature relations: Optimum, between 27° and 30° C. Minimum, between 6° and 9° C. Maximum, 37° C.

Source: Six isolates from cankers of cowpea stems.

Habitat: Causes canker disease of cow-

peas, *Vigna spp.*, and disease of the red kidney bean, *Phaseolus vulgaris*.

38. Xanthomonas nakatae (Okabe, 1933) Dowson, 1943. (*Bacterium nakatae* Type B, Okabe, Jour. Soc. Trop. Agr., Formosa, *5*, 1933, 161; Dowson, Trans. Brit. Mycol. Soc., *26*, 1943, 12.)

na'ka.tae. Named for K. Nakata, a Japanese plant pathologist; M.L. gen.noun *nakatae* of Nakata.

Rods 0.3 to 0.4 by 1.1 to 2.5 microns. Encapsulated. Motile with a single polar flagellum. Gram-negative.

Gelatin: Liquefied. Brown color.

Beef-extract agar colonies: Amber-yellow, circular, smooth, glistening, margins entire. Medium turns brown.

Broth: Moderate turbidity with yellow ring. Medium turns brown.

Milk: Casein precipitated and digested. Tyrosine crystals produced. Brown color.

Nitrites not produced from nitrates.

Indole not produced.

Hydrogen sulfide produced (slight).

Acid but no gas from glucose, sucrose, maltose and lactose.

Starch: Active hydrolysis.

Temperature relations: Optimum, between 30° and 32° C. Minimum, 10° C. Maximum, 39° C.

No growth in beef extract broth plus 2 per cent salt.

Aerobic.

Distinctive character: Differs from Type A in that it produces a brown pigment in culture. (Description of Type A not seen.)

Source: Isolated from water-soaked to brown leaf spots on jute.

Habitat: Pathogenic on jute, *Corchorus capsularis*.

39. Xanthomonas papavericola (Bryan and McWhorter, 1930) Dowson, 1939. (*Bacterium papavericola* Bryan and McWhorter, Jour. Agr. Res., *40*, 1930, 9; Dowson, Zent. f. Bakt., II Abt., *100*, 1939, 190.)

pa.pa.ve.ri'co.la. L. *papaver* the poppy; M.L. neut.n. *Papaver* generic name of poppy; L. v. *colo* to dwell; M.L. fem.n. *papavericola* poppy dweller.

Rods, 0.6 to 0.7 by 1.0 to 1.7 microns, occurring in chains. Encapsulated. Motile with a single polar flagellum. Gram-negative.

Gelatin: Liquefied.

Beef agar colonies: Mustard-yellow to primuline-yellow, circular, margins entire.

Broth: Turbidity prompt with a yellow ring and an incomplete pellicle.

Milk: Soft coagulation; peptonization and production of tyrosine crystals.

Nitrates: A weak reaction for nitrites after 10 days.

Indole not produced.

Hydrogen sulfide produced.

Lipolytic (Starr and Burkholder, Phytopath., *32*, 1942, 600).

Acid but no gas from glucose, galactose, fructose, sucrose, lactose, maltose, glycerol and mannitol.

Starch hydrolyzed.

Pectate medium liquefied.

Temperature relations: Optimum, between 25° and 30° C. Maximum, 35° C.

No growth in broth plus 5 per cent salt.

Aerobic.

Source: Isolated from black spots on leaves, buds and pods of poppy.

Habitat: Pathogenic on poppy, *Papaver rhoeas*.

40. **Xanthomonas alfalfae** (Riker et al., 1935) Dowson, 1943. (*Bacterium alfalfae* Riker, Jones and Davis, Jour. Agr. Res., *51*, 1935, 177; Dowson, Trans. Brit. Mycol. Soc., *26*, 1943, 11.)

al.fal'fae. Spanish alfalfa (lucerne); M.L. gen.noun *alfalfae* of alfalfa.

Rods 0.45 by 2.4 microns. Motile with a single polar flagellum. Gram-negative.

Gelatin: Liquefied.

Nutrient agar slant: Growth abundant, filiform, smooth, glistening, butyrous, pale yellow.

Broth: Turbid in 24 hours. Light sediment.

Milk: Casein precipitated and digested. Ammonia produced slowly in a nitrate medium.

Acid but no gas from glucose, maltose, lactose, arabinose and salicin (Patel, Kulkarni and Dhande, Indian Phytopath., *2*, 1949, 166). No acid in yeast broth plus sugars.

Starch hydrolyzed.

Aerobic.

Temperature relations: Optimum, between 24° and 32° C. Minimum, below 4° C. Maximum, below 36° C.

Source: Six single-cell cultures isolated from diseased alfalfa.

Habitat: Pathogenic on the leaves of alfalfa, *Medicago sativa*.

41. **Xanthomonas acernea** (Ogawa, 1937) Burkholder, 1948. (*Pseudomonas acernea* Ogawa, Ann. Phyt. Soc. Japan, *7*, 1937, 123; Burkholder, in Manual, 6th ed., 1948, 165.)

a.cer'ne.a. L. *acerneus* made of maple.

Rods 0.2 to 0.6 by 0.5 to 1.2 microns. Motile with a single polar flagellum. Gram-negative.

Gelatin: Liquefied.

Agar colonies: Round, smooth, convex, white to citron-yellow, glistening, translucent with amorphous structure.

Broth: Turbid.

Milk: Slowly cleared, slightly acid. No coagulation.

Nitrites produced from nitrates.

Hydrogen sulfide produced.

No gas produced in peptone water plus sugars.

Starch not hydrolyzed.

Temperature relations: Optimum, about 32° C. Thermal death point, 59° C.

Aerobic.

Source: From diseased leaves of *Acer trifidum* in Japan.

Habitat: Causes a disease in *Acer spp.* and in *Aesculus turbinata* and *Koelrenteria paniculata*.

42. **Xanthomonas carotae** (Kendrick, 1934) Dowson, 1939. (*Phytomonas carotae* Kendrick, Jour. Agr. Res., *49*, 1934, 504; Dowson, Zent. f. Bakt., II Abt., *100*, 1939, 190.)

ca.ro'tae. L. *carota* the carrot; M.L. gen.noun *carotae* of the carrot.

Rods 0.42 to 0.85 by 1.38 to 2.75 microns. Motile with 1 or 2 polar flagella. Gram-negative.

Gelatin: Liquefied.

Potato-glucose agar colonies: Circular, smooth, glistening, entire, straw-yellow in color.

Milk: Casein precipitated and milk cleared; alkaline.

Nitrites not produced from nitrates.

Indole not produced.

Acid but no gas from glucose, d-galactose, xylose, d-mannose, l-arabinose, sucrose, lactose, raffinose, trehalose, d-mannitol and glycerol. No acid from maltose or rhamnose.

Starch not hydrolyzed.

Pectate medium liquefied.

Optimum temperature, between 25° and 30° C.

Tolerates 4 per cent salt at pH 7.

Aerobic.

Source: Two original isolations from diseased carrots and a reisolation from inoculated carrots were used for the description.

Habitat: Pathogenic on leaves of *Daucus carota* var. *sativa*.

43. **Xanthomonas hederae** (Arnaud, 1920) Dowson, 1939. (*Bacterium hederae* Arnaud, Compt. rend. Acad. Sci., Paris, *171*, 1920, 121; Dowson, Zent. f. Bakt., II Abt., *100*, 1939, 190.)

he'de.rae. L. *hedera* the ivy; M.L. fem.n. *Hedera* generic name of ivy; M.L. gen.noun. *hederae* of ivy.

Description taken from Burkholder and Guterman (Phytopath., *22*, 1932, 783).

Rods 0.6 by 2.13 microns. Motile with a single polar flagellum. Gram-negative.

Gelatin: Liquefied.

Beef-extract-agar slants: Growth good, filiform, amber-yellow, butyrous.

Broth: Turbid.

Milk: Casein precipitated and digested. Milk becomes alkaline.

Nitrites not produced from nitrates.

Hydrogen sulfide produced.

Indole not produced.

Not lipolytic (Starr and Burkholder, Phytopath., *32*, 1942, 600).

Acid from glucose, fructose, galactose, xylose, sucrose, lactose and glycerol. Alkali from salts of acetic, citric, lactic, malic and succinic acids. The following are not utilized: arabinose, rhamnose, maltose, salicin, cellulose and formic acid.

Starch not hydrolyzed.

Pectate medium not liquefied.

Aerobic, facultative.

Source: Isolated from diseased ivy leaves.

Habitat: Pathogenic on ivy, *Hedera helix*.

44. **Xanthomonas phormicola** (Takimoto, 1933) Dowson, 1943. (*Bacterium phormicola* Takimoto, Jour. Plant Protect., *20*, 1933, 777; Dowson, Trans. Brit. Mycol. Soc., *26*, 1943, 12.)

phor.mi'co.la. Gr. dim. *phormium* the name of a plant; M.L. neut.n. *Phormium* generic name of New Zealand flax; L. v. *colo* to dwell; M.L. fem.n. *phormicola* the *Phormium* dweller.

Description translated by Dr. K. Togashi.

Rods 0.5 to 0.6 by 1.0 to 2.0 microns. Motile with a single flagellum. Gram-negative.

Gelatin: Liquefied.

Agar colonies: Light yellow, then waxy yellow; butyrous, then viscid.

Broth: Turbid; pellicle formed.

Milk: Casein coagulated slowly and precipitated, then digested. Alkaline.

Nitrites not produced from nitrates.

Indole not produced.

Hydrogen sulfide produced.

No gas from sucrose, glucose, lactose or glycerol.

No acid from various sugars in broth.

Temperature relations: Optimum, about 29° C. Minimum, about 0° C. Maximum, 39° C.

Aerobic.

Source: Species isolated from New Zealand flax, *Phormium tenax*.

Habitat: Causes a leaf stripe of *Phormium tenax*.

45. **Xanthomonas geranii** (Burkholder, 1937) Dowson, 1939. (*Phytomonas geranii* Burkholder, Phytopath., *27*, 1937, 560; Dowson, Zent. f. Bakt., II Abt., *100*, 1939, 190.)

ge.ra'ni.i. Gr. *geranium* geranium, crane's bill; M.L. neut.n. *Geranium* generic name; M.L. gen.noun *geranii* of *Geranium*.

Rods 0.75 to 2.0 microns. Motile with a single polar flagellum. Gram-negative.

Gelatin: Liquefied.

Beef-extract agar slants: Moderate to

good filiform growth, glistening, primuline-yellow. Develops in 24 hours.

Broth: Turbid in 24 hours. No pellicle but a moderate sediment.

Milk: Becomes clear with a heavy casein precipitate. Peptonization with crystal formation.

Nitrates reduced to ammonia.

Indole not produced.

Hydrogen sulfide produced.

Lipolytic (Starr and Burkholder, Phytopath., *32*, 1942, 600).

Acid from glucose, galactose, fructose, xylose, rhamnose, lactose, sucrose, raffinose and glycerol. Alkaline reaction from salts of citric, malic, malonic and succinic acids. No growth in arabinose or formic, hippuric, maleic or tartaric acids.

Starch not hydrolyzed.

Pectate medium liquefied.

Aerobic.

Distinctive characters: Pathogenic on *Geranium spp.*, not on the house geranium, *Pelargonium hortorum*.

Relationship to other species: Similar in culture to *Xanthomonas pelargonii*.

Source: Three cultures isolated from *Geranium sanguineum*.

Habitat: Pathogenic on *Geranium sanguineum*, *G. maculatum*, *G. pratense* and *G. sylvaticum*.

46. **Xanthomonas antirrhini** (Takimoto, 1920) Dowson, 1943. (*Pseudomonas antirrhini* Takimoto, Bot. Mag. Tokyo, *34*, 1920, 257; Dowson, Trans. Brit. Mycol. Soc., *26*, 1943, 11.)

an.tir.rhi′ni. Gr. *antirrhinum* the plant snapdragon; M.L. gen.noun *antirrhini* of the snapdragon.

Description from Elliott (Man. Bact. Plant Path., 1930, 93).

Rods 0.3 to 0.4 by 0.8 to 1.2 microns. Encapsulated. Motile with polar flagella. Gram-negative.

Gelatin: Liquefied.

Agar colonies: Circular, glistening, white, later yellow.

Milk: Coagulated and casein digested.

Nitrites produced from nitrates.

No gas produced.

Aerobic.

Temperature relations: Optimum, between 26° and 27° C. Maximum, 34° C.

Habitat: Causes a leaf spot of *Antirrhinum majus*.

47. **Xanthomonas heterocea** (Vzoroff, 1930) Săvulescu, 1947. (*Phytomonas heterocea* Vzoroff, Bull. North Caucasian Plant Prot. Sta. Roztoff-on-Don, *6–7*, 1930, 263; Săvulescu, Anal. Acad. Romane, III, *22*, 1947, 11.)

he.te.ro′ce.a. Gr. adj. *heterus* another, different.

Description taken from Rev. App. Myc., *10*, 1931, 628.

Rods 0.4 to 0.6 by 1.0 to 2.0 microns. Motile. Gram-negative.

Gelatin: Slow liquefaction.

Agar colonies: Circular, 2 mm in diameter, convex, smooth, semi-transparent, glistening, yellow to amber. Pitted surface.

Milk: No coagulation. At first acid, later alkaline.

Nitrites produced from nitrates.

Indole not produced.

Hydrogen sulfide produced.

Acid from glucose, galactose, arabinose, xylose, sucrose, maltose, salicin, glycerol and mannitol. Does not ferment lactose, inulin, ethyl alcohol, esculin, adonitol or dulcitol.

Optimum temperature, between 25° and 30° C.

Source: Isolated from diseased tobacco in the North Caucasus.

Habitat: Pathogenic on *Nicotiana tabacum*.

48. **Xanthomonas badrii** Patel et al., 1950. (Patel, Kulkarni and Dhande, Indian Phytopath., *3*, 1950, 104.)

bad′ri.i. From the given name of Badri Uppal, Indian plant pathologist; M.L. gen.noun *badrii* of Badri.

Rods, 0.7 to 1.0 by 1.4 to 1.8 microns, occurring singly and rarely in chains. Motile with a single polar flagellum. Gram-negative.

Gelatin: Liquefied.

Nutrient agar colonies: Smooth, glistening, entire, empire-yellow; growth slow.

Milk: Cleared in 8 days. Litmus reduced.

Loeffler's blood serum: Liquefied.

Nitrites not produced from nitrates.

Indole not produced.

Ammonia produced.

Methyl red negative; acetylmethylcarbinol not produced.

Acid but no gas from glucose, lactose, sucrose, mannitol and salicin.

Optimum temperature, 31° C.

Source: Isolated from leaf spot of *Xanthium strumarium* in India.

Habitat: Pathogenic on *Xanthium strumarium*.

49. **Xanthomonas gummisudans** (McCulloch, 1924) Starr and Burkholder, 1942. (*Bacterium gummisudans* McCulloch, Phytopath., *14*, 1924, 63; also see Jour. Agr. Res., *27*, 1924, 229; Starr and Burkholder, Phytopath., *32*, 1942, 600.)

gum.mi.su'dans. L. *gummi* gum; L. v. *sudo* to sweat, exude; M.L. part.adj. *gummisudans* exuding gum.

Rods 0.6 to 0.8 by 1.0 to 2.8 microns. Encapsulated. Motile with a single polar flagellum. Gram-negative.

Gelatin: Liquefied.

Beef-peptone agar colonies: Amberyellow, circular, transparent, smooth, with definite margins.

Broth: Moderately turbid with a yellow ring.

Milk: Soft curd which is digested with formation of tyrosine crystals.

Nitrites not produced from nitrates.

Indole not produced.

Hydrogen sulfide produced.

Lipolytic (Starr and Burkholder, *loc. cit.*).

Acid from glucose and sucrose.

Temperature relations: Optimum, 30° C. Minimum, 2° C. Maximum, 36° C.

Aerobic.

Source: From gummy lesions on gladiolus leaves.

Habitat: Pathogenic on leaves of gladioli.

50. **Xanthomonas nigromaculans** (Takimoto, 1927) Dowson, 1943. (*Bacterium nigromaculans* Takimoto, Jour. Plant Protect., Tokyo, *14*, 1927, 522; Dowson, Trans. Brit. Mycol. Soc., *26*, 1943, 12.)

ni.gro.ma'cu.lans. L. *niger* black; L. v. *maculo* to spot; M.L. part.adj. *nigromaculans* spotting with black.

Description translated by Dr. K. Togashi.

Rods 0.6 to 0.9 by 1.5 to 2.8 microns. Motile with 1 or 2 polar flagella. Gram-negative.

Gelatin: Liquefied.

Agar colonies: Yellow, circular, entire, smooth, glistening.

Broth: Growth moderate with yellow pellicle.

Milk: Coagulation and digestion of the casein.

Nitrites not produced from nitrates.

Indole not produced.

No acid or gas from glucose, sucrose, lactose, mannitol or glycerol in peptone water.

Temperature relations: Optimum, between 27° and 28° C. Minimum, 0° C. Maximum, 33° C.

Aerobic.

Comment: A *forma specialis* that is pathogenic on *Zinnia spp.* has been described (Hopkins and Dowson, Trans. Brit. Mycol. Soc., *32*, 1949, 253).

Source: Isolated from lesions on leaf and petioles of burdock.

Habitat: Pathogenic on leaves and petioles of *Arctium lappa*, the burdock.

51. **Xanthomonas axonopodis** Starr and Garces, 1950. (*Xanthomonas axonoperis* (sic) Starr and Garces, Rev. Fac. Nal. de Agron. de Medellin, *12*, 1950, 75.)

ax.on.o'pod.is. Gr. noun *axon* axis; Gr. noun *pous* foot; M.L. mas.n. *Axonopus* generic name of a grass; M.L. gen.noun *axonopodis* of *Axonopus*.

Rods 0.4 by 1.0 to 3.0 microns. Encapsulated. Motile by means of a single polar flagellum. Gram-negative.

Gelatin: Not liquefied.

Yeast extract agar: Growth slow; small, yellow colonies appear in 7 days.

Peptone sucrose agar: Growth slow; yellow colonies 1 mm in diameter appear in 7 days.

Potato-glucose agar: No growth.

Broth: Slight turbidity in two days; slimy pellicle in 2 weeks. Yellowish ring produced.

Milk: Litmus not reduced.

Nitrites not produced from nitrates.

Indole not produced.

Hydrogen sulfide not produced.

Non-lipolytic.

Tyrosine in a caseinate medium: Growth slight; no color reaction.

Carbohydrate utilization difficult to determine because of meager growth. Glucose, sucrose and trehalose probably utilized. Lactose, maltose, raffinose, dulcitol, glycerol, mannitol, sorbitol, dextrin, inulin, aesculin and salicin utilization doubtful. Starch hydrolyzed.

Pectate medium not liquefied.

Temperature relations: Optimum, 30° C. Minimum, 5° C. Maximum, 37° C.

Moderate growth in broth plus 1 per cent NaCl; no growth with 1.5 per cent NaCl.

Chemical tolerance: Optimum pH between 6.6 and 7.6. Minimum, 5.8.

Source: Isolated from diseased grass, *Axonopus scoparius*, in Colombia.

Habitat: Pathogenic on *Axonopus spp.*

52. **Xanthomonas oryzae** (Uyeda and Ishiyama, 1926) Dowson, 1943. (*Pseudomonas oryzae* Uyeda and Ishiyama, Proc. Third Pan-Pacific Sci. Congr., Tokyo, *2*, 1926, 2112; Dowson, Trans. Brit. Mycol. Soc., *26*, 1943, 12.)

o.ry′zae. Gr. *oryza* rice; M.L. fem.n. *Oryza* generic name of rice; M.L. gen.noun *oryzae* of *Oryza*.

Rods 0.5 to 0.8 by 1.0 to 2.0 microns. Motile with a single polar flagellum. Gram-negative.

Gelatin: No liquefaction.

Nutrient agar colonies: Circular, smooth, glistening, wax-yellow.

Milk: Slightly acid.

Nitrites not produced from nitrates.

Hydrogen sulfide produced.

Acid but no gas from glucose, lactose and sucrose.

Optimum temperature, between 26° and 30° C.

Strict aerobe.

Source: Isolated from a leaf blight of rice.

Habitat: Pathogenic on rice, *Oryza sativa*.

53. **Xanthomonas celebensis** (Gäumann, 1923) Dowson, 1943. (*Pseudomonas celebensis* Gäumann, Ztschr. f. Pflanzenkrank., *33*, 1923, 11; Meded. Inst. voor Plantenziek., Buitenzorg, *59*, 1923, 17;

Dowson, Trans. Brit. Mycol. Soc., *26*, 1943, 11.)

ce.le.ben′sis. Celebes, an island name; M.L. adj. *celebensis* of Celebes.

Rods 0.9 by 1.5 microns. Motile by a single polar flagellum. Gram-negative.

Agar colonies: Grayish yellow.

Broth: Thin pellicle.

Milk: Coagulated and cleared.

Nitrites not produced from nitrates.

Sodium selenite: Brick red.

Starch hydrolyzed.

Source: From vascular bundles of diseased bananas from the Celebes.

Habitat: Causes the blood disease of banana.

54. **Xanthomonas panici** (Elliott, 1923) Săvulescu, 1947. (*Bacterium panici* Elliott, Jour. Agr. Res., *26*, 1923, 157; Săvulescu, Anal. Acad. Romane, III, *22*, 1947, 11.)

pa′ni.ci. L. *panicum* Italian panic grass; M.L. neut.n. *Panicum* generic name; M.L. gen.noun *panici* of *Panicum*.

Rods 0.69 by 1.66 microns. Encapsulated. Motile with 1, rarely 2, polar flagella. Gram-negative.

Gelatin: Liquefaction slow.

Beef agar colonies: Circular, white, smooth, glistening, margins at first entire, later undulate.

Broth: Moderate turbidity in 24 hours. Thin pellicle. Medium brownish.

Milk: Alkaline and clears.

Nitrites produced from nitrates.

Indole not produced.

Hydrogen sulfide produced.

No acid or gas from carbohydrates.

Starch: Hydrolysis moderate.

Temperature relations: Optimum, 33° C. Minimum, 5° C. Maximum, 45° C.

pH range for growth, pH 5.4 to 10.0. Optimum pH, between 6.15 and 6.3.

Aerobic.

Distinctive characters: Differs from *Pseudomonas andropogoni* in that it liquefies gelatin, produces nitrites from nitrates and does not infect sorghum and broom corn.

Source: Isolation from water-soaked lesions on leaves, sheaths and culms of millet collected in Wisconsin and in S. Dakota.

Habitat: Pathogenic on proso millet, *Panicum miliaceum*.

55. Xanthomonas proteamaculans (Paine and Stansfield, 1919) Burkholder, 1948. (*Pseudomonas proteamaculans* Paine and Stansfield, Ann. Appl. Biol., *6*, 1919, 38; Burkholder, in Manual, 6th ed., 1948, 169.)

pro.te.a.ma'cu.lans. Gr. *Proteus* a god; M.L. noun *Protea* a plant generic name; L. v. *maculo* to spot; M.L. part.adj. *proteamaculans* spotting *Protea*.

Rods 0.6 to 0.8 by 0.8 to 1.6 microns. Motile with 1 to 3 polar flagella. Grampositive (Paine and Stansfield). Gram-negative (Dowson, personal communication, August, 1953).

Gelatin: Liquefied.

Agar slant: Growth wet-shining, dirty white with a faint yellow tinge.

Broth: Turbid in 24 hours. Slight ring.

Milk: Acid with soft curd after 2 days. Later a separation of whey.

Nitrites produced from nitrates.

Acid and gas from glucose, sucrose and mannitol. No acid or gas from lactose.

Starch: Slight hydrolysis.

Source: Repeated isolation from a leafspot of *Protea* in England.

Habitat: Pathogenic on *Protea cynaroides*.

56. Xanthomonas manihotis (Arthaud-Berthet, 1912) Starr, 1946. (*Bacillus manihotus* (sic) Arthaud-Berthet, in Bondar, Chacaras and Quintaes, *5* (4), 1912, 15; Starr, Jour. Bact., *51*, 1946, 136.)

ma.ni.ho'tis. M.L. *Manihot* a plant generic name; M.L. gen.noun *manihotis* of *Manihot*.

Description from Burkholder (Phytopath., *32*, 1942, 147).

Rods 0.35 to 0.93 by 1.4 to 2.8 microns. Mostly non-motile. One isolate showed a few cells with a single polar flagellum. Amaral (Instit. Biol., São Paulo, Arq., *13*, 1942, 120) states that the species is motile with a single polar flagellum. Gramnegative.

Gelatin: Liquefied.

Beef-extract-peptone agar slant: Growth raised, ivory-colored, smooth, shiny, with edges entire.

Potato-glucose agar: Growth abundant, white to hyaline, very mucoid.

Broth: Turbid with a whitish granular ring.

Litmus milk: Litmus reduced and milk clears. With return of color, litmus is purple.

Indole not produced.

Hydrogen sulfide produced.

Nitrites produced from nitrates (Drummond and Hipolito, Ceres, *2*, 1941, 298).

Asparagine not used as a nitrogen and carbon source. No growth in nitrate synthetic broth.

Weak growth but slight acid production in synthetic medium plus glucose, d-galactose, d-fructose, d-xylose, maltose or sucrose. No growth in rhamnose, l-arabinose, d-lactose, glycerol, mannitol or salicin. Good growth with alkaline reaction in same medium plus salts of the following acids: acetic, citric, malic, maleic or succinic. The salts of formic, hippuric, lactic and tartaric acids were not utilized.

Starch hydrolyzed.

Pectate medium liquefied.

Lipolytic action slight.

Aerobic.

Temperature relations: Optimum, 30° C. Minimum, 5° C. Maximum, 38° C.

Source: First isolated from the cassava, *Manihotus utilissima*, in Brazil.

Habitat: Produces a wilt disease on various species of *Manihotus*.

57. Xanthomonas rubrisubalbicans (Christopher and Edgerton, 1930) Săvulescu, 1947. (*Phytomonas rubrisubalbicans* Christopher and Edgerton, Jour. Agr. Res., *41*, 1930, 266; Săvulescu, Anal. Acad. Romane, III, *22*, 1947, 11.)

ru.bri.sub.al'bi.cans. L. *ruber* red; L. *subalbicans* whitish; M.L. adj. *rubrisubalbicans* red whitish.

Short rods with polar flagella. Encapsulated. Gram-negative.

Gelatin: No liquefaction.

Bacto-glucose agar colonies: Circular, glistening, viscid, milky gray to buff. Margins translucent, entire.

Broth: Turbid after 24 hours. Pellicle and a ropy sediment.

Indole produced.

Hydrogen sulfide produced.

No acid or gas from carbohydrates.

Starch hydrolyzed.

Optimum temperature, 30° C.
Optimum pH, 6.8 to 8.0.
Source: Isolated many times from mottled stripe of sugar cane in Louisiana.
Habitat: Pathogenic on sugar cane, Johnson's grass and sorghum.

58. Xanthomonas cannae (Bryan, 1921) Săvulescu, 1947. (*Bacterium cannae* Bryan, Jour. Agr. Res., *21*, 1921, 152; Săvulescu, Anal. Acad. Romane, III, *22*, 1947, 12.)

can'nae. Gr. *canna* a reed; M.L. fem.n. *Canna* generic name; M.L. gen.noun *cannae* of *Canna*.

Rods 0.5 to 0.7 by 1.0 to 2.0 microns. Encapsulated. Motile with 1 to 3 polar flagella. Gram-negative.

Gelatin: Slow liquefaction.

Agar slants: Growth filiform, white, moist, with thin margins and granular centers.

Broth: Turbid; heavy sediment.

Milk: Alkaline and clears.

Nitrites produced from nitrates.

Indole not produced.

Hydrogen sulfide produced.

No acid produced from carbohydrates.

Temperature relations: Optimum, 35° C. Minimum, 5° C. Maximum, 40° C.

Aerobic.

Source: Isolated from diseased canna leaves collected in Washington, D. C. and in Illinois.

Habitat: Causes a disease in *Canna indica*.

59. Xanthomonas conjac (Uyeda, 1910) Burkholder, 1948. (*Pseudomonas conjac* Uyeda, Bot. Mag. Tokyo, *24*, 1910, 182; Burkholder, in Manual, 6th ed., 1948, 171.)

con'jac. M.L. *conjac* the specific epithet of *Amorphophallus konjac*, the host.

Description from Elliott (Man. Bact. Plant Path., 1930, 121).

Rods 0.75 to 1.0 by 1.5 microns. Motile with 1 to 4 polar flagella. Presumably Gram-negative although the original description records this species as Gram-positive (Burkholder).

Gelatin colonies: Circular to irregular, light yellow.

Broth: Pellicle formed.

Milk: Coagulated.

Conjac: Liquefied.

Nitrites produced from nitrates.

Indole produced.

Hydrogen sulfide produced.

Gas from glucose.

Optimum temperature, 24° C.

Habitat: Pathogenic on *Amorphophallus konjac*.

60. Xanthomonas zingiberi (Uyeda, 1908) Săvulescu, 1947. (Eine neue species, Uyeda, Cent. f. Bakt., II Abt., *17*, 1907, 383; *Pseudomonas zingiberi* Uyeda, Rept. Imp. Agr. Exp. Sta., Japan, No. 35, 1908, 114; Săvulescu, Anal. Acad. Romane, III, *22*, 1947, 13.)

zin.gi'be.ri. Gr. indecl. *zingiberi* ginger.

Description from Stapp (in Sorauer, Handb. d. Pflanzenkrank., *2*, 5 Aufl., 1928, 65).

Rods 0.5 to 1.1 by 0.75 to 1.8 microns. Non-motile at first, later a polar flagellum develops. Gram-negative.

Gelatin: Liquefied.

Agar colonies: White.

Milk: Coagulation and peptonization of the casein.

Nitrites produced from nitrates.

Indole not produced.

Hydrogen sulfide produced.

No gas from glucose.

Temperature relations: Optimum, 28° C. Minimum, 5° C. Maximum, 40° C.

Source: Isolated from ginger plant showing a rot at the base of the sprouts.

Habitat: Pathogenic on ginger, *Zingiber officinale*.

Addendum: *Species incertae sedis.* Two additional groups of yellow, polar-flagellate species are described in this addendum although they are not typical of the genus *Xanthomonas* in all respects. The first is a group of three species of plant pathogens. One of these species is non-motile, but it appears to be closely related to the two polar-flagellate species with which it is associated. Plant pathologists have placed these three species in *Xanthomonas* even though they do not possess all of the characteristics of the species in this genus *sensu stricto*. The non-water-soluble, yellow pigment differs from that found in true xanthomonads. Likewise none of the three species liquefies gelatin. Neither do they show the gummy growth of true xanthomonads, and they differ in other important characteristics. The second group comprises eleven species which are not pathogenic to plants so far as is known. They have been isolated from the surface of leaves, soil and similar materials. All produce a non-water-soluble, yellow pigment, but no one has as yet undertaken a comparative study of cultures to determine which of these species, if any, are true xanthomonads.

Key to **Xanthomonas Addendum.**

I. Plant pathogens.
  A. Non-motile.
        1. *Xanthomonas stewartii.*
  B. Polar flagellate.
    1. Litmus milk alkaline. Pathogenic on *Iris spp.*
        2. *Xanthomonas tardicrescens.*
    2. No change in litmus milk. Pathogenic on sugar cane, *Saccharum officinarum.*
        3. *Xanthomonas albilineans.*
II. Saprophytic species.
  A. Gelatin liquefied.
    1. Nitrites produced from nitrates.
      a. Acid but no gas from glucose.
        4. *Pseudomonas trifolii.*
        5. *Pseudomonas xanthe.*
      aa. Action on glucose not recorded.
        6. *Pseudomonas caudata.*
    2. Nitrites not produced from nitrates.
      a. Litmus milk acid; ferments lactose.
        7. *Pseudomonas perlurida.*
      aa. Litmus milk slimy, alkaline.
        8. *Pseudomonas ochracea.*
  B. Gelatin not liquefied.
    1. Nitrites produced from nitrates.
      a. Do not attack cellulose.
        b. Does not attack phenol.
        9. *Pseudomonas cerevisiae.*
        bb. Attacks phenol.
        10. *Pseudomonas pictorum.*
      aa. Attack cellulose.
        b. Litmus milk acid but no digestion.
        11. *Pseudomonas arguta.*
        bb. No growth in litmus milk.
        12. *Pseudomonas subcreta.*
    2. Nitrites not produced from nitrates; may or may not hydrolyze agar.
      a. Butter-colored pellicle on litmus milk.
        13. *Pseudomonas lacunogenes.*
      aa. No surface pellicle.
        14. *Pseudomonas segnis.*

Group I. –Plant pathogens.

1. **Xanthomonas stewartii** (Erw. Smith, 1914) Dowson, 1939. (Sweet corn bacillus, Stewart, N. Y. Agr. Exp. Sta. Bull. 130, 1897, 423; *Bacterium stewarti* (sic) Smith, Bacteria in Relation to Plant Diseases, *3*, 1914, 89; *Xanthomonas stewarti* (sic) Dowson, Zent. f. Bakt., II Abt., *100*, 1939, 190.)

ste.war'ti.i. Stewart patronymic; M.L. gen.noun *stewartii* of Stewart.

Description from Smith (U. S. Dept. Agr., Div. Veg. Phys. and Path., Bull. 28, 1901).

Rods 0.4 to 0.7 by 0.9 to 2.0 microns. Encapsulated. Non-motile (McCulloch, Phytopath., *8*, 1918, 440). Gram-negative.

Gelatin: No liquefaction.

Nutrient agar colonies: Small, round, yellow.

Broth: Growth feeble with whitish ring and yellow precipitate.

Milk: Yellow ring but no visible action on the milk. Slightly acid.

Nitrites not produced from nitrates. McNew (Phytopath., *28*, 1938, 773) states that less virulent strains assimilate only organic nitrogen; those of intermediate virulence assimilate nitrogen from inorganic salts without reduction of nitrates to nitrites; virulent strains reduce nitrates to nitrites.

Hydrogen sulfide not produced.

Indole production slight or none.

Reduction of methylene blue in Dunham's solution feeble or doubtful.

Acid but no gas from glucose, galactose, sucrose, mannitol and glycerol. No acid from maltose. Acid from fructose, arabinose and xylose (McNew, *loc. cit.*); also from lactose and mannose (Dowson, *op. cit.*, *100*, 1939, 190).

Starch not hydrolyzed.

Temperature relations: Optimum, 30° C. Maximum, 39° C. Minimum, 8° C.

Chemical tolerance: Optimum pH between 6.0 and 8.0. Limits, about pH 4.5 to 8.5.

8 per cent salt restricts growth.

Strict aerobe.

Source: From wilted sweet corn.

Habitat: Pathogenic on corn, *Zea mays*. Sweet corn very susceptible and field corn slightly so.

2. Xanthomonas tardicrescens (McCulloch, 1937) Dowson, 1943. (*Bacterium tardicrescens* McCulloch, Phytopath., *27*, 1937, 135; Dowson, Trans. Brit. Mycol. Soc., *26*, 1943, 12.)

tar.di.cres'cens. L. adj. *tardus* slow; L.

part.adj. *crescens* growing; M.L. adj. *tardicrescens* slow growing.

Rods 0.6 to 0.8 by 1.58 microns. Motile with a polar flagellum. Gram-negative.

Gelatin: No liquefaction.

Beef-extract agar colonies: Circular, mustard-yellow, edges entire, 1.0 to 1.5 mm in diameter.

Broth: Light clouding.

Milk: Slightly alkaline. Clearing after 5 to 6 weeks.

Nitrites produced from nitrates.

Indole not produced.

Hydrogen sulfide not produced, or feebly so.

Acid but no gas from glucose, fructose, galactose, arabinose, xylose and rhamnose. Alkaline reaction from salts of citric, malic and succinic acids.

Starch not hydrolyzed.

Not lipolytic (Starr and Burkholder, Phytopath., *32*, 1942, 603).

Temperature relations: Optimum, 26° C. Maximum, 32° C. Minimum, 5° C. (McCulloch, Phytopath., *28*, 1938, 648).

Chemical tolerance: Optimum pH between 6.5 and 7.5. Growth slight at 5.8 and 8.0 (McCulloch, *loc. cit.*).

No growth with 3 per cent salt (McCulloch, *loc. cit.*).

Aerobic.

Distinctive character: Very slow grower.

Source: Isolated by McCulloch and by Burkholder from blighted iris leaves.

Habitat: Pathogenic on *Iris spp.*

3. Xanthomonas albilineans (Ashby, 1929) Dowson, 1943. (*Bacterium albilineans* Ashby, Trop. Agr., Trinidad, *6*, 1929, 135; Dowson, Trans. Brit. Mycol. Soc., *26*, 1943, 11.)

al.bi.li'ne.ans. L. adj. *albus* white; L. part.adj. *lineans* striping; M.L. adj. *albilineans* white-striping.

Description from Martin, Carpenter and Weller (The Hawaiian Planters' Record, *36*, 1932, 184).

Rods, 0.25 to 0.3 by 0.6 to 1.0 micron, occurring singly or in chains. Motile with a polar flagellum. Gram-negative.

Agar colonies: After 7 to 10 days, minute transparent drops, moist, shining. Honey-yellow to Naples-yellow.

Gelatin: No liquefaction.

Milk: Growth, but no visible change in the milk.

No growth with ammonium salts, nitrates or asparagine as a source of nitrogen.

No growth in peptone water without carbohydrates. Invertase secreted.

Starch not hydrolyzed.

Temperature relations: Optimum, about 25° C. Maximum, 37° C.

Distinctive characters: Differs from *Xanthomonas vasculorum*, which produces a large gummy type of colony and which is a very active organism biochemically. The two pathogens also differ in the type of lesion they produce on sugar cane.

Source: Isolated by D. S. North (Colonial Sugar Ref. Co., Sydney, N. S. Wales, Agr. Rept., 8, 1926, 1) from white stripe and leaf scald of sugar cane in Australia.

Habitat: Vascular pathogen of sugar cane, *Saccharum officinarum*.

Group II.—Saprophytic species.

4. Pseudomonas trifolii Huss, 1907. (Huss, Cent. f. Bakt., II Abt., *19*, 1907, 68; *Xanthomonas trifolii* James, Canadian Jour. Microbiol., *1*, 1955, 479.)

tri.fo′li.i. L. *trifolium* trefoil, clover; M.L. neut.n. *Trifolium* generic name of clover; M.L. gen.noun *trifolii* of *Trifolium*.

Rods, 0.5 to 0.7 by 0.75 to 2.0 microns, occurring singly, in pairs and in chains. Motile, possessing a single polar flagellum. Gram-negative.

Gelatin colonies: Convex, smooth, moist, glistening, grayish yellow.

Gelatin stab: Napiform liquefaction.

Agar colonies: Small, circular, grayish, becoming brownish yellow.

Agar slant: Yellowish, becoming brownish yellow streak, lacerate margin.

Broth: Turbid, with grayish yellow pellicle and sediment.

Litmus milk: Slowly coagulated; alkaline; with yellow ring.

Potato: Thick, yellowish, flat, smooth, glistening.

Hydrogen sulfide produced.

Indole produced.

Acid from glucose, sucrose, xylose, arabinose and mannitol. No acid from lactose.

Nitrites produced from nitrates.

Cultures have an agreeable odor.

Volutin formed.

Aerobic, facultative.

Optimum temperature, between 33° and 35° C.

Source: Isolated from clover hay.

Habitat: Evidently a common organism on the leaves of plants.

5. Pseudomonas xanthe Zettnow, 1916. Cent. f. Bakt., I Abt., Orig., 77, 1916, 220.)

xan′the. Gr. adj. *xanthus* yellow.

Rods 0.5 to 0.6 by 0.4 to 1.4 microns. Motile, possessing a single or occasionally two or more very long (20 microns) polar flagella. Gram-negative.

Gelatin colonies: Circular, yellow, granular.

Gelatin stab: Pale yellow surface growth. Brownish yellow under surface colonies. Saccate liquefaction.

Agar slant: Dark yellow, glistening, with dark yellow sediment in water of condensation. Pigment not water-soluble.

Broth: Turbid.

Milk becomes rose-yellow in 4 weeks without any other change.

Potato: Grayish yellow to brownish growth.

Indole produced.

Nitrites produced from nitrates.

Acid produced from glucose, sucrose and maltose.

Starch hydrolyzed.

Blood serum not liquefied.

Aerobic, facultative.

Optimum temperature, 30° C.

Source: Air contamination.

6. Pseudomonas caudata (Wright, 1895) Conn, 1919. (*Bacillus caudatus* Wright, Memoirs Nat. Acad. Sci., 7, 1895, 444; Conn, Jour. Agr. Res., *16*, 1919, 313.)

cau.da′ta. L. noun *cauda* a tail; M.L. adj. *caudatus* having a tail.

Rods long, granular, slender, occurring singly, in pairs and in chains. Appear like cocci in old cultures. Motile, possessing a polar flagellum (Conn). Gram-negative.

Gelatin colonies: Yellow, translucent, smooth, undulate.

Gelatin stab: Villous growth in stab. Crateriform liquefaction.

Agar slant: Yellow to orange, glistening, translucent, slightly spreading. May lose power to form pigment.

Broth: Turbid, with yellow sediment.

Litmus milk: Unchanged.

Potato: Dark yellow, raised, rough, spreading.

Indole not produced.

Nitrites and ammonia produced from nitrates.

Ammonia produced from peptone.

Starch digested.

Aerobic, facultative.

Optimum temperature, 25° C.

Habitat: Water and soil.

7. **Pseudomonas perlurida** Kellerman et al., 1913. (Kellerman, McBeth, Scales and Smith, Cent. f. Bakt., II Abt., *39*, 1913, 516; also see McBeth, Soil Sci., *1*, 1916, 472.)

per.lu'ri.da. L. prefix *per* very; L. *luridus* pale yellow, sallow; M.L. adj. *perluridus* very sallow.

Rods 0.4 by 1.0 micron. Motile with one to three polar flagella. Gram-negative.

Gelatin stab: Liquefied.

Agar slant: Moderate, flat, faint yellow growth.

Broth: Turbid in 5 days.

Litmus milk: Acid. Peptonization after 16 days.

Potato: Scant, yellow growth with bleaching along line of growth.

Indole not produced.

Nitrites not produced from nitrates.

Ammonia produced.

Acid from glucose, maltose, lactose, sucrose, starch, glycerol and mannitol.

Aerobic, facultative.

Optimum temperature, 20° C.

Source: Soil from Virginia, Louisiana and Missouri.

Habitat: Soil.

8. **Pseudomonas ochracea** (Zimmermann, 1890) Chester, 1901. (*Bacillus ochraceus* Zimmermann, Bakt. unserer Trink- und Nutzwässer, Chemnitz, *1*, 1890, 60; Chester, Man. Determ. Bact., 1901, 316.)

och.ra'ce.a. Gr. noun *ochra* ochre; M.L. adj. *ochraceus* of the color of ochre.

Rods, 0.7 to 0.8 by 1.2 to 4.5 microns, occurring in pairs and longer chains. Slow, undulatory motion (Zimmermann). Polar flagella (Lehmann and Neumann, Bakt. Diag., 1 Aufl., *2*, 1896, 255). Gram-negative.

Gelatin colonies: Pale yellow to golden, ochre-yellow, slightly raised, with slightly fringed margin, granular.

Gelatin stab: Yellowish to yellow-gray surface growth. Infundibuliform liquefaction. Pale yellow to ochre-yellow sediment.

Agar colonies: Thin, flat, yellowish, smooth.

Agar slant: Thin, yellowish gray to ochraceous growth.

Broth: Slightly turbid, with pale yellow sediment.

Litmus milk: Medium becomes slimy; alkaline.

Potato: Ochre-yellow streak.

Indole produced.

Nitrites not produced from nitrates.

Hydrogen sulfide produced.

Aerobic, facultative.

Optimum temperature, 35° C.

Source: Chemnitz tap water.

Habitat: Water.

9. **Pseudomonas cerevisiae** Fuhrmann, 1906. (Cent. f. Bakt., II Abt., *16*, 1906, 309.)

ce.re.vi'si.ae. L. *cerevisia* beer; M.L. gen.noun *cerevisiae* of beer.

Rods straight or slightly curved, 0.6 by 1.5 to 2.0 microns, occurring singly and in chains. Motile, possessing a tuft of four to six polar flagella. Gram-negative.

Gelatin colonies: Circular, white, slightly contoured, becoming brownish yellow.

Gelatin stab: Slight yellowish growth in stab. No liquefaction.

Agar colonies: Thin, spreading, contoured.

Agar slant: Moist, glistening, thin, pale yellow, spreading, contoured.

Litmus milk: Slow coagulation.

Potato: Yellowish brown, spreading growth.

Indole not produced.

Nitrites produced from nitrates.

No gas from glucose.

Aerobic, facultative.

Optimum temperature, 30° C.

Source: Isolated from beer.

Habitat: Unknown.

10. **Pseudomonas pictorum** Gray and Thornton, 1928. (Cent. f. Bakt., II Abt., *73*, 1928, 89.)

pic.to′rum. Named for the Picts, a Scottish tribe; M.L. neut.pl.gen.n. *pictorum* of the Picts.

Rods 0.5 to 0.8 by 1.5 to 5.0 microns. Motile, usually with a single polar flagellum. Gram-negative.

Gelatin colonies: Circular, greenish yellow, convex, smooth, glistening, entire.

Gelatin stab: No liquefaction.

Agar colonies: Circular, yellow, convex, smooth, glistening, entire.

Agar slant: Filiform, yellow, convex, smooth, glistening, entire.

Broth: Turbid.

Nitrites produced from nitrates.

Starch not hydrolyzed.

Acid from glucose and maltose.

Attacks phenol.

Aerobic, facultative.

Optimum temperature, 25°C.

Source: One culture from soil.

Habitat: Soil.

11. **Pseudomonas arguta** McBeth, 1916. (Soil Science, *1*, 1916, 465.)

ar.gu′ta. L. part.adj. *argutus* clear, bright.

Rods 0.3 by 0.8 micron. Motile with one or two polar flagella. Gram-negative.

Gelatin stab: Moderate, yellowish growth. No liquefaction in 30 days.

Agar colonies: Circular, slightly convex, soft, grayish white, granular, entire.

Agar slant: Scant, grayish white growth.

Potato agar slant: Moderate, yellowish, glistening growth.

Broth: Turbid.

Ammonia cellulose agar: Enzymatic zone 2 to 3 mm in 30 days.

Filter paper broth: Paper is reduced to loose flocculent mass which disintegrates very readily on slight agitation. More rapid decomposition when the broth contains ammonium sulfate, potassium nitrate, peptone or casein as source of nitrogen.

Litmus milk: Acid, not digested.

Potato: No growth.

Indole not produced.

Nitrites produced from nitrates.

Ammonia not produced.

Acid from glucose, maltose, lactose and starch. No acid from glycerol, mannitol or sucrose.

Aerobic, facultative.

Optimum temperature, 20° C.

Source: Isolated twice from California soils.

Habitat: Soil.

12. **Pseudomonas subcreta** McBeth and Scales, 1913. (Bur. Plant Industry, U. S. Dept. Agr., Bull. 266, 1913, 37.)

sub.cre′ta. L. pref. *sub-* somewhat; L. *creta* chalk; M.L. adj. *subcretus* somewhat chalky.

Rods 0.3 by 1.4 microns. Motile with one to five polar flagella. Gram-negative.

Gelatin stab: Filiform growth, no liquefaction.

Cellulose agar: No surface growth. Moderate, generally faint yellow growth in medium, area of growth sunken.

Agar slant: Glistening, smooth, moist, vitreous to faint yellow growth.

Starch agar: Enzymatic zone 2 to 4 mm.

Broth: No growth.

Litmus milk: No growth.

Potato: Growth scant, concave due to slight liquefaction, white to faint yellow. Bleached around growth.

Indole not produced.

Trace of nitrites produced from nitrates.

Ammonia not produced.

Acid from glucose, lactose, maltose, sucrose and starch. No acid from glycerol or mannitol.

Aerobic, facultative.

Optimum temperature, 20° C.

Habitat: Soil.

13. **Pseudomonas lacunogenes** Goresline, 1933. (Jour. Bact., *26*, 1933, 447.)

la.cu.no′ge.nes. L. *lacuna* a hollow; L. *gigno* to produce; M.L. adj. *lacunogenes* producing hollows.

Short rods, 0.2 to 0.3 by 1.0 to 1.2 microns, with pointed ends, occurring singly or in pairs. Motile with a single polar flagellum from 2 to 15 microns in length. Gram-negative.

Plain gelatin stab: No growth.

Nutrient gelatin stab: Growth brownish yellow, half-way down stab, heavier at surface. No liquefaction.

Nutrient agar colonies: Small, yellow; surface of the agar pitted or dimpled. After 5 days colonies 5 to 7 mm in diameter, orange-yellow, slightly raised, surrounded by a depression.

Nutrient agar slant: Growth heavy, light orange-yellow; consistency of warm butter; edge entire, slightly raised. Shallow depression formed on each side of streak. Agar softened beneath growth.

Nutrient broth: Turbid in 48 hours. Light orange-yellow pellicle; considerable, viscous sediment.

Litmus milk: Alkaline; butter-colored pellicle. Reduction in bottom of tube after 10 days. No curd. No digestion.

Potato: Growth moderate, orange-yellow, smooth. No darkening.

Indole not produced.

Nitrites not produced from nitrates.

Starch agar plates not hydrolyzed.

Utilizes arabinose, galactose, lactose, fructose, maltose, melezitose, raffinose, starch, xylose, glucose, mannose, sucrose, pectin, rhamnose, salicin and dextrin. No growth in dulcitol, erythritol, glycerol, sorbitol, mannitol or inulin.

Temperature relations: Optimum, 28° C. Good growth at 25° C. Moderate growth at 20° and at 37° C. No growth at 10° and at 42° C.

Limits of pH: 5.4 to 10.0.

Aerobic, facultative.

Distinctive characters: Softens agar; considerable change in viscosity of agar due to this digestion; utilization of ammonium sulfate as nitrogen source.

Source: Three cultures isolated from an experimental trickling filter receiving creamery wastes.

Habitat: Probably widely distributed in nature.

14. **Pseudomonas segnis** Goresline, 1933. (Jour. Bact., *26*, 1933, 452.)

seg'nis. L. adj. *segnis* slow, tardy.

Short rods, 0.2 to 0.3 by 1.0 to 1.2 microns, with pointed ends, occurring singly or in pairs. Motile with a single polar flagellum. Gram-negative.

Plain gelatin stab: No growth.

Nutrient gelatin stab: Growth yellow, half-way down stab, best at surface. No liquefaction.

Nutrient agar colonies: Very small, light yellow surface pitted. After 5 days colonies 5 mm in diameter.

Nutrient agar slant: Growth heavy, orange-yellow, consistency of warm butter; edge entire, slightly raised; slight depression formed on each side of growth. Agar softened beneath growth.

Nutrient broth: Turbid in 48 hours. No pellicle or surface growth. Moderate amount of sediment. Old cultures with a yellow ring at surface and occasionally a loose membrane.

Litmus milk: Slightly alkaline after 10 days. No reduction. No surface growth.

Potato: Scant yellow-orange growth. No darkening.

Indole not produced.

Nitrites not produced from nitrates.

Hydrogen sulfide not produced.

Starch not hydrolyzed.

Arabinose, glucose, galactose, lactose, fructose, maltose, mannose, xylose, sucrose, melezitose and raffinose utilized.

Temperature relations: Optimum, 28° C. Good growth at 25° C. Moderate growth at 20° and at 37° C. No growth at 10° and at 42° C.

Limits of pH: 5.8 to 9.0.

Aerobic, facultative.

Distinctive characters: Softens agar; considerable change in viscosity of agar due to this digestion.

Source: Isolated from an experimental trickling filter receiving creamery wastes.

Habitat: Probably widely distributed in nature.

Genus III. **Acetobacter** *Beijerinck*, 1898.*

(*Acetobacter* Beijerinck, quoted from Kral's Sammlung v. Mikroorg., Prague, 1898, 7; *Acetobacterium* in Ludwig's abstract of Hoyer, Bijdrage tot de kennis van de azijnbacterien,

---

* Revised by Dr. Reese H. Vaughn, Univ. of California, Berkeley, California, June, 1943, and Davis, California, March, 1954.

Thesis, Leiden, 1898, 115 pp., Delft, in Cent. f. Bakt., II Abt., *4*, 1898, 857; *Acetobacter* Beijerinck, Proc. Kon. Akad. v. Wetenschapp., Amsterdam, *2*, 1900, 503; *Acetobacter* Beijerinck, Arch. néerl. d. sciences exact. et natur., Sér. II, *6*, 1901, 212; *Acetobacter* in Fuhrmann, Beiheft Bot. Centralbl., Orig., *19*, 1905, 8; *Acetimonas* Orla-Jensen, Cent. f. Bakt., II Abt., *22*, 1909, 312; *Acetobacter* Winslow et al., Jour. Bact., *5*, 1920, 201; *Acetomonas* Leifson, Antonie van Leeuwenhoek, *20*, 1954, 109.)

A.ce.to.bac'ter. L. noun *acetum* vinegar; M.L. mas.n. *bacter* the masculine form of the Gr. neut.n. *bactrum* a rod or staff; M.L. mas.n. *Acetobacter* vinegar (acetic) rod.

Individual cells ellipsoidal to rod-shaped, occurring singly, in pairs or in short or long chains. Motile with polar flagella*, or non-motile. Involution forms may be spherical, elongated, filamentous, club-shaped, swollen, curved or may even appear to be branched. Young cells Gram-negative; old cells often Gram-variable. Obligate aerobes; as a rule strongly catalase-positive, sometimes weakly so. Oxidize various organic compounds to organic acids and other oxidation products which may undergo further oxidation. Common oxidation products include acetic acid from ethyl alcohol, gluconic and 5-ketogluconic acid from glucose, dihydroxy-acetone from glycerol, sorbose from sorbitol, etc. Nutritional requirements vary from simple to complex. Development generally best in yeast infusion or yeast autolysate media with added ethyl alcohol or other oxidizable substrates. Optimum temperature varies with the species. Widely distributed in nature where they are particularly abundant in plant materials undergoing alcoholic fermentation; of importance to man for their role in the completion of the carbon cycle and for the production of vinegar.

It is recognized that there are marked morphological and physiological similarities between species of *Acetobacter* and *Pseudomonas* (see Vaughn, Jour. Bact., *46*, 1943, 394; and Stanier, Jour. Bact., *54*, 1947, 191, among others). However, the species of *Acetobacter* may be differentiated from all other *Pseudomonadaceae* by their unique ability to oxidize significant quantities of ethanol under the extremely acidic conditions imposed by the presence of from about 2 to more than 11 per cent acetic acid.

The evidence also indicates a significant difference in the end-products of hexose and disaccharide oxidation. The species of *Acetobacter* produce gluconic and 5-ketogluconic acids from both glucose and maltose whereas species of *Pseudomonas* oxidize glucose to gluconic and 2-ketogluconic acids and maltose to maltobionic acid (see Pervozvanski, Khim. Referat. Zhur., *7*, 1939, 43; Lockwood, Tabenkin and Ward, Jour. Bact., *42*, 1941, 51; Stodola and Lockwood, Jour. Biol. Chem., *171*, 1947, 213; Kluyver, Deley and Rijven, Antonie van Leeuwenhoek, *16*, 1950, 1; and Foda and Vaughn, Jour. Bact., *65*, 1953, 233, among others).

The type species is *Acetobacter aceti* (Beijerinck) Beijerinck.

Key to the species of genus **Acetobacter.**

I. Oxidize acetic acid to carbon dioxide and water.
    A. Utilizes ammonium salts as a sole source of nitrogen (Hoyer's solution).†
                1. *Acetobacter aceti.*

---

* Leifson (Bact. Proc., 53rd Gen. Meeting Soc. Amer. Bact., 1953, 34, and Antonie van Leeuwenhoek, *20*, 1954, 102), in a study of the flagellation of cultures of *Acetobacter*, reports that the species of *Acetobacter* that oxidize acetic acid are peritrichous, and that the species that do not oxidize acetic acid ordinarily have four polar flagella. Further photographs such as can be obtained with the electron microscope must, however, be obtained before the exact point of attachment of the flagella can be determined with certainty.

† It is not known with certainty whether *Acetobacter pasteurianus* and *Acetobacter kuetzingianus* are capable of using inorganic nitrogen as a sole source of nitrogen for growth. See *Acetobacter rancens* Beijerinck to which these two species are very closely related. Also see Frateur, La Cellule, *53*, 1950, 316–320.

Species Nos. 2 to 3b inclusive will, however, utilize ammonium salts if supplied with

B. Do not utilize ammonium salts as a sole source of nitrogen.
  1. Forms a thick, zoogloeal, cellulose membrane on the surface of liquid media.
  2. *Acetobacter xylinum.*
  2. Do not form a thick, zoogloeal, cellulose membrane on the surface of liquid media.
  3. *Acetobacter rancens.*
  3a. *Acetobacter pasteurianus.*
  3b. *Acetobacter kuetzingianus.*
II. Do not oxidize acetic acid.
  A. Form pigments in glucose media.
    1. Dark brown to blackish pigment.
    4. *Acetobacter melanogenus.*
    2. Pink to rose pigment.
    5. *Acetobacter roseus.*
  B. Do not form pigments.
    1. Optimum temperature, between 30° and 35° C.
    6. *Acetobacter suboxydans.*
    2. Optimum temperature, between 18° and 21° C.
    7. *Acetobacter oxydans.*

1. **Acetobacter aceti** (Beijerinck, 1898) Beijerinck, 1900. (Mycodermes, Pasteur, Compt. rend. Acad. Sci., Paris, *54*, 1862, 265; Pasteur, *ibid.*, *55*, 1862, 28; *Mycoderma aceti* Pasteur, Ann. Sci. d. École Normal superiore, *1*, 1864, 103–158; *Bacterium aceti* Beijerinck, Cent. f. Bakt., II Abt., *4*, 1898, 211; *Acetobacter aceti* Beijerinck, published as a synonym in Kral's Sammlung v. Mikroorg., Prague, 1898, 7; Beijerinck, Proc. Kon. Akad. v. Wetensch., Amsterdam, *2*, 1900, 503.)

a.ce′ti. L. noun *acetum* vinegar; L. gen. noun *aceti* of vinegar.

Beijerinck's description of this organism, which forms the basis of the description given here, is based on Pasteur's earlier description.*

Rods, 0.4 to 0.8 by 1.0 to 2.0 microns, occurring singly and in long chains, frequently showing large club-shaped forms. Stain yellow with iodine solution. Motility variable. Motile cells possess a single polar flagellum (Vaughn, Jour. Bact., *46*, 1943, 394).

Beer gelatin containing 10 per cent sucrose: Large, shiny colonies are formed.

Liquid media: Forms slimy pellicle; may also form a ring or turbidity without pellicle.

Acid from glucose, ethanol, propanol and glycol. No acid from arabinose, fructose, galactose, sorbose, sucrose, maltose, lactose, raffinose, dextrin, starch, glycogen, inulin, methanol, isopropanol, butanol, isobutanol, pentanol, glycerol, erythritol, mannitol, dulcitol or acetaldehyde (Henneberg, Die deutsch. Essigind., *2*, 1898, 147).

Distinctive characters: Marked oxidative power causing rapid and complete oxidation of substrate such as glucose or ethyl alcohol; ability to utilize inorganic nitrogen salts as a sole source of nitrogen (Hoyer, Inaug. Diss., Leiden, 1898, 43; Beijerinck, Cent. f. Bakt., II Abt., *4*, 1898, 215); growth and oxidative activity in association with fermenting yeasts (Vaughn, Jour. Bact., *36*, 1938, 360).

Optimum temperature, 30° C. Growth occurs between 10° and 42° C.

Habitat: Vinegar, souring fruits, vegetables and beverages.

other required nutrients (Stokes and Karsen, Jour. Bact., *49*, 1945, 495; Foda and Vaughn, Jour. Bact., *65*, 1953, 79).

* Beijerinck (*op. cit.*, *4*, 1898, 211) explains the relationship of Pasteur's organism to those described by others as follows: "Two of the many varieties of B. (*Bacterium*) *rancens* have been described by Henneberg under the names B. *oxydans* and B. *acetosum*. Hansen erroneously named this species B. *aceti* as did Brown also. Neither Hansen nor Brown knew B. *aceti* of Pasteur."

2. **Acetobacter xylinum** (Brown, 1886) Holland, 1920. (*Bacterium xylinum* Brown, Jour. Chem. Soc., London, *49*, 1886, 439; Holland, Jour. Bact., *5*, 1920, 216.)

xy'li.num. Gr. adj. *xylinus* of cotton; L. neut.n. *xylinum* cotton.

Rods, about 2 microns long, occurring singly and in chains. The cells have a slimy envelope which gives the cellulose reaction.

A zoogloeal film forms on all liquid media in which growth occurs; the nature of the medium influences the thickness of the film which may vary from 2 to 250 millimeters. The film becomes cartilagenous and falls to the bottom if disturbed.

X-ray pattern studies made by Khouvine, Champetier and Sutra (Compt. rend. Acad. Sci. Paris, *194*, 1932, 208) and by Barsha and Hibbert (Can. Jour. Research, *10*, 1934, 170) have shown that the cellulose contained in the membranes formed by *Acetobacter xylinum* is identical with cotton cellulose.

Acid from glucose, ethanol, propanol and glycol. No acid from arabinose, fructose, galactose, maltose, lactose, raffinose, dextrin, starch, methanol, isopropanol, butanol, isobutanol, pentanol, mannitol or acetaldehyde (Henneberg, Die deutsch. Essigind., *2*, 1898, 147).

Distinctive character: The production of thick, leathery, zoogloeal, cellulosic membranes on the surface of liquids.

Optimum temperature, 28° C.

Habitat: Vinegar, souring fruits, vegetables and beverages.

3. **Acetobacter rancens** Beijerinck, 1898. (*Bacterium rancens* Beijerinck, Cent. f. Bakt., II Abt., *4*, 1898, 211; Beijerinck, in Kral's Sammlung v. Mikroorg., Prague, 1898, 4.)

ran'cens. L. part.adj. *rancens* putrid, stinking.

The following description is taken in part from a study of a culture of *Acetobacter rancens* received from Kluyver by Vaughn; also see Frateur (La Cellule, *53*, 1950, 339).

Rods with the usual morphological appearance of cultures of acetic-acid bacteria. Gram-negative. Molitility variable. Motile cells possess a single polar flagellum (Vaughn, Jour. Bact., *46*, 1943, 394). Involu-

tion forms commonly appear as filaments and enlarged cells.

Wort agar slant: Growth abundant, butyrous, pale-buff in color in one week.

Yeast infusion, glucose, calcium carbonate slant: Growth abundant, butyrous and cream-colored in one week.

With petri-dish cultures, well isolated colonies are large, smooth and butyrous on the above-mentioned media.

Broth cultures containing peptone or yeast infusion form a mucilaginous, slimy pellicle. Beijerinck (*op. cit.*, *4*, 1898, 211) called this polysaccharide pellicle cellulose-like and intimated that the mucilaginous material in the pellicle was somewhat different from that produced by *Acetobacter xylinum*. The pellicle material stained blue when treated with iodine and hydriodic acid.

Minimum nutritional requirements: Pantothenic acid, nicotinic acid, p-aminobenzoic acid, thiamine, valine, alanine, isoleucine, histidine, cystine, proline, aspartic or glutamic acid, mineral salts and an oxidizable substrate such as alcohol, glucose, etc. (Foda and Vaughn, Jour. Bact., *65*, 1953, 79).

Acid from glucose, ethanol, propanol, butanol, glycol, adonitol, mannitol and sorbitol. No acid from numerous other compounds tested.

Distinctive character: Production of a thin, mucilaginous, slimy, polysaccharide membrane on the surface of liquids as compared with the thick, true cellulose membrane of *Acetobacter xylinum* grown under the same conditions. Beijerinck (*op. cit.*, *4*, 1898, 211) reported the production of a cellulose-like membrane with some cultures of *Acetobacter rancens*.

Source: Isolated from shavings in the quick-vinegar process.

Habitat: Found in fermented grain mash, malt beverages, mother of vinegar, and souring fruits.

Beijerinck (Cent. f. Bakt., II Abt., *4*, 1898, 211) thought that the next two species were hardly more than varieties of *Acetobacter rancens*; also see Frateur (La Cellule, *53*, 1950, 339).

3a. **Acetobacter pasteurianus** (Hansen, 1879) Beijerinck, 1916. (*Mycoderma pasteurianum* Hansen, Compt. rend. d. Trav. d. Lab. d. Carlsberg, *1*, 1879, 96; Beijerinck, Proc. Sect. Sci., Kon. Akad. v. Wetenschappen, Amsterdam, *18*, 1916, 1199.) pas.teur.i.a′nus. Named for Pasteur, French chemist and bacteriologist; M.L. adj. *pasteurianus* of Pasteur.

Rods, 0.4 to 0.8 by 1.0 micron, occurring singly and in chains, at times showing thick, club-shaped forms. Motility variable. Motile cells possess a single polar flagellum (Vaughn, Jour. Bact., *46*, 1943, 394). Stain blue with iodine.

Wort gelatin colonies: Small, circular, entire, gray, slimy.

Forms a dry, wrinkled, folded pellicle on double beer with one per cent alcohol.

Meat infusion gelatin: Growth widespread; later rosette form, toothed.

Acid from glucose, ethanol, propanol and glycol. No acid from arabinose, fructose, galactose, sorbose, sucrose, maltose, lactose, raffinose, dextrin, starch, glycogen, inulin, methanol, isopropanol, butanol, isobutanol, pentanol, glycerol, erythritol, mannitol, dulcitol or acetaldehyde (Henneberg, Die deutsch. Essigind., *2*, 1898, 147).

Optimum temperature, 30° C. Growth occurs between 5° and 42° C.

Habitat: Vinegar; beer and beer wort.

3b. **Acetobacter kuetzingianus** (Hansen, 1894) Bergey et al., 1923. (*Bacterium kützingianum* (sic) Hansen, Compt. rend. d. Trav. d. Lab. d. Carlsberg, *3*, 1894, 191; Bergey et al., Manual, 1st ed., 1923, 35.) kuet.zing.i.a′nus. Named for Kuetzing, a German botanist; M. L. adj. *kuetzingianus* of Kuetzing.

Short, thick rods, occurring singly, rarely forming chains of notable length. Capsule stains blue with iodine and with potassium iodide. Non-motile.

Double beer gelatin colonies: Small, entire, with vermiform surface.

Wort gelatin colonies: Small, entire, with surface free of wrinkles.

Double beer: Forms a rather thick, folded pellicle. Distinguished from *Acetobacter aceti* in showing a heavier growth above the surface of the medium.

Acid from glucose, ethanol, propanol and glycol. No acid from arabinose, fructose, galactose, sorbose, sucrose, maltose, lactose, raffinose, dextrin, starch, glycogen, inulin, methanol, isopropanol, butanol, isobutanol, pentanol, glycerol, erythritol, mannitol, dulcitol or acetaldehyde (Henneberg, Die deutsch. Essigind., *2*, 1898, 147).

Optimum temperature, 34° C.; minimum, between 6° and 7° C.; maximum, 42° C.

Habitat: Beer. Found in double beer.

4. **Acetobacter melanogenus** Beijerinck, 1911. (Cent. f. Bakt., II Abt., *29*, 1911, 175.) me.la.no′ge.nus. Gr. adj. *melas, melanis* black; Gr. v. *gennao* to produce; M.L. adj. *melanogenus* black-producing.

Rods. Non-motile or motile. Motile cells possess a single polar flagellum (Vaughn, Jour. Bact., *46*, 1943, 394).

Gelatin: Apparent liquefaction probably caused by acid, not an enzyme. When held on artificial media for some time, the power of liquefying gelatin is lost, probably due to a slower production of acid. Deep brown pigment produced; gelatin becomes insoluble in boiling water and in trypsin solution.

Beer- or wort-gelatin plates: Characteristic dark brown, wide-spreading, diffuse areas.

Tap water - agar - glucose - peptone - potassium phosphate-iron citrate-chalk medium: In 24 hours at 30° C., black, spreading, diffuse areas.

Produces the pigment from peptone or yeast autolysate if maltose or glucose is present as a source of carbon. When grown in glucose-peptone broth or agar with $CaCO_3$ at 25° to 30° C., the pigment is produced after one to several weeks.

Pigment: The pigment causing the brown coloration is an aromatic substance which is blackened by iron salts. Reduces alkaline solutions of silver and mercury, blackening them (Beijerinck, *op. cit.*, *29*, 1911, 175).

Minimum nutritional requirements: Pantothenic acid, nicotinic acid, p-aminobenzoic acid, thiamine, mineral salts and an oxidizable substrate such as alcohol, glucose, etc. (Gray and Tatum, Proc. Nat'l. Acad. Sci., *30*, 1944, 404, and Foda and Vaughn, Jour. Bact., *65*, 1953, 79).

Acetic acid produced from alcohol. Gluconic and 5-ketogluconic acids produced from glucose and maltose.

Oxidizes mannitol to fructose; sorbitol to sorbose; and glycerol to dihydroxyacetone. Produces acid from arabinose, xylose, glucose, fructose, galactose and maltose. Some strains do not attack maltose.

Distinctive character: The formation of dark brown to black pigment in media containing glucose.

Source: Isolated from beer.

Habitat: Causes light-colored beer to become darker brown. It is a very strong beer-vinegar bacterium. Also found in souring fruits.

5. Acetobacter roseus Vaughn, 1942. (*Bacterium hoshigaki* var. *rosea* Takahashi and Asai, Zent. f. Bakt., II Abt., *82*, 1930, 390; Vaughn, Wallerstein Lab. Communications, *5*, No. 14, 1941, 20.)

ro'se.us. L. adj *roseus* rose-colored.

Rods, 0.7 to 0.9 by 1.5 to 1.8 microns, generally occurring singly, in pairs, often in chains. Non-motile. Pellicle on fluid media yields no starch or cellulose reaction.

Koji (a mixture of rice and mold spores used to start fermentation of Japanese bread and saké) extract agar colonies: Small, granular, circular, glistening, umbonate, becoming brownish.

Wort agar colonies: Circular, milky white, becoming brownish in the center and yellowish at the periphery.

Koji extract agar streak: Grayish white, glistening with ciliate margin, becoming purple-brown to brown.

Koji extract: Turbid, with thin film ascending on wall of tube.

Bouillon: Turbid with ring formation.

Yeast infusion glucose agar: Colonies similar to those on wort agar.

Yeast infusion glucose broth: Turbid with thin, ascending film.

Red color produced on saké-wort agar and all media containing calcium carbonate.

Acid from glucose, fructose, galactose, arabinose, glycerol, mannitol, ethanol and propanol. No acid from maltose, sucrose, lactose, raffinose, dextrin, starch, inulin, sorbitol, glycogen, isodulcitol or methanol.

Optimum temperature, between 30° and 35° C.; minimum, between 10° and 15° C.; maximum, between 40° and 41° C.

Thermal death point, 50° C. for 5 minutes.

Distinctive character: The formation of a rose to red pigment in suitable media, particularly those containing glucose and calcium carbonate.

Note: Vaughn (*loc. cit.*) has proposed the name *Acetobacter roseus* to replace the name *Acetobacter hoshigaki*. As originally described, this organism was given the name *Bacterium hoshigaki* var. *rosea* by Takahashi and Asai (*op. cit.*, *82*, 1930, 390) without the authors having first named and described the species *Bacterium hoshigaki*. The Japanese word "hoshigaki" has been used in a confusing manner, *viz.* *Bacterium industrium* var. *hoshigaki* (Takahashi and Asai, *loc. cit.*) and *Bacterium hoshigaki* var. *glucuronicum* I, II and III (Takahashi and Asai, Jour. Agr. Chem. Soc. Japan, *9*, 1933, 351 and Zent. f. Bakt., II Abt., *87*, 1933, 385). None of these Japanese names are in the form of true binomials.

Source: Isolated from fermenting mash of dried persimmons (hoshigaki); also from souring figs and dates.

6. Acetobacter suboxydans Kluyver and de Leeuw, 1923. (Paper read at the convention of the Dutch Society of Microbiology, Utrecht, December, 1923; see Tijdschrift v. Vergelijkende Geneeskunde, *10*, Afl. 2–3, 1924.)

sub.ox'y.dans. L. pref. *sub-* somewhat, slightly; Gr. adj. *oxys* sharp; M.L. part.adj. *oxydans* oxidizing; M.L. part.adj. *suboxydans* slightly oxidizing.

Short rods. Occur singly or in chains. Non-motile. Morphologically like *Acetobacter rancens*.

Forms a very thin, hardly visible pellicle on fluid media.

Wort agar colonies: Very small, circular, slightly yellow.

Minimum nutritional requirements: Pantothenic acid, nicotinic acid, p-aminobenzoic acid, valine, alanine, isoleucine, histidine, cystine, proline, mineral salts and an oxidizable substrate such as alcohol, glucose, etc. (Landy and Dicken, Jour. Biol. Chem., *146*, 1942, 109; Lampen, Underkofler and Peterson, Jour. Biol. Chem., *146*, 1942, 277; Underkofler, Bantz and Peterson, Jour. Bact., *45*, 1943, 183; Stokes and Larsen, Jour. Bact., *49*, 1945, 495).

Acid from ethanol, propanol, glycol, glucose, glycerol and sorbitol.

Optimum temperature, 30° C.

Distinctive character: Partial oxidation of substrates as indicated by the formation of calcium 5-ketogluconate crystals on the surface of agar slants containing glucose and calcium carbonate.

Source: Isolated from spoiled beer.

Habitat: Beer; also found in souring fruits and wine vinegar.

7. Acetobacter oxydans (Henneberg, 1897) Bergey et al., 1923. (*Bacterium oxydans* Henneberg, Cent. f. Bakt., II Abt., *3*, 1897, 223; Bergey et al., Manual, 1st ed., 1923, 36.)

ox'y.dans. Gr. adj. *oxys* sharp; M.L. part.adj. *oxydans* oxidizing.

Rods, 0.8 to 1.2 by 2.4 to 2.7 microns, occurring singly and in chains. Motile cells possess a single polar flagellum (Vaughn, Jour. Bact., *46*, 1943, 394). The chains show bud-like swellings.

Gelatin colonies: Circular, becoming irregular in shape with peculiar ramifications.

Minimum nutritional requirements: Pantothenic acid, nicotinic acid, p-aminobenzoic acid, valine, alanine, isoleucine, histidine, cystine, proline, mineral salts and an oxidizable substrate such as alcohol, glucose, etc. (Foda and Vaughn, Jour. Bact., *65*, 1953, 79).

Acid from arabinose, fructose, glucose, galactose, sucrose, maltose, raffinose, dextrin, ethanol, propanol, erythritol, mannitol, glycol or glycerol. No acid from sorbose, lactose, starch, glycogen, inulin, methanol, isopropanol, butanol, isobutanol, pentanol, dulcitol or acetaldehyde (Henneberg, Die deutsch. Essigind., *2*, 1898, 147).

Optimum temperature, between 18° and 21° C.

Distinctive characters: Low optimum temperature for growth and oxidation of substrates; also the ability to oxidize a large number of substrates.

Habitat: Beer, souring fruits, wine vinegar.

Genus IV. **Aeromonas** *Kluyver and van Niel, 1936.** *

(Zent. f. Bakt., II Abt., *94*, 1936, 398.)

A.e.ro.mo'nas. Gr. mas.n. *aër* air, gas; Gr. fem.n. *monas* unit, monad; M.L. fem.n. *Aeromonas* gas (-producing) monad.

Short (rarely more than 3 microns), rod-shaped cells. Motile by means of polar flagella, usually monotrichous; occasionally non-motile. Gram-negative. Heterotrophic, oxidizing various organic compounds. Carbohydrates fermented with the production of H_2, CO_2 and 2,3-butylene glycol. Methyl red negative. Slow or no fermentation of lactose. The majority of species thus far described are from water or are known to be pathogenic to marine and fresh-water animals such as fish and amphibians.

Physiologically these organisms appear to be identical with certain species found in the family *Enterobacteriaceae*. The chief differences between the species in *Aeromonas* and those in *Paracolobactrum* Borman, Stuart and Wheeler are found in the arrangement of their flagella, in the less active fermentation of carbohydrates by the former, and in their pathogenicity.

The type species is *Aeromonas liquefaciens* (Beijerinck) Kluyver and van Niel.

Key to the species of genus **Aeromonas.**

I. Motile.
  A. Originally isolated from water.

---

* Prepared by Dr. S. F. Snieszko, U. S. Fish and Wildlife Service, Leetown via Kearneysville, West Virginia, August, 1953.

1. Not proven to be pathogenic for fish and amphibians.
    1. *Aeromonas liquefaciens.*
 2. Generally regarded as the cause of an infectious edema of carp and other fish.
    2. *Aeromonas punctata.*
B. Originally isolated from a septicemia in frogs (red leg).
    3. *Aeromonas hydrophila.*
II. Non-motile. Pathogenic for fish, particularly *Salmonidae.*
    4. *Aeromonas salmonicida.*

1. **Aeromonas liquefaciens** (Beijerinck, 1900) Kluyver and van Niel, 1936. (*Aerobacter liquefaciens* Beijerinck, Cent. f. Bakt., II Abt., *6*, 1900, 199; Kluyver and van Niel, Zent. f. Bakt., II Abt., *94*, 1936, 399.) li.que.fa′ci.ens. L. v. *liquefacio* to liquefy; L. part.adj. *liquefaciens* liquefying.

Description taken from Beijerinck (*op. cit.*, *6*, 1900, 199) and from E. M. Miles and A. A. Miles (Jour. Gen. Microbiol., *5*, 1951, 299).

Rods, 0.4 to 0.8 by 1.5 to 3.0 microns, with parallel sides and rounded ends. Filaments common in "rough" colony forms. Motile by means of a single polar flagellum about 5 to 6 microns long. Gram-negative.

Gelatin stab: Liquefaction marked and commonly saccate, good growth.

Horse blood agar colonies: 2 to 3 mm in diameter, round, entire, raised, smooth, moist, opaque, semi-translucent, grayish white, forming a dirty brown-yellow coloration after 3 to 5 days at room temperature; non-hemolytic.

Broth: Growth abundant, turbid, with a moderate, readily disintegrable sediment and delicate pellicle.

Loeffler's serum: Growth abundant, but no digestion.

Litmus milk: Acid; coagulated; digested.

Potato: Growth abundant, moist and glistening, light brown.

Indole is produced.

Nitrites but not ammonia produced from nitrates (Beijerinck); ammonia produced, presumably from peptones (Miles and Miles).

Methyl red test negative.

Citric acid and salts of citric acid may be utilized as sole sources of carbon.

Ammonium sulfate, uric acid and asparagine may be utilized as sources of nitrogen.

Catalase produced.

Hydrogen sulfide produced.

Urea not attacked.

Methylene blue reduced.

Starch hydrolyzed (Miles and Miles); starch not hydrolyzed (Beijerinck).

Acid and gas from glucose, galactose, fructose, mannose, maltose, sucrose, mannitol, glycerol and starch. Acid from lactose, raffinose, inositol and sorbitol. Slight acid from salicin at 22° C. but none at 37° C. Glucose fermented with the production of 2,3-butanediol. Arabinose, rhamnose and dulcitol not attacked.

Aerobic, facultative.

Temperature relations: Optimum, 37° C.; good growth on ordinary laboratory media at 20° C.

Produces a characteristic black-rot in hen eggs.

Pathogenic to mice, also to frogs, causing a fatal bacteriemia.

Source: Found rarely in canal mud, generally in certain marshes and swamps.

Habitat relationships uncertain. Those that believe this organism to be identical with *Aeromonas punctata* would associate it with a disease of carp, eels and other fishes.

2. **Aeromonas punctata** (Zimmermann, 1890, *emend.* Lehmann and Neumann, 1896) Snieszko, *comb. nov.* (*Bacillus punctatus* Zimmermann, Bakt. unserer Trink- und Nutzwässer, Chemnitz, *1*, 1890, 38; *Bacterium punctatum* Lehmann and Neumann, Bakt. Diag., 1 Aufl., *2*, 1896, 238; *Pseudomonas punctata* Chester, Man. Determ. Bact., 1901, 147; also see Schäperclaus, Ztschr. f. Fischerei, *28*, 1930, 289.) punc.ta′ta. L. noun *punctum* a point, a small hole; M.L. adj. *punctata* full of points.

Rods, 0.7 by 1.0 to 1.5 microns, occurring singly, in pairs and in chains. Motile with a single polar flagellum. Gram-negative.

Gelatin colonies: Small, circular, gray, erose to filamentous, punctiform.

Gelatin stab: Crateriform liquefaction. No pellicle.

Agar slant: Gray, smooth, filamentous.

Broth: Turbid with delicate pellicle.

Litmus milk: Acid; coagulated; peptonized.

Potato: Brownish yellow to brownish red color.

Indole is produced.

Hydrogen sulfide is produced.

Acid and gas from glucose broth (Lehmann and Neumann, *op. cit.*, 1896, 238).

Aerobic, facultative.

Optimum temperature, between 25° and 30° C.

Distinctive characters: There does not seem to be any real difference between this organism and *Aeromonas liquefaciens* Kluyver and van Niel. Schäperclaus (Fischkrankheiten, Braunschweig, 1 Aufl., 1935, 46; Ztschr. f. Fischerei, *37*, 1939, 7) recognizes definite varieties of this species: some are non-pathogenic, others are pathogenic to carp, and still others are pathogenic to eels.

Source: From Chemnitz tap water (Zimmermann). Commonly found in water of the River Main (Lehmann and Neumann, *op. cit.*, 238; also see *op. cit.*, 7 Aufl., *2*, 1927, 47).

Habitat: Found in water supplies, especially those in which carp, eels and other fishes occur. Causes an infectious edema in carp (*Cyprinus*) (Schäperclaus, *op. cit.*, 1930, 289; see Zent. f. Bakt., II Abt., *105*, 1942, 49) and other fishes.

3. **Aeromonas hydrophila** (Chester, 1901) Stanier, 1943. (*Bacillus hydrophilus fuscus* Sanarelli, Cent. f. Bakt., *9*, 1891, 222; *Bacillus hydrophilus* Chester, Manual Determ. Bact., 1901, 235; *Proteus hydrophilus* Bergey et al., Manual, 1st ed., 1923, 211; Stanier, Jour. Bact., *46*, 1943, 213.)

hy.dro'phi.la. Gr. noun *hydōr* water; Gr. *philus* loving; M.L. adj. *hydrophilus* water-loving.

Description taken from Emerson and Norris (Jour. Exp. Med., *7*, 1905, 32) and from E. M. Miles and A. A. Miles (Jour. Gen. Microbiol., *5*, 1951, 299).

Rods, 0.6 by 1.3 microns, occurring singly and in chains. Motile, with a single polar flagellum (Kulp and Borden, Jour. of Bact., *44*, 1942, 673). Gram-negative.

Gelatin colonies: Small, circular, gray, translucent, stippled.

Gelatin stab: Napiform liquefaction.

Agar colonies: Whitish, raised, moist, stippled.

Horse blood agar colonies: 2 to 3 mm in diameter, round, entire, raised, smooth, moist, semi-translucent, grayish white, forming a dirty brown-yellow coloration after 3 to 5 days at room temperature; marked hemolysis.

Agar slant: Thin, whitish, glassy, spreading, becoming yellowish and opalescent.

Broth: Turbid, with heavy pellicle.

Loeffler's serum: Growth abundant, but no digestion.

Litmus milk: Acid; coagulated; peptonized.

Potato: Yellowish brown, moist, slightly raised.

Indole is produced.

Nitrites produced from nitrates.

Ammonium sulfate, uric acid and asparagine may serve as sources of nitrogen.

Catalase produced.

Hydrogen sulfide produced.

Urea not attacked.

Methylene blue reduced.

Acid and gas from glucose, galactose, fructose, mannose, maltose, sucrose, mannitol, glycerol and starch. Acid and gas from salicin at 22° C. but not at 37° C. Acid from glycogen and dextrin. Glucose fermented with the production of 2,3-butanediol. Lactose, arabinose, raffinose, rhamnose, dulcitol, sorbitol and inositol not attacked.

In the fermentation of beet molasses, Murphy, Watson, Muirhead and Barnwell (Canad. Jour. Tech., *29*, 1951, 375) found this organism to yield up to 96 per cent of theoretical 2,3-butanediol and acetoin. This is a higher yield than the same authors found for *Aerobacter aerogenes*.

Starch hydrolyzed.

Gas ratio $H_2:CO_2 = 1:4.71$. Methyl red negative, acetylmethylcarbinol positive, indole negative, citrate positive (Speck and Stark, Jour. Bact., *44*, 1942, 697).

Aerobic, facultative.

Optimum temperature, 37° C.

Produces a characteristic black-rot in hen eggs.

Pathogenic for frogs, salamanders, fish, mice, guinea pigs and rabbits, causing hemorrhagic septicemia. Causes a hemorrhagic septicemia in snakes. In this case the disease is transmitted by mites (Camin, Jour. of Parasitol., *34*, 1948, 345).

Source: Isolated from frogs dead of septicemia (red leg).

Habitat: Water and infected fresh-water animals.

4. Aeromonas salmonicida (Lehmann and Neumann, 1896) Griffin, 1954. (Bacillus der Forellenseuche, Emmerich and Weibel, Arch. f. Hyg., *21*, 1894, 1; *Bacterium salmonicida* Lehmann and Neumann, Bakt. Diag., 1 Aufl., *2*, 1896, 240; see Mackie, Arkwright, Pryce-Tannatt, Mottram, Johnston and Menzies, Final Rept. of the Furunculosis Committee, H. M. Stationery Office, Edinburgh, 1935; Griffin, Trans. Amer. Fish. Soc., *83*, (1953) 1954, 241.)

sal.mo.ni′ci.da. L. noun *salmo, salmonis* salmon; L. v.suffix *-cida* from L. v. *caedo* to cut, kill; M.L. fem.n. *salmonicida* salmon-killer.

Description taken from Griffin (Trans. Amer. Fish. Soc., *82* (1952) 1953, 129).

Rods, 1.0 by 1.7 to 2.0 microns, with rounded ends, occurring singly, in pairs or in chains. Non-motile. Gram-negative.

Gelatin stab: Crateriform to infundibuliform liquefaction in 1 to 3 days; complete liquefaction in 7 days. Growth filiform, beaded, best at top. Medium turns light brown near the surface of old cultures.

Agar colonies: Circular, punctiform in 24 hours and 1 to 2 mm in diameter in 4 to 5 days, convex, entire, semi-translucent. Colonies and medium turn brown in old cultures.

Agar slant: Growth abundant, butyrous, glistening, filiform, opaque to transparent, odorless, colorless. A soluble, brown, melanin-like pigment forms in 3 to 5 days. A bright salmon-pink color develops when β-2-thienylalanine is present (Griffin, Snieszko and Friddle, Jour. Bact., *65*, 1953, 658).

Colonies developed on trypticase agar quickly turn a violet-black color after the addition of 1 per cent aqueous *p*-phenylenediamine (Griffin, Proc. 52nd Gen. Meeting, Soc. Amer. Bact., Boston, 1952, 53; also see Vet. Med., *48*, 1953, 280).

Broth: Moderate to strong clouding; no ring or pellicle; moderate, flocculent sediment. Medium may clear in the upper layers and some growth may adhere to walls of test tubes of old cultures.

Litmus milk: Slight and temporary acidification. Complete peptonization in one week.

Rabbit blood agar: Beta-hemolysis in 2 days.

Indole not produced.

Nitrites produced from nitrates.

Ammonia produced in tryptic digest of casein-yeast extract medium.

Hydrogen sulfide not produced.

Methyl red negative; acetylmethylcarbinol not produced; sodium citrate does not serve as a sole source of carbon.

Urea not attacked.

Acid and gas from glucose, fructose, maltose, galactose, arabinose, mannose, starch, dextrin, glycogen, salicin, esculin and mannitol. Lactose, sucrose, xylose, rhamnose, trehalose, melibiose, cellobiose, raffinose, melizitose, inulin, amygdalin, methyl glucoside, glycerol, erythritol, adonitol, sorbitol and dulcitol not attacked.

Starch hydrolyzed.

Arginine and methionine are essential for growth; asparagine and leucine are highly stimulative while lysine is only moderately so (unpublished data, Griffin).

Temperature relations: Optimum, between 20° and 25° C. Minimum, 6° C. Maximum, 34.5° C.

Aerobic, facultative.

Pathogenic for most fresh-water fish, particularly those belonging to *Salmonidae*.

Source: From dead fish, of the family *Salmonidae*, taken from a fish hatchery in Southern Germany.

Habitat: Found in fresh-water lakes, streams, rivers and fish ponds throughout Europe and also in the United States and Canada. Causes a furunculosis in infected fish; also occurs in apparently normal fish.

Note: *Species incertae sedis.* At least twelve additional species that appear to be identical with or closely related to the four species described in full have been reported in the literature. These were isolated from water, aquatic animals (midge larvae, leeches, fishes) or dairy products. It should also be noted that at least one plant pathogen (*Xanthomonas proteamacu-* *lans*) is listed in the MANUAL as producing acid and gas from glucose and related sugars. A monographic study of these organisms is needed. The descriptions of some species that were found before 1900 appear to be as adequate as are the early descriptions of *Aeromonas liquefaciens.* No attempt has been made to determine which specific epithet or epithets have priority.

Genus V. Photobacterium Beijerinck, 1889, emend. Breed and Lessel, 1954.*

(Beijerinck, Arch. néerl. d. Sci. exact. et natur., *23*, 1889, 401; *Photobacter* Beijerinck, Proc. Sect. Sci., Kon. Akad. v. Wetensch., Amsterdam, *3*, 1900, 352; ? *Photomonas* Orla-Jensen (*nomen nudum*), Jour. Bact., *6*, 1921, 271; Breed and Lessel, Antonie van Leeuwenhoek, *20*, 1954, 60.)

Pho.to.bac.te'ri.um. Gr. noun *phōs* light; Gr. neut.dim.n. *bacterium* a small rod; M.L. neut.n. *Photobacterium* light (-producing) bacterium.

Coccobacilli and occasional rods which, in the presence of glucose and asparagine, tend to ramify in a manner analogous to that of bacteroids. Polar flagellate when motile. The type species is normally non-motile but shows motility in young cultures (Kluyver). May or may not liquefy gelatin. Produce acid, or acid and visible gas (H_2 and CO_2), from glucose and other carbohydrates but not from lactose. Luminescent. Growth and luminescence best, or even exclusively, on salt-water media containing 3 to 5 per cent salt. Found on dead fish and other salt-water animals and in sea water. Reports by various authors indicate that the luminescent, coccoid and rod-shaped bacteria found living symbiotically in the tissues of the phosphorescent organs of various cephalopods and deep-sea fishes also belong to this genus. Other coccoid and rod-shaped luminescent bacteria found in the blood of crustacea and caterpillars appear to be parasitic or even pathogenic.

The type species is *Photobacterium phosphoreum* (Cohn) Ford.

Key to the species of genus Photobacterium.†

I. Coccobacilli which produce acid and gas from glucose.
  A. Saprophytic on dead fish, crustacea, meat and similar products.
    1. *Photobacterium phosphoreum.*
  B. Symbiotic, found in the photogenic organ of a cephalopod.
    2. *Photobacterium pierantonii.*
II. Short rods which produce acid but no gas from glucose.
  A. No growth at 37° C.
    3. *Photobacterium fischeri.*
  B. Grows well at 37° C.
    4. *Photobacterium harveyi.*

1. Photobacterium phosphoreum (Cohn, 1878) Ford, 1927. (*Micrococcus phosphoreus* Cohn, see letter addressed to J. Penn, Verzameling van stukken betref- fende het geneeskundig staatstoezicht in Nederland, 1878, 126; *Bacterium phosphorescens* Fischer, Cent. f. Bakt., *3*, 1888, 107; *Photobacterium phosphorescens* Bei-

---

* Prepared by Prof. Robert S. Breed and Mr. Erwin F. Lessel, Jr., Cornell University, Geneva, New York, February, 1954.

† See Spencer (Jour. Gen. Microbiol., *13*, 1955, 111) for a recent discussion of the classification of this group.

jerinck, Arch. néerl. d. Sci. exact. et natur., *23*, 1889, 401; *Photobacter phosphoreum* Beijerinck, Folia Microbiologica, Delft, *4*, 1916, 15; Ford, Textb. of Bact., 1927, 615.)

phos.pho're.um. Gr. v. *phosphoreo* to bring light; M.L. adj. *phosphoreus* light-bearing.

Description taken from Fischer (*op. cit.*, 1888, 107) and Beijerinck (*op. cit.*, 1889, 401).

Coccobacilli, 0.5 to 2.0 microns; occasional rods are 0.5 to 1.0 micron. In the presence of glucose, especially glucose and asparagine combined, some of the cells tend to branch and to take the form of bacteroids. Frequently occur as zoogloeae. Non-motile (Fischer); some cells show a sluggish motility (Beijerinck); (Johnson, personal communication, 1953, stated that even electron micrographs failed to reveal flagella); actively motile on suitable media (Kluyver, personal communication, June, 1953); Leifson (personal communication, July, 1953) reports that an occasional cell of culture L342 from Delft shows monotrichous flagellation. Stain lightly with aniline dyes. Gram-negative (Manual, 3rd ed., 1930, 178).

Gelatin: No liquefaction.

Agar slant: Grayish white layer (Manual, *loc. cit.*).

Broth: Slightly turbid with thin pellicle (Manual, *loc. cit.*).

Potato: Ordinary acid potato, no growth; neutralized with sodium phosphate, thin brownish growth (Chester, Ann. Rept. Del. Col. Agr. Exp. Sta., *9*, 1897, 124).

Proteolytic enzymes not secreted.

Glucose, fructose, maltose and galactose are anaerobically fermented with the production of gas. This is a butanediol fermentation that produces H_2 and CO_2 (Kluyver, personal communication, 1953).

Aerobic, facultatively anaerobic.

Minimum temperature, between 5° and 10° C.

Quality of luminescence: Bluish green.

Salt tolerance: To assure phosphorescence and good growth, the osmotic tension of inorganic salt solutions used for cultivation should be equivalent to that produced in a 3 per cent sodium chloride solution.

Distinctive characters: Coccoid bacteria which do not liquefy gelatin and which produce acid and gas from glucose but not from lactose. In the presence of glucose, especially when combined with asparagine, the cells swell up greatly and lose their luminescent property. Luminescence on organic matter occurs only when there is a sufficient proportion of inorganic salt.

Comments: Several publications which antedate that of Fischer (*op. cit.*, 1888, 107) allude to the fact that the binomial *Bacterium phosphorescens* might have been effectively published earlier than 1888. One reference (Anonymous, Nature, *35*, 1886–1887, 377) cites Hermes, the Director of the Berlin Aquarium, as having published an article in which he describes and names as *Bacterium phosphorescens* a luminescent organism obtained from a specimen of cod (*Gadus callarias*) at the Berlin Aquarium; this was the same organism which Fischer secured from the Berlin Aquarium and which he named *Bacterium phosphorescens*. A second reference (Ludwig, Cent. f. Bakt., *2*, 1887, 404) states that Hermes demonstrated before the Berlin Society the phosphorescent bacterium from the Berlin Aquarium under the name *Bacterium phosphorescens*. Other references (Anonymous, Gesell. deutsch. Naturforsch. u. Aerzte, Tageblatt, *60*, 1887, 77 and 254) showed that Hermes used this organism several times for demonstration purposes in the Aquarium and before the Society. As Hermes' publication has not been found, and as the binomial *Bacterium phosphorescens* is not effectively published in any of the three references given directly above, Fischer is credited here as the author of this binomial.

Considerable confusion exists in the literature concerning this species, most of which can be elucidated by the following: (1) Fischer (Ztschr. f. Hyg., *2*, 1887, 54–92) described an organism, isolated from sea water from the West Indies, which he named *Bacillus phosphorescens*; (2) a second species of phosphorescent bacteria, obtained from the Berlin Aquarium, was described, but not named, by Fischer in a supplement to the work cited above (*ibid.*, 92–95); Lehmann (Cent. f. Bakt., *5*, 1889, 785) also described an organism obtained from the

Berlin Aquarium, and he states that it is identical with the one which Fischer obtained from this same source; (3) in a later paper (Cent. f. Bakt., *3*, 1888, 107), Fischer identified the second species, as well as phosphorescent bacteria that he isolated from dead fish from the Baltic and North Seas, as *Bacterium phosphorescens*. Some authors, *e.g.* Lehmann and Neumann (Bakt. Diag., 1 Aufl., *2*, 1896, 198; and other editions), Migula (Syst. d. Bakt., *2*, 1900, 433) and Chester (Man. Determ. Bact., 1901, 181), when referring to *Bacterium phosphorescens* Fischer, quote the supplement to Fischer's paper in the Ztschr. f. Hyg., *2*, 1887, 92, as the source of the name *Bacterium phosphorescens*, whereas the first use of this binomial by Fischer was in the Cent. f. Bakt., *3*, 1888, 107. This failure to give an exact reference has caused confusion in later publications, especially since *Bacillus phosphorescens* is the only binomial proposed, or even used, by Fischer in his paper published in the Ztschr. f. Hyg., *2*, 1887, 54–95, which also contains a description of the organism he later identified as *Bacterium phosphorescens*. Still other writers (Gorham, in Dahlgren, Jour. Franklin Inst., *180*, 1915, 517 and insert following 714) have used the name *Bacillus phosphorescens* in lieu of *Bacterium phosphorescens*, thus augmenting the confusion.

Relationships to other species of bacteria: Beijerinck regards *Photobacterium phosphorescens* Beijerinck as identical with *Micrococcus phosphoreus* Cohn (Folia Microbiologica, Delft, *4*, 1916, 15, footnote 4) but different from *Photobacterium pfleugeri* Ludwig (Arch. néerl. d. Sci. exact. et natur., *24*, 1891, 369).

Source: Isolated from cod (*Gadus callarias*) from the Baltic Sea; also found on haddock (*Melanogrammus aeglifinus*) and on lobster (*Homarus sp.*).

Habitat: Found on dead fish and in sea water, so far as known.

2. **Photobacterium pierantonii** (Zirpolo, 1918) Krassilnikov, 1949. (*Micrococcus pierantonii* Zirpolo, Boll. del. Societa dei Natural. in Napoli, *31*, (1918) 1919, 75; *Photobacterium pierantonii*, incorrectly ascribed to Bergey et al. by Krassilnikov,

Guide to the Bacteria and Actinomycetes, Izd. Akad. Nauk, U.S.S.R., Moskau, 1949, 514.)

pie.ran.to′ni.i. M.L. gen.noun *pierantonii* of Pierantoni; named for Prof. U. Pierantoni, an Italian scientist.

Original description supplemented by material taken from Meissner (Cent. f. Bakt., II Abt., *67*, 1926, 204).

Cocci, 0.8 micron in diameter, and short rods, 0.8 by 1.0 to 2.0 microns. Occasionally vacuolated. Motile or non-motile, the motile cells possessing a single flagellum or a tuft of 2 to 4 flagella. Gram-negative.

Gelatin colonies: Circular, luminous.

Gelatin stab: No liquefaction.

Sepia agar colonies: Circular, white, convex, smooth and serrate with an intense, greenish luminescence.

Egg glycerol agar slant: Yellowish green, luminous streak.

Broth: Turbid.

Indole not produced.

Acid and gas from glucose and maltose. Some strains produce acid but no gas from lactose and sucrose.

Aerobic.

Optimum temperature, 33° C.

Optimum pH for growth, 9.0. No growth at pH 5.0.

Optimum pH for luminescence, 8.0. No luminescence at pH 5.0.

Quality of luminescence: Greenish.

Source: Isolated from the photogenic organ of the cephalopod *Rondeletia minor*.

Habitat: Apparently found only in *Rondeletia minor* but may also be found in closely related species.

3. **Photobacterium fischeri** Beijerinck, 1889. (Einheimischer Leuchtbacillus, Fischer, Cent. f. Bakt., *3*, 1888, 107; Beijerinck, Arch. néerl. d. Sci. exact. et natur., *23*, 1889, 401; *Vibrio fischeri* Lehmann and Neumann, Bakt. Diag., 1 Aufl., *2*, 1896, 342; *Achromobacter fischeri* Bergey et al., Manual, 3rd ed., 1930, 220.)

fisch′er.i. M.L. gen.noun *fischeri* of Fischer; named for Prof. Bernhard Fischer, one of the earliest students of luminescent bacteria.

Description taken from Fischer (*op. cit.*, 1888, 107), Beijerinck (*op. cit.*, 1889, 401) and

Johnson and Shunk (Jour. Bact., *31*, 1936, 589).

Short, thick rods, 0.4 to 0.8 by 1.0 to 2.5 microns, with rounded ends, occurring singly and in pairs. Occasional rods slightly curved, ends slightly pointed. Not encapsulated. Motile. Johnson, Zworykin and Warren (Jour. Bact., *46*, 1943, 167) made pictures with the electron microscope of a culture which they identified with this species; the organism showed a tuft of polar flagella. Gram-negative.

Sea-water gelatin colonies: After 48 hours, colonies small (less than 0.5 mm in diameter), circular, entire, homogeneous, with slight liquefaction.

Sea-water gelatin stab: Slight, infundibuliform liquefaction, sometimes slightly beaded, tending to become crateriform in old cultures.

Nutrient sea-water agar colonies: Small, circular, smooth, entire, slightly raised, homogeneous, iridescent. Old colonies become yellowish with margins slightly serrate.

Sea-water agar slant: Growth abundant, grayish to yellowish, smooth, viscous, homogeneous, iridescent.

Growth on autoclaved fish: Moderate, grayish to yellowish, smooth, glistening, luminescent, no odor of putrefaction.

Sea water containing 0.2 per cent peptone: Moderate growth, mostly near the surface; very thin pellicle; sediment found in old tubes.

Milk: No growth. Milk with 2.8 per cent sodium chloride: Slight growth and luminescence, but no action on the milk.

Potato plugs resting on cotton saturated in sea water: Growth fairly abundant, spreading, slightly brownish, luminous.

Blood serum: No growth.

Indole not produced.

Hydrogen sulfide is produced.

Acid but no gas from glucose (Gorham, in Dahlgren, Jour. Franklin Inst., *180*, 1915, 517 and insert following 714). Acid from glycerol, fructose, galactose, mannose, maltose, cellobiose, dextrin and salicin. No acid or gas from lactose, sucrose, arabinose, xylose, fucose, rhamnose, trehalose, raffinose, glycogen, inulin, adonitol, dulcitol, inositol, sorbitol, erythritol, arabitol or alpha-methyl-glycoside.

Starch hydrolysis is doubtful or very slight.

Decarboxylates glutamic acid to form γ-aminobutyric acid and CO_2 ; decarboxylates lysine (Pearson, Jour. Cell. and Comp. Physiol., *41*, 1953, 65).

Alanine, arginine, aspartic acid, glutamic acid and threonine are capable of serving as sole nitrogen sources for this organism (Pearson, Jour. Tenn. Acad. Sci., *27*, 1952, 229).

Nitrites produced from nitrates.

Ammonia produced in peptone media.

Aerobic, facultatively anaerobic.

Temperature relations: Optimum, between 25° and 28° C. Minimum, between 5° and 10° C. No growth at 37° C.

Optimum temperature for luminescence, 28° C. Weak at 10° C., none at 5° nor at 37° C.

Optimum pH for luminescence, between 7.4 and 7.8; less intense at 7.0 and 8.2. Fischer (Erg. d. Plankton Expedition d. Humboldt-Stiftung, *4*, 1894) noted that this organism grows best in alkaline media.

Quality of luminescence: Orangish, maintained for 5 to 8 weeks (Beijerinck); greenish (Johnson and Shunk). Luminescence favored by the presence of glycerol in the medium.

Salt tolerance: The osmotic tension of inorganic salt solutions used as media for this species must be equivalent to that produced in a 2.8 to 3.0 per cent sodium chloride solution to assure luminescence and good growth.

Not pathogenic for white rats.

Distinctive character: Luminescence on organic matter occurs only when there is a sufficient proportion of inorganic salt present.

Source: Isolated from sea water at Kiel and from herring.

Habitat: Frequently found on dead fish, crustacea and other salt-water animals and in coastal sea water. Phosphorescent bacteria also occur on meat and even on soldier's wounds where they produce no known harmful effects. No food poisoning has been traced to meat on which these organisms have grown (Niven, Circular No. 2, American Meat Inst. Foundation, 1951, 1–11).

4. Photobacterium harveyi (Johnson and Shunk, 1936) Breed and Lessel, 1954. (*Achromobacter harveyi* Johnson and Shunk, Jour. Bact., *31*, 1936, 587; Breed and Lessel, Antonie van Leeuwenhoek, *20*, 1954, 61.)

har'vey.i. M.L. gen.noun *harveyi* of Harvey; named for E. N. Harvey.

Description taken from Johnson and Shunk (*op. cit.*, 1936, 587).

Rods, 0.5 to 1.0 by 1.2 to 2.5 microns, occurring singly or in pairs, with rounded ends. Occasionally slightly curved; ends occasionally slightly pointed. Non-spore-forming. Not encapsulated. Motile by means of a single, polar flagellum 2 to 3 times the length of the cell. Gram-negative.

Sea-water gelatin colonies: After 24 hours at 20° C., circular, about 1.5 mm in diameter or larger, margin slightly undulate, sunken due to the beginning of lique-faction, interior somewhat zonate; colonies surrounded by a halo of numerous small secondary colonies, circular and finely granular. In crowded plates a large number of gas bubbles are formed. Luminescent.

Sea-water gelatin stab: Rapid saccate liquefaction complete in 5 days at 22° C. Abundant flocculent sediment.

Sea-water agar colonies: Mostly very large, 6 to 8 cm in diameter in 24 hours, flat, highly iridescent, circular with undulate margin, or composed of narrow and close or wide filamentous growth. Occasionally small colonies appear that are circular, with entire or slightly undulate margin, often producing irregular secondary growth, surface always smooth. Luminescent.

Sea-water agar slant: Growth abundant, spreading, grayishly viscous, homogeneous, iridescent, the medium becoming rapidly alkaline when inoculated at an initial pH of 7.0. With fish decoctions added to the medium, luminescence is much brighter and growth becomes brownish after several days.

Growth on autoclaved fish: Abundant, smooth, glistening, yellowish, becoming dirty brown after several days. Mild putre-factive odor. Luminescence very brilliant.

Sea water containing 0.2 per cent peptone: Abundant uniform turbidity, thin pellicle, sediment accumulating over a period of several days. Luminescence at surface only unless the tube is shaken.

Milk, with or without the addition of 2.8 per cent salt: No growth.

Potato plugs resting on cotton saturated with sea water: Growth slight, somewhat spreading, slightly brownish. Luminous.

Indole produced (Gore's method).

Hydrogen sulfide is produced (ZoBell and Fantham method).

Fixed acid from glucose, fructose, mannose, galactose, sucrose, maltose, mannitol, dextrin, glycogen, trehalose, cellobiose; slowly from salicin. Non-fixed acid from melezitose; slight acid from sorbitol, disappearing in 24 hours. No acid from glycerol, xylose, arabinose, dulcitol, inositol, adonitol, erythritol, arabitol, lactose, raffinose, rhamnose, fucose or alpha methyl glucoside.

Starch agar: Wide zone of hydrolysis.

Nitrites produced from nitrates.

Ammonia produced in peptone media (Hansen method).

Aerobic, facultatively anaerobic.

Temperature relations: Optimum, between 35° and 39° C. Abundant growth between 22° and 25° C.

Optimum temperature for luminescence, between 20° and 40° C.

Optimum pH for luminescence, between pH 7.4 and 7.8.

Quality of luminescence (to completely dark-adapted eyes): Yellowish green to green on fish and typically green on sea-water agar or gelatin.

Not pathogenic for white rats or amphipods.

Distinctive character: Luminescence not favored by the presence of glycerol in the medium.

Source: Isolated from a dead amphipod (*Talorchestia sp.*) at Woods Hole, Massachusetts.

Habitat: Sea water.

Note: *Species incertae sedis.* Additional luminescent bacteria which probably belong in this genus have been reported in the literature. However many of the descriptions are not adequate enough to permit the determination of the identity and relationships of these organisms.

Genus VI. **Azotomonas** *Stapp, 1940.* *

(Stapp, Zent. f. Bakt., II Abt., *102*, 1940, 18; not *Azotomonas* Orla-Jensen, Cent. f. Bakt., II Abt., *24*, 1909, 484.)

A.zo.to.mo'nas. Gr. *azous* without life; Fr. noun *azote* nitrogen; Gr. fem.n. *monas* unit, monad; M.L. fem.n. *Azotomonas* nitrogen (-fixing) monad.

Rod- to coccus-shaped cells. Motile by means of 1 to 3 polar flagella. No fat-like reserve food granules in the cells. Chemo-heterotrophic. Produce acid and sometimes gas from glucose and other sugars and alcohols. Many carbon compounds other than sugars are used as sources of energy. Indole is produced. Aerobic. Active in the fixation of atmospheric nitrogen. Found in soil.

The type species is *Azotomonas insolita* Stapp.

Key to the species of genus **Azotomonas.**

I. Acid and gas from glucose.
  1. *Azotomonas insolita.*

II. Acid but no gas from glucose.
  2. *Azotomonas fluorescens.*

1. **Azotomonas insolita** Stapp, 1940. (Abstracts of Communications, Third Internat. Congr. for Microbiol., Sect. VIII, 1939, 306; abst. in Proc. Soil Sci. Soc. of America, *4*, 1939, 244; Zent. f. Bakt., II Abt., *102*, 1940, 1.)

in.so'li.ta. L. adj. *insolitus* unusual.

Coccoid rods 0.6 to 1.2 by 0.6 to 1.8 microns. Motile by means of 1 to 3 polar flagella. Gram-negative.

Gelatin: No liquefaction.

Agar colonies: Flat, whitish, entire, weakly fluorescent.

Agar slant: Glistening, white growth.

Broth: Strongly turbid; sediment; pellicle.

Milk: Unchanged.

Potato: Growth somewhat dry, not slimy, dirty gray, spreading.

Hydrogen sulfide is produced.

Acid and gas from adonitol, arabinose, dextrin, glucose, galactose, glycerol, inositol, lactose, fructose, maltose, mannose, mannitol, raffinose, rhamnose, salicin, sorbitol, starch, sucrose and xylose.

Starch is hydrolyzed.

Nitrites produced from nitrates.

Atmospheric nitrogen is fixed.

Ammonium salts are utilized.

Aerobic.

Temperature relations: Optimum, between 25° and 30° C. Minimum, between 7.0° and 9.5° C. Maximum, 48° C. Good growth at 37° C. Thermal death point, 60° C.

Limits of pH, 3.3 to 9.5.

Source: Isolated from a mixture of chopped cotton husks and rice hulls.

Habitat: Soil.

2. **Azotomonas fluorescens** Krassilnikov, 1947. (Quoted from Krassilnikov, Guide to the Bacteria and Actinomycetes, Izd. Akad. Nauk, U.S.S.R., Moskau, 1949, 420.)

flu.o.res'cens. L. noun *fluor* a flux; M.L. v. *fluoresco* to fluoresce; fluor-spar, a fluxing mineral which is fluorescent; M.L. part.adj. *fluorescens* fluorescing.

Translated by Dr. A. Petraitis, New York State Experiment Station, Geneva, New York.

Rod-shaped cells, 0.5 to 0.8 by 2.0 to 5.0 microns, which become shorter in old cultures. Motile by means of one to three polar flagella. Gram-negative.

Gelatin: Slow liquefaction.

Inorganic media with or without nitrogen: Good growth.

Colonies are wide, smooth and glistening.

A slightly yellowish or violet fluorescent pigment is produced which diffuses through the medium.

Milk: Peptonized.

---

* Rearranged by Dr. A. W. Hofer, New York State Experiment Station, Cornell University, Geneva, New York, November, 1953.

Acid but no gas from various sugars and alcohols.
Starch is hydrolyzed.
Fixes nitrogen.

Nitrites not produced from nitrates.
Aerobic.
Source: Isolated from soil.
Habitat: Soil.

Genus VII. **Zymomonas** *Kluyver and van Niel, 1936.**

(Kluyver and van Niel, Zent. f. Bakt., II Abt., *94*, 1936, 399; *Saccharomonas* Shimwell, Jour. Inst. Brewing, *56* (N.S. *47*), 1950, 179.)

Zy.mo'mo.nas or Zy.mo.mo'nas. Gr. noun *zyme* leaven, ferment; Gr. noun *monas* a unit, monad; M.L. fem.n. *Zymomonas* fermenting monad.

Rod-shaped cells, occasionally ellipsoidal. Motile cells are lophotrichous. Anaerobically ferment glucose with the production of carbon dioxide, ethyl alcohol and some lactic acid. Found in fermenting beverages such as pulque, palm juice and beer.

The type species is *Zymomonas mobilis* (Lindner) Kluyver and van Niel.

1. **Zymomonas mobilis** (Lindner, 1928) Kluyver and van Niel, 1936. (*Termobacterium mobile* Lindner, Atlas d. Mikrosk. Grundl. d. Gärungsk., 3 Aufl., *2*, 1928, Taf. 68; also see Lindner, 50 Jubiläumsber. Westpreuss. Bot.-Zool. Vereins, 1928, 253; *Pseudomonas lindneri* Kluyver and Hoppenbrouwers, Arch. f. Mikrobiol., *2*, 1931, 259; *Zymomonas mobile* (sic), Kluyver and van Niel, Zent. f. Bakt., II Abt., *94*, 1936, 399; *Saccharomonas lindneri* Shimwell, Jour. Inst. Brewing, *56* (N. S. *47*), 1950, 179.)

mo'bi.lis. L. adj. *mobilis* movable, motile.

Short rods with rounded ends, 1.4 to 2.0 by 4.0 to 5.0 microns. Occur usually as pairs with a central constriction and rarely as short chains. Motile with polar flagella. Gram-negative.

Peptone gelatin: Poor growth.

Peptone agar: Poor growth.

Wort agar: White, round, raised colonies 1 mm in diameter. Good growth. Still better growth where 2 per cent sucrose or yeast extract with sucrose is added. Chalk may be added to neutralize acid.

Wort gelatin stab: Uniform growth in stab; no surface growth. No liquefaction.

Broth: Poor growth in peptone or yeast extract broth unless sugars are added.

Carbon dioxide, ethyl alcohol and some lactic acid produced from glucose and fructose but not from mannose. Ferments sucrose usually after a somewhat prolonged lag period. May produce as much as 10 per cent alcohol.

Catalase-positive.

Anaerobic, although with a certain oxygen tolerance of aerobic growth in the presence of fermentable sugars.

Optimum temperature, 30° C.

Distinctive character: Apart from the production of some lactic acid, the fermentation resembles the alcoholic fermentation produced by yeasts.

Source: Isolated from the fermenting sap (pulque) of *Agave americana* in Mexico and from fermenting palm juice (*Arenga saccharifera*) in Sumatra and Java (Roelofsen, Natuurwetenschappelijk Tijdschrift voor Ned-. Indie, *101*, 1941, 374).

Habitat: Found in fermenting plant juices in tropical countries (Mexico and Indonesia).

2. **Zymomonas anaerobia** (Shimwell, 1937) Kluyver, *comb. nov.* (*Achromobacter anaerobium* Shimwell, Jour. Inst. Brewing, *43*, 1937, 507; *Saccharomonas anaerobia* Shimwell, *op. cit.*, *56* (N. S. *47*), 1950, 179 (type species of genus *Saccharomonas* Shimwell).)

an.a.e.ro'bi.a. Gr. pref. *an* not; Gr. noun *aër* air; Gr. noun *bius* life; M.L. adj. *anaerobius* not living in air.

Rods, 1.0 to 1.5 by 2.0 to 3.0 microns, plump with rounded ends. Cells occasionally clump together to form rosette-like clusters. Young cells actively motile with lophotrichous flagella, old cells become non-motile. Not encapsulated. Gram-negative.

Glucose-beer-gelatin stab: Dense, filiform to beaded growth in stab; no surface growth. No liquefaction.

---

* Prepared by Prof. A. J. Kluyver, Technische Hogeschool, Delft, Holland, December, 1953.

Glucose-beer-agar colonies: When incubated in CO_2, irregularly circular, entire, convex, about 1 mm in diameter, cream-colored by reflected light, brown by transmitted light, thinly butyrous, granular.

Glucose-beer-agar slant: Normally there is no growth although there may be a slight growth after prolonged incubation. Filiform or beaded, creamy white, thinly butyrous, non-adherent growth when incubated in CO_2.

Glucose-beer-agar stab: Dense, filiform to beaded growth in stab; no surface growth.

Yeast extract, sugar-free beer: No growth.

Beer, 2 per cent glucose: Densely turbid, later becoming clear with a heavy sediment.

Yeast extract glucose broth: Growth only in deep medium; slight deposit on walls of tube; dense sediment at bottom.

Indole not produced.

Glucose and fructose readily fermented; maltose, sucrose, lactose and ethyl alcohol not attacked.

Acetylmethylcarbinol and diacetyl not produced.

Nitrites not produced from nitrates.

Anaerobic, microaeroduric (not microaerophilic).

Temperature relations: Optimum, 30° C.; thermal death point, 60° C. for 5 minutes.

pH range for growth, 3.4 to 7.5.

Distinctive characters: Does not grow in any medium unless glucose or fructose is present. Shimwell (loc. cit.) recognizes a non-motile variety of this species. A related or perhaps identical species has been described as the cause of "cider sickness" in England (see Barker, Ann. Rept. Nat. Fruit and Cider Inst. Long Ashton, 1948).

A comparative study of cultures of Zymomonas mobilis, Z. anaerobia and the cider organism made in 1951 shows that these organisms are closely related. Z. anaerobia did show fermentation of sucrose although the cider organism did not show this fermentation (Kluyver, personal communication).

Source: Isolated from beer, from the surface of brewery yards and from the brushes of cask-washing machines.

Habitat: Plant juices or extracts containing glucose.

Note: *Species incertae sedis*. Additional species which probably belong in this genus but which have not been well described have been reported from beer and cider.

Genus VIII. **Protaminobacter** den Dooren de Jong, 1926.*

(Bijdrage tot de kennis van het mineralisatieproces. Thesis, Rotterdam, 1926, 159.)

Pro.ta.mi.no.bac'ter. Gr. sup.adj. *prōtus* first; M.L. noun *aminum* an amine; M.L. mas.n. *bacter* masculine form of Gr. neut.n. *bactrum* rod or staff; M.L. mas.n. *Protaminobacter* protamine rod.

Cells motile or non-motile. Capable of dissimilating alkylamines. Pigmentation frequent. Soil or water forms.

Recently Slepecky and Doetsch (Bact. Proc., 54th Gen. Meeting, Soc. of Amer. Bact., 1954, 44) have isolated 23 fresh cultures of polar flagellate organisms that utilize alkylamines. Of these, one resembled a known species of *Protaminobacter*, but all showed the general characters of organisms placed in the genus *Pseudomonas*. The authors question the recognition of the genus *Protaminobacter* on a biochemical basis only.

The type species is *Protaminobacter alboflavus* den Dooren de Jong.

Key to the species of genus **Protaminobacter.**

I. Non-motile. Gelatin colonies light yellow to colorless.
                    1. *Protaminobacter alboflavus.*

II. Motile. Gelatin colonies red.
                    2. *Protaminobacter ruber.*

---

* Prepared by Prof. D. H. Bergey, Philadelphia, Pennsylvania, June, 1929; further revision by Prof. Robert S. Breed, New York State Experiment Station, Geneva, New York, July, 1953.

1. **Protaminobacter alboflavus** den Dooren de Jong, 1926. (Thesis, Rotterdam, 1926, 159; also see Cent. f. Bakt., II Abt., *71*, 1927, 218.)

al.bo.fla′vus. L. adj. *albus* white; L. adj. *flavus* yellow; M.L. adj. *alboflavus* whitish yellow.

Rods. Non-motile. Gram-negative.

Gelatin colonies: Circular, dry, light yellow or colorless.

Gelatin stab: No liquefaction.

Agar colonies: Circular, opaque, pigment bright red, yellow, light gray or colorless.

Amine agar colonies: Circular, white to dark yellow.

See Table I for list of organic substances utilized.

Catalase produced.

Aerobic, facultative.

Optimum temperature, 30° C.

Distinctive characters: The author recognizes four varieties of this species which he differentiates on the basis of organic substances attacked (see Table) and pigment produced. Variety α shows light yellow growth on gelatin, bright red on agar and yellow on amine agar. Variety β is light yellow on gelatin, yellow on agar and dark yellow on amine agar. Variety γ is light yellow on gelatin, light gray on agar and yellow on amine agar. Variety δ is colorless on gelatin and agar and white on amine agar.

Habitat: Soil and water.

2. **Protaminobacter ruber** den Dooren de Jong, 1926. (Thesis, Rotterdam, 1926, 159; also see Cent. f. Bakt., II Abt., *71*, 1927, 218.)

ru′ber. L. *ruber* red.

Rods. Motile with a single polar flagellum (Weaver, Samuels and Sherago, Jour. Bact., *35*, 1938, 59). Gram-negative.

Gelatin colonies: Circular, red, dry.

Gelatin stab: No liquefaction.

Agar colonies: Circular, red, opaque.

Amine agar colonies: Circular, dark red.

The following organic acids are attacked: Acetic, lactic, β-oxybutyric, glycerinic, succinic, malonic, formic, methyl formic, glutaric, maleinic, fumaric, malic, tartaric, citric and quinic.

The following amino compounds are

TABLE I.—*Organic Substances Utilized as a Source of Carbon by Varieties (biotypes) of* **Protaminobacter alboflavus**

	α	β	γ	δ
Organic acids:				
Acetic	+	+	+	+
Valerianic	+	+	0	+
α-crotonic	+	+	+	+
Undecyclic	0	0	0	+
Lactic	+	0	0	+
β-oxybutyric	+	+	+	+
Succinic	+	+	+	+
Formic	+	+	+	+
Glutaric	0	+	0	+
Adipic	0	0	0	+
Fumaric	+	+	+	+
Malic	+	+	+	+
Tartaric	0	+	0	0
Citric	+	+	+	+
β-phenylpropionic	+	0	0	0
Quinic	+	+	0	0
Amino compounds:				
α-alanin	0	0	+	+
α-aminocapronic acid	+	0	+	0
Leucin	+	+	0	0
Propionamid	+	0	+	0
Capronamid	+	0	+	0
Uric acid	+	0	0	0
Hippuric acid	+	0	0	0
Alcohol:				
Ethyl	+	+	+	+
Sugar:				
Glucose	+	+	+	0
Amines:				
Ethyl	+	+	+	+
Diethyl	+	+	0	0
Propyl	+	+	+	+
Isopropyl	0	+	0	0
Dipropyl	+	+	0	0
Tripropyl	+	0	0	0
Butyl	+	0	+	0
Isobutyl	+	+	+	+
Diisobutyl	+	+	0	0
Amyl	+	+	+	+
Diamyl	0	+	0	0
Ethanol	+	+	+	+
Glucosamin	+	+	+	0
Benzyl	+	0	+	0

attacked: Sarcosin, betain, hippuric acid, asparagine, propionamid, capronamid, lactamid, succinamid, allantoin and uric acid. Glucose fermented.

Catalase produced.
Aerobic, facultative.
Optimum temperature, 30° C.
Habitat: Soil and water.

Genus IX. Alginomonas Thjøtta and Kåss, 1945.*

(Thjøtta and Kåss, Norske Videnskaps-Akad., Oslo, I Mat.- Naturv. Klasse, No. 5, 1945, 17; also see Kåss, Lid and Molland, *ibid.*, No. 11, 1945, 8.)

Al.gi.no.mo'nas. L. fem.n. *alga* seaweed; M.L. adj. *alginicus* pertaining to alginic acid from seaweed; Gr. noun *monas* a unit, monad; M.L. fem.n. *Alginomonas* alginic-acid (-decomposing) monad.

Coccoid rods which are motile with one to four polar flagella. Gram-negative. Fluorescent. Gelatin is usually liquefied. Carbohydrates are not utilized. Citric acid is not used as a sole source of carbon. Alginic acid is decomposed. Found on algae and in sea water and soil.

As the type of flagellation has not been determined for all of the species here included in the genus, it may be found later that some of these species do not belong in *Alginomonas* as here defined.

The type species is *Alginomonas nonfermentans* Kåss et al.

Key to the species of genus Alginomonas.

I. Gelatin is liquefied.
    A. Grow on potato.
        1. Gray to grayish brown growth on potato.
                1. *Alginomonas nonfermentans.*
        2. Pinkish or ivory-colored growth on potato.
           a. Pink growth on potato.
                2. *Alginomonas terrestralginica.*
           aa. Ivory-colored growth on potato.
                3. *Alginomonas alginovora.*
    B. No growth on potato.
                4. *Alginomonas fucicola.*
II. Gelatin not liquefied in seven days.
                5. *Alginomonas alginica.*

1. **Alginomonas nonfermentans** Kåss et al., 1945. (Kåss, Lid and Molland, Norske Videnskaps-Akad., Oslo, 1 Mat.-Naturv. Klasse, No. 11, 1945, 9.)

non.fer.men'tans. L. prefix *non-* not, non-; L. v. *fermento* to ferment; M.L. part. adj. *nonfermentans* non-fermenting.

Small, coccoid rods. Motile with one to four polar flagella. Gram-negative.

Good growth on ordinary media.
Gelatin: Liquefaction.
Agar colonies: Smooth, fluorescent.
Broth: Turbid; sediment; no pellicle.
Litmus milk: Coagulated; peptonized; reduced.

Potato: Abundant, grayish brown growth.

Indole not produced.

Hydrogen sulfide is produced.

Alginic acid is decomposed without the production of acid or gas.

Carbohydrates are not utilized.

Citric acid cannot be used as a sole source of carbon.

Nitrites produced from nitrates.

Aerobic.

Grows at 37° C.

Chemical tolerance: No growth at pH 9.6.

---

* Prepared by Prof. Th. Thjøtta, Microbiological Institute, University of Oslo, Oslo, Norway, January, 1955.

No growth in 6 per cent sodium chloride broth.

Source: Five strains were isolated from soil.

Habitat: Presumably soil.

2. Alginomonas terrestralginica (Waksman et al., 1934) Kåss et al., 1945. (*Bacterium terrestralginicum* Waksman, Carey and Allen, Jour. Bact., *28*, 1934, 217; Kåss, Lid and Molland, Norske Videnskaps-Akad., Oslo, 1 Mat.-Naturv. Klasse, No. 11, 1945, 9.)

ter.res.tral.gi'ni.ca. L. noun *terrestris* land, earth; M.L. adj. *alginicus* pertaining to alginic acid from seaweed; M.L. adj. *terrestralginicus* land-alginic; presumably intended to mean an alginic bacterium from the soil.

Long rods, 1.0 to 1.5 by 1.5 to 2.5 microns, with somewhat rounded ends, usually occurring singly but also in pairs, occasionally in chains of shorter rods. Motile. Granular. Gram-negative.

Alginic acid plate: Colonies small, whitish in appearance with a slight metallic sheen.

Alginic acid liquid medium: Medium at first clouded. Later a pellicle is formed on the surface of the medium; it is soon broken up due to active gas formation. Reaction of medium becomes slightly alkaline.

Gelatin medium: Slow growth throughout stab, slow liquefaction at surface of medium at 18° C.

Agar liquefaction: None.

Glucose broth: Abundant turbidity; some sediment; no pellicle; slightly fluorescent.

Litmus milk: Acid; milk coagulated; only limited digestion of coagulum.

Potato: Abundant, pinkish, compact, dry growth on surface of plug, the rest of the plug becoming gray with a tendency to darkening.

Starch plate: Limited growth along streak; no diastase.

Aerobic to facultatively anaerobic.

Optimum temperature, 30° C.

Source: Isolated from New Jersey soil.

Habitat: Soil.

3. Alginomonas alginovora (Waksman et al., 1934) Kåss et al., 1945. (*Bacterium alginovorum* Waksman, Carey and

Allen, Jour. Bact., *28*, 1934, 215; Kåss, Lid and Molland, Norske Videnskaps-Akad., Oslo, I Mat.-Naturv. Klasse, No. 11, 1945, 9.)

al.gi.no'vo.ra. L. fem.n. *alga* seaweed; M.L. noun *acidum alginicum* alginic acid (derived from seaweed); L. v. *voro* to devour; M.L. adj. *alginovorus* alginic acid-destroying.

Rods, 0.75 to 1.2 by 1.5 to 2.0 microns, with rounded to almost elliptical ends, especially when single, occurring frequently in pairs and even in chains. Encapsulated. Actively motile. Gram-negative.

Alginic acid plate: Colony large, white in appearance, with coarse, granular center, entire margin. Clears up turbidity caused by alginic acid on the plate. No odor.

Alginic acid liquid medium: Heavy pellicle formation. Active production of an enzyme, alginase, which brings about the disappearance of alginic precipitate in sea-water medium.

Salt-water medium: A slimy pellicle of a highly tenacious nature is produced, the whole medium later turning to a soft jelly.

Sea-water gelatin: Active and rapid liquefaction in two to six days at 18° C.; highly turbid throughout the liquefied zone.

Agar liquefaction: Extensive softening of agar, no free liquid.

Sea-water glucose broth: Abundant, uniform turbidity with surface pellicle; some strains give heavier turbidity, and others heavier pellicle.

Litmus milk containing 3.5 per cent salt: No apparent growth.

Potato moistened with sea water: Moist, spreading, ivory-colored growth; heavy sediment in free liquid at the bottom.

Starch plate: Abundant, cream-colored, slimy growth; extensive diastase production.

Aerobic to microaerophilic.

Optimum temperature, 20° C.

Source: Isolated from sea water, sea-bottom sediments and from the surface of algal growth in the sea.

Habitat: Very common in the sea.

4. Alginomonas fucicola (Waksman et al., 1934) Kåss et al., 1945. (*Bacterium fucicola* Waksman, Carey and Allen, Jour. Bact.,

28, 1934, 213; Kåss, Lid and Molland, Norske Videnskaps-Akad., Oslo, I Mat.-Naturv. Klasse, No. 11, 1945, 9.)

fu.ci'co.la. L. mas.n. *fucus* a seaweed; M. L. noun *Fucus* a genus of brown seaweeds; L.v. *colo* to inhabit; M.L. noun *fucicola* the *Fucus* dweller.

Short rods, 0.6 to 1.0 by 1.0 to 1.5 microns, with ends rounded to almost coccoid; slightly curved. Actively motile with twirling motion. Gram-negative.

Alginic acid plate: Colonies finely granular, entire; at first whitish, turning brown in three to five days, and later almost black, producing a deep brown, soluble pigment.

Alginic acid liquid medium: Limited growth on surface in the form of a pellicle. Frequently produces no growth at all.

Sea-water gelatin: Active liquefaction; no growth on stab; thin, fluorescent growth throughout liquefied zone.

Agar liquefaction: Positive, although limited; only softening of agar.

Sea-water glucose broth: Faint turbidity; no pellicle; no sediment.

Litmus milk containing salt: No apparent growth.

Potato moistened with sea water: No growth.

Starch plate: No growth.

Aerobic.

Optimum temperature, 20° C.

Source: Isolated from sea water near the surface of the sand bottom.

Habitat: Rare in sea water.

5. **Alginomonas alginica** (Waksman et al., 1934) Kåss et al., 1945. (*Bacterium alginicum* Waksman, Carey and Allen, Jour. Bact., *28*, 1934, 213; Kåss, Lid and Molland, Norske Videnskaps-Akad., Oslo, I Mat.-Naturv. Klasse, No. 11, 1945, 9.)

al.gi'ni.ca. L. fem.n. *alga* seaweed; M.L. adj. *alginicus* pertaining to alginic acid from seaweed.

Rods short to almost spherical, 0.6 to 1.0 micron in diameter. Encapsulated. Sluggishly motile. Gram-negative.

Alginic acid plate: White, finely granulated colonies with entire margin. Does not clear up the turbidity in plate. Odor produced resembles that of old potatoes.

Alginic acid liquid medium: Thin pellicle; weak alginase formation.

Sea-water gelatin: Thin growth throughout gelatin stab; no liquefaction in 7 days at 18° C.

Agar liquefaction: None.

Sea-water glucose broth: Uniform but very limited turbidity; no pellicle; no sediment.

Litmus milk containing salt: No apparent growth.

Potato moistened with sea water: Moist, spreading, cream-colored growth; heavy sediment in free liquid at bottom.

Starch plate: Limited, pale blue growth; no diastase.

Aerobic.

Optimum temperature, 20° C.

Source: Isolated from sea water and from the surface of algal growth.

Habitat: Common in sea water.

Genus X. **Mycoplana** *Gray and Thornton, 1928.**

(Cent. f. Bakt., II Abt., *73*, 1928, 82.)

My.co.pla'na. Gr. *myces* fungus; Gr. *planus* a wandering; M.L. fem.n. *Mycoplana* fungus wanderer.

Cells branching, especially in young cultures. Frequently banded when stained. Polar flagellate.† Capable of using phenol or similar aromatic compounds as a sole source of energy. Grow well on standard culture media. From soil.

The type species is *Mycoplana dimorpha* Gray and Thornton.

---

* Prepared by Prof. Robert S. Breed, Cornell University, Geneva, New York, January, 1954.

† The orginal statements regarding the flagellation of these species are contradictory. The first reads "Polar, peritrichous"; the second "Polar or peritrichous".—Editors.

Key to the species of genus **Mycoplana.**

I. Gelatin not liquefied.

        1. *Mycoplana dimorpha.*

II. Gelatin liquefied.

        2. *Mycoplana bullata.*

1. **Mycoplana dimorpha** Gray and Thornton, 1928. (Cent. f. Bakt., II. Abt., *73*, 1928, 82.)

di.mor'pha. Gr. adj. *dimorphus* two forms.

Short, curved and irregular rods, 0.5 to 0.7 by 1.25 to 4.5 microns, showing branching especially in young cultures. Originally reported as "polar, peritrichous". Drawings show some cells with a polar flagellum and others where the several flagella shown could represent a tuft of polar flagella. Cultures preserved in the American Type Culture Collection have been retested (T. H. Lord, Manhattan, Kansas; F. E. Clark, Beltsville, Maryland) and show typical pseudomonad cells, i.e., straight rods with a single polar flagellum. Meanwhile P. H. H. Gray (Macdonald College, Quebec) reports that his cultures still show branching cells on the media he uses. Gram-negative.

Gelatin colonies: Circular, buff, smooth, resinous, entire.

Gelatin stab: No liquefaction. Growth filiform.

Agar colonies: Circular, buff, convex, smooth, glistening, entire.

Agar slant: Filiform, white, convex, glistening, entire.

Broth: Turbid, with surface ring.

Nitrites not produced from nitrates, but gas evolved in fermentation tubes.

Starch hydrolyzed.

No acid from carbohydrate media.

Attacks phenol.

Aerobic.

Optimum temperature, below 30° C.

Source: Only one strain was found in soil by Gray and Thornton (*loc. cit.*). Wood (Aust. Jour. Marine and Freshwater Res., *4*, 1953, 184) identifies 1010 cultures out of 2969 cultures isolated from Australian marine habitats as belonging to this species. Some appeared on submerged glass slides as attached forms. A diversity of characters was found in these cultures, indicating that many of them should not have been identi-fied as belonging to this species or even to this genus. For example, while it is stated in one place that carbohydrate fermentation is feeble, it is stated in another place that about 50 per cent of the cultures actively fermented maltose and sucrose, these sugars being fermented more actively than glucose. Some cultures are reported as attacking cellulose, others as attacking alginates or even chitin. In other words many of the cultures identified as *Mycoplana dimorpha* possessed characters not ascribed to the species by Gray and Thornton. Apparently all cultures from marine habitats that were Gram-negative branching forms were identi-fied as *Mycoplana dimorpha* unless they showed a yellow, pink or lemon-yellow chro-mogenesis. Wood's work would indicate that branching, polar flagellate species of very diverse physiologies exist in marine habitats that are as yet scarcely studied from the standpoint of the species present. M. E. Norris of the Pacific Fisheries Experiment Station, Vancouver, B. C. reports (personal communication, May, 1954) that she also finds Gram-negative, branching, polar flagellate organisms in sea water.

Habitat: Probably widely distributed in soil. Possibly also found in marine habitats.

2. **Mycoplana bullata** Gray and Thorn-ton, 1928. (Cent. f. Bakt., II Abt., *73*, 1928, 83.)

bul.la'ta. L. adj. *bullatus* with a knob.

Rods curved or irregular in shape, branch-ing, 0.8 to 1.0 by 2.25 to 4.5 microns. Origi-nally stated to be either "polar or peri-trichous" in its flagellation, but recent studies show that the American Type Cul-ture Collection culture of this organism is polar flagellate. It resembles *Mycoplana dimorpha* in this respect. Gram-negative.

Gelatin colonies: Circular, buff, smooth, glistening; edge diffuse Gelatin partially liquefied.

Gelatin stab: Saccate liquefaction.

Agar colonies: Circular, white, convex, smooth, glistening, entire.

Agar slant: Filiform, white, convex, smooth, glistening, entire.

Broth: Turbid.

Nitrites not produced from nitrates. Gas, presumably N_2, in fermentation tubes.

Starch not hydrolyzed.

No acid from carbohydrate media.

Attacks phenol.

Aerobic.

Optimum temperature, below 30°C.

Source: Two strains isolated from soil.

Habitat: Probably widely distributed in soil. Possibly also found in marine habitats.

Note: *Species incertae sedis.* Other bacteria from sea water, fresh water and soil have been described as belonging in this genus. Their relationships to the species described by Gray and Thornton (Cent. f. Bakt., II Abt., *73*, 1928, 82) have not yet been definitely established.

Genus XI. Zoogloea Cohn, 1854.*

(Nov. Act. Acad. Caes. Leop.-Carol. Nat. Cur., *24*, 1854, 123.)

Zo.o.gloe'a. Gr. adj. *zous* living; Gr. *gloea* glue; M.L. fem.n. *Zoogloea* living glue.

Rod-shaped cells embedded in a gelatinous matrix. Free-floating forms found in fresh water that contains organic matter. Occur as compact masses or as branched forms. Cells may become detached and motile in which case they are monotrichous.

The original description of this genus follows:

Zoogloea. Cellulae minimae bacilliformes hyalinae, gelatina hyalina in massas globosas, uvaeformes, mox membranaceae consociatae, dein singulae elapsae, per aquam vacillantes.

This may be freely translated as follows:

Zoogloea. Transparent, very small, rod-shaped cells embedded in transparent, gelatinous, clustered, spherical masses. Afterwards become detached as individuals swimming to and fro in the water.

Zoogloea termo Cohn, 1854, the type species (monotypy) of this genus, is generally thought to be unrecognizable. While awaiting further study of this problem by modern methods, it is recommended that *Zoogloea ramigera* Itzigsohn be accepted as the type species of *Zoogloea* Cohn.

1. **Zoogloea ramigera** Itzigsohn, 1867, *emend.* Blöch, 1918. (Itzigsohn, Sitzungsber. d. Gesellschaft naturf. Freunde, Berlin, Nov. 19, 1867, 30; Blöch, Cent. f. Bakt., II Abt., *48*, 1918, 44–62.)

ra.mi'ge.ra. L. *ramus* a branch; L. v. *gero* to bear; M.L. adj. *ramigerus* branch-bearing.

Description taken from Blöch (*loc. cit.*), who made the first cultural studies of this species, Butterfield (Public Health Reports, *50*, 1935, 671) and Wattie (Pub. Health Reports, *57*, 1942, 1519).

Rods, 1 by 2 to 4 microns, with rounded ends. Numerous cells are found embedded in a gelatinous, branching matrix (see Koch, Beiträge z. Biol. d. Pflanzen, *2*, Heft 8, 1877, 399, Taf. XIV, and Butterfield, *op. cit.*, 1935, plates I–IV). Free cells are motile with a single, long, polar flagellum. Gram-negative.

Blöch reports no growth at 25° C. on gelatin, poor growth on nutrient agar, good growth in nutrient broth, weak growth in peptone water, very good growth in hay infusions, good growth in yeast extract water, no growth in liquid manure, no growth in beer wort, no growth on potato and no growth on yellow sugar beet. Butterfield reports that growth is best in aerated liquid media.

Nitrites not produced from nitrates.

Ammonia produced from peptones.

Indole not produced.

Hydrogen sulfide not produced.

Methyl red negative; acetylmethylcarbinol not produced.

---

* Revised by Mrs. James B. Lackey née Elsie Wattie, University of Florida, Gainesville, Florida, March, 1954.

Blöch reports that sugars are utilized in developing cell substances. Wattie finds that there is evidence of slight acid production from glucose, lactose, xylose and mannitol, whereas Butterfield finds no action on all sugars tested. In addition to the sugars named above, these included sucrose, arabinose, galactose, mannose, cellobiose, raffinose, melizitose, dextrin and salicin.

Pure-culture "activated sludges" formed by this species have been shown to produce a high rate of oxidation of the pollutional material in sewage (synthetic and natural), oxidizing about 50 per cent of the 5-day biochemical oxygen demand in a 5-hour aeration period and about 80 per cent in a 24-hour interval. Nitrogenous materials are not included in this oxidation as this species is not capable of such action.

Temperature relations: Optimum, between 28° and 30° C. Good growth at 20° and at 37° C. Minimum, 4° C.

Optimum pH, 7.0 to 7.4.

Strict aerobe.

Distinctive characters: Oxidizes sewage and other organic solutions. Also see McKinney and Horwood (Sewage and Ind. Wastes, *24*, 1953, 117), who found other floc-forming organisms besides *Zoogloea ramigera* in activated sludge; these were identified as *Bacillus cereus, Escherichia intermedia, Paracolobactrum aerogenoides* and *Nocardia actinomorpha*. A species of *Flavobacterium* was also found in the flocs in association with these species.

Source: Originally (1867) found in a culture of decomposing algae. It has been repeatedly found in materials containing decomposing plant materials and sewage and is especially common in the flocs formed in the activated sludge process of purifying sewage.

Habitat: Produces zoogloeal masses in water containing decomposing organic matter. Common.

2. **Zoogloea filipendula** Beger, 1928.

(Kl. Mitt. d. Ver. f. Wasser-, Boden- und Lufthyg., Berlin-Dahlem, *4*, 1928, 143; also see Beger, Zent. f. Bakt., I Abt., Orig., *154*, 1949, 61.)

fi.li.pen'du.la. L. noun *filum* a thread; L. adj. *pendulus* hanging down; M.L. adj. *filipendulus* thread hanging down.

Description prepared by Prof. H. Beger, Berlin-Dahlem, Germany.

Cells coccoid (0.8 micron in diameter) to rod-shaped (0.8 by 2.0 microns). The cells are surrounded by a gelatinous mass which varies in size from 1.5 to 2.0 by 4.5 cm and which is composed of numerous, more or less spherical masses 3 to 5 mm long. The largest cells completely fill the newly formed globules which lie at the end of filaments hanging downward from zoogloeal masses suspended from the under surface of pump pistons and other submerged objects; the cells in the older globules are smaller (0.4 by 0.7 micron) and are found near the surface of the globule, the interior being relatively free of cells.

Several other bacteria are found in association with this species. As a result, the gelatinous mass appears rust-colored (covered with iron bacteria) when found in acid waters and grayish white when isolated from water that is neutral.

Nutrient gelatin: Only the small forms, such as those found in older globules, are able to grow on this medium. Substantial growth occurs at the bottom of the stab in 48 hours.

Source: Isolated from pump pistons and other submerged objects from a waterworks near Berlin.

Habitat: Found in water contaminated with sewage or industrial wastes.

Note: *Species incertae sedis:* For species that resemble those placed in the genus *Zoogloea* Cohn in many important respects, see *Nevskia ramosa* Famintzin and *Myconostoc gregarium* Cohn. Additional species have also been placed in the genus *Zoogloea*.

Genus XII. **Halobacterium** *Elazari-Volcani, 1940.**

(Elazari-Volcani, Studies on the Microflora of the Dead Sea. Thesis, Hebrew Univ., Jerusalem, 1940, V and 59; not *Halibacterium* Fischer, Ergebnisse der Plankton-Expedition der

* Prepared by Dr. B. Elazari-Volcani, The Weizmann Institute of Science, Rehovoth, Israel, February, 1955.

Humboldt-Stiftung, 1894, 19; not *Halophilus* Sturges and Heideman (*nomen nudum*), Abst. of Bact., *8*, 1924, 14; not *Halobacterium* Schoop (*nomen nudum*), Zent. f. Bakt., I Abt., Orig., *134*, 1935, 26; *Halobacter* Anderson, Applied Microbiol., *2*, 1954, 66.)

Ha.lo.bac.te'ri.um. Gr. noun *hals* salt; Gr. dim.noun *bacterium* a small rod; M.L. neut.n. *Halobacterium* the salt bacterium.

Obligate halophilic, rod-shaped bacteria which are highly pleomorphic. Require at least 12 per cent salt for growth, and will live even in saturated brine solutions. Motile species are polar flagellate; some species are non-motile. Gram-negative. Usually chromogenic, producing non-water-soluble, carotenoid pigments which vary in shade from colorless to orange or even brilliant red. Carbohydrates may or may not be attacked without the production of visible gas. Nitrates are reduced, occasionally with the production of gas. Found in tidal pools, especially in the tropics, salt ponds, salt seas or other places where heavy brines occur naturally; also found on salted fish, salted hides and similar materials.

The type species is *Halobacterium salinarium* Elazari-Volcani.

Key to the species of genus **Halobacterium**.

I. Gas not produced from nitrates.
  A. Nitrites not produced from nitrates.
    1. Pale pink to scarlet chromogenesis.
                1. *Halobacterium salinarium.*
    2. Pink to dark red chromogenesis.
                2. *Halobacterium cutirubrum.*
  B. Nitrites produced from nitrates.
                3. *Halobacterium halobium.*
II. Gas produced from nitrates.
  A. Produces acid from glucose.
                4. *Halobacterium marismortui.*
  B. Does not produce acid from glucose.
                5. *Halobacterium trapanicum.*

1. **Halobacterium salinarium** (Harrison and Kennedy, 1922) Elazari-Volcani, 1940. (*Pseudomonas salinaria* Harrison and Kennedy, Trans. Royal Soc. of Canada, *16*, 1922, 121; *Flavobacterium* (*Halobacterium*) *salinarium* Elazari-Volcani, Studies on the Microflora of the Dead Sea. Thesis, Hebrew Univ., Jerusalem, 1940, 59.)

sa.li.na'ri.um. L. adj. *salinarius* of salt works.

Occurs as spheres and rods. The spheres are 0.8 to 1.4 microns in diameter. The rods, 0.6 to 1.5 by 1.0 to 6.0 microns, occur singly as ovoid, amoeboid, clavate, cuneate, truncate, spindle- and club-shaped, pyriform and other irregular forms. Age of culture and nature of medium influence the size and shape of cells. Reproduction is by means of fission but apparently also by budding. Motile by means of a polar flagellum at one or both poles. Gram-negative.

Does not grow on ordinary culture media unless supplemented with 16 to 35 per cent sodium chloride and 2 per cent $MgSO_4 \cdot 7H_2O$ (Katznelson and Lochhead, Jour. Bact., *64*, 1952, 97). Grows well on salted fish and hides.

Gelatin (salt): Slow liquefaction (Katznelson and Lochhead, *loc. cit.*).

Codfish agar colonies (16 to 30 per cent salt): In seven days punctiform, smooth, raised, entire, granular, pale pink to scarlet (Ridgway chart), 1.5 mm in diameter.

Milk salt agar (24 to 35 per cent salt): Pink colonies 4 to 5 mm in diameter, becoming scarlet.

Putrefactive odor. Definite proteolytic zones develop (Lochhead, Can. Jour. Res., *10*, 1934, 275).

Codfish agar slant (16 to 35 per cent salt): In seven days moderate, filiform, slightly raised, glistening, smooth, translucent, bright red, viscid. Unpleasant odor.

Milk salt agar slants (24 to 35 per cent

salt): Filiform, slightly raised, smooth, glistening, butyrous, bright red (Lochhead, *loc. cit*).

Broth (5 to 35 per cent salt): No growth. Good growth when grown according to directions of Katznelson and Lochhead (*op. cit.*, 1952, 97).

Codfish broth (25 per cent salt): Turbid, dense, pink sediment; imperfect, pink pellicle.

Potato immersed in brine: No growth.

Indole not produced.

Hydrogen sulfide is produced.

No indication of action on carbohydrates.

Starch not hydrolyzed.

Cannot utilize inorganic nitrogen as a sole source of nitrogen. Tests (Warburg respirometer) show active oxidation of amino acids (such as serine, glutamic acid and aspartic acid); also active oxidation of glycerol.

Nitrites not produced from nitrates (Lochhead, *op. cit.*, 1934, 275).

Aerobic.

Optimum temperature, 37° C. Grows at 22° C.

Optimum salinity, 28 to 32 per cent (Lochhead, *loc. cit.*). When the salt concentration is reduced to 8 per cent, cells are ruptured.

Distinctive characters: See *Halobacterium cutirubrum*.

Source: Isolated from cured codfish (Harrison and Kennedy, *op. cit.*, 1922, 121) and salted fish (Browne, Absts. Bact., *6*, 1922, 25, and Proc. Soc. Exp. Biol. and Med., *19*, 1922, 321); also from salted hides (Lochhead, *op. cit.*, 1934, 275).

Habitat: Produces a reddening of salted fish and hides where untreated solar salt is used. Abundant in tidal pools along shores of tropical seas. Reddens the water in the pools where solar salt is produced as soon as the brine is concentrated to 18 per cent salt. Common on untreated solar salt.

2. **Halobacterium cutirubrum** (Lochhead, 1934) Elazari-Volcani, 1940. (*Serratia cutirubra* Lochhead, Can. Jour. Research, *10*, 1934, 275; *Flavobacterium (Halobacterium) cutirubrum* Elazari-Volcani, Studies on the Microflora of the Dead Sea. Thesis, Hebrew Univ., Jerusalem, 1940, 59.)

cu.ti.ru'brum. L. noun *cutis* the skin; L. adj. *ruber* red; M.L. adj. *cutirubrus* skin-red.

Occurs as spheres and rods. The spheres are 1.0 to 2.0 microns in diameter, and the rods measure 0.7 to 4.0 by 1.5 to 8.0 microns. Age of culture and nature of medium influence the size and shape of cells. Rod forms are motile with a single polar flagellum; coccoid forms are motile when young. Gram-negative.

No growth on ordinary media.

Milk agar (20 per cent salt to saturation; optimum 28 to 32 per cent) colonies: 3 to 4 mm in diameter, round and slightly convex, pink to dark red (rose dorée, Ridgway chart).

Milk agar slants: Growth filiform, slightly spreading, rather flat with smooth, glistening surface and membranous consistency. Proteolytic action.

Liquid media: No or slight growth. Good growth when grown according to directions of Katznelson and Lochhead (Jour. Bact., *64*, 1952, 97).

Gelatin (salt): Pronounced liquefaction.

Indole not produced (Lochhead, *op cit.*, 1934, 275); faint positive (Gibbons, Jour. Biol. Board Canada, *3*, 1936, 75).

Hydrogen sulfide is produced.

Tests (Warburg respirometer) show slow oxidation of amino acids (such as serine, glutamic acid and aspartic acid); also slow oxidation of glycerol.

Nitrites not produced from nitrates.

Diastatic action negative.

No carbohydrate fermentation.

Aerobic.

Optimum temperature, 37°C.

Salt tolerance: Halophilic, obligate. No rupturing of cells occurs when the salt concentration is reduced to 8 per cent; rupturing occurs when the salt concentration is 4 per cent.

Distinctive characters: Resembles *Halobacterium salinarium*. Differs from it in morphology and cultural characters, particularly as regards color and consistency. More actively proteolytic. Slower oxidative action on amino acids and glycerol. Rupturing of cells does not occur as rapidly when the salt concentration is reduced.

Source: Isolated from salted hides which were presumably salted with solar salt.

Habitat: Sea water and solar salt.

3. Halobacterium halobium (Petter, 1931) Elazari-Volcani, 1940. (Microbe du rouge de morue, Le Dantec, Ann. Inst. Past., *5*, 1891, 656; also see Le Dantec, Compt. rend. Soc. Biol., Paris, *61*, 1906, 136; *Bacillus halobius ruber* Klebahn, Mitteil. a. d. Inst. f. allg. Bot. i. Hamburg, *4*, 1919, 47; abst. in Cent. f. Bakt., II Abt., *52*, 1921, 123; *Bacterium halobium* Petter, Proc. Kon. Acad. v. Wetensch. Amsterdam, *34*, 1931, 1417; also see Petter, Over roode en andere bacteriën van gezouten visch. Thesis, Utrecht, 1932; *Flavobacterium (Halobacterium) halobium* Elazari-Volcani, Studies on the Microflora of the Dead Sea. Thesis, Hebrew Univ., Jerusalem, 1940, V and 59.)

ha.lo′bi.um. Gr. noun *hals* salt; Gr. noun *bius* life; M.L. adj. *halobius* living on salt.

Rods, the length of which varies greatly with the medium and age of culture: 0.6 to 0.9 by 2.0 to 6.0 microns in young cultures grown on agar (30 per cent NaCl + 1 per cent peptone "Poulenc"); 2.0 to 27.0 microns long in liquid peptone media, occurring singly. (Klebahn described rods up to 45 microns in liquid media; in old cultures (horse-serum agar), irregular involution forms appear which are round, ovoid or coccus-like, 1.0 to 1.5 by 1.7 to 2.7 microns.) Cells from opaque colonies contain characteristic gas vacuoles. The cells are very sensitive to changes in salt concentration; below 12 per cent NaCl and in water, they swell and form ovoid, amoeboid and club-, spindle-, drumstick- and pear-shaped artefacts. Because of these irregular forms, the organism was described by several investigators as polymorphic (Cloake, Dept. of Scientific and Ind. Research, Food Investigation Board No. 18, London, 1923). Slightly motile with a pendulum-like movement; flagella observed with electron microscope (Houwink, Jour. Gen. Microbiol., *15*, 1956, 146). Gram-negative.

Agar colonies (30 per cent NaCl + 1 per cent peptone "Poulenc"): Circular, transparent or opaque; color varies from almost white to orange, red, violet and purple; the color of the colony also changes during the course of growth.

Broth (30 per cent NaCl + 1 per cent peptone "Poulenc"): Pellicle; turbid; colored sediment.

Asparagine broth (30 per cent NaCl + 3 per cent asparagine): No growth.

Indole not produced.

No acid from glucose, sucrose or maltose (tests made in 30 per cent salt + 1 per cent peptone + 2 per cent carbohydrate).

Nitrites produced from nitrates; no gas is produced.

Catalase-positive.

Aerobic.

Optimum temperature, 37° C.

Salt tolerance: Halophilic, obligate; grows above 12 per cent NaCl up to saturation.

Distinctive character: The pigment is soluble in methanol, ethanol, acetone, chloroform, carbon disulfide, benzol, petroleum ether, toluene and xylene. The carotenoids are named bacterio-ruberine α and β.

Source: Seven different strains were isolated from reddened, salted codfish and herring.

Habitat: Produces a red discoloration on salted herring and codfish.

4. Halobacterium marismortui Elazari-Volcani, 1940. (*Flavobacterium (Halobacterium) maris-mortui* (sic) Elazari-Volcani, Studies on the Microflora of the Dead Sea. Thesis, Hebrew Univ., Jerusalem, 1940, V and 48.)

ma.ris.mor′tu.i. L. noun *mare* the sea; L. gen.noun *maris* of the sea; L. adj. *mortuus* dead; M.L. gen.noun *marismortui* of the Dead Sea.

Rods, the length and shape varying greatly with the medium: in Dead Sea water + 1 per cent proteose peptone, the cells occur singly and measure 0.5 by 1.5 to 3.0 microns; in 24 per cent salt + 1 per cent peptone and on agar + peptone + salt and on Dead Sea water + peptone + agar, the cells are spheroids which measure 1.0 to 1.5 microns in diameter. Non-motile. When stained, the rods burst while the spheroids retain their shape. Gram-negative.

Gelatin stab (18 per cent salt + 1 per cent peptone + 30 per cent gelatin): Surface growth. No liquefaction (2 months).

Agar colonies (24 per cent salt + 1 per

cent proteose peptone + 2 per cent KNO₃): Circular, smooth, entire, raised to convex, butyrous, glistening, opaque with a slightly transparent margin which is less colored, orange-brown, orange-red or orange-yellow.

Agar slant (24 per cent salt + 1 per cent peptone + 2 per cent KNO₃): Growth moderate, filiform, raised to convex, glistening, smooth, butyrous, opaque, orange-red.

Broth (24 per cent salt + 1 per cent peptone): Turbid; orange-red pellicle; slightly viscous sediment.

Asparagine broth (24 per cent salt + 1 per cent asparagine): Turbid.

Indole not produced.

Acid from glucose, fructose, mannose and glycerol; slight acid from xylose and salicin (tests made in 24 per cent salt + 1 per cent peptone + 1 per cent carbohydrate during 3 weeks).

Starch not hydrolyzed.

Nitrites rapidly produced from nitrates; gas is produced (tests made in 24 per cent salt + 1 per cent peptone + 2 per cent KNO₃).

Aerobic.

Optimum temperature, 30° C.

Salt tolerance: Halophilic, obligate; grows in 18 per cent to saturated salt solutions; slight growth in 15 per cent salt.

Distinctive character: The pigment produces a blue color with concentrated sulfuric acid, thus suggesting a carotenoid; it is very soluble in pyridine, less soluble in methanol, ethanol and chloroform, slightly soluble in acetone, very slightly so in benzol and insoluble in xylene and petroleum ether.

Source: Isolated from Dead Sea water.

Habitat: Salt lakes.

5. Halobacterium trapanicum (Petter, 1931) Elazari-Volcani, 1940. (*Bacterium trapanicum* Petter, Proc. Kon. Acad. v. Wetensch. Amsterdam, *34*, 1931, 1417; also see Petter, Over roode en andere bacteriën van gezouten visch. Thesis, Utrecht, 1932; *Flavobacterium* (*Halobacterium*) *trapanicum* Elazari-Volcani, Studies on the Microflora of the Dead Sea. Thesis, Hebrew Univ., Jerusalem, 1940, V and 59.)

tra.pa'ni.cum. M.L. adj. *trapanicus* pertaining to "Trapani" salt.

Rods, 0.6 by 1.5 to 3.5 microns. The length and shape of the cells may vary greatly with the medium: in Dead Sea water + 1 per cent proteose peptone, the cells occur singly and are 0.45 to 0.55 by 1.5 to 4.8 microns with occasional rods measuring 8.0 to 16.0 microns in length; in 24 per cent salt + 1 per cent peptone, the short rods predominate; in 24 per cent salt + 1 per cent peptone + 2 per cent KNO₃ agar, the cells are ovoid, measuring 1.0 to 1.5 microns in diameter. Non-motile. Gram-negative.

Gelatin stab (18 per cent salt + 1 per cent peptone + 30 per cent gelatin): Surface growth. No liquefaction (2 months).

Agar colonies (24 per cent salt + 1 per cent proteose peptone + 2 per cent KNO₃): Small (1 to 2 mm in diameter), circular, smooth, entire, convex, glistening, transparent, light orange or slightly colorless.

Agar slant (24 per cent salt + 1 per cent peptone + 2 per cent KNO₃): Growth moderate, filiform, raised, glistening, smooth, opaque or slightly transparent, light orange.

Broth (Dead Sea water + 1 per cent peptone): Orange-rose pellicle; turbid; orange sediment. In 24 per cent salt + 1 per cent peptone: orange-rose ring; turbid; orange sediment.

Asparagine broth (24 per cent salt + 1 per cent asparagine): Moderately turbid.

Indole not produced.

No acid from arabinose, xylose, glucose, fructose, galactose, mannose, lactose, sucrose, maltose, raffinose, inulin, dextrin, glycerol, mannitol or salicin (tests made in 24 per cent salt + 1 per cent peptone + 1 per cent carbohydrate during 3 weeks).

Starch not hydrolyzed.

Nitrites rapidly produced from nitrates; gas is produced (tests made in 24 per cent salt + 1 per cent peptone + 2 per cent KNO₃).

Catalase-positive.

Aerobic.

Optimum temperature, between 30° and 37° C.

Salt tolerance: Halophilic, obligate; grows in 18 per cent to saturated salt solutions; slight growth in 15 per cent salt.

Distinctive character: The pigment produces a blue color with concentrated sulfuric acid, thus suggesting a carotenoid. Very soluble in pyridine; less soluble in methanol, ethanol and chloroform; slightly soluble in acetone, very slightly so in benzol; insoluble in xylene and petroleum ether.

Source: Isolated from "Trapani" salt from a cannery in Bergen (Norway) and from the water of the Dead Sea.

Habitat: Sea salt, sea-water brine and salt lakes.

FAMILY V. CAULOBACTERACEAE HENRICI AND JOHNSON, 1935, EMEND. BREED.*

(Includes the typical families and genera of *Caulobacteriales* (sic) Henrici and Johnson, Jour. Bact., *29*, 1935, 4 and *ibid.*, *30*, 1935, 83. The Order *Caulobacterales* Henrici and Johnson was redefined as a Sub-order, *Caulobacteriineae* (sic), by Breed, Murray and Hitchens, Bact. Rev., *8*, 1944, 255. The present emendation reduces the Order *Caulobacterales*, as originally defined, to the status of a family in the Sub-order *Pseudomonadineae* Breed, Murray and Smith.)

Cau.lo.bac.ter.a'ce.ae. M.L. neut.n. *Caulobacter* the type genus of the family; *-aceae* ending to denote a family; M.L. fem.pl.n. *Caulobacteraceae* the *Caulobacter* family.

Non-filamentous, rod-shaped bacteria normally attached by branching or unbranching stalks to a substrate. In one floating form the stalks are branched. Cells occur singly, in pairs or in short chains. The cells are asymmetrical in that a stalk is developed at one end of the cell or ferric hydroxide or other material is secreted from one side of the cell to form stalks. Cells are polar flagellate in the free-living state, non-motile in the attached forms. Gram-negative. Multiply by transverse fission, the daughter cells remaining in place or swimming away as swarm cells. Typically fresh- or salt-water forms.

The family *Caulobacteraceae*, as here defined, includes the genera *Caulobacter* Henrici and Johnson, *Gallionella* Ehrenberg, *Siderophacus* Beger and *Nevskia* Famintzin.

The species in this family as presented here have close affinities with the species in the family *Pseudomonadaceae*. In all cases where motility has been observed and stains made, polar flagella have been found. It seems probable that when the life histories of these sedentary bacteria have been investigated, it will be found that practically all, if not all, of these attached forms develop a motile stage. Such a stage permits the distribution of the species in its environment.

The stalked bacteria studied by Henrici and Johnson (*op. cit.*, *30*, 1935, 83) were of fresh-water origin. Bacteria of this type are found, however, equally if not more abundantly in marine habitats where they play their part in the fouling of underwater surfaces. ZoBell and Upham (Bull. Scripps Inst. of Oceanography, LaJolla, California, *5*, 1944, 253) summarize this situation as follows: "Many of the bacteria found in sea water are sessile or periphytic, growing preferentially or exclusively attached to solid surfaces. The sessile habit of marine bacteria is most pronounced when they are growing in very dilute nutrient solutions, such as sea water, to which nothing has been added. . . . Most sessile bacteria appear to attach themselves tenaciously to solid surfaces by exuding a mucilaginous holdfast. A few have stalks. Some of the sessile bacteria grow on the walls of the culture receptacle without clouding the medium itself.".

The submerged-slide technique as employed by Henrici (Jour. Bact., *25*, 1933, 277) and

---

* Redefined and rearranged by Prof. Robert S. Breed, Cornell University, Geneva, New York, December, 1953. Prof. Herbert Beger, Institut für Wasser-, Boden- und Lufthygiene, Berlin-Dahlem, Germany, has given this section a further revision so as to include genera and species not previously recognized in the MANUAL, February, 1954.

by ZoBell and Allen (Proc. Soc. Exper. Biol. and Med., *30*, 1933, 1409) has proved to be most useful for studying bacteria that live attached to a substrate.

The species included in *Pasteuria* Metchnikoff and *Blastocaulis* Henrici and Johnson reproduce by a curious form of fission or budding. They have been transferred to a new Order, *Hyphomicrobiales* Douglas.

Key to the genera of family **Caulobacteraceae.**

I. Long axis of cell coincides with axis of stalk. Stalks slender.
Genus I. *Caulobacter*, p. 213.
II. Long axis of cell transverse to long axis of stalk. Stalks may be twisted and branched.
A. Stalks are band-shaped or rounded. Contain ferric hydroxide.
1. Stalks band-shaped and twisted. Dumb-bell-shaped in cross section.
Genus II. *Gallionella*, p. 214.
2. Stalks horn-shaped, not twisted. Round in cross section.
Genus III. *Siderophacus*, p. 216.
B. Stalks lobose, composed of gum. Forming zoogloea-like colonies. Free-floating.
Genus IV. *Nevskia*, p. 216.

Genus I. **Caulobacter** Henrici and Johnson, 1935.

(Jour. Bact., *29*, 1935, 4; *ibid.*, *30*, 1935, 83.)

Cau.lo.bac′ter. L. noun *caulis* a plant stem or stalk; M.L. noun *bacter* masculine form of Gr. neut.n. *bactrum* a rod; M.L. mas.n. *Caulobacter* stalk rod.

Stalked, curved, rod-shaped bacteria, the long axis of the elongated cells coinciding with the long axis of the stalks. Young cells motile by means of a single polar flagellum. Old cells attached to submerged objects by a stalk that is a continuation of the cell. A holdfast is developed at the distal end. Multiplication of cells is by transverse binary fission. Periphytic, growing upon submerged surfaces.

The type species is *Caulobacter vibrioides* Henrici and Johnson *emend.* Bowers et al.

1. **Caulobacter vibrioides** Henrici and Johnson, 1935, *emend.* Bowers et al., 1954. (Henrici and Johnson, Jour. Bact., *30*, 1935, 83; Bowers, Weaver, Grula and Edwards, Jour. Bact., *68*, 1954, 194.)

vib.ri.oi′des. L.v. *vibro* to vibrate; M.L. noun *Vibrio* name of a genus; Gr. noun *eidus* shape, form; M.L. adj. *vibrioides* resembling a vibrio.

Cells elongated, curved, vibrio-like, with rounded ends, 0.5 to 1.2 by 1.5 to 3.0 microns; filamentous forms occasionally produced. Young cells actively motile with a single polar flagellum; older cells develop a stalk at the flagellated end. The stalk has a central filament or tube and a membrane that is continuous with the cell wall. Organisms attached singly or in rosettes, with stalks attached to a common holdfast. Usually surrounded by a slime layer. Gram-negative.

Gelatin: Surface growth and filiform growth in stab without liquefaction.

Agar colonies: Surface colonies up to 5 mm in diameter, round, smooth, slightly raised, glistening, finely granular in the center, grayish white, with center and reverse side becoming brownish yellow. Subsurface colonies dense, brownish yellow, lenticular, up to 0.5 mm in diameter and 1.0 mm in length.

Agar slant: Growth filiform, grayish white, glistening, viscid.

Broth: Moderate turbidity with slightly viscid sediment.

Litmus milk: Unchanged.

Potato: Little or no growth.

Indole not produced.

Nitrites not produced from nitrates.

No acid or gas from carbohydrates.

Requires riboflavin, phosphates, iron and an organic source of energy for growth. Glucose, maltose or casamino acids are used as sources of carbon and energy; sodium bicarbonate, sodium lactate, sodium acetate

or glycerol not utilized. Ammonium sulfate or casamino acids used as sources of nitrogen; ammonium nitrate not utilized.
Optimum temperature, 30° C.
Aerobic, facultative.
Source: Found frequently in Lake Alexander, Minnesota, and other fresh-water lakes (Henrici and Johnson, *op. cit.*, *30*, 1935, 83). Also found in well-water in Kentucky (Bowers et al., *op. cit.*).
Habitat: Water, where it grows upon firm substrates.*

Genus II. Gallionella Ehrenberg, 1838.†

(Ehrenberg, Die Infusionsthierchen, 1838, 166; not *Gaillonella* Bory de St. Vincent, Dict. Classique d'Hist. Nat., *4*, 1823, 393; *Didymohelix* Griffith, Ann. Mag. Nat. Hist., Ser. 2, *12*, 1853, 438.)

Gal.li.o.nel′la. Named for Benjamin Gaillon, receiver of customs and zoologist (1782–1839) in Dieppe, France; M.L. dim.ending -*ella*; M.L. fem.n. *Gallionella* a generic name.

Cells kidney-shaped or rounded. Placed at the end of the stalk with the long axis of the cell transverse to the long axis of the stalk. Stalks secreted by the cells are slender and twisted. Branch dichotomously or in the form of umbels. Stalks more or less dumb-bell or bisquit-shaped in cross section. Composed of ferric hydroxide, completely dissolving in weak acids. Two polar flagella are present when the cells are motile. Gram-negative. Multiplication by fission of the cells, the daughter cells remaining at first at the end of the stalk; later they may be liberated as swarm cells. Grow only in iron-bearing waters. Do not store manganese compounds. From both fresh and salt water. When the first species was discovered the twisted stalks were thought to be a chain of diatoms.

The type species is *Gallionella ferruginea* Ehrenberg.

Key to the species of genus Gallionella.

I. Stalks branched.
   A. Stalks dichotomously branched.
      1. Stalks slender, spirally twisted.
         a. Cells small, stalks very slender.
            1. *Gallionella ferruginea.*

---

* The papers by Houwink (Antonie van Leeuwenhoek, *21*, 1955, 29) and by Kandler, Zehender and Huber (Arch. f. Mikrobiol., *21*, 1954, 57) were received after the manuscript covering the family *Caulobacteraceae* was prepared. They give further information regarding the structure and function of the stalk of *Caulobacter sp.* Clearly the stalks developed by species in this genus are quite different in nature from the stalks of ferric hydroxide or gum secreted by the cells of other species placed in other genera of this family.

† *Gallionella* Ehrenberg is accepted and is continued in use in this edition of the MANUAL although under a strict interpretation of Rules of Nomenclature it should apparently be regarded as a homonym and therefore illegitimate. *Gaillonella* Bory de St. Vincent, proposed as the name of a genus of algae, appears to have priority (see Internat. Bull. Bact. Nomen. and Tax., *2*, 1951, 96). However, *Gaillonella* B. de St. V. is no longer used by students of diatoms so that *Gallionella* E. may be retained as a *genus conservandum* in bacteriology without causing confusion. Unless *Gallionella* E. is retained, the little used *Didymohelix* Griffith must be again introduced into the MANUAL with the formation of a series of new combinations.

The situation is complicated because the final settlement of this problem of nomenclature requires action both by the Judicial Commission of the International Association of Microbiologists and the Special Committee on *Diatomaceae* of the International Botanical Congress. The majority of the special students of iron bacteria have accepted and used *Gallionella* E., *e.g.* Molisch (1910), Naumann (1921), Cholodny (1924), Butkevich (1928), Dorff (1934), Henrici and Johnson (1934), Beger (1941) and Pringsheim (1952).

aa. Cells longer, stalks broader.

2. *Gallionella major*.

2. Stalks short, thick, not definitely in spirals.

3. *Gallionella minor*.

B. Stalks branching in simple or compound umbels.

4. *Gallionella umbellata*.

II. Stalks unbranched.

5. *Gallionella infurcata*.

1. Gallionella ferruginea Ehrenberg, 1836. (*Gaillonella ferruginea* (sic) Ehrenberg, Vorl. Mittheil. ü. d. wirkl. Vorkommen fossiler Infusionen u. ihre grosse Verbreitung, Ann. Phys., Ser. 2, *8*, 1836, 217; *Gallionella ferruginea* Ehrenberg, Die Infusionthierchen, 1838, 166; *Didymohelix ferruginea* Griffith, Ann. Mag. Nat. Hist., Ser. 2, *12*, 1853, 438.)

fer.ru.gi'ne.a. L. adj. *ferrugineus* of the color of iron rust.

Kidney-shaped cells. The full grown bacteria are 0.5 to 0.6 by 1.2 to 1.5 microns. The cells secrete colloidal ferric hydroxide from the concave portion of the cell, forming band-like stalks 0.6 to 3.3 microns in width and as much as 200 microns and more in length. A rotatory motion of the cells gives rise to a spiral twisting of the stalks.

In the older studies, the stalks were described as the organism, the minute cells at the tip having been dislodged or at least overlooked. The cells lie at the tip of the stalk and multiply by transverse binary fission. This gives rise to a dichotomous branching of the stalks. Stalks become very long and slender, with smooth edges.

Not cultivated in artificial media.

Distribution: Usually the branched stalks are attached separately in great numbers to solid surfaces. They may, however, float in irregular flocs distributed throughout the water. Less commonly they form balls up to 3.0 microns in diameter. In these the stalks radiate from a center and such groups have been described as *Gloeosphaera ferruginea* Rabenhorst. In a third variety, solid tubercles richly encrusted with ferric compounds are formed. These are found in old pipelines or they may occur free in nature. These tubercles have been named *Sphaerothrix latens* Perfiliev.

Habitat: Found in cool springs and brooks

which carry reduced iron in solution; also found in wells, in storage basins in waterworks and in pipe lines.

2. Gallionella major Cholodny, 1927. (Trav. Station. biolog. du Dniepre Acad. des Sci. de l'Ukraine, Classe Sci. Phys. et Math., *3*, Livre 4, 1927.)

ma'jor. L. comp. adj. *major* larger.

Very similar to *Gallionella ferruginea*, but the cells are distinctly larger (1.0 by 3.0 microns). Stalks are 3.0 to 6.0 microns broad. Some cells that fail to divide reach a length of 7 microns or more; these form stalks of double the normal width.

The cells contain one or more vacuoles, apparently filled with an iron compound.

Source: Found in springs near Krassnodar (Caucasus).

Habitat: Found in iron-bearing waters.

3. Gallionella minor Cholodny, 1924. (Ber. d. deutsch. Bot. Ges., *42*, 1924, 42; also see Cholodny, Die Eisenbakterien, Pflanzenforschung, Heft 4, 1926, 47.)

mi'nor. L. comp. adj. *minor* smaller.

Cells as in *Gallionella ferruginea*, but stalks are shorter, thicker and more band-like than twisted. After division, cells do not separate as quickly as in *Gallionella ferruginea*. The branches gradually become encrusted until the stalks are quite obscured. Branches of stalks are not more than 20 to 30 microns long.

Source: Found in a small spring near the Biological Station in Dniepre. Also found by Beger (Ber. d. deutsch. Bot. Ges., *62*, 1944, 11) in material from Camerun in Africa.

Habitat: Found in iron-bearing waters.

4. Gallionella umbellata Beger, 1949. (*Gallionella ferruginea* Palm, Svensk. Bot.

Tidskr., *27*, 1933, 360; not *Gallionella ferruginea* Ehrenberg, Die Infusionthierchen, 1838, 166; Beger, Ber. d. deutsch. Bot. Ges., *52*, 1949, 9.)

um.bel.la′ta. L. noun *umbella* umbrella; M.L. adj. *umbellatus* umbel-like.

Five to six cells are formed at the end of the stalks before separation. The cells are kidney-shaped and 1.0 by 2.0 microns in size. The stalks then divide into 5 to 6 branches forming a simple umbel. This process of cell division and growth of branches continues until finally the whole mass appears composed of umbels.

Source: From leaf mold found in streams in British-Gambia.

Habitat: Found in tropical, iron-bearing streams.

5. Gallionella infurcata Beger, 1937. (*Spirophyllum sp.*, Suessenguth, Cent. f. Bakt., II Abt., 1927, 69 and 339; Beger, Gas- und Wasserfach, *80*, 1937, 887; *Spirophyllum infurcatum* Beger, *ibid.*, 889.)

in.fur.ca′ta. L. prep. *in* in; L. noun *furca* fork; M.L. adj. *furcatus* forked; M.L. adj. *infurcatus* forked.

Stalks twisted but not branched. Cells coccoid, 1 micron in diameter. After fission into two cells, they become detached from the stalk.

Source: Found in water basins in the Botanical Garden of München-Nymphenburg.

Habitat: Found in iron-bearing waters.

Genus. III. **Siderophacus** *Beger, 1944.*

(Ber. d. deutsch. Bot. Ges., *61*, 1944, 12.)

Si.de.ro′pha.cus. Gr. noun *siderus* iron; Gr. noun *phacus* lentil; M.L. mas.n. *Siderophacus* iron lentil.

The stalks are horn-shaped, without branches, and do not form twisted bands; they are round to ovoid in transverse section. Cells biconcave or rod-like; after division they separate from the stalk. Ferric hydroxide is stored in the stalks.

The type species is *Siderophacus corneolus* (Dorff) Beger.

1. Siderophacus corneolus (Dorff, 1934) Beger, 1944. (*Gallionella corneola* Dorff, Die Eisenorganismen, Pflanzenforschung, Heft 16, 1934, 25; Beger, Ber. d. deutsch. Bot. Ges., *61*, 1944 12.)

cor.ne′o.lus. L. adj. *corneolus* horny, firm.

Stalks 15 to 30 microns long, broader at the top than at the base. Three to eight stalks arise from a broad holdfast. Cells 0.6 to 1.0 by 2.5 to 3.0 microns.

Source: Found in an iron-bearing rivulet near Lot-Malmby, Central Sweden; also found near Berlin.

Habitat: Found in iron-bearing waters.

Genus IV. **Nevskia** *Famintzin, 1892.*

(Bull. Acad. Imp. Sci., St. Pétersb., Sér. IV, *34* (N.S. *2*), 1892, 484.)

Nev′ski.a. *Neva* a river at Leningrad; M.L. fem.n. *Nevskia* of the Neva.

Stalked bacteria, the long axis of the rod-shaped cells being set at right angles to the axis of the stalk. Stalks lobose, dichotomously branched and composed of gum. Multiplication of cells by transverse binary fission. Grow in zoogloea-like masses in water.

The type species is *Nevskia ramosa* Famintzin.

1. Nevskia ramosa Famintzin, 1892. (Bull. Acad. Imp. Sci., St. Pétersb., Sér. IV, *34* (N. S. *2*), 1892, 484.)

ra.mo′sa. L. adj. *ramosus* branched.

Globular, bush-like or plate-like colonies of gummy consistency which float upon the surface of water. Colonies composed of gummy material arranged in dichotomously branched stalks arising from a common base, with the bacterial cells contained in the gum, a single cell at the tip of each stalk. At times cells are set free from the stalks to start new colonies.

Rod-shaped cells set with their long axis

at right angles to the axis of the broad, lobe-like stalk. Cells 2 by 6 to 12 microns, containing a number of highly refractile globules of fat or sulfur. Multiplication by binary fission.

Not cultivated on artificial media.

Note: *Nevskia pediculata* Henrici and Johnson is now regarded as a *Lactobacillus*. See *Lactobacillis brevis* Bergey et al., syn. *Betabacterium vermiforme* Mayer.

Source: Found in the aquarium in the Botanical Garden, St. Petersburg. Similar but smaller organisms found by Henrici and Johnson (Jour. Bact., *30*, 1935, 63) in a jar of water from the lily pond of the University of Minnesota greenhouse in Minneapolis.

Habitat: Found in water.

FAMILY VI. SIDEROCAPSACEAE PRIBRAM, 1929.*

(Tribe *Siderocapseae* Buchanan, Jour. Bact., *2*, 1915, 615; Pribram, Jour. Bact., *18*, 1929, 377.)

Si.de.ro.cap.sa'ce.ae. M.L. fem.n. *Siderocapsa* type genus of the family; -*aceae* suffix to denote a family; M.L. fem.pl.n. *Siderocapsaceae* the *Siderocapsa* family.

Cells spherical, ellipsoidal or bacilliform. Frequently embedded in a thick, mucilaginous capsule in which iron or manganese compounds may be deposited. Motile stages, where known, are polar flagellate. Free-living in surface films or attached to the surface of submerged objects. Form deposits of iron and manganese compounds. Autotrophic, facultatively autotrophic and heterotrophic species are included in the family. Found in fresh water.

The morphology of the bacteria of this family is best determined after dissolving the iron or manganese compounds with weak acids and staining with Schiff's reagent.

The type genus is *Siderocapsa* Molisch.

Key to the genera of family **Siderocapsaceae**.

I. Cells surrounded by capsular matter with iron compounds deposited either on the surface or throughout the capsular material.
  A. Cells coccoid.
    1. Cells in masses in a common capsule.
        Genus I. *Siderocapsa*, p. 218.
    2. Cells always in pairs in a gelatinous capsule.
        Genus II. *Siderosphaera*, p. 220.
  B. Cells ellipsoidal to bacilliform.
    1. Cells heavily encapsulated but do not possess a torus.†
      a. Cells in chains in a gelatinous capsule.
        b. Chains of ellipsoidal cells embedded in a gelatinous capsule, the outlines of which follow the form of the cells.
          Genus III. *Sideronema*, p. 220.
      bb. Rods in pairs or chains in surface films.

---

* Manuscript prepared by Prof. Robert S. Breed, Cornell University, Geneva, New York, December, 1953; further revision with the introduction of additional genera and species by Prof. Dr. Herbert Beger, Institut für Wasser-, Boden- und Lufthygiene, Berlin-Dahlem, Germany, March, 1954.

† The so-called torus is a marginal thickening of a thin capsule. The torus is heavily impregnated with iron compounds so that the torus of an individual cell looks like the link of a chain or, if incomplete, like a horseshoe.

Genus IV. *Ferribacterium*, p. 221.

aa. Coccoid to rod-shaped cells in masses in a gelatinous capsule. Usually show an irregular arrangement of cells.

Genus V. *Sideromonas*, p. 222.

2. Cells with a thin capsule with a torus.

a. Torus completely surrounds the cells.

Genus VI. *Naumanniella*, p. 223.

aa. Torus open at one pole giving the wall the appearance of a horseshoe.

Genus VII. *Ochrobium*, p. 225.

II. Non-encapsulated cells which form deposits of iron compounds in the cell wall, on the surface of the cells or in the surrounding medium.

A. Cells coccoid.

Genus VIII. *Siderococcus*, p. 225.

B. Cells rod-shaped.

1. Found in neutral or alkaline waters.

Genus IX. *Siderobacter*, p. 226.

2. Found in acid mine wastes.

Genus X. *Ferrobacillus*, p. 227.

Genus I. **Siderocapsa** *Molisch, 1909.*

(Ann. Jard. Bot. Buitenzorg, 2 Sér., Supp. 3, 1909, 29; also see Die Eisenbakterien, Jena, 1910, 11.)

Si.de.ro.cap′sa. Gr. noun *siderus* iron; L. noun *capsa* a box; M.L. fem.n. *Siderocapsa* iron box.

One to many spherical to ellipsoidal, small cells embedded without definite arrangement in a primary capsule. The primary capsules may be surrounded by a large secondary capsule, and these may then be united into larger colonies. Iron compounds are predominantly stored on the surface of the primary capsule, and when a secondary capsule is present, it is also completely covered.

The type species is *Siderocapsa treubii* Molisch.

Key to the species of genus **Siderocapsa.**

I. Several cells in each capsule.

A. Attached forms.

1. Cells small; up to 8 in number in each capsule.

1. *Siderocapsa treubii.*

2. Cells larger; up to 100 and more in each capsule.

2. *Siderocapsa major.*

B. Plankton forms.

1. Primary capsules 3.5 to 9 microns in diameter, each containing 2 to 8 cells.

3. *Siderocapsa coronata.*

2. Primary capsules 10 to 20 microns in diameter, each containing up to 60 or more cells.

4. *Siderocapsa eusphaera.*

II. Only one cell in each capsule. Cells always small.

A. Capsules attached.

5. *Siderocapsa monoeca.*

B. Capsules form unattached iron flocs.

6. *Siderocapsa botryoides.*

1. **Siderocapsa treubii** Molisch, 1909. (*Siderocapsa Treubii* (sic) Molisch, Ann. Jard. Bot. Buitenzorg, 2 Sér., Supp. 3, 1909, 29; also see Die Eisenbakterien, Jena, 1910, 11.)

treu'bi.i. M.L. gen.noun *treubii* of Treub; named for Prof. Treub, director of the Tropical Garden at Buitenzorg, Java.

Cocci, 0.4 to 0.6 micron in diameter. As many as 8 cells may be embedded in zoogloeal masses surrounded by ferric hydroxide and other iron or manganese compounds; these masses are 1.8 to 3.6 microns in diameter.

Deposits ferric hydroxide on the surfaces of water plants.

Regarded by Hardman and Henrici (Jour. Bact., *37*, 1939, 97) as a heterotrophic organism that utilizes the organic radicle of organic iron compounds, depositing the iron as a waste product on the capsules of the colonies.

Source: Found attached to the roots, root hairs and leaves of water plants (*Elodea, Nymphaea, Sagittaria, Salvinia, etc.*) in Java.

Habitat: Widely distributed in fresh water. Epiphytic on submerged plants or on other objects. Abundant in alkaline, hard-water lakes of the drainage type in Minnesota and Wisconsin according to Hardman and Henrici (*ibid.*, 103). Absent in neutral or acid soft-water lakes of the seepage type.

2. **Siderocapsa major** Molisch, 1909. (Ann. Jard. Bot. Buitenzorg, 2 Sér., Supp. 3, 1909, 29; also see Die Eisenbakterien, Jena, 1910, 13.)

ma'jor. L. comp.adj. *major* larger.

Cells colorless, coccus-like, short rods, 0.7 by 1.8 microns. A colony may consist of 100 or more cells in the same mucilaginous capsule.

Similar to *Siderocapsa treubii* except that the cells are larger and the gelatinous capsule is less sharply defined. May be free-floating in surface films or may be attached to submerged objects.

Forms intermediate between *Siderocapsa major* and *Siderocapsa treubii* have been observed by Hardman and Henrici (Jour. Bact., *37*, 1939, 97).

Source: Found on the surface of a *Spirogyra sp.* near Prague.

Habitat: Widely distributed in fresh water.

3. **Siderocapsa coronata** Redinger, 1931. (Arch. f. Hydrobiol., *22*, 1931, 410.)

co.ro.na'ta. L. part.adj. *coronatus* crowned.

Coccoid cells, about 1.0 micron in diameter, occurring in the primary capsule in groups of 2 to 8. These groups are surrounded by secondary gelatinous capsules which may unite into foamy, irregular masses 5 to 10 or more cm in diameter. The capsular material contains deposits of iron and manganese. Free-floating. Yellowish to dark brown in color.

Source: Found in water from Upper Lake, Lunz, Austria. Foamy masses are formed in the winter time. Ruttner (Arch. f. Hydrobiol., *32*, 1937, 167) reports that the distribution of this organism in Alpine lakes is related to the oxygen stratification therein: it was found most frequently at depths of from 17.5 to 27.5 meters, where the oxygen range was 0.12 to 0.30 mg per liter. 4.66 mg per liter was the highest oxygen tension at which it was found.

Habitat: Presumably widely distributed in water.

4. **Siderocapsa eusphaera** Skuja, 1948. (Symbolae Bot. Upsal., *9* (3), 1948, 12.)

eu.sphae'ra. Gr. prep. *eu* true; Gr. noun *sphaera* ball, sphere; M.L. noun *eusphaera* a true sphere.

Cells coccus-shaped, 1 to 2 microns in diameter, 2 to 60 and more in a primary capsule. The latter are 10 to 20 microns in diameter and are surrounded by a large secondary capsule up to 50 microns in diameter. The secondary capsules are united into large colonies with a common mucilaginous layer. The secondary capsule stores compounds of iron and manganese.

Source: Found in lakes in Sweden; found in the plankton at levels where the oxygen tension is low.

Habitat: Presumably widely distributed in fresh-water lakes.

5. **Siderocapsa monoeca** Naumann, 1922. (*Siderocapsa monoica* (sic) Naumann, Kgl. Svensk. Vetensk. Akad. Handl., I, *62*, 1922, 49.)

mo.noe'ca. Gr. adj. *monus* alone, solitary; Gr. noun *oecus* house, dwelling; M.L. adj. *monoecus* solitary dwelling.

Cells single, coccus-shaped or ellipsoidal, 0.5 to 0.7 micron in diameter, surrounded by a more or less thick layer of iron and manganese compounds in which, at least when young, a rounded space is kept free. The cell may be seen in this clear space. Although the cells are found in great numbers in close proximity to each other, they are distinctly isolated. Form iron and manganese deposits on the surface of water plants and submerged objects.

Source: Isolated from the surface of *Potamogeton natans* in Sweden.

Habitat: Found in ponds, rivers and waterworks; presumably widely distributed.

6. **Siderocapsa botryoides** Beger, 1949. (Zent. f. Bakt., I Abt., Orig., *154*, 1949, 65.)

bot.ry.o.i'des or bot.ry.oi'des. Gr. adj. *botryoides* like a bunch of grapes.

Cells coccus-shaped, spherical or ellipsoidal, 0.6 to 0.8 micron in diameter. With the capsule they are 0.8 to 2.0 microns in diameter, lying singly only when young, later forming spherical to clustered colonies up to 0.3 cm long.

The encrusted colonies form iron or manganese flocs.

Source: Found in wells and waterworks near Berlin.

Habitat: Presumably widely distributed.

Genus II. **Siderosphaera** *Beger, 1944*.

(Ber. d. deutsch. Bot. Ges., *62*, (1944) 1950, 7.)

Si.de.ro.sphae'ra. Gr. noun *siderus* iron; L. noun *sphaera* ball, sphere; M.L. fem.n. *Siderosphaera* iron sphere.

Small, coccoid cells, always occurring in pairs and embedded in a primary capsule. After cell division the daughter pairs, with the primary capsules, are surrounded by a new, common capsule. This division continues up to the formation of eight pairs and results in a round, ball-shaped *Gloeocapsa*-like stage which stores compounds of iron. A number of these balls unite to form larger flocs which may lie on the surface of bottom mud in fresh-water ditches and swamps.

The type species is *Siderosphaera conglomerata* Beger.

1. **Siderosphaera conglomerata** Beger, 1950. (Ber. d. deutsch. Bot. Ges., *62*, (1944) 1950, 7.)

con.glo.me.ra'ta. L. part.adj. *conglomeratus* rolled together.

Cocci, 1.0 to 1.2 microns in diameter, each with a sheath about 2.0 microns in diameter. These cells divide to form 2, 4 or, at times, 8 pairs of cells in a clear, spherical, gelatinous colony 8 to 10 microns in diameter.

Spherical to ellipsoidal flocs containing

these colonies may be as much as 500 microns in diameter. In general appearance these flocs resemble those formed by *Siderocapsa coronata* found in the Upper Lake at Lunz. When dilute HCl is added, the jelly-like colonies may be liberated as the iron salts dissolve. Manganese salts are apparently not present.

Source: Found in a small ditch near Lunz (Austrian Alps).

Habitat: Found on the surface of mud in bogs.

Genus III. **Sideronema** *Beger, 1941*.

(Zent. f. Bakt., II Abt., *103*, 1941, 321.)

Si.de.ro.ne'ma. Gr. noun *siderus* iron; Gr. noun *nema* thread; M.L. neut.n. *Sideronema* iron thread.

Coccoid cells occurring in short chains which are enclosed in a gelatinous sheath. The cell membrane contains an abundance of ferric hydroxide whereas the sheath is relatively devoid of this substance. Non-motile and unattached. Found in iron-bearing waters.

The type species is *Sideronema globuliferum* Beger.

1. **Sideronema globuliferum** Beger, 1941. (*Sideronema globulifera* (sic) Beger, Zent. f. Bakt., II Abt., *103*, 1941, 321.)

glob.u.li.fe'rum. L. dim.noun *globulus* a small sphere, globule; L. v. *fero* to bear, carry; M.L. adj. *globuliferus* globule-bearing.

Cells coccoid, round to egg-shaped, 4.8 to 5.0 by 6.5 microns. Occur in chains (3 to 8 cells) which are enclosed in a gelatinous sheath 1.6 microns thick; the cells in these chains are non-confluent. Ferric hydroxide is found in the cell membrane but only sparingly so in the sheath. Non-motile and unattached.

Source: Found on glass slides submerged in spring water near Magdeburg, Germany.

Habitat: Presumably widely distributed in iron-bearing waters.

Genus IV. **Ferribacterium** *Brussoff, 1916.*

(Brussoff, Cent. f. Bakt., II Abt., *45*, 1916, 547; *Sideroderma* Naumann, Kungl. Svenska Vetenskapsakad. Handl., *62*, 1922, 54.)

Fer.ri.bac.te'ri.um. L. noun *ferrum* iron; Gr. dim.noun *bacterium* a small rod; M.L. neut.n. *Ferribacterium* iron rodlet.

Rods, with rounded or square ends, usually occurring in pairs, sometimes appearing singly or in short chains. Motility occasionally observed; presumably the cells are polar flagellate. In most cultures the cells are enclosed in a gelatinous capsule which is ordinarily surrounded by deposits of iron compounds. Produces a pellicle on the surface of liquid media and water. Found in iron- or manganese-bearing water.

The type species is *Ferribacterium duplex* Brussoff.

1. **Ferribacterium duplex** Brussoff, 1916. (Brussoff, Cent. f. Bakt., II Abt., *45*, 1916, 547; *Sideroderma duplex* Naumann, Kgl. Svenska Vetenskapsakad. Handl., *62*, 1922, 55 and 63.)

du'plex. L. adj. *duplex* two-fold, double.

Rods, with rounded ends, 1.2 by 2.5 to 5.0 microns, occurring usually in pairs, sometimes singly or in short chains. Reported as non-motile. Cells enclosed in a gelatinous capsule which is ordinarily surrounded by iron compounds. According to Sauer (Inaug. Diss., Kiel, 1934, 33) the cells are motile and Gram-negative.

Peat-infusion agar: In old cultures the gelatinous capsule is surrounded by a dark sheath, never by an iron secretion; the sheath is generally ellipsoidal. Irregular forms are also found.

Iron ammonium citrate broth: Pellicle scarcely visible, appearing yellow under the microscope.

Iron peptone broth: Produces a barely visible pellicle which appears yellow under the microscope.

Water: A pellicle is formed which is weakly iridescent or of a metallic sheen.

Aerobic.

Source: Isolated from an ochre-colored sediment from two samples of tap-water from Breslau labelled "Schwentniger" and "Pirschamer".

Habitat: Found in iron-bearing waters.

2. **Ferribacterium rectangulare** (Naumann, 1922) Beger, *comb. nov.* (*Sideroderma rectangulare* Naumann, Kungl. Svenska Vetenskapsakad. Handl., *62*, No. 4, 1922, 54; *Sideroderma tenue* Naumann, *loc. cit.*)

rec.tang.u.la're. L. adj. *rectus* straight; L. adj. *angularis* angular; M.L. adj. *rectangularis* rectangular.

Rods, with square ends, 0.5 by 3.0 microns. Embedded in capsularaterial in m pairs. Iron compounds deposited outside the capsules which are found in surface films. No motility observed.

Aerobic.

Comment: The differences between the two species placed by Naumann (*loc. cit.*) in the genus *Sideroderma* are not very significant. Moreover, as surface-film organ-isms, these are so much like *Ferribacterium duplex* Brussoff that they clearly belong in the same genus.

Source: Found in the Anebodae region of Sweden.

Habitat: Found in fresh water, in swampy ditches and in small streams.

Genus V. Sideromonas *Cholodny, 1922.*

(Cholodny, Ber. d. deutsch. Bot. Ges., *40*, 1922, 326; also see Die Eisenbakterien, Pflanzenforschung, Heft 4, 1926, 55; *Siderothece* Naumann, Kungl. Svenska Vetenskapsakad. Handl., *62*, No. 4, 1922, 18; *Siderocystis* Naumann, *ibid.*, 42; also see Dorff, Die Eisenorganismen, Pflanzenforschung, Heft 16, 1934, 12; and Beger, Ber. d. deutsch. Bot. Ges., *62*, (1944) 1950, 8.)

Si.de.ro.mo'nas. Gr. noun *siderus* iron; Gr. noun *monas* a unit, monad; M.L. fem.n. *Sideromonas* iron monad.

Short, coccoid to rod-shaped cells each embedded in a rather large, sharply outlined capsule. The number of cells may increase within the capsule, and older capsules may unite to form larger colonies, the outlines of which are ill-defined. The capsules are impregnated with iron or manganese compounds or are completely encrusted with them.

The type species is *Sideromonas confervarum* Cholodny.

1. **Sideromonas confervarum** Cholodny, 1922. (Cholodnyi (sic), Ber. d. deutsch. Bot. Ges., *40*, 1922, 326; also see Cholodny, Die Eisenbakterien, Pflanzenforschung, Heft 4, Jena, 1926, 55.)

con.fer.va'rum. M.L. fem.n. *Conferva* a genus of algae; M.L. gen.pl.noun *confervarum* of *confervae*

Coccobacteria, 0.5 to 0.6 by 0.8 to 1.0 micron, occurring in chains embedded in gelatinous masses 10 to 100 microns in diameter. Chains become visible when the gelatinous mass is treated with formalin followed by dilute HCl, washed in water and stained with gentian violet or carbolfuchsin. No motility observed.

Form deposits of iron salts within the gelatinous mass surrounding the chains.

Probably facultative autotrophic (Dorff, Tabulae Biologicae, *16*, 1933, 222).

Cause the algal cells that are surrounded by the zoogloeal masses to become darker green than normal.

Source: Found on the surface of algae (*Conferva*) in water containing iron salts near Kiew (Ukraine); also found near Berlin, Central and Southern Sweden, Hungary and Moravia.

Habitat: Widely distributed on freshwater green algae.

2. **Sideromonas duplex** (Naumann, 1922) Beger, *comb. nov.* (*Siderocystis duplex* Naumann, Kungl. Svenska Vetenskapsakad. Handl., *62*, No. 4, 1922, 43.)

du'plex. L. adj. *duplex* two-fold, double.

Slender rods with rounded ends, 0.5 by 1.5 to 3.0 microns, occurring singly or in pairs. Embedded in capsules that may fuse to form zoogloeal masses. Iron compounds impregnate the capsular material. No motility observed.

Comment: The differences between this species and *Ferribacterium duplex* Brussoff are slight; cultural studies may show these two to be identical.

Source: Found in the Aneboda region of Sweden.

Habitat: Found on submerged objects in swampy ditches and small streams.

3. **Sideromonas vulgaris** (Naumann, 1922) Beger, *comb. nov.* (*Siderocystis vulgaris* Naumann, Kungl. Svenska Vetenskapsakad. Handl., *62*, No. 4, 1922, 42.)

vul.ga'ris. L. adj. *vulgaris* common.

Slender rods measuring 0.5 by 2.5 microns. Rods, several to many placed irregularly in a gelatinous envelope, form, when old, zoogloea-like masses as much as 7.5 microns in diameter. The rods are surrounded by primary capsules which are impregnated with iron compounds and which later fuse.

Reported by Dorff (Tabulae Biologicae, *16*, 1938, 221) to be autotrophic.

Comment: The characters of the genus *Siderocystis*, as described by Naumann (*loc. cit.*), do not seem adequate to distinguish it from the genus *Sideromonas*, established earlier by Cholodny.

Source: Found in the Aneboda region in Sweden.

Habitat: Forms deposits on submerged objects in ditch and river waters.

4. **Sideromonas major** (Naumann, 1922) Beger, *comb. nov.* (*Siderothece major* Naumann, Kungl. Svenska Vetenskapsakad. Handl., *62*, No. 4, 1922, 17; *Siderothece minor* Naumann, *loc. cit.*; *Siderocystis minor* Naumann, *ibid.*, 43.)

ma′jor. L. comp.adj. *major* larger.

Rods broader than those of *Sideromonas vulgaris*, 0.5 to nearly 1.5 by 1.0 to 1.5 microns. Each rod is surrounded by a large primary capsule; the capsules later fuse and form a gelatinous envelope in which the cells are irregularly arranged. Form zoogloea-like masses up to 10 microns in diameter. Iron compounds deposited within the capsular substance.

Possibly autotrophic (Dorff, Tabulae Biologicae, *16*, 1938, 221).

Aerobic.

Comments: While there are some differences in the sizes of the organisms placed by Naumann in the three different species named above, such differences may, in reality, not be significant: these differences may be due to variations in the nutritive value of the water in which each of the organisms was growing.

Source: Found in the Aneboda region in Sweden.

Habitat: Develop concretionary deposits (microscopic particles) on submerged objects in swampy ditch and river waters; also found in wells and pipes in waterworks.

Genus VI. **Naumanniella** *Dorff, 1934.*

(Die Eisenorganismen, Pflanzenforschung, Heft 16, 1934, 19.)

Nau.man.ni.el′la. M.L. dim.ending *-ella*; M.L. fem.n. *Naumanniella* named for Einar Naumann, a Swedish limnologist.

Cells ellipsoidal or rod-shaped with rounded ends, occurring singly or in short chains; the rods may be straight or curved and frequently are constricted in the middle. Each cell is surrounded by a small capsule and a marginal thickening (torus) heavily impregnated with iron and manganese compounds. Gelatinous capsules of the type found in *Siderocapsa* are absent. Cell division occurs simultaneously with constriction and separation of the torus. The species in this genus have not been cultured. Found at the surface and in or on the bottom mud of iron-bearing water.

The type species is *Naumanniella neustonica* Dorff.

Key to the species of genus **Naumanniella.**

I. Cells rod-shaped.
   A. Cells occur singly.
      1. Cell diameter greater than 1.2 microns with the torus.
         a. Cells with the torus 1.8 to 3.3 by 4.0 to 10.0 microns.
            1. *Naumanniella neustonica.*
        aa. Cells with the torus 1.2 to 1.5 by 3.1 to 3.6 microns.
            2. *Naumanniella minor.*
      2. Cells 1 by 2 microns with the torus.

B. Cells occur in chains.

II. Cells ellipsoidal.

3. *Naumanniella pygmaea.*

4. *Naumanniella catenata.*

5. *Naumanniella elliptica.*

1. **Naumanniella neustonica** Dorff, 1934. (Die Eisenorganismen, Pflanzenforschung, Heft *16*, 1934, 21.)

neus.to′ni.ca. Gr. adj. *neustus* swimming, floating; M.L. adj. *neustonicus* of the neuston (surface film).

Cells, including the torus, 1.8 to 3.3 by 4.9 to 10 microns; never curved but may be slightly constricted. Without the torus the cells measure 2.5 by 6.0 microns. Occur singly in the surface film of water, rarely on submerged plants.

Source: Found on the surface of iron-bearing water from wells near Freienwalde (1931) and Stolzenhagen (1932) in Mark Brandenburg; also isolated at Brisbane, Australia.

Habitat: Widely distributed in swamp water.

2. **Naumanniella minor** Dorff, 1934. (Die Eisenorganismen, Pflanzenforschung, Heft *16*, 1934, 21.)

mi′nor. L. comp.adj. *minor* smaller.

Cells, including the torus, 1.2 to 1.5 by 3.1 to 3.6 microns; occur singly in the form of rods which frequently are curved or spiral-shaped. The cells are 0.9 by 3.0 microns irrespective of the torus. Usually found in or on the bottom mud of fresh-water ponds and swampy areas.

Source: Found at Wurms (Rhein) in the bottom of a well which contained iron-bearing water.

Habitat: Widely distributed in swamp water; also found on ore or on the submerged leaves of water plants.

3. **Naumanniella pygmaea** Beger, 1949. (Zent. f. Bakt., I Abt., Orig., *154*, 1949, 65.)

pyg.mae′a. Gr. adj. *pygmaeus* dwarfish.

Small, straight rods, with rounded ends, 1 by 2 microns with the torus. Occur singly.

Source: Isolated from pipes and deep wells of waterworks near Berlin. Found on the surface of the gelatinous mass formed by *Zoogloea filipendula* Beger.

Habitat: Presumably widely distributed.

4. **Naumanniella catenata** Beger, 1941. (Zent. f. Bakt., II Abt., *103*, 1941, 32.)

ca.te.na′ta. L. part.adj. *catenatus* in chains.

Cells 0.4 to 0.5 by 4.6 to 5.2 microns; with the torus, 1.0 to 1.2 by 4.9 to 5.5 microns. Cells elongated or slightly curved with thick walls impregnated with iron. After division the cells remain connected in chains of several to many (3 to 12). These cells are joined together in such a manner that, because of the iron-impregnated, marginal thickenings and the relatively clear cells inside, they give the appearance of a chain with elongated links. Non-motile and unattached.

Source: Found on glass slides submerged in spring water near Magdeburg, Germany.

Habitat: Presumably widely distributed in or on the bottom mud of iron-bearing waters.

5. **Naumanniella elliptica** Beger, 1949. (Zent. f. Bakt., I Abt., Orig., *154*, 1949, 63 and 65.)

el.lip′ti.ca. Gr. adj. *ellipticus* defective, elliptical.

Cells ellipsoidal, 2.0 by 2.5 to 3.0 microns, with a pronounced torus.

Source: Found in pipes and deep wells of waterworks near Berlin. Found on masses of *Crenothrix polyspora* threads lying on the bottom mud.

Habitat: Presumably widely distributed in or on the bottom mud of iron-bearing waters.

Genus VII. **Ochrobium** *Perfiliev, 1921.*

(Perfiliev, in Wislouch, Bull. Institut Hydrobiol., Russia, 1921; *Sideroderma* in part, Naumann, Kungl. Svenska Vetenskapsakad. Handl., *62*, Part 4, (1921) March 20, 1922, 32; also see Naumann, Zent. f. Bakt., II Abt., *78*, 1929, 514.)

O.chro′bi.um. Gr. noun *ochra* yellow ochre, iron oxide; Gr. noun *bius* life, dwelling; M.L. neut.n. *Ochrobium* ochre-dweller.

Ellipsoidal to rod-shaped cells that are partially surrounded by a marginal thickening (torus) that is heavily impregnated with iron. This torus remains open at one end so that it resembles a horseshoe. The cells are surrounded by a delicate, transparent capsule that contains a very small amount of iron. Polar flagellate. Widely distributed in fresh water.

The type species is *Ochrobium tectum* Perfiliev.

1. **Ochrobium tectum** Perfiliev, 1921. (Perfiliev, in Wislouch, Bull. Institut Hydrobiol., Russia, 1921; also see Nachrichten des Sapropelkommittees, Leningrad, 1922, 1; and Verhandl. Intern. Verein. f. theor. und angew. Limnologie (1925)3, T. 3, 1927; *Sideroderma limneticum* Naumann, Kungl. Svenska Vetenskapsakad. Handl., *62*, 1922, 32.)

tec′tum. L. v. *tego* to cover; L. past part. *tectus* covered.

Cells small, ellipsoidal to rod-shaped, 0.5 to 3.0 by 1.5 to 5.0 microns. Each cell is surrounded by a heavily iron-impregnated torus which is open at one pole. Pairs of cells appear like a pair of horseshoes with the open ends together. The cells are covered with a delicate outer capsule, and they may be united in small colonies. When motile, they bear two unequal polar flagella.

Comment: The cells are much like those found in the algal genus *Pteromonas*, only smaller.

Source: Originally found in the region about Leningrad; then found independently by Naumann (Zent. f. Bakt., II Abt., *78*, 1929, 514) in Sweden and later by Beger (Zent. f. Bakt., I Abt., Orig., *154*, 1949, 65) in wells of waterworks near Berlin.

Habitat: Widely distributed in iron-bearing waters.

Genus VIII. **Siderococcus** *Dorff, 1934.*

(Die Eisenorganismen, Pflanzenforschung, Jena, Heft 16, 1934 9.)

Si.de.ro.coc′cus. Gr. noun *siderus* iron; Gr. noun *coccus* a berry, sphere; M.L. mas.n. *Siderococcus* iron coccus.

Cells cocciform and of small size. Lack a gelatinous capsule. Not encrusted with iron compounds; these are deposited entirely outside of the cells.

The type species is *Siderococcus limoniticus* Dorff.

1. **Siderococcus limoniticus** Dorff, 1934. (Die Eisenorganismen, Pflanzenforschung, Jena, Heft 16, 1934, 9.)

li.mo.ni′ti.cus. Gr. noun *limōn* meadow, bog; M.L. noun *limonitum* limonite, a mineral, ferrous iron oxide; M.L. adj. *limoniticus* of limonite.

Cocci 0.2 to 0.5 micron in diameter. No evident capsule. Utilize inorganic iron compounds and deposit them outside of the cells.

In liquid cultures, the cells produce, on a glass slide, a sharply marked zone beneath the surface in which iron compounds are deposited on the slide. When the iron compounds are dissolved with dilute HCl, very tiny cocci are left on the slide.

Source: Isolated from limonite deposits in a bay of Teufelsee near Freienwalde, Austria. Also found in Russian and Swedish iron ore deposits as well as in Java, Sumatra and Borneo.

Habitat: Widely distributed in swamps and lakes where limonite deposits are forming.

2. **Siderococcus communis** Dorff, 1934.
(Die Eisenorganismen, Pflanzenforschung, Jena, Heft 16, 1934, 9.)

com.mu′nis. L. adj. *communis* common.

Cocci to short rods, 0.4 to 1.0 micron in diameter, occurring singly or in chains. No capsules observed. Utilize organic iron compounds (ferrous ammonium citrate) and produce precipitates of ferric oxide.

Do not grow in water containing inorganic iron compounds such as iron carbonate. Do not grow on glass slides submerged in water containing organic iron compounds but are found in the precipitate that is formed.

Source: Found in many European countries and in North America.

Habitat: Widely distributed in water containing organic iron compounds.

Genus IX. Siderobacter Naumann, 1922.

(Kungl. Svenska Vetenskapsakad. Handl., *62*, No. 4, 1922, 55.)

Si.de.ro.bac′ter. Gr. noun *siderus* iron; M.L. noun *bacter* the masculine form of the Gr. neut. n. *bactrum* a small rod; M.L. mas.n. *Siderobacter* iron rodlet.

Cells bacilliform with rounded ends; occur singly, in pairs or in short chains or are united to form colonies. Lack a gelatinous capsule. Iron or manganese compounds are deposited on the surfaces or in the membranes of the cells; the deposit may also be entirely outside of the cells. Flagellated cells may occur. Found in neutral or alkaline waters.

The type species is *Siderobacter linearis* Naumann.

Key to species of genus Siderobacter.

I. Cells less than 1.0 micron in diameter. Found on the surface of zoogloeal masses.
    A. Cells less than 0.5 micron in diameter.
            1. *Siderobacter gracilis.*
    B. Cells 0.8 micron in diameter.
            2. *Siderobacter brevis.*
II. Cells 1.0 micron or greater than 1.0 micron in diameter.
    A. Cells 1.0 micron in diameter.
            3. *Siderobacter linearis.*
    B. Cells greater than 1.0 micron in diameter.
       1. Cells in pairs and 1.5 microns in diameter.
            4. *Siderobacter duplex.*
      2. Cells 2.5 microns in diameter. Participate in the formation of iron and lime concretions of macroscopic size.
            5. *Siderobacter latus.*

1. **Siderobacter gracilis** Beger, 1949.
(Zent. f. Bakt., I Abt., Orig., *154*, 1949, 65.)

gra′ci.lis. L. adj. *gracilis* slim, slender.

Cells 0.4 by 3.0 microns. Encrusted cells are 5.0 to 7.0 microns long. Occur singly. Participate in the formation of deposits of iron compounds.

Source: Found on the surface of masses of *Zoogloea filipendula*. This species formed thick coatings on the walls of two wells supplying rapid sand filters near Berlin, Germany. The filters required frequent washing because the coatings were easily detached.

Habitat: Found in the cool waters of deep wells.

2. **Siderobacter brevis** Beger, 1949.
(Zent. f. Bakt., I Abt., Orig., *154*, 1949, 65.)

bre′vis. L. adj. *brevis* short.

Cells, 0.8 to 1.0 by 3.0 to 4.0 microns, usually occurring singly. Participate in the formation of deposits of iron compounds.

Source: Found on the surface of masses of *Zoogloea filipendula*. This species formed thick coatings on the walls of two wells supplying rapid sand filters near Berlin, Germany. The filters required frequent washing because the coatings were easily detached.

3. **Siderobacter linearis** Naumann, 1922.

(Kungl. Svenska Vetenskapsakad. Handl., *62*, 1922, 55.)

li.ne.a′ris. L. adj. *linearis* linear.

The type species of genus *Siderobacter* Naumann.

Cells 1.0 by 5.0 microns after the encrusting iron compounds have been dissolved away with dilute HCl. Opaque, encrusted cells, 1.2 by 7.0 microns. Always occur singly in contrast to the larger-celled *Siderobacter duplex*, where the cells occur in pairs.

Source: Found in the Aneboda region in Sweden.

Habitat: Found in surface films and on submerged objects.

4. **Siderobacter duplex** Naumann, 1922. (Kungl. Svenska Vetenskapsakad. Handl., *62*, No. 4, 1922, 55.)

du′plex. L. adj. *duplex* two-fold, double.

Cells, 1.5 by 3.5 microns after encrusting iron compounds are removed with dilute HCl, occurring in pairs.

Source: Found in the Aneboda region in Sweden.

Habitat: Found in surface films on the water of swamps and small streams.

5. **Siderobacter latus** Beger, 1941. (Zent. f. Bakt., I Abt., Orig., *154*, 1949, 63 and 66.)

la′tus. L. adj. *latus* broad.

Straight or occasionally curved cells, 2.5 by 6.0 to 15.0 microns, usually occurring singly. Participate in the formation of iron and lime concretions.

Source: Found on concretions on the brick walls of two wells supplying a rapid sand filter near Berlin, Germany.

Habitat: Found in the cool waters of deep wells.

Genus X. **Ferrobacillus** *Leathen and Braley, 1954.**

(Bact. Proc. 54th General Meeting, Soc. of Amer. Bact., 1954, 44.)

Fer.ro.ba.cil′lus. L. noun *ferrum* iron, here meaning ferrous iron; L. dim.noun *bacillus* a small rod; M.L. noun *Ferrobacillus* ferrous-iron rodlet.

Short, plump, rod-shaped cells occurring singly and in pairs, seldom in chains; the cells are not united to form colonies. Oxidize ferrous iron to the ferric state in acid environments. Optimum reaction, pH 3.5.

The type species is *Ferrobacillus ferrooxidans* Leathen and Braley.

1. **Ferrobacillus ferrooxidans** Leathen and Braley, 1954. (Ferrous iron oxidizing bacterium, Leathen, McIntyre and Braley, Bact. Proc. 52nd General Meeting, Soc. of Amer. Bact., 1952, 15; also see Leathen, Braley and McIntyre, Appl. Microbiol., *1*, 1953, 65; Leathen and Braley, Bact. Proc. 54th General Meeting, Soc. of Amer. Bact., 1954, 44.)

fer.ro.o′xi.dans. L. noun *ferrum* iron; Gr. adj. *oxys* sharp, acid; M.L. v. *oxido* to oxidize or make acid; M.L. part.adj. *ferrooxidans* iron-oxidizing.

Rods 0.6 to 1.0 by 1.0 to 1.6 microns. Motile, presumably polar flagellate. Gram-negative.

Ferrous iron-silica gel: Colonies are small and raised with irregular margins. Young colonies are glistening and tan, but gradu-

ally become granular and brown with oxidizing iron. A tan to brown area of oxidized iron is frequently found around the colony.

Liquid ferrous iron medium (Leathen, McIntyre and Braley, Science, *114*, 1951, 280): Rapidly oxidized; forms a precipitate of ferric hydroxide or basic ferric sulfate.

Acid thiosulfate liquid medium: Not oxidized.

Optimum reaction, pH 3.5. Oxidation retarded below pH 2.2 and above pH 4.6.

Optimum temperature, between 15° and 20° C.

Strictly autotrophic. Derives energy by the oxidation of ferrous iron to the ferric state. Utilizes the CO_2 of the atmosphere as a source of carbon.

Aerobic.

*Description of genus and species prepared by Wm. W. Leathen, Mellon Institute, Pittsburgh, Pennsylvania.

Distinctive characters: By catalytic action, this species increases by several fold the amount of sulfuric acid normally formed by the atmospheric oxidation of pyritic materials found in bituminous coal seams and associated rock strata.

Comment: This organism closely resembles *Thiobacillus ferrooxidans* and may, in fact, be identical with it. However Temple and Colmer (Jour. Bact., *59*, 1950, 317) report that *Thiobacillus ferrooxidans* oxidizes thiosulfate while Leathen and Braley (*op. cit.*, 1954, 44) report that *Ferrobacillus ferrooxidans* does not oxidize thiosulfate. The latter workers (personal communication, May, 1954) further report that the transfer of even minute traces of ferrous iron medium to an acid thiosulfate medium may cause decomposition of the thiosulfate, evidenced by the development of turbidity due to the formation of colloidal sulfur; this purely chemical reaction involving thiosulfate may easily be misinterpreted as a bacterial oxidation of this same substrate.

Source: Isolated from bituminous coal mine drainages and from waters receiving such discharges.

Habitat: Indigenous to bituminous coal regions. Frequently form relatively hard granules of ferric iron in which many bacteria are entrapped.

FAMILY VII. SPIRILLACEAE MIGULA, 1894.

(Migula, Arb. Bact. Inst. Karlsruhe, *1*, 1894, 237; *Spirillobacteriaceae* Orla-Jensen, Jour. Bact., *6*, 1921, 264.)

Spi.ril.la′ce.ae. M.L. neut.n. *Spirillum* type genus of the family; -aceae ending to denote a family; M.L. fem.pl.n. *Spirillaceae* the *Spirillum* family.

Cells simple, curved or spirally twisted rods. These frequently remain attached to each other after transverse division to form chains of spirally twisted cells. Cells are rigid and usually motile by means of a single flagellum (rarely two) or a tuft of polar flagella. Gram-negative. Frequently oxidative in their physiology. Aerobic or facultatively anaerobic, although a few strict anaerobes occur among the vibrios (*Desulfovibrio* and *Vibrio*). Largely water forms, although some are parasitic or pathogenic on higher animals and man.

Key to the genera of family **Spirillaceae.**

I. Curved, vibrio-like rods that are rarely united into a complete ring.
  A. Cells curved; rods never united at the end into a ring-shaped cell. Usually possess a single, polar flagellum.
    1. Curved rods that are not known to attack cellulose.
      a. Aerobic to anaerobic, heterotrophic vibrios.
                Genus I. *Vibrio*, p. 229.
      aa. Anaerobic, facultatively autotrophic vibrios that produce hydrogen sulfide or methane.
        b. Reduce sulfates to hydrogen sulfide.
                Genus II. *Desulfovibrio*, p. 248.
        bb. Reduce carbon dioxide to methane.
                Genus III. *Methanobacterium*, p. 250.
    2. Curved rods that attack cellulose.
      a. Vibrio-like cells.
                Genus IV. *Cellvibrio*, p. 250.
      aa. Pointed, sickle-shaped cells.
                Genus V. *Cellfalcicula*, p. 252.
  B. Curved rods that join ends to form a complete ring.
                Genus VI. *Microcyclus*, p. 253.

II. Crescent-shaped to spiral cells that are frequently united into spiral chains of cells.
  A. Cells not embedded in zoogloeal masses.
    1. Spiral cells with polar flagellation.
      a. Possess a tuft of polar flagella.
               Genus VII. *Spirillum*, p. 253.
      aa. Possess a single, polar flagellum.
               Genus VIII. *Paraspirillum*, p. 257.
    2. Crescent-shaped cells with a tuft of flagella attached to the middle of the concave side of the cell.
               Genus IX. *Selenomonas*, p. 258.
  B. Crescent- to spiral-shaped cells embedded in a spherical mass of jelly. Found in fresh water.
               Genus X. *Myconostoc*, p. 260.

Genus I. Vibrio Müller, 1773.*

(Müller, Vermium terrestrium et fluviatilum, *1*, 1773, 39; *Pacinia* Trevisan, Atti d. Accad. Fisio-Medico-Statistica in Milano, Ser. 4, *3*, 1885, 83; *Microspira* Schroeter, in Cohn, Kryptogamen-Flora von Schlesien, *3*, 1, 1886, 168.)

Vib'ri.o. L. v. *vibro* to move rapidly to and fro, to vibrate; M.L. mas.n. *Vibrio* that which vibrates.

Cells short, curved, single or united into spirals. Motile by means of a single, polar flagellum which is usually relatively short; rarely two or three flagella in one tuft. Grow well and rapidly on the surfaces of standard culture media. Heterotrophic organisms varying greatly in their nutritional requirements. Aerobic, facultative anaerobic and anaerobic species. Widely distributed as saprophytic forms in salt- and fresh-water and in soil; also occur as parasites and as pathogens.

See Genus I, *Pseudomonas*, of Family IV, *Pseudomonadaceae*, for a discussion of the borderline between the genus *Vibrio* and the genus *Pseudomonas*.

Few comparative studies have been made on the species in this genus; it is therefore impossible to prepare a really satisfactory differential key.

The type species is *Vibrio comma* (Schroeter) Winslow et al.

Key to the species of genus Vibrio.

I. Aerobic species.
  A. Produce acid but no gas from glucose and usually from other sugars (one luminescent, one halophilic and several agar-digesting species fail to produce acid from glucose).
    1. Not luminescent, not able to digest agar and do not attack benzene ring compounds or oxidize oxalates so far as known.
      a. Found in fresh water or in the body fluids of animals, including man.
        b. Liquefy gelatin.
          c. Indole produced.
            d. Nitrites produced from nitrates.
              e. Milk not coagulated.
                f. Cause of cholera.
                  1. *Vibrio comma.*
               ff. Cholera-like vibrio from fresh water.
                  2. *Vibrio berolinensis.*

---

* Revised by Prof. Robert S. Breed, Cornell University, Geneva, New York, January, 1954; the section covering the microaerophilic and anaerobic animal pathogens was reviewed by Dr. E. V. Morse, College of Agriculture, University of Wisconsin, Madison, Wisconsin, May, 1955.

ee. Milk coagulated.
        3. *Vibrio metschnikovii.*
dd. Nitrites not produced from nitrates.
        4. *Vibrio proteus.*
cc. Indole not produced.
    d. Found in the human buccal cavity.
        5. *Vibrio sputigenus.*
    dd. Cause of abscesses in the African toad.
        6. *Vibrio xenopus.*
bb. Does not liquefy gelatin.
        7. *Vibrio leonardii.*
aa. Require sea-water or heavy brine media for growth on fresh isolation.
    b. Isolated from sea water.
        c. A diffusible dark brown pigment is usually produced in gelatin
        media.
                8. *Vibrio marinopraesens.*
        cc. A buff-colored pigment is produced on sea-water agar. No diffusible
        pigment produced.
                9. *Vibrio phytoplanktis.*
    bb. Found growing in brines.
        c. Acid from glucose.
                10. *Vibrio costicolus.*
        cc. No acid from glucose.
                11. *Vibrio halonitrificans.*
2. Luminescent, digest agar, attack benzene ring compounds or oxidize oxalates.
    a. Produce luminescence especially on neutral media containing sea water or
    the equivalent salt content.
        b. Gelatin liquefied.
            c. Require alkaline sea water or equivalent media for growth.
                d. Optimum growth temperature, between 25° and 28° C.
                        12. *Vibrio luminosus.*
                dd. Optimum growth temperature, between 30° and 32° C.
                        13. *Vibrio indicus.*
            cc. Found in fresh water and in intestinal contents.
                    14. *Vibrio albensis.*
        bb. Does not liquefy gelatin.
                15. *Vibrio pierantonii.*
    aa. Not as above.
        b. Digest agar either actively or at least soften it.
            c. Found in soil and in rotting organic matter.
                d. Decomposes both cellulose and agar.
                        16. *Vibrio agarliquefaciens.*
                dd. Liquefies agar only.
                        17. *Vibrio andoii.*
            cc. Found in sea water with rotting algae.
                d. Nitrites produced from nitrates.
                    e. Colonies on agar are white to gray.
                        18. *Vibrio beijerinckii.*
                    ee. Colonies on agar are pale yellow becoming bright yellow
                    then pale brown.
                        19. *Vibrio fuscus.*

        dd. Nitrites not produced from nitrates.
               20. *Vibrio granii.*
   bb. Not as above.
      c. Soil organisms that are known to attack benzene ring compounds.
        d. Soil organism that attacks naphthalene.
              21. *Vibrio neocistes.*
        dd. Soil organism that attacks phenol and m-cresol.
              22. *Vibrio cyclosites.*
     cc. Soil organisms that are known to attack oxalates.
        d. Grows well on calcium oxalate agar. White colonies.
              23. *Vibrio oxaliticus.*
        dd. Forms film on bottom of liquid oxalate media. Rose-red to
           blood-red chromogenesis on oxalate agar.
              24. *Vibrio extorquens.*
B. Do not attack carbohydrates.
   1. Soil organism that is known to attack naphthalene.
              25. *Vibrio cuneatus.*
   2. Not as above.
      a. Do not liquefy gelatin.
        b. From fresh water.
              26. *Vibrio percolans.*
        bb. Requires sea-water media for growth on fresh isolation.
              27. *Vibrio adaptatus.*
     aa. Liquefy gelatin.
        b. Causes a disease in fresh-water fishes.
              28. *Vibrio piscium.*
        bb. Requires sea-water media for growth on fresh isolation.
              29. *Vibrio hyphalus.*
II. Anaerobic to microaerophilic species (all parasitic, normally pathogenic).
  A. Microaerophilic species that are pathogenic to warm-blooded animals.
   1. Cause of abortion in cattle and sheep.
              30. *Vibrio fetus.*
   2. Not as above.
      a. Cause of swine dysentery.
              31. *Vibrio coli.*
     aa. Cause of dysentery in cattle and related animals.
              32. *Vibrio jejuni.*
  B. Strict anaerobes.
      a. Produces gas and bad odors in protein media.
              33. *Vibrio niger.*
     aa. Does not produce gas and bad odors in protein media.
              34. *Vibrio sputorum.*

    1. **Vibrio comma** (Schroeter, 1886) Winslow et al., 1920. (Kommabacillus, Koch, Berliner klin. Wochenschr., *21*, 1884, 479; *Spirillum cholerae asiaticae* Zopf, Die Spaltpilze, 3 Aufl., 1885, 69; *Microspira comma* Schroeter, in Cohn, Kryptogamen Flora v. Schlesien, *3*, 1, 1886, 168; *Vibrio cholerae* Neisser, Arch. f. Hyg., *19*, 1893, 199; Winslow, Broadhurst, Buchanan, Krum- wiede, Rogers and Smith, Jour. Bact., *5*, 1920, 204.)

    com'ma. Gr. *comma* a comma.

    Slightly curved rods, 0.3 to 0.6 by 1.0 to 5.0 microns, occurring singly and in spiral chains. Cells may be long, thin and delicate or short and thick. May lose their curved form on artificial cultivation. Motile, possessing a single polar flagellum. Gram-negative.

Gelatin colonies: Small, yellowish white.

Gelatin stab: Rapid, napiform liquefaction.

Agar colonies: Circular, whitish brown, moist, glistening, translucent, slightly raised, entire.

Agar slant: Brownish gray, moist, glistening.

McConkey's medium: Good growth, colonies colorless when young, soon pinkish, medium becomes darker red.

Broth: Slightly turbid, with fragile, wrinkled pellicle and flocculent precipitate.

Peptone water: Characteristic rapid growth, chiefly at surface, where, after 6 to 9 hours, a delicate membrane is formed; little turbidity, deposit apparently derived from pellicle (Topley and Wilson, Princip. Bact. and Immun., 2nd ed., 1936, 388). Readily isolated from the surface film of 0.1 per cent peptone water.

Litmus milk: Alkaline at the top and slightly acid at bottom; generally not coagulated; peptonized; reduced.

Potato: Dirty white to yellowish, moist, glistening, spreading growth.

Blood serum: Abundant growth, sometimes slow liquefaction.

Blood agar: The blood pigment is digested forming a greenish zone around colonies; a true soluble hemolysin is not formed (the El Tor vibrio also digests blood pigment but in addition produces a soluble hemolysin; otherwise it is said to be indistinguishable from the typical cholera vibrio).

Indole produced.

Cholera-red reaction, which depends on production of indole and reduction of nitrates, is positive.

Hydrogen sulfide produced.

Acid but no gas from glucose, fructose, galactose, maltose, sucrose and mannitol. Slowly from glycerol. Does not attack lactose, inulin or dulcitol.

Group I of Heiberg (Classification of *Vibrio cholerae* and Cholera-like Vibrios. Copenhagen, 1935) ferments mannose and sucrose but not arabinose.

Hydrolyzes starch actively in alkaline media.

Nitrites produced from nitrates.

High alkali but low acid tolerance: optimum pH, between 7.6 and 8.0; for isolation on Dieudonne's medium, pH 9.0 to 9.6.

Aerobic, grows best in abundant oxygen; under strict anaerobiosis may fail to grow altogether.

Optimum temperature, 37° C. Maximum, 42° C. Minimum, 14° C.

Source: Isolated from the intestinal contents of cholera patients in Egypt and India.

Habitat: Found in the intestinal contents of cholera patients and carriers.

The relationships existing among the cholerigenic and non-pathogenic water vibrios, although studied intensively, have not yet been completely defined. As a working scheme, based on somatic (O) and flagellar (H) antigen studies, Gardner and Vankatraman (Jour. Hyg., *35*, 1935, 262–282) suggest the one shown in the graph on the following page.

Linton (Bact. Rev., *4*, 1940, 275) has outlined a classification of the vibrios based upon their protein and polysaccharide structures. Using chemical methods, it was found that one polysaccharide and one protein was commonly obtained from each strain of vibrio; when exceptions occurred, it was invariably noted that the strain was undergoing dissociation. Given a single protein and polysaccharide in each vibrio, it was possible to divide the strains into six groups, which were numbered in the order of their discovery as shown in the table.

A chemical grouping of the cholerigenic and water vibrios.

Group	Protein Type	Polysaccharide Type
I	I	I
II	I	II
III	II	I₁
IV	II	I
V	II	III
VI	I	III

The strains of Groups I and II possess the same protein and different polysaccha-

Cholera group of vibrios.

(Biochemically similar. Common H antigen.)

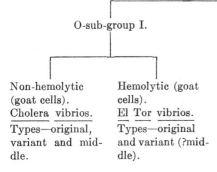

O-sub-group I.

O sub-groups II, III, IV, V, VI and individual races (mostly hemolytic). Paracholera, cholera-like, and some El Tor vibrios.

Non-hemolytic (goat cells).
Cholera vibrios.
Types—original, variant and middle.

Hemolytic (goat cells).
El Tor vibrios.
Types—original and variant (?middle).

(Types within sub-groups underlined.)

rides. These are derived from cases of cholera and have the serological and biochemical characteristics of O-Group I, *Vibrio cholera*. Group I strains are more common than those of Group II, which have, however, been isolated from epidemics with a high mortality. The phospholipid fraction is common to both types when isolated in the early part of an epidemic but is not found in strains of other groups. The harmless water vibrios, which are so heterogeneous serologically (Taylor and Ahuja, Indian Jour. Med. Res., *26*, 1938, 8–32), form a single chemical group with a homogeneous structure. They fall into Group III, which differs in its protein structure from the authentic cholera vibrios and which resembles Group II in its polysaccharide. The vibrios of Group IV, which came from El Tor and from chronic vibrio carriers, are believed, on epidemiological grounds, to be harmless, although serological methods have failed to distinguish them from cholerigenic vibrios. Group V, which, like III and IV, contains protein II, consists, like Group IV, of strains from chronic vibrio carriers. Group VI strains are only rarely isolated in nature, and representatives of this group are generally found among collections of old laboratory strains. They appear to be the result of polysaccharide variation from Group I after long-continued growth on artificial media.

2. **Vibrio berolinensis** Neisser, 1893. (Arch. f. Hyg., *19*, 1893, 200.)

be.ro.li.nen'sis. M.L. *Berolinum* place name, Berlin; M.L. adj. *berolinensis* of Berlin.

Curved rods, somewhat smaller than those of *Vibrio comma*, frequently occurring in pairs. Pleomorphic. Motile by means of a single, polar flagellum. Gram-negative.

Gelatin colonies: Small, grayish, slightly granular, fragmented; very slow liquefaction.

Gelatin stab: Slow, napiform liquefaction.

Agar slant: Grayish yellow, moist, glistening growth.

Broth: Turbid, with gray pellicle.

Litmus milk: No coagulation, no acid.

Potato: Brownish streak.

Indole produced.

Nitrites produced from nitrates.

Not pathogenic for mice, pigeons or guinea pigs.

Aerobic, facultative.

Optimum temperature, 37° C. Minimum, above 10° C. Maximum, less than 60° C.

Source: Isolated from filtered Spree river water.

Habitat: Presumably widely distributed in polluted water.

3. **Vibrio metschnikovii** Gamaléia, 1888. (*Vibrio metschnikovi* (sic) Gamaléia, Ann. Inst. Past., *2*, 1888, 482.)

metsch.ni.ko'vi.i. Named for Metschnikoff, a Russian bacteriologist; M.L. mas. gen.n. *metschnikovii* of Metschnikoff.

Curved rods, somewhat shorter and thicker than those of *Vibrio comma*. Long, slender chains of cells are formed in old cultures. Motile by means of a single, polar flagellum. In the animal body the cells are nearly coccoid. Gram-negative.

Gelatin colonies: Like those of *Vibrio comma*.

Gelatin stab: Rapid, napiform liquefaction.

Agar slant: Yellowish, plumose, moist, glistening growth.

Broth: Turbid, with thin, white pellicle.

Litmus milk: Acid, coagulated (eighth day); not peptonized.

Potato: Delicate, brownish growth.

Indole produced.

Nitrites produced from nitrates.

Aerobic, facultative.

Optimum temperature, 37° C. Maximum, less than 45° C.

Pathogenic for pigeons, fowls and guinea pigs.

Source: Isolated from fowl dead of a cholera-like disease.

Habitat: Found in the intestinal contents of chickens, pigeons and other animals suffering from a cholera-like disease.

4. **Vibrio proteus** Buchner, 1885. (Kommabacillus der cholera nostras, Finkler and Prior, Deutsche med. Wochenschr., 1884, 632; Buchner, Sitzungsber. d. Gesel. f. Morph. u. Physiol., München, Heft 1, 1885, 10.)

pro'te.us. Gr. noun *Proteus* a sea-god who could change his form; M.L. mas.n. *Proteus* a generic name.

Description supplemented by material taken from Lehmann and Neumann (Bakt. Diag., 7 Aufl., *2*, 1927, 541).

Curved rods, 0.4 to 0.6 by 2.4 microns, often pointed at both ends. Motile by means of a single, polar flagellum. Gram-negative.

Gelatin colonies: Small, gray, circular, granular, entire; rapid liquefaction with the formation of large craters.

Gelatin stab: Rapid, saccate liquefaction.

Agar slant: Dirty grayish, plumose growth.

Broth: Turbid, with fetid odor.

Litmus milk: Slightly acid; coagulated; peptonized.

Potato: Grayish, slimy layer.

Indole not produced; indole reaction weak (Lehmann and Neumann).

Hydrogen sulfide production very slight.

Gas not produced from glucose.

Nitrites not produced from nitrates.

Aerobic, facultative.

Optimum temperature, 30° C.

Source: Isolated from feces of patients suffering from cholera nostras (gastroenteritis).

Habitat: Found in the intestinal contents in cholera nostras and cholera infantum.

5. **Vibrio sputigenus** (Migula, 1900) Bergey et al., 1923. (Vibrio aus Sputum, Brix, Hyg. Rundschau, *4*, 1894, 913; *Microspira sputigena* Migula, Syst. d. Bakt., *2*, 1900, 981; Bergey et al., Manual, 1st ed., 1923, 80.)

spu.ti'ge.nus. L. noun *sputum* spit, sputum; Gr. v. *gennaō* to bear; M.L. adj. *sputigenus* sputum-borne.

Slightly curved rods, about the same size and form as those of *Vibrio comma*, occurring singly, occasionally three or four in a chain. Motile by means of a single, polar flagellum. Gram-negative.

Gelatin colonies: Small, circular, slightly granular, yellowish, becoming brownish.

Gelatin: Crateriform liquefaction.

Agar slant: Grayish white, moist.

Broth: Turbid, no pellicle formed.

Litmus milk: Acid; coagulated.

Potato: Thin, gray layer, spreading.

Indole not produced.

Nitrites not produced from nitrates.

Aerobic, facultative.

Optimum temperature, 37° C.

Source: Isolated from sputum.

6. **Vibrio xenopus** Schrire and Greenfield, 1930. (Trans. Roy. Soc. So. Africa, *17*, 1930, 309.)

xe'no.pus. Gr. adj. *xenus* alien, strange; Gr. noun *pus, podis* a foot; M.L. mas.n. *Xenopus* strange foot, a genus of toads.

Spiral forms, occurring singly and in pairs. Non-motile. Gram-negative.

Gelatin stab: Slow, crateriform liquefaction.

Agar colonies: Small, white, glistening, slimy, entire.

Agar slant: Grayish white, slimy, entire growth.

Broth: Turbid with flocculent sediment.

Litmus milk: Unchanged.

Potato: Not reported.

Indole not produced.

Blood serum peptonized.

Starch not hydrolyzed.

Acid from glucose, fructose, maltose, glycerol and sorbitol.

Nitrites produced slowly from nitrates.

Aerobic, facultative.

Optimum temperature, 37° C.

Source: Isolated from an abscess of the pectoral muscle of an African toad.

7. Vibrio leonardii Métalnikov and Chorine, 1928. (Ann. Inst. Past., *42*, 1928, 1647.)

le.o.nar′di.i. M.L. gen.noun *leonardii* of Leonard; named for A. G. Leonard.

Curved rods with rounded ends, 0.5 to 1.0 by 2.0 to 3.0 microns. Motile by means of 1 to 3 polar flagella. Gram-negative.

Gelatin stab: No liquefaction.

Agar colonies: Small, transparent, circular, having a characteristic odor.

Broth: Turbid, with thin pellicle.

Litmus milk: No coagulation, acid, with reduction of litmus.

Potato: Slight, colorless growth.

Coagulated blood serum not liquefied.

Indole not produced.

Hydrogen sulfide produced.

Acid and gas from glucose, fructose, galactose, lactose, sucrose and mannitol. No acid or gas from maltose or glycerol.

Nitrites produced from nitrates.

Aerobic, facultative.

Optimum temperature, 30° C.

Habitat: Highly pathogenic for insects such as *Galleria mellonella* L. (wax moth) and *Pyrausta nubialis* Hübn. (European corn borer).

8. Vibrio marinopraesens ZoBell and Upham, 1944. (Bull. Scripps Inst. of Oceanography, Univ. Calif., *5*, 1944, 256.)

ma.ri.no.prae′sens. L. adj. *marinus* of the sea; L. part.adj. *praesens* present; M.L. adj. *marinopraesens* present in the sea.

Curved rods, 0.4 to 0.5 by 1.2 to 2.4 microns, occurring singly and in spiral chains. Polar staining. Motile by means of one or two polar flagella. Gram-negative.

Note: All differential media except the fresh-water broth, litmus milk and potato were prepared with sea water.

Gelatin colonies: Circular, 1 mm in diameter, dense center, brown discoloration of gelatin.

Gelatin stab: Stratiform above, infundibuliform below; complete liquefaction in 5 days; brown discoloration of gelatin.

Agar colonies: Convex, circular, 0.5 mm in diameter, entire, translucent.

Agar slant: Abundant, filiform, glistening, butyrous growth with no pigment.

Sea-water broth: Heavy turbidity; slight viscid sediment; surface ring.

Fresh-water broth: No visible growth.

Litmus milk: Completely decolorized.

Potato: No visible growth.

Indole not produced.

Hydrogen sulfide rapidly produced.

Acid but no gas from glucose and maltose. Glycerol, xylose, lactose, sucrose, mannitol and salicin not fermented.

Starch is hydrolyzed.

Non-lipolytic.

Nitrites not produced from nitrates.

Ammonia produced from peptone but not from urea.

Casein not digested.

Aerobic, facultative.

Optimum temperature, between 20° and 25° C.

Source: Isolated from sea water.

Habitat: Common; probably widely distributed.

9. Vibrio phytoplanktis ZoBell and Upham, 1944. (Bull. Scripps Inst. of Oceanography, Univ. Calif., *5*, 1944, 261.)

phy.to.plank′tis. Gr. neut.n. *phytum* plant; Gr. adj. *planctus* wandering; M.L. neut.n. *plankton* (*planctum*) plankton; M.L. neut.n. *phytoplankton* plant plankton; M.L. adj. *?phytoplanktis* of the phytoplankton.

Curved rods, 0.5 to 0.6 by 2.0 to 5.4 microns, occurring mostly singly with some short spiral chains. Bipolar staining. Motile by means of a single polar flagellum. Gram-negative.

Note: All differential media except the

fresh-water broth, litmus milk and potato were prepared with sea water.

Gelatin colonies: Diffuse, irregular; waxy appearance, slightly depressed; rapid liquefaction.

Gelatin stab: Slow, crateriform, liquefaction becoming stratiform. Buff pigment.

Agar colonies: 1 to 2 mm in diameter, translucent, smooth, convex, circular.

Agar slant: Luxuriant, echinulate; watery appearance; slightly mucoid, glistening growth with buff or cream pigment.

Sea-water broth: Heavy turbidity; abundant, flocculent sediment; surface ring.

Fresh-water broth: No visible growth.

Litmus milk: No visible change.

Potato: No visible growth.

Indole not produced.

Hydrogen sulfide is produced.

Acid but no gas from glucose, maltose and sucrose. Glycerol, xylose, lactose, mannitol and salicin not fermented.

Starch not hydrolyzed.

Non-lipolytic.

Nitrites not produced from nitrates.

Ammonia produced from peptone but not from urea.

Casein is digested.

Aerobic, facultative (good anaerobic growth).

Optimum temperature, between 20° and 25° C.

Source: Isolated from sea water and marine phytoplankton.

Habitat: Presumably widely distributed.

10. **Vibrio costicolus** Smith, 1938. (Roy. Soc. Queensland, Proc. for 1937, *49*, 1938, 29.)

cos.ti′co.lus. L. noun. *costa* rib; L. v. *colo* to dwell; M.L. adj. *costicolus* rib dwelling (from bacon).

Curved rods, 0.5 by 2.0 to 4.0 microns; old cells coccoid. Actively motile by means of a single, polar flagellum. Young cultures show pronounced beaded staining. Gramnegative.

No growth on media which does not contain salt. Limit for growth, 2 to 23 per cent NaCl; optimum, 6 to 12 per cent.

Gelatin stab: No liquefaction. However, some strains liquefy within 2 days at 32° C.; these may represent a distinct variety or a separate species.

Agar colonies: Circular, entire, convex, glistening, non-viscid.

Agar slant: Abundant, filiform, transparent or translucent growth.

Broth: Pellicle formation varies from absent to pronounced, whitish and non-coherent.

Litmus milk: Not coagulated.

Potato: Sparse, moist, brownish growth.

Indole not produced.

Hydrogen sulfide produced.

Acid from glucose, fructose, sucrose, mannose, mannitol and glycerol. No acid from galactose, lactose, maltose, rhamnose, raffinose, arabinose, xylose, sorbitol, dextrin, starch or salicin.

Acetylmethylcarbinol not produced.

Non-lipolytic.

Nitrites produced from nitrates.

Catalase-positive.

Aerobic, facultative.

Optimum temperature, between 30° and 35° C.; temperature range, 2° to 42° C.

Related organisms: Robinson (A Possible Explanation of Microbial Halophilism, Thesis, McGill University, 1950, 92 pp.) isolated a similar organism from bacon-curing brines in Canada. At concentrations of 11.7 and 17.5 per cent NaCl, cells are spirillum-shaped and sluggishly motile. Pellicle formed on broth. Gelatin liquefied. Acetylmethylcarbinol produced. Catalase and urease absent. Acid from raffinose and inulin. No acid from mannose, dulcitol, cellobiose, adonitol or ethyl alcohol. Organism will note grow in absence of salts, but NaCl may be replaced by KCl, NaBr, $Na_2S_2O_3$, LiCl or $MgCl_2$ (also see Flannery, Doetsch and Hansen, Jour. Bact., *64*, 1952, 713–17).

Source: Isolated from the tainted ribs of bacon and tank brines in bacon factories in Australia.

Habitat: Found in cured meats and meat-curing brines.

11. **Vibrio halonitrificans*** Smith, 1938.

---

* This organism is, in reality, a denitrifier, not a nitrifier, and therefore this name is inappropriate.

(Roy. Soc. Queensland, Proc. for 1937, *49*, 1938, 29.)

ha.lo.ni.tri'fi.cans. Gr. noun *hals, halis* the sea salt; M.L. part.adj. *nitrificans* nitrifying; M.L. adj. *halonitrificans* nitrifying salt.

Curved rods, usually 0.3 by 1.2 to 2.5 microns, occurring singly. Motile by means of a single, polar flagellum. No marked variation in form in media of varied salinity. Stain somewhat faintly with the usual stains. Gram-negative.

No growth on media which does not contain salt. Limit for growth, 1 to 23 per cent salt; optimum growth in 4.0 to 6.0 per cent salt.

Gelatin stab: Liquefied within 7 days at 35° C.; at 20° C. shallow, superficial liquefaction was evident in 20 days.

Agar colonies: Light amber, glistening, convex, transparent, non-viscid, slightly spreading.

Agar slants: Growth slow at 4° C., colonies appearing in 14 days.

Nutrient and nitrate broths: Growth. No growth, however, when covered with a paraffin oil seal.

Litmus milk: Not coagulated; growth slight or absent.

Potato: Growth moist, fairly abundant, whitish.

Indole not produced.

Hydrogen sulfide not produced.

Glucose, fructose, sucrose, mannose, rhamnose, galactose, lactose, maltose, raffinose, sorbitol and glycerol not fermented.

Acetylmethylcarbinol not produced.

Non-lipolytic.

Nitrites produced from nitrates.

Catalase-negative.

Aerobic.

Temperature relations: Optimum, between 30° and 35° C. Slow growth at 4° C. Killed in 10 minutes in 6 per cent saline broth at 55° C.

Limiting reactions for growth, pH 5.4 and pH 9.2.

Not pathogenic for guinea pigs or mice.

Source: Five strains were isolated from tank brines from bacon-curing factories in Australia. The strains showed little variation in characters. Except for its ability to liquefy gelatin, this species resembles the organisms isolated by Sturges and Heideman (Absts. Bact., *7*, 1923, 11; *ibid.*, *8*, 1924, 14; *ibid.*, *9*, 1925, 2) in the U. S. A.

Habitat: Known to be found in meat-curing brines but probably more widely distributed.

12. **Vibrio luminosus** Beijerinck, 1888. (*Vibrio luminosus* (*nomen nudum*) Beijerinck, Botan. Zeitg., *46*, 1888, 763; *Photobacterium luminosum* Beijerinck, Arch. Néerl. d. Sci. Exact. et Natur., *23*, 1889, 401; *Microspira luminosa* Migula, Syst. d. Bakt., *2*, 1900, 1015.)

lu.mi.no'sus. L. adj. *luminosus* luminous.

Small rods having the size and form of the cholera vibrio when grown in media containing little nitrogen and carbohydrates. Sometimes form chains of vibrios which resemble spirilla. In richer media the cells become much larger. Motile. Gram-negative (Chester, 1897).

Gelatin: Liquefied. In presence of 0.5 per cent asparagine and 0.5 per cent peptone, offensive odors not produced. Putrefaction of the gelatin occurs when the nitrogen source is insufficient.

Peptonized meat bouillon gelatin: No growth. Good growth and luminescence with the addition of 3.0 to 3.5 per cent of sea salt, potassium chloride or magnesium chloride.

Agar: Growth rapid, shines feebly.

Sea-water broth: Produces forms which resemble the bacteroids of legume bacteria.

Blood serum: No growth. Addition of 3.0 to 3.5 per cent of sea salt, potassium chloride or magnesium chloride allows good growth and luminescence.

Nitrates not reduced.

Indigo-blue not readily reduced.

Salt tolerance: In order to assure phosphorescence and good growth, the osmotic tension of inorganic salt solutions used for cultivation should be equivalent to that produced in a 3 per cent sodium chloride solution.

Optimum temperature for growth and luminescence, between 25° and 28° C.

Aerobic.

Quality of luminescence: Bluish green, persisting for 1 to 2 weeks.

Distinctive characters: Develops only

on neutral or feebly alkaline media: a slight quantity of acid completely prevents growth and the production of luminescence. Luminescence occurs on organic matter only when a sufficient proportion of inorganic salt is present.

Source: Isolated in Holland from coastal sea water, dead sea fish and crustacea.

Habitat: Found in coastal sea water, on dead fish, crustacea and other salt-water animals, on meat and even on soldiers' wounds where they produce no known harmful effects. No food poisoning has ever been traced to meat on which these organisms have grown (Niven, Circular No. 2, American Meat Inst. Foundation, 1951, 1–11).

13. **Vibrio indicus** (Beijerinck, 1889) Lehmann and Neumann, 1896. (*Bacillus phosphorescens* Fischer, Ztschr. f. Hyg., *2*, 1887, 58; also see Anonymous, Sitzber. d. Gesell. naturf. Freunde zu Berlin, 1886, 162; *Photobacterium indicum* Beijerinck, Arch. Néerl. d. Sci. Exact. et Natur., *23*, 1889, 401; not *Photobacterium phosphorescens* Beijerinck, *loc. cit.*; Lehmann and Neumann, Bakt. Diag., 1 Aufl., *2*, 1896, 341; *Pseudomonas phosphorescens* Bergey et al., Manual, 3rd ed., 1930, 177.)

in′di.cus. L. adj. *indicus* of India.

Description taken from Fischer (*op. cit.*, 1887, 58) and Beijerinck (*op. cit.*, 1889, 401).

Small, thick rods 2 to 3 times as long as wide with rounded ends; occasionally spiral and short, irregularly-curved filamentous forms are found. Motile. Stain lightly with aniline dyes. Gram-negative (Chester, 1897).

Gelatin colonies: After 36 hours, small, circular, grayish white, punctiform. Liquefaction, forming a slightly concave surface.

Blood serum: Grayish white, slimy growth.

Potato: Thin, white layer in 2 to 3 days.

Cooked fish: Abundant growth. Entire surface covered with a grayish white, slimy growth. Bluish white phosphorescence.

Alkaline broth: Slight turbidity in 24 hours. Pellicle in 3 days.

Acid broth: No turbidity. No phosphorescence.

Milk: No growth.

No gas produced

Nitrates not reduced.

Indigo-blue not readily reduced.

Not pathogenic for laboratory animals.

Salt tolerance: To assure phosphorescence and good growth, the osmotic tension of inorganic salt solutions used for cultivation should be equivalent to that produced in a 3 per cent sodium chloride solution.

Optimum temperature for growth and luminescence, between 30° and 32° C. Minimum, 15° C.

Aerobic.

Quality of luminescence: Bluish to green, persisting for 1 to 2 weeks.

Distinctive character: Luminescence on organic matter occurs only when a sufficient proportion of inorganic salt is present.

Source: Isolated from sea water of the West Indies.

Habitat: Found in coastal sea water and on dead fish, crustacea and other salt-water animals; they are also found on meat and even on soldiers' wounds where they produce no known harmful effects. No food poisoning has been traced to meat on which these organisms have grown (Niven, Circular No. 2, American Meat Inst. Foundation, 1951, 1–11).

14. **Vibrio albensis** Lehmann and Neumann, 1896. (Elbe vibrio, Dunbar, Deutsche med. Wochnschr., *19*, 1893, 799; Lehmann and Neumann, Bakt. Diag., 1 Aufl., *2*, 1896, 340; *Microspira dunbari* Migula, Syst. d. Bakt., *2*, 1900, 1013.)

al.ben′sis. M.L. adj. *albensis* pertaining to the (river) Elbe.

Early descriptions merely report this organism as morphologically and culturally (except for phosphorescence and pathogenicity) indistinguishable from *Vibrio comma*. Some of the early workers even failed to observe phosphorescence. Description taken from Gorham (in Dahlgren, Jour. Franklin Inst., *180*, 1915, table following 714) and Warren (Jour. Bact., *49*, 1945, 549); also see Sonnenschein (Cent. f. Bakt., I Abt., Orig., *123*, 1931, 92).

Curved rods, 1.2 by 2.1 microns, occurring singly and in pairs. Motile by means of a single, polar flagellum. Not encapsulated. Gram-negative.

Gelatin colonies: Small, yellowish white. Gelatin stab: Liquefaction. Growth at the surface and along the stab.

Agar: Abundant growth.

Agar slant: Growth dull and wrinkled.

Blood agar: Good growth and luminescence; beta hemolysis.

Broth: Pellicle formed.

Koser's citrate medium: Growth and luminescence.

Milk: Growth.

Potato: Luxuriant growth.

Indole produced.

Hydrogen sulfide not produced.

Acid but no gas from glucose and sucrose. No acid or gas from lactose.

Starch hydrolyzed.

Gives a cholera-red reaction, i.e., produces both indole and nitrites.

Nitrites produced from nitrates.

Optimum salt concentration, 0.9 per cent.

Temperature relations: Optimum, 22° C.; growth at 37.5° C.

Aerobic, facultative.

Distinctive characters: Morphologically and culturally like *Vibrio comma*. Luminescent. Pathogenic to guinea pigs and pigeons.

Source: Originally isolated from the Elbe River. If *Vibrio phosphorescens* Jermoljewa (Cent. f. Bakt., I Abt., Orig., *100*, 1926, 170) is accepted as identical with this species, then it has also been found in the intestinal contents of three cholera patients, one gastroenteritis and one typhoid patient; Jermoljewa (*ibid.*, 171) also isolated his organism from the bile of a cadaver. Sonnenschein (*op. cit.*, *123*, 1931, 92) reisolated this species from a fish taken from the Elbe River and found that it maintained its ability to luminesce when grown in ox bile.

Habitat: Found in fresh water, in human feces and in bile. Probably widely distributed.

15. **Vibrio pierantonii** (Zirpolo, 1918) Meissner, 1926. (*Bacillus pierantonii* Zirpolo, Boll. Soc. Nat. Napoli, *30*, (1917) 1918, 206; Meissner, Cent. f. Bakt., II Abt., *67*, 1926, 200.)

pier.an.to'ni.i. M.L. gen.noun *pierantonii*

of Pierantoni; named for Prof. U. Pierantoni, an Italian scientist.

Rods, 0.5 by 1.5 microns, with rounded ends. Rods curved and vibrio-shaped according to Meissner (*ibid.*, 201). Motile by means of one to three polar flagella. Gram-negative.

Gelatin colonies: Circular and irregularly lobulate.

Gelatin stab: No liquefaction.

Agar colonies: Circular, light green, smooth, entire.

Glycerol agar slant: Slightly luminous streak.

Broth: Turbid, with pellicle.

Indole not produced.

Acid from glucose and maltose. Some strains also attack lactose, sucrose and mannitol.

Best growth in alkaline media.

Aerobic, facultative.

Optimum temperature, 37° C.

Source: Isolated from the photogenic organ of the cephalopod *Sepiola intermedia* Naef.

16. **Vibrio agarliquefaciens** (Gray and Chalmers, 1924) Bergey et al., 1934. (*Microspira agar-liquefaciens* (sic) Gray and Chalmers, Ann. Appl. Biol., *11*, 1924, 325; Bergey et al., Manual, 4th ed., 1934, 119.)

a.gar.li.que.fac'i.ens. Malay agar, a jelly from seaweeds; L. v. *liquefacio* to liquefy; M.L. part.adj. *agarliquefaciens* liquefying agar.

Short, curved rods, usually c-shaped, with occasional s-shaped and coccoid forms. Cells 2.0 microns long by 0.5 to 0.7 micron broad; 3.0 to 5.0 microns long in division stages. Coccoid forms stained, 0.5 to 0.7 micron long. Motile by means of a single, polar flagellum. Gram stain not reported.

Gelatin stab: Very slight surface growth after one month; the streak then shows a beaded line. No liquefaction.

Agar colonies: Surface colonies appear as a whitish growth in a depression, surrounded by a white ring. The colony is later surrounded by a ring of liquid agar. Deep colonies show a clear area and may be irregular, oval or angular.

Agar slant: A deep groove is cut along

the inoculation streak, whitish growth along sides. The gel is later much weakened.

Broth: Slightly turbid. No pellicle.

Acid from glucose, lactose and maltose. No acid from sucrose or glycerol.

Starch hydrolyzed.

Decomposes cellulose and agar. The presence of one per cent glucose prevents the liquefaction of agar.

Nitrites produced from nitrates.

Utilizes ammonium salts as a source of nitrogen.

Aerobic.

Temperature relations: Optimum, 25° C.; will grow at 16° but not at 34° C.

Habitat: Soil.

17. **Vibrio andoii** Aoi and Orikura, 1928. (Eine neue Agarzersetzende Bodenbakterienart, Aoi, Cent. f. Bakt., II Abt., *63*, 1924, 30; Aoi and Orikura, Cent. f. Bakt., II Abt., *74*, 1928, 331.)

an.do′i.i. M.L. gen.noun *andoii* of Andoi; named for Andoi, a Japanese scientist.

Curved rods with more or less tapering ends, c- or s-shaped, 0.5 to 0.8 by 1.5 to 2.5 microns. Motile by means of a single, polar flagellum. Gram-negative.

Gelatin: No growth.

Peptone agar media: No growth.

Peptone broth: No growth.

Litmus milk: No growth.

Potato: No growth.

Ammonium sulfate agar colonies: Punctiform, circular, concave, surrounded with a clear zone.

Ammonium sulfate agar slant: Growth grayish, becoming straw-yellow, sinking into the medium as the agar liquefies.

Glucose, fructose, galactose, mannose, xylose and "konjac" assimilated. Konjac, a Japanese food in tablets and strips, resembles gelatinized agar; it is prepared from the tuber of the konjac plant, *Amorphophallus rivieri.*

Starch hydrolyzed.

Cellulose and lignin not attacked.

Xylan decomposed.

Cellobiose decomposed.

Aerobic, facultative.

Temperature relations: Optimum, between 25° and 28° C. Minimum, 8° C. Maximum, 37° C.

Optimum pH, between 6.8 and 7.5.

Distinctive characters: When grown symbiotically with a second, unnamed species found in rotted manure, the latter species is able to hydrolyze cellulose in straw, probably because the first species (*Vibrio andoii*) decomposes the xylan that protects the cellulose from the action of the second species.

Source: Isolated from rotted stable manure.

Habitat: Presumably decomposing organic matter.

18. **Vibrio beijerinckii** Stanier, 1941. (Tyrosine vibrio of the sea, Beijerinck, Proc. Sect. Sci., Kon. Akad. Vetenschappen, Amsterdam, *13*, 1911, 1072; Stanier, Jour. Bact., *42*, 1941, 539.)

beij.er.inck′i.i. M.L. gen.noun *beijerinckii* of Beijerinck; named for Prof. M. W. Beijerinck, the Dutch biologist who first discovered this species.

Small, curved rods, 0.4 to 1.0 by 2.0 to 6.0 microns, usually single, sometimes occurring in short chains; in older cultures, occur mostly as straight rods. Actively motile by means of polar flagella. Encapsulated. Gram-negative.

Sea-water peptone agar colonies: Round, smooth, glistening, mucoid, entire. White to gray in color. After 24 hrs, 3 to 4 mm in diameter. The agar softens and clears for a distance of 3 to 5 mm from the edge of the colony, the outer edge of the gelase field being sharply defined. The colonies eventually grow to as much as 10 mm in diameter with a gelase margin of 2 to 3 cm.

Sea-water nitrate agar: Growth is slower than with peptone, but pigment production is much more marked. After 48 hours, colonies are 1 mm in diameter with a dark brown to black center and a colorless margin. Pigmented granules may be seen lying among the cells.

Sea-water peptone agar slant: Abundant growth after 24 hours, spreading, slightly raised, smooth, glistening, mucoid, dirty-white to dark gray in color. Agar digestion is evidenced only by a general softening of the slant. After several days, a pale brown, diffusible pigment is produced by some strains.

Sea-water nutrient gelatin slant: Good, filiform, gray growth after 24 hours, with considerable liquefaction. Slant completely liquefied after one week.

Sea-water nutrient gelatin stab: Fair, filiform growth after 24 hours, best at surface. Napiform liquefaction, complete after 7 to 10 days.

Sea-water peptone broth: Heavily turbid after 24 hours. Gray pellicle and flocculent; gray sediment. Later a light brown, soluble pigment is formed.

Indole not produced.

Hydrogen sulfide not produced.

Very slight or no acid from glucose, galactose, maltose, lactose and cellobiose. Arabinose, xylose and sucrose not fermented. Agar is extensively softened but not liquefied. Cellulose, chitin and alginic acid not attacked.

Starch is rapidly hydrolyzed.

Nitrites produced from nitrates.

Ammonia and nitrates utilized as sole sources of nitrogen.

Urease-negative.

Catalase-positive.

Aerobic.

Optimum temperature, 23° C.; grows between 5° and 30° C.

Salt range: 0.25 to 6.0 per cent. Optimum, between 2.0 and 4.0 per cent.

Source: Found in sea-water and, in the winter months, in the plankton; also found in fresh water and in sewage. Isolated both in Holland and in California. Along the coast of California it appears to be the most common species of marine agar-digester.

Habitat: Widely distributed in sea water and also in fresh water.

19. **Vibrio fuscus** Stanier, 1941. (Jour. Bact., *42*, 1941, 540.)

fus'cus. L. adj. *fuscus* dark or tawny.

Small, slightly curved rods, 0.7 by 1.5 to 5.0 microns, usually occurring singly, sometimes in short chains. Very actively motile by means of a single, polar flagellum. Not encapsulated. Gram-negative.

Sea-water peptone agar colonies: 1 mm in diameter after 48 hours; round, smooth, glistening, translucent, entire, pale yellow and slightly sunken in the agar. Colonies several mm in diameter after 7 days, be-

coming bright yellow, then pale brown. They are sharply sunken into the agar and are surrounded by a narrow, sharply defined gelase field. Liquefaction does not occur except on heavily seeded plates.

Sea-water peptone agar slant: Fair growth after 48 hours, filiform, smooth, glistening, translucent, pale yellow, slightly sunken in the agar. Later a pale yellow, diffusible pigment may be produced, and the streak tends to become light brown in color. On old slants the agar is slightly liquefied.

Sea-water nutrient gelatin slant: Filiform, smooth, pale yellow growth after 48 hours with slight liquefaction; liquefaction almost complete after 7 days.

Sea-water gelatin stab: Filiform growth after 48 hours with slight liquefaction; colorless; growth best at surface. Later the liquefaction becomes stratiform and almost complete.

Sea-water peptone broth: Good growth after 48 hours; turbid with a granular sediment and yellow pellicle.

Indole not produced.

Hydrogen sulfide not produced.

Glucose, galactose, sucrose, maltose, lactose, xylose and cellobiose attacked. Arabinose not utilized. Cellulose is attacked to a slight extent, and agar is softened and sometimes liquefied. Chitin and alginic acid are not attacked.

Starch not hydrolyzed.

Nitrites produced from nitrates.

Urease-negative.

Catalase-positive.

Aerobic.

Optimum temperature, between 20° and 25° C. Grows between 5° and 30° C.

Salt range, 1.0 to 5.0 per cent. Optimum, between 2.0 and 4.0 per cent.

Source: Found only once in a marine cellulose-enrichment culture in California.

Habitat: Presumably salt water.

20. **Vibrio granii** (Lundestad, 1928) Stanier, 1941. (*Bacterium granii* Lundestad, Cent. f. Bakt., II Abt., *75*, 1928, 330; Stanier, Jour. Bact., *42*, 1941, 538.)

gra'ni.i. M.L. gen.noun *granii* of Gran; named for Prof. H. H. Gran, who first detected agar-liquefying bacteria.

Rods, 0.6 to 0.8 by 1.4 to 2.4 microns, with

rounded ends, occurring singly, in pairs, and at times in short chains. Motile. Polar flagellate (Stanier, *loc. cit.*). Gram-negative.

Fish-gelatin colonies: Punctiform, black, glistening.

Fish-gelatin stab: Slow, crateriform liquefaction.

Sea-weed agar colonies: Circular, flat, opaque, glistening, white, slimy, entire. Agar is dissolved.

Fish-agar slant: Flat, white, elevated, glistening, undulate growth. Liquefaction.

Broth: Turbid with grayish white, slimy sediment.

Indole not produced.

No action on sugars.

Starch usually hydrolyzed.

Nitrites not produced from nitrates.

Aerobic, facultative.

Optimum temperature, between 20° and 25° C. Minimum, between 0° and 5° C. Maximum, between 30° and 32° C.

Source: Isolated from sea-water of the Norwegian Coast.

Habitat: Presumably found in sea water and on sea weeds.

21. **Vibrio neocistes** Gray and Thornton, 1928. (Cent. f. Bakt., II Abt., *73*, 1928, 92.)

ne.o.cis′tes. Gr. adj. *neus* new; Gr. noun *ciste* box; M.L. fem.gen.n. *neocistes* of Newark, a city.

Curved rods 0.5 to 1.0 by 1.0 to 4.0 microns. Motile by means of one to three polar flagella. Gram stain not recorded.

Gelatin colonies: Liquefied.

Gelatin stab: Liquefied. Medium reddened.

Agar colonies: Circular or amoeboid, buff to brownish, convex, smooth, glistening, entire.

Agar slant: Filiform, fluorescent, raised, smooth, glistening, undulate.

Broth: Turbid.

Acid from glucose.

Starch not hydrolyzed.

Nitrites not produced from nitrates.

Attacks naphthalene.

Aerobic, facultative.

Optimum temperature, between 30° and 35° C.

Habitat: Soil.

22. **Vibrio cyclosites** Gray and Thornton, 1928. (Cent. f. Bakt., II Abt., *73*, 1928, 92.)

cyc.lo.si′tes. Gr. noun *cyclus* a ring: Gr. v. *sīteō* to eat; M.L. adj. *cyclosites* feeding on rings, *i.e.*, on ring compounds.

Curved rods 0.5 to 1.0 by 1.5 to 4.0 microns. Motile by means of a single, polar flagellum. Gram-negative.

Gelatin colonies: Circular, buff to brown, flat, smooth, glistening, entire.

Gelatin stab: No liquefaction.

Agar colonies: Circular to irregular, pale buff (later greenish), smooth, entire.

Agar stab: Filiform, greenish buff, raised, smooth, undulate.

Broth: Turbid.

Indole not reported.

Acid from glucose.

Starch not hydrolyzed.

Nitrites not produced from nitrates.

Attacks phenol and *m*-cresol.

Aerobic, facultative.

Optimum temperature, between 30° and 35° C.

Habitat: Soil.

23. **Vibrio oxaliticus** Bhat and Barker, 1948. (Jour. Bact., *55*, 1948, 359.)

ox.a.li′ti.cus. Gr. noun *oxalis* sorrel, a sour plant; Gr. adj. *lyticus* dissolving; M.L. adj. *oxaliticus* intended to mean decomposing oxalate.

Curved rods 0.4 by 1.3 microns. Actively motile by means of a single, polar flagellum. Not encapsulated. Gram-negative.

Nutrient agar colonies: Small, moist, raised, entire; no chromogenesis. Pin-point in size in 48 hours, growing slowly until they reach a diameter of 1.5 mm in 6 days.

Nutrient broth: Moderate growth after 24 hours, appearing at first as a thin film while a slight, general turbidity develops in another 24 to 48 hours.

Calcium oxalate agar: Growth rapid and colonies small; medium becomes alkaline.

Oxalate broth: Becomes turbid following the formation of a slight surface film.

Oxalates and pyruvates support growth within 3 to 4 days when added to a mineral medium as the sole carbon source; formates support growth only when the incubation period is extended. The following do not support growth under any of the above conditions when added to the mineral medium: butyrates, citrates, lactates, malates, malonates, succinates, tartrates or glucose.

Indole not produced.

Hydrogen sulfide not produced.

Nitrites not produced from nitrates.

Aerobic.

Source: Five strains were isolated from Boston, Mass., and Berkeley, California, soils by inoculation of soil into a medium containing potassium oxalate and other minerals in distilled water. All soil samples tested showed the presence of this species. Ayers, Rupp and Johnson (U. S. Dept. Agr. Bull. No. 782, 1919, 38 pp.) and den Dooren de Jong (Dissertation, Delft, 1926, Table XVIII) tested over 125 strains of bacteria without finding any that decomposed oxalate. Bassilik (Jahrb. wiss. Bot., *53*, 1913, 255) found only three strains out of 90 tested which decomposed oxalate, two slowly; the third was the species described by him (*Vibrio extorquens*).

Habitat: Widely distributed in soil.

24. **Vibrio extorquens** (Bassalik, 1913) Bhat and Barker, 1948. (*Bacillus extorquens* Bassalik, Jahrb. f. wiss. Bot., *53*, 1913, 255; Bhat and Barker, Jour. Bact., *55*, 1948, 367; *Pseudomonas extorquens* Janota, Med. Doswiadczalna i Mikrobiol., *2*, 1950, 131; see Biol. Abstracts, *25*, 1951, Abs. no. 34148.)

ex.tor'quens. L. part.adj. *extorquens* twisting out.

Slightly curved rods, 1.5 by 3.0 microns. Motile by means of a single, polar flagellum. Gram-negative.

Gelatin media: Poor growth. Colonies small (less than 1 mm in diameter in 7 days), round, entire, butyrous. Surface colonies dirty yellow to yellowish red, eventually becoming a beautiful red color. No liquefaction.

Oxalate and similar mineral media: Growth rapid and abundant.

Peptone-agar colonies: Growth slower than on gelatin.

Liquid oxalate media. Grows rapidly as a rose-colored film on the bottom and walls of the flask, leaving the liquid clear.

Potato: Slow growth with darkening of potato.

Litmus milk: Not coagulated. Reaction becomes alkaline but growth is poor.

Aerobic, facultative.

Optimum temperature, between 25° and 30° C. Poor growth at 37° C.

Optimum pH: Prefers media with an alkaline reaction.

Distinctive characters: In old cultures in liquid calcium oxalate media and especially in media made with plant materials containing oxalate crystals, the cells become encrusted with a surface deposit. This appears to be calcium carbonate and is easily dissolved with dilute acid, especially dilute HCl.

Source: Originally isolated by adding the excreta of earthworms that had ingested plant materials containing oxalate crystals to a liquid medium containing ammonium oxalate. Pure cultures were isolated with difficulty by using a silica gel medium containing ammonium oxalate. Later these organisms were found to be generally present in forest and garden soils in Switzerland.

Habitat: Presumably widely distributed in soil.

25. **Vibrio cuneatus** Gray and Thornton, 1928. (Cent. f. Bakt., II Abt., *73*, 1928, 92.)

cu.ne.a'tus. L. part.adj. *cuneatus* wedge-shaped.

Curved rods, 1.0 by 1.0 to 3.0 microns, the cells tapering at one extremity. Motile by means of one to five polar flagella. Gram-negative.

Gelatin colonies: Liquefied.

Gelatin stab: Liquefied.

Agar colonies: Circular to amoeboid, white to buff, flat to convex, smooth, translucent, border entire.

Agar slant: Filiform, whitish, smooth, glistening.

Indole production not recorded.

No acid from carbohydrate media.

Starch not hydrolyzed.

Nitrites not produced from nitrates.

Attacks naphthalene.

Aerobic, facultative.

Optimum temperature, between 30° and 35° C.

Source: One strain was isolated from soil from Rothamsted, England.

Habitat: Soil.

26. **Vibrio percolans** Mudd and Warren, 1923. (Jour. Bact., *8*, 1923, 447.)

per'co.lans. L. v. *percolo* to filter through; L. part.adj. *percolans* filtering through.

Curved rods, 0.3 to 0.4 by 1.5 to 1.8 microns, occurring singly or in short chains. Pleomorphic. Actively motile by means of 1 to 3 polar flagella. Gram-negative.

Gelatin stab: No liquefaction.

Agar colonies: Circular, slightly convex, amorphous, entire.

Agar slant: Bluish white, glistening streak.

Broth: Turbid. Pellicle, sediment.

Litmus milk: Unchanged.

Potato: White, slimy streak.

Coagulated blood serum not liquefied.

Indole not produced.

No action on carbohydrates.

Starch not hydrolyzed.

Nitrites not produced from nitrates.

Passes through bacterial filters (Berkefeld V candles).

Aerobic, facultative.

Optimum temperature, 30° C.

Non-pathogenic.

Relationships to other species: Except for polar flagellation, this species has characters much like those of *Alcaligenes faecalis* Castellani and Chalmers. The two species are frequently confused. For example Lehmann and Neumann renamed *Alcaligenes faecalis* as *Vibrio alcaligenes* in their Bakt. Diag., 7 Aufl., *2*, 1927, 548, in the mistaken idea that the former organism is polar flagellate. Leifson and Hugh (personal communication, 1954), who recognize the species *Vibrio alcaligenes*, report that *Vibrio alcaligenes* produces nitrites from nitrates and that it does not hydrolyze urea (with possible rare exceptions). They report also that *Vibrio alcaligenes* occurs more frequently in the intestine than does *Alcaligenes faecalis* Petruschky.

Source: Isolated from a hay infusion.

Habitat: Water.

27. **Vibrio adaptatus** ZoBell and Upham, 1944. (Bull. Scripps Inst. of Oceanography, Univ. Calif., *5*, 1944, 258.)

a.dap.ta′tus. L. part.adj. *adaptatus* fitted, adapted.

Curved rods, 0.4 to 0.5 by 1.6 to 2.3 microns, only slightly curved, occurring singly and sometimes in pairs. Motile by means of a single, polar flagellum. Gram-negative.

Note: All differential media except the fresh-water broth, litmus milk and potato were prepared with sea water.

Gelatin colonies: Pin-point, yellow.

Gelatin stab: No liquefaction. Yellow, filiform growth along stab.

Agar colonies: Punctiform, yellow, opaque, pulvinate, smooth.

Agar slant: Luxuriant, filiform, shiny growth with waxy yellow pigment.

Sea-water broth: Moderate turbidity; thick, yellow pellicle; slight, flocculent sediment.

Fresh-water broth: Moderate growth.

Litmus milk: No visible change.

Potato: No visible growth.

Indole not produced.

Hydrogen sulfide not produced.

Glucose, sucrose, maltose, lactose, xylose, glycerol, mannitol and salicin not fermented.

Starch not hydrolyzed.

Non-lipolytic.

Nitrites not produced from nitrates.

Ammonia produced from peptone but not from urea.

Casein not digested.

Aerobic, facultative (poor anaerobic growth).

Optimum temperature, between 20° and 25° C.

Source: Isolated from sea water and from marine sediments.

Habitat: Common; probably widely distributed.

28. **Vibrio piscium** David, 1927. (Cent. f. Bakt., I Abt., Orig., *102*, 1927, 46.)

pis′ci.um. L. noun *piscis* a fish; L. gen.pl. *piscium* of fishes.

Curved rods 0.3 to 0.5 by 2.0 microns. Motile by means of a single, polar flagellum. Gram-negative.

Gelatin colonies: Circular, granular, opaque.

Gelatin stab: Napiform liquefaction.

Agar colonies: Yellowish, circular, smooth, entire, iridescent.

Agar slant: Light yellow, transparent streak.

Broth: Slightly turbid; thin pellicle.

Litmus milk: Soft coagulum. Peptonized, alkaline.

Potato: Brownish red streak.

Indole produced.

Hydrogen sulfide produced.

No action in sugar media.

Nitrites not produced from nitrates.

Pathogenic for frogs.

Aerobic, facultative.

Optimum temperature, between 18° and 20° C.

Habitat: Causes epidemic infection in fish.

29. **Vibrio hyphalus** ZoBell and Upham, 1944. (Bull. Scripps Inst. of Oceanography, Univ. Calif., *5*, 1944, 277.)

hy.pha'lus. Gr. adj. *hyphalus* under the sea, submarine.

Curved rods, 0.6 by 1.6 to 4.0 microns, with rounded ends, occurring singly. Motile by means of one or occasionally two polar flagella. Granular staining. Gram-negative.

Note: All differential media except the fresh-water broth, litmus milk and potato were prepared with sea water.

Gelatin colonies: Circular or irregular with liquefaction; yellowish gray.

Gelatin stab: Napiform liquefaction. Filiform growth along line of stab.

Agar colonies: 2 to 3 mm in diameter, circular, undulate, convex, radial folds, smooth.

Agar slant: Abundant, echinulate, glistening, gummy growth with pale pink pigment.

Sea-water broth: Scant pellicle; moderate turbidity; moderate, flocculent sediment.

Fresh-water broth: No visible growth.

Litmus milk: No visible change.

Potato: No visible growth.

Indole not produced.

Hydrogen sulfide is produced.

No acid or gas from glucose, sucrose, lactose, glycerol, xylose, mannitol or salicin.

Starch not hydrolyzed.

Non-lipolytic.

Nitrites produced from nitrates.

Ammonia produced from peptone but not from urea.

Casein is digested.

Aerobic, facultative.

Optimum temperature, between 20° and 25° C.

Source: Isolated from marine bottom deposits.

Habitat: Probably widely distributed.

30. **Vibrio fetus** Smith and Taylor, 1919. (*Spirillum* causing abortion in sheep, MacFadyean and Stockman, Rept. Dept. Comm. Ministry Agric. on Epizootic Abortion, London, 1909, 156; also see MacFadyean and Stockman, *ibid.*, 1913, 111; *Spirillum* associated with infectious abortion, Smith, Jour. Exp. Med., *28*, 1918, 701; Smith and Taylor, *ibid.*, *30*, 1919, 299.)

fe'tus. L. noun *fetus* a fetus; L. mas.gen.n. *fetus* of a fetus.

Description taken primarily from Plastridge, Williams, Easterbrooks, Walker and Beccia (Storrs Agr. Exp. Sta., Bull. 281, 1951, 11) and from Rhoades (Bact. Proc., 53rd Gen. Meeting, Soc. Amer. Bact., San Francisco, 1953, 34).

Curved rods that are minute, comma- and S-shaped forms on initial isolation. On transfer, very long, filamentous forms may appear. 0.2 to 0.5 by 1.5 to 5.0 microns. Motile, the comma forms possessing a single, polar flagellum, and the S forms usually possessing a single flagellum at each pole. Prolonged incubation and transfer to dry slants or semisolid media produces coccoid forms with one or more flagella. Occasionally encapsulated. Granules present in older cultures. Gram-negative.

Gelatin: No or poor growth on ordinary gelatin; with the addition of proper nutriments, good to excellent growth may occur in 3 to 5 days. No liquefaction.

Agar plates: No growth. Reich, Morse and Wilson (Amer. Jour. Vet. Res., *17*, 1956, 140), however, report growth when cultures are incubated in an atmosphere of either helium or nitrogen.

Agar slant: No surface growth by freshly isolated strains; laboratory strains produce a scant, grayish white, glistening surface growth. Good growth is obtained when cultures are incubated in an atmosphere of helium or nitrogen (Reich et al., *loc. cit.*).

Sub-surface agar colonies: Small, yellow, opaque.

Blood agar plates (in 10 per cent CO_2 atmosphere): Growth.

Thiol agar (prepared by adding 35.0 gm of granular agar and 0.05 gm of glutathione to 1.0 liter of thiol medium (supplied in dehydrated form by Difco Laboratories) and adjusting the pH to 8.9): Moderate growth. Colonies vary from small (1 mm in diameter), transparent and convex to translucent or opaque, light tan colonies up to 3 mm in diameter. Masses of growth are translucent and light gray or light tan.

Broth: A viscid ring pellicle may appear; faint clouding of the medium occurs; a filmy, stringy deposit may settle out.

Litmus milk: No growth.

Potato: No growth.

Indole not produced.

Hydrogen sulfide not produced.

Nitrites produced from nitrates (Bryner and Frank, Amer. Jour. Vet. Res., *16*, 1955, 76).

Blood serum slant: Feeble growth. No liquefaction.

No gas from carbohydrates. No change or slightly acid from glucose, lactose and sucrose. No acid from the following carbohydrates when each was added to a medium of beef infusion with peptone, agar and Andrade's indicator: glucose, fructose, galactose, arabinose, raffinose, trehalose, sucrose, maltose, lactose, dextrin, inulin, salicin, dulcitol, mannitol and sorbitol.

Temperature relations: Optimum, 37° C. Minimum, 15° C. Maximum, 40.5° C. Withstands 55° C. for 5 minutes.

Strains isolated from cases of abortion are catalase-positive (Bryner and Frank, *loc. cit.*).

Salt tolerance: Tolerates 1.5 to 2.0 per cent NaCl in a semisolid medium.

Bile tolerance: Most strains grow in a semisolid medium containing 10 per cent fresh ox bile; all strains grow in 5 per cent ox bile media (Schneider and Morse, Cornell Vet., *45*, 1955, 84).

Aerobic to microaerophilic.

Pathogenicity: Infection with *Vibrio fetus* (vibriosis) causes abortion in cattle and sheep. Pathogenic for guinea pigs, hamsters and embryonated chicken eggs (see Webster and Thorp, Amer. Jour. Vet. Res.,

14, 1953, 118; Ristic and Morse, *ibid.*, 399; and Ristic, Morse, Wipf and McNutt, *ibid.*, *15*, 1954, 309). Non-pathogenic to rabbits, rats and mice when injected intraperitoneally.

Source: Twenty-two strains were isolated from the placentas or fetuses of cows having abortion.

Habitat: Causes abortion in cattle and sheep.

31. **Vibrio coli** Doyle, 1948. (Comma-shaped microorganisms, Whiting, Doyle and Spray, Purdue Univ. Agr. Exp. Sta. Bull. 257, 1921, 12; Vibrio of swine dysentery, Doyle, Amer. Jour. Vet. Res., *5*, 1944, 3; Doyle, *ibid.*, *9*, 1948, 50.)

co'li. Gr. noun *colum* or *colon* the large intestine, colon; M.L. gen.noun *coli* of the colon.

Description taken from Doyle (*loc. cit.*) and Hauduroy et al. (Dict. d. Bact. Path., 2nd ed., 1953, 649).

Curved rods, comma- and sometimes spiral-shaped, 0.2 to 0.5 by 1.5 to 5.0 microns. Motile by means of a single, polar flagellum. Gram-negative.

Agar colonies: Transparent and colorless. Good growth only when the medium contains 10 per cent of defibrinated blood and when the atmosphere contains 15 per cent CO_2 ; abundant growth in the moisture of condensation.

Gelatin: Not liquefied.

Litmus milk: No growth; not coagulated.

Indole not produced.

Glucose, sucrose, lactose, maltose and mannitol not utilized.

Nitrites not produced from nitrates.

Coagulated blood serum not hemolyzed.

Pathogenicity: Injection causes no disease in calves, rabbits, rats, mice, guinea pigs or chickens. Injection causes dysentery in swine.

Source: Isolated from the mucosa of the colon of a swine which had died of dysentery.

Habitat: Causes dysentery in swine.

32. **Vibrio jejuni** Jones et al., 1931. (Jones, Orcutt and Little, Jour. Exp. Med., *53*, 1931, 853.)

je.ju′ni. L. adj. *jejunus* insignificant, meagre; M.L. noun *jejunum* the jejunum.

Pleomorphic, occurring in three different forms in the same culture: the first forms are short, slightly convoluted and actively motile with either a single polar flagellum or a single flagellum at each pole; the second are less active and have two or more complete coils; the remaining forms are extremely long and rarely motile. In older cultures clumps occur, and these usually degenerate into fragments and granules. Gram-negative.

Blood agar: Within 4 or 5 days the condensation fluid becomes slightly turbid; delicate lines then appear at the border of the agar. After several transfers these lines become well defined, and a delicate film spreads over the nether portion of the slant.

Gelatin: Not liquefied.

Coagulated blood serum not liquefied.

Carbohydrates not utilized.

Aerobic.

Optimum pH, 7.6. No growth in either slightly acid or definitely alkaline media.

Temperature relations: Optimum, 37.5° C. (Merchant, Vet. Bact. and Virology, 4th ed., 1950, 343). Killed in 5 minutes at 55° C.

Pathogenicity: Non-pathogenic to laboratory animals under the usual conditions. Some strains produce multiple necrotic foci of the liver when injected intraperitoneally into white mice. Febrile reactions are produced in rabbits when injected intravenously with certain strains. The enteritis produced experimentally in calves is less severe than that occurring spontaneously.

Source: Isolated from the small intestine of calves suffering from diarrhoea.

Habitat: Causes diarrhoea in cows and calves where it is found in the small intestine and feces.

33. **Vibrio niger** (Rist, 1898) Prévot, 1948. (*Spirillum nigrum* Rist, Thèse méd., Paris, 1898; also see Cent. f. Bakt., I Abt., *30*, 1901, 299; Prévot, Man. d. Classif. Bact. Anaér., 2nd ed., 1948, 124.)

ni′ger. L. adj. *niger* black.

Description taken from Rist (*op. cit.*, 1901, 299) and Hauduroy et al. (Dict. d. Bact. Path., 2nd ed., 1953, 658).

Long, slender, comma- or S-shaped cells rounded at the ends; 1.0 to 2.0 by 3.0 microns. Motile. Possess a black granule which swells the cell and which may be terminal. Gram-negative.

Glucose agar colonies: Lenticular, dark black, opaque, 2 to 3 mm in diameter.

Deep agar colonies: Lenticular, black, cloudy; gas is produced.

Deep blood serum agar colonies: Small, thin, delicate, non-hemolytic.

Brain medium: Blackened; hydrogen sulfide, ethanol and butyric and lactic acids are produced.

Gelatin colonies: Black, opaque; putrid odor. No liquefaction.

Glucose broth: Dark gray turbidity; putrid odor; gas and hydrogen sulfide are produced.

Peptone broth: Poor growth.

Milk: Coagulated slowly then digested.

Coagulated ascitic fluid: Not liquefied.

Indole not produced.

Hydrogen sulfide produced.

Neutral red reduced.

Obligate anaerobe.

Temperature relations: Growth range, 21° to 37° C. Death occurs at 55° C. Can withstand freezing.

Pathogenicity: Fatal for guinea pigs in two weeks; macroscopic lesions not demonstrable.

Source: Isolated from purulent otitis, mastoiditis and pulmonary gangrene; also isolated from cases of meningitis and appendicitis.

Habitat: Found rather frequently in man under pathological conditions.

34. **Vibrio sputorum** Prévot, 1940. (An anaerobic vibrio from bronchitis, Tunnicliff, Jour. Inf. Dis., *15*, 1914, 350; A small anaerobic vibrio from Vincent's angina, Smith, *ibid.*, *46*, 1930, 307; Prévot, Man. de Classif. des Bact. Anaér., Paris, 1940, 85.)

spu.to′rum. L. noun *sputum* spit, sputum; L. gen.pl. noun *sputorum* of sputa.

Description taken from Prévot (*loc. cit.*) and from Macdonald (Motile, Non-sporulating, Anaerobic Rods of the Oral Cavity, Toronto, 1953, 53).

Straight or slightly curved rods, 0.5 to

0.8 by 2.0 to 8.0 microns, occurring singly, in pairs or in short chains. Active, darting motility by means of 1 to 3 polar flagella. Gram-negative.

Grows only in media to which body fluids (blood, ascites, etc.) have been added or in other enriched media.

Ascitic fluid broth: Almost imperceptible turbidity.

Thioglycollate broth: Light, floccular turbidity.

Blood agar colonies: After 5 days, smooth, convex, grayish yellow, dull and translucent with a finely fimbriate margin. Less than 0.5 mm in diameter. Frequently surrounded by a narrow zone of green.

Coagulated blood serum: Cloth-like growth. No odor.

Nitrites produced from nitrates by some strains.

Indole not produced.

Hydrogen sulfide produced.

Carbohydrates not utilized.

Optimum pH, 7.2. Feeble growth between pH 6.0 and 9.7.

Serology: Cross-reacting, somatic antigens have been demonstrated.

Anaerobic.

Optimum temperature, 37° C. Growth feeble at 27° and 45° C. No growth at 20° C.

Source: Isolated by Prévot from a case of bronchitis.

Habitat: Found in the human oral cavity and in fusospirochetal diseases of the mouth.

Genus II. Desulfovibrio *Kluyver and van Niel, 1936.** *

(Kluyver and van Niel, Zent. f. Bakt., II Abt., *94*, 1936, 369; *Sporovibrio* Starkey, Arch. f. Mikrobiol., *9*, 1938, 300.)

De.sul.fo.vib′ri.o. L. pref. *de* from; L. *sulfur* sulfur; L. v. *vibro* to vibrate; M.L. mas.n. *Vibrio* that which vibrates, a generic name; M.L. mas.n. *Desulfovibrio* a vibrio that reduces sulfur compounds.

Slightly curved rods of variable length, usually occurring singly but sometimes in short chains which have the appearance of spirilla. Swollen pleomorphic forms are common. Actively motile by means of a single polar flagellum. Strict anaerobes which reduce sulfates to hydrogen sulfide. Found in sea water, marine mud, fresh water and soil.

The type species is *Desulfovibrio desulfuricans* (Beijerinck) Kluyver and van Niel.

1.ᶜ **Desulfovibrio desulfuricans** (Beijerin k, 1895) Kluyver and van Niel, 1936. (*Bacterium hydrosulfureum ponticum* Zelinsky, Proc. Russ. Phys. and Chem. Soc., *25*, 1893, 298; *Spirillum desulfuricans* Beijerinck, Cent. f. Bakt., II Abt., *1*, 1895, 1; Kluyver and van Niel, Zent. f. Bakt., II Abt., *94*, 1936, 369; *Sporovibrio desulfuricans* Starkey, Koninkl. Nederland. Akad. v. Wetenschappen, Proc., *41*, 1938, 426; also in Arch. f. Mikrobiol., *9*, 1938, 268.)

de.sul.fur′i.cans. L. pref. *de* from; L. noun *sulfur* sulfur; M.L. part.adj. *desulfuricans* reducing sulfur compounds.

Slightly curved rods, 0.5 to 1.0 by 1 to 5 microns, usually occurring singly but sometimes in pairs and short chains which cause them to look like spirilla. Swollen pleomor-

phic forms are common. Older cells appear black due to precipitated ferric sulfide. Actively motile, possessing a polar flagellum. Stains readily with carbol fuchsin. Gram-negative.

Gelatin: No liquefaction.

Grows best in fresh-water media. Fails to develop in sea water upon initial isolation.

Produces opalescent turbidity in absence of oxygen in mineral media enriched with sulfate and peptone.

Media containing iron salts and sulfur compounds blackened. Bacteria found associated with precipitated ferrous sulfide.

Peptone-glucose agar colonies (in absence of air): Small, circular, slightly raised, dull, entire, soft in consistency.

Peptone, asparagine, glycine, alanine,

---

* Prepared by Dr. Claude E. ZoBell, Scripps Institution of Oceanography, La Jolla, California, January, 1943; revised January, 1953.

aspartic acid, ethanol, propanol, butanol, glycerol, glucose, lactate, succinate and malate known to be utilized as hydrogen donors. Some varieties oxidize H_2 .

Produces up to 3100 mg H_2S per liter.

Nitrites not produced from nitrates.

Reduces sulfate to hydrogen sulfide; also reduces sulfites, thiosulfates and hyposulfites.

Temperature relations: Optimum, between 25° and 30° C. Maximum, between 35° and 40° C.

Chemical tolerance: Optimum pH, between 6 and 7.5. Limits for growth, between pH 5 and 9.

Cytochrome is produced.

Anaerobic.

Habitat: Soil, sewage and water.

2. Desulfovibrio aestuarii (van Delden, 1904) ZoBell, 1948. (*Microspira aestuarii* van Delden, Cent. f. Bakt., II Abt., *11*, 1904, 81; ZoBell, in Manual, 6th ed., 1948, 208.)

aes.tu.a′ri.i. L. noun *aestuarium* an estuary, inlet; L. gen.noun *aestuarii* of an estuary.

Morphologically indistinguishable from *Desulfovibrio desulfuricans* described above, although it has a greater tendency to pleomorphism and is slightly larger. Motile, possessing a polar flagellum. Gram-negative.

Gelatin: No liquefaction.

Grows preferentially in media prepared with sea water or 3 per cent mineral salt solution enriched with sulfate and peptone. According to Baars (Over Sulfaatreductie door Bakterien, Diss. Delft, 1930, 164 pp.) the marine species can be acclimatized to tolerate hypotonic salt solutions, but Rittenberg (Studies on Marine Sulfate-Reducing Bacteria, Thesis, Univ. of Calif., 1941, 115 pp.) was unable to confirm this observation. Likewise Rittenberg was unable to acclimatize *D. aestuarii* to tolerate temperatures exceeding 45° C. or to produce endospores.

Produces faint turbidity in absence of oxygen in sea water enriched with sulfate and peptone. Organisms most abundant in sediment.

Agar colonies: Small, circular, slightly raised, darker centers, entire, soft consistency.

Peptone, asparagine, glycine, alanine, glucose, fructose, ethanol, butanol, glycerol, acetate, lactate and malate known to be utilized in presence of sulfate. Some strains utilize molecular hydrogen as the sole source of energy.

Reduces sulfate to hydrogen sulfide. Also reduces sulfites, thiosulfates and hyposulfites.

Produces up to 950 mg of hydrogen sulfide per liter.

Nitrites not produced from nitrates.

Temperature relations: Optimum, between 25° and 30° C. Maximum, between 35° and 40° C.

Chemical tolerance: Optimum pH, between 6 and 8. Limits for growth, between pH 5.5 and 8.5.

Anaerobic.

Habitat: Sea water, marine mud, brine and oil wells.

3. Desulfovibrio rubentschikii (Baars, 1930) ZoBell, 1948. (*Vibrio rübentschickii* (sic) Baars, Over Sulfaatreductie door Bakterien, Diss. Delft, 1930, 89; ZoBell, in Manual, 6th ed., 1948, 208.)

ru.ben.tschi′ki.i. M.L. gen.noun *rubentschikii* of Rubentschik; named for Dr. L. Rubentschik.

Slightly curved rods, 0.5 to 1.0 by 1 to 5 microns, usually occurring singly, sometimes in pairs and short chains. Actively motile, possessing a polar flagellum. Gram-negative. Morphologically indistinguishable from *Desulfovibrio desulfuricans*.

Reduces sulfate to hydrogen sulfide; also reduces sulfites, thiosulfates and hyposulfites.

Culturally and physiologically like *D. desulfuricans* except that *D. rubentschikii* utilizes propionic, butyric, valeric, palmitic and stearic acids and galactose, sucrose, lactose and maltose.

Anaerobic.

Habitat: Soil and ditch water.

Genus III. **Methanobacterium** *Kluyver and van Niel, 1936.**

(Zent. f. Bakt., II Abt., *94*, 1936, 399.)

Me.tha.no.bac.te'ri.um. Gr. noun *methy* wine; M.L. noun *methanum* methane; Gr. neut.n. *bacterium* a small rod; M.L. noun *Methanobacterium* the methane (-producing) rodlet.

Straight or slightly curved rods, sometimes united in bundles or long chains. Reported to be non-motile. Anaerobic. Chemo-heterotrophic or chemo-autotrophic, oxidizing various organic or inorganic compounds and reducing carbon dioxide to methane. Gram-negative.

The anaerobic genus *Methanobacterium* was proposed by Kluyver and van Niel in 1936 with an indication that they regarded Söhngen's methane bacterium as the type species of the genus. Later, Barker (1936) found organisms that he regarded as identical with those previously isolated by Söhngen, and he proposed the name *Methanobacterium söhngenii* for this species. While the organisms belonging to this genus are reported to be non-motile, the curved form of their cells and their physiology places them near the species placed in *Desulfovibrio*.

The type species is *Methanobacterium soehngenii* Barker.

1. **Methanobacterium soehngenii** Barker, 1936. (Methane bacterium, Söhngen, Dissertation, Delft, 1906; Barker, Arch. f. Mikrobiol., *7*, 1936, 433.)

soehn.ge'ni.i. M.L. gen.noun *soehngenii* of Söhngen; named for Prof. N. L. Söhngen, the bacteriologist who first studied this organism.

Rods straight to slightly curved, moderately long. Non-motile. Gram-negative.

In liquid cultures, cells are characteristically joined into long chains which often lie parallel to one another so as to form bundles.

Acetate and n-butyrate but not propionate are fermented with the production of methane and carbon dioxide.

Ethyl and n-butyl alcohols not fermented. Obligate anaerobe.

Source: Enrichment cultures containing acetate or butyrate as the only organic compound. Four strains were isolated from acetate enrichment cultures. The cultures were highly purified but not strictly pure.

Habitat: Canal mud, sewage. Probably occurs widely in fresh-water sediments where anaerobic conditions prevail.

Genus IV. **Cellvibrio** *Winogradsky, 1929.†*

(Ann. Inst. Pasteur, *43*, 1929, 577.)

Cell.vib'ri.o. L. noun *cella* a room, cell; L. v. *vibro* to vibrate; M.L. mas.n. *Vibrio* that which vibrates, a generic name; M.L. mas.n. *Cellvibrio* cell vibrio, but here the *cell* is an abbreviation of cellulose, hence, cellulose vibrio.

Long slender rods, slightly curved, with rounded ends, showing deeply staining granules which appear to be concerned in reproduction. Monotrichous. Most species produce a yellow or brown pigment with cellulose. Oxidize cellulose, forming oxycellulose. Growth on ordinary culture media is feeble. Found in soil.

The type species is *Cellvibrio ochraceus* Winogradsky.

Key to the species of genus **Cellvibrio.**

I. No growth on glucose or starch agar.
   A. Ochre-yellow pigment produced on filter paper.
                              1. *Cellvibrio ochraceus.*

---

* Revised by Prof. Robert S. Breed, Cornell University, Geneva, New York, May, 1955.

† Revised by Prof. Robert S. Breed, Cornell University, Geneva, New York, with the assistance of Prof. Onorato Verona, University of Pisa, Pisa, Italy, September, 1953.

II. Growth on glucose and starch agar.
    A. Poor growth on starch agar.
        1. Cream-colored pigment which becomes brown with age is produced on filter paper.
                2. *Cellvibrio flavescens.*
    B. Abundant growth on starch agar.
        1. Scant growth on glucose agar.
            a. Intense yellow pigment produced on filter paper.
                3. *Cellvibrio fulvus.*
        2. Abundant growth on glucose agar.
            a. No pigment produced on filter paper.
                4. *Cellvibrio vulgaris.*

1. **Cellvibrio ochraceus** Winogradsky, 1929. (Ann. Inst. Pasteur, *43*, 1929, 549, 601.) och.ra′ce.us. Gr. noun *ochra* ochre; M.L. adj. *ochraceus* like ochre, rust-colored.

Plump, curved rods with rounded ends, 2.0 to 4.0 microns long, rarely occurring as spirals. Chromatic granule frequently found in center. Motile by means of a single flagellum. Gram-negative.

Produces diffuse, light ochre-colored, mucilaginous colonies on cellulose silica gel medium.

No action or growth on plain agar. No growth on peptone, glucose, starch or tragacanth gum agar.

Grows well on hydrocellulose agar without producing clearings.

Cellulose is oxidized to acid oxycellulose without the production of reducing substances or volatile by-products; a soluble, non-reducing product may be formed.

Filter paper streaks: Entire paper colored ochre-yellow in 48 hrs.

Aerobic, facultative.

Optimum temperature, 20° C.

Distinctive character: Rapid, ochre-colored growth.

Habitat: Soil. Disintegrates vegetable fibers.

2. **Cellvibrio flavescens** Winogradsky, 1929. (Ann. Inst. Pasteur, *43*, 1929, 608.) fla.ves′cens. L. v. *flavesco* to become golden yellow; L. part.adj. *flavescens* becoming yellow.

Plump, curved rods, flexuous, with rounded ends, 0.5 by 2.5 to 5.0 microns. Show metachromatic granules. Motile by means of a single flagellum. Gram-negative.

Produces diffuse, cream-colored growth becoming brownish; mucilaginous colonies on cellulose silica gel medium.

Good growth on peptone agar. Colonies 1 mm in 4 days. Grows poorly on glucose, starch and gum agars.

Filter paper streaks: Almost as rapid in growth as *Cellvibrio ochraceus* and colors entire paper in 2 to 3 days.

Aerobic, facultative.

Optimum temperature, 20° C.

Distinctive characters: Smaller, less curved rods which grow on a greater variety of media than *Cellvibrio ochraceus* but which do not attack cellulose as readily.

Source: Isolated from a pile of old damp sawdust. A variety of this organism has been isolated from sea water by Kadota (Bull. Japan. Soc. Sci. Fish., *16*, 1951, 63–70).

Habitat: Soil. Disintegrates vegetable fibers.

3. **Cellvibrio fulvus** Stapp and Bortels, 1934. (Culture Y, Dubos, Jour. Bact., *15*, 1928, 230; Stapp and Bortels, Zent. f. Bakt., II Abt., *90*, 1934, 42.) ful′vus. L. adj. *fulvus* deep yellow.

Slightly curved rods, 0.3 to 0.4 by 1.5 to 3.0 microns. Show involution forms. Motile by means of a single, polar flagellum. Gram-negative.

Cellulose is decomposed. Grows on filter paper with an intense egg-yellow color which in older cultures may deepen to rust brown.

Glucose agar: Very scant growth.

Sucrose agar: Very slight growth.

Maltose agar: Abundant yellow growth.

Lactose agar: Fairly abundant yellow growth.

Starch agar: Very abundant, bright yellow growth which later turns brown.

Nutrient broth: No growth.

Temperature relations: Optimum, between 25° and 30° C. Minimum, 5° C. Maximum, between 32° and 35° C. No growth at 37° C. Thermal death point, between 39° and 40° C.

Aerobic.

Source: Isolated from forest soil in Germany and from soil in the United States.

Habitat: Widely distributed in soils.

4. Cellvibrio vulgaris Stapp and Bortels, 1934. (Culture Co, Dubos, Jour. Bact., *15*, 1928, 230; Stapp and Bortels, Zent. f. Bakt., II Abt., *90*, 1934, 44.)

vul.ga′ris. L. adj. *vulgaris* common.

Curved rods, 0.3 by 2.9 to 4.0 microns. Show involution forms. Motile by means of a single polar flagellum. Gram-negative.

Cellulose is decomposed. Grows on filter paper without the formation of pigment.

Glucose agar: Abundant growth. No pigment.

Sucrose agar: Abundant, slightly yellow growth.

Maltose agar: Abundant, yellowish growth.

Lactose agar: Very heavy growth.

Starch agar: Very abundant, yellowish growth.

Nutrient broth: No growth.

Temperature relations: Optimum, between 25° and 30° C. Minimum, 5° C. Maximum, between 32° and 35° C. No growth at 37° C. Thermal death point, between 44° and 45° C.

Aerobic.

Source: Isolated from forest soil in Germany and from soils in the United States.

Habitat: Widely distributed in soils.

Genus V. **Cellfalcicula** *Winogradsky, 1929.***

(Ann. Inst. Pasteur, *43*, 1929, 616.)

Cell.fal.ci′cu.la. L. noun *cella* a room, cell; M.L. noun *cellulosum* cellulose; L. noun *falcicula* a sickle; M.L. fem.n. *Cellfalcicula* cell sickle, but here the *cell* is an abbreviation of cellulose, hence, cellulose sickle.

Short rods or spindles, not exceeding 2 microns in length, with pointed ends, containing metachromatic granules. Old cultures show coccoid forms. Monotrichous. Oxidize cellulose, forming oxycellulose. Growth on ordinary culture media is feeble. Soil bacteria.

The type species is *Cellfalcicula viridis* Winogradsky.

1. Cellfalcicula viridis Winogradsky, 1929. (Ann. Inst. Pasteur, *43*, 1929, 616.)

vi′ri.dis. L. adj. *viridis* green.

Plump, small spindles, 0.7 by 2.0 microns, with rounded ends. Motile by means of a single flagellum. Gram-negative.

Produces diffuse green, mucilaginous colonies on cellulose silica gel medium.

Filter paper streaks: Rapid spreading growth colored green in 3 days at 30° C.

Hydrocellulose agar: Growth rapid, green; minute, yellowish green, mucous colonies on streaking.

No growth on peptone, glucose, starch or gum agar.

Aerobic, facultative.

Optimum temperature, 20° C.

Habitat: Soil.

2. Cellfalcicula mucosa Winogradsky, 1929. (Ann. Inst. Pasteur, *43*, 1929, 621.)

mu.co′sa. L. adj. *mucosus* slimy.

Plump, curved spindles, with slightly pointed ends. Motile by means of a single polar flagellum. Contain a single chromatic granule. Gram-negative.

Produces diffuse, cream-colored, mucilaginous colonies on cellulose silica gel medium.

Hydrocellulose agar: Abundant grayish growth.

No growth on peptone, glucose, starch or gum agar.

Aerobic, facultative.

Optimum temperature, 20° C.

Habitat: Soil.

* Revised by Prof. Robert S. Breed, Cornell University, Geneva, New York, September, 1937.

3. **Cellfalcicula fusca** Winogradsky, 1929. (Ann. Inst. Pasteur, *43*, 1929, 622.) fus'ca. L. adj. *fuscus* dark, tawny.

Plump, curved spindles, 0.5 by 1.2 to 2.5 microns, with slightly pointed ends and a central chromatic granule. Motile by means of a single, polar flagellum. Gram-negative. Produces diffuse, brownish, slightly marbled or veined colonies on cellulose silica gel medium.

Filter paper streak: Paper becomes a partially transparent, dry, non-mucilaginous pellicle adherent to gel.

Aerobic, facultative.

Optimum temperature, 20° C.

Source: Isolated from a pile of old, damp sawdust.

Habitat: Probably rotting wood.

Genus VI. **Microcyclus** *Ørskov, 1928.**

(Cent. f. Bakt., I Abt., Orig., *107*, 1928, 180; also see Riassunti d. Communicazioni, VI Cong. Internaz. d. Microbiol., Roma, *1*, 1953, 24.)

Mic.ro.cyc'lus. Gr. adj. *micrus* small, little; Gr. *cyclus* round, circle; M.L. mas.n. *Microcyclus* small circle.

Small, slightly curved, non-motile rods which form a closed ring during growth. These rings grow into bodies which subdivide again into rod-shaped elements as at the beginning. Encapsulated. Attack few sugars and then only slowly. From fresh-water ponds and from soil.

The type species is *Microcyclus aquaticus* Ørskov.

1. **Microcyclus aquaticus** Ørskov, 1928. (Cent. f. Bakt., I Abt., Orig., *107*, 1928, 180; also see Riassunti d. Communicazioni, VI Cong. Internaz. d. Microbiol., Roma, *1*, 1953, 24.)

a.qua'ti.cus. L. adj. *aquaticus* living in water.

Very small, slightly curved rods about 1 micron in length. During growth, the rods form closed rings 2 to 3 microns in diameter. The next stage is a body consisting of horseshoe-shaped halves that are fastened together without visible divisional lines. These halves further subdivide into separate rods; the rods then form rings and start the cycle of growth all over again. Form and capsule are seen most distinctly with direct agar microscopy and direct India ink agar microscopy. Encapsulated. Non-motile. Gram-negative.

Gelatin: No liquefaction in one month.

Agar colonies: Round, smooth edges, butyrous. This species is not fastidious in its growth requirements, although colonies are small. It grows well on tap-water agar plus 0.5 per cent peptone.

No acid from glucose, sucrose, lactose, maltose, adonitol, dulcitol, sorbitol, inositol, rhamnose and salicin. After six weeks, slight acid in arabinose and xylose.

Indole not produced.

Non-hemolytic.

Grows at temperatures between 5° and 30° C. No growth at 37° C.

Source: Originally found in the waters of a woodland lake. Later isolated from fresh-water ponds and occasionally from soil. Sturges (Absts. of Bact., *7*, 1923, 11) briefly reports the presence of organisms with the same unusual morphology in ham-curing brines.

Habitat: Presumably widely distributed in fresh water and in soil.

Genus VII. **Spirillum** *Ehrenberg, 1832.†*

(Physik. Abhandl. k. Akad. Wissensch. Berlin, 1832, 38.)

Spi.ril'lum. Gr. noun *spira* a spiral; M.L. dim.neut.n. *Spirillum* a small spiral, generic name.

---

* Prepared by Dr. J. Ørskov, Director, Statens Seruminstitut, Copenhagen, Denmark, November, 1953.

† Revised by Prof. Robert S. Breed, Cornell University, Geneva, New York, April, 1954, based on a Monograph by Giesberger, Inaug. Diss., Delft, Nov. 30, 1936.

Cells form either long screws or portions of a turn. Volutin granules are usually present. Usually motile by means of a tuft of polar flagella (5 to 20) which may occur at one or both ends of the cells. Aerobic, growing well on ordinary culture media except for one saprophyte and the pathogenic species; these have not yet been cultivated. Usually found in fresh and salt water containing organic matter.

The type species is *Spirillum undula* (Müller) Ehrenberg.

Key to the species of genus Spirillum.

I. One micron or less in diameter.
   A. Volutin granules present.
      1. Slow to rapid liquefaction of gelatin.
         a. Grayish to brown growth on potato.
                                 1. *Spirillum undula.*
        aa. Light yellowish orange growth on potato.
                                 2. *Spirillum serpens.*
      2. No liquefaction of gelatin. Of small size (0.5 micron in diameter).
         a. Colonies on agar white becoming brownish black and slightly wrinkled.
                                 3. *Spirillum itersonii.*
        aa. Colonies on agar white and smooth.
                                 4. *Spirillum tenue.*
   B. No volutin granules observed.
      1. Single flagellum. From sea water.
                                 5. *Spirillum virginianum.*
      2. Tuft of flagella. From blood of rats and mice.
                                 6. *Spirillum minus.*
II. Over 1 micron in diameter.
   A. Grow poorly or not at all on peptone agar media.
      1. Grows poorly on peptone agar and potato.
                                 7. *Spirillum kutscheri.*
      2. Has not been cultivated on artificial media. Very evident volutin granules.
                               8. *Spirillum volutans.*
   B. Grows abundantly on peptone media. Cells may be deformed with fat droplets.
                               9. *Spirillum lipoferum.*

1. Spirillum undula (Müller, 1786) Ehrenberg, 1832. (*Vibrio undula* Müller, Animalcula infusoria et marina, 1786; Ehrenberg, Physik. Abhandlungen d. k. Berl. Akad., 1832, 38.)

un′du.la. L. noun *unda* a wave; M.L. dim.fem.n. *undula* a small wave.

Stout threads, 0.9 micron in diameter, with one-half to three turns. The wave lengths are 6 microns. Width of spiral, 3.0 microns. Tufts of three to nine flagella at each pole. Volutin granules present. Gram-negative.

Gelatin colonies: The surface colonies are circular, granular, greenish yellow, entire.

Gelatin stab: Thick, white, rugose surface growth. Very slow liquefaction.

Agar colonies: Grayish white, smooth.

Broth: Turbid.

Potato: Grayish brown growth.

Indole not produced.

Catalase-positive.

Nitrites not produced from nitrates.

Aerobic, facultative.

Optimum temperature, 25° C.

Cohn (Beitrage z. Biol. d. Pflanzen, *1*, Heft 2, 1875, 132) reports that he could not distinguish this organism from *Vibrio prolifer* Ehrenberg.

Habitat: Putrid and stagnant water.

2. Spirillum serpens (Müller, 1786) Winter, 1884. (*Vibrio serpens* Müller, Animalcula infusoria et marina, 1786, 43;

Winter, in Rabenhorst's Kryptogamen-Flora, *1*, Die Pilze, 1884, 63.)

ser'pens. L. v. *serpo* to crawl or creep; L. part. adj. *serpens* creeping.

Long, curved rods with two to three wave-like undulations, 0.8 to 1.0 micron in diameter; wave length, 8 to 9 microns. Width of spiral, 1.5 to 1.8 microns. Volutin granules in cytoplasm. Motile, possessing tufts of flagella at both poles. Gram-negative.

Gelatin colonies: Yellowish to brownish, granular, entire.

Gelatin stab: Yellowish surface growth. Slow liquefaction.

Agar colonies: Heavy cream-colored growth.

Agar slant: Grayish, with yellowish center, granular, entire.

Broth: Turbid.

Litmus milk: Unchanged.

Potato: Clear orange-yellow growth.

Indole not produced.

Catalase-positive.

Nitrites not produced from nitrates.

Aerobic, facultative.

Optimum temperature, 35° C.

Habitat: Stagnant water.

3. **Spirillum itersonii** Giesberger, 1936. (Inaug. Diss., Utrecht, 1936, 46 and 57.)

i.ter.so'ni.i. M.L. gen.noun *itersonii* of Iterson; named for G. van Iterson, a Dutch bacteriologist.

The smallest of the spirilla isolated from water. First observed by van Iterson (Proc. Kon. Akad. v. Wetensch. Amsterdam, *5*, 1902, 685).

Small spirals, 0.5 micron in diameter. Wave length, 3 to 3.5 microns. Spiral width, 1 to 1.5 microns. Motile by means of bipolar tufts of flagella. Gram-negative.

Gelatin stab: No liquefaction.

Grows readily on peptone agar. White colonies becoming brownish black and slightly wrinkled.

Potato: Brownish orange growth.

Acid from glucose, fructose, ethyl alcohol, n-propyl alcohol, n-butyl alcohol and glycerol. Utilizes acetic, propionic, n-butyric, tartaric, fumaric, lactic, citric and succinic acids.

Grows well in peptone broth. Also utilizes ammonium compounds.

Catalase-positive.

Anaerobic growth in the presence of nitrates when organic or ammonia nitrogen is also available.

Optimum temperature, 30° C.

Source: Isolated from water.

Habitat: Water.

4. **Spirillum tenue** Ehrenberg, 1838. (Die Infusionsthierchen als vollkommende Organismen. Leipzig, 1838; also see Bonhoff, Arch. f. Hyg., *26*, 1896, 162.)

te'nu.e. L. adj. *tenuis* thin.

Slender spirals 0.7 micron in diameter. Wave lengths, 4.5 to 5.0 microns; width of wave, 1.5 to 1.8 microns. Actively motile in peptone water by means of tufts of flagella at each pole. Volutin granules present. Gram-negative.

Gelatin stab: No liquefaction.

Agar colonies: White, smooth.

Peptone agar slant: Heavy growth.

Potato: Light brown growth.

Acid from glucose and fructose. Slight acid from several other sugars and glycerols. Utilizes salts of acetic, propionic, n-butyric, tartaric, lactic, citric, malic and succinic acids.

Ammonia compounds are used as a source of nitrogen.

Catalase-positive.

Optimum temperature, 30° C.

Source: Isolated from putrefying vegetable matter.

Habitat: Putrefying materials.

5. **Spirillum virginianum** Dimitroff, 1926. (Jour. Bact., *12*, 1926, 19.)

vir.gi.ni.a'num. M.L. adj. *virginianus* Virginian; named for the State of Virginia.

Spirals consisting of ½ to 3 complete turns in young cultures, older cultures showing 7 turns; 0.6 to 0.9 by 3 to 11 microns. No volutin granules observed (Giesberger, Inaug. Diss., Delft, 1936, 60). Motile by means of a single, polar flagellum on one or both ends. Gram-negative.

Gelatin colonies: Entire, convex, circular, moist, colorless.

Gelatin stab: Growth along entire stab. No liquefaction (Dimitroff, *op. cit.*, *12*, 1926, 31). Active liquefaction (Giesberger, *op. cit.*, 1936, 65).

Agar colonies: Dew drop, convex, entire, moist, colorless.

Agar slant: Dew drop, isolated colonies.

Broth: Cloudy, no flocculation.

Uschinsky's protein-free medium: Abundant growth.

Litmus milk: No growth.

Loeffler's blood serum: Convex, isolated dew drop colonies. No liquefaction.

Potato: No growth.

Methyl red negative; acetylmethylcarbinol not produced.

Indole not produced.

Hydrogen sulfide not produced.

No acid or gas from carbohydrates.

Lactates and citrates utilized (Giesberger, *loc. cit.*).

Nitrites not produced from nitrates.

Aerobic, facultative.

Optimum temperature, 35° C.

Source: Isolated from mud on an oyster shell.

Habitat: Probably the muddy bottom of brackish water.

6. **Spirillum minus** Carter, 1888. (Carter, Sci. Mem. Med. Officers Army India, *3*, 1888, 45; *Spirochaeta muris* Wenyon, Jour. Hyg., *6*, 1906, 580.)

mi'nus. L. comp.adj. *minus* less, smaller.

Description taken from Adachi (Jour. Exp. Med., *33*, 1921, 647) and Giesberger (Inaug. Diss., Delft, 1936, 67).

Short thick cells, 0.5 by 3.0 microns, having 2 or 3 windings which are thick, regular and spiral. Actively motile by means of bipolar tufts of flagella. Gram-negative.

Has not been cultivated on artificial media.

Aerobic, facultative.

Pathogenic for man, monkeys, rats, mice and guinea pigs.

This species is regarded by some as a spirochaete. Because of its habitat and wide distribution it has been described under many different names. It is possible that some of these names indicate varieties or even separate species. See Beeson (Jour.

Amer. Med. Assoc., *123*, 1943, 332) for important literature.

Source: Found in the blood of rats and mice.

Habitat: A cause of rat-bite fever. Widely distributed.

7. **Spirillum kutscheri** Migula, 1900. (*Spirillum undula majus* Kutscher, Cent. f. Bakt., I Abt., *18*, 1895, 614; Migula, Syst. d. Bakt., *2*, 1900, 1024.)

ku'tsche.ri. M.L. gen.noun *kutscheri* of Kutscher; named for K. H. Kutscher, the German bacteriologist who first isolated this organism.

Stout, spiral-shaped threads 1.5 microns in diameter. Wave lengths, 10.5 to 12.5 microns; width, 3.0 to 4.5 microns. The spiral form may be lost on continued cultivation. Volutin granules present. Motile by means of tufts of flagella at the poles. Gram-negative.

Gelatin plate: Surface colonies are transparent and round; deep colonies are dark brown.

Gelatin stab: Slow liquefaction.

Agar colonies grow poorly; granular. Deep colonies yellowish green to dark brown.

Agar slant: Delicate, transparent growth.

Potato: Limited growth.

Utilizes malic and succinic acids.

Grows well on peptone broth. Also utilizes ammonia compounds.

Catalase-positive.

Optimum temperature, between 22° and 27° C.

Source: Isolated from putrid materials and liquid manure.

Habitat: Putrefying liquids.

8. **Spirillum volutans** Ehrenberg, 1832. (Prototype, *Vibrio spirillum* Müller, Animalcula infusoria et marina, 1786; Ehrenberg, Physik. Abhandlungen d. k. Akad. Berlin, 1832, 38.)

vo'lu.tans. L. v. *voluto* to tumble about; L. part.adj. *volutans* tumbling about.

The largest of the spirilla; probably first seen by Müller.

Spiral-shaped cells 1.5 microns in diameter. Wave length, 13 to 14 microns;

width 4 to 5 microns. Slightly attenuated ends. Dark granules of volutin are present in the cytoplasm. Motile, possessing a tuft of ten to fifteen flagella at each pole. Gram-negative.

Migula (Syst. d. Bakt., *2*, 1900, 1025) reports that this species has not been cultivated on artificial media and that the cultures described by Kutscher (Ztschr. f. Hyg., *20*, 1895, 58) as *Spirillum volutans* are of a different species. Vahle (Cent. f. Bakt., II Abt., *25*, 1910, 237) later describes the cultural characters of an organism which he regards as identical with Kutscher's organism. Giesberger (Inaug. Diss., Delft, 1936, 65) saw what he felt was the true *Spirillum volutans* but could not cultivate it.

Optimum temperature, 35° C.

Habitat: Stagnant water.

9. **Spirillum lipoferum** Beijerinck, 1925. (*Azotobacter spirillum* Beijerinck, Kon. Akad. Wetensch. Amsterdam, *30*, 1923, 431, quoted from Giesberger, Inaug. Diss., Delft., 1936, 24; Beijerinck, Cent. f. Bakt., II Abt., *63*, 1925, 353.)

li.po'fe.rum. Gr. noun *lipus* fat; L. v. *fero* to carry; M.L. adj. *lipoferus* fat-bearing.

Curved cells with one-half to one spiral turn. Contain minute fat droplets which may deform the cells. Motile by means of a tuft of polar flagella. Gram-negative.

Calcium malate agar colonies: Circular, small, transparent, dry. The malate is oxidized to calcium carbonate. Cells contain fat droplets.

Peptone agar colonies: More abundant development. Cells lack fat droplets and are typically spirillum in form.

Glucose peptone broth: Cells actively motile with large fat droplets.

Fixes atmospheric nitrogen in partially pure cultures, i.e., free from *Azotobacter* and *Clostridium* (Beijerinck, *loc. cit.*). Schröder (Cent. f. Bakt., II Abt., *85*, 1932, 17) failed to find fixation of nitrogen when she used cultures derived from a single cell. Aerobic.

Optimum temperature, 22° C.

Beijerinck regards this as a transitional form between *Spirillum* and *Azotobacter*. Giesberger (*op. cit.*, 1936, 64) thinks it a *Vibrio*.

Habitat: Garden soil.

Genus VIII. **Paraspirillum** *Dobell, 1912.* *

(Arch. f. Protistenk., *24*, 1912, 97.)

Pa.ra.spi.ril'lum. Gr. pref. *para* beside; M.L. neut.n. *Spirillum* a genus of bacteria; M.L. neut.n. *Paraspirillum Spirillum*-like (organisms).

Cells spiral or S-shaped, tapering toward the ends, with a well marked thickening toward the middle of the body; resemble much elongated and spirally twisted spindles. Motile by means of a single, polar flagellum. Found in fresh water.

Dobell (*loc. cit.*) believes that this organism belongs to the *Spirillaceae* rather than to the *Spirochaetaceae*.

The type species is *Paraspirillum vejdovskii* Dobell.

1. **Paraspirillum vejdovskii** Dobell, 1912. (Arch. f. Protistenk., *24*, 1912, 97.)

vej.dov'ski.i. M.L. gen.noun *vejdovskii* of Vejdovský; named for Prof. F. Vejdovský.

Spiral or S-shaped rods, tapering toward the ends, 8 to 25 microns in length, averaging 15 microns. Width, in the middle, 1.5 to to 2.0 microns. A definite spherical to ellipsoidal nucleus is present. The cytoplasm immediately about the nucleus is hyaline

or very finely granular. Volutin granules are numerous between the hyaline area and the ends of the cell. Locomotion is screw-like, resembling that characteristic of species of *Spirillum*. The motion is reversible, and cells may swim in either direction. In motion the cell seems to be rigid, but it may increase or decrease the amount of bending. Sometimes the cell is much-curved, at other

---

* Prepared by Prof. R. E. Buchanan, Iowa State College, Ames, Iowa, July, 1952.

times it is almost straight. A single, polar flagellum is demonstrable; such a flagellum may occur at each end. Division of the cell is transverse and is preceded by a division of the nucleus.

This organism has not been cultivated.

Source: Encountered only once in a culture of *Oscillatoriae* in water from the River Granta near Cambridge, England.

Habitat: Fresh water.

Genus IX. **Selenomonas** von Prowazek, 1913.*

(Von Prowazek, Cent. f. Bakt., I Abt., Orig., *70*, 1913 (July), 36; *Selenomastix* Woodcock and Lapage, Quart. Jour. Micro. Sci., *59* (N.S.), 1913 (November), 433.)

Se.le.no.mo'nas. Gr. noun *selene* the moon; Gr. noun *monas* a unit, monad; M.L. fem.n. moon monad.

Cells kidney- to crescent-shaped with blunt ends. Motile by means of a tuft of flagella attached to the middle of the concave side. The flagella are thicker at the base than at the free end and are usually about one and a half times as long as the cell. Gram-negative. Anaerobic. Parasites found in the alimentary tracts of mammals, including man.

Three species are described, and it is possible that when comparative studies are made the three will be found to belong to but a single species. On the other hand it is equally possible that not only these three but also additional species will be recognized (Lessel and Breed, Bact. Rev., *18*, 1954, 167).

The type species is *Selenomonas palpitans* Simons.

Key to the species of genus **Selenomonas**.

I. Found in the coeca of guinea pigs.

      1. *Selenomonas palpitans.*

II. Found in the human mouth cavity.

      2. *Selenomonas sputigena.*

III. Found in the rumen juices of ruminants.

      3. *Selenomonas ruminantium.*

1. **Selenomonas palpitans** Simons, 1922. (Guinea pig selenomonad, da Cunha, Brasil Medico, *29*, 1915, 33; *Selenomonas palpitans* Simons (*nomen dubium*), Cent. f. Bakt., I Abt., Orig., *87*, 1921, 50; Simons, in Boskamp, *ibid.*, *88*, 1922, 58.)

pal'pi.tans. L. part.adj. *palpitans* trembling.

Description taken from Boskamp (*loc. cit.*).

Kidney- to crescent-shaped cells with blunt ends, 1.8 to 2.3 by 6.8 to 9.1 microns. Motile by means of a tuft of flagella on the concave side of the cell. The flagella are thicker at the base than at the free end and are usually about one to one and a half times as long as the cell. A highly refractive granule is found on the concave side at the base of the tuft of flagella; this granule stains with nuclear stains and appears to be

a true nucleus, dividing as the cell divides. Boskamp (*ibid.*, 65) was unable to determine whether this division was mitotic or amitotic. With Giemsa's stain the cytoplasm is blue whereas the chromatin material, the cell membrane and the flagella stain red. Gram-negative.

Anaerobic (?) as presumed by Boskamp (*ibid.*, 68–69) from the fact that these organisms, in feces, died quickly when exposed to air; they likewise did not grow aerobically on ordinary media.

Source: Found in the cecum of a guinea pig.

Habitat: Found in the ceca of guinea pigs. Not found in the buccal cavity, the stomach or the small intestine. Decrease rapidly in number in the upper large intestine and disappear entirely in the lower part.

---

* Prepared by Mr. Erwin F. Lessel, Jr., Cornell University, Geneva, New York, January, 1954.

2. **Selenomonas sputigena** (Flügge, 1886, *emend.* Mühlens, 1909) Dobell, 1932. (*Spirillum sputigenum* Flügge, Die Mikroorganismen, 2 Aufl., 1886, 387; Mühlens, Cent. f. Bakt., I Abt., Orig., *48*, 1909, 524; *Selenomonas sputigena* Boskamp (*nomen provisorium*), Cent. f. Bakt., I Abt., Orig., *88*, 1922, 70; Dobell, Antony van Leeuwenhoek and His "Little Animals". New York, 1932, 239, plate XXIV, and 245, footnote 2; *Vibrio sputigenus* Prévot, Man. de Classif. des Bact. Anaér., Paris, 1e ed., 1940, 85; not *Vibrio sputigenus* Bergey et al., Manual, 1st ed., 1923, 80.)

spu.ti'ge.na. L. noun *sputum* spit, sputum; L. v. *gigno* to produce; M.L. adj. *sputigenus* sputum-produced.

Description taken from Mühlens (*op. cit.*, 1909, 524). Also see Hoffmann and von Prowazek (Cent. f. Bakt., I Abt., Orig., *41*, 1906, 820), von Prowazek (*ibid.*, *70*, 1913, 36) and Macdonald (Thesis, Univ. of Toronto, 1953, 95 pp.).

Comma- and crescent-shaped cells, thicker and longer than the cholera vibrio, occasionally occurring in pairs in the form of an S. Motility is vibratory, rotating, whirling and boring in nature. Dobell (*op. cit.*, 1932, 245) feels that the type of motility depicted in Leeuwenhoek's drawing (*ibid.*, 239, plate XXIV, Fig. B, with motion shown in C to D) is so characteristic of *Spirillum sputigenum* that the organism labelled Fig. B by Leeuwenhoek is, in all probability, *Spirillum sputigenum* Miller. Hoffmann and von Prowazek (*op. cit.*, 1906, 820) describe this organism as a crescent-shaped rod with a thick flagellum that appears to be attached on the concave side. Mühlens (*op. cit.*, 1909, 525) reports 1 to 3 flagella, the majority of the organisms having a single thick flagellum (a tuft of flagella) on the concave side. Von Prowazek (*op. cit.*, 1913, 36) later shows excellent figures of these thick flagella treated with Giemsa's stain. These figures show that the thick flagellum is really a tuft of flagella which may separate like the bristles of a paint brush. Stains pale red with Giemsa's stain.

Horse-serum agar stab: Fine, hazy colonies develop in the low portions. Growth begins in 1 to 3 days as fine, cloudy colonies with somewhat thicker, yellowish centers and increases to a thick streak, opaque in the center and cloudy-transparent at the edges.

Kutscher's placenta agar: Good growth. Anaerobic growth in the lower two-thirds of stab and shake cultures. No visible gas produced.

Serum broth: No growth.

The following characters are from Macdonald (*op. cit.* 1953):

Blood agar: Growth occurred only when plates were reduced immediately after streaking. Colonies were smooth, convex, grayish yellow, and less than 0.5 mm in diameter.

Difco thioglycollate broth: Growth heavy and granular in 48 hrs. The best fluid medium in which to maintain cultures.

Difco thioglycollate agar shake cultures: Irregularly shaped, yellow colonies.

Litmus milk: Acid and coagulated.

Acid from glucose and sucrose. Slight acid from mannitol.

Indole not produced.

Hydrogen sulfide not produced.

Nitrites produced from nitrates.

Optimum temperature, 37°C. Growth range, from 20° to 45° C. The pH range for growth is 4.5 to 8.6 with the best growth between 5.5 and 8.6.

Not pathogenic for guinea pigs injected subcutaneously or intracardially, nor for mice injected intraperitoneally.

Distinctive characters: Early investigators described an organism of this type but were unable to culture it, *e.g.* Lewis (Lancet, Sept. 20, 1884, who regarded the organism he found as identical with the cholera vibrio) and Miller (The Microorganisms of the Human Mouth, Philadelphia, 1890, 75); Miller also gives an excellent discussion of the early work. Mühlens (*op. cit.*, 1909, 526) described a variety of this species with smaller cells.

While Macdonald describes this species as peritrichous, he reports (personal communication) that others have felt that his electron micrographs could be interpreted as showing a cluster of flagella attached at the middle of the concave side of the crescent-shaped cells, and that in dark field examination he observed, as had earlier workers, a single heavy flagellum attached at the middle of the concavity. The so-called nuclear body shows plainly in the electron micrographs.

Source: Isolated from the buccal cavity of man.

Habitat: Found in the buccal cavity.

3. **Selenomonas ruminantium** (Certes, 1889) Wenyon, 1926. (*Ancyromonas ruminantium* Certes, Bull. Soc. Zool., France, *14*, 1889, 70; *Selenomastix ruminantium* Woodcock and Lapage, Quart. Jour. Micro. Sci., *59* (N.S.), 1913–1914, 433; Wenyon, Protozoology. *1*, 1926, 311.)

ru.mi.nan'ti.um. L. part.adj. *ruminans, ruminantis* ruminating; M.L. neut.pl.n. *ruminantia* ruminants; M.L. pl.gen.noun *ruminantium* of ruminants.

Rigid, crescent-shaped cells which measure 2 to 3 by 9.5 to 11 microns. Woodcock and Lapage (*op. cit.*, 434) state that the cells are only slightly crescentic and never assume the S shape as reported by Certes (*op. cit.*, 439); furthermore, they report that the curve lies in but one plane. A tuft of flagella which attains a length of 8.0 to 9.5 microns springs from the center of the concavity. The protoplasm stains homogeneously except at the base of the flagella where a deeply staining mass is easily demonstrable. Reproduction is by binary fission transverse to the long axis of the cell and through the flagellar region. Each half of the flagella passes to one of the two pear-shaped daughter cells where it is attached near the blunt end; later the flagella undergo an apparent shift in position to the center of the concavity.

Probably anaerobic but does not grow on ordinary media either aerobically or anaerobically.

Woodcock and Lapage (*op. cit.*, 445 ff.) found ellipsoidal, non-motile organisms mixed abundantly with the motile crescents and felt that these might represent a stage in the life history of the crescents although they could not demonstrate this. Wenyon (*op. cit.*, 311) also thinks that a rounded flagellate organism may be a stage of the crescent-shaped organism, but he presents no proof to support this conclusion.

Source: Found by Certes (*op. cit.*, 70) by microscopical examination of rumen juice of cattle, sheep and deer. Later found by Woodcock and Lapage (*op. cit.*, 433) very abundantly in the rumen juice of goats.

Habitat: Found as a predominant organism on microscopical examination of rumen juices from herbivorous mammals.

Genus X. **Myconostoc** *Cohn, 1875.***

(Beiträge z. Biol. d. Pflanzen, *1*, Heft 3, 1875, 183.)

My.co.nos'toc. Gr. noun *myces* fungus; M.L. neut.n. *Nostoc* a genus of algae; M.L. neut.n. *Myconostoc* fungus nostoc.

Curved, colorless cells occurring singly or in curved or spiral chains. Embedded in small, spherical, gelatinous masses. Found in fresh- or sulfur-water containing decomposing organic matter.

The type species is *Myconostoc gregarium* Cohn.

1. **Myconostoc gregarium** Cohn, 1875. (Cohn, Beiträge z. Biol. d. Pflanzen, *1*, Heft 3, 1875, 183; *Spirosoma gregarium* Migula, Syst. d. Bakt., *2*, 1900, 960.)

gre.gar'i.um. L. adj. *gregarius* of or belonging to a flock or group.

Cells curved to comma-shaped, 1 by 5 to 10 microns, often joined together as spiral chains which may resemble horse-shoes or which may twist around each other to form coiled, non-septate, non-motile, colorless filaments. The filaments are usually enclosed in a spherical, solid, microscopic, gelatinous mass which measures 10 to 17 microns in diameter; these masses may clump together and form a cluster, usually on the surface of the water, which is visible to the naked eye. Excellent illustrations depicting the nature of this species are shown in Zopf (Die Spaltpilze, 3 Aufl., 1885, 23).

---

* Prepared by Mr. Erwin F. Lessel, Jr., Cornell University, Ithaca, New York, September, 1953.

When the gelatinous mass disintegrates, swarm cells are formed which are presumably polar flagellate. The individual cells are granular and stain rather poorly.

During reproduction, the filaments become somewhat elongated and expand the gelatinous mass to an ellipsoidal shape. As the gelatinous sphere undergoes transverse fission, there is a concomitant division of the filament, the daughter cells finally separating from each other. Lankester (Quart. Jour. Micros. Sci., *13*, (N.S.), 1873, 408) erroneously believed this gelatinous form to be a stage in the life cycle of a *Spirillum*, probably *Spirillum undula* Ehrenberg.

These organisms have not been cultivated on artificial media.

Source: Found in the surface scum of sulfur-water in a jar with decomposing algae, especially *Spirogyra sp.* (Cohn, *op. cit.*, 1875, 183). Also found by Migula (*op. cit.*, 1900, 960) in peat bogs between Weingarten and Karlsruhe. Hansgirg (Österr. Vot. Ztschr., *38*, 1888, 265) frequently found this organism among his algal cultures in Bohemia.

Habitat: Fresh-water ponds.

ORDER II. CHLAMYDOBACTERIALES BUCHANAN, 1917.*

(Buchanan, Jour. Bact., *2*, 1917, 162.)

Chla.my.do.bac.te.ri.a'les. M.L. fem.pl.n. *Chlamdobacteriaceae* type family of the order *Chlamydobacteriales*; *-ales* ending to denote an order; M.L. fem.pl.n. *Chlamydobacteriales* the *Chlamydobacteriaceae* order.

Colorless, alga-like bacteria which occur in trichomes. May or may not be ensheathed. They may be unbranched or may show false branching. False branching arises from a lateral displacement of the cells of the trichome within the sheath; this gives rise to a new trichome so that the sheath is branched while the trichomes are separate. The sheaths may be composed of an organic matrix impregnated with iron or manganese oxides, or they may be composed of an organic matrix free from these oxides. Gram-negative. Reproduction may be by flagellate swarm spores or by non-motile conidia. Endospores of the type found in *Bacillus* are never developed. Fresh-water and marine forms.

Key to the families of order **Chlamydobacteriales.**

I. Conidia, when formed, are motile by means of a sub-polar tuft of flagella.
   A. Possesses trichomes in which false branching may occur. Motile swarm cells may be formed.

Family I. *Chlamydobacteriaceae*. p. 262.

   B. Possesses ensheathed, unbranching trichomes which may be very long (0.5 cm). Found in fresh water.

Family II. *Peloplocaceae*, p. 270.

II. Non-motile conidia are produced.

Family III. *Crenotrichaceae*, p. 272.

FAMILY I. CHLAMYDOBACTERIACEAE MIGULA, 1894.

(Arb. bakt. Inst. Hochschule, Karlsruhe, *1*, 1894, 237.)

Chla.my.do.bac.te.ri.a'ce.ae. Gr. noun *chlamys, chlamydis* a cloak; Gr. neut.n. *bacterium* a small rod; *-aceae* ending to denote a family; M.L. fem.pl.n. *Chlamydobacteriaceae* the family of the sheathed bacteria.

Bacteria which occur in trichomes and which frequently show false branching. Sheaths, when present, may or may not be impregnated with ferric and/or manganese oxides. Cells divide transversely. Swarm cells, if developed, are usually motile by means of a tuft of flagella. Usually found in fresh water.

Key to the genera of family **Chlamydobacteriaceae.**

I. Trichomes surrounded by sheaths which are usually not impregnated with iron or manganese oxides and which do not dissolve in hydrochloric acid. Large forms, mostly sessile.

---

* Rearranged and revised by Prof. Robert S. Breed, Cornell University, Geneva, New York, November, 1953; further revision, with the introduction of an additional family and genera and species, by Prof. Dr. Herbert Beger, Institut für Wasser-, Boden- und Lufthygiene, Berlin-Dahlem, Germany, January, 1955.

Genus I. *Sphaerotilus*, p. 263.

II. Trichomes surrounded by sheaths impregnated with oxides of iron or manganese which dissolve in strong hydrochloric acid. Free-living or sessile.

A. Individual trichomes, each with a sheath.

Genus II. *Leptothrix*, p. 264.

B. Sheaths contain more than one trichome; the trichomes are sometimes in a fan-like arrangement.

Genus III. *Toxothrix*, p. 269.

Genus I. **Sphaerotilus** *Kützing, 1833.*

(Kützing, Linnaea, *8*, 1833, 385; *Cladothrix* Cohn, Beitr. z. Biol. d. Pflanz., *1*, Heft 3, 1875, 185.)

Sphae.ro′ti.lus. Gr. noun *sphaera* a sphere; Gr. noun *tilus* anything shredded, flock, down; M.L. mas.n. *Sphaerotilus* sphere down.

Attached or free-floating, colorless trichomes showing false branching, though this may be rare in some species. When examined under the electron microscope, the sheath shows a homogeneous structure. Sheath may become yellowish or brown with the deposition of iron oxide. The deposition of iron is dependent on environmental factors, not on the physiological ability to store iron. Trichomes consist of rod-shaped or ellipsoidal cells surrounded by a firm sheath. Multiplication occurs both by non-motile conidia and by motile swarm cells, the latter with a subpolar tuft of flagella. Gram-negative so far as known. Found in fresh water.

The systematic positions of the species placed in *Sphaerotilus*, *Leptothrix* and related genera are uncertain. Pringsheim (Phil. Trans. Roy. Soc. London, Series B, *233*, 1949, 605, and Biol. Reviews, *24*, 1949, 200) would combine some of the species now placed in *Leptothrix* with *Sphaerotilus natans* and broaden the definition of *Sphaerotilus* to include other species here placed in *Leptothrix* and *Clonothrix*. However, Beger and Bringmann (Zent. f. Bakt., II Abt., *107*, 1953, 318) indicate differences in the structures of the sheaths of *Sphaerotilus* and *Leptothrix* and give other reasons why it may be better to keep the earlier groupings as they have been.

The type species is *Sphaerotilus natans* Kützing.

1. **Sphaerotilus natans** Kützing, 1833. (Kützing, Linnaea, *8*, 1833, 385; not *Sphaerotilus natans* Sack, Cent. f. Bakt., II Abt., *65*, 1925, 116.)

na′tans. L. part.adj. *natans* swimming.

Colorless, slimy trichomes which attain a length of several millimeters. The trichomes are ensheathed, show false branching and are either free-floating or attached at one end by means of a small disc. The individual cells are cylindrical, 1 by 2 to 6 microns, and vacuolated (Lackey and Wattie, U. S. Pub. Health Ser., Pub. Health Repts., *55*, 1940, 975).

Multiplication occurs through the formation of conidia within the sheath of the vegetative cells, from which they swarm out at one end, swim about for a time, then attach themselves to objects and develop into delicate trichomes.

Gelatin rapidly liquefied, requires organic nitrogen, does not grow in the ordinary peptone solution, grows best with low concentrations of meat extract (Zikes, Cent. f. Bakt., II Abt., *43*, 1915, 529). See Stokes (Jour. Bact., *67*, 1954, 278) for a recent study of the cultural and physiological characteristics of this species.

Distinctive characters: This species thrives in great tassels on solid substrata covered by dirty running water. These tassels are composed of trichomes of bacterial cells held together by slimy, tubular sheaths. The latter may become softened and dissolved, releasing *Pseudomonas*-like swarm cells. The same organism grows in a quite different state in quiet waters with only a little organic matter, forming branched structures occurring in trichomes, the sheaths of which are not slimy. A third form is produced when ferrous compounds and very little organic substance are present. The sheaths become brittle and glass-like in appearance by deposition of ferric hydroxide in a hard colloidal form. Prings-heim (Endeavour, *11*, 1952, 209) states that under these conditions it is identical with *Leptothrix ochracea*, which looks ochre-like in bulk but never brown under the microscope.

Source: Originally found in polluted waters. May become a real nuisance in sewage purification plants of the activated sludge type (Lackey and Wattie, *op. cit.*, 1940, 975) and in streams polluted with sulfite liquor from pulp and paper mills (Lackey, Mimeographed Rept., U. S. Pub. Health Ser., 1941).

Habitat: Stagnant and running water, especially sewage-polluted streams. Widely distributed throughout the world in fresh water.

2. **Sphaerotilus dichotomus** (Cohn, 1875) Migula, 1900. (*Cladothrix dichotoma* Cohn, Beitr. z. Biol. d. Pflanz., *1*, Heft 3, 1875, 185; Migula, Syst. d. Bakt., *2*, 1900, 1033.)

di.cho'to.mus. Gr. adj. *dichotomus* divided, forked.

The identity of this species as distinct from *Sphaerotilus natans* has been questioned. In his text, Cohn reports the diameter of the trichomes to be 0.3 micron. This clearly is an error as his figures at 600✕ show the diameter of the trichomes to be greater than the diameter of *Bacillus anthracis* spores shown at the same magnification. Such spores are 1.3 to 1.5 microns in diameter.

Zikes (Cent. f. Bakt., II Abt., *43*, 1915, 529) gives the following differential characters: Cells smaller than those of *Sphaerotilus natans*, 1.5 to 2.5 microns; false branching constant; grows best in high concentrations of meat extract; will grow in ordinary peptone solutions; can utilize inorganic nitrogen; liquefies gelatin slowly.

Source: Isolated by Cohn from water containing *Myconostoc*.

Habitat: Comparatively unpolluted fresh water capable of sustaining algae.

3. **Sphaerotilus fluitans** (Migula, 1895) Schikora, 1899. (*Streptothrix fluitans* Migula, in Engler and Prantl, Die natürl. Pflanzen-fam., *1*, 1a, 1895, 38; Schikora, Ztschr. f. Fischerei, *7*, 1899, 1–28.)

flu'i.tans. L. part.adj. *fluitans* floating.

Very thin, attached trichomes as much as 1 cm in length. The trichomes are surrounded by a soft sheath from which almost spherical conidia issue, usually attaching themselves to the exterior of the sheath where they multiply.

Source: Found attached to pieces of wood and stems of plants in running water.

Habitat: Fresh water.

Genus II. **Leptothrix** *Kützing, 1843.*

(Kützing, Phycologia Generalis, 1843, 198; not *Leptotrichia* Trevisan, Reale Ist. Lombardo di Sci. e Lettere, Ser. 2, *12*, 1879, 138.)

Lep'to.thrix. Gr. adj. *leptus* fine, small; Gr. noun *thrix* hair; M.L. fem.n. *Leptothrix* fine hair.

Trichomes of cylindrical, colorless cells with a sheath at first thin and colorless, later thicker, yellow or brown, encrusted with iron or manganese oxide. The oxides may be dissolved by dilute acid, whereupon the inner cells show up well. If the sheath contains manganese oxide, it does not dissolve completely in weak acids. When examined under the electron microscope, the sheath shows an alveolar structure. Multiplication is by cell division with individual cells occasionally slipping out of the sheath as reproductive cells. These are sometimes motile with a tuft of flagella. False branching may occur. Gram-negative and not acid-fast so far as known. Usually found in fresh water.

The type species is *Leptothrix ochracea* Kützing.

Key to the species of genus **Leptothrix.**

I. Trichomes straight, not spirally twisted.
 A. Trichomes free-floating and unbranched. Sheath thin.

1. Trichomes 1 to 3 microns thick.
>>> 1. *Leptothrix ochracea.*
2. Trichomes 0.4 to 0.5 micron thick.
>>> 2. *Leptothrix thermalis.*
B. Trichomes attached.
>>> 1. Attachment is by means of a holdfast.
>>> a. Trichomes arise singly, each from its own holdfast.
>>> b. Sheath very thin, encrusted only at the base of the trichome.
>>>>> 3. *Leptothrix sideropous.*
>>> bb. Sheaths thick.
>>> c. Trichomes showing no or only a few false branches. Cells up to 1 micron thick.
>>>>> 4. *Leptothrix discophora.*
>>> cc. Trichomes always with numerous false branches. Cells 1.4 microns thick.
>>>>> 5. *Leptothrix major.*
>> aa. Numerous trichomes arising from a common holdfast.
>>> b. Sheaths not tapering to the tip. Trichomes form sessile, hemispherical clusters.
>>>>> 6. *Leptothrix lopholea.*
>>> bb. Sheaths tapering to the tip. Trichomes usually form free-living colonies in which the trichomes radiate like the spokes of a wheel.
>>>>> 7. *Leptothrix echinata.*
>> 2. Attached by gelatinous masses.
>>>>> 8. *Leptothrix epiphytica.*
II. Trichomes spirally twisted (except in a variety of *Leptothrix pseudovacuolata*).
>> A. Epiphytic, growing twisted around thread-like algae.
>>>>> 9. *Leptothrix volubilis.*
>> B Free-living in water or on the surface of mud.
>>> 1. Trichomes very thin; sheaths tapering slowly to the tip, ending in a sharp point.
>>> a. Cells 0.3 micron in diameter.
>>>>> 10. *Leptothrix skujae.*
>>> aa. Cells 0.9 micron in diameter.
>>>>> 11. *Leptothrix winogradskii.*
>>> 2. Trichomes thick, sometimes not twisted; sheaths rounded at the tip.
>>>>> 12. *Leptothrix pseudovacuolata.*

1. **Leptothrix ochracea** (Roth, 1797) Kützing, 1843. (*Conferva ochracea* Roth, Catal. bot. I, 1797, Table V, Fig. 2; also see Dillwyn, Syn. Conf., 1802, Table 62; Kützing, Phycologia generalis, 1843, 198.)

o.chra′ce.a. Gr. noun *ochra* yellow ochre; M.L. adj. *ochraceus* like ochre.

Description taken from Kützing (*loc. cit.*) and Cataldi (Estudio Fisiológico y Sistemático de Algunas Chlamydobacteriales. Thesis, University of Buenos Aires, 1939, 58 and 66).

Cells rod-like, colorless, 0.8 to 1.0 micron. Motile. Trichomes long, free-floating, never attached to a substrate, never branching, 1 micron in thickness. Young trichomes sur-rounded by a delicate sheath which later becomes yellow to brown in color. Sheath alveolar, completely dissolving in dilute hydrochloric acid. When the sheath becomes very thick, the trichomes slip out of the sheath and secrete a new one so that many empty sheaths are found. Presumably polar flagellate swarm cells have been observed. Not acid-fast. Gram-negative.

Gelatin: No liquefaction.

Iron citrate and ammonium agar colonies: Filamentous and spreading, with wavy edges.

Manganese acetate agar colonies: Filamentous, not very large.

Iron citrate and ammonium agar slant:

Growth very abundant, spreading over the entire surface; iridescent.

Peptone and manganese acetate broth: Abundant growth in the form of loose flakes.

Indole not produced.

Hydrogen sulfide not produced.

Acetylmethylcarbinol not produced.

Nitrites produced from nitrates.

Optimum temperature, 28° C.

Optimum pH, 8.0.

Aerobic, but growth favored by the presence of CO_2.

Habitat: Found in iron-bearing, fresh waters; widely distributed.

2. Leptothrix thermalis (Molisch, 1925) Dorff, 1934. (*Chlamydothrix thermalis* Molisch, Sc. Rept. Tohoku Imp. Univ., 4 ser. Biol., Sendae, Japan, *1*, 1923, 135 (or possibly *1*, 1925, 146); Dorff, Die Eisenorganismen, Pflanzenforschung, Heft 16, 1934, 38.)

ther.ma'lis. Gr. noun *thermē* heat; M.L. adj. *thermalis* pertaining to heat.

Unbranched trichomes, 0.4 to 0.5 micron thick, united in bundles. Surrounded by a sheath which may store iron and turn brown.

Source: From warm and hot spring waters in Japan.

Habitat: Found in warm and hot (37° to 74° C.) spring waters.

3. Leptothrix sideropous (Molisch, 1910) Cholodny, 1926. (*Chlamydothrix sideropous* Molisch, Die Eisenbakterien, 1910, 14; Cholodny, Die Eisenbakterien, Pflanzenforschung, Heft 4, 1926, 25.)

si.de'ro.pous. Gr. adj. *sideropus* or *sideropous* iron-footed.

Description taken from Molisch (*op. cit.*, 1910, 14) and Cataldi (Estudio Fisiológico y Sistemático de Algunas Chlamydobacteriales. Thesis, University of Buenos Aires, 1939, 62 and 66).

Cells rod-shaped, 0.5 to 0.8 micron. Motile. Trichomes short and unbranched. Sheath very thin and colorless, giving an iron reaction only at the base of the trichome. Attached by a broad holdfast which gives a marked iron reaction. Not acid-fast. Gram-negative.

Gelatin: No liquefaction.

Iron citrate and ammonium agar colonies: Very filamentous. Colonies and filaments encompassed by a spattering of rust-colored spots.

Manganese acetate agar colonies: Large and filamentous, the filaments being strongly colored.

Iron citrate and ammonium agar slant: Growth in the form of isolated colonies; strongly colored.

Manganese acetate agar slant: Abundant growth which adheres to the medium except in those places covered with water of condensation.

Peptone and manganese acetate broth: Firm pellicle with a metallic sheen.

Indole not produced.

Hydrogen sulfide not produced.

Acetylmethylcarbinol not produced.

Nitrites produced from nitrates.

Optimum temperature, between 25° and 28° C.

Optimum pH, 8.0.

Aerobic; growth not favored by the presence of CO_2.

Habitat: Found growing on the surfaces of objects submerged in water; widely distributed.

4. Leptothrix discophora (Schwers, 1912) Dorff, 1934. (*Megalothrix discophora* Schwers, Cent. f. Bakt., II Abt., *33*, 1912, 273; *Leptothrix crassa* Cholodny, Cent. f. Bakt., II Abt., *61*, 1924, 292; Dorff, Die Eisenorganismen, Pflanzenforschung, Heft 16, 1934, 31.)

dis.co'pho.ra. Gr. noun *discus* a disc; Gr. adj. *phorus* bearing; M.L. adj. *discophorus* disc-bearing.

Description taken from Schwers (*op. cit.*, 1912, 273) and Cataldi (Estudio Fisiológico y Sistemático de Algunas Chlamydobacteriales. Thesis, University of Buenos Aires, 1939, 60 and 66).

Cells 0.5 by 0.8 micron. Motile. Trichomes long, slender, articulated, composed of elements of varying length showing false branching (Cholodny, Cent. f. Bakt., II Abt., *61*, 1924, 297). Usually attached to a submerged substrate, but may be free-floating. A sheath, thick (10 to 15 microns) at the base, tapering toward the free tip and heavily impregnated with iron oxide, surrounds the trichomes. Reproduction by motile swarm cells liberated from the tip and also by the emergence of the trichome from the sheath, with subsequent breaking up into individual, non-motile cells. Not acid-fast. Gram-negative.

Gelatin not liquefied.

Iron citrate and ammonium agar colonies: More or less rounded, with oily inclusions, filamentous border.

Manganese acetate agar colonies: Filamentous growth, the filaments being rather large and showing false branching.

Iron citrate and ammonium agar slant: Growth only in the water of condensation, rarely on the slant.

Peptone and manganese acetate broth: Abundant growth in the form of loose flakes.

Indole not produced.

Hydrogen sulfide not produced.

Acetylmethylcarbinol not produced.

Nitrites produced from nitrates.

Optimum temperature, between 25° and 28° C.

Optimum pH, 8.5.

Aerobic; growth not favored by the presence of CO_2.

Habitat: Found in fresh water; widely distributed.

5. **Leptothrix major** Dorff, 1934. (Dorff Die Eisenorganismen, Pflanzenforschung, Heft 16, 1934, 35; also see Beger and Bringmann, Zent. f. Bakt., II Abt., *107*, 1953, 323.)

ma'jor. L. comp.adj. *major* larger.

Trichomes, up to 1 and more cm in length, attached by a holdfast, richly branched, forming tufts. Trichomes composed of rod-like cells, 1.4 by 5 to 10 microns, which contain small false vacuoles. Giant cells up to 75 microns in length. Two trichomes may be found in the same sheath. The sheath may be as much as 12 microns in thickness, tapering to the tip, storing manganese and iron. Resembles the sheath of *Leptothrix discophora* but is firmer in texture. Light to dark brown in color.

Source: From the Spree River near Berlin.

Habitat: Found in fresh-water streams.

6. **Leptothrix lopholea** Dorff, 1934. (Die Eisenorganismen, Pflanzenforschung, Heft 16, 1934, 33.)

lo.pho'le.a. Gr. noun *lophus* a crest; M.L. dim.adj. *lopholeus* somewhat crested or tufted.

Short, slender unbranched trichomes, uniform in diameter, attached to a substrate, 5 to 13 trichomes arising from a common holdfast. Trichomes 20 to 33 microns long, cells 0.5 by 1.0 to 1.3 microns.

Sheaths composed of iron oxide; dissolve completely in dilute hydrochloric acid.

Trichomes slip out of the sheath as in *Leptothrix ochracea*.

Habitat: Water.

7. **Leptothrix echinata** Beger, 1935. (Zent. f. Bakt., II Abt., *92*, 1935, 401.)

e.chi.na'ta. Gr. noun *echinus* the hedgehog; M.L. adj. *echinatus* like the hedgehog, bristly.

Similar to the preceding species but occurring in larger colonies, 20 to 50 trichomes arising from a common holdfast. Trichomes are shorter (9 to 10 microns).

Sheath is thicker at the base and tapers toward the free tip of the trichome, which is slightly spiral. The sheath contains an organic matrix visible after treatment in dilute hydrochloric acid.

Habitat: Found in water, especially in manganese-bearing waters.

8. **Leptothrix epiphytica** (Migula, 1895) Schoenichen and Kalberlah, 1900. (*Streptothrix epiphytica* Migula, in Engler and Prantl, Die natürl. Pflanzenfam., *1*, 1a, 1895, 36 and 38; *Chlamydothrix epiphytica* Migula, Syst. d. Bakt., *2*, 1900, 1033; Schoenichen and Kalberlah, Eyferth's Einfachste Lebensformen, 3rd ed., 1900, 46.)

e.pi.phy'ti.ca. Gr. prep. *epi'* upon; Gr. noun *phytum* plant; M.L. adj. *epiphyticus* epiphytic, growing on plants.

Chains of cells enclosed in short, colorless trichomes which are surrounded by thick, gelatinous masses; the gelatinous masses are attached to algae, but never in groups or clusters.

Habitat: Widely distributed in fresh water containing algae.

9. **Leptothrix volubilis** Cholodny, 1924. (*Lyngbya epiphytica* Hieronymus, in Kirchner, in Engler and Prantl, Die natürl. Pflanzenfam., *1*, 1a, 1898, 67; Cholodny, Zent. f. Bakt., II Abt., *61*, 1924, 292; *Chlamydothrix epiphytica* Naumann, Ber. d. deutsch. bot. Gesellsch., *46*, 1928, 141; not *Chlamydothrix epiphytica* Migula, Syst. d. Bakt., *2*, 1900, 1033; *Leptothrix epiphytica* Dorff, Die Eisenorganismen, Pflanzenforschung, Heft 16, 1934, 32; not *Leptothrix epiphytica* Schoenichen and Kalberlah, Eyferth's Einfachste Lebensformen, 3rd ed., 1900, 46.)

vo.lu′bi.lis. L. adj. *volubilis* twisting spirally around a support, twining.

Cells rod-shaped and colorless, measuring 1 by 2 microns. The cells are enclosed in long, cylindrical, unbranched trichomes which grow in a spiral fashion around threads of *Oedogonium, Tolypothrix*, etc. The bacterial trichomes are, in turn, surrounded by cylindrical, ochre-yellow sheaths, about 3 microns in diameter, which are encrusted with iron. The cells may leave the sheaths as in *Leptothrix ochracea*.

Habitat: Found in fresh water containing algae.

10. **Leptothrix skujae** Beger, 1953. (*Leptothrix tenuissima* Skuja, Symbolae Botanicae Upsaliensis, *9*, 1948, 33; not *Leptothrix tenuissima* Naegeli, in Kützing, Species Algarum, 1849, 265; Beger, in Beger and Bringmann, Zent. f. Bakt., II Abt., *107*, 1953, 331.)

sku′jae. M.L. gen.noun *skujae* of Skuja; named for H. Skuja, the Swedish algologist who first described this species.

Unattached trichomes, generally without false branching, spirally wound together, 0.3 to 0.4 micron in diameter. The surrounding sheath is as much as 18 microns in diameter and tapers toward the tip. Cells rod-shaped and colorless, with a few granules lying in chains.

Resembles *Leptothrix discophora* Dorff.

Source: From Store Halsjön, Prov. Uppland, Sweden. Found between other water plants and in the plankton.

Habitat: Found near the shore in lakes.

11. **Leptothrix winogradskii** Cataldi, 1939. (Estudio Fisiológico y Sistemático de Algunas Chlamydobacteriales. Thesis, University of Buenos Aires, 1939, 58.)

wi.no.grad′ski.i. M.L. gen.noun *winogradskii* of Winogradsky; named for S. Winogradsky, a Russian bacteriologist.

Cells 0.9 micron in diameter. Motile, presumably polar flagellate. Trichomes very long, never attached. Sheath 1.5 microns thick. Not acid-fast. Gram-negative.

Gelatin not liquefied.

Iron citrate and ammonium agar colonies: Very filamentous, terminate in spirals, lusterless red.

Manganese acetate agar colonies: Very filamentous, red to bright chestnut in color.

Iron citrate and ammonium agar slant: Colonies quite large and distinct, pale white.

Manganese acetate agar slant: Filaments long, red to chestnut-colored and intertwined much as are cotton fibers.

Peptone and manganese acetate broth: Filaments quite long and intertwined like cotton fibers.

Indole not produced.

Hydrogen sulfide not produced.

Acetylmethylcarbinol not produced.

Nitrites produced from nitrates.

Optimum temperature, 37° C.

Optimum pH, between 5.0 and 9.8.

Aerobic; growth favored by the presence of CO_2.

Source: Isolated from fresh water in the neighborhood of Buenos Aires.

Habitat: Presumably widely distributed.

12. **Leptothrix pseudovacuolata** (Perfiliev, 1925) Dorff, 1934. (*Spirothrix pseudovacuolata* Perfiliev, Verh. d. Int. Verein. f. theor. u. angew. Limnologie, 1925, Stuttgart, 1927; Dorff, Die Eisenorganismen, Pflanzenforschung, Heft 16, 1934, 36.)

pseu.do.va.cu.o.la′ta. Gr. adj. *pseudes* false; L. adj. *vacuus* empty; M.L. noun *vacuola* a vacuole; M.L. adj. *pseudovacuolatus* having false vacuoles.

Trichomes, 85 to 250 microns in length, unbranched, spirally wound, occasionally straight. Strongly encrusted with ferric hydroxide. Spirals 20 to 24 microns from crest to crest.

Cells rounded at the ends, thin-walled, granular, 1.7 to 2.8 by 3.5 to 30 microns. Apparently heterotrophic.

Habitat: Found in bottom muds of deep lakes with very low oxygen content.

Genus III. Toxothrix Molisch, 1925.

(Molisch, Sci. Rept. Tahoku Imp. Univ., 4 Ser., Biol., 1925, 144; Cryptothrix Perfiliev, Zur Mikroflora des Sapropels, Nachrichten des Sapropelkomitees Leningrad, 1, 1922.)

Tox'o.thrix. Gr. noun toxum a bow; Gr. noun thrix, trichis a thread; M.L. fem.n. Toxothrix bent thread.

Trichomes composed of cylindrical, colorless cells with a thin primary sheath; the latter soon becomes impregnated with iron oxide. The trichomes lie loosely, longitudinally together, in slightly spirally twisted rolls. The continued repetition of this process leads to the development of a thick, secondary sheath from which parallel bundles may separate. False branching may occur. The sheaths do not completely dissolve in weak acids. Cells may slip out of the sheath and may become motile swarm spores.

The type species is Toxothrix trichogenes (Molisch) Beger.

Key to the species of genus Toxothrix.

I. Long, unattached trichomes not in a gelatinous layer.
1. Toxothrix trichogenes.
II. Short trichomes lying in a gelatinous layer.
2. Toxothrix gelatinosa.

1. **Toxothrix trichogenes** (Cholodny, 1924) Beger, 1953. (Leptothrix trichogenes Cholodny, Cent. f. Bakt., II Abt., 61, 1924, 296; Toxothrix ferruginea Molisch, Sci. Rept. Tahoku Imp. Univ., 4 Ser., Biol., 1925, 13; Chlamydothrix trichogenes Naumann, Zent. f. Bakt., II Abt., 78, 1929, 513; Sphaerotilus trichogenes Pringsheim, Biol. Reviews, Cambridge, 24, 1949, 234; Beger, in Beger and Bringmann, Zent. f. Bakt., II Abt., 107, 1953, 332.)

tri.cho'ge.nes. Gr. noun thrix, trichis hair; Gr. v. gennao to bear; M.L. adj. trichogenes hair-producing.

Found in trichomes up to 400 microns in length; composed of rod-shaped cells which are 0.5 by 1.0 to 2.0 microns. Surrounded by a tubular sheath which splits later so that arched, fan-shaped groups of threads or irregular groups are formed as the trichomes grow in length. Do not lie in a gelatinous layer. The tubular sheath is longitudinally and somewhat spirally striated with lines about 0.2 micron apart. No false branching. Iron oxide is deposited in

the sheaths. The number and diameters of the longitudinally placed trichomes are variable. Giant cells are frequently present. The sheaths, when empty, decay rapidly. The trichomes may slip out of their sheaths.

This species has been cultivated by Teichmann (Vergleichende Untersuchungen über die Kultur und Morphologie einiger Eisenorganismen, Inaug. Diss., Prague, 1935).

Beger and Bringmann (op. cit., 1953, 332) report a form of this species in which the sheaths do not split; the cells are 0.5 by 2.0 to 4.0 microns.

Source: This species has been described from springs, wells, small rivers, water works and rice fields.

Habitat: Found in cool, fresh, iron-bearing waters.

2. **Toxothrix gelatinosa** Beger, 1953. (Beger, in Beger and Bringmann, Zent. f. Bakt., II Abt., 107, 1953, 333.)

ge.la.ti.no'sa. L. part.adj. gelatus congealed; M.L. adj. gelatinosus gelatinous.

The trichomes are up to 22 microns in

length; including the sheath, they measure 1.5 to 1.7 microns in diameter. Several trichomes arising from the same point and each trichome developing a few false branches produces a fan-shaped appearance. All trichomes end at approximately the same distance from the starting point. The trichomes are bent so that the entire fan-shaped group arches somewhat. The individual cells are rod-shaped, 0.5 by 3.0 microns. Iron oxide is deposited in the sheath. Around this, a gelatinous mass is formed, as much as 22 microns in length and ovoid in form. Iron is not deposited in this gelatinous mass.

Source: Found on slides submerged in an aquarium in Berlin in which *Cabomba* was growing.

Habitat: Found in fresh water.

FAMILY II. PELOPLOCACEAE BEGER, Fam. Nov.

Pe.lo.plo.ca'ce.ae. M.L. fem.n. *Peloploca* type genus of the family; -*aceae* ending to denote a family; M.L. fem.pl.n. *Peloplocaceae* the *Peloploca* family.

Long, unbranched trichomes usually enclosed in a thin, delicate sheath. Cells within the trichomes, when in the living state, contain false vacuoles which are easily discerned by a reddish gleam of light which they emit; the cytoplasm of the cell appears bluish white. Generally non-motile, but motile species may occur. Reproduction is by transverse fission of the cells. Unattached forms found in fresh-water ponds with decomposing algae.

Key to the genera of family **Peloplocaceae.**

I. Trichomes lie parallel to each other in bundles or bands.

Genus I. *Peloploca*, p. 270.

II. Trichomes occur singly.

Genus II. *Pelonema*, p. 271.

Genus I. **Peloploca** Lauterborn, 1913.

(Allgem. bot. Ztschr., *19*, 1913, 99.)

Pe.lo'plo.ca. Gr. adj. *pĕllos* or *pĕlos* dark-colored; Gr. noun *plocē* a twining, a braid or a twist; M.L. fem.n. *Peloploca* dark-colored braid or twist.

Trichomes of cylindrical, colorless cells with no evident sheath. Occur as motionless bundles or bands. Cells contain false vacuoles which emit a reddish gleam of light. Nonmotile. Occur in fresh-water ponds where *Chara sp.* is undergoing decomposition. Frequently overlooked because the trichomes resemble plant fibers.

The type species is *Peloploca undulata* Lauterborn.

1. **Peloploca undulata** Lauterborn, 1913. (Allgem. bot. Ztschr., *19*, 1913, 99.)

un.du.la'ta. L. adj. *undulatus* undulated, with waves.

Cells 6 to 10 microns long. The trichomes are spirally twisted into wavy bundles that are tightly wound together. The bundles reach a length of 60 to 150 microns. Nonmotile.

Source: Found in Germany in ponds where *Chara sp.* was growing.

Habitat: Presumably widely distributed in fresh-water ponds.

2. **Peloploca taeniata** Lauterborn, 1913. (Allgem. bot. Ztschr., *19*, 1913, 99.)

tae.ni.a'ta. L. adj. *taeniatus* band-like.

Cells 3.0 to 4.0 microns long. Trichomes united into rather broad, frequently twisted bands. These may have the appearance of a grating or lattice because of the presence of pseudovacuoles in the individual cells.

The bands may reach a length of 700 microns.

Source: Found in Germany in ponds where *Chara sp.* was growing; also found by Beger (1954) in decomposing plant materials on the surface of bottom mud along with *Beggiatoa, Thiospira, Zoogloea* and similar types of bacteria.

Habitat: Presumably widely distributed in fresh-water ponds.

Genus II. **Pelonema** Lauterborn, 1915.

(Verhandl. Naturhist.-med. Verein z. Heidelberg, N.F. *13*, 1915, 408.)

Pe.lo.ne'ma. Gr. adj. *pellos* or *pelos* dark-colored; Gr. noun *nema* filament; M.L. neut.n. *Pelonema* dark-colored filament.

Long, unbranching trichomes, occurring singly, which are either straight or spirally twisted. The trichomes are enclosed in a very thin, delicate sheath. Non-motile, but may become motile. Within the trichomes are cylindrical, colorless cells which contain one or several to many false vacuoles which emit a reddish gleam of light. Found on the surfaces of ponds and lakes which contain decomposing algae and which are poorly aerated.

The type species is *Pelonema tenue* Lauterborn.

Key to the species of genus **Pelonema.**

I. Cells contain a single false vacuole.
  A. Cells 8 to 12 microns long; trichomes are straight and attain a length of up to 300 microns.

   1. *Pelonema tenue.*

  B. Cells 4 to 6 microns long; trichomes are straight and are 200 or more microns long.

   2. *Pelonema hyalinum.*

II. Cells contain several to many false vacuoles.
  A. Trichomes are straight, measuring up to 500 microns in length.

   3. *Pelonema pseudovacuolatum.*

  B. Trichomes are spirally twisted, reaching a length of 40 to 160 microns.

   4. *Pelonema spirale.*

1. **Pelonema tenue** Lauterborn, 1915. (Verhandl. Naturhist.- med. Verein z. Heidelberg, N.F. *13*, 1915, 408.)

te'nu.e. L. adj. *tenuis* slender.

Straight trichomes, up to 300 microns long, which may become motile when the water in which they are growing is low in oxygen content. Cells are 2 by 8 to 12 microns. Each cell contains a single false vacuole which nearly fills the cell; the vacuole is irregular in shape and emits but a small reddish gleam of light.

Source: From pools in the Rheinebene, Germany, where *Chara* was growing.

Habitat: Presumably widely distributed in fresh-water ponds and lakes which contain decomposing algae.

2. **Pelonema hyalinum** Koppe, 1923. (*Pelonema hyalina* (sic) Koppe, Archiv. f. Hydrobiologie, *14*, 1923, 625.)

hy.a.li'num. Gr. adj. *hyalinus* of crystal, glass; M.L. adj. *hyalinus* hyaline.

Straight trichomes which measure 200 or more microns in length. The cells, 2 by 4 to 6 microns, contain a single false vacuole which is quite large and slightly refractive; the vacuole is rectangular in shape and has rounded edges.

Source: From water from Little Plöner Lake, Schleswig-Holstein, Germany.

Habitat: Found in the upper algae-containing layers of deep fresh-water lakes.

3. **Pelonema pseudovacuolatum** Lauterborn, 1915. (Verhandl. Naturhist.- med. Verein z. Heidelberg, N.F. *13*, 1915, 408.)

pseu.do.va.cu.o.la'tum. Gr. adj. *pseudes* false; L. adj. *vacuus* empty; M. L. noun *vacuola* a vacuole; M.L. adj. *pseudovacuolatus* having false vacuoles.

Straight trichomes measuring up to 500

microns in length. The cells are 2 by 4 microns and possess several small false vacuoles which are sharply but irregularly outlined. The cytoplasm of the cells emits a marked bluish gleam of light.

Source: From pools and shallow lakes which contained an abundance of decomposing algae.

Habitat: Found in fresh water.

4. **Pelonema** (?) **spirale** Lauterborn,

1915. (Verhandl. Naturhist.-med. Verein z. Heidelberg, N.F. *13*, 1915, 408.)

spi.ra′le. Gr. noun *spira* a spiral; M.L. adj. *spiralis* spiral.

Spirally twisted trichomes, 1.0 to 1.5 by 40 to 160 microns, with a wave length of 8 to 14 microns. The cells contain numerous, small but long false vacuoles.

Source: From a pool in Germany rich in *Chara*.

Habitat: Found in fresh water.

FAMILY III. CRENOTRICHACEAE HANSGIRG, 1888.

(Oesterr. bot. Ztschr., *36*, 1888, 228.)

Cre.no.tri.cha′ce.ae. M.L. fem.n. *Crenothrix* type genus of the family; -*aceae* ending to denote a family; M.L. fem.pl.n. *Crenotrichaceae* the *Crenothrix* family.

Trichomes attached to a firm substrate and show differentiation of base and tip. Unbranched or show false branching. Sheaths may be thin, delicate and not encrusted with oxides of iron or manganese, or they may be plainly visible, thin and colorless at the tip and thick and encrusted with iron or manganese oxides at the base. Cells disc-shaped to cylindrical, dividing to produce spherical, non-motile conidia. Individual cells may also slip out of the sheath to grow into new trichomes. Found in fresh and salt waters.

Key to the genera of family **Crenotrichaceae.**

I. Attached trichomes which are swollen at the free end.
A. Sheath thick, storing iron or manganese oxides.
Genus I. *Crenothrix*, p. 272.
B. Sheath very delicate, always colorless.
Genus II. *Phragmidiothrix*, p. 273.
II. Attached trichomes which are tapered at the free end.
Genus III. *Clonothrix*, p. 274.

Genus I. **Crenothrix** *Cohn, 1870.*

(Beitr. z. Biol. d. Pflanz., *1*, Heft 1, 1870, 108.)

Cre′no.thrix. Gr. noun *crēnus* a fountain, spring; Gr. noun *thrix, trichis* a hair; M.L. fem.n. *Crenothrix* fountain hair.

Trichomes attached to a firm substrate and swollen at the free end. Unbranched or show false branching. The sheaths surrounding the trichomes are plainly visible, thin and colorless at the tip and encrusted with iron or manganese oxides at the base. Cells disc-shaped to cylindrical, dividing to produce spherical, non-motile conidia of two types: micro- and macroconidia. Individual cells may also slip out of the sheath and form new trichomes. Found in stagnant and running waters which contain organic matter and iron salts.

The type species is *Crenothrix polyspora* Cohn.

1. **Crenothrix polyspora** Cohn, 1870. (Beitr. z. Biol. d. Pflanz., *1*, Heft 1, 1870, 108.)

po.ly′spo.ra. Gr. adj. *poly* many; Gr.

noun *sporus* a seed; M.L. noun *spora* a spore; M.L. adj. *polysporus* many-spored.

Trichomes long (up to 1 cm), articulated, unbranched and sessile. There is considerable variation in the diameter of the individual trichomes, the base measuring 1.5 to 5.0 microns and the swollen tip measuring 6.0 to 9.0 microns. Each trichome is surrounded by a colorless sheath which later may become rust-colored and heavily encrusted, especially at the base, with depositions of ferric hydroxide and, to a lesser extent, manganese oxides. The ensheathed trichomes may reach a diameter of 12 microns or more. Cells within the trichomes are usually about 1.5 times as long as they are wide and are more or less rectangular in shape.

During reproduction the cells divide by longitudinal and transverse fission into nonmotile conidia of two types: microconidia, which are 1 to 2 microns in diameter, and macroconidia, which measure about 5 microns in diameter; intermediate forms may also occur. When the tip of the sheath ruptures, the conidia are extruded; these may attach themselves to some object and grow into trichomes, or they may germinate upon the exterior of the sheath from which they were liberated, giving rise to new trichomes attached to the surface of the older one, thus simulating false branching. The conidia often form a zoogloeal mass, but only in the presence of dissolved iron.

In addition to the above-mentioned types of reproductive cells, Cohn (*ibid.*, 120) observed a third structure which he conditionally alluded to as a spore. These cells originate from the swollen terminal cell which is usually ellipsoidal in shape and sometimes as much as seven times as long as it is wide (3.67 by 26.25 microns). The protoplasm of this terminal cell becomes finely granular and eventually emerges from the sheath. From these cells, short, colorless *Oscillaria*-like trichomes are produced which contain no more than eight cylindrical cells measuring 5 to 6 by 10 to 12 microns. The trichomes have a characteristic, slow, gliding motion and are surrounded by a fine, transparent membrane, but no sheath. Subsequent authors, when describing this species, have usually failed to mention this third type of reproductive cell observed by Cohn.

Cultivation: Has not been grown on artificial media in pure culture. Grows readily in water containing organic matter regardless of the iron content of the water.

Related species: Cholodny believed *Clonothrix fusca* to be identical with *Crenothrix polyspora*. However, *Clonothrix fusca* shows genuine false branching and produces conidia by fission in only one plane so that the trichomes taper toward the tip instead of expanding (see Kolk, Amer. Jour. Bot., *25*, 1938, 11, for a differentiation of these two species).

Comments: Zopf (Entwicklungsgesch. Unters. ü. *Crenothrix polyspora*, die Ursache der Berliner Wasserkalamitat. Berlin, 1879, 2) regards *Leptothrix kuehniana* Rabenhorst as identical with *Crenothrix polyspora* Cohn, and there seems to be much evidence in favor of considering the two species as identical. If Cohn's organism proves to be identical with Rabenhorst's, then the specific epithet *kuehniana* has priority over *polyspora*; however, until the relationship of the two organisms has been clarified, the name *Crenothrix polyspora* is retained here.

Source: This organism is wide-spread in water pipes, drain pipes and springs where the water contains iron. It frequently fills pipes under such circumstances and causes a real nuisance. Found by Cohn in samples of water from springs in the neighborhood of Breslau, Germany.

Habitat: Found in stagnant or running waters containing organic matter and iron salts. Harmless, but frequently becomes bothersome in water pipes and city water supplies; grows as thick, brownish masses.

Genus II. **Phragmidiothrix** *Engler, 1883*.

(Vierter Ber. d. Commission z. wissensch. Unters. d. deutsch. Meere in Kiel für 1877 bis 1881, I Abt., 1883, 187.)

Phrag.mi′di.o.thrix. Gr. noun *phragma* fence; Gr. noun *eidus* form, shape; Gr. noun *thrix, trichis* hair; M.L. fem.n. *Phragmidiothrix* fence-like hair.

Trichomes are articulated, unbranched and attached, the free ends being swollen. Surrounding the trichomes are very thin, delicate, colorless sheaths which do not store iron or manganese compounds. The cells are small and disc-shaped and are uniform in size. Conidia of the same diameter as the cells are produced. Found in salt water.

Hansgirg (Bot. Ztg., *49*, 1891, 313) concluded that *Phragmidiothrix* should be included in the genus *Crenothrix*, and that the genus *Crenothrix* should be divided into two sections, *Eucrenothrix* and *Phragmidiothrix*.

The type species is *Phragmidiothrix multiseptata* (Engler) Engler.

1. **Phragmidiothrix multiseptata** (Engler, 1882) Engler, 1883. (*Beggiatoa multiseptata* Engler, Verhandl. bot. Ver. Brandenburg, *24*, 1882, 19; Engler, Vierter Ber. d. Commission z. wissensch. Unters. d. deutsch. Meere in Kiel für 1877 bis 1881, I Abt., 1883, 187; also see Zopf, Die Spaltpilze, 1883, 104.)

mul.ti.sep.ta'ta. L. mas.n. *multus* much; L. adj. *septatus* fenced; M.L. adj. *multiseptatus* much-fenced, with many septa.

Colorless trichomes, several millimeters long, which form grayish white tufts. The trichomes are sessile; when young they are 1.5 microns wide, but when older they measure 2 to 3 microns at their bases and 5 to 6 microns at their tips. Very thin, delicate sheaths which are not encrusted with iron or manganese oxides surround the tri-chomes. The cells are disc-shaped, their width being 1.5 to 4.0 microns while their length is only ¼ to ½ this size. Each cell has a very thin, colorless membrane and some hyaline granules.

When mature, the cells in the upper portion of the trichomes divide longitudinally and transversely and form uniformly sized conidia (1 micron in diameter). These conidia may be extruded, may become free by decomposition of the sheath, or they may germinate within the sheath. The extruded conidia may produce zoogloeal masses before they germinate.

Source: From the body of a crustacean (*Gammarus locusta*) from sea water; also found on seaweeds in polluted water on the shores of the northern Adriatic.

Habitat: Found in polluted salt water.

Genus III. **Clonothrix** *Roze, 1896.*

(Roze, Jour. de Botanic, *10*, 1896, 325; also proposed independently by Schorler, Cent. f. Bakt., II Abt., *12*, 1904, 689.)

Clo'no.thrix. Gr. noun *clōn, clōnis* twig, slip; Gr. noun *thrix, trichis* hair; M.L. fem.n. *Clonothrix* twig hair.

Attached trichomes showing false branching as in *Sphaerotilus*. Sheaths organic, encrusted with iron or manganese, broader at the base and tapering toward the tip. Cells colorless, cylindrical. Reproduction by spherical conidia formed in chains by transverse fission of cells; conidia formation acropetal, limited to short branches of the younger portions of the trichomes.

The type species is *Clonothrix putealis* (Kirchner) Beger.

1. **Clonothrix putealis** (Kirchner, 1878) Beger, 1953. (*Glaucothrix putealis* Kirchner, Kryptogamen-Flora von Schlesien, *2*, 1, 1878, 229; *Clonothrix fusca* Roze, Jour. de Botanic, *10*, 1896, 325; Beger, in Beger and Bringmann, Zent. f. Bakt., II Abt., *107*, 1953, 327.)

pu.te.a'lis. L. adj. *putealis* belonging to a well.

Ensheathed trichomes, up to 0.6 mm long, which show false branching and which taper towards the tip; the bases of the trichomes measure 7 microns and the tips measure 2 microns in diameter. The sheaths may become encrusted with oxides of manganese and/or iron, particularly those of manganese. Sheath encrustations may reach a thickness of 24 microns when manganese oxides are prevalent and 10 microns when iron oxides are abundant. Cells cylindrical with rounded ends, 2 by 10 microns, becoming larger toward the base and smaller toward the tips of the trichomes.

Multiplication by extrusion of single cells

or by rather uniform, spherical, non-motile conidia formed into short trichomes in chains of 2 to 6 or more, their diameters being about 2 microns.

Historical: This organism was described by Roze as a blue-green alga, but subsequent observers have failed to find pigment. It was described independently by Schorler (Cent. f. Bakt., II Abt., *12*, 1904, 689) who also gave it the name *Clonothrix fusca*. Cholodny considered it identical with *Crenothrix polyspora*, but Kolk (Amer. Jour. Bot., *25*, 1938, 11) has clearly differentiated these species.

Source: From a well in Proskaŭ, Schlesien.

Habitat: Widely distributed in rivers and streams with gravelly, manganese-bearing bottoms; also found in water works and pipe lines, where it may cause technical difficulties. May occur in dark brown masses that are large enough to be seen readily in tap water.

ORDER III. HYPHOMICROBIALES DOUGLAS, Ordo Nov.*

Hy.pho.mi.cro.bi.a'les. M.L. fem.pl.n. *Hyphomicrobiaceae* type family of the order; *-ales* ending to denote an order; M.L. fem.pl.n. *Hyphomicrobiales* the *Hyphomicrobiaceae* order.

Multiplication is by budding or by budding and longitudinal fission. Buds may be sessile or may be borne at the tip of a slender filament which arises from the pole of a mature cell or from a filament connecting two cells. Cells may occur singly or in pairs but are found more commonly in aggregates. In some types the aggregates consist of groups of cells attached to a surface by stalks which appear to radiate from a common holdfast; in others the aggregates consist of free-floating cell groups in which the cells are attached to one another by the filament engendered in the budding process. Branching of the filament may result in groups which contain several hundred cells. Cells are ovoid, ellipsoidal, spherical or pyriform. If motile, the cells possess a single polar flagellum. Specialized resting stages have not been found. Gram-negative so far as known. Metabolism may be heterotrophic or photosynthetic. Found in the mud and water of fresh-water ponds and streams; also parasitic on fresh-water crustacea.

Key to the Families of Order Hyphomicrobiales.

I. Buds borne upon filaments.

        Family I. *Hyphomicrobiaceae*, p. 276.

II. Buds sessile.

        Family II. *Pasteuriaceae*, p. 278.

FAMILY I. HYPHOMICROBIACEAE BABUDIERI, 1950.

(Rendiconti dell'Istituto Superiore di Sanita, *13*, 1950, 589.)

Hy.pho.mi.cro.bi.a'ce.ae. M.L. neut.n. *Hyphomicrobium* type genus of the family; *-aceae* ending to denote a family; M.L. fem.pl.n. *Hyphomicrobiaceae* the *Hyphomicrobium* family.

These organisms occur mainly as free-floating groups in which the cells are attached to one another by a slender, sometimes branched, filament. Daughter-cell formation is initiated by the outgrowth of a filament from the pole of a mature cell or from some point on a filament connecting two mature cells. The daughter cell is formed by enlargement of the tip of the filament. Gram-negative.

Key to the genera of family Hyphomicrobiaceae.

I. Chemoheterotrophic. Motile.

        Genus I. *Hyphomicrobium*, p. 277.

---

* New material prepared by and old material rearranged by Prof. H. C. Douglas, Department of Microbiology, School of Medicine, University of Washington, Seattle, Washington. December, 1953.

II. Photoheterotrophic. Non-motile.

Genus II. *Rhodomicrobium*, p. 277.

Genus I. **Hyphomicrobium** *Stutzer and Hartleb, 1898.*

(Mitteil. d. landwirtsch. Inst. d. k. Univ. Breslau, 1898; abst. in Cent. f. Bakt., II Abt., *5*, 1899, 678.)

Hy.pho.mi.cro'bi.um. Gr. noun *hyphē* thread; Gr. adj. *micrus* small; Gr. noun *bius* life; M.L. neut.n. *Hyphomicrobium* thread (-producing) microbe.

Daughter cells may remain attached to the filaments which connect them to the mother cells or may tear free of the filament as the result of active movement by means of a single, polar flagellum. Gram-negative. Non-pigmented. Metabolism is chemoheterotrophic and oxidative. Aerobic. Found in soil and in fresh water.

The type species is *Hyphomicrobium vulgare* Stutzer and Hartleb.

1. **Hyphomicrobium vulgare** Stutzer and Hartleb, 1898. (Saltpeterpilz, Stutzer and Hartleb, Cent. f. Bakt., II Abt., *3*, 1897, 621; Stutzer and Hartleb, Mitteil. d. landwirtsch. Inst. d. k. Univ. Breslau, 1898; abst. in Cent. f. Bakt., II Abt., *5*, 1899, 678.)

vul.ga're. L. adj. *vulgaris* common.

Description taken from Stutzer and Hartleb (*loc. cit.*), Kingma-Boltjes (Arch. f. Mikrobiol., *7*, 1936, 188) and Mevius (Arch. f. Mikrobiol., *19*, 1953, 1).

Mature cells are ovoid, measuring 0.5 by 1.0 micron; immature cells are spherical. Motile by means of a single, polar flagellum. Daughter cells are borne on filaments measuring approximately 0.2 micron or less in diameter and varying in length from one to several times the length of mature cells. The predominant growth habit is that of a dense clump of cells from which filaments radiate outward. Branching of the filament occurs but is not common. Daughter cells may tear free of the filaments and exist as single, motile cells with motility sometimes persisting even after the cell has produced a filament of considerable length. Cells in pairs, connected by a filament, are common. Gram-negative.

Gelatin: No growth.

Formate-nitrate agar or silica gel plates: Colonies are colorless, 0.5 to 1.0 mm in diameter, slightly elevated, entire.

Peptone agar colonies: Much smaller than those above.

Peptone broth: Poor growth.

Formate-nitrate broth: Growth occurs as a light, cream-colored, granular sediment.

Chemoheterotrophic, oxidative. Growth occurs in mineral media at pH 7.0 to 7.5 with ammonium or nitrate as a nitrogen source and formate, formaldehyde, methanol, acetate or lactate as a carbon source. Some growth occurs in mineral media without an added carbon source at the expense of organic compounds in the air.

Sucrose not attacked.

Asparagine not utilized.

Aerobic.

Temperature range for growth, 20° to 37° C.

Source: Isolated from soil and water. Commonly found in enrichment cultures for nitrifying bacteria and in activated sludge. Babudieri (Rendiconti Istit. Super. di Sanita, Roma, *13*, 1950, 589) has found this species as a contaminant in *Leptospira canicola* cultures.

Habitat: Widely distributed in soil and in fresh water.

Genus II. **Rhodomicrobium** *Duchow and Douglas, 1949.*

(Jour. Bact., *58*, 1949, 409.)

Rho.do.mi.cro'bi.um. Gr. noun *rhodum* the rose; Gr. adj. *micrus* small; Gr. noun *bius* life; M.L. neut.n. *Rhodomicrobium* red (-producing) microbe.

The daughter cells remain attached to the filaments connecting them to the mother cells.

Non-motile. Gram-negative. Colonies are salmon-pink to orange-red in color. Photohetero-trophic. Anaerobic. Found in mud and in fresh water.

The type species is *Rhodomicrobium vannielii* Duchow and Douglas.

1. **Rhodomicrobium vannielii** Duchow and Douglas, 1949. (Duchow and Douglas, Jour. Bact., *58*, 1949, 409; also see Murray and Douglas, Jour. Bact., *59*, 1950, 157; and Volk and Pennington, Jour. Bact., *59*, 1950, 169.)

van.niel'i.i. M.L. gen.noun *vannielii* of van Niel; named for C. B. van Niel, an American bacteriologist.

Mature cells are ovoid, measuring 1.2 by 2.8 microns; immature cells are spherical. Non-motile. The cells are connected by filaments which are approximately 0.3 micron in diameter and from one to several times the length of a mature cell. A mature cell may produce as many as three daughter cells: one by formation of a primary filament from the pole of the cell, and one or two more by lateral outgrowths of new filaments from the primary filament upon which the first daughter cell is borne. Because of the tendency of the cells to remain attached to the filament, the predominant growth habit is that of an aggregate containing many cells. Gram-negative.

Agar: In shake tubes, colonies are dark orange-red, irregular, 2 to 3 mm in diameter and have a rough, convoluted surface.

Broth: Turbid in young cultures, becoming granular and flocculent; salmon-pink to deep orange-red, depending on the density of growth.

Photoheterotrophic. Cells contain bacteriochlorophyll and carotenoid pigments. Growth occurs in the presence of light in a mineral medium containing an organic hydrogen donor and bicarbonate; organic growth factors are not required. Suitable hydrogen donors are ethanol, propanol, butanol, acetate, propionate, butyrate, valerate, caproate, lactate and malate.

Glucose, mannose, fructose, mannitol, citrate, tartrate, formate, thiosulfate and sulfide are not utilized.

Anaerobic.

Optimum temperature, between 25° and 30° C.

Source: Isolated from mud and water from Washington State.

Habitat: Commonly found in mud, pond, lake and stream waters.

FAMILY II. PASTEURIACEAE LAURENT, 1890, EMEND. HENRICI AND JOHNSON, 1935.

(Laurent, Compt. rend. Acad. Sci., Paris, *3*, 1890, 754; Henrici and Johnson, Jour. Bact., *30*, 1935, 84.)

Pas.teu.ri.a'ce.ae. M.L. fem.n. *Pasteuria* type genus of the family; *-aceae* ending to denote a family; M.L. fem.pl.n. *Pasteuriaceae* the *Pasteuria* family.

Stalked bacteria with spherical or pear-shaped cells; if cells are elongated, the long axis of the cell coincides with the axis of the stalk. Stalks may be very short or absent, but when present they are usually very fine and at times arranged in whorls attached to a common holdfast. Cells multiply by longitudinal fission and/or by budding. Mostly periphytic; one species is parasitic.

The descriptions of the members of this family are largely based upon microscopic examinations of collected materials such as parasitized daphnias (fresh-water crustacea) or glass slides submerged at various depths for about two weeks in Lake Alexander, Minnesota (Henrici, Jour. Bact., *25*, 1932, 277). A few crude cultures were obtained in two liquid media: one containing a mineral solution with precipitated cellulose and ammonium salts as a source of nitrogen, the other being a solution of $MgSO_4$ and K_2HPO_4 in tap water to which bits of the exoskeleton of marine crabs were added. No growth took place on agar media so that no pure cultures were obtained. Cultures were incubated at room temperature in the dark. Further information regarding the organisms belonging to the genera of this family is greatly needed.

Key to the genera of family **Pasteuriaceae.**

I. Stalks lacking; cells sessile.

Genus I. *Pasteuria*, p. 279.

II. Stalks long and slender, often in whorls.

Genus II. *Blastocaulis*, p. 279.

Genus I. **Pasteuria** Metchnikoff, 1888.

(Ann. Inst. Past., *2*, 1888, 166.)

Pas.teu'ri.a. M.L. gen.n. *Pasteuria* of Pasteur; named for Louis Pasteur, the French scientist.

Pear-shaped cells attached to each other or to a firm substrate by holdfasts secreted at the narrow end. Multiplication is by longitudinal fission and by budding of spherical or ovoid cells at the free end. Non-motile. Non-pigmented. Parasitic on fresh-water crustacea.

The type species is *Pasteuria ramosa* Metchnikoff.

1. **Pasteuria ramosa** Metchnikoff, 1888. (Ann. Inst. Past., *2*, 1888, 166.)

ra.mo'sa. L. adj. *ramosus* much-branched.

Cells 1 to 2 by 4 to 5 microns. Non-motile. Non-pigmented. Cells grow attached to each other in cauliflower-like masses, multiplying by longitudinal fission or by intracellular bodies which are extruded as buds, apparently reproductive in nature; at times these colonies break up into smaller ones and continue to separate until all of the individual cells are liberated. Cells and methods of reproduction resemble those of *Chamaesiphon*, a genus of blue-green algae (Henrici and Johnson, Jour. Bact., *30*, 1935, 71). Gram stain not recorded.

Related species: Free-living organisms which resembled *Pasteuria ramosa* were found by Henrici and Johnson (*ibid.*, 71 and 77) in Lake Alexander, Minnesota; these appeared frequently on glass slides submerged in the lake water; they produced reproductive bodies apparently by budding rather than by an endogenous formation. Photomicrographs are shown in Henrici and Johnson (*ibid.*, 93, plate 3, fig. 4). ZoBell and Allen (Proc. Soc. Exp. Biol. and Med., *30*, 1933, 1409) and ZoBell and Upham (Bull. Scripps Inst. Oceanography, LaJolla, California, *5*, 1944, 243) used a submerged-slide technique in sea water and found similar bacteria.

Source: From the body cavities of *Daphnia pulex* and *D. magna*.

Habitat: Parasitic on fresh-water crustacea so far as known.

Genus II. **Blastocaulis** Henrici and Johnson, 1935.

(Jour. Bact., *30*, 1935, 84.)

Blas.to.cau'lis. Gr. noun *blastus* a sprout, shoot, bud; Gr. noun *caulis* a stalk; M.L. fem.n. *Blastocaulis* a bud stalk.

Pear-shaped or globular cells attached to a firm substrate by long, slender stalks with a holdfast at the base; stalks may occur singly or may arise in clusters from a common holdfast. Not cultivable on artificial media. Found on firm substrates in fresh water.

The type species is *Blastocaulis sphaerica* Henrici and Johnson.

1. **Blastocaulis sphaerica** Henrici and Johnson, 1935. (Jour. Bact., *30*, 1935, 84.)

sphae'ri.ca. Gr. adj. *sphaericus* spherical. Cells spherical, 1 to 2 microns in diameter.

The cells are attached to long, slender stalks which radiate from a common center; as many as 8 stalks may be attached to a common holdfast; usually they are attached directly to a glass slide, occasionally to algae or other organisms or to some amorphous debris. Multiplication is by budding, the buds being globular in shape. The smaller cells stain solidly, but the larger cells that are budding show a differentiation of the protoplasm: the free end stains deeply while that part of the cell which is attached to the stalk stains more faintly. Young cells are Gram-positive, but budding individuals are Gram-negative.

Temperature relations: Found only in lake water where temperatures do not exceed 23° C.

Comments: It is believed that the characteristic growth of this organism in whorls may be best explained by assuming that when the buds germinate they first undergo a simple fission, perhaps producing clusters of cells, and that then, from these clusters, the individual cells secrete stalks which thus radiate from a common holdfast.

Related species: Similar stalked bacteria which reproduce by budding are illustrated by Henrici and Johnson (ibid., 77 and 91) but are not named or described in detail.

Source: From glass slides submerged in Lake Alexander, Minnesota.

Habitat: Presumably widely distributed in fresh-water ponds. Does not occur closer to the shore than the 2-meter contour. Found constantly in the open lake at all depths up to 13 meters. Occurs more abundantly in the fall months than in the summer.

ORDER IV. EUBACTERIALES BUCHANAN, 1917.

(Jour. Bact., *2*, 1917, 102.)

Eu.bac.te.ri.a'les. Gr. pref. *eu-* well, true; Gr. neut.n. *bacterium* a small rod; *-ales* ending to denote an order; M.L. fem.pl.n. *Eubacteriales* the order of the true bacteria.

Simple, undifferentiated, rigid cells which are either spherical or straight rods. In some families, for example *Corynebacteriaceae*, a certain amount of pleomorphism occurs. Only the simplest forms of branching occur, and these only rarely. There are many non-motile as well as motile species. The flagella are usually arranged peritrichously, but monotrichous species do occur in groups where the flagellation is normally peritrichous; such conditions appear to have been developed from ancestral peritrichous species. Typical endospores occur in one family (*Bacillaceae*). All of the species in certain families are definitely Gram-negative; in other families and groups, where the majority of species are Gram-positive, at least in certain stages of growth, species occur which lose their Gram stain so readily that they are generally classed as Gram-negative. Reproduction is by transverse fission; occasionally the cells divide in two or three planes perpendicular to each other, thereby forming tetrads or packets of eight cells. The pigments of chromogenic species are commonly non-water-soluble and of a carotenoid nature; other pigments do occur however, some of which show slight powers of diffusion into agar media. None of these pigments have the ability to carry out photosynthesis. The order includes saprophytes, parasites and many pathogenic species; the latter cause diseases of both animals and plants. Found in salt and fresh waters, air, soil and in the bodies of animals and plants.

Key to the families of order **Eubacteriales.**

I. Cells rod-shaped (rarely large, yeast-like cells). Gram-negative.
   A. Aerobic or facultatively anaerobic.
      1. Large ovoid to rod-shaped cells which may be yeast-like in appearance. Free-living in soil. Fix free nitrogen.
           Family I. *Azotobacteraceae*, p. 283.
      2. Not as above.
         a. Heterotrophic rods which may not require organic nitrogen for growth. Usually motile by means of one to six flagella. Frequently form nodules or tubercles on roots of plants or show violet chromogenesis. Colonies usually large and slimy, especially on mannitol agar.
              Family II. *Rhizobiaceae*, p. 285.
     aa. Not as above.
         b. Straight rods which grow readily on ordinary peptone media. May or may not ferment sugars anaerobically with the production of organic acids.
           c. Glucose usually attacked oxidatively or not at all. Only rarely are species able to ferment glucose anaerobically. Produce little or no acid in litmus milk. May or may not reduce nitrates. Many yellow chromogens. Some species digest agar, others chitin. Primarily found as saprophytes in foods, in soil and in fresh and salt water.
              Family III. *Achromobacteraceae*, p. 296.

cc. Ferment glucose anaerobically, frequently producing visible gas (CO_2 + H_2) from glucose and sometimes lactose. Reduce nitrates (rare exceptions). Frequently found in the alimentary, respiratory and urinary tracts of vertebrates, others are free-living, while still others are plant pathogens.

Family IV. *Enterobacteriaceae*, p. 332.

bb. Usually small, motile or non-motile rods. Obligate animal parasites which usually require body fluids for growth. Many fail to grow on ordinary media. The majority do not ferment glucose anaerobically.

Family V. *Brucellaceae*, p. 394.

B. Anaerobic to microaerophilic, rod-shaped organisms which sometimes show branching.

Family VI. *Bacteroidaceae*, p. 423.

II. Cells spherical to rod-shaped. Usually Gram-positive, though some cocci and anaerobic spore-forming rods lose the Gram stain readily.

A. Cells do not form endospores.

1. Cells spherical, occurring in masses, tetrads or packets of eight cells.

a. Spherical cells. Gram-positive. Aerobic or anaerobic.

Family VII. *Micrococcaceae*, p. 454.

aa. Cells spherical. Gram-negative. Aerobic or anaerobic. Frequently occur in pairs.

Family VIII. *Neisseriaceae*, p. 480.

2. Cells either spherical, occurring in chains, or rod-shaped. Gram-positive, but cells may lose the Gram stain readily in old cultures.

a. Cells rod-shaped, no pleomorphism or branching of cells. Rarely or never ferment glucose anaerobically.

Family IX. *Brevibacteriaceae*, p. 490.

aa. Not as above.

b. Gram-positive cocci and rods which frequently form chains of cells. Cells ferment sugars anaerobically with the production of lactic, acetic, propionic, butyric, etc. acids. Microaerophilic to anaerobic.

c. Homo- and hetero-fermentative cocci and rods whose chief product in fermentation is lactic acid. Do not reduce nitrates.

Family X. *Lactobacillaceae*, p. 505.

cc. Rod-shaped bacteria whose distinctive product in fermentation is propionic acid, butyric acid or ethanol. All produce CO_2 .

Family XI. *Propionibacteriaceae*, p. 569.

bb. Cells generally rod-shaped but wedge and club forms are common. The cells are usually found in angular or picket formations due to snapping division. Old cells are frequently Gram-negative. Not active in the anaerobic fermentation of sugars. May or may not reduce nitrates.

Family XII. *Corynebacteriaceae*, p. 578.

B. Rod-shaped cells that produce endospores. Aerobic and anaerobic. Some anaerobic species lose the Gram stain readily.

Family XIII. *Bacillaceae*, p. 613.

FAMILY I. AZOTOBACTERACEAE BERGEY, BREED AND MURRAY, 1938.*

(*Azotobacteriaceae* (sic) Bergey, Breed and Murray, Preprint, Manual, 5th ed., October, 1938, v and 71.)

A.zo.to.bac.te.ra'ce.ae. M.L. mas.n. *Azotobacter* type genus of the family; *-aceae* ending to denote a family; M.L. fem.pl.n. *Azotobacteraceae* the *Azotobacter* family.

Relatively large rods or even cocci, sometimes almost yeast-like in appearance. Cells without endospores. The type of flagellation in this genus has been definitely established as peritrichous. Gram-negative. Obligate aerobes, usually growing in a film on the surface of the culture medium. Capable of fixing atmospheric nitrogen when provided with carbohydrate or other energy source. Grow best on media deficient in nitrogen. Soil and water bacteria.

There is a single genus.

Genus I. **Azotobacter** *Beijerinck, 1901.*

(Cent. f. Bakt., II Abt., 7, 1901, 567.)

A.zo.to.bac'ter. Gr. adj. *azous* without life; Fr. noun *azote* nitrogen; M.L. mas.n *bacter* the masculine equivalent of Gr. neut.n. *bactrum* a rod or staff; M.L. mas.n. *Azotobacter* nitrogen rod.

Description same as for the family.

The type species is *Azotobacter chroococcum* Beijerinck.

1. **Azotobacter chroococcum** Beijerinck, 1901. (Cent. f. Bakt., II Abt., 7, 1901, 567; also see *ibid.*, *9*, 1902, 3.)

chro.o.coc'cum. Gr. noun *chroa* color, complexion; Gr. noun *coccus* a grain; M.L. neut.n. *chroococcum* colored coccus.

Rods, 2.0 to 3.0 by 3.0 to 6.0 microns, occurring in pairs and packets and occasionally in chains. The cells show three or four refractile granules. The organisms are surrounded by a slimy membrane of variable thickness, usually becoming brownish in older cultures, due possibly to the conversion of tyrosine to melanin. The coloring matter is insoluble in water, alcohol, ether or chloroform. Motile by means of numerous peritrichous flagella (Hofer, Jour. Bact., *47*, 1944, 415). Gram-negative.

Grows in absence of organic nitrogen.

Gelatin colonies: Very small, circular, yellow, granular, later becoming yellowish brown.

Gelatin stab: Only slight growth in the stab. No liquefaction.

Mannitol agar stab: Gray, may become brownish.

Nutrient broth: No growth even in the presence of glucose; peptone utilized with difficulty.

Litmus milk: Becoming clearer in 10 to 14 days.

Potato: Glossy, barely visible, slimy to wrinkled; may become yellowish, brownish yellow or chocolate-brown.

The organism fixes atmospheric nitrogen and gives off CO_2, utilizing glucose and sucrose. Other generally used carbon compounds are fructose, maltose, mannitol, inulin, dextrin, galactose, arabinose, starch, glycerol, ethyl alcohol, acetate, butyrate, citrate, lactate, malate, propionate and succinate.

Nitrate: Improves growth in amounts less than 1 gm per liter; greater amounts are toxic.

Fixes nitrogen moderately actively.

Chemical analysis: Four-day cultures grown upon mannitol agar, when dried, are found to contain less than 0.5 per cent of hemicelluloses, less than 20 per cent of crude protein, less than 5 per cent of ash, and more than 30 per cent of lignin-like materials (Greene, Soil Sci., *39*, 1935, 327). The nitrogen fraction contains less than 1 per

---

* Revised by Dr. A. W. Hofer, New York State Experiment Station, Cornell University, Geneva, New York, June, 1938; further revision by Dr. A. W. Hofer, May, 1954.

cent of amide nitrogen, less than 1 per cent of humin nitrogen and about 1 per cent of basic nitrogen.

Aerobic.

Optimum temperature, between 25° and 28° C.

Distinctive characters: Inability to grow in peptone media, even in the presence of glucose; frequent occurrence of a dark brown or black pigment.

Source: Isolated from soil.

Habitat: Occurs naturally in the majority of neutral or alkaline field soils.

2. Azotobacter agilis Beijerinck, 1901. (Cent. f. Bakt., II Abt., *7*, 1901, 577.)

a'gi.lis. L. adj. *agilis* quick, agile.

Rods, 4 to 6 microns in length, almost spherical. Actively motile by means of numerous, peritrichous flagella (Hofer, Jour. Bact., *47*, 1944, 415). Some strains are reported to be non-motile. Gram-negative.

Grows in absence of organic nitrogen.

Gelatin: No liquefaction.

Mannitol agar colonies: Circular, grayish white, translucent with whitish center.

Washed agar colonies: Show slight bluish green fluorescence. The presence of a fluorescent pigment is readily demonstrated by placing cultures under ultraviolet light, 3600 A. Examination by paper chromotography indicates that this pigment is not fluorescin, the pigment found in fluorescent pseudomonads (Johnstone, Jour. Bact., *69*, 1955, 481).

Mannitol agar slant: Grayish, translucent, fluorescent.

Plain agar slant: Yellowish white, smooth, glistening, translucent with opaque center.

Broth: Turbid, with sediment.

Litmus milk: Becoming clear in 10 to 14 days.

Potato: Yellowish white, slimy, becoming yellowish brown.

In the presence of organic acids, a greenish or reddish pigment is formed.

The organism fixes atmospheric nitrogen actively and gives off CO_2.

Aerobic.

Chemical analysis: Four-day cultures grown upon mannitol agar, when dried, con-

tain more than 4 per cent of hemicelluloses, more than 45 per cent of crude protein, more than 7 per cent of ash, and less than 4 per cent of lignin-like materials. The nitrogen fraction contains more than 1 per cent amide nitrogen, more than 1 per cent humin nitrogen, and 2 per cent or more of basic nitrogen (Greene, Soil Sci., *39*, 1935, 327).

Optimum temperature, between 25° and 28° C.

Distinctive characters: Lack of a brown pigment; occasional fluorescence; growth in peptone broth containing glucose.

Comment: A non-chromogenic variety of this species has been recognized by Kluyver and van den Bout (Arch. f. Mikrobiol., *7*, 1936, 263).

Source: Originally isolated from canal water at Delft.

Habitat: Occurs in water and soil.

3. Azotobacter indicus Starkey and De, 1939. (*Azotobacter indicum* (sic) Starkey and De, Soil Sci., *47*, 1939, 337.)

in'di.cum. L. adj. *indicus* of India.

Ellipsoidal rods, 0.5 to 1.2 by 1.7 to 2.7 microns when grown on nitrogen-free glucose agar. One of the distinctive characteristics is the presence of two large, round, highly refractive bodies in the cells, one usually at each end. Motile by means of numerous peritrichous flagella (Hofer, Jour. Bact., *47*, 1944, 415). Gram-negative.

The organism grows slowly but in time produces large amounts of slime. Has high acid tolerance, since it grows from pH 3 to 9.

Sucrose or glucose agar plates: Colonies are colorless, round, very much raised and uniformly turbid, having much the appearance of heavy starch paste. After two weeks, a buff to light brown color develops.

Mannitol agar slant: Grows very poorly.

Peptone agar slant with 0.5 per cent glucose: Limited grayish growth.

Nutrient broth: No growth.

Liquid media: Generally turbid with some sediment.

Fixes atmospheric nitrogen readily with either glucose or sucrose as source of energy.

Aerobic.

Optimum temperature, 30° C.

Distinctive characters: Tolerance of acidity; wide limits of pH tolerated; abundant slime production; large globules of fat within cells.

Relationships to other species: Derx (Kon. Nederl. Akad. v. Wetensch., Amsterdam, Proc. Sect. Sci., *53*, 1950, 145; Ann. Bogoriensis, *1*, 1950, 1) has made this species the type species of a new genus, *Beijerinckia*, because the organisms in the new genus differ in morphology and physiology in important respects from the organisms in the genus *Azotobacter* proper. Further comparative studies should be made before this separation is accepted.

Source: Isolated from soils of India and Java.

Habitat: Soils.

FAMILY II. RHIZOBIACEAE CONN, 1938.

(Jour. Bact., *36*, 1938, 321.)

Rhi.zo.bi.a′ce.ae. M.L. neut.n. *Rhizobium* type genus of the family; *-aceae* ending to denote a family; M.L. fem.pl.n. *Rhizobiaceae* the *Rhizobium* family.

Cells without endospores, rod-shaped, sparsely flagellated (one polar or lateral flagellum or 2 to 4 peritrichous ones); some species are non-motile. Usually Gram-negative. One genus (*Chromobacterium*) produces a violet pigment. Grow aerobically on ordinary culture media containing glucose. Glucose and sometimes other carbohydrates are utilized without appreciable acid formation. Saprophytes, symbionts and pathogens; the latter are usually plant pathogens forming abnormal growths on roots and stems.

Key to genera of family **Rhizobiaceae.**

I. Cells capable of fixing free nitrogen when growing symbiotically on the roots of *Leguminosae.*

Genus I. *Rhizobium*, p. 285.

II. Either plant pathogens which attack roots or produce hypertrophies on stems or free-living non-chromogenic soil or water forms. Do not fix nitrogen.

Genus II. *Agrobacterium*, p. 288.

III. Usually free-living soil and water forms which produce a violet chromogenesis.

Genus III. *Chromobacterium*, p. 292.

Genus I. **Rhizobium** Frank, 1889.*

(*Phytomyxa* Schroeter, in Cohn, Kryptogamen-Flora von Schlesien, *3*, 1886, 134; Frank, Ber. d. deutsch. bot. Gesellsch., *7*, 1889, 380.)

Rhi.zo′bi.um. Gr. noun *rhiza* a root; Gr. noun *bius* life; M.L. neut.n. *Rhizobium* that which lives in a root.

Rods which measure 0.5 to 0.9 by 1.2 to 3.0 microns. Motile when young, commonly changing to bacteroidal forms (a) upon artificial culture media containing alkaloids or glucosides, or in which acidity is increased, or (b) during symbiosis within the nodule. Gram-negative. Aerobic. Heterotrophic, growing best with extracts of yeast, malt or other plant materials. Nitrites may be produced from nitrates. Nitrites are not utilized. Gelatin is not liquefied or is very slightly liquefied after long incubation. Optimum temperature, 25° C. This group is capable of producing nodules on the roots of *Leguminosae* and of fixing free nitrogen during this symbiosis.

The type species is *Rhizobium leguminosarum* Frank.

*Original revision by Dr. and Mrs. O. N. Allen, University of Wisconsin, Madison, Wisconsin, January, 1938; further revision by Dr. O. N. Allen, September, 1953.

Key to the species of genus **Rhizobium.**

I. Litmus milk alkaline.
    A. Forms a serum zone in milk. Young cells peritrichous.
        1. Causes formation of root nodules on species of the genera *Lathyrus, Pisum, Vicia* and *Lens.* Bacteroids irregular with x-, y-, star- and club-shaped forms.

                                                1. Rhizobium leguminosarum.

        2. Causes formation of root nodules on *Phaseolus vulgaris, P. multiflorus* and *P. angustifolius.* Bacteroids, vacuolated rods, few branched forms.

                                                2. Rhizobium phaseoli.

        3. Causes formation of nodules on species in the genus *Trifolium.* Bacteroids pear-shaped, swollen, vacuolated. Pentoses usually not fermented.

                                                3. Rhizobium trifolii.

    B. No serum zone formed in milk. Monotrichous cells usually occur; in some cases all motile cells are monotrichous.
        1. Causes formation of nodules on species of the genus *Lupinus* and on *Ornithopus sativus.* Bacteroids vacuolated, rods seldom branched.

                                                4. Rhizobium lupini.

        2. Causes formation of nodules on *Soja max.* Bacteroids long, slender rods, seldom vacuolated or branched.

                                            5. Rhizobium japonicum.[*]

II. Litmus milk acid. Forms a serum zone in milk. Causes formation of root nodules on species of the genera *Melilotus, Medicago* and *Trigonella.* Bacteroids club-shaped, branched. Young cells peritrichous.

                                              6. Rhizobium meliloti.

---

1. Rhizobium leguminosarum Frank, 1890, *emend.* Baldwin and Fred, 1929. (Frank, Landwirtschäftliche Jahrbücher, *19*, 1890, 563; Baldwin and Fred, Jour. Bact., *17*, 1929, 146.)

le.gu.mi.no.sa′rum. M.L. fem.pl.n. *Leguminosae* old family name of the legumes; M.L. fem.pl.gen.n. *leguminosarum* of legumes.

Rods, 0.5 to 0.9 by 1.2 to 3.0 microns. Motile by means of peritrichous flagella. Bacteroids commonly irregular with x-, y-, star- and club-shaped forms. Vacuolate forms predominate. Gram-negative.

Growth on mannitol agar is rapid, with tendency to spread. Streak is raised, glistening, semi-translucent, white, slimy and occasionally viscous. Considerable gum is formed.

Slight acid production from glucose, galactose, mannose, lactose and maltose.

Aerobic.

Optimum temperature, 25° C.

Source: Isolated from root nodules on *Lathyrus, Pisum* (pea), *Vicia* (vetch) and *Lens* (lentil).

Habitat: Widely distributed in soils where the above-mentioned legumes are grown.

2. Rhizobium phaseoli Dangeard, 1926. (Le Botaniste, Sér. *16*, 1926, 197.)

pha.se′o.li. Gr. noun *phaselus* the kidney bean; L. noun *phaseolus* the kidney bean; M.L. mas.n. *Phaseolus* generic name of the bean; M.L. gen.noun *phaseoli* of *Phaseolus.*

Rods. Motile by means of peritrichous flagella. Bacteroids are usually rod-shaped, often vacuolated with few branched forms.

---

[*] No specific name has been proposed for the organism causing the formation of nodules on plants that are members of the so-called "cowpea" group. Data showing possible interrelationships of certain plant species of the soybean and cowpea cross-inoculation groups prompted Walker and Brown (Soil Science, *39*, 1935, 221–225) to propose a consolidation of the two groups to be recognized as being inoculated by a single species, *Rhizobium japonicum.* Results obtained by Reid and Baldwin (Proc. Soil Sci. Soc. Amer. for 1936, *1*, 1937, 219) show these inter-relationships to include the lupine group also.

Usually smaller than in *Rhizobium legumi-nosarum* and *R. trifolii*. Gram-negative.

Growth on mannitol agar is rapid with tendency to spread. Streak inoculation is raised, glistening, semi-translucent, white, slimy. Occasionally mucilaginous, but this character is not so marked as in *Rhizobium trifolii*.

Very slight acid formation from glucose, galactose, mannose, sucrose and lactose.

Aerobic.

Optimum temperature, 25° C.

Source: Isolated from root nodules of *Phaseolus vulgaris* (kidney bean), *P. angustifolius* (bean) and *P. multiflorus* (scarlet runner) (Burrill and Hansen, Ill. Agr. Exp. Sta. Bul. 202, 1917, 137).

Habitat: Widely distributed in the soils in which beans are grown.

3. Rhizobium trifolii Dangeard, 1926.

(Le Botaniste, Sér. *16*, 1926, 191.)

tri.fo′li.i. L. noun *trifolium* clover, trefoil; M.L. neut.n. *Trifolium* generic name of clover; M.L. gen.noun *trifolii* of clover.

Rods. Motile by means of peritrichous flagella. Bacteroids from nodules are pear-shaped, swollen and vacuolated, rarely x- or y-shaped. Gram-negative.

Growth on mannitol agar is rapid. The colonies are white becoming turbid with age. Frequently mucilaginous. Streak cultures transparent at first. Growth mucilaginous, later flowing down the agar slant and accumulating as a slimy mass at the bottom. Produces large amounts of gum.

Slight acid production from glucose, galactose, mannose, lactose and maltose.

Aerobic.

Optimum temperature, 25° C.

Source: Isolated from root nodules of species of *Trifolium* (clover).

Habitat: Widely distributed in the soils where clover grows.

4. Rhizobium lupini (Schroeter, 1886) Eckhardt et al., 1931.

(*Phytomyxa lupini* Schroeter, in Cohn, Kryptogamen-Flora von Schlesien, *3*, I, 1886, 135; Eckhardt, Baldwin and Fred, Jour. Bact., *21*, 1931, 273.)

lu.pi′ni. L. noun *lupinus* the lupine; M.L.

mas.n. *Lupinus* generic name of lupine; M.L. gen.noun *lupini* of *Lupinus*.

Rods. Motile by means of 1 to 4 flagella, usually 2 or 3. Bacteroids are vacuolate rods, seldom if ever branched. Gram-negative.

Growth on yeast water, mannitol agar is scant to moderate with alkaline reaction.

Beef-peptone gelatin: Little growth with extremely slow liquefaction.

On galactose an alkaline reaction serves to differentiate *Rhizobium lupini* from all fast-growing rhizobia (*R. phaseoli, R. meliloti, R. trifolii* and *R. leguminosarum*). An initial alkaline reaction followed more quickly by an acid reaction on rhamnose and xylose separates *R. lupini* from slow-growing *R. japonicum* and the *Rhizobium sp.* from cowpea.

In general *Rhizobium lupini* produces slight to moderate acidity on pentose sugars and no change or alkaline reaction on hexoses, disaccharides or trisaccharides.

Litmus milk: No serum zone; no reduction; slight alkaline reaction.

Meager growth on potato and parsnip slants and on carrot agar.

Aerobic.

Optimum temperature, 25° C.

Source: Isolated from root nodules on *Lupinus* (lupine), *Serradella* and *Ornithopus*.

Habitat: Widely distributed in soils in which these legumes grow.

5. Rhizobium japonicum (Kirchner, 1895) Buchanan, 1926.

(*Rhizobacterium japonicum* Kirchner, Beiträge z. Biol. d. Pflanzen, *7*, 1895, 213; Buchanan, Proc. Iowa Acad. Sci., *33*, 1926, 81.)

ja.po′ni.cum. M.L. adj. *japonicus* of Japan.

Rods. Motile by means of monotrichous flagella. Bacteroids of nodules are long and slender with only occasional branched and swollen forms. Gram-negative.

Growth on mannitol agar is slow and scant. The streak is slightly raised, glistening, opaque, white, butyrous, with little gum formation.

Pentose sugars give better growth than the hexoses.

Little if any acid formed from carbohydrates. Acid slowly formed from xylose and arabinose.

Aerobic.

Optimum temperature, 25° C.

Source: Isolated from root nodules on *Soja max* (soy bean).

Habitat: Widely distributed in soils where soy beans are grown.

6. Rhizobium meliloti Dangeard, 1926. (Le Botaniste, Sér. *16*, 1926, 194.)

me.li.lo'ti. Gr. noun *meli* honey; Gr. noun *lotus* the lotus; Gr. noun *melilotus* melilot or sweet clover; M.L. fem.n. *Melilotus* generic name of sweet clover; M.L. gen.noun *meliloti* of *Melilotus*.

Rods. Motile by means of peritrichous flagella. Bacteroids club-shaped and branched. Gram-negative.

Growth on mannitol agar is fairly rapid. The streak is raised, glistening, opaque, pearly white, butyrous. Considerable gum is formed.

Acid from glucose, galactose, mannose and sucrose.

Aerobic.

Optimum temperature, 25° C.

Source: Isolated from root nodules of *Melilotus* (sweet clover), *Medicago* and *Trigonella*.

Habitat: Widely distributed in soils in which these legumes grow.

Genus II. **Agrobacterium** *Conn, 1942.**

(Jour. Bact., *44*, 1942, 359.)

Ag.ro.bac.te'ri.um. Gr. noun *agrus* a field; Gr. dim.neut.n. *bacterium* a small rod; M.L neut.n. *Agrobacterium* field rodlet or bacterium.

Small, short rods which are typically motile by means of 1 to 4 peritrichous flagella (if only one flagellum, lateral attachment is as common as polar). Ordinarily Gram-negative. On ordinary culture media they do not produce visible gas nor sufficient acid to be detectable by litmus. In synthetic media, enough CO_2 may be produced to show acid with brom thymol blue or sometimes with brom cresol purple. Gelatin is either very slowly liquefied or not at all. Free nitrogen cannot be fixed, but other inorganic forms of nitrogen (nitrates or ammonium salts) can ordinarily be utilized. Optimum temperature, between 25° and 30°C. Found in soil, in plant roots in the soil or in the stems of plants where they produce hypertrophies; occasionally from marine sources.

The type species is *Agrobacterium tumefaciens* (Smith and Townsend) Conn.

Key to the species of genus **Agrobacterium.**

I. Plant pathogens.
    A. Nitrites produced from nitrates, sometimes only to a slight extent.
        1. Produce galls on angiosperms.
            a. Indole production slight.
                1. *Agrobacterium tumefaciens.*
            aa. Indole not produced.
                2. *Agrobacterium gypsophilae.*
        2. Produces galls on gymnosperms.
                3. *Agrobacterium pseudotsugae.*
    B. Nitrites not produced from nitrates.
        1. Pathogenic to apples.
                4. *Agrobacterium rhizogenes.*
        2. Pathogenic to raspberries and blackberries.
                5. *Agrobacterium rubi.*

---

* Originally prepared by Prof. H. J. Conn, New York State Experiment Station, Cornell University, Geneva, New York, September, 1943; revised by Prof. Walter H. Burkholder, Cornell University, Ithaca, New York, July, 1954.

II. Not pathogenic to plants.
  A. From soil. Grows on potato. Nitrates completely assimilated; test for nitrites may
  be negative.
                    6. *Agrobacterium radiobacter.*
  B. From marine mud. Does not grow on potato. Nitrites produced from nitrates.
                    7. *Agrobacterium stellulatum.*

1. **Agrobacterium tumefaciens** (Smith and Townsend, 1907) Conn, 1942. (*Bacterium tumefaciens* Erw. Smith and Townsend, Science, *25* (N.S.), 1907, 672; Conn, Jour. Bact., *44*, 1942, 359.)

tu.me.fa'ci.ens. L. part.adj. *tumefaciens* tumor-producing.

Description taken from Riker, Banfield, Wright, Keitt and Sagen (Jour. Agr. Res., *41*, 1930, 507), Sagen, Riker and Baldwin (Jour. Bact., *28*, 1934, 571) and Hendrickson, Baldwin and Riker (Jour. Bact., *28*, 1934, 597).

Rods, 0.7 to 0.8 by 2.5 to 3.0 microns, occurring singly or in pairs. Encapsulated. Motile by means of 1 to 4 flagella. Gram-negative.

Agar colonies: Small, white, circular, smooth, glistening, translucent, entire.

Broth: Slightly turbid, with thin pellicle.

Litmus milk: Slow coagulation. Litmus reduced. Neutral to alkaline.

Indole production slight.

Slight acid from glucose, fructose, arabinose, galactose, mannitol and salicin.

Starch not hydrolyzed.

Nitrites produced from nitrates to a very slight extent.

Optimum temperature, between 25° and 28° C.

Facultative anaerobe.

Distinctive characters: Causes a gall formation, parenchymatous in character, which, because of its soft nature, is subject to injury and decay.

Agrobacterium tumefaciens strongly absorbs congo red and aniline blue in contrast to little or no absorption by *A. rhizogenes*. *A. tumefaciens* makes abundant growth on sodium selenite agar and calcium glycerophosphate medium with mannitol in contrast to no growth or a very slight trace by *A. rhizogenes* (Hendrickson et al., *loc. cit.*).

Comment: A variety of this species that causes galls on blueberry has been described by Demaree and Smith (Phytopath., *42*, 1952, 88).

Source: Isolated from galls on plants.

Habitat: Causes galls on Paris daisy and is cross-inoculable on over 40 families.

2. **Agrobacterium gypsophilae** (Brown, 1934) Starr and Weiss, 1943. (*Bacterium gypsophilae* Brown, Jour. Agr. Res., *48*, 1934, 1109; Starr and Weiss, Phytopath., *33*, 1943, 316.)

gyp.so'phi.lae. Gr. noun *gypsus* chalk; Gr. adj. *philus* loving; M.L. fem.n. *Gypsophila* chalk-lover, generic name; M.L. gen.noun *gypsophilae* of *Gypsophila.*

Rods, 0.2 to 0.8 by 0.4 to 1.4 microns. Motile by means of 1 to 4 flagella. Encapsulated. Gram-negative.

Gelatin: Liquefaction slow, beginning after 1 month.

Beef-infusion agar colonies: Circular, Naples-yellow, smooth or rough, butyrous.

Broth: Turbid in 24 hours.

Milk: Coagulation and peptonization.

Indole not produced.

Hydrogen sulfide: A trace may be produced.

Acid but no gas from glucose, sucrose, maltose, mannitol and glycerol. No acid from lactose.

Starch not hydrolyzed.

Nitrites produced from nitrates.

Aerobic, facultative.

Distinctive characters: Differs from *Xanthomonas beticola* in starch hydrolysis and hydrogen sulfide production; furthermore, these two species cannot be cross-inoculated.

Source: Isolated from several galls on *Gypsophila.*

Habitat: Produces galls in *Gypsophila paniculata* and related plants.

3. **Agrobacterium pseudotsugae** (Hansen and Smith, 1937) Săvulescu, 1947. (*Bacterium pseudotsugae* Hansen and R. E. Smith, Hilgardia, *10*, 1937, 576; Săvulescu, Anal. Acad. Romane, III, *22*, 1947, 10.)

pseu.do.tsu'gae. Gr. adj. *pseudes* false; Jap. noun *tsuga* an evergreen; M.L. fem.n. *Tsuga* generic name of hemlock; M.L. fem.n. *Pseudotsuga* false *Tsuga*, a generic name; M.L. gen.noun *pseudotsugae* of *Pseudotsuga*.

Rods 0.5 to 1.5 by 1.9 to 3.9 microns. Probably motile; type of flagellation doubtful. Gram-negative.

Gelatin: Liquefied.

Nutrient agar slant: Growth scant, flat, glistening, smooth, translucent, whitish.

Broth: Growth slight. No sediment.

Milk: No acid.

Hydrogen sulfide production slight.

Acid but no gas from glucose, fructose, galactose and maltose. No acid or gas from lactose, sucrose or glycerol.

Starch not hydrolyzed.

Nitrites produced from nitrates.

Facultative aerobe.

Source: Isolated from galls on Douglas fir in California.

Habitat: Pathogenic on Douglas fir, *Pseudotsuga taxifolia*.

4. **Agrobacterium rhizogenes** (Riker et al., 1930) Conn, 1942. (*Bacterium rhizogenes* Riker, Banfield, Wright, Keitt and Sagen, Jour. Agr. Res., *41*, 1930, 536; Conn, Jour. Bact., *44*, 1942, 359.)

rhi.zo'ge.nes. Gr. noun *rhiza* a root; Gr. v. *genneō* to produce; M.L. adj. *rhizogenes* root-producing.

Rods, 0.4 by 1.4 microns, occurring singly. Motile by means of 1 to 4 flagella. Encapsulated. Not acid-fast. Gram-negative.

Gelatin: No liquefaction.

Agar colonies: Circular, smooth, convex, finely granular; optical characters, translucent through gray to almost white.

Agar slant: Moderate, filiform, translucent, raised, smooth, slimy.

Broth: Turbid, with heavy pellicle.

Litmus milk: Acid, slow reduction.

Indole not produced.

Nitrites not produced from nitrates.

Acid but no gas from arabinose, xylose, rhamnose, glucose, galactose, mannose, maltose, lactose, salicin and erythritol. No acid or gas from fructose, sucrose, raffinose, melezitose, starch, dextrin, inulin, aesculin, dulcitol or mannitol.

Starch not hydrolyzed.

Optimum temperature, between 20° and 28° C.

Aerobic.

Distinctive characters: *Agrobacterium rhizogenes* differs from *Agrobacterium tumefaciens* by stimulating root formation instead of soft, parenchymatous crown galls. *A. rhizogenes* lacks the ability of *A. tumefaciens* to utilize simple nitrogenous compounds as KNO_3. *A. rhizogenes* absorbs congo red and brom thymol blue slightly and aniline blue not at all. Will not grow on sodium selenite agar (see *A. tumefaciens* for response to same materials). Does not infect tomato.

Source: Isolated from hairy-root of apple and other plants.

Habitat: Pathogenic on apple, etc.

5. **Agrobacterium rubi** (Hildebrand, 1940) Starr and Weiss, 1943. (*Phytomonas rubi* Hildebrand, Jour. Agr. Res., *61*, 1940, 694; Starr and Weiss, Phytopath., *33*, 1943, 316.)

ru'bi. L. noun *rubus* the blackberry; L. noun *Rubus* generic name of blackberry; L. gen.noun *rubi* of *Rubus*.

Rods, 0.6 by 1.7 microns, occurring singly, in pairs or in short chains. Motile by means of 1 to 4 flagella. Gram-negative.

Gelatin: No liquefaction.

Potato-mannitol-agar slants: Growth slow, moderate, filiform, white to creamy white, with butyrous consistency later becoming leathery.

Broth: Turbid in 36 to 48 hours.

Milk: A slight serum zone; pink color; acid and curd formed.

Hydrogen sulfide not produced.

Indole not produced.

Acid from glucose, d-galactose, d-mannose, d-fructose, d-xylose, d-arabinose, sucrose and maltose. None from lactose (Pinckard, Jour. Agr. Res., *50*, 1935, 933).

Starch not hydrolyzed.

Nitrites not produced from nitrates.

Ferric ammonium citrate, uric acid, oxamide, succinimide, l-asparagine, l-tyrosine, l-cystine, d-glutamic acid and yeast extract can be used as a source of nitrogen (Pinckard, *loc. cit.*).

Temperature relations: Optimum, 28° C. Minimum, 8° C. Maximum, 36° C. (Pinckard, *loc. cit.*).

Distinctive characters: Differs from *Agrobacterium tumefaciens* in that it does not utilize nitrates and grows much more slowly on ordinary media. Infects only members of the genus *Rubus*. Starr and Weiss (Phytopath., *33*, 1943, 317) state that this species, unlike *Agrobacterium tumefaciens* and *Agrobacterium rhizogenes*, does not utilize asparagin as a sole source of carbon and nitrogen.

Source: Isolated from raspberry canes, *Rubus spp.*

Habitat: Pathogenic on black and purple cane raspberries, on blackberries and, to a lesser extent, on red raspberries.

6. Agrobacterium radiobacter (Beijerinck and van Delden, 1902) Conn, 1942. (*Bacillus radiobacter* Beijerinck and van Delden, Cent. f. Bakt., II Abt., *9*, 1902, 3; Conn. Jour. Bact., *44*, 1942, 359.)

ra.di.o.bac'ter. L. noun *radius* a ray, beam; M.L. *bacter* masculine equivalent of Gr. neut.n. *bactrum* a rod or staff; M.L. mas.n. *radiobacter* ray rod.

Small rods, 0.15 to 0.75 by 0.3 to 2.3 microns, occurring singly, in pairs and, under certain conditions, in star-shaped clusters. Motile with one to four flagella. Prevailingly Gram-negative, but an occasional culture is variable.

Nutrient gelatin stab: No liquefaction.

Agar slant: Flat, whitish slimy layer.

Mannitol-calcium-glycerophosphate agar streak plates: Abundant, raised, slimy growth surrounded by a brown halo with an outer zone of white precipitate (Riker et al., Jour. Agr. Res., *41*, 1930, 524).

Broth: Turbid; heavy ring or pellicle if veal infusion is present.

Litmus milk: Serum zone with pellicle in one week; usually turns a chocolate-brown in 2 weeks; same in plain milk, but with less browning.

Potato: Raised slimy mass becoming brownish; potato may be browned.

Starch not hydrolyzed.

No organic acid or visible gas from sugars; nearly all sugars, glycerol and mannitol are utilized with the production of CO_2.

Nitrates completely assimilated; test for nitrites may be negative (Hofer, Jour. Bact., *41*, 1941, 202).

Temperature relations: Optimum, 28° C. Minimum, near 1° C. Maximum, 45° C.

Aerobic.

Media containing KNO_3, K_2HPO_4 and glycerol, ethanol or propanol become alkaline to phenol red (Sagen, Riker and Baldwin, Jour. Bact., *28*, 1934, 581).

Growth occurs in special alkaline media of pH 11.0 to 12.0 (Hofer, Jour. Amer. Soc. Agron., *27*, 1935, 228).

Hydrogen sulfide produced if grown in ZoBell and Feltham's medium (ZoBell and Feltham, Jour. Bact., *28*, 1934, 169).

Distinctive characters: Browning of mannitol-calcium-glycerophosphate agar; inability to cause plant disease or to produce nodules on roots of legumes; complete utilization of nitrate (the nitrate disappears) in the peptone-salt medium of Riker et al. (Riker et al., Jour. Agr. Res., *41*, 1930, 529) and failure to absorb congo red (Riker et al., *ibid.*, 528).

This species bears at least superficial resemblances to certain *Rhizobium spp.* but may be distinguished from them by the first two characters listed above and by the following in addition: Growth at a reaction of pH 11 to 12; heavy ring or pellicle formation on veal infusion broth; hydrogen sulfide production in the mannitol-tryptone medium of ZoBell and Feltham (ZoBell and Feltham, *op. cit.*, 1934, 169); production of milky white precipitate on nitrate-glycerol-soil-extract agar.

Source: Isolated from soil.

Habitat: Soil around the roots of plants, especially legumes.

7. Agrobacterium stellulatum Stapp and Knösel, 1954. (Zent. f. Bakt., II Abt., *108*, 1954, 244.)

stel.lu.la'tum. L. noun *stella* star; M.L. adj. *stellulatus* resembling a small star.

Rods, 0.2 to 0.8 by 0.3 to 2.1 microns, occurring singly or in pairs; in certain media, star-like clusters are found. Motile by means of a single, polar flagellum. Not acid-fast. Gram-negative.

Gelatin: No liquefaction.

Peptone agar colonies: Small, round, smooth, gray, glistening.

Peptone agar slant: Growth is poor, widely spread, colorless to whitish, translucent and resembles droplets of moisture.

Mannitol-calcium-glycerophosphate agar slant: Weak growth resembling a film of droplets of moisture.

Broth: Slightly turbid; no pellicle; very small sediment.

Broth with KNO$_3$: Acid toward phenol red.

Sea-water medium 2216: Weak growth; good formation of star-shaped clusters.

Carrot agar: Very weak growth.

Iron-manganese-carrot juice: Very weak development; no surface growth; no star-shaped clusters.

Iron-manganese-sea water-carrot juice: Good growth; thin, easily destroyed, surface film; no star-shaped clusters.

Litmus milk: Slight growth with a neutral to alkaline reaction; litmus slowly decolorized; no peptonization.

Potato: No growth.

Indole not produced.

Nitrites produced from nitrates.

Congo red is weakly absorbed.

No growth at pH 4.5.

Optimum temperature, between 15° and 25° C.

Distinctive characters: May be distinguished from *Agrobacterium radiobacter* and *A. tumefaciens* by weak growth on bouillon or bouillon agar, by forming star-like clusters on sea-water medium 2216, by weak growth on calcium-glycerophosphate agar, by weak absorption of Congo red, by failure to grow on potato, by very weak growth on carrot agar or Fe-Mn-carrot juice and by forming star-like clusters on Fe-Mn-sea water-carrot juice.

Source: Isolated from marine mud.

Habitat: Marine sources.

Genus III. **Chromobacterium** *Bergonzini, 1881.**

(*Cromobacterium* (sic) Bergonzini, Ann. Societa d. Naturalisti in Modena, Ser. 2, *14*, 1881, 153.)

Chro.mo.bac.te′ri.um. Gr. noun *chroma* color; Gr. noun *bacterium* a small rod; M.L. neut.n. *Chromobacterium* colored rod.

Rods which measure 0.4 to 0.8 by 1.0 to 5.0 microns. Motile by means of 1 to 4 or more flagella. Gram-negative. A violet pigment (violacein) is produced which is soluble in alcohol but not in water or chloroform. Grow on ordinary culture media, usually forming acid from glucose, sometimes from maltose and sucrose, but not from lactose. Gelatin is liquefied, sometimes slowly. Indole is not produced. Nitrites usually produced from nitrates; the nitrites are frequently further reduced to nitrogen and possibly nitrous oxide. Some strains grow well at 4° C. while others grow well at 37° C. with a maximum temperature of between 40° and 42° C.; none grow at both 4° and 37° C. Usually saprophytic soil and water bacteria. Occasionally pathogenic to animals and man.

The type species is *Chromobacterium violaceum* (Schroeter) Bergonzini.

Discussion: The most characteristic feature of this group is its production of a violet pigment. The chemistry of this pigment has been well worked out by Tobie (Bull. Assoc. Diplomes Microbiol., Fac. Pharm. de Nancy, No. 18, 1939, 7). Since violacein appears to be chemically related to indigo, peritrichous organisms producing the latter pigment may tentatively be placed in this genus pending further study (Tobie, Jour. Bact., *35*, 1938, 11). Cultures of violet bacteria are difficult to maintain in culture collections and are frequently

---

* Prepared by Prof. Robert S. Breed, New York State Experiment Station, Cornell University, Geneva, New York, from Cruess-Callaghan and Gorman, Scientific Proc. Royal Dublin Society, *21*, 1935, 213, in January, 1938; further revision, July, 1955, with the assistance of Dr. Ethel T. Eltinge, Mount Holyoke College, South Hadley, Massachusetts, and Dr. W. C. Tobie, Old Greenwich, Connecticut.

lost (Sneath, Jour. Gen. Microbiol., *13*, 1955, p. I, has recently reported that these organisms are highly sensitive to traces of hydrogen peroxide in the medium). They have a tendency to produce mucous, gummy, gelatinous or even leathery growths (Corpe, Jour. Bact., *66*, 1953, 470).

The separation of the true violet chromogens into three species is in accord with the recommendations of Cruess-Callaghan and Gorman (Sci. Proc. Royal Dublin Soc., *21*, 1938, 213). Their conclusions were based on a study of 18 named cultures from culture collections and 6 freshly isolated cultures. Others have studied this same problem. For example, Hans and Bicknell (Bact. Proc. 53rd Gen. Meeting Soc. Amer. Bact., San Francisco, 1953, 33) agree that only a few species should be recognized. Eltinge (personal communication, Sept., 1955), after a study of a collection of 88 cultures, reports that the group may readily be separated into cultures that will grow at 4° but not at 37° C. and cultures that will not grow at 4° but do grow at 37° to 42° C. This seems to be one of the most constant of the differences in characters, and it is used in the classification drawn up by Cruess-Callaghan and Gorman.

There is a partial correlation between the growth-temperature relationships and the ability to reduce nitrate (Eltinge, Antonie van Leeuwenhoek, *22*, 1956, 139). Some cultures (*Chromobacterium violaceum*) that may give a negative test for nitrite production actually reduce the nitrate so rapidly with the production of free gas that they have sometimes been reported in the literature as failing to reduce nitrate. Other cultures merely reduce the nitrate to nitrite (*Chromobacterium janthinum*), while still other cultures do not attack nitrate at all.

Corpe (Jour. Bact., *62*, 1951, 515) found that he could readily isolate these organisms by adding sterile rice grains to moistened soil. The latter observation confirms an earlier observation by Beijerinck (Folia Microbiologica, *4*, 1916, 207) who added wheat bran or fibrin to tap-water infusions in order to develop these violet bacteria. Starchy substances appear to stimulate growth, as all grow abundantly on potato with a yellow growth that usually turns to a dark violet or purple.

A number of organisms have been classed as species of *Chromobacterium* because they develop a bluish chromogenesis without regard to the fact that their pigments are not chemically the same as violacein. The majority of these cultures are polar flagellate and have been shown to belong to the genus *Pseudomonas*. Frequently these blue pigments are water-soluble and have a tendency to become rose-colored.

The violet organisms differ in important respects from the organisms placed in *Serratia*. The latter produce prodigiosin and belong with the coliform group. The violet organisms show the same type of gummy colony growth that is characteristic of many of the species found in *Rhizobiaceae*, their carbohydrate metabolism is like that of the species in this family, and they possess the same unusual type of monotrichous to peritrichous flagellation. The position of the violet bacteria in the family *Rhizobiaceae* appears to be a natural one.

In recent years these violet bacteria have been found in fatal septicemias in man and animals (see Sippel, Medina and Atwood, (good bibliography), Jour. Amer. Vet. Med. Assoc., *124*, 1954, 467; Audebaud, Ganzin, Ceccaldi and Merveille, Ann. Inst. Past., *87*, 1954, 413; and Black and Shahan, Jour. Amer. Med. Assoc., *110*, 1938, 1270). These pathogenic organisms have frequently been identified as *Chromobacterium violaceum* Bergonzini because they produce a violet pigmentation. However, by definition, this species does not grow at 37° C. In the early literature *C. janthinum* Zopf was sometimes regarded as a separate species, while in other cases *C. violaceum* and *C. janthinum* were regarded as identical. Inasmuch as both Schroeter and Bergonzini, the investigators who first described *C. violaceum*, grew their organisms at room temperature, and inasmuch as descriptions list them as growing at room temperature while *C. janthinum* is normally described as growing *best* at room temperature, Cruess-Callaghan and Gorman emended the descriptions of these two species in such a way as to make *C. violaceum* the organism which will not grow at 37° C. while they describe *C. janthinum* as growing at 37° C. In view of these emended descriptions, the violet organisms isolated from warm-blooded animals should be identified as *C. janthinum* not as *C. violaceum.*

Key to the species of genus Chromobacterium.

I. Fresh-water and soil oganisms that produce a violet chromogenesis.
    A. No growth at 37° C.
        1. Gelatin stab may show violet ring or pellicle.
                1. *Chromobacterium violaceum.*
        2. Gelatin stab develops heavy membranous growth on liquefied gelatin. Usually violet in color.
            2. *Chromobacterium amethystinum.*
    B. Growth at 37° C.
            3. *Chromobacterium janthinum.*
II. Optimum growth in media containing 12 per cent salt. Chromogenesis bluish to blue-brown or yellowish.
            4. *Chromobacterium marismortui.*

1. Chromobacterium violaceum (Schroeter, 1872) Bergonzini, 1881. (*Bacteridium violaceum* Schroeter, Beiträge z. Biol. d. Pflanzen, *1*, Heft 2, 1872, 126; *Cromobacterium violaceum* (sic) Bergonzini, Ann. Societa d. Naturalisti in Modena, Ser. 2, *14*, 1881, 153.)

vi.o.la′ce.um. L. adj. *violaceus* violet-colored.

Slender rods, 0.8 to 1.0 by 2.0 to 5.0 microns, occurring singly and in chains. Motile, usually by means of a single flagellum, but some cells show several flagella arranged peritrichously. Gram-negative.

Gelatin colonies: Circular, gray, entire, sometimes with a violet center.

Gelatin stab: Infundibuliform liquefaction, sometimes with violet ring or pellicle and sediment.

Agar colonies: Whitish, flat, glistening, moist, becoming violet.

Agar slant: Violet, moist, sometimes gummy, shiny, spreading growth.

Broth: Slightly turbid; violet ring; granular to viscid sediment.

Litmus milk: Violet ring or pellicle. Digestion slow. Alkaline.

Potato: Growth yellow to dark violet.

Löffler's blood serum: Slow liquefaction.

Indole not produced.

Acid from glucose and usually from maltose and sucrose. No acid from lactose.

Nitrites produced from nitrates and frequently reduced further to a gas (N_2).

Aerobic, facultative.

Temperature relations: Optimum, between 25° and 30° C. Slight growth between 2° and 4° C. No growth at 37° C.

Source: Isolated from slices of cooked potato which had been exposed to air contamination and then incubated at room temperature.

Habitat: Soil and water.

2. Chromobacterium amethystinum (Chester, 1897) Holland, 1920. (*Bacillus membranaceus amethystinus* Eisenberg, Bakt. Diag., 1891, 421; *Bacterium amethystinus* (sic) Chester, Ann. Rept. Del. Col. Agr. Exp. Sta., *9*, 1897, 117; Holland, Jour. Bact., *5*, 1920, 222.)

a.me.thys′ti.num. Gr. adj. *amethystinus* of amethyst.

Rods, 0.5 to 0.8 by 1.0 to 1.4 microns, occurring singly. Motile with a single or occasionally with peritrichous flagella. Gram-negative.

Gelatin colonies: Thin, bluish, becoming violet, crumpled.

Gelatin stab: Heavy, violet-black pellicle. Liquefied.

Agar colonies: Deep violet, surface rugose.

Agar slant: Thick, moist, gummy, rugose, yellowish white growth, becoming violet sometimes with a metallic luster.

Broth: Pellicle; violet sediment; fluid becoming violet.

Litmus milk: Violet pellicle. Digestion turning alkaline.

Potato: Yellow to deep violet, rugose, spreading growth.

Indole not produced.

Usually no acid from glucose, maltose or sucrose. No acid from lactose.

Nitrites produced from nitrates.

Aerobic, facultative.

Temperature relations: Optimum, 30° C. Good growth in 7 days between 2° and 4° C. No growth at 37° C.

Comment: The most characteristic feature of the original culture of this species was its ability to grow a heavy, folded, membranous pellicle on gelatin stabs and other media. The original culture also sometimes produced a metallic sheen. If the descriptions of all of the cultures regarded by Cruess-Callaghan and Gorman (Scientific Proc. Royal Dublin Soc., *21*, 1935, 219) as *C. amethystinum* are taken into account, there really are no other important characters by which this species can be separated from *C. violaceum*. Moreover, those that have studied many cultures of these violet organisms over a long period of time, with replatings to purify, report that this membranous growth may develop on almost any subculture of typical *C. violaceum*. The formation of this heavy, folded growth should therefore probably be regarded as a dissociation phenomenon. Further comparative studies will presumably show that *C. amethystinum* should be regarded as a variant form of *C. violaceum*.

Source: Isolated once by Jolles from spring water from Spalato.

Habitat: Water.

3. **Chromobacterium janthinum** (Zopf, 1883) Holland, 1920. (*Bacterium janthinum* Zopf, Die Spaltpilze, 1 Aufl., 1883, 68; Holland, Jour. Bact., *5*, 1920, 222.)

jan'thi.num. Gr. adj. *janthinus* violet-colored.

Rods, 0.5 to 0.8 by 1.5 to 5.0 microns, occurring singly. Motile with peritrichous flagella. Gram-negative.

Gelatin colonies: Circular, yellow, becoming violet.

Gelatin stab: White to violet surface growth. Infundibuliform liquefaction.

Agar colonies: Creamy center, violet margin.

Agar slant: Yellowish, moist, gummy, glistening growth becoming deep violet.

Broth: Turbid, with light violet pellicle.

Litmus milk: Violet cream layer. Litmus decolorized from below. Rapid digestion.

Potato: Violet to violet-black, spreading growth.

Indole not produced.

Acid from glucose. No acid from maltose, lactose or sucrose.

Nitrites generally produced from nitrates.

Aerobic, facultative.

Temperature relations: Optimum, 30° C. No growth between 2° and 4° C. Grows well at 37° C.

Source: Isolated from pieces of pig's bladder floating on badly contaminated water.

Habitat: Water and soil. This appears to be the species that causes a fatal septicemia in animals and man.

4. **Chromobacterium marismortui** Elazari-Volcani, 1940. (Studies on the Microflora of the Dead Sea. Thesis, Hebrew Univ., Jerusalem, 1940, VII and 76.)

ma.ris.mor'tu.i. L. noun *mare* the sea; L. gen. noun *maris* of the sea; L. adj. *mortuus* dead; M.L. gen. noun *marismortui* of the Dead Sea.

Rods, the length of which varies greatly with the concentration of salt and media. On agar media, in 3 to 24 per cent salt, the cells are usually 0.5 by 1.3 to 3.0 microns; in liquid media, 4.5 to 13.0 microns. Occur singly and in pairs. In 0.5 and 30 per cent salt and in Dead Sea water, the cells are usually very long, twisted threads. Motile by means of 4 to 6 peritrichous flagella. Gram-negative.

Gelatin stab (12 per cent salt-1 per cent proteose peptone-15 per cent gelatin): Filiform, blue-brown, nailhead surface growth. Very slight infundibuliform liquefaction after six weeks.

Agar colonies (12 per cent salt-1 per cent proteose peptone-2 per cent KNO_3): Circular, smooth, entire, slightly convex and concentrically ringed with dark brown centers followed by blue-brown, gray-brown and yellow rings and a colorless transparent margin. On removing the colony, a print remains in the agar consisting of three zones: a blue center, a brownish gray inner ring and a blue outer ring. Colonies colored only when well separated and at an optimum salt concentration of 12 per cent.

Agar slant (12 per cent salt-1 per cent proteose peptone-2 per cent KNO₃): Moderate, filiform, slightly raised, smooth, slightly transparent growth with a blue-brown margin; leaves a colored print in the agar.

Broth (12 per cent salt-1 per cent peptone): Very turbid; white pellicle; broth turns brown, the color disappearing after several days.

Indole not produced.

Acid without gas from glucose, galactose, maltose, lactose, arabinose and xylose.

Starch not hydrolyzed.

Nitrites produced from nitrates; no gas is produced.

Aerobic.

Optimum temperature, 30° C.

Salt tolerance: Halotolerant, growing in 0.5 to 30 per cent salt and in Dead Sea water. Optimum growth at 12 per cent salt.

Source: Isolated from the water of the Dead Sea.

Habitat: Found in places where the salt content of water is high.

FAMILY III. ACHROMOBACTERACEAE BREED, 1945.

(*Achromobacteriaceae* (sic) Breed, Jour. Bact., *50*, 1945, 124.)

A.chro.mo.bac.te.ra′ce.ae. M.L. mas.n. *Achromobacter* type genus of the family; *-aceae* ending to denote a family; M.L. fem.pl.n. *Achromobacteraceae* the *Achromobacter* family.

Small to medium-sized rods which are usually uniform in shape. Motile by means of peritrichous flagella or non-motile. Gram-negative. May or may not liquefy gelatin. Growth on agar slants is non-chromogenic to yellow, orange, brown or even red; the pigment does not diffuse through the agar and apparently is carotenoid in nature. May produce acid but no gas from glucose and sometimes from other sugars; lactose is very rarely or never attacked. Certain species liquefy agar and/or attack alginates, others digest chitin. May or may not reduce nitrates. Litmus milk may be unchanged, slightly acid (not enough to be curdled) or alkaline. No luminescent species are known. Generally found as salt-water, fresh-water or soil forms, less commonly found as parasites or pathogens. Some plant pathogens may belong here.

Key to the genera of family **Achromobacteraceae.**

I. Do not attack agar, alginates or chitin. Not active in the production of acid from sugars, especially lactose.
    A. Non-chromogenic on ordinary agar media, although the type species of *Achromo bacter* produces yellow chromogenesis on potato.
        1. Litmus milk alkaline. No acid from carbohydrates.

Genus I. *Alcaligenes*, p. 297.

        2. Litmus milk slightly acid (not enough to be curdled), unchanged or alkaline. Small amounts of acid are usually produced from hexoses.

Genus II. *Achromobacter*, p. 300.

    B. Yellow, orange, brown or red chromogenesis produced on ordinary agar media; the pigment is non-water-soluble.

Genus III. *Flavobacterium*, p. 309.

II. Attack agar, alginates or chitin. Slightly more active in the fermentation of sugars than is the previous group, some even attacking lactose. Non-chromogenic or chromogenic, usually with yellow or orange, always non-water-soluble pigments.
    A. Attack agar and/or alginates.

Genus IV. *Agarbacterium*, p. 322.

    B. Attack chitin and sometimes horny substances.

Genus V. *Beneckea*, p. 328.

Genus I. **Alcaligenes** *Castellani and Chalmers, 1919.**

(Manual Trop. Med., 3rd ed., 1919, 936.)

Al.ca.li'ge.nes. Arabic *al* the; Arabic noun *galīy* the ash of saltwort; French noun *alcali* alkali; English *alkali*; Gr. v. *gennaio* to produce; M.L. mas.n. *Alcaligenes* alkali-producing (bacteria).

Rods which are either motile by means of peritrichous flagella or non-motile. Gram-negative. May or may not liquefy gelatin and solidified blood serum. Litmus milk turned alkaline, with or without peptonization. Carbohydrates not utilized. Acetylmethylcarbinol not produced. Chromogenesis, when it occurs, is grayish yellow, brownish yellow or yellow. Generally found in the intestinal tracts of vertebrates or in dairy products.

The type species is *Alcaligenes faecalis* Castellani and Chalmers.

Key to the species of genus **Alcaligenes.**

I. Gelatin not liquefied.
   A. Motile.

1. *Alcaligenes faecalis.*

   B. Non-motile.
   1. Produces ropiness in milk.

2. *Alcaligenes viscolactis.*

   2. Found in the intestinal tract.

3. *Alcaligenes metalcaligenes.*

II. Gelatin liquefied.
   A. Motile.
   1. Milk peptonized; blood serum liquefied.

4. *Alcaligenes bookeri.*

   2. Milk not peptonized; blood serum not liquefied.

5. *Alcaligenes recti.*

   B. Non-motile.

6. *Alcaligenes marshallii.*

1. **Alcaligenes faecalis** Castellani and Chalmers, 1919. (*Bacillus faecalis alcaligenes* Petruschky, Cent. f. Bakt., I Abt., *19*, 1896, 187; *Bacterium alcaligenes* Mez,† Mikroskopische Wasseranalyse, Berlin, 1898, 63; Castellani and Chalmers, Manual Trop. Med., 1919, 936.)

fae.ca'lis. L. noun *faex, faecis* dregs; M.L. adj. *faecalis* fecal.

Description from Petruschky (*op. cit.*, 1896, 187) as supplemented by Dr. Einar Leifson and Dr. Rudolph Hugh, Loyola University, Chicago, Illinois.

Rods, 0.5 by 1.0 to 2.0 microns, occurring singly, in pairs and chains. Normally not encapsulated. Motile by means of peritrichous flagella. Gram-negative.

Gelatin colonies: Circular, grayish, translucent.

Gelatin stab: Gray surface growth. No liquefaction.

Agar colonies: Opaque, entire, non-chromogenic.

Agar slant: White, glistening, non-chromogenic.

---

* Revised by Prof. H. J. Conn, New York State Experiment Station, Geneva, New York, June, 1938; further revision by Prof. Robert S. Breed, New York State Experiment Station, Geneva, New York, October, 1954.

† While Mez (1898) proposed the binomial *Bacterium alcaligenes* earlier than Castellani and Chalmers (1919) proposed the binomial *Alcaligenes faecalis*, the specific epithet *alcaligenes* is unusable when the genus *Alcaligenes* is recognized. The use of the specific epithet *alcaligenes* in the latter genus produces a tautonym, and tautonyms are illegitimate under the Bacteriological Code of Nomenclature (Sect. 5, Rule 18).

Broth: Turbid; thin pellicle; viscid sediment. Gives off ammonia.

Litmus milk: Alkaline. No other detectable changes.

Potato: Scant to abundant, yellowish to brownish growth. No detectable acid or gas produced from carbohydrates.

Indole not produced.

Nitrites may or may not be produced from nitrates.

Urea not hydrolyzed.

The growth of this species has been tested on 18 amino acids, 12 aliphatic amines, 4 amides, 5 miscellaneous organic nitrogen compounds and 3 inorganic nitrogen compounds. Only aspartic acid, asparagine, histidine and glutathione supported sufficient continued growth to give appreciable turbidity in broth and a final pH close to 8.0. Almost all of the aliphatic amines were toxic (Denault, Cleverdon and Kulp, Jour. Bact., 66, 1953, 465).

No characteristic odor.

Aerobic.

Optimum temperature, between 25° and 37° C.

Relationships to other species: This peritrichous organism is very frequently confused with a polar flagellate organism having almost identical characters. The polar flagellate species has been placed in the genus Vibrio. See discussions under Vibrio percolans Mudd and Warren and Vibrio alcaligenes Lehmann and Neumann.

Source: Isolated from feces, abscesses related to the intestinal tract and occasionally from the blood stream. Miles (Jour. Gen. Microbiol., 4, 1950, 434) reports that an organism having all the characteristics of this species caused a fatal red leg in a batch of European tree-frogs (Hyla arborea L.) received at the London Zoological Gardens.

Habitat: Less commonly found in the intestine than is Vibrio alcaligenes Lehmann and Neumann. Widely distributed in decomposing organic matter. Generally considered to be non-pathogenic.

2. **Alcaligenes viscolactis** (Mez, 1898) Breed, comb. nov.* (Bacillus lactis viscosus Adametz, Milchztg., 18, 1889, 941; also see Landwirtschl. Jahrb., 20, 1891, 185; and Cent. f. Bakt., 9, 1891, 698; Mez, Mikroskopische Wasseranalyse, Berlin, 1898, 61; Alcaligenes viscosus Weldin, Iowa State Coll. Jour. Sci., 1, 1927, 186.)

vis.co.lac'tis. L. noun viscum glue, birdlime; L. gen.noun lactis of milk; M.L. viscolactis of slimy milk.

Description taken from Long and Hammer (Iowa State Coll. Jour. of Sci., 10, 1936, 262), supplemented by Dr. Rudolph Hugh, Loyola University, Chicago, Illinois.

Rods, 0.6 to 1.0 by 0.8 to 2.6 microns, occurring singly, in pairs or in short chains. Frequently found as almost spherical cells. Non-motile. Capsules produced in milk cultures. Gram-negative.

Gelatin colonies: Small, gray becoming yellowish.

Gelatin stab: White surface growth, sometimes with villous growth in stab. No liquefaction.

Agar colonies: After 3 to 4 days, circular, 4 to 6 mm in diameter, white, viscid, shining, entire.

Agar slant: Abundant, white, spreading, viscid, shining growth.

Broth: Turbid with thin pellicle and some sediment. Ropiness generally produced.

Litmus milk: Ropiness produced. Pellicle formed. Alkaline. No coagulation.

Potato: Moderately heavy, dirty white, spreading, shining growth.

Indole not produced.

Hydrogen sulfide not produced.

Acid production from carbohydrates slight, if at all.

Lipolytic.

Methyl red test negative.

Acetylmethylcarbinol not produced.

---

* The discovery that Mez (1898) used a binomial for this species before Weldin did in 1927 has made it necessary to propose a new combination. The specific epithet viscolactis, which is derived directly from the epithets in the original trinomial, Bacillus lactis viscosus Adametz, 1889, is in reality to be preferred over the much-used epithet viscosus. In the genus Bacterium, in which Alcaligenes viscolactis is frequently placed, the epithet viscosum has been applied to at least five quite different species of bacteria.

Nitrites ordinarily not produced or produced only in trace amounts from nitrates.

Growth occurs at 10° and at 20° C. Variable growth at 37° and at 40° C.

Aerobic.

Long and Hammer (*ibid.*, 264) have described a variety of this species which does not produce ropiness in milk. For a recent discussion of this species see Jones (Food Research, *19*, 1954, 246).

Source: Originally isolated from water.

Habitat: Found in water and around dairy barns and dairy utensils. Produces ropiness in milk.

3. Alcaligenes metalcaligenes Castellani and Chalmers, 1919. (Manual Trop. Med., 1919, 936.)

met.al.ca.li′ge.nes. Gr. *meta* in common with; M.L. adj. *alcaligenes* alkali-producing; M.L. adj. *metalcaligenes* resembling alcaligenes, originally an epithet in the trinomial *Bacillus faecalis alcaligenes*.

Rods, 0.6 by 1.5 microns, with rounded ends, occurring singly and in pairs. Nonmotile. Gram-negative.

Gelatin stab: No liquefaction.

Agar colonies: Circular, raised, smooth, amorphous, entire, gray.

Agar slant: Gray, scant, filiform, contoured, viscid growth.

Broth: Membranous pellicle with heavy sediment.

Litmus milk: Alkaline.

Potato: Scant, glistening, smooth, sometimes faint pink growth.

Indole not produced.

No action on carbohydrates.

Starch not hydrolyzed.

Nitrite production from nitrates variable.

Blood serum not liquefied.

Aerobic, facultative.

Optimum temperature, 22° C.

Habitat: Intestinal canal.

4. Alcaligenes bookeri (Ford, 1903) Bergey et al., 1923. (Bacillus A of Booker, Trans. Ninth Internat. Med. Congress, *3*, 1887, 598; *Bacillus bookeri* Ford, Studies from the Royal Victoria Hospital, Montreal, *1*, 1903, 31; Bergey et al., Manual, 1st ed., 1923, 236.)

boo′ke.ri. M.L. gen.noun *bookeri* of

Booker; named for W. D. Booker, the bacteriologist who first isolated this species.

Rods, 0.5 by 1.5 to 2.0 microns, occurring singly. Motile by means of peritrichous flagella. Gram-negative.

Gelatin colonies: Circular, brown, variable in size.

Gelatin stab: Slow, saccate liquefaction, becoming stratiform.

Agar colonies: Thin, transparent, with opaque center and indistinct margin.

Agar slant: Abundant, yellowish to yellowish brown growth.

Broth: Turbid, with viscid sediment. No pellicle.

Litmus milk: Alkaline. Soft curd. Litmus reduced. Peptonization.

Potato: Luxuriant, yellowish white, moist growth. Medium is darkened.

Indole not produced.

No acid or gas from carbohydrate media.

Nitrites not produced from nitrates.

Blood serum: Yellowish brown growth. Gradual liquefaction.

No characteristic odor.

Aerobic, facultative.

Optimum temperature, 37° C.

Source: Isolated from alvine discharges of children suffering with cholera infantum.

Habitat: Intestinal canal.

5. Alcaligenes recti (Ford, 1903) Bergey et al., 1923. (*Bacterium recti* Ford, Studies from the Royal Victoria Hospital, Montreal, *1*, 1903, 31; Bergey et al., Manual, 1st ed., 1923, 236.)

rec′ti. L. adj. *rectus* straight; L. *intestinum rectum* the straight gut; M.L. neut.n. *rectum* rectum; M.L. gen.noun *recti* of the rectum.

Rods, 0.5 by 1.5 to 2.0 microns, occurring singly, in pairs and in chains. Motile by means of peritrichous flagella. Gram-negative.

Gelatin colonies: Variable in size and shape, circular to oval, brown.

Gelatin stab: Rapid, saccate liquefaction.

Agar colonies: Large, grayish white with opaque center. Slightly spreading.

Agar slant: Grayish white, echinulate.

Broth: Turbid. No pellicle.

Litmus milk: Alkaline. No peptonization.

Potato: Luxuriant, moist, brownish red.

Indole not produced.

No acid or gas from carbohydrate media.

Nitrites produced from nitrates.

Blood serum: Abundant white growth. No liquefaction.

No characteristic odor.

Aerobic, facultative.

Optimum temperature, 37° C.

Source: Isolated but once from cecum and rectum (Ford).

Habitat: Intestinal canal.

6. **Alcaligenes marshallii** Bergey et al., 1923. (Bacillus B of Marshall, Cent. f. Bakt., II Abt., *11*, 1903, 739; *Bacterium lactis marshalli* Conn, Esten and Stocking, Ann. Rept. Storrs Agr. Exp. Station, 1906, 141; Bergey et al., Manual, 1st ed., 1923, 237.)

mar.shal'li.i. M.L. gen.noun *marshallii* of Marshall; named for Prof. C. E. Marshall, the American bacteriologist who first isolated this species.

Rods, 0.3 by 1.2 microns, occurring singly. Non-motile. Gram-negative.

Gelatin colonies: Gray, granular, irregular, glistening.

Gelatin stab: Slow, infundibuliform liquefaction.

Agar slant: Growth filiform, gray to creamy white, raised, becoming lemon-yellow.

Broth: Turbid, with gray ring and viscid sediment.

Litmus milk: Alkaline; slimy; peptonized; strong odor.

Potato: Luxuriant, lemon-yellow, smooth growth.

Indole not produced.

No acid or gas from carbohydrates.

Nitrites not produced from nitrates.

Aerobic, facultative.

Optimum temperature, 30° C.

Habitat: Milk.

Genus II. **Achromobacter** *Bergey et al., 1923.**

(Manual, 1st ed., 1923, 132.)

A.chro.mo.bac'ter. Gr. adj. *achromus* colorless; M.L. noun *bacter* the masculine equivalent of the Gr. neut.n. *bactrum* a rod or staff; M.L. mas.n. *Achromobacter* colorless rodlet.

Non-pigment-forming (at least no pigment formed on agar or gelatin) rods. Motile by means of peritrichous flagella or non-motile. Gram-negative. Litmus milk faintly acid to unchanged or alkaline. Occur in salt- to fresh-water and in soil.

The type species is *Achromobacter liquefaciens* (Eisenberg) Bergey et al.

Key to the species of genus **Achromobacter.**

I. Motile. Flagella peritrichous.
  A. Gelatin liquefied.
    1. Litmus milk unchanged.
      a. Nitrites not produced from nitrates.
                    1. *Achromobacter liquefaciens.*
      aa. Nitrites produced from nitrates.
        b. Produces acid from glucose and sucrose.
                    2. *Achromobacter iophagus.*
        bb. Does not produce acid from glucose or sucrose.
                    3. *Achromobacter thalassius.*
    2. Litmus milk reaction acid or alkaline. Nitrites produced from nitrates.
      a. Litmus milk acid.
                    4. *Achromobacter delicatulus.*
      aa. Litmus milk alkaline.
                    5. *Achromobacter xerosis.*

---

* Prepared by Prof. Robert S. Breed, Cornell University, Geneva, New York, October, 1954.

B. Gelatin not liquefied.
  1. Litmus milk unchanged.
    a. Acid from glucose.
      b. Nitrites produced from nitrates.

                  6. *Achromobacter aquamarinus.*
      bb. Nitrites not produced from nitrates.

                  7. *Achromobacter guttatus.*
    aa. No acid from carbohydrate media.
      b. Attacks phenol and naphthalene.

                  8. *Achromobacter cycloclastes.*
      bb. Action on phenol and naphthalene not recorded.

                  9. *Achromobacter pestifer.*
  2. Litmus milk slightly acid.

                  10. *Achromobacter superficialis.*
II. Non-motile.
  A. Gelatin liquefied.
    1. Nitrites slowly produced from nitrates.

                  11. *Achromobacter stenohalis.*
    2. Nitrites not produced from nitrates.

                  12. *Achromobacter butyri.*
  B. Gelatin not liquefied.
    1. Acid from glucose.
      a. Litmus milk unchanged. Action on nitrates not recorded.

                  13. *Achromobacter eurydice.*
    aa. Litmus milk acid; litmus reduced in 5 days. Nitrites produced from nitrates.

                  14. *Achromobacter delmarvae.*
    2. No acid from glucose.

                  15. *Achromobacter parvulus.*

1. Achromobacter liquefaciens (Eisenberg, 1891) Bergey et al., 1923. (*Bacillus liquefaciens* Eisenberg, Bakt. Diag., 3 Aufl., 1891, 112; not *Bacillus liquefaciens* Doyen, Jour. d. connaiss. médic., *57*, Vᵉ Sér., 1889, 108; not *Bacillus liquefaciens* Lustig, Diagnostica dei batteri delle acque, Torino, 1st ed., 1890, 99; also see translation of 2nd ed. by Teuscher, Diagnostik der Bakterien des Wassers, 1893, 86; not *Bacillus liquefaciens* Tataroff, Inaug. Diss., Dorpat, 1891, 29; Bergey et al., Manual, 1st ed., 1923, 135.)

li.que.fa′ci.ens. L. part.adj. *liquefaciens* liquefying.

Description as emended by Bergey et al. (*loc. cit.*).

Short, rather thick rods with rounded ends. Occur singly (Bergey et al.). Actively motile (Eisenberg). Possess peritrichous flagella (Bergey et al.). Gram-negative (Bergey et al.).

Gelatin colonies: Circular, gray, entire, slimy. Liquefaction. In time, a putrid odor is produced.

Gelatin stab: Napiform liquefaction.

Agar slant: Dirty white, spreading growth.

Broth: Turbid (Bergey et al.).

Litmus milk: Unchanged (Bergey et al.).

Potato: Light yellow growth.

Indole not produced (Bergey et al.).

Nitrites not produced from nitrates (Bergey et al.).

Aerobic.

Does not grow at 37° C. (Eisenberg). Optimum temperature, between 20° and 25° C. (Bergey et al.).

Comments: The early descriptions of this organism are so incomplete that, as yet, it has been impossible to reisolate a culture that can be accepted as the type culture of this species. Bergey, in 1923, selected this organism as the type species of the genus *Achromobacter* as he undoubtedly held with other early students of water organisms that it was one of the commonest species to be found in polluted waters. The description given in the Manual (1st ed., 1923, 135) is taken directly from the Frankland's translation of Eisenberg's original description of this species. As Eisenberg's description makes no mention of certain characteristics, e.g. Gram stain, type of flagellation and action on nitrates, now regarded as very important for the identification of species of this type, Bergey added these characters out of his own studies made on Schuylkill River water; these added characters are indicated above.

Related species: The Franklands (Microorganisms in Water. London, 1894, 461) state that the *Bacillus liquefaciens* of Eisenberg resembles very closely the *Bacillus liquefaciens* of Lustig (*op. cit.*, 1890, 99). They then describe the similar organism that they isolated from unfiltered, Thames River water under the name *Bacillus liquidus*. This species differs from the Eisenberg organism in that it produces a thick, flesh-colored, moist expansion on potato. It is also stated to reduce powerfully nitrates to nitrites. Horrocks (Bact. Exam. of Water. London, 1901, 54) discusses all of these common, gelatin-liquefying bacteria found in water and adds a description of *Bacillus liquefaciens* based on his own studies of cultures. Additional characters are given. He states that no gas is produced in a glucose gelatin stab, that milk remains unchanged, that there is a diffuse growth in broth with an abundant deposit of sediment, that nitrates are reduced to nitrites and ammonia, that no indole is produced and that there is no chromogenesis on agar. He adds that it is a short, motile bacillus, often occurring in pairs, that neither forms spores nor grows well at 37° C. His description of the chromogenesis produced on potato indicates that he regards the *B. liquidus* of the Franklands as identical with the *B. liquefaciens* of Eisenberg. Horrocks describes the growth on potato as variable: sometimes it has a light yellow color, at other times it has a flesh-colored tint changing to reddish brown.

Because none of the early students of this organism made flagella stains and because one of the most conspicuous of the gelatin-liquefying species that would occur on the gelatin plates used so commonly before 1900 in isolating water bacteria is *Pseudomonas fluorescens* Migula, it is noteworthy that there is no mention of greenish fluorescence in any of the descriptions referred to above. Likewise, the chromogenesis of *P. fluorescens* on potato is described by early students of this species as an uncharacteristic brown (Flügge, Die Mikroorganismen, 2 Aufl., 1886, 289) or as a rather thick, yellowish gray, spreading growth which gradually becomes a light sepia-brown (Migula, Syst. d. Bakt., *2*, 1900, 886). In searching for cultures of a peritrichous, gelatin-liquefying water organism, the organism most likely to be mistaken for it would be a non-fluorescent strain of *P. fluorescens*. From the fact that several investigators have recently searched for an organism that has the characters of *Achromobacter liquefaciens* Bergey et al. without finding a peritrichous species that conforms in all respects with the description of *Bacillus liquefaciens* as given here, it appears that early statements reporting this organism as common in water are based on a failure to distinguish between polar flagellate and peritrichous gelatin-liquefying water organisms.

Source: Isolated from water.

Habitat: Found in water.

2. **Achromobacter iophagus** (Gray and Thornton, 1928) Bergey et al., 1930. (*Bacterium iophagum* Gray and Thornton, Cent. f. Bakt., II Abt., *73*, 1928, 89; Bergey et al., Manual, 3rd ed., 1930, 204.)

i.o'pha.gus. Gr. noun *ius* poison; Gr. v. *phagein* to devour; M.L. adj. *iophagus* poison-devouring.

Rods 0.8 to 1.0 by 1.0 to 5.0 microns. Motile by means of peritrichous flagella. Gram-negative.

Gelatin colonies: Quickly liquefied.

Gelatin stab: Liquefaction.

Agar colonies: Circular or amoeboid, whitish, flat, raised, smooth, translucent, entire.

Agar slant: Filiform, white to buff, flat, undulate.

Broth: Turbid.

Litmus milk: Unchanged.

Acid from glucose and sucrose. Occasionally from maltose and glycerol.

Starch hydrolyzed.

Nitrites produced from nitrates.

Attacks phenol and naphthalene.

Aerobic, facultative.

Optimum temperature, between 30° and 35° C.

Source: Fifteen cultures were isolated from soil.

Habitat: Soil.

3. Achromobacter thalassius ZoBell and Upham, 1944. (Bull. Scripps Inst. of Oceanography, Univ. of Calif., *5*, 1944, 279.)

tha.las'si.us. Gr. adj. *thalassius* of the sea.

Rods, 0.6 to 0.7 by 0.8 to 2.3 microns, with some variation in shape, occurring singly, in pairs and in short chains; many cells lie side by side. Motile by means of peritrichous flagella. Gram-negative, but cell walls tend to retain stain.

All media except the fresh-water broth, litmus milk and potato were prepared with sea water.

Gelatin colonies: 1 mm in diameter, circular, white.

Gelatin stab: Napiform liquefaction. Filiform growth along line of stab.

Agar colonies: Punctiform, rough, translucent, raised.

Agar slant: Moderate, glistening, beaded, watery, butyrous growth with no pigment.

Sea-water broth: No pellicle; slight turbidity; scant, powdery sediment.

Fresh-water broth: Fair growth.

Litmus milk: No visible change. Casein not digested.

Potato: No visible growth.

Indole not produced.

Hydrogen sulfide not produced.

Glucose, lactose, maltose, sucrose, xylose, mannitol, glycerol and salicin not utilized.

Starch not hydrolyzed.

Non-lipolytic.

Of 19 amino acids tested, none was required for growth; preformed growth factors also were not required (Campbell and Williams, Food Research, *16*, 1951a, 506).

Ammonium chloride and the 19 amino acids which were tested may serve as sources of nitrogen; the amino acids may also be utilized as carbon sources (Campbell and Williams, *loc. cit.*).

Nitrites produced from nitrates.

Ammonia produced from peptone but not from urea.

Trimethylamine not produced from trimethylamine oxide, betaine, choline or acetyl choline (Campbell and Williams, Jour. Bact., *62*, 1951b, 250).

Inorganic sulfur may serve as a source of sulfur (Campbell and Williams, *op. cit.*, 1951a, 506).

Aerobic, facultative.

Optimum temperature, between 20° and 25° C.

Source: Isolated from marine bottom deposits.

4. Achromobacter delicatulus (Jordan, 1890) Bergey et al., 1923. (*Bacillus delicatulus* Jordan, Report Mass. State Bd. of Health, 1890, 837; Bergey et al., Manual, 1st ed., 1923, 137.)

de.li.ca'tu.lus. L. adj. *delicatus* dainty, delicate; M.L. dim.adj. *delicatulus* somewhat delicate.

Original descriptions supplemented by Bergey (*loc. cit.*) from his private notes.

Rods, 1.0 by 2.0 microns, occurring singly (Jordan). Motile by means of peritrichous flagella. Gram-negative (Bergey).

Gelatin colonies: Whitish, homogeneous; radiate margin.

Gelatin stab: Infundibuliform liquefaction.

Agar slant: Whitish, glistening.

Broth: Turbid; gray pellicle; sediment.

Litmus milk: Acid.

Potato: Thin, gray streak.

Indole not produced (Bergey).

Of 19 amino acids tested, none was required for growth; preformed growth factors also were not required (Campbell and Williams, Food Research, *16*, 1951a, 506).

Ammonium chloride and the 19 amino acids which were tested may serve as sources of nitrogen; the amino acids may also be utilized as carbon sources (Campbell and Williams, *loc. cit.*).

Nitrites produced from nitrates.

Trimethylamine produced from trimethylamine oxide, choline and acetyl choline but not from betaine (Campbell and Williams, Jour. Bact., *62*, 1951b, 250).

Inorganic sulfur may serve as a source of sulfur (Campbell and Williams, *op. cit.*, 1951a, 506).

Aerobic, facultative.

Optimum temperature, between 30° and 35° C.

Source: Isolated from the effluent of a septic tank (Jordan). From water (Bergey). Steinhaus (personal communication, 1951) has now shown that the culture which he identified (No. 45, Jour. Bact., *42*, 1941, 771) as belonging to this species belongs in the paracolon group.

Habitat: Presumably widely distributed in nature.

5. **Achromobacter xerosis** Groupé et al., 1954. (Groupé, Pugh, Levine and Herrmann, Jour. Bact., *68*, 1954, 10.)

xe.ro′sis. Gr. adj. *xerus* dry; M.L. adj. *xerosis* dry.

Pleomorphic rods measuring 0.5 by 2.0 to 3.0 microns in young cultures; in older cultures the cells may be as much as 10 to 25 microns in length. Motile by means of peritrichous flagella. Not encapsulated. Gram-negative.

Gelatin: Liquefaction.

Agar colonies: White to grayish white, 1.0 to 1.5 mm in diameter, dry, membranous, circular, low convex, adherent; tan, granular and radially wrinkled with a lobate edge on prolonged incubation.

Broth containing peptone and other complex nitrogenous materials: Pellicle formed. No acid from broth containing glucose, galactose or maltose.

Litmus milk: Alkaline; litmus reduced after 7 days.

Potato: Growth yellowish to brownish, dry and wrinkled.

Acid produced on inorganic nitrogen base agar containing glucose, galactose or maltose as the sole carbon source. Growth, but no acid, on agar containing sucrose; no growth on agar containing arabinose, rhamnose, raffinose, xylose, lactose, salicin, mannitol or sorbitol.

Starch is hydrolyzed.

Indole not produced.

Hydrogen sulfide production slight.

Citrate utilized as the sole source of carbon.

Nitrites produced from nitrates.

Aerobic.

Good growth at 28° and 37° C. No growth at 45° C.

Produces xerosin, a metabolic substance that has a modifying effect on certain viral lesions in mice.

Source: Isolated from soil.

6. **Achromobacter aquamarinus** ZoBell and Upham, 1944. (Bull. Scripps Inst. of Oceanography, Univ. of Calif., *5*, 1944, 264.)

a.qua.ma.ri′nus. L. noun *aqua* water; L. adj. *marinus* of the sea; M.L. adj. *aquamarinus* pertaining to sea water.

Rods, 0.8 by 1.2 to 2.0 microns, with rounded ends, occurring singly. Motile by means of a few peritrichous flagella. Gram-negative.

All media except the fresh-water broth, litmus milk and potato were prepared with sea water.

Gelatin colonies: 2 mm in diameter, convex, circular, entire, whitish.

Gelatin stab: Poor growth, no liquefaction, no pigment.

Agar colonies: 2 mm in diameter, convex, smooth, circular.

Agar slant: Moderate, beaded, glistening, butyrous growth with no pigment.

Sea-water broth: Surface ring; moderate turbidity; heavy, viscous sediment.

Fresh-water broth: Poor growth.

Litmus milk: No visible change. Casein not digested.

Potato: No visible growth.

Indole not produced.

Hydrogen sulfide not produced.

Acid but no gas from glucose and maltose. Lactose, sucrose, xylose, salicin, glycerol and mannitol not utilized.

Starch not hydrolyzed.

Lipolytic.

Of 19 amino acids tested, none was required for growth; preformed growth factors also were not required (Campbell and Williams, Food Research, *16*, 1951a, 506).

Ammonium chloride and the 19 amino acids which were tested may serve as sources of nitrogen; the amino acids (except valine) may also be utilized as carbon sources (Campbell and Williams, *loc. cit.*).

Nitrites rapidly produced from nitrates.

Ammonia produced from peptone but not from urea.

Trimethylamine not produced from trimethylamine oxide, betaine, choline or acetyl choline (Campbell and Williams, Jour. Bact., *62*, 1951b, 250).

Inorganic sulfur may serve as a source of sulfur (Campbell and Williams, *op. cit.*, 1951a, 506).

Aerobic, facultative.

Optimum temperature, between 20° and 25° C.

Source: Isolated from sea water and from submerged slides.

Habitat: Sea water.

7. **Achromobacter guttatus** (Zimmermann, 1890) Bergey et al., 1923. (*Bacillus guttatus* Zimmermann, Bakt. unserer Trink-u. Nutzwässer, Chemnitz, *1*, 1890, 56; Bergey et al., Manual, 1st ed., 1923, 140.)

gut.ta'tus. L. adj. *guttatus* drop-like.

Description prepared by Dr. J. M. Rush, Clemson Agricultural College, Clemson South Carolina, from the original description by Zimmermann, from the emended description of Bergey et al. (*loc. cit.*), and from a study of 74 freshly isolated cultures.

Rods, 0.9 to 1.0 micron, occurring singly and in chains. Motile by means of peritrichous flagella. Gram-negative.

Gelatin colonies: Circular, gray, smooth, entire.

Gelatin stab: No liquefaction.

Agar colonies: Small, gray, smooth, entire, circular, convex.

Agar slant: Growth moderate, gray, filiform, butyrous.

Nutrient broth: Turbid.

Litmus milk: Unchanged.

Potato: Light tan, slimy growth.

Indole not produced.

Hydrogen sulfide produced in small amounts on lead acetate agar.

Acid from glucose. No acid or gas produced from other carbohydrates. Sguros and Hartsell (Jour. Bact., *64*, 1952, 811) report that the dissimilation of glucose is predominately aerobic in nature.

Starch not hydrolyzed.

Methyl red test negative.

Acetylmethylcarbinol not produced.

Citrate utilized.

Of 19 amino acids tested, none was required for growth; preformed growth factors also were not required (Campbell and Williams, Food Research, *16*, 1951a, 506).

Ammonium chloride and the 19 amino acids which were tested may serve as sources of nitrogen; the amino acids may also be utilized as carbon sources (Campbell and Williams, *loc. cit.*).

Nitrites not produced from nitrates.

Ammonia produced slowly from peptone.

Urease not produced.

Trimethylamine not produced from trimethylamine oxide, betaine, choline or acetyl choline (Campbell and Williams, Jour. Bact., *62*, 1951b, 250).

Inorganic sulfur may serve as a source of sulfur (Campbell and Williams, *op. cit.*, 1951a, 506).

Non-hemolytic.

Pathogenicity: Not lethal to white mice when injected in massive doses. Does not produce soft rot on carrots, potatoes or turnips.

Aerobic, facultative.

Optimum temperature, 25° C. Growth range, 15° to 30° C.

Comments: Zimmermann emphasizes the resemblance of the gelatin colonies to drops of liquid and reports that spherical spores appear to be formed in chains of cells; spores are not reported by subsequent investigators. Zimmermann also reports that gelatin is liquefied slowly (after 4 weeks).

Source: Originally isolated from Chemnitz tap water; also isolated from meat, fish, soil and water.

Habitat: Apparently widely distributed in water and foodstuffs.

8. **Achromobacter cycloclastes** (Gray and Thornton, 1928) Bergey et al., 1930 (*Bacterium cycloclastes* Gray and Thornton, Cent. f. Bakt., II Abt., *73*, 1928, 89; Bergey et al., Manual, 3rd ed., 1930, 212.)

cy.clo.clas'tes. Gr. noun *cyclus* a ring; Gr. adj. *clastus* broken; M.L. noun *cycloclastes* a ring breaker.

Rods, 1.0 to 1.5 by 1.5 to 8.0 microns.

Motile by means of 1 to 12 peritrichous flagella. Gram-negative.

Gelatin colonies: Circular, white, raised, smooth, glistening, entire.

Gelatin stab: No liquefaction. Nail-head growth.

Agar colonies: Circular to amoeboid, white, flat to convex, smooth, glistening, translucent with opaque center, entire.

Agar slant: Filiform, pale buff, raised, smooth, glistening, undulate growth.

Broth: Turbid.

Litmus milk: Unchanged.

No acid from carbohydrate media.

Starch not hydrolyzed.

Nitrites produced from nitrates.

Attacks phenol and naphthalene.

Aerobic, facultative.

Optimum temperature, between 30° and 35° C.

Source: Three cultures were isolated from soil.

Habitat: Soil.

9. **Achromobacter pestifer** (Frankland and Frankland, 1888) Bergey et al., 1923. (*Bacillus pestifer* G. and P. Frankland, Philosoph. Trans. Roy. Soc., London, B, *178*, 1888, 277; Bergey et al., Manual, 1st ed., 1923, 140.)

pes'ti.fer. L. noun *pestis* plague, pestilence; L. v. *fero* to carry; M.L. adj. *pestifer* plague-carrying.

Description prepared by Dr. J. M. Rush, Clemson Agricultural College, Clemson, South Carolina, from the original description by Frankland and Frankland, from the emended description of Bergey et al. (*loc. cit.*), and from a study of 102 freshly isolated cultures.

Rods, 1.0 by 2.3 microns, occurring singly and occasionally in chains. Motile by means of peritrichous flagella. Gram-negative.

Gelatin colonies: Gray, smooth, irregular.

Gelatin stab: No liquefaction.

Agar colonies: Circular, convex, smooth, translucent.

Agar slant: Growth moderate, filiform, butyrous, smooth.

Nutrient broth: Turbid; thin pellicle.

Litmus milk: Unchanged.

Potato: Gray, filiform growth.

Indole not produced.

Hydrogen sulfide not produced on lead acetate agar.

No action on carbohydrates.

Starch not hydrolyzed.

Methyl red test negative.

Acetylmethylcarbinol not produced.

Citrate not utilized.

Nitrites produced from nitrates.

Ammonia not produced from peptone.

Urease not produced.

Trimethylamine oxide not reduced.

Non-hemolytic.

Pathogenicity: Not lethal to white mice when injected in massive doses. Does not produce soft rot on carrots, potatoes or turnips.

Aerobic, facultative.

Optimum temperature, 25° C. Growth range, 10° to 30° C.

Source: Originally isolated from air; also isolated from water, cabbage, meat and soil.

Habitat: Presumably widely distributed in water, soil and foodstuffs.

10. **Achromobacter superficialis** (Jordan, 1890) Bergey et al., 1923. (*Bacillus superficialis* Jordan, Report Mass. State Bd. of Health, 1890, 833; Bergey et al., Manual, 1st ed., 1923, 144.)

su.per.fi.ci.a'lis. L. adj. *superficialis* superficial.

Original description supplemented by Bergey (*loc. cit.*) from his private notes.

Rods, 1.0 by 2.2 microns, occurring singly (Jordan). Motile by means of peritrichous flagella. Gram-negative (Bergey).

Gelatin colonies: Small, circular, gray, translucent.

Gelatin stab: Scant surface growth. Slow liquefaction.

Agar slant: Limited, gray, filiform growth. Abundant growth (Steinhaus, Jour. Bact., *42*, 1941, 771).

Broth: Slightly turbid.

Litmus milk: No change; later becomes slightly acid.

Potato: No growth (Jordan). Limited growth (Bergey).

Indole not produced (Bergey).

Of 19 amino acids tested, none was required for growth; preformed growth factors also were not required (Campbell and Williams, Food Research, *16*, 1951a, 506).

Ammonium chloride and the 19 amino acids which were tested may serve as sources of nitrogen; the amino acids (except alanine and aspartic acid) may also be utilized as carbon sources (Campbell and Williams, *loc. cit.*).

Nitrites not produced from nitrates.

Trimethylamine not produced from trimethylamine oxide, betaine, choline or acetyl choline (Campbell and Williams, Jour. Bact., *62*, 1951b, 250).

Inorganic sulfur may serve as a source of sulfur (Campbell and Williams, *op. cit.*, 1951a, 506).

Aerobic, facultative.

Optimum temperature, between 25° and 30° C.

Source: Sewage. Gibbons (Contrib. to Canadian Biol. and Fish., *8*, 1934, 279) reports this species as occurring in the slime and feces of the cod (*Gadus callarias*) and dogfish (*Squalus acanthias*). An organism apparently identical with this species has been found by Steinhaus (*op. cit.*, 1941, 764) in the intestines of beetle larvae (*Urographus fasciata* DeG.).

Habitat: Presumably widely distributed in nature.

11. **Achromobacter stenohalis** ZoBell and Upham, 1944. (ZoBell and Upham, Bull. Scripps Inst. of Oceanography, Univ. of Calif., *5*, 1944, 257; *Acinetobacter stenohalis* Brisou and Prévot, Ann. Inst. Past., *86*, 1954, 727.)

ste.no.ha′lis. Gr. adj. *stenus* narrow; *hals, halis* salt; M.L. gen.noun *stenohalis* of narrow salt (tolerance).

Rods, 0.8 to 0.9 by 0.8 to 1.6 microns, occurring singly, in pairs and in short chains. Non-motile. Encapsulated. Gram-negative.

All media except the fresh-water broth, litmus milk and potato were prepared with sea water.

Gelatin colonies: 1 mm in diameter, whitish, circular, convex, entire. No pigment.

Gelatin stab: Very slow, crateriform liquefaction. Napiform in 50 days.

Agar colonies: Small, circular, opalescent, convex with slightly raised margin, smooth; lobate edge.

Agar slant: Moderate, beaded, glistening, opalescent growth with no pigment.

Sea-water broth: Moderate turbidity; viscid sediment; no pellicle or ring.

Fresh-water broth: No visible growth.

Litmus milk: No visible change. Casein not digested.

Potato: No visible growth.

Indole not produced.

Hydrogen sulfide not produced.

No acid or gas from glucose, lactose, maltose, sucrose, mannitol, glycerol, xylose or salicin.

Starch not hydrolyzed.

Non-lipolytic.

Nitrites slowly produced from nitrates.

Ammonia produced from peptone but not from urea.

Aerobic, facultative (poor anaerobic growth).

Optimum temperature, between 20° and 25° C.

Source: Isolated from sea water, marine mud and marine phytoplankton.

Habitat: Sea water.

12. **Achromobacter butyri** Bergey et al., 1923. (*Micrococcus butyri-aromafaciens* Keith, The Technology Quarterly, *10*, 1897, 247; Bergey et al., Manual, 1st ed., 1923, 148; *Acinetobacter butyri* Brisou and Prévot, Ann. Inst. Past., *86*, 1954, 727.)

bu′ty.ri. Gr. noun *butyrum* butter; M.L. gen.noun *butyri* of butter.

Rods, 0.5 to 1.0 micron, nearly spherical, occurring singly and in pairs. Non-motile. Gram-negative.

Gelatin colonies: White, circular, smooth, glistening.

Gelatin stab: White surface growth; liquefaction with white sediment.

Agar slant: Abundant, white, glistening growth.

Broth: Turbid, with ring and sediment.

Litmus milk: Reaction unchanged. Aromatic odor.

Potato: Slow and limited, white growth

Of 19 amino acids tested, none was required for growth; preformed growth factors also were not required (Campbell and Williams, Food Research, *16*, 1951b, 506).

Ammonium chloride and the 19 amino acids which were tested may serve as sources of nitrogen; the amino acids may also be utilized as carbon sources (Campbell and Williams, *op. cit.*, 1951a, 506).

Nitrites not produced from nitrates.

Trimethylamine not produced from trimethylamine oxide, betaine, choline or acetyl choline (Campbell and Williams, Jour. Bact., *62*, 1951a, 250).

Inorganic sulfur may serve as a source of sulfur (Campbell and Williams, *loc. cit.*).

Aerobic, facultative.

Optimum temperature, 25° C.

Habitat: Milk.

13. Achromobacter eurydice (White, 1912) Bergey et al., 1925.

(*Bacterium eurydice* White, U. S. Dept. of Agr., Bur. of Entomol., Circ. 157, 1912, 3, and U. S. Dept. of Agr. Bull. 810, 1920, 15; Bergey et al., Manual, 2nd ed., 1925, 170; *Acinetobacter eurydice* Brisou and Prévot, Ann. Inst. Past., *86*, 1954, 727.)

eu.ry'di.ce. Gr. fem.n. *Eurydice* the wife of *Orpheus.*

Small, slender rods with slightly rounded ends; occur singly and in pairs. Non-motile. Gram-negative.

Gelatin stab: A bluish gray growth occurs along the line of inoculation. No liquefaction.

Glucose agar colonies: Bluish gray, circular, smooth glistening, entire.

Broth: Uniform turbidity with viscid sediment.

Potato: Slight, grayish growth.

Litmus milk: Unchanged.

Acid from glucose, but little or no action on other carbohydrates.

Of 19 amino acids tested, none was required for growth; preformed growth factors also were not required (Campbell and Williams, Food Research, *16*, 1951a, 506).

Ammonium chloride and the 19 amino acids which were tested may serve as sources of nitrogen; the amino acids may also be utilized as carbon sources (Campbell and Williams, *loc. cit.*).

Trimethylamine not produced from trimethylamine oxide, betaine, choline or acetyl choline (Campbell and Williams, Jour. Bact., *62*, 1951b, 250).

Inorganic sulfur may serve as a source of sulfur (Campbell and Williams, *op. cit.*, 1951a, 506).

Aerobic, facultative.

Innocuous when fed to bees. Not pathogenic when inoculated subcutaneously in rabbits.

Source: Occurs as a secondary invader in European foulbrood of bees.

Habitat: Unknown.

14. Achromobacter delmarvae Smart, 1932.

(Jour. Bact., *23*, 1932, 41; also see Jour. Agr. Research, *51*, 1935, 363; *Acinetobacter delmarvae* Brisou and Prévot, Ann. Inst. Past., *86*, 1954, 727.)

del.mar'vae. M.L. gen.noun *delmarvae* of Delmarva; named for Delmarva, the name given to an area comprising portions of the states of Delaware, Maryland and Virginia.

Short rods which average 0.75 by 1.5 microns; rounded ends; occur singly, in pairs and in short chains. Non-motile. Gram-negative.

Gelatin colonies: Similar to agar colonies.

Gelatin stab: Scant growth. No liquefaction.

Beef-infusion agar colonies: Small, circular, raised, glistening, translucent, bluish white, amorphous; margin entire; edges smooth.

Agar stab: Abundant growth. Surface growth round, smooth, glistening, bluish white, raised. Filiform growth the whole length of stab, but growth best at top.

Agar slant: Abundant, filiform, raised, glistening, smooth, translucent, bluish white growth; no odor; old cultures slightly viscid. Medium unchanged.

Nutrient broth: Turbid. Delicate, white pellicle. Sediment abundant, white, slightly stringy. No odor. Color of medium unchanged.

Sterile milk: Slow growth. No peptonization. Coagulation in 12 to 14 days. Milk turns chocolate-brown beginning at top.

Litmus milk: Acid, with reduction of litmus in 5 days. Coagulation, with return of pink color in 12 to 14 days. Browning of medium.

Potato: Abundant, grayish white, glistening, smooth, raised growth. Medium changes from white to smoke-gray.

Indole not produced.
Hydrogen sulfide not produced.
Acid but no gas from glucose, lactose, glycerol and mannitol. Alkaline reaction and no gas from sucrose.
Nitrites produced from nitrates in 7 days at 26° C.
Ammonia not produced.
Diastatic action weak.
Optimum pH, 7.0.
Temperature relations: Optimum, 26° C. Good growth up to 31° C. Very slight growth at 37° and at −8° C.
Facultative anaerobe.
Source: Isolated from fresh strawberries from Delaware, Maryland and Virginia.
Habitat: Unknown.

15. **Achromobacter parvulus** (Conn, 1922) Breed, *comb. nov.* (Culture B, Conn and Collison, New York Agr. Exp. Sta. Bull. 494, 1922, 12; *Bacterium parvulum* Conn, *ibid.*, 26; not *Bacterium parvulum*

Banning, Cent. f. Bakt., II Abt., *8*, 1902, 396 and 565.)

par'vu.lus. L. dim.adj. *parvulus* very small.

Very small rods, 0.1 to 0.2 by 0.3 to 0.5 micron. Non-motile. Gram-negative.

Gelatin plate: Punctiform colonies. No liquefaction.

Agar plate: Punctiform colonies.

Grows poorly in liquid media.

Indole not produced.

No acid from glucose, lactose, sucrose, glycerol or ethanol in either liquid or solid media.

Starch not digested.

Nitrites produced from nitrates.

Optimum temperature, 25° C.

Strictly aerobic.

Distinctive character: Causes strong volatilization of ammonia from a mixture of horse manure and urine.

Source: Isolated from manure.

Habitat: Soil.

Genus III. **Flavobacterium** *Bergey et al., 1923.**

(Manual, 1st ed., 1923, 97.)

Fla.vo.bac.te'ri.um. L. adj. *flavus* yellow; Gr. dim.neut.n. *bacterium* a small rod; M.L. neut.n. *Flavobacterium* a yellow bacterium.

Gram-negative, rod-shaped bacteria. Motile by means of peritrichous flagella or non-motile. Characteristically produce yellow, orange, red, or yellow-brown pigmentation, the hue often depending upon the nutrient medium. Some strains produce only a gray-yellow pigmentation on peptone meat-extract agar, but these have a more pronounced pigmentation on other media, *e.g.*, nutrient gelatin, potato or litmus milk agar. Pigments are not soluble in the medium, and those which have been studied are carotenoid in nature. Commonly proteolytic. Fermentative metabolism usually is not conspicuous; acid reactions commonly do not develop from carbohydrates when available nitrogen-containing organic compounds are in the medium. Gas is not produced from carbohydrates according to the usual cultural tests. Nutritional requirements usually are not complex. Aerobic to facultatively anaerobic. Occur in water and soil. Some species are pathogenic.

The type species is *Flavobacterium aquatile* (Frankland and Frankland) Bergey et al.

Key to the species of genus **Flavobacterium.**

I. Non-motile.
   A. Produce a pigmentation which varies with the cultural conditions.
      1. Litmus milk modified. Gelatin liquefied.
         a. Litmus milk peptonized. Yellow to orange pigmentation produced on potato.
            b. Nitrites not produced from nitrates. Litmus milk slowly peptonized. No growth at 37° C.
               1. *Flavobacterium aquatile.*

* Prepared by Prof. Owen B. Weeks, Agricultural Experiment Station, University of Idaho, Moscow, Idaho, and Prof. Robert S. Breed, Cornell University, Geneva, New York, October, 1954.

bb. Nitrites produced from nitrates. Litmus milk rapidly peptonized. Growth at 37° C.

2. *Flavobacterium fucatum.**

aa. Litmus milk not peptonized. Yellow or orange pigmentation produced on potato.

b. Orange pigmentation produced on potato. Soft curd develops in litmus milk; no change in reaction.

c. Yellow-gray growth on nutrient agar.

3. *Flavobacterium ferrugineum.*

cc. Orange growth on nutrient agar.

4. *Flavobacterium arborescens.*

bb. Yellow pigmentation on potato. Litmus milk becomes slightly acid.

5. *Flavobacterium balustinum.**

2. Litmus milk not modified. Gelatin not liquefied.

6. *Flavobacterium solare.*

B. Produce a yellow pigmentation which shows no pronounced change under various cultural conditions.

1. Fresh-water forms or marine forms described from growth in media prepared with fresh water; do not require salt for growth.*

a. Litmus milk modified. Gelatin liquefied.

b. Litmus milk becomes alkaline. Abundant growth on potato.

7. *Flavobacterium lutescens.*

bb. Litmus milk becomes slightly acid. Scant growth on potato.

8. *Flavobacterium dormitator.**

aa. Litmus milk not modified. Gelatin not liquefied.

b. Grows on potato.

9. *Flavobacterium peregrinum.*

bb. Does not grow on potato.

10. *Flavobacterium breve.*

2. Marine form which requires at least 3 per cent salt in media and which grows abundantly in media containing as much as 24 per cent salt.

11. *Flavobacterium halmephilum.*

II. Motile.

A. Produce a pigmentation which varies with the cultural conditions.

1. Fresh-water forms or marine forms described from growth in media prepared with fresh water.*

a. Litmus milk modified.

b. Orange to rust-colored growth on potato.

12. *Flavobacterium rhenanum.*

bb. Yellow growth on potato.

13. *Flavobacterium harrisonii.*

aa. Litmus milk not modified.

b. White to red-yellow growth on nutrient agar. Scant growth on potato and nutrient agar.

14. *Flavobacterium diffusum.**

bb. Light yellow to brown growth on nutrient agar. Abundant growth on potato and nutrient agar.

15. *Flavobacterium rigense.*

---

* The marine bacteria studied by Harrison had their cultural properties established using media prepared with fresh water. These forms have been arranged with the non-marine species.

2. Marine forms which have been described from growth in media prepared with sea water.*
   a. Acid from glucose in nutrient broth.
      b. Yellow growth on nutrient agar; orange growth on gelatin.
         16. *Flavobacterium halohydrium.*
      bb. Buff to yellow growth on nutrient agar; faint yellow growth on gelatin.
         17. *Flavobacterium neptunium.*
   aa. No acid from glucose in nutrient broth.
      b. Nitrites produced from nitrates.
         18. *Flavobacterium okeanokoites.*
      bb. Nitrites not produced from nitrates.
         19. *Flavobacterium marinovirosum.*
B. Produce a pigmentation which shows no pronounced change under various cultural conditions.
   1. Fresh-water forms or marine forms described from growth in media prepared with fresh water.*
      a. Litmus milk modified.
         b. Litmus milk peptonized and becomes alkaline. Gelatin liquefied.
           c. Indole produced. Pigmentation yellow.
              20. *Flavobacterium suaveolens.*
           cc. Indole not produced. Pigmentation amber-yellow.
              21. *Flavobacterium marinum.**
         bb. Litmus milk becomes slightly acid. Gelatin not liquefied.
           22. *Flavobacterium lactis.*
      aa. Litmus milk not modified.
         b. Gelatin liquefied.
           23. *Flavobacterium devorans.*
         bb. Gelatin not liquefied.
           24. *Flavobacterium invisibile.*
   2. Marine forms which have been described from growth in media prepared with sea water.
      a. Grows in litmus milk. Pigmentation yellow.
         25. *Flavobacterium marinotypicum.*
      aa. Does not grow in litmus milk. Pigmentation bright orange.
         26. *Flavobacterium piscicida.*

---

1. Flavobacterium aquatile (Frankland and Frankland, 1889) Bergey et al., 1923. (*Bacillus aquatilis* G. and P. Frankland, Ztschr. f. Hyg., *6*, 1889, 381; *Flavobacterium aquatilis* (sic) Bergey et al., Manual, 1st ed., 1923, 100.)

a.qua'ti.le. L. adj. *aquatilis* living in water.

Description prepared by Prof. Owen B. Weeks (see Jour. Bact., *69*, 1955, 649) from a study of Culture F36 (ATCC 11947) isolated from water by Dr. E. Windle Taylor, Metropolitan Water Board, London, England, from the same deep wells in chalk that were studied by the Franklands.

Rods, 0.5 to 0.7 by 1.0 to 3.0 microns, approaching coccobacillary form in young cultures; filamentous forms, 10 to 40 microns long, occur in liquid or on solid media. Nonmotile. Gram-negative.

Gelatin: Giant colonies irregular, mucoid and uniformly raised with a conspicuous center. Yellow, becoming orange. Limited liquefaction.

Agar colonies: Smooth, 1 to 3 mm in diameter, entire, glistening, transparent, light yellow becoming brownish yellow. At 10° C., or when there is abundant growth, red components are most conspicuous. Where sucrose is added to the agar, the

---

* See footnote on preceding page.

growth becomes more mucoid without an increase in pigmentation.

Agar slants: Growth moderate, mucoid, glistening, transparent, filiform. An increase in organic nitrogen-containing compounds causes growth to become non-mucoid, opaque, wrinkled and adherent. Frequent transfers are necessary for survival.

Proteose peptone (2 per cent) agar: Gray-yellow growth.

Broth: Faintly turbid.

Litmus milk: Litmus reduced; yellow surface ring; no acid in 7 days at 20° to 25° C.; casein slowly digested (14 to 20 days).

Potato: Growth scant to moderate, white to faint yellow at 20° to 25° C.; potato darkens and pigment becomes bright orange at 10° C.

Indole not produced.

Hydrogen sulfide production slight.

Glycerol, xylose, arabinose, glucose, fructose, galactose, mannose, cellobiose, sucrose, maltose, lactose and raffinose are utilized as principal carbon sources under aerobic conditions; ethanol, sodium citrate, dextrin, starch, dulcitol, mannitol and salicin are not utilized under these conditions.

Glucose and ammonium chloride usually do not support growth when used as the sources of carbon and nitrogen.

Acid from glucose, galactose, mannose, sucrose and maltose when included in semi-synthetic media, agar slants or broths (acid reactions not detectable with indicators in peptone-beef-extract-containing media).

Optimum pH, between 7.2 and 7.4. Growth between pH 6.5 and 7.8. Final pH of unbuffered 1 per cent glucose broth, 5.9; if peptone-beef-extract is also present in the broth, the final pH is 6.5.

Acetylmethylcarbinol not produced.

Methyl red test negative.

Nitrites not produced from nitrates.

Urease-negative.

Catalase-positive.

Aerobic.

Temperature relations: Growth range, 10° to 30° C. No growth at 37° C.

Distinctive characters: Differs from other non-motile species of *Flavobacterium* by a number of cultural properties which, when combined, serve to differentiate the species. These properties are yellow pigmentation becoming yellow-brown or orange, slow growth and poor survival on meat-extract-peptone media, inability to reduce nitrates to nitrites and failure to grow at 37° C. and under anaerobic conditions.

Source: Isolated from the water of deep wells in the chalk region of Kent, England, where it occurred as a practically pure culture. Found abundantly and reisolated by Taylor, 1941, from the same source (personal communication).

Habitat: Found in water containing a high percentage of calcium carbonate.

2. **Flavobacterium fucatum** Harrison, 1929. (Canadian Jour. of Research, *1*, 1929, 232.)

fu.ca'tum. L. adj. *fucatus* colored, painted.

Rods, 0.8 to 1.0 by 2.5 to 3.5 microns, slightly bent with rounded ends. Granular with diphtheroid forms at 37° C. Non-motile. Gram-negative.

Gelatin colonies: Circular, yellow, entire, paler at edges.

Gelatin stab: Crateriform liquefaction.

Agar colonies: Circular, buff-yellow, smooth, shiny, convex to pulvinate, granular, entire.

Agar slant: Moderate, light buff-yellow, spreading, shiny, smooth growth.

Ammonium phosphate agar: Good growth in 6 days.

Broth: Turbid, becoming clear; pellicle and yellow sediment.

Litmus milk: Alkaline. Peptonized. Clear serum. Yellow sediment.

Potato: Growth abundant, pale buff-yellow, smooth, spreading, becoming orange-yellow.

Indole not produced.

Hydrogen sulfide not produced.

No acid from glucose, lactose or sucrose.

Nitrites produced from nitrates.

Traces of ammonia produced.

Loeffler's blood serum not liquefied. Light buff-yellow growth becoming ochraceus salmon.

Aerobic, facultatively anaerobic.

Optimum temperature, between 20° and 25° C.

Source: Repeatedly isolated from living halibut obtained at 30 to 50 fathoms, Pacific Ocean. Also isolated by Gibbons (Contrib. to Canadian Biol. and Fish., 8, 1934, 279) from cod (*Gadus callarias*) and dogfish (*Squalus acanthias*).

Habitat: Found on the skin of sea fish.

3. Flavobacterium ferrugineum Sickles and Shaw, 1934. (Jour. Bact., 28, 1934, 421.)

fer.ru.gi'ne.um. L. adj. *ferrugineus* resembling iron rust.

Small, slender rods, less than 0.5 by 0.7 to 1.0 micron, occurring singly and in pairs. Non-motile. Gram-negative.

Gelatin: Liquefaction in one week at 37° C.; at room temperature liquefaction slower, napiform; yellow sediment along line of puncture.

Blood agar colonies: Dull, rust-colored, 1 mm in diameter, round, entire, umbilicate, rather dry.

Agar colonies: Similar to blood agar colonies but yellowish gray in color.

Blood agar slants: Moderate, rust-colored, rather dry growth.

Agar slants: Growth very slight, thin, yellowish gray.

Beef-infusion broth: No growth.

Beef extract broth: Moderate, even turbidity. Adding non-type-specific carbohydrate (pneumococcus) results in a heavier growth with yellow sediment.

Litmus milk: Soft curd (2 weeks); slight reduction of litmus; no change in reaction.

Potato: Moderate growth, bright orange in color. Potato darkened.

Acid but no gas from glucose, lactose, sucrose, maltose, dextrin and inulin; very slight action on mannitol; no action on salicin.

Very active hydrolysis of starch.

Limits of growth: Optimum pH, between 7.0 and 7.5. Minimum, 6.5. Maximum, 9.0.

Temperature relations: Optimum, between 35° and 37° C. Minimum, 22° C. Maximum, 39° C. Thermal death point, 52° C. for 10 minutes. Enzyme produced by strain against pneumococcus carbohydrate withstands 56° C. for 10 minutes.

Aerobic, facultatively anaerobic.

Distinctive character: Decomposes the non-type-specific carbohydrate obtained from a degraded type I pneumococcus.

Source: Several strains were isolated from swamps and other uncultivated soils.

Habitat: Soil.

4. Flavobacterium arborescens (Frankland and Frankland, 1889) Bergey et al., 1923. (*Bacillus arborescens* Frankland and Frankland, Ztschr. f. Hyg., 6, 1889, 379; also see Tils, Ztschr. f. Hyg., 9, 1890, 312; and Wright, Mem. Nat. Acad. Sci., 7, 1894, 446, var. a and b; Bergey et al., Manual, 1st ed., 1923, 113.)

ar.bo.res'cens. L. part.adj. *arborescens* becoming tree-like.

Rods, 0.5 by 2.5 microns, occurring singly and in chains. Long, wavy threads are formed in broth. Non-motile (Frankland and Frankland). Gram-negative (Zimmermann, Bakt. unserer Trink- u. Nutzwässer, 2, 1894, 20).

Gelatin colonies: Colonies at first filamentous and branching as seen under low magnification. Center becomes yellowish and the border becomes translucent and arborescent.

Gelatin stab: Liquefaction with yellow deposit.

Agar slant: Slow, dirty orange growth.

Broth: Turbid; yellow sediment; no pellicle.

Litmus milk: Slow coagulation; litmus reduced. Reaction neutral (Wright, *op. cit.*, 1894, 447).

Potato: Deep orange, luxuriant growth.

No growth in nitrate solution; nitrites not produced.

Aerobic, facultatively anaerobic.

Optimum temperature, 30° C.

Ravenel (Mem. Nat. Acad. Sci., 8, 1896, 39) reports a non-liquefying strain of this species. This may have been *Flavobacterium solare* Lehmann and Neumann.

Source: Isolated from river and lake water.

Habitat: Water.

5. Flavobacterium balustinum Harrison, 1929. (Canadian Jour. of Research, 1, 1929, 234.)

bal.us.ti'num. Etymology uncertain.

Rods, 0.6 by 2.0 to 4.0 microns, forming short chains. Non-motile. Gram-negative.

Gelatin colonies: Circular, bright yellow center, entire.

Gelatin stab: Liquefaction.

Agar colonies: Punctiform, cadmium-yellow, convex, shiny, transparent.

Agar slant: Egg-yolk-yellow, semi-transparent streak, smooth, shiny, becoming brownish yellow.

Ammonium phosphate agar: Slight, yellow growth.

Broth: Turbid with yellow sediment.

Litmus milk: Slightly acid with yellow sediment.

Potato: Scant, yellow growth.

Indole not produced.

Hydrogen sulfide not produced.

Faint acid from glucose. No action on lactose or sucrose.

Nitrites produced from nitrates in trace amounts.

Ammonia not produced.

Loeffler's blood serum: Not liquefied. Egg-yolk-like growth.

Aerobic, facultatively anaerobic.

Optimum temperature, between 20° and 25° C.

Source: Isolated from living halibut obtained at 30 to 50 fathoms, Pacific Ocean.

Habitat: Found on the skins of fishes.

6. **Flavobacterium solare** (Lehmann and Neumann, 1896) Bergey et al., 1923. (*Bacterium solare* Lehmann and Neumann, Bakt. Diag., 1 Aufl., *2*, 1896, 258; Bergey et al., Manual, 1st ed., 1923, 116.)

so.la're. L. adj. *solaris* of the sun, solar, with rays.

Rods, 0.3 to 0.4 micron in width, forming short or long, strongly twisted threads. Non-motile. Gram-negative.

Gelatin colonies: Circular, yellow, glistening, translucent; projecting rays.

Gelatin stab: Yellow, arborescent growth in stab. No liquefaction. Surface growth is lemon-yellow.

Agar slant: Pale yellow, raised, arborescent growth.

Broth: Clear. No gas from sugar broths.

Litmus milk: Unchanged.

Potato: Dull white growth becoming yellow.

Indole not produced.

Hydrogen sulfide not produced.

Nitrites not produced from nitrates.

Aerobic, facultatively anaerobic.

Optimum temperature, 30° C.

Distinctive character: Resembles *Flavobacterium arborescens* Bergey et al. in type of growth.

Source: Isolated from Würzburg tap water. Gibbons (Contrib. to Canadian Biol. and Fish., *8*, 1934, 279) reports this species as occurring in the slime of a skate (*Raja erinacea*) and of a hake (*Urophycis tenuis*).

Habitat: Found in fresh and salt water.

7. **Flavobacterium lutescens** (Migula, 1900) Bergey et al., 1923. (Bacillo giallo, Lustig, Diagnostica dei batteri delle acque, Torino, 1890, 91; also see translation of 2nd ed. by Teuscher, Diagnostik der Bakterien des Wassers, 1893, 78; *Bacterium lutescens* Migula, Syst. d. Bakt., *2*, 1900, 476; Bergey et al., Manual, 1st ed., 1923, 114.)

lu.tes'cens. L. part.adj. *lutescens* becoming muddy.

Rods, 0.5 by 0.95 micron, occurring singly and in pairs. Non-motile. Gram-negative.

Gelatin colonies: Circular, yellow, lobate.

Gelatin stab: Slow liquefaction.

Agar slant: Growth pale yellow, becoming golden yellow.

Broth: Turbid.

Litmus milk: Alkaline.

Potato: Luxuriant, golden yellow growth.

Indole not produced.

Nitrites produced from nitrates.

Aerobic, facultatively anaerobic.

Optimum temperature, between 30° and 35° C.

Source: Isolated from water. Gibbons (Contrib. to Canadian Biol. and Fish., *8*, 1934, 279) reports this species as occurring in the slime of the cod (*Gadus callarias*).

Habitat: Found in fresh and salt water.

8. **Flavobacterium dormitator** (Wright, 1895) Bergey et al., 1923. (*Bacillus dormitator* Wright, Memoirs Nat. Acad. Sci., *7*,

1895, 442; Bergey et al., Manual, 1st ed., 1923, 115.)

dor.mi.ta'tor. L. noun *dormitator* a sleeper, a sluggard.

Original description supplemented by material taken from Harrison (Canadian Jour. of Research, *1*, 1929, 233), whose cultures differed in some particulars from Wright's.

Rods with conical ends, occurring singly, in pairs and in chains. Non-motile. Gram-negative (Harrison).

Gelatin colonies: Small, yellow, slightly granular. Liquefaction.

Gelatin stab: Infundibuliform liquefaction; yellow sediment.

Agar slant: Yellow, glistening, translucent growth.

Ammonium phosphate agar: Slight, yellow growth.

Broth: Turbid with slight pellicle and yellow sediment.

Litmus milk: Slightly acid; litmus reduced. Harrison reports no reduction.

Potato: Slight, transparent, yellow growth.

Indole not produced (Harrison).

Acid from glucose, sucrose, glycerol and mannitol. No acid from lactose, raffinose or inulin (Harrison).

Nitrites produced from nitrates in trace amounts (Harrison).

Aerobic, facultatively anaerobic.

Optimum temperature, 30° C.

Source: Originally isolated from fresh water at Philadelphia. Later isolated by Harrison (*loc. cit.*) from the skin of halibut taken from the Pacific Ocean off Canada. Gibbons (Contrib. to Canadian Biol. and Fish., *8*, 1934, 279) reports this species as occurring in the slime of a haddock (*Melanogrammus aeglefinus*).

Habitat: Found in fresh and salt water.

9. **Flavobacterium peregrinum** Stapp and Spicher, 1954. (Zent. f. Bakt., II Abt., *108*, 1954, 113.)

per.e.gri'num. L. adj. *peregrinus* strange, foreign.

Straight rods, 0.5 to 0.8 by 2.4 microns, occurring singly and in pairs. Non-motile. Gram-negative.

Gelatin colonies: Circular, entire, yellow; radial grooves.

Gelatin stab: Yellow surface growth; no growth in the stab. No liquefaction.

Nutrient agar colonies: Mucoid, yellow, shiny; hyaline margins.

Glucose agar: Slowly developing yellow growth.

Nutrient broth: Turbid with a white sediment.

Litmus milk: Unchanged.

Potato: Yellow streak.

Indole not produced.

No acid or gas from glucose, sucrose, lactose, glycerol or mannitol in nutrient broth.

Starch not hydrolyzed.

Nitrites not produced from nitrates.

Slow development in a mineral, glucose agar.

Aerobic.

Distinctive characters: Resembles *Flavobacterium breve* Bergey et al. culturally. The herbicide 2,4-dichlorophenoxyacetic acid is utilized as a sole source of carbon in an otherwise inorganic medium. Destroys 2,4-D in the soil, presumably by opening the benzene ring.

Source: Isolated in Germany from soil-enrichment cultures containing 2,4-D.

Habitat: Found in soil.

10. **Flavobacterium breve** (Lustig, 1890) Bergey et al., 1923. (Der kurze Canalbacillus, Mori, Ztschr. f. Hyg., *4*, 1888, 53; *Bacillus canalis parvus* Eisenberg, Bakt. Diag., 1891, 362; *Bacillus brevis* Lustig, Diagnostica dei batteri delle acque, Torino, 1890, 52; *Bacterium canale* Mez, Mikroskopische Wasseranalyse, Berlin, 1898, 55; *Flavobacterium brevis* (sic) Bergey et al., Manual, 1st ed., 1923, 116.)

bre've. L. adj. *brevis* short.

Rods, 0.8 to 1.0 by 2.5 microns, showing polar staining. Non-motile. Gram-negative.

Gelatin colonies: Minute, pale yellow, compact growth in 2 to 3 weeks.

Gelatin stab: Thin, yellowish growth on the surface in 3 weeks. Beaded growth in stab. No liquefaction.

Agar slant: Yellowish growth in 2 to 3 days.

Broth: Turbid with white sediment.

Blood serum: Light gray-colored growth in 2 to 3 days.

Litmus milk: Action not recorded.

Potato: No growth.

Aerobic, facultatively anaerobic.

Optimum temperature, 35° C.

Pathogenic for laboratory animals.

Source: Found constantly in Berlin drain water.

Habitat: Sewage.

11. Flavobacterium halmephilum Elazari-Volcani, 1940. (Studies on the Microflora of the Dead Sea. Thesis. Hebrew Univ., Jerusalem, 1940, VIII and 85.)

hal.me′phi.lum. Gr. noun *halme* brine, sea water; Gr. adj. *philus* loving; M.L. adj. *halmephilus* sea-water-loving.

Rods, 0.5 to 0.6 by 0.7 to 2.0 microns, occurring singly and in pairs; morphology and size unchanged as salt concentrations vary. Non-motile. Gram-negative.

Gelatin stab (12 per cent salt-1 per cent proteose peptone-15 per cent gelatin): Scant growth; no liquefaction after a month.

Agar colonies (12 per cent salt-1 per cent proteose peptone-2 per cent KNO_3): Circular, smooth, entire, convex, glistening, opaque, yellowish.

Agar slant (12 per cent salt-1 per cent proteose peptone-2 per cent KNO_3): Moderate, filiform, raised, smooth or slightly rugose, opaque, yellowish growth.

Broth (12 per cent salt-1 per cent peptone): Turbid; delicate pellicle or ring and granular, flaky sediment; broth turns yellowish.

Indole not produced.

No acid or gas from glucose, fructose, galactose, mannose, lactose, sucrose, maltose, arabinose, xylose, raffinose, inulin, dextrin, glycerol, mannitol or salicin.

Starch not hydrolyzed.

Nitrites produced from nitrates in trace amounts.

Aerobic.

Optimum temperature, 30° C.

Salt tolerance: Halotolerant, not growing in 0.5 per cent salt, but growing strongly in 3 to 24 per cent and moderately in 30 per cent salt and in Dead Sea water.

Source: Isolated from the water of the Dead Sea.

Habitat: Found in places where the salt content of water is high.

12. Flavobacterium rhenanum (Migula, 1900) Bergey et al., 1948. (Burri's Rhine water bacillus, Frankland and Frankland, Microorganisms in Water, 1894, 483; *Bacillus rhenanus* Migula, Syst. d. Bakt., *2*, 1900, 713; *Flavobacterium rhenanus* (sic) Bergey et al., Manual, 6th ed., 1948, 433.)

rhe.na′num. L. adj. *rhenanus* pertaining to the Rhine.

Original description supplemented by Bergey (*loc. cit.*) from his private notes as indicated; Steinhaus (Jour. Bact., *42*, 1941, 762 and 772) apparently found the same organism and has added other characters.

Rods, 0.7 by 2.5 to 3.5 microns, with rounded ends, occurring singly and in chains (Burri). Motile, possessing peritrichous flagella (Bergey). Gram-negative (Bergey).

Gelatin colonies: Convex, colorless, transparent, becoming yellowish.

Gelatin stab: Infundibuliform liquefaction.

Agar colonies: Small, smooth, convex, entire.

Agar slant: Bright yellow growth (Steinhaus).

Glycerol agar slant: Thin, shining, honey-colored. Growth dry and tough.

Broth: Turbid, with orange-colored pellicle and sediment.

Litmus milk: Soft coagulum, becoming slightly alkaline with yellow ring.

Potato: Moist, glistening, thin, flat, orange to rust-colored growth.

Indole not produced (Bergey).

Hydrogen sulfide not produced (Steinhaus).

Acid from glucose, maltose and sucrose but not from lactose (Steinhaus).

Starch not hydrolyzed (Steinhaus).

Nitrites produced from nitrates (Bergey).

Aerobic, facultatively anaerobic.

Optimum temperature, 30° C.

Source: Isolated from Rhine River water (Burri). From water (Bergey). From eggs in the ovary of a walking stick (*Diapheromera femorata* Say) (Steinhaus).

Habitat: Presumably widely distributed in nature.

13. **Flavobacterium harrisonii** Bergey et al., 1923. (Variety No. 6, Harrison, Rev. gén. du Lait, *5*, 1905, 129; *Bacillus lactis harrisonii* Conn, Esten and Stocking, Ann. Rept. Storrs Agr. Exp. Sta., 1906, 169; Bergey et al., Manual, 1st ed., 1923, 104.)

har.ri.so'ni.i. M.L. gen.noun *harrisonii* of Harrison; named for Prof. F. C. Harrison, the Canadian bacteriologist who first isolated this species.

Rods, 0.25 to 0.75 by 0.3 to 3.5 microns, occurring singly and occasionally in short chains. Motile by means of peritrichous flagella. Gram-negative.

Gelatin colonies: Small, gray, glistening, lobular, citron-yellow, slimy.

Gelatin stab: Villous growth in stab. Slow crateriform to napiform liquefaction.

Agar slant: Growth luxuriant, viscous, spreading, becoming dirty to brownish citron-yellow.

Broth: Turbid, with viscid ring and gelatinous sediment; sweetish odor; alkaline.

Litmus milk: Colorless to gray and slimy, becoming yellow, alkaline.

Potato: Luxuriant, yellow, spreading, slimy growth.

Indole not produced.

Glucose, lactose, maltose and sucrose broths turn alkaline with a disagreeable odor. Reaction of glycerol broth remains neutral.

Aerobic, facultatively anaerobic.

Optimum temperature, 25° C.

Source: Isolated from slimy milk.

Habitat: Unknown.

14. **Flavobacterium diffusum** (Frankland and Frankland, 1889) Bergey et al., 1923. (*Bacillus diffusus* G. and P. Frankland, Ztschr. f. Hyg., *6*, 1889, 396; Bergey et al., Manual, 1st ed., 1923, 100.)

dif.fu'sum. L. adj. *diffusus* spreading, diffuse.

Original description supplemented by Harrison (Canadian Jour. Res., *1*, 1929, 233) as indicated.

Rods, 0.5 by 1.5 microns, occurring singly and in chains. Motile, possessing peritrichous flagella. Gram-negative (Harrison).

Gelatin colonies: Thin, bluish green, spreading, later faint yellow.

Gelatin stab: Thin, glistening, yellowish green surface growth. Slow, crateriform liquefaction.

Agar slant: Thin, light yellow, glistening growth (Frankland and Frankland); capucine-buff (yellow-red-yellow) growth (Harrison).

Broth: Turbid, with greenish yellow sediment.

Litmus milk: Unchanged (Harrison).

Potato: Thin, smooth, greenish yellow, glistening growth.

Indole not produced (Harrison).

Slight acid from glucose. No acid from sucrose or lactose (Harrison).

Nitrites produced from nitrates (Harrison).

Aerobic, facultatively anaerobic.

Optimum temperature, between 25° and 30° C.

Source: Originally found in soil. Found also by Tataroff (Die Dorpater Wasserbakterien, Dorpat, 1891, 58) in fresh water and by Harrison from the skin of halibut from both the Atlantic and Pacific shores of Canada.

Habitat: Soil, fresh and sea waters.

15. **Flavobacterium rigense** Bergey et al., 1923. (*Bacillus brunneus rigensis* Bazarewski, Cent. f. Bakt., II Abt., *15*, 1905, 1; Bergey et al., Manual, 1st ed., 1923, 100.)

ri.gen'se. M.L. adj. *rigensis* pertaining to Riga; named for Riga, the city where this species was isolated.

Rods, 0.75 by 1.7 to 2.5 microns, occurring singly. Motile by means of peritrichous flagella. Gram-negative.

Gelatin colonies: Circular, entire to undulate, grayish white, homogeneous.

Gelatin stab: Smooth, yellowish surface growth. Infundibuliform liquefaction. Brownish yellow sediment.

Agar slant: Narrow, whitish streak, becoming yellowish brown, spreading. Pigment is water- and alcohol-soluble but insoluble in ether.

Broth: Turbid with pellicle and brownish sediment. Cells encapsulated.

Litmus milk: Unchanged.

Potato: Yellow, spreading growth which turns brownish.

Indole not produced.

Hydrogen sulfide not produced.

Acid from glucose in nutrient broth (Mindach, Butler University Botanical Studies, *9*, 1949, 21).

Nitrites produced from nitrates.

Aerobic, facultatively anaerobic.

Optimum temperature, 30° C. Brownish colors develop best at lower temperatures; orange-yellow colors develop best at 37° C.

Habitat: Soil.

16. Flavobacterium halohydrium ZoBell and Upham, 1944. (Bull. Scripps Inst. of Oceanography, Univ. of Calif., *5*, 1944, 278.)

ha.lo.hy'dri.um. Gr. noun *hals* salt; Gr. noun *hydor* water; Gr. dim.noun *hydrium* a small quantity of water; M.L. noun *halohydrium* (probably intended to mean) salt water.

Short rods, 0.6 by 0.8 to 1.0 micron, occurring singly. Motile by means of many peritrichous flagella. Gram-negative.

All media except the fresh-water broth, litmus milk and potato were prepared with sea water.

Gelatin colonies: Small, circular, orange.

Gelatin stab: Napiform liquefaction becoming crateriform. Beaded along line of stab.

Agar colonies: 2 mm in diameter, pulvinate, circular, entire, smooth.

Agar slant: Moderate, glistening, echinulate, butyrous growth with yellow pigment.

Sea-water broth: Yellow surface ring; heavy turbidity; moderate, viscid sediment.

Fresh-water broth: No visible growth.

Litmus milk: No visible change.

Very poorly tolerant of increases or decreases in salinity.

Potato: No visible growth.

Indole not produced.

Hydrogen sulfide not produced.

Acid but no gas from glucose, lactose, maltose, sucrose and salicin. Does not ferment glycerol, mannitol or xylose.

Starch is hydrolyzed.

Casein is hydrolyzed.

Non-lipolytic.

Nitrites not produced from nitrates.

Ammonia produced from peptone but not from urea.

Aerobic, facultatively anaerobic.

Optimum temperature, between 20° and 25° C.

Source: Isolated from sea water and marine mud.

Habitat: Sea water.

17. Flavobacterium neptunium ZoBell and Upham, 1944. (Bull. Scripps Inst. of Oceanography, Univ. of Calif., *5*, 1944, 278.)

nep.tu'ni.um. Gr. adj. *neptunius* pertaining to Neptune; named for Neptune, mythical god of the sea.

Rods, 0.5 to 0.6 by 1.6 to 4.5 microns, occurring singly and in short chains; many cells are bent rods. Motile by means of long, peritrichous flagella. Gram-negative.

All media except the fresh-water broth, litmus milk and potato were prepared with sea water.

Gelatin colonies: Small, circular, darker centers, sink in gelatin, faintly yellow.

Gelatin stab: Slow, napiform liquefaction. Filiform growth along line of stab.

Agar colonies: 2 mm in diameter, circular, smooth, entire, convex, dark centers with buff pigment.

Agar slant: Luxuriant, echinulate, glistening, slightly mucoid growth with buff to yellow pigment. Agar discolored brown.

Sea-water broth: Heavy pellicle; scant turbidity; scant sediment.

Fresh-water broth: No visible growth.

Litmus milk: No visible change.

Potato: No visible growth.

Indole not produced.

Hydrogen sulfide not produced.

Acid but no gas from glucose, lactose, maltose and salicin. Does not ferment glycerol, mannitol, xylose or sucrose.

Starch is hydrolyzed.

Casein not hydrolyzed.

Non-lipolytic.

Nitrites not produced from nitrates.

Ammonia produced from peptone but not from urea.

Aerobic, facultatively anaerobic.

Optimum temperature, between 20° and 25° C.

Source: Isolated from marine bottom deposits.

Habitat: Sea water.

18. **Flavobacterium okeanokoites** ZoBell and Upham, 1944. (Bull. Scripps Inst. of Oceanography, Univ. of Calif., *5*, 1944, 270.)

o.ke.a.no.ko.i′tes. Gr. mas.n. *oceanus* the ocean; Gr. fem.n. *coite, coites* bed; M.L. fem.gen.n. *okeanokoites* of the ocean bed.

Rods, 0.8 to 0.9 by 1.2 to 1.6 microns, with rounded ends, occurring singly and in long chains; many cells are coccoid. Motile by means of peritrichous flagella. Gram-negative.

All media except the fresh-water broth, litmus milk and potato were prepared with sea water.

Gelatin colonies: Small, circular, convex, entire, rust- or orange-colored; digest gelatin.

Gelatin stab: Slow, napiform liquefaction; yellow growth.

Agar colonies: 2 mm in diameter, circular, entire, smooth, convex.

Agar slant: Moderate, filiform, glistening, butyrous growth with yellow pigment.

Sea-water broth: No pellicle; moderate turbidity; moderate, viscid sediment.

Fresh-water broth: Good growth.

Litmus milk: No visible change.

Potato: No visible growth.

Indole not produced.

Hydrogen sulfide is produced.

No acid or gas from glucose, lactose, maltose, sucrose, glycerol, mannitol, xylose or salicin.

Starch not hydrolyzed.

Casein is hydrolyzed.

Non-lipolytic.

Nitrites slowly produced from nitrates.

Ammonia produced from peptone but not from urea.

Aerobic, facultatively anaerobic.

Optimum temperature, between 20° and 25° C.

Source: Isolated from marine mud.

Habitat: Sea water.

19. **Flavobacterium marinovirosum** ZoBell and Upham, 1944. (Bull. Scripps Inst. of Oceanography, Univ. of Calif., *5*, 1944, 271.)

ma.ri.no.vi.ro′sum. L. adj. *marinus* of the sea; L. adj. *virosus* slimy; M.L. adj. *marinovirosus* probably intended to mean a marine slimy organism.

Rods, 0.7 to 0.8 by 0.8 to 2.8 microns, with rounded ends, occurring singly and in long chains. Motile by means of peritrichous flagella. Gram-negative.

All media except the fresh-water broth, litmus milk and potato were prepared with sea water.

Gelatin colonies: Small, circular, raised, rust-colored; gelatin slowly digested.

Gelatin stab: Crateriform liquefaction becoming stratiform. Light orange pigment.

Agar colonies: 1 to 2 mm, circular, convex, entire, smooth.

Agar slant: Moderate, filiform, glistening, mucoid growth with grayish yellow pigment.

Sea-water broth: Heavy turbidity; no pellicle; abundant, viscid sediment.

Fresh-water broth: Good growth.

Litmus milk: No visible change.

Potato: No visible growth.

Indole not produced.

Hydrogen sulfide is produced.

Does not ferment glycerol, glucose, lactose, maltose, sucrose, mannitol, xylose or salicin.

Starch not hydrolyzed.

Casein not hydrolyzed.

Non-lipolytic.

Nitrites not produced from nitrates.

Ammonia produced from peptone but not from urea.

Aerobic, facultatively anaerobic.

Optimum temperature, between 20° and 25° C.

Source: Isolated from sea water and marine mud.

Habitat: Sea water.

20. **Flavobacterium suaveolens** Soppeland, 1924. (Jour. Agr. Res., *28*, 1924, 275.)

sua.ve′o.lens. L. adj. *suaveolens* having a sweet odor.

Rods, 0.6 to 0.8 by 1.0 to 1.2 microns, with rounded ends, occurring singly and in pairs. Motile by means of peritrichous flagella. Gram-negative on plain agar; Gram-positive in young culture on milk powder agar.

Gelatin stab: Rapid, stratiform liquefaction. Medium becomes brown.

Agar colonies: Small, circular, smooth, yellow, amorphous, undulate margin.

Agar slant: Moderate, flat, glistening, opaque, butyrous, yellow, with aromatic odor.

Broth: Turbid with scant sediment. Aromatic odor, becoming cheesy.

Litmus milk: Peptonized. Alkaline.

Potato: Abundant, yellow, glistening growth becoming brown.

Indole produced.

Nitrites not produced from nitrates.

Hydrogen sulfide produced.

Slight acid but no gas from glucose, sucrose and glycerol. No acid from lactose.

Starch is hydrolyzed.

Blood serum is liquefied.

Aerobic, facultatively anaerobic.

Optimum temperature, 25° C.

Source: Isolated from dairy wastes.

Habitat: Unknown.

21. Flavobacterium marinum Harrison, 1929. (Canadian Jour. of Research, *1*, 1929, 234.)

ma.ri'num. L. adj. *marinus* marine, of the sea.

Rods, 0.8 by 1.2 to 1.3 microns, with rounded ends, occurring singly and in pairs. Motile by means of 4 to 5 peritrichous flagella. Encapsulated. Gram-variable; show blue granules in Gram-negative rods.

Gelatin colonies: Circular, iridescent, whitish margin with pale yellow center. Liquefaction.

Gelatin stab: Saccate to stratiform liquefaction.

Agar colonies: Circular, pale yellow, smooth, convex, granular; reticulate edge.

Agar slant: Amber-yellow, slightly raised, spreading, smooth, glistening, transparent growth.

Ammonium phosphate agar: Scant growth.

Broth: Turbid, sediment.

Litmus milk: Alkaline. Digestion without coagulation. Clear serum.

Potato: Abundant, amber-yellow, becoming dirty yellow, spreading, glistening growth.

Indole not produced.

Hydrogen sulfide not produced.

Faint acidity from glucose; no action on lactose or sucrose.

Nitrites not produced from nitrates. Trace of ammonia formed.

Loeffler's blood serum not liquefied. Faint yellow, spreading growth.

Aerobic, facultatively anaerobic.

Optimum temperature, between 20° and 25° C.

Source: Isolated from living halibut obtained at 30 to 50 fathoms, Pacific Ocean. Gibbons (Contrib. to Canadian Biol. and Fish., *8*, 1934, 279) reports this species as occurring in the slime and feces of cod (*Gadus callarias*), halibut (*Hippoglossus hippoglossus*) and skate (*Raja erinacea*).

Habitat: Skin and feces of fishes.

22. Flavobacterium lactis Bergey et al., 1923. (*Bacillus aromaticus lactis* Grimm, Cent. f. Bakt., II Abt., *8*, 1902, 584; Bergey et al., Manual, 1st ed., 1923, 108.)

lac'tis. L. noun *lac* milk; L. gen.noun *lactis* of milk.

Rods, 0.7 to 1.0 by 3.5 to 4.0 microns, occurring singly, in pairs and in chains. Motile by means of peritrichous flagella. Gram-negative.

Gelatin colonies: Circular, light yellow, slimy, concentrically ringed, undulate.

Gelatin stab: Slimy surface growth. No liquefaction.

Agar slant: Slimy, yellowish, smooth, moist.

Broth: Turbid, with abundant sediment.

Litmus milk: Slightly acid.

Potato: Growth thick, slimy, brownish, with yellowish margin.

Indole not produced.

Nitrites not produced from nitrates.

Cultures have pleasant odor.

Aerobic, facultatively anaerobic.

Optimum temperature, 25° C.

Source: Isolated from milk.

Habitat: Unknown.

23. Flavobacterium devorans (Zimmermann, 1890) Bergey et al., 1923. (*Bacillus devorans* Zimmermann, Bakt. unserer Trink- u. Nutzwässer, Chemnitz, *1*, 1890, 48; Bergey et al., Manual, 1st ed., 1923, 102.)

de'vo.rans. L. part.adj. *devorans* consuming, devouring.

Original description supplemented by Bergey (*loc. cit.*) from his private notes as indicated.

Rods, 0.7 by 0.9 to 1.2 microns, occurring singly, in pairs and in chains. Motile (Zimmermann) by means of peritrichous flagella (Bergey). Gram-negative (Zimmermann).

Gelatin colonies: Circular, white, granular to filamentous, becoming yellowish gray.

Gelatin stab: Slow, infundibuliform liquefaction.

Agar slant: Thin, gray, spreading growth.

Broth: Turbid.

Litmus milk: Unchanged.

Potato: No growth (Zimmermann). Yellowish gray streak (Bergey).

Indole not produced.

Nitrites not produced from nitrates (Bergey).

Aerobic, facultatively anaerobic.

Optimum temperature, between 25° and 30° C.

Source: Isolated from water at Chemnitz (Zimmermann). From water (Bergey). From the alimentary tract of the nine-spotted lady beetle (*Coccinella novemnotata* Habst.) (Steinhaus, Jour. Bact., *42*, 1941, 764).

24. **Flavobacterium invisibile** (Vaughan, 1892) Bergey et al., 1923. (*Bacillus invisibilis* Vaughan, American Jour. Med. Sci., *104*, 1892, 191; *Flavobacterium invisibilis* (sic) Bergey et al., Manual, 1st ed., 1923, 109.)

in.vi.si'bi.le. L. adj. *invisibilis* invisible.

Rods, 0.6 to 0.7 by 1.2 to 2.0 microns, occurring singly. Motile by means of peritrichous flagella. Gram-negative.

Gelatin colonies: Pale yellow, burr-like, with irregular margin.

Gelatin stab: Scant growth on surface. Good growth in stab. No liquefaction.

Agar colonies: White, convex, smooth, serrate.

Agar slant: Limited, thick, white streak.

Broth: Turbid.

Litmus milk: Unchanged.

Potato: No growth.

Indole not produced.

Nitrites not produced from nitrates.

Aerobic, facultatively anaerobic.

Optimum temperature, 35° C.

Habitat: Water.

25. **Flavobacterium marinotypicum** ZoBell and Upham, 1944. (Bull. Scripps Inst. of Oceanography, Univ. of Calif., *5*, 1944, 268.)

ma.ri.no.ty'pi.cum. L. adj. *marinus* of the sea; Gr. adj. *typicus* conformable, typical; M.L. adj. *marinotypicus* probably intended to mean typical of the sea.

Rods, 0.5 to 0.7 by 1.4 to 2.0 microns, occurring almost entirely as single cells. Motile by means of four or more peritrichous flagella. Gram-negative.

All media except the fresh-water broth, litmus milk and potato were prepared with sea water.

Gelatin colonies: Very minute and yellow; slow liquefaction.

Gelatin stab: Crateriform liquefaction becoming stratiform. Filiform along line of stab.

Agar colonies: Minute, circular, entire, convex, yellow.

Agar slant: Scant, filiform, butyrous, shiny growth with yellow pigment.

Sea-water broth: Scant, yellowish pellicle; heavy turbidity; slight, viscid sediment.

Fresh-water broth: Good growth.

Litmus milk: Decolorized; neutral; greenish pellicle; slow peptonization.

Potato: Abundant, shiny, greenish yellow growth. Potato darkened.

Indole not produced.

Hydrogen sulfide is produced.

Acid but no gas from glucose and glycerol. Does not ferment lactose, sucrose, mannitol, xylose or salicin.

Starch not hydrolyzed.

Non-lipolytic.

Nitrites not produced from nitrates.

Ammonia produced from peptone but not from urea.

Aerobic, facultatively anaerobic.

Optimum temperature, between 20° and 25° C.

Source: Isolated from sea water and marine mud.

Habitat: Sea water.

26. **Flavobacterium piscicida** Bein.

1954. (Bulletin of Marine Sciences of the Gulf and Caribbean, *4*, 1954, 110.)

pis.ci'ci.da. L. noun *piscis* a fish; L. v. L. adj. suffix *-cidus* from L. v. *caedo* to cut, kill; M.L. noun *piscicida* fish killer.

Straight rods, 0.6 to 0.8 by 1.2 to 1.8 microns, occurring singly and in chains. Motile by means of peritrichous flagella. Gram-negative.

All media except fresh-water broth and litmus milk were prepared with sea water.

Gelatin stab: Rapid, crateriform liquefaction.

Agar colonies: Spreading, irregular, glistening: edges undulate to lobate.

Agar slant (1.0 per cent peptone): Glistening, yellow-orange growth.

Peptone broth (1 per cent): Ammonia not produced.

Nutrient broth: No growth.

Sea-water broth: Heavy turbidity; pellicle.

Litmus milk: No growth.

Indole not produced.

Hydrogen sulfide not produced.

Glucose, fructose, sucrose, maltose, lactose, mannitol and salicin not attacked.

Starch not hydrolyzed.

Nitrites not produced from nitrates.

Urease-negative.

Pathogenic for fish, killing schoolmasters (*Lutjanus apodus*) in five minutes and sand perch (*Eucinostomus pseudogula*), killifish (*Fundulus similis*) and mollies (*Mollienesia latipinna*) within 24 hours.

Distinctive characters: Requires sea water for growth. Little or no pigmentation appears when the peptone concentration is 0.1 per cent; intense pigmentation occurs with 1.0 per cent peptone sea-water media.

Source: Isolated from "red tide" water from the vicinity of Whitewater Bay on the southwest coast of Florida during an outbreak of mass mortality of fishes.

Habitat: Found in sea water. Known to occur off the coast of Florida.

Genus IV. **Agarbacterium** *Angst, 1929.**

(Puget Sound Biol. Sta. Pub., 7, 1929, 52.)

A.gar.bac.te'ri.um. Malayan noun *agar* agar, a jelly from seaweed; Gr. neut.dim.n. *bacterium* a small rod; M.L. neut.n. *Agarbacterium* agar (-digesting) rodlet.

Short to medium-sized rods which are either motile by means of peritrichous flagella or non-motile; some species are included here in which the position of the flagella is unknown but which possess other characters of this genus.[†] Gram-negative. May or may not possess non-diffusible pigments. Carbohydrates are feebly attacked, if at all, some species producing acid but no gas. Agar is digested. Found primarily on decomposing seaweed and in sea water; also found in fresh water and soil.

The type species is *Agarbacterium aurantiacum* Angst.

Key to the species of genus **Agarbacterium**.

I. Motile.
  A. Type of flagellation not determined.
    1. Chromogenic.
      a. Acid from lactose and mannitol.
          1. *Agarbacterium aurantiacum*.
      aa. No acid from lactose or mannitol.
          2. *Agarbacterium rhodomelae*.

* Prepared by Prof. Robert S. Breed, Cornell University, Geneva, New York, October, 1955.

† The type of flagellation of the type species, *Agarbacterium aurantiacum* Angst, has not been determined. In the event that this species is proved to be polar flagellate, the genus *Agarbacterium* should be placed in the family *Pseudomonadaceae*. The peritrichous, Gram-negative agar-digesting species should then remain in a separate genus in the family *Achromobacteraceae*, where they are presently located.

2. Non-chromogenic.
    a. Abundant growth on potato.
            3. *Agarbacterium mesentericum.*
    aa. No growth on potato.
            4. *Agarbacterium reducans.*
B. Flagellation peritrichous.
    1. Gelatin liquefied.
            5. *Agarbacterium amocontactum.*
    2. Gelatin not liquefied.
            6. *Agarbacterium pastinator.*
II. Non-motile.
  A. Acid from glucose or mannitol.
    1. Acid from glucose but not from mannitol.
            7. *Agarbacterium uliginosum.*
    2. Acid from mannitol but not from glucose.
            8. *Agarbacterium bufo*
  B. No acid from glucose or mannitol.
    1. Grow on fish agar slant.
      a. Cells measure up to 4.0 microns in length.
            9. *Agarbacterium polysiphoniae.*
      aa. Cells do not measure up to 4.0 microns in length.
        b. Pellicle produced in broth.
            10. *Agarbacterium ceramicola.*
        bb. Pellicle not produced in broth.
            11. *Agarbacterium boreale.*
    2. Does not grow on fish agar slant.
            12. *Agarbacterium delesseriae.*

1. **Agarbacterium aurantiacum** Angst, 1929. (Puget Sound Biol. Sta. Pub., 7, 1929, 53.)

aur.an.ti'a.cum. L. part.adj. *aurans, aurantis* overlaying with gold; M.L. noun *aurantium* the orange; M.L. adj. *aurantiacus* orange-colored.

Short rods, 0.6 by 0.8 micron, with rounded ends, occurring singly and in pairs. Not encapsulated. Motile. Gram-negative.

All media contained a decoction made by boiling or autoclaving fronds of *Iridaea*, a sea weed, in sea water or in a 3 per cent salt solution.

Gelatin colonies: Circular, sunken, entire, crateriform, granular; growth is slow.

Fish gelatin slant: Abundant, filiform, flat, glistening, smooth, opaque, orange, butyrous growth.

Fish gelatin stab: Stratiform liquefaction; growth best at top.

Agar colonies: Circular, smooth, flat, erose, granular; growth is slow.

Agar slant: Abundant, filiform, flat, glistening, smooth, opaque, orange, butyrous growth.

Fish agar slant: Abundant, filiform, flat, dull, smooth, opaque, orange, butyrous growth.

Meat agar slant: Abundant, filiform, raised, dull, smooth to wrinkled, opaque, orange, butyrous growth.

Broth: Turbid, no sediment; membranous pellicle.

Plain milk unchanged; surface growth orange.

Potato: Abundant, filiform, flat, dull, smooth, orange, butyrous growth; the potato becomes grayed.

Indole not produced.

Hydrogen sulfide not produced.

Slight acid from lactose and mannitol. No acid from glucose, sucrose, xylose, rhamnose or arabinose.

Starch not hydrolyzed.

Agar digested; cellulose not attacked.

Nitrites not produced from nitrates.

Aerobic.

Methylene blue reduced.

Temperature relations: Optimum, between 20° and 28° C. Minimum, between 5° and 10° C. Maximum, less than 36° C.

Comment: By subsequent designation, Breed (Riassunti delle Comunicazioni, VI Cong. Internaz. di Microbiol., Roma, *1*, 1953, 13) selected this species as the type for the genus *Agarbacterium* Angst. It was felt that this species could be reisolated and reidentified more readily than could the other species placed in this genus by Angst.

Source: Isolated from the fronds of *Porphyra perforata*.

Habitat: Found on marine algae.

2. **Agarbacterium rhodomelae** (Lundestad, 1928) Breed, *comb. nov.* (*Bacterium rhodomelae* Lundestad, Cent. f. Bakt., II Abt., *75*, 1928, 331.)

rho.do′me.lae. M.L. noun *Rhodomela* a genus of red algae; M.L. gen.noun *rhodomelae* of *Rhodomela*.

Rods, 0.5 to 0.8 by 1.2 to 2.0 microns, with rounded ends, occurring singly, in pairs and, at times, in short chains. Motile. Gramnegative.

Fish gelatin colonies: Circular, slightly glistening, opaque, white.

Fish gelatin stab: Rapid, infundibuliform liquefaction.

Seaweed agar colonies: Circular, flat, thin, transparent, glistening, entire. Agar is dissolved.

Glucose agar slant: Growth moderate, white, becoming orange-yellow, flat, opaque, glistening; undulate margin.

Broth: Turbid; pellicle; grayish yellow, slimy sediment.

Indole not produced.

Carbohydrates not attacked.

Starch very slightly hydrolyzed.

Nitrites not produced from nitrates.

Aerobic, facultatively anaerobic.

Temperature relations: Optimum, bebetween 20° and 25° C. Minimum, 0° C. Maximum, between 30° and 32° C.

Source: Isolated from water from the Norwegian Coast.

Habitat: Sea water.

3. **Agarbacterium mesentericum** Angst, 1929. (*Agarbacterium mesentericus* (sic) Angst, Puget Sound Biol. Sta. Pub., *7*, 1929, 52.)

me.sen.te′ri.cum. Gr. neut.n. *mesenterium* the mesentery; M.L. adj. *mesentericus* like the mesentery.

Short rods, 0.6 by 0.8 micron, with rounded ends, occurring singly and in pairs. No encapsulated. Motile. Gram-negative.

All media contained a decoction made by boiling or autoclaving fronds of *Iridaea*, a seaweed, in sea water or a 3 per cent salt solution.

Fish gelatin colonies: Circular, sunken, granular, irregular, crateriform; growth is rapid.

Fish gelatin slant: Abundant, spreading, flat, glistening, smooth, translucent, white, butyrous growth. Liquefaction.

Fish gelatin stab: Infundibuliform liquefaction; growth best at top.

Agar colonies: Circular, concentrically ringed, flat, entire, granular; growth is moderate.

Agar slant: Abundant, filiform, raised, glistening, finely wrinkled when old or dry, opaque, buff, membranous growth.

Fish agar slant: Abundant, filiform, flat, glistening, concentrically ringed, opaque, white, butyrous growth.

Meat agar slant: Abundant, spreading, flat, glistening, smooth, opaque, white, butyrous growth.

Broth: Moderately turbid; no sediment; membranous pellicle.

Plain milk unchanged.

Potato: Abundant, spreading, raised, glistening, wrinkled, buff to yellowish, membranous growth; the potato becomes grayed.

Indole not produced.

Hydrogen sulfide not produced.

Acid from mannitol. No acid from glucose, lactose, xylose, rhamnose or arabinose.

Starch is hydrolyzed.

Agar is digested; cellulose not attacked.

Nitrites not produced from nitrates.

Aerobic.

Methylene blue reduced.

Temperature relations: Optimum, between 20° and 28° C. Minimum, less than 5° C. Maximum, between 36° and 45° C.

Source: Isolated from fronds of *Nereocystis luetkeana*.

Habitat: Found on marine algae.

4. Agarbacterium reducans Angst, 1929. (Puget Sound Biol. Sta. Pub., *7*, 1929, 57.)

re.du′cans. L. part. adj. *reducans* bringing back, reducing.

Short rods, 0.6 by 0.8 micron, with rounded ends, occurring singly and in pairs. Not encapsulated. Motile. Gram-negative.

All media contained a decoction made by boiling or autoclaving fronds of *Iridaea*, a seaweed, in sea water or a 3 per cent salt solution.

Fish gelatin colonies: Circular, sunken, entire, crateriform, granular; growth is rapid.

Fish gelatin slant: Abundant, filiform, sunken, glistening, smooth, opaque, buff, butyrous growth.

Fish gelatin stab: Crateriform liquefaction; growth best at top.

Agar colonies: Circular, smooth, flat, entire, granular; growth is moderate.

Agar slant: Abundant, filiform, flat, glistening. smooth, opaque, buff, butyrous growth.

Fish agar slant: Abundant, filiform, flat, glistening, smooth, opaque, white, butyrous growth.

Meat agar slant: Abundant, echinulate, flat, glistening, smooth, opaque, white, butyrous growth.

Broth: Turbid, no sediment; no pellicle.

Plain milk unchanged.

Potato: No growth.

Indole not produced.

Hydrogen sulfide not produced.

Acid from sucrose, rhamnose, arabinose and mannitol. No acid from lactose or xylose.

Starch is hydrolyzed.

Agar is digested; cellulose not attacked.

Aerobic.

Methylene blue reduced.

Temperature relations: Optimum, between 25° and 28° C. Minimum, less than 5° C. Maximum, between 36° and 45° C.

Source: Isolated from *Nereocystis luetkeana*.

Habitat: Found on marine algae.

5. Agarbacterium amocontactum (ZoBell and Allen, 1935) Breed, *comb. nov.* (*Flavobacterium amocontactum* ZoBell and Allen, Jour. Bact., *29*, 1935, 246.)

a.mo.con.tac′tum. L. v. *amo* to like, love; L. noun *contactus* contact; M.L. adj. *amocontactus* presumably means contact-loving.

Slender rods, 0.4 to 0.7 by 1.6 to 2.3 microns, with rounded ends, occurring singly and in irregular clumps. Encapsulated. Actively motile by means of peritrichous flagella. Stain very lightly. Gram-negative.

Gelatin stab: Good, filiform growth with rapid, saccate liquefaction.

Agar colonies: Circular, 2 to 4 mm in diameter, yellow.

Agar slant: Abundant, filiform, smooth, glistening, bright yellow growth with a butyrous consistency. Originally agar was liquefied, but this property was lost following artificial cultivation.

Sea-water broth: Good growth with ring at surface. Strongly turbid; abundant, viscid sediment; no odor.

Milk: No growth.

Potato: No growth.

Potato dialyzed in sea water: Slight, yellow growth.

Indole not produced.

Hydrogen sulfide produced.

No acid from glucose, lactose, sucrose, xylose or mannitol.

Starch not hydrolyzed.

Agar is digested.

Nitrites produced from nitrates.

Ammonia produced from peptone.

Aerobic, facultatively anaerobic.

Optimum temperature, between 18° and 21° C.

Optimum reaction, pH 8.0.

Distinctive character: Adheres firmly to submerged glass slides and cannot be removed with running water.

Source: Many cultures were isolated from glass slides submerged in sea water.

Habitat: Sea water.

6. Agarbacterium pastinator (Goresline, 1933) Breed, *comb. nov.* (*Achromobacter pastinator* Goresline, Jour. Bact., *26*, 1933, 442.)

pas.ti.na'tor. L. noun *pastinator* one who digs or trenches the ground.

Short rods, 0.4 by 1.5 microns, occurring singly and in pairs. Motile by means of two to five peritrichous flagella. Gram-negative.

Plain gelatin stab: No growth.

Nutrient gelatin stab: Surface growth very scant. No liquefaction.

Nutrient agar colonies: At first tiny, almost colorless, becoming yellowish and ring-like. Agar liquefied rapidly.

Nutrient agar slant: Growth good, flat not thick. Agar liquefied along streak often to the depth of a quarter of an inch. Pocket formed at bottom of slant filled with a rather viscous, yellowish fluid.

Nutrient broth: Slight turbidity after 5 days. Subsurface but no surface growth. No sediment.

Litmus milk: Slightly acid after 20 days. No curd. Only a trace of reduction at bottom of tube.

Potato: No growth.

Indole not produced.

Hydrogen sulfide not produced.

Acid from glucose, fructose, arabinose, galactose, sucrose, maltose, lactose, mannose, melezitose, raffinose, rhamnose, salicin, pectin, starch and dextrin. No growth in dulcitol, erythritol, mannitol, sorbitol, glycerol, xylose or inulin.

Starch is hydrolyzed.

Agar is digested.

Temperature relations: Optimum, 28° C. Good growth at 25° C. Moderate growth at 20° and at 37° C. No growth at 10° or at 42° C.

Limits of growth: pH 5.9 to 9.0.

Facultative anaerobe.

Distinctive characters: Digests agar rapidly; colonies sink through to the glass of the Petri dish. Fehling's solution is reduced by the liquefied agar. There is considerable change in the viscosity of the agar due to the digestion.

Source: Isolated from a trickling filter receiving creamery wastes.

Habitat: Probably widely distributed in nature.

7. **Agarbacterium uliginosum** (ZoBell and Upham, 1944) Breed, *comb. nov.* (*Flavobacterium uliginosum* ZoBell and Upham, Bull. Scripps Inst. of Oceanography, Univ. Calif., *5*, 1944, 263.)

u.li.gi.no'sum. L. adj. *uliginosus* wet, damp.

Rods, 0.4 to 0.6 by 1.2 to 3.9 microns, some slightly curved, occurring mostly singly with some short chains. Non-motile. Gram-negative.

All differential media except the freshwater broth, litmus milk and potato were prepared with sea water.

Gelatin colonies: 1 mm in diameter, orange, sunken.

Gelatin stab: Infundibuliform liquefaction. Yellow pigment. Gelatin discolored brown.

Agar colonies: Sunken, uneven, irregular, gummy; agar is liquefied. Orange to yellow pigment is produced, and agar is discolored brown.

Agar slant: Luxuriant, yellowish orange, glistening, filiform, adherent growth; agar slowly liquefied.

Sea-water broth: Moderately turbid; dense, yellow pellicle; slightly viscid sediment.

Fresh-water broth: No visible growth.

Litmus milk: Completely decolorized; neutral.

Potato: No visible growth.

Indole not produced.

Hydrogen sulfide not produced.

Acid but no gas from xylose, glucose, maltose, lactose, sucrose and salicin. Glycerol and mannitol not fermented.

Starch not hydrolyzed.

Agar rapidly liquefied. However, after prolonged laboratory cultivation, this organism gradually loses its ability to digest agar.

Nitrites rapidly produced from nitrates.

Ammonia produced from peptone but not from urea.

Casein digested.

Non-lipolytic.

Aerobic, obligate.

Optimum temperature, between 20° and 25° C.

Source: Isolated from marine bottom deposits.

8. Agarbacterium bufo Angst, 1929. (Puget Sound Biol. Sta. Pub., 7, 1929, 53.)

bu'fo. L. noun *bufo* the toad.

Short rods, 0.6 by 0.8 micron, with rounded ends, occurring singly and in pairs. Not encapsulated. Non-motile. Gram-negative.

All media contained a decoction made by boiling or autoclaving fronds of *Iridaea*, a seaweed, in sea water or a 3 per cent salt solution.

Fish gelatin colonies: Circular, sunken, crateriform, granular, yellow; growth is slow.

Fish gelatin slant: Scant, filiform, flat, glistening, smooth, translucent, white to yellowish, butyrous growth.

Fish gelatin stab: Stratiform liquefaction; growth best at top.

Agar colonies: Circular, concentrically ringed, sunken, entire, granular, yellow; growth is slow.

Agar slant: Abundant, filiform, raised, glistening, contoured, opaque, yellow, membranous growth.

Fish agar slant: Abundant, filiform, flat, glistening, smooth, opaque, yellow to orange, butyrous growth.

Meat agar slant: Abundant, filiform, flat, glistening, contoured, opaque, yellow to orange, butyrous growth surrounded by a white halo.

Broth: Moderately turbid; scant sediment; granular, membranous pellicle.

Plain milk unchanged; surface growth yellow.

Potato: No growth.

Indole not produced.

Hydrogen sulfide not produced.

Slight acid from mannitol. No acid from glucose, sucrose, lactose, xylose, rhamnose or arabinose.

Starch not hydrolyzed.

Agar digested; cellulose not attacked.

Nitrites produced from nitrates.

Aerobic.

Methylene blue reduced.

Temperature relations: Optimum, between 25° and 28° C. Minimum, between 5° and 10° C. Maximum, less than 36° C.

Source: Isolated from *Odonthalia kamtschatica*.

Habitat: Found on marine algae.

9. Agarbacterium polysiphoniae (Lundestad, 1928) Breed, *comb. nov.* (*Bacterium polysiphoniae* Lundestad, Cent. f. Bakt., II Abt., 75, 1928, 331.)

po.ly.si.pho'ni.ae. M.L. noun *Polysiphonia* a genus of red algae; M.L. gen.noun *polysiphoniae* of *Polysiphonia*.

Rods, 0.5 to 0.6 by 2.0 to 4.0 microns, with rounded ends, occurring singly. Non-motile. Gram-negative.

Fish gelatin colonies: Circular, slightly glistening, bright yellow, transparent, with dense center.

Fish gelatin stab: Slight, yellowish growth on surface. Slow, saccate liquefaction.

Seaweed agar colonies: Circular, flat, light yellow, with concentric rings and diffuse margin. Agar is disintegrated.

Fish agar slant: Yellow, flat growth with undulate margin.

Broth: Turbid; flocculent pellicle; yellowish sediment.

Indole not produced.

Carbohydrates not attacked.

Starch slightly hydrolyzed.

Nitrites not produced from nitrates.

Aerobic, facultatively anaerobic.

Temperature relations: Optimum, 25° C. Minimum, between 5° and 10° C. Maximum, between 27° and 30° C.

Source: Isolated from sea water from the Norwegian Coast.

Habitat: Sea water.

10. Agarbacterium ceramicola (Lundestad, 1928) Breed, *comb. nov.* (*Bacterium ceramicola* Lundestad, Cent. f. Bakt., II Abt., 75, 1928, 332.)

ce.ram.i'co.la. M.L. noun *Ceramium* a genus of red algae; L. v. *colo* to dwell; M.L. fem.n. *ceramicola* the *Ceramium* dweller.

Rods, 0.5 to 0.6 by 1.4 to 2.4 microns, with rounded ends, occurring singly and lying side by side. Non-motile. Gram-negative.

Fish gelatin colonies: Circular, glistening, transparent, yellow.

Fish gelatin stab: Slight, yellow surface growth. Crateriform liquefaction.

Sea-water agar colonies: Circular, flat, transparent, glistening, light yellow; diffuse margin. Agar is disintegrated.

Fish agar slant: Moderate, yellow, flat, entire, glistening, opaque growth.

Broth: Light yellow pellicle and sediment. Indole production not recorded. Carbohydrates not attacked. Starch slightly hydrolyzed. Nitrite production not recorded. Aerobic, facultatively anaerobic. Temperature relations: Optimum, 23° C. Minimum, between 5° and 10° C. Maximum, between 27° and 30° C. Source: Isolated from water from the Norwegian Coast. Habitat: Sea water.

11. Agarbacterium boreale (Lundestad, 1928) Breed, *comb. nov.* (*Bacterium boreale* Lundestad, Cent. f. Bakt., II Abt., *75*, 1928, 333.)

bo.re.a'le. L. adj. *borealis* northern.

Rods, 0.5 to 0.6 by 1.6 to 2.6 microns, with rounded ends, occurring singly. Non-motile. Gram-negative.

Fish gelatin colonies: Circular, opaque, glistening, concentrically ringed, yellow.

Fish gelatin stab: Yellow with crateriform liquefaction.

Sea-water agar colonies: Circular, flat, opaque, glistening, light yellow; diffuse margin. Agar is disintegrated.

Fish agar slant: Yellow, flat, glistening, opaque, entire growth.

Broth: Finely flocculent, yellow sediment. Indole production not recorded. Carbohydrates not attacked. Starch slightly hydrolyzed. Nitrite production not recorded. Aerobic, facultatively anaerobic. Temperature relations: Optimum, 23° C.

Minimum, between 5° and 10° C. Maximum, between 27° and 30° C. Source: Isolated from water from the Norwegian Coast. Habitat: Sea water.

12. Agarbacterium delesseriae (Lundestad, 1928) Breed, *comb. nov.* (*Bacterium delesseriae* Lundestad, Cent. f. Bakt., II Abt., *75*, 1928, 332.)

de.les.se'ri.ae. M.L. noun *Delesseria* a genus of red algae; M.L. gen.noun *delesseriae* of *Delesseria*.

Rods, 0.5 to 0.6 by 1.6 to 2.6 microns, with rounded ends, occurring singly. Non-motile. Gram-negative.

Fish gelatin colonies: Circular, transparent, glistening, concentrically ringed, yellow.

Fish gelatin stab: Crateriform liquefaction; yellow sediment.

Seaweed agar colonies: Circular, flat, concentrically ringed, light yellow. Agar is disintegrated.

Fish agar slant: No growth.

Broth: Turbid with flocculent pellicle and sediment, light yellow. Indole production not recorded. Carbohydrates not attacked. Starch slightly hydrolyzed. Nitrite production not recorded. Aerobic, facultatively anaerobic. Temperature relations: Optimum, 23° C. Minimum, between 5° and 10° C. Maximum, between 27° and 30° C. Source: Isolated from water from the Norwegian Coast. Habitat: Sea water.

Genus V. **Beneckea** *Campbell, gen. nov.** *

Be.neck'e.a. M.L. fem.gen.n. *Beneckea* of Benecke; named for W. Benecke, the German bacteriologist who was the first to isolate chitin-decomposing bacteria.

Small to medium-sized rods. Motile by means of peritrichous flagella. Gram-negative. May or may not produce chromogenesis. Acid usually produced from carbohydrates. Chitin is digested. Found in salt- and fresh-water and in soil.

The type species is *Beneckea labra* (Campbell and Williams) Campbell.

Key to the species of genus **Beneckea.**

I. Gelatin not liquefied.
   A. Nitrites produced from nitrates.

1. *Beneckea labra.*

---

* Prepared by Dr. L. Leon Campbell, Jr., State College of Washington, Pullman, Washington, June, 1954.

B. Nitrites not produced from nitrates.

        2. *Beneckea ureasophora.*

II. Gelatin liquefied.

  A. Nitrites produced from nitrates.

    1. Acid from sucrose.

        3. *Beneckea chitinovora.*

    2. No acid from sucrose.

        4. *Beneckea hyperoptica.*

  B. Nitrites not produced from nitrates.

    1. Acid from sucrose.

        5. *Beneckea indolthetica.*

    2. No acid from sucrose.

        6. *Beneckea lipophaga.*

1. **Beneckea labra** (Campbell and Williams, 1951) Campbell, *comb. nov.* (*Achromobacter labrum* Campbell and Williams, Jour. Gen. Microbiol., *5*, 1951, 894.)

la'bra. Gr. adj. *labrus* greedy.

Rods, 0.2 to 0.4 by 0.8 to 1.1 microns, occurring singly, in pairs and occasionally in clumps. Motile by means of peritrichous flagella. Gram-negative.

Gelatin stab: No liquefaction.

Agar colonies: Circular, smooth, entire, flat, glistening, opaque, non-pigmented to pale cream.

Agar slants: Abundant, filiform, smooth, glistening, opaque, non-pigmented growth.

Broth: Moderately turbid: surface growth adherent to the walls of the tubes.

Litmus milk: Acid in 6 days.

Indole not produced.

Hydrogen sulfide not produced.

Acid but no gas from glucose, fructose, maltose, dextrin, mannose, trehalose and cellobiose. No acid from lactose, sucrose, arabinose, rhamnose, xylose, raffinose, inulin, mannitol, salicin, dulcitol, inositol, melezitose or adonitol.

Glucose, fructose, sucrose, maltose, lactose, dextrin, mannose, arabinose, rhamnose, xylose, raffinose, inulin, mannitol, salicin, galactose, trehalose, inositol, cellobiose, melezitose, adonitol, chitin, glycogen, starch, butyrate, valerate, asparaginate, succinate, malate, fumarate (0.5 per cent), levulinate, β-alanine, glucosamine, ethanol and tertiary butanol are utilized as carbon sources. Dulcitol, cellulose, malonate, salicylate, oxalate, mandelate, benzoate (0.5 per cent), propionate, n-amyl alcohol, methanol, n-propanol, iso-amyl alcohol and lumichrome are not utilized as carbon sources.

Starch is hydrolyzed.

Chitin is hydrolyzed.

Non-lipolytic.

Nitrites produced from nitrates.

Ammonia produced from peptone.

Urease-negative.

Casein not hydrolyzed.

Trimethylamine not produced from trimethylamine oxide, choline or betaine.

Aerobic, facultative.

Optimum temperature, between 20° and 30° C. Grows at 4° C.

Source: Isolated from marine mud.

Habitat: Found in sea water.

2. **Beneckea ureasophora** (Campbell and Williams, 1951) Campbell, *comb. nov.* (*Achromobacter ureasophorum* Campbell and Williams, Jour. Gen. Microbiol., *5*, 1951, 894.)

u.re.a.so'pho.ra. Gr. noun *urum* urine; M.L. noun *urea* urea; M.L. noun *ureasum* urease; Gr. adj. *phorus* bearing; M.L. adj. *ureasophorus* urease-bearing.

Small rods, 0.2 by 0.8 micron, occurring singly. Motile by means of peritrichous flagella. Gram-negative.

Gelatin stab: No liquefaction.

Agar colonies: Circular, raised, glistening, entire, translucent, non-pigmented.

Agar slant: Abundant, filiform, glistening, translucent, non-pigmented growth.

Broth: Slightly turbid with a stringy sediment.

Litmus milk: Acid in 6 days.

Indole not produced.

Hydrogen sulfide not produced.

Acid but no gas from glucose, fructose,

maltose, sucrose, mannose, trehalose and cellobiose. No acid from lactose, dextrin, arabinose, rhamnose, xylose, raffinose, inulin, salicin, dulcitol, inositol, melezitose or adonitol.

Glucose, fructose, sucrose, maltose, lactose, dextrin, mannose, arabinose, rhamnose, xylose, raffinose, inulin, mannitol, salicin, dulcitol, galactose, trehalose, inositol, cellobiose, melezitose, adonitol, glycogen, starch, chitin, asparaginate, succinate, malate, lactate, pyruvate (0.3 per cent), acetate, β-alanine, glucosamine, ethanol, methanol and tertiary butanol are utilized as carbon sources. Fumarate (0.5 per cent), malonate, tartrate, citrate, levulinate, propionate, salicylate, valerate, oxalate, butyrate, mandelate, benzoate (0.5 per cent), n-amyl alcohol, iso-amyl alcohol, n-propanol and lumichrome are not utilized as carbon sources.

Starch is hydrolyzed.

Chitin is hydrolyzed.

Non-lipolytic.

Nitrites not produced from nitrates.

Ammonia is produced from peptone.

Urease-positive.

Casein not hydrolyzed.

Trimethylamine not produced from trimethylamine oxide, choline or betaine.

Aerobic, facultative.

Optimum temperature, between 20° and 30° C. Growth at 4° C.

Source: Isolated from marine mud.

Habitat: Found in sea water.

3. **Beneckea chitinovora** (Benecke, 1905) Campbell, *comb. nov.* (*Bacillus chitinovorus* Benecke, Bot. Zeitung, *63*, 1905, 227.)

chi.ti.no'vo.ra. M.L. noun *chitinum* chitin; L. v. *voro* to devour; M.L. adj. *chitinovorus* chitin-destroying.

Rods, 0.75 by 2.0 microns, occurring occasionally in pairs and in chains. Motile by means of peritrichous flagella. Gramnegative.

Gelatin stab: Liquefaction.

Mineral agar containing chitin: Good growth if no sugar is added to produce acid. Non-chromogenic.

Peptone mineral agar containing chitin:

Good growth if reaction is neutral to slightly alkaline.

Peptone broth: Turbid with heavy, slimy, whitish to brownish pellicle.

Acid from glucose and sucrose.

Nitrites produced from nitrates.

Ammonia produced in peptone-chitin media.

Salt in concentrations up to 1.5 per cent is favorable for growth. Maximum, 4 per cent.

Optimum temperature, 20° C.

Source: Isolated at Kiel from media containing decomposing crab shells and from media containing purified chitin; also from soil.

Habitat: Brackish water and soil.

4. **Beneckea hyperoptica** (Campbell and Williams, 1951) Campbell, *comb. nov.* (*Achromobacter hyperopticum* Campbell and Williams, Jour. Gen. Microbiol., *5*, 1951, 894.)

hy.per.op'ti.ca. Gr. adj. *hyperopticus* disdainful.

Small rods, 0.2 by 0.6 micron, occurring singly and in small clumps. Motile by means of peritrichous flagella. Gram-negative.

Gelatin stab: Crateriform liquefaction.

Agar colonies: Small, punctiform, glistening, opaque, non-pigmented.

Agar slant: Beaded, glistening, opaque, non-pigmented growth.

Broth: Moderately turbid; surface ring adherent to the walls of the tubes; slightly stringy sediment.

Litmus milk: Alkaline, with slight peptonization in 4 days.

Indole not produced.

Hydrogen sulfide not produced.

Acid but no gas from glucose, maltose, mannose, trehalose and cellobiose. No acid from fructose, lactose, sucrose, galactose, arabinose, dextrin, rhamnose, xylose, raffinose, inulin, mannitol, inositol, melezitose or adonitol.

Glucose, sucrose, dextrin, mannose, raffinose, galactose, cellobiose, starch, glycogen, chitin, glucosamine and acetate are utilized as carbon sources. Succinate, malate, fumarate (0.5 per cent), lactate, malonate, tartrate, citrate, pyruvate (0.3 per cent), levulinate, β-alanine, asparaginate, propionate, salicylate, valerate, oxalate, butyrate, mandelate, benzoate (0.5 per cent), ethanol, methanol, iso-amyl alcohol, n-amyl alcohol, tertiary butanol, n-propanol and lumichrome are not utilized as carbon sources.

Starch is hydrolyzed.

Chitin is hydrolyzed.

Lipolytic.

Nitrites produced from nitrates.

Ammonia produced from peptone.

Urease-negative.

Casein is hydrolyzed.

Trimethylamine not produced from trimethylamine oxide, choline or betaine.

Growth not inhibited by 10 per cent NaCl.

Aerobic, facultative.

Optimum temperature, between 20° and 30° C. Growth at 4° C.

Source: Isolated from marine mud.

Habitat: Found in sea water.

5. **Beneckea indolthetica** (Campbell and Williams, 1951) Campbell, *comb. nov.* (*Flavobacterium indoltheticum* Campbell and Williams, Jour. Gen. Microbiol., *5*, 1951, 894.)

in.dol.the'ti.ca. M.L. noun *indolum* indole; Gr. adj. *theticus* positive; M.L. adj. *indoltheticus* indole-positive.

Rods, 0.4 to 0.9 by 1.0 to 1.5 microns, occurring singly, in pairs and in occasional clumps. Motile by means of peritrichous flagella. Gram-negative.

Gelatin stab: Crateriform liquefaction.

Agar colonies: Circular, smooth, entire, opaque, yellow to yellow-orange.

Agar slant: Yellow to yellow-orange, smooth, opaque growth.

Broth: Turbid; slight surface scum; yellow to orange sediment.

Litmus milk: Acid in 2 days.

Indole is produced.

Hydrogen sulfide not produced.

Acid but no gas from glucose, fructose, sucrose, maltose, dextrin, mannose, raffinose, trehalose and cellobiose. No acid from lactose, arabinose, rhamnose, xylose, inulin, mannitol, salicin, dulcitol, inositol, melezitose or adonitol.

Glucose, fructose, sucrose, maltose, dextrin, mannose, raffinose, salicin, cellobiose, trehalose, pyruvate (0.3 per cent), acetate,

chitin, starch, glycogen and glucosamine are utilized as carbon sources. Lactose, arabinose, rhamnose, xylose, inulin, mannitol, dulcitol, galactose, inositol, melezitose, adonitol, succinate, malate, fumarate (0.5 per cent), lactate, malonate, tartrate, citrate, levulinate, β-alanine, asparaginate, propionate, salicylate, valerate, oxalate, butyrate, mandelate, benzoate (0.5 per cent), ethanol, methanol, n-amyl alcohol, iso-amyl alcohol, tert.-butanol, n-propanol and lumichrome are not utilized as carbon sources.

Starch is hydrolyzed.

Chitin is hydrolyzed.

Non-lipolytic.

Nitrites not produced from nitrates.

Ammonia produced from peptone.

Urease-negative.

Casein is hydrolyzed.

Trimethylamine not produced from trimethylamine oxide, choline or betaine.

Growth inhibited by 10 per cent NaCl.

Aerobic, facultative.

Optimum temperature, between 20° and 30° C. No growth at 4° C.

Source: Isolated from marine mud.

Habitat: Found in sea water.

6. **Beneckea lipophaga** (Campbell and Williams, 1951) Campbell, *comb. nov.* (*Achromobacter lipophagum* Campbell and Williams, Jour. Gen. Microbiol., *5*, 1951, 894.)

li.po'pha.ga. Gr. noun *lipus* fat; Gr. v. *phagein* to devour; M.L. noun *lipophaga* fat-destroyer.

Small rods, 0.4 by 1.0 micron, occurring singly, in pairs and in small clumps. Motile by means of peritrichous flagella. Gram-negative.

Gelatin stab: Saccate liquefaction.

Agar colonies: Circular, smooth, entire, glistening, opaque, non-pigmented.

Agar slant: Abundant, filiform, glistening, opaque, non-pigmented growth.

Broth: Uniformly turbid.

Litmus milk: Acid in 4 days with slight peptonization.

Indole not produced.

Hydrogen sulfide not produced.

Acid but no gas from glucose, maltose and mannose. No acid from fructose, lactose, sucrose, dextrin, arabinose, rhamnose, xylose, raffinose, inulin, mannitol, sorbitol, salicin, dulcitol, trehalose, inositol, cellobiose, melezitose or adonitol.

Glucose, fructose, sucrose, maltose, lactose, dextrin, mannose, arabinose, rhamnose, xylose, raffinose, inulin, mannitol, salicin, dulcitol, galactose, trehalose, inositol, cellobiose, melezitose, adonitol, glycogen, starch, chitin, asparaginate, succinate, malate, fumarate (0.5 per cent), lactate, pyruvate (0.3 per cent), acetate, β-alanine, glucosamine, ethanol, methanol and tertiary butanol are utilized as carbon sources. Malonate, tartrate, citrate, levulinate, propionate, salicylate, valerate, oxalate, butyrate, mandelate, benzoate (0.5 per cent), n-amyl alcohol, n-propanol and lumichrome are not utilized as carbon sources.

Starch is hydrolyzed.

Chitin is hydrolyzed.

Nitrites not produced from nitrates.

Ammonia produced from peptone.

Urease-negative.

Casein is hydrolyzed.

Trimethylamine is produced from trimethylamine oxide but not from choline or betaine.

Growth not inhibited by 10 per cent NaCl.

Aerobic, facultative.

Optimum temperature, between 20° and 30° C. Growth at 4° C.

Source: Isolated from marine mud.

Habitat: Found in sea water.

Addendum: *Species incertae sedis.* Benton (Jour. Bact., *29*, 1935, 449) describes but does not name 17 types of chitinovorous bacteria isolated from water, mud and plankton of fresh-water lakes, from decaying May fly nymph shells, intestinal contents of fish, frogs, bats, snipe and crayfish, and from shore soil, composts, etc. Twelve types are reported to be monotrichous, two to be peritrichous, and the position of the flagella is not given in three types. Of two Gram-positive types, one may have been a spore-former and the other an organism belonging in the family *Corynebacteriaceae.* Two of the 17 types digested cellulose.

ZoBell and Rittenberg (Jour. Bact., *35*, 1938, 275) isolated and studied but did not name 31 cultures of chitinoclastic bacteria from marine sources. Out of 16 cultures studies intensively, all were Gram-negative. All but 4 of the 31 cultures were motile. One culture was a coccus and two species were vibrios. None of these cultures digested cellulose.

Hock (Jour. Marine Res., *4*, 1941, 105) describes two species of motile rods that attack chitin without, however, determining the type of flagellation. If these species are reisolated and found to be peritrichous, they should be placed in the genus *Beneckea* Campbell.

In addition to the cultures described above, Campbell and Williams (Jour. Gen. Microbiol., *5*, 1951, 894) isolated and described three other chitinoclastic species which they identified as belonging to the genera *Pseudomonas* or *Micrococcus.*

FAMILY IV. ENTEROBACTERIACEAE RAHN, 1937.*
(Zent. f. Bakt., II Abt., *96*, 1937, 280.)

En.te.ro.bac.te.ri.a′ce.ae. M.L. noun *enterobacterium* an intestinal bacterium; *-aceae* ending to denote a family; M.L. fem.pl.n. *Enterobacteriaceae* the family of the enterobacteria.

Straight rods. Motile by means of peritrichous flagella or non-motile. Gram-negative. Grow well on artificial media. All species attack glucose producing acid or acid and visible

---

* The late Prof. Robert S. Breed, Cornell University, Geneva, New York, and Prof. E. G. D. Murray, University of Western Ontario, Canada, have prepared the general sections for family *Enterobacteriaceae*, October, 1955. Other contributors, as noted, have prepared the sections covering the various groups within this family.

gas (H_2 present); some species even attack alginates or pectins. Characteristically, nitrites are produced from nitrates (exceptions in *Erwinia*). Antigenic composition is best described as a mosaic which results in serological interrelationships among the several genera, even extending to other families. Many species live in the intestines of man and other animals, frequently causing intestinal disturbances, while others are parasitic on plants, some causing blights and soft rots; still other species are saprophytic, causing decomposition of dead organic materials.

NOTE: Early attempts to develop a satisfactory basis for the recognition of species among the coliform-dysentery-typhoid group of bacteria are reviewed by Winslow, Kligler and Rothberg (Jour. Bact., *4*, 1919, 429); these were based largely on differences in motility, production of indole, ability to liquefy gelatin and, more particularly, differences in the ability to ferment carbohydrates, especially such compounds as glucose, lactose, sucrose, dulcitol and salicin. The more recent attempts to express differences in species of coliform bacteria by means of the IMViC reactions are reviewed by Parr (Amer. Jour. Public Health, *26*, 1936, 39; also see Bact. Rev., *3*, 1939, 1), this cryptic symbol indicating the indole test, methyl-red acid determination, acetylmethylcarbinol production (Voges-Proskauer reaction) and the utilization of salts of citric acid. Stuart, Griffin and Baker (Jour. Bact., *36*, 1938, 391) and Griffin and Stuart (Jour. Bact., *40*, 1940, 83) have applied these tests plus cellobiose fermentation to a study of a long series of cultures.

Meanwhile, the Kauffmann and White Antigenic Schema has been successfully applied to the recognition of serological groups and types among the organisms placed in the coliform-dysentery-typhoid group. Studies by Kauffmann (*Enterobacteriaceae*. Munksgaard, Copenhagen, 1954, 225–254) and Edwards and Ewing (Identification of *Enterobacteriaceae*. Burgess Pub. Co., Minneapolis, 1955, 164–176) and others have shown that many cultures previously identified as *Aerobacter aerogenes* Beijerinck are, culturally and serologically, *Klebsiella pneumoniae* Trevisan. For this reason it has been recommended by the above-mentioned authors that these two species should be combined as *Klebsiella pneumoniae* Trevisan, this name having priority over *Aerobacter aerogenes* Beijerinck. However, because investigators (Kligler, Jour. Inf. Dis., *15*, 1914, 187; Stuart, Griffin and Baker, Jour Bact., *38*, 1938, 391; Osterman and Rettger, Jour. Bact., *42*, 1941, 721; and others) have previously shown that it is difficult to draw a borderline between the usually non-motile, non-gelatin-liquefying *Aerobacter aerogenes* and the usually motile, gelatin-liquefying *Aerobacter cloacae* Bergey et al., the union of the species *Klebsiella pneumoniae* and the species *Aerobacter aerogenes* causes *A. aerogenes* and *A. cloacae* to be placed in separate genera. The placing of the latter species in a genus (*Cloaca* Castellani and Chalmers) is an arrangement that is equally as unsatisfactory as is the present arrangement. While awaiting a better solution of this problem, it has been felt advisable to retain *Aerobacter aerogenes* as a species distinct from *Klebsiella pneumoniae* and to retain the genera *Aerobacter* Beijerinck and *Klebsiella* Trevisan.

From the standpoint of taxonomy, too little attention has been given by the majority of the authors who have proposed adjustments in the classification of the species related to the coliform organisms to the wide distribution and diversity of species that possess characteristics that place them in this group. It has long been known that the coliform organisms that occur in dairy products are frequently derived from grain, and that they occur on the panicles of the grass family in open fields where there is no reason to think that they originated from fecal contamination (Rogers, Clark and Evans, Jour. Inf. Dis., *17*, 1915, 137; Rogers, Univ. of Wisc. Studies in Science, No. 2, 1918, 104 pp.; Thomas and McQuillin, Proc. Soc. Appl. Bact., *15*, 1952, 41; Henriksen, Acta Path. et Microbiol. Scand., *34*, 1954, 249–285 and others). Some of these non-encapsulated organisms, identified as *Aerobacter aerogenes* Beijerinck, produce a yellow chromogenesis. Although saprophytic coliform organisms from cotton fiber, bagasse (sugar cane fiber), hemp, jute and grain have been recognized as responsible for various types of respiratory diseases in man, it has not been demonstrated how closely these saprophytes are related to *Klebsiella pneumoniae*. This important problem needs careful review from a variety of viewpoints.

Serological studies support the cultural studies that show that the species of *Serratia* Bizio *sensu stricto* belong in the coliform group (Breed and Breed, Cent. f. Bakt., II Abt., *71*, 1927, 435). These widely distributed red organisms are found growing not only on starchy foods but also on other foods and on such tropical products as dried coconut (copra), latex and even in palm buds undergoing a soft rot. Likewise, Thjøtta and Kåss (Norske Videnskaps-Akad., Oslo, I Mat.-Naturv. Klasse, No. 5, 1945, 17) have shown that the bacteria which decompose alginates sometimes have all the characteristics of coliform organisms except that they possess the power to attack these substances that resist attack by the common coliform bacteria. Too few students of the coliform group test their cultures to see whether they will produce soft rots (*Erwinia carotovora* Holland). Still fewer students of coliform bacteria determine the type of flagellation possessed by the organisms they study, although it is well known to students of fish diseases (Schäperclaus, Fischkrankheiten, 2 Aufl., 1941, Braunschweig, 296 pp.) that several motile (polar flagellate) and nonmotile species of *Pseudomonadaceae* are easily mistaken for coliform or paracolon bacteria. Some of these (*Aeromonas punctata* Snieszko and other species in the genus *Aeromonas* Kluyver and van Niel) are common in water as they cause diseases of carp, salmon and other fish as well as diseases of frogs.

Borman, Stuart and Wheeler (Jour. Bact., *48*, 1944, 351), Kauffmann (*op. cit.*, 1954), Edwards and Ewing (*op. cit.*, 1955) and others have recently suggested rearrangements in the classification of the species that belong in the family *Enterobacteriaceae*. Only the future can determine which of the views of these authors best expresses the relationships of the bacteria that belong in this family.—The Editors.

Key to the tribes of family **Enterobacteriaceae.**

I. Lactose fermented anaerobically, usually within 48 hours, but in one genus (*Paracolobactrum*) the fermentation may be delayed as much as 30 days.
  A. Prodigiosin not produced.
    1. Do not produce protopectinase. Not parasitic on plants.
      Tribe I. *Escherichieae*, p. 334.
    2. May produce protopectinase. Parasitic on plants, frequently causing soft rots, blights, etc.
      Tribe II. *Erwinieae*, p. 349.
  B. Prodigiosin produced.
      Tribe III. *Serratieae*, p. 359.
II. Lactose rarely fermented anaerobically.
  A. Urea decomposed within 48 hours (except by *Proteus inconstans*).
      Tribe IV. *Proteeae*, p. 364.
  B. Urea not decomposed within 48 hours.
      Tribe V. *Salmonelleae*, p. 368.

TRIBE I. ESCHERICHIEAE BERGEY, BREED AND MURRAY, 1938.

(Preprint, Manual, 5th ed., 1938 (October), vi.)

Esch.er.i.chi′e.ae. M.L. fem.n. *Escherichia* type genus of the tribe; *-eae* ending to denote a tribe; M.L. fem.pl.n. *Escherichieae* the *Escherichia* tribe.

Rods that are either motile by means of peritrichous flagella or occasionally non-motile. Gelatin not liquefied except slowly by *Aerobacter cloacae* and by *Paracolobactrum arizonae*. Ferment glucose and lactose with the production of acid and visible gas within 24 hours at 37° C. or within 48 hours at 25° to 30° C. Some forms produce acid and gas from lactose slowly, occasionally not at all. Do not produce soft rots of vegetables.

Key to the genera of tribe **Escherichieae.**

I. Alginic acid is not decomposed with the production of acid and gas.
   A. Lactose is fermented *within 48 hours.*
      1. *Acetylmethylcarbinol not produced; methyl red test positive; salts of citric acid may or may not be used as sole sources of carbon.

   Genus I. *Escherichia*, p. 335.
      2. *Acetylmethylcarbinol produced; methyl red test negative; salts of citric acid used as sole sources of carbon.
         a. Usually not encapsulated; from feces, milk, dairy products, grain and other saprophytic sources.

   Genus II. *Aerobacter*, p. 341.
         aa. Usually encapsulated; from respiratory, intestinal and urogenital tracts.

   Genus III. *Klebsiella*, p. 344.
   B. Lactose fermentation is consistently delayed, and occasionally lactose is not fermented at all.

   Genus IV. *Paracolobactrum*, p. 346.
II. Alginic acid is decomposed with the production of acid and gas.

   Genus V. *Alginobacter*, p. 348.

Genus I. **Escherichia** *Castellani and Chalmers, 1919.*†

(Castellani and Chalmers, Man. Trop. Med., 3rd ed., 1919, 941; *Citrobacter* Werkman and Gillen, Jour. Bact., *23*, 1932, 173; *Enterobacter* Rahn (in part), Cent. f. Bakt., II Abt., *96*, 1937, 281.)

Esch.er.i'chi.a. M.L. gen.noun *Escherichia* of Escherich; named for Prof. Theodor Escherich, who first isolated the type species of this genus.

Short rods. Motile or non-motile. Gram-negative. Glucose and lactose are fermented with the production of acid and gas. Acetylmethylcarbinol is not produced. Methyl red test positive. Carbon dioxide and hydrogen are produced in approximately equal volumes from glucose. Generally not able to utilize uric acid as a sole source of nitrogen. Found in feces; occasionally pathogenic to man (enteritis, peritonitis, cystitis, etc.). Widely distributed in nature.

The type species is *Escherichia coli* (Migula) Castellani and Chalmers.

Key to the species of genus **Escherichia.**

I. Citric acid and salts of citric acid are not utilized as sole sources of carbon. Hydrogen sulfide not produced.
   A. Usually not pigmented although a yellow pigment is sometimes produced.

   1. *Escherichia coli.*
   B. Golden brown to red pigment produced.

   2. *Escherichia aurescens.*
II. Citric acid and salts of citric acid are utilized as sole sources of carbon.
   A. Hydrogen sulfide produced.

   3. *Escherichia freundii.*
   B. Hydrogen sulfide not produced.

   4. *Escherichia intermedia.*

---

* Levine (Jour. Bact., *1*, 1916, 153) was the first to show the inverse correlation between the methyl red and Voges-Proskauer tests and used these characters for the primary separation of the *Escherichia coli* section from the *Aerobacter aerogenes* section of the coliform group (Amer. Jour. Public Health, *7*, 1917, 784).

† Prepared by Prof. M. W. Yale, New York State Experiment Station, Geneva, New York, July, 1943; revised by Prof. Robert S. Breed, Cornell University, Geneva, New York, in consultation with investigators that have made special studies of this genus, October, 1955.

1. **Escherichia coli** (Migula, 1895) Castellani and Chalmers, 1919. (*Bacterium coli commune* Escherich, Fortschr. d. Med., *3*, 1885, 518; *Bacillus escherichii* Trevisan, I generi e le specie delle Batteriacee, 1889, 15; *Bacillus coli* Migula, in Engler and Prantl, Naturlich. Pflanzenfam., *1*, la, 1895, 27; *Bacterium coli* Lehmann and Neumann, Bakt. Diag., 1 Aufl., *2*, 1896, 224; Castellani and Chalmers, Man. Trop. Med., 3rd ed., 1919, 941.)

co′li. Gr. noun *colum* or *colon* the large intestine, colon; L. gen.noun *coli* of the colon.

Rods, usually 0.5 by 1.0 to 3.0 microns, varying from almost coccoid forms to long rods, occurring singly, in pairs and in short chains. Motile or non-motile; motile strains possess peritrichous flagella. Usually not encapsulated. Non-spore-forming. Gram-negative.

Gelatin colonies: Opaque, moist, grayish white, entire.

Gelatin stab: Grayish white, spreading, undulate growth. No liquefaction.

Agar colonies: Usually white, sometimes yellowish white, entire to undulate, moist, homogeneous. Atypical forms occur frequently.

Agar slant: Usually white, sometimes yellowish white, moist, glistening, spreading growth.

Broth: Turbid; heavy, grayish sediment; no pellicle.

Litmus milk: Rapid acid production with development of gas; usually coagulated; curd may or may not be broken up; no peptonization of the curd. Litmus may or may not be reduced.

Potato: Abundant, grayish to yellowish, spreading growth.

Blood agar plates: Different strains vary widely in their action, some being hemolytic (Buchgraber and Hilkó, Zent. f. Bakt., I Abt., Orig., *133*, 1935, 449).

Indole usually produced.

No hydrogen sulfide produced in peptone iron agar (Levine, Epstein and Vaughn, Amer. Jour. Public Health., *24*, 1934, 505; Tittsler and Sandholzer, Amer. Jour. Public Health, *27*, 1937, 1240). More sensitive indicators give positive tests for hydrogen sulfide (Hunter and Weiss, Jour. Bact., *35*, 1938, 20).

Methyl red test positive (Clark and Lubs, Jour. Inf. Dis., *17*, 1915, 160); Voges-Proskauer test negative (Durham, Jour. Exp. Med., *5*, 1901, 373); inverse correlation between methyl red and Voges-Proskauer tests (Levine, Jour. Bact., *1*, 1916, 153).

Acid and gas from glucose, fructose, galactose, lactose, maltose, arabinose, xylose, rhamnose and mannitol. Sucrose, raffinose, salicin, esculin, dulcitol and glycerol may or may not be fermented. Variable fermentation of sucrose and salicin (Sherman and Wing, Jour. Bact., *33*, 1937, 315; Tregoning and Poe, Jour. Bact., *34*, 1937, 473). Inulin, pectin and adonitol rarely fermented. Dextrin, starch, glycogen and inositol not fermented. Cellobiose (Jones and Wise, Jour. Bact., *11*, 1926, 359) and α-methyl-glucoside (Koser and Saunders, Jour. Bact., *24*, 1932, 267) not fermented. See Twort (Proc. Royal Soc. London, *79*, 1907, 329) for utilization of unusual glucosides, Dozois et al. (Jour. Bact., *30*, 1935, 189; and *32*, 1936, 499) for utilization of certain sugar alcohols and their anhydrides, and Poe and Klemme (Jour. Biol. Chem., *109*, 1935, 43) for utilization of rare sugars. See Winslow, Kligler and Rothberg (Jour. Bact., *4*, 1919, 429) for review of literature relative to classification.

Gas ratio: Approximately equal volumes of carbon dioxide and hydrogen, ratio 1:1, are produced from glucose (Harden and Walpole, Proc. Roy. Soc., Ser. B, *77*, 1905, 399; Rogers, Clark and Davis, Jour. Inf. Dis., *14*, 1914, 411).

Trimethyleneglycol not produced from glycerol by anaerobic fermentation (Braak, Onderzoekingen over Vergisting van Glycerine. Thesis, Delft, 1928, 166; Werkman and Gillen, Jour. Bact., *23*, 1932, 167).

Citric acid and salts of citric acid not utilized as sole sources of carbon (Koser, Jour. Bact., *8*, 1923, 493).

Nitrites produced from nitrates.

Uric acid not utilized as a sole source of nitrogen (Koser, Jour. Inf. Dis., *23*, 1918, 377); uracil utilized as a sole source of nitrogen (Mitchell and Levine, Jour. Bact., *35*, 1938, 19).

Fecal odor produced.

Catalase-positive.

Aerobic, facultatively anaerobic.

Heat resistance: Usually destroyed in 30 minutes at 60° C., but certain heat-resistant strains may withstand this exposure (Ayers and Johnson, Jour. Agr. Res., *3*, 1914, 401; Stark and Patterson, Jour. Dairy Sci., *19*, 1936, 495).

Growth requirements: Good growth on ordinary laboratory media. Optimum growth temperature, between 30° and 37° C. Growth takes place at 10° and 45° C. Gas produced from glucose at 45° to 46° C. Eijkmann test positive (Eijkmann, Cent. f. Bakt., I Abt., Orig., *37*, 1904, 74; Perry and Hajna, Jour. Bact., *26*, 1933, 419).

Serology: A large number of serological types which seem to differ in pathogenic significance are included in this species as defined here. While it has long been known that *E. coli* is serologically heterogeneous, Kauffmann and his associates have brought some semblance of order to the mass of divergent types present in this species. Among significant contributions to the establishment of a scheme of serological classification, the following may be listed: Kauffmann (Acta. Path. et Microbiol. Scand., *20*, 1942, 21; *21*, 1944, 20; Jour. Immunol., *57*, 1947, 71), Knipschildt (Undersogelser over Coligruppens Serologi. A. Busk, Copenhagen, 1945) and Vahlne (Serological typing of the colon bacteria. Gleerupska Univ. Bokhandeln, Lund, 1945).

Like the salmonellas and shigellas, strains of *E. coli* are divided into groups on the basis of their heat-stable somatic (O) antigens. The O groups are subdivided on the basis of sheath, envelope or capsular (K) antigens, which have the property of inhibiting O agglutination just as the Vi antigen inhibits the O agglutination of *Salmonella typhosa*. The ability of these K antigens to inhibit O agglutination is annulled by heating, and they are divided into three categories (L, B, A) by their physical properties, particularly by the resistance to heat of their ability to inhibit O agglutination and to bind their respective agglutinins. Finally, the organisms are divided into serotypes on the basis of their flagellar (H) antigens. To date, approximately 135 O groups, 75 K antigens and 40 H antigens have been recognized and characterized. Since these antigens may occur in different combinations, it is obvious that the number of serotypes existent within the species is much greater than the number recognized to date.

Within recent years there has been a great increase in interest in the serology of *E. coli* due to the association of certain serotypes with severe outbreaks of infantile diarrhea. Among the earlier papers dealing with this problem are those of Bray (Jour. Path. and Bact., *57*, 1945, 239), Bray and Beaven (Jour. Path. and Bact., *60*, 1946, 395), Giles, Sangster and Smith (Arch. Dis. Childhood, *24*, 1949, 45) and Kauffmann and Dupont (Acta Path. et Microbiol. Scand., *27*, 1950, 552). Since these papers were published, the observations of the abovementioned investigators have been confirmed by a great number of workers in many different countries. While it is not yet clear how many different strains of *E. coli* may be involved in the etiology of infantile diarrhea, the following have been found repeatedly in association with the disease: 026:B6; 055:B5; 0111:B4; 0127:B8; and 0128:B12.

For a comprehensive summary of the association of *E. coli* serotypes with infantile diarrhea and other pathological conditions, see Kauffmann (*Enterobacteriaceae*, 2nd edition, E. Munksgaard, Copenhagen, 1954).

Comments: Many varieties of this species have been given specific or varietal names. The majority of these varieties, a number of which are based on differences in sugar fermentations, are not now regarded as significant. Other varieties have been established on the basis of the production of a yellow pigment, a lack of motility, differences in the appearance of colonial growth, a failure to coagulate milk, an inability to produce indole or on the basis of isolation from different regions of the intestine or other differences in habitat, etc.

Source: Originally isolated by Escherich from the feces of breast-fed infants.

Habitat: Found as a normal inhabitant of the intestines of man and of other vertebrates. Widely distributed in nature. Frequently causes infections of the urogenital tract and diarrhea in infants. Invades the circulation in agonal stages of diseases.

1a. Escherichia coli var. *communis* (Escherich, 1885) Breed, *comb. nov.* (*Bacterium coli commune* Escherich, Fortschr. d. Med., *3*, 1885, 518.)

Includes strains of *Escherichia coli* which do not ferment sucrose or salicin. See Topley and Wilson (Princ. of Bact. and Immun., *1*, 1931, 446).

Source: Isolated from feces.

1b. Escherichia coli var. *acidilactici* (Topley and Wilson, 1931) Yale, 1939. (Milchsäurebacterium, Hueppe, Mit. d. kais. Gesund., *2*, 1884, 340; *Bacillus acidi lactici* Zopf, Die Spaltpilze, 1885, 87; *Escherichia acidilactici* Bergey et al., Manual, 1st ed., 1923, 199; *Bacterium coli* var. *acidi lactici* Topley and Wilson, Princ. of Bact. and Immun., *1*, 1931, 446; Yale, in Manual, 5th ed., 1939, 393.)

Includes strains of *Escherichia coli* which do not attack sucrose or salicin. It is generally thought that Hueppe's cultures were contaminated with a spore-former.

Source: Isolated from milk.

1c. Escherichia coli var. *neapolitana* (Topley and Wilson, 1931) Yale, 1939. (Neapeler Bacterien, Emmerich, Deut. med. Wochnschr., *10*, 1884, 299; *Bacillus neapolitanus* Flügge, Die Mikroorganismen, 1886, 270; *Escherichia neapolitana* Castellani and Chalmers, Man. Trop. Med., 3rd ed., 1919, 942; *Bacterium coli* var. *neapolitanum* Topley and Wilson, Princ. of Bact. and Immun., *1*, 1931, 446; Yale, in Manual, 5th ed., 1939, 393.)

Includes strains of *Escherichia coli* which ferment sucrose and salicin.

Source: Isolated from cholera patients and cadavers; originally thought to be the cause of cholera.

1d. Escherichia coli var. *communior* (Topley and Wilson, 1931) Yale, 1939. (*Bacillus coli communior* Durham, Jour. Exp. Med., *5*, 1900, 353; *Bacterium coli* var. *communior* Topley and Wilson, Princ. of Bact. and Immun., *1*, 1931, 446; Yale, in Manual, 5th ed., 1939, 393.)

Includes strains of *Escherichia coli* which ferment sucrose but not salicin. Levine (Iowa Eng. Exp. Sta. Bull. 62, 1921, 38) recognizes a strain which ferments salicin.

Source: Isolated from feces.

2. Escherichia aurescens (Parr, 1937) Malligo et al., 1955. (*Bacterium aurescens* Parr, Proc. Soc. Exp. Biol. and Med., *35*, 1937, 563; not *Bacterium aurescens* Migula, Syst. d. Bakt., *2*, 1900, 466; Malligo, Parr and Robbins, Jour. Bact., *70*, 1955, 498.)

au.res'cens. L. v. *auresco* to gild, to become golden; L. part.adj. *aurescens* becoming golden.

Rods similar in shape, size and arrangement with those of *Escherichia coli*. Motile. Not encapsulated. Gram-negative.

Gelatin: No liquefaction.

Agar colonies: Golden brown to red, insoluble, carotenoid pigment produced. Red develops best on a Bacto-peptone, Leibig's meat extract agar.

Broth: Pigmented sediment.

Litmus milk: Acidified and coagulated as in *Escherichia coli*.

Indole is produced.

Hydrogen sulfide not produced.

Acid and gas from glucose, lactose, salicin, galactose and mannitol. Sucrose, dulcitol, cellobiose, alpha-methyl-d-glucoside, inositol, raffinose, inulin and adonitol not attacked. Power to produce gas from sugars may be lost.

The products of the anaerobic dissimilation of glucose are ethanol, formic, acetic, lactic and succinic acids, carbon dioxide and hydrogen (Neish, personal communication, 1954).

Methyl red test is positive.

Voges-Proskauer test is negative.

Citrate not utilized as a sole source of carbon.

Nitrites produced from nitrates.

Aerobic.

Grows well at 22° and 37° C.

Distinctive characters: Golden brown, reddish yellow or red pigment, depending on the medium. Pigments are yellow-orange, carotenoid pigments, not like the prodigiosin of *Serratia*. Power to produce pigments may be lost.

Source: Isolated from human feces

(Parr), from an infected eye (Kluyver) and from contaminated water supplies (Tittsler, Jour. Bact., *33*, 1937, 450).

Habitat: Found in fecal matter.

3. **Escherichia freundii** (Braak, 1928) Yale, 1939. (*Bacterium freundii* Braak, Onderzoekingen over Vergisting van Glycerine. Thesis, Delft, 1928, 140; *Citrobacter freundii* Werkman and Gillen, Jour. Bact., *23*, 1932, 176 (type species of genus *Citrobacter* Werkman and Gillen, *ibid.*, 173); Yale, in Manual, 5th ed., 1939, 394.)

freun'di.i. M.L. gen.noun *freundii* of Freund; named for A. Freund, who first observed that trimethyleneglycol was a product of fermentation (1881).

Short rods, with rounded ends, occurring singly, in pairs and in short chains. Motile or non-motile. Gram-negative.

Gelatin stab: Liquefaction by 4 out of 15 cultures (Werkman and Gillen, *op. cit.*, 1932, 177). No liquefaction by any strains (Tittsler and Sandholzer, Jour. Bact., *29*, 1935, 353; Carpenter and Fulton, Amer. Jour. Pub. Health, *27*, 1937, 822).

Agar slant: Smooth, gray, shining, filiform, butyrous growth.

Litmus milk: Acid in 2 days; coagulation may or may not take place; no peptonization.

Potato: Abundant, yellowish white growth.

Indole may or may not be produced (Werkman and Gillen, *op. cit.*, 1932, 177; Tittsler and Sandholzer, *op. cit.*, 1935, 353).

Hydrogen sulfide produced in proteose peptone, ferric citrate agar (Levine, Epstein and Vaughn, Amer. Jour. Pub. Health, *24*, 1934, 505; Tittsler and Sandholzer, Amer. Jour. Pub. Health, *27*, 1937, 1240).

Methyl red test positive. Voges-Proskauer test negative (Koser, Jour. Bact., *9*, 1924, 59). Some strains give a positive methyl red and a positive Voges-Proskauer test (Parr, Jour. Bact., *36*, 1938, 1).

Acid and gas from glucose, fructose, galactose, arabinose, xylose, raffinose, lactose, maltose, mannose, rhamnose, trehalose, glycerol, mannitol and sorbitol. Sucrose, salicin, dulcitol, adonitol and inositol may or may not be fermented. Cellobiose usually fermented while α-methyl-glucoside may or may not be fermented (Tittsler and Sandholzer, *op. cit.*, 1935, 353; Carpenter and Fulton, *op. cit.*, 1937, 822). No acid or gas from amygdalin, dextrin, erythritol, glycogen, inulin or melezitose.

Trimethyleneglycol produced from glycerol by anaerobic fermentation (Braak, *op. cit.*, 1928, 146; Werkman and Gillen, *op. cit.*, 1932, 167).

Citric acid utilized as a sole source of carbon.

Nitrites produced from nitrates.

Uric acid not utilized as a sole source of nitrogen (Koser, *op. cit.*, 1924, 59; Werkman and Gillen, *op. cit.*, 1932, 167).

Catalase-positive.

Aerobic, facultatively anaerobic.

Growth requirements: Good growth on ordinary laboratory media. Optimum growth temperature, between 30° and 37° C. Gas not produced in Eijkman test when carried out at 45° to 46° C. (Levine, Epstein and Vaughn, *op. cit.*, 1934, 505). No gas at 44° C. (Wilson, Med. Res. Council, London, Special Rept., Ser. 206, 1935, 165).

Serology: This species, like *Escherichia coli*, is divisible into serological types. The serology of *E. freundii* has not been studied as extensively as that of *E. coli*. In fact study of these organisms has been confined almost exclusively to aberrant cultures of the group which ferment lactose slowly. The cultures which ferment lactose slowly or not at all have long caused difficulty in the diagnosis of enteric infections since they often are mistaken for members of the genus *Salmonella*. It is only within the past two years that reliable and rapid methods of differentiation of this species from salmonellas through KCN and decarboxylase tests have become available (Møller, Acta. Path. et Microbiol. Scand., *26*, 1954, 115 and 158).

The slow lactose-fermenting organisms of the *E. freundii* group have been designated as the Bethesda-Ballerup group (Edwards, West and Bruner, Jour. Bact., *55*, 1948, 711). Since these are often confused with salmonellas, it was natural that they should have attracted greater attention among medical bacteriologists than typical *E. freundii* cultures. Through the work of

Edwards, West and Bruner (Jour. Bact., *55*, 1948, 711), Bruner, Edwards and Hopson (Jour. Inf. Dis., *85*, 1949, 290) and West and Edwards (U. S. Pub. Health Service Monograph 22, 1954), 32 O groups and 87 H antigens have been established. When the sera used in the classification of Bethesda-Bellerup cultures were used in the examination of normal strains of *E. freundii*, it was found that either or both the O and H antigens of the majority of *E. freundii* cultures could be recognized. Thus, in view of the similarity of their biochemical reactions and their close serological relationships, it seems better to regard the Bethesda-Ballerup group as a variety of the species *E. freundii*. Subsequent biochemical investigations have confirmed this view.

Comments: In 1932, Werkman and Gillen (Jour. Bact., *23*, 1932, 177), following the custom prevalent at that time, established the citrate-positive coliform organisms in a separate genus, *Citrobacter*, and subdivided this genus into seven species on the basis of action on gelatin and on differences in their fermentation of sucrose, esculin, salicin, dulcitol and similar compounds. Five of the seven species described by Werkman and Gillen produced H_2S in proteose peptone-ferric citrate agar and, following Vaughn and Levine (Jour. Bact., *44*, 1942, 502), are all regarded here as belonging to *Escherichia freundii*.

Source: Isolated from canal water in Holland.

Habitat: Normally found in soil and water and, to a varying degree, in the intestinal canals of man and other animals. Widely distributed in nature.

4. Escherichia intermedia (Werkman and Gillen, 1932) Vaughn and Levine, 1942.

(*Citrobacter intermedium* Werkman and Gillen, Jour. Bact., *23*, 1932, 178; Vaughn and Levine, Jour. Bact., *44*, 1942, 498.)

in.ter.me′di.a. L. adj. *intermedius* intermediate.

Short rods, with rounded ends, occurring singly, in pairs and in short chains in young nutrient agar or broth cultures. Actively motile by means of peritrichous flagella or non-motile. Gram-negative.

Gelatin stab: No liquefaction after 60 days at 20° C.

Agar slant: Smooth to wrinkled surface; grayish white, abundant, raised, butyrous growth.

Levine's eosine-methylene blue agar: Well isolated colonies vary from 1 to 4 mm in diameter. No confluence of neighboring colonies. Colonies are slightly to moderately raised with surfaces varying from flat to convex and usually smooth and glistening but sometimes dull, rough and granular.

By transmitted light two types of colonies have been observed: (1) colonies having almost the same appearance throughout but with a distinctly lighter center, the color being similar to the medium; (2) colonies having a dark brownish central area which diffuses out to a lighter margin.

By reflected light three types of colonies have been observed: (1) dark, button-like, concentrically ringed colonies possessing a strong, greenish metallic sheen so characteristic for *Escherichia coli*; (2) colonies with dark, purplish, wine-colored centers surrounded by a light pink zone; some colonies are concentrically ringed; (3) pink colonies with no suggestion of sheen but sometimes concentrically ringed.

Nutrient broth: Turbid; slight ring at surface.

Litmus milk: Acid; sometimes coagulated and reduced; no proteolysis.

Potato: Abundant, white to ivory- colored growth.

Indole may or may not be produced.

Hydrogen sulfide not detected in proteose peptone ferric citrate agar.

Acid or acid and gas produced from xylose, arabinose, rhamnose, glucose, fructose, mannose, galactose, lactose, maltose, trehalose and mannitol. No acid or gas from melezitose, amygdalin or erythritol. Sucrose, raffinose, cellobiose, α-methyl-glucoside, adonitol, dulcitol, glycerol, inositol, sorbitol, starch, aesculin, salicin and sodium malonate may or may not be fermented.

Fermentation of glucose: The end products characteristic for the genus *Escherichia* are produced. Carbon dioxide and hydrogen gases are produced in approximately equimolar proportions (gas ratio, 1:1) besides significant quantities of ethanol and acetic, lactic and succinic acids with only traces of formic acid. Acetylmethylcarbinol and 2,3-butylene glycol have not been found (Voges-Proskauer test negative).

Salts of citric acid are utilized as sole sources of carbon.

Nitrites produced from nitrates.

Catalase-positive.

Aerobic, facultatively anaerobic.

Temperature requirements: Growth at 10° and at 45° to 46° C. Optimum growth temperature, between 30° and 37° C. Gas not produced in Eijkman tests, although some cultures show growth at 45° to 46° C.

Salt tolerance: Most cultures ferment glucose in the presence of sodium chloride in a concentration of 6.0 to 7.0 per cent. A few cultures tolerate 8.0 per cent sodium chloride.

Optimum pH, about 7.0. Growth occurs between pH 5.0 and pH 8.0.

Serology: As noted under *Escherichia freundii*, the serology of the citrate-positive species placed in *Escherichia* has not been studied extensively. So far as known, no studies have been made to determine whether there are detectable serological differences between the citrate-positive cultures that produce hydrogen sulfide in proteose peptone, ferric citrate agar (*E. freundii* as defined by Vaughn and Levine, Jour. Bact., *44*, 1942, 502) and the citrate-positive cultures that do not produce hydrogen sulfide on the same medium (*E. intermedia* as defined by Vaughn and Levine, loc. cit.).

Comments: Vaughn and Levine (loc. cit.) have given reasons for combining two of the seven species of *Citrobacter* described by Werkman and Gillen (Jour. Bact., *23*, 1932, 177) that do not produce hydrogen sulfide into a single species for which they use the name *Escherichia intermedia*. It should be noted that the description as given above is based on their definition. The specific epithet *intermedia* is used here in a more restricted sense than is the general term "intermediates," which is frequently applied to all citrate-positive species of coliform organisms.

Habitat: Normally found, to a varying degree, in soil, water and in the intestinal canals of man and other animals. Widely distributed in nature.

Genus II. **Aerobacter** Beijerinck, *1900*.*

(Cent. f. Bakt., II Abt., *6*, 1900, 193.)

A.e.ro.bac′ter. Gr. mas.n. *aër* air, gas; M.L. noun *bacter* the masculine equivalent of Gr. neut. n. *bactrum* a small rod; M.L. mas.n. *Aerobacter* a gas (-producing) rod.

Short rods. Motile or non-motile, the motile species possessing peritrichous flagella. Gram-negative. Grow readily on ordinary media. Ferment glucose and lactose with the production of acid and gas. Produce two or more times as much carbon dioxide as hydrogen from glucose. Methyl red test negative; Voges-Proskauer test positive. Trimethyleneglycol not produced from glycerol by anaerobic fermentation. Citric acid and salts of citric acid are utilized as sole sources of carbon. Aerobic, facultatively anaerobic. Widely distributed in nature.

The type species is *Aerobacter aerogenes* (Kruse) Beijerinck.

Key to the species of genus **Aerobacter.**

I. †Glycerol fermented with the production of acid and gas. Gelatin not liquefied (rarely liquefied).

1. *Aerobacter aerogenes.*

---

* Prepared by Prof. M. W. Yale, New York State Experiment Station, Geneva, New York, July, 1943; revised by Prof. Robert S. Breed, Cornell University, Geneva, New York, in consultation with investigators who have made special studies of this genus, October, 1955.

† Kligler (Jour. Inf. Dis., *15*, 1914, 187) found the fermentation of glycerol to be inversely correlated with gelatin liquefaction and considered the former the more reliable as a charac-

II. Glycerol fermented with the production of no visible gas. Gelatin liquefied.
2. *Aerobacter cloacae.*

1. **Aerobacter aerogenes** (Kruse, 1896) Beijerinck, 1900. (*Bakterium lactis aërogenes* (sic) Escherich, Fortschr. d. Med., *3*, 1885, 520; *Bacillus aerogenes* Kruse, in Flügge, Die Mikroorganismen, *2*, 1896, 340; not *Bacillus aerogenes* Miller, Deutsche med. Wochnschr., *12*, 1886, 119; *Bacterium aerogenes* Chester, Ann. Rept. Del. Col. Agr. Exp. Sta., *9*, 1897, 53; not *Bacterium aerogenes* Miller, *op. cit.*, 1886, 119; Beijerinck, Arch. néerl. d. sci. exact. et nat., *4*, 1900, 1.)

a.e.ro′ge.nes. Gr. mas.n. *aër* air, gas; Gr. v. *gennaio* to produce; M.L. adj. *aerogenes* gas-producing.

Rods, 0.5 to 0.8 by 1.0 to 2.0 microns, occurring singly. Frequently encapsulated. Usually non-motile. Gram-negative.

Gelatin colonies: Thick, porcelain-white, opaque, moist, smooth, entire.

Gelatin stab: Thick, spreading, white, opaque surface growth. No liquefaction.

Agar colonies: Thick, white, raised, moist, smooth, entire; more convex than those of *Escherichia coli* and often mucoid.

Agar slant: Abundant, thick, white, moist, glistening, spreading growth.

Broth: Turbid; pellicle; abundant sediment.

Litmus milk: Acid with coagulation; no peptonization.

Potato: Thick, yellowish white to yellowish brown, spreading growth with nodular outgrowths over the surface.

Indole may or may not be produced (Ford, Studies from the Royal Victoria Hospital, Montreal, *1*, 1901–1903, 16; Bardsley, Jour. of Hyg. (Eng.), *34*, 1934, 38; Wilson, Med. Res. Council, London, Spec. Rept. Ser. 206, 1935, 161).

Hydrogen sulfide not produced in peptone iron agar (Levine, Epstein and Vaughn, Amer. Jour. Pub. Health, *24*, 1934, 505; Tittsler and Sandholzer, Amer. Jour. Pub.

Health, *27*, 1937, 1240). More sensitive indicators give positive tests for hydrogen sulfide (Hunter and Weiss, Jour. Bact., *35*, 1938, 20).

Acid and gas from glucose, fructose, galactose, arabinose, lactose, maltose, raffinose, cellobiose, salicin, esculin, starch, dextrin, glycerol, mannitol, sorbitol and inositol; α-methyl-glucoside is usually fermented (Koser and Saunders, Jour. Bact., *24*, 1932, 267). Sucrose, inulin, dulcitol and adonitol may or may not be fermented. Protopectin not fermented. Variable fermentation of sucrose and mannitol (Sherman and Wing, Jour. Bact., *33*, 1937, 315).

Gas ratio: Two or more volumes of carbon dioxide to one of hydrogen are produced from glucose (Harden and Walpole, Proc. Roy. Soc., Series B, *77*, 1905, 399; Rogers, Clark and Davis, Jour. Inf. Dis., *14*, 1914, 411).

Trimethyleneglycol not produced from glycerol by anaerobic fermentation (Braak, Onderzoekingen over Vergisting van Glycerine. Thesis, Delft, 1928, 212; Werkman and Gillen, Jour. Bact., *23*, 1932, 167).

Methyl red test negative (Clark and Lubs, Jour. Inf. Dis., *17*, 1915, 160); Voges-Proskauer test positive (Durham, Jour. Exp. Med., *5*, 1901, 373); inverse correlation between methyl red and Voges-Proskauer tests (Levine, Jour. Bact., *1*, 1916, 153).

Citric acid and salts of citric acid may be utilized as sole sources of carbon (Koser, Jour. Bact., *8*, 1923, 493).

Uric acid may be utilized as a sole source of nitrogen (Koser, Jour. Inf. Dis., *23*, 1918, 377).

Sodium hippurate is hydrolyzed (Hajna and Damon, Amer. Jour. Hyg., *19*, 1934, 545).

Nitrites produced from nitrates.

Catalase-positive.

Aerobic, facultatively anaerobic.

---

ter for differentiating species due to occasional loss of gelatin-liquefying ability. This was confirmed by Levine (Amer. Jour. Pub. Health, *7*, 1917, 784), who reports that the two characters do not correlate perfectly. Griffin and Stuart (Jour. Bact., *40*, 1940, 93 ff.) find a similar correlation of characters but feel that, because these characters do not correlate perfectly, it would be better to combine the two species into a single species.

Growth requirements: Good growth on ordinary laboratory media. Optimum temperature, about 30° C. Grows better at temperatures below 30° C. than does *Escherichia coli* Castellani and Chalmers. Usually destroyed in 30 minutes at 60° C., but certain heat-resistant strains may withstand this exposure (Ayers and Johnson, Jour. Agr. Res., *3*, 1914, 401; Stark and Patterson, Jour. Dairy Sci., *19*, 1936, 495). Gas not produced in Eijkmann test when carried out at 45° to 46° C. (Eijkmann, Cent. f. Bakt., I Abt., Orig., *37*, 1904, 74; Levine, Epstein and Vaughn, Amer. Jour. Pub. Health, *24*, 1934, 505).

Comments: Thompson (Jour. Bact., *28*, 1934, 41) has reported a variety of this organism which shows a transverse arrangement of the capsule.

Relationships to other species: Regarded by Escherich (*op. cit.*, 1885, 520) as possibly identical with Hueppe's Milchsäurebacterium (Mit. d. kais. Gesund., *2*, 1884, 340; *Escherichia coli* var. *acidilactici*). However, because he did not have a culture of Hueppe's organism for comparison, Escherich gave the name *Bakterium lactis aërogenes* to his own organism.

Source: Isolated from the feces of breast-fed infants.

Habitat: Normally found on grains and plants and, to a varying degree, in water, milk, dairy products and the intestinal canals of man and other animals. Widely distributed in nature.

2. Aerobacter cloacae (Jordan, 1890) Bergey et al., 1923. (*Bacillus cloacae* Jordan, Rept. Mass. State Bd. of Health, Part II, 1890, 836; also see Jordan, Jour. Hyg., *3*, 1903, 1; *Bacterium cloacae* Lehmann and Neumann, Bakt. Diag., 1 Aufl., *2*, 1896, 239; Bergey et al., Manual, 1st ed., 1923, 207.)

clo.a'cae. L. noun *cloaca* a sewer; L. gen.noun *cloacae* of a sewer.

Rods, 0.5 to 1.0 by 1.0 to 2.0 microns, occurring singly. Usually motile by means of peritrichous flagella. Not encapsulated. Gram-negative.

Gelatin colonies: Thin, circular, bluish, translucent.

Gelatin stab: Slow liquefaction. Liquefy-ing power sometimes lost (Kligler, Jour. Inf. Dis., *15*, 1914, 199).

Agar colonies: Circular, thick, opaque with white center, entire.

Agar slant: Porcelain-white, smooth, glistening, spreading growth.

Broth: Turbid; thin pellicle.

Litmus milk: Acid; coagulation; gas; slow peptonization.

Potato: Yellowish, moist, glistening growth.

Indole not produced (Levine, Epstein and Vaughn, Amer. Jour. Pub. Health, *24*, 1934, 505; Wilson, Med. Res. Council, London, Spec. Rept. Ser. 206, 1935, 161).

Hydrogen sulfide not produced in peptone iron agar (Levine, Epstein and Vaughn, *op. cit.*, 1934, 505).

Acid and gas from glucose, fructose, galactose, arabinose, xylose, lactose, maltose, raffinose, dextrin, salicin, trehalose, mannitol, sorbitol, cellobiose and α-methylglucoside. Sucrose usually fermented. Inulin, esculin, starch, dulcitol, rhamnose and protopectin not attacked. Glycerol fermented with no visible gas (Kligler, *op. cit.*, 1914, 187; Levine, Amer. Jour. Pub. Health, 7, 1917, 784). Starch rarely fermented (Levine, *loc. cit.*). See Winslow, Kligler and Rothberg (Jour. Bact., *4*, 1919, 429) for a review of the literature.

Gas ratio: Glucose fermented with at least two volumes of carbon dioxide to one of hydrogen (Rogers, Clark and Davis, Jour. Inf. Dis., *14*, 1914, 411).

Methyl red test negative; Voges-Proskauer test positive.

Citric acid and salts of citric acid may be utilized as sole sources of carbon (Koser, Jour. Bact., *8*, 1923, 493).

Uric acid may be utilized as a sole source of nitrogen (Koser, Jour. Inf. Dis., *23*, 1918, 377).

Sodium hippurate not hydrolyzed (Hajna and Damon, Amer. Jour. Hyg., *19*, 1934, 545).

Nitrites produced from nitrates.

Fecal odor produced.

Catalase-positive.

Aerobic, facultatively anaerobic.

Growth requirements: Good growth on ordinary laboratory media. Optimum temperature, between 30° and 37° C. Gas not produced in Eijkmann test when carried out at 45° to 46° C. (Levine, Epstein and Vaughn, *op. cit.*, 1934, 505).

Comments: In the original description of this species, Jordan (*op. cit.*, 1890, 836) makes no report of the action of this organism on sugars. The cultures used by Th. Smith (The Fermentation Tube, 1893, 215) produced acid and gas actively from glucose and sucrose and less actively from lactose. The ratio of hydrogen to carbon dioxide, as determined by Smith, was approximately 1:2.

Source: Isolated from sewage from the Lawrence Experiment Station, Massachusetts.

Habitat: Found in human and other animal feces and in sewage, soil and water.

Genus III. **Klebsiella** *Trevisan, 1885.**

(Atti della accad. Fisio-Medico-Statistica in Milano, Ser. 4, *3*, 1885, 105.)

Kleb.si.el'la. M.L. dim.ending -*ella*; M.L. fem.n. *Klebsiella* named for Edwin Klebs (1834–1913), an early German bacteriologist.

Short rods, somewhat plump with rounded ends, occurring mostly singly. Encapsulated in the mucoid phase. Non-motile. Gram-negative. Gelatin not liquefied. Fermentation reactions are variable, but usually a number of carbohydrates are fermented. Acetylmethylcarbinol may or may not be produced. Nitrites are produced from nitrates. Aerobic, growing well on ordinary culture media. Encountered frequently in the respiratory, intestinal and urogenital tracts of man, but these organisms may be isolated from a variety of animals and materials.

The type species is *Klebsiella pneumoniae* (Schroeter) Trevisan.

Key to the species of genus **Klebsiella.**

I. Acetylmethylcarbinol produced. Frequently associated with acute inflammations of the respiratory tract.

1. *Klebsiella pneumoniae.*

II. Acetylmethylcarbinol not produced. Frequently associated with nasal infections.

A. Acid and gas usually produced from glucose. Found associated with ozena and other chronic diseases of the respiratory tract.

2. *Klebsiella ozaenae.*

B. Usually acid but no gas from glucose. Found associated with rhinoscleroma.

3. *Klebsiella rhinoscleromatis.*

1. Klebsiella pneumoniae (Schroeter, 1886) Trevisan, 1887. (Pneumoniecoccus, Friedländer, Arch. f. path. Anat., *87*, 1882, 319; *Bacterium pneumonie crouposae* Zopf, Die Spaltpilze, 3 Aufl., 1885, 66; *Klebsiella crouposa* Trevisan, Atti della Accad. Fisio-Medico-Statistica in Milano, Ser. 4, *3*, 1885, 105; *Hyalococcus pneumoniae* Schroeter, in Cohn, Kryptogamen-Flora von Schlesien, *3*(1), 1886, 152; *Bacillus pneumoniae* Flügge, Die Mikroorganismen, 2 Aufl., 1886, 204; Trevisan, Rend. d. R. Istit. Lombardo, Ser. 2, *20*, 1887, 94.)

pneu.mo'ni.ae. Gr. noun *pneumonia* inflammation of the lungs, pneumonia; M.L. gen.noun *pneumoniae* of pneumonia.

Common name: Friedländer's bacillus; pneumobacillus.

Rods, 0.3 to 0.5 by 5.0 microns, often 4 to 5 times as long as broad, with rounded ends, occurring singly and in pairs. Encapsulated. Non-motile. Gram-negative.

Gelatin colonies: Dirty white, smooth, opaque, entire, slightly raised.

Gelatin stab: Dirty white surface growth. Filiform growth in stab. Gas bubbles are produced. No liquefaction.

---

* Prepared by Prof. Robert S. Breed, Cornell University, Geneva, New York, in consultation with investigators who have made special studies of this genus, October, 1955.

Agar colonies: White, shiny, convex, smooth, glistening, entire.

Agar slants: Slimy, white, somewhat translucent, raised growth.

Broth: Turbid; thick ring or film.

Litmus milk: Acid; no coagulation.

Potato: Yellowish, slimy, raised growth. Gas is produced.

Indole not produced.

Hydrogen sulfide not produced.

Acid and gas from glucose. Acid and gas may be produced from lactose. Acid from sucrose, maltose, salicin, arabinose, rhamnose, xylose, mannitol, adonitol, inositol and sorbitol. Acid may or may not be produced from dulcitol.

Acetylmethylcarbinol usually produced.

Methyl red test negative.

Ammonium citrate utilized as a sole source of carbon.

Nitrites produced from nitrates.

Urea may or may not be slowly decomposed.

Aerobic, facultatively anaerobic.

Optimum temperature, 37° C.

Pathogenicity: Lethal for mice.

Serology: Cultures belonging to this species are classified serologically on the basis of their O and K (capsule) antigens. Kauffmann (Acta Path. et Microbiol. Scand., *26*, 1949, 38) and Ørskov (Acta Path. et Microbiol. Scand., *34*, 1954, 145) demonstrated four somatic groups in the klebsiellas, in each of which was found a variety of capsular antigens. Due to technical difficulties caused by the prominent capsules possessed by most cultures, the O antigens of *Klebsiella* cultures usually are not determined, and serological examination is confined to the determination of the capsular antigens of the strains. Through the work of a number of investigators, 72 capsule types have been recognized. Of these, types 1 to 6 inclusive (A to F of the earlier literature) occur in the respiratory tract of man and occasionally are found in other locations. The remaining capsule types exhibit no such preference and are widely distributed in nature. They occur frequently in respiratory and urinary infections, in the blood stream and in feces.

Comment: From the foregoing, it may be seen that no method has been found to differentiate the majority of *Klebsiella pneumoniae* cultures from organisms commonly classified as *Aerobacter aerogenes*, and this situation has caused confusion. Identical cultures are classified by some workers as types of *Klebsiella pneumoniae* and by others as *Aerobacter aerogenes*. The source from which an organism was isolated often has dictated the genus into which it is placed. Until such time as the relationships of the two genera are clarified, it is inevitable that confusion will continue.

Source: Isolated from the lungs in cases of lobar pneumonia.

Habitat: Associated with pneumonia and other inflammations of the respiratory tract.

2. **Klebsiella ozaenae** (Abel, 1893) Bergey et al., 1925. (*Bacillus mucosus ozaenae* Abel, Cent. f. Bakt., *13*, 1893, 167; *Bacillus ozaenae* Abel, *ibid*., 172; *Bacterium ozaenae* Lehmann and Neumann, Bakt. Diag., 1 Aufl., *2*, 1896, 204; Bergey et al., Manual, 2nd ed., 1925, 266.)

o.zae'nae. L. fem.n. *ozaena* ozena; L. fem.gen.n. *ozaenae* of ozena.

Plump rods, 1.25 microns in width and of variable length, occurring singly. Encapsulated. Non-motile. Gram-negative.

Gelatin colonies: Small, white, convex, slimy, translucent.

Gelatin stab: Translucent, slimy surface growth. Filiform growth in stab. No liquefaction.

Agar slant: Slimy, cream-like, spreading growth.

Broth: Turbid; gray ring and sediment.

Litmus milk: Unchanged or slightly acid but not coagulated; no gas.

Potato: Creamy, spreading growth; never shows gas production.

Indole not produced.

Acetylmethylcarbinol not produced.

Acid may or may not be produced from glucose; lactose is fermented weakly, if at all (Lehmann and Neumann, Bakt. Diag., 4 Aufl., *2*, 1907, 299). Acid and gas from glucose, lactose, sucrose, maltose and mannitol (Julianelle, Jour. Bact., *30*, 1935, 536).

Nitrites produced from nitrates (Julianelle, *ibid*., 535).

Aerobic, facultatively anaerobic.
Optimum temperature, 37° C.

Pathogenicity: Lethal for mice 3 to 4 days after subcutaneous inoculation; rats and guinea pigs become sick; rabbits are immune.

Comment: Henriksen (Acta Path. et Microbiol. Scand., *34*, 1954, 249, 259, 266, 271, 276 and 291) believes this and the following species to be distinguishable from *Klebsiella pneumoniae* because both *K. ozaenae* and K. *rhinoscleromatis* give the IMViC reactions found in the genus *Escherichia* whereas *K. pneumoniae* possesses the IMViC characters found in the genus *Aerobacter*.

Source: Isolated from cases of ozena.

Habitat: Frequently occurs in ozena and in non-stinking, pure atrophic rhinitis.

3. **Klebsiella rhinoscleromatis** Trevisan, 1887. (Rhinoscleromabacillus, von Fritsch, Wien. med. Wochenschr., *32*, 1882, 968; also see Cornil, Progrès Medical, *11*, 1883, 587; Trevisan, Rend. d. R. Istit. Lombardo, Ser. 2, *20*, 1887, 95.)

rhi.no.scle.ro′ma.tis. M.L. adj. *rhinoscleromatis* pertaining to rhinoscleroma.

Original description supplemented by material taken from Edwards and Ewing (Identification of *Enterobacteriaceae*, Burgess Pub. Co., Minneapolis, 1955, 166 and 167).

Rods, with rounded ends, about 0.8 by 1.6 to 2.4 microns, occurring singly, in pairs, and occasionally in short chains. Encapsulated. Non-motile. Gram-negative.

Gelatin colonies: Circular, yellowish white, convex, entire.

Gelatin stab: White, convex surface growth. No liquefaction.

Agar colonies: White, translucent, smooth, glistening.

Agar slant: Moist, white, translucent, spreading growth.

Broth: Turbid; tough pellicle.

Litmus milk: Unchanged.

Potato: Yellowish white, slimy, frequently showing gas production.

Indole not produced.

Hydrogen sulfide not produced.

Gas not ordinarily produced from glucose; acid produced from lactose slowly if at all (Lehmann and Neumann, Bakt. Diag., 4 Aufl., *2*, 1907, 299). Acid from sucrose, salicin, inositol and adonitol. Acid may or may not be produced from dulcitol. d-Tartrate and mucate not fermented.

Acetylmethylcarbinol not produced.

Methyl red test positive.

Citrate not utilized as sole source of carbon.

Nitrites produced from nitrates.

Urea not decomposed.

Aerobic, facultatively anaerobic.

Optimum temperature, 37° C.

Comment: See comment under *Klebsiella ozaenae.*

Source: Isolated from nasal secretions in rhinoscleroma.

Genus IV. **Paracolobactrum** *Borman et al., 1944.**

(Paracolibacille, Widal and Nobecourt, Semaine Méd., *17*, 1897, 285; Borman, Stuart and Wheeler, Jour. Bact., *48*, 1944, 361.)

Pa.ra.co.lo.bac′trum. Gr. prep. *para* (in composition) alongside of, like; M.L. noun *Colobactrum* a genus of bacteria; M.L. neut.n. *Paracolobactrum* that which resembles *Colobactrum.*

Short rods. Gram-negative. Fermentation of lactose is consistently delayed; occasionally lactose is not fermented. Glucose is fermented with the production of visible gas. Certain forms attack carbohydrates characteristically at 20° to 30° C. but not at 37° C.; the production of acetylmethylcarbinol may likewise be influenced by incubation temperature. Antigenic relationships to other genera in the family are common, even with respect to major antigens. Found in surface water, soil, grains and the intestinal tracts of animals, including man.

---

* Prepared by Dr. E. K. Borman, Director, Bureau of Laboratories, State Department of Health, Hartford, Connecticut, October, 1955.

The type species is *Paracolobactrum aerogenoides* Borman et al.

Key to the species of genus **Paracolobactrum.**

I. Acetylmethylcarbinol produced.

                              1. *Paracolobactrum aerogenoides.*

II. Acetylmethylcarbinol not produced.

    A. Ammonium citrate utilized as a sole source of carbon.

        1. Gelatin not liquefied.

                            2. *Paracolobactrum intermedium.*

        2. Gelatin slowly liquefied.

                            3. *Paracolobactrum arizonae.*

    B. Ammonium citrate not utilized as a sole source of carbon.

                            4. *Paracolobactrum coliforme.*

1. Paracolobactrum aerogenoides Borman et al., 1944. (Para-aerogenes, Stuart, Wheeler, Rustigian and Zimmerman, Jour. Bact., *45*, 1943, 117; Borman, Stuart and Wheeler, Jour. Bact., *48*, 1944, 361.)

a.e.ro.ge.no.i'des. M.L. adj. *aerogenes* gas-producing, a specific epithet; Gr. noun *eidus* resembling, like; M.L. adj. *aerogenoides* (*Aerobacter*) *aerogenes*-like.

Characters as for *Aerobacter aerogenes* Beijerinck and *Aerobacter cloacae* Bergey et al. except for consistently delayed fermentation of lactose.

Primarily non-pathogenic.

Comments: Møller (Acta Path. et Microbiol. Scand., *35*, 1954, 262 and 272) has named the non-gelatin-liquefying, *Aerobacter aerogenes*-like paracolons the *Hafnia* Group, type species *Hafnia alvei* Møller (*ibid.*, 272). The organisms in the *Hafnia* Group are motile at 22° becoming less motile at 36° and non-motile at 38° C.

Source: Isolated from cases of human gastroenteritis.

Habitat: Found in surface water, soil, grains and the intestinal tracts of animals, including man.

2. Paracolobactrum intermedium Borman et al., 1944. (Para-freundii, Stuart, Wheeler, Rustigian and Zimmerman, Jour. Bact., *45*, 1943, 117; Borman, Stuart and Wheeler, Jour. Bact., *48*, 1944, 361.)

in.ter.me'di.um. L. adj. *intermedius* intermediate.

Characters as for *Escherichia freundii* Yale and *Escherichia intermedia* Vaughn and Levine except for consistently delayed fermentation of lactose.

Relationships to other species: The Ballerup Group (Bruner, Edwards and Hopson, Jour. Inf. Dis., *85*, 1949, 290) and the Bethesda Group (Edwards, West and Bruner, Jour. Bact., *55*, 1948, 712) have been combined by recent investigators (West and Edwards, U. S. Dept. Health, Education and Welfare Monograph, No. 22, 1954, 34; Kauffmann, *Enterobacteriaceae.* Ejnar Munksgaard, Copenhagen, 1954, 210). While these workers recognize the combined groups as being identical with *Paracolobactrum intermedium* Borman et al., they do not distinguish between them and *Escherichia freundii* Yale.

Source: Isolated from cases of human gastroenteritis.

Habitat: Found in surface water, soil, grains and the intestinal tracts of animals, including man.

3. Paracolobactrum arizonae (Kauffmann, 1940) Borman, *comb. nov.* (*Salmonella sp.*, Dar es salaam Type var. from Arizona, Caldwell and Ryerson, Jour. Inf. Dis., *65*, 1939, 245; *Salmonella arizona* (sic) Kauffmann, Acta Path. et Microbiol. Scand., *17*, 1940, or *19*, 1942; Arizona culture, Edwards, Cherry and Bruner, Jour. Inf. Dis., *73*, 1943, 236; Arizona Group, Edwards, Jour. Bact., *49*, 1945, 513.)

a.ri.zo'nae. M.L. noun *Arizona* Arizona; M.L. gen.noun *arizonae* of Arizona.

Rods. Motile by means of peritrichous flagella. Gram-negative.

Gelatin: Slow liquefaction.

Potassium cyanide medium: No growth (exceptions are rare).

Indole not produced.

Hydrogen sulfide produced.

Acid and gas from glucose. Characteristically, lactose is fermented in 7 to 10 days (sometimes earlier, sometimes in 3 weeks, rarely not at all). Salicin rarely fermented. Adonitol, dulcitol, inositol and sucrose not attacked.

Methyl red test is positive.

Acetylmethylcarbinol not produced.

Ammonium citrate utilized as a sole source of carbon.

Urea not hydrolyzed.

Serology: Ninety-seven serotypes, with their antigenic formulas, are listed by Edwards and Ewing (Identification of Enterobacteriaceae. Burgess Pub. Co., Minneapolis, 1955, 89). These authors stress the strong serological relationship between this species and those in the genus Salmonella.

Pathogenic for guinea pigs and rabbits.

Comment: Kauffmann (Enterobacteriaceae. Munksgaard, Copenhagen, 2nd ed., 1954, 147) proposed the generic name Arizona for the organisms in the Arizona Group but did not name a type species.

Source: Isolated by Caldwell and Ryerson (op. cit., 1939, 245) from horned lizards, Gila monsters and chuckawallas. Found in snakes by Hinshaw and McNeill (Cornell Vet., 34, 1944, 248). Also reported by Edwards (op. cit., 1945, 513) and by Edwards et al. (Canad. Jour. Microbiol., 2, 1956, 281) from infants.

Habitat: Apparently widely distributed in lizards, snakes and warm-blooded animals.

4. **Paracolobactrum coliforme** Borman et al., 1944. (Para-coli, Stuart, Wheeler, Rustigian and Zimmerman, Jour. Bact., 45, 1943, 117; Borman, Stuart and Wheeler, Jour. Bact., 48, 1944, 361.)

co.li.for′me. Gr. noun colum the colon, here used in the genitive in reference to the specific epithet coli; L. noun forma appearance; M.L. adj. coliformis resembling (Escherichia) coli.

Characters as for Escherichia coli Castellani and Chalmers except for consistently delayed fermentation of lactose.

Source: Isolated from cases of human gastroenteritis.

Habitat: Found in surface water, soil, grains and the intestinal tracts of animals, including man.

Genus V. **Alginobacter** Thjøtta and Kåss, 1945.*

(Thjøtta and Kåss, Norske Videnskaps-Akad., Oslo, I Mat.-Naturv. Klasse, No. 5, 1945, 17; also see Kåss, Lid and Molland, ibid., No. 11, 1945, 15.)

Al.gi′no.bac.ter. M.L. noun acidum alginicum alginic acid; M.L. mas.n. bacter the masculine equivalent of the Gr. neut.n. bactrum a rod; M.L. mas.n. Alginobacter the alginic acid (-decomposing) rod.

Short rods which are motile by means of peritrichous flagella. Acetylmethylcarbinol production is positive although faint. Methyl red test is positive. Citric acid may be utilized as a sole source of carbon. Alginic acid and glucose are decomposed with the production of acid and gas; lactose is more slowly fermented. Non-pathogenic organisms from soil.

The type species is Alginobacter acidofaciens Kåss, Lid and Molland.

1. **Alginobacter acidofaciens** Kåss et al., 1945. (Kåss, Lid and Molland, Avhandl. Norske Videnskaps-Akad., Oslo, I Mat.-Naturv. Klasse, No. 11, 1945, 17.)

a.ci.do.fa′ci.ens. L. adj. acidus sour; M.L. neut.n. acidum acid; L.v. facio to make; M.L. part.adj. acidofaciens acid-producing.

Short rods occurring singly, occasionally in pairs or short chains. Encapsulated. Motile by means of peritrichous flagella. Gram-negative.

Good growth on ordinary media.

Gelatin: Good growth. No liquefaction.

Agar colonies: Large, smooth, coniform. No pigment produced.

---

* Prepared by Prof. Th. Thjøtta, Microbiological Institute, University of Oslo, Oslo, Norway, January, 1955.

Broth: Turbid, with sediment. No pellicle formed.

Litmus milk: Acid after 24 hours.

Potato: Abundant, yellowish gray growth.

Indole not produced.

Hydrogen sulfide production is abundant.

Alginic acid is decomposed with the production of acid and gas.

Acid and gas from glucose and lactose (slow). Acid from fructose, arabinose, galactose, raffinose, xylose, maltose, sucrose, salicin, glycerol, dulcitol, iso-dulcitol, mannitol and sorbitol; dextrin is usually attacked. No acid from starch or inulin.

Acetylmethylcarbinol is produced (faintly).

Methyl red test is positive.

Citric acid, as well as sodium alginate, can be used as a sole source of carbon.

Nitrites produced from nitrates.

Blood agar: No hemolysis.

Aerobic, facultatively anaerobic.

Temperature relations: Optimum, 30° C.; good growth at 37° C.; grows at 4° and 45° C.

Chemical tolerance: Grows at pH 9.6.

Grows in 6 per cent sodium chloride broth.

Source: Five strains were isolated from soil.

Habitat: Presumably soil.

TRIBE II. ERWINIEAE WINSLOW ET AL., 1920.

(Jour. Bact., *5*, 1920, 209.)

Er.wi.ni'e.ae. M.L. fem.n. *Erwinia* type genus of the tribe; -*eae* ending to denote a tribe; M.L. fem.pl.n. *Erwinieae* the *Erwinia* tribe.

Characters as for the genus.

There is a single genus.

Genus VI. **Erwinia** *Winslow et al., 1917.**

(Jour. Bact., *2*, 1917, 560.)

Er.wi'ni.a. M.L. gen.noun *Erwinia* of Erwin; named for Erwin F. Smith, pioneer American plant pathologist.

Motile rods which normally do not require organic nitrogen compounds for growth. Produce acid with or without visible gas from a variety of sugars. In some species the number of carbon compounds attacked is limited, and lactose may not be fermented. May or may not liquefy gelatin. May or may not produce nitrites from nitrates. Invade the tissues of living plants and produce dry necroses, galls, wilts and soft rots. In the latter case, a protopectinase destroys the middle lamellar substance.

The type species is *Erwinia amylovora* (Burrill) Winslow et al.

Key to the species of genus **Erwinia.**

I.† Pathogens that cause dry necroses, galls or wilts in plants but not a soft rot (*Erwinia sensu stricto*).

* Completely revised by Prof. Walter H. Burkholder, Cornell University, Ithaca, New York, July, 1954.

† The genus *Erwinia* as defined here is heterogeneous in nature and is composed of at least two distinct groups. The first group constitutes *Erwinia* proper and does not produce visible gas from sugars. Waldee (Iowa State Coll. Jour. Sci., *19*, 1945, 435) has suggested that the species in this first group be placed in a separate family, *Erwiniaceae*.

A. Gelatin liquefied.
  1. White colonies.

                1. *Erwinia amylovora.*

  2. Yellow colonies.
    a. Coagulate milk.
      b. Hydrolyzes starch.

                2. *Erwinia vitivora.*

      bb. Does not hydrolyze starch.

                3. *Erwinia milletiae.*

    aa. Does not coagulate milk.

                4. *Erwinia cassavae.*

B. Gelatin not liquefied.
  1. Luxuriant growth.

                5. *Erwinia salicis.*

  2. Very slight growth.

                6. *Erwinia tracheiphila.*

II.* Pathogens that normally cause soft rots in plants (belong in the genus *Pectobacterium* Waldee).
  A. Gas produced in sugar media.
    1. Gelatin liquefied.
      a. Coagulates milk.

                7. *Erwinia chrysanthemi.*

      aa. Does not coagulate milk.

                8. *Erwinia carnegieana.*

    2. Gelatin not liquefied.
      a. Hydrolyzes starch.

                9. *Erwinia dissolvens.*

      aa. Does not hydrolyze starch.

                10. *Erwinia nimipressuralis.*

  B. Gas usually produced in sugar media, but certain isolates are non-aerogenic.
    1. Growth with ethanol, dulcitol, malonate or hippurate.

                11. *Erwinia carotovora.*

    2. No growth with ethanol, dulcitol, malonate or hippurate.

                12. *Erwinia atroseptica.*

  C. Gas not produced in sugar media.
    1. Gelatin liquefied.
      a. Hydrolyzes starch.

                13. *Erwinia ananas.*

      aa. Do not hydrolyze starch.
        b. White colonies.

                14. *Erwinia aroideae.*

        bb. Yellow colonies.
          c. Grows in Uschinsky's solution.

                15. *Erwinia citrimaculans.*

---

* The second group of species usually causes soft rots but includes a few not very typical species. Waldee (*loc. cit.*) has proposed that the species that cause typical soft rot be placed in a new genus, *Pectobacterium*, with *Pectobacterium carotovorum* as the type species. The new genus is retained in the family *Enterobacteriaceae*. Waldee would place the atypical species in other genera, *Erwinia dissolvens* for example being placed in the genus *Aerobacter*. As further comparative studies are needed before such changes can be made with confidence, the older arrangement is allowed to stand in this edition of the MANUAL.

cc. Does not grow in Uschinsky's solution.
16. *Erwinia mangiferae*.

2. Gelatin not liquefied.

17. *Erwinia rhapontici*.

1. **Erwinia amylovora** (Burrill, 1882) Winslow et al., 1920. (*Micrococcus amylovorus* Burrill, Illinois Indust. Univ., 11th Rept., 1882, 142; Winslow et al., Jour. Bact., *5*, 1920, 209.)

a.my.lo'vo.ra. Gr. noun *amylum* fine meal, starch; L. v. *voro* to devour; M.L. adj. *amylovorus* starch-destroying.

Description taken mainly from Ark (Phytopath., *27*, 1937, 1).

Rods, 0.7 to 1.0 by 0.9 to 1.5 microns, occurring singly, in pairs and sometimes in short chains. Motile by means of peritrichous flagella. Gram-negative.

Gelatin colonies: Circular, whitish, amorphous, entire.

Gelatin stab: Slow crateriform liquefaction confined to the upper layer.

Agar colonies: Circular, grayish white, moist, glistening; irregular margins.

Broth: Turbid; thin, granular pellicle.

Potato: Growth white, moist, glistening. Medium not softened. No odor. No pigment.

Litmus milk: Coagulated after 3 to 4 days to a pasty condition, with a separation of whey. At first acid, becoming alkaline. Litmus reduced. There is a gradual digestion of the casein.

Blood serum: Growth similar to that on agar. No liquefaction.

Dunham's solution: Rapid growth, but clouding not dense.

Indole not produced.

Growth in synthetic media containing $(NH_4)_2HPO_4$, which serves as a source of nitrogen, and various carbohydrates.

Acid without gas from glucose, sucrose, arabinose, mannose, fructose, maltose, cellobiose, raffinose, salicin and amygdalin. Xylose, rhamnose, dulcitol and starch not fermented. Acid production from lactose and galactose variable. Utilizes salts of citric, malic and hippuric acids. Action on salts of lactic and succinic acids variable. Salts of benzoic, maleic, malonic, oxalic, tartaric and valeric acids are not utilized.

Acetylmethylcarbinol produced.

Nitrites not produced from nitrates.

Most of the strains give a positive test for ammonia in broth, a few show only a slight positive test.

Asparagine fermented with production of alkali. Glycine, valine, isoleucine, glutamic acid, cystine, tyrosine, tryptophane and urea not fermented.

Minimum temperature, between 3° and 8° C. Maximum, below 37° C.

Optimum pH, 6.8. Minimum pH, between 4.0 and 4.4. Maximum pH, 8.8.

Source: Isolated from the blossoms, leaves and twigs of pear and apple trees.

Habitat: Attacks a large number of species in several tribes of the family *Rosaceae* (Elliott, Manual Bact. Plant Pathogens, 1951, 30).

2. **Erwinia vitivora** (Baccarini, 1894) du Plessis, 1940. (*Bacillus vitivora* Baccarini, Bull. della Soc. Bot. Ital., 1894, 235; du Plessis, Dept. Agr. and Forestry Union of S. Africa, Science Bul. 214, 1940, 58.)

vi.ti'vo.ra. L. noun *vitis* the grape vine; L. v. *voro* to devour; M.L. adj. *vitivorus* grape-vine-destroying.

Rods, 0.74 (0.44 to 1.10) by 1.46 (0.95 to 2.19) microns. Cells sometimes dumbbell-shaped. Motile by means of peritrichous flagella. Encapsulated. Gram-negative.

Gelatin: Liquefaction.

Agar colonies: First punctiform, irregularly circular or lenticular, ultimately circular, raised to pulvinate, glistening, spreading, light to orange-yellow. Agar becomes brown.

Broth: Turbid in 24 hrs; whitish to lemon-yellow pellicle.

Milk: Litmus reduced. Thread-like to spongy curd formed. Yellow whey about curd. Yellow growth on top of plain milk. Medium acid.

Uschinsky's solution: Slowly becomes turbid; pellicle; sediment is whitish yellow.

Hydrogen sulfide produced.

Acid produced from glucose, fructose,

xylose, lactose, sucrose, mannitol and salicin. No acid from raffinose or inulin.

Starch hydrolyzed.

Nitrites produced from nitrates.

Facultatively anaerobic.

Temperature relations: Optimum, 25° C. Minimum, between 5° and 10° C. Maximum, between 35° and 40° C.

Optimum pH, 6.0. Minimum pH, 4.2.

Source: Isolated by du Plessis from various localities in South Africa.

Habitat: Causes a disease of grape vines in South Africa, Italy and France.

3. Erwinia milletiae (Kawakami and Yoshida, 1920) Magrou, 1937. (*Bacillus milletiae* Kawakami and Yoshida, Bot. Mag., Tokyo, *34*, 1920, 110; Magrou, in Hauduroy et al., Dict. d. Bact. Path., 1937, 213.)

mil.le′ti.ae. M.L. noun *Milletia* a genus of flowering plants; M.L. gen.noun *milletiae* of *Milletia*; named for A. J. Millett, a botanist.

Rods, 0.4 to 0.6 by 0.9 to 2.5 microns. Motile by means of peritrichous flagella. Encapsulated. Gram-negative.

Gelatin: Liquefaction begins after 8 days.

Agar colonies: Circular, flat, smooth, shiny, opaque, waxy yellow, entire.

Broth: Turbid; heavy precipitate.

Milk: No coagulation. Clears with alkaline reaction.

Conjac: No liquefaction.

Acid but no gas from galactose, fructose, lactose, maltose, sucrose and mannitol. No acid from glycerol.

Starch not hydrolyzed.

Nitrites produced from nitrates.

Growth in 0.2 per cent but not in 0.3 per cent of the following acids in sucrose peptone broth: Acetic, citric, oxalic and tartaric.

Aerobic.

Grows well at 32° C. Thermal death point, 53° C for 10 min.

Source: Isolated from galls on the Japanese wisteria in various localities in Japan.

Habitat: Causes galls on the Japanese wisteria, *Milletia japonica*.

4. Erwinia cassavae (Handsford, 1938) Burkholder, 1948. (*Bacterium cassavae* Handsford, Ann. Rept. Dept. Agr. Uganda for 1937, II, 1938, 48; Burkholder, in Manual, 6th ed., 1948, 466.)

cas.sa′vae. M.L. *cassava* from the Haytian *kasabi*, the common name of species of *Manihot*; M.L. gen.noun *cassavae* of Manihot.

Rods. Motile by means of a few peritrichous flagella. Not encapsulated. Gramnegative.

Gelatin is slowly liquefied.

Agar colonies: Smooth, lens-shaped, entire, translucent and of uniform structure. Yellow.

Broth: Turbid with a ring; a yellow precipitate forms in old cultures.

Milk becomes alkaline. Not cleared.

Acid but no gas from glucose, sucrose, maltose and glycerol but not from lactose.

Methyl red test negative. Acetylmethylcarbinol produced (Dowson, Zent. f. Bakt., II Abt., *100*, 1939, 183).

Nitrites rapidly produced from nitrates.

Facultatively anaerobic.

Source: Isolated from necrotic lesions on cassava leaves in Uganda.

Habitat: Pathogenic on cassava, *Manihot sp.*

5. Erwinia salicis (Day, 1924) Chester, 1939. (*Bacterium salicis* Day, Oxford For. Mem., *3*, 1924, 14; Chester, in Bergey et al., Manual, 5th ed., 1939, 406.)

sa′li.cis. L. noun *salix, salicis* the willow; M.L. noun *Salix* generic name of the willow.

Description taken from Dowson (Ann. Appl. Biol., *24*, 1937, 542).

Rods, 0.5 to 0.7 by 0.8 to 2.2 microns, occurring singly or in pairs, rarely in chains, with rounded ends. Motile by means of 5 to 7 long peritrichous flagella. Gramnegative.

Gelatin stab: Beaded growth. No liquefaction.

Infusion agar: Colonies appear slowly, circular, with slightly uneven margins, pale brown by transmitted light, pale gray by reflected.

Infusion agar slants: Growth thin, nearly transparent.

Broth: Moderate, uniform turbidity; no pellicle.

Litmus milk: No change.

Potato: Bright yellow, later fading to pale brown, spreading, abundant, glistening, slimy growth.

No growth in Cohn's solution.

Indole not produced.

Hydrogen sulfide not produced.

Acid but no gas from glucose, galactose, mannose, xylose, maltose, sucrose, raffinose, glycerol, mannitol and salicin. No growth in arabinose, fructose, rhamnose, inulin or dextrin.

Starch not hydrolyzed.

Acetylmethylcarbinol produced. Methyl red test negative (Dowson, Zent. f. Bakt., II Abt., *100*, 1939, 183).

Nitrites produced from nitrates (Dowson).

Ammonia not produced.

Temperature relations: Optimum, between 29° and 30° C. Minimum, between 5° and 10° C. Maximum, between 33° and 37° C. Thermal death point, between 50° and 52° C.

Aerobic, facultatively anaerobic.

Source: Isolated from the cricket-bat willow (*Salix caerulea*) and from the white willow (*Salix alba*).

Habitat: Causes a water-mark disease of willow in England.

6. **Erwinia tracheiphila** (Erwin Smith, 1895) Holland, 1920. (*Bacillus tracheiphilus* Erwin Smith, Cent. f. Bakt., II Abt., *1*, 1895, 364; Holland, Jour. Bact., *5*, 1920, 215.)

tra.che.i'phi.la. Gr. adj. *tracheia* rough, the *tracheia arteria*, or rough artery, is the trachea; Gr. adj. *philus* loving; M.L. adj. *tracheiphilus* trachea-loving, i.e., growing in the tracheae or vessels of the fibro-vascular bundles.

Rods, 0.5 to 0.7 by 1.2 to 2.5 microns, with rounded ends, occurring singly and in pairs, more rarely in fours. Motile by means of peritrichous flagella. Encapsulated. Gram-negative.

Gelatin colonies: Small, circular, grayish white, smooth, glistening. Show internal striae by transmitted light.

Gelatin stab: Surface growth thin, spreading, grayish white. Slight filiform growth in depth. No liquefaction.

Agar colonies: Small, circular, grayish white, smooth, glistening.

Agar slant: Growth gray, smooth, filiform, moist, glistening.

Broth: Slight turbidity; no ring or pellicle.

Potato: Growth white or color of substratum, smooth, moist, glistening. No action on the starch. Does not soften the middle lamella of potato cells.

Litmus milk: Not coagulated. Reaction unchanged. Litmus not reduced. Not peptonized.

Egg albumen: Not digested.

Blood serum: No liquefaction.

Cohn's solution: No growth.

Uschinsky's solution: Weak growth.

Fermi's solution: Weak growth.

Indole not produced in Dunham's solution.

Hydrogen sulfide production feeble.

Acid without gas from glucose, sucrose and fructose; growth in closed arm. Acid from glycerol. No growth in closed arm with lactose, maltose, dextrin, glycerol or mannitol. No acid from lactose.

Starch not hydrolyzed.

Nitrites not produced from nitrates.

Ammonia production moderate.

Cannot utilize asparagine, ammonium lactate or tartrate as source of nitrogen.

Growth in broth with 1.0 per cent NaCl retarded; inhibited with 2.0 per cent.

Very sensitive to acid (phenolphthalein).

Temperature relations: Optimum, between 25° and 30° C. Minimum, about 8° C. Maximum, between 34° and 35° C. Thermal death point, 43° C. for one hour.

Aerobic, facultatively anaerobic.

Source: Isolated from various cucurbits.

Habitat: Causes the wilt of cucumber; also affects cantaloupes, muskmelons, pumpkins and squashes.

7. **Erwinia chrysanthemi** Burkholder et al., 1953. (Burkholder, McFadden and Dimock, Phytopath., *43*, 1953, 524.)

chrys.an'the.mi. M.L. neut.n. *Chrysanthemum* a genus of flowering plants; M.L. gen.noun *chrysanthemi* of *Chrysanthemum*.

Rods, 0.7 by 2.10 microns, occurring singly and in pairs. Motile by means of a varying number of peritrichous flagella. Gram-negative.

Gelatin: Liquefaction.

Beef-extract peptone agar slants: Growth moderate, slightly iridescent and butyrous with wavy margins. Certain strains produce a slate-gray pigment in old cultures.

Broth: Lightly turbid; pellicle forms in 18 hours and sinks to the bottom of the tube.

Litmus milk: Becomes lavender in 2 to 3 days. Soft curd within a week with one-half the medium whey. Pink.

Fermi's, Uschinsky's and Clara's solutions: White, turbid growth.

Indole not produced.

Hydrogen sulfide produced.

Krumwiede's triple sugar agar: Agar becomes yellow but turns entirely red at the end of 2 to 3 weeks.

Endo agar: Growth pink; no change in the color of the medium.

Desoxycholate agar: Colonies yellow.

Acid from a synthetic solution plus the following: glucose, galactose, arabinose, xylose, rhamnose, sucrose, dulcitol, glycerol, mannitol, ethanol (5 per cent) or salicin. Gas produced from most of the above-mentioned compounds. Alkali produced from the sodium salts of citric, hippuric, malonic and uric acids. Delayed action in lactose; maltose weak.

Gas in 3 days in formate ricinoleate broth and in Krumwiede's triple sugar agar. Occasional bubbles in pectate medium. In sugar broth, especially sucrose, bromthymol-blue is decolorized.

Starch not hydrolyzed, but solidified ammonium pectate medium is liquefied.

Methyl red test negative.

Acetylmethylcarbinol produced.

Nitrites produced from nitrates.

Only occasional and very slight growth in 5 per cent salt.

Temperature relations: Optimum, between 40° and 41° C. Growth at 6° C. Good growth at 37° C.

Source: Isolated from blight of chrysanthemum, sedum and celery.

Habitat: Pathogenic on chrysanthemum, sedum and celery. Causes a soft rot on many fleshy vegetables.

8. **Erwinia carnegieana** Lightle et al., 1942. (Lightle, Standring and Brown, Phytopath., *32*, 1942, 310.)

car.ne.gie.a'na. M.L. adj. *carnegieanus* of *Carnegiea* the generic name of a cactus.

Rods, 1.12 to 1.79 by 1.56 to 2.90 microns. Motile by means of peritrichous flagella. Encapsulated. Gram-positive (Lightle et al.). Gram-negative; old cultures show Gram-positive granules in cells (Burkholder).

Gelatin: Slow liquefaction.

Agar colonies: Round, slightly raised, smooth, grayish white, wet-shining, entire.

Broth: Abundant growth.

Uschinsky's solution: Turbid; slight ring and sediment.

Milk: Litmus pink to reduced. No curdling.

Hydrogen sulfide produced (Burkholder).

Acid and gas from glucose, galactose, fructose, maltose, sucrose, raffinose, mannitol and salicin. Acid and gas from lactose and xylose and alkali from sodium tartrate (Burkholder).

Starch not hydrolyzed (Burkholder).

Nitrites produced from nitrates.

No odor.

Aerobic.

Thermal death point, 59° C.

Source: Isolated from rotting tissue of the giant cactus (*Carnegiea gigantia*).

Habitat: Pathogenic on the giant cactus, but not on carrots.

9. **Erwinia dissolvens** (Rosen, 1922) Burkholder, 1948. (*Pseudomonas dissolvens* Rosen, Phytopath., *12*, 1922, 497; Burkholder, in Manual, 6th ed., 1948, 472.)

dis.sol'vens. L. part.adj. *dissolvens* dissolving.

Rods, 0.5 to 0.9 by 0.7 to 1.2 microns, occurring in pairs, rarely in chains. First described as motile by means of a single flagellum, later as non-motile. Encapsulated. Gram-negative.

Gelatin: Not liquefied.

Agar colonies: Round, entire, white, opaque, glistening, butyrous, emitting a strong odor of decaying vegetables.

Broth: Turbid; heavy surface growth consisting of a ring and floccules or compact slimy masses and streamers; abundant sediment.

Uschinsky's solution: Good growth, but not viscid.

Litmus milk: Acid, coagulated.

Indole produced.

Hydrogen sulfide not produced.

Acid and gas from glucose, galactose, mannitol, sucrose, maltose, lactose and glycerol.

Starch hydrolyzed.

Nitrites produced from nitrates.

Good growth in 3 per cent salt. Growth retarded at 4 per cent.

Optimum temperature, 30° C.

Source: Isolated from rotting corn stalks.

Habitat: Pathogenic to maize.

10. **Erwinia nimipressuralis** Carter, 1945. (Illinois Nat. Hist. Survey Bull. 23, 1945, 423.)

ni.mi.pres.su.ra'lis. L. adv. *nimis* overmuch; L. noun *pessura* pressure; M.L. adj. *nimipressuralis* with excessive pressure.

Rods, most of which measure 0.34 to 0.68 by 0.68 to 1.35 microns. Motile by means of as many as 6 peritrichous flagella. Capsules not observed. Gram-negative.

Gelatin: No liquefaction.

Potato glucose agar: Colonies circular, smooth, whitish cream, entire, flat to slightly raised and usually opaque. Gas produced when medium is stabbed.

Broth: Abundant with thin pellicle or flocculent surface growth; sediment scant and viscid; gas produced in nutrient broth plus glucose was 47 per cent CO_2 and 2.4 per cent hydrogen. CO_2 varied with age of culture, more being produced in young cultures.

Milk: Acid, coagulated. Litmus and bromocresol purple are reduced. Not peptonized.

Indole not produced.

Hydrogen sulfide produced.

Acid and gas produced from arabinose, rhamnose, xylose, glucose, fructose, galactose, mannose, lactose, maltose, trehalose, melibiose, cellobiose, mannitol, sorbitol and salicin; no acid or gas from inulin, dextrin or filterpaper; variable results from sucrose, raffinose, melezitose, dulcitol, glycerol and elm sawdust. Pectin is not fermented.

Starch not hydrolyzed.

Methyl red test positive.

Acetylmethylcarbinol produced.

Nitrites produced from nitrates.

Facultatively anaerobic.

Temperature relations: Optimum, between 24° and 30° C. Minimum, 5° C. or lower. Maximum, 37° C. Thermal death point, between 45° and 55° C.

Optimum pH for growth, between 6.8 and 7.5. Minimum, 4.6. Maximum, 10.0+.

Source: Isolated from five different trees affected with wet wood.

Habitat: Pathogenic in trunk wood of elms, *Ulmus americana, U. pumila, U. fulva* and *U. procera.*

11. **Erwinia carotovora** (Jones, 1901) Holland, 1920. (*Bacillus carotovorus* Jones, Cent. f. Bakt., II Abt., *7*, 1901, 12; Holland, Jour. Bact., *5*, 1920, 222; *Pectobacterium carotovorum* Waldee, Iowa State Coll. Jour. Sci., *19*, 1945, 469.)

ca.ro.to'vo.ra. L. noun *carota* carrot; L. v. *voro* to devour; M.L. adj. *carotovorus* carrot-destroying.

Description taken from Burkholder and Smith (Phytopath., *39*, 1949, 893).

Rods, 0.7 by 1.0 to 2.0 microns. Motile by means of 1 to 6 peritrichous flagella. No capsules observed. Gram-negative.

Gelatin: Liquefaction.

Beef-extract peptone agar slants: Growth moderate, filiform, grayish white, iridescent and butyrous. Medium unchanged.

Broth: Moderately turbid with a slight ring but seldom a pellicle; white sediment.

Litmus milk: Coagulation in 4 days. Litmus reduced; slight separation of whey but little or no peptonization.

Potato plug: Slight growth.

Endo agar: Colonies circular, at first pink turning deep red with a metallic luster. Medium turns red.

Blood serum: Growth much as on agar. Not liquefied.

Krumwiede's triple sugar agar: Turns yellow.

Uschinsky's solution: Growth light to none.

Desoxycholate agar. Good growth. Colonies pink.

Diastase-negative.

Indole not produced.

Hydrogen sulfide not produced.

Methyl red test positive. Acetylmethylcarbinol not produced. Certain strains vary with respect to these two characters.

All strains produce acid and many produce gas from glucose, galactose, fructose, arabinose, xylose, rhamnose, cellobiose, lactose, maltose, raffinose, sucrose, glycerol, mannitol and salicin. Ethanol (5 per cent), dulcitol, erythritol and the sodium salts of hippuric, malonic, tartaric and uric acids are also utilized.

Starch not hydrolyzed, and cellulose not attacked; pectates liquefied.

Nitrites produced from nitrates.

Ammonium salts, potassium nitrate, peptone, gelatin and yeast extract utilized, but not aspartic acid. Asparagine may be utilized as both a carbon and a nitrogen source, but tyrosine can not be so utilized.

5 per cent salt retards and 7 per cent inhibits growth.

Aerobic.

Temperature relations: Optimum, approximately 27° C. Minimum, 6° C. Maximum, between 35° and 37° C.

Pathogenicity: Causes a rapid soft rot of roots, rhizomes, fruits and the fleshy stems of a variety of plants.

Source: Isolated from rotted carrots.

Habitat: Causes a soft rot in carrot, cabbage, celery, cucumber, egg-plant, iris, muskmelon, hyacinth, onion, parsnip, pepper, potato, radish, tomato, turnip and other plants.

12. **Erwinia atroseptica** (van Hall, 1902) Jennison, 1923. (*Bacillus atrosepticus* van Hall, Inaug. Diss., Amsterdam, 1902, 134; Jennison, Ann. Missouri Bot. Gard., *10*, 1923, 43; *Pectobacterium atrosepticum* Patel and Kulkarni, Indian Phytopath., *4*, 1951, 80.)

at.ro.sep'ti.ca. L. adj. *ater* black; Gr. adj. *septicus* producing a putrefaction; M.L. adj.*atrosepticus* producing a black rot.

Description taken from Burkholder and Smith (Phytopath., *39*, 1949, 892).

Rods, 0.7 by 1.0 to 2.0 microns. Motile by means of 1 to 6 flagella; old cells are frequently non-motile. No capsules observed. Gram-negative.

Gelatin: Liquefaction.

Beef-extract peptone agar slants: Growth moderate, filiform, grayish white, iridescent and butyrous. Medium unchanged.

Broth: Moderately turbid with a slight ring, seldom a slight pellicle; later a white sediment.

Litmus milk: Coagulation in 4 days. Litmus reduced; slight separation of whey but little or no peptonization.

Potato plug: Slight growth.

Endo agar: Colonies circular, at first pink, later deep red with a metallic luster. Medium turns red.

Krumwiede's triple sugar agar: Yellow.

Fermi's solution: Slight to no turbidity.

Desoxycholate agar: Good growth. Colonies pink.

Indole not produced.

Hydrogen sulfide not produced.

All strains produce acid and many produce gas from glucose, galactose, fructose, arabinose, xylose, rhamnose, cellobiose, lactose, maltose, raffinose, sucrose, glycerol, mannitol and salicin.

Ethanol, dulcitol, erythritol and the sodium salts of hippuric, malonic, tartaric and uric acids are not utilized. Differs from *Erwinia carotovora* in this respect.

Starch not hydrolyzed, and cellulose not attacked; pectates liquefied.

Methyl red positive; acetylmethylcarbinol not produced.

Nitrites produced from nitrates.

Ammonium salts, potassium nitrate, peptone, gelatin and yeast extract utilized, but not aspartic acid. Asparagine may be utilized as both a carbon and a nitrogen source, but tyrosine can not be so utilized.

5 per cent salt retards and 7 per cent inhibits growth.

Aerobic.

Temperature relations: Optimum, approximately 27° C. Minimum, 3° C. Maximum, between 32° and 35° C.

Source: Isolated from the stems of potatoes affected with black-leg.

Habitat: Causes a black rot on the stems and tubers of potatoes and other vegetables.

13. **Erwinia ananas** Serrano, 1928. (Serrano, Philippine Jour. Sci., *36*, 1928, 271; *Pectobacterium ananas* Patel and Kulkarni, Indian Phytopath., *4*, 1951, 80.)

a′na.nas. M.L. noun *Ananas* generic name of the pineapple.

Note: Not to be confused with *Pseudomonas* (*Phytomonas*) *ananas* Serrano, *loc. cit.*

Short rods, 0.6 by 0.9 micron, with rounded ends, occurring singly, in pairs and in short chains. Motile by means of peritrichous flagella. Encapsulated. Gram-negative.

Gelatin stab: Stratiform liquefaction with a deep, chrome-yellow sediment.

Potato glucose agar: After 24 hours, circular, 3 mm in diameter, convex, dense, homogeneous, entire, moist, straw-yellow, mottled, becoming primulin-yellow. Plates have a molasses odor. Show two types of colonies: rough and smooth. Rough colonies have crenate margins.

Potato glucose agar slant: Growth straw-yellow, raised, becoming primulin-yellow, moist, glistening.

Broth: Turbid; straw-colored pellicle and ring.

Glucose broth: Growth sulfur-yellow.

Litmus milk: Coagulated, faintly acid, becoming alkaline.

Potato: Copious growth, moist, glistening, spreading, becoming primulin-yellow.

Indole not produced.

Slight amount of hydrogen sulfide produced.

Blood serum: Moderate growth, slightly raised, mustard-yellow to primulin-yellow. No liquefaction after 3 months.

Cohn's solution: No growth.

Phenol-negative.

Diastase-positive.

No gas from carbohydrates. Acid from glucose, lactose, sucrose, mannitol, raffinose, glycerol, salicin, dextrin, maltose, fructose and mannose. No acid from arabinose, xylose, amygdalin, rhamnose, inositol, inulin, dulcitol, adonitol, asparagine or starch.

Small amount of alcohol and aldehyde produced.

Nitrites produced from nitrates.

Slight amount of ammonia produced.

Source: Isolated from the pineapple (*Ananas sativus*) and sugar cane (*Saccharum officinarum*).

Habitat: Causes a brown rot of the fruitlets of pineapple.

14. **Erwinia aroideae** (Townsend, 1904) Holland, 1920. (*Bacillus aroideae* Townsend, U. S. Dept. Agr., Bur. Plant Ind. Bull. 60, 1904, 40; Holland, Jour. Bact., *5*, 1920, 222; *Pectobacterium aroideae* Waldee, Iowa State Coll. Jour. Sci., *19*, 1945, 472.)

a.ro.i′de.ae. Gr. noun *arum* the plant wake robin; M.L. pl.noun *Aroideae* the name of the *Arum* subfamily; M.L. gen.noun *aroideae* of an aroid.

Description taken from Townsend (*op. cit.*, 1904, 40) and supplemented by studies made by Burkholder.

Rods, 0.5 by 2.0 to 3.0 microns; occasionally a few very small rods occur. Motile by means of 2 to 8 peritrichous flagella. Gram-negative.

Gelatin: Liquefaction.

Beef-peptone agar slants: Light to moderate growth, filiform, white to cream.

Broth: Turbid; no pellicle.

Litmus milk: Coagulation in 3 days. Litmus reduced. One-fourth of tube whey.

Potato plug: White with tinge of yellow.

Endo agar slants: Streak deep red and medium deep red.

Krumwiede's triple sugar agar: Turns yellow but later a red color appears at top of slant.

Fermi's solution: Flocculent and white.

Uschinsky's solution: Very turbid with heavy sediment.

Desoxycholate agar: Pink, later yellowish.

Indole not produced.

Hydrogen sulfide produced.

Acid but no gas from glucose, galactose, fructose, arabinose, xylose, lactose, sucrose, glycerol, mannitol and salicin. Maltose doubtful. Alkaline reaction in sodium citrate, and only slight growth in tartrate in 10 days.

Methyl red test weakly positive; acetylmethylcarbinol produced.

No growth in ethanol, dulcitol, sodium hippurate and malonate.

Starch not hydrolyzed; ammonium pectate medium liquefied.

Nitrites rapidly produced from nitrates.

Good growth in 5 per cent salt, and a delayed but good growth in 7 per cent salt.

Aerobic.

Good growth at 37° C.; light growth at 40° C., but none at 42° C.

Distinctive characters: Differs from the non-aerogenic strains of *Erwinia atroseptica* and *E. carotovora* in the production of hydrogen sulfide, in its high temperature range and in its great turbidity in Uschinsky's solution. Acetylmethylcarbinol is also produced. Its fermentation is more like that of *E. atroseptica* than that of *E. carotovora*.

Source: Isolated from rotted calla lily.

Habitat: Causes a soft rot of calla. Affects raw potato, egg-plant, cauliflower, radish, cucumber, cabbage, parsnip, turnip, salsify and tomato (ripe and green).

15. Erwinia citrimaculans (Doidge, 1917) Magrou, 1937. (*Bacillus citrimaculans* Doidge, Ann. Appl. Biol., *3*, 1917, 53; Magrou, in Hauduroy et al., Dict. d. Bact. Path., 1937, 203.)

ci.tri.ma′cu.lans. M.L. noun *Citrus* generic name of the citrus fruits; L. part. adj. *maculans* spotting; M.L. adj. *citrimaculans* citrus-spotting.

Rods, 0.45 to 0.7 by 0.8 to 3.2 microns. Motile by means of peritrichous flagella. Encapsulated. Gram-positive. Dowson (Zent. f. Bakt., II Abt., *100*, 1939, 184) thinks that this species is Gram-negative.

Gelatin: Liquefaction.

Agar colonies: Subcircular, yellow, with dense grumose centers.

Broth: Turbid, with pellicle and sediment.

Milk: Coagulated, with precipitation of casein and extrusion of whey. Not peptonized. Litmus gradually reduced.

Blood serum: Not liquefied.

Indole is produced.

Cohn's solution: No growth.

Uschinsky's solution: Growth present.

No growth in broth over chloroform.

Acid without visible gas from glucose, sucrose, fructose, galactose, maltose and mannitol. No acid from lactose, glycerol, dextrin or starch.

Nitrites produced from nitrates with evolution of gas.

Ammonia produced in broth.

Diastase-negative.

Methylene blue and neutral red reduced.

Pigment insoluble in water, alcohol, ether, chloroform, carbon bisulfide, dilute acid or alkalis.

A turbid growth is produced in 10 per cent salt.

Facultatively anaerobic.

Temperature relations: Optimum, 35° C. Maximum, 43° C. Thermal death point, 62° C. for 10 minutes.

Source: Isolated from diseased lemons and oranges.

Habitat: Causes a spot disease of citrus. In nature attacks lemons, oranges, naartjes and has also been successfully inoculated into limes, shaddock, grapefruit and citron. Seville oranges are resistant.

16. Erwinia mangiferae (Doidge, 1915) Bergey et al., 1923. (*Bacillus mangiferae* Doidge, Ann. Appl. Biol., *2*, 1915, 1; Bergey et al., Manual, 1st ed., 1923, 173.)

man.gi′fer.ae. M.L. noun *Mangifera* generic name of the mangoes; M.L. gen.noun *mangiferae* of the mango.

Rods, 0.6 by 1.5 microns, with rounded ends, occurring singly and in chains. Motile by means of peritrichous flagella. Encapsulated. Gram-negative.

Gelatin stab: Medium liquefied in 10 to 17 days. Growth yellow.

Agar colonies: Glistening, yellowish; undulate borders.

Agar slant: Growth yellow, glistening.

Broth: Turbid; yellow ring.

Litmus milk: Slow coagulation at 37° C. Slight acidity. Casein slowly dissolved. Litmus reduced.

Potato: Growth spreading, glistening, yellowish. Medium not discolored.

Cohn's solution: Slight turbidity.

Uschinsky's solution: No growth.

Fermi's solution with starch jelly: No growth.

Indole produced in peptone solution.

Phenol-negative.

No hydrogen sulfide produced.

Feeble acid production without gas from glucose, lactose, sucrose, fructose and glycerol. No growth in closed arm with lactose and glycerol; more or less growth in closed arm with glucose, sucrose, fructose, maltose, raffinose and mannitol.

Diastase-negative.

Produces an enzyme capable of dissolving

the middle lamella but without action on cellulose.

Nitrites produced from nitrates.

No ammonia in broth.

Pigment insoluble in water, alcohol, ether, chloroform or dilute acids.

Temperature relations: Optimum, 30° C. Minimum, between 5° and 6° C. Maximum, 45° C. Thermal death point, 60° C.

Source: Isolated from the mango in Africa.

Habitat: Causes a disease of the mango (*Mangifera indica*).

17. **Erwinia rhapontici** (Millard, 1924) Burkholder, 1948. (*Phytomonas rhapontica* (sic) Millard, Univ. Leeds and Yorkshire Council for Agr. Ed. Bul. 134, 1924, 111; *Erwinia rhapontici* Burkholder, in Manual, 6th ed., 1948, 475; *Pectobacterium rhapontici* Patel and Kulkarni, Indian Phytopath., *4*, 1951, 80.)

rha.pon'ti.ci. Gr. neut.n. *rhaponticum* specific epithet of *Rheum rhaponticum*, rhubarb; M.L. gen.noun. *rhapontici* of rhubarb.

Description taken from Metcalfe (Ann. of Appl. Biol., *27*, 1940, 502), where he suggests that this species belongs in *Erwinia*.

Rods, 0.5 to 0.8 by 1.2 to 1.5 microns. Motile by means of 3 to 7 peritrichous flagella. Gram-negative.

Gelatin stab: Beaded growth. No liquefaction.

Infusion agar: Colonies circular, convex, smooth, glistening, translucent, with margins entire, 2 to 3 mm in diameter in 48 hours at 25° C.

Rhubarb agar: Colonies slightly larger, often with a yellowish tinge.

Tryptophane broth: Turbid with fragile pellicle, a slight rim and slight flocculent deposit.

Milk: Acid in 3 to 4 days with or without slight curd separation. No clotting.

Indole not produced.

Hydrogen sulfide not produced.

Cohn's solution: Moderate growth.

Acid but no gas from arabinose, xylose, glucose, galactose, fructose, mannose, lactose, maltose, sucrose, mannitol, glycerol and salicin.

Acetylmethylcarbinol produced.

Growth in citrate solution.

Starch not hydrolyzed.

Nitrites produced from nitrates.

Chromogenesis: Water-soluble, pinkish pigment in various media.

Growth from 0° to 37° C. and possibly higher.

Distinctive characters: Differs from *Erwinia aroideae* in that it does not liquefy gelatin nor clot milk and is chromogenic. It also has a limited host range.

Source: Isolated from rotting rhubarb crowns. Metcalfe used 6 strains from various sources in describing this pathogen.

Habitat: Causes a crown-rot of rhubarb (*Rheum rhaponticum*).

TRIBE III. SERRATIEAE BERGEY, BREED AND MURRAY, 1938.

(Preprint, Manual, 5th ed., 1938 (October), vi.)

Ser.ra.ti'e.ae. M.L. gen.noun *Serratia* type genus of the tribe; -*eae* ending to denote a tribe; M.L. fem.pl.n. *Serratieae* the *Serratia* tribe.

Characters as for the genus.

There is a single genus.

Genus VII. **Serratia** Bizio, 1823, **emend.** Breed and Breed, 1927.*

(Bizio, Polenta porporina, Biblioteca italiana o sia Giornale de lettera, scienze e arti, *30*, 1823, 288; *Zoogalactina* Sette, Memoria storico-naturale sull'arrossimento straordinario di alcune sostanze alimentose osservato nella provincia di Padova l'anno 1819. Venezia,

---

* Revised by Prof. Robert S. Breed, New York State Experiment Station, Geneva, New York, November, 1937; further revision by Prof. Robert S. Breed, July, 1955.

8°, 1824, 51; *Coccobacterium* Schmidt and Weis, Die Bakterien, 1902, 10; *Erythrobacillus* Fortineau, Compt. rend. Soc. Biol., Paris, *58*, 1905, 104; *Dicrobactrum* Enderlein, Sitzber. Gesell. Naturf. Freunde, Berlin, 1917, 309; Breed and Breed, Cent. f. Bakt., II Abt., *71*, 1927, 435.)

Ser.ra'ti.a. M.L. fem.n. *Serratia* named for Serafino Serrati, the Italian physicist who invented a steam boat at Florence before 1787.

Small, peritrichous rods. Gram-negative. Produce characteristic red pigments; white to rose-red strains that lack brilliant colors are common. Gelatin is rapidly liquefied. Milk is coagulated and digested. Typical species produce CO_2 and frequently H_2 from glucose and other sugars; acetic, formic, succinic and lactic acids, acetylmethylcarbinol and 2,3-butylene glycol are also produced. Coagulated blood serum is liquefied. Nitrates are reduced. Aerobic. Saprophytic on decaying plant or even animal materials.

A characteristic feature of the species belonging to *Serratia* is the variability of their pigmentation. Heavily pigmented to white cultures probably occur in all species. In some cultures of *Serratia marcescens* Bizio, white strains arise so readily that growth on agar slants may appear as a mosaic of white and orange-red. Colonies are frequently white as they first appear, usually becoming orange-red later. In the work done by Breed and Breed (*loc. cit.*) it was found that pigment developed better on the Bacto-Peptone, Liebig meat-extract media then generally used than on new, improved media containing casein digest, yeast extract and similar growth-promoting substances. Recently Harned (personal communication, 1955) found mannitol- and sorbitol-peptone media to give profuse pigmentation while no pigment is produced on improved peptone media containing glucose. Prodigiosin dissolved in alcohol is red in acid and orange in alkaline solutions. Old cultures on agar slants become a deep magenta-red.

The red pigment found in the various species of *Serratia* has been named prodigiosin. A series of chemical studies (see Wrede and Rothhaas, Ztschr. Physiol. Chem., *215*, 1933, 67; *ibid.*, *222*, 1934, 203; and *ibid.*, *226*, 1934, 95 for a bibliography) defined the structure of this compound as a tripyrrl methene. This pigment has been shown by a number of investigators to be active *in vitro* against a number of pathogenic protozoa and fungi. It is even indicated by clinical studies (Weir, Egeberg, Lack and Leiby, Amer. Jour. Med. Sci., *224*, 1952, 70) that this compound has some promise as a therapeutic agent in the treatment of disseminated coccidioidomycosis, and methods have been devised for securing appreciable quantities of this pigment by submerged culture (Harned, Applied Microbiol., *2*, 1954, 365). There is, however, indication that prodigiosin is not a single pigment as there is much variation in the amount and type of pigment produced in various cultures belonging to the same species. Some cultures are heavily pigmented, and in these cases there is some diffusion of pigment through the agar indicating some water solubility. Other heavily pigmented strains quite regularly show a fuchsin-like sheen on the surface, a character not found in the case of other cultures. Other cultures never produce the common orange-red pigment that turns to a magenta-red in old cultures. These less heavily pigmented strains maintain a constant rose-red color while still other strains produce no chromogenesis whatever. Some of the non-chromogenic strains that are known to have been derived from chromogenic strains have failed to produce color on any medium or condition of growth that has been tried. It has been noted that when the color of normally pigmented strains is extracted in alcohol, the residual cells still show a rose-red color suggesting that there is a rose-red pigment present that is not soluble in alcohol (Breed).

The type species is *Serratia marcescens* Bizio.

Key to the species of genus **Serratia**.

I. Pigment not especially water-soluble, readily soluble in alcohol.
    A. No visible gas from glucose.
        1. Inconspicuous pellicle, if any, on plain gelatin.

                              1. *Serratia marcescens*.

2. Brilliant orange-red pellicle on plain gelatin.

2. *Serratia indica.*

B. Produce enough H₂ with the CO₂ from glucose to show gas in fermentation tubes.

1. Acetylmethylcarbinol produced.

3. *Serratia plymuthica.*

2. Acetylmethylcarbinol not produced.

4. *Serratia kiliensis.*

II. Pigment soluble in water and in alcohol.

5. *Serratia piscatorum.*

1. **Serratia marcescens** Bizio, 1823. (Bizio, Polenta porporina, Biblioteca italiana o sia Giornale de lettera, scienze e arti, *30*, 1823, 288; *Zoagalactina imetrofa* Sette, Memoria storico-naturale sull'arrossimento straordinario di alcune sostanze alimentose osservato nella provincia di Padova l'anno 1819. Venezia, 8°, 1824, 51; *Monas prodigiosa* Ehrenberg, Bericht ü. d. z. Bekannt-machung geeigneten Verhandlungen d. Kgl. preuss. Acad. d. Wissenschaften, 1849, 354.) mar.ces′cens. L. part.adj. *marcescens* pining away, decaying.

Description taken largely from Breed and Breed (Jour. Bact., *9*, 1924, 545).

Short rods, sometimes almost spherical, 0.5 by 0.5 to 1.0 micron, occurring singly and occasionally in chains of 5 or 6 elements. Motile by means of four peritrichous flagella. Eight to ten flagella occur on cells grown at 20° to 25° C. (de Rossi, Rivista d'Igiene, *14*, 1903, 000). Gram-negative.

Gelatin colonies: Thin, slightly granular, gray becoming red, circular, slightly undulate. Medium liquefied rather quickly.

Gelatin stab: Infundibuliform liquefaction. Sediment in liquefied medium usually red on top, white in the depth.

Agar colonies: Circular, thin, granular, white becoming red. R and S colonies with mucoid variants (Reed, Jour. Bact., *34*, 1937, 255).

Agar slant: White, smooth, moist layer, taking on an orange-red to fuchsin color in three or four days, sometimes with a metallic luster.

Broth: Turbid; may form a red ring at surface or slight pellicle; gray sediment.

Litmus milk: Acid reaction with soft coagulum. A red surface growth develops. Little or no digestion takes place.

Potato: At first a white line appears which rapidly turns red. The growth is luxuriant and frequently shows a metallic luster.

Indole not produced.

Production of hydrogen sulfide: Produced from cysteine, cystine or organic sulfur compounds containing either of these molecules. Produced from sulfur but not from sulfites, sulfates or thiosulfates (Tarr, Biochem. Jour., *27*, 1933, 1869; also see *ibid.*, *28*, 1934, 192).

Produces acetic, formic, succinic and levolactic acids, ethanol, acetylmethylcarbinol, 2,3-butylene glycol, CO₂ and a trace of H₂ from glucose (Pederson and Breed, Jour. Bact., *16*, 1928, 183).

Grows poorly or not at all in distilled water containing urea, potassium chloride and glucose.

Acetylmethylcarbinol is produced (Breed).

Nitrites produced from nitrates.

Pigment soluble in alcohol, ether, chloroform, benzol and carbon bisulfide (Schneider, Arb. bakt. Hochsch. Karlsruhe, *1*, 1894, 210). Pigment may diffuse through the agar, i.e., shows solubility in water where strains are very deeply pigmented (Breed). Pigment not produced at 35° C.

Sodium formate broth (Stark and England, Jour. Bact., *29*, 1935, 26): Cultures do not produce visible gas (Breed).

Odor of trimethylamine is produced.

Aerobic, facultatively anaerobic.

Optimum temperature, between 25° and 30° C. No growth at 37° C.

Source: Isolated by Bizio and Sette from growth on corn meal mush (polenta).

Habitat: Found in water, soil, milk and foods and in silk worms and other insects.

2. **Serratia indica** (Eisenberg, 1886) Bergey et al., 1923. (*Bacillus indicus* Eisenberg, Bakt. Diag., 1 Aufl., 1886, 1: *Micrococ-*

cus indicus Koch, Berichte ueber die Reise zur Erforschung der Cholera, 1887; Bergey et al., Manual, 1st ed., 1923, 88; Breed and Breed, Jour. Bact., *11*, 1926, 76.)

in'di.ca. L. adj. *indicus* pertaining to India.

Small rods, 0.5 by 1.0 to 1.5 microns. Motile by means of four peritrichous flagella. Gram-negative.

Gelatin colonies: Resemble those of *Serratia marcescens* Bizio.

Gelatin stab: Liquefaction occurs rather quickly. Brilliant orange-red pellicle on plain gelatin.

Agar colonies: Pink, slightly serrate, spreading, with green iridescence.

Agar slant: Luxuriant, dirty white layer. Pigment produced best in alkaline media.

Broth: Turbid, white sediment.

Litmus milk: Acid and coagulated. Digestion complete in 10 days.

Potato: Luxuriant growth with or without pigment production.

Indole not produced.

Produces same products (except H_2) from glucose as does *Serratia marcescens* (Pederson and Breed, Jour. Bact., *16*, 1928, 183).

Growth with pigment production in distilled water containing urea, potassium chloride and glucose.

Acetylmethylcarbinol is produced (Breed).

Nitrites produced from nitrates.

Coagulated blood serum is liquefied.

Odor of trimethylamine is produced.

Sodium formate broth: Cultures do not produce visible gas (Breed).

Aerobic, facultatively anaerobic.

Optimum temperature, between 25° and 35° C. No growth at 37° C.

Pathogenic for laboratory animals.

Comment: A non-gelatin-liquefying strain of this species has been reported (see Breed, in Manual, 6th ed., 1948, 481).

Relationship to other species: Cultures of this organism lose their ability to produce the orange-red pellicle on gelatin and then become practically indistinguishable from cultures of *Serratia marcescens*. This would indicate that this so-called species is a rough strain of the former species (Breed). See Reed (Jour. Bact., *34*, 1937, 255) for a

discussion of dissociation phenomena in this genus.

Source: Isolated from the alimentary tract of a Java ape in India; also from a milk can from Ithaca, N. Y.

Habitat: Presumably widely distributed. Not common.

3. **Serratia plymuthica** (Lehmann and Neumann, 1896) Bergey et al., 1923. (Roter Bacillus aus Plymouth, Fischer, Ztschr. f. Hyg., *2*, 1887, 74; *Bacterium plymuthicum* Lehmann and Neumann, Bakt. Diag., 1 Aufl., *2*, 1896, 264; Bergey et al., Manual, 1st ed., 1923, 88.)

ply.mu'thi.ca. M.L. adj. *plymuthicus* pertaining to Plymouth.

Distinct rods, 0.6 by 1.5 to 2.0 microns, with rounded ends, occurring singly and in short chains. Motile by means of peritrichous flagella. Gram-negative.

Gelatin colonies: Like those of *Serratia marcescens* Bizio. Original culture mucoid.

Gelatin stab: Crateriform liquefaction. Liquefaction as in *Serratia marcescens*.

Agar colonies: Like mucoid variants of *Serratia marcescens*.

Agar slant: Sometimes show metallic luster. Pigment as in *Serratia marcescens*.

Broth: Growth like that of *Serratia marcescens*.

Litmus milk: Acid and coagulated.

Potato: Growth violet-pink, with or without metallic luster.

Strong fecal odor produced.

Gas from glucose, lactose and sucrose, 70 to 80 per cent of it being CO_2, the remainder is H_2. Gas is also produced in asparagine solutions.

Acetylmethylcarbinol is produced (Breed).

Sodium formate broth: Cultures produce abundant gas (Breed).

Coagulated blood serum is liquefied.

Pigment is soluble in alcohol and ether and sometimes slightly so in water.

Aerobic, facultatively anaerobic.

Optimum temperature, 30° C.

Source: Isolated from the water supply of Plymouth, England.

Habitat: Found in water and in various foods.

4. **Serratia kiliensis** (Lehmann and Neumann, 1896) Bergey et al., 1923. (Bacterium h, Breunig, Inaug. Diss., Kiel, 1888; *Bacillus ruber balticus* Kruse, in Flügge, Die Mikroorganismen, 3 Aufl., *2*, 1896, 303; *Bacterium kiliense* Lehmann and Neumann, Bakt. Diag., 1 Aufl., *2*, 1896, 263; *Serratia keilensis* (sic) Bergey et al., Manual, 1st ed., 1923, 90.)

ki.li.en'sis. M.L. adj. *kiliensis* pertaining to Kiel.

Description taken from Kruse (*op. cit.*, 1896, 303) and from Bergey et al. (*op. cit.*, 1923, 90).

Slender rods, 0.7 to 0.8 by 2.5 to 5.0 microns, occurring singly. Motile by means of four peritrichous flagella. Gram-negative.

Deep gelatin colonies: Bright yellow. Gelatin liquefied slowly, usually becoming rose red.

Glucose gelatin stab: Rapid liquefaction. Occasional gas bubbles (Breed).

Agar colonies: Small, red becoming magenta, smooth.

Agar slant: Bright red becoming darker in old cultures.

Agar stab: Turbid, strongly pigmented water of condensation.

Broth: Turbid; usually reddened.

Litmus milk: Acid; at 20° C., coagulated slowly and pigment produced; at 35° C., coagulated rapidly and no pigment produced.

Potato: Slight, red growth becoming luxuriant and darker.

Indole not produced.

Acid and gas from carbohydrates (Lehmann and Neumann, *op. cit.*, 1896, 263). Gas from glucose, lactose and sucrose, 20 to 30 per cent of it being CO_2 (Bergey). Optically inactive lactic acid is produced and not more than a trace of acetylmethylcarbinol or 2,3-butylene glycol (Pederson and Breed, Jour. Bact., *16*, 1928, 183).

Sodium formate broth: Gas is produced (Breed).

Acetylmethylcarbinol not produced by the Král culture (Breed).

Nitrites and free nitrogen are produced from nitrates.

Coagulated blood serum is liquefied.

Pigment produced at 37° C. Pigment especially soluble in alcohol.

Optimum temperature, 30° C.

Aerobic.

Relationships to other species: It is not certain whether Breunig's original culture was a heavily pigmented strain of *Serratia marcescens* or whether it was of the type described above. Cultures of both types have been widely distributed as the Kiel bacillus. Descriptions drawn up by Kruse (*op. cit.*, 1896, 303) and Lehmann and Neumann (*op. cit.*, 1896, 263) state that this bacterium produces visible gas, while Migula, in 1900, gives a description which fits *Serratia marcescens*. Moreover, cultures obtained under this name from various laboratories in Europe and America are sometimes of one type and sometimes of the other. As the Král culture distributed as *Bacillus ruber balticus* is widely known and has now been shown to differ from *Serratia marcescens* in that it is a distinct rod in ordinary media, forms visible gas from carbohydrates and even more abundant gas from sodium formate media, the name *Serratia kiliensis* is used here for the Král culture. *Serratia kiliensis* is a distinct rod like *Serratia plymuthica* but fails to produce acetylmethylcarbinol. This use of the name *Serratia kiliensis* given here also accords with the description drawn up by Bergey for the first edition of the Manual based on the study of a culture which he obtained many years previously from Europe (Breed).

Source: Isolated from water at Kiel, Germany.

Habitat: Presumably widely distributed.

5. **Serratia piscatorum** (Lehmann and Neumann, 1896) Breed, 1939. (Microbe rouge de la sardine, du Bois Saint-Sévrin, Ann. Inst. Past., *8*, 1894, 155; *Bacterium piscatorum* Lehmann and Neumann, Bakt. Diag., 1 Aufl., *2*, 1896, 263; Breed, in Manual, 5th ed., 1939, 427; *Serratia urinae* Gurevitch and Weber, Amer. Jour. Clin. Pathol., *20*, 1950, 49.)

pis.ca.to'rum. L. noun *piscator* a fisherman; L. gen.pl.noun *piscatorum* of fishermen.

Short rods, 0.5 by 0.6 micron, occurring in pairs, sometimes in fours or, in broth, in long filaments. Actively motile. Gram-negative.

Gelatin colonies: Small, yellowish gray becoming pink, very slimy. Carmine-red pellicle. Liquefaction.

Gelatin stab: Rapid liquefaction. Grayish pellicle which becomes red after 24 hours and later precipitates. Slimy.

Agar colonies: Dull, white to pinkish growth.

Broth: Rapid turbidity; thick, slimy, white pellicle which later turns red; purplish sediment; liquid becomes pink and syrupy; in old cultures the broth is brown.

Potato: At 37° to 39° C., red pigment visible after 8 hours. At room temperatures growth is at first white and slimy, later red.

Strong odor of trimethylamine.

Distinctive characters: Pigment soluble in alcohol. Good pigment production at 37° to 39° C. The original cultures were heavily pigmented, and thus the pigment showed some solubility in water as does that of *Serratia marcescens* Bizio under similar conditions. The original cultures were slimy, but slimy (mucoid) cultures also occur in *S. marcescens*.

Comments: In recent years cultures of *Serratia* have been isolated from various human infections (Gurevitch and Weber, *loc. cit.*; Wheat, Zuckerman and Rantz, Arch. Internal Med., *88*, 1951, 461; Vernon and Hepler, Quart. Bull., Northwestern Univ. Med. School, *28*, 1954, 366). In some of these cases, new names have been given to the organisms isolated without adequate justification, for these organisms seem to possess the same characters as do those that were originally isolated from felons on the hands of men handling fish.

Source: Isolated in 1893 from a box of oil-packed sardines at a canning factory in France. Also found in the red pus from fishermen and sardine-factory workers suffering from felons. In these lesions this organism is associated with an anaerobe, but by itself it is not pathogenic.

Habitat: Presumably widely distributed.

TRIBE IV. PROTEEAE CASTELLANI AND CHALMERS, 1919.

(Manual of Trop. Med., 3rd ed., 1919, 932.)

Pro.te′e.ae. Gr. noun *Proteus* type genus of the tribe; *-eae* ending to denote a tribe; M.L. fem.pl.n. *Proteeae* the *Proteus* tribe.

Characters as for the genus.

There is a single genus.

Genus VIII. **Proteus Hauser, *1885*.***

(Hauser, Sitzber. d. phys.-med. Sozietät zu Erlangen, 1885, 156; *Liquidobacterium* Orla-Jensen, Cent. f. Bakt., II Abt., *22*, 1909, 337; *Spirilina* Hueppe, Wiesbaden, 1886, 146; *Eisenbergia* Enderlein, Sitzber. Ges. Naturf. Freunde, Berlin, 1917, 315.)

Pro′te.us. Gr. noun *Proteus* an ocean god who took many shapes.

Straight rods. Motile by means of peritrichous, occasionally very numerous, flagella; generally actively motile at 25° C., but at 37° C. motility may be weak or absent.† Gram-negative. Two species (*Proteus vulgaris* and *P. mirabilis*) produce amoeboid colonies which show a swarming phenomenon on solid media devoid of bile salts. On moist agar the remaining species produce colonies which spread to some extent. Spreading colonies can usually be induced to swarm. Pleomorphism is characteristic only of young, actively swarm-

* Revised by Prof. C. A. Stuart, Brown University, Providence, Rhode Island, July, 1955.

† See Leifson, Carhart and Fulton (Jour. Bact., *69*, 1955, 73) for a recent discussion of the type of flagellation found in this genus.

ing cultures. Glucose and usually various other carbohydrates, but not lactose, are fermented with the production of acid and usually visible gas; one species usually produces only acid. Phenylpyruvic acid is produced from phenylalanine by an oxidative deamination, and leucine is rendered alkaline by an oxidative decarboxylation. Urea may or may not be decomposed. Trimethylamine oxide is reduced. Primarily from fecal matter and other putrefying materials.

The type species is *Proteus vulgaris* Hauser.

Key to the species of genus **Proteus**.

I. Urea hydrolyzed.
    A. No acid or gas from mannitol.
        1. Acid and gas from maltose.
                1. *Proteus vulgaris.*
        2. No acid or gas from maltose.
           a. Indole not produced.
                2. *Proteus mirabilis.*
           aa. Indole is produced.
                3. *Proteus morganii.*
    B. Acid and sometimes gas from mannitol.
                4. *Proteus rettgeri.*
II. Urea not hydrolyzed.
                5. *Proteus inconstans.*

1. **Proteus vulgaris** Hauser, 1885. (Hauser, Sitzungsber. d. phys.-mediz. Sozietät zu Erlangen, 1885, 156; *Bacterium vulgare* Lehmann and Neumann, Bakt. Diag., 1 Aufl., *2*, 1896, 243.)

vul.ga′ris. L. adj. *vulgaris* common.

Rods, 0.5 to 1.0 by 1.0 to 3.0 microns, occurring singly, in pairs and frequently in long chains. Actively motile by means of peritrichous flagella. Gram-negative.

Gelatin colonies: Irregular, swarming; rapid liquefaction.

Gelatin stab: Rapid, stratiform liquefaction.

Agar colonies: Opaque, gray, swarming.

Agar slant: Thin, bluish gray growth, spreading over the entire surface.

Broth: Markedly turbid, usually with a thin pellicle.

Litmus milk: Slightly acid, becoming markedly alkaline; quick peptonization.

Potato: Abundant, creamy to yellowish gray growth, becoming brown.

Putrefactive odor produced.

Indole is produced.

Hydrogen sulfide produced from cysteine, cystine or organic sulfur compounds containing either of these molecules; also produced from sulfur and thiosulfates (Tarr,

Biochem. Jour., *27*, 1933, 1869; *28*, 1934, 192). Lead acetate turned brown.

Acid and gas from glucose, fructose, galactose, maltose and sucrose. No acid or gas from dextrin, lactose or mannitol. See Moltke (Contributions to the Characterization and Systematic Classification of *Bac. proteus vulgaris* (Hauser). Levin and Munksgaard, Copenhagen, 1927, 156) for other fermentation characters. The ratio of H_2 to CO_2 is 1:1 (Speck and Stark, Jour. Bact., *44*, 1942, 687).

Acetylmethylcarbinol not produced.

Sodium citrate may be utilized as a sole source of carbon.

Nitrites produced from nitrates.

Phenylpyruvic acid is produced from phenylalanine, and leucine is rendered alkaline.

Aerobic, facultatively anaerobic.

Optimum temperature, 37° C.

Pathogenic for fish and other animals such as dogs, guinea pigs and mice (Wyss, Ztschr. f. Hyg., *27*, 1898, 143).

Distinctive characters: X-strains of Weil and Felix. Lehmann-Neumann-Breed, Determinative Bact., Eng. Trans., 7th Ed., *2*, 1931, 493: "The discovery of proteus strains which may be agglutinated by typhus serum is of very great importance. These are the so-called X-strains from typhus patients found by Weil and Felix. They first cultivated strains X and X₂ from the urine of typhus patients and later the famous X₁₉ . The two former were agglutinated weakly, the latter strongly (up to 1:50,000). The diagnosis of typhus by agglutination with strain X₁₉ proved to be excellent and the reaction took place in the serum of almost 100 per cent of those suffering from the disease. . . . The typhus strains of proteus have recently been divided into the two types of Felix and Weil, the H forms and the O forms. The former grows as a thin opaque film, the latter lacks this character and grows as non-spreading slimy colonies; frequently without distinct flaella. . . " (For further description of H and O forms, see Moltke, *op. cit.*, 1927, 156.)

The X₂ and X₁₉ strains mostly ferment maltose.

Relationship to other species: Hauser described *Proteus vulgaris* as a rapid gelatin-liquefier and *Proteus mirabilis* as a slow liquefier. Wenner and Rettger (Jour. Bact., *4*, 1919, 332) found the property of gelatin liquefaction too variable to serve as a basis for separation of species. They suggested that this differentiating character be set aside and that the two species be differentiated on the basis of maltose fermentation, the species fermenting the sugar receiving the name *Proteus vulgaris*, and the species failing to attack it, *Proteus mirabilis*. This suggestion was accepted by Bergey et al., (Manual, 1st ed., 1923) and by Weldin (Iowa Jour. Sci., *1*, 1927, 147); their work was confirmed by Rustigian and Stuart (Jour. Bact., *45*, 1943, 198) and by Thornton (Jour. Bact., *48*, 1944, 123). Also see Moltke (*op. cit.*, 1927, 156).

Source: Isolated from putrid meat, infusions and abscesses.

Habitat: Found on putrefying materials.

2. **Proteus mirabilis** Hauser, 1885. (Hauser, Sitzungsber. d. phys.-med. Sozietät zu Erlangen, 1885, 156; *Bacterium mirabilis* (sic) Chester, Ann. Rept. Del. Col. Agr. Exp. Sta., *9*, 1897, 101.)

mi.ra'bi.lis. L. adj. *mirabilis* wonderful, surprising.

Short rods, 0.5 to 0.6 by 1.0 to 3.0 microns, occurring singly, in pairs and frequently in long chains. Motile by means of peritrichous flagella. Gram-negative.

Gelatin colonies: Irregular, swarming.

Gelatin stab: Slow, stratiform liquefaction.

Agar colonies: Gray, irregular, swarming.

Agar slant: Thin, bluish gray growth, spreading over the surface.

Broth: Turbid; thin, gray pellicle; sediment.

Litmus milk: Slightly acid, becoming alkaline; peptonized.

Potato: Dirty gray, spreading growth.

Putrefactive odor produced.

Indole not produced.

Hydrogen sulfide is produced.

Acid and gas from glucose, fructose, galactose, xylose and trehalose. Acid and gas usually produced slowly from sucrose. No acid or gas from lactose, maltose, dextrin or mannitol.

Most of the XK strains do not attack maltose.

Sodium citrate is usually utilized as a sole source of carbon.

Acetylmethylcarbinol frequently produced weakly.

Nitrites produced from nitrates.

Phenylpyruvic acid is produced from phenylalanine, and leucine is rendered alkaline.

Aerobic, facultatively anaerobic.

Optimum temperature, 37° C.

Source: Isolated from putrid meat, infusions and abscesses. Also reported as a cause of gastroenteritis (Cherry and Barnes, Amer. Jour. Pub. Health, *36*, 1946, 484).

Habitat: Found on putrefying materials.

3. **Proteus morganii** (Winslow et al., 1919) Rauss, 1936. (Organism No. 1, Morgan, Brit. Med. Jour., *1*, 1906, 908; *Bacillus morgani* Winslow, Kligler and Rothberg, Jour. Bact., *4*, 1919, 481; *Salmonella morgani* Castellani and Chalmers, Man. Trop. Med., 3rd ed., 1919, 939; *Bacterium morgani* Holland, Jour. Bact., *5*, 1920, 215; Rauss, Jour. Path. and Bact., *42*, 1936, 183.)

mor.ga'ni.i. M.L. gen.noun *morganii* of Morgan; named for H. de R. Morgan, the bacteriologist who first studied this organism.

Common name: Morgan's bacillus, type 1.

Rods, 0.4 to 0.6 by 1.0 to 2.0 microns, occurring singly. Motile by means of peritrichous flagella. See Rauss (*loc. cit.*) for a discussion of flagellation and its relation to the swarming characteristic. Gram-negative.

Gelatin colonies: Bluish gray, homogeneous, smooth, entire.

Gelatin stab: No liquefaction.

Agar colonies: Grayish white, smooth, glistening growth. May show a tendency to spread somewhat on moist agar.

Broth: Turbid.

Litmus milk: Neutral or becoming alkaline.

Potato: Dirty white, limited growth.

Indole is produced.

Hydrogen sulfide not produced.

Acid and a small amount of gas from glucose, fructose, galactose and mannose; rarely from xylose. Does not attack lactose, sucrose, maltose, arabinose, raffinose, dextrin, salicin, mannitol, dulcitol, sorbitol, adonitol or inositol.

Acetylmethylcarbinol not produced.

Sodium citrate not utilized as a sole source of carbon.

Nitrites are produced from nitrates.

Phenylpyruvic acid is produced from phenylalanine, and leucine is rendered alkaline.

Aerobic, facultatively anaerobic.

Optimum temperature, 37° C.

Source: Isolated from the feces of infants with summer diarrhoea.

Habitat: Found in the intestinal canal and in normal or diarrhoeal stools.

4. **Proteus rettgeri** (Hadley et al., 1918) Rustigian and Stuart, 1943. (*Bacterium rettgeri* Hadley, Elkins and Caldwell, Rhode Island Agr. Exp. Sta. Bull. 174, 1918, 169; *Shigella rettgeri* Weldin, Iowa State Coll. Jour. Sci., *1*, 1927, 181; *Proteus entericus* Rustigian and Stuart, Jour. Bact., *45*, 1943, 198; Rustigian and Stuart, Proc. Soc. Exp. Biol. and Med., *53*, 1943, 241.)

rett'ge.ri. M.L. gen.noun *rettgeri* of Rettger; named for L. F. Rettger, the Amer-

ican bacteriologist who, in 1904, isolated this species.

Rods, 0.5 to 0.8 micron long, occurring singly, in pairs and occasionally in chains. Usually non-motile at 37° C., but actively motile variants possessing peritrichous flagella can be obtained at 25° C. Gram-negative.

Gelatin colonies: Small, grayish, translucent, entire.

Gelatin stab: No liquefaction.

Agar colonies: Small, grayish, translucent, entire. May show a tendency to spread on moist agar.

Agar slant: Filiform to echinulate, grayish, thin, moist, translucent growth.

Broth: Turbid; flocculent to viscid sediment.

Litmus milk: Alkaline in eight days, becoming translucent.

Potato: Luxuriant, grayish growth.

Indole is produced.

Hydrogen sulfide not produced.

Acid and occasionally slight gas from glucose, fructose, galactose, adonitol and mannitol. Salicin, inositol and rhamnose may or may not be fermented. Slow and sometimes weak acid from sucrose. Lactose and maltose are not fermented.

Acetylmethylcarbinol is not produced.

Sodium citrate is utilized as a sole source of carbon.

Nitrites are produced from nitrates.

Phenylpyruvic acid is produced from phenylalanine, and leucine is rendered alkaline.

Aerobic, facultatively anaerobic.

Optimum temperature, 37° C.

Source: Originally isolated from a cholera-like epidemic among chickens; recently isolated from sporadic and epidemic gastroenteritis patients.

Habitat: Found in fecal matter.

5. **Proteus inconstans** (Ornstein, 1921) Shaw and Clarke, 1955. (*Bacillus inconstans* Ornstein, Ztschr. f. Hyg., *91*, 1921, 152; Anaerogenic paracolon, type 29911, Stuart, Wheeler, Rustigian and Zimmerman, Jour. Bact., *45*, 1943, 111; also see Stuart, Wheeler and McGann, Jour. Bact., *52*, 1946, 431; Providence Group, Kauffmann, *Enterobacteriaceae*. Munksgaard, Copenhagen,

1st ed., 1951, 249; Shaw and Clarke, Jour. Gen. Microbiol., *13*, 1955, 155.)

in.con'stans. L. adj. *inconstans* inconstant, changeable.

Rods. Motile by means of peritrichous flagella. Gram-negative.

Gelatin: No liquefaction.

Indole produced.

Hydrogen sulfide produced from an adequate sulfur base.

Acid and usually slight gas from glucose. Sucrose and adonitol are frequently utilized although the former may require prolonged incubation. Glycerol may or may not be attacked. Other carbohydrates usually not attacked.

Methyl red test is positive.

Acetylmethylcarbinol not produced.

Ammonium citrate usually utilized as a sole source of carbon.

Nitrites produced from nitrates.

Phenylpyruvic acid is produced from phenylalanine, and leucine is rendered alkaline (see Proom, Jour. Gen. Microbiol., *13*, 1955, 173 and 174).

Urea not hydrolyzed, except rarely (Shaw and Clarke, *op. cit.*, 1955, 158).

Serology: One hundred and fifty-six serotypes have been recognized (Edwards and Ewing, Identification of *Enterobacteriaceae*. Burgess Pub. Co., Minneapolis, 1955, 162).

Pathogenicity: Some cultures have been established as etiological agents of gastroenteritis.

Comment: Kauffmann (*Enterobacteriaceae*. Munksgaard, Copenhagen, 2nd ed., 1954, 317) proposed the generic name *Providencia* for the organisms in the Providence Group but did not name a type species.

Source: Isolated from gastroenteritis patients.

Habitat: Found in urinary tract infections and in outbreaks and sporadic cases of diarrhoea in man.

TRIBE V. SALMONELLEAE BERGEY, BREED AND MURRAY, 1938.

(Preprint, Manual, 5th ed., 1938 (October), vi.)

Sal.mo.nel'le.ae. M.L. fem.n. *Salmonella* type genus of the tribe; *-eae* ending to denote a tribe; M.L. fem.pl.n. *Salmonelleae* the *Salmonella* tribe.

Rods that are either motile by means of peritrichous flagella or non-motile. Gram-negative. No spreading growth on ordinary (2 to 3 per cent) agar. Gelatin not liquefied (exceptions have been noted, but these are rare). Milk not peptonized. Numerous carbohydrates are attacked with the production of acid or of acid and visible gas. Lactose, sucrose and salicin are not ordinarily attacked. Acetylmethylcarbinol is not produced. Urea not hydrolyzed. Found in the bodies of warm-blooded animals, including man, and occasionally in reptiles; frequently found in the food eaten by these animals.

Key to the genera of tribe Salmonelleae.

I. Motile by means of peritrichous flagella (occasional strains of typhoids are nonmotile, and strains of *Salmonella gallinarum* are frequently non-motile). Hydrogen sulfide usually produced. Ammonium citrate normally utilized.

Genus IX. *Salmonella*, p. 368.

II. Non-motile. Hydrogen sulfide not produced. Ammonium citrate not utilized.

Genus X. *Shigella*, p. 384.

Genus IX. Salmonella *Lignières, 1900.*[*]

(Rec. de méd. vét., Sér. 8, *7*, 1900, 389.)

Sal.mo.nel'la. M.L. dim.ending *-ella*; M.L. fem.n. *Salmonella* named for D. E. Salmon, an American bacteriologist.

---

[*] Prepared by Dr. Gertrude Kalz, McGill University, Montreal, P.Q., Canada, July, 1955.

Rods which are usually motile by means of peritrichous flagella, although non-motile forms may occur. Gram-negative. Gelatin not liquefied. Indole not produced. Hydrogen sulfide production is variable. Acid is produced from glucose, mannitol, maltose and sorbitol. Gas production is usually observed (exceptions are *Salmonella typhosa* and *Salmonella gallinarum*, but gas production may also be absent in other species or serotypes). Lactose, sucrose, salicin and adonitol are not attacked. The fermentation of other carbohydrates is variable. Acetylmethylcarbinol is not produced. Methyl red test is positive. Nitrites are produced from nitrates. Ammonium citrate is usually utilized. Urea not hydrolyzed. KCN-sensitivity is negative (Möller, VI Internat. Cong. Microbiol., Rome, *2*, 1953, 316). All known forms are pathogenic for man and/or other animals.

The type species is *Salmonella choleraesuis* (Smith) Weldin.

Any organism showing the above-mentioned characters should be verified as a member of the genus *Salmonella* by antigenic analysis. For most practical purposes the use of polyvalent or group antisera will suffice. Exact antigenic characterization and bacteriophage typing for epidemiological purposes is the task of *Salmonella* centers. Although many strains of *Salmonella* are atypical, these may be looked upon as exceptions which do not invalidate the definition of the genus.

Attempts to subdivide the genus *Salmonella* into valid species from the taxonomic point of view have met with great difficulties. The Kauffman-White Schema (1955) (Edwards and Ewing, Identification of *Enterobacteriaceae*, Burgess Publishing Co., Minneapolis, 1955, 52–60) lists 343 names. It is generally agreed that the vast majority of the organisms named do not deserve species rank but should be considered as serological types. This fact has been officially recognized by the *Enterobacteriaceae* Subcommittee in the addendum to the report presented at the 6th International Congress for Microbiology, September 8, 1953, in Rome. "It is the recommendation of the Subcommittee that from the date of publication of this report all new serological types of *Salmonella* should be described by formula only and not by name." The adoption of this proposal would lead to the undesirable situation that 343 or more *Salmonella* types would be given names similar to those given to species, if not by meaning, certainly by implication, and that others would be known by antigenic formula only. The suggestion by Kauffmann and Edwards (Internat. Bull. of Bact. Nomen. and Taxon., *2*, 1952, 5) to divide the genus into three species, namely, *Salmonella choleraesuis* as type species, *Salmonella typhosa* on the basis of well recognized differences from other members and *Salmonella enterica* to serve as species for all serological types, appears too narrow and also somewhat contradictory as it practically means that two type species are chosen.

Recent observations by various workers on the transduction of antigenic characters raises the question whether such changes also occur under natural conditions and should be taken into consideration in epidemiological conclusions. It is as yet uncertain whether these changes are permanent or whether reversion to the original characters occurs. Until more exact knowledge on these factors is available, the possibility must be appreciated and taken into account in epidemiological tracings.

It is hardly possible to propose a classification for the salmonellas which can include all the factors established for the large number of types. However, the genus is composed of disease-producing organisms, and the first and foremost duty of any classification scheme is to make it workable under practical routine conditions. "Systems of nomenclature are for man's convenience and cannot hope to be wholly logical as to represent faithfully the evolution of all living things" (Andrewes, Acta Path. et Microb. Scand., *28*, 1951, 211). From this point of view it seems justified to accord species rank to those organisms which are easily identified because they are commonly encountered and/or cause rather well established syndromes.

Key to the species of genus **Salmonella.**

I. Affect both man and other animals.
  A. Occur singly but not in pairs or chains.

1. No acid or gas from arabinose.

           1. *Salmonella choleraesuis.*

2. Acid and gas from arabinose.

           2. *Salmonella typhimurium.*

B. Occurs singly, in pairs and occasionally in short chains.

           3. *Salmonella enteritidis.*

II. Affect either man or other animals.

  A. Exclusively or predominantly affect man.

    1. Acid but no gas from glucose.

           4. *Salmonella typhosa.*

    2. Acid and gas from glucose.

      a. Occur singly but not in pairs.

        b. Acid and gas from xylose.

           5. *Salmonella hirschfeldii.*

        bb. No acid or gas from xylose.

           6. *Salmonella paratyphi.*

      aa. Occurs singly and in pairs.

           7. *Salmonella schottmuelleri.*

B. Most commonly affect animals other than man.

    1. Acid and gas from glucose.

      a. Causes abortion in mares and other animals but not in sheep.

           8. *Salmonella abortivoequina.*

      aa. Causes abortion in sheep but not in other animals.

           9. *Salmonella abortusovis.*

    2. Acid but no gas from glucose.

           10. *Salmonella gallinarum.*

1. **Salmonella choleraesuis** (Smith, 1894) Weldin, 1927. (Probably not the *Bacillus* of swine plague, Klein, Report of the Medical Officer of the Local Gov. Bd., England, 1877–78, Supplement, 168; *Bacterium* of swine plague, Salmon, U. S. Dept. Agr. Bur. Anim. Ind. Ann. Rept., 1885, 212; *Bacterium* of hog cholera, Salmon, *ibid.*, 1886, 20; Bakterium der Schweinepest, Selander, Cent. f. Bakt., *3*, 1888, 361; *Pasteurella salmoni* Trevisan, I generi e le specie delle Batteriacee, 1889, 21; *Bacterium cholerae suis* Th. Smith, U. S. Dept. Agr. Bur. Anim. Ind., Bull. 6, 1894, 9; Weldin, Iowa Sta. Coll. Jour. Sci., *1*, 1927, 155.)

cho.le.rae.su'is. Gr. noun *cholera* cholera; L. noun *sus* swine, hog; M.L. gen. noun *suis* of a hog; M.L. gen. noun *choleraesuis* of hog cholera.

Rods, 0.6 to 0.7 by 2.0 to 3.0 microns, occurring singly. Motile by means of four to five peritrichous flagella. Gram-negative.

Gelatin colonies: Grayish, smooth, flat, glistening, irregular.

Gelatin stab. Flat, grayish, surface growth. No liquefaction.

Agar colonies: Grayish, moist, smooth, translucent.

Agar slant: Grayish, moist, smooth, translucent growth.

Broth: Turbid; thin pellicle; grayish white sediment.

Litmus milk: Slightly acid, becoming alkaline, opalescent, translucent to yellowish gray.

Potato: Grayish white streak becoming brownish.

Indole not produced.

Hydrogen sulfide production is variable.

Acid and gas from glucose, mannitol, maltose, sorbitol and xylose. Action on dulcitol, rhamnose and d-tartrate is variable. l-Tratrate, dl-tartrate and mucate may or may not show late fermentation. No action on lactose, sucrose, salicin, adonitol, arabinose, inositol or trehalose.

Sodium citrate is utilized.

Nitrites produced from nitrates.

Trimethylamine produced from trimethylamine oxide (Wood and Baird, Jour. Fish. Res. Board Canada, *6*, 1943, 198).

Aerobic, facultatively anaerobic.

Optimum temperature, 37° C.

Antigenic structure: 6, 7: c: 1, 5.

Pathogenicity: Lethal for mice and rabbits on subcutaneous inoculation.

Comment: Schütze et al. (Jour. of Hyg., 1934, 341) have given a special name to the hydrogen sulfide-producing variety of this species.

Habitat: The natural host is the pig, where it is an important secondary invader in the virus disease hog cholera. Does not occur as a natural pathogen in other animals. Occasionally gives rise to acute gastroenteritis and enteric fever in man.

2. **Salmonella typhimurium** (Loeffler, 1892) Castellani and Chalmers, 1919. (*Bacillus typhi murium* Loeffler, Cent. f. Bakt., *11*, 1892, 192; Castellani and Chalmers, Man. Trop. Med., 3rd ed., 1919, 939.)

ty.phi.mu'ri.um. Gr. noun *typhus* a stupor, here used in the sense of typhoid; L. noun *mus* the mouse; L. gen.noun *murium* of mice; M.L. gen.noun *typhimurium* of typhoid of mice.

See Edwards and Bruner (Kentucky Agr. Exp. Sta. Bull. 400, 1940, 43) for a discussion of this species.

Rods, 0.5 by 1.0 to 1.5 microns, occurring singly. Motile by means of peritrichous flagella. Gram-negative.

Gelatin colonies: Small, circular, grayish, granular, becoming yellowish brown.

Gelatin stab: Flat surface growth. No liquefaction.

Agar colonies: Small, circular, grayish, entire to undulate.

Agar slant: Filiform, grayish, moist, entire growth.

Broth: Turbid.

Litmus milk: Slightly acid, becoming alkaline.

Potato: Grayish white streak.

Indole not produced.

Hydrogen sulfide is produced.

Acid and gas from glucose, mannitol, maltose, sorbitol and arabinose. Mucate and l-tartrate are attacked. Action on dulcitol, inositol, rhamnose, trehalose, xylose, d-tartrate and dl-tartrate is variable. No action on lactose, sucrose, salicin or adonitol.

Sodium citrate may or may not be utilized.

Nitrites produced from nitrates.

Trimethylamine produced from trimethylamine oxide (Wood and Baird, Jour. Fish. Res. Board Canada, *6*, 1943, 198).

Aerobic, facultatively anaerobic.

Optimum temperature, 37° C.

Antigenic structure: 1, 4, 5, 12: i: 1, 2.

Comment: A variety of this organism which lacks antigen 5 has been reported by Kauffmann (Ztschr. f. Hyg., *116*, 1934, 368).

Source: Isolated during a mouse typhoid epidemic in the Hygienic Institute of Greifswald, Germany.

Habitat: Causes food poisoning in man. A natural pathogen for all warm-blooded animals. This type occurs more frequently than any other type not confined to a specific host. Also found in snakes by Hinshaw and McNeil (Amer. Jour. Vet. Res., *6*, 1945, 264).

3. **Salmonella enteritidis** (Gaertner, 1888) Castellani and Chalmers, 1919. (*Bacillus enteritidis* Gaertner, Correspond. d. Allgemein. Artzl. Verein Thuringen, *17*, 1888, 573; Castellani and Chalmers, Man. Trop. Med., 3rd ed., 1919, 930.)

en.te.ri'ti.dis. Gr. noun *enterum* gut, intestine; M.L. noun *enteritis* a disease of the intestines, enteritis; M.L. gen.noun *enteritidis* of enteritis.

Rods, 0.6 to 0.7 by 2.0 to 3.0 microns, occurring singly, in pairs and occasionally in short chains. Motile by means of peritrichous flagella. Gram-negative.

Gelatin colonies: Circular, gray, translucent, granular, entire.

Gelatin stab: Abundant surface growth. No liquefaction.

Agar colonies: Circular, gray, translucent, moist, smooth, entire. Deskowitz and Buchbinder (Jour. Bact., *29*, 1935, 294) describe a variant that produces a soluble yellow pigment where certain peptone is present in the agar. Antigenic structure not determined.

Agar slant: Grayish white, opalescent, smooth, moist, undulate growth.

Broth: Turbid; thin pellicle; grayish white sediment.

Litmus milk: Slightly acid, becoming

alkaline, opalescent, translucent to yellowish gray.

Potato: Abundant, moist, yellowish brown to brown growth.

Indole not produced.

Hydrogen sulfide is produced.

Acid and gas from glucose, mannitol, maltose, sorbitol, xylose, rhamnose and trehalose. Fermentation of arabinose, dulcicitol, l-tartrate, d-tartrate, dl-tartrate and mucate is variable. No action on lactose, sucrose, salicin, adonitol or inositol.

Sodium citrate may or may not be utilized.

Nitrites produced from nitrates.

Trimethylamine produced from trimethylamine oxide (Wood and Baird, Jour. Fish. Res. Board Canada, 6, 1943, 198).

Aerobic, facultatively anaerobic.

Optimum temperature, 37° C.

Antigenic structure: 1, 9, 12: g, m: —.

Comment: Varieties of this species have been recognized on the basis of differences in biochemical behavior.

Source: Isolated from feces in an epidemic of meat poisoning at Frankenhausen, Germany.

Habitat: Widely distributed, occurring in man. Also found in domestic and wild animals, particularly rodents.

4. **Salmonella typhosa** (Zopf, 1884) White, 1930. (Bacillus des Abdominal-Typhus, Eberth, Arch. f. path. Anat., *81*, 1880, 58; also see *ibid.*, *83*, 1881, 486; Typhus Bacillen, Gaffky, Mitteil. a. d. kaiserl. Gesundheitsamte, *2*, 1884, 372; *Bacterium typhosum* Zopf, Die Spaltpilze, 2 Aufl., 1884, 90; *Bacillus typhosus* Zopf, Die Spaltpilze, 3 Aufl., 1885, 126; not *Bacillus typhosus* Klebs, Hand. d. path. Anat., 1880; also see Arch. f. exp. Path. u. Pharmac., *13*, 1881, 392; *Bacillus typhi* Schroeter, in Cohn, Kryptogamen-Flora v. Schlesien, *3*, 1886, 165; *Bacillus typhi abdominalis* Flügge, Die Mikroorganismen, 2 Aufl., 1886, 198; *Bacterium (Eberthella) typhi* Buchanan, Jour. Bact., *3*, 1918, 53 (type species of genus *Eberthella* Buchanan, *loc. cit.*); *Salmonella typhi* Warren and Scott, Jour. of Hyg., *29*, 1930, 416; White, Jour. of Hyg., *29*, 1930, 443.)

ty.pho′sa. Gr. noun *typhus* a stupor, here

used in the sense of typhoid; M.L. adj. *typhosus* pertaining to typhoid.

Rods, 0.6 to 0.7 by 2.0 to 3.0 microns, occurring singly, in pairs and occasionally in short chains. Motile by means of peritrichous flagella; sometimes non-motile. Gram-negative.

Gelatin colonies: Grayish, transparent to opaque, with leaf-like surface markings.

Gelatin stab: Thin, white, opalescent growth. No liquefaction.

Agar colonies: Grayish, transparent to opaque.

Agar slant: Whitish gray, glistening, echinulate, entire to undulate growth.

Broth: Turbid; moderate sediment; delicate pellicle in old cultures.

Litmus milk: Slight, transient acidity, followed by a return to neutral or to slight alkalinity.

Potato: Delicate, moist, slightly spreading, barely visible growth.

Indole not produced.

Hydrogen sulfide usually produced.

Acid but no gas from glucose, mannitol, maltose, sorbitol and trehalose. Fermentation of arabinose, dulcitol, xylose, inositol and d-tartrate is variable. No action on lactose, sucrose, salicin, adonitol, rhamnose, l-tartrate or dl-tartrate. Mucate may or may not show late fermentation.

Sodium citrate may or may not be utilized.

Nitrites produced from nitrates.

Trimethylamine produced from trimethylamine oxide (Wood and Baird, Jour. Fish. Res. Board Canada, 6, 1943, 198).

Aerobic, facultatively anaerobic.

Optimum temperature, 37° C.

Antigenic structure: 9, 12, (Vi): $d_1 : d_2$. By means of Vi phages, distinct types can be recognized which are of epidemiological importance.

Pathogenic for laboratory animals on parenteral inoculation.

Source: Isolated from human cases of typhoid fever, from contaminated water and from foods. Isolated once from a chicken by Henning, Onderstepoort, South Africa.

Habitat: The cause of typhoid fever.

5. **Salmonella hirschfeldii** Weldin, 1927. (*Bacillus paratyphosus* β5, Weil, Wien. klin.

Wochnschr., *30*, 1917, 1061; Paratyphoid C
bacillus, Hirschfeld, Lancet, *1*, 1919, 296;
Weldin, Iowa State Coll. Jour. Sci., *1*, 1927,
161.)

hirsch.fel′di.i. M.L. gen.noun *hirschfeldii* of Hirschfeld; named for L. Hirschfeld, who worked with this organism.

Rods, 0.3 to 0.5 by 1.0 to 2.5 microns, occurring singly. Motile by means of peritrichous flagella. Gram-negative.

Gelatin colonies: Grayish, smooth, flat,
glistening, irregular.

Gelatin stab: Flat, grayish surface
growth. No liquefaction.

Agar colonies: Grayish, moist, smooth,
translucent.

Broth: Turbid.

Litmus milk: Slightly acid, becoming
alkaline.

Indole not produced.

Hydrogen sulfide produced.

Acid and gas from glucose, mannitol,
maltose, sorbitol, dulcitol and xylose. d-Tartrate and l-tartrate are attacked. Fermentation of arabinose, rhamnose and trehalose is variable. No action on lactose,
sucrose, salicin, adonitol, inositol, dl-tartrate or mucate.

Sodium citrate is utilized.

Nitrites produced from nitrates.

Trimethylamine produced from trimethylamine oxide (Wood and Baird, Jour. Fish.
Res. Board Canada, *6*, 1943, 198).

Aerobic, facultatively anaerobic.

Optimum temperature, 37° C.

Antigenic structure: 6, 7, Vi: c, 1, 5.

Source: Isolated from cases of enteric
fever in man.

Habitat: A natural pathogen of man
causing enteric fever.

6. Salmonella paratyphi (Kayser, 1902)
Castellani and Chalmers, 1919. (*Bacterium
paratyphi* Typus A, Brion and Kayser,
Münch. med. Wochnschr., *49*, 1902, 611;
Bacterium paratyphi Kayser, Cent. f. Bakt.,
I Abt., Orig., *31*, 1902, 426; Castellani and
Chalmers, Man. Trop. Med., 3rd ed., 1919,
938.)

pa.ra.ty′phi. Gr. prep. *para* alongside of,
therefore resembling; Gr. noun *typhus* a
stupor, here meaning typhoid fever, the
typhus abdominalis; M.L. noun *paratyphus*

paratyphoid; M.L. gen.noun *paratyphi* of
paratyphoid.

Rods, 0.6 by 3.0 to 4.0 microns, occurring
singly. Usually motile by means of peritrichous flagella. Gram-negative.

Gelatin colonies: Bluish gray, homogeneous, smooth, glistening, entire to slightly
undulate.

Gelatin stab: Fair surface growth. No
liquefaction.

Agar colonies: Grayish, homogeneous,
smooth, glistening, entire to slightly undulate.

Agar slant: Filiform, grayish, smooth,
glistening growth.

Broth: Turbid; slight, grayish sediment.

Litmus milk: Slightly acid.

Potato: Limited, dirty white streak.

Indole not produced.

Hydrogen sulfide not produced by most
strains.

Acid and gas from glucose, mannitol,
maltose, sorbitol, arabinose and trehalose.
Fermentation of dulcitol and rhamnose is
variable. No action on lactose, sucrose,
salicin, adonitol, xylose, inositol, l-tartrate,
d-tartrate, dl-tartrate or mucate.

Sodium citrate not utilized.

Nitrites produced from nitrates.

Trimethylamine produced from trimethylamine oxide (Wood and Baird, Jour. Fish.
Res. Board Canada, *6*, 1943, 198).

Aerobic, facultatively anaerobic.

Optimum temperature, 37° C.

Antigenic structure: 1, 2, 12: a: —.

Source: Isolated from cases of enteric
fever in man.

Habitat: A natural pathogen of man causing enteric fever. Not known to be a natural
pathogen of other animals.

7. Salmonella schottmuelleri (Winslow et al., 1919) Bergey et al., 1923. (Bacilli
paratyphique, Achard and Bensaude Soc.
méd. des Hôp. de Paris, *13*, 1896, 679; *Bacillus paratyphi alcaligenes* Schottmüller,
Deutsche med. Wochnschr., *32*, 1900, 511;
Bacterium paratyphi Typus B, Brion and
Kayser, Münch. med. Wochnschr., *49*, 1902,
611; *Bacillus schottmulleri* Winslow, Kligler
and Rothberg, Jour. Bact., *4*, 1919, 479;
Bergey et al., Manual, 1st ed., 1923, 213.)

schott.muel′le.ri. M.L. gen.noun *schott-*

muelleri of Schottmüller; named for Prof.
H. Schottmüller, who isolated this organism
in 1899.

Rods, 0.6 to 0.7 by 2.0 to 3.0 microns,
occurring singly and in pairs. Usually motile
by means of peritrichous flagella. Gram-
negative.

Gelatin stab: No liquefaction.

Agar colonies: Small, circular, bluish
gray, transparent, homogeneous, entire to
undulate.

Broth: Turbid; thin, gray pellicle and
sediment. Fecal odor.

Litmus milk: Slightly acid, becoming
alkaline.

Potato: Grayish white, viscous growth.

Indole not produced.

Hydrogen sulfide is produced.

Acid and gas from glucose, mannitol,
maltose, sorbitol, arabinose, xylose and
trehalose. Mucate and l-tartrate are attacked. Fermentation of dulcitol, inositol,
rhamnose and dl-tartrate is variable. No
action on lactose, sucrose, salicin, adonitol
or d-tartrate.

Sodium citrate may or may not be utilized.

Nitrites produced from nitrates.

Trimethylamine produced from trimethylamine oxide (Wood and Baird, Jour. Fish.
Res. Board Canada, *6*, 1943, 198).

Aerobic, facultatively anaerobic.

Optimum temperature, 37° C.

Antigenic structure: 1, 4, 5, 12: b: 1, 2.

Source: Isolated from cases of enteric
fever in man. Not a natural pathogen of
other animals.

Habitat: A natural pathogen of man
causing enteric fever. Also found rarely
in cattle, sheep, swine, lower primates and
chickens.

8. **Salmonella abortivoequina** (Good
and Corbett, 1916) Bergey et al., 1923. (*Bacillus abortivus equinus* Good and Corbett,
Jour. Inf. Dis., *13*, 1913, 53; *Bacillus abortus
equi* Meyer and Boerner, Jour. Med. Res.,
29, 1913, 330; *Bacillus abortivo-equinus* Good
and Corbett, Jour. Inf. Dis., *18*, 1916, 586;
Bacillus abortus equinus Weiss and Rice,
Jour. Med. Res., *35*, 1917, 403; *Bacillus
abortivus* Winslow, Kligler and Rothberg,
Jour. Bact., *4*, 1919, 477; Bergey et al., Man-

ual, 1st ed., 1923, 217; *Salmonella abortus-
equi* Bergey et al., Manual, 2nd ed., 1925,
236.)

a.bor.ti.vo.e.qui'na. L. adj. *abortivus*
pertaining to abortion; L. adj. *equinus* pertaining to horses; M.L. adj. *abortivoequinus*
pertaining to aborting horses.

Rods, 0.2 to 0.5 by 1.5 microns, occurring
singly, occasionally in pairs. Motile by
means of peritrichous flagella. Gram-negative.

Gelatin: No liquefaction.

Indole not produced.

Hydrogen sulfide not produced.

Acid and gas from glucose, mannitol,
maltose, sorbitol, xylose, arabinose and
rhamnose. l-Tartrate and dl-tartrate are
attacked. Fermentation of dulcitol and
trehalose is variable. l-Tartrate may or may
not show late fermentation. No action on
lactose, sucrose, salicin, adonitol, inositol
or mucate.

Sodium citrate is utilized.

Nitrites produced from nitrates.

Trimethylamine produced from trimethylamine oxide (Wood and Baird, Jour. Fish.
Res. Board Canada, *6*, 1943, 198).

Antigenic structure: 4, 12: —, e, n, x.

Isolated from the afterbirth of mares that
had aborted.

Habitat: A natural pathogen of mares,
causing abortion; also infectious for guinea
pigs, rabbits, goats and cows, producing
abortion.

9. **Salmonella abortusovis** (Lovell,
1931) Schütze et al., 1934. (*Bacillus para-
typhi abortus ovis* Schermer and Ehrlich,
Cent. f. Bakt., I Abt., Ref., *73*, 1922, 252;
Bacterium abortus ovis Lovell, Jour. Path.
and Bact., *34*, 1931, 13; Schütze, Jordan,
Kauffmann, Scott, White and St. John-
Brooks, Jour. of Hyg., *34*, 1934, 340.)

a.bor.tus.o'vis. L. noun *abortus* abortion;
L. gen.noun *abortus* of abortion; L. noun
ovis a sheep; L. gen.noun *ovis* of a sheep;
M.L. gen.noun *abortusovis* of abortion of a
sheep.

Rods, 0.6 by 3.0 to 4.0 microns, occurring
singly. Usually motile by means of peritrichous flagella. Gram-negative.

Gelatin: No liquefaction.

Indole not produced.

Hydrogen sulfide production is variable. Acid and gas from glucose, mannitol, maltose and sorbitol. d-Tartrate is attacked. Fermentation of arabinose, dulcitol, rhamnose and xylose is variable. l-Tartrate may or may not show and dl-tartrate usually does not show late fermentation. No action on lactose, sucrose, salicin, adonitol, inositol, trehalose or mucate.

Sodium citrate is utilized.

Trimethylamine produced from trimethylamine oxide (Wood and Baird, Jour. Fish. Res. Board Canada, *6*, 1943, 198).

Antigenic structure: 4, 12: c: 1, 6.

Source: Isolated from cases of abortion in sheep.

Habitat: Not known to infect any animal other than sheep.

10. **Salmonella gallinarum** (Klein, 1889) Bergey et al., 1925. (*Bacillus gallinarum* Klein, Cent. f. Bakt., *5*, 1889, 689; *Bacterium pullorum* Rettger, Jour. Med. Res., *21* (N.S. *16*), 1909, 117; *Salmonella pullorum* Bergey et al., Manual, 1st ed., 1923, 218; Bergey et al., Manual, 2nd ed., 1925, 236; *Salmonella gallinarum-pullorum* Taylor J., Bensted, Boyd, Carpenter, Dowson, Lovell, Taylor, E. W., Thornton, Wilson and Shaw, Internat. Bull. of Bact. Nomen. and Taxon., *2*, 1952, 140.)

gal.li.na′rum. L. noun *gallina* a hen; L. gen. pl. noun *gallinarum* of hens.

Rods, 0.3 to 0.6 by 0.8 to 2.5 microns, with rounded ends, occurring singly or, in blood, in short chains. Usually non-motile. Gram-negative.

Gelatin colonies: Small, grayish white, finely granular, circular entire.

Gelatin stab: Slight, grayish white surface growth with slight, grayish, filiform growth in stab. No liquefaction.

Agar colonies: Moist, grayish, circular, entire.

Agar slant: Thin, gray, irregular, moist, glistening streak.

Broth: Turbid; heavy, flocculent sediment.

Litmus milk: Reaction unchanged, becoming translucent. No coagulation.

Potato: Slight, grayish growth.

Indole not produced.

Hydrogen sulfide production is variable.

Acid but no gas from glucose, mannitol, maltose and sorbitol. Action on dulcitol, rhamnose, trehalose, xylose, d-tartrate, l-tartrate and mucate is variable. dl-Tartrate may or may not show late fermentation. No action on lactose, sucrose, salicin, adonitol or inositol.

Sodium citrate may or may not be utilized.

Nitrites produced from nitrates.

Trimethylamine produced from trimethylamine oxide (Wood and Baird, Jour. Fish. Res. Board Canada, *6*, 1943, 198).

Aerobic, facultatively anaerobic.

Optimum temperature, 37° C.

Antigenic structure: 1, 9, 12: —, —.

Comment: A variety of this species which differs from the parent strain in its slow fermentation of maltose and by its inability to ferment d-tartrate and to produce hydrogen sulfide has been reported by Kauffmann (Zent. f. Bakt., I Abt., Orig., *132*, 1934, 337).

Source: Isolated from chickens and other birds as well as from calves, hogs, rabbits and man.

Habitat: The causative agent of fowl typhoid (clearly to be distinguished from fowl cholera) and identical with Moore's infectious leukemia of fowls. Causes white diarrhoea in young chicks. Infectious for rabbits and all poultry, canaries and certain wild birds (quail, grouse, pheasant) by feeding or by inoculation. Occasionally produces food poisoning or gastroenteritis in man (Mitchell, Garlock and Broh-Kahn, Jour. Inf. Dis., *79*, 1946, 57).

The following table gives exact antigenic analyses of the 343 *Salmonella* serotypes which were recognized by 1955 (serotypes which have since been recognized are not included here). This table affords additional information for those who are equipped to carry identifications of antigenic patterns beyond the broad groupings. For details of preparations of antigens and of group- and single-factor antisera, the extensive studies of Kauffmann (*Enterobacteriaceae*, 2nd ed., Ejnar Munksgaard, Copenhagen, 1954) should be consulted.

THE KAUFFMANN-WHITE SCHEMA (1955)

Diagnostic Antigenic Schema (according to Edwards and Ewing, Identification of *Enterobacteriaceae*. Burgess Publ. Co., Minneapolis, 1955, 52–60).

Reprinted by permission.

Group	No.	Serotype	Somatic Antigens	Flagellar Antigens	
				Phase 1	Phase 2
A	1	*Salmonella paratyphi*	1, 2, 12	a	—
	2	*Salmonella kisangani*	1, 4, 5, 12	a	1, 2
	3	*Salmonella hessarek*	4, 12	a	1, 5
	4	*Salmonella fulica*	4, 5, 12	a	1, 5
	5	*Salmonella arechavaleta*	4, 5, 12	a	1, 7
	6	*Salmonella bispebjerg*	1, 4, 12	a	e, n, x
	7	*Salmonella abortivoequina*	4, 12	—	e, n, x
	8	*Salmonella tinda*	1, 4, 12, 27	a	e, n, z_{15}
	9	*Salmonella schottmuelleri*	1, 4, 5, 12	b	1, 2
	10	*Salmonella limete*	1, 4, 12, 27	b	1, 5
	11	*Salmonella schleissheim*	4, 12, 27	b, z_{12}	—
	12	*Salmonella abony*	1, 4, 5, 12	b	e, n, x
	13	*Salmonella abortusbovis*	1, 4, 12, 27	b	e, n, x
	14	*Salmonella wagenia*	1, 4, 12, 27	b	e, n, z_{15}
	15	*Salmonella wien*	4, 12	b	1, w
	16	*Salmonella abortusovis*	4, 12	c	1, 6
	17	*Salmonella altendorf*	4, 12	c	1, 7
	18	*Salmonella bury*	4, 12, 27	c	z_6
	19	*Salmonella stanley*	4, 5, 12	d	1, 2
	20	*Salmonella cairo*	1, 4, 12, 27	d	1, 2
	21	*Salmonella schwarzengrund*	1, 4, 12, 27	d	1, 7
B	22	*Salmonella sarajane*	4, 12, 27	d	e, n, x
	23	*Salmonella duisburg*	4, 12	d	e, n, z_{15}
	24	*Salmonella salinatis*	4, 12	d, e, h	d, e, n, z_{15}
	25	*Salmonella saintpaul*	1, 4, 5, 12	e, h	1, 2
	26	*Salmonella reading*	4, 12	e, h	1, 5
	27	*Salmonella kaposvar*	4, 5, 12	e, (h)	1, 5
	28	*Salmonella kaapstad*	4, 12	e, h	1, 7
	29	*Salmonella chester*	4, 5, 12	e, h	e, n, x
	30	*Salmonella sandiego*	4, 5, 12	e, h	e, n, z_{15}
	31	*Salmonella derby*	1, 4, 12	f, g	—
	32	*Salmonella essen*	4, 12	g, m	—
	33	*Salmonella hato*	4, 5, 12	g, m, s	—
	34	*Salmonella california*	4, 12	g, m, t	—
	35	*Salmonella kingston*	1, 4, 12, 27	g, s, t	—
	36	*Salmonella budapest*	1, 4, 12	g, t	—
	37	*Salmonella typhimurium*	1, 4, 5, 12	i	1, 2
	38	*Salmonella sp.*	1, 4, 12, 27	i	1, w
	39	*Salmonella texas*	4, 5, 12	k	e, n, z_{15}

Group	No.	Serotype	Somatic Antigens	Flagellar Antigens Phase 1	Flagellar Antigens Phase 2
	40	*Salmonella bredeney*	1, 4, 12, 27	l, v	1, 7
	41	*Salmonella kimuenza*	1, 4, 12, 27	l, v	e, n, x
	42	*Salmonella brandenburg*	4, 12	l, v	e, n, z_{15}
	43	*Salmonella banana*	4, 5, 12	m, t	—
	44	*Salmonella heidelberg*	4, 5, 12	r	1, 2
	45	*Salmonella coeln*	4, 5, 12	y	1, 2
	46	*Salmonella ball*	1, 4, 12	y	e, n, x
B	47	*Salmonella kiambu*	4, 12	z	1, 5
	48	*Salmonella indiana*	4, 12	z	1, 7
	49	*Salmonella stanleyville*	4, 5, 12	z_4 , z_{23}	1, 2
	50	*Salmonella haifa*	1, 4, 5, 12	z_{10}	1, 2
	51	*Salmonella ituri*	1, 4, 12	z_{10}	1, 5
	52	*Salmonella brancaster*	1, 4, 12	z_{29}	—
	53	*Salmonella sanjuan*	6, 7	a	1, 5
	54	*Salmonella austin*	6, 7	a	1, 7
	55	*Salmonella oslo*	6, 7	a	e, n, x
	56	*Salmonella denver*	6, 7	a	e, n, z_{15}
	57	*Salmonella brazzaville*	6, 7	b	1, 2
	58	*Salmonella edinburg*	6, 7	b	1, 5
	59	*Salmonella georgia*	6, 7	b	e, n, z_{15}
	60	*Salmonella leopoldville*	6, 7	b	z_6
	61	*Salmonella choleraesuis*	6, 7	c	1, 5
	62	*Salmonella hirschfeldii*	6, 7, Vi	c	1, 5
	63	*Salmonella typhisuis*	6, 7	c	1, 5
	64	*Salmonella decatur*	6, 7	c	1, 5
	65	*Salmonella birkenhead*	6, 7	c	1, 6
	66	*Salmonella sp.*	6, 7	c	e, n, z_{15}
	67	*Salmonella mission*	6, 7	d	1, 5
	68	*Salmonella amersfoort*	6, 7	d	e, n, x
	69	*Salmonella livingston*	6, 7	d	l, w
C_1	70	*Salmonella lomita*	6, 7	e, h	1, 5
	71	*Salmonella norwich*	6, 7	e, h	1, 6
	72	*Salmonella braenderup*	6, 7	e, h	e, n, z_{15}
	73	*Salmonella montevideo*	6, 7	g, m, s	—
	74	*Salmonella menston*	6, 7	g, s, t	—
	75	*Salmonella garoli*	6, 7	i	1, 6
	76	*Salmonella thompson*	6, 7	k	1, 5
	77	*Salmonella daytona*	6, 7	k	1, 6
	78	*Salmonella singapore*	6, 7	k	e, n, x
	79	*Salmonella concord*	6, 7	l, v	1, 2
	80	*Salmonella irumu*	6, 7	l, v	1, 5
	81	*Salmonella bonn*	6, 7	l, v	e, n, x
	82	*Salmonella potsdam*	6, 7	l, v	e, n, z_{15}
	83	*Salmonella colorado*	6, 7	l, w	1, 5
	84	*Salmonella jerusalem*	6, 7	l, w	z_{10}
	85	*Salmonella nessziona*	6, 7	l, z_{13}	1, 5
	86	*Salmonella makiso*	6, 7	l, z_{28}	z_6
	87	*Salmonella oranienburg*	6, 7	m, t	—
	88	*Salmonella virchow*	6, 7	r	1, 2

THE KAUFFMANN-WHITE SCHEMA (1955)—*Continued*

Group	No.	Serotype	Somatic Antigens	Flagellar Antigens	
				Phase 1	Phase 2
	89	*Salmonella infantis*	6, 7	r	1, 5
	90	*Salmonella colindale*	6, 7	r	1, 7
	91	*Salmonella papuana*	6, 7	r	e, n, z_{15}
	92	*Salmonella richmond*	6, 7	y	1, 2
	93	*Salmonella bareilly*	6, 7	y	1, 5
C_1	94	*Salmonella hartford*	6, 7	y	e, n, x
	95	*Salmonella mikawashima*	6, 7	y	e, n, z_{15}
	96	*Salmonella aequatoria*	6, 7	z_4 , z_{23}	e, n, z_{15}
	97	*Salmonella kralendyk*	6, 7	z_4 , z_{24}	—
	98	*Salmonella eschweiler*	6, 7	z_{10}	1, 6
	99	*Salmonella mbandaka*	6, 7	z_{10}	e, n, z_{15}
	100	*Salmonella tennessee*	6, 7	z_{29}	—
	101	*Salmonella lille*	6, 7	z_{38}	—
	102	*Salmonella curacao*	6, 8	a	1, 6
	103	*Salmonella narashino*	6, 8	a	e, n, x
	104	*Salmonella nagoya*	6, 8	b	1, 5
	105	*Salmonella gatuni*	6, 8	b	e, n, x
	106	*Salmonella shipley*	6, 8	b	e, n, z_{15}
	107	*Salmonella banalia*	6, 8	b	z_6
	108	*Salmonella utah*	6, 8	c	1, 5
	109	*Salmonella bronx*	6, 8	c	1, 6
	110	*Salmonella belem*	6, 8	c	e, n, x
	111	*Salmonella quiniela*	6, 8	c	e, n, z_{15}
	112	*Salmonella muenchen*	6, 8	d	1, 2
	113	*Salmonella manhattan*	6, 8	d	1, 5
	114	*Salmonella newport*	6, 8	e, h	1, 2
	115	*Salmonella kottbus*	6, 8	e, h	1, 5
	116	*Salmonella lindenburg*	6, 8	i	1, 2
	117	*Salmonella takoradi*	6, 8	i	1, 5
C_2	118	*Salmonella bonariensis*	6, 8	i	e, n, x
	119	*Salmonella litchfield*	6, 8	l, v	1, 2
	120	*Salmonella manchester*	6, 8	l, v	1, 7
	121	*Salmonella fayed*	6, 8	l, w	1, 2
	122	*Salmonella bovismorbificans*	6, 8	r	1, 5
	123	*Salmonella hidalgo*	6, 8	r	e, n, z_{15}
	124	*Salmonella tananarive*	6, 8	y	1, 5
	125	*Salmonella praha*	6, 8	y	e, n, z_{15}
	126	*Salmonella sp.*	6, 8	z_4 , z_{23}	—
	127	*Salmonella duesseldorf*	6, 8	z_4 , z_{24}	—
	128	*Salmonella tallahassee*	6, 8	z_4 , z_{32}	—
	129	*Salmonella hadar*	6, 8	z_{10}	e, n, x
	130	*Salmonella glostrup*	6, 8	z_{10}	e, n, z_{15}
	131	*Salmonella sanga*	(8)	b	1, 7
	132	*Salmonella virginia*	(8)	d	—
	133	*Salmonella emek*	(8), 20	g, m, s	—
	134	*Salmonella kentucky*	(8), 20	i	z_6

THE KAUFFMANN-WHITE SCHEMA (1955)—*Continued*

Group	No.	Serotype	Somatic Antigens	Flagellar Antigens	
				Phase 1	Phase 2
C₂	135	*Salmonella amherstiana*	(8)	l, (v)	1, 6
	136	*Salmonella hindmarsh*	(8)	r	1, 5
	137	*Salmonella corvallis*	(8), 20	z_4 , z_{23}	—
	138	*Salmonella albany*	(8), 20	z_4 , z_{24}	—
D	139	*Salmonella miami*	1, 9, 12	a	1, 5
	140	*Salmonella sendai*	1, 9, 12	a	1, 5
	141	*Salmonella saarbruecken*	1, 9, 12	a	1, 7
	142	*Salmonella lomalinda*	9, 12	a	e, n, x
	143	*Salmonella durban*	9, 12	a	e, n, z_{15}
	144	*Salmonella onarimon*	1, 9, 12	b	1, 2
	145	*Salmonella alabama*	9, 12	c	e, n, z_{15}
	146	*Salmonella typhosa*	9, 12, Vi	d	—
	147	*Salmonella ndolo*	9, 12	d	1, 5
	148	*Salmonella strasbourg*	9 . . .	d	1, 7
	149	*Salmonella zega*	9, 12	d	z_6
	150	*Salmonella jaffna*	9, 12	d	z_{35}
	151	*Salmonella eastbourne*	1, 9, 12	e, h	1, 5
	152	*Salmonella israel*	9, 12	e, h	e, n, z_{15}
	153	*Salmonella berta*	9, 12	f, g, t	—
	154	*Salmonella enteritidis*	1, 9, 12	g, m	—
	155	*Salmonella blegdam*	9, 12	g, m, q	—
	156	*Salmonella pensacola*	9, 12	g, m, t	—
	157	*Salmonella dublin*	1, 9, 12	g, p	—
	158	*Salmonella rostock*	1, 9, 12	g, p, u	—
	159	*Salmonella moscow*	9, 12	g, q	—
	160	*Salmonella neasden*	9, 12	g, s, t	e, n, x
	161	*Salmonella seremban*	9, 12	i	1, 5
	162	*Salmonella marylebone*	9, 12	k	1, 2
	163	*Salmonella claibornei*	1, 9, 12	k	1, 5
	164	*Salmonella mendoza*	9, 12	l, v	1, 2
	165	*Salmonella panama*	1, 9, 12	l, v	1, 5
	166	*Salmonella kapemba*	9, 12	l, v	1, 7
	167	*Salmonella goettingen*	9, 12	l, v	e, n, z_{15}
	168	*Salmonella daressalaam*	1, 9, 12	l, w	e, n
	169	*Salmonella napoli*	1, 9, 12	l, z_{13}	e, n, x
	170	*Salmonella javiana*	1, 9, 12	l, z_{28}	1, 5
	171	*Salmonella shoreditch*	9, 12	r	e, n, z_{15}
	172	*Salmonella haarlem*	9 . . .	z	e, n, x
	173	*Salmonella wangata*	9, 12	z_4 , z_{23}	—
	174	*Salmonella portland*	9, 12	z_{10}	1, 5
	175	*Salmonella canastel*	9, 12	z_{29}	1, 5
	176	*Salmonella sp.*	9, 12	z_{35}	z_6
	177	*Salmonella fresno*	9, 12	z_{38}	—
	178	*Salmonella gallinarum*	1, 9, 12	—	—
	179	*Salmonella pullorum*	9, 12	—	—

The Kauffmann-White Schema (1955)—*Continued*

Group	No.	Serotype	Somatic Antigens	Flagellar Antigens Phase 1	Phase 2
	180	*Salmonella oxford*	3, 10	a	1, 7
	181	*Salmonella butantan*	3, 10	b	1, 5
	182	*Salmonella shangani*	3, 10	d	1, 5
	183	*Salmonella vejle*	3, 10	e, h	1, 2
	184	*Salmonella muenster*	3, 10	e, h	1, 5
	185	*Salmonella anatum*	3, 10	e, h	1, 6
	186	*Salmonella nyborg*	3, 10	e, h	1, 7
	187	*Salmonella newlands*	3, 10	e, h	e, n, x
	188	*Salmonella meleagridis*	3, 10	e, h	l, w
	189	*Salmonella westhampton*	3, 10	g, s, t	—
	190	*Salmonella zanzibar*	3, 10	k	1, 5
	191	*Salmonella nchanga*	3, 10	l, v	1, 2
	192	*Salmonella london*	3, 10	l, v	1, 6
E_1	193	*Salmonella give*	3, 10	l, v	1, 7
	194	*Salmonella clerkenwell*	3, 10	l, w	z
	195	*Salmonella uganda*	3, 10	l, z_{13}	1, 5
	196	*Salmonella elizabethville*	3, 10	r	1, 7
	197	*Salmonella simi*	3, 10	r	e, n, z_{15}
	198	*Salmonella weltevreden*	3, 10	r	z_6
	199	*Salmonella amager*	3, 10	y	1, 2
	200	*Salmonella orion*	3, 10	y	1, 5
	201	*Salmonella bolton*	3, 10	y	e, n, z_{15}
	202	*Salmonella stockholm*	3, 10	y	z_6
	203	*Salmonella lexington*	3, 10	z_{10}	1, 5
	204	*Salmonella coquilhatville*	3, 10	z_{10}	1, 7
	205	*Salmonella cairina*	3, 10	z_{35}	z_6
	206	*Salmonella macallen*	3, 10	z_{36}	—
	207	*Salmonella goerlitz*	3, 15	e, h	1, 2
	208	*Salmonella newington*	3, 15	e, h	1, 6
	209	*Salmonella selandia*	3, 15	e, h	1, 7
	210	*Salmonella cambridge*	3, 15	e, h	l, w
E_2	211	*Salmonella newbrunswick*	3, 15	l, v	1, 7
	212	*Salmonella kinshasa*	3, 15	l, z_{13}	1, 5
	213	*Salmonella tuebingen*	3, 15	y	1, 2
	214	*Salmonella binza*	3, 15	y	1, 5
	215	*Salmonella manila*	3, 15	z_{10}	1, 5
	216	*Salmonella minneapolis*	(3), (15), 34	e, h	1, 6
	217	*Salmonella canoga*	(3), (15), 34	g, s, t	—
E_3	218	*Salmonella thomasville*	(3), (15), 34	y	1, 5
	219	*Salmonella illinois*	(3), (15), 34	z_{10}	1, 5
	220	*Salmonella harrisonburg*	(3), (15), 34	z_{10}	1, 6
	221	*Salmonella chittagong*	(1), 3, 10, (19)	b	z_{35}
E_4	222	*Salmonella niloese*	1, 3, 19	d	z_6
	223	*Salmonella senftenberg*	1, 3, 19	g, s, t	—

THE KAUFFMANN-WHITE SCHEMA (1955)—*Continued*

Group	No.	Serotype	Somatic Antigens	Flagellar Antigens	
				Phase 1	Phase 2
E₄	224	*Salmonella taksony*	1, 3, 19	i	z_6
	225	*Salmonella krefeld*	1, 3, 19	l, w	y
	226	*Salmonella schoeneberg*	1, 3, 19	z	e, n, z_{15}
	227	*Salmonella simsbury*	1, 3, 19	z_{27}	—
F	228	*Salmonella marseille*	11	a	1, 5
	229	*Salmonella luciana*	11	a	e, n, z_{15}
	230	*Salmonella pharr*	11	b	e, n, z_{15}
	231	*Salmonella chandans*	11	d	e, n, x
	232	*Salmonella chingola*	11	e, h	1, 2
	233	*Salmonella aberdeen*	11	i	1, 2
	234	*Salmonella veneziana*	11	i	e, n, x
	235	*Salmonella pretoria*	11	k	1, 2
	236	*Salmonella abaetetube*	11	k	1, 5
	237	*Salmonella maracaibo*	11	l, v	1, 5
	238	*Salmonella senegal*	11	r	1, 5
	239	*Salmonella rubislaw*	11	r	e, n, x
	240	*Salmonella solt*	11	y	1, 5
	241	*Salmonella sp.*	11	z_{10}	1, 2
	242	*Salmonella telhashomer*	11	z_{10}	e, n, x
G	243	*Salmonella atlanta*	13, 23	b	—
	244	*Salmonella ibadan*	13, 22	b	1, 5
	245	*Salmonella mississippi*	1, 13, 23	b	1, 5
	246	*Salmonella mishmarhaemek*	1, 13, 23	d	1, 5
	247	*Salmonella friedenau*	13, 22	d	1, 6
	248	*Salmonella grumpensis*	13, 23	d	1, 7
	249	*Salmonella telelkebir*	13, 23	d	e, n, z_{15}
	250	*Salmonella wichita*	1 13, 23	d	z_{37}
	251	*Salmonella habana*	1, 13, 23	f, g	—
	252	*Salmonella sp.*	13, 23	g, s, (t)	—
	253	*Salmonella borbeck*	13, 22	l, v	1, 6
	254	*Salmonella worthington*	1, 13, 23	l, w	z
	255	*Salmonella worcester*	1, 13, 23	m, t	e, n, x
	256	*Salmonella nachshonim*	1, 13, 23	z	1, 5
	257	*Salmonella poona*	13, 22	z	1, 6
	258	*Salmonella bristol*	13, 22	z	1, 7
	259	*Salmonella delplata*	1, 13, 23	z_4, z_{23}	—
	260	*Salmonella cubana*	1, 13, 23	z_{29}	—
	261	*Salmonella clifton*	13, 22	z_{29}	1, 5
H	262	*Salmonella heves*	6, 14, 24	d	1, 5
	263	*Salmonella florida*	(1), 6, 14, 25	d	1, 7
	264	*Salmonella albuquerque*	6, 14, 24	d	z_6
	265	*Salmonella onderstepoort*	(1), 6, 14, 25	e, h	1, 5
	266	*Salmonella caracas*	(1), 6, 14, 25	g, m, s	—
	267	*Salmonella boecker*	6, 14	l, v	1, 7

THE KAUFFMANN-WHITE SCHEMA (1955)—*Continued*

Group	No.	Serotype	Somatic Antigens	Flagellar Antigens	
				Phase 1	Phase 2
H	268	*Salmonella horsham*	(1), 6, 14, 25	l, v	e, n, x
	269	*Salmonella madelia*	(1), 6, 14, 25	y	1, 7
	270	*Salmonella carrau*	6, 14, 24	y	1, 7
	271	*Salmonella homosassa*	(1), 6, 14, 25	z	1, 5
	272	*Salmonella sundsvall*	(1), 6, 14, 25	z	e, n, x
	273	*Salmonella siegburg*	6, 14, 18	z_4 , z_{23}	—
	274	*Salmonella uzaramo*	(1) 6, 14, 25	z_4 , z_{24}	—
I	275	*Salmonella brazil*	16	a	1, 5
	276	*Salmonella hull*	16	b	1, 2
	277	*Salmonella hvittingfoss*	16	b	e, n, x
	278	*Salmonella vancouver*	16	c	1, 5
	279	*Salmonella gaminara*	16	d	1, 7
	280	*Salmonella nottingham*	16	d	e, n, z_{15}
	281	*Salmonella weston*	16	e, h	z_6
	282	*Salmonella szentes*	16	k	1, 2
	283	*Salmonella orientalis*	16	k	e, n, z_{15}
	284	*Salmonella shanghai*	16	l, v	1, 6
	285	*Salmonella salford*	16	l, v	e, n, x
	286	*Salmonella rowbarton*	16	m, t	—
	287	*Salmonella lisboa*	16	z_{10}	1, 6
	288	*Salmonella jacksonville*	16	z_{29}	—
Further groups	289	*Salmonella kirkee*	17	b	1, 2
	290	*Salmonella bleadon*	17	(f), g, t	—
	291	*Salmonella matadi*	17	к	e, n, x
	292	*Salmonella morotai*	17	l, v	1, 2
	293	*Salmonella michigan*	17	l, v	1, 5
	294	*Salmonella carmel*	17	l, v	e, n, x
	295	*Salmonella usumbura*	18	d	1, 7
	296	*Salmonella memphis*	18	k	1, 5
	297	*Salmonella cerro*	18	z_4 , z_{23}	—
	298	*Salmonella blukwa*	18	z_4 , z_{24}	—
	299	*Salmonella minnesota*	21	b	e, n, x
	300	*Salmonella seattle*	28	a	e, n, x
	301	*Salmonella langford*	28	b	e, n, z_{15}
	302	*Salmonella kaltenhausen*	28	b	z_6
	303	*Salmonella mundonobo*	28	d	1, 7
	304	*Salmonella taunton*	28	k	e, n, x
	305	*Salmonella sp.*	28	l, v	e, n, z_{15}
	306	*Salmonella chicago*	28	r	1, 5
	307	*Salmonella kibusi*	28	r	e, n, x
	308	*Salmonella pomona*	28	y	1, 7
	309	*Salmonella telaviv*	28	y	e, n, z_{15}
	310	*Salmonella ezra*	28	z	1, 7
	311	*Salmonella urbana*	30	b	e, n, x
	312	*Salmonella godesburg*	30	g, m	—

Group	No.	Serotype	Somatic Antigens	Flagellar Antigens	
				Phase 1	Phase 2
	313	*Salmonella landau*	30	i	1, 2
	314	*Salmonella morehead*	30	i	1, 5
	315	*Salmonella donna*	30	l, v	1, 5
	316	*Salmonella matopeni*	30	y	1, 2
	317	*Salmonella bodjonegoro*	30	z_4 , z_{24}	—
	318	*Salmonella adelaide*	35	f, g	—
	319	*Salmonella gambia*	35	i	e, n, z_{15}
	320	*Salmonella monschaui*	35	m, t	—
	321	*Salmonella alachua*	35	z_4 , z_{23}	—
	322	*Salmonella kasenyi*	38	e, h	1, 5
	323	*Salmonella korovi*	38	g, m, s	—
	324	*Salmonella mgulani*	38	i	1, 2
	325	*Salmonella inverness*	38	k	1, 6
	326	*Salmonella lindi*	38	r	1, 5
Further	327	*Salmonella emmastad*	38	r	1, 6
groups	328	*Salmonella freetown*	38	y	1, 5
	329	*Salmonella colombo*	38	y	1, 6
	330	*Salmonella champaign*	39	k	1, 5
	331	*Salmonella riogrande*	40	b	1, 5
	332	*Salmonella johannesburg*	1, 40	b	e, n, x
	333	*Salmonella duval*	1, 40	b	e, n, z_{15}
	334	*Salmonella allandale*	1, 40	k	1, 6
	335	*Salmonella waycross*	41	z_4 , z_{23}	—
	336	*Salmonella uphill*	42	b	e, n, x
	337	*Salmonella weslaco*	42	z_{36}	—
	338	*Salmonella berkeley*	43	a	1, 5
	339	*Salmonella milwaukee*	43	f, g	—
	340	*Salmonella ahuza*	43	k	1, 5
	341	*Salmonella kingabwa*	43	y	1, 5
	342	*Salmonella niarembe*	44	a	l, w
	343	*Salmonella deversoir*	45	c	e, n, x

In accordance with the opinion of the majority of the Subcommittee members, the symbols used to express the O antigens of *Salmonella* have been changed from Roman to Arabic numerals.

It was shown by Edwards and Moran (Proc. Soc. Exp. Biol. and Med., *66*, 1947, 230) that *Salmonella sp.* (Type Senftenberg) and *Salmonella sp.* (Type Simsbury) each could be transformed into the other. Bruner and Edwards (Jour. Bact., *55*, 1948, 449) found that in certain instances antigen 3, 10 could be changed to antigen 3, 15 and again reversed to 3, 10. Bruner (Jour. Bact., *57*, 1949, 387) obtained typical cultures of *Salmonella sp.* (Type (Oranienburg) from certain strains of *Salmonella sp.* (Type Montevideo). These antigenic changes, all of which were produced by induced variation, are of great interest and undoubtedly throw light on phylogeny and evolution within the group. Further, it is highly probable that such changes occur in nature. However, the epidemiological significance of the various *Salmonella* types is well established, and observations such as those cited above in no way detract from the value of antigenic typing in the study of the epidemiology of *Salmonella* infections. For this reason the types are listed in the schema as they are found in nature.

No antigenic relationship exists between the H antigens z_1 , z_2 , z_3 , etc. The symbol z affixed by the numeral was chosen to denote these antigens, as no other letters of the alphabet were available.

Genus X. Shigella *Castellani and Chalmers, 1919.**

(Man. Trop. Med., 3rd ed., 1919, 936.)

Shi.gel'la. M.L. dim.ending -*ella*; M.L. fem.n. *Shigella* named for Prof. Kiyoshi Shiga, the Japanese bacteriologist who first discovered the dysentery bacillus in 1898.

Rods that are non-motile. Gram-negative. Gelatin not liquefied. Indole may or may not be produced. Hydrogen sulfide not produced. Numerous carbohydrates are attacked with the production of acid but no visible gas (some cultures of serotype *Shigella flexneri* 6 produce visible gas from glucose and from other fermentable substrates). Lactose is ordinarily not attacked, but some species attack this sugar very slowly. Salicin, inositol and adonitol are not attacked. Acetylmethylcarbinol is not produced. Methyl red test is usually positive. Ammonium citrate is not utilized. Nitrites are produced from nitrates. May or may not produce trimethylamine from trimethylamine oxide (Wood, Baird and Keeping, Jour. Bact., *46*, 1943, 106). Urea is not hydrolyzed. Aerobic. Possess distinctive antigenic structures. Pathogenic, causing dysenteries, or non-pathogenic species, all living in the bodies of warm-blooded animals. Found in polluted water supplies and in flies.

See Bensted (Dysentery Bacilli—*Shigella*. A brief historical review. Canad. Jour. Microbiol., *2*, 1956, 163–174) for a helpful review.

Key to the species of genus Shigella.

I. No acid from mannitol.
    A. No acid from arabinose or rhamnose. Indole not produced.
                1. *Shigella dysenteriae.*
    B. Acid from arabinose; acid may or may not be produced from rhamnose. Indole may or may not be produced.
        1. Acid from rhamnose; late and irregular acid from arabinose. Indole produced.
                2. *Shigella schmitzii.*
        2. No acid from rhamnose; acid from arabinose slow. Indole not produced (except Type 7).
                3. *Shigella arabinotarda* (Large-Sachs Group).
II. Acid from mannitol.
    A. No acid from lactose.
        1. No acid from rhamnose; acid usually produced from xylose. Agglutination with polyvalent specific serum (Types 1 to 11).
                4. *Shigella boydii.*
        2. Variable acid production from rhamnose; no acid from xylose or dulcitol. No trimethylamine from trimethylamine oxide. Agglutination with polyvalent specific serum (Types 1 to 6).
                5. *Shigella flexneri.*
        3. Acid from dulcitol. Trimethylamine from trimethylamine oxide.
                6. *Shigella alkalescens.*
    B. Acid from lactose late.
        1. Indole not produced. Agglutination with specific serum.
                7. *Shigella sonnei.*
        2. Indole produced.
                8. *Shigella dispar.*

1. Shigella dysenteriae (Shiga, 1898) Castellani and Chalmers, 1919. (Bacillus of Japanese dysentery, Shiga, Cent. f. Bakt., I Abt., *23*, 1898, 599; not Bacillus of Japanese dysentery, Ogata, Cent. f. Bakt., *11*, 1892, 264 (*Bacillus dysenteriae* Migula); *Bacillus dysenteriae* Shiga, Cent. f. Bakt., I Abt., *24*, 1898, 817; *Bacillus shigae* Chester, Man.

---

* Prepared by Dr. Julien Dumas, Pasteur Institute, Paris, France, August, 1955.

Determ. Bact., 1901, 228; Castellani and Chalmers, Man. Trop. Med., 3rd ed., 1919, 935.)

dy.sen.te'ri.ae. Gr. noun *dysenteria* dysentery; M.L. gen.noun *dysenteriae* of dysentery.

Rods, 0.4 to 0.6 by 1.0 to 3.0 microns, occurring singly. Non-motile. Gram-negative.

Gelatin: Surface growth. No liquefaction.

Agar colonies: Circular, 1.0 to 1.5 mm in diameter, raised, gray, opaque, shiny, entire. After 48 hours there is spreading, and the centers of the colonies become thickened.

Broth: Slightly turbid in several hours, increasing after 18 hours to a homogeneous turbidity.

Litmus milk: Slightly acid, slowly becoming slightly alkaline.

Potato: Growth shiny, slowly turning brown.

Indole not produced.

Hydrogen sulfide not produced.

Acid but no gas from glucose, fructose, galactose, raffinose and sometimes from glycerol (positive reaction with Stern's medium). Xylose, maltose, sucrose, mannitol, dulcitol, arabinose, rhamnose, salicin and adonitol not attacked.

Kligler's medium: Red slope; yellow butt; no gas.

Nitrites produced from nitrates.

Trimethylamine not produced from trimethylamine oxide.

Catalase not produced.

Aerobic, facultatively anaerobic.

Optimum temperature, 37° C. No growth at 45° C.

Antigenic structure: The O antigen of *Shigella dysenteriae* consists of a non-antigenic phospholipid and an antigenic toxic protein together with a polysaccharide responsible for the serological reactions (Boivin and Mesrobeanu, 1937; Morgan and Patridge, 1940). All strains have an identical antigenic structure; they also have a minor antigen, identical with that of *Shigella ambigua* Weldin, which does not interfere with slide agglutination.

Toxin production: Among the dysentery bacilli only *Shigella dysenteriae* produces an active exotoxin in liquid media which can be changed into an anatoxin (toxoid) by the action of formalin and heat (Ramon, Dumas and Saïd Bilal, 1926).

Pathogenicity: Avirulent but toxic for man causing epidemic bacillary dysentery. This is the only dysentery bacillus pathogenic for laboratory animals (rabbits, mice, monkeys and dogs), producing lesions similar to those found in man.

Dissociation: Dissociates spontaneously into S and R variants. The latter, which lack the O antigen, can produce an active exotoxin.

Source: Isolated from widespread epidemics of dysentery.

Habitat: A cause of dysentery in man and monkeys. Found only in feces of the sick.

2. **Shigella schmitzii** (Weldin and Levine, 1923) Hauduroy et al., 1937. (*Shigella parashigae* Remlinger and Dumas, Ann. Inst. Past., *29*, 1915, 493; Bazillus Schmitz, Schmitz, Ztschr. f. Hyg., *84*, 1917, 449; *Bacillus dysenteriae* "Schmitz", Murray, Jour. Roy. Army Med. Corps, *31*, 1918, 257; *Bacillus ambiguus* Andrewes, Lancet, *194*, 1918, 560; *Bacterium schmitzii* Weldin and Levine, Abst. Bact., *7*, 1923, 13; *Shigella ambigua* Weldin, Iowa State College Jour. Sci., *1*, 1927, 177; Hauduroy et al., Dict. d. Bact. Path., 1937, 496.)

schmit'zi.i. M.L. gen.noun *schmitzii* of Schmitz; named for Dr. K. E. F. Schmitz of Roumania.

Morphology and cultural characters on agar, gelatin, broth, milk and potato are identical with those of *Shigella dysenteriae*.

Indole always produced.

Hydrogen sulfide not produced.

Acid from glucose, galactose, fructose, maltose and rhamnose; irregular acid production within 4 days from arabinose. No acid from lactose, sucrose, mannitol, dulcitol, sorbitol, salicin, xylose or glycerol (negative reaction with Stern's medium).

Nitrites not produced from nitrates.

Trimethylamine not produced from trimethylamine oxide.

Catalase not produced.

Aerobic, facultatively anaerobic.

Temperature relations: Optimum, 37° C. No growth at 45° C.

Antigenic character: Possesses a major antigen specific to this species only and a minor antigen (reacting feebly) in common with *Shigella dysenteriae*.

Source: Isolated from the stools of dysentery patients.

Habitat: Found in cases of human dysentery, especially in Europe; relatively uncommon.

3. **Shigella arabinotarda** Christensen and Gowen, 1944. (See Large and Sankaran, Jour. Roy. Army Med. Corps, *63*, 1934, 231; and Sachs, Jour. Roy. Army Med. Corps, *80*, 1943, 92; Christensen and Gowen, Jour. Bact., *47*, 1944, 171.)

a.rab.i.no.tar'da. M.L. *arabinosum* arabinose; L. adj. *tardus* late; M.L. adj. *arabinotardus* (probably intended to mean) producing a late or slow fermentation of arabinose.

These organisms, frequently referred to as the Large-Sachs Q-group, comprise six recognized serotypes, which are known as Q 771, Q 1167, Q 1030, Q 454, Q 902 and 599-52; there is little doubt that Dudgeon and Urquhart's para-shiga is included (Med. Res. Council Special Report Series No. 40, 1919).

The morphology and cultural characters on agar, gelatin, broth, potato and milk are identical with those of *Shigella dysenteriae*.

Indole not produced (except by serotype Q 902).

Hydrogen sulfide not produced.

Acid from glucose, galactose, fructose, sorbitol and arabinose (slowly). No acid from lactose, mannitol, dulcitol (except serotype Q 1030) or rhamnose (except serotype Q 902).

Nitrites produced from nitrates.

Trimethylamine not produced from trimethylamine oxide.

Aerobic, facultatively anaerobic.

Temperature relations: Optimum, 37° C. No growth at 45° C.

Antigenic structure: Each type possesses a type-specific particular O antigen and lacks a group antigen; therefore there is no cross reaction with other species. There is a thermolabile capsular L antigen which can mask the O agglutination; thus diagnostic tests are best with broth cultures with destruction of L antigen.

Source: Found only in the stools from cases of dysentery.

Habitat: Relatively uncommon in outbreaks of dysentery due to *Shigella flexneri*.

4. **Shigella boydii** Ewing, 1949. (Jour. Bact., *57*, 1949, 634 and 635.)

boyd'i.i. M.L. gen.noun *boydii* of Boyd; named for Col. J. S. K. Boyd, the English bacteriologist who has made a special study of dysentery organisms.

Rods. Non-motile. Some strains of serotype 2 may be encapsulated (Ewing). Gram-negative.

Gelatin: No liquefaction.

Indole produced by serotypes 5, 7 and 11.

Hydrogen sulfide not produced.

Acid but no gas from mannitol (except for certain strains of serotypes 3, 6 and 10), glucose, arabinose and occasionally from sucrose and maltose.

Nitrites produced from nitrates.

Antigenic structure: *Shigella boydii* is distinguished from *Shigella flexneri* by possessing a type-specific major O antigen and by lacking a group antigen. Some have minor antigens, which fact explains their serological relationships.

Certain strains of *Shigella boydii* 2, 3, 5 and 7 may have K antigens, particularly antigen L, which masks the O agglutination. In this case the agglutination should be made in tubes with boiled cultures (Madsen).

To determine the serological type, unabsorbed anti-boydii 1, 2, 3 and 5 sera are used, but anti-boydii 4 serum should be absorbed with *Shigella alkalescens* and serum 6 with *Shigella sonnei* in phase II. With encapsulated *Shigella boydii* 2, a serum may be prepared which causes swelling of the capsule of an organism of type 2 when a capsule is present.

There are eleven serotypes, which are represented by the following recognized strains: 170, P288, 5DI, P274, P143, D19, Lavington, 112, 1296/7, 430 and 34.

Relationships to other species: *Shigella boydii* 1 has antigenic relationships with serotype 4, and *Shigella boydii* 3 with serotype 6. However by far the most important serological relationships are those of *Shigella boydii* 6 with *Shigella sonnei* in phase II, *Shigella dispar* and with fraction A of *Shigella alkalescens* (Wheeler and Ewing, 1946). In addition, *Shigella boydii* 6 has an antigen identical with that of *Shigella sonnei* in phase II and less important relationships with *Shigella flexneri* 1 and 4. Several types of *Shigella boydii* have antigenic fractions identical with those of *Escherichia coli* O53, and *Shigella boydii* 5 has fractions identical with those of *Escherichia coli* O79 (Ewing, Hucks and Taylor, Jour. Bact., *63*, 1952, 319).

Source: Isolated from feces in cases of dysentery.

Habitat: Found only in the feces of the sick; occurs only in a low proportion of cases of bacillary dysentery.

5. Shigella flexneri Castellani and Chalmers, 1919. (*Bacillus dysenteriae* Flexner, Phil. Med. Jour., *6*, 1900, 414; not *Bacillus dysenteriae* Shiga, Cent. f. Bakt., I Abt., *24*, 1898, 817; *Bacillus paradysenteriae* Collins, Jour. Inf. Dis., *2*, 1905, 620; Castellani and Chalmers, Man. Trop. Med., 3rd ed., 1919, 937; *Shigella paradysenteriae* Weldin, Iowa State Coll. Jour. Sci., *1*, 1927, 178.)

flex'ne.ri. M.L. gen.noun *flexneri* of Flexner; named for Simon Flexner, the bacteriologist who first isolated this species.

Rods, 0.5 by 1.0 to 1.5 microns, occurring singly, often filamentous and irregularly shaped in old cultures. Non-motile. Gramnegative.

Culturally identical with the other members of the genus except that growth in broth is more abundant.

Gelatin: No liquefaction.

Indole is produced (except by serotype 6).

Hydrogen sulfide not produced.

Acid but no gas from glucose and arabinose; irregularly from rhamnose, sucrose and maltose. Mannitol is fermented (except by certain strains of serotypes 4 and 6). Lactose, dulcitol, xylose, sorbitol, salicin and adonitol are not attacked.

Nitrites produced from nitrates.

Trimethylamine not produced from trimethylamine oxide.

Aerobic, facultatively anaerobic.

Optimum temperature, 37° C. No growth at 45.5° C.

Antigenic structure: The somatic antigen, extracted by diethyleneglycol, consists of a protein together with a polyoside and a phospholipid. The protein, dissociated with difficulty from the polyosides, is obtained in a pure state by a pancreatic digestion. In an acid medium, the toxicity of the antigen is related to the protein fraction and in an alkaline medium to the polyoside. The polyoside heptene is responsible for the serological characters (Tal and Goebel, 1950).

The structure of the O antigen of *Shigella flexneri* is much more complex than those of the other shigellas. These organisms have a major type antigen and several minor group antigens (Murray, Jour. Roy. Army Med. Corps, *31*, 1918, 257; Andrewes and Inman, Med. Res. Council, Special Rept. Ser. No. 42, London, 1919). Andrewes has identified five groups of major antigens: V, W, X, Y and Z; type Y is composed of variable proportions of the other four antigens. The mosaic of minor antigens determines constant cross agglutinations among the various types of *Shigella flexneri*, although there is not any serological relationship with the other groups of shigellas. Boyd has ascertained that the instability of the O antigen is due to a modification of the antigenic structure of the mutants which are developed in artificial media. In each cell the specific type antigen diminishes or disappears, and thus the organism retrogresses toward a type common to every strain.

The group diagnosis of *Shigella flexneri* is determined by agglutination with polyvalent serum; the diagnosis of the type is then determined by a monospecific serum obtained after absorption of the group agglutinins. Certain varieties of *Shigella flexneri* 6 are O-inagglutinable because they have a K antigen which is similar to the surface antigen B of *Escherichia coli* (Madsen). On boiling the emulsion for an hour to inhibit the B antigen, the organism becomes agglutinable. *Shigella flexneri* has no important serological relationships with the other shigellas but has antigenic fractions identical with those of *Salmonella poona* and *Salmonella worthington.*

There is no correlation between the serotypes and the biochemical characters except for *Shigella flexneri* 3, which acidifies rhamnose, and *Shigella flexneri* 6, which has particular biochemical characters.

Serotype *Shigella flexneri* 6 contains strains each of which possesses biochemical properties at variance with those of the other strains as well as with those of the other serotypes of this species: strain Boyd 88 produces acid from mannitol and glucose and sometimes late acid from dulcitol; strain *Shigella* (Type Manchester) produces acid and gas from mannitol and glucose and late acid and gas from dulcitol; *Shigella* (Type Newcastle) does not ferment mannitol but produces acid and gas from glucose and late acid and gas from dulcitol.

Other varieties of *Shigella flexneri* have been reported as not fermenting mannitol: Nelson (1948) isolated non-mannitol-fermenting strains whose type antigens were similar to those of *Shigella flexneri* 4 (Boyd 103). *Shigella rabaulensis* Munford and Mohr (1944) and *Shigella rio* de Assis and Stafkowsky (1948) also belong to this group: *S. rabaulensis* has an R antigen which, although belonging to the group antigen, is specific for *S. rabaulensis*; *S. rio* is a degenerate variant of *S. rabaulensis*. Denier and Huet (Bull. Soc. Path. Exot., *5*, 1912, 263) isolated a strain, which they called Saigon Bacillus, in Indo China which does not ferment mannitol; it produces acid without gas from glucose, maltose and occasionally from rhamnose and xylose in 12 to 24 days; it does not ferment mannitol, lactose, sucrose, dulcitol or sorbitol and it produces indole; it has a type 4 major antigen and minor antigens similar to those of several other serotypes of *Shigella flexneri*. Pacheco, Rubinsten, Piéchaud and Kirch suggest that the name *Shigella saigonensis* be used to include all strains of *S. flexneri* which do not ferment mannitol.

Source: Isolated from feces in cases of dysentery.

Habitat: The most common cause of dysentery epidemics and sometimes of infantile gastroenteritis. Found in the feces of the sick and in the feces of convalescents or of carriers of dysentery bacilli.

6. Shigella alkalescens (Andrewes, 1918) Weldin, 1927. (*Bacillus alkalescens* Andrewes, Lancet, *194*, 1918, 560; Weldin, Iowa State Coll. Jour. Sci., *1*, 1927, 179; *Proshigella alkalescens* Borman, Stuart and Wheeler, Jour. Bact., *48*, 1944, 363.)

al.ka.les'cens. Arabic *al* the; Arabic noun *qalīy* the ashes of saltwort, etc.; M.L. part.adj. *alkalescens* alkaline-making.

Rods, 0.5 by 1.0 to 1.5 microns, occurring singly and in pairs. Non-motile. Gram-negative.

Cultures in gelatin, on agar, in broth and on potato are similar to those of *Shigella flexneri* Castellani and Chalmers.

Litmus milk: Turns blue in 4 to 10 days; whey produced in 3 to 5 days.

Indole is produced.

Hydrogen sulfide not produced.

Acid but no gas from glucose, mannitol, xylose, rhamnose, maltose, dulcitol, sorbitol and occasionally from sucrose. Lactose, dextrin and salicin are not attacked.

Nitrites produced from nitrates.

Trimethylamine produced from trimethylamine oxide; trimethylamine also produced from choline.

Aerobic, facultatively anaerobic.

Optimum temperature, 37° C. Growth at 45.5° C.

Not generally accepted as pathogenic.

Distinctive characters: Produces trimethylamine from choline. Certain strains (serotypes 1 and 2) have the property of agglutinating the erythrocytes of man, monkeys, dogs or sheep (Griffith, 1948).

Source: Isolated from the feces of convalescents from dysentery and from healthy individuals; also isolated from a blood culture by Starkey (Jour. Canad. Med. Assn., *31*, 1934, 41) and from cases of bacilluria by Snyder and Hanner (Jour. Inf. Dis., *60*, 1937, 51).

Habitat: Found in the intestinal canal. Suspected as a cause of diarrhoea.

7. Shigella sonnei (Levine, 1920) Weldin, 1927. (Group III of Sonne, Sonne, Cent. f. Bakt., I Abt., Orig., *75*, 1915, 408; *Bacillus* *dispar* (in part) Andrewes, Lancet, *194*, 1918, 560 (see *Shigella dispar*); *Bacterium sonnei* Levine, Jour. Inf. Dis., *27*, 1920, 31; Weldin, Iowa State Coll. Jour. Sci., *1*, 1927, 182; *Proshigella sonnei* Borman, Stuart and Wheeler, Jour. Bact., *48*, 1944, 363.)

son'ne.i. M.L. gen.noun *sonnei* of Sonne; named for Dr. Carl Sonne, who worked with this organism.

Rods. Non-motile. Gram-negative.

Gelatin: No liquefaction.

Agar colonies: Cultures dissociate readily, and after the first transfers variants develop which modify their appearance and antigenic structure. Three, and sometimes even four, colony forms may develop (Wheeler and Mickle, 1951). Phase I colony: circular, gray, convex, 2 to 4 mm in diameter, entire, smooth, glistening; readily emulsified in normal saline. Phase II colony: granular, glistening, 5 mm in diameter, translucent edge, irregular; readily emulsified in normal saline. Goebel et al. describe phase IIr colonies similar to the phase II colonies of Wheeler and phase IIs colonies, small (1 to 2 mm in diameter), smooth and glistening, which have a distinctive antigenic structure. The organisms of these colonies emulsify readily (Baker and Goebel, 1949). The colonies in phase II of *Shigella sonnei* do not grow on certain selective media, SS agar or desoxycholate agar (Leifson).

Broth: Many strains make the medium turbid just as do cultures of *Shigella flexneri*; some form heavy flakes by spontaneous agglutination of the cells. In broth cultures the variation S → R is common. These colonies are flat, 8 to 10 mm in diameter, gray, undulate, rugose with irregular, sometimes lobate, edges. Spontaneous agglutination occurs in normal saline.

Milk: Coagulated in 4 to 30 days.

Indole not produced.

Acid but no gas from lactose (2 to 30 days) or sucrose (10 to 40 days). Acid from glucose, fructose, maltose, galactose, mannitol, arabinose, raffinose and rhamnose in 24 hours. Dulcitol, inositol, adonitol and xylose usually not attacked.

Nitrites produced from nitrates.

Trimethylamine produced from trimethylamine oxide.

Aerobic, facultatively anaerobic.

Optimum temperature, 37° C. Growth at 45.5° C.

Antigenic structure: Antigens of phase I, extracted in an aqueous solution of glycerol, and those of phase IIs, extracted in a 50 per cent solution of pyridine, are protein lipocarbohydrates of a nearly similar chemical composition.

The serum prepared with living organisms in phase I agglutinates bacteria in phases I and II, while that prepared with organisms in phase II agglutinates only bacteria in phase II. The agglutination of phase II organisms by the antiserum of phase I is explained by the presence of bacteria undergoing phase II mutation. The antiserum prepared with the organisms of phase IIs agglutinates the organisms of phase IIs and of phase IIr but has no effect on the organisms of phase I. On the contrary, the antigens of phases I and IIs are strongly specific (Goebel). *Shigella sonnei* in phase II has antigenic components common to *Shigella boydii* 6, *Shigella boydii* 4, *Shigella alkalescens* and *Shigella dispar*.

Distinctive characters: Appearance of broth cultures and of agar colonies; slow fermentation of lactose.

Comments: Some strains of *Shigella sonnei* do not ferment lactose, make milk alkaline or ferment xylose or rhamnose in 24 hours. Other strains which do not attack rhamnose have the same biochemical reactions as *Shigella boydii* 6 (D 10). The cells of these colonies in phase I and phase II are agglutinated by the anti-sonnei serum absorbed by D 19 (Rubinsten and Piéchaud, Ann. Inst. Past., *82*, 1952, 770).

Hammarström (Lancet, *1*, 1947, 102; and Acta med. Scand., *133*, 1949, Suppl. No. 223) has classified the strains of *Shigella sonnei* into 68 types by means of eleven specific bacteriophages and one non-specific bacteriophage tending to show whether the culture is in the typable form, R. Types 3 and 5 are the most common, then types 7, 8, 12, 16, 53 and 19. This method is of great epidemiological value.

Source: Isolated from feces in cases of dysentery or gastroenteritis; also isolated from drinking water (Green and MacLeod, 1943).

Habitat: A cause of dysentery in man; causes diarrhoea in infants and adults.

8. Shigella dispar (Andrewes, 1918) Bergey et al., 1930. (*Bacillus ceylanensis B* (sic), Castellani, Jour. Hyg., *7*, 1907, 9; *Bacillus dispar* (in part) Andrewes, Lancet, *194*, 1918, 560 (see *Shigella sonnei*; Andrewes included in *Bacillus dispar* all lactose-fermenting members of the dysentery group); *Castellanus castellanii* Cerruti, Jour. Trop. Med. and Hyg., *33*, 1930, 207; Bergey et al., Manual, 3rd ed., 1930, 364; *Proshigella dispar* Borman, Stuart and Wheeler, Jour. Bact., *48*, 1944, 363.)

dis'par. L. adj. *dispar* unlike.

Rods. Non-motile. Gram-negative.

Culturally resembles *Shigella sonnei* Weldin.

Gelatin: No liquefaction.

Milk is sometimes slowly coagulated.

Indole is produced.

Hydrogen sulfide not produced.

Acid from xylose and occasionally from lactose and dulcitol.

Nitrites produced from nitrates.

Trimethylamine produced from trimethylamine oxide.

Antigenic structure: The antigens of this species may be identical with those of *Shigella boydii* 5, *Shigella flexneri* 6 and certain strains of *Escherichia coli*.

Dissociation: The S colonies do not dissociate into phase II but change rather rapidly into S → R variants.

Relationships to other species: Culturally resembles *Shigella sonnei* Weldin but differs from the latter biochemically and serologically.

Kauffman and Frantzen combine *Shigella alkalescens* and *S. dispar*, placing them in a group they call the "Alkalescens-Dispar Group." This was done to include these two organisms in the *Escherichia coli anaerogenes* group because they have O and K antigens similar to those found in the genus *Escherichia*. O agglutination may be masked by the K antigen or by a capsular A antigen. Frantzen described eight biochemical and serological groups of Alkalescens-Dispar. The diagnosis of the groups is determined by the agglutination of a boiled emulsion with one of the eight specific sera. The O antigens of these eight groups have fractions similar to the somatic antigens of certain varieties of *Escherichia coli*. Oftentimes the biochemical and serological characters show no relationship, except in the case of *Shigella alkalescens* Type 1, which has stable biochemical characters.

Source: Isolated from the feces and intestines of persons suffering from dysentery.

Habitat: Most frequently found in the urine of persons having cystitis, pyelitis or pyelonephritis, in the blood of persons ill with septicemia and in the feces of dysentery patients or of healthy individuals. Pathogenic for the urinary tract; very rarely causes dysentery.

In the accompanying table is presented the nomenclatural and taxonomic schema of the genus *Shigella* as proposed by Ewing (Jour. Bact., *57*, 1949, 633), as modified by the Shigella Commission in 1950 and as amended and extended by that Commission in 1953 (Enterobacteriaceae Subcommittee Reports, 1954). The schema is based in part upon biochemical characteristics, in part upon intragroup antigenic relationships and in part upon tradition. In this text Arabic numerals instead of Roman numerals have been employed to designate serotypes; this change was made to avoid possible confusion between the letters V and X and the Roman numerals V and X. However, when writing the formula for a *Shigella* serotype, Roman numerals have still been employed to designate the type-specific antigen.

NOMENCLATURE OF SEROSUBGROUPS AND SEROTYPES OF SPECIES OF *Shigella*

(Edwards and Ewing, Identification of *Enterobacteriaceae*. Burgess Publ. Co., Minneapolis, 1955, Fig. 4, 99.)

Reprinted by permission.

Shigella Commission 1953	Shigella Commission 1950	Ewing 1949	Kauffmann and Ferguson 1947	Wheeler 1944	Boyd 1940, 1946	Boyd 1938	Weil, Black and Farsetta 1944	English* (older)	German†	Other
Subgroup A: *Shigella dysenteriae*										
1	1	I							Shiga-Kruse	*Bacterium shigae*
2	2	II							I	*Shigella ambigua, S. schmitzii, B. ambiguus*
3	3	III								Q771, type 8524-‡, *S.arabinotarda A*-§
4	4	IV								Q1167, *S. arabinotarda B*-§
5	5	V								Q1030
6	6	VI								Q454
7	7	VII								Q902
8										Serotype 599-52

NOMENCLATURE OF SEROSUBGROUPS AND SEROTYPES OF SPECIES OF *Shigella* (*Continued*)

Shigella Commission 1953	Shigella Commission 1959	Ewing 1949 Type	Ewing 1949 Abbreviated antigenic formula	Kauffmann and Ferguson 1947	Wheeler 1944	Boyd 1940, 1946	Boyd 1938	Weil, Black, and Farsetta, 1944	English* (older)	Germant	Other
Subgroup B: *Shigella flexneri*											
1a	1a	I	I:4	1b	I	I	V	I	V	B, C	Flexner
1b	1b	I	I:4,6	1a	I			I, III	VZ	A	Strong, Hiss-Russell
2a	2a	II	II:4	2a	IIa	II	W	II	W	D	
2b	2b	II	II:7,8,9	2b	IIb			II, VII	WX	DX	
3	3	III	III:6,7	3	III	III		III	Z	H	Lentz Y2
4a	4a	IV	IV:4	4a	IV	IV	103	IV		F	
4b	4b	IV	IV:6	4b	IV	IV	103Z	III, IV		J	*Shigella saigonensis, S. rio*
	4									F	
5	5	V	—:7,8,9	5	V	V	P. 119	V (V, VII)		G	
6	6	VI	—:4	6	VI	VI	88	VI		L	*Shigella newcastle*
X	X	X			X			VII	X		
Y	Y	Y			Y			VIII	Y	Y	Hiss-Russell
Subgroup C: *Shigella boydii*											
1	1	I				I	170	IX			
2	2	II				II	P. 288	X			
3	3	III				III	D. 1	XI			
4	4	IV					P. 274	XIV		R	
5	5	V					P. 143	XIII			
6	6	VI					D. 19	XII			

	7	7	VII						N	Lavington, type T, *Shigella etousae*
	8								P	Serotype 112
	9									Serotype 1296/7
	10									Serotype 430
	11									Serotype 34
Subgroup D: *Shigella sonnei*	*Shigella sonnei*	*Shigella sonnei*	*Shigella sonnei*						E	Sonne-Duval, Sonne III, *Shigella ceylonensis A*

* Andrewes and Inman (1919), Murray (1918), Gettings (1919).
† Kruse (1900), Sartorius and Reploh (1932), Seeliger (1949).
‡ Gober et al. (1944).
§ Christensen and Gowen (1944).

FAMILY V. BRUCELLACEAE, Nom. Nov.

(*Parvobacteriaceae* Rahn, Zent. f. Bakt., II Abt., *96*, 1937, 281.)

Bru.cel.la′ce.ae. M.L. fem.n. *Brucella* type genus of the family; -*aceae* ending to denote a family; M.L. fem.pl.n. *Brucellaceae* the *Brucella* family.

Small, coccoid to rod-shaped cells which occur singly, in pairs, in short chains or in groups; filamentous and pleomorphic forms are occasionally found. Motile and non-motile species occur, the motile species possessing from one to eight peritrichous flagella; with certain of the motile species, motility can be demonstrated only at lower temperatures (18° to 26° C.). May or may not be encapsulated. May or may not show bipolar staining. Gram-negative. V (phosphopyridene nucleotide) and/or X (hemin) factors are sometimes required for growth; blood serum and similar enrichment materials may be required or may enhance growth. Increased CO_2 tension may also favor growth, especially on primary isolation. Gelatin usually not liquefied. Carbohydrates may or may not be attacked with the production of acid but no gas. Nitrites may or may not be produced from nitrates. Aerobic, facultatively anaerobic. Some invade living tissues; infection in some cases may take place by penetration of the organism through mucous membranes or through the unbroken skin. Parasites and pathogens which affect warm-blooded animals, including man, rarely cold-blooded animals.

Key to the genera of family **Brucellaceae**.

I. Non-motile at 37° C., but may be motile at lower temperatures.
  A. Predominantly occur singly or in masses.
    1. Cells predominantly occur singly and do not occur in masses.
      a. Grow on peptone media but may require blood serum or similar enrichment materials for growth.
        b. Show, or tend to show, bipolar staining.
          c. Attacks carbohydrates.
                Genus I. *Pasteurella*, p. 395.
          cc. Does not attack carbohydrates.
                Genus II. *Bordetella*, p. 402.
        bb. Does not show bipolar staining.
                Genus III. *Brucella*, p. 404.
      aa. Requires V (phosphopyridene nucleotide) and/or X (hemin) factors for growth.
                Genus IV. *Haemophilus*, p. 406.
    2. Cells predominantly occur singly and show pleomorphism and/or occur in masses.
      a. Growth occurs on ordinary media; increased CO_2 tension enhances growth, especially on primary isolation.
                Genus V. *Actinobacillus*, p. 414.
      aa. Growth occurs on infusion media only after growth in chick embryo.
                Genus VI. *Calymmatobacterium*, p. 418.
  B. Predominantly occur as diplobacilli.
                Genus VII. *Moraxella*, p. 419.
II. Motile at 37° C.
  A. Optimum temperature for growth, 37° C. Litmus milk becomes strongly alkaline.
                Genus II. *Bordetella*, p. 402.
  B. Optimum temperature for growth, between 28° and 30° C. Litmus milk unchanged.
                Genus VIII. *Noguchia*, p. 421.

Genus I. **Pasteurella** *Trevisan, 1887.**

(*Octopsis* Trevisan, Atti della Accad. Fisio-Medico-Statistica, Milano, Ser. 4, *3*, 1885, 102; Trevisan, Rendiconti Reale Instituto Lombardo di Scienze e Lettere, 1887, 94; *Coccobacillus* Gamaleïa, Cent. f. Bakt., *4*, 1888, 167; *Eucystia* Enderlein, Sitzber. Gesell. Naturf. Freunde, Berlin, 1917, 317.)

Pas.teu.rel'la. M.L. dim.ending *-ella*; M.L. fem.n. *Pasteurella* named for Louis Pasteur, the French scientist.

Small, ellipsoidal to elongated rods which show bipolar staining by special methods. Gram-negative. Gelatin not liquefied. Milk not coagulated. The majority of species ferment carbohydrates but produce only a small amount of acid; no or slight lactose fermentation; no gas production. Aerobic, facultatively anaerobic. May require low oxidation-reduction potential on primary isolation. Parasitic on man, other animals and birds.

The type species is *Pasteurella multocida* (Lehmann and Neumann) Rosenbusch and Merchant.

Key to the species of genus **Pasteurella.**

I. Grow on ordinary media.
  A. Non-motile. No change or slight acid in milk without coagulation.
    1. Indole produced. Hydrogen sulfide produced.
      a. Gelatin not liquefied.
          1. *Pasteurella multocida.*
      aa. Gelatin liquefied.
          2. *Pasteurella septicaemiae.*
    2. Indole not produced.
      a. Lactose usually attacked. Blood agar is hemolyzed.
          3. *Pasteurella haemolytica.*
      aa. Lactose not attacked.
        b. Gelatin liquefied.
            4. *Pasteurella anatipestifer.*
        bb. Gelatin not liquefied.
          c. Nitrites produced from nitrates.
              5. *Pasteurella pestis.*
          cc. Nitrites not produced from nitrates.
              6. *Pasteurella pfaffii.*
  B. Non-motile at 37° C. Motile and flagellated at 18° to 26° C. Milk alkaline.
          7. *Pasteurella pseudotuberculosis.*
II. Do not grow on plain agar or in liquid media without special enrichment.
  A. Acid not produced from sucrose.
          8. *Pasteurella tularensis.*
  B. Acid produced from sucrose.
          9. *Pasteurella novicida.*

1. **Pasteurella multocida** (Lehmann and Neumann, 1899) Rosenbusch and Merchant, 1939. (Virus der Wildseuche, Hueppe, Berlin. klin. Wochnschr., *23*, 1886, 797; Bactérie ovoide, Lignières, Recueil de Méd. Vétér., *75*, 1898, 836 (Bull. Soc. Centr.

---

* The manuscript covering this genus was prepared by Prof. Robert S. Breed with the assistance of Mr. Erwin F. Lessel, Jr. and Mrs. Eleanore Heist Clise, Cornell University, Geneva, New York, and was reviewed by Dr. I. A. Merchant, Division of Veterinary Medicine, Iowa State College, Ames, Iowa, October, 1955.

Méd. Vétér., N.S. *60*, 1898, 836); *Bacillus septicaemiae haemorrhagicae* Sternberg, Man. of Bact., 1893, 408; *Bacterium multocidum* Lehmann and Neumann, Bakt., Diag., 2 Aufl., *2*, 1899, 196; Rosenbusch and Merchant, Jour. Bact., *37*, 1939, 85.)

mul.to'ci.da. L. adj. *multus* many; L. v. L. adj.suffix *-cidus* from L. v. *caedo* to cut, kill; M.L. adj. *multocidus* many-killing, i.e., killing many kinds (of animals).

Description taken from Schütze (Med. Res. Council, Syst. of Bact., London, *4*, 1929, 451) who prepared it from studies of 230 strains described by 17 authors during the years 1908 to 1926.

Short, ellipsoidal rods, 0.3 to 1.25 microns in length, occurring singly, in pairs, rarely in chains. Non-motile. Show bipolar staining. Gram-negative.

Gelatin: No liquefaction.

Agar: Fine, translucent growth; characteristic odor. A complex dissociation pattern is shown. Many strains recovered from normal respiratory passages and from some chronic infections are in the mucoid phase and generally show a relatively lower virulence. Strains from acute cases of fowl cholera and hemorrhagic septicemia are in the fluorescent (iridescent) phase and are highly virulent (Carter, Canadian Journal Comp. Med. and Vet. Sci., *16*, 1952, 150).

Blood agar: No hemolysis.

Broth: Uniform turbidity; characteristic odor.

Milk: No change in reaction; no coagulation.

Potato: No visible growth.

Indole is produced.

Hydrogen sulfide is produced.

Acid but no gas from glucose, mannitol (usually), sucrose, fructose, sorbitol, galactose, mannose, xylose (usually) and trehalose (usually). No acid from lactose, dulcitol, arabinose (usually), amygdalin, maltose (usually), raffinose, rhamnose, adonitol, dextrin, inulin, glycerol, salicin (usually) or erythritol. Groupings based on differences in sugar fermentations using xylose, arabinose, dulcitol, etc. do not appear to be natural ones.

Nitrites produced from nitrates.

Temperature relations: Optimum, 37° C. Killed at temperatures above 45° C.

Aerobic to facultatively anaerobic.

Four distinct serological types, A, B, C and D, have been recognized (Carter, Amer. Jour. Vet. Res., *16*, 1955, 481).

Virulent for laboratory animals, especially mice and rabbits.

Distinctive characters: Grows on ordinary media. Bile salts inhibit growth.

Relationships of this species: Few species of bacteria have been given so many different names as the organism causing the so-called chicken cholera of birds and the hemorrhagic septicemia of mammals. Pasteur (Compt. rend. Acad. Sci., Paris, *90*, 1880, 230, 952 and 1030) was one of the first to recognize this species in chickens, but the earliest scientific name given to the species appears to be the completely forgotten *Micrococcus gallicidus* given by the early American bacteriologist, Burrill (Amer. Naturalist, *17*, 1883, 320; also see Jour. Roy. Micro. Soc., London, *3*, 1883, 399). The specific epithet given by Zopf (Die Spaltpilze, 3 Aufl., 1885, 57) in the binomial *Micrococcus choleraegallinarum* has been much more widely used, especially for the organism isolated from birds.

At about the same time, Bollinger (Microparasiten bei eine neue Wild- und Rinderseuche, München, 1879) had found the hemorrhagic septicemia organism in animals, and apparently the first name given this organism was the trinomial *Bacterium bipolare multocidum* Kitt (Sitz. Gesell. Morphol. u. Physiol., München, *1*, 1885, 24). This trinomial was changed to a binomial, *Bacterium multocidum*, by Lehmann and Neumann (Bakt. Diag., 2 Aufl., *2*, 1899, 196). Later, as indicated above, this was changed to *Pasteurella multocidum* (Rosenbusch and Merchant, Jour. Bact., *37*, 1939, 85). Because of the early use of the epithet *multocidum* and because of its appropriateness, it was used in the 6th edition of the MANUAL on the recommendation of many students of animal diseases, and its use is continued in this edition. Meanwhile, Topley and Wilson introduced the entirely new binomial *Pasteurella septica* (Princip. Bact. and Immunol., 1st ed., *1*, 1931, 488), and this name is currently widely used in England because of its appropriateness and because of the widespread use of *-septica* as a combining form in such specific epithets as *aviseptica, boviseptica, suiseptica,* etc. Names of this type were apparently introduced about 1896.

The confusion that exists in regard to the scientific name of this species should be clarified by appropriate action taken by the International Judicial Commission on Bacteriological Nomenclature. A strict application of the Priority Rule in the Bacteriological Code would apparently result in the introduction of a specific epithet *gallicidus* never used in the literature except by its author. A careful review of the early literature might even reveal some other binomial validly published before 1883. No attempt is made here to list the various names that have been used for this species as found in various animals such as man, children, calves, buffaloes, goats, sheep, swine, horses, cats, dogs, ferrets, rats, mice, rabbits, guinea pigs, fowls, ducks, swans, wild pigeons, pheasants, canaries, etc.

Source: Early isolations were from fowls, cattle and rabbits.

Habitat: The cause of chicken cholera and hemorrhagic septicemia in warm-blooded animals.

2. **Pasteurella septicaemiae** (Bergey et al., 1925) Breed, *comb. nov.* (*Bacillus septicaemiae anserum exsudativae* Riemer, Cent. f. Bakt., I Abt., Orig., *37*, 1904, 648; *Eberthella septicaemiae* Bergey et al., Manual, 2nd ed., 1925, 250.)

sep.ti.cae′mi.ae. Gr. adj. *septicus* putrefactive, septic; Gr. noun *haema* blood; M.L. noun *septicaemia* septicemia; M.L. gen. noun *septicaemiae* of septicemia.

Small rods, 0.1 by 0.3 to 1.0 micron, occurring singly, frequently in pairs, the one behind the other, and in threads.

Non-motile. Gram-negative.

Gelatin colonies: Small, white, circular.

Gelatin stab: Slight, infundibuliform liquefaction, becoming complete in several weeks.

Agar colonies: Circular, transparent, smooth, homogeneous, entire.

Agar slant: Soft, grayish white streak, slightly viscid, becoming transparent.

Does not grow on Endo agar.

Broth: Slight, uniform turbidity; slight pellicle formation.

Litmus milk: Unchanged.

Potato: No growth.

Blood serum: Yellowish white streak, the medium becoming brownish and slowly liquefied.

Indole is produced after several days.

Hydrogen sulfide is produced.

Slight acid but no gas from glucose. No acid from lactose.

Aerobic.

Optimum temperature, 37° C.

Not pathogenic for white mice, guinea pigs, chickens or pigeons. Mildly pathogenic for ducks.

Source: Isolated from blood, exudates and all of the internal organs of geese.

Habitat: Cause of a fatal septicemia in young geese.

3. **Pasteurella haemolytica** Newsom and Cross, 1932. (Jour. Amer. Vet. Med. Assoc., *80* (N.S. *33*), 1932, 715.)

hae.mo.ly′ti.ca. Gr. noun *haema* blood; Gr. adj. *lyticus* dissolving; M.L. adj. *haemolyticus* blood-dissolving.

Bipolar staining. Similar in its general characteristics to *Pasteurella multocida.*

Blood agar: Hemolysis.

Indole not produced.

Acid from glucose, dextrin, fructose, galactose, glycerol (usually), inositol, lactose (usually), maltose, mannitol, raffinose, sorbitol, sucrose and xylose. No acid from arabinose, dulcitol, inulin, mannose, rhamnose or salicin.

No cross-agglutination between *Pasteurella multocida* and this species.

Avirulent for rabbits.

Source: Twenty strains were isolated from cases of pneumonia in sheep and cattle.

Habitat: Occurs in pneumonia of sheep and cattle.

4. **Pasteurella anatipestifer** (Hendrickson and Hilbert, 1932) Hauduroy et al., 1953. (*Pfeifferella anatipestifer* Hendrickson and Hilbert, The Cornell Veterinarian, *22*, 1932, 239; *Pasteurella* (?) *anapestifer* (sic) Hauduroy et al., Dict. d. Bact. Path., 2ᵉ ed., 1953, 367.)

a.na.ti.pes′ti.fer. L. fem.n. *anas, anatis*

duck; L. fem.n. *pestis* plague; L. v. *fero* to carry; L. adj. *pestifer* pestilence-carrying; M.L. adj. *anatipestifer* duck-plague-carrying.

Description prepared by Prof. D. W. Bruner, New York State Veterinary College, Cornell University, Ithaca, New York.

Short rods, 0.3 to 0.5 by 1.0 to 2.5 microns, occurring singly, in pairs and in short chains. Non-motile. Gram-negative.

Gelatin stab: Liquefaction.

Blood agar colonies: Small, circular, transparent, entire. No hemolysis.

Plain broth (horse meat): Slight, uniform turbidity that becomes more dense at 48 hours of incubation at 37° C. After several days a bluish ring forms at the surface where contact is made with the test tube. No pellicle is formed. The organism remains viable in this medium for about two weeks.

Löffler's blood serum: Liquefaction.

Coagulated egg medium (Dorset): Liquefaction.

Huddleson's thionin medium: Growth.

Huddleson's basic fuchsin medium: Growth.

Glycerol phosphate agar: No growth.

Bile (10 per cent) in serum agar: Growth.

Bile (40 per cent) in serum agar: No growth.

Litmus milk: No visible change.

Indole not produced.

Hydrogen sulfide produced in slight amounts.

Potato: No growth.

Sodium thioglycollate medium: Growth in a ring about 1 cm below the surface.

No acid from glucose or other carbohydrates.

Nitrites not produced from nitrates.

May require CO_2 for isolation, but becomes aerobic after several transfers.

Optimum temperature, 37° C.

Not pathogenic for laboratory animals; however, with ducks it may produce death following intravenous infection of a freshly isolated culture. Not established as the causative agent in so-called new duck disease.

Source: Isolated from cases of septicemia in ducklings on Long Island, New York, 1932. Reisolated from Long Island ducklings

by Bruner and Fabricant (Cornell Veterinarian, *44*, 1954, 461).

Habitat: Associated with a disease of ducklings.

5. **Pasteurella pestis** (Lehmann and Neumann, 1896) Holland, 1920. (Bacille de la peste, Yersin, Ann. Inst. Past., *8*, 1894, 666; Pest Bacillus, Aoyama, Ztschr. f. Hyg., *21*, 1895, 165; *Bacterium pestis* Lehmann and Neumann, Bakt. Diag., 1 Aufl., *2*, 1896, 194; Holland, Jour. Bact., *5*, 1920, 219.)

pes'tis. L. noun *pestis* plague, pestilence.

Rods, 1.0 by 2.0 microns, occurring singly. Characteristic bladder, safety-pin and ring involution forms. Non-motile. Polar staining. Gram-negative.

Gelatin colonies: Flat, gray, with granular margin.

Gelatin stab: Flat surface growth. Arborescent growth in stab. No liquefaction.

Agar colonies: Grayish white, translucent, iridescent, undulate.

Agar slant: Growth grayish, viscid, thin, moist, translucent. Growth slow, favored by the addition of blood or sodium sulfite.

Broth: Turbid or clear with flocculi in the fluid. Old cultures show a pellicle with streamers into the fluid (stalactites). Becomes alkaline more slowly than *Pasteurella pseudotuberculosis*. See Bessonowa and Lenskaja (Cent. f. Bakt., I Abt., Orig., *119*, 1930, 430).

Litmus milk: Slightly acid or unchanged. No coagulation.

Potato: Scant, grayish growth.

Indole not produced.

Lactose and rhamnose not attacked. Variable action on glycerol.

Nitrites produced from nitrates.

Temperature relations: Optimum, between 25° and 30° C. Minimum, 0° C. Maximum, between 43° and 45° C.

Aerobic, facultatively anaerobic.

Comments: *Pasteurella pestis* and *P. pseudotuberculosis* are not definitely distinguishable by serological methods (Schütze, Med. Res. Council, Syst. of Bact., London, *4*, 1929, 478, and Wu Lien-teh, in Chun, Pollitzer and Wu, "Plague", National Quarantine Service, Shanghai, 1936). However Thal and Chen (Jour. Bact., *69*, 1955,

103) recently reported biochemical methods by which *P. pestis* and *P. pseudotuberculosis* can readily be differentiated: on ordinary urea (Difco) slants with phenol red as indicator, the former does not affect the medium whereas the latter produces a red coloration of the medium; with desoxycholate citrate agar, the colonies of *P. pestis* are rather scant, reddish and pin-point in size after 48 hours at 37° C., while those of *P. pseudotuberculosis* are abundant, large, opaque and, like the medium in general, become yellow.

Source: Isolated from buboes, blood, pleural effusion, spleen and liver of infected rodents and man; also from sputum in pneumonic plague and from infected fleas.

Habitat: The causative organism of plague in man and in rats, ground squirrels and other rodents. Infectious for mice, guinea pigs and rabbits. Transmitted from rat to rat and from rat to man by the infected rat flea.

6. **Pasteurella pfaffii** (Hadley et al., 1918) Hauduroy et al., 1953. (Bacillus der Kanarienvögelseuche, Pfaff, Cent. f. Bakt., I Abt., Orig., *38*, 1905, 276; *Bacterium pfaffi* (sic) Hadley, Elkins and Caldwell, Rhode Island Agr. Exp. Sta. Bull. 174, 1918, 169; *Pasteurella pfaffi* (sic) Hauduroy et al., Dict. d. Bact. Path., 2e ed., 1953, 377.)

pfaf'fi.i. M.L. gen.noun *pfaffii* of Pfaff; named for Dr. Franz Pfaff of Prague, who isolated this species.

Description taken largely from Hadley et al. (*op. cit.*, 1918, 180).

Rods, 0.5 by 1.0 to 2.0 microns, occurring singly. Non-motile. Gram-negative.

Gelatin colonies: Small, grayish, translucent.

Gelatin stab: No liquefaction.

Agar colonies: Small, yellowish gray, homogeneous, translucent, entire. No odor.

Agar slant: Slight, yellowish gray, translucent streak.

Broth: Turbid; flocculent sediment (Pfaff, *op. cit.*, 1905, 280).

Litmus milk: Unchanged.

Potato: Moderate, whitish streak.

Indole not produced.

Hydrogen sulfide not produced.

Acid but no gas from glucose, fructose, arabinose, xylose, maltose, dextrin, salicin and mannitol. Lactose, sucrose, raffinose, inulin, adonitol and dulcitol not attacked.

Nitrites not produced from nitrates.

Aerobic, facultatively anaerobic.

Optimum temperature, 37° C.

Pathogenic for canaries, sparrows, pigeons, white mice, guinea pigs and rabbits. Not pathogenic for chickens (Pfaff, *loc. cit.*).

Source: First encountered in an epidemic of septicemia in canaries. Caused a necrotic enteritis.

Habitat: Not known from other sources.

7. **Pasteurella pseudotuberculosis** (Pfeiffer, 1889) Topley and Wilson, 1931. (*Bacillus pseudotuberkulosis* (sic) Pfeiffer, Ueber die bacilläre Pseudotuberculose bei Nagethieren, Leipzig, 1889, 5; *Streptobacillus pseudotuberculosis rodentium* Preisz, Ann. Inst. Past., *8*, 1894, 231; Topley and Wilson, Princip. Bact. and Immun., 1st ed., *2*, 1931, 825.)

pseu.do.tu.ber.cu.lo'sis. Gr. adj. *pseudes* false; L. noun *tuberculum* a small swelling; M.L. neut.n. *tuberculosis* tuberculosis; M.L. noun *pseudotuberculosis* pseudotuberculosis.

The tabular description by Eisenberg (Bakt. Diag., 3 Aufl., 1891, 294) is very incomplete. Description taken from Topley and Wilson (Princip. Bact. and Immun., 2nd ed., 1936, 607) and from Bessonowa, Lenskaja and Molodtzowa (Office Internat. d'Hyg. Publ., *29*, 1937, 2106).

Small rods which vary in size and shape: ellipsoidal or coccoid forms are 0.8 by 0.8 to 2.0 microns, with rounded ends, occurring singly; rod-shaped forms are 0.6 by 1.5 to 5.0 microns, with rounded ends, occurring singly, in groups or in short chains; occasionally long, curved, filamentous forms occur. Motile by means of one to six peritrichous flagella. Not acid-fast. Gram-negative.

Gelatin stab: After 7 days at 22° C., good filiform growth extending to bottom of tube. No liquefaction.

Agar colonies: After 24 hours at 37° C., circular, 0.5 to 1.0 mm in diameter, umbonate, granular, translucent, grayish yellow, butyrous; edge entire; dull, finely granular or beaten-copper surface; differentiated into a raised, more opaque center and a flat, clearer periphery with radial striation.

Agar slant: After 48 hours at 37° C., growth moderate, confluent, raised, grayish yellow, translucent, with glistening, wavy or beaten-copper surface and an irregularly lobate edge.

Blood agar plate: Good growth. No hemolysis.

Broth: After 24 hours at 37° C., moderate growth with moderate turbidity which later clears. Viscous sediment. Incomplete surface and ring growth. Becomes alkaline more rapidly than does *Pasteurella pestis*.

Litmus milk: Usually slightly alkaline.

Potato: After 7 days at 22° C., a thin, yellowish membrane appears which later turns brown.

Indole not produced.

Hydrogen sulfide produced.

Acid but no gas from glucose, maltose, arabinose, xylose, rhamnose, salicin, glycerol and mannitol. Sometimes acid from sucrose.

Methyl red test positive.

Acetylmethylcarbinol not produced.

Nitrites produced from nitrates.

Ammonia is produced.

Methylene blue is reduced.

Catalase-positive.

Aerobic, facultatively anaerobic.

Temperature relations: Optimum, 30° C. Minimum, 5° C. Maximum, 43° C. Thermal death point, 60° C. for 10 minutes.

Pathogenicity: Infectious for mice, rats, dogs, cats and horses.

Distinctive characters: Motile with peritrichous flagella and H antigen at 22° C.; non-motile, non-flagellated and no H antigen at 37° C.; this change occurs near 30° C.; non-motile strains grown at 37° C. develop flagella when grown at 22° C. (Preston and Maitland, Jour. Gen. Microbiol., 7, 1952, 117).

Comments: See description of *Pasturella pestis* for comments regarding the differentiation of these two species.

Source: Isolated from a guinea pig inoculated with material from a horse suspected of having glanders.

Habitat: Schütze (Syst. of Bact. in

Relation to Med., Med. Res. Counc., London, 4, 1929, 474) states that this species appears to be widely distributed in nature, having been found in soil, dust, water, fodder and milk. It causes pseudotuberculosis in the following animals: horse, cow, goat, rabbit, hare, guinea pig, mouse, wild rat, cat, dog, monkey, hen, turkey, pigeon and canary. The organism has been isolated from human blood, spleen, liver, gall bladder, appendix and cerebro-spinal fluid.

8. **Pasteurella tularensis** (McCoy and Chapin, 1912) Bergey et al., 1923. (*Bacterium tularense* McCoy and Chapin, Jour. Inf. Dis., *10*, 1912a, 61; McCoy and Chapin, Public Health Bull. 53, U. S. Treas. Dept., Public Health Service, 1912b, 17; Bergey et al., Manual, 1st ed., 1923, 267.)

tu.la.ren'sis. M.L. adj. *tularensis* pertaining to Tulare County; named for Tulare, the county in California in which tularemia was first observed.

Description taken from McCoy and Chapin (*op. cit.*, 1912a, 61, and *op. cit.*, 1912b, 17) and from Francis (U. S. Hygienic Lab. Bull. 130, 1922). Further revision by Francis, 1947.

Equal numbers of cocci and rods; 0.2 by 0.2 to 0.7 micron, occurring singly. Extremely pleomorphic (Hesselbrock and Foshay, Jour. Bact., *49*, 1945, 209). Capsules rare or absent. Non-motile. May show bipolar staining. Gram-negative.

No growth on plain agar or in liquid media without special enrichment (Tamura and Gibby, Jour. Bact., *45*, 1943, 361). Filterable through Berkefeld filters.

Growth occurs on coagulated egg yolk (McCoy and Chapin), on blood glucose cystine agar (Francis), on blood agar, glucose blood agar and glucose serum agar. The addition of fresh, sterile rabbit spleen to the surfaces of the last three media favors the growth of the organism.

Forms minute, viscous colonies after 2 to 5 days which may attain a diameter of 4 mm if well separated. Growth readily emulsifiable.

Growth on blood media is gray. May cause green discoloration of the blood.

Rough, smooth and mucoid variants have not been reported.

Hydrogen sulfide produced in a cystine medium.

Slight acid without gas may be produced from glucose, glycerol, maltose, mannose, fructose and dextrin.

Growth soluble in sodium ricinoleate.

Aerobic. No growth anaerobically.

Temperature relations: Optimum, 37° C. Thermal death point, 56° C. for 10 minutes. Survives best at low temperatures, even −70° C.

Pathogenicity: Penetrates unbroken skin to cause infection. Buboes and areas of necrosis produced in human and animal tissue. Infectious for man and most rodents, including rabbits, guinea pigs, rats, mice, squirrels, ground hogs, muskrats, beavers, water rats and lemmings.

Source: Originally isolated from California ground squirrels and later from more than 30 other forms of wild life in the United States and elsewhere. Found in lesions in man and animals with natural or experimental infections. Found especially in the livers, blood, lymph nodes and spleens of animals.

Habitat: The cause of tularemia in man; transmitted from wild animals to man by blood-sucking insects, by contact with infected animals or by drinking water. Disease known in North America, Japan, Russia, Norway, Sweden, Austria, Turkey, Czechoslovakia and Central Germany. See Burroughs, Holdenreid, Longanecker and Meyer (Jour. Inf. Dis., *76*, 1945, 115) for a complete list of known vertebrate hosts.

9. Pasteurella novicida Larson et al., 1955. (Larson, Wicht and Jellison, Public Health Reports, *70*, 1955, 253.)

no.vi′ci.da. L. adj. *novus* new; L. v. n.suffix -*cida* from L. v. *caedo* to cut, kill; M.L. noun *novicida* new-killer.

Description prepared by Jellison, April, 1955.

Coccoid to ovoid or short, rod-shaped cells, 0.20 to 0.28 by 0.28 micron in tissues, 0.7 by 1.7 microns in liquid media and 0.47 by 0.47 to 0.94 micron on solid media. Capsules not observed. Non-motile. Gram-negative.

No growth on plain agar without special enrichment.

Gelatin (without added cystine): Growth. No liquefaction.

Glucose cystine agar colonies: 6 to 7 mm in diameter, translucent.

Glucose cystine blood agar colonies: 8 mm in diameter, gray with a definite blue cast, smooth, slightly elevated, glistening, amorphous, entire. Good growth on primary isolation.

Yeast extract agar colonies: 3 mm in diameter, clear, convex, glistening; edges are smooth.

Yeast extract- or cystine-containing agar shakes: After 8 days at room temperature, at 30° or at 37° C., growth occurs on the surface and at a depth not exceeding 0.7 cm. Surface colonies are 5 mm in diameter, and those within the agar are 1 mm or less.

Horsemeat infusion agar: When infected liver or spleen is smeared over the surface, growth occurs only in the immediate vicinity of small pieces of tissue which adhere to the medium.

Blood agar colonies: 4 mm in diameter; resemble those on glucose cystine blood agar. No hemolysis.

Peptone broth: Abundant growth; moderately uniform turbidity; no pellicle; no surface growth; slight sediment which disintegrates on shaking.

Litmus milk: Unchanged.

Potato: No growth.

Indole not produced.

Hydrogen sulfide is produced.

Acid but no gas from glucose, fructose, sucrose and mannose.

Methyl red test is negative.

Acetylmethylcarbinol not produced.

Nitrites not produced from nitrates.

Ammonia is not produced.

Methylene blue is reduced.

Catalase-positive.

Aerobic, facultatively anaerobic.

Temperature relations: Optimum, 37° C. Thermal death point, 60° C. for 10 minutes.

Pathogenicity: Pathogenic for white mice, guinea pigs and hamsters. Produces lesions in experimental animals similar to those found in tularemia. Rabbits, white rats and pigeons are somewhat resistant; not known to infect man.

Relationships to other species: This organism is very similar to *Pasteurella tularensis* in gross appearance of cultures, in microscopic appearance and in pathogenicity. It is distinguished from *P. tula-* *rensis* and other species of *Pasteurella* by serological and fermentation tests.

Source: Isolated from a water sample taken from Ogden Bay, Utah.

Habitat: Water.

Genus II. Bordetella *Moreno-López, 1952.**

(Microbiol. Española, *5*, 1952, 177.)

Bor.de.tel'la. M.L. dim.ending -*ella*; M.L. fem.n. *Bordetella* named for Jules Bordet, who, with O. Gengou, first isolated the organism causing pertussis.

Minute coccobacilli. Motile and non-motile species occur. Gram-negative. On primary isolation, some species are dependent on complex media; all are hemolytic. Carbohydrates are not fermented. Litmus milk becomes alkaline. A dermonecrotic toxin is produced. Parasitic. Cause whooping cough or an infection clinically resembling it.

The type species is *Bordetella pertussis* (Holland) Moreno-López.

Key to the species of genus Bordetella.

I. Non-motile.
  A. No growth on plain agar in the smooth phase.
      1. *Bordetella pertussis.*
  B. Moderately rapid growth on plain agar with brown coloring of the medium.
      2. *Bordetella parapertussis.*
II. Motile.
      3. *Bordetella bronchiseptica.*

1. Bordetella pertussis (Holland, 1920) Moreno-López, 1952. (Microbe de coqueluche, Bordet and Gengou, Ann. Inst. Past., *20*, 1906, 731; *Hemophilus pertussis* Holland, Jour. Bact., *5*, 1920, 219; Moreno-López, Microbiol. Española, *5*, 1952, 177.)

per.tus'sis. L. prep. *per* very, severe; L. noun *tussis* cough; M.L. noun *pertussis* whooping cough; M.L. gen.noun *pertussis* of whooping cough.

Minute coccobacilli, 0.2 to 0.3 by 1.0 micron, occurring singly, in pairs and occasionally in short chains. Capsules may be demonstrated by a special technique (Lawson, Jour. Lab. Clin. Med., *25*, 1940, 435). Non-motile. Show a tendency to bipolar staining. Gram-negative.

No growth on the usual laboratory media. Adapted by repeated transfer with heavy inoculum; adaptation accompanied by a loss of original characteristics.

Bordet-Gengou medium containing at least 15 per cent blood is excellent for isolation and maintenance. Charcoal may be used to replace blood in certain agar media (Pollock, Brit. Jour. Exp. Path., *28*, 1947, 295).

Bordet-Gengou agar colonies: Smooth, raised, entire, pearly, glistening. Surrounded by a zone of hemolysis with indefinite periphery. Growth in 3 to 4 days.

Special liquid medium: Turbid; sediment is ropy.

Litmus milk: Alkaline in 12 to 14 days (after adaptation).

Indole not produced.

Carbohydrates not attacked.

Citrate not utilized as a sole source of carbon.

Nitrites not produced from nitrates.

Urea not split.

Catalase-positive.

Aerobic.

Optimum temperature, between 35° and 37° C.

Serologically homogeneous when first isolated (Phase I of Leslie and Gardner, Jour. Hyg., *31*, 1931, 423). Shows cross

---

* Prepared by Dr. Margaret Pittman, National Institutes of Health, Bethesda, Maryland, February, 1953.

agglutination with *Bordetella parapertussis* and *B. bronchiseptica. B. pertussis* antitoxin neutralizes toxin of *B. parapertussis* and of *B. bronchiseptica.*

Source: Isolated from the respiratory tract in cases of whooping cough.

Habitat: Etiologically associated with whooping cough.

2. Bordetella parapertussis (Eldering and Kendrick, 1937) Moreno-López, 1952. (Eldering and Kendrick, Jour. Bact., *33*, 1937, 71; *Bacillus para-pertussis* Eldering and Kendrick, Jour. Bact., *35*, 1938, 561; *Haemophilus parapertussis* Topley and Wilson, Princip. Bact. and Immun., 3rd ed., *1*, 1946, 802; Moreno-López, Microbiol. Española, *5*, 1952, 177.)

pa.ra.per.tus'sis. Gr. prep. *para* alongside of, resembling; M.L. noun *pertussis* a specific epithet; M.L. adj. *parapertussis* (*Bordetella*) *pertussis*-like.

Morphologically similar to *Bordetella pertussis*. Non-motile. Gram-negative.

Bordet-Gengou agar colonies: Like those of *B. pertussis*; surrounding medium is darkened followed by hemolysis. Growth in 1 to 2 days.

Peptone agar colonies: Like those on Bordet-Gengou agar. Brown coloring of medium.

Broth: Ropy sediment; brown coloring of medium.

Litmus milk: Alkaline in 2 to 4 days.

Indole not produced.

Carbohydrates not attacked.

Citrate utilized as a sole source of carbon.

Nitrites not produced from nitrates.

Urea usually split.

Catalase-positive.

Aerobic.

Optimum temperature, about 37° C.

Serologically homogeneous. Shows cross agglutination with *Bordetella pertussis* and *B. bronchiseptica*. Toxin neutralized by antitoxin of *B. pertussis* and of *B. bronchiseptica.*

Source: Isolated from the respiratory tract in cases of a whooping-cough-like disease.

Habitat: Etiologically associated with a whooping-cough-like disease.

3. Bordetella bronchiseptica (Ferry, 1912) Moreno-López, 1952. (Short, narrow bacillus, Ferry, Amer. Vet. Rev., *37*, 1910, 499; also see McGowan, Jour. Path. and Bact., *15*, 1911, 372; *Bacillus bronchicanis* Ferry, Jour. Inf. Dis., *8*, 1911, 402; *Bacillus bronchisepticus* Ferry, Amer. Vet. Rev., *41*, 1912, 79; *Bacterium bronchisepticus* Evans, Jour. Inf. Dis., *22*, 1918, 580; *Alcaligenes bronchisepticus* Bergey et al., Manual, 1st ed., 1923, 234; *Brucella bronchiseptica* Topley and Wilson, Princip. Bact. and Immun., 1st ed., *1*, 1931, 508; *Haemophilus bronchisepticus* Topley and Wilson, *ibid.*, 3rd ed., *1*, 1946, 787; Moreno-López, Microbiol. Española, *5*, 1952, 177.)

bron.chi.sep'ti.ca. Gr. noun *bronchus* the trachea; Gr. adj. *septicus* putrefactive, septic; M.L. adj. *bronchisepticus* apparently intended to mean "with an infected bronchus."

Morphologically similar to *Bordetella pertussis*. Motile by means of peritrichous flagella. Gram-negative.

Gelatin colonies: Similar to those on agar. No liquefaction.

Nutrient agar colonies: Smooth, raised, entire, pearly, glistening. No brown discoloration of medium.

Blood agar colonies: Similar to those on agar; surrounded by a zone of hemolysis. Rapid growth.

Broth: Turbid; thin, gray pellicle; ropy sediment.

Litmus milk: Alkaline in 1 to 2 days.

Indole not produced.

Carbohydrates not attacked.

Citrate utilized as a sole source of carbon.

Nitrites often produced from nitrates (Topley and Wilson).

Urea and asparagin are split.

Catalase-positive.

Aerobic.

Optimum temperature, 37° C.

Shows cross agglutination with *Bordetella pertussis* and *B. parapertussis*. Toxin indistinguishable from that of *B. pertussis* and of *B. parapertussis.*

Source: Isolated from dogs affected with distemper.

Habitat: Etiologically associated with bronchopneumonia in rodents, bronchopneumonia complicating distemper in dogs and occasionally with a whooping-cough-like disease in man.

Genus III. **Brucella** *Meyer and Shaw, 1920.**

(Jour. Inf. Dis., *27*, 1920, 173.)

Bru.cel'la. L. dim.ending -*ella*; M.L. fem.n. *Brucella* named for Sir David Bruce, who first recognized the organism causing undulant fever.

Short, rod-shaped to coccoid cells, 0.5 by 0.5 to 2.0 microns. Encapsulated. Non-motile. Gram-negative. Gelatin is not liquefied. No gas produced from carbohydrates. Urea is hydrolyzed. Parasitic, invading all animal tissues and producing infection of the genital organs, the mammary gland and the respiratory and intestinal tracts. Pathogenic for various species of domestic animals and man.

It has been found that a measurement of urease activity of the cells cannot be used as a means of differentiating the species in *Brucella* (Sanders and Warner, Jour. Bact., *62*, 1951, 591).

The differentiation of the species of *Brucella* by the bacteriostatic action of dyes depends upon the medium used. When tryptose agar (Difco) is used, basic fuchsin and thionin should be used in a final dilution of 1:100,000.

There are several forms of the R and mucoid types of *Brucella spp.* (Huddleson, Mich. Agr. Exp. Sta. Mem. 6, 1952). The true R type differs from the S type in its lack of pathogenicity, its antigenic properties, its susceptibility to agglutination by exposure of suspensions to heat and to acriflavine in concentration of 1:2000 and in its colonial appearance. The mucoid types differ antigenically, morphologically and culturally. Colonies on agar are spherical or flat, regular in contour, grayish to reddish yellow in appearance. Suspensions are agglutinated by heat and acriflavine; they are not always agglutinated by special agglutinating sera. There is no change in their growth characteristics on media containing either basic fuchsin or thionin.

For recent literature concerning this group of organisms, see Hoyer (Brucellosis, Amer. Assoc. Adv. Sci., Washington, 1950, 9), Pacheco and Thiago de Mello (Jour. Bact., *59*, 1950, 689), Sanders and Huddleson (Amer. Jour. Vet. Res., *11*, 1950, 75), Polding (Indian Vet. Jour., *27*, 1950, 170), Marr and Wilson (Proc. Soc. Exp. Biol. and Med., *75*, 1950, 438), Sanders and Warner (Jour. Bact., *62*, 1951, 591), White and Wilson (Jour. Bact., *61*, 1951, 239), Huddleson (Mich. Agr. Exp. Sta. Mem. 5, 1952, 67 pp.), Renoux (Ann. Inst. Past., *82*, 1952, 1), Pickett, Nelson and Liberman (Jour. Bact., *66*, 1953, 210), Cruickshank (Jour. Hyg., *52*, 1954, 105) and Pickett and Nelson (Jour. Bact., *69*, 1955, 333). For literature discussing a wasting disease of chickens caused by these organisms, see Dubois (Rev. Vet., *67*, 1910, 490), Huddleson and Emmel (Mich. State Coll. Agr. Exp. Sta., Tech. Bull. 103, 1929), Gillman and Brunett (Cornell Vet., *20*, 1930, 371) and Wilson (Jour. Hyg., *4*, 1933, 516).

The type species is *Brucella melitensis* (Hughes) Meyer and Shaw.

Key to the species of genus **Brucella.**

I. Grow in special media containing basic fuchsin.
    A. Grows in media containing thionin.
                1. *Brucella melitensis.*
    B. Does not grow in media containing thionin.
                2. *Brucella abortus.*
II. Does not grow in media containing basic fuchsin; grows in media containing thionin.
                3. *Brucella suis.*

---

* Revised by Prof. I. F. Huddleson, Michigan State College, East Lansing, Michigan, December, 1942; further revision, May, 1955.

DIFFERENTIAL CHARACTERS OF THE THREE SPECIES OF GENUS *Brucella*.

Species (a)	Infectivity for Guinea Pigs (a), 30 Days	Requires CO_2 for Isolation, 5 Per Cent	H_2S Formation, 4 Days	Urease Activity, 4 hr.	Catalase Activity, 30 Min.	Growth in the Presence of		Sugar Fermentation (c)					
						Thionin (b)	Basic fuchsin (b)	Glucose	Inositol	Maltose	Mannose	Rhamnose	Trehalose
Brucella melitensis type I	++++	0	-, ±	-, ++	++	++++	++++	+	0	0	0	0	0
Brucella abortus type I	++++	++	++	-, ++	+	0	++++	+	+	0	+	+	0
Brucella abortus type II	++++	++	++	-, ++	+	0	0	+	+	0	0	±	0
Brucella abortus type III	++++	++	++	-, ++	+	++++	++++	+	+	0	0	±	0
Brucella suis type I	++++	0	++++	++++	++++	++++	0	+	0	+	+	0	+
Brucella suis type II	++++	0	-, ±	++++	++++	++++	0	+	0	+	+	0	+
Brucella suis type III	++++	0	-, ±	++++	++++	++++	++++	+	0	+	+	0	+

(a) Type S, primary isolation; (b) Final conc., 10^{-5}; (c) Pickett and Nelson (Jour. Bact., *69*, 1955, 333).

Brucella melitensis. As indicated in the table, cultures of this species show some variation in characteristics. These variations, in turn, show some relationship to geographical distribution and/or to the host animal. The cultures described under I appear to be most typical of the species (Polding, Indian Jour. Vet. Res., *27*, 1950, 170).

Brucella abortus. The cultures described in the table under I are regarded as possessing the characteristics that are most typical for the species. The cultures described under II were first described by Wilson (Jour. of Hyg., *4*, 1933, 516) from cattle in France. Cultures showing the characters under III appear to come mainly from Asian countries (Indonesia, India, Iran, Turkey). Wilson and Miles (in Topley and Wilson, Princip. Bact. and Immun., 3rd ed., *1*, 1946, 820) record similar cultures from Southern Rhodesia.

Brucella suis. The cultures described in the table under I are regarded as typical of the species. Those described under II are representative of the Thomsen strain. Wilson and Miles (*ibid.*, 821) state that *Br. suis* strains from Denmark are more susceptible to all dyes than strains from America, although their differential susceptibility is the same. Those described under type III are representative of cultures isolated largely since 1949 from man and hogs from the hog-raising areas of central United States.

1. **Brucella melitensis** (Hughes, 1892) Meyer and Shaw, 1920. (Bruce, Practitioner, *39*, 1887, 161; also see *ibid.*, *40*. 1888, 241; and Rept. Army Med. Dept., London, *32*, 1890, Append. No. 4, 465; *streptococcus Miletensis* (sic) Hughes, The Mediterranean Naturalist, *2*, February 1, 1892, 325; *Micrococcus melitensis* Bruce, Ann. Inst. Past., *7*, April, 1893, 289; Hughes, La Riforma Med., *3*, Aug. or Sept., 1893, 789; also see Ann. Inst. Past., *7*, Aug., 1893, 630; Meyer and Shaw, Jour. Inf. Dis., *27*, 1920, 173.)

me.li.ten'sis. L. adj. *melitensis* of or pertaining to the Island of Malta.

Short, ellipsoidal rods, 0.3 to 0.4 micron in length, occurring singly, in pairs and rarely in short chains. Non-motile. Not acid-fast. Gram-negative.

Gelatin colonies: Small, clear, entire.

Gelatin stab: Slow growth. No liquefaction.

Agar colonies: Small, circular, convex, amorphous, smooth, glistening, entire, bluish green, grayish if R type.

Agar slant: Growth moist, honey-like, entire. After a week the agar is turned brownish and crystals may appear.

Broth: After 10 days, moderately turbid with grayish sediment. Reaction alkaline; pH 8.0 or higher.

Litmus milk: Unchanged at 24 hours; later becomes alkaline.

Potato: Scant, grayish growth becoming brownish.

Growth enhanced on peptone media of pH 7.0.

Indole not produced.

Glucose is fermented.

Nitrites produced from nitrates, often with complete disappearance of the nitrite (ZoBell and Meyer, Jour. Inf. Dis., *51*, 1932, 99). Because of the latter fact, reports in the literature are apparently contradictory.

Ammonia produced in slight amounts from urea.

Aerobic.

Temperature relations: Optimum, 37° C. No growth at 6° or at 45° C. Killed at 59° C.

Optimum pH (in an agar medium), between 7.0 and 7.2.

Comments: Strains of this species show wide differences in urease and catalase activity in cells of smooth-intermediate colonial types (Sanders and Warner, Amer. Jour. Vet. Res., *14*, 1953, 388).

Distinctive character: Requires no increased CO_2 tension.

Source: Isolated by Bruce (*op. cit.*, 1887, 161) from the spleen in fatal cases of Malta fever.

Habitat: Chief host is the milch goat. The cause of undulant fever (brucellosis) in man, of abortion in goats and of a wasting disease of chickens. May infect cows and hogs and may be excreted in their milk. Infectious for all domestic animals.

2. **Brucella abortus** (Schmidt and Weis, 1901) Meyer and Shaw, 1920. (Bacillus of abortion, Bang, Ztschr. f. Thiermed., *1*, 1897, 241; *Bacterium abortus* Schmidt and Weis, Bakterierne, 1901, 266; Meyer and Shaw, Jour. Inf. Dis., *27*, 1920, 173.)

ab.or'tus. L. noun *abortus, abortūs* abortion.

The morphological and cultural characters are similar to those of *Brucella melitensis* with the following exceptions: Requires 5 per cent CO_2 for isolation; becomes aerobic after several transfers; the browning of the medium in agar slant culture is less marked; S cultures can be differentiated from those of *B. melitensis*, but not from those of *B. suis*, by the agglutinin absorption test.

Optimum pH for growth (in an agar medium), between 7.0 and 7.2; optimum pH for isolation (in an agar medium with an atmosphere of 5 per cent CO_2), between 7.5 and 7.8. pH drops to 7.1 or 7.2.

Source: Isolated from the tissues and milk of infected cattle and hogs and from blood in human cases of undulant fever.

Habitat: Chief host is the milch cow. Causes infectious abortion in cattle; the same effects are produced in mares, sheep, rabbits, guinea pigs and all other domestic animals. Causes undulant fever (brucellosis) in man and a wasting disease in chickens.

3. **Brucella suis** Huddleson, 1929. (Organism resembling *Bacillus abortus*, Anonymous, U.S.D.A. Ann. Rept. Secy. Dept., Rept. of Chief Bur. Animal Ind., 1914, 86 (30); authorship established by Traum in North Amer. Vet., *1*, No. 2, 1920; described as *Bacillus abortus* by Good and Smith, Jour. Bact., *1*, 1916, 415; Huddleson, Undulant Fever Symposium, Amer. Pub. Health Assoc., (Oct., 1928) 1929, 24; also see Michigan Agr. Exp. Sta. Tech. Bull. 100, 1929, 12.)

su'is. L. noun *sus* the hog, swine; L. gen.noun *suis* of the hog.

The morphological and cultural characters are similar to those of *Brucella melitensis*.

S cultures of *Brucella suis* can be differentiated from S cultures of *Brucella melitensis*, but not from S cultures of *Brucella abortus*, by the agglutinin absorption test.

Source: Isolated from urogenital and many other organs of swine.

Habitat: Chief host is the hog. Causes abortion in swine, undulant fever (brucellosis) in man and a wasting disease in chickens. Also infectious for horses, dogs, cows, monkeys, goats and laboratory animals.

Genus IV. **Haemophilus** *Winslow et al., 1917.**

(*Hemophilus* (sic) Winslow, Broadhurst, Buchanan, Krumwiede, Rogers and Smith, Jour. Bact., *2*, 1917, 561.)

Hae.mo'phi.lus. Gr. noun *haema* blood; Gr. adj. *philus* loving; M.L. mas.n. *Haemophilus* the blood lover.

---

* Prepared by Dr. Margaret Pittman, National Institutes of Health, Bethesda, Maryland, August, 1955.

Minute, rod-shaped cells which are sometimes thread-forming and pleomorphic. Non-motile. Gram-negative. Strict parasites, growing only in the presence of certain growth accessory substances. May or may not be pathogenic. Found in various lesions and secretions, as well as in normal respiratory tracts, of vertebrates.

The type species is *Haemophilus influenzae* (Lehmann and Neumann) Winslow et al.

Key to the species of genus **Haemophilus.**

I. Affect warm-blooded animals.
  A. Affect the respiratory tract or the conjunctiva.
    1. Dependence on V (phosphopyridine nucleotide) and X (hemin) determined.
      a. Require both V and X for growth.
          1. *Haemophilus influenzae.*
          2. *Haemophilus aegyptius.*
          3. *Haemophilus suis.*
          4. *Haemophilus haemolyticus.*
          5. *Haemophilus gallinarum.*
    aa. Require either V or X for growth, but not both.
      b. Require V but not X for growth.
          6. *Haemophilus parainfluenzae.*
          7. *Haemophilus parahaemolyticus.*
      bb. Require X but not V for growth.
          8. *Haemophilus aphrophilus.*
          9. *Haemophilus influenzae-murium.*
         10. *Haemophilus ovis.*
    2. Exact dependence on V and X undetermined.
         11. *Haemophilus putoriorum.*
  B. Affect the genital region.
    1. Require X but not V for growth.
         12. *Haemophilus ducreyi.*
         13. *Haemophilus haemoglobinophilus.*
    2. Exact dependence on V and X unknown.
         14. *Haemophilus citreus.*
II. Affects cold-blooded animals. Requires diphosphothiamine but not V or X for growth.
         15. *Haemophilus piscium.*

1. Haemophilus influenzae (Lehmann and Neumann, 1896) Winslow et al., 1917. (Influenzabacillus, Pfeiffer, Deutsche med. Wochnschr., *18*, 1892, 28; also see Ztschr. f. Hyg., *13*, 1893, 357; *Bacterium influenzae* Lehmann and Neumann, Bakt. Diag., 1 Aufl., *2*, 1896, 187; Winslow, Broadhurst, Buchanan, Krumwiede, Rogers and Smith, Jour. Bact., *2*, 1917, 561.)

in.flu.en'zae. Italian noun *influenza* influenza; M.L. gen.noun *influenzae* of influenza.

Common name: The Pfeiffer Bacillus.

Very small rods, 0.2 to 0.3 by 0.5 to 2.0 microns, occurring singly and in pairs, occasionally in short chains and at times in the form of long threads. Some strains are encapsulated. Frequently show a marked tendency to bipolar staining. Non-motile. Gram-negative.

Requires both the factors V and X for growth in all media.

Gelatin colonies: No growth.

Gelatin stab: No growth.

Blood agar colonies: Small, circular, transparent, homogeneous, entire. Satel. litism with *Micrococcus.*

V and X transparent agar colonies: 1 to 2 mm in diameter, bluish sheen or iridescent in transmitted light.

Blood agar slant: Thin, filiform, transparent growth.

Chocolate agar slant: Luxuriant growth.

Blood broth: Slightly turbid. No hemolysis.

Litmus milk with blood: Rendered very slightly alkaline by some strains.

Sterilized potato slant: No growth.

Fresh, unheated, sterile potato added to broth favors development.

Indole is produced by some strains.

Various carbohydrates are attacked by some strains, provided a suitable medium is used, while other strains do not attack any of the carbohydrates. Mannitol and lactose are never fermented.

Nitrites produced from nitrates.

Aerobic, facultatively anaerobic; CO_2 may favor primary isolation.

Temperature relations: Optimum, 37° C. Minimum, between 25° and 27° C. Maximum, 43° C. Killed in thirty minutes at 55° C.

Pathogenic; strains may or may not be encapsulated.

Six serological types (a–f) of *Haemophilus influenzae* are recognized on the basis of precipitation of immune serum by capsular substance. Strains from cerebrospinal fluid are usually of type b. The majority of the strains from the respiratory tract are not type-specific, but they may cause infection.

Source: Isolated by Pfeiffer from cases of influenza; also found in the nasopharynx, in sputum, sinuses, conjunctiva, cerebrospinal fluid, blood and in pus from joints.

Habitat: Found in the respiratory tract. A cause of acute respiratory infections, of acute conjunctivitis and of purulent meningitis of children, rarely of adults. Regarded by Pfeiffer and by others to be the cause of influenza.

2. **Haemophilus aegyptius** (Trevisan, 1889) Pittman and Davis, 1950. (Koch, Wiener med. Wochnschr., *33*, 1883, 1550; reprinted in Arb. a. d. kaiserl. Gesundheitsamte, *3*, 1887, Anlage 2, 19; Weeks, Arch. Ophthalmol., *15* (old series), 1886, 441; also see New York Med. Record, *31*, 1887, 571; *Bacillus aegyptius* Trevisan, I generi e le specie delle Batteriacee, 1889, 13; *Bacterium aegyptiacum* Lehmann and Neumann, Bakt. Diag., 2 Aufl., *2*, 1899, 191; *Hemophilus conjunctivitidis* Bergey et al., Manual, 1st ed., 1923, 270; Pittman and Davis, Jour. Bact., *59*, 1950, 413.)

ae.gyp'ti.us. L. adj. *aegyptius* Egyptian. Common name: The Koch-Weeks Bacillus.

Rods, 0.25 to 0.5 by 1.0 to 2.5 microns, occurring singly, occasionally in short chains and at times in the form of threads. Show bipolar staining. Non-motile. Gram-negative.

Requires both the factors V and X for growth.

Blood agar colonies: Very small, circular, transparent, homogeneous, entire. No hemolysis. Satellitism with *Micrococcus*.

V and X transparent agar colonies: 1 to 2 mm in diameter, bluish sheen in transmitted light.

V and X broth: Turbid.

Indole not produced.

Weak acidity but no gas from glucose, fructose and galactose. No acid from xylose, maltose, sucrose, lactose or mannitol.

Nitrites produced from nitrates.

Aerobic, facultatively anaerobic.

Optimum temperature, between 34° and 37° C. Growth range, 25° to 40° C.

Pathogenic for man.

Serologically homogeneous or closely related to, and distinct from, *Haemophilus influenzae*. Agglutinates human red blood cells.

Source: Isolated from conjunctiva.

Habitat: Causes acute or subacute infectious conjunctivitis in warm climates.

3. **Haemophilus suis** Hauduroy et al., 1937. (*Hemophilus influenzae suis* Lewis and Shope, Jour. Exp. Med., *54*, 1931, 361; Hauduroy et al., Dict. d. Bact. Path., 1937, 258.)

su'is. L. noun *sus* a hog, swine; L. gen.noun *suis* of swine.

Morphologically resembles *Haemophilus influenzae*.

Requires both the factors V and X for growth (Lewis and Shope, *op. cit.*, 1931, 361). Requires V but not X; serum added to Levinthal agar stimulates growth (Alexander, in Dubos, Bacterial and Mycotic Infections of Man, 2nd ed., 1952, 528).

Blood agar colonies: Very minute. No

hemolysis. Satellitism with contaminating organism.

Chocolate blood agar colonies: 1.0 to more than 2.0 mm in diameter, grayish, semi-transparent, circular, flattened with a sharply contoured edge. Grows more feebly than does *Haemophilus influenzae.*

Litmus milk containing blood: No change.

Indole not produced.

Weak acidity from maltose and sucrose.

Nitrites produced from nitrates.

Slightly pathogenic, if at all, for laboratory animals.

Aerobic, facultatively anaerobic.

Optimum temperature, 37° C.

Serologically heterogeneous. Some cross aggutination occurs with *Haemophilus influenzae.* There is one type-specific group based on capsular substance, but no relationship to the 6 types of *Haemophilus influenzae* (Alexander, *loc. cit.*).

Source: Isolated from the respiratory tract and heart blood of cases of swine influenza.

Habitat: With the swine influenza virus, causes typical swine influenza (Shope, Jour. Exp. Med., *54*, 1931, 373).

4. **Haemophilus haemolyticus** Bergey et al., 1923. (Bacillus X, Pritchett and Stillman, Jour. Exp. Med., *29*, 1919, 259; also see Stillman and Bourn, Jour. Exp. Med., *32*, 1920, 665; Bergey et al., Manual, 1st ed., 1923, 269.)

hae.mo.ly'ti.cus. Gr. noun *haema* blood; Gr. adj. *lyticus* loosening, dissolving; M.L. adj. *haemolyticus* blood-dissolving.

Morphologically similar to *Haemophilus influenzae.* Non-motile. Gram-negative.

Requires both the factors V and X for growth (Rivers, Johns Hopkins Hosp. Bull., *33*, 1922, 149).

Blood agar colonies: Resemble those of *Haemophilus influenzae,* but these are surrounded by a zone of hemolysis.

Blood agar slant: Thin, filiform, transparent growth.

Blood broth: Turbid, showing hemolysis.

Blood milk mixture: Slightly alkaline.

Sterile, unheated potato favors development.

Indole produced by some strains.

Various carbohydrates fermented by some strains, while other strains do not attack carbohydrates.

Nitrites produced from nitrates.

Aerobic, facultatively anaerobic.

Optimum temperature, 37° C.

Usually non-pathogenic; on rare occasions causes subacute endocarditis.

Habitat: Found in the upper respiratory tract of man.

5. **Haemophilus gallinarum** (Delaplane et al., 1934) Eliot and Lewis, 1934. (*Bacillus hemoglobinophilus coryzae gallinarum* de Blieck, Tijdsch. v. Diergeneensk., *58*, 1931, 310; also see Vet. Jour., *88*, 1932, 9; Delaplane, Erwin and Stuart, R. I. State Coll. Sta. Bull. 244, May, 1934; Eliot and Lewis, Jour. Amer. Vet. Med. Assoc., *84*, 1934, 878.)

gal.li.na'rum. L. noun *gallina* a hen; L. fem.pl.gen.n. *gallinarum* of hens.

Common name: The fowl coryza bacillus.

Small coccobacilli occurring singly, in pairs and in short chains. At times very pleomorphic with long filaments. Non-motile. Show bipolar staining. Gram-negative.

Requires both the factors V and X for growth (Schalm and Beach, Jour. Bact., *31*, 1936, 161; Delaplane and Stuart, Jour. Agr. Res., *63*, 1941, 29). Fails to grow on certain media which support the growth of *Haemophilus influenzae* (Delaplane et al., *op. cit.*, 1934; Gregory, Am. Jour. Vet. Res., *5*, 1944, 72).

Requires approximately 1.0 per cent sodium chloride in media for growth.

Blood agar colonies: 0.3 mm or less in diameter, smooth, translucent, becoming more opaque with age.

Filtered chocolate agar colonies: 0.5 to 0.6 mm in diameter, convex, smooth, translucent to slightly opaque, glistening.

Indole not produced.

Glucose fermented; final pH, 6.4.

Nitrites produced from nitrates.

Aerobic, facultatively anaerobic; CO_2 favors growth.

Optimum temperature, 37° C. Killed in 4 to 6 minutes at 55° C.

Pathogenic for fowls.

Source: Isolated from the nasal exudates of fowls.

Habitat: Causes Type I fowl coryza

characterized by rapid onset and short duration; in association with coccobacilliform bodies of Nelson, causes Type III fowl coryza characterized by rapid onset and long duration (Nelson, Jour. Exp. Med., *67*, 1938, 847).

6. Haemophilus parainfluenzae Rivers, 1922. (Johns Hopkins Hosp. Bull., *33*, 1922, 429.)

pa.ra.in.flu.en'zae. Gr. prep. *para* alongside of, resembling; M.L. noun *influenzae* a specific epithet; M.L. adj. *parainfluenzae* (*Haemophilus*) *influenzae*-like.

Morphologically similar to *Haemophilus influenzae*. Non-motile. Gram-negative.

Requires the V factor for growth.

Blood agar colonies: Resemble those of *Haemophilus influenzae*. No hemolysis.

Blood agar slant: Thin, filiform transplant.

Broth containing yeast extract: Floccular sediment.

Indole produced by some strains from the cat.

Various carbohydrates fermented by some strains, while other strains do not attack carbohydrates.

Nitrites produced from nitrates.

Aerobic, facultatively anaerobic.

Optimum temperature, 37° C.

Usually non-pathogenic; occasionally causes subacute endocarditis.

Habitat: Found in the upper respiratory tract of man and cat.

7. Haemophilus parahaemolyticus Pittman, 1953. (Haemolytic influenza bacillus, Fildes, Brit. Jour. Exp. Path., *5*, 1924, 69; *Hemophilus parainfluenzae*, hemolytic, Valentine and Rivers, Jour. Exp. Med., *45*, 1927, 993; Pittman, Jour. Bact., *65*, 1953, 750.)

pa.ra.hae.mo.ly'ti.cus. Gr. prep. *para* alongside of, resembling; M.L. noun *haemolyticus* a specific epithet; M.L. adj. *parahaemolyticus* (*Haemophilus*) *haemolyticus*-like.

Usually larger and stain more heavily and unevenly than the other influenza bacilli. Vary from coccoid to long, tangled thread forms with much pleomorphism. Non-motile. Gram-negative.

Requires the V factor for growth in all media.

Blood agar colonies: 1 to 3 mm in diameter, slightly opaque, homogeneous, entire, friable, surrounded by a large, clear zone of hemolysis.

Blood agar slant: Thin, filiform, slightly opaque growth. Death occurs in a few days.

Broth: Stringy, floccular sediment; clear supernatant.

Indole usually not produced.

Weak acidity from glucose and usually from sucrose and maltose.

Nitrites produced from nitrates.

Aerobic, facultatively anaerobic.

Optimum temperature, 37° C.

Habitat: Found in the upper respiratory tract; frequently associated with acute pharyngitis and occasionally causes subacute endocarditis.

8. Haemophilus aphrophilus Khairat, 1940. (Jour. Path. and Bact., *50*, 1940, 497.)

a.phro'phi.lus. Gr. noun *aphrus* foam; Gr. adj. *philus* loving; M.L. adj. *aphrophilus* foam-loving.

Coccobacilli, 0.4 by 1.5 to 2.0 microns, occurring singly and in irregular clumps. After repeated culture long, curved and occasionally filamentous forms occur. Non-motile. Gram-negative.

Requires the X factor for growth in air containing CO_2, but not in the absence of air.

Gelatin stab: Slight growth at 37° C. No liquefaction.

Blood agar colonies: After one day, 0.15 to 0.4 mm in diameter, circular, entire, convex, smooth, glistening, translucent, butyrous. After three days, 0.5 to 0.7 mm in diameter with olive-green discoloration of agar.

Tryptic digest broth: Faint, uniform turbidity with discrete colonies adhering to glass.

Litmus milk: Slightly acid after 14 days.

Indole not produced.

Acid but no gas from glucose, maltose and lactose in 2 to 4 days and from starch and glycogen in 9 to 10 days. No acid from galactose, fructose, raffinose, xylose, mannitol, dulcitol, sorbitol, salicin or inulin.

Nitrites produced from nitrates.

Microaerophilic, facultatively anaerobic. Grows best in the presence of CO_2.

Optimum temperature, 37° C. Killed in 10 minutes at 60° C.

Non-pathogenic for guinea pigs and mice.

Source: Isolated from the blood and heart valve of a case of endocarditis.

Habitat: Found in the blood and on the heart valve of one case of endocarditis.

9. Haemophilus influenzae-murium

(Kairies and Schwartzer, 1936) Lwoff, 1939. (*Bacterium influenzae murium* (sic) Kairies and Schwartzer, Cent. f. Bakt., I Abt., Orig., *137*, 1936, 351; *Haemophilus influenzae murium* (sic) Lwoff, Ann. Inst. Past., *62*, 1939, 168.)

in.flu.en'zae-mu'ri.um. Italian noun *influenza* influenza; L. noun *mus*, *muris* mouse; M.L. gen.noun *influenzae-murium* influenza of mice.

Small, short, thick coccobacilli occurring singly and at times in the form of threads. Filterable forms pass through 0.4- to 0.6-micron pores. Non-motile. Shows bipolar staining. Gram-negative.

Requires the factor X for growth (Ivanovics and Ivanovics, Cent. f. Bakt., I Abt., Orig., *139*, 1937, 184).

Gelatin: No liquefaction.

Levinthal agar colonies: Up to 4 mm in diameter, round, convex, glistening, bluish, transparent. Resemble *Haemophilus influenzae* colonies. Become opaque and whitish with age.

Blood agar colonies. Whitish. No hemolysis.

Chocolate agar: Good growth.

Endo agar: Red colonies in 2 to 3 days.

Levinthal or egg broth: Uniformly turbid.

Milk not coagulated.

Indole not produced.

Acid from glucose, fructose, lactose, maltose and sucrose. No acid from mannite.

Aerobic.

Optimum temperature, 37° C.

Slightly pathogenic for mice but not for guinea pigs.

Serologically homogeneous and distinct from *Haemophilus influenzae*, *Pasteurella* and *Salmonella typhosa*.

Source: Isolated from the noses and pharynges of mice.

Habitat: Causes conjunctivitis and respiratory infections in mice.

10. Haemophilus ovis Mitchell, 1925.

(Jour. Amer. Vet. Assoc., *68*, 1925, 8.)

o'vis. L. fem.n. *ovis* a sheep; L. gen.noun *ovis* of a sheep.

Small, short, somewhat pleomorphic rods occurring singly and at times in short chains. Coccoid forms occur in old cultures. Non-motile. Gram-negative.

Requires the X factor when newly isolated. After serial passage on chocolate agar, slight growth on plain agar medium. Primary isolation best on chocolate blood agar.

Gelatin slant: Very slight growth in 4 days.

Gelatin stab: No growth.

Chocolate blood agar colonies: After 24 to 36 hours, pinhead in size, discrete, moist, viscid, translucent; become gray, scaly and adherent to the medium with age.

Blood broth: No hemolysis.

Plain broth: After adaptation, turbid. Floating ropy strands. Slimy sediment.

Litmus milk: No change.

Potato: No growth.

Indole not produced.

Acid but no gas from glucose, fructose, galactose, sucrose, raffinose, sorbitol, mannitol, mannose and maltose. Weak acidity from lactose and xylose. No acid from arabinose, rhammose, salicin or inositol.

Nitrites produced from nitrates.

Aerobic.

Optimum temperature, 37° C. Slight growth at 28° C.

Pathogenic for guinea pigs and sheep.

Source: Isolated from the lungs of sheep.

Habitat: Causes bronchial pneumonia and generalized hemorrhagic involvement in sheep.

11. Haemophilus putoriorum Hauduroy et al., 1937.

(*Bacterium influenzae putoriorum multiforme* Kairies, Ztschr. f. Hyg., *117*, 1935, 12; Hauduroy et al., Dict. d. Bact. Path., 1937, 258.)

pu.to.ri.o'rum. M.L. mas.n. *Putorius*

generic name of ferret; M.L. gen.pl.noun *putoriorum* of ferrets.

Coccoid to bacillary rods with a strong pleomorphic tendency. Non-motile. Show bipolar staining. Gram-negative.

Growth requirement for V and X unknown. Growth reliable only on media containing blood. On ordinary media growth occurs only in the vicinity of other bacteria. Less hemoglobinophilic than is *Haemophilus influenzae*.

Levinthal agar colonies: Young colonies are small with elevated centers and transparent peripheries; older colonies are flat with bluish, glassy appearance in transmitted light and bluish gray with whitish luster in reflected light.

Agar slant: Poor, thin growth when subcultured from Levinthal agar.

Broth: Lightly turbid; fine granules.

Odor like that of *Haemophilus influenzae*.

Non-pathogenic for laboratory animals when inoculated in pure culture. Intracutaneous inoculation produces a marked hemorrhagic lesion.

Serologically, different strains are related but not homogeneous. Distinct from *Haemophilus influenzae* and *Haemophilus suis*.

Source: Isolated from the respiratory tracts of ferrets.

Habitat: Found in the respiratory tracts of ferrets.

12. **Haemophilus ducreyi** (Neveu-Lemaire, 1921) Bergey et al., 1923. (Ducrey, Riforma Med., *5*, 1889, 98; also see Cong. internat. de dermatol. et syph., Compt. rend., Paris, 1890, 229; Monatsh. f. prakt. Dermatol., *9*, 1889, 387; and *ibid*, *21*, 1895, 57, abstract in Cent. f. Bakt., I Abt., *18*, 1895, 290; Streptobacillus of soft chancre, Unna, Monatsh. f. prakt. Dermatol., *14*, 1892, 485; also see *ibid*, *21*, 1895, 61; *Bacillus ulceris cancrosi* Kruse, in Flügge, Die Mikroorganismen, 3 Aufl., *2*, 1896, 456; *Coccobacillus ducreyi* Neveu-Lemaire, Précis Parasitol. Hum., 5th ed., 1921, 20; Bergey et al., Manual, 1st ed., 1923, 271.)

du.crey'i. M.L. gen.noun *ducreyi* of Ducrey; named for A. Ducrey, the bacteriologist who first isolated this organism.

Small rods, 0.5 by 1.5 to 2.0 microns, with rounded ends, occurring singly and in short chains. Non-motile. Gram-negative.

Requires the X factor (Lwoff, Ann. Inst. Past., *62*, 1939, 168) and other enrichment for growth.

Gelatin colonies: No growth.

Gelatin stab: No growth.

Blood agar colonies: Small, grayish, glistening. Slight zone of hemolysis around the colony in three or four days (Teague and Deibert, Jour. Med. Research, *43*, 1922, 61).

Best growth is obtained on clotted rabbit, sheep or human blood heated to 55° C. for 15 minutes and in casein digest agar containing blood (Teague and Deibert, Jour. Urology, *4*, 1920, 543).

Aerobic, facultatively anaerobic.

Optimum temperature, 37° C.

Habitat: The cause of soft chancre (chancroid).

13. **Haemophilus haemoglobinophilus** (Lehmann and Neumann, 1907) Murray, 1939. (*Bacillus haemoglobinophilus canis* Friedberger, Cent. f. Bakt., I Abt., Orig., *33*, 1903, 401; *Bacterium haemoglobinophilus* Lehmann and Neumann, Bakt. Diag., 4 Aufl., *2*, 1907, 270; Murray, in Manual, 5th ed., 1939, 309.)

hae.mo.glo.bi.no'phi.lus. Gr. noun *haema* blood; L. noun *globus* a sphere; M.L. noun *haemoglobinum* hemoglobin; Gr. adj. *philus* loving; M.L. adj. *haemoglobinophilus* hemoglobin-loving.

Small rods, 0.2 to 0.3 by 0.5 to 2.0 microns, occurring singly, in pairs and in short chains. Non-motile. Gram-negative.

Requires the X factor for growth.

Blood agar colonies: Small, clear, transparent, entire. Old colonies become opaque.

Blood broth: Turbid.

Blood milk mixture: Doubtful development.

Indole is produced.

Acid but no gas from glucose, fructose, galactose, mannitol, sucrose and xylose. No acid from maltose, lactose, dextrin, arabinose or glycerol (Rivers, Jour. Bact., *7*, 1922, 579).

Nitrites produced from nitrates.

Aerobic, facultatively anaerobic.

Optimum temperature, 37° C.

Habitat: Occurs in large numbers in preputial secretions of dogs.

14. **Haemophilus citreus** Diernhofer, 1949. (Wiener tierärztl. Monatsschr., *36*, 1949, 582.)

cit're.us. L. adj. *citreus* of the citron; M.L. adj. *citreus* lemon-colored.

Rods, 0.5 by 1.0 to 2.0 microns, occurring singly and in short chains; frequently pleomorphic with long threads. Non-motile. Stain poorly and unevenly, showing bipolar bodies. Gram-negative.

Gelatin plus blood: No liquefaction.

Plain agar: No growth.

Blood agar containing 20 to 30 per cent blood and 1.0 per cent glucose is optimum for isolation. Colonies are 1 to 2 mm in diameter, flat, moist and entire. Some strains produce a narrow zone of hemolysis around the colonies. Become slightly yellow; lemon-yellow when massed by loop.

V and X agar colonies: Very small, transparent, colorless.

Serum, pus, fresh milk, potato extract and yeast extract added to chocolate agar stimulate luxuriant growth.

Indole is produced.

Weak acid from glucose.

Nitrites produced from nitrates.

Non-pathogenic for mice, guinea pigs and calves. Does not induce disease in the genital tracts of cattle.

Aerobic.

Grows at 37° C. Killed in 30 minutes at 50° C.

Source: Isolated from genital secretions from acute and chronic cases of vesicular exanthema (exanthema coitale) in cattle.

15. **Haemophilus piscium** Snieszko et al., 1950. (Snieszko, Griffin and Friddle, Jour. Bact., *59*, 1950, 699.)

pis'ci.um. L. noun *piscis* fish; M.L. gen.pl.noun *piscium* of fishes.

Rods, in lesions measuring 0.5 to 0.7 by 2.0 microns, in cultures measuring 0.8 to 1.0 by 1.0 to 3.0 microns, occurring singly, in pairs, in irregular groups and occasionally as filaments up to 12.0 microns in length. Non-motile. May show bipolar staining. Gram-negative.

Requires diphosphothiamine or adenosine triphosphate for growth (Griffin, Arch. Biochem., *30*, 1951, 100). Supplied by peptic digest of fish tissue or 5 per cent sterile, unheated potato extract; V and X factors are not required. X in presence of diphosphothiamine increases growth response (Griffin, Yale Jour. Biol. and Med., *24*, 1952, 411).

Fish extract gelatin colonies: Same as on agar. No liquefaction.

Fish extract gelatin stab: Growth best near surface, filiform. No liquefaction.

Fish extract agar colonies: 1 to 3 mm in diameter, circular, entire, convex, opaque, smooth, cream-colored. S variants are butyrous, R variants are compact and tough.

Blood agar: Beta hemolysis.

Fish extract agar slant: In 2 to 3 days, growth is filiform, slightly glistening, cream-colored. S variants are butyrous, R variants are brittle.

Fish extract broth: R variants show transient clouding, then granular; adherent to walls; clearing of medium; scant pellicle or ring within a week. S variants remain uniformly clouded for several days.

Fish extract litmus milk: No change.

Potato: No visible growth.

Indole not produced.

Acid but no gas in 2 to 3 days in fish extract broth with glucose, fructose or sucrose; slowly with maltose, trehalose or starch; weak and slowly with mannose, galactose, cellobiose or dextrin. No acid with arabinose, xylose, rhamnose, lactose, melibiose, raffinose, melezitose, inulin or alcohols.

Methyl red test positive; Voges-Proskauer test negative after one week. Fish extract used in media.

Nitrites produced from nitrates.

Aerobic, facultatively anaerobic.

Optimum temperature, between 20° and 25° C. No growth at 35° C., slow growth at 7° C.

Pathogenic for trout.

Source: Isolated from trout with ulcer disease.

Habitat: Found in infected trout. A cause of ulcer disease in trout.

Genus V. Actinobacillus *Brumpt, 1910.**

(Brumpt, Précis de Parasitologie, Paris, 1st ed., 1910, 849; *Cladascus* Enderlein (in part), Sitzber. Ges. Naturf. Freunde, Berlin, 1917, 316; *Pfeifferella* Buchanan, Jour. Bact., *3*, 1918, 54; not *Pfeifferella* Labbé, Sporozoa, in Das Tierreich, Lief. 5, 1899, 60; *Malleomyces* Pribram, Klassifikation der Schizomyceten, Leipzig, 1933, 11 and 93; not *Malleomyces* Hallier, Ztschr. f. Parasitenkunde, 1870, 119; *Loefflerella* Gay et al., Agents of Disease and Host Resistance, Indianapolis, 1935, 782.)

Ac.ti.no.ba.cil′lus. Gr. noun *actis, actinis* a ray, beam; L. dim.noun *bacillus* a small rod; M.L. noun *Actinobacillus* ray bacillus or rod.

Small to medium-sized, coccoid to rod-shaped cells which rarely grow into filaments; under special conditions the filaments may show some branching. Non-motile. There is a tendency to show bipolar staining. Gram-negative. Colonies may be mucous or stringy, especially when freshly isolated, and white, grayish white, yellowish or bluish in color. Aerobic to facultatively anaerobic. Microaerophilic in primary cultures. Acid but no gas from carbohydrates, when fermented. Pathogenic for animals; some species attack man.

The type species is *Actinobacillus lignieresii* Brumpt.

Key to the species of genus **Actinobacillus**.

I. Little or no growth on potato.
  A. Growth in milk.
    1. Nitrites not produced from nitrates. Non-pigmented growth on glycerol agar.
        1. *Actinobacillus lignieresii.*
    2. Nitrites produced from nitrates.
        2. *Actinobacillus equuli.*
  B. No growth in milk.
    1. Growth on ordinary agar or broth.
        3. *Actinobacillus actinomycetemcomitans.*
    2. No growth on ordinary agar or broth.
        4. *Actinobacillus actinoides.*
II. Good growth on potato. Yellowish growth on glycerol agar.
        5. *Actinobacillus mallei.*

1. **Actinobacillus lignieresii** Brumpt, 1910. (Actinobacilo, Lignières and Spitz, Boletin d. Agr. y Ganaderia, Buenos Aires, *11*, 1902, 169; Actinobacille, Lignières and Spitz, Cent. f. Bakt., I Abt., Orig., *35*, 1903, 454; *Actinobacillus Lignièresi* (sic) Brumpt, Précis de Parasitol., Paris., 1st ed., 1910, 849.)

lig.ni.e.re′si.i. M.L. gen.noun *lignieresii* of Lignières; named for J. Lignières, one of the bacteriologists who first isolated this organism.

Rod-shaped cells, 0.4 by 1.15 to 1.25 microns, on primary isolation; later, especially on agar, cocco-bacillary and diplococcal forms occur. Streptobacillary forms appear in serum broth, and in old cultures, principally in serum broth, involution

forms occur. Non-motile. Frequently show bipolar staining. Gram-negative.

Gelatin: Growth sparse, if at all. No liquefaction.

Infusion-peptone-agar: Good growth, favored by the addition of serum or blood. Primary cultures succeed when granules are broken. Surface colonies measure 1 mm and may reach 2 to 3 mm in diameter; translucent and bluish, later opaque. Colonies in primary isolations may be rather firmly attached to the agar surface; when touched by the tip of the needle a ropy thread may be pulled off, the colony finally jerking to the tip of the needle leaving a rough spot on the agar surface. In subcultures the ropiness gradually is lost, but the growth continues to be mucous.

---

* Prepared by Prof. Dr. H. Haupt, University of Giessen, Giessen, Germany, April, 1955.

Glycerol-agar: Growth non-pigmented (Thompson, Jour. Bact., *26*, 1933, 224).

Broth: Moderate growth, favored by the addition of serum and peptone. Freshly isolated strains grow in the form of small granules which adhere to the walls of the tube or are collected on its bottom, leaving the broth fairly clear. On the surface, a fine, fragile pellicle is formed. Later generations may grow rather diffusely. No change in reaction of medium. No odor.

Coagulated serum and Loeffler serum: Good growth. A whitish, opaque layer is produced. No proteolysis.

Litmus milk: Most strains produce no change, some strains produce a slight reddening after 4 to 6 days. No coagulation.

Potato: On natural potato, little or no growth; on potato rendered alkaline, a rather feeble, shining and yellowish gray layer may be formed.

Indole produced in small amounts.

Hydrogen sulfide not produced.

Acid but no gas within 48 hours from glucose, maltose, sucrose and mannitol; some strains, after longer incubation, also produce acid from lactose, galactose, raffinose, glycerol and salicin. No acid within 10 days from arabinose, rhamnose, adonitol, dulcitol, inositol, sorbitol or inulin.

Nitrites not produced from nitrates.

Aerobic, facultatively anaerobic; primary cultures are microaerophilic.

Temperature relations: Optimum, 37° C. Slight growth at 20° C. Killed in 1½ hours at 52°, in 1 hour at 54°, in 10 minutes at 62° and in 1 minute at 100° C.; on agar slants, survival for 10 to 12 days.

No exotoxin is produced.

Pathogenic for cattle and swine. A few cases have been reported in man. Rabbits and guinea pigs are slightly susceptible to inoculation.

Serologically homogeneous (Haupt, Arch. f. wissen. u. prakt. Tierheilk., *67*, 1934, 516); related serologically to *Actinobacillus mallei* Thompson (Thompson, Jour. Bact., *26*, 1933, 225).

Source and Habitat: Usually isolated from actinobacillosis of cattle. This condition is often clinically diagnosed as "actinomycosis". Lesions are found in soft tissues, usually in lymph nodes and in muscles of the tongue ("wooden tongue"), where granulomatous tumors are formed. Eventually these break down to form abscesses, the pus containing small grayish white granules.

2. **Actinobacillus equuli** (van Straaten, 1918) Haupt, 1934. (*Bacillus nephritidis equi* Meyer, Transvaal Dept. Agr. Rept. Gov. Bac., 1908–1909, 122; *Bacterium viscosum equi* Magnusson, Svensk. Veterinärtidskr., 1917, 81; also see Jour. Comp. Path. and Therap., *32*, 1919, 143; *Bacillus equuli* van Straaten, Verslag van den Werksaamheden der Rijksseruminrichting voor 1916–1917, Rotterdam, 1918, 75; *Bacillus equirulis*, incorrectly attributed to van Straaten by de Blieck and van Heelsbergen, Tijdschr. v. Diergeneesk., *46*, 1919, 496; *Bacterium pyosepticum viscosum* Miessner, Deutsch. tierärztl. Wochnschr., *29*, 1921, 185; *Shigella equirulis* Edwards, Kentucky Agr. Exp. Sta. Res. Bul. 320, 1931; Haupt, Arch. f. wissen. u. prakt. Tierheilk., *67*, 1934, 514.)

e.quu'li. L. noun *equulus* a small young horse, a foal; L. gen.noun *equuli* of a foal.

Description taken largely from Edwards (*op. cit.*, 1931).

Rods, 0.3 to 0.4 by 0.5 to 0.8 micron, occurring singly, in chains and in filaments. The prevailing forms in rough, mucoid colonies are short, oval rods, and in smooth, non-mucoid colonies, long filaments and chains prevail. Capsules have been described, but their existence is uncertain. Non-motile. Gram-negative.

Gelatin colonies: Similar to those on agar. No liquefaction.

Agar slant: Grayish white, viscid growth covering the surface. Viable 8 to 10 days.

Infusion-peptone-agar: Good growth. Colonies 3 to 6 mm in diameter in 48 hours. In primary cultures rough type colonies prevail with lobulated surface and mucous or stringy consistency; in later generations smooth type colonies with glistening smooth surface and of soft (non-mucous) consistency prevail.

Broth: Masses are formed on the wall of the tube. At times a thin, grayish pellicle is formed. Grayish, tough, ropy sediment. Eventually there is diffuse turbidity which is highly viscous. Viability, 2 to 4 weeks.

Litmus milk: Slowly acidified; slimy, viscid. Sometimes coagulated and reduced. No caseolysis.

Potato: No visible growth.

Indole not produced.

Hydrogen sulfide is produced.

Acid but no gas from glucose, fructose, xylose, lactose, galactose, maltose, sucrose, mannitol and raffinose. Dextrin usually fermented. No action on rhamnose, dulcitol, sorbitol or inositol. Usually no action on salicin, adonitol or arabinose.

Acetylmethylcarbinol not produced.

Uric and citric acids not utilized.

Nitrites produced from nitrates.

Trimethylamine not produced from trimethylamine oxide (Wood et al., Jour. Bact., *46*, 1943, 100).

Optimum temperature, 37° C. Does not grow at 45.5° C. (Stuart et al., Jour. Bact., *46*, 1943, 105).

Aerobic, facultatively anaerobic.

Non-hemolytic.

Not pathogenic for small experimental animals. Produces abscesses and joint-ill when infected subcutaneously into horses.

Serologically heterogeneous (Edwards); related serologically to *Actinobacillus lignieresii* Brumpt and to *A. mallei* Thompson (Haupt, *op. cit.*, 1934, 524).

Source: Isolated from cases of joint-ill in foals.

Habitat: Generally a harmless inhabitant of the intestinal canal of solipeds; causes joint-ill and nephritis purulenta chiefly in foals 1 to 4 days old, sometimes in adolescent solipeds.

3. **Actinobacillus actinomycetemcomitans** Topley and Wilson, 1936. (*Bacterium actinomycetem comitans* Klinger, Cent. f. Bakt., I Abt., Orig., *62*, 1912, 198; *Bacterium comitans* Lieske, Morph. u. Biol. d. Strahlenpilze, 1921, 233; *Actinobacillus actinomycetem comitans* Topley and Wilson, Princip. of Bact. and Immun., 1st ed., *1*, 1931, 253 and 256; Topley and Wilson, *ibid.*, 2nd ed., 1936, 279.)

ac.ti.no.my.ce.tem.co′mi.tans. Gr. noun *actis, actinis* a ray; Gr. noun *myces, mycetis* a fungus; M.L. noun *actinomyces* ray fungus; L. part.adj. *comitans* accompa-

nying; M.L. part.adj. *actinomycetemcomitans* accompanying an actinomycete.

Description taken from Topley and Wilson (*loc. cit.*), Colebrook (Brit. Jour. Exp. Path., *1*, 1920, 197) and Bayne-Jones (Jour. Bact., *10*, 1925, 572).

Cocco-bacilli, occurring as rods, 1.0 to 1.5 microns long, or as cocci, 0.6 to 0.8 micron in diameter, in densely packed masses. Non-motile. Gram-negative.

Generally will grow on nutrient media under aerobic as well as anaerobic conditions; increased CO_2 tension accelerates growth (Holm, Riassunti delle Comunicazioni, VI Congresso Internaz. di Microbiologia, Roma, *1*, 1953, 407; also see Acta Path. et Microbiol. Scand., *34*, 1954, 235; abst. of the latter paper in Biol. Abst., *29*, 1955, No. 6185).

Gelatin: No liquefaction.

Agar colonies: Small, transparent, hemispherical, tough, adherent.

Glucose agar: Growth thin, dry, granular, hard, slightly yellow, adherent.

Liquid gelatin or broth: At 37° C., numerous, isolated, translucent granules, 0.5 to 1.0 mm in diameter; adherent granules are formed along the walls of the tube. In a few days they fuse into a grayish white mass, forming a ring around the tube and a pellicle over the surface. Later the granules become opaque and grayish white.

Glucose broth: Turbid. Yellowish flakes.

Milk: No growth.

Potato: No growth.

Acid but no gas from glucose and lactose.

Aerobic, facultatively anaerobic.

No growth at 22° C.

Not pathogenic for laboratory animals. Toxic to rabbits on injection, but a true infection is not set up.

Distinctive character: Manner of growth in liquid gelatin.

Relationship to other species: Comparative investigations may show this organism to be identical with *Actinobacillus lignieresii* Brumpt.

Source: Originally isolated from lesions of actinomycosis; also found in a jaw infection in a young woman (Thjøtta and Sydnes, Acta Path. et Microbiol. Scand., *28*, 1951, 27; abst. in Biol. Abst., *25*, 1951, No. 28469) and in mice (Vallée and Gaillard, Ann. Inst. Past., *84*, 1953, 647).

Habitat: Found in human cases of actinomycosis either alone or in mixture with the Gram-positive bacilli of Wolff and Israel (1891).

4. **Actinobacillus actinoides** (Smith, 1918) Topley and Wilson, 1931. (*Bacillus actinoides* Th. Smith, Jour. Exp. Med., *28*, 1918, 342; Topley and Wilson, Princip. of Bact. and Immun., 1st ed., *1*, 1931, 253 and 256.)

ac.ti.no.i′des. Gr. noun *actis, actinis* a ray; Gr. noun *eidus* shape, form; M.L. adj. *actinoides* ray-like.

In tissues the organisms appear as delicate rods, 0.4 to 0.5 micron in width, arranged in groups. In cultures, coccoid or bacillary forms occur. In the condensation water of coagulated blood serum, small, round, mulberry-like flakes up to 1 mm in diameter may be seen which consist of sheathed filaments, each filament terminating in club-like expansions. The sheaths as well as the clubs are unstainable and enclose chains of minute bacilli. Cells from cultures on agar containing tissue, milk or blood appear in the form of rods without capsules or clubs. Non-motile. Gram-negative.

Nutrient agar with or without blood: Uncertain growth. Serial transfers on this medium generally fail.

Broth: No growth.

Potato: No growth.

Litmus milk: No growth.

An accumulation of fatty substances in the cultures has been reported.

Optimum temperature, 37° C.

Not pathogenic for laboratory animals.

Distinctive characters: For isolation bits of tissue are brought into the condensation water of coagulated serum, the tubes being sealed with wax. Serial transfers may be successful on the same medium held under increased CO_2 tension (microaerophilic conditions). Appearance of mulberry-like granules.

Relationship to other species: A resemblance between *Actinobacillus actinoides* Topley and Wilson and *Streptobacillus moniliformis* Levaditi et al. has been noted by Dienes and Edsall (Proc. Soc. Exp. Biol.,

N. Y., *36*, 1937, 740); however, in view of its inability to infect laboratory animals and because of its bacillary morphology in calf lungs, Topley and Wilson (Princip. of Bact. and Immun., 3rd ed., 1946, 393) feel that *A. actinoides* should be treated separately from *S. moniliformis*.

Comments: Heilmann (Jour. Inf. Dis., *69*, 1941, 32) discusses the question raised by Klieneberger (Jour. Path. and Bact., *40*, 1935, 93; also see *ibid.*, *42*, 1936, 587), Dawson and Hobby (Proc. 3rd Intern. Cong. of Microb., New York, 1939, 177) and others on *Asterococcus*-like forms originating from cultures of *Streptobacillus moniliformis* Levaditi et al.

Source: Isolated by Th. Smith from an enzootic of chronic pneumonia in calves; in five cases the only cultivable organism, in four cases associated with other pathogenic species and in three cases absent. Th. Smith raises the question of some noncultivable, unrecognized microorganism. No other authors have observed similar cases. Jones has isolated an organism resembling *Actinobacillus actinoides* Topley and Wilson from a pneumonia in old white rats (Jour. Exp. Med., *33*, 1922, 441).

Habitat: Pathogenic, affecting calves and probably other domestic animals.

5. **Actinobacillus mallei** (Zopf, 1885) Thompson, 1933. (Rotz-Bacillus, Loeffler and Schütz, in Struck, Deutsch. med. Wochnschr., *8*, 1882, 707; *Bacillus mallei* Zopf, Die Spaltpilze, 3 Aufl., 1885, 89; *Pfeifferella mallei* Buchanan, Jour. Bact., *3*, 1918, 54 (type species of genus *Pfeifferella* Buchanan, *loc. cit.*); Thompson, Jour. Bact., *26*, 1933, 226; see *ibid.*, *25*, 1933, 44; *Malleomyces mallei* Pribram, Klassifikation der Schizomyceten, Leipzig und Wien, 1933, 93 (type species of genus *Malleomyces* Pribram, *loc. cit.*).)

mal′le.i. L. noun *malleus* the disease glanders; L. gen.noun *mallei* of glanders.

Common name: Glanders bacillus.

Description taken largely from Kelser (Man. Vet. Bact., 4th ed., 1943, 325).

Slender rods, 0.3 to 0.5 by 1.5 to 4.0 microns, with rounded ends, usually occurring singly, in pairs and in groups; in culture preparations, sometimes occur as filaments.

Branching involution forms occur on glycerol agar. Show irregular staining. Nonmotile. Gram-negative.

Gelatin: Poor growth. Usually no liquefaction. May be slowly liquefied (Jordan, General Bact., 11th ed., 1935, 491).

Agar colonies: Moist, grayish white layer, translucent, ropy, with regular borders. Later become yellowish or yellowish brown.

Agar slants: Glistening, moist, ropy, grayish white growth.

Glycerol agar: Yellowish growth (Thompson, op. cit., *26*, 1933, 224).

Loeffler's serum: Good growth. Moist, viscid, yellowish colonies develop after 36 to 48 hours.

Broth: Turbid, sometimes with a thin pellicle; slimy or ropy sediment.

Litmus milk: Coagulation usually occurs after a week with some acid production. Litmus may or may not be reduced.

Potato: After 36 to 48 hours, pale yellow "honey-drop-like" colonies, later becoming darker, reddish yellow or chocolate-colored. The medium sometimes has a faint greenish tinge around the growth.

Indole not produced.

Carbohydrates usually not fermented. Some strains produce small amounts of acid from glucose.

Nitrites not produced from nitrates.

Aerobic, facultatively anaerobic.

Optimum temperature, 37° C. No growth below 20° or above 44° C.

Serologically related to *Actinobacillus lignieresii* Brumpt (Thompson, Jour. Bact., *26*, 1933, 225) and to *Actinobacillus equuli* Haupt (Haupt, Arch. f. wissensch. u. prakt. Tierheilk., *67*, 1934, 514).

Distinctive characters: Culture media of slightly acid reaction (pH 6.6) are best suited for growth; on potato, honey-drop-like colonies are formed which later darken.

Source: Isolated by Loeffler and Schütz from the lesions of a horse affected with glanders.

Habitat: The cause of glanders naturally occurring in solipeds; *Felidae* and man occasionally are affected. Transmissible to guinea pigs, cats, field mice and to rabbits and dogs, generally not to the white mouse.

Genus VI. **Calymmatobacterium** *Aragão and Vianna, 1913.**

(Aragão and Vianna, Mem. do Inst. Oswaldo Cruz, *5*, 1913, 221; also see Aragão, Brasil Medico, 1919, 74; and *ibid.*, 1933, 473; *Donovania* Anderson, De Monbreun and Goodpasture, Jour. Exp. Med., *81*, 1945, 25.)

Ca.lym.ma.to.bac.te'ri.um. Gr. noun *calymma* mantel, sheath; Gr. dim.neut.n. *bacterium* a small rod; M.L. noun *Calymmatobacterium* the sheathed rodlet.

Pleomorphic rods which exhibit single or bipolar condensations of chromatin and which occur singly and in clusters. May or may not be encapsulated. Non-motile. Gram-negative. Growth outside of the human body occurs only in the yolk sac or amniotic fluid of developing chick embryo or in a medium containing embryonic yolk; after adaptation, growth may occur in meat infusion media. Pathogenic for man causing granulomatous lesions, particularly in the inguinal region.

The type species is *Calymmatobacterium granulomatis* Aragão and Vianna.

1. **Calymmatobacterium granulomatis** Aragão and Vianna, 1913. (Epithelial cell parasites, Donovan, Indian Med. Gaz., *40*, 1905, 414; Aragão and Vianna, Mem. do Inst. Oswaldo Cruz, *5*, 1913, 221; Donovan bodies, Dienst, Greenblatt and Sanderson, Jour. Inf. Dis., *62*, 1938, 112; also see Anderson, Science, *97*, 1943, 560; *Donovania*

granulomatis Anderson, De Monbreun and Goodpasture, Jour. Exp. Med., *81*, 1945, 25.)

gra.nu.lo'ma.tis. L. dim.noun *granulum* a small grain; Gr. suffix *-oma*, *-omatis* a swelling or tumor; M.L. noun *granuloma* a granuloma; M.L. gen.noun *granulomatis* of a granuloma.

---

* Revised by Dr. Otto Bier, Department of Immunology, Instituto Biológico, São Paulo, Brazil, May, 1955.

Pleomorphic rods, 1 to 2 microns in length, with rounded ends, occurring singly and in clusters. Intracellular forms are usually encapsulated. Non-motile. Gram-negative.

Originally this organism was described as being non-cultivable on ordinary media; lately, however, it has been shown by Dunham and Rake (Amer. Jour. Syphilis, Gonorrhea and Venereal Diseases, *32*, 1948, 145) and by Rake and Oskay (Jour. Bact., *55*, 1948, 667) that, after adaptation, growth can be effected on artificial media.

Chick embryo: Grows readily in yolk sac and feebly in amniotic fluid of developing chick embryo.

Embryonic yolk medium: Growth occurs.

Levinthal beef heart infusion agar colonies (after adaptation): At first shiny and translucent, increasing in size until the larger colonies measure 1.5 mm in diameter; gradually become gray, later brownish (Rake and Oskay, *ibid.*, 668).

Distinctive characters: Encapsulated forms readily demonstrated by means of Wright's stain as blue bacillary bodies surrounded by well defined, dense, pinkish capsules. Non-encapsulated forms are variable in morphology. Characteristic safety-pin forms may be demonstrated.

Not pathogenic for the common experimental animals.

Source: Isolated from granulomatous lesions of man.

Habitat: Human lesions. The cause of granuloma inguinale.

Genus VII. **Moraxella** *Lwoff, 1939.**

(*Diplobacillus* McNab, Klinische Monatsbl. f. Augenheilk., *42*, 1904, 65; not *Diplobacillus* Weichselbaum, Cent. f. Bakt., *2*, 1887, 212; Lwoff, Ann. Inst. Past., *62*, 1939, 168.)

Mo.rax.el′la. M.L. dim.ending -*ella*; M.L. fem.n. *Moraxella* named for V. Morax, the bacteriologist who first isolated the type species of this genus.

Small, short, rod-shaped cells which occur as diplobacilli and which are sometimes described as diplococci; occasionally occur singly. Non-motile. Gram-negative. Do not require V (phosphopyridine nucleotide) or X (hemin) factors for growth; growth is, however, dependent upon or improved with the addition of serum or ascitic fluid. Litmus milk is unchanged or becomes alkaline. Carbohydrates generally not attacked. Actively proteolytic, liquefying inspissated blood serum and even egg media. Oxidase-positive. Aerobic. Found as parasites and pathogens in warm-blooded animals, being especially found in association with diseases of the eye.

The type species is *Moraxella lacunata* (Eyre) Lwoff.

Key to the species of genus **Moraxella.**

I. Does not grow in gelatin.
    1. *Moraxella lacunata.*
II. Grow in gelatin.
    A. Gelatin readily liquefied. No change in litmus milk.
        2. *Moraxella liquefaciens.*
    B. Gelatin slowly liquefied. Litmus milk becomes alkaline with partial coagulation.
        3. *Moraxella bovis.*

1. **Moraxella lacunata** (Eyre, 1899) Lwoff, 1939. (Diplobacille de la conjunctivite subaigue, Morax, Ann. Inst. Past., *10*, 1896, 337; Diplobacillus of chronic conjunctivitis, Axenfeld, Cent. f. Bakt., I Abt., *21*, 1897, 1; *Bacterium conjunctivitis* Chester, Ann. Rept. Del. Col. Agr. Exp. Sta., *9*, 1897, 66; not *Bacterium conjunctivitis* Chester, *ibid.*, 67; *Bacillus lacunatus* Eyre, Jour. Path. and Bact., *6*, 1899, 5; not *Bacillus lacunatus* Wright, Memoirs Nat. Acad. Sci., *7*, 1895, 435; *Bacterium duplex* Lehmann and

* Revised by Prof. E. G. D. Murray, University of Western Ontario, London, Canada, April, 1955.

Neumann, Bakt. Diag., 2 Aufl., *2*, 1899 (July), 193; *Bacterium conjunctivitidis* Chester, Man. Determ. Bact., 1901, 120; not *Bacterium conjunctivitidis* Migula, Syst. d. Bact., *2*, 1900, 509; *Diplobacillus moraxaxenfeld* McNab, Klinische Monatsbl. f. Augenheilk., *42*, 1904, 64; *Bacillus duplex* Hewlett, Med. Res. Council Syst. of Bact., *2*, 1929, 417; Lwoff, Ann. Inst. Past., *62*, 1939, 173.)

la.cu.na'ta. L. noun *lacuna* a hollow or cavity; M.L. adj. *lacunatus* pitted.

Short rods, 0.4 to 0.5 by 2.0 microns, occurring singly, in pairs and in short chains, with ends rounded or square in the chains. Non-motile. Gram-negative.

Requires the addition of blood serum for growth in bouillon or peptone water.

Gelatin colonies: No growth.

Gelatin stab: No growth.

Blood agar colonies: No growth on primary isolation. Growth on subculture is difficult. Certain strains are not surrounded by zones of hemolysis, while others are (Oag, Jour. Path. and Bact., *54*, 1942, 128).

Serum agar colonies: No growth on primary isolation.

Löffler's blood serum: Slow but definite liquefaction with deep pitting around the colonies.

Ascitic broth: Turbid with slight, grayish sediment.

Blood milk mixture: Doubtful development.

Litmus milk: No growth.

Potato: No growth.

Various carbohydrates and mannitol are attacked.

Aerobic, facultatively anaerobic.

Optimum temperature, 37° C.

Comments: Audureau (Ann. Inst. Past., *64*, 1940, 128) reports a variety of this organism which differs from the parent strain in that it does not liquefy serum.

Source: Isolated from conjunctiva.

Habitat: Causes subacute infectious conjunctivitis, or angular conjunctivitis.

2. **Moraxella liquefaciens** (McNab, 1904) Murray, 1948. (Diplobacille liquéfiant, Pettit, Annales d'oculistique, March, 1899, 166; also see Thesis, Paris, 1900, 223; *Diplobacillus liquefaciens* McNab, Klinische

Monatsbl. f. Augenheilk., *42*, 1904, 64; Murray, in Manual, 6th ed., 1948, 591.)

li.que.fa'ci.ens. L. part.adj. *liquefaciens* dissolving.

Rods, 1.0 to 1.5 by 2.0 microns, with rounded ends, occurring in pairs and sometimes singly. Capsules not demonstrated. Non-motile. Stain uniformly with basic aniline dyes. Gram-negative.

Will barely grow in bouillon or peptone water without the addition of blood serum.

Gelatin colonies: Round, 1.5 to 2.0 mm in diameter, yellowish white.

Gelatin stab: Rapid liquefaction.

Blood agar: Ready growth in primary and subculture.

Ascitic agar colonies: Grayish, thick, round, viscous.

Peptone agar colonies: Same as above, but less abundant growth.

Coagulated serum: Liquefaction in 3 to 4 days; eventually complete.

Plain broth: Poor growth, if any. Slight, uniform turbidity.

Ascitic broth: Abundant growth in 24 hours at 35° C. Uniform turbidity. Later sediment and an opaque pellicle.

Milk: No growth. No coagulation.

Potato: Slight, yellowish white, viscous growth.

Optimum temperature, between 20° and 37° C. Killed at 55° C for 15 minutes.

Aerobic.

Not pathogenic for laboratory animals.

Source: Isolated from cases of conjunctivitis associated with corneal ulceration in man.

Habitat: Conjunctivitis in man so far as known.

3. **Moraxella bovis** (Hauduroy et al., 1937) Murray, 1948. (Diplobacillus, Allen, Jour. Amer. Vet. Med. Assn., *54*, 1918, 307; Diplobacillus, Jones and Little, Jour. Exp. Med., *38*, 1923, 139; *Hemophilus bovis* Hauduroy et al., Dict. d. Bact. Path., 1937, 247; Murray, in Manual, 6th ed., 1948, 591.)

bo'vis. L. noun *bos* cow, ox; L. gen.noun *bovis* of an ox or cow.

Short, plump rods, 0.5 by 1.5 to 2.0 microns, with rounded ends, usually occurring in pairs and in short chains. Encapsulated. Non-motile. Gram-negative.

Gelatin: Slow growth at 22° C. Very slow liquefaction.

Blood agar colonies: After 24 hours, round, translucent, grayish white, surrounded by a narrow, clear zone of hemolysis; deep colonies tiny with a clear hemolytic zone, usually 1.5 mm in diameter. After 48 hours, surface colonies somewhat flattened, 3.5 to 4.0 mm in diameter; deep colonies ellipsoidal and biconvex with hemolytic area 2.5 to 3.0 mm in diameter.

Blood agar slants: After 24 hours at 38° C., heavy, viscid, grayish white growth.

Coagulated serum: Liquefaction.

Broth: Slow growth; slight turbidity; considerable sediment.

Litmus milk: Alkaline. Partial coagulation.

Potato: No growth.

Indole not produced.

No acid from glucose or other carbohydrates.

Nitrites not produced from nitrates.

Aerobic.

Optimum temperature, 36° C. Killed at 58° to 59° C. in five minutes.

Not pathogenic for laboratory animals.

Source: Isolated from acute cases of ophthalmia (pink eye) of cattle.

Genus VIII. Noguchia Olitsky et al., 1934.*

(Olitsky, Syverton and Tyler, Jour. Exp. Med., 60, 1934, 382.)

No. gu'chi.a. M.L. noun *Noguchia* named for Hideyo Noguchi, the bacteriologist who isolated the type species of this genus.

Small, slender rods. Encapsulated. Motile by means of peritrichous flagella. Gram-negative. Produce a mucoid type of growth which, on initial isolation, occurs with some difficulty on ordinary media. Aerobic to facultatively anaerobic. Optimum temperature, between 28° and 30° C. Found in the conjunctiva of man and animals affected by a follicular type of disease.

The type species is *Noguchia granulosis* (Noguchi) Olitsky et al.

Key to the species of genus Noguchia.

I. Produce acid from carbohydrates.
   A. Produces acid from raffinose, maltose and salicin.
      1. *Noguchia granulosis.*
   B. Does not produce acid from raffinose, maltose or salicin.
      2. *Noguchia simiae.*
II. Does not produce acid from carbohydrates.
      3. *Noguchia cuniculi.*

1. **Noguchia granulosis** (Noguchi, 1928) Olitsky et al., 1934. (*Bacterium granulosis* Noguchi, Jour. Exp. Med., *48*, 1928, Supplement 2, 21; Olitsky, Syverton and Tyler, Jour. Exp. Med., *60*, 1934, 382.)

gra.nu.lo'sis. L. noun *granulum* a small grain; Gr. suffix *-osis*; M.L. fem.n. *granulosis* pathological condition characterized by collection of granules; M.L. gen.noun *granulosis* of granulosis.

Rods measuring 0.25 to 0.3 by 0.8 to 1.2 microns in young cultures; involution forms occur in old cultures on blood agar. Motile by means of a single flagellum which usually arises from one of the poles but which occasionally appears as if attached to one side. Gram-negative.

No growth on plain agar or broth.

Blood agar colonies: Minute, round, shiny, somewhat raised, almost transparent or slightly grayish in 48 hours; later the colonies increase in size and are grayish, opalescent and somewhat sticky. Old colonies have a brownish or yellowish tint.

Semi-solid *Leptospira* medium: Grayish white, diffuse growth forming a delicate zone 1 cm deep.

Liquid *Leptospira* medium: Diffuse,

* Arranged by Prof. C. D. Kelly, McGill University, Montreal, P.Q., Canada, October, 1938.

slightly cloudy growth; sticky, grayish sediment at the bottom of the tube in old cultures.

Acid from glucose, fructose, mannose, sucrose, galactose, maltose, salicin, xylose, mannitol, dextrin, arabinose, amygdalin and lactose. Small amount of acid from raffinose, inulin, rhamnose and trehalose. No acid from dulcitol, sorbitol or inositol.

Aerobic, facultatively anaerobic.

Temperature relations: Optimum, between 15° and 30° C. Grows at 37° C.

Optimum pH, 7.8.

Non-pathogenic for rabbits, guinea pigs, rats and mice.

Distinctive characters: Non-motile when cultured on *Leptospira* medium or on blood agar plates at 30° to 37° C.; motile when grown on horse blood agar slants at 30° C. or on *Leptospira* medium or blood agar plates at 15° C. Carbohydrates are attacked. Agglutination reactions.

Source: Isolated from cases of trachoma of American Indians at Albuquerque, New Mexico.

Habitat: Regarded by Noguchi and by others as a cause of trachoma in man. Produces a granular conjunctivitis in monkeys and apes.

2. **Noguchia simiae** (Olitsky et al., 1933) Olitsky et al., 1934. (*Bacterium simiae* Olitsky, Syverton and Tyler, Jour. Exp. Med., *57*, 1933, 875; Olitsky, Syverton and Tyler, *ibid.*, *60*, 1934, 382.)

si'mi.ae. L. noun *simia* ape; L. gen.noun *simiae* of an ape.

Slender rods, 0.2 to 0.3 by 0.8 to 1.2 microns, with pointed ends, occurring singly, in pairs, in short chains or in a parallel arrangement of two or three cells. Encapsulated. Motile by means of flagella which are really of the peritrichous type, although normally not more than one flagellum is found attached near the end but usually not in the polar position; occasionally two separated flagella are observed in lateral positions. Gram-negative.

Gelatin colonies: More mucoid and more raised than those on agar.

Gelatin stab: Arachnoid growth along line of inoculation. No liquefaction.

Agar colonies: Small, circular, grayish, translucent, smooth, convex, slightly raised with a sticky or mucoid consistency.

Agar slants: Grayish white to white, moist, mucoid, raised, glistening growth. Growth is more profuse when blood is added.

Blood agar colonies: More highly translucent and colorless during early growth than those on plain agar, becoming grayish after two or three days.

Leptospira medium: Homogeneous, dense growth in a 0.5 cm, sharply defined layer with a slight, nebulous, uniform opacity about 1 cm below. In three or four days the lower layer becomes more dense and in time extends to the bottom of the tube.

Broth: Uniformly turbid; slight, grayish sediment; no pellicle.

Litmus milk: Unchanged.

Potato: Light tan, spreading, abundant growth.

Indole not produced.

Acid but no gas from glucose, fructose, mannose, galactose, xylose, arabinose and rhamnose. Small amount of acid from dextrin. Some strains produce a small amount of acid from sucrose, lactose, inulin and mannitol. Raffinose, salicin, dulcitol, amygdalin, maltose, trehalose, sorbitol and inositol are not attacked.

Nitrites not produced from nitrates.

Aerobic, facultatively anaerobic.

Temperature relations: Optimum, between 28° and 30° C. Thermal death point, 56° C. for thirty minutes.

Serological reactions: Rabbit antiserum is specific for all strains, and there is no cross agglutination with *Noguchia granulosis*.

Distinctive characters: Attacks carbohydrates. Agglutination reactions.

Source: Isolated from inflammatory type, Type II, of spontaneous conjunctival folliculosis in monkeys (*Macacus rhesus*).

Habitat: Causes conjunctival folliculosis in monkeys (*Macacus rhesus*).

3. **Noguchia cuniculi** Olitsky et al., 1934. (Olitsky, Syverton and Tyler, Jour. Exp. Med., *60*, 1934, 382.)

cu.ni'cu.li. L. noun *cuniculus* rabbit; L. gen.noun *cuniculi* of a rabbit.

Small, slender rods, 0.2 to 0.3 by 0.5 to 1.0 micron, with pointed ends. Capsules formed are of much finer texture than those surrounding *Noguchia granulosis* or *Noguchia simiae*. Motile by means of six to eight peritrichous flagella. Not acid-fast. Gram-negative.

Gelatin agar colonies: Grayish, mucoid, confluent.

Gelatin stab: Tenuous, arborescent, non-spreading growth. No liquefaction.

Agar colonies: Small, spherical, translucent, slightly grayish, smooth, somewhat convex, moist, mucoid, entire.

Agar slants: Slightly grayish, translucent, coalescent, glistening, mucoid, homogeneous, non-spreading growth. The water of syneresis appears uniformly cloudy or milky depending on the amount of growth.

Blood agar colonies: More profuse, more grayish and less translucent than those on plain agar.

Leptospira medium: After 24 hours there is a faint, nebulous surface growth followed by an ingrowing sac-like mass, with its base 5 mm across, lying at the center of the under surface and extending for 5 mm into the medium. The area spreads laterally until at about two or three days there is a uniform, opaque, whitish layer about 1 cm thick which progresses slowly until the bottom of the tube is reached in about seven days.

Broth: Uniformly turbid; no pellicle.

Litmus milk: Unchanged.

Potato: Faint, buff-colored (changing to brown after five days), non-spreading, sparse surface growth.

Indole not produced.

No acid or gas from glucose, fructose, mannose, mannitol, sucrose, raffinose, inulin, galactose, maltose, salicin, xylose, dextrin, arabinose, amygdalin, lactose, dulcitol, rhamnose, trehalose, sorbitol or inositol.

Nitrites not produced from nitrates.

Aerobic, facultatively anaerobic.

Temperature relations: Optimum, between 28° and 30° C. Thermal death point, 56° C. for 15 to 30 minutes.

Serological reactions: Rabbit antiserum is specific for all strains, and there is no cross agglutination with *Noguchia granulosis* or *Noguchia simiae*.

Distinctive characters: No action on carbohydrates. Agglutination.

Source: Isolated from spontaneous conjunctival folliculosis, Type II, of rabbits.

Habitat: Causes conjunctival folliculosis in rabbits.

FAMILY VI. BACTEROIDACEAE BREED, MURRAY AND SMITH, Fam. Nov.*

Bac.te.ro.i.da′ce.ae. M.L. noun *Bacteroides* type genus of the family; -aceae ending to denote a family; M.L. fem.pl.n. *Bacteroidaceae* the *Bacteroides* family.

Rods, with rounded or pointed ends, which vary in size from minute, filterable forms to long, filamentous, branching forms; marked pleomorphism may occur. May be motile or non-motile, the motile species possessing peritrichous flagella (rarely, motility has been observed without demonstrable flagella). Gram-negative. Body fluids are frequently required for growth and are always stimulative. Simple carbohydrates are usually fermented with the production of acid; gas may be produced in glucose or peptone media. Normally these are strict anaerobes, but occasionally microaerophilic species occur. Found primarily in the intestinal tracts and mucous membranes of warm-blooded animals. Sometimes pathogenic.

* Prof. Robert S. Breed, Cornell University, Geneva, New York, Prof. E. G. D. Murray, University of Western Ontario, Canada, and Dr. Nathan R. Smith, Senior Bacteriologist, Retired, Plant Industry Station, U. S. Department of Agriculture, Beltsville, Maryland, have prepared the general sections for Family *Bacteroidaceae*, June, 1955. Other contributors as noted have prepared the sections covering special groups within this family.

Key to the genera of family **Bacteroidaceae.**

I. Simple, rarely pleomorphic, rod-shaped cells which are strict anaerobes.
 A. Cells with diameters greater than 0.3 micron.
  1. Cells with rounded ends.
     Genus I. *Bacteroides*, p. 424.
  2. Cells with pointed ends.
     Genus II. *Fusobacterium*, p. 436.
 B. Cells with diameters 0.15 micron or less.
     Genus III. *Dialister*, p. 440.
II. Highly pleomorphic rods, some of which may be facultative anaerobes.
 A. Strict anaerobes.
     Genus IV. *Sphaerophorus*, p. 441.
 B. Facultative anaerobes.
     Genus V. *Streptobacillus*, p. 451.

Genus I. **Bacteroides** *Castellani and Chalmers, 1919.**

(Castellani and Chalmers, Man. Trop. Med., 3rd ed., 1919, 959; *Ristella* Prévot, Ann. Inst. Past., *60*, 1938, 289; *Capsularis* Prévot, *ibid.*, 290; *Zuberella* Prévot, *loc. cit.*)

Bac.te.ro.i'des. M. L. noun *bacter* the masculine equivalent of Gr. neut.n. *bactrum* a staff or rod; Gr. noun *idus* form, shape; M.L. noun *Bacteroides* rod-like.

Rods, with rounded ends, occurring singly, in pairs or in short chains; sometimes pleomorphic. Some species are encapsulated. Motile and non-motile species occur, the motile species possessing peritrichous flagella. Gram-negative. May or may not require enriched culture media. Usually ferment glucose, rarely lactose or sucrose. Nitrites not produced from nitrates. Gas may or may not be produced in peptone media. Anaerobic. Found in the alimentary and urogenital tracts of man and other animals; some species are pathogenic.

The type species is *Bacteroides fragilis* (Veillon and Zuber) Castellani and Chalmers.

Key to the species of genus **Bacteroides.**

I. Non-motile. Sub-genus *Ristella* Prévot (Ann. Inst. Past., *60*, 1938, 289).
 A. Not encapsulated.
  1. Gas produced in culture media.
   a. Gelatin not liquefied.
    b. Serum or ascitic fluid not required for growth.
     c. Attack carbohydrates.
      d. Simple, rod-shaped cells.
        1. *Bacteroides fragilis*
        2. *Bacteroides furcosus.*
        3. *Bacteroides perfoetens.*
        4. *Bacteroides incommunis.*
        5. *Bacteroides insolitus.*
      dd. Pleomorphic cells.
        6. *Bacteroides thetaiotaomicron.*
        7. *Bacteroides trichoides.*
        8. *Bacteroides terebrans.*
        9. *Bacteroides halosmophilus.*
     cc. Does not attack carbohydrates.
        10. *Bacteroides putidus.*

---

* Revised by Dr. C. D. Kelly, Department of Bacteriology, McGill University, Montreal, P.Q., Canada, March, 1955.

bb. Requires serum or ascitic fluid for growth. Produces a black pigment on blood agar.

11. *Bacteroides melaninogenicus.*

aa. Gelatin liquefied.

b. Attack carbohydrates.

12. *Bacteroides ovatus.*
13. *Bacteroides convexus.*

bb. Do not attack carbohydrates.

14. *Bacteroides coagulans.*
15. *Bacteroides putredinis.*

2. Gas not produced in culture media.

a. Gelatin is liquefied.

16. *Bacteroides uncatus.*
17. *Bacteroides tumidus.*
18. *Bacteroides exiguus.*
19. *Bacteroides uniformis.*
20. *Bacteroides vulgatus.*
21. *Bacteroides distasonis.*

aa. Gelatin not liquefied.

b. Action on cellulose not recorded.

22. *Bacteroides capillosus.*
23. *Bacteroides cylindroides.*
19. *Bacteroides uniformis.*
20. *Bacteroides vulgatus.*
21. *Bacteroides distasonis.*

bb. Attacks cellulose.

24. *Bacteroides succinogenes.*

aaa. Action on gelatin not recorded.

25. *Bacteroides glutinosus.*
26. *Bacteroides destillationis.*

B. Encapsulated. Sub-genus *Capsularis* Prévot (*ibid.*, 290).

1. Requires serum or ascitic fluid for growth.

27. *Bacteroides viscosus.*

2. Does not require serum or ascitic fluid for growth.

28. *Bacteroides variabilis.*

II. Motile. Sub-genus *Zuberella* Prévot (*loc. cit.*).

A. Gas produced in culture media.

29. *Bacteroides serpens.*

B. No gas produced in culture media.

30. *Bacteroides variegatus.*

1. **Bacteroides fragilis** (Veillon and Zuber, 1898) Castellani and Chalmers, 1919. (*Bacillus fragilis* Veillon and Zuber, Arch. Méd. Exp. et Anat. Path., *10*, 1898, 870; Castellani and Chalmers, Man. Trop. Med., 3rd ed., 1919, 959; *Ristella fragilis* Prévot, Ann. Inst. Past., *60*, 1938, 290 (type species of genus *Ristella* Prévot, *loc. cit.*).)

fra′gi.lis. L. adj. *fragilis* fragile.

Rods, with rounded ends, staining more deeply at the poles, occurring singly and in pairs. Non-motile. Gram-negative.

Gelatin: No liquefaction; small amount of gas.

Agar colonies: Small, gray, irregular.

Broth: Turbid.

Litmus milk: No coagulation. Slight amount of gas.

Indole not produced.

Hydrogen sulfide not produced.

Acid from fructose, maltose, sucrose, galactose, glucose and arabinose. Some strains produce acid from lactose (Weinberg et al., Les Microbes Anaérobies, 1937, 720).

Nitrites not produced from nitrates.

Anaerobic.

Optimum temperature, 37° C.

Pathogenicity: Some strains produce subcutaneous abscesses in rabbits, guinea pigs or mice.

Source and habitat: From acute appendicitis, pulmonary gangrene, abscesses of the urinary tract and septicemias in man.

2. **Bacteroides furcosus** (Veillon and Zuber, 1898) Hauduroy et al., 1937. (*Bacillus furcosus* Veillon and Zuber, Arch. Méd. Exp. et Anat. Path., *10*, 1898, 517; Hauduroy et al., Dict. d. Bact. Path., 1937, 61; *Ristella furcosa* Prévot, Ann. Inst. Past., *60*, 1938, 291.)

fur.co'sus. L. adj. *furcosus* forked.

Small rods with forked ends. Non-motile. Gram-negative.

Gelatin: No liquefaction.

Agar: Deep colonies very small, transparent, regular, yellowish. No gas.

Blood agar: Small, moist colonies with irregular edges.

Broth: Slow growth; fine precipitate; little gas with sourish, fetid odor.

Milk: No coagulation.

Coagulated egg white not digested.

Coagulated serum not digested.

Acid and gas from glucose, maltose, sucrose and mannitol. No action on lactose or inulin.

Anaerobic.

Optimum temperature, 37° C.

Pathogenicity: Produces subcutaneous abscesses in guinea pigs.

Source: Isolated from cases of appendicitis and from lung abscesses.

Habitat: Found in cases of appendicitis and similar infections in man.

3. **Bacteroides perfoetens** (Tissier, 1905) Hauduroy et al., 1937. (*Cocco-Bacillus anaerobius perfoetens* Tissier, Thèse Méd., Paris, 1900, 70; *Coccobacillus perfoetans* (sic) Tissier, Ann. Inst. Past., *19*, 1905, 110; Hauduroy et al., Dict. d. Bact. Path., 1937, 67; *Ristella perfoetens* Prévot, Ann. Inst. Past., *60*, 1938, 291.)

per.foe'tens. L. pref. *per* very; L. part.

adj. *foetens* stinking; M.L. adj. *perfoetens* very stinking.

Small, ellipsoidal rods, 0.6 to 0.8 by 0.8 to 1.0 micron, occurring singly, in pairs, in short chains or in irregular groups. Nonmotile. Gram-negative.

Gelatin: No growth.

Glucose agar: Deep colonies lenticular, with bubbles of fetid gas.

Glucose broth: Rapid growth, with powdery precipitate and fetid gas.

Milk: Unchanged.

Indole not produced.

Acid from glucose and sucrose. Some strains produce acid from lactose.

Anaerobic.

Optimum temperature, 37° C.

Not pathogenic.

Source: Isolated from the intestines of infants with diarrhoea.

Habitat: Found in the intestinal tract of man.

4. **Bacteroides incommunis** Eggerth and Gagnon, 1933. (Eggerth and Gagnon, Jour. Bact., *25*, 1933, 402; *Ristella incommunis* Prévot, Ann. Inst. Past., *60*, 1938, 291.)

in.com.mu'nis. L. adj. *incommunis* not common.

Rods, 0.5 to 1.5 by 1.0 to 3.0 microns, occurring singly. Non-motile. Stain solidly. Gram-negative.

Gelatin: No liquefaction.

Blood agar colonies: Elevated, slightly yellowish, 1 mm in diameter. One strain formed soft colonies; the other was stringy when emulsified.

Broth: Growth is diffuse.

Milk: Acidified but not coagulated; coagulates promptly on boiling.

Indole not produced.

Hydrogen sulfide is produced.

Acid and a small amount of gas from amygdalin, arabinose, cellobiose, dextrin, fructose, galactose, glucose, inulin, lactose, maltose, mannose, raffinose, rhamnose, sucrose and xylose. One strain fermented glycogen and starch. No action on esculin, glycerol, mannitol, melezitose, salicin, sorbitol or trehalose.

Nitrites not produced from nitrates.

Peptone: No gas.

Anaerobic.

Non-pathogenic for white mice or rabbits.

Source: Two strains were isolated from human feces.

Habitat: Probably the intestinal canals of mammals.

5. Bacteroides insolitus Eggerth and Gagnon, 1933. (Eggerth and Gagnon, Jour. Bact., *25*, 1933, 408; *Ristella insolita* Prévot, Ann. Inst. Past., *60*, 1938, 291.)

in.so.li'ta. L. adj. *insolitus* unusual.

Short, thick rods, 1 to 2 microns long, often occurring as slender, curved cells, 2 to 3 microns long. Non-motile. Gram-negative.

Gelatin: No liquefaction in 45 days.

Blood agar colonies: Minute, transparent.

Broth: Heavy, diffuse growth.

Milk: Acidified and coagulated in 30 to 35 days.

Indole is produced.

Hydrogen sulfide is produced.

Acid but no gas from fructose, galactose, glucose, glycerol, lactose, maltose and mannose. No acid or gas from esculin, amygdalin, arabinose, cellobiose, dextrin, glycogen, inulin, mannitol, melezitose, raffinose, rhamnose, salicin, sorbitol, starch, sucrose, trehalose or xylose.

Nitrites not produced from nitrates.

Anaerobic.

Non-pathogenic for white mice or rabbits.

Distinctive characters: Brom cresol purple and phenol red are rapidly decolorized in a meat infusion broth. A small amount of gas is produced from peptone.

Source: One strain was isolated from human feces.

Habitat: Probably the intestinal canals of mammals.

6. Bacteroides thetaiotaomicron (Distaso, 1912) Kelly, *comb. nov.* (*Bacillus thetaiotaomicron* Distaso, Cent. f. Bakt., I Abt., Orig., *62*, 1912, 444; *Bacteroides tethaiotaomicron* (sic) Castellani and Chalmers, Man. Trop. Med., 3rd ed., 1919, 960; *Sphaerocillus thetaiotaomicron* Prévot, Ann. Inst. Past., *60*, 1938, 300.)

the.ta.i.o.ta.o'mi.cron. M.L. noun *thetaiotaomicron* a combination of the Greek letters theta, iota and omicron, so used

because the pleomorphic rods of this species have the shapes of these letters.

Description taken from Distaso (*op. cit.*, 1912, 444); a more complete description will be found in Eggerth and Gagnon (Jour. Bact., *25*, 1933, 399).

Short, plump to elliptical rods which sometimes have a bar across them, thus causing the organism to resemble the Greek letter theta. Motile (Distaso). Non-motile (Eggerth and Gagnon). Stain solidly or only at the poles. Gram-negative.

Gelatin: No liquefaction.

Glucose agar colonies: Large, transparent, entire; sometimes gas bubbles are produced.

Broth: Turbid.

Egg albumen broth: Albumen not attacked.

Litmus milk: Acid, coagulated. Curd shrinks with expulsion of turbid whey.

Indole is produced.

Hydrogen sulfide produced (Eggerth and Gagnon).

Acid and gas from esculin, amygdalin, arabinose, fructose, inulin, lactose, cellobiose, dextrin, galactose, glucose, glycogen, maltose, mannose, melezitose, raffinose, rhamnose, salicin, starch, sucrose, trehalose and xylose. Four strains fail to produce gas from any sugar. No acid or gas from glycerol, mannitol or sorbitol (Eggerth and Gagnon).

Nitrate reduction not recorded (Distaso). Nitrites not produced from nitrates (Eggerth and Gagnon).

Peptone: No gas (Eggerth and Gagnon).

Anaerobic.

Distinctive characters: Resembles *Bacteroides variabilis* but is not encapsulated, does not liquefy gelatin, usually produces gas from sugars and ferments melezitose and trehalose. Differs from *Bacteroides uniformis* in morphology, in producing gas from sugars and in fermenting rhamnose (Eggerth and Gagnon).

Source: Isolated frequently from human feces.

Habitat: Intestinal canals of mammals (common).

7. Bacteroides trichoides (Potez and Compagnon, 1922) Hauduroy et al., 1937. (*Bacillus trichoides* Potez and Compagnon,

Compt. rend. Soc. Biol., Paris, *87*, 1922, 339; Hauduroy et al., Dict. d. Bact. Path., 1937, 78; *Ristella trichoides* Prévot, Ann. Inst. Past., *60*, 1938, 292.)

tri.cho.i'des. Gr. adj. *trichoides* hair-like. Rods, 0.3 by 5.0 microns, with rounded ends. Pleomorphic with long filaments in cultures. Non-motile. Gram-negative.

Gelatin: No liquefaction.

Glucose agar: Deep colonies lenticular, tenacious, whitish.

Martin broth: Uniform turbidity in 2 to 3 days followed by flocculent precipitate and clearing.

Milk: Acid and coagulation.

Coagulated egg white: Not digested.

Coagulated serum: Not digested.

Hydrogen sulfide produced.

Acid and gas from glucose, maltose, sucrose, fructose, lactose and mannitol. Gas but no acid from glycerol.

Neutral red decolorized.

Anaerobic.

Optimum temperature, 37° C.

Pathogenicity: Produces subcutaneous abscesses in rabbits.

Source: One strain was isolated from a case of cholecystitis.

Habitat: Presumably found in various infections in man.

8. **Bacteroides terebrans** (Brocard and Pham, 1934) Kelly, *comb. nov.* (*Bacillus terebrans* Brocard and Pham, Compt. rend. Soc. Biol., Paris, *117*, 1934, 997; *Ristella terebrans* Prévot, Ann. Inst. Past., *60*, 1938, 291.)

te.re'brans. L. part.adj. *terebrans* perforating.

Rods, 2 to 3 microns long, with rounded ends. Pleomorphic with swollen bodies and chromatic granules. Non-motile. Gramnegative.

Gelatin: No liquefaction.

Glucose agar: Deep colonies spherical with irregular edges. Some gas.

Glucose broth: Uniform turbidity; some gas with foul odor.

Milk: Acid but no coagulation.

Coagulated egg white: Not digested.

Coagulated serum: Not digested.

Growth inhibited by bile.

Hydrogen sulfide not produced.

Acid and gas from glucose, fructose, maltose, lactose, sucrose and mannitol.

Neutral red decolorized.

Anaerobic.

Optimum temperature, 37° C.

Pathogenicity doubtful.

Source: Two strains were isolated from cases of gangrenous erysipelas associated with a streptococcus.

Habitat: Presumably found in various infections in man.

9. **Bacteroides halosmophilus** Baumgartner, 1937. (Baumgartner, Food Research, *2*, 1937, 321; *Ristella halosmophila* Prévot, Man. de Class. et de Déterm. des Bact. Anaérobies, 1940, 47.)

ha.los.mo'phi.lus. Gr. noun *hals* salt; Gr. noun *ōsmus* a pushing, thrust; Gr. adj. *philus* loving; M.L. adj. *halosmophilus* salt-pressure-loving.

Rods, with rounded ends and frequently curved, varying in size and shape, the average size being 0.5 by 2.0 to 3.0 microns, occurring singly, in pairs and occasionally in chains. Pleomorphic. Non-motile. Gramnegative.

Gas is produced.

NaCl-nutrient gelatin: No liquefaction in 21 days.

NaCl-nutrient broth: Uniform turbidity; sparse, granular sediment.

NaCl-agar colonies: After 4 to 6 days, 2 to 3 mm in diameter, finely granular, smooth, moist, low convex, round, entire, translucent, buff-colored, readily emulsified in 15 per cent NaCl solution.

NaCl-agar streak: Buff-colored, transparent, beaded.

NaCl cooked meat medium: Gas produced. Meat slightly reddened in 4 days. Slight fetid odor.

Indole not produced.

Hydrogen sulfide produced in trace amounts.

Acid and gas from glucose, maltose and glycerol. No acid from lactose, sucrose, inulin, mannitol, dulcitol or salicin.

Starch not hydrolyzed.

Nitrites not produced from nitrates in 21 days.

Halophilic; more than 4 per cent NaCl is

required in the medium for growth. Optimum, 12.5 to 15 per cent.

Optimum pH, between 7.4 and 7.6. Limits of pH, 5.5 to 8.5.

Anaerobic.

Temperature relations: Optimum, 35° C. Slight growth at 22° C. No growth at 56° C.

Source: Isolated from salted Mediterranean anchovies; frequently isolated from the fish muscle and the solar salt (the probable infecting agent) in which the fish is packed.

Habitat: Probably sea water.

10. **Bacteroides putidus** (Weinberg et al., 1937) Kelly, *comb. nov.* (*Bacillus gracilis putidus* Tissier and Martelly, Ann. Inst. Past., *16*, 1902, 865; *Bacillus putidus* Weinberg et al., Les Microbes Anaérobies, 1937, 790; not *Bacillus putidus* Kern, Arb. bakt. Inst. Karlsruhe, *1*, Heft 4, 1896, 400; *Ristella putida* Prévot, Ann. Inst. Past., *60*, 1938, 291.)

pu′ti.da. L. adj. *putidus* stinking, fetid.

Small, thin, straight rods, occurring singly or in short chains; longer forms occur in older cultures. Non-motile. Gram-negative.

Gelatin: No liquefaction.

Glucose agar: Deep colonies lenticular in 48 hours, later becoming irregular. No gas.

Broth: Turbidity in 48 hours with a powdery precipitate. No gas. Putrid odor.

Milk: No action.

Albumin: Broken down to proteoses and amines with the production of hydrogen sulfide and acetic, butyric and valerianic acids.

Fibrin is digested with the production of gas.

Urea is broken down.

No action on carbohydrates.

Fats are saponified.

Anaerobic.

Growth occurs at 37° C. or at room temperature.

Source: Isolated from putrefying meat.

Habitat: Found in decomposing organic matter.

11. **Bacteroides melaninogenicus** (Oliver and Wherry, 1921) Roy and Kelly, 1939. (*Bacterium melaninogenicum* Oliver and Wherry, Jour. Inf. Dis., *28*, 1921, 341; *Ris-*

tella melaninogenica Prévot, Ann. Inst. Past., *60*, 1938, 290; Roy and Kelly, in Manual, 5th ed., 1939, 569.)

me.la.ni.no.ge′ni.cus. Gr. adj. *melas* black; M.L. noun *melaninum* melanin; Gr. adj. *genicus* of the family; M.L. adj. *melaninogenicus* melanin-producing.

Description taken from Oliver and Wherry (*op. cit.*, 1921, 341) and Burdon (Jour. Inf. Dis., *42*, 1928, 161).

Rods, 0.8 by 1.0 to 3.0 microns. Non-motile. Gram-negative.

Serum gelatin stab: Dense, flocculent growth at 37° C. No liquefaction.

Blood agar slant: Confluent, black, dry layer. The blood is disintegrated in one to two weeks, forming melanin. The medium becomes colorless.

Sodium phosphate broth: Turbid.

Litmus milk: Slow acidification but no coagulation.

Blood serum slant: Fairly luxuriant, white, moist layer.

Acid from fructose, glucose, lactose, maltose, sucrose and mannitol. No acid from galactose.

Growth is stimulated by the X factor, but there is very little growth stimulation by the V factor (Schwabacher, Lucas and Rimington, Jour. Gen. Microbiol., *1*, 1947, 109).

Anaerobic.

Optimum temperature, 37° C.

Non-pathogenic for rabbits, guinea pigs or white mice (Burdon).

Distinctive characters: Growth very poor unless fresh body fluids are added to the medium. Grows more readily in mixed culture. When grown on a medium containing haemoglobin, a black pigment is produced.

Comments: Schwabacher et al. (*loc. cit.*) have shown that the black pigment produced by this species is, in reality, hematin, not melanin; the specific epithet *melaninogenicus* is, therefore, inappropriate, and they recommend renaming this species. Renaming, however, is contrary to internationally accepted rules governing nomenclature.

Source: Isolated from the oral cavity, external genitalia, an infected surgical wound, urine and feces (Oliver and Wherry).

Habitat: Inhabits healthy mucous membranes of mammals but may take a part in various pathological processes (Burdon).

12. Bacteroides ovatus Eggerth and Gagnon, 1933. (Eggerth and Gagnon, Jour. Bact., *25*, 1933, 405; *Pasteurella ovata* Prévot, Ann. Inst. Past., *60*, 1938, 292.)

o. va'tus. L. adj. *ovatus* ovate, egg-shaped.

Small, ellipsoidal rods, 0.5 to 1.0 by 1.0 to 2.0 microns, occurring singly. Non-motile. Stain solidly. Gram-negative.

Gelatin: Liquefaction in 4 days.

Blood agar colonies: Soft, grayish elevated colonies, 1.0 to 1.5 mm in diameter.

Broth: Diffuse, heavy growth.

Milk: Acidified and coagulated in 4 days.

Indole is produced.

Hydrogen sulfide is produced.

Acid and a small amount of gas from esculin, amygdalin, cellobiose, dextrin, fructose, galactose, glucose, glycogen, inulin, lactose, maltose, mannose, raffinose, rhamnose, starch, sucrose and xylose. No acid or gas from arabinose, glycerol, mannitol, melezitose, salicin, sorbitol or trehalose.

Nitrites not produced from nitrates.

Peptone: No gas.

Anaerobic.

Non-pathogenic for white mice or rabbits.

Source: One strain was isolated from human feces.

Habitat: Probably the intestinal canals of mammals.

13. Bacteroides convexus Eggerth and Gagnon, 1933. (Eggerth and Gagnon, Jour. Bact., *25*, 1933, 406; *Pasteurella convexa* Prévot, Ann. Inst. Past., *60*, 1938, 292.)

con. vex'us. L. adj. *convexus* convex.

Thick, ellipsoidal rods, 0.8 to 1.5 microns long, occurring singly or in pairs. In glucose broth, the rods are usually 2.0 to 3.0 microns long. Non-motile. Gram-negative.

Gelatin: Liquefaction in 20 to 30 days.

Blood agar colonies: Elevated, grayish, somewhat opaque colonies, 1.0 to 1.5 mm in diameter.

Broth: Heavy diffuse growth.

Milk: Acidified and coagulated in 4 days.

Indole not produced.

Hydrogen sulfide is produced.

Acid and a small amount of gas from esculin, amygdalin, cellobiose, dextrin, fructose, galactose, glucose, glycogen, inulin, lactose, maltose, mannose, raffinose, starch, sucrose and xylose. No acid or gas from arabinose, glycerol, mannitol, melezitose, rhamnose, salicin, sorbitol or trehalose.

Nitrites not produced from nitrates.

Peptone: No gas.

Anaerobic.

Non-pathogenic for white mice or rabbits.

Source: Five strains were isolated from human feces.

Habitat: Probably the intestinal canals of mammals.

14. Bacteroides coagulans Eggerth and Gagnon, 1933. (Eggerth and Gagnon, Jour. Bact., *25*, 1933, 409; *Pasteurella coagulans* Prévot, Ann. Inst. Past., *60*, 1938, 292.)

co. a'gu.lans. L. part.adj. *coagulans* curdling, coagulating.

Rods, 0.5 to 2.0 microns long. Show bipolar staining. Non-motile. Gram-negative.

Gelatin: Liquefied in 8 to 12 days.

Blood agar colonies: Soft, transparent, 0.5 mm in diameter.

Broth: Diffuse growth.

Milk: Coagulated in 8 days without acid production. The coagulum partly redissolves after 3 to 4 weeks.

Indole is produced.

Hydrogen sulfide is produced.

Nitrites not produced from nitrates.

Anaerobic.

Non-pathogenic for white mice or rabbits.

Distinctive characters: No acid or gas from carbohydrates. A small amount of gas is produced from peptone. Phenol red and brom cresol purple are decolorized in a meat infusion broth.

Source: One strain was isolated from human feces.

Habitat: Probably the intestinal canals of mammals.

15. Bacteroides putredinis (Weinberg et al., 1937) Kelly, *comb. nov.* (Bacillus A, Heyde, Beitr. z. klin. Chirurg., *76*, 1911, 1; *Bacillus putredinis* Weinberg et al., Les Microbes Anaérobies, 1937, 755; not *Bacillus putredinis* Trevisan, Add. ad Gen., p. 36;

see DeToni and Trevisan, in Saccardo, Sylloge Fungorum, *8*, 1889, 1025; *Ristella putredinis* Prévot, Ann. Inst. Past., *60*, 1938, 291.)

put.re'di.nis. L. noun *putredo* putridity; M.L. gen.noun *putredinis* of putridity.

Straight rods, 0.8 by 3.0 to 4.0 microns, with rounded ends, one of which may be swollen. Non-motile. Gram-negative.

Gelatin: Liquefaction. Foul odor.

Agar: Deep colonies small, round to arborescent. No gas.

Broth: Rapid growth; uniform turbidity. No gas; foul odor.

Milk: Rapid growth; casein precipitated and peptonized. Small amount of gas; foul odor.

Coagulated serum: Digested.

Indole is produced.

Hydrogen sulfide produced in broth.

No acid or gas from carbohydrates.

Anaerobic.

Optimum temperature, 37° C.

Pathogenicity: Produces local abscesses in animals when mixed with *Escherichia coli.*

Source: Fifteen strains were isolated from cases of acute appendicitis.

Habitat: From cases of acute appendicitis and presumably found in similar infections in man.

16. **Bacteroides uncatus** Eggerth and Gagnon, 1933. (Eggerth and Gagnon, Jour. Bact., *25*, 1933, 404; *Ristella uncata* Prévot, Ann. Inst. Past., *60*, 1938, 291.)

un.ca'tus. L. adj. *uncatus* hooked at the tip.

Rods, ordinarily 5 to 8 microns long, with extreme variations in size and form; curved and hooked forms are common. Non-motile. Gram-negative.

Gelatin: Liquefaction in 16 days.

Blood agar colonies: Very minute and transparent.

Broth: Turbid; growth is slow and light.

Milk: Not acidified or coagulated.

Indole not produced.

Hydrogen sulfide not produced.

Acid but no gas after 8 to 30 days of incubation from dextrin, fructose, galactose, glucose, lactose, maltose, raffinose, rhamnose, salicin, starch and sucrose. No acid from esculin, amygdalin, arabinose, cello-

biose, glycerol, glycogen, inulin, mannitol, mannose, melezitose, sorbitol, trehalose or xylose.

Nitrites not produced from nitrates.

Peptone: No gas.

Anaerobic.

Non-pathogenic for white mice or rabbits.

Source: One strain was isolated from human feces.

Habitat: Probably the intestinal canals of mammals.

17. **Bacteroides tumidus** Eggerth and Gagnon, 1933. (Eggerth and Gagnon, Jour. Bact., *25*, 1933, 405; *Ristella tumida* Prévot, Ann. Inst. Past., *60*, 1938, 292.)

tu'mi.dus. L. adj. *tumidus* swollen.

Small, thick, ellipsoidal rods, 1.0 to 1.5 microns long, occurring singly. On glucose broth there are many swollen forms, 1.0 to 4.0 by 1.5 to 10.0 microns, which stain irregularly; the bodies of these swollen forms are usually very pale, with only the ends staining. Non-motile. Stain solidly. Gram-negative.

Gelatin: Liquefaction in 12 to 20 days.

Blood agar colonies: Soft, grayish, elevated colonies, 1 mm in diameter.

Broth: Heavy, diffuse growth.

Milk: Acidified but not coagulated.

Indole not produced.

Hydrogen sulfide is produced.

Acid but no gas from dextrin, fructose, galactose, glucose, glycogen, inulin, lactose, maltose, mannose, raffinose, sorbitol, starch and sucrose. No acid or gas from esculin, amygdalin, arabinose, cellobiose, glycerol, mannitol, melezitose, rhamnose, salicin, trehalose or xylose.

Nitrites not produced from nitrates.

Peptone: No gas.

Anaerobic.

Non-pathogenic for white mice or rabbits.

Source: Four strains were isolated from human feces.

Habitat: Probably the intestinal canals of mammals.

18. **Bacteroides exiguus** Eggerth and Gagnon, 1933. (Eggerth and Gagnon, Jour. Bact., *25*, 1933, 407; *Ristella exigua* Prévot, Ann. Inst. Past., *60*, 1938, 292).

ex.i'gu.us. L. adj. *exiguus* small and narrow.

Very small, slender rods, 0.5 to 1.0 micron long, occurring singly and in pairs. Non-motile. Gram-negative.

Gelatin: Liquefaction in 16 to 20 days.

Blood agar colonies: These are of two types: one is pin-point in size, the other is large, gray, moist and 1.0 to 1.5 mm in diameter.

Broth: Diffusely clouded.

Milk: Acidified and may or may not be coagulated in 35 to 40 days.

Indole not produced.

Hydrogen sulfide not produced.

Acid but no gas from fructose, galactose, glucose, lactose, maltose, mannose, sucrose and trehalose. One strain ferments raffinose. No acid or gas from esculin, amygdalin, arabinose, cellobiose, dextrin, glycerol, glycogen, inulin, mannitol, melezitose, rhamnose, salicin, sorbitol, starch or xylose.

Nitrites not produced from nitrates.

Peptone: No gas.

Anaerobic.

Non-pathogenic for white mice or rabbits.

Source: Two strains were isolated from human feces.

Habitat: Probably the intestinal canals of mammals.

19. **Bacteroides uniformis** Eggerth and Gagnon, 1933. (Eggerth and Gagnon, Jour. Bact., *25*, 1933, 400; *Ristella uniformis* Prévot, Ann. Inst. Past., *60*, 1938, 291.)

u.ni.for'mis. L. adj. *uniformis* of a single form.

Small rods, 0.8 to 1.5 microns long, with rounded ends, occurring singly. Non-motile. Stain heavier at poles and around periphery. Gram-negative.

Gelatin: Liquefaction by two strains in 15 to 40 days. No liquefaction by six strains.

Blood agar colonies: Transparent, soft, elevated, 0.5 to 0.75 mm in diameter.

Broth: Diffuse growth.

Milk: Acidified and coagulated in 8 to 12 days.

Indole is produced.

Hydrogen sulfide produced slowly or not at all.

Acid but no gas from esculin, amygdalin, arabinose, cellobiose, dextrin, fructose,

galactose, glucose, glycogen, inulin, lactose, maltose, mannose, melezitose, raffinose, salicin, starch, sucrose, trehalose and xylose. No acid or gas from glycerol, mannitol, rhamnose, sorbitol, dulcitol, erythritol or inositol.

Nitrites not produced from nitrates.

Peptone: No gas.

Anaerobic.

Non-pathogenic for white mice or rabbits.

Distinctive characters: Produces indole. Resembles *Bacteroides vulgatus*.

Source: Eight strains were isolated from human feces.

Habitat: Probably the intestinal canals of mammals.

20. **Bacteroides vulgatus** Eggerth and Gagnon, 1933. (Eggerth and Gagnon, Jour. Bact., *25*, 1933, 401; *Pasteurella vulgata* Prévot, Ann. Inst. Past., *60*, 1938, 292.)

vul.ga'tus. L. adj. *vulgatus* common.

Ellipsoidal rods, 0.7 to 2.5 microns long, usually occurring singly, sometimes in pairs; one strain forms filaments 10.0 microns long. Morphology very variable in glucose broth. Non-motile. Stain solidly, although some strains show bipolar staining. Gram-negative.

Gelatin: Liquefaction in 4 to 20 days by all but one strain.

Blood agar colonies: Soft, translucent, grayish, elevated, 1.5 to 2.0 mm in diameter. Half of the strains are hemolytic.

Broth: Heavy and diffuse growth.

Milk: Acidified. Coagulated by some strains in 5 to 25 days.

Indole not produced.

Hydrogen sulfide is produced.

Acid and a small amount of gas from arabinose, dextrin, fructose, galactose, glucose, glycogen, inulin, lactose, maltose, mannose, raffinose, rhamnose, starch, sucrose and xylose. Seven strains fermented esculin. No acid or gas from amygdalin, cellobiose, glycerol, mannitol, melezitose, salicin, sorbitol, trehalose, dulcitol, erythritol or inositol.

Nitrites not produced from nitrates.

Anaerobic.

Non-pathogenic for white mice or rabbits.

Distinctive characters: Does not form indole; does not produce gas from peptone.

This is the commonest *Bacteroides* species found in the feces of adults. Differs from *Bacteroides incommunis* in that it does not ferment amygdalin and cellobiose but does ferment glycogen and starch. Liquefies gelatin.

Source: Thirty-eight strains were isolated from human feces.

Habitat: Probably the intestinal canals of mammals.

21. Bacteroides distasonis Eggerth and Gagnon, 1933. (Eggerth and Gagnon, Jour. Bact., *25*, 1933, 403; *Ristella distasonis* Prévot, Ann. Inst. Past., *60*, 1938, 291.)

dis.ta.so′nis. M.L. gen.noun *distasonis* of Distaso; named for A. Distaso, a Roumanian bacteriologist.

Rods, 0.5 to 0.8 by 1.5 to 2.5 microns, with rounded ends, occurring singly; some strains show a few bacilli 5.0 to 8.0 microns long. Non-motile. Stain solidly. Gram-negative.

Gelatin: No liquefaction by 16 strains; liquefaction by the remaining four strains in 35 to 50 days.

Blood agar colonies: Soft, grayish, elevated, 1.0 to 1.5 mm in diameter. Two strains are markedly hemolytic.

Broth: Growth is diffuse.

Milk: Acidified. All but 4 strains coagulate milk.

Indole not produced.

Hydrogen sulfide is produced.

Acid but no gas from amygdalin, cellobiose, dextrin, fructose, galactose, glucose, inulin, lactose, maltose, mannose, melezitose, raffinose, rhamnose, salicin, sucrose, trehalose and xylose. Fifteen strains ferment esculin. Fifteen strains slowly ferment starch. No acid or gas from arabinose, glycogen, glycerol, mannitol or sorbitol.

Nitrites not produced from nitrates.

Peptone: No gas.

Anaerobic.

Non-pathogenic for white mice or rabbits.

Distinctive characters: Usually fails to liquefy gelatin. Fails to ferment arabinose.

Source: Twenty strains were isolated from human feces.

Habitat: Probably the intestinal canals of mammals.

22. Bacteroides capillosus (Tissier, 1908) Kelly, *comb. nov.* (*Bacillus capillosus* Tissier, Ann. Inst. Past., *22*, 1908, 189; *Ristella capillosa* Prévot, Ann. Inst. Past., *60*, 1938, 292.)

ca.pil.lo′sus. L. adj. *capillosus* very hairy.

Long, thick rods, 1 by 4 to 5 microns, occurring singly or in chains; curved and filamentous forms are present, and they may become tangled. Non-motile. Gram-negative.

Gelatin: No liquefaction.

Agar: Deep colonies fine, granular, irregular, fimbriate. No gas produced.

Broth: Slight turbidity.

Milk: Growth but no change.

Coagulated egg white not digested.

Indole not produced.

Hydrogen sulfide not produced.

Slight acid from glucose. No acid from lactose or sucrose.

Anaerobic.

Optimum temperature, 37° C.

Not pathogenic.

Source: Isolated twice from the intestines of infants.

Habitat: Found in the intestinal tract of man.

23. Bacteroides cylindroides (Rocchi, 1908) Kelly, *comb. nov.* (*Bacterium cylindroides* Rocchi, Lo stato actuale delle nostre cognizioni sui germi anaerobi Gamberine e Parmezziani, Bologna, 1908; *Ristella cylindroides* Prévot, Ann. Inst. Past., *60*, 1938, 292.)

cy.lin.dro.i′des. Gr. noun *cylindrus* a cylinder; Gr. noun *idus* form, shape; M.L. adj. *cylindroides* cylinder-shaped.

Large, filamentous rods, 6 to 8 microns long, with granular, swollen areas. Non-motile. Gram-negative.

Gelatin:No liquefaction.

Glucose agar: Deep colonies small, round.

Glucose broth: Turbid with light deposit.

Milk: Unchanged.

Albumin not digested.

Acid from glucose and sucrose. No acid from lactose, galactose, mannitol or dulcitol.

Anaerobic.

Grows only at 18° C.

Not pathogenic.

Source: Isolated from the intestines of man.

Habitat: Found in the intestinal tract of man.

24. Bacteroides succinogenes Hungate, 1950. (Bact. Revs., *14*, 1950, 1.)

suc.ci.no'ge.nes. L. noun *succinum* amber; M.L. noun *acidum succinicum* succinic acid (derived from amber); Gr. v. *gennaio* to produce; M.L. adj. *succinogenes* succinic acid-producing.

Original description supplemented by material from Bryant and Doetsch (Jour. Dairy Sci., *37*, 1954, 1176).

Rods, 0.3 to 0.4 by 1.0 and 2.0 microns when grown on cellulose agar, often appearing slightly curved and with pointed ends. Occur singly and in pairs. In old cultures the rods are replaced by spherical and ellipsoidal forms of variable size. In media containing either glucose or cellobiose, the rods are larger, usually quite pleomorphic and occasionally show rosette arrangements of cells. Non-motile. Show bipolar staining. Gram-negative.

Gelatin: No liquefaction.

Cellulose agar colonies: Definite clear zone of cellulose digestion with no microscopically visible colony, but rods may be observed microscopically at the periphery of the area cleared of cellulose.

Rumen fluid-glucose-cellobiose agar colonies: Deep colonies are lenticular, 1 to 3 mm in diameter; surface colonies are entire, slightly convex, translucent to opaque, often with "frosted glass" appearance. Non-pigmented or, occasionally, yellow.

Liquid rumen fluid-glucose-cellobiose medium: Evenly turbid growth which rapidly clears with age.

Indole not produced.

Hydrogen sulfide not produced.

Acid from glucose, cellobiose, cellulose and pectin. Acid may or may not be produced from maltose, lactose, trehalose and dextrin. No acid from xylose, arabinose, galactose, fructose, sucrose, mannitol, glycerol, inositol, inulin, salicin, gum arabic or xylan.

Starch may or may not be hydrolyzed.

Esculin not hydrolyzed.

Acetylmethylcarbinol not produced.

Produces mainly succinic and acetic acids and shows a net carbon dioxide uptake in cellulose or cellobiose fermentations.

Nitrites not produced from nitrates.

Casein is digested.

Anaerobic.

Temperature relations: Optimum, about 40° C. No growth at 22° or 45° C.

Final pH in liquid rumen fluid-glucose medium, about 5.5.

Distinctive characters: Ferments cellulose very rapidly. Certain volatile fatty acids present in rumen fluid are required for growth (Bryant and Doetsch, Sci., *120*, 1954, 944; Jour. Dairy Sci., *38*, 1955, 340).

Source: Isolated from bovine rumen contents.

Habitat: Probably the reticulo-rumen of ruminants.

25. Bacteroides glutinosus (Guillemot and Hallé, 1904) Hauduroy et al., 1937. (*Bacillus glutinosus* Guillemot and Hallé, Arch. Méd. Exp. et Anat. Path., *16*, 1904, 599; Hauduroy et al., Dict. d. Bact. Path., 1937, 61; *Ristella glutinosa* Prévot, Ann. Inst. Past., *60*, 1938, 292.)

glu.ti.no'sus. L. adj. *glutinosus* glutinous.

Long rods, 0.8 by 6.0 to 8.0 microns, filamentous forms attaining a length of 32.0 microns. Occur singly or in entangled clumps in pus, mostly in clumps and rarely singly in cultures. Not encapsulated. Non-motile. Gram-negative.

Gas not produced.

Agar stab: Growth slow; colonies lenticular, whitish, very cohesive.

Anaerobic.

Optimum temperature, 37° C.; killed at 55° C.

Pathogenicity: Pleural pus containing this organism did not prove fatal to guinea pigs and rabbits when inoculated into the pleura.

Distinctive characters: Feeble growth; very cohesive colonies.

Source: Isolated from cases of purulent pleurisies.

Habitat: Found in respiratory apparatus, especially the pleura; not common.

26. Bacteroides destillationis (Weinberg et al., 1937) Kelly, *comb. nov.* (Anaero-

bic bacillus, Tunnicliff, Jour. Inf. Dis., *13*, 1913, 289; *Bacterium destillationis* Weinberg et al., Les Microbes Anaérobies, 1937, 762; *Ristella destillationis* Prévot, Ann. Inst. Past., *60*, 1938, 291.)

des.til.la.ti.o'nis. L. prep. *de* from, down; L. noun *stillatio* a dropping down; L. noun *destillatio* a dripping down; L. gen.noun *destillationis* of a distillation.

Rods, 0.3 by 2.0 microns, occurring singly or in clumps; filaments are formed. Non-motile. Gram-negative.

Gas is not produced.

Serum or ascitic fluid favors growth.

Plain agar: No growth.

Goat blood agar colonies: Round, convex, white becoming yellowish, very cohesive; growth in water of condensation is grayish white and mucoid.

Blood agar and ascitic fluid agar stabs: Colonies are lenticular, coherent, mucoid.

Loeffler's serum: Smooth colonies.

Potato: Smooth, moist, adherent growth.

Nutrient broth: No growth.

Glucose bouillon: Growth occurs as irregular, mucoid zoogloea; no turbidity.

Anaerobic.

Optimum temperature, 37° C.; killed at 55° C.

Pathogenicity: Toxic but not pathogenic to guinea pigs when inoculated in large numbers. Following two inoculations (18 days apart) with the water of condensation from cultures in Loeffler's blood serum, a pulmonary congestion and broncho-pneumonia with atelectasis, culminating in death, were produced in guinea pigs.

Source: Isolated from a case of chronic bronchitis.

Habitat: Found in the human respiratory tract; not common.

27. Bacteroides viscosus Hauduroy et al., 1937. (*Coccobacterium mucosum anaerobicum* Klinger, Cent. f. Bakt., I Abt., Orig., *62*, 1912, 186 (type species (monotypy) of genus *Coccobacterium* Klinger, *loc. cit.*); *Bacterium mucosum* Weinberg et al., Les Microbes Anaérobies, 1937, 727; not *Bacterium mucosum* Mez, Mikroskopische Wasseranalyse, Berlin, 1898, 57; Hauduroy et al., Dict. d. Bact. Path., 1937, 81; *Capsularis*

mucosus Prévot, Ann. Inst. Past., *60*, 1938, 293.)

vis.co'sus. L. adj. *viscosus* sticky, viscous.

Short, ellipsoidal rods, 0.4 by 1.0 to 2.0 microns. Pleomorphic on culture media. Encapsulated. Non-motile. Show bipolar staining. Gram-negative.

Serum gelatin: Liquefaction.

Serum agar: Deep colonies small, lenticular; gas with fetid odor.

Serum broth: Mucoid growth in bottom of tube; gas and fetid odor.

Indole produced in serum broth.

Hydrogen sulfide produced in serum broth.

Anaerobic.

Growth only at 37° C.

Pathogenicity: Produces subcutaneous abscesses in rabbits, guinea pigs and mice.

Distinctive characters: Grows only if serum is added to the medium.

Source: One strain was isolated from a brain abscess following bronchiectasis in man.

Habitat: Presumably found in various infections in man.

28. Bacteroides variabilis (Distaso, 1912) Castellani and Chalmers, 1919. (*Bacillus variabilis* Distaso, Cent. f. Bakt., I Abt., Orig., *62*, 1912, 441; Castellani and Chalmers, Man. Trop. Med., 3rd ed., 1919, 960; *Capsularis variabilis* Prévot, Ann. Inst. Past., *60*, 1938, 293.)

va.ri.a'bi.lis. L. adj. *variabilis* variable.

Short rods, with rounded ends, occurring singly; some cells appear as long, flexuous rods. Encapsulated. Non-motile. Gram-negative.

Gelatin: No growth on plain gelatin (Distaso); liquefaction (Eggerth and Gagnon, Jour. Bact., *25*, 1933, 400).

Blood agar colonies: Smooth, glistening, elevated and very mucoid, about 1.0 mm in diameter.

Broth: Diffuse growth.

Litmus milk: Unchanged (Distaso); acidified and some strains coagulating in 25 to 35 days (Eggerth and Gagnon).

Indole is produced.

Hydrogen sulfide is produced.

Acid and gas from glucose, lactose and sucrose (Distaso). Acid but no gas from esculin, amygdalin, arabinose, cellobiose, dextrin, fructose, galactose, glycogen, inulin, lactose, glucose, maltose, mannose, raffinose, rhamnose, salacin, starch, sucrose and xylose. No acid or gas from glycerol, mannitol, melezitose, sorbitol or trehalose (Eggerth and Gagnon).

Nitrites not produced from nitrates (Eggerth and Gagnon).

Peptone: No gas.

Anaerobic.

Optimum temperature, 37° C.

Non-pathogenic for white mice or rabbits.

Distinctive characters: Encapsulated.

Source: Isolated from human feces by Distaso and by Eggerth and Gagnon (8 strains).

Habitat: Probably the intestinal canals of mammals.

29. **Bacteroides serpens** (Veillon and Zuber, 1898) Hauduroy et al., 1937. (*Bacillus serpens* Veillon and Zuber, Arch. Méd. Exp. et Anat. Path., *10*, 1898, 870; Hauduroy et al., Dict. d. Bact. Path., 1937, 74; *Zuberella serpens* Prévot, Ann. Inst. Past., *60*, 1938, 293 (type species of genus *Zuberella* Prévot, *ibid.*, 290).)

ser'pens. L. part.adj. *serpens* creeping.

Thick rods, with rounded ends, occurring singly, in pairs or in short chains. Motile. Gram-negative.

Gelatin: Slow liquefaction, with gas.

Agar colonies: Punctiform.

Deep agar colonies: Small colonies in 48 hours, ray-like growth later. Gas produced.

Broth: Turbid, then flocculent growth; some gas with foul odor.

Litmus milk: Acidified and coagulated in six days with no digestion.

Coagulated egg white and serum not liquefied.

Hydrogen sulfide not produced.

Acid from fructose, galactose, maltose and lactose.

Anaerobic.

Optimum temperature, 37° C.

Experimental pathogenicity: Some strains produce abscesses in rabbits, guinea pigs and mice.

Source and habitat: Acute appendicitis, mastoiditis, pulmonary gangrene, bile tract of dog and sea water.

30. **Bacteroides variegatus** (Distaso, 1912) Castellani and Chalmers, 1919. (*Bacillus variegatus* Distaso, Cent. f. Bakt., I Abt., Orig., *62*, 1912, 445; Castellani and Chalmers, Man. Trop. Med., 3rd ed., 1919, 960; *Zuberella variegata* Prévot, Ann. Inst. Past., *60*, 1938, 293.)

va.rie.ga'tus. L. part.adj. *variegatus* variegated.

Rods occurring singly and in chains. Motile by means of peritrichous flagella. Gram-negative.

Gelatin stab: No liquefaction.

Glucose agar colonies: Small, translucent, entire. No gas produced.

Broth: Turbid; no gas.

Litmus milk: Acid, coagulated.

Coagulated egg white: Not digested.

Indole is produced.

Acid but no gas from glucose or lactose.

Anaerobic.

Optimum temperature, 37° C.

Source: Isolated from the intestines of man.

Habitat: Found in the intestinal tract of man.

Genus II. **Fusobacterium** *Knorr, 1922.**

(Knorr, Cent. f. Bakt., I Abt., Orig., *87*, 1922, 536; *Fusocillus* Prévot, Ann. Inst. Past., *60*, 1938, 300.)

Fu.so.bac.te'ri.um. L. noun *fusus* a spindle; Gr. dim.noun *bacterium* a small rod; M.L. noun *Fusobacterium* a spindle rodlet.

Straight or curved rods, usually with tapering ends, occurring singly, in pairs and sometimes in short chains; filaments are common. Motile (*Fusocillus*) and non-motile species occur; the motile species may show oscillation of both ends of the rod or movements of

---

* Revised by Dr. Heiner Hoffman, College of Dentistry, New York University, New York City, New York, May, 1955.

translation. Gram-negative. Stain with more or less distinct granules which may become Gram-positive. Surface colonies are butyrous, round, entire and, especially in early cultivation, may appear as clouded, white flecks in a water-clear medium. Glucose is usually fermented. Possess fastidious nutrient requirements for growth. Anaerobic to microaerophilic. Limited pathogenicity for man and laboratory animals. Found in the buccal cavity and various infections of man.

Although it is now known that the genus *Fusiformis* Hoelling is based on a type species, *Fusiformis termitidis* Hoelling, which presumably belongs in the genus *Cytophaga* Winogradsky, some bacteriologists continue to use this generic name for the anaerobic, fusiform bacteria found in the human mouth. The latter organisms are closely related to the anaerobic, Gram-negative species found in the human intestine, and the generic name *Fusobacterium* Knorr appears to be the legitimate name for this group.

The type species is *Fusobacterium fusiforme* (Veillon and Zuber) Hoffman.

Key to the species of genus Fusobacterium.

I. Long rods, attaining a length of 8 to 16 microns.
    A. Acid from maltose.
                1. *Fusobacterium fusiforme.*
    B. No acid from maltose.
                2. *Fusobacterium polymorphum.*
II. Short rods, usually not exceeding 4 microns in length.
    A. Motile.
                3. *Fusobacterium praeacutum.*
    B. Non-motile.
        1. Milk unchanged.
            a. Stubby, spindle-shaped cells.
                4. *Fusobacterium nucleatum.*
            aa. Slender, pointed cells.
                5. *Fusobacterium vescum.*
        2. Milk acidified and coagulated.
                6. *Fusobacterium biacutum.*

1. **Fusobacterium fusiforme** (Veillon and Zuber, 1898) Hoffman, *comb. nov.* (Bacille de la pourriture d'hôpital, Vincent, Ann. Inst. Past., *10*, 1896, 495; *Bacillus fusiformis* Veillon and Zuber, Arch. de Méd. Expér. et Anat. Path. (Paris), sér 1, *10*, 1898, 540; not *Bacillus fusiformis* Gottheil, Cent. f. Bakt., II Abt., *7*, 1901, 724; Le bacille fusiforme, Vincent, *op. cit.*, *13*, 1899, 613; *Bacillus hastilis* Seitz, Ztschr. f. Hyg., *30*, 1899, 47; *Corynebacterium fusiforme* Lehmann and Neumann, Bakt. Diag., 4 Aufl., *2*, 1907, 529; *Fusiformis dentium* Hoelling, Arch. f. Protistenk., *19*, 1910, 239; *Fusobacterium plauti-vincenti* Knorr, Cent. f. Bakt., I Abt., Orig., *89*, 1923, 5; *Fusiformis fusiformis* Topley and Wilson, Princip. of Bact. and Immun., 1st ed., 1931, 300.)

fu.si.for′mis. L. noun *fusus* a spindle; L. noun *forma* shape; M.L. adj. *fusiformis* spindle-shaped.

Original description supplemented by material taken from Hine and Berry (Jour. Bact., *34*, 1937, 523).

Straight or slightly curved rods, 0.5 to 1.0 by 8.0 to 16.0 microns, occurring in pairs with blunt ends together and outer ends pointed, sometimes in short, curved chains or long spirillum-like threads. Granules present. Non-motile. Gram-negative.

No gas or odor produced.

Gelatin: No growth.

Colonies: Circular, 1 to 3 mm in diameter, shaped like a low cone, surface resembles hammered copper or may be wrinkled and pitted; regular edge.

Plain agar: No growth.

Meat infusion agar: Growth.

Serum agar shake culture: After 36 hours, colonies spherical, up to 0.5 mm in diameter, thin, yellowish brown.

Serum agar plate: Matted growth. Medium around colonies becomes turbid from the precipitation of protein. No surface growth.

Ascitic fluid agar: Growth by most strains.

Serum broth: Milky turbidity.

Peptone broth: No growth.

Liver broth: No turbidity; grayish white, flaky precipitate.

Indole not produced.

Hydrogen sulfide not produced.

Acid from glucose, fructose, sucrose, maltose and sometimes from lactose. No acid from inulin or mannitol (Hine and Berry).

Pathogenicity: Associated with Vincent's angina. Non-pathogenic for white mice (Hauduroy et al., Dict. d. Bact. Path., Paris, 1953, 259).

Anaerobic.

Temperature relations: Survives 60° C. for 2 but not for 5 minutes.

Relationship to other species: There has been a continuous discussion in the literature regarding the identity of Vincent's organism (Vincent, op. cit., 1896, 495) with that reported by Plaut (Deutsch. med. Wochnschr., 20, 1894, 922). A review of Plaut's work indicates that he dealt primarily with a mixed culture, one of the organisms present being the "Miller'schen Bacillus," which appears to have been *Selenomonas sputigena* Dobell. Early German workers (e.g. Knorr) have favored the idea that Plaut's organism is really identical with Vincent's organism, but Vincent and other French investigators have maintained that the two organisms are distinct. The French viewpoint, which seems to be the correct one, is well summarized by Weinberg et al. (Les Microbes Anaérobies, 1937, 804) and by Prévot (Ann. Inst. Past., 60, 1938, 285). Plaut's organism is so vaguely described that it should be placed among the *species incertae sedis*; it is doubtful whether it can be definitely reidentified.

Source: Isolated from cases of hospital gangrene (Vincent); also isolated from gingival crevices in normal mouths, from cases with deep caries, inflamed areas around crowns and fillings, pyorrhetic pockets, Vincent's infection and from the mouths of three monkeys and two rabbits (Hine and Berry).

Habitat: Found in mouth cavities with gangrenous lesions as well as in normal mouth cavities.

2. Fusobacterium polymorphum Knorr, 1923. (Cent. f. Bakt., I Abt., Orig., *89*, 1923, 19.)

po.ly.mor'phum. Gr. adj. *poly* many; Gr. noun *morphē* form, shape; Gr. adj. *polymorphus* multiform, of many shapes.

Original description supplemented by material taken from Hine and Berry (Jour. Bact., *34*, 1937, 522) and from Prévot and Peyré (Ann. Inst. Past., *73*, 1947, 1124).

Rods, 0.2 to 0.5 by 8.0 to 16.0 microns, occurring in pairs with the pointed ends adjoining, often occurring in long threads (250 microns). Pronounced pleomorphism. Non-motile. Gram-negative.

Neither gas nor odor is produced.

Gelatin: No liquefaction.

Plain agar: Slight growth.

Meat infusion agar: Good growth.

Serum agar plates (alkaline): After 2 to 3 days, colonies 0.5 mm or larger in diameter, lens-shaped with offshoots.

Rabbit blood (5 per cent) agar colonies: Round, 1 to 2 mm in diameter, convex, grayish white, smooth, glistening, entire.

Ascitic fluid agar: Good growth.

Glucose bouillon: Uniformly turbid.

Peptone broth: No growth.

Douglas' broth: Good growth at bottom of tube under anaerobic conditions; uniform turbidity on shaking.

Tenacious sediment in liquid media.

Milk: Partially coagulated.

Coagulated serum or egg white: Not digested.

Indole not produced (Knorr); indole is produced (Hine and Berry, and Prévot and Peyré).

Hydrogen sulfide not produced (Knorr); hydrogen sulfide produced in trace amounts (Prévot and Peyré).

Acid usually produced from glucose, fructose and sucrose. No acid from lactose, maltose, inulin or mannitol (Hine and Berry). Only glucose and fructose are fermented (Prévot and Peyré).

Neutral red is reduced.

Nitrites not produced from nitrates.

Anaerobic.

Temperature relations: Optimum, 37° C.; growth range, 31° to 43° C. (Hoffman, Oral Surg., *5*, 1952, 1088). Survives 50° C. for 15 minutes, 52° C. for 10 minutes and 56° C. for 5 minutes (Hine and Berry).

Optimum pH, between 7.0 and 8.2 (Hauduroy et al., Dict. d. Bact. Path., 1953, 259); between 6.9 and 7.7 (Hoffman, *op. cit.*, 1952, 1088).

Non-pathogenic for guinea pigs and mice.

Source: One strain was isolated from a deposit on teeth in a case of gingivitis (Knorr); also isolated from gingival crevices in normal mouths, from cases with deep caries, inflamed areas around crowns and fillings, pyorrhetic pockets, Vincent's infection and from the mouths of three monkeys and two rabbits (Hine and Berry); also found in a case of acute appendicitis (Prévot and Peyré).

Habitat: Presumably the buccal cavity.

3. **Fusobacterium praeacutum** (Tissier, 1908) Hoffman, *comb. nov. (Coccobacillus praeacutus* Tissier, Ann. Inst. Past., *22*, 1908, 189; *Zuberella praeacuta* Prévot, Ann. Inst. Past., *60*, 1938, 293.)

prae.a.cu'tum. L. pref. *prae* very, quite; L. adj. *acutus* sharp; M.L. adj. *praeacutus* quite sharp.

Short rods, with pointed ends, occurring singly and in chains. Swollen forms present in old cultures. Motile by means of peritrichous flagella. Gram-negative.

Gelatin: No liquefaction.

Agar: Deep colonies lenticular. Abundant gas production.

Broth: Turbid with powdery precipitate.

Milk: Unchanged.

Coagulated egg white: Not digested.

Milk fats are saponified.

Indole not produced.

Acid from glucose. No acid or gas from lactose or sucrose.

Anaerobic.

Optimum temperature, between 22° and 37° C.

Not pathogenic.

Source: Isolated from the intestines of infants.

Habitat: Found in the intestinal tract of man.

4. **Fusobacterium nucleatum** Knorr, 1923. (Cent. f. Bakt., I Abt., Orig., *89*, 1923, 17.)

nu.cle.a'tum. L. adj. *nucleatus* having a kernel, nucleated.

Original description supplemented by material taken from Hine and Berry (Jour. Bact., *34*, 1937, 520) and from Robin (Ann. Inst. Past., *74*, 1948, 259).

Spindle-shaped rods, 1 by 4 microns, occurring singly and often in pairs. One or two granules are present. Non-motile. Gram-negative.

Disagreeable odor produced on cultivation; no gas is produced.

Gelatin: No liquefaction.

Plain agar: Scant growth.

Meat infusion agar: Good growth.

Serum agar plate: Deep colonies lens-shaped with offshoots.

Rabbit blood (5 per cent) agar colonies: Round, 0.5 to 1.0 mm in diameter, convex, grayish white, smooth, glistening, entire.

Ascitic fluid agar: No growth by most strains.

Peptone broth: No growth.

Plain liver broth: No growth.

Liver broth with serum: After 1 to 3 days, flocculent deposit on the pieces of liver.

Douglas' broth: Good growth at bottom of tube under anaerobic conditions; uniform turbidity on shaking.

Milk: No coagulation.

Indole not produced (Knorr); indole produced (Hine and Berry, and Robin).

Hydrogen sulfide not produced (Knorr); hydrogen sulfide is produced (Robin).

Acid from glucose, usually from fructose and sometimes from sucrose and lactose. No acid from maltose, inulin or mannitol (Hine and Berry). Glucose, fructose, galactose and sucrose are fermented, lactose only feebly (Robin).

Neutral red reduced.

Nitrites produced from nitrates.

Proteins not digested.

Pathogenic for mice.

Anaerobic.

Temperature relations: Optimum, between 35° and 37° C. (Hauduroy et al.

Dict. d. Bact. Path., 1953, 259). Survives 56° C. for 15 minutes but not 60° C. for 10 minutes (Hine and Berry).

Source: One strain was isolated from a deposit on teeth in a healthy mouth (Knorr); also isolated from gingival crevices in normal mouths, from cases with deep caries, inflamed areas around crowns and fillings, pyorrhetic pockets, Vincent's infection and from the mouths of three monkeys and two rabbits (Hine and Berry); also found in an actinomycosis of the face (Robin).

Habitat: Presumably the buccal cavity.

5. **Fusobacterium vescum** (Eggerth and Gagnon, 1933) Hoffman, *comb. nov.* (*Bacteroides vescus* Eggerth and Gagnon, Jour. Bact., *25*, 1933, 406; *Fusiformis vescus* Prévot, Ann. Inst. Past., *60*, 1938, 300.)

ves'cus. L. adj. *vescus* small, weak.

Slender, pointed rods, 1 to 2 microns long, which are sometimes slightly curved. Non-motile. Show bipolar staining. Gram-negative.

Gelatin: Liquefaction in 8 to 25 days.

Blood agar colonies: Very minute and transparent.

Broth: Diffusely clouded.

Milk: Neither acidified nor coagulated.

Indole not produced.

Hydrogen sulfide not produced.

Acid but no gas from cellobiose (in 30 days), dextrin, glucose, maltose, mannose and rhamnose. No acid or gas from esculin, amygdalin, arabinose, galactose, mannitol, melezitose, raffinose, salicin, sorbitol, starch, sucrose, trehalose, xylose, glycerol, glycogen, inulin, lactose or fructose.

Nitrites not produced from nitrates.

Peptone: No gas.

Anaerobic.

Non-pathogenic for white mice or rabbits.

Source: One strain was isolated from human feces.

Habitat: Probably the intestinal canals of mammals.

6. **Fusobacterium biacutum** Weinberg and Prévot, 1926. (Compt. rend. Soc. Biol., Paris, *95*, 1926, 519.)

bi.a.cu'tum. L. adv. *bis* twice; L. adj. *acutus* sharp, pointed; L. part.adj. *biacutus* two-pointed.

Rods, 0.4 to 0.5 by 1.4 to 3.0 microns, with pointed ends, occurring singly, in pairs or sometimes in short chains. Non-motile. Gram-negative.

Gelatin: No liquefaction.

Veillon's agar: Rapid growth. Colonies lens-shaped. Gas is produced which breaks up the medium.

Plain broth: Poor growth.

Glucose broth: Turbid. Medium rapidly acidified. Good growth.

Indole not produced.

Small amount of hydrogen sulfide produced.

Milk: Acid and coagulation in 2 to 8 days. Curd not digested.

Casein and coagulated egg-white not digested.

Acid from glucose, fructose, galactose, maltose and lactose.

Neutral red reduced.

Does not require blood serum for growth. Anaerobic.

Killed in 60 minutes at 60° C.

Pathogenic for guinea pigs.

Source: Six strains were isolated from a case of appendicitis.

Habitat: Unknown.

Genus III. **Dialister** *Bergey et al., 1923*[*]

(Manual, 1st ed., 1923, 271.)

Di.a.lis'ter. Etymology uncertain.

Minute, filterable, rod-shaped cells, with rather pointed ends, occurring singly, in pairs and in short chains. Non-motile. Gram-negative. Require fresh, sterile tissue or ascitic fluid for growth. Glucose is fermented. Anaerobic. Parasitic. Found, associated with influenza, in the respiratory tract.

The type species is *Dialister pneumosintes* (Olitsky and Gates) Bergey et al.

---

[*] Arranged by Dr. A. Parker Hitchens, University of Pennsylvania, Philadelphia, Penna., March, 1946.

1. **Dialister pneumosintes** (Olitsky and Gates, 1921) Bergey et al., 1923. (*Bacterium pneumosintes* Olitsky and Gates, Jour. Exp. Med., *33*, 1921, 713; also see *ibid.*, *35*, 1922, 813; Bergey et al., Manual, 1st ed., 1923, 271.)

pneu.mo.sin'tes. Gr. noun *pneuma* air; Gr. noun *sintes* a spoiler, thief; M.L. adj. *pneumosintes* breath-destroying.

Original description supplemented by material taken from Dack (Bact. Revs., *4*, 1940, 250).

Very short rods, 0.15 to 0.3 (in glucose broth, 0.5 to 1.0) micron in length, the width measuring ½ to ⅓ the length, occurring singly and occasionally in pairs, short chains or masses. The ends are rather pointed. Non-motile. Gram-negative.

Passes Berkefeld V and N filters.

Blood agar colonies: Small, clear, circular, entire, translucent.

Growth occurs in media containing fresh, sterile, rabbit kidney and ascitic fluid. Under strict anaerobic conditions, there is good growth on rabbit blood glucose agar plates.

Glucose broth in which *Escherichia coli* or *Bacillus mesentericus* (non-spore stage) has grown favors growth.

Indole not produced.

Acid but no gas from glucose. Neither acid nor gas from maltose, lactose, sucrose, inulin or mannitol.

Nitrites not produced from nitrates.

Methylene blue not reduced.

Catalase-negative.

Anaerobic.

Optimum temperature, 37° C. Does not survive 56° C. for half an hour.

Optimum pH, between 7.4 and 7.8. No growth at pH 7.0 or pH 8.0.

Pathogenic for rabbits and guinea pigs. Intratracheal injections of mass cultures into rabbits produces a rise in temperature in 24 hours and sometimes a conjunctivitis and a mononuclear leucopenia. Non-pathogenic to monkeys when injected intratracheally.

Source: Isolated from filtered nasopharyngeal secretions from influenza patients in the early hours of the disease.

Habitat: Found in the nasopharyngeal washings of man.

2. **Dialister granuliformans** (Pavlović, 1929) Bergey et al., 1934. (*Bacterium granuliformans* Pavlović, Cent. f. Bakt., I Abt., Orig., *112*, 1929, 432; Bergey et al., Manual, 4th ed., 1934, 341.)

gra.nu.li.for'mans. L. noun *granula* a small grain; L. part.adj. *formans* forming; M.L. adj. *granuliformans* granule-forming.

Small rods. Non-motile. Gram-negative.

Passes through Chamberland L₂ filters.

Agar colonies: Very small, transparent. No gas.

Broth: Turbid.

Litmus milk: Unchanged.

Indole not produced.

Acid from glucose, sucrose and mannitol. Anaerobic to microaerophilic.

Optimum temperature, 37° C.

Pathogenic for rabbits.

Source: Isolated from the respiratory tract in cases of influenza.

Habitat: Found in the mucous membrane of the respiratory tract.

Genus IV. **Sphaerophorus** *Prévot, 1938.**†

(*Spherophorus* (sic) Prévot, Ann. Inst. Past., *60*, 1938, 297; *Spherocillus* (sic) Prévot, *loc. cit.*; *Necrobacterium* Thjøtta, in Lahelle and Thjøtta, Acta Path. et Microbiol. Scand., *22*, 1945, 310; not *Spherophorus* Persoon, Einige Bemerkungen über der Flechten. Neue Annalen d. Bot., edited by Dr. Paulus Usteri, *7*, 1794, 1–32.)

Sphae.ro'pho.rus. Gr. noun *sphaera* sphere; Gr. adj. *phorus* bearing; M.L. noun *Sphaerophorus* that which bears spheres.

---

* Revised by Prof. Robert S. Breed, Cornell University, Geneva, New York; assisted by Dr. Heiner Hoffman, College of Dentistry, New York University, New York City, New York, June, 1955.

† The generic name *Sphaerophorus* Prévot, type species *Sphaerophorus necrophorus* Prévot, was used in the 6th ed. of the Manual, 1948, 578, and is continued in use in this edition.

Straight or curved rods, with rounded ends, which show a marked pleomorphism; filamentous and branching forms occur. Motile and non-motile species. Gram-negative. May or may not require enriched culture media. Usually ferment glucose, rarely lactose or sucrose. Nitrites not produced from nitrates. Gas may or may not be produced in peptone media. Anaerobic. Found in the alimentary and urogenital tracts of man and other animals; also found in various gangrenous or purulent infections in man.

The type species is *Sphaerophorus necrophorus* (Flügge) Prévot.

Key to the species of genus **Sphaerophorus**.

I. Non-motile. Sub-genus *Sphaerophorus* Prévot (Ann. Inst. Past., *60*, 1938, 297).
   A. Gas produced in culture media.
      1. Do not require serum or ascitic fluid for growth.
         a. Gelatin not liquefied.

           1. *Sphaerophorus necrophorus*.
           2. *Sphaerophorus inaequalis*.
           3. *Sphaerophorus varius*.
           4. *Sphaerophorus siccus*.
           5. *Sphaerophorus necroticus*.
           6. *Sphaerophorus necrogenes*.
           7. *Sphaerophorus ridiculosus*.
         aa. Gelatin liquefied slowly.

           8. *Sphaerophorus gulosus*.
      2. Require serum or ascitic fluid for growth.
           9. *Sphaerophorus mortiferus*.
          10. *Sphaerophorus gonidiaformans*.
          11. *Sphaerophorus freundii*.
          12. *Sphaerophorus pyogenes*.
   B. No gas produced in culture media.
      1. Do not require serum or ascitic fluid for growth.
         a. Slow coagulation of milk.

          13. *Sphaerophorus influenzaeformis*.
         aa. No coagulation of milk.

          14. *Sphaerophorus floccosus*.

After the manuscript was prepared in this way, it was discovered that *Sphaerophorus* Prévot is an illegitimate homonym of *Sphaerophorus* Persoon (Einige Bemerkungen über der Flechten. Neue Annalen d. Bot., edited by Dr. Paulus Usteri, *7*, 1794, 1–32). Persoon included two species of lichens in this genus, and the name continues in use among botanists (see for example, Fink, Lichen Flora of the United States, 1935, 78). Dr. Prévot's attention has been called to this unfortunate situation in order that he may make such adjustments in nomenclature as he feels are desirable. The problem of adjusting the nomenclature is complicated by the fact that Thjøtta, in Lahelle and Thjøtta (Acta Path. et Microbiol. Scand., *22*, 1945, 310), without noting the previous proposal of *Sphaerophorus* Prévot, 1938, has proposed *Necrobacterium* as the name of the genus in which he would place the necrosis bacillus. However, no use is made of a scientific name for the necrosis bacillus in the paper by Lahelle and Thjøtta. Neither is the binomial *Necrobacterium necrophorum* used by Lahelle (*Necrobacterium*, Thesis, Univ. Oslo, 1947, 166), this binomial appearing first as *Necrobacterium necrophorus* (sic) in Jonsen and Thjøtta, Acta Path. et Microbiol. Scand., *25*, 1948, 698. It is unfortunate that so many authors fail to observe conventional requirements established in order to produce stability in nomenclature. If the definition given above for *Sphaerophorus* is accepted, then it would appear that the correct name for the necrosis bacillus is *Necrobacterium necrophorum*. Some may feel that this name should be ascribed to Thjøtta 1945 by implication although this binomial was not actually published until 1948 by Jonsen and Thjøtta.—Editors

2. Require serum or ascitic fluid for growth.
    a. Gelatin not liquefied.
      b. Acid from glucose.

                15. *Sphaerophorus abscedens.*

      bb. No acid from glucose.

                16. *Sphaerophorus caviae.*

    aa. Gelatin liquefied slowly.

                17. *Sphaerophorus glycolyticus.*

II. Motile. Sub-genus *Sphaerocillus* Prévot (*loc. cit.*).

                18. *Sphaerophorus bullosus.*

1. **Sphaerophorus necrophorus** (Flügge, 1886) Prévot, 1938. (Bacillus der Kälberdiphtherie, Loeffler, Mitteil. kaiserl. Gesundheitsamte, *2*, 1884, 493; *Bacillus diphtheriae vitulorum* Flügge, Die Mikroorganismen, 2 Aufl., 1886, 265; *Bacillus necrophorus* Flügge, *ibid.*, 273; *Streptothrix cuniculi* Schmorl, Deutsch. Ztschr. f. Tiermed., *17*, 1891, 376; *Bacillus funduliformis* Hallé, Inaug. Diss., Paris, 1898; *Bacillus thetoides* Rist, Thèse de Paris, 1898; *Actinomyces necrophorus* Lehmann and Neumann, Bakt. Diag., 2 Aufl., *2*, 1899, 434; *Cohnistreptothrix cuniculi* Chalmers and Christopherson, Ann. Trop. Med., *10*, 1916, 273; *Bacteroides funduliformis* Bergey et al., Manual, 3rd ed., 1930, 373; Prévot, Ann. Inst. Past., *60*, 1938, 298; *Spherophorus funduliformis* Prévot, *loc. cit.*; *Bacterium funduliforme* Dack, Jour. Inf. Dis., *62*, 1938, 169; *Necrobacterium necrophorus* (sic) Jonsen and Thjøtta, Acta Path. et Microbiol. Scand., *25*, 1948, 698.)

ne.cro'pho.rus. Gr. adj. *necrus* dead; Gr. adj. *phorus* bearing; M.L. adj. *necrophorus* necrosis-producing.

Rods, 0.5 to 1.5 by 1.5 to 3.0 microns in pathological processes. Extremely pleomorphic, especially in cultures, showing filamentous forms up to 80 to 100 microns in length and even branching forms, as reported by some authors. Schmorl (Deutsch. Ztschr. f. Tiermed., *17*, 1891, 376) states that the short forms are motile, whereas Lahelle (*Necrobacterium*, Oslo, 1947, 166) and other recent investigators report this species to be non-motile and non-flagellated. Gramnegative.

Foul odor produced in all media.

Gelatin: No liquefaction.

Agar colonies: Small, circular, opaque,

dirty white; yellowish center under low power lens; floccose margin.

Agar stab: Yellowish colonies along needle track; gas bubbles are produced.

Blood agar: Hemolysis of human and rabbit erythrocytes; weak hemolysis of ox erythrocytes; no hemolysis of horse, sheep or goat erythrocytes.

Broth: Turbid, flocculent growth; gas and a cheese-like odor are produced.

Litmus milk: Coagulation then digestion of the coagulum; neutral reaction after 1 week.

Coagulated egg white: No digestion.

Indole is produced.

Hydrogen sulfide is produced.

Acid and gas from glucose, fructose and maltose. No acid or gas from lactose, sucrose, mannitol or glycerol.

Nitrites not produced from nitrates.

Ammonia not produced.

Anaerobic.

Temperature relations: Optimum, between 30° and 40° C. No growth at 21° or at 45° C. Sparse growth at 22° and at 44° C.

Optimum pH, between 7.5 and 7.8.

Hemotoxin is produced.

Pathogenicity: Some strains are pathogenic for rabbits, guinea pigs and mice but not for white rats.

Comments: Dack, Dragstedt, Johnson and McCullough (Jour. Inf. Dis., *62*, 1938, 169) made a comparative study of *Sphaerophorus funduliformis* and *Sphaerophorus necrophorus* with respect to their growth requirements, their colonial morphologies, their cell morphologies on different media, their biochemical reactions, their pathogenicities for rabbits and their abilities to ulcerate the colons of experimental animals. Their study indicated that no distinction exists between these two organisms. Although strain variations in morphology were noted, Dack et al. (*ibid.*, 180) regarded these variations as insufficient for the differentiation of species. Likewise, differences were observed with regard to pathogenicity. When injected subcutaneously into rabbits, various strains of these organisms produced a gradient of virulence which ranged from slightly virulent to lethal. As there is no clear-cut method for separating *Sphaerophorus funduliformis* and *Sphaerophorus necrophorus*, Dack et al. (*loc. cit.*) consider these two organisms as constituting a single species, *Sphaerophorus necrophorus*.

Source: Isolated from the female genital tract, urinary infections, puerperal infections, acute appendicitis, otitis, pulmonary gangrene, liver abscesses, septicaemias, intestinal tracts and chronic ulcerative colitis; also isolated from cases of diphtheria in cattle with multiple sclerotic abscesses, from gangrenous dermatitis in horses and mules and from multiple necrotic foci in the livers of cattle and hogs.

Habitat: Presumably a normal inhabitant of the mucous membranes of man and other animals.

2. **Sphaerophorus inaequalis** (Eggerth and Gagnon, 1933) Prévot, 1938. (*Bacteroides inaequalis* Eggerth and Gagnon, Jour. Bact., *25*, 1933, 407; Prévot, Ann. Inst. Past., *60*, 1938, 298.)

in.ae.qua′lis. L. adj. *inaequalis* unequal.

Rods which show wide variation in size and form. Marked pleomorphism on blood agar: some forms are coccoid, 0.5 micron in diameter, while others are slender filaments, 3.0 to 12.0 microns long, which are often curved or hooked. On glucose agar and in glucose broth, the cells occur as small ellipsoids, 1.0 to 2.0 microns long, which may form short chains. Non-motile. Show bipolar staining. Gram-negative.

Gelatin: No liquefaction in 45 days.

Blood agar colonies: Pin-point in size.

Broth: Diffusely clouded.

Milk: Acidified but not coagulated.

Indole is produced.

Hydrogen sulfide is produced.

Acid but no gas from esculin, amygdalin, arabinose, fructose, galactose, glucose, lactose, maltose, mannose, raffinose, salicin,

sucrose and xylose. No acid or gas from cellobiose, dextrin, glycerol, glycogen, inulin, mannitol, melezitose, rhamnose, sorbitol, starch or trehalose.

Nitrites not produced from nitrates.

Anaerobic.

Non-pathogenic for white mice or rabbits.

Distinctive characters: Produces a small amount (5 per cent in Smith tube) of gas from peptone water in the complete absence of carbohydrates; none of this gas is absorbed by alkali. Rapidly decolorizes brom cresol purple and phenol red in meat infusion broth; slowly or not at all in peptone water.

Source: One strain was isolated from human feces.

Habitat: Probably the intestinal canals of mammals.

3. **Sphaerophorus varius** (Eggerth and Gagnon, 1933) Prévot, 1938. (*Bacteroides varius* Eggerth and Gagnon, Jour. Bact., *25*, 1933, 409; Prévot, Ann. Inst. Past., *60*, 1938, 299.)

va′ri.us. L. adj. *varius* diverse, varied.

Slender rods, 1 to 2 microns long, on blood agar; on glucose agar the cells are longer and thicker, measuring 2 to 3 microns in length; ellipsoidal or coccoid forms are found in glucose broth. Non-motile. Shows uneven staining. Gram-negative.

Gelatin: No liquefaction in 45 days.

Blood agar colonies: Very flat cones, 2 to 3 mm in diameter.

Broth: Diffusely clouded.

Milk: Not acidified or coagulated.

Indole is produced.

Hydrogen sulfide is produced.

Acid and gas from fructose, galactose, glucose and mannose. No acid or gas from esculin, amygdalin, arabinose, cellobiose, dextrin, glycerol, glycogen, inulin, lactose, maltose, mannitol, melezitose, raffinose, rhamnose, salicin, sorbitol, starch, sucrose, trehalose or xylose.

Nitrites not produced from nitrates.

Anaerobic.

Non-pathogenic for white mice or rabbits.

Distinctive characters: Gas is produced from peptone. Brom cresol purple and phenol red are decolorized in a meat infusion broth.

Source: Two strains were isolated from human feces.

Habitat: Probably the intestinal canals of mammals.

4. **Sphaerophorus siccus** (Eggerth and Gagnon, 1933) Prévot, 1938. (*Bacteroides siccus* Eggerth and Gagnon, Jour. Bact., *25*, 1933, 410; Prévot, Ann. Inst. Past., *60*, 1938, 299.)

sic'cus. L. adj. *siccus* dry.

Short, thick rods about 1.0 micron long; in glucose broth the cells are coccoid and often grow in short chains. Non-motile. Gram-negative.

Gelatin: No liquefaction.

Blood agar colonies: Elevated, dry, difficult to emulsify, 1.0 to 1.5 mm in diameter.

Broth: Growth occurs as a powdery sediment with a clear supernatant fluid.

Indole not produced.

Hydrogen sulfide is produced.

Milk: Unchanged.

Acid but no gas from fructose. No acid or gas from glucose, glycerol, mannitol, sorbitol, arabinose, salicin, trehalose, amygdalin, cellobiose, glycogen, rhamnose, xylose or lactose.

Nitrites not produced from nitrates.

Anaerobic.

Non-pathogenic for white mice or rabbits.

Distinctive characters: Gas is produced in small amounts from peptone. Phenol red and brom cresol purple are decolorized in meat infusion broth.

Source: Two strains were isolated from human feces.

Habitat: Probably the intestinal canals of mammals.

5. **Sphaerophorus necroticus** (Nativelle, 1936) Prévot, 1938. (*Bacillus necroticus* Nativelle, 1936, see Weinberg et al., Les Microbes Anaérobies, 1937, 693; Prévot, Ann. Inst. Past., *60*, 1938, 298.)

ne.cro'ti.cus. Gr. noun *necrus* a dead body; M.L. adj. *necroticus* necrotic.

Short, thin, irregular rods, with a few long forms, some showing bipolar staining in young cultures. In 10 to 18 hours, central, deep-staining, ovoid swellings appear in the rods; these are not spores. After 24 hours to several days, the rods disappear, and only amorphous elements remain. Non-motile. Gram-negative.

Gelatin: No liquefaction.

Agar: Deep colonies small, lenticular. Gas is produced.

Glucose broth: Diffuse growth which settles as a heavy, sticky deposit. Gas and fetid odor.

Milk: No acid, coagulation or peptonization.

Coagulated egg white not liquefied.

Indole is produced.

Acid from glucose, fructose, lactose, sucrose, galactose and maltose. No acid from mannitol, dextrin, inulin, amygdalin, salicin, arabinose or glycerol.

Anaerobic.

Optimum temperature, 37° C.

Pathogenicity: Slightly pathogenic in pure culture. Pathogenicity more marked if mixed with *Escherichia coli*.

Source: One strain was isolated from a case of gangrenous appendicitis.

Habitat: Presumably found in necrotic tissues of man.

6. **Sphaerophorus necrogenes** (Weinberg et al., 1937) Prévot, 1938. (Bacillus, Kawamura, Jour. Jap. Soc. Vet. Sci., *5*, 1926, 22; *Bacillus necrogenes* Weinberg et al., Les Microbes Anaérobies, 1937, 681; Prévot, Ann. Inst. Past., *60*, 1938, 298.)

ne.cro'ge.nes. Gr. adj. *necrus* dead; Gr. v. *gennaio* to produce; M.L. adj. *necrogenes* necrosis-producing.

Rods and very long filaments (50 to 100 microns) with swellings. Non-motile. Gram-negative.

Gas is produced.

Serum and ascitic fluid may or may not favor growth.

Gelatin: No liquefaction. Good growth; gas.

Serum agar colonies: Small, whitish, appearing in 2 or 3 days; slight gas.

Glucose agar colonies: Small, whitish; less growth than on serum agar.

Agar stab: Small, punctiform colonies; gas.

Glucose bouillon: Turbid; gas; sediment and then clarification.

Liver broth: Abundant growth; gas; grayish white sediment in 3 to 5 days, the broth clearing.

Milk: Not coagulated; cheesy odor.

Anaerobic.

Optimum temperature, 37° C.; killed at 58° C.

Pathogenicity: Causes necrotic suppurations in domestic fowls, especially hens. Pathogenic for mice, guinea pigs and rabbits; subcutaneous injection of 0.1 to 1.0 cc produces local edema and metastatic, necrotic abscesses in the lungs and liver, killing in 4 to 10 days. Intramuscular injection of 0.1 cc produces purulent inflammation and necrosis, followed by death, in chickens and pigeons.

Source: Isolated from an epidemic abscess of chickens.

Habitat: Found in domestic fowls; not common.

7. **Sphaerophorus ridiculosus** Prévot, 1948. (Ann. Inst. Past., *75*, 1948, 387.)

ri.di.cu.lo′sus. L. adj. *ridiculosus* laughable, droll.

Extremely pleomorphic rods, especially on initial isolation and when subject to the action of penicillin; the most frequent form is a round mass, 3 to 4 microns in diameter, bearing two rod-shaped appendices which are diametrically opposed or which form an obtuse angle with each other; in old cultures the predominant forms are straight or curved rods, 0.8 by 2.5 to 10.0 microns, the short forms often showing bipolar staining. Non-motile. Robinow's procedures show what appears to be a conjugation of cells with a true nuclear cycle. Gram-negative.

Much gas and slight odor are produced.

Gelatin: No liquefaction.

Agar stab: Lenticular colonies; abundant gas.

Glucose bouillon: Rapid and abundant turbidity; abundant gas; fetid odor.

Peptone broth: Turbid; gas.

Milk: Coagulated in 5 days.

Coagulated proteins: Not attacked.

Indole and skatole not produced.

Hydrogen sulfide slightly produced.

Glucose, fructose, sucrose, lactose, maltose and galactose are attacked. Glycerol is not utilized.

Starch is feebly attacked.

Ammonia (0.04 g) and a volatile acid (0.096 g of acetic and butyric acids) are produced (per 100 cc of culture).

Lactic acid is produced.

Acetylmethylcarbinol not produced.

Nitrites not produced from nitrates.

Neutral red is reduced.

Anaerobic.

Optimum temperature, 37° C.

Neither toxin nor hemolysin produced.

Pathogenicity: Lesions not produced in mice or guinea pigs.

Source: Isolated from a lesion in a jaw unsuccessfully treated with penicillin.

Habitat: Found in human lesions; probably more widely distributed than this.

8. **Sphaerophorus gulosus** (Eggerth and Gagnon, 1933) Prévot, 1938. (*Bacteroides gulosus* Eggerth and Gagnon, Jour. Bact., *25*, 1933, 398; Prévot, Ann. Inst. Past., *60*, 1938, 298.)

gu.lo′sus. L. adj. *gulosus* gluttonous.

Small, elliptical rods, 0.8 to 1.0 by 1.0 to 2.0 microns, on blood agar plates; in addition to these elliptical forms, small cocci, rods with marked bipolar staining, swollen rods 2 to 3 by 3 to 4 microns, and longer rods up to 6 microns occur in glucose broth. Nonmotile. Stain deeper around periphery. Gram-negative.

Gelatin: Liquefaction in 2 to 3 weeks.

Blood agar colonies: Soft, gray, entire, elevated, 2 mm in diameter.

Broth: Heavy and diffuse growth.

Milk: Acidified and coagulated in 4 to 20 days.

Indole is produced.

Hydrogen sulfide is produced.

Acid and a very small amount of gas from esculin, amygdalin, arabinose, cellobiose, dextrin, fructose, galactose, glycogen, inulin, lactose, glucose, maltose, mannitol, mannose, melezitose, raffinose, rhamnose, salicin, sorbitol, starch, sucrose, trehalose and xylose. Sorbitol and mannitol require 2 to 3 weeks for fermentation. Neither acid nor gas from glycerol, dulcitol, erythritol or inositol.

Nitrites not produced from nitrates.

Peptone: No gas.

Anaerobic.

Non-pathogenic for white mice or rabbits.

Source: Seven strains were isolated from human feces.

Habitat: Probably the intestinal canals of mammals.

9. Sphaerophorus mortiferus (Harris, 1901) Prévot, 1938. (*Bacillus mortiferus* Harris, Jour. Exp. Med., *6*, 1901, 519; Prévot, Ann. Inst. Past., *60*, 1938, 299.)

mor.ti'fer.us. L. noun *mors* death; L. gen.noun *mortis* of death; L. v. *fero* to bear; M.L. adj. *mortiferus* death-bearing.

Rods, 0.6 by 2.0 microns, with rounded ends, occurring singly, in pairs or in short chains, with filamentous and pleomorphic forms, some showing metachromatic granules. Non-motile. Gram-negative.

Serum or ascitic fluid is required for growth.

Hydrocele gelatin: No liquefaction. No gas.

Hydrocele agar: Deep colonies small, irregular, translucent, granular, light brown. Surface colonies small, regular or fringed, 1 to 2 mm in diameter, yellowish brown; fecal odor.

Glucose-human blood agar: Gas with a disagreeable odor; browning of the hemoglobin.

Hydrocele broth: Growth with heavy, viscous, whitish deposit and foul-smelling gas.

Hydrocele milk: Acid but no coagulation. In 6 days the milk is peptonized.

Indole produced in hydrocele broth.

Hydrogen sulfide produced in hydrocele broth.

Anaerobic.

Optimum temperature, 37° C.

Pathogenic for guinea pigs, rabbits and mice.

Source: Isolated from a liver abscess of man.

Habitat: Presumably found in various infections in man.

10. Sphaerophorus gonidiaformans (Tunnicliff and Jackson, 1925) Prévot, 1938. (*Bacillus gonidiaformans* Tunnicliff and Jackson, Jour. Inf. Dis., *36*, 1925, 430; *Actinomyces gonadiformis* (sic) Bergey et al., Manual, 3rd ed., 1930, 469; *Bacteroides gonidiaformans* Hauduroy et al., Dict. d. Bact.

Path., 1937, 62; Prévot, Ann. Inst. Past., *60*, 1938, 299.)

go.ni.di.a.for'mans. Gr. noun *gone* offspring, seed; M.L. noun *gonidium* gonidium; L. part. adj. *formans* forming; M.L. adj. *gonidiaformans* gonidia-forming.

Rods, 0.5 by 1.0 to 3.0 microns, with rounded ends; gonidia form within the rods, developing into short or long, wavy filaments. Non-motile. Show bipolar staining; also show red granules with Giemsa stain. Gram-negative.

Serum or ascitic fluid is required for growth.

Gelatin: No liquefaction. No growth.

Blood agar colonies: Thick,whitish, moist, entire.

Glucose media: Slight gas produced.

Broth: Slight development; flocculent sediment.

Litmus milk: No growth.

Potato: No growth.

No acid or gas from glucose, salicin, mannitol or inulin.

Anaerobic.

Optimum temperature, 37° C.

Pathogenic for rabbits and guinea pigs.

Source: Isolated from tonsils.

Habitat: Presumably the pharynx.

11. Sphaerophorus freundii (Hauduroy et al., 1937) Prévot, 1938. (Freund, Cent. f. Bakt., I Abt., Orig., *88*, 1922, 9; Bacterium of Freund, Weinberg et al., Les Microbes Anaérobies, 1937, 706; *Bacteroides freundii* Hauduroy et al., Dict. d. Bact. Path., 1937, 57; *Sphaerophorus freundi* (sic) Prévot, Ann. Inst. Past., *60*, 1938, 299.)

freun'di.i. M.L. gen.noun *freundii* of Freund; named for F. Freund, the bacteriologist who first described this species.

Short, ellipsoidal rods, 0.3 to 0.35 by 0.8 to 1.0 micron, occurring singly, in pairs and in chains. Pleomorphic in cultures with irregular filaments and swollen forms. Non-motile. Show bipolar staining. Gram-negative.

Serum or ascitic fluid is required for growth.

Gelatin: No liquefaction.

Ascitic agar: Deep colonies lenticular in 1 to 3 days, small, yellowish.

Serum glucose agar: Deep colonies lenticular. Gas produced.

Glucose agar: Surface colonies pinhead, dew-drop, opaque, yellowish.

Glucose serum broth: Turbidity; thin flocculent growth. Gas produced with fetid odor.

Serum milk: Coagulated in 3 days. Not peptonized.

Indole is produced in glucose broth.

Hydrogen sulfide is produced in glucose broth.

Coagulated hydrocele fluid not liquefied.

Acid and gas from glucose, maltose, sucrose and mannitol. Ethanol and butyric and lactic acids are produced from carbohydrates.

Anaerobic.

Optimum temperature, 37° C.

Pathogenic for rabbits and guinea pigs.

Source: One strain was isolated from a purulent meningitis following otitis in man.

Habitat: Found in various infections in man.

12. **Sphaerophorus pyogenes** (Hauduroy et al., 1937) Prévot, 1938. (Buday, Cent. f. Bakt., I Abt., Orig., *77*, 1916, 453; *Bacillus pyogenes anaerobius* Béla-Johan, Cent. f. Bakt., I Abt., Orig., *87*, 1922, 290; not *Bacillus pyogenes anaerobius* Kruse, in Flügge, Die Mikroorganismen, 3 Aufl., *2*, 1896, 244; *Bacteroides pyogenes* Hauduroy et al., Dict. d. Bact. Path., 1937, 69; Prévot, Ann. Inst. Past., *60*, 1938, 299.)

py.o′ge.nes. Gr. noun *pyum* pus; Gr. v. *gennaio* to produce; M.L. adj. *pyogenes* pus-producing.

Short, ellipsoidal rods, occurring singly, in short chains and as pleomorphic, filamentous forms. Non-motile. Show bipolar staining. Gram-negative.

Serum or ascitic fluid is required for growth; isolation in culture media is easier after animal passage.

Serum agar: Deep colonies small, punctiform. Some gas produced. Surface colonies fine, transparent, with flat borders, 0.5 mm in diameter.

Ascitic broth: The optimum concentration of ascitic fluid is from 30 to 50 per cent. Flocculent growth with a foamy layer on the surface. Gas produced.

Tarozzi broth with liver: Rapid growth with turbidity and later a flocculent deposit. Foamy layer on the surface.

Hydrogen sulfide not produced.

Anaerobic.

Optimum temperature, 37° C.

Pathogenicity: Pathogenic for rabbits and guinea pigs when pus from a lesion is injected. Cultures other than those in ascitic broth show no pathogenicity.

Source: Isolated from abscesses of the liver and lungs following septic war wounds; also isolated from the blood stream following tonsillectomies.

Habitat: Found in various infections in man.

13. **Sphaerophorus influenzaeformis** (Russ, 1905) Prévot, 1938. (*Bacillus influenzaeformis* Russ, Cent. f. Bakt., I Abt., Orig., *39*, 1905, 357; *Bacteroides russii* Hauduroy et al., Dict. d. Bact. Path., 1937, 73; Prévot, Ann. Inst. Past., *60*, 1938, 299.)

in.flu.en.zae.for′mis. M.L. noun *influenza* influenza; L. noun *forma* shape; M.L. adj. *influenzaeformis* influenza-like.

Short rods, 0.5 by 1.5 microns, with rounded ends; some strains are pleomorphic with involution forms and swollen filaments. Non-motile. Show bipolar staining. Gram-negative.

Gelatin: No liquefaction.

Agar: Deep colonies lenticular, sometimes surrounded by a number of smaller colonies. No gas.

Glucose agar: Surface colonies semi-transparent, dew-drop, grayish.

Peptone broth: No growth.

Glucose broth: Uniform turbidity which deposits as a granular mass. No gas produced.

Milk: Slow growth with coagulation in several weeks. No gas or digestion of coagulum.

Indole produced in glucose broth.

Hydrogen sulfide produced in glucose broth.

Anaerobic.

Optimum temperature, 37° C.

Pathogenicity: One strain was pathogenic for rabbits, mice and guinea pigs.

Source: One strain was isolated from a

perianal abscess and two strains from purulent meningitis in man.

Habitat: Found in various infections in man.

14. Sphaerophorus floccosus (Weinberg et al., 1937) Prévot, 1938. (*Streptobacillus pyogenes floccosus* Courmont and Cade, Arch. Méd. Exp., *12*, 1900, 393; *Bacillus floccosus* Weinberg et al., Les Microbes Anaérobies, 1937, 698; not *Bacillus floccosus* Kern, Arb. bakt. Inst. Karlsruhe, *1*, Heft 4, 1896, 424; *Bacteroides floccosus* Hauduroy et al., Dict. d. Bact. Path., 1937, 55; Prévot, Ann. Inst. Past., *60*, 1938, 299.)

floc.co'sus. L. adj. *floccosus* full of flocks of wool.

Small, ellipsoidal rods, 1 micron long, occurring singly, in pairs and in chains. Nonmotile. Show bipolar staining. Gram-negative.

Gelatin: No liquefaction

Deep agar: Growth slow, appearing as a light haze. No gas produced.

Blood agar: Translucent colonies surrounded by a zone of alpha hemolysis.

Broth: Rapid, flocculent growth on sides of tube; no turbidity; no gas; slight fetid odor.

Milk: Poor growth; no coagulation.

Coagulated serum: Small, whitish colonies. No liquefaction.

Potato: No growth.

Anaerobic.

Optimum temperature, 37° C.

Non-pathogenic for mice. Produces lesions in rabbits, guinea pigs and dogs.

Source: Isolated from blood in pyemia of man.

Habitat: Presumably found in various infections in man.

15. Sphaerophorus abscedens Tardieux and Monteverde, 1951. (Tardieux and Monteverde, in Tardieux, Ann. Inst. Past., *80*, 1951, 276.)

ab.sce'dens. L. part.adj. *abscedens* going away, disappearing.

Pleomorphic rods which, on initial culturing, occur as ellipsoidal forms, 2 to 3 microns in diameter, and as elongated forms with lateral or terminal, spheroidal swellings and metachromatic granules. With subsequent transfers, the short forms predominate, especially in liquid media, and pleomorphism is retained in agar stabs. The ellipsoidal forms show bipolar staining. Non-motile. Gram-negative.

Serum or ascitic fluid is required for growth.

Neither gas nor odor produced.

Gelatin: No liquefaction.

Serum agar stab: Colonies punctiform, becoming lenticular.

Glucose serum broth: Homogeneous turbidity.

In glucose broth, the end-products of fermentation are acetic, butyric and lactic acids, ammonia, a slight amount of hydrogen sulfide, indole and sometimes cresol and acetylmethylcarbinol. Amines, alcohols and ketones are not produced.

Peptone broth: Eventually becomes turbid; indole is produced.

Milk: Unchanged.

Coagulated proteins not attacked.

Glucose and galactose are attacked.

Nitrites not produced from nitrates.

Anaerobic.

Neither toxin nor hemolysin produced.

Non-pathogenic for rabbits, guinea pigs or mice.

Source: One strain was isolated from the pus of an abscess on a cow; a second strain was isolated from the pus of an abscess which developed on the heel of a man bitten by a dog.

Habitat: Found in warm-blooded animals so far as known.

16. Sphaerophorus caviae (Vinzent, 1928) Prévot, 1938. (*Streptobacillus caviae* Vinzent, Ann. Inst. Past., *42*, 1928, 533; *Bacteroides caviae* Hauduroy et al., Dict. d. Bact. Path., 1937, 53; Prévot, Ann. Inst. Past., *60*, 1938, 299.)

ca'vi.ae. M.L. gen.noun *caviae* of *Cavia*; M.L. noun *Cavia* generic name of the cavy, or guinea pig.

Small rods, usually 0.3 to 0.5 by 1.0 to 1.5 microns, sometimes curved, occurring singly and in chains. Pleomorphic in old cultures with long, filamentous forms. Non-motile. Gram-negative.

Serum or ascitic fluid is required for growth.

Serum gelatin: No liquefaction.

Serum agar: Surface colonies small, translucent, slightly raised, adherent to medium in 48 hours. Deep colonies lenticular, 2 mm in size in 48 hours. Colonies difficult to break up. No gas.

Serum broth: Supernatant fluid clear with small, stellate colonies which tend to adhere to walls of the tube. No gas.

Milk: Unchanged.

Coagulated egg white and serum not liquefied.

Indole not produced in serum peptone water.

Hydrogen sulfide not produced.

No acid or gas from carbohydrates.

Anaerobic.

Optimum temperature, 37° C.

Pathogenic for guinea pigs, rabbits and mice.

Source: Isolated from epidemic benign cervical adenitis of guinea pigs.

Habitat: Infected guinea pigs so far as known.

17. **Sphaerophorus glycolyticus** Tardieux and Ernst, 1951. (Tardieux and Ernst, in Tardieux, Ann. Inst. Past., *80*, 1951, 278.)

gly.co.ly′ti.cus. Gr. adj. *glycus* sweet; Gr. adj. *lyticus* dissolving; M.L. adj. *glycolyticus* sugar-dissolving.

Pleomorphic rods which, on initial culturing, occur as ellipsoidal forms, 2 to 3 microns in diameter, and as elongated forms with lateral or terminal, spheroidal swellings and metachromatic granules. With subsequent transfers, the short forms predominate, especially in liquid media, and pleomorphism is retained in agar stabs. The ellipsoidal forms show bipolar staining. Non-motile. Gram-negative.

Serum or ascitic fluid is required for growth.

No gas, but abundant odor is produced.

Gelatin: Slow liquefaction (sometimes only after 1 month).

Agar stab: Colonies are punctiform or lenticular.

Glucose broth: Abundant, homogeneous turbidity.

In glucose broth, the end-products of fermentation are acetic, butyric and lactic acids, hydrogen sulfide, ammonia, acetone and traces of aldehydes and skatole. Amines and alcohols are not produced.

Peptone serum broth: Very slight turbidity.

Milk: Rapid coagulation and digestion. Coagulated proteins not attacked.

Acid but no gas from glucose, fructose, galactose, sucrose, lactose, maltose and glycerol.

Starch is not hydrolyzed.

Nitrites not produced from nitrates.

Neutral red is reduced, progressively recoloring.

Anaerobic.

Survives for several minutes at 70° C.

Neither toxin nor hemolysin produced.

Pathogenic for guinea pigs but not for rabbits.

Source: Two strains were isolated from genital infections and a third from a war wound.

Habitat: Human sources so far as known.

18. **Sphaerophorus bullosus** (Distaso, 1912) Breed, *comb. nov.* (*Bacillus bullosus* Distaso, Cent. f. Bakt., I Abt., Orig., *62*, 1912, 443; *Bacteroides bullosus* Castellani and Chalmers, Man. Trop. Med., 3rd ed., 1919, 960; *Spherocillus bullosis* (sic) Prévot, Ann. Inst. Past., *60*, 1938, 300 (type species of genus *Sphaerocillus* Prévot, *ibid.*, 297).)

bul.lo′sus. L. noun *bulla* a knob; M.L. adj. *bullosus* knobbed.

Small rods with rounded ends; at times long, slender, bifurcating forms occur with an enlargement at one pole or in the center. Motile by means of peritrichous flagella. Show bipolar staining. Gram-negative.

Gelatin: No liquefaction.

Glucose agar colonies: Deep colonies very small with fimbriate margin. Gas is produced.

Glucose broth: Flocculent growth falling to bottom. Some gas produced.

Litmus milk: Slight acidity. No coagulation.

Indole not produced.

Acid from glucose. No acid from lactose or sucrose.

Anaerobic.

Optimum temperature, 37° C.

Source: Isolated from the intestinal tract.

Habitat: Found in the intestinal tract.

Genus V. **Streptobacillus** *Levaditi et al., 1925.**

(*Streptothrix* Schottmüller, Dermat. Wochnschr., *58*, 1914, Supplement, 77; not *Streptothrix* Corda, Prachtflora Europaeischer Schimmelbildung, 1839; *Actinomyces* Lieske, Morph. u. Biol. d. Strahlenpilze, Leipzig, 1921, 31; not *Actinomyces* Harz, in Bollinger, Centbl. f. med. Wissensch., *15*, 1877; 485; Levaditi, Nicolau and Poincloux, Compt. rend. Acad. Sci., Paris, *180*, 1925, 1188; not *Streptobacillus* Ueke, Cent. f. Bakt., I Abt., *23*, 1898, 996; *Asterococcus* (in part) Heilman, Jour. Inf. Dis., *69*, 1941, 32; *Proactinomyces* (in part) Krassilnikov, Guide to the Actinomycetes, Izd. Akad. Nauk, U.S.S.R., Moskau, 1941, 76.)

As *Streptobacillus* Levaditi et al., 1925, is generally used as the generic name of the organisms in this genus, it is retained for use in this edition of the MANUAL although *Streptobacillus* Ueke, 1898, type species *S. terrae* Ueke, clearly antedates it. *Streptobacillus* Ueke is now generally regarded as a synonym of *Bacillus* Cohn, for the type species of Ueke's genus is an aerobic sporeformer while *Streptobacillus moniliformis* Levaditi et al. is a nonsporeformer. Possibly *Haverhillia* Parker and Hudson (Amer. Jour. Path., *2*, 1926, 357), type species *Haverhillia multiformis* Parker and Hudson (*loc. cit.*), should be accepted as the legitimate name for the rat-bite-fever organism. However, except for a purely morphological comparison based on stained smears (van Rooyen, Jour. Path. and Bact., *43*, 1936, 455), no direct comparative studies of the rat-bite-fever organism and the organism that caused the epidemic in Haverhill, Massachusetts have been made as yet, and the latter was regarded as having been transmitted by ingested milk, not by rat bites. Until the relationship of the two species is established by further research, it has seemed advisable not to complicate further the problems of nomenclature by using the generic name *Haverhillia* Parker and Hudson at this place.

Strep.to.ba.cil'lus. Gr. adj. *streptus* pliant; L. dim.noun *bacillum* a small rod; M.L. noun *bacillus* a rodlet; M.L. noun *Streptobacillus* pliant rodlet.

Pleomorphic bacilli which vary from short rods to long, interwoven filaments which have a tendency to fragment into chains of bacillary and coccobacillary elements. Under certain conditions *Monilia*-like swellings are formed along the length of each filament. Not encapsulated. Non-motile. Not acid-fast. Gram-negative. Require media enriched with ascitic fluid or blood serum for good growth. Discrete, colorless or grayish to whitish colonies are formed on solid media. Flocculent, whitish growth at the bottom of fluid media. Spontaneous L-phase variation occurs. Aerobic, facultative; anaerobic conditions sometimes produce the best growth on primary isolation. Parasitic to pathogenic for rats, mice and other mammals.

The type species is *Streptobacillus moniliformis* Levaditi et al.

1. **Streptobacillus moniliformis** Levaditi et al., 1925. (*Streptothrix muris ratti* Schottmüller, Dermat. Wochnschr., *58*, 1914, Supplement, 77; *Nocardia muris* de Mello and Pais, Arq. Hig. Pat. Exot., *6*, 1918, 183; *Actinomyces muris ratti* Lieske, Morph. u. Biol. d. Strahlenpilze, Leipzig, 1921, 31; Levaditi, Nicolau and Poincloux, Compt. rend. Acad. Sci., Paris, *180*, 1925, 1188; *Haverhillia multiformis* Parker and Hudson, Amer. Jour. Path., *2*, 1926, 357; *Actinomyces muris* Topley and Wilson, Princip. of Bact. and Immun., 2nd ed., 1936, 274; *Asterococcus muris* Heilman, Jour. Inf. Dis., *69*, 1941, 32; *Proactinomyces muris* Krassilnikov, Guide to the Actinomycetes, Izd. Akad. Nauk, U.S.S.R., Moskau, 1941, 76; *Haverhillia moniliformis* Prévot, in Hauduroy et al., Dict. d. Bact. Path., 2e ed., 1953, 266.)

mo.ni.li.for'mis. L. noun *monile* a necklace; L. noun *forma* shape; M.L. adj. *moniliformis* necklace-like.

Highly pleomorphic rods, 0.1 to 0.5 by 2.0 or 5.0 to 10.0 or 15.0 microns, with rounded or occasionally pointed ends, forming long, wavy, curved or looped filaments up to 100 to 150 microns in length. In young

* Prepared by Dr. E. A. Freundt, Statens Seruminstitut, Copenhagen, Denmark, April, 1955.

cultures the filaments are homogeneous and composed of single cells; with increasing age, fine granules and alternate light and dark bands appear in the filaments together with a tendency to fragment into irregular, bacillary and coccobacillary elements which give the typical streptobacillary appearance. Under certain conditions, large, spindle-shaped or spherical swellings, sometimes packed with granules, are very common, occurring anywhere, terminally, subterminally or centrally, in the rods and filaments. Besides these cellular swellings, extracellular, ether-soluble, oil-droplet-like globules are very characteristic; these have been shown to consist mainly of cholesterol (Partridge and Klieneberger, Jour. Path. and Bact., *52*, 1941, 219). The morphology, to a considerable extent, depends upon the medium, culture conditions and the age of the culture. Under favorable conditions the cells tend to be regular and rod-shaped, while under unfavorable conditions pleomorphism is most pronounced. In smears from pathological material, such as exudates or blood from infected animals, the cells occur only as rods or occasionally as short filaments which lie singly or in clumps without definite arrangement. True branching has often been reported, but it is now generally recognized that branching does not occur. Not encapsulated. Non-motile. The *Monilia*-like swellings take stains more intensely than do the filaments; they do not take the spore stain. Not acid-fast. Gramnegative; sometimes reported to be weakly and irregularly Gram-positive in very young cultures.

Requires media enriched with ascitic fluid, blood serum or whole blood. CO_2 generally does not stimulate growth. Moisture is essential for good growth; incubation of cultures on solid media in incubators with a moisture-saturated atmosphere is recommended.

Gelatin: No liquefaction.

Plain and glucose agar or broth: No growth with recently isolated strains; occasionally very slight growth after prolonged artificial culture.

Ascitic fluid or serum agar: Discrete colonies, 1.0 to 2.5 mm in diameter after 3 days, circular or irregularly round with sharp edges, low-convex, colorless or grayish to whitish, smooth glistening surface, butyrous consistency. Smaller colonies (type X colonies of Brown and Nunemaker, Bull. Johns Hopkins Hosp., *70*, 1942, 201; α colonies of Ørskov, Acta Path. et Microbiol. Scand., *19*, 1942, 575), which have a rough and more coarsely granular appearance, are sometimes found; these colonies are intermediate in size and structure between those of the streptobacilli and those of the L_1 forms.

Horse-blood agar colonies: Similar to those on serum agar. No hemolysis or change of color.

Loeffler's serum colonies: Smaller than those on serum agar, being less than 1 mm in diameter.

Ascitic fluid and serum broth: Whitish, flocculent growth at the bottom or along the side of the tube in 24 hours; growth occurs either as small, compact balls or granules with perfectly clear supernatant fluid or as soft, fluffy masses, occasionally with some general turbidity. No surface growth. No odor.

Medium composed of equal parts of glycerol extract of potato and infusion broth to which egg yolk is added (Parker and Hudson, *op. cit.*, 1926, 357): Excellent growth.

Milk: Growth generally poor; good growth is reported by some authors. No coagulation.

Indole not produced.

Hydrogen sulfide produced in slight or moderate amounts.

Acid from glucose, fructose, maltose, galactose, mannose, glycogen, dextrin and starch. Sucrose, lactose and salicin may or may not be attacked. No acid from xylose, inulin, dulcitol, rhamnose, arabinose, inositol, raffinose, sorbitol, trehalose, glycerol or mannitol.

Nitrites not produced from nitrates.

Urea not hydrolyzed.

Methylene blue is rapidly reduced.

Sodium tellurite not reduced.

Catalase-negative.

Oxidase-negative.

Aerobic, facultatively anaerobic; anaerobic conditions sometimes produce the best growth on primary isolation.

Optimum temperature, between 35° and 38° C. No or scant growth at 22° C.

Optimum pH, between 7.0 and 8.0. Viability rapidly lost with decrease in pH

Pathogenicity: Usually highly virulent for mice, although certain strains of mice may be rather resistant. Intravenous or intraperitoneal inoculation with 0.1 to 0.5 ml of broth culture causes a fatal sepsis, death occurring in 24 to 48 hours, or a chronic disease characterized by purulent polyarthritis, anemia, emaciation, diarrhea, conjunctivitis and transient or permanent paralysis involving the hindpart of the body. At necropsy nothing distinctive is found in acute cases; the spleen and lymph nodes are considerably enlarged in subacute and chronic infections, and focal or confluent necroses are frequently found in the spleen and liver. Intracutaneous and subcutaneous injections cause local abscesses and arthritis and occasionally generalized infection. Bronchopneumonia and sepsis are frequently produced by intranasal instillation. Generalized infection has been produced by feeding experiments; the portal of entry in such cases appears to be the submaxillary and cervical lymph nodes (Freundt, Acta Path. et Microbiol. Scand., 38, 1956, 231.) Passage in 9- to 10-day-old chick embryos causes thickening, edema and hemorrhagic lesions of the chorio-allantoic membrane and invasion of the embryo. Rats, rabbits and guinea pigs are generally resistant, although rabbits have been reported to be susceptible to certain strains.

Antigenic structure: Mice and rat strains from three different sources (Levaditi et al., op. cit., 1925, 1188; Mackie, van Rooyen and Gilroy, Brit. Jour. Exp. Path., 14, 1933, 132; Strangeways, Jour. Path. and Bact., 37, 1933, 45) were found to be identical by agglutinin absorption tests (van Rooyen, Jour. Path. and Bact., 43, 1936, 460).

L-phase variation: In most bacteria in which the L-phase variation is known, abnormal culture conditions are generally necessary to induce the development of L-type colonies on solid media. All strains of Streptobacillus moniliformis, on the other hand, develop L colonies spontaneously, though in a variable number. The L-phase variant of S. moniliformis is known as L_1 (Klieneberger, Jour. Path. and Bact., 40, 1935, 93). Klieneberger's original theory,

that L_1 was a symbiont of S. moniliformis, was opposed by Dienes (Jour. Inf. Dis., 65, 1939, 24; Jour. Bact., 44, 1942, 37), Dawson and Hobby (Proc. 3rd Internat. Congr. for Microbiol., New York, (1939) 1940, Sect. I, 177), Heilman (op. cit., 1941, 32), Brown and Nunemaker (op. cit., 1942, 201) and Ørskov (op. cit., 1942, 575), among others; it is now generally accepted, also by Klieneberger-Nobel herself (Jour. Gen. Microbiol., 3, 1949, 434), that L_1 is a variant form of S. moniliformis.

L-phase colony: The L_1 colony is definitely smaller than that of the bacillary form, measuring about 0.1 to 0.2 mm in diameter. It contains a round, dark brown center embedded in the agar and consists of tiny, coccoid or coccobacillary elements. The central spot is surrounded by a delicate, translucent, peripheral zone made up of swollen bodies, extracellular fatty droplets and an amorphous substance. L_1 is extremely resistant to penicillin, while the streptobacilli are very sensitive to this antibiotic. Cross absorption tests between L_1 and the bacillary phase have shown that although they share a common antigen, the L phase is deficient in another antigen that is found in the bacillary form (Klieneberger, Jour. Hyg., 42, 1942, 485). Reversion of L_1 to the streptobacillus form is extremely difficult to obtain on solid media, whereas this reversion generally occurs in fluid or semi-solid media. The stability of L_1, even in fluid media, increases with the number of subcultures on solid media. L_1 cultures are non-pathogenic when reversion to the bacillary form in the inoculated animal is prevented. Vaccines prepared from L_1 do not protect against infections by streptobacilli (Freundt, op. cit., 1956, 246).

Relationships and nomenclature of this species: Streptothrix muris ratti Schottmüller and Haverhillia multiformis Parker and Hudson are included here as synonyms of Streptobacillus moniliformis Levaditi et al. However, because no comparative studies have been made with authentic cultures of these three organisms, the change in nomenclature that would be indicated if it were established that these organisms are identical has not been made at this time.

Source: Isolated from cases of spontaneous polyarthritis in mice, from the naso-pharynx and infected middle-ears of laboratory and wild rats, from cervical abscesses in guinea pigs and from the blood and joint fluids of humans suffering from rat bite fever. Similar organisms, which many regard as identical with *Streptobacillus moniliformis* Levaditi et al., have been reported as the cause of Haverhill fever (Erythema arthriticum epidemicum); the Haverhill epidemic in the United States (1926), which has given name to the disease when not contracted by rat bite, was un-doubtedly caused by ingestion of infected milk, and the portal of entry was thought to be intestinal.

Comment: Another type of rat-bite fever (Soduku) is caused by *Spirillum minus* Carter. Clinically the two etiologically distinct diseases may be indistinguishable. Mixed infections may occur.

Habitat: Commonly found as an inhabitant of the naso-pharynx of rats. Occurs as the etiological agent of an epizootic septic polyarthritis in mice and of one type of rat-bite fever.

FAMILY VII. MICROCOCCACEAE PRIBRAM, 1929.*

(Jour. Bact., *18*, 1929, 385.)

Mi.cro.coc.ca'ce.ae. M.L. mas.n. *Micrococcus* type genus of the family; -aceae ending to denote a family; M.L. fem.pl.n. *Micrococcaceae* the *Micrococcus* family.

Cells in their free condition spherical; during division, somewhat elliptical. Endospores not produced (except in *Sarcina ureae* under special conditions). Division is primarily in two or three planes; some anaerobic cells divide only in a single plane, producing chains. If the cells remain in contact after division, they are frequently flattened in the plane of last division. They occur singly or in pairs, tetrads, packets, irregular masses or even in chains. Motility is rare. Gram-positive although the free-living and saprophytic species may decolorize so readily that they are sometimes reported as Gram-variable or even as Gram-negative. Many species form a non-water-soluble, yellow, orange, pink or red pigment. The aerobic species produce abundant growth on ordinary culture media and are capable of slight anaerobic growth. Anaerobic to aerotolerant species also occur. Heterotrophic. No visible gas is produced by the aerobic species from carbohydrates, which are frequently fermented. The anaerobic species sometimes produce gas, such as methane, carbon dioxide and hydrogen. Gelatin is often slowly liquefied. Free-living, saprophytic to parasitic or even pathogenic. The typical aerobic micrococci frequently live on the skin, in skin glands or in the skin gland secretions of *Vertebrata*; however, sea-water and soil forms may occur. The anaerobic species live primarily in decomposing organic materials.

Key to the genera of family **Micrococcaceae.**

I. Aerobic to facultatively anaerobic species. Also includes some obligate anaerobes that occur in packets (*Sarcina*).

    A. Cells are generally found in irregular masses; occasionally they are single or in pairs.

        1. Action on glucose, if any, is oxidative. Aerobic.

                Genus I. *Micrococcus*, p. 455.

        2. Glucose fermented anaerobically with the production of acid. Facultatively anaerobic.

                Genus II. *Staphylococcus*, p. 464.

    B. Cells normally occur in tetrads or packets of eight cells.

        1. Parasitic species occurring in tetrads. White to pale yellow chromogenesis. Non-motile.

                Genus III. *Gaffkya*, p. 446.

---

* Arranged by Prof. Robert S. Breed, Cornell University, Geneva, New York, October, 1955.

2. Cells occur in packets. White, yellow, orange and red chromogenesis. Usually non-motile.

Genus IV. *Sarcina*, p. 467.

II. Obligate anaerobes occurring singly or in pairs, chains or masses but never in packets; tetrads are rarely formed.

A. Methane produced from various organic compounds.

Genus V. *Methanococcus*, p. 473.

B. Methane not produced.

Genus VI. *Peptococcus*, p. 474.

Genus I. **Micrococcus** *Cohn, 1872.**†

(Cohn, Beiträge z. Biol. d. Pflanzen, *1*, Heft 2, 1872, 153;
Urococcus Miquel, Ann. Microg., *1*, 1888, 518.)

Mi.cro.coc′cus. Gr. adj. *micrus* small; Gr. noun *coccus* a grain, berry; M.L. mas.n. *Micrococcus* small coccus.

Cells in irregular masses (never in packets). The group is regarded as Gram-positive although some species lose their power to retain the Gram stain so quickly that they are frequently reported as Gram-negative. Some species are motile or show motile varieties. Growth on agar usually abundant; some species form no pigment but others form yellow, orange or red pigment. Catalase-positive so far as known. Glucose broth slightly acid, lactose broth generally neutral. Gelatin frequently liquefied, but never rapidly. Saprophytic, facultatively parasitic or parasitic. Never truly pathogenic.

The type species is *Micrococcus luteus* (Schroeter) Cohn.

Key to the species of genus **Micrococcus**.

I. May or may not reduce nitrates to nitrites. No free nitrogen or nitrous oxide gas produced from nitrates.

A. No pink or red pigment produced on agar media in young cultures.

1. Nitrites not produced from nitrates.

a. Utilize $NH_4H_2PO_4$ as a sole source of nitrogen.‡

b. Yellow pigment produced on agar media. Not acido-proteolytic.

1. *Micrococcus luteus.*

---

* Revised by Prof. G. J. Hucker and Prof. Robert S. Breed, New York State Experiment Station, Cornell University, Geneva, New York, April, 1954.

† In revising the material covering the micrococci for the 7th edition of the MANUAL, it has become evident that there is a very real difference between the fundamental physiologies of such free-living species as those found in soil, sea water and brines, and those that are familiar as pus-forming, enterotoxin-producing staphylococci. The former are able to satisfy their needs for nitrogen and carbon from such simple compounds as ammonium phosphate and glucose, ammonium tartrate or asparagine and glucose. On the other hand, the staphylococci require more complex nitrogenous compounds in order to grow. It is believed that when suitable investigations can be completed, it will prove desirable to separate the mass-forming cocci into the two genera *Micrococcus* Cohn, 1872, and *Staphylococcus* Rosenbach, 1884. In the present edition both of these genera are recognized. However, only two species have been placed in the genus *Staphylococcus*; further investigations may show that other parasitic or pathogenic species should be included therein.

‡ That is, will grow and produce acid (sometimes slowly) on slants containing 1.5 per cent washed agar, 0.1 per cent ammonium phosphate, 1.0 per cent glucose, 0.02 per cent potassium chloride and 0.02 per cent magnesium sulfate. Add brom-cresol-purple as an indicator (Hucker, N. Y. State Exp. Sta. Tech. Bul. 100, 1924, 25; also Tech. Bul. 101, 1924, 36-40).

bb. No pigment produced on agar media.
    c. Not acido-proteolytic.
        d. Utilizes urea as a sole source of nitrogen.
            2. *Micrococcus ureae.*
        dd. Does not utilize urea.
            3. *Micrococcus freudenreichii.*
    cc. Acido-proteolytic in litmus milk.
        9. *Micrococcus caseolyticus.*
aa. Do not utilize $NH_4H_2PO_4$ as a sole source of nitrogen.
    b. Grow well at 25° C.
        c. Yellow pigment produced.
            4. *Micrococcus flavus.*
        cc. No pigment produced.
            5. *Micrococcus candidus.*
    bb. No growth at 25° C; grows well at 10° C.
        6. *Micrococcus cryophilus.*
2. Nitrites produced from nitrates.
    a. Do not utilize chitin. Utilize $NH_4H_2PO_4$ as a sole source of nitrogen. Ordinarily found in dairy products.
        b. Yellow pigment produced on agar media. Not acido-proteolytic.
            c. Gelatin liquefied.
                7. *Micrococcus conglomeratus.*
            cc. Gelatin not liquefied.
                8. *Micrococcus varians.*
        bb. Usually not chromogenic. Actively acido-proteolytic in litmus milk.
            9. *Micrococcus caseolyticus.*
    aa. Utilizes chitin. Found in sea water.
        10. *Micrococcus colpogenes.*
B. Pink, orange-red or red pigment produced on agar media in young cultures.
    1. Not obligately halophilic.
        a. Gelatin liquefied slowly. Produces rose-colored pigment.
            11. *Micrococcus roseus.*
        aa. Gelatin not liquefied.
            b. Non-motile. Produces light, flesh-colored pigment on agar slants.
                12. *Micrococcus rubens.*
        bb. Motile. Produces a bright red pigment.
            13. *Micrococcus agilis.*
    2. Obligately halophilic (requires at least 12 per cent salt for growth).
        14. *Micrococcus morrhuae.*
II. Free nitrogen gas and sometimes nitrous oxide produced from nitrates.
    A. Will not grow in media containing more than 6 per cent salt. Produces a mixture of nitrogen and nitrous oxide gases from nitrates.
        15. *Micrococcus denitrificans.*
    B. Grows in 4 to 12 per cent salt. Gas produced from nitrates is largely nitrogen.
        16. *Micrococcus halodenitrificans.*

    1. Micrococcus luteus (Schroeter, 1872) Cohn, 1872. (*Bacteridium luteum* Schroeter,   Beitr. z. Biol. d. Pflan., *1*, Heft 2, 1872, 119; Cohn, *ibid.*, 153; not *Micrococcus luteus* Lehmann and Neumann, Bakt. Diag., 1 Aufl., *2*, 1896, 161.)

lu′te.us. L. adj. *luteus* golden-yellow.

Spheres, 1.0 to 1.2 microns in diameter, occurring in pairs and fours. Non-motile. Gram-positive.

Gelatin colonies: Yellowish white to yellow, raised, with undulate margin.

Gelatin stab: No liquefaction (Schroeter, in Cohn, Kryptog. Flora v. Schlesien, *3*, I, 1886, 144).

Agar colonies: Small, yellowish, glistening, raised.

Agar slant: Citron-yellow, smooth growth.

Broth: Clear, with yellowish sediment.

Litmus milk: Usually slightly acid, not coagulated.

Potato: Thin, glistening, citron-yellow growth.

Indole not produced.

Acid from glucose, sucrose and mannitol. No acid from lactose.

Starch not hydrolyzed.

Nitrites not produced from nitrates.

Ammonia produced from peptone.

Utilizes $NH_4H_2PO_4$ as a source of nitrogen; also utilizes ammonium tartrate, growth occurring after 6 weeks in Cohn's solution (Cohn, *op. cit.*, 1872, 153).

Saprophytic.

Aerobic.

Optimum temperature, 25° C. (Eisenberg, Bakt. Diag., 1891, 39).

Comments: It is recommended that Culture number 398, *Micrococcus luteus*, of the American Type Culture Collection be accepted as the type culture for this species. This culture has been retested (September, 1955) and has been found to grow slowly in Cohn's solution without added sugar after 6 weeks under conditions similar to those used by Cohn in 1872. On reinoculation, this culture now develops within 2 weeks in Cohn's solution.

Source: Isolated by Schroeter from dust contaminations on cooked potato.

Habitat: Found in milk and dairy products and on dust particles.

2. **Micrococcus ureae** Cohn, 1872. (Bei-

träge *z*. Biol. d. Pflanzen, *1*, Heft 2, 1872, 158.)

u′re.ae. Gr. noun *urum* urine; M.L. noun *urea* urea; M.L. gen.noun *ureae* of urea.

Spheres, 0.8 to 1.0 micron in diameter, occurring singly, in pairs and in clumps. Never in chains. Non-motile. Gram-variable.

Gelatin colonies: Small, white, translucent, slimy, becoming fissured.

Gelatin stab: Slight, white growth. Very slow or no liquefaction.

Agar colonies: White, slightly raised.

Agar slant: Grayish white, raised, glistening, butyrous growth.

Broth: Turbid, with viscid sediment.

Litmus milk: Slightly alkaline; litmus slowly reduced.

Milk: Acid.

Potato: Slight, grayish to pale olive growth.

Indole not produced.

Acid produced from glucose, lactose, sucrose and mannitol.

Starch not hydrolyzed.

Nitrites not produced from nitrates.

Urea fermented to ammonium carbonate.

Ammonium salts are utilized.

Ammonia produced from peptone.

Saprophytic.

Aerobic.

Optimum temperature, 25° C.

Source: Isolated from fermenting urine.

Habitat: Found in stale urine and in soil containing urine.

3. **Micrococcus freudenreichii** Guillebeau, 1891. (Landwirtsch. Jahrb. d. Schweiz, *5*, 1891, 135.)

freud.en.reich′i.i. M.L. gen.noun *freudenreichii* of Freudenreich; named for E. von Freudenreich, a Swiss bacteriologist.

Spheres, 2.0 microns in diameter, occurring singly and in clumps, rarely in short chains. Non-motile. Gram-positive.

Milk gelatin colonies: Small, white, opaque.

Milk gelatin stab: Infundibuliform liquefaction.

Agar colonies: White, slimy.

Agar streak: White, smooth growth.

Broth: Turbid, with white sediment.

Litmus milk: Acid; coagulated; peptonized.

Potato: Moderate, white to yellow growth.

Indole not produced.

Does not utilize urea as a source of nitrogen.

Acid from glucose, lactose and sucrose. Some strains form acid from mannitol, others from glycerol.

Starch not hydrolyzed.

Nitrites not produced from nitrates.

Ammonia produced from peptone.

Ammonium salts are utilized.

Saprophytic.

Aerobic.

Optimum temperature, 20° C.

Habitat: Found in milk and dairy utensils.

4. **Micrococcus flavus** Trevisan, 1889. (*Micrococcus flavus liquefaciens* Flügge, Die Mikroorganismen, 2 Aufl., 1886, 174; Trevisan, I generi e le specie delle Batteriacee, Milan, 1889, 34.)

fla′vus. L. adj. *flavus* yellow.

Spheres, 0.8 to 0.9 micron in diameter, occurring singly, in clumps and occasionally in fours. Occasionally cultures are found that are motile with a single flagellum, otherwise they are non-motile. Gram-variable.

Gelatin colonies: Small, circular, yellowish to yellowish brown, somewhat serrate margin, granulated, sharply contoured.

Gelatin stab: Yellow, wrinkled surface growth with slow, crateriform liquefaction.

Agar colonies: Small, pale yellowish, homogeneous, entire.

Agar-slant: Growth canary-yellow, somewhat dry, wrinkled, raised, entire.

Broth: Turbid with yellowish ring and sediment.

Litmus milk: Slightly acid; soft coagulum formed with slight reduction; slowly peptonized.

Potato: Slight, canary-yellow growth.

Indole not produced.

Acid is generally formed from glucose and lactose. Sucrose, glycerol and mannitol generally not fermented.

Starch not hydrolyzed.

Nitrites not produced from nitrates.

Generally produces growth on $NH_4H_2PO_4$ media.

Ammonia produced from peptone.

Non-pathogenic.

Aerobic.

Optimum temperature, 25° C.

Source: Original source not given.

Habitat: Found in skin gland secretions, milk, dairy products and dairy utensils.

5. **Micrococcus candidus** Cohn, 1872. (Beiträge z. Biol. d. Pflanzen, *1*, Heft 2, 1872, 160.)

can′di.dus. L. adj. *candidus* shining white.

Spheres 0.5 to 0.7 micron in diameter, occurring singly. Non-motile. Gram-positive.

Gelatin colonies: White, granular, with irregular or entire margin.

Gelatin stab: White surface growth. Filiform. No liquefaction.

Agar colonies: Punctiform, white, smooth, entire, iridescent.

Agar slant: Smooth, white, glistening, iridescent growth.

Broth: Turbid with pellicle.

Litmus milk: Slightly acid; not coagulated.

Potato: Thick, porcelain-white, glistening growth.

Indole not produced.

Acid from glucose, sucrose, lactose and glycerol.

Starch not hydrolyzed.

Nitrites not produced from nitrates.

Ammonia produced from peptone.

Ammonium salts not utilized.

Non-pathogenic.

Aerobic.

Optimum temperature, 25° C.

Source: Originally appeared as white colonies on cooked potato exposed to dust contaminations.

Habitat: Found in skin secretions, milk and dairy products.

6. **Micrococcus cryophilus** McLean et al., 1951. (McLean, Sulzbacher and Mudd, Jour. Bact., *62*, 1951, 723.)

cry.o′phi.lus. Gr. noun *cryus* cold, frost;

Gr. adj. *philus* loving; M.L. adj. *cryophilus* frost-loving.

Spherical cells, the average diameter being 1.6 microns, occasional large cells measuring 3.6 and small cells measuring 1.0 micron in diameter, occurring singly, in pairs, in chains and in clusters. Nuclear bodies which vary in size and position have been observed in the cell. There is evidence that these bodies represent various stages of a mitotic and a meiotic process (DeLamater and Woodburn, Jour. Bact., *64*, 1952, 793; Hunter, Exp. Cell Res., *9*, 1955, 231). However, compare Bisset (Jour. Bact., *67*, 1954, 41). Non-motile; occasional cells are motile by means of peritrichous flagella. Gram-stains of veal infusion agar smears show Gram-positive cells with a predominant number of Gram-negative cells irrespective of the age of the culture.

Gelatin: No liquefaction.

Agar slant: Creamy white, glistening, filiform, moderately heavy growth.

Yeast extract agar: Growth same as above but heavier; old cultures become faint pink in color.

Veal infusion agar: Growth same as above; old cultures become brownish yellow.

Yeast extract and nutrient broths: A ring is formed.

Ulrich milk (Science, *99*, 1941, 352): Alkaline in 2 days; slight reduction of methylene blue indicator in 4 days.

Indole not produced.

Hydrogen sulfide not produced.

No acid from glucose, lactose, sucrose, maltose, xylose, cellobiose, mannitol, dulcitol or salicin.

Sodium citrate does not serve as a sole source of carbon.

Nitrites not produced from nitrates.

Ammonium phosphate does not serve as a sole source of nitrogen.

Urease is produced.

Oxidase not produced.

Blood agar: No hemolysis.

Catalase-positive.

Aerobic.

Temperature relations: Optimum, 9.8° C. Minimum, −4.0° C. Maximum, between 23° and 24° C.

Optimum pH, between 6.8 and 7.2. Growth occurs between pH 5.5 and 9.5.

Source: Isolated by McLean (Food Technology, *5*, 1951, 7) from a finished package of pork sausage prepared from frozen meat.

Habitat: Found in frozen meat products so far as known.

7. **Micrococcus conglomeratus** Migula, 1900. (Citronengelber Diplococcus, Bumm, Der Mikroorganismus der gonorrhoischen Schleimhauterkrankungen, 1 Aufl., 1885, 17; *Micrococcus citreus conglomeratus* Flügge, Die Mikroorganismen, 2 Aufl., 1886, 182; Migula, Syst. d. Bakt., *2*, 1900, 146.)

con.glo.me.ra'tus. L. part.adj. *conglomeratus* rolled together.

Spheres, 0.8 to 1.2 microns in diameter, occurring singly, in pairs, in fours and in large clumps. Non-motile. Gram-variable.

Gelatin colonies: Small, circular, yellow with radiate margin.

Gelatin stab: Slow crateriform liquefaction.

Agar colonies: Luxuriant, moist, sulfur-yellow.

Agar slant: Growth light yellow, plumose, slightly rugose, somewhat dull with raised center and transparent margin.

Broth: Turbid, with light orange ring and sediment.

Milk: Generally acid but not sufficient to curdle.

Potato: No growth.

Indole not produced.

Acid from glucose and lactose generally, sometimes from sucrose. Mannitol and glycerol generally not fermented.

Starch not hydrolyzed.

Nitrites produced from nitrates.

Ammonia produced from peptone.

Utilizes $NH_4H_2PO_4$ as a source of nitrogen.

Blood not hemolyzed.

Non-pathogenic.

Aerobic.

Optimum temperature, 25° C.

Resistant to drying and heat.

Source: Found in gonorrhoeal pus and in dust.

Habitat: Infections, milk, dairy products, dairy utensils, water. Common.

8. **Micrococcus varians** Migula, 1900.
(*Merismopedia flava varians* Dyar, Ann. N.
Y. Acad. Sci., *8*, 1895, 346; Migula, Syst. d.
Bakt., *2*, 1900, 135.)

va'ri.ans. L. part.adj. *varians* varying.

Spheres, 0.8 to 1.0 micron in diameter, occurring singly, in pairs and in fours. Occasionally cultures are found that are motile
with a single flagellum, otherwise they are
non-motile. Gram-variable.

Gelatin colonies: Small, circular, whitish
to yellow, capitate, moruloid.

Gelatin stab: Scant growth. No liquefaction.

Agar colonies: Small, yellow, raised,
glistening.

Agar slant: Plumose, yellow, variegated
growth.

Broth: Turbid, with yellow, granular
sediment.

Litmus milk: Acid; coagulated on boiling.

Potato: Raised, dry, bright yellow, glistening growth.

Indole not produced.

Acid from glucose, lactose, sucrose, raffinose and frequently from glycerol and
mannitol. No acid from salicin or inulin.

Starch not hydrolyzed.

Nitrites produced from nitrates.

Ammonia produced from peptone.

Utilizes $NH_4H_2PO_4$ as a source of nitrogen.

Saprophytic.

Aerobic.

Optimum temperature, 25° C.

Source: Original strains found in a contaminated jar of sterilized milk.

Habitat: Has been found in body secretions, dairy products, dairy utensils, dust
and water, including sea water.

9. **Micrococcus caseolyticus** Evans,
1916. (Jour. Inf. Dis., *18*, 1916, 455.)

ca.se.o.ly'ti.cus. L. noun *caseus* cheese;
Gr. adj. *lyticus* able to loose; M.L. adj.
caseolyticus casein-dissolving.

Spheres, variable in size, occurring in
clumps. Non-motile. Gram-positive.

Gelatin stab: Liquefaction generally begins after first day and continues rapidly.

Agar colonies: Yellow to orange (Evans,
loc. cit.); pearly white (Hucker, N. Y. Agr.
Exp. Sta. Tech. Bull. 102, 1924, 17).

Agar stroke: Yellow to orange (Evans, *op.
cit.*, *18*, 1916, 455); pearly white (Hucker,
op. cit., 1924, 17); luxuriant growth.

Broth: Generally grows with smooth turbidity although certain strains give heavy
precipitate with clear supernatant fluid.

Litmus milk: Acid, peptonized. Whey
generally clear.

Potato: Scant, white growth. Certain
strains may show yellow pigment.

Indole not produced.

Acid from glucose, lactose, maltose, mannitol and glycerol. No action on raffinose.

Forms dextrorotatory lactic acid (Orla-
Jensen, The Lactic Acid Bacteria, 1919, 80).

Nitrites usually produced from nitrates.

Asparagin and urea decomposed by some
strains.

Utilizes $NH_4H_2PO_4$ as a source of nitrogen.

Aerobic.

Optimum temperature, 22° C.

Saprophytic.

Source: Eight cultures from a bovine
udder.

Habitat: Milk, dairy utensils and dairy
products, especially cheese.

10. **Micrococcus colpogenes** Campbell
and Williams, 1951. (Jour. Gen. Microbiol.,
5, 1951, 897 and 904).

col.po'ge.nes. Gr. noun *colpus* bosom,
fold; Gr. v. *gennaio* to bear; M.L. adj.
colpogenes fold-producing.

Cocci occurring in clumps and occasionally in pairs. Non-motile. Gram-positive.

Gelatin stab: No liquefaction.

Agar colonies: Circular, smooth, entire,
raised, glistening, yellow.

Agar slant: Filiform, glistening, yellow
streak.

Broth: Moderately turbid; slight, granular sediment.

Litmus milk: Unchanged.

Indole not produced.

Hydrogen sulfide not produced.

No acid or gas from glucose, lactose, sucrose, maltose, fructose, dextrin, mannose,
arabinose, rhamnose, xylose, raffinose, inulin, mannitol, salicin, dulcitol, galactose,
trehalose, inositol, cellobiose, melezitose or
adonitol. Fumarate (0.5 per cent), lactate,
malonate, tartrate, citrate, levulinate,

β-alanine, asparaginate, propionate, salicylate, valerate, oxalate, butyrate, mandelate, benzoate (0.5 per cent), starch, ethanol, methanol, n-amyl alcohol, isoamyl alcohol, tertiary-butanol, n-propanol and lumichrome not utilized.

Starch not hydrolyzed.

Chitin is hydrolyzed, ammonia and reducing sugars being produced in 6 days.

Glucose, maltose, mannitol, malate, pyruvate (0.3 per cent), acetate, succinate, glycogen, chitin and glucosamine are utilized as carbon sources.

Casein is hydrolyzed.

Non-lipolytic.

Nitrites produced from nitrates.

Urease is produced.

Trimethylamine not produced from trimethylamine oxide, choline or betaine.

Growth is inhibited by 10 per cent but not by 4 per cent sodium chloride.

Aerobic.

Optimum temperature, between 20° and 30° C. Does not grow at 4° C.

Source: Two strains were isolated from marine mud from the Gulf of Mexico.

Habitat: Found in sea water and marine mud.

11. Micrococcus roseus Flügge, 1886. (Rosafarbiger Diplococcus, Bumm, Der Mikroorganismus der gonorrhoischen Schleimhauterkrankungen, 1 Aufl., 1885, 25; Flügge, Die Mikroorganismen, 2 Aufl., 1886, 183.)

ro'se.us. L. adj. *roseus* rose-colored.

Spheres, 1.0 to 1.5 microns in diameter, occurring singly and in pairs. Non-motile. Gram-variable.

Gelatin colonies: Rose surface growth, usually with slow liquefaction.

Agar colonies: Circular, entire, rose-red surface colonies.

Agar slant: Thick, rose-red, smooth, glistening growth.

Broth: Slightly turbid with rose-colored sediment.

Litmus milk: Unchanged to alkaline; usually reddish sediment after 14 days.

Potato: Raised, rose-red, smooth, glistening growth.

Acid from glycerol and mannitol.

Starch not hydrolyzed.

Usually produces nitrites from nitrates.

Utilizes $NH_4H_2PO_4$ as a source of nitrogen.

Aerobic.

Optimum temperature, 25° C.

Saprophytic.

Source: Dust contamination.

Habitat: Widespread, as it occurs in dust.

12. Micrococcus rubens Migula, 1900. (*Micrococcus tetragenus ruber* Bujwid, in Schneider, Arb. Bakt. Inst. Karlsruhe, *1*, Heft 2, 1894, 215; Migula, Syst. d. Bakt., *2*, 1900, 177.)

ru'bens. L. part.adj. *rubens* being red, reddish.

Description taken from Migula (*loc. cit.*) and Breed (Jour. Bact., *45*, 1943, 455).

Spheres, the average diameter being 2.1 microns; large cells measure 4.0 microns and small cells 1.3 microns in diameter; occur in fours and in irregular masses, generally not singly or in pairs. Non-motile. Gram-negative to Gram-variable.

Gelatin colonies: After several days, small, pink or flesh-colored, shiny, butyrous, 0.5 to several mm in diameter. Smaller colonies have regular edges; larger colonies have lobate edges.

Gelatin streak: Thick, shiny, flesh-colored to carmine-red growth, generally spreading.

Gelatin stab: Scant, whitish growth along line of stab; surface growth flesh-red. No liquefaction after several weeks, but a slight softening of the medium underneath the growth.

Agar slant: Luxuriant, thick, spreading, slimy, flesh-colored growth.

Broth: Bright red, slimy sediment. No pellicle.

Milk: Generally acid curd followed by slight peptonization.

Acid from glucose, sucrose, mannitol and glycerol. No action on lactose or starch.

Nitrites produced from nitrates.

Pigment soluble in ether, benzol, carbon bisulfide, chloroform and alcohol. Not soluble in water (Schneider, *op. cit.*, 1894, 215).

Aerobic.

Grows well between 26° and 37° C.

Saprophytic.

Source: Original culture isolated by Buj-wid in Bern, Switzerland, and sent to Mi-gula at Karlsruhe, Germany.

Habitat: Unknown.

13. **Micrococcus agilis** Ali-Cohen, 1889. (Cent. f. Bakt., *6*, 1889, 36.)

a'gi.lis. L. adj. *agilis* agile.

Spheres, 1.0 micron in diameter, occurring singly, in pairs and in fours. Motile by means of one or two flagella. Gram-variable.

Gelatin colonies: Small, gray, becoming distinctly rose-colored.

Gelatin stab: Thin, whitish growth in stab. On surface thick, rose-red, glistening growth. Generally no liquefaction.

Agar slant: Growth glistening, dark rose-red, lobed with much variation in color.

Broth: Slightly turbid, with slight, rose-colored ring and pink sediment.

Litmus milk: Slightly acid, pink sediment.

Potato: Slow growth as small, rose-colored colonies.

Loeffler's blood serum: Pink, spreading, shiny, abundant. Slow liquefaction.

Indole not produced.

Acid from glucose, sucrose, inulin, gly-cerol and mannitol. No acid from raffinose.

Nitrites produced (trace).

Ammonia formed (trace).

Does not utilize $NH_4H_2PO_4$ as source of nitrogen.

Aerobic.

Optimum temperature, 25° C.

Saprophytic.

Source: Isolated from water.

Habitat: Water, sea water and on sea fish.

14. **Micrococcus morrhuae** Klebahn, 1919. (*Micrococcus (Diplococcus) morrhuae* Klebahn, Mitteil. a. d. Inst. f. allg. Bot. i. Hamburg, *4*, 1919, 47; abst. in Cent. f. Bakt., II Abt., *52*, 1921, 123.)

mor'rhu.ae. M.L. gen.noun *morrhuae* of *Morrhua*; M.L. fem.n. *Morrhua* a genus of codfish.

Original description supplemented by material taken from Petter (Proc. Kon. Acad. v. Wetensch. Amsterdam, *34*, 1931, 1417; also see Petter, Over roode en andere bacteriën van gezouten visch. Thesis, Utrecht, 1932) and Elazari-Volcani (Studies on the Microflora of the Dead Sea Thesis, Hebrew Univ., Jerusalem, 1940, V and 65).

Spheres, 1.0 to 1.5 microns in diameter, occurring singly, in pairs, in short chains and in tetrads. In 30 per cent salt + 1 per cent peptone ("Poulenc"), the spheres are 0.9 to 2.7 microns in diameter and occur singly or in pairs or tetrads; in the same agar medium, they appear mostly as cocci, diplococci, streptococci and staphylococci, tetrads being poorly developed. Non-motile. Gram-negative.

Gelatin stab (15 per cent salt): Surface growth and liquefaction.

Agar colonies (24 per cent salt + 1 per cent proteose peptone + 2 per cent KNO_3): Circular, smooth, entire, raised to convex, amorphous, opaque, orange-red.

Agar slant: Growth filiform, raised, slightly glistening, smooth, butyrous, opaque, orange-red.

Broth (24 per cent salt + 1 per cent proteose peptone): Slightly turbid; orange-red sediment.

Indole not produced.

No acid or gas from arabinose, xylose, glucose, fructose, galactose, mannose, lactose, sucrose, maltose, raffinose, inulin, dextrin, glycerol, mannitol or salicin (all tests were made in 24 per cent salt + 1 per cent peptone + 1 per cent carbohydrate during 3 weeks).

Starch not hydrolyzed.

Nitrites produced from nitrates; no gas is produced (tests made in 24 per cent salt + 1 per cent peptone + 2 per cent KNO_3).

Catalase-positive.

Aerobic.

Salt tolerance: Halophilic, obligate; grows with no morphological changes in 9 to 30 per cent salt. When the organism is transferred to water, its morphology does not change, and it grows when reinoculated into salt-containing media.

Optimum temperature, between 30° and 37° C.

Distinctive character: The pigment produced by this organism gives a blue color with concentrated sulfuric acid, thus suggesting a carotenoid; it is not soluble in methanol, ethanol, acetone, ether, chloroform, dioxam, ethylacetate, benzol, petroleum ether, xylene or pyridine.

Comment: Also see description of *Sarcina littoralis* Poulsen.

Source: Isolated from reddened, salted codfish and herring and from Dead Sea water.

Habitat: Found in sea-water brine, sea salt and salt lakes; also found to be associated with a red discoloration of salted fish.

15. Micrococcus denitrificans Beijerinck, 1910, *emend.* Sijderius, 1946. (Beijerinck, Cent. f. Bakt., II Abt., *25*, 1910, 53; also see Elema, De bepaling van de oxydatie reductie potentiaal in bacteriën cultures en hare betekenis voor de stofwisseling. Thesis, Delft, 1932; Sijderius, Heterotrophe bacteriën die thiosulfaat oxyderon. Thesis, Amsterdam, 1946.)

de.ni.tri'fi.cans. L. prep. *de* away from; L. noun *nitrum* soda; M.L. noun *nitrum* nitrate, niter; M.L. v. *denitrifico* to denitrify; M.L. part.adj. *denitrificans* denitrifying.

Description prepared by Dr. W. Verhoeven, Delft, Holland.

Non-motile coccus, 1 micron in diameter. Some spindle-shaped, even rod-like forms may be observed in young cultures. In old cultures the typical coccus form is predominant. Sometimes aggregates are observed. Gram-negative.

Grows readily on peptone media. Rather salt resistant; develops in media containing no salt to 6 per cent salt.

Gelatin stab: No liquefaction.

Agar colonies: Circular, entire, smooth, glistening, white, opaque.

Broth: Turbid, no pellicle.

Milk: Unchanged.

Indole not produced.

Hydrogen sulfide not produced.

No acid or gas produced from glucose.

Nitrates and nitrites are hydrogen acceptors in dissimilation, being reduced to nitrous oxide and nitrogen. Ammonia is not produced.

Urease activity negative.

Catalase-positive.

Aerobic.

Temperature range, 5° to 37° C. Optimum, between 25° and 30° C.

In denitrification, ethanol, propanol, glycerol, mannitol, glucose, formate, acetate, lactate, succinate, fumarate, citrate, valerionate or asparagine are suitable hydrogen donators.

Grows under autotrophic conditions on thiosulfates as oxidation substrates with the formation of sulfates and sulfuric acid. Sijderius (*op. cit.*, 1946) suggests that *Thiobacillus novellus* Starkey is the same as *Micrococcus denitrificans* Beijerinck.

Grows readily under autotrophic conditions in a hydrogen atmosphere. Also produces good growth on a mineral medium with nitrate in a hydrogen atmosphere, if certain growth factors are added to the medium.

The relationship of *Micrococcus denitrificans* to *Micrococcus halodenitrificans* Robinson and Gibbons (Can. Jour. Botany, *30*, 1952, 147) has not been determined. Presumably the latter organism is an obligate, halophilic adaptate of *Micrococcus denitrificans* (Verhoeven, Koster and van Nievelt, Jour. Microbiol. and Serology, *20*, 1954, 279).

Source: Isolated from nitrate media inoculated with soil.

Habitat: Presumably widely distributed in soil.

16. Micrococcus halodenitrificans Robinson and Gibbons, 1952. (Robinson and Gibbons, Can. Jour. Botany, *30*, 1952, 147; also see Robinson, *ibid.*, *30*, 1952, 155, and Robinson, Gibbons and Thatcher, Jour. Bact., *64*, 1952, 69.)

ha.lo.de.ni.tri'fi.cans. Gr. noun *hals*, *halis* salt; L. prep *de* away from; L. noun *nitrum* soda; M.L. noun *nitrum* nitrate, niter; M.L. v. *denitrifico* to denitrify; M.L. part.adj. *halodenitrificans* salt denitrifying.

Description prepared by Dr. N. E. Gibbons, Ottawa, Canada.

Spherical cells 0.5 micron in diameter. Occur singly or in pairs. Salt concentration has little effect on morphology. Gram-negative.

Does not grow on media containing less than four per cent salt. Grows readily in peptone media.

Gelatin stab: Liquefied.

Agar colonies: Circular, entire, convex, butyrous, glistening, opaque, cream-colored.

Broth: Turbid, no pellicle.

Milk: Unchanged.

Indole not produced.

Hydrogen sulfide not produced.

No acid or gas produced from glucose.

Nitrates and nitrites are reduced to nitrogen and nitrous oxide. Ammonia is not produced.

Urease activity negative.

Catalase-positive.

Aerobic.

Temperature range, 0° to 32° C. Optimum, 20° C.

Salt range: Limits of growth, 4 to 23 percent salt. Optimum, 4.4 to 8.8 per cent NaCl. Will not grow in the presence of other sodium and potassium salts, including sodium ammonium phosphate and ammonium sulfate.

Relationship to the denitrifying micrococcus described by Beijerinck (Cent. f. Bakt., II Abt., *25*, 1910, 53) is being studied.

Source: Isolated from Wiltshire bacon-curing brines in Canada.

Habitat: Presumably widely distributed in natural and artificial brines.

Genus II. **Staphylococcus** *Rosenbach, 1884.**†

(*Staphylococcus* Ogston (*nomen nudum*), Jour. Anat. et. Physiol., Paris, *17*, 1883, 27; Rosenbach, Mikroorganismen bei den Wundinfektionskrankheiten des Menschen, Wiesbaden, 1884, 27; *Aurococcus* Winslow and Rogers, Jour. Inf. Dis., *3:* 1906, 540; *Albococcus* Winslow and Rogers, *ibid.*, 541; also see Evans, Bradford and Niven, Int. Bull. of Bact. Nomen. and Taxon., *5*, 1955, 61.)

Staph.y.lo.coc′cus. Gr. noun *staphyle* bunch of grapes; Gr. noun *coccus* a grain, berry; M.L. mas.n. *Staphylococcus* the grape-like coccus.

Spherical cells occurring singly, in pairs, in tetrads and in irregular clusters, especially when growing in broth. Non-motile. Gram-positive. Many strains produce an orange or yellow pigment, particularly on media containing high levels of NaCl. Most strains produce acetoin from glucose, ammonia from arginine, reduce nitrates and ferment a variety of carbohydrates. Require an organic source of nitrogen (amino acids) and two or more vitamins for growth in a synthetic medium. Growth in a nutritionally adequate broth is abundant, usually with a heavy, uniform turbidity and a slight ring pellicle. Growth on agar media is usually abundant. Strongly catalase-positive. Facultative with respect to oxygen requirement, growing very well anaerobically in the presence of a fermentable carbohydrate but growing even better aerobically. Coagulase-positive strains produce a variety of toxins and are thus potentially pathogenic and may cause food poisoning. Frequently found on the skin, in skin glands, on the nasal and other mucous membranes of warm-blooded animals and in a variety of food products.

The type species is *Staphylococcus aureus* Rosenbach.

Key to the species of genus **Staphylococcus**.

I. Ferments mannitol. Coagulase-positive.

                              1. *Staphylococcus aureus.*

II. Does not ferment mannitol. Coagulase-negative.

                              2. *Staphylococcus epidermidis.*

---

* Revised by Dr. J. B. Evans, American Meat Institute Foundation, University of Chicago, Chicago, Illinois, April, 1955.

† While Rosenbach describes the orange and the white pus-forming staphylococci of Ogston as two separate species, he states that he finds no difference between them other than the difference in chromogenesis. He describes them under the names *Staphylococcus aureus* and *Staphylococcus albus*. White colonies occur frequently as variants and may be the only type present in a culture. These should not be considered a different species but merely a white variety of *Staphylococcus aureus*. The name *Staphylococcus albus* should never be used for these or for any other white staphylococci.

1. Staphylococcus aureus Rosenbach, 1884. (*Staphylococcus pyogenes aureus* Rosenbach, Mikroorganismen bei den Wundinfektionskrankheiten des Menschen, 1884, 19; *Staphylococcus pyogenes albus* Rosenbach, *ibid.*, 21; *Staphylococcus aureus* Rosenbach, *ibid.*, 27; *Staphylococcus albus* Rosenbach, *loc. cit.*; *Staphylococcus pyogenes citreus* Passet, Aetiologie der eiterigen phlegmone des Menschen, Berlin, 1885, 9; *Micrococcus aureus* Zopf, Die Spaltpilze, 3 Aufl., 1885, 57; *Micrococcus pyogenes* Lehmann and Neumann, Bakt. Diag., 1 Aufl., *2*, 1896, 165; *Micrococcus citreus* Migula, Syst. d. Bakt., *2*, 1900, 147; *Micrococcus albus* Buchanan, Veterinary Bact., 1911, 196; *Staphylococcus citreus* Bergey et al., Manual, 1st ed., 1923, 55.)

au're.us. L. adj. *aureus* golden.

Spheres, 0.8 to 1.0 micron in diameter, occurring singly, in pairs, in short chains and in irregular clumps. Non-motile. Grampositive.

Chromogenesis: Typical *Staphylococcus aureus* cultures rather readily develop variants that grow as dirty white colonies. Such colonies quite frequently develop strains that again produce the typical orange chromogenesis. On the other hand cultures occur which are white on original isolation. Such colonies usually do not develop orange variants although they are identical in other cultural characters and in their physiological characters with the orange strains. Some designate these white forms as *Staphylococcus albus*, as did Rosenbach, and regard them as belonging to a separate species.

Passet used the name *Staphylococcus pyogenes citreus* for the organisms that produce the yellower (more lemon-colored) colonies. He distinguished these from the darker yellow (more orange-colored) colonies described by Rosenbach under the name *Staphylococcus aureus*. Passet secured his *Staphylococcus citreus* cultures from aseptically drawn pus. He reports that the yellow organisms were identical with the orange organisms except for the difference in chromogenesis. Later investigators have sometimes reported other differences in characters without referring back to Passet's original description, in which no such differences in characters are noted.

Gelatin stab: Saccate liquefaction with white to yellowish pellicle and white or yellow to orange sediment.

Agar colonies: Circular, smooth, orange to white, glistening, butyrous, entire.

Agar slant: Abundant, opaque, smooth, flat, moist, white to yellowish or orange growth.

Broth: Turbid, becoming clear; yellowish ring and sediment.

Litmus milk: Acid, coagulated.

Acid from glucose, lactose, sucrose, mannitol and glycerol. No acid from raffinose, salicin or inulin.

Optically inactive or levo-rotatory lactic acid is produced (Orla-Jensen, The Lactic Acid Bacteria, 1919, 81).

Acetoin produced from glucose.

Starch and esculin not hydrolyzed.

Sodium hippurate usually hydrolyzed.

Nitrites produced from nitrates.

Amino acids are required as a source of nitrogen.

Thiamin and nicotinic acid are required for growth.

Does not utilize $NH_4H_2PO_4$ as a source of nitrogen.

Ammonia produced from peptone and arginine.

Blood agar: Beta hemolysis normally produced.

Catalase-positive.

Aerobic, facultatively anaerobic.

Optimum temperature, 37° C. Grows at 10° and 45° C., these temperatures being very near the minimum and maximum temperatures respectively.

Very salt tolerant, growing vigorously in media containing 10 per cent NaCl.

Certain strains, under favorable conditions, produce not only exotoxins (hematoxin, dermatoxin, lethal toxin, etc.) but also a potent enterotoxin which is a significant cause of food poisoning (Dolman and Wilson, Jour. Immunology, *35*, 1938, 13).

Pathogenic.

Distinctive characters: Normally coagulase-positive (human or rabbit plasma). Ferments both glucose and mannitol under anaerobic conditions.

Source: Isolated from pus in wounds.

Habitat: Found particularly on nasal mucous membrane and skin (hair follicles). The cause, outstandingly, of furunculosis, pyaemia, osteomyelitis, suppuration of wounds, and food poisoning. Very common.

2. Staphylococcus epidermidis (Winslow and Winslow, 1908) Evans, 1916. (*Staphylococcus epidermidis albus* Welch, Amer. Jour. Med. Sci., Phila., *102* (N.S.), 1891, 441; *Albococcus epidermidis* Winslow and Winslow, The Systematic Relationships of the Coccaceae, New York, 1908, 201; Evans, Jour. Inf. Dis., *15*, 1916, 849; *Micrococcus epidermidis* Hucker, N. Y. Agr. Exp. Sta. Tech. Bull. 102, 1924, 21.)

e.pi.der'mi.dis. Gr. noun *epidermis* the outer skin; M.L. gen.noun *epidermidis* of the epidermis.

Spheres, 0.5 to 0.6 micron in diameter, occurring singly, in pairs and in irregular groups. Non-motile. Gram-positive.

Gelatin stab: White surface growth with slow saccate liquefaction.

Agar colonies: Circular, smooth; generally pale, translucent white.

Broth (containing a fermentable carbohydrate): Heavy, uniform turbidity; ring pellicle.

Litmus milk: Acid.

Acid is usually produced from glucose, fructose, maltose, sucrose, trehalose and glycerol. Acid may be produced from mannose, galactose and lactose. No acid from xylose, arabinose, raffinose, inulin, sorbitol or mannitol.

Amino acids are required as a source of nitrogen.

Some of the B vitamins, usually including biotin, are required for growth.

Nitrites produced from nitrates.

Catalase-positive.

Aerobic, facultatively anaerobic.

Grows readily at 37° C.

Very salt tolerant, growing vigorously in media containing 10 per cent NaCl.

Parasitic rather than pathogenic.

Distinctive characters: Coagulase-negative. Ferments glucose but not mannitol under anaerobic conditions.

Source: Originally isolated from small stitch-abscesses and other skin wounds.

Habitat: Skin and mucous membranes of man and other animals.

Genus III. **Gaffkya** *Trevisan, 1885.** *

(Trevisan, Atti d. Accad. Fisio-Medico-Statistica in Milano, Ser 4, *3*, 1885, 106; *Tetracoccus* von Klecki, Cent. f. Bakt., *15*, 1894, 360.)

Gaff'ky.a. M.L. fem.n. *Gaffkya* named for Prof. Georg Gaffky, a German bacteriologist.

Occur in the animal body and in special media as tetrads, while in ordinary culture media the cells occur in pairs and irregular masses. Gram-positive. Aerobic to facultatively anaerobic. Parasitic.

The type species is *Gaffkya tetragena* (Gaffky) Trevisan.

Key to the species of genus **Gaffkya**.

I. White, viscid growth on potato. Found in the mucous membranes of the respiratory tract.

1. *Gaffkya tetragena.*

II. No growth on potato. Causes a disease of lobsters.

2. *Gaffkya homari.*

1. Gaffkya tetragena (Gaffky, 1883) Trevisan, 1885. (*Micrococcus tetragenus* Gaffky, Arch. f. Chirurg., *28*, 1883, 500; Trevisan, Atti d. Accad. Fisio-Medico-Statistica in Milano, Ser. 4, *3*, 1885, 106.)

tet.ra'ge.na. Gr. pref. *tetra-* four; Gr. v. *gennaio* to produce; M.L. adj. *tetragenus* produced in fours.

Spheres, 0.6 to 0.8 microns in diameter, with a pseudocapsule (in body fluids) sur-

---

* Revised by Prof. G. J. Hucker, New York State Experiment Station, Geneva, New York, March 1943; further revision, November, 1955.

rounding four of the elements, thus forming typical tetrads. Gram-positive.

Gelatin colonies: Small, 1 to 2 mm in diameter, white convex.

Gelatin stab: Thick, white surface growth. No liquefaction.

Agar colonies: Circular, white, smooth, glistening, entire. Reimann (Jour. Bact., *31*, 1936, 385) has described eleven colony-form variants for this species.

Agar slant: White, moist, glistening growth.

Broth: Clear, with gray viscous sediment.

Litmus milk: Slightly acid.

Potato: White, viscid growth.

Indole not produced.

Hydrogen sulfide not produced.

Acid from glucose, lactose and glycerol.

Starch not hydrolyzed.

Nitrites not produced from nitrates.

Ammonium salts not utilized.

Biotin, L-tyrosine and L-glutamate are required for growth (Aaronson, Bact. Proc., 51st Gen. Meeting Soc. Amer. Bact., Chicago, 1951, 58).

Aerobic, facultatively anaerobic.

Optimum temperature, 37° C.

Pathogenic for mice and guinea pigs; rabbits are less susceptible.

Source: Isolated from sputum in tuberculosis; also from air and skin.

Habitat: Mucous membrane of the respiratory tract.

2. **Gaffkya homari** Hitchner and Snieszko, 1947. (Micrococci of the *Gaffkya* type, Snieszko and Taylor, Science, *105*, 1947, 500; Hitchner and Snieszko, Jour. Bact., *54*, 1947, 48.)

ho.ma'ri. M.L. noun *Homarus* generic name of the lobster; M.L. gen.noun *homari* of the lobster.

Spheres, 0.8 to 1.1 microns in diameter, occurring in tetrads. Encapsulated in lobster blood but not in artificial media. Non-motile. Gram-positive.

Gelatin: No liquefaction.

Agar colonies: Circular, 1 to 2 mm in diameter, grayish white, raised.

Agar slants: Scant, beaded growth.

Broth: Scant growth with granular sediment.

Litmus milk: Slightly acid.

Potato: No growth.

Indole not produced.

Hydrogen sulfide not produced.

Acid but no gas from glucose, lactose, sucrose, maltose, raffinose, mannitol, glycerol and salicin. Dulcitol not attacked.

Starch not hydrolyzed.

Acetylmethylcarbinol not produced.

Nitrites not produced from nitrates.

Urease not produced.

Ammonium salts do not serve as a sole source of nitrogen.

Biotin, calcium pantothenate, thiamin, nicotinic acid and a number of amino acids are required for growth (Aaronson, Bact. Proc., 51st Gen. Meeting, Soc. Amer. Bact., Chicago, 1951, 58).

Optimum temperature, between 30° and 35° C. Growth range, 6° to 44° C.

Aerobic, facultatively anaerobic.

Human blood agar: Beta-hemolytic.

Pathogenic for lobsters.

Source: Isolated from diseased lobsters (*Homarus americanus*) from Maine.

Genus IV. **Sarcina** *Goodsir, 1842.**

(Edinborough Med. and Surg. Jour., *57*, 1842, 430.)

Sar.ci'na. L. noun *sarcina* a package; M.L. fem.n. *Sarcina* a generic name.

Spheres. Division occurs, under favorable conditions, in three perpendicular planes, producing regular packets. Usually non-motile, although motile species may occur. Gram-positive, but the Gram stain may be lost rather readily. Aerobic growth on agar abundant, often with the production of a yellow, orange or red pigment; the growth of the anaerobic species

---

* Revised by Prof. Robert S. Breed, New York State Experiment Station, Geneva, New York, March, 1943; further revision by Prof. Jan Smit, Landbouwhoogeschool, Wageningen, The Netherlands, February, 1949.

is less abundant and non-pigmented even when the conditions for growth are favorable. Glucose broth generally slightly acid, lactose broth generally neutral. Gelatin frequently liquefied. Nitrites may or may not be produced from nitrates. Saprophytic and facultatively parasitic species occur.

The type species is *Sarcina ventriculi* Goodsir.

Key to the species of genus **Sarcina**.

I. Microaerophilic to anaerobic.
  A. Utilize sugars. Do not produce methane. Subgenus *Zymosarcina* Smit (Die Garungs-sarcinen. Pflanzenforschung, Jena, Heft 14, 1930, 26).
    1. Cellulose reaction positive. Slow coagulation in litmus milk.

1. Sarcina ventriculi.

    2. Cellulose reaction negative. Litmus milk not coagulated.

2. Sarcina maxima.

  B. Do not utilize sugars. Produce methane from carbon dioxide. Sub-genus *Methanosarcina* Kluyver and van Niel (Zent. f. Bakt., II Abt., *94*, 1936, 400).
    1. Methanol not utilized.

3. Sarcina methanica.

    2. Methanol utilized.

4. Sarcina barkeri.

II. Aerobic.
  A. Urea not converted to ammonium carbonate. Sub-genus *Sarcinococcus* Breed (in Manual, 6th ed., 1948, 285).
    1. Not halophilic.
      a. Yellow pigment produced.
        b. Milk alkaline; coagulated.

5. Sarcina lutea.

        bb. Milk alkaline; not coagulated.

6. Sarcina flava.

      aa. Orange pigment produced.

7. Sarcina aurantiaca.

    2. Halophilic, red chromogen.

8. Sarcina litoralis.

  B. Urea converted into ammonium carbonate. Sub-genus *Urosarcina* Miquel (Annales de Micrographie, *1*, 1888, 517).

9. Sarcina hansenii.

10. Sarcina ureae.

1. **Sarcina ventriculi** Goodsir, 1842, *emend.* Beijerinck, 1905. (Goodsir, Edinborough Med. and Surg. Jour., *57*, 1842, 430; Beijerinck, Proc. Sect. Sci., Kon Akad. v. Wetensch., Amsterdam, *7*, 1905, 580; also see Beijerinck, *ibid.*, 8, 1911, 1237; *Zymosarcina ventriculi* Smit, Die Gärungssarcinen. Pflanzenforschung, Jena, Heft 14, 1930, 26.)

ven.tri'cu.li. L. noun *ventriculus* the stomach; L. gen.noun *ventriculi* of the stomach.

Description taken in part from Smit (*loc. cit.*).

Large spheres, 3.5 to 4.0 microns in diameter, occurring in packets of 8, 16, 32 or more elements. Non-motile. Gram-positive.

Growth occurs only in sugar media containing peptones.

Gelatin: No liquefaction.

Deep glucose agar colonies: Multilenticular, surrounded by a cloudy zone. Abundant gas.

Glucose agar slant: Round, whitish colonies, several millimeters in diameter.

Glucose broth: Abundant, flaky growth. Abundant gas. Acid. No turbidity.

Plain peptone water: No growth.

Sugar peptone water: Abundant growth. Gas.

Milk: Slow growth. Acid and coagulation.

Indole not produced.

Acid and gas from glucose, fructose, sucrose, maltose, lactose and galactose. No acid from xylose, arabinose, raffinose, mannitol, dulcitol, salicin, starch, glycerol or inulin.

Cellulose reaction positive.

Neutral red broth changed to fluorescent yellow.

Utilizes peptones, wort and yeast water as sources of nitrogen. Cannot utilize amino acids or inorganic nitrogen.

Coagulated proteins not attacked.

Nitrites not produced from nitrates.

Principal products of metabolism are carbon dioxide and ethanol.

Microaerophilic to anaerobic.

Temperature relations: Optimum, 30° C. Minimum, 10° C. Maximum, 45° C. Killed in ten minutes at 65° C.

Optimum pH, between 1.5 and 5.0; pH limits for growth, 0.9 to 9.8.

Non-pathogenic.

Comments: *Sarcina ventriculi* Goodsir is often described as small, aerobic cocci, isolated from the stomach, which grow on sugar-free media and which do not attack sugars (see Bergey et al., Manual, 1st to 5th eds., 1923 to 1939). This mistake originated with Falkenheim (Arch. f. exp. Path u. Pharmak., *19*, 1885, 339). Beijerinck (*op. cit.*, 1905, 580) was the first to grow pure cultures of *Sarcina ventriculi* and to recognize its anaerobic nature.

Source: Originally found by making a microscopic examination of vomit. Found in cases of duodenal ulcer, never in cases of stomach cancer (Smit).

Habitat: Found in the stomach, garden soil, dust, sand and mud.

2. **Sarcina maxima** Lindner, 1888. (Lindner, Die Sarcina- Organismen der Gärungsgewerbe. Inaug. Diss., Berlin, 1888, 54; *Zymosarcina maxima* Smit, Die Gärungssarcinen. Pflanzenforschung, Jena, Heft 14, 1930, 22.)

max'i.ma. L. sup.adj. *maximus* greatest.

Description taken from Weinberg, Nati-

velle and Prévot (Les Microbes Anaérobies, 1937, 1030) and from Smit (*op. cit.*, 1930, 22).

Large spheres, 4.0 to 4.5 microns in diameter, occurring in regular packets of 8, 16, 32 or more elements. Non-motile. Grampositive.

Growth occurs only in sugar media containing peptones.

Gelatin: No liquefaction.

Deep glucose agar colonies: Multilenticular. Abundant gas produced.

Glucose agar slant: Round, whitish colonies.

Glucose broth: Abundant growth, flaky, gaseous, marked acidification. Disagreeable butyric odor. No turbidity.

Sugar peptone water: Abundant growth, flaky, gaseous, followed by acidification.

Milk: Not coagulated.

Acid and gas from glucose, fructose, galactose, maltose, sucrose and lactose.

Cellulose reaction negative.

Neutral red broth changed to fluorescent yellow.

Utilizes peptones, yeast water or broth as source of nitrogen. Cannot utilize amino acids or inorganic nitrogen.

Coagulated proteins not attacked.

Principal products of metabolism are carbon dioxide, butyric and acetic acids.

Microaerophilic to anaerobic.

Temperature relations: Optimum, 30° C. Minimum, 15° C. Maximum, 40° C. Killed in twenty minutes at 55° C.

pH limits of growth, 1.0 to 9.5.

Non-pathogenic.

Source: Isolated from fermenting malt mash.

Habitat: Acidified flour pastes, wheat bran; seldom in soils. Also intestinal contents of guinea pigs (Crecelius and Rettger, Jour. Bact., *46*, 1943, 10).

3. **Sarcina methanica** (Smit, 1930) Weinberg et al., 1937. (Methaansarcine, Söhngen, Inaug. Diss., Delft, 1906, 104; *Zymosarcina methanica* Smit, Die Gärungssarcinen. Pflanzenforschung, Jena, Heft 14, 1930, 25; Weinberg, Nativelle and Prévot, Les Microbes Anaérobies, 1937, 1032.)

me.tha'ni.ca. Gr. noun *methy* wine; M.L.

noun *methanum* methane; M.L. adj. *methanicus* pertaining to methane.

Description taken from Weinberg et al. (*loc. cit.*) and from Smit (*op. cit.*, 1930, 25).

Spheres, 2.0 to 2.5 microns in diameter, occurring in packets of 8 or more cocci. Non-motile. Gram-variable.

Growth in solutions of calcium acetate and possibly of butyrate and inorganic ammonium salts. Carbon dioxide is needed for methane production.

In acetate-agar (with addition of some H_2S and $NaHCO_3$): Colonies of 50 to 100 microns are formed, showing gas production.

Cultural characters as yet unknown.

Carbohydrates and ethanol not fermented.

Cellulose reaction negative.

Principal products from the metabolism of calcium acetate and butyrate are methane, carbon dioxide and calcium carbonate.

Peptones not attacked.

Utilizes ammonium salts as source of nitrogen. No organic nitrogen compounds utilized.

Strict anaerobe. Killed by a short contact with the air.

Optimum temperature, between 35° and 37° C.

Non-pathogenic.

Distinctive characters: Utilizes ammonium salts and acyclic acids producing methane and carbonic acid.

Source: Isolated from sediment in methane fermentation (Weinberg et al.). Isolated from mud (Smit).

Habitat: Swamp waters and mud; fermenting sewage sludge.

4. **Sarcina barkeri** Schnellen, 1947. (*Sarcina barkerii* (sic) Schnellen, Inaug. Diss., Delft, 1947, 63; also see Kluyver and Schnellen, Arch. of Biochem., *14*, 1947, 57.)

bar'ke.ri. M.L. gen.noun *barkeri* of Barker; named for H. A. Barker, who has made studies of organisms of this type.

Spheres, 1.5 to 2.0 microns in diameter, occurring mostly in packets of 8 or less. Non-motile. Gram-positive.

Growth occurs in solutions of methanol and inorganic ammonium salts.

Methanol agar (with inorganic salts and some Na_2S) colonies: 0.5 to 1.0 mm in diameter, whitish.

Carbohydrates not fermented.

Cellulose-negative.

Methane is produced from carbonic acid and bicarbonates. Sodium acetate is more slowly attacked with the production of carbon dioxide, part of which is reduced to methane. Other alcohols and salts are not utilized.

Nitrites not produced from nitrates.

Peptones and other sources of organic nitrogen are not utilized.

Catalase-negative.

Optimum temperature, 30° C.

Optimum pH, 7.0.

Non-pathogenic.

Distinctive characters: Methanol is utilized with the production of methane, carbon dioxide and water. From mixtures of carbon monoxide or carbon dioxide and hydrogen, methane is produced. Pure carbon monoxide is utilized with the production of carbon dioxide and methane.

Source: Isolated from mud.

Habitat: Found in mud and sewage sludge.

5. **Sarcina lutea** Schroeter, 1886. (In Cohn, Kryptogamen-Flora v. Schlesien, *3*, 1, 1886, 154.)

lu'te.a. L. adj. *luteus* yellow.

Spheres, 1.0 to 1.5 microns in diameter, occurring in packets in all media. Gram-positive.

Gelatin colonies: Circular, up to 5 mm in diameter, sulfur-yellow, sinking into the medium.

Gelatin stab: Slow, infundibuliform liquefaction.

Agar colonies: Yellow, coarsely granular, circular, raised, moist, glistening, entire.

Agar slant: Sulfur- to chrome-yellow, smooth, soft growth.

Broth: Clear with abundant, yellow sediment.

Litmus milk: Coagulated, becoming alkaline.

Potato: Sulfur- to chrome-yellow, raised, sometimes limited growth.

Slight indole production.

Hydrogen sulfide is produced.

No acid from glucose, lactose or sucrose.

Nitrites generally produced from nitrates.

Aerobic.

Optimum temperature, 25° C.

Habitat: Air, soil and water; also found on skin surfaces.

6. Sarcina flava de Bary, 1887. (Vorlesungen über Bakterien, 1887, 151.)

fla'va. L. adj. *flavus* yellow.

Spheres, 1.0 to 2.0 microns in diameter, occurring in packets of 16 to 32 cells. Grampositive.

Gelatin colonies: Small, circular, yellowish.

Gelatin stab: Slowly liquefied.

Agar slant: Yellow streak.

Broth: Slowly becoming turbid with whitish, later yellowish, sediment.

Litmus milk: Alkaline, not coagulated.

Potato: Yellow streak.

Indole not produced.

Nitrites not produced from nitrates.

Aerobic.

Optimum temperature, between 30° and 35° C.

Habitat: Air, water and soil.

7. Sarcina aurantiaca Flügge, 1886. (Die Mikroorganismen, 1886, 180.)

au.ran.ti'a.ca. M.L. noun *aurantium* the orange; M.L. adj. *aurantiacus* orangecolored.

Spheres which occur in packets in all media. Gram-positive.

Gelatin colonies: Small, circular, dark yellow, entire, sinking into the medium.

Gelatin stab: Infundibuliform liquefaction.

Agar slant: Slightly raised, orange-yellow to orange-red, soft, smooth growth.

Broth: Flocculent turbidity with abundant sediment.

Litmus milk: Coagulation and digestion.

Potato: Raised, yellow-orange, glistening to dull, granular growth.

Slight indole production.

Hydrogen sulfide not produced.

Nitrites not produced from nitrates.

Aerobic.

Optimum temperature, 30° C.

Habitat: Air and water.

8. Sarcina litoralis Poulsen, 1879. (Poulsen, Vidensk. Meddel. naturh. Foren. i Copenhagen, *1* and *2*, 1879–1880, 231; *Halococcus litoralis* Schoop, Deutsch. Tierärztl. Wochnschr., *43*, 1935, 817.)

li.to.ra'lis. L. adj. *litoralis* pertaining to the shore.

Description taken from Lochhead (Can. Jour. Res., *10*, 1934, 280).

Spheres, 1.2 to 1.6 microns in diameter, occurring singly, in pairs, fours, short chains and in packets, the arrangement varying with the medium, temperature, salt concentration and age of culture. Non-motile. Gram-variable, with rather more positive than negative cells.

No growth in ordinary media.

Salt gelatin: Growth slow, with no liquefaction.

Starch media (20 per cent salt): Colonies usually 1 to 3 mm in diameter, round, entire, convex with a waxy appearance, brickred with a pale border, color appearing gradually.

Starch media slants (20 per cent salt): Growth filiform, slightly raised, entire. Coral-red in color. Slight decrease in shade as cultures age.

Liquid media: No growth.

Potato: In 20 per cent salt, scant growth. Slight, chalky pink development near the top.

Indole not produced.

Diastatic action negative.

Nitrites produced from nitrates.

Halophilic, obligate; growth in 16 to 32 per cent salt. Optimum growth in 20 to 24 per cent salt.

Aerobic.

Optimum temperature, 37° C.

Comments: It appears quite possible that this species is identical with *Micrococcus morrhuae* Klebahn. Tetrads are mentioned by the majority of investigators, but few if any mention packets. Comparative studies using suitable methods for growing these organisms are needed.

Source: Isolated from seashore mud near Copenhagen; also from salted hides and salted fish.

Habitat: Sea-water brine or sea salt.

9. **Sarcina hansenii** (Miquel, 1893) Breed, *comb. nov.** (*Urosarcina hansenii* Miquel, Annales de Micrographie, *5*, 1893, 225 (type species (monotypy) of genus *Urosarcina* Miquel, *ibid.*, *1*, 1888, 517); also see Miquel and Cambier, Traité de Bactériologie, 1903, 628.)

han.se′ni.i. M.L. gen.noun *hansenii* of Hansen; named for Emil Christian Hansen, a Danish scientist who worked on fermentation problems.

Spheres, variable in size, ordinarily occurring in tetrads or packets, sometimes in irregular forms.

Growth occurs in various media.

Gelatin colonies: White, becoming yellow after 48 hours. Growth may occur in streaks. No liquefaction.

Broth: No turbidity; yellow deposit on walls of tube.

Urea is converted into ammonium carbonate.

Optimum temperature, 30° C. Growth occurs at room temperature.

Comment: The original description makes no mention of motility, of spore formation or of the Gram stain.

Relationships to other species: Hauduroy et al. (Dict. d. Bact. Path., 2ᵉ ed., 1953, 542) regard this species as probably identical with the following species. If the two species are identical, Miquel's description antedates that of Beijerinck.

Source: Isolated from water and dust.

Habitat: Presumably widely distributed.

10. **Sarcina ureae** (Beijerinck, 1901) Löhnis, 1911. (*Planosarcina ureae* Beijerinck, Cent. f. Bakt., II Abt., *7*, 1901, 52; Löhnis, Landwirtsch. bakteriol. Praktikum, 1911, 138.)

u′re.ae. Gr. noun *urum* urine; M.L. noun *urea* urea; M.L. gen.noun *ureae* of urea.

Original description supplemented by material taken from Gibson (Arch. f. Mikrobiol., *6*, 1935, 73).

Spheres, 1.0 to 2.5 microns in diameter, occurring singly, in pairs and in packets. Endospores of an unusual type are produced; they measure 0.8 to 1.0 micron in diameter and are centrally located. Motile, each sphere possessing a single, long flagellum. Gram-positive.

Gelatin colonies: Small, circular, flat, microscopically coarsely granular, gray, becoming opaque; old colonies generally become slightly yellowish or brownish.

Gelatin stab: Thread-like or beaded, gray to yellowish gray, glistening or dull growth. No liquefaction (Beijerinck); may or may not produce slow liquefaction (several weeks or months) (Gibson).

Agar colonies: Same as those on gelatin.

Agar slant: Growth gray, opaque and glistening, becoming slightly yellowish in old cultures.

Glucose agar stab: Gray, glistening surface growth becoming whitish or yellowish in the center and slightly irregular.

Broth: Turbid; later, an easily dispersed sediment is produced; a granular precipitate may be formed on the walls of the tube.

Milk: No change, but alkaline after several weeks if a heavy inoculum is used.

Potato: No growth on acid potato; brownish growth on potato rendered alkaline with Na_2CO_3 .

Indole not produced.

Hydrogen sulfide not produced.

No acid from glucose.

Starch not hydrolyzed.

Nitrites produced from nitrates (Gibson); sea-water forms do not reduce nitrates (Wood, Jour. Bact., *51*, 1946, 287).

Urea is converted into ammonium carbonate.

Aerobic.

Temperature relations: Optimum, 20° C. Maximum, under 37° C. Spore-containing cells resist heating to 80° C. for 10 minutes (Beijerinck) and 100° C. for 5 minutes (Gibson). The majority of vegetative cells are destroyed at 65° C. for 15 minutes; in dense suspensions, some survive 70° C. for 15 minutes (Gibson).

Optimum pH, about 8.8. Limits of pH, 6.4 and 9.4.

Spore formation: For abundant spore formation, solid media containing am-

---

* Description prepared by Prof. Robert S. Breed, Cornell University, Geneva, New York, October, 1955.

monium salts and sub-optimal concentrations of other nutrients should be used; also, the reactions of the media should approach the limiting acidity for growth, and the incubation temperature should not exceed 22° C.

Motility: After 24 hours, primary cultures on agar, in peptone water and in broth are non-motile whereas those on urea agar are actively motile.

Source: Isolated from urine and from garden soil. Also found in sea water (Wood, *loc. cit.*).

Habitat: Presumably widely distributed.

Genus V. **Methanococcus** *Kluyver and van Niel, 1936,* **emend.** *Barker, 1936.**

(Kluyver and van Niel, Zent. f. Bakt., II Abt., *94*, 1936, 400; Barker, Arch. f. Mikrobiol., *7*, 1936, 430.)

Me.tha.no.coc'cus. Gr. noun *methy* wine; M.L. noun *methanum* methane; Gr. noun *coccus* a berry; M.L. noun *coccus* a spherical cell; M.L. mas.n. *Methanococcus* methane coccus.

Spherical cells, occurring singly, in pairs, or in masses. Motile or non-motile. Gram-variable. Chemo-heterotrophic, fermenting various organic compounds with the production of methane. Anaerobic. Saprophytes.

The type species is *Methanococcus mazei* Barker.

1. **Methanococcus mazei** Barker, 1936. (Pseudosarcina, Mazé, Compt. rend. Soc. Biol., Paris, *78*, 1915, 398; Barker, Arch. f. Mikrobiol., *7*, 1936, 430.)

ma'ze.i. M.L. gen.noun *mazei* of Mazé; named for P. Mazé, the French bacteriologist who first gave a clearly recognizable description of this type of methane organism.

Small, spherical cells occurring singly, in large, irregular masses or in regular cysts of various sizes and forms. Non-motile. Stains readily with erythrosine. Gram-variable.

Grows in a mineral medium containing acetate, fermenting the acetate vigorously.

Ferments acetate and butyrate with the production of methane and carbon dioxide. Ethanol and butanol not attacked.

Ammonia nitrogen utilized, but not nitrate nitrogen. Yeast extract is not beneficial.

Anaerobic.

Optimum temperature, between 30° and 37° C.

Source: Isolated from garden soil, sewage sludge, black mud containing hydrogen sulfide and from the feces of herbivorous animals.

Habitat: One of the most active methane-producing organisms found in nature.

2. **Methanococcus vannielii** Stadtman and Barker, 1951. (Jour. Bact., *62*, 1951, 269.)

van.niel'i.i. M.L. gen.noun *vannielii* of van Niel; named for C. B. van Niel, the American bacteriologist who developed the carbon dioxide reduction theory of methane formation.

Cocci, often slightly ellipsoidal, which vary from 0.5 to 4.0 microns in diameter and which frequently occur in pairs. Motile. Cells disintegrate on drying. Stain readily with erythrosine. Gram stain not recorded.

Agar deep colonies: 0.5 to 1.0 mm in diameter, lenticular and light brown with edges regular or slightly lobate.

Acetate, propionate, butyrate, succinate, glucose, ethanol and methanol are not attacked when incorporated in a mineral-bicarbonate medium of pH 8.0 at a concentration of 0.5 per cent; under similar conditions, formate supports good growth.

Sodium formate in concentrations of 1.5 per cent permits maximum growth; at the 2 and 3 per cent levels, growth is slower, and in 5 per cent sodium formate there is no growth.

Formate, the only organic compound known to support growth, is fermented to

---

* Prepared by Prof. H. A. Barker, University of California, Berkeley, California, October, 1955.

methane, carbon dioxide and, under some conditions, hydrogen.

Chemical tolerance: pH range for growth, 7.4 to 9.2. Optimum pH, about 8.0.

Anaerobic.

Source: Isolated by enrichment procedures from black mud from the east shore of San Francisco Bay.

Habitat: Presumably found in similar materials elsewhere.

Genus VI. **Peptococcus** *Kluyver and van Niel, 1936.* *

(Zent. f. Bakt., II Abt., *94*, 1936, 400.)

Pep.to.coc'cus. Gr. v. *pepto* to cook, digest; Gr. noun *coccus* a grain, berry; M.L. mas.n. *Peptococcus* the digesting-coccus.

Spherical bacteria occurring singly, in pairs, tetrads or masses. Non-motile. Gram-positive. Anaerobic. Chemoheterotrophic, fermenting a variety of organic compounds. With one exception, the species here described are all from human sources.

Cardon and Barker (Jour. Bact., *52*, 1946, 633) have proposed the generic name *Anaerococcus* as a provisional name to include the Gram-positive, anaerobic occci which occur in a more or less irregular and variable arrangement.

The present classification of the species in this genus is based on morphological and various physiological characters. However, recent work has shown that the presence of fatty acids and sulfur compounds exerts a marked influence on the morphology and/or biochemical behavior of these organisms; consequently, in choosing criteria for the classification of the species in this genus, it seems exigent to use those obtained with standardized media. With the use of rather ill-defined media, at least thirty anaerobic cocci have been recognized and described; however, with standardized media, Hare and his associates have divided the anaerobic cocci into only nine groups. Thus, future work may show that some or even many of the species here regarded as distinct are, in reality, identical with each other. (See Hare, Wildy, Billett and Twort, Jour. Hyg., *50*, 1952, 295; Hare, Atti del VI Congresso Internaz. di Microbiologia, Roma, *1*, 1953, 55; and Thomas and Hare, Jour. Clin. Path., *7*, 1954, 300; also see Foubert and Douglas, Jour. Bact., *56*, 1948, 25.)

The type species is *Peptococcus niger* (Hall) Kluyver and van Niel.

Key to the species of genus **Peptococcus.**

I. Produce gas in visible quantities in culture media.
  A. Agar colonies black.
    1. *Peptococcus niger.*
  B. Agar colonies not black.
    1. Gelatin liquefied.
      2. *Peptococcus activus.*
    2. Gelatin not liquefied.
      a. Indole produced, nitrate reduced, glutamate fermented.
        3. *Peptococcus asaccharolyticus.*
        4. *Peptococcus aerogenes.*
      aa. Indole not produced, nitrate not reduced, glutamate not fermented.
        5. *Peptococcus prevotii.*
II. Do not produce gas in visible quantities in culture media.
  A. Ferment sugars. Glycine not fermented.
    1. Lactose fermented.
      6. *Peptococcus grigoroffii.*
    2. Lactose not fermented.
      7. *Peptococcus constellatus.*
      8. *Peptococcus saccharolyticus.*

---

* Prepared by Prof. H. C. Douglas, University of Washington, Seattle, Washington, December, 1954.

B. None or only slight fermentation of sugars. Glycine fermented.
  1. Gelatin liquefied; cell size variable.
    9. *Peptococcus glycinophilus.*
    10. *Peptococcus variabilis.*
  2. Gelatin not liquefied; cell size uniform.
    11. *Peptococcus anaerobius.*

1. Peptococcus niger (Hall, 1930) Kluyver and van Niel, 1936. (*Micrococcus niger* Hall, Jour. Bact., *20*, 1930, 409; Kluyver and van Niel, Zent. f. Bakt., II Abt., *94*, 1936, 400.)

ni′ger. L. adj. *niger* black.

Small spheres, 0.6 micron in diameter, occurring in irregular masses, occasionally in pairs. Gram-positive.

Gelatin: After 5 days a dark sediment is produced which gradually gets more and more intensely black. No liquefaction.

Deep agar colonies: Slow growth. At first very tiny, colorless, irregularly globular, smooth, dense. Small bubbles of gas are sometimes produced. After several days colonies become brown, then black. If exposed to air, colonies fade to a dull gray. Medium not discolored.

Blood agar slant colonies: After 4 or 5 days, minute, black, round, smooth, glistening, 0.5 mm in diameter. Non-hemolytic.

Coagulated blood serum: Minute, brown colonies appear on the 8th day. No liquefaction.

Broth: After 4 or 5 days, uniform turbidity and slight production of gas which contains hydrogen sulfide. Black sediment.

Brain medium: Turbid after 4 or 5 days at 37° C. Uniform gas production about the 6th day. Discoloration of the medium not marked.

Milk: No change.

No acid from carbohydrates. Black sediment produced.

Strict anaerobe.

Optimum temperature, 37° C. No growth below 30° C.

Non-pathogenic for guinea pigs and rabbits.

Distinctive characters: Formation of a water-insoluble, black pigment. Growth slow, visible after 2 to 4 days.

Source: Isolated from the urine of an aged woman.

Habitat: Unknown.

2. Peptococcus activus (Prévot and Taffanel, 1945) Douglas, *comb. nov.* (*Staphylococcus activus* Prévot and Taffanel, Ann. Inst. Past., *71*, 1945, 152.)

ac′ti.vus. L. adj. *activus* active.

Original description supplemented by material from Foubert (Thesis, Univ. of Washington, 1947) and Whiteley (Thesis, Univ. of Washington, 1951).

Spherical cells, 0.75 to 1.0 micron in diameter, occurring singly, in pairs, tetrads and irregular groups. Non-motile. Not encapsulated. Gram-positive.

Gelatin: Liquefaction.

Agar colonies: 0.5 to 1.0 mm in diameter, smooth, entire, convex, opaque, grayish white, butyrous.

Growth in fluid medium: In peptone yeast extract broth, growth moderately heavy in 72 hours; no odor; coarsely granular; gas is produced. Growth not enhanced by glucose.

Litmus milk: Reduced.

Indole is produced.

Hydrogen sulfide is produced.

Acid from glucose, galactose, fructose, mannose, maltose and sucrose. No acid from raffinose, starch, inulin, salicin, glycerol or mannitol. Cell suspensions ferment serine, threonine and purines to CO_2, NH_3, H_2 and unidentified products.

Nitrites produced from nitrates; nitrites are reduced.

Egg albumen, beef serum and casein attacked slowly.

Coagulase-negative.

Catalase-positive.

Anaerobic.

Optimum temperature, 37° C. Growth occurs between 30° and 37° C.

Optimum pH, between 7.0 and 8.0; pH range, 6.5 to 8.5.

Non-hemolytic.

Distinctive characters: Gas production; active utilization of glucose and other sugars; proteolytic activity.

Source: Isolated from the blood of a patient suffering from puerperal septicemia.

Habitat: Human sources so far as known.

3. Peptococcus asaccharolyticus (Distaso, 1912) Douglas, *comb. nov.* (*Staphylococcus asaccharolyticus* Distaso, Cent. f. Bakt., I Abt., Orig., *62*, 1912, 445; *Micrococcus asaccharolyticus* Hall, in Manual, 6th ed., 1948, 246.)

a.sac.cha.ro.ly'ti.cus. Gr. pref. *a* not; Gr. noun *sacchar* sugar; Gr. adj. *lyticus* able to loose; M.L. adj. *asaccharolyticus* not digesting sugar.

Description taken from Prévot (Ann. Sci. Nat., Sér. Bot. et Zool., *15*, 1933, 211).

Large spheres, 1.0 to 1.2 microns in diameter, occurring in very large clusters and in pairs and short chains. Gram-positive.

Gelatin: At 37° C. growth resembles tufts of cotton which precipitate. No liquefaction.

Deep agar colonies: Very delicate, pinpoint, transparent. A few bubbles of gas are produced.

Broth: Turbid. Growth settles at the bottom of the tube as a sort of viscous zoogloea. Unpleasant odor produced.

Peptone water: Turbid.

Milk: Feebly acidified but not coagulated.

Indole is produced.

Carbohydrates not attacked.

Egg albumen not attacked.

Anaerobic.

Distinctive characters: Large size; unpleasant odor; production of indole; production of gas.

Source: Isolated from the large intestine of a man with intestinal intoxication.

Habitat: Intestine. Not common.

4. Peptococcus aerogenes (Schottmüller, 1912) Douglas, *comb. nov.* (*Staphylococcus aerogenes* Schottmüller, Cent. f. Bakt., I Abt., Orig., *64*, 1912, 270; *Micrococcus aerogenes* Bergey et al., Manual, 1st ed., 1923, 70; not *Micrococcus aerogenes* Miller, Deutsch. med. Wochnschr., *12*, 1886, 119.)

a.e.ro'ge.nes. Gr. noun *aër* air; Gr. v. *gennaio* to produce; M.L. adj. *aerogenes* gas-producing.

Description taken from Prévot (Ann. Sci.

Nat., Sér. Bot. et Zool., *15*, 1933, 212), Foubert and Douglas (Jour. Bact., *56*, 1948, 25) and Whiteley (Jour. Bact., *63*, 1952, 163, and Thesis, Univ. of Washington, 1951).

Spheres, 0.75 to 1.0 micron in diameter, occurring singly, in pairs, tetrads and irregular masses. Non-motile. Not encapsulated. Gram-positive.

Gelatin: No liquefaction.

Agar colonies: Circular, 0.5 to 2.0 mm in diameter, smooth, entire, low convex, opaque, grayish white, butyrous.

Growth in fluid medium: In peptone yeast extract broth, growth is moderate, coarsely granular; slight to moderate gas production. Growth and gas production not enhanced by glucose but markedly stimulated by 0.5 per cent glutamate.

Litmus milk: Reduced.

Indole is produced.

Hydrogen sulfide is produced.

Cell suspensions decompose glutamate, serine, threonine, histidines and purines to CO_2, H_2, NH_3 and acids. The acids produced are butyric and acetic from glutamate, acetic from serine, propionic from threonine, and acetic and lactic from purines and histidines. Chemical analyses show that only traces of glucose are utilized (Foubert and Douglas). Prévot states that some strains produce small amounts of acid from glucose and fructose.

Nitrites produced from nitrates; nitrites are reduced.

Egg albumen, beef serum and casein not attacked.

Coagulase-negative.

Catalase-positive.

Anaerobic.

Optimum temperature, 37° C. Growth between 25° and 37° C.

Optimum pH, between 7.0 and 8.0; pH range, 5.5 to 8.5.

Non-hemolytic.

Distinctive characters: Gas production; sugars utilized slowly if at all; fermentation of amino acids and purines. Foubert and Douglas (*op. cit.*, 1948, 29) found no essential differences between cultures of this species and those of *Peptococcus asaccharolyticus*. Future work will probably show the two species to be identical.

Source: Isolated from twenty cases of puerperal fever (Schottmüller), from infected tonsils (Prévot) and from the female genital tract (Foubert and Douglas).

Habitat: Female genital tract and tonsils so far as known.

5. Peptococcus prevotii (Foubert and Douglas, 1948) Douglas, *comb. nov.* (*Micrococcus prevotii* Foubert and Douglas, Jour. Bact., *56*, 1948, 25.)

pre.vo′ti.i. M.L. gen.noun *prevotii* of Prévot; named for A. Prévot, a French bacteriologist.

Spherical cells, 0.6 to 1.5 microns in diameter, occurring singly, in pairs, tetrads and irregular groups. Non-motile. Not encapsulated. Gram-positive.

Gelatin: No liquefaction.

Agar colonies: Circular, 0.5 to 1.0 mm in diameter, smooth, entire, low convex, translucent or opaque, gray to grayish white, butyrous.

Growth in fluid medium: In peptone yeast extract broth, moderately heavy growth in 72 hours, coarsely granular; no odor; gas is produced. Growth of some strains enhanced slightly by glucose.

Litmus milk: Litmus reduced.

Indole not produced.

Hydrogen sulfide production slight, if at all.

All strains utilize small amounts of glucose. Some strains produce slight acidity in glucose, fructose, galactose, mannose, maltose and raffinose. Cell suspensions decompose serine, threonine and purines with the formation of CO_2, NH_3, H_2 and unidentified products. Glutamate, histidine and other amino acids not decomposed.

Nitrites not produced from nitrates; nitrites not reduced.

Egg albumen, beef serum and casein not attacked.

Coagulase-negative.

Catalase-positive.

Anaerobic.

Optimum temperature, 37° C. Growth between 25° and 37° C.

Optimum pH, between 6.5 and 8.5.

Non-hemolytic.

Distinctive characters: Distinguished from *Peptococcus aerogenes* by its failure to produce indole, to reduce nitrates and to ferment glutamate and histidine.

Source: Isolated from the female genital tract; also from tonsils, from a bottle of plasma and from skin.

Habitat: From human sources so far as known.

6. Peptococcus grigoroffii (Prévot, 1933) Douglas, *comb. nov.* (*Micrococcus* A, Grigoroff, Thèse de Geneve, 1905; *Micrococcus grigoroffi* (sic) Prévot, Ann. Sci. Nat., Sér. Bot. et Zool., *15*, 1933, 219.)

gri.go.rof′fi.i. M.L. gen.noun *grigoroffii* of Grigoroff; named for S. Grigoroff, the bacteriologist who first isolated this organism.

Small spheres, averaging 0.7 micron in diameter, occurring singly or in irregular masses. Gram-positive.

Gelatin: Colonies appear in four days. No liquefaction.

Deep agar colonies: After three days, round, lenticular, yellowish.

Glucose broth: Turbid after two days with whitish sediment. Neither gas nor fetid odor produced. The medium is acidified.

Milk: Good growth; acid; coagulation.

Acid from glucose, fructose, maltose, lactose and sorbitol.

Anaerobic.

Optimum temperature, 37° C.

One strain is slightly pathogenic.

Distinctive characters: This is the only anaerobic coccus growing in irregular masses that coagulates milk. Lactose is fermented.

Source: Five strains were isolated from the appendix by Grigoroff; one strain was isolated from an appendix by Prévot.

Habitat: Human digestive tract. Not common.

7. Peptococcus constellatus (Prévot, 1924) Douglas, *comb. nov.* (*Diplococcus constellatus* Prévot, Compt. rend. Soc. Biol., Paris, *91*, 1924, 426.)

con.stel.la′tus. L. adj. *constellatus* studded with stars.

Description taken in part from Prévot

(Ann. Sci. Nat., Sér. Bot. et Zool., *15*, 1933, 158).

Spheres, 0.5 to 0.6 micron in diameter, occurring in pairs and tetrads, rarely in very short chains, never in clusters. Gram-positive.

Gelatin: Good growth. No liquefaction.

Deep agar colonies: At first very small, lenticular, biconvex, thick, opaque, yellowish, 0.5 to 1.5 mm in diameter. Each colony is surrounded by many small satellite colonies visible microscopically.

Broth: Growth slow, poor. After 48 hours a slight, homogeneous turbidity is formed; it quickly clears leaving a slight, powdery sediment. Neither gas nor odor is produced.

Glucose broth: Growth rapid, abundant. Proteins not attacked.

Blood broth: Good growth; no hemolysis.

Milk: Poor growth; no change.

Peptone water: Good growth; not acidified; indole not produced.

Acid but no gas from glucose and arabinose. Slight acid from glycerol. No acid from lactose, inulin, mannitol or dulcitol.

Neutral red broth: Unchanged.

Anaerobic.

Optimum temperature, 37° C. Feeble growth at 22° C. Not thermo-resistant.

Optimum pH, between 6.0 and 8.0.

Distinctive character: The microscopic appearance of agar colonies, each of which is surrounded by a constellation of satellites.

Source: Isolated from a case of chronic, cryptic tonsillitis; later isolated from pus in acute appendicitis.

Habitat: Found in the digestive tract, especially the lymphoid tissues, such as tonsils, etc.

8. **Peptococcus saccharolyticus** (Foubert and Douglas, 1948) Douglas, *comb. nov.* (*Micrococcus saccharolyticus* Foubert and Douglas, Jour. Bact., *56*, 1948, 30 and 31.)

sac.cha.ro.ly'ti.cus. Gr. noun *sacchar* sugar; Gr. adj. *lyticus* able to loose; M.L. adj. *saccharolyticus* sugar-digesting.

Spheres, 0.6 to 1.0 micron in diameter, occurring singly, in pairs, tetrads and irregular groups. Non-motile. Not encapsulated. Gram-positive.

Gelatin: No liquefaction.

Agar colonies: Circular, 0.5 to 1.0 mm in diameter, smooth, entire, low convex, opaque, grayish white, butyrous.

Growth in fluid medium: In peptone yeast extract broth, growth is moderate and stimulated by glucose. Cultures are turbid with a white, powdery sediment. No visible gas production. Faint, fruity odor.

Litmus milk: Slight reduction of litmus. Indole not produced.

Hydrogen sulfide not produced.

Acid but no visible gas from glucose, fructose, mannose and glycerol. Arabinose, galactose, maltose, lactose, raffinose, starch, inulin, salicin, mannitol, lactate and malate not utilized. Glucose fermented to CO_2, ethanol, acetic acid, formic acid and traces of lactic acid.

Nitrites produced from nitrates; nitrites are reduced.

Egg albumen, beef serum and casein not attacked.

Coagulase-negative.

Catalase-positive.

Anaerobic.

Optimum temperature, 37° C. Growth between 25° and 37° C.

Optimum pH, between 7.0 and 7.5; pH range, 5.5 to 8.5.

Non-hemolytic.

Distinctive characters: Saccharolytic; no visible gas produced; characteristic fermentation products from glucose.

Comments: There seems to be little difference between this and the preceding species.

Source: Isolated from bottles of plasma; also from the human skin.

Habitat: Probably the skin of man.

9. **Peptococcus glycinophilus** (Cardon and Barker, 1946) Douglas, *comb. nov.* (*Diplococcus glycinophilus* Cardon and Barker, Jour. Bact., *52*, 1946, 629.)

gly.ci.no'phi.lus. M.L. noun *glycinum* glycine; Gr. adj. *philus* loving; M.L. adj. *glycinophilus* glycine-loving.

Original description supplemented by material from Foubert (Thesis, University of Washington, 1947).

Spheres, 0.7 to 2.5 microns in diameter, the average being about 1.2 microns, occasionally rod-shaped, occurring in pairs, short chains, tetrads and irregular groups. Non-motile. Not encapsulated. Gram-positive.

Growth does not occur on complex nitrogenous or sugar-containing media to any observable extent in the absence of added glycine; furthermore, ordinary distilled water is frequently toxic to this organism, and glass-distilled water or a 1:1 mixture of glass-distilled and tap water is recommended in the preparation of media.

Gelatin: Liquefaction.

Agar plate colonies: Circular, up to 0.5 mm in diameter, smooth, entire, convex, opaque, grayish white, butyrous.

Growth in fluid medium: Slow but abundant growth in peptone yeast extract medium containing 0.3 per cent added glycine; coarsely granular; no odor; no gas.

Litmus milk: Partial reduction.

Indole not produced.

Hydrogen sulfide not produced.

Glycine or glycine-containing peptides are fermented. Other amino acids, organic acids and carbohydrates are not utilized. Glycine is decomposed to CO_2, NH_3 and acetic acid; under certain conditions H_2 may also be formed in addition to the above products.

Nitrites produced from nitrates; nitrites are reduced.

Coagulase-negative.

Catalase-positive.

Anaerobic.

Optimum temperature, 37° C.

Optimum pH, 7.2; pH range, 6.0 to 8.5.

Non-hemolytic.

Distinctive characters: Large cell size; distinctive catabolism. The predominant organism in anaerobic enrichment cultures prepared by inoculating mud into 1 per cent glycine in tap water.

Source: Isolated from mud in the tidal areas of San Francisco Bay.

Habitat: Mud and soil.

10. **Peptococcus variabilis** (Foubert and Douglas, 1948) Douglas, *comb. nov.* (*Micrococcus variabilis* Foubert and Douglas, Jour. Bact., *56*, 1948, 25.)

va.ri.a′bi.lis. L. adj. *variabilis* variable.

Original description supplemented by material from Douglas (Jour. Bact., *62*, 1951, 517).

Spheres, 0.5 to 1.5 microns in diameter, occurring singly, in pairs, tetrads and irregular groups. Non-motile. Not encapsulated. Gram-positive.

Gelatin: Liquefaction.

Agar colonies: Circular, 0.5 to 1.0 mm in diameter, smooth, entire, low convex, opaque, grayish white, butyrous.

Growth in fluid medium: In peptone yeast extract broth, growth moderately heavy, cloudy; no odor; no visible gas. Growth not enhanced by glucose.

Litmus milk: Slight reduction.

Indole not produced.

Hydrogen sulfide is produced.

Cell organisms and growing cultures decompose glycine to CO_2, NH_3 and acetic acid. Other amino acids, purines, lactate and malate not decomposed. No acid production or growth enhancement by sugars although chemical analyses show that small amounts of glucose are utilized by all strains.

Nitrites not produced from nitrates; nitrites not reduced.

Coagulase-negative.

Catalase-positive.

Anaerobic.

Optimum temperature, 37° C. Growth between 25° and 37° C.

Optimum pH, 7.0; pH range, 6.5 to 8.5.

Non-hemolytic.

Distinctive characters: No visible gas production; glycine fermented to CO_2, NH_3 and acetic acid; liquefaction of gelatin and variable cell size distinguish this species from *Peptococcus anaerobius.*

Source: Isolated from the female genital tract; also from a normal tonsil and a draining sinus.

Habitat: Human sources so far as known.

11. **Peptococcus anaerobius** (Hamm, 1912) Douglas, *comb. nov.* (Anaerobic staphylococcus, Jungano, Compt. rend. Soc. Biol., Paris, *59*, 1907, 707; *Staphylococcus anaerobius* Hamm, Die puerperale Wundinfektion, Berlin, 1912; not *Staphylococcus anaerobius* Heurlin, Bakt. Unters. d. Keimgehaltes im Genitalkanale d. fiebernden Wöchnerinnen, Helsingfors, 1910, 120;

Micrococcus anaerobius Hall, in Manual, 6th ed., 1948, 247).

an.a.e.ro'bi.us. Gr. pref. *an* not; Gr. noun *aër* air; Gr. noun *bius* life; M.L. adj. *anaerobius* not living in air.

Description taken from Prévot (Ann. Sci. Nat., Sér. Bot. et Zool., *15*, 1933, 209), Foubert (Thesis, Univ. of Washington, 1947) and Douglas (Jour. Bact., *62*, 1951, 517).

Spheres, 0.5 to 0.6 micron in diameter, occurring singly, in pairs, tetrads and masses. Non-motile. Not encapsulated. Gram-positive.

Gelatin: No liquefaction.

Agar colonies: 0.5 to 1.0 mm in diameter, circular, smooth, entire, low convex, opaque, grayish, opalescent, butyrous.

Growth in fluid medium: In peptone yeast extract broth, growth moderate, cloudy to granular; no visible gas production. Growth not enhanced by glucose.

Litmus milk: Reduced.

Indole not produced.

Hydrogen sulfide is produced.

Cell suspensions and growing cultures decompose glycine to CO_2, NH_3 and acetic acid. Other amino acids are not fermented. Purines, lactate and malate not attacked. Sugars attacked slowly or not at all.

Nitrites not produced from nitrates.

Egg albumen, beef serum and casein not attacked.

Coagulase-negative.

Catalase-positive.

Anaerobic.

Optimum temperature, 37° C. Growth between 25° and 37° C.

Optimum pH, 7.0; pH range, between 6.0 and 8.0.

Non-hemolytic.

Distinctive characters: No visible gas produced; sugars utilized slowly or not at all; glycine fermented to CO_2, NH_3 and acetic acid; failure to liquefy gelatin and uniform cell size distinguish this species from *Peptococcus variabilis*.

Source: Isolated by Jungano from inflamed appendices and from a case of cystitis; also from an infected tonsil (Prévot).

Habitat: From human sources so far as known.

FAMILY VIII. NEISSERIACEAE PRÉVOT, 1933.

(Ann. Sci. Nat., Sér. Bot., *15*, 1933, 119.)

Neis.se.ri.a'ce.ae. M.L. fem.n. *Neisseria* type genus of the family; *-aceae* ending to denote a family; M.L. fem.pl.n. *Neisseriaceae* the *Neisseria* family.

Spherical cells occurring in pairs or in masses. Giant cells common in young cultures. Non-motile. Gram-negative. Pigment may or may not be produced. Some species grow poorly immediately after isolation without mammalian body fluids. Aerobic, facultatively anaerobic and anaerobic. Optimum temperature, 37°C. All known species are parasitic.

Key to the genera of family **Neisseriaceae.**

I. Cells, approximately 1.0 micron in diameter, occur in pairs with the adjacent sides usually flattened. Aerobic or facultatively anaerobic.

Genus I. *Neisseria*, p. 480.

II. Cells, usually less than 0.5 micron in diameter, occur in pairs and masses. Anaerobic.

Genus II. *Veillonella*, p. 485.

Genus I. **Neisseria** Trevisan, 1885.*

(Trevisan, Atti della Accademia Fisio-Medico-Statistica in Milano, Ser. 4, *3*, 1885, 105; *Gonococcus* Lindau, in Just's Bot. Jahresber., I Abt., Orig., *26*, 1898, 100.)

---

* Revised by Dr. Sara E. Branham, National Institutes of Health, Bethesda, Maryland, and Dr. Michael J. Pelczar, University of Maryland, College Park, Maryland, December, 1952. Reviewed by Prof. E. G. D. Murray, McGill University, Montreal, P. Q., Canada.

Neis.se′ri.a. M.L. fem.n. *Neisseria* named for Dr. Albert Neisser, who discovered the organism causing gonorrhoea in 1879.

Cocci occurring in pairs with the adjacent sides flattened. Gram-negative. Five species produce a yellow, a greenish yellow or a tan pigment. Growth on non-enriched media may be poor. Biochemical activities are limited. Few carbohydrates are utilized. Indole not produced. Nitrates not reduced. Catalase is abundantly produced. Aerobic or facultatively anaerobic. Some species are hemolytic. Parasites of animals so far as known.

The type species is *Neisseria gonorrhoeae* Trevisan.

Key to the species of genus Neisseria.

I. Grow best on special culture media containing blood, blood serum or similar enrichment fluids (especially with added glucose) at 35° to 37° C.; growth rare below 25° C. Non-chromogenic.

    A. Acid from glucose, not from maltose. Will grow anaerobically.

          1. *Neisseria gonorrhoeae.*

    B. Acid from glucose and maltose. No growth anaerobically.

          2. *Neisseria meningitidis.*

II. Grow well on ordinary culture media at 22° C.

    A. Non-chromogenic.

      1. No acid from any carbohydrate. Moist colonies on agar. From human nasal secretions.

          3. *Neisseria catarrhalis.*

      2. Acid from glucose, fructose, maltose and sucrose.

        a. Dry, crumbly colonies on agar. Sometimes hemolytic.

          4. *Neisseria sicca.*

        aa. Growth slow and delicate. Hemolytic.

          5. *Neisseria haemolysans.*

    B. Chromogenic, especially on Loeffler's serum medium or on Dorsett's egg medium*.

      1. No acid from any carbohydrate.

        a. Greenish yellow chromogenesis.

          6. *Neisseria flavescens.*

        aa. Light brown to tan chromogenesis.

          7. *Neisseria caviae.*

      2. Acid from carbohydrates.

        a. No acid from fructose. Greenish yellow chromogenesis.

          8. *Neisseria subflava.*

        aa. Acid from fructose.

          b. No acid from sucrose. Greenish yellow chromogenesis.

          9. *Neisseria flava.*

          bb. Acid from sucrose. Greenish yellow chromogenesis.

          10. *Neisseria perflava.*

---

1. **Neisseria gonorrhoeae** Trevisan, 1885. (Micrococcus der Gonorrhoe, Neisser, Vorl. Mitteil., Cent. f. Medicinische Wissenchaft, *17*, 1879, 497; Trevisan, Atti della Accademia Fisio-Medico-Statistica in Milano, Ser. 4, *3*, 1885 105; *Micrococcus gonorrhoeae* Flügge, Die Mikroorganismen, 2 Aufl., 1886, 156; *Gonococcus neisseri* Lindau, in Just's Bot. Jahresber., I Abt., Orig., *26*, 1898, 100.)

go.nor.rhoe′ae. Gr. noun *gonorrhoea* gonorrhea; M.L. gen.noun *gonorrhoeae* of gonorrhea.

Common name: Gonococcus.

Spheres, 0.6 to 1.0 micron in diameter, occurring singly and in pairs, the sides flat-

---

* Abel's modification. See M. Levine and H. Schoenlein, A Compilation of Culture Media. Baltimore, 1930, 792.

tened where they are in contact. Gram-negative.

Grows best on media with the addition of body fluids (blood, ascites, etc.) or other specially prepared media.

Colonies are small and transparent, eventually (2 to 4 days) developing a lobate margin, grayish white with a pearly opalescence by transmitted light. Larger colonies form on special media.

Acid from glucose. No acid from fructose, maltose, sucrose, mannitol or other sugars.

Optimum temperature, 37° C. No growth below 25° C.

Aerobic to facultatively anaerobic. Many strains develop more readily with increased CO_2 tension.

Source: Originally found in purulent venereal discharges. Also found in blood, conjunctiva, joints and cerebrospinal fluid.

Habitat: The cause of gonorrhea and other infections of man. Not found in other animals.

2. **Neisseria meningitidis*** (Albrecht and Ghon, 1903) Holland, 1920. (*Diplococcus intracellularis meningitidis* Weichselbaum, Fortschr. d. Med., *5*, 1887, 583; *Neisseria weichselbaumii* Trevisan, I generi e le specie delle Batteriacee, 1889, 32; *Micrococcus intracellularis* Migula, Syst. d. Bakt., *2*, 1900, 189; *Micrococcus meningitidis* Albrecht and Ghon, Cent. f. Bakt., I Abt., Orig., *33*, 1903, 498; Holland, Jour. Bact., *5*, 1920, 224.)

me.nin.gi'ti.dis. Gr. fem.n. *meninx*, *meningis* the membrane enclosing the brain; M.L. fem.n. *meningitis*, *meningitidis* inflammation of the meninges.

Common name: Meningococcus.

In 1898, Councilman, Mallory and Wright (Epidemic Cerebrospinal Meningitis and its Relation to other Forms of Meningitis, Boston, 1898) definitely established the Gram-negative coccus as the cause of epidemic meningitis.

Spheres, 0.6 to 1.0 micron in diameter, occasionally larger; occur singly, in pairs with adjacent sides flattened or occasionally in tetrads. Gram-negative.

Good growth is obtained on media containing blood, blood serum and other enrichment fluids with added glucose. Best growth on special media.

Blood agar plates are generally employed to isolate the organism. The colonies are small, slightly convex, transparent, glistening. Colonies are larger on special media.

Older cultures may show growth on nutrient agar or glucose agar properly prepared. Semi-solid media are especially favorable for growth and are often used for isolation. With recently isolated strains frequent transplantation is necessary to keep the organism alive; older strains survive longer. Cultures should be kept at 35° to 37° C.

Acid from glucose and maltose. No acid from other carbohydrates.

Nitrites not produced from nitrates.

Optimum temperature, between 36° and 37° C. No growth at 22° C.

Aerobic.

Source: Originally found in the cerebrospinal fluid. Also found in the nasopharynx, in the blood, in the conjunctiva, in pus from joints and in petechiae in the skin.

Habitat: Nasopharynx of man; not found in other animals. Cause of epidemic cerebrospinal fever (meningitis).

Four main groups of *Neisseria meningitidis* have been differentiated on the basis of agglutination reactions with immune serum. The Subcommittee on *Neisseria* of the International Committee on Bacteriological Nomenclature of the International Association of Microbiologists has suggested

---

* The binomial *Neisseria intracellularis*, used in the first five editions of the MANUAL, proved confusing because the names *Micrococcus intracellularis*, *Diplococcus intracellularis* and *Streptococcus intracellularis* have been used loosely for unrelated organisms. *Neisseria weichselbaumii* has also been so rarely used and at the same time is so loosely used that any attempt to introduce it now is inadvisable despite rights or priority. The equally available name *Neisseria meningitidis* was therefore adopted for the 6th edition of the MANUAL and is hereby continued. It has the obvious advantage of association with the common name, meningococcus, which has been repeatedly used in the literature.

(Proceedings 5th International Congress for Microbiology, Rio de Janeiro, Brasil, 1950, Internat. Bull. Bact. Nomen. and Taxon., *4*, 1954, 95) that these groups be designated as A, B, C and D. Relationships of these groups to older classifications of the meningococcus are shown in the accompanying table.

Aerobic, facultatively anaerobic.

Source: Nasopharynx, saliva and respiratory tract.

Habitat: Human mucous membrane of the respiratory tract. Often associated with other organisms in inflammations of the mucous membrane.

RELATIONSHIPS AMONG THE VARIOUS CLASSIFICATIONS OF MENINGOCOCCI.

Dopter and Pauron,* 1914	Gordon and Murray,* 1915	Griffith; Scott,* 1916	Nicolle, Debains and Jouan,* 1918	Evans (Tropin Groups),* 1920	Common use, 1940	Recommended by Committee,* 1950
Meningococcus	I III	I	A	R	I	A
Para-meningo-coccus	II	II	B	S	II	B
	IV			Z	IV	D
			C		II alpha	C
			D**			

*Dopter and Pauron, Compt. rend. Soc. Biol., Paris, *77*, 1914, 231; Gordon and Murray, Jour. Roy. Army Med. Corps, *25*, 1915, 411; Griffith, Local Govt. Bd. Rept., New Series, No. 110, 1916, 41; Scott, *ibid.*, 56; Nicolle, Debains and Jouan, Ann. Inst. Past., *32*, 1918, 150; Evans, U. S. Pub. Health Ser., Hyg. Lab. Bull. 124, 1920, 43; Sub-Committee on *Neisseria* of the Internat. Comm. on Bact. Nomenclature, Proceedings, 5° Congresso Internacional de Microbiologia, Rio de Janeiro, 1950 (in press).

** Relation of this D to other groups is unknown.

3. **Neisseria catarrhalis** (Frosch and Kolle, 1896) Holland, 1920. (*Micrococcus catarrhalis* Frosch and Kolle, in Flügge, Die Mikroorganismen, 3 Aufl., *2*, 1896, 154; Holland, Jour. Bact., *5*, 1920, 224.)

ca.tar.rhal'is. Gr. adj. *catarrhus* downflowing, catarrh; M.L. adj. *catarrhalis* of catarrh.

Spheres 0.6 to 1.0 micron in diameter as a rule. Occur singly, in pairs with adjacent sides flattened and sometimes in fours. Gram-negative.

Blood agar colonies: Small, circular, rather convex, grayish white to dirty white, sometimes erose.

Broth: Turbid, often with a slight pellicle.

No acid from any of the carbohydrates.

Optimum temperature, 37° C. Grows well at 22° C.

4. **Neisseria sicca** (von Lingelsheim, 1908) Bergey et al., 1923. (*Diplococcus pharyngis siccus* von Lingelsheim, Klin. Jahrb., *15*, 1906, 409; *Diplococcus siccus* von Lingelsheim, Ztschr. f. Hyg., *59*, 1908, 476; Bergey et al., Manual, 1st ed., 1923, 43.)

sic'ca. L. adj. *siccus* dry.

Spheres 0.6 to 1.0 micron in diameter, occurring singly and in pairs with adjacent sides flattened. Gram-negative.

Blood agar colonies: Grayish, somewhat dry, crumbling when an effort is made to remove them. Often the whole colony can be pushed about over the medium. Sometimes corrugated on the surface and firmly adherent to the medium. Sometimes hemolytic.

Often difficult to emulsify; precipitates spontaneously in normal salt solution.

Acid from glucose, fructose, maltose and sucrose.

Optimum temperature, 37° C. Grows at 22° C.

Aerobic, facultatively anaerobic.

Source: Nasopharynx, saliva and sputum.

Habitat: Mucous membrane of the respiratory tract of man.

5. Neisseria haemolysans Thjøtta and Böe, 1938. (Acta path. et microbiol. Scand., Suppl., *37*, 1938, 527.)

hae.mo′ly.sans. Gr. noun *haema* blood; Gr. v. *lyo* to loose; M.L. part.adj. *haemolysans* dissolving blood.

Spheres, 0.6 to 1.0 micron or more in diameter, occurring singly and in pairs with adjacent sides flattened. Type strain shows some very large cells. Gram-negative.

Blood agar colonies: Smooth, non-chromogenic, surrounded by a zone of clear beta hemolysis by the second or third day. Growth slow and delicate.

Gelatin not liquefied.

Acid from glucose, fructose, maltose and sucrose, but not from any other carbohydrate.

Indole not produced.

Nitrites not produced from nitrates.

Aerobic, facultatively anaerobic.

Source: Bronchial secretions, nasopharynx.

Habitat: Human mucous membrane of the respiratory tract.

6. Neisseria flavescens Branham, 1930. (U. S. Public Health Service, Pub. Health Reports, *45*, 1930, 845.)

fla.ves′cens. L. v. *flavesco* to become golden yellow; L. part.adj. *flavescens* becoming golden yellow.

Biscuit-shaped cocci occurring in flattened pairs; usually 0.6 to 1.0 micron in diameter. Gram-negative.

Glucose agar: Poor growth.

Blood agar: Grows well, colonies less moist and less transparent than those of the meningococcus. Develops a golden yellow pigment. Is greenish yellow on Loeffler's blood serum medium.

Semi-solid agar: Good growth with pellicle formation.

No acid from any carbohydrates.

Optimum temperature, 37° C; grows well at 22° C.

Aerobic, facultatively anaerobic.

Serologically, a homogeneous group.

Source: Cerebrospinal fluid in cases of meningitis.

Habitat: Probably mucous membrane of respiratory tract of man.

7. Neisseria caviae Pelczar, 1953. (*Neisseria* from guinea pig, Pelczar, Hajek and Faber, Jour. Inf. Dis., *85*, 1949, 239; Pelczar, Jour. Bact., *65*, 1953, 744.)

ca′vi.ae. M.L. fem.n. *Cavia* generic name of the guinea pig; M.L. gen.noun *caviae* of *Cavia*.

Spheres, 0.6 to 1.0 micron in diameter, occurring predominantly in pairs with flattened sides, though small clusters of cells are present. Gram-negative.

Trypticase soy agar colonies: Approximately 2 mm in diameter, circular, convex, entire with smooth glistening surface. Consistency butyrous, becoming viscid.

Chromogenesis: Growth on Loeffler's slants is a distinct light caramel to dirty brown color. Distinctly different from the grayish white or yellow to yellowish green chromogenesis of other species in the genus.

No acid from any carbohydrate.

Positive oxidase test with para-aminodimethylaniline monohydrochloride reagent.

Hemolysis: Some strains weakly hemolytic against rabbit blood.

Optimum temperature, 37° C; grows at 22° C.

Aerobic, facultatively anaerobic.

Source: Isolated from the pharyngeal region of guinea pigs.

Habitat: Pharyngeal region of guinea pigs and perhaps also in the pharyngeal region of other animals.

8. Neisseria subflava Bergey et al., 1923. (Chromogenic group III, Elser and Huntoon, Jour. Med. Res., *20* (N.S. *15*), 1909, 415; Bergey et al., Manual, 1st ed., 1923, 44.)

sub.fla′va. L. prefix *sub* less than, somewhat; L. adj. *flavus* yellow; L. adj. *subflavus* yellowish.

Spheres, 0.6 to 1.0 micron in diameter,

occurring singly and in pairs with adjacent sides flattened. Gram-negative.

Blood agar colonies: Small, round, smooth, convex, yellowish gray. Sometimes translucent and very adherent to the agar.

Chromogenesis: The bacterial growth is usually a pale greenish yellow on Loeffler's serum medium.

Acid from glucose and maltose. No acid from fructose, sucrose or mannitol.

Optimum temperature, 37° C., but grows at 22° C.

Easily confused with *Neisseria meningitidis*.

Source: Nasopharynx.

Habitat: Human mucous membrane of the respiratory tract.

9. **Neisseria flava** Bergey et al., 1923. (Chromogenic Group II, Elser and Huntoon, Jour. Med. Res., *20* (N.S. *15*), 1909, 415; Bergey et al., Manual, 1st ed., 1923, 43.)

fla'va. L. adj. *flavus* yellow.

Spheres, 0.5 to 1.0 micron in diameter, occurring singly and in pairs with adjacent sides flattened. Gram-negative.

Blood agar colonies: Small, circular, raised, smooth, glistening, yellowish.

Chromogenesis best seen on Loeffler's serum medium; greenish yellow.

Acid from glucose, fructose and maltose. No acid from sucrose.

Optimum temperature, 37° C. Grows at 22° C.

Source: Nasopharynx and cerebrospinal fluid in cases of meningitis (very rare).

Habitat: Human mucous membrane of respiratory tract.

10. **Neisseria perflava** Bergey et al., 1923. (Chromogenic group I, Elser and Huntoon, Jour. Med. Res., *20* (N.S. *15*), 1909, 415; Bergey et al., Manual, 1st ed., 1923, 43.)

per.fla'va. L. prefix *per* very; L. adj. *flavus* yellow; M.L. adj. *perflavus* very yellow.

Spheres, 0.6 to 1.0 micron in diameter, occurring singly and in pairs with adjacent sides flattened. Gram-negative.

Blood agar colonies: Small, circular, raised, yellowish, smooth, shining. Growth is often adherent to the medium.

Chromogenesis best seen on Loeffler's serum medium; usually a bright greenish yellow.

Acid from glucose, fructose, maltose and sucrose.

Optimum temperature, 37° C. Grows at 22° C.

Aerobic, facultatively anaerobic.

Source: Nasopharynx, saliva and sputum.

Habitat: Mucous membrane of respiratory tract of man. The most common of the chromogenic *Neisseria*.

Genus II. **Veillonella** *Prévot, 1933.**

(Prévot, Ann. Sci. Nat., Sér. Bot., *15*, 1933, 118; also see Langford, Faber and Pelczar, Jour. Bact., *59*, 1950, 349–356.)

Veil.lo.nel'la. M.L. dim.ending -*ella*; M.L. fem.n. *Veillonella* named for A. Veillon, the French bacteriologist who isolated the type species.

Small cocci, generally 0.3 to 0.4 micron in diameter, occurring in masses, in pairs or in short chains. Cells undifferentiated and united by an interstitial substance of ectoplasmic nature. Gram-negative. Good growth on usual culture media. Pronounced biochemical activity. Anaerobic. Occur as parasites in the mouths, the intestines and the urogenital and respiratory tracts of man and other animals.

The present classification of the species in this genus is based on morphological and various physiological characters. However, recent work has shown that the presence of fatty acids and sulfur compounds exerts a marked influence on the morphology and/or biochemical behavior of these organisms; consequently, in choosing criteria for the classification of the species in this genus, it seems exigent to use those obtained with specified media. With the use of rather ill-defined media, at least thirty anaerobic cocci have been recog-

* Prepared by Dr. Michael J. Pelczar, University of Maryland, College Park, Maryland, December, 1954.

nized and described; however, with standardized media, Hare and his associates have divided the anaerobic cocci into only nine groups. Thus, future work may show that some or even many of the species here regarded as distinct are, in reality, identical with each other. (See Hare, Wildy, Billett and Twort, Jour. Hyg., *50*, 1952, 295; Hare, Atti del VI Congresso Internaz. di Microbiologia, Roma, *1*, 1953, 55; and Thomas and Hare, Jour. Clin. Path., *7*, 1954, 300.)

The type species is *Veillonella parvula* (Veillon and Zuber) Prévot.

Key to the species of genus **Veillonella.**

I. Gas produced in culture media.
  A. Acid from glucose.
  1. *Veillonella parvula.*
  B. Carbohydrates not attacked.
    1. Rancid odor not produced in broth.
    2. *Veillonella alcalescens.*
    2. Slight rancid odor produced in broth.
    3. *Veillonella discoides.*
II. Gas not produced in culture media.
  A. Gelatin not liquefied.
    1. Indole produced in trace amounts. Cells measure 0.8 to 1.0 micron in diameter.
    4. *Veillonella reniformis.*
    2. Indole not produced. Cells measure 1.5 to 2.0 microns in diameter.
    5. *Veillonella orbiculus.*
  B. Gelatin is liquefied.
    6. *Veillonella vulvovaginitidis.*

1. **Veillonella parvula** (Veillon and Zuber, 1898) Prévot, 1933. (*Staphylococcus parvulus* Veillon and Zuber, Arch. Méd. Exp., 1898, 542; Prévot, Ann. Sci. Nat., Sér. Bot., *15*, 1933, 119.)

par'vu.la. L. dim.adj. *parvulus* very small.

Very small spheres, 0.2 to 0.4 micron in diameter, occurring in pairs, in very short chains or in masses. Gram-negative.

Gelatin: No liquefaction.

Semi-solid agar (Veillon) colonies: At first punctiform, becoming lenticular, reaching a diameter of 2 mm. Gas bubbles produced.

Blood agar colonies: Usually surrounded by a clear halo; weakly hemolytic.

Agar slant: Transparent, bluish, minute colonies.

Peptone broth: Turbid; fine sediment.

Glucose broth: Turbid. Faintly fetid odor. Gas produced contains CO_2, H_2 and H_2S.

Serum broth: Very abundant, rapid growth.

Milk: No acid. No coagulation. Some strains produce gas.

Indole is produced.

Hydrogen sulfide is produced.

Acid and gas from glucose. Slight amount of acid from fructose, galactose and sucrose. Mannitol, maltose and inulin feebly attacked by some strains.

Nitrites produced from nitrates.

Coagulated protein not attacked.

Ammonia not produced.

Strictly anaerobic.

Temperature relations: Optimum, 37° C. Feeble growth at 22° C.

Optimum pH, between 6.5 and 8.0.

Distinctive characters: Fermentation of polypeptides to produce hydrogen, carbon dioxide, hydrogen sulfide and indole; fermentation of sugars; hemolysis of blood; production of nitrites from nitrates.

Source: Isolated by Veillon and Zuber from appendixes, buccal cavities and lungs. Of the 13 strains studied by Prévot, three were isolated from pulmonary gangrene, one from an appendix, one from alveolar pyorrhea, five from amniotic fluid, two from abscesses and pulmonary congestion and one from the buccal cavity of a normal rabbit. Found in suppurative lesions or pus.

Occasionally pathogenic, invading the tissues, causing suppurations either alone or in association with other pyogenic organisms.

Habitat: Found normally as a harmless parasite in the natural cavities, especially the mouths and digestive tracts, of man and other animals.

1a. *Veillonella parvula* var. *minima* Prévot, 1933. (*Staphylococcus minimus* Gioelli, Boll. R. Accad. Med. di Genova, 1907; abst. in Cent. f. Bakt., I Abt., Ref., *42*, 1908–09, 595; Prévot, Ann. Sci. Nat., Sér. Bot., *15*, 1933, 125.)

mi′ni.ma. L. sup.adj. *minimus* smallest.

Differs from *Veillonella parvula* only in that it is slightly smaller in size (0.2 to 0.3 micron). Growth only at 37° C. No growth on gelatin. Growth on the wall of the culture tube in fine flakes, not clouding the medium. No plasmolysis in a 5 per cent salt solution.

Source: Isolated from a periuterine abscess.

1b. *Veillonella parvula* var. *branhamii* Prévot, 1933. (Anaerobic micrococcus, Branham, Jour. Inf. Dis., *41*, 1927, 203; also see *ibid.*, *42*, 1928, 230; *Micrococcus branhamii* Bergey et al., Manual, 3rd ed., 1930, 92; Prévot, Ann. Sci. Nat., Sér. Bot., *15*, 1933, 126.)

bran.ham′i.i. M.L. gen.noun *branhamii* of Branham; named for Dr. Sara E. Branham, an American bacteriologist who has made a special study of these organisms.

Serologically distinct from *Veillonella parvula*. Gelatin slowly liquefied by one strain.

Source: Isolated from nasal washings in two cases of influenza.

1c. *Veillonella parvula* var. *thomsonii* Prévot, 1933. (Anaerobic diplococcus, Thomson, Jour. Trop. Med. and Hyg., *26*, 1923, 227; also see Ann. Pickett-Thomson Res. Lab., *1*, 1924–25, 105 and 164; Prévot, Ann. Sci. Nat., Sér. Bot., *15*, 1933, 126.)

thom.so′ni.i. M.L. gen.noun *thomsonii* of Thomson; named for Dr. David Thomson of London, England, the first to isolate this variety.

Differs but slightly from *Veillonella parvula* in that it requires some accessory growth factor found in serum or other body fluids or tissues.

Source: Isolated from the throats of persons with measles or scarlet fever.

2. **Veillonella alcalescens*** Prévot, 1933. (*Micrococcus gazogenes alcalescens anaerobius* Lewkowicz, Arch. Méd. Expt., *13*, 1901, 633; *Micrococcus gazogenes* Hall and Howitt, Jour. Inf. Dis., *37*, 1925, 112; not *Micrococcus gazogenes* Choukévitch, Ann. Inst. Past., *25*, 1911, 350; Prévot, Ann. Sci. Nat., Sér. Bot., *15*, 1933, 127; *Veillonella gazogenes* Murray in, Manual, 5th ed., 1939, 287.)

al.ca.les′cens. M.L. v. *alcalesco* to make alkaline; M.L. part.adj. *alcalescens* alkaline-making.

Spheres, 0.3 to 0.7, averaging 0.4, micron in diameter, occurring in irregular masses, in pairs, in short chains or singly. Gram-negative.

Gelatin: No liquefaction.

Agar deep colonies: At first punctiform, becoming lenticular. Gas bubbles appear after 16 to 18 hours.

Blood agar colonies: Minute. Several strains produce a greenish pigment. No hemolysis.

Peptone broth: Gas produced. Broth becomes slightly alkaline.

Milk: Gas but no acid. No coagulation.

Indole not produced.

Hydrogen sulfide not produced.

Egg white and coagulated serum not attacked.

Carbohydrates not attacked.

Nitrites not produced from nitrates.

Ammonia and hydrogen produced in small amounts.

Strictly anaerobic.

---

* Under the present International Bacteriological Code of Nomenclature, the specific epithet *alcalescens* is the correct epithet for this species. The epithet *gazogenes* cannot be reestablished on the transfer to a new genus (*Veillonella*) as it was illegitimate when it was first proposed by Hall and Howitt.

Temperature relations: Optimum, 37° C. Some strains grow at 22° C.

Optimum pH, between 6.0 and 8.0. Growth occurs in broth at pH 5.5.

Slowly plasmolyzed in 5 per cent NaCl solution.

Non-pathogenic (Lewkowicz's strains). Two strains (Prévot's) were pathogenic for rabbits.

Distinctive characters: Differs from *Veillonella parvula* in that it does not ferment sugars, does not produce hydrogen sulfide nor indole, is not hemolytic, does not produce nitrites from nitrates and does not develop fetid odors.

Source: Isolated from the mouth of a healthy infant (Lewkowicz). Twenty-four strains were isolated from human saliva (Hall and Howitt). Of the fifteen strains isolated by Prévot, one was from alveolar pyorrhoea, one from a case of pulmonary gangrene, five from tonsils, one from an appendix, two from cases of measles, three from cases of scarlet fever and two from normal guinea pigs and rabbits.

Habitat: Prevalent in the salivas of man and other animals.

2a. *Veillonella alcalescens* var. *gingivalis* Prévot, 1933. (Kleiner Micrococcus, Ozaki, Cent. f. Bakt., I Abt., Orig., *62*, 1912, 83; *Micrococcus gingivalis* Bergey et al., Manual, 1st ed., 1923, 69; Prévot, Ann. Sci. Nat., Sér. Bot., *15*, 1933, 133.)

gin.gi.va'lis. L. noun *gingiva* a gum; M.L. adj. *gingivalis* pertaining to a gum.

Differs from *Veillonella alcalescens* by its ability to grow at 22° C. and by the fact that glucose, although favoring growth, is not fermented.

Source: Isolated from the oral cavity. Two strains were isolated from the intestines (Prévot).

2b. *Veillonella alcalescens* var. *minutissima* Prévot, 1933. (*Micrococcus minutissimus* Oliver and Wherry, Jour. Inf. Dis., *28*, 1931, 342; Prévot, Ann. Sci. Nat., Sér. Bot., *15*, 1933, 134.)

mi.nu.tis'si.ma. L. sup.adj. *minutissimus* smallest.

Differs from *Veillonella alcalescens* only in that the usual carbohydrates favor

growth and that the gas produced is not absorbed by sodium hydroxide and is not inflammable.

Non-pathogenic for rabbits, guinea pigs or white mice (Oliver and Wherry).

Source: Two strains were isolated from a mixed infection in aphthous ulcers of the gingival and buccal mucosa of a case of post-poliomyelitic paralysis.

2c. *Veillonella alcalescens* var. *syzygios* Prévot, 1933. (*Syzygiococcus scarlatinae* Herzberg, Cent. f. Bakt., I Abt., Ref., *90*, 1928, 575; *Micrococcus syzygios scarlatinae* Herzberg, Cent. f. Bakt., I Abt., Orig., *111*, 1929, 373; *Micrococcus syzygios* Bergey et al., Manual, 3rd ed., 1930, 92; Prévot, Ann. Sci. Nat., Sér. Bot., *15*, 1933, 134.)

sy.zy'gi.os. Gr. adj. *syzygios* yoked together.

Differs from *Veillonella alcalescens* only by its ability to grow under an atmospheric pressure of 4 cm of mercury with the production of hydrogen sulfide in small amounts by some strains and the production of nitrites from nitrates.

Source: Isolated by Herzberg in 30 per cent of normal mouths and in 100 per cent of salivas from scarlet fever patients.

3. **Veillonella discoides** (Prévot, 1933) Pelczar, *comb. nov.* (*Neisseria discoides* Prévot, Ann. Sci. Nat., Sér. Bot., *15*, 1933, 106.)

dis.co.i'des. Gr. adj. *discoides* disc-shaped.

Spheres, 0.6 to 0.7 micron in diameter, occurring in pairs or tetrads. Gram-negative.

Gelatin: No liquefaction.

Agar deep colonies: Lenticular, up to 1 mm in diameter. Grows in a narrow disc about 1 cm below the surface. Gas produced.

Broth: Turbid; fine, granular precipitate. Slight rancid odor and inflammable, explosive gas produced.

Peptone water: Gas produced.

Milk: No action.

Indole not produced.

Hydrogen sulfide not produced.

Coagulated proteins: No digestion.

Carbohydrates not attacked.

Neutral red glucose broth: Becomes pink, but no further change.

Strictly anaerobic.

Temperature relations: Optimum, 37° C. No growth at 28° C.

Optimum pH, between 7.0 and 8.0.

Non-pathogenic.

Distinctive characters: Colonies grow in narrow zone 1 cm below the surface of an agar stab; gas produced from peptones.

Source: Isolated from bronchial mucus and from elsewhere in the respiratory system; also from dental and tonsillary focal infections.

Habitat: Found in the human buccal cavity and probably also in other warm-blooded animals.

4. Veillonella reniformis (Cottet, 1900) Pelczar, *comb. nov.* (*Diplococcus reniformis* Cottet, Compt. rend. Soc. Biol., *52*, 1900, 421; *Micrococcus reniformis* Oliver and Wherry, Jour. Inf. Dis., *28*, 1921, 341; *Neisseria reniformis* Prévot, Ann. Sci. Nat., Sér. Bot., *15*, 1933, 102.)

re.ni.for'mis. L. noun *ren* kidney; L. noun *forma* shape; M.L. adj. *reniformis* kidney-shaped.

Spheres, 0.8 to 1.0 micron in diameter, bean-shaped, occurring in pairs. Gram-negative.

Gelatin: No liquefaction.

Agar deep colonies: Appear in 24 to 48 hours; at first punctiform, then lenticular; small, 0.3 to 0.5 mm in diameter. No gas produced.

Agar slant: Minute, bluish white, dew-drop colonies.

Broth: Turbid in 24 hours; flocculent precipitate rapidly formed, clearing the medium. No gas produced, but a rancid odor is present.

Peptone water: Very meager growth.

Milk: Unchanged.

Indole produced in trace amounts.

Coagulated proteins: No digestion.

Acid from glucose in slight amounts by only one strain.

Strictly anaerobic.

Temperature relations: Optimum, 37° C. No growth at 22° C.

Optimum pH, 7.0. Limits of pH, 6.0 to 8.0.

Pathogenic.

Distinctive character: Odor of rancid butter.

Source: Isolated in several cases from suppurations of the urogenital system.

Habitat: Presumably found in bodies of warm-blooded animals.

5. Veillonella orbiculus (Tissier, 1908) Pelczar, *comb. nov.* (*Diplococcus orbiculus* Tissier, Ann. Inst. Past., *22*, 1908, 204; *Neisseria orbiculata* (sic) Prévot, Ann. Sci. Nat., Sér. Bot., *15*, 1933, 109.)

or.bi'cu.lus. L. mas.dim.n. *orbiculus* small disc.

Spheres, 1.5 to 2.0 microns in diameter, occurring in pairs. Gram-negative.

Gelatin: No growth at 22° C.

Agar deep colonies: After 36 to 48 hours, large, lenticular, very regular, whitish, almost transparent. Gas not produced.

Broth: Turbid; sediment.

Milk: No coagulation.

Egg white: Not attacked.

Proteoses attacked without the production of indole.

Acid from glucose and feebly from lactose. No acid from sucrose.

Strictly anaerobic.

Temperature relations: Optimum, 37° C. No growth at 22° C.

Non-pathogenic.

Distinctive characters: Large size; no gas production.

Source: Isolated from the feces of young children.

Habitat: Found in the intestinal canal. Not common.

6. Veillonella vulvovaginitidis (Reynes, 1947) Pelczar, *comb. nov.* (*Neisseria vulvovaginitis* (sic) Reynes, Ann. Inst. Past., *73*, 1947, 601.)

vul.vo.va.gi.ni'ti.dis L. fem.n. *vulva* a covering, vulva; L. fem.n. *vagina* vagina; Gr. suffix *-itis* inflammation of; M.L. noun *vulvovaginitidis* vulvovaginitis.

Spheres, about 0.8 to 1.0 micron in diameter, occurring in pairs or in very short chains, rarely singly, often in masses of 5 to 10 cells. Not encapsulated. Non-motile. Gram-negative.

Gelatin: Liquefaction.

Agar deep colonies: Small. No gas bubbles produced. Cultures have a slightly disagreeable, rancid odor. Survive over two months.

Peptone water: Very meager growth which precipitates.

Glucose broth: Uniformly turbid; slight, white sediment. No acidification detectable by chemical titration. Ammonia produced with a mixture of propionic and acetic acids. No lactic or succinic acid. Volatile amines, aldehydes and acetone are present, but no alcohol, acetylmethylcarbinol, phenol or cresol.

Milk: Digested.

Coagulated serum and fibrin: Partially attacked.

Indole and skatole not produced.

Nitrites not produced from nitrates.

Neutral red and phenosafranin are not reduced.

Non-hemolytic.

Strictly anaerobic.

Temperature relations: Grows well at 35° C. but not at 25° C.

Not pathogenic for mice or guinea pigs.

Distinctive characters: Digestion of milk and liquefaction of gelatin. Survival for two months.

Source: Isolated from pus from a case of vulvovaginitis in a child.

Habitat: Found in the urogenital tract of man. Distribution in nature unknown.

FAMILY IX. BREVIBACTERIACEAE BREED, 1953.*

(Riassunti delle Comunicazioni, VI Congresso Internaz. di Microbiol., Roma, *1*, 1953, 13; also see Atti del VI Congresso Internaz. di Microbiol., Roma, *1*, 1955, 10.)

Brev.i.bac.te.ri.a'ce.ae. M.L. neut.n. *Brevibacterium* type genus of the family; *-aceae* suffix to denote a family; M.L. fem.pl.n. *Brevibacteriaceae* the *Brevibacterium* family.

Cells without endospores. Rod-shaped, varying from a quite short, almost coccoid form to a rather long, straight, unbranched rod. Motile or non-motile, the motile species being peritrichous or, occasionally, monotrichous. Gram-positive. Red, reddish orange, yellow or brown pigments may be produced. Carbohydrates may or may not be attacked. Aerobic and facultatively anaerobic species occur. Found in dairy products, soil, salt and fresh water and decomposing substances of a great variety of types.

Key to the genera of family **Brevibacteriaceae.**

I. Short, almost coccoid, unbranched rods which do not form filaments. Acid usually produced from simple carbohydrates.
Genus I. *Brevibacterium*, p. 490.

II. Long, unbranched rods which may form filaments; the filaments may subdivide into coccoid elements. Carbohydrates not utilized.
Genus II. *Kurthia*, p. 503.

Genus I. **Brevibacterium** Breed, 1953.

(Riassunti delle Comunicazioni, VI Congresso Internaz. di Microbiol., Roma, *1*, 1953, 13; also see Atti del VI Congresso Internaz. di Microbiol., Roma, *1*, 1955, 12.)

Brev.i.bac.te'ri.um. L. adj. *brevis* short; Gr. dim.noun *bacterium* a small rod; M.L. neut.n. *Brevibacterium* a short rodlet.

Typically short, unbranching rods. Generally non-motile; type of motility of motile species peritrichous or uncertain. Sometimes chromogenic, with non-water-soluble reddish, reddish orange, yellow or brown pigments. May or may not reduce nitrates. Glucose broth usually becomes acid; lactose not fermented. Proteolytic action varies with the species.

* Prepared by Prof. Robert S. Breed, Cornell University, Geneva, New York, October. 1954.

Aerobic and facultatively anaerobic. Rarely microaerophilic. Found in dairy products, soil, salt- and fresh-water and decomposing substances of a great variety of types.

The type species is *Brevibacterium linens* (Weigmann) Breed.

Key to the species of genus **Brevibacterium.**

I. Non-motile.
  A. Red, rose, yellow, brownish yellow or orange pigmentation produced on agar.
    1. Red or rose chromogenesis.
      a. Litmus milk slowly digested; becomes alkaline with a yellow sediment.
          1. *Brevibacterium linens.*
      aa. Litmus milk slowly digested; becomes alkaline with a clear, reddish fluid.
          2. *Brevibacterium erythrogenes.*
    2. Yellow to brownish yellow or orange chromogenesis.
      a. Nitrites not produced from nitrates.
        b. Orange-red chromogenesis on agar.
          3. *Brevibacterium fulvum.*
        bb. Light greenish yellow chromogenesis on agar.
          4. *Brevibacterium insectiphilium.*
        bbb. Surface colonies flesh-colored. Deep colonies brown.
          5. *Brevibacterium brunneum.*
      aa. Nitrites produced from nitrates.
        b. Pale lemon-yellow to orange-yellow chromogenesis on agar.
          c. Pale lemon-yellow chromogenesis on agar.
            6. *Brevibacterium vitarumen.*
          cc. Orange-yellow chromogenesis on agar.
            7. *Brevibacterium maris.*
        bb. Brownish yellow to pale greenish yellow chromogenesis on agar.
          8. *Brevibacterium fuscum.*
  B. White, grayish white or gray on agar.
    1. Nitrites not produced from nitrates.
      a. Require agar made with sea water for initial growth.
        b. Gelatin not liquefied.
          9. *Brevibacterium minutiferula.*
        bb. Gelatin liquefied.
          c. Acid produced from maltose; found associated with marine sedentary organisms.
            d. Gelatin colonies irregular and sunken.
              10. *Brevibacterium sociovivum.*
            dd. Gelatin colonies circular and raised.
              11. *Brevibacterium immotum.*
          cc. Acid not produced from maltose; found on the skin of marine fish.
            12. *Brevibacterium marinopiscosum.*
      aa. Does not require agar made with sea water for initial growth.
          13. *Brevibacterium tegumenticola.*
    2. Nitrites produced from nitrates.
      a. Requires agar made with sea water for initial growth.
          14. *Brevibacterium stationis.*
      aa. Do not require agar made with sea water for initial growth.
        b. Gelatin liquefied.
          15. *Brevibacterium quale.*
        bb. Gelatin not liquefied.
          16. *Brevibacterium ammoniagenes.*

3. Nitrite production not recorded.

                  17. *Brevibacterium healii.*

II. Motile.

  A. Gelatin not liquefied.

    1. Grayish white on agar slant.

                  18. *Brevibacterium incertum.*

    2. Pinkish orange to yellow on agar slant.

                  19. *Brevibacterium imperiale.*

  B. Gelatin liquefied.

    1. Grayish white on agar slant.

                  20. *Brevibacterium lipolyticum.*

    2. Yellow to yellow-brown on agar slant.

      a. Orange chromogenesis on potato.

                  21. *Brevibacterium acetylicum.*

    aa. Yellow chromogenesis on potato.

      b. Sulfur-yellow streak on potato.

                  22. *Brevibacterium sulfureum.*

      bb. Abundant, thickened, yellow growth on potato.

                  23. *Brevibacterium helvolum.*

---

1. **Brevibacterium linens** (Weigmann, 1910) Breed, 1953. (Organismus IX, Wolff, Milchwirt. Zent., *5*, 1909, 145; *Bacterium linens* Weigmann, in Wolff, Cent. f. Bakt., II Abt., *28*, 1910, 422, and in Weigmann, Mykologie der Milch, *62*, 1911, 220; Breed, Riassunti delle Comunicazioni, VI Congresso Internaz. di Microbiol., Roma, *1*, 1953, 13; also see Atti del VI Congresso Internaz. di Microbiol., Roma, *1*, 1955, 13.)

li'nens. L. part.adj. *linens* spreading over, smearing.

Also see Steinfatt (Milchwirt. Forsch., *9*, 1930, 7), Kelly (Jour. Dairy Sci., *20*, 1937, 239) and Albert, Long and Hammer (Iowa Agr. Exp. Sta. Res. Bul. 328, 1944).

Rods. Average 0.6 by 2.5 microns when grown 1 to 2 days on tryptone glucose extract agar. Non-motile (Wolff, *op. cit.*, 1909, 145). Gram-positive (Kelly, *op. cit.*, 1937, 239).

Gelatin colonies: At 18° C., punctiform at first; after 12 days about 1 mm in diameter, compact, circular, shiny, brownish yellow to red-brown. Liquefaction.

Gelatin stab: At 21° C., crateriform liquefaction, becoming infundibuliform on extended incubation. Rate of liquefaction varies considerably with different cultures, some completing it in 15 days, others not completing it even on long incubation.

Agar colonies: On tryptone glucose ex-

tract agar at 21° C. after 1 to 2 days, colonies convex, glistening, entire and cream-colored, becoming brown on extended incubation; diameters 2 to 5 mm. On special cheese agar with incubation in oxygen, luxuriant growth, the color becoming bright orange to reddish brown in 4 or 5 days.

Agar stab: Heavy surface growth on tryptone glucose extract agar at 21° C. with no growth along the line of inoculation.

Agar slant: On tryptone glucose extract agar at 21° C. after 2 days, growth abundant, glistening, filiform, non-viscid and cream-colored. After extended incubation the color usually is brown. On special cheese agar in an atmosphere of oxygen, the growth is bright orange to reddish brown in 4 or 5 days.

Broth: Turbidity and sediment.

Potato: At 21° C. after 5 days, growth is scant, smooth, glistening and varies in color from grayish to brownish orange.

Litmus milk: At 21° C. the changes are very slow. After 6 or 7 days the reaction becomes alkaline and a yellow sediment appears. After approximately 10 days some digestion is evident, complete digestion generally requiring several weeks to over a month. A distinct ammoniacal odor, more or less objectionable, produced in old cultures. No coagulation. Ropiness often produced on extended incubation.

Indole not produced.

Hydrogen sulfide produced in broth and in agar by some cultures but not by others.

No acid or gas from arabinose, dextrin, glucose, dulcitol, galactose, inulin, lactose, fructose, maltose, mannitol, raffinose, rhamnose, salicin, sorbitol, sucrose or xylose.

Ethyl, propyl, butyl and amyl alcohols oxidized largely to corresponding acids; hexyl and heptyl alcohols attacked much less actively.

Nitrites produced from nitrates.

Methyl red test negative.

Acetylmethylcarbinol not produced.

Natural fats not hydrolyzed.

Catalase rapidly produced in or on various media.

Aerobic.

Temperature relations: Optimum, about 21° C. Growth at 8° and 37° C. but not at 45° C.

Heat resistance low, cultures being killed at 62.8° C. in a few minutes.

Growth in the pH range 6.0 to 9.8; no growth at pH 5.0 or below.

Salt tolerant, cultures growing readily in a concentration of 15 per cent salt in broth or skim milk, with certain cultures apparently capable of growing somewhat in much higher concentrations.

Relationships to other species: Closely related to or identical with *Bacterium erythrogenes* Lehmann and Neumann.

Source: Originally isolated by Wolff from the surface flora of various soft cheeses.

Habitat: Widely distributed in and especially on the surface of dairy products including blue, brick, camembert, limburger, oka and cheddar cheeses, butter, milk and cream. Also found in various feeds including grains, silage, green plants, hay and straw, and in water, soil, manure and air.

2. Brevibacterium erythrogenes (Lehmann and Neumann, 1896) Breed, 1953.

(*Bacterium lactis erythrogenes* Grotenfelt, Fortschr. d. Med., *7*, 1889, 41; *Bacterium erythrogenes* Lehmann and Neumann, Bakt. Diag., 1 Aufl., *2*, 1896, 253; Breed, Riassunti delle Comunicazioni, VI Congresso Internaz. di Microbiol., Roma, *1*, 1953, 13;

also see Atti del VI Congresso Internaz. d Microbiol., Roma, *1*, 1955, 13.)

e.ryth.ro'ge.nes. Gr. adj. *erythrus* red; Gr. v. *gennaio* to produce; M.L. adj. *erythrogenes* producing a red (color).

Rods, 0.3 to 0.5 by 1.0 to 1.4 microns, in broth often up to 4.3 microns long, occurring singly and having rounded ends. Non-motile. Stain with the usual aniline dyes. Gram-positive (Lehmann and Neumann, *op. cit.*, 1896, 253).

Gelatin colonies: Small, circular, grayish, becoming yellow, sinking into the medium. Crateriform liquefaction. Yellow sediment. Medium becomes rose-colored.

Gelatin stab: Surface growth a whitish, later yellow, circular, thin layer. Weak growth in stab. Slow liquefaction at the surface, the liquid becoming red with a yellow sediment. The solid portion assumes a weak rose color.

Agar stab: Moist, fairly luxuriant, yellow growth, the medium assuming a rose to wine color.

Broth: Turbid, yellow. Pellicle (Fuller and Johnson, Jour. Exp. Med., *4*, 1899, 609).

Litmus milk: Acid. Slow coagulation, having a clear fluid which becomes blood-red in color. Reaction becomes alkaline.

Sterile milk: Casein slowly precipitated, later peptonized. Reaction neutral or alkaline. A stratum of blood-red serum is seen above the precipitated casein and above this is a yellowish white layer of cream. Produces an intensive sweet odor that becomes disagreeable.

Potato: Growth rapid, spreading, grayish, later yellow. On incubation a deep golden yellow color develops after 6 to 8 days. A darkening of the medium occurs around the culture but soon disappears; later the whole potato becomes a weak yellowish red.

Indole not produced (Fuller and Johnson, *loc. cit.*). Indole produced (Chester, Manual Determ. Bact., 1901, 174).

Slight hydrogen sulfide production (Matzuschita, Bakt. Diagnostik, 1902, 220).

Blood serum: Liquefied (Fuller and Johnson, *op. cit.*, 1899, 609). Not liquefied (Hefferan, Cent. f. Bakt., II Abt., *11*, 1903, 457).

No gas from carbohydrates.

Nitrites produced from nitrates.

Red pigment insoluble in water, alcohol,

ether, chloroform and benzol; soluble (Hefferan, *op. cit.*, 1903, 529). Yellow pigment insoluble.

Distinctive character: Milk becomes blood-red in 12 to 20 days.

Non-pathogenic for mice (Fuller and Johnson, *op. cit.*, 1899, 609).

Optimum temperature, between 28° and 35° C.

Aerobic (Fuller and Johnson, *loc. cit.*). Facultatively anaerobic (Hefferan, *op. cit.*, 1903, 530).

Source: Isolated from red milk by Hueppe in Wiesbaden in 1886. Isolated from feces of a child by Baginsky (Cent. f. Bakt., *6*, 1889, 137). Isolated from Ohio River water by Fuller and Johnson (*op. cit.*, 1899, 609). Isolated from Mississippi River water by Hefferan (*op. cit.*, 1903, 456). Burri and Staub (Landwirtsch. Jahrb. d. Schweiz, *40*, 1926, 1006) isolated an organism of this type from Emmenthal cheese; they regarded it as closely related to or possibly identical with this species.

Habitat: Probably widely distributed in nature.

3. **Brevibacterium fulvum** (Zimmermann, 1890) Breed, 1953. (*Bacillus fulvus* Zimmermann, Bakt. unserer Trink- u. Nutzwässer, Chemnitz, *1*, 1890, 44; Breed, Riassunti delle Comunicazioni, VI Congresso Internaz. di Microbiol., Roma, *1*, 1953, 14; also see Atti del VI Congresso Internaz. di Microbiol., Roma, *1*, 1955, 14.) ful'vum. L. adj. *fulvus* deep yellow.

Rods, 0.8 by 0.9 to 1.3 microns, occurring singly and in pairs. Non-motile. Gram-positive.

Gelatin colonies: Circular, convex, reddish yellow.

Gelatin stab: Convex, reddish yellow surface growth. Good growth in stab. Slow liquefaction.

Agar slant: Orange-red, glistening streak.

Broth: Turbid with yellow sediment.

Litmus lactose broth: Acid, or acid then alkaline (Dyar, Ann. N. Y. Acad. Sci., *8*, 1895, 368).

Potato: Slowly spreading, yellowish, glistening growth.

Indole produced (Dyar, *loc. cit.*).

Nitrites not produced from nitrates (Bergey).

Aerobic, facultatively anaerobic.

Optimum temperature, 30° C.

Source: Isolated from Chemnitz and Döbeln tap water (Zimmermann). From dust and water (Dyar).

Habitat: Water.

4. **Brevibacterium insectiphilium** (Steinhaus, 1941) Breed, 1953. (*Bacterium insectiphilium* Steinhaus, Jour. Bact., *42*, 1941, 777; Breed, Riassunti delle Comunicazioni, VI Congresso Internaz. di Microbiol., Roma, *1*, 1953, 13; also see Atti del VI Congresso Internaz. di Microbiol., Roma, *1*, 1955, 13.)

in.sec.ti.phi'li.um. L. noun *insectum* an insect; Gr. adj. *philius* friendly; M.L. *insectiphilium* friendly to insects.

Rods, 0.8 to 1.2 by 1.0 to 2.8 microns, occurring singly. At times appearing almost as cocci or coccobacilli. Non-motile. Gram-positive.

Gelatin stab: Liquefaction.

Agar colonies: Light greenish yellow, circular, entire, raised, glistening, smooth, opaque.

Agar slant: Filiform, raised, smooth, glistening, opaque growth.

Broth: Moderate turbidity; slight, viscid sediment.

Litmus milk: Alkaline, peptonization and slow reduction.

Potato: Greenish yellow, thick, moist growth.

Indole not produced.

Hydrogen sulfide not produced.

No acid from glucose, lactose, sucrose, maltose, fructose, mannitol, galactose, arabinose, xylose, dextrin, salicin, rhamnose, raffinose, trehalose, sorbitol, inulin, dulcitol, glycerol, adonitol or mannose.

Starch slightly hydrolyzed.

Nitrites not produced from nitrates.

Aerobic.

Source: Isolated from the body wall of the bagworm, *Thyridopteryx ephemeraeformis* Haw.

Habitat: Unknown.

5. **Brevibacterium brunneum** (Copeland, 1899) Breed, *comb. nov.* (*Bacillus*

brunneus Copeland, Rept. Filtration Comm. Pittsburgh, 1899, 348.)

brun'ne.um. M.L. adj. *brunneus* dark brown.

Cells rod-shaped, 0.5 micron in width. Non-motile. Gram stain not recorded.

Gelatin colonies: Surface colonies are flesh-colored; deep colonies are brownish. Liquefaction.

Gelatin stab: Beaded growth along the stab; gelatin turns deep brown; sunken, flesh-colored surface growth.

Agar slant: Growth slight, very thin, glistening, spreading.

Broth: Not turbid; no pellicle.

Potato: Red to reddish brown streak.

Plain milk: Coagulated; casein digested; brownish whey.

Litmus milk: Reaction unchanged.

Indole not produced.

No acid from glucose, lactose or sucrose.

Nitrites not produced from nitrates.

Coagulated blood serum: No visible growth.

Growth at 18° and 37° C. Thermal death point, about 50° C.

Relationships to other species: This organism seems to be the same as *Corynebacterium bruneum* as described by Lehmann and Neumann (Bakt. Diag., 7 Aufl., *2*, 1927, 708); this species is reported to be Gram-positive.

Source: Isolated from Pittsburgh tap water.

6. **Brevibacterium vitarumen** (Knutsen, 1928) Breed, *comb. nov.* (*Flavobacterium vitarumen* Knutsen, in Bechdel, Honeywell, Dutcher and Knutsen, Jour. Biol. Chem., *80*, 1928, 234.)

vi.ta.ru'men L. noun *vita* life; L. noun *rumen* throat, gullet, rumen; M.L. noun *vitarumen* rumen-life.

Rod-shaped cells, 0.5 to 1.5 by 0.5 to 3.0 microns, with rounded ends, occuring singly and occasionally in pairs. Non-motile. Gram-positive.

Gelatin: No liquefaction.

Gelatin colonies: Similar to those on agar.

Agar colonies: Those on the surface are 1 to 4 mm in diameter, while the embedded colonies are somewhat smaller.

Agar slant: Growth filiform and pale lemon-yellow.

Lead acetate agar: No growth.

Endo medium: No growth.

Broth: Turbid, becoming clear; sediment; no pellicle.

Litmus milk: Turns acid; slight reduction of litmus; no curd.

Indole and skatole are not produced.

Acid from glucose, sucrose and maltose. No acid from xylose, lactose, mannitol, inositol, sorbitol or dulcitol.

Starch not hydrolyzed.

Cellulose not attacked.

Nitrites produced from nitrates.

Distinctive characters: Produces vitamin B complex in the rumina of cows. Because of this, cattle, unlike any other species of animal yet studied, have the ability to grow to maturity, to produce normal offspring and to produce milk of normal dietary composition on a ration that carries an insufficient amount of vitamin B complex to support growth and well being in rats.

Comments: Dutcher (personal communication, January, 1955) states that it is now evident that the chief substance synthesized by this species was riboflavin and that many other species of bacteria are now known that are more efficient as synthesizers of riboflavin than is this species.

Source: Isolated from the fermented rumen contents of a Holstein cow.

Habitat: Found in the rumina of cows and, presumably, other ruminants where it constitutes about 90 per cent of the microflora as manifested on plain nutrient agar.

7. **Brevibacterium maris** (Harrison, 1929) Breed, 1953. (*Flavobacterium maris* Harrison, Canadian Jour. Research, *1*, 1929, 232; Breed, Riassunti delle Comunicazioni, VI Congresso Internaz. di Microbiol., Roma, *1*, 1953, 14; also see Atti del VI Congresso Internaz. di Microbiol., Roma, *1*, 1955, 14.)

mar'is. L. noun *mare* the sea; L. gen.noun *maris* of the sea.

Rods, 0.7 to 0.8 by 1.0 to 1.2 microns, occurring singly and in pairs. At 37° C., coccoid. Encapsulated. Non-motile. Gram-positive.

Gelatin colonies: Punctiform, red-orange, granular, entire.

Gelatin stab: Red-orange surface growth; filiform growth in stab. No liquefaction.

Agar colonies: Circular, orange-yellow, smooth, glistening, convex.

Agar slant: Growth moderate, orange-yellow, becoming cadmium-orange to red-orange, spreading, glistening.

Broth: Clear with orange pellicle and sediment.

Litmus milk: At first faintly alkaline, becoming faintly acid with orange sediment.

Potato: Scant growth.

Indole not produced.

Hydrogen sulfide not produced.

Faint acidity from glucose. No action on lactose or sucrose.

Nitrites produced from nitrates.

Traces of ammonia produced.

For the action of this species on cholesterol, see Arnaudi (Rendiconti Ist. Lombardo Sci. e Lett., *83*, 1950, 1).

Loeffler's blood serum not liquefied.

Aerobic, facultatively anaerobic.

Optimum temperature, between 20° and 25° C.

Source: Isolated from the skin of fishes. Steinhaus (Jour. Bact., *42*, 1941, 771) found a similar organism in the intestine of a caterpillar.

Habitat: Unknown.

8. **Brevibacterium fuscum** (Zimmermann, 1890) Breed, 1953. (*Bacillus fuscus* Zimmermann, Bakt. unserer Trink- u. Nutzwässer, Chemnitz, *1*, 1890, 70; Breed, Riassunti delle Comunicazioni, VI Congresso Internaz. di Microbiol., Roma, *1*, 1953, 14; also see Atti del VI Congresso Internaz. di Microbiol., Roma, *1*, 1955, 14.)

fus'cum. L. adj. *fuscus* dark, tawny.

Rods, 0.6 by 1.5 microns, occurring singly. Non-motile. Gram-positive.

Gelatin colonies: Small, with brownish center and yellowish border. Heavy, undulate growth.

Gelatin stab: Gray, filiform growth in stab. Slow crateriform liquefaction.

Agar colonies: Circular, brownish yellow to brownish orange, smooth, slightly convex, entire.

Agar slant: Growth greenish yellow, plumose, smooth, raised, undulate.

Broth: Turbid, with pellicle and heavy chrome-yellow sediment.

Litmus milk: Slightly acid, becoming alkaline, with yellow ring.

Potato: Thick, moist, dark chrome-yellow streak. Eventually spreads over entire surface.

Indole not produced.

Nitrites produced from nitrates (Dyar, Ann. N. Y. Acad. Sci., *8*, 1895, 361 and 373).

Aerobic, facultatively anaerobic.

Optimum temperature, 20° C.

Comment: Dyar (*ibid.*, 375) has described a variety of this species which liquefies gelatin more slowly and more completely than does the parent strain.

Source: Isolated from Zwönitz River water.

Habitat: Water.

9. **Brevibacterium minutiferula** (Steinhaus, 1941) Breed, 1953. (*Bacterium minutiferula* Steinhaus, Jour. Bact., *42*, 1941, 778; Breed, Riassunti delle Comunicazioni, VI Congresso Internaz. di Microbiol., Roma, *1*, 1953, 13 and 14; also see Atti del VI Congresso Internaz. di Microbiol., Roma, *1*, 1955, 13.)

mi.nu.ti.fe'ru.la. L. part.adj. *minutus* small (literally, diminished); L. noun *ferula* a rod; M.L. noun *minutiferula* a small rod.

Very small rods, 0.4 to 0.9 by 0.7 to 1.0 micron, occurring singly. Non-motile. Gram-positive.

Gelatin stab: No liquefaction.

Agar colonies: Colorless to faint gray, circular, smooth, entire, glistening.

Agar slant: Very thin, transparent, glistening growth.

Broth: Slight turbidity and sediment.

Litmus milk: No change at first; slightly acid after one week.

Indole not produced.

Hydrogen sulfide not produced.

Acid from glucose after 4 days. Slight acid from sucrose. Lactose and maltose not fermented.

Starch not hydrolyzed.

Nitrites not produced from nitrates.

Aerobic.

Source: Isolated from a triturated specimen of the mud-dauber wasp, *Sceliphron cementarium* Dru.

Habitat: Unknown.

10. Brevibacterium sociovivum (ZoBell and Upham, 1944) Breed, 1953. (*Bacterium sociovivum* ZoBell and Upham, Bull. Scripps Inst. Oceanography, La Jolla, *5*, 1944, 269; Breed, Riassunti delle Comunicazioni, VI Congresso Internaz. di Microbiol., Roma, *1*, 1953, 14; also see Atti del VI Congresso Internaz. di Microbiol., Roma, *1*, 1955, 14.)

so.ci.o.vi'vum. L. noun *socius* companion, partner; L. v. *vivo* to live; M.L. adj. *sociovivus* partner living.

Rods, 0.5 to 0.8 by 3.0 to 4.0 microns, with rounded ends, occurring singly, in pairs and in chains. Non-motile. Gram-positive, but tends to destain, leaving Gram-positive cell wall and granules.

All differential media except the freshwater broth, litmus milk and potato were prepared with sea water.

Gelatin colonies: Irregular, sunken, grayish white; filamentous margin.

Gelatin stab: Crateriform liquefaction becoming stratiform.

Agar colonies: 2 to 4 mm in diameter, circular, convex, smooth, entire, darker center.

Agar slant: Luxuriant, beaded, glistening, butyrous growth with no pigment.

Sea-water broth: No pellicle; no turbidity; heavy, flocculent sediment.

Fresh-water broth: Fair growth.

Litmus milk: Decolorized; neutral; completely peptonized in 20 days.

Potato: Abundant, dull, light cream-colored growth. Potato darkened.

Indole not produced.

Hydrogen sulfide not produced.

Acid but no gas from glucose, maltose and mannitol. No acid from glycerol, lactose, sucrose or salicin.

Starch is hydrolyzed.

Non-lipolytic.

Nitrites not produced from nitrates.

Ammonia produced from peptone but not from urea.

Casein is digested.

Aerobic, facultatively anaerobic.

Optimum temperature, between 20° and 25° C.

Source: Found associated with sedentary organisms in the sea.

Habitat: Commonly found on submerged surfaces and on sessile diatoms in sea water.

11. Brevibacterium immotum (ZoBell and Upham, 1944) Breed, 1953. (*Bacterium immotum* ZoBell and Upham, Bull. Scripps Inst. Oceanography, *5*, 1944, 271; Breed, Riassunti delle Comunicazioni, VI Congresso Internaz. di Microbiol., Roma, *1*, 1953, 14; also see Atti del VI Congresso Internaz. di Microbiol., Roma, *1*, 1955, 14.)

im.mo'tum. L. adj. *immotus* motionless.

Rods, 0.8 by 3.1 to 8.6 microns, with rounded ends, occurring singly, in pairs and in long chains. Non-motile. Gram-positive, but tends to destain, leaving Gram-positive outline and granules.

All differential media except the freshwater broth, litmus milk and potato were prepared with sea water.

Gelatin colonies: Small, circular, raised, gray, slowly digest gelatin.

Gelatin stab: Crateriform liquefaction becoming infundibuliform. Beaded growth along line of stab. No pigment.

Agar colonies: 1 to 2 mm in diameter, circular, convex, smooth, lobate margin, darker centers.

Agar slant: Luxuriant, glistening, echinulate, mucoid growth with no pigment.

Sea-water broth: No pellicle; moderate turbidity; abundant, flocculent sediment.

Fresh-water broth: Scant growth.

Litmus milk: Decolorized; neutral; partly peptonized in 20 days.

Potato: Luxuriant, mucoid, creamy growth which darkens potato.

Indole not produced.

Hydrogen sulfide not produced.

Acid but no gas from glucose, maltose, xylose and mannitol. No acid from glycerol, lactose, sucrose or salicin.

Starch is hydrolyzed.

Non-lipolytic.

Nitrites not produced from nitrates.

Ammonia produced from peptone but not from urea.

Casein is digested.

Aerobic, facultatively anaerobic.

Optimum temperature, between 20° and 25° C.

Source: Found associated with marine sedentary organisms.

Habitat: Not known from other sources.

12. Brevibacterium marinopiscosum (ZoBell and Upham, 1944) Breed, 1953. (*Bacterium marinopiscosus* (sic) ZoBell and Upham, Bull. Scripps Inst. Oceanography, La Jolla, *5*, 1944, 258; Breed, Riassunti delle Comunicazioni, VI Congresso Internaz. di Microbiol., Roma, *1*, 1953, 14; also see Atti del VI Congresso Internaz. di Microbiol., Roma, *1*, 1955, 13.)

ma.ri.no.pis.co'sum. L. adj. *marinus* of the sea; L. adj. *piscosus* abounding in fish; M.L. adj. *marinopiscosus* literally, marine abounding in fish.

Rods, 1.2 to 1.6 by 2.0 to 4.7 microns, with rounded ends, showing granular staining and occurring singly, in pairs and in long chains. Non-motile. Gram-positive, but many cells tend to decolorize leaving Gram-positive granules.

All differential media except the fresh-water broth, litmus milk and potato were prepared with sea water.

Gelatin colonies: Gray, circular, convex, 1 mm in diameter. No pigment.

Gelatin stab: Liquefaction napiform, becoming crateriform to stratiform with age. Complete in 50 days.

Agar colonies: 2 to 4 mm in diameter, circular, convex, entire, smooth; irregular edge.

Agar slant: Luxuriant, beaded, glistening, butyrous growth with no pigment.

Sea-water broth: No turbidity; abundant flocculent sediment; slight surface ring.

Fresh-water broth: Good growth.

Litmus milk: Decolorized; neutral; top peptonized.

Potato: Heavy, white, raised, mucoid, dull growth. Potato darkened.

Indole not produced.

Hydrogen sulfide not produced.

Acid but no gas from glucose and mannitol. No acid from maltose, lactose, sucrose, glycerol, xylose or salicin.

Starch is hydrolyzed.

Non-lipolytic.

Nitrites not produced from nitrates.

Ammonia produced from peptone but not from urea.

Casein is digested.

Aerobic, facultatively anaerobic.

Optimum temperature, between 20° and 25° C.

Source: Found on the skin of marine fish.

Habitat: Not known from other sources.

13. Brevibacterium tegumenticola (Steinhaus, 1941) Breed, 1953. (*Bacterium tegumenticola* Steinhaus, Jour. Bact., *42*, 1941, 775; Breed, Riassunti delle Comunicazioni, VI Congresso Internaz. di Microbiol., Roma, *1*, 1953, 13; also see Atti del VI Congresso Internaz. di Microbiol., Roma, *1*, 1955, 13.)

te.gu.men.ti'co.la. L. noun *tegumentum* cover, skin; L. suffix *cola* dweller; M.L. noun skin dweller.

Small rods, 0.5 to 0.8 by 1.0 to 1.5 microns, with a tendency to be ellipsoidal on solid media. Non-motile. Gram-positive.

Gelatin stab: Generally no liquefaction, although variable.

Agar colonies: Tiny (1 mm), white, convex, glistening, circular, entire.

Agar slant: Filiform, glistening, grayish white growth.

Broth: Slight turbidity; sediment.

Litmus milk: No change.

Indole not produced.

Hydrogen sulfide not produced.

Acid slowly produced from glucose and maltose. Acid from sucrose. Lactose not fermented.

Starch not hydrolyzed.

Nitrites not produced from nitrates.

Source: Isolated from the integument of the bed-bug, *Cimex lectularius* L.

Habitat: Unknown.

14. Brevibacterium stationis (ZoBell and Upham, 1944) Breed, 1953. (*Achromobacter stationis* ZoBell and Upham, Bull. Scripps Inst. of Oceanography, Univ. of Calif., *5*, 1944, 273; Breed, Riassunti delle Comunicazioni, VI Congresso Internaz. di Microbiol., Roma, *1*, 1953, 14; also see Atti del VI Congresso Internaz. di Microbiol., Roma, *1*, 1955, 13.)

sta.ti.o'nis. L. noun *statio, stationis* that

which is fixed in position, a station; L. gen. noun *stationis* of a fixed position.

Ovoid rods, 0.4 by 0.5 to 0.6 micron, occurring singly or in chains of two to three. Non-motile. Gram-positive, but easily destained.

All media except the fresh-water broth, litmus milk and potato were prepared with sea water.

Gelatin colonies: 0.5 to 1.0 mm in diameter, circular, convex, grayish white.

Gelatin stab: Very slow, napiform liquefaction.

Agar colonies: 1 to 2 mm in diameter, convex, smooth, colorless; lobate edge.

Agar slant: Moderate, glistening, filiform, butyrous growth with no pigment.

Sea-water broth: Heavy pellicle; no turbidity; granular growth along walls; scant sediment.

Fresh-water broth: Good growth.

Litmus milk: Becomes alkaline. Casein not digested.

Potato: No visible growth.

Indole not produced.

Hydrogen sulfide not produced.

Acid but no gas from glucose. Lactose, maltose, sucrose, mannitol, glycerol, xylose and salicin not utilized.

Starch not hydrolyzed.

Non-lipolytic.

Of 19 amino acids tested, none was required for growth; preformed growth factors also were not required (Campbell and Williams, Food Research, *16*, 1951a, 506).

Ammonium chloride and the 19 amino acids which were tested may serve as sources of nitrogen; the amino acids may also be utilized as carbon sources (Campbell and Williams, *loc. cit.*).

Nitrites rapidly produced from nitrates.

Ammonia produced from peptone but not from urea.

Trimethylamine not produced from trimethylamine oxide, betaine, choline or acetyl choline (Campbell and Williams, Jour. Bact., *62*, 1951b, 250).

Inorganic sulfur may serve as a source of sulfur (Campbell and Williams, *op. cit.*, 1951a, 506).

Aerobic, facultatively anaerobic.

Optimum temperature, between 20° and 25° C.

Source: Isolated from a film of marine fouling organisms.

Habitat: Sea water.

15. Brevibacterium quale (Steinhaus, 1941) Breed, 1953. (*Bacterium qualis* (sic) Steinhaus, Jour. Bact., *42*, 1941, 774; Breed, Riassunti delle Comunicazioni, VI Congresso Internaz. di Microbiol., Roma, *1*, 1953, 13; also see Atti del VI Congresso Internaz. di Microbiol., Roma, *1*, 1955, 13.)

qua'le. L. proun.adj. *qualis* of what sort?

Short rods, very short on solid media, frequently ellipsoidal in shape. In fluid media, 0.5 to 0.7 by 1.4 to 2.2 microns, occurring singly. Non-motile. Gram-positive.

Gelatin stab: Liquefaction.

Agar colonies: Small (1 mm), white, glistening, transparent, circular, entire.

Agar slant: Filiform, smooth, glistening.

Broth: Almost clear; slight turbidity in serum and glucose broth.

Litmus milk: No change.

Indole not produced.

Hydrogen sulfide not produced.

Acid from glucose, sucrose and maltose. Lactose not fermented.

Starch not hydrolyzed.

Slight production of nitrites from nitrates.

Source: Isolated from the alimentary tract of the tarnished plant bug, *Lygus pratensis* L.

Habitat: Unknown.

16. Brevibacterium ammoniagenes (Cooke and Keith, 1927) Breed, 1953. (*Bacterium ammoniagenes* Cooke and Keith, Jour. Bact., *13*, 1927, 315; Breed, Riassunti delle Comunicazioni, VI Congresso Internaz. di Microbiol., Roma, *1*, 1953, 14; also see Atti del VI Congresso Internaz. di Microbiol., Roma, *1*, 1955, 14.)

am.mo.ni.a'gen.es. M.L. noun *ammonia* ammonia, from Gr. noun Ammon (Jupiter), worshipped in Egypt in the form of a ram; Gr. v. *gennaio* to produce; M.L. adj. *ammoniagenes* ammonia producing.

Rods with rounded ends, 0.8 by 1.4 to 1.7 microns, occurring singly. Not encapsulated. Non-motile. Gram-positive.

Gelatin stab: No liquefaction.

Agar colonies: Circular, flat, smooth, entire, gray. Occasionally a faint yellow chromogenesis is produced.

Agar slant: Growth moderate, smooth, flat, opaque, glistening, butyrous, amorphous. No odor.

Agar stab: Filiform growth more abundant near the surface.

Broth: Moderate turbidity near the surface; flocculent sediment.

Litmus milk: Slightly alkaline.

Indole not produced.

No action on carbohydrates.

Nitrites produced from nitrates (personal communication, test of A.T.C.C. cultures, numbers 6871 and 6872, by W. A. Clark, 1954).

Urea is fermented forming ammonia.

Blood serum not liquefied.

Aerobic, facultatively anaerobic.

Optimum temperature, 30° C. Killed at 55° C. in ten minutes.

Optimum pH, between 7.0 and 8.5; does not grow readily in media with more acid or more alkaline reaction than this.

Not pathogenic for rabbits or guinea pigs.

Source: Isolated from the feces of infants. Cause of a diaper rash of infants.

Habitat: Presumably widely distributed in putrefying materials.

17. Brevibacterium healii (Buchanan and Hammer, 1915) Breed, 1953. (*Bacterium healii* Buchanan and Hammer, Iowa Agr. Exp. Sta. Research Bull. 22, 1915, 249; Breed, Riassunti delle Comunicazioni, VI Congresso Internaz. di Microbiol., Roma, *1*, 1953, 14; also see Atti del VI Congresso Internaz. di Microbiol., Roma, *1*, 1955, 14.)

hea'li.i. M.L. gen.noun *healii* of Healy; named for Dr. Healy.

Rods 0.5 to 0.7 by 2.2 to 12.9 microns; chains and filaments common. Not encapsulated. Non-motile. Gram-positive.

Produces a slight flocculent growth in Uschinsky's solution.

Gelatin stab: Heavy growth with stratiform liquefaction beginning at surface. Villous to arborescent growth along the stab.

Agar stab: Heavy white, brittle surface growth. Villous to arborescent growth along line of inoculation.

Agar streak: White, hard, arborescent growth; no tendency to stringiness.

Agar colonies: Large, white, rhizoid.

Broth: No turbidity; forms a pellicle which sinks either entirely or in part.

Litmus milk: Slightly acid, becoming slimy, coagulated and peptonized.

Potato: Heavy white, shiny, non-viscous growth.

Indole not produced.

Acid but no gas from glucose, fructose, maltose, sucrose, salicin and starch. No acid from mannitol, lactose, raffinose or inulin.

Grows well at room temperature. Does not survive 80° C. for 5 minutes.

Distinctive character: Morphologically this species resembles the species in *Kurthia;* further study may show that it should be transferred from *Brevibacterium* to *Kurthia*.

Source: Isolated from bitter and slimy milk by Dr. Healy of Kentucky; also from dairy products by Esten.

Habitat: Dairy products, and presumably widely distributed in decomposing organic materials.

18. Brevibacterium incertum (Steinhaus, 1941) Breed, 1953. (*Bacterium incertum* Steinhaus, Jour. Bact., *42*, 1941, 776; Breed, Riassunti delle Comunicazioni, VI Congresso Internaz. di Microbiol., Roma, *1*, 1953, 14; also see Atti del VI Congresso Internaz. di Microbiol., Roma, *1*, 1955, 13.)

in.cer'tum. L. adj. *incertus* uncertain.

Short rods, 0.5 to 0.8 by 1.0 to 1.5 microns, occurring singly and occasionally in pairs. Young cultures motile. Monotrichous (Steinhaus, personal communication, 1955). After 48 hours generally non-motile. Gram-positive; after 48 hours many cells become Gram-negative.

Gelatin stab: No liquefaction.

Agar colonies: Tiny, grayish white, smooth, almost transparent. Does not grow well on nutrient agar.

North's gelatin chocolate agar slant: Filiform, thin, transparent growth. Brown color of chocolate medium changes to yellowish green.

Blood agar: Alpha hemolysis at first; after three days, beta hemolysis.

Broth: Almost clear; very slight growth.

Litmus milk: No change.

Indole not produced.

Hydrogen sulfide not produced.

Acid but no gas from glucose, sucrose, fructose, mannose and maltose. No fermentation of lactose, rhamnose, galactose, mannitol, dulcitol, inositol or sorbitol.

Acetylmethylcarbinol not produced.

Starch not hydrolyzed.

Nitrites not produced from nitrates.

Microaerophilic.

Source: Isolated from the ovaries of the lyreman cicada, *Tibicen linnei* Smith and Grossbeck.

Habitat: Unknown.

19. Brevibacterium imperiale (Steinhaus, 1941) Breed, 1953. (*Bacterium imperiale* Steinhaus, Jour. Bact., *42*, 1941, 777; Breed, Riassunti delle Comunicazioni, VI Congresso Internaz. di Microbiol., Roma, *1*, 1953, 14; also see Atti del VI Congresso Internaz. di Microbiol., Roma, *1*, 1955, 13.)

im.pe.ri.al'e. L. adj. *imperialis* imperial; from specific epithet of name of insect host.

Small rods, 0.5 to 0.8 by 1.0 to 1.7 microns, occurring singly and in pairs.

A few cells are motile in young cultures. Monotrichous; occasionally the flagellum is lateral (Steinhaus, personal communication, 1955). Gram-positive.

Gelatin stab: No liquefaction.

Agar colonies: Circular, entire, almost translucent, pinkish orange to yellow pigment.

Agar slant: Filiform, glistening, opaque growth.

Broth: Slight to moderate turbidity; slight sediment.

Litmus milk: No change at first, later slightly acid.

Potato: Heavy, glistening, moist growth; reddish to yellowish orange.

Indole not produced.

Hydrogen sulfide not produced.

Acid but no gas from glucose, sucrose, maltose, fructose, mannitol, galactose, arabinose, xylose, salicin, raffinose, trehalose, sorbitol, mannose, adonitol and esculin, and slight acid from lactose and dextrin. Inulin, dulcitol, glycerol, rhamnose, adonitol and inositol not fermented.

Starch not hydrolyzed.

Nitrites not produced from nitrates.

Aerobic.

Source: Isolated from the alimentary tract of the imperial moth, *Eacles imperialis* Dru.

Habitat: Unknown.

20. Brevibacterium lipolyticum (Huss, 1908) Breed, 1953. (*Bactridium lipolyticum* Huss, Cent. f. Bakt., II Abt., *20*, 1908, 474 Breed, Riassunti delle Communicazioni, VI Congresso Internaz. di Microbiol., Roma, *1*, 1953, 14; also see Atti del VI Congresso Internaz. di Microbiol., Roma, *1*, 1955, 14.)

li.po.ly'ti.cum. Gr. noun *lipus* animal fat; Gr. adj. *lyticus* dissolving; M.L. adj. *lipolyticus* fat-dissolving.

Small, coccoid rods, 0.3 to 0.5 by 0.7 to 1.4 microns, occasionally as long as 3.5 microns. Cells coccoid on gelatin media, forming chains resembling those of the streptococci. Motile by means of peritrichous flagella. Gram-positive.

Gelatin colonies: Circular, grayish to transparent with irregular margin.

Gelatin stab: Infundibuliform liquefaction.

Agar colonies: Circular, gray, smooth, butyrous, glistening, entire. Old colonies brownish yellow.

Whey agar: Growth on surface and along the stab; surface growth may become faintly yellowish.

Whey: Heavy turbidity at 20° C.; forms a heavy precipitate after 8 days.

Broth: Turbid; granular sediment.

Litmus milk: Coagulated, peptonized and becoming alkaline.

Potato: Moist, glistening, yellowish white growth.

Acid from glucose, sucrose, raffinose, xylose, mannitol and glycerol. Lactose not fermented.

Indole reaction faint.

Hydrogen sulfide not produced.

Fats are split in milk, giving rise to a rancid odor and a bitter taste.

Reduction of nitrates questionable.

Aerobic, facultatively anaerobic.

Temperature relations: Optimum, 35° C. Growth at 14° but not above 45° C.

Comments: This species is definitely not *Bacterium lipolyticum* Evans (Jour. Inf. Dis., *22*, 1918, 576). The latter organism is a non-motile, non-gelatin-liquefying species which possesses the characteristic diphtheroid morphology and which does not ferment sugars and related compounds; furthermore, it is less actively lipolytic than is the species described by Huss (*op. cit.*, 1908, 474). Huss' organism appears to occur less frequently than that described by Evans.

Source: Isolated from the udder of a cow giving abnormal milk.

Habitat: Found in milk and in dairy products.

21. Brevibacterium acetylicum (Levine and Soppeland, 1926) Breed, *comb. nov.* (*Flavobacterium acetylicum* Levine and Soppeland, Bull. 77, Engineering Exp. Sta., Iowa State Agr. College, 1926, 46.)

a.ce.ty'li.cum. L. neut.n. *acetum* vinegar; M.L. neut.n. *acetylum* the organic radical acetyl; M.L. adj. *acetylicus* pertaining to acetyl.

Rods, 0.9 by 1.1. microns, with rounded ends, occurring singly and in pairs. Motile (Levine and Soppeland). Peritrichous as determined by O. B. Weeks, January, 1955, from A.T.C.C. cultures 953 and 954. Gram-positive.

Gelatin stab: Stratiform liquefaction.

Agar colonies: Irregular in form, yellow, smooth, flat, amorphous, entire.

Agar slant: Growth abundant, echinulate, flat, peach-yellow, smooth, butyrous.

Broth: Ring growth on surface. Turbid with a scant sediment.

Litmus milk: Slight acidity with a granular curd; peptonized; litmus reduced.

Potato: Moderate, orange growth.

Indole not produced.

Acid from glucose.

Starch is hydrolyzed.

Acetylmethylcarbinol is produced.

Nitrites not produced from nitrates.

Blood serum: Liquefaction.

Aerobic, facultatively anaerobic.

Optimum temperature, 22° C.

Source: Isolated from skimmed milk.

Habitat: Unknown.

22. Brevibacterium sulfureum (Bergey et al., 1923) Breed, *comb. nov.* (*Bacterium punctans sulfureum* Zettnow, Cent. f. Bakt.,

I Abt., Orig., *77*, 1916, 222; *Flavobacterium sulfureum* Bergey et al., Manual, 1st ed., 1923, 103.)

sul.fu're.um. L. adj. *sulfureus* of sulfur, from sulfur-colored growth.

Rods, 0.5 to 0.7 by 0.7 to 1.5 microns. Motile by means of peritrichous flagella. Gram-positive.

Gelatin colonies: Very small, barely visible, becoming brownish yellow, granular.

Gelatin stab: Spreading growth on the surface only; later, crateriform liquefaction.

Agar slant: Sulfur-yellow growth.

Broth: Turbid.

Litmus milk: Alkaline; peptonized; yellow.

Potato: Sulfur-yellow streak.

Indole not produced.

No acid from glucose.

Nitrites not produced from nitrates.

Blood serum: Sulfur-yellow growth. Partial liquefaction.

Aerobic, facultatively anaerobic.

Optimum temperature, 25° C.

Source: Isolated from air.

Habitat : Unknown.

23. Brevibacterium helvolum (Zimmermann, 1890) Lochhead, 1955. (*Bacillus helvolus* Zimmermann, Die Bakt. unserer Trink- und Nutzwässer, Chemnitz, *1*, 1890, 52; *Bacterium helvolum* Lehmann and Neumann, Bakt. Diag., 1 Aufl., *2*, 1896, 254; *Corynebacterium helvolum* Kisskalt and Berend, Cent. f. Bakt., I Abt., Orig., *81*, 1918, 446; not *Corynebacterium helvolum* Jensen, Proc. Linn. Soc. New So. Wales, *59*, 1934, 37; *Flavobacterium helvolum* Bergey et al., Manual, 1st ed., 1923, 114; Lochhead, Internat. Bull. of Bact. Nomen. and Taxon., *5*, 1955, 115.)

hel'vo.lum. L. adj. *helvolus* pale yellow.

Description given below is taken directly from the original description by Zimmermann (*op. cit.*, 1890, 52) except as indicated. Lehmann and Neumann add certain characters to the original description from a study of a culture from air that agreed with Zimmermann's culture. The description in Migula (Syst. d. Bakt., *2*, 1900, 324) is accurately paraphrased from Zimmermann's original description.

Short rods which at first hang very closely together usually in pairs, also in fours or longer chains. Later, however, longer chains are regularly formed. The diameter of the cells is about 0.5, the length 1.5 to 2.5, microns, at times as long as 4.5 microns. The rods rotate on their long axis (Lehmann and Neumann state that their culture was non-motile). Gram-positive.

Gelatin plates: The colonies within the gelatin are small, spherical bodies that are bright yellow in color. The colonies on the surface are highly convex, bright yellow, tiny drops which lie in a shallow depression. When examined under low magnification, the colonies beneath the surface appear as pale yellowish to brownish, granular, circular, sharply contoured discs. The colonies on the surface also show a sharp contour for some time; however, they later become somewhat irregular in contour and appear much darker brown by transmitted light.

Gelatin stab: An elevated growth is formed at first on the surface. This is a definite Naples-yellow in color. This growth gradually spreads until it almost reaches the glass wall of the test tube. By this time the gelatin is liquefied in a shallow layer. There is little development along the stab. The liquefaction proceeds slowly.

Agar slant: There is an abundant, rather rapid growth that is of a definite light yellow color as on gelatin. (Lemon-yellow, Lehmann and Neumann.)

Bouillon broth: The broth becomes somewhat lighter in color with little turbidity at first; then flecks form and settle, appearing as a yellowish white sediment.

Potato: The yellow growth is abundant, becoming thickened and glistening. The color becomes somewhat greenish but not enough to call it sulfur-yellow.

Indole is not produced (Lehmann and Neumann).

Hydrogen sulfide is actively produced (Lehmann and Neumann).

No gas produced from glucose (Lehmann and Neumann).

Milk is coagulated (Lehmann and Neumann).

Optimum temperature, about 25° C.

Aerobic.

The specific epithet *helvolus* is suggested because of its pale yellow chromogenesis on agar plates.

Comments: It will be seen that the description by Zimmermann differs in several important respects from that given in the 6th edition of the Manual, 1948, 395; the latter was taken largely from Jensen (Proc. Linn. Soc. New So. Wales, *59*, 1934, 37). The morphology of the Zimmermann organism both as described by him and also by Lehmann and Neumann is that of a simple, unbranching rod. There is no suggestion of a pleomorphic morphology, snapping division or branching. The description given by Jensen is indicative of a different species, and when Lochhead compared a culture of Jensen's organism with cultures of related organisms, he found it (personal communication, 1954) to be identical with cultures of *Bacterium globiforme* Conn, the organism selected as the type species of the genus *Arthrobacter* Conn and Dimmick. Zimmermann's organism clearly was a *Brevibacterium* as defined here, not a *Corynebacterium* as defined by Lehmann and Neumann (Bakt. Diag., 1 Aufl., *2*, 1896, 380). *Brevibacterium* represents a segregation of species placed by Lehmann and Neumann in *Bacterium*.

Source: Isolated from Chemnitz tap water (Zimmermann); also found as a dust contaminant in Würzburg (Lehmann and Neumann).

Habitat: Presumably widely distributed in nature.

Genus II. **Kurthia** *Trevisan, 1885.*

(Trevisan, Atti della Accad. Fisio- Medico- Statistica in Milano, Ser. 4, *3*, 1885, 92; *Zopfius* Wenner and Rettger, Jour. Bact., *4*, 1919, 334.)

Kurth'i.a. M.L. fem.n. *Kurthia* named for H. Kurth, the German bacteriologist who described the type species.

Long rods with somewhat rounded ends. In liquid media the cells are aligned in evenly curved chains; in gelatin media filaments form which may subdivide into coccoid elements. Not encapsulated. Motile with peritrichous flagella. Gram-positive. Carbohydrates not attacked. Facultatively anaerobic. Found in decomposing materials.

The type species is *Kurthia zopfii* (Kurth) Trevisan.

Key to the species of genus **Kurthia.**

I. Gelatin not liquefied.
  A. Hydrogen sulfide not produced; putrid odor produced in cultures.
                         1. *Kurthia zopfii.*
  B. Hydrogen sulfide produced; no putrid odor produced in cultures.
                         2. *Kurthia variabilis.*
II. Gelatin rapidly liquefied.
                         3. *Kurthia bessonii.*

1. **Kurthia zopfii** (Kurth, 1883) Trevisan, 1885. (*Bacterium zopfii* Kurth, Bericht. d. deutsch. Bot. Gesellschaft, *1*, 1883, 97; Trevisan, Atti della Accad. Fisio-Medico-Statistica in Milano, Ser. 4, *3*, 1885, 92.)

zop′fi.i. M.L. gen.noun *zopfii* of Zopf; named for W. Zopf, a German botanist.

Description based on original descriptions and that of Wenner and Rettger (Jour. Bact., *4*, 1919, 350).

Rods, 0.8 by 3.5 microns, with rounded ends. In liquid media, long, evenly curved chains are formed; in gelatin media the chains are twisted, braided and clumped into knots. From these knots filaments push out, laterally then anteriorly, which may subdivide into coccoid elements. Not encapsulated. Motile by means of peritrichous flagella. Gram-positive.

Gelatin colonies: Radiate, filamentous, gray.

Gelatin stab: Arborescent growth in stab. No liquefaction.

Agar colonies: Fimbriate.

Agar slant: Spreading, gray, fimbriate growth.

Broth: Slow, moderate growth; putrid, ammoniacal odor produced.

Litmus milk: No change.

Potato: Moderate, gray growth; medium becoming dark.

Carbohydrates not attacked.

Indole not produced.

Hydrogen sulfide not produced.

Nitrites not produced from nitrates.

Aerobic, facultatively anaerobic.

Optimum temperature, between 25° and 30° C.

Comments: Some workers make a distinction between *Kurthia zopfii* Trevisan and *Kurthia zenkeri* Bergey et al., mainly on their ability or inability to form an arborescent growth in a gelatin stab. However, according to Chester (Man. Determ. Bact., 1901, 249), division of these organisms into two species does not seem advisable: the formation of an arborescent growth is too variable a character on which to base species differentiation. This view is also shared by Wenner and Rettger (*op. cit.*, 1919, 351).

Source: Isolated from hen manure.

Habitat: Found in decomposing materials.

2. **Kurthia variabilis** Severi, 1946. (Giorn. di Batteriol. e Immunol., *46*, 1946, 107.)

va.ri.a′bi.lis. L. adj. *variabilis* variable.

Rods, 0.7 by 1.5 to 2.0 microns, frequently curved, growing out into filaments 10 to 30 microns long; these filaments later divide in two or form short chains. Motile by means of peritrichous flagella. Gram-positive.

Gelatin stab: No liquefaction. Grayish growth along the stab.

Agar colonies: 1 to 2 mm in diameter, grayish white, glossy, smooth; regular margins.

Agar slant: Slender, grayish white, translucent, slightly viscid.

Broth: Moderate, uniform turbidity; thin membrane. Sediment at first slight, later abundant.

Litmus milk unchanged.

Methylene blue not reduced.

Neutral red reduced.

Potato: Growth slender, moist and white. Coagulated blood serum: Growth viscous, mucoid, white.

Indole not produced.

Hydrogen sulfide produced.

No action on carbohydrates or alcohols, of which the following were tested: glucose, fructose, galactose, lactose, maltose, sucrose, starch, dextrin, salicin, glycerol, sorbitol, dulcitol and mannitol.

Nitrites not produced from nitrates.

Ammonia produced in peptone solutions.

Temperature relations: Optimum, between 37° and 39° C. Minimum, 17° C. Maximum, 45° C.

Aerobic, facultatively anaerobic.

Not pathogenic for guinea pigs.

Source: Isolated from feces in a case of food poisoning.

Habitat: Found in decomposing materials.

3. **Kurthia bessonii** (Hauduroy et al., 1937) Severi, 1946. (Bacille isolé des selles, Besson, Tech. microbiol. et sérothérap., Paris, 7ᵉ ed., 1924, 920; *Listerella bessoni* (sic) Hauduroy et al., Dict. d. Bact. Path., Paris, 1ᵉ ed., 1937, 271; Severi, Giorn. di Batteriol. e Immunol., *34*, 1946, 107.)

bes.son'i.i. M.L. gen.noun *bessonii* of Besson; named for A. Besson, the bacteriologist who first described this organism.

Description taken from Hauduroy et al. (*op. cit.*, 1937, 271).

Rods, 0.7 by 1.0 to 8.0 or even 12.0 microns, which form filaments. Actively motile by means of peritrichous flagella. Grampositive.

Gelatin colonies: Thin and spreading; fimbriate margins.

Gelatin stab: Rapid liquefaction.

Agar colonies: Thinner in center than at margins; lacerate edges.

Broth: Slightly turbid; thin, fragile pellicle; slight precipitate. Odor ammoniacal and putrid.

Litmus milk: Alkaline and digested.

Indole not produced.

Hydrogen sulfide not produced.

Little or no action on carbohydrates. Slight action on glycerol.

Coagulated blood serum: Liquefied.

Neutral red partially and slowly reduced.

Source: Isolated from normal and diarrheal human feces.

Habitat: Believed to be widely distributed in putrid organic matter.

FAMILY X. LACTOBACILLACEAE WINSLOW ET AL., 1917.*

(Winslow, Broadhurst, Buchanan, Krumwiede, Rogers and Smith, Jour. Bact., *2*, 1917, 561; *Lactobacteriaceae* (sic) Orla-Jensen, Jour. Bact., *6*, 1921, 266; *Streptobacteriaceae* Bergey, Breed and Murray, Preprint, Manual, 5th ed., 1938, 71.)

The generic name *Lactobacter* proposed by Beijerinck (Cent. f. Bakt., II Abt., *6*, 1900, 200) was used by him to designate a physiological genus that included both the lactic acid cocci and the lactic acid rods. No species are described so that the status of this name is questionable.

Lac.to.ba.cil.la'ce.ae. L. noun *lac, lactis* milk; L. mas.dim.n. *bacillus* a little rod; *-aceae* ending to denote a family; M.L. fem.pl.n. *Lactobacillaceae* the *Lactobacillus* family.

---

* The following have been consulted in regard to the general arrangement of the genera recognized in this family: Prof. E. G. D. Murray, McGill University, Montreal, P.Q., Canada; Prof. J. M. Sherman, Cornell University, Ithaca, New York; Dr. C. F. Niven, Jr., American Meat Institute Foundation, The University of Chicago, Chicago, Illinois; Dr. L. DS. Smith, Montana Agricultural Experiment Station, Bozeman, Montana; and Prof. C. S. Pederson, New York State Experiment Station, Geneva, New York, March, 1955. The descriptions of the anaerobic species are taken largely from Dr. A.-R. Prévot, Pasteur Institute, Paris, France.

Long or short rods or cocci which divide like rods in one plane only, producing chains, occasionally tetrads; filamentous as well as so-called false branching forms sometimes occur. Usually non-motile but may be motile, the motile species possessing peritrichous flagella. Gram-positive. Pigment production is rare; a few species produce a yellow, orange, red or rusty brown pigment. Gelatin liquefaction is rare among the microaerophilic species but is more common among the strict anaerobes. Surface growth on all media is poor or absent. Carbohydrates are essential for good development; they are fermented to lactic acid, sometimes with volatile acids, alcohol and carbon dioxide as by-products. Nitrites not produced from nitrates, but among the strict anaerobes there are a few species that are known to reduce nitrates and some that have not been tested for nitrate reduction. Microaerophilic to anaerobic. Found regularly in the mouth and intestinal tract of man and other animals, in food and dairy products and in fermenting vegetable juices; a few species are highly pathogenic.

Key to the tribes of family **Lactobacillaceae**.

I. Cocci occurring singly, in pairs and in chains (rarely tetrads).

Tribe I. Streptococceae, p. 506.

II. Rods, occurring singly, in pairs and in chains. Individual cells may be very long or even filamentous.

Tribe II. Lactobacilleae, p. 541.

TRIBE I. STREPTOCOCCEAE TREVISAN, 1889.

(I generi e le specie delle Batteriacee, 1889, 29.)

Cells spherical or elongate, dividing in one plane only, usually occurring in pairs or in chains. Gelatin is rarely liquefied. None of the species grows abundantly on solid media. The microaerophilic species attack carbohydrates and polyhydroxy alcohols, producing lactic acid by homofermentation or lactic and acetic acids, alcohol and carbon dioxide by heterofermentation; the strictly anaerobic species attack protein decomposition products, organic acids and usually carbohydrates with the production of carbon dioxide, hydrogen and other products. Microaerophilic to anaerobic. Catalase-negative. May or may not be pathogenic; some pathogenic species grow poorly without blood serum or other enrichment fluids. Found in various lesions and in the normal mouths and intestines of man and other animals, in food and dairy products and in fermenting plant juices.

Key to the genera of tribe **Streptococceae.**

I. Facultatively anaerobic to microaerophilic.

    A. Homofermentative, producing only traces of end-products other than lactic acid from carbohydrates.

        1. Produce dextro rotatory lactic acid from glucose.

            a. Parasites which grow poorly on artificial media. Cells usually in pairs, often elongated. Bile-soluble.

Genus I. Diplococcus, p. 507.

            aa. Parasites and saprophytes. Normally form short or long chains. Not soluble in bile solutions.

Genus II. Streptococcus, p. 508.

        2. Produces a racemic mixture of lactic acid from glucose. Occurs singly, as tetrads, pairs or even short chains.

Genus III. Pediococcus, p. 529.

B. Heterofermentative, producing considerable amounts of carbon dioxide, ethanol and acetic acid as well as lactic acid from carbohydrates.

Genus IV. *Leuconostoc*, p. 531.

II. Strictly anaerobic (one species becomes aerotolerant with repeated transfers).

Genus V. *Peptostreptococcus*, p. 533.

Genus I. **Diplococcus** *Weichselbaum, 1886.**

(Wiener med. Jahrb., *82*, 1886, 483.)

Dip.lo.coc′cus. Gr. adj. *diplous* double; Gr. noun *coccus* a grain, berry; M.L. mas.n. *Diplococcus* paired coccus.

Cells usually in pairs, sometimes in chains. Young cells Gram-positive. Parasites, sometimes growing poorly or not at all on artificial media. Fermentative powers usually high, most strains producing acid from glucose, lactose, sucrose and inulin. The organisms in this genus are soluble in a 10 per cent bile solution.

The type species is *Diplococcus pneumoniae* Weichselbaum.

1. **Diplococcus pneumoniae** Weichselbaum, 1886. (Microbe septicémique du salive, Pasteur, Chamberland and Roux, Compt. rend. Acad. Sci., Paris, *92*, 1881, 159; Micrococcus of rabbit septicemia, Sternberg, National Board of Health Bull., Washington, *2*, 1881, 781; Coccus lancéolé, Talamon, Communication à la Société anatom. de Paris, *58*, 1883, 475; Weichselbaum, Wiener med. Jahrb., *82*, 1886, 485; Pneumoniemikrococcus or Pneumococcus, Fränkel, Ztschr. f. klin. Medizin, *10*, 1886, 402.)

pneu.mo′ni.ae. Gr. noun *pneumon* the lungs; M.L. fem.n. *pneumonia* pneumonia; M.L. gen.noun *pneumoniae* of pneumonia.

Common name: Pneumococcus.

The organisms occur as oval or spherical forms typically in pairs, occasionally singly or in short chains, 0.5 to 1.25 microns. The distal ends of each pair of organisms tend to be pointed or lancet-shaped. Encapsulated. Non-motile. Young cells are Gram-positive.

Gelatin stab: Filiform or beaded growth. No liquefaction.

Infusion agar colonies: Small, transparent, grayish, entire. Elevation high, convex, glistening, mucoid to watery.

On blood agar the colonies are elevated at the center with concentric elevations and depressions. Hemolysis usually slight but often marked in anaerobic culture; met-

hemaglobin formation with green zone around colony.

Beef heart infusion broth: Uniform turbidity with variable amount of sediment.

Addition of glucose, serum, whole blood or ascitic fluid enhances growth.

Meat extract media: Growth irregular, usually poor if any.

Inulin serum water: Usually acid with coagulation.

Litmus milk: Usually acid with coagulation.

Potato: No growth.

Whole bile or 10 per cent solutions of sodium taurocholate or sodium glycocholate added to actively growing broth cultures will dissolve the organisms. It is customary to use from 0.1 to 0.5 ml of bile for each 0.5 ml of culture.

Aerobic, facultative.

Optimum temperature, 37° C. Usually no growth between 18° and 22° C.

Optimum initial pH, 7.8.

Source: Sputum, blood and exudates in pneumonia; cerebrospinal fluid in meningitis; mastoiditis; otitis media; peritonitis; empyema; pericarditis; endocarditis; arthritis; saliva and secretions of respiratory tract in normal persons. Commonest cause of lobar pneumonia.

Habitat: The respiratory tract of man and animals.

---

* Revised by Prof. E. G. D. Murray, McGill University, Montreal, P.Q., Canada, September, 1938; further revision by Lt. Col. Elliott S. Robinson, M.C., Washington, D. C., January, 1944.

At present thirty-one serotypes of *Diplococcus pneumoniae* are recognized on the basis of serological reactions, chiefly the Neufeld "Quellung" phenomenon as induced by type-specific immune rabbit serums. Following the description of Pneumococcus 1 by Neufeld and Händel (Arb. a. d. k. Gesundheitsamte, *34*, 1910, 293), Dochez and Gillespie (Jour. Amer. Med. Assoc., *61*, 1913, 727) divided the species into Types 1, 2, 3 and a heterogeneous group 4; Cooper, Edwards and Rosenstein (Jour. Exp. Med., *49*, 1929, 461) separated Types 4 to 13 from the strains previously designated as group 4, and later Cooper, Rosenstein, Walter and Peizer (Jour. Exp. Med., *55*, 1932, 531) continued the classification to Type 32. Due to marked cross-reactions, it was subsequently decided that Type 6 was identical with Type 26, and that Types 15 and 30 were identical. This resulted in the deletion of the Cooper Types 26 and 30, thus leaving thirty of the original thirty-two types. Type 33 (Wilder) has been described by Walter, Blount, Beattie and Cotler (Jour. Inf. Dis., *66*, 1940, 181) as a distinct type; sufficient recognition has been accorded to justify the acceptance of this type, thereby making a total of thirty-one types of the species. In a still more recent publication, Walter, Guevin, Beattie, Cotler and Bucca (Jour. Immunol., *41*, 1941, 279) recommend the addition of nine new types and eight subtypes. These, together with new strains reported by Kauffmann, Mørch and Schmith (Jour. Immunol., *39*, 1940, 397), if eventually recognized, would make a total of fifty-five types. Eddy still more recently, taking into account all known types, raises the number of recognized types to seventy five (U. S. Public Health Repts., *59*, 1944, 449–468).

NOTE: Pneumococci, regardless of serological type, manifest three chief culture phases (or stages): Mucoid, Smooth and Rough. The Mucoid (M) form corresponds to that previously designated as Smooth (S) and represents the typical phase of the species; Smooth (S) supersedes the earlier term Rough (R); and the present Rough (R) form is a relatively newly described variant. The most frequently observed dissociative trend is M → S → R. Serological types are recognizable only in the Mucoid form due to the presence of type-specific polysaccharides in the capsular material; both Smooth and Rough forms are devoid of capsular material but possess species-specific antigens common to all members of the species. Smooth and Rough forms are non-pathogenic, possess distinctive growth characteristics and require special technic for accurate observations. The cultural characteristics given are those of the mucoid and smooth phases only, e.g., see growth in broth.

Genus II. **Streptococcus** *Rosenbach*, 1884.*

(Mikroorganismen bei den Wundinfectionskrankheiten des Menschen. Wiesbaden, 1884, 22.)

Strep.to.coc′cus. Gr. adj. *streptus* pliant; Gr. noun *coccus* a grain, berry; M.L. mas.n. *Streptococcus* pliant coccus.

Cells spherical or ovoid, rarely elongated into rods, occurring in pairs or short or long chains. Capsules are not regularly discernible but may become conspicuous with some species under certain conditions. Non-motile except a few strains in the enterococcus group. Gram-positive. No pigments are produced with the exception of an occasional strain in Lancefield's groups B and D, which may produce brick-red pigment or yellow pigments under appropriate environmental conditions. A fermentable carbohydrate or polyhydroxy alcohol is necessary for satisfactory growth in artificial media. Growth in broth culture is variable in character. Rough variants may show granular growth that tends to settle out quickly, leaving a clear supernatant. Smooth variants may show uniform turbidity with little tendency to settle out. Such variants may be noted within one species. A pellicle is never formed. Growth on agar surface is usually scanty. Colonies are small, usually less

---

* Revised by Dr. C. F. Niven, Jr., American Meat Institute Foundation, The University of Chicago, Chicago, Illinois, in consultation with Professors J. M. Sherman and Harry W. Seeley, Cornell University, Ithaca, New York, November, 1953.

than 1 millimeter in diameter. Colony variants within one species may range from rough to smooth (matt to glossy) to mucoid. Subsurface colonies are usually lenticular. Carbohydrate fermentation is homofermentative with dextro rotatory lactic acid as the dominant end-product. Carbon dioxide is produced in very small quantities or not at all from sugar fermentation. Ethanol, acetic acid and formic acid may be produced in appreciable quantities from glucose if allowed to ferment in alkaline media (Gunsalus and Niven, Jour. Biol. Chem., *145*, 1942, 131). Many of the streptococci oxidize a number of the alcohols, glycols and short-chain fatty acids (Gunsalus and Wood, Jour. Bact., *44*, 1942, 523; Gunsalus and Umbreit, Jour. Bact., *49*, 1945, 347; Niven, Evans and White, Jour. Bact., *49*, 1945, 105; Wolin, Evans and Niven, Jour. Bact., *64*, 1952, 531), but the energy derived from these respiratory mechanisms is not utilized directly for growth. However, some enterococcus cultures may show moderately superior growth under aerobic conditions (Seeley and Van-Demark, Jour. Bact., *61*, 1951, 27). The cytochrome systems are absent; catalase-negative. Do not reduce nitrate to nitrite. Facultative with respect to oxygen. Not soluble in ten per cent bile. Proteolytic strains found only in the enterococcus group. All streptococci are fastidious with respect to their nutritional requirements, thereby requiring a number of the B vitamins and amino acids for growth. The nutritional requirements are, in general, species specific, but some variations may be noted within one species. Some strains require an unsaturated fatty acid or increased carbon dioxide tension for growth. In some instances, the nutritional requirements may be of aid in the identification of a species. The reader is referred to Dubos (Bacterial and Mycotic Infections of Man. Lippincott, 1948, 240) for a general summary of the nutritional requirements for most of the species. Serological tests, specifically the Lancefield precipitin technique, have proved to be of distinct value in classifying the streptococci. In general, all streptococci except those in the viridans group possess a serologically active, group specific "C" substance (polysaccharide), thus allowing them to be placed into serological groups by the precipitin technique. One serological group may comprise more than one species. Also, one serological group may possess a number of established serological types based upon the presence of capsular type-specific antigens and detected by the agglutinin or precipitin technique. Thus far, little relationship has been noted between serological type specificity and species specificity as established by their respective physiological characteristics. Several instances are known in which certain strains of streptococci possess common type antigens but belong to different serological groups. Members of the viridans group possess demonstrable type antigens but, for the most part, they have been of little taxonomic value. The streptococci are commonly found wherever organic matter containing sugars is accumulated. They occur regularly in the mouth and intestine of man and other animals, in dairy and other food products and in fermenting plant juices. Some species are pathogenic.

The arrangement of the species presented is in harmony with the suggestions of Sherman (Bact. Rev., *1*, 1937, 3) in which the facultative streptococci are separated into four general groups: the pyogenic, the viridans, the enterococcus and the lactic groups. The arrangement of the species into these four categories was based upon a series of common physiological characteristics possessed by the respective groups, the most important of which was their temperature limits for growth. However, as new species are recognized, the individuality of each group naturally becomes less distinct, and the difficulties of placing the new species, which may possess characteristics of more than one group, are increased. For example, *Streptococcus uberis* Diernhofer, a member of the viridans group, possesses certain characteristics that would tempt one to place it in the enterococcus group, while *Streptococcus acidominimus* Ayers and Mudge, also a member of the viridans group, might be considered a member of the pyogenic group.

The type species is *Streptococcus pyogenes* Rosenbach.

It is difficult to draw up a workable key for streptococci. Keys, of necessity, emphasize single characters or, at most, only a few characters, and these are not necessarily the most important characters of a species. Before the identify of a *Streptococcus* culture should be regarded as established, the complete physiological pattern should be determined and compared with the complete physiological patterns of the species in the genus.

Key to the species of genus **Streptococcus.**

THE PYOGENIC GROUP

I. No growth at 10° or 45° C. (some exceptions in *Streptococcus sanguis*). No growth in 6.5 per cent NaCl broth, at pH 9.6 or in 0.1 per cent methylene blue milk. No reduction of litmus before curdling milk. Tyrosine not decarboxylated.
A. Sodium hippurate not hydrolyzed.
　1. High CO$_2$ tension not required for rapid growth on blood agar. Cells and colonies not "minute." Ammonia produced from arginine.
　　a. No viscous polysaccharide produced in 5 per cent sucrose broth. Inulin not fermented.
　　　b. Fibrinolytic.
　　　　c. Beta hemolytic. Ferments trehalose but not sorbitol.
　　　　　d. Glycerol not fermented. Lancefield group A.
　　　　　　　1. *Streptococcus pyogenes.*
　　　　　dd. Glycerol fermented aerobically. Lancefield group C.
　　　　　　　2. *Streptococcus equisimilis.*
　　　bb. Not fibrinolytic.
　　　　c. Beta hemolytic.
　　　　　d. Trehalose not fermented, but sorbitol fermented. Glycerol fermented aerobically. Lancefield group C.
　　　　　　　3. *Streptococcus zooepidemicus.*
　　　　　dd. Trehalose, sorbitol and glycerol not fermented. Lancefield group C.
　　　　　　　4. *Streptococcus equi.*
　　　　cc. Not beta hemolytic. Trehalose fermented. Sorbitol usually fermented. Glycerol not fermented. Lancefield group C.
　　　　　　　5. *Streptococcus dysgalactiae.*
　　aa. Viscous polysaccharide produced in 5 per cent sucrose broth. Inulin usually fermented. May or may not be beta hemolytic. Lancefield group H.
　　　　　　　6. *Streptococcus sanguis.**
　2. High CO$_2$ tension required for rapid growth on blood agar. "Minute" cells and colonies. Ammonia produced from arginine. Lancefield group F and Type I, group G.
　　　　　　　7. *Streptococcus anginosus.*
B. Sodium hippurate hydrolyzed.
　1. Ammonia produced from arginine. Glycerol fermented aerobically. May be beta hemolytic. Final pH in glucose broth, 4.2 to 4.8. Lancefield group B.
　　　　　　　8. *Streptococcus agalactiae.*

THE VIRIDANS GROUP

　2. Ammonia not produced from arginine. Glycerol not fermented. Not hemolytic. Final pH in glucose broth, 5.6 to 6.5.
　　　　　　　9. *Streptococcus acidominimus.*
II. No growth at 10° C. Growth at 45° C. (exceptions in *Streptococcus mitis*). No ammonia

---

* Although no group antigen has been demonstrated for *Streptococcus sanguis*, this species and the group H streptococci are similar enough in other characteristics to warrant their association. See detailed description of this species.

from arginine (exceptions in *Streptococcus mitis*). Not beta hemolytic. No growth in 6.5 per cent NaCl broth, at pH 9.6 or in 0.1 per cent methylene blue milk. No reduction of litmus before curdling milk. Tyrosine not decarboxylated.

A. No growth at 50° C. Growth in 2 per cent NaCl broth.
   1. Starch not hydrolyzed. No growth on 40 per cent bile blood agar.
      a. Indifferent (gamma hemolytic) on blood agar. Raffinose and inulin fermented. Large, mucoid colonies produced on 5 per cent sucrose and raffinose agar.

                         10. *Streptococcus salivarius*

      aa. Greening (alpha hemolytic) on blood agar. Inulin not fermented. Raffinose may or may not be fermented. Mucoid colonies not produced on 5 per cent sucrose agar.

                         11. *Streptococcus mitis*.

   2. Starch hydrolyzed. Growth on 40 per cent bile blood agar.
      a. Lactose fermented.

                         12. *Streptococcus bovis*.

      aa. Lactose not fermented.

                         13. *Streptococcus equinus*.

B. Growth at 50° C. No growth in 2 per cent NaCl broth.

                         14. *Streptococcus thermophilus*.

III. Growth at 10° and 45° C. Ammonia produced from arginine.
A. No growth in 6.5 per cent NaCl broth, at pH 9.6 or in 0.1 per cent methylene blue milk. Tyrosine not decarboxylated. Not hemolytic. Litmus milk not reduced before curdling.

                         15. *Streptococcus uberis*.

The Enterococcus Group

B. Growth in 6.5 per cent NaCl broth, at pH 9.6 and in 0.1 per cent methylene blue milk. Tyrosine decarboxylated. Lancefield group D.
   1. Not beta hemolytic.
      a. Gelatin not liquefied.

                         16. *Streptococcus faecalis*.

      aa. Gelatin liquefied.

                         16a. *Streptococcus faecalis* var. *liquefaciens*.

   2. Beta hemolytic.
      a. Mannitol and sorbitol fermented. Litmus reduced before curdling milk. May or may not liquefy gelatin.

                         16b. *Streptococcus faecalis* var. *zymogenes*.

      aa. Mannitol and sorbitol not fermented. Litmus not reduced before curdling milk. Gelatin not liquefied.

                         17. *Streptococcus durans*.

The Lactic Group

IV. Growth at 10° but not at 45° C. No growth in 6.5 per cent NaCl broth or at pH 9.6. Tyrosine not decarboxylated. Growth in 0.1 per cent methylene blue milk; reduces litmus before curdling milk. Not hemolytic. Lancefield group N.
A. Growth at 40° C., in 4 per cent NaCl broth, at pH 9.2 and in 0.3 per cent methylene blue milk. Produces ammonia from arginine. Maltose fermented.

                         18. *Streptococcus lactis*.

B. No growth at 40° C., in 4 per cent NaCl broth, at pH 9.2 or in 0.3 per cent methylene blue milk. Ammonia not produced from arginine. Maltose usually not fermented.

                         19. *Streptococcus cremoris*.

1. **Streptococcus pyogenes** Rosenbach, 1884. (Fehleisen, Ueber Erysipel, Deut. Zeit. f. Chir., *16*, 1882, 391; Erysipelkokken, Fehleisen, Die Aetiologie des Erysipels, Berlin, 1883; Rosenbach, Mikroorganismen bei den Wundinfectionskrankheiten des Menschens, 1884, 22; *Streptococcus erysipelatos* (sic) Rosenbach, *loc. cit.*; *Micrococcus scarlatinae* and *Streptococcus scarlatinae* Klein, Report of the Medical Officer of the Local Government Board for 1885–1886, No. 8, 1887, 85; *Streptococcus hemolyticus* Rolly, Cent. f. Bakt., I Abt., Orig., *61*, 1911, 87; *Streptococcus epidemicus* Davis, Jour. Am. Med. Assoc., *58*, 1912, 1852; Jour. Inf. Dis., *15*, 1914, 378; *ibid.*, *19*, 1916, 236.)

py.o′ge.nes. Gr. noun *pyum* pus; Gr. v. *gennaio* to produce; M.L. adj. *pyogenes* pus-producing.

Spherical or ovoid cells, 0.6 to 1 micron in diameter in cultures, usually spherical in blood and inflammatory exudates, occurring in chains or pairs; in broth culture, usually long chains. Gram-positive.

Serology: Constitutes Lancefield's group A (Jour. Exp. Med., *57*, 1933, 571). May be subdivided into serological types by the precipitin technique on the basis of the capsular protein M antigen. This antigen, which can be destroyed by certain proteolytic enzymes, is associated with virulence, and the antibodies to which it gives rise are primarily concerned with the specific protective action of immune sera (Lancefield, The Harvey Lectures, Ser. XXXVI, 1940–1941, 251). At least 40 types have been identified. May also be subdivided into types by the agglutination technique (Griffith, Jour. Hyg., *34*, 1934, 542) on the basis of the capsular T substance. The T substance is not associated with virulence. The M and T substances are independent and may occur in various combinations in different strains. Some strains may lack either or both type-specific antigens.

Action on blood: Surface and submerged colonies are beta hemolytic (Brown, Rockefeller Inst. Med. Res., Monograph 9, 1919, 14). In rare instances, some strains have been noted to lose their hemolytic properties when cultured aerobically. Two soluble antigenic hemolysins (streptolysins) produced in fluid cultures; influenced by constitution of medium and presence of serum. Streptolysin O is reversibly oxygen-labile; streptolysin S is very sensitive to heat and acids but is stable to oxygen (Todd, Jour. Path. Bact., *47*, 1938, 423).

Colony form: Mucoid, matt and glossy variants are ordinarily observed (Todd, Brit. Jour. Exp. Path., *9*, 1928, 1). The matt colony type contains the type-specific M substance and may or may not be virulent. Mucoid variants also possess the M substance in addition to the serologically inactive capsular substance, hyaluronic acid (Kendall *et al.*, Jour. Biol. Chem., *118*, 1937, 61). The glossy forms are always avirulent and contain little or no M substance.

Fibrinolytic (Tillett, Bact. Rev., *2*, 1938, 161). Only very rare strains fail to dissolve human fibrin.

Temperature relations: Optimum temperature, approximately 37° C. No growth at 10° or 45° C. Does not survive 60° C. for 30 minutes.

Tolerance tests: Fails to grow in presence of 6.5 per cent NaCl or in skim milk containing 0.1 per cent methylene blue. No growth in broth adjusted to pH 9.6 or on blood agar containing 40 per cent bile.

Litmus milk: Acid, seldom curdled, litmus reduced slowly or not at all.

Final pH in glucose broth, 4.8 to 6.0.

Acid characteristically produced from glucose, maltose, lactose, sucrose, salicin and trehalose. No acid from inulin, raffinose, arabinose, glycerol, mannitol, sorbitol or dulcitol. Rare strains noted that fail to ferment lactose, salicin or trehalose, or may ferment mannitol.

Starch not actively hydrolyzed, although some strains are reported to hydrolyze this substance under certain conditions (Crowley, Jour. Gen. Microbiol., *4*, 1950, 156).

Gelatin is not liquefied, and casein is not digested as detected by the usual cultural methods. However, under certain conditions some strains elaborate an extracellular proteinase that destroys the type-specific M antigen (except for type 28). It also is able to digest casein, gelatin and fibrin (Elliott, Jour. Exp. Med., *81*, 1945, 573).

Sodium hippurate not hydrolyzed. Esculin usually split.

Ammonia produced from arginine.

Erythrogenic toxin associated with scarlet fever rash produced by most strains.

Source: Originally isolated from infected wounds by Rosenbach (op. cit., 1884, 22). Also found in the human mouth, throat and respiratory tract and in inflammatory exudates, blood stream and lesions in human disease of varied character. Occasionally encountered in the udder of the cow and in laboratory animals. May be found in dust from sick rooms, hospital wards, schools, theaters and other public places.

Habitat: Primarily the human body, where it causes the formation of pus or even fatal septicemias.

2. Streptococcus equisimilis Frost and Engelbrecht, 1936.

(Type B, Ogura, Jour. Jap. Soc. Vet. Sci., 8, 1929, 174; Frost and Engelbrecht, A Revision of the Genus Streptococcus, privately published, 1936, 3 pp.; also see The Streptococci, 1940, 45; Human C, Sherman, Bact. Reviews, 1, 1937, 35.)

e.qui.si'mi.lis. L. noun equus horse; L. adj. similis resembling; M.L. adj. equisimilis literally horse-like, but intended to mean "resembling Streptococcus equi".

Morphology and general cultural characteristics resemble those of Streptococcus pyogenes. Matt colonies are characteristically produced. Gram-positive.

Serology: Belongs to Lancefield's group C. Several types have been established. Griffith's agglutinative types 7, 20 and 21 belong to this species. The type-specific antigens are proteins digestible with trypsin.

Action on blood: Beta hemolytic. Soluble hemolysins produced, one of which is identical with streptolysin O.

Fibrinolytic.

Temperature relations: No growth at 10° or 45° C. Does not survive 60° C. for 30 minutes.

Tolerance tests: Fails to grow in presence of 6.5 per cent NaCl or at pH 9.6. Does not grow in skim milk containing 0.1 per cent methylene blue, but Edwards (Kentucky Agr. Exp. Station Bull. 356, 1935) reported growth in an infusion-casein digest broth containing 0.000025 molar methylene blue, thus indicating a tolerance to methylene blue higher than that of Streptococcus pyo-

genes. Occasionally grows on 40 per cent bile blood agar.

Litmus milk: Lactose-fermenting strains produce an acid reaction. Milk may be curdled; litmus not reduced before curdling.

Final pH in glucose broth, between 4.6 and 5.4.

Acid from glucose, maltose, sucrose and trehalose. Glycerol fermented when incubated aerobically. May or may not ferment lactose and salicin. No acid from arabinose, raffinose, inulin, mannitol or sorbitol.

Starch and esculin may or may not be hydrolyzed. Gelatin not liquefied. Sodium hippurate not hydrolyzed.

Ammonia produced from arginine.

Distinctive characters: Members of this species may be confused with Streptococcus pyogenes but may be differentiated from the latter by their ability to ferment glycerol aerobically and to hydrolyze starch and by their generally greater tolerance to methylene blue and bile. For positive identification, the Lancefield precipitin technique must be relied upon.

Source: Occasionally associated with erysipelas and puerperal fever. The normal human nose and throat, vagina and skin. Sometimes found in respiratory tract of domestic animals.

Habitat: Human upper respiratory tract and vagina.

3. Streptococcus zooepidemicus Frost and Engelbrecht, 1936.

(Animal pyogenes, Type A of Edwards, Jour. Bact., 27, 1934, 527; Frost and Engelbrecht, A Revision of the Genus Streptococcus, privately published, 1936, 3 pp.; also see The Streptococci, 1940, 25; Streptococcus pyogenes animalis Seelemann, Deutsche tierarzt. Wchnschr., 50, 1942, 8 and 48.)

zo.ö.e.pi.de'mi.cus. Gr. noun zōum an animal; Gr. adj. epidēmius among people, prevalent, epidemic; M.L. adj. zoöepidemicus prevalent among animals.

Morphology and general cultural characteristics resemble those of Streptococcus pyogenes. Mucoid colonies are common. May produce capsular hyaluronic acid.

Serology: Belongs to Lancefield's group C.

Action on blood: Beta hemolytic. The

soluble hemolysin produced is distinct from streptolysins O and S.

Not fibrinolytic.

Temperature relations: No growth at 10° or 45° C. Does not survive 60° C. for 30 minutes.

Tolerance tests: Same as for *Streptococcus pyogenes*.

Litmus milk: Acid, usually does not curdle. Does not reduce litmus before curdling.

Final pH in glucose broth, between 4.6 and 5.0.

Acid from glucose, lactose, sucrose, sorbitol and salicin. May ferment maltose. No acid from the pentoses, trehalose, raffinose, inulin, glycerol or mannitol.

Starch usually hydrolyzed. Sodium hippurate not hydrolyzed. Gelatin not liquefied; esculin split.

Ammonia produced from arginine.

Distinctive characters: This species may be distinguished from closely allied species by its ability to ferment sorbitol but not trehalose and by its inability to lyse human fibrin.

Source: Blood stream, inflammatory exudates and lesions of diseased animals. Not known from man.

Habitat: Disease process of domestic and laboratory animals. (Horse: endometritis, fetus. Hog: Septicemia. Cow: septicemia, metritis, fetus. Fowls: slipped tendon. Guinea pig: lymphadenitis. Rabbit: septicemia. Fox: pneumonia.)

4. Streptococcus equi Sand and Jensen, 1888. (*Bacillus adenitis equi* Baruchello, Soc. veter. de Venetie, Undine, 1886; also see Baruchello, Giornale di anatomia, fisiologica et patologia degli animali domestici, Pisa, Sept., 1887; Sand and Jensen, Deutsche Ztschr. f. Tiermed., *13*, 1888, 436, dated December 27, 1887, Veterinary Congress, Copenhagen, 1887.)

e'qui. L. noun *equus* horse; L. gen.noun. *equi* of a horse.

Ovoid or spherical cells 0.6 to 1 micron in diameter; sometimes in pus the long axes of the cells are transverse to the long axis of the chain and at other times parallel with the long axis of the chain, in the latter case resembling streptobacilli; bacillary forms

are not rare; occur in pairs, short or long chains; very long chains common in broth cultures. Capsules often pronounced in blood of infected mice and when grown in serum. Gram-positive.

Generally poor growth in broth culture; growth increased by serum.

Serology: Belongs to Lancefield's group C. Cultures are generally poor antigens for production of agglutinating serum.

Action on blood: Beta hemolytic. The blood agar colonies are small and watery and dry out rapidly leaving flat, glistening colonies.

Growth in serum broth yields a soluble hemolysin that is distinct from streptolysins O and S.

Not fibrinolytic.

Temperature relations: Optimum temperature, 37° C. Growth slow at 20° C. No growth at 10° or 45° C. Does not survive 60° C. for 30 minutes.

Tolerance tests: Fails to grow in presence of 6.5 per cent NaCl or in skim milk containing 0.1 per cent methylene blue. No growth in media adjusted to pH 9.6 or on blood agar containing 40 per cent bile.

Litmus milk: No change.

Final pH in glucose broth, between 4.8 and 5.5.

Acid from glucose, maltose, sucrose and salicin. No acid from arabinose, lactose, trehalose, raffinose, inulin, glycerol, mannitol or sorbitol.

Sodium hippurate not hydrolyzed. Gelatin not liquefied; esculin not split.

Ammonia produced from arginine.

High virulence for mice, but low or no virulence for rabbits and guinea pigs.

Distinctive characters: This species is distinctive by its inability to ferment trehalose, sorbitol, glycerol or lactose.

Source: Pus from lesions and mucous membrane of upper respiratory tract of horses.

Habitat: Found only in strangles in horses.

5. Streptococcus dysgalactiae Diernhofer, 1932. (Diernhofer, Milchw. Forsch., *13*, 1932, 368; Group II, Minett, Proc. 12th Internat. Vet. Cong., *2*, 1934, 511; *Streptococcus pseudoagalactiae* Plastridge and

Hartsell, Jour. Inf. Dis., *61*, 1937, 110; see Little, Proc. Soc. Exp. Biol. Med., *41*, 1939, 254.)

dys.ga.lac′ti.ae. Gr. prefix *dys* ill, hard; Gr. noun *galactia* pertaining to milk; M.L. noun *dysgalactia* loss or impairment of milk secretion, dysgalactia; M.L. gen.noun *dysgalactiae* of dysgalactia.

Spherical or ovoid cells occurring in chains of medium length. Gram-positive.

Serology: Belongs to Lancefield's group C. Those cultures associated with suppurative polyarthritis(joint-ill) in lambs appear to belong to a distinct serological type of which the type antigen is a capsular protein (Blakemore, Elliott and Hart-Mercer, Jour. Path. Bact., *52*, 1941, 57).

Action on blood: Greening (alpha hemolytic). Soluble hemolysin not produced.

Colony form: Matt colonies may be produced similar to those of *Streptococcus pyogenes*.

Not fibrinolytic.

Temperature relations: No growth at 10° or 45° C. Does not survive 60° C. for 30 minutes.

Tolerance tests: Fails to grow in presence of 6.5 per cent NaCl or at pH 9.6. Does not grow in skim milk containing 0.1 per cent methylene blue. Does not grow on 40 per cent bile blood agar.

Litmus milk: Lactose-fermenting strains produce acid reaction with occasional curdling. Litmus not reduced before curdling.

Final pH in glucose broth: bovine strains, between 5.0 and 5.2; ovine strains, between 4.4 and 4.9.

Acid from glucose, maltose, sucrose and trehalose. Lactose, sorbitol and salicin may or may not be fermented. No acid from raffinose, inulin, glycerol or mannitol.

Esculin may or may not be hydrolyzed. Gelatin not liquefied. Sodium hippurate hydrolyzed by some bovine strains but not by ovine strains.

Ammonia produced from arginine.

Relationships: This non-hemolytic species needs further study to establish definitely its identity, the relationship of the ovine and bovine strains and its serological relationship to group C.

Source: Isolated from milk and udder of cows with acute but mild mastitis. Also from various tissues and organs of lambs suffering from suppurative polyarthritis.

Habitat: Probably of bovine and ovine origin.

6. **Streptococcus sanguis** White, 1946. (Serological group H, Hare, Jour. Path. Bact., *41*, 1935, 499; *Streptococcus* s.b.e., Loewe, Plummer, Niven and Sherman, Jour. Am. Med. Assoc., *130*, 1946, 257; White, in White and Niven, Jour. Bact., *51*, 1946, 717.)

san′guis. L. noun *sanguis* blood.

Spherical or ovoid cells 0.8 to 1.2 microns in diameter, occurring in medium or long chains. Cultures grown aerobically may show occasional rod-shaped cells. Gram-positive.

Serology: Two serological types (I and II) have been established among the non-hemolytic strains. Some cultures possess both type antigens (Washburn, White and Niven, Jour. Bact., *51*, 1946, 723). Dodd (Proc. Soc. Exp. Biol. Med., *70*, 1949, 598) placed both types within serological group H as established by Hare and indicated that this group contained at least 5 serological types. Porterfield (Jour. Gen. Microbiol., *4*, 1950, 92) reported that types I and I/II belonged to group H but that type II was serologically distinct.

Action on blood: The original group H streptococci as established by Hare were described as narrow-zoned beta hemolytic colonies on blood agar which had a tendency to throw off non-hemolytic variants. No soluble hemolysin could be demonstrated. As originally described, *Streptococcus sanguis* produced alpha reaction on blood agar, but one strain produced narrow-zone beta hemolysis (White and Niven, Jour. Bact., *51*, 1946, 717).

Colony forms: Matt or glossy type colonies may be produced, usually 0.7 to 0.9 mm in diameter on blood agar after 48 hours at 37° C.

Not fibrinolytic.

Temperature relations: No growth at 10° C. May or may not grow at 45° C. A few cultures may survive 60° C. for 30 minutes.

Tolerance tests: Fails to grow in presence of 6.5 per cent NaCl or in skim milk containing 0.1 per cent methylene blue. Most cultures grow on blood agar containing 40 per cent bile.

Litmus milk: Acid produced; may be curdled; litmus not reduced before curdling.

Final pH in glucose broth, between 4.6 and 5.2.

Acid from glucose, maltose, lactose, sucrose, trehalose and salicin. The majority of the cultures ferment inulin but not raffinose. Arabinose, xylose, glycerol, mannitol and sorbitol not fermented.

Nearly all cultures synthesize a polysaccharide (dextran) from sucrose in broth culture (Niven, Kiziuta and White, Jour. Bact., 51, 1946, 711) or on sucrose agar when incubated anaerobically (Hehre, Jour. Exp. Med., 83, 1946, 147). This polysaccharide cross reacts with type II pneumococcus antiserum.

Starch usually not hydrolyzed. Gelatin not liquefied.

Sodium hippurate not hydrolyzed. Esculin usually split.

Ammonia produced from arginine.

Relationships: Although the identity of non-hemolytic Streptococcus sanguis with the hemolytic group H streptococci has not yet been clearly established, their close relationship appears to warrant combining them into one species at this time. Further serological studies are needed to firmly establish the validity of this grouping. Although most Streptococcus sanguis cultures react with group H sera, attempts to prepare group H sera from Streptococcus sanguis cultures have been unsuccessful.

Source: The original group H strains were isolated from normal human throats. They were not believed to be associated with any serious human infections.

Streptococcus sanguis was originally isolated from so-called vegetation on heart valves from cases of subacute bacterial endocarditis and appeared to be one of the most common streptococci associated with this disease. Occasionally isolated from infected sinuses and teeth and from house dust.

Habitat: Unknown. Probably man.

7. **Streptococcus anginosus** Andrewes and Horder, 1906. (Andrewes and Horder, Lancet, 2, 1906, 708, 775 and 852; Minute

beta hemolytic streptococcus, Long and Bliss, Jour. Exp. Med., 60, 1934, 619; also see Long, Bliss and Walcott, ibid., 633, and Bliss, Jour. Bact., 33, 1937, 625.)

an.gi.no'sus. L. adj. anginosus pertaining to angina.

Minute cocci, one-half to two-thirds the size of Streptococcus pyogenes, occurring singly, in pairs, short chains and in small or large masses. Gram-positive, but may decolorize readily.

Serology: Comprises Lancefield's group F and type I group G. At least 4 serological types within group F have been established. The type-specific antigens in type I group F, and type I group G appear to be chemically and serologically identical.

Action on blood: Very minute colonies appear on blood agar after incubation for 48 to 96 hours; they are surrounded by minute zones of beta hemolysis. The hemolytic zones may appear before the colonies are visible to the naked eye. Growth and hemolysis greatly aided by incubation under 10 per cent carbon dioxide (Deibel, Thesis, Univ. of Chicago, 1952). Soluble hemolysin produced, but may be difficult to demonstrate (Long and Bliss, Jour. Inf. Dis., 61, 1937, 96). Streptolysin O or S not produced. Non-hemolytic strains reported by Rantz (Jour. Inf. Dis., 71, 1942, 61).

Colony forms: Matt colonies usually not produced. Under the microscope, colonies are finely granular and may appear wrinkled and crenated.

Not fibrinolytic.

Temperature relations: No growth at 10° C. and, with few exceptions, no growth at 45° C. Does not survive 60° C. for 30 minutes.

Tolerance tests: Does not grow in broth containing 6.5 per cent NaCl or at pH 9.6. No growth on 40 per cent bile blood agar or in skim milk containing 0.1 per cent methylene blue.

Litmus milk: Acid produced by the lactose-fermenting strains. Milk may be curdled by some strains. Litmus not reduced before curdling.

Final pH in glucose broth, between 4.5 and 5.2.

Acid from glucose, maltose, sucrose and salicin. Lactose and trehalose usually fermented. Raffinose fermented by the group G strains. Inulin, glycerol, mannitol and sorbitol not fermented.

Starch not hydrolyzed. Gelatin not liquefied.

Sodium hippurate not hydrolyzed. Esculin split.

Ammonia produced from arginine.

Oxidizes butyric acid with the production of hydrogen peroxide (Niven, Evans and White, Jour. Bact., *49*, 1945, 105).

Requires folic acid for growth in simplified media (Niven, Washburn and Sherman, Jour. Bact., *51*, 1946, 128).

Requires high carbon dioxide tension or an unsaturated fatty acid for growth in simplified media (Deibel, Thesis, Univ. of Chicago, 1952).

Comments: All of the minute streptococci do not adhere to the original description of *Streptococcus anginosus* as given by Andrewes and Horder. The minute streptococci comprise a homogeneous group based upon physiological characteristics other than those originally employed by these investigators; also it will be noted that this species, as herein described, contains representatives that belong to two different serological groups. Further study of these microorganisms is needed to establish definitely the validity of this precedent. Minor differences between the group F and the minute group G streptococci may warrant the establishment of two separate varieties within this species or an ultimate separation into two separate species (Sherman, Bact. Rev., *1*, 1937, 3).

Source: Human throat, sinuses, abscesses, vagina, skin, feces. Has been associated with glomerular nephritis and various types of mild respiratory diseases.

Habitat: Human respiratory tract.

8. **Streptococcus agalactiae** Lehmann and Neumann, 1896. (Streptococcus de la mammite, Nocard and Mollereau, Ann. Inst. Past., *1*, 1887, 109; *Streptococcus nocardi* Trevisan, I generi e le specie delle Batteriacee, 1889, 30; *Streptococcus agalactiae contagiosae* Kitt, Bakterienkunde, Wien, 1893, 322; Lehmann and Neumann, Bakt. Diag., 1 Aufl., *2*, 1896, 126; *Strepto-*

coccus mastitidis Migula, Syst. d. Bakt., *2*, 1900, 19.)

a.ga.lac'ti.ae. Gr. noun *agalactia* want of milk, agalactia; M.L. gen.noun *agalactiae* of agalactia.

Spherical or ovoid cells 0.6 to 1.2 microns in diameter, occurring in chains of seldom less than four cells and frequently very long. Chains may appear to be composed of paired cocci.

Serology: Constitutes Lancefield's group B. May be subdivided into a number of serological types by the precipitin technique on the basis of the capsular carbohydrate "S" substance. The type-specific polysaccharides appear to have a direct relationship to virulence, and the antibodies to which they give rise are concerned with the specific protective action of immune sera. Some strains may lack the "S" substance.

There is a difference of opinion as to whether the serological types indigenous to man and cattle are distinct (Lancefield, Harvey Lectures, Ser. XXXVI, 1940, 251; Simmons and Keogh, Austral. Jour. Exp. Biol. Med. Sci., *18*, 1940, 151; Brown, Proc. Fifth Internat. Congress Microbiol., Rio de Janeiro, 1950, in press).

Action on blood: About half the strains produce narrow but clear zones of hemolysis on blood agar. A few may produce broad zones of hemolysis. The other strains produce greening (alpha hemolytic) reaction. The hemolytic strains produce a soluble hemolysin that is moderately sensitive to heat and acid and that is distinct from streptolysins O and S.

Some strains produce a yellow, orange or brick-red pigment in stab cultures. May also be noted as an orange sediment in broth cultures, especially when starch is added.

Not fibrinolytic.

Temperature relations: Optimum temperature, 37° C. No growth at 10° or 45° C. Does not survive 60° C. for 30 minutes.

Tolerance tests: Usually grows in presence of 4 per cent NaCl but not in 6.5 per cent NaCl. Does not grow in milk containing 0.1 per cent methylene blue or in broth adjusted to pH 9.6. Usually grows on blood agar containing 40 per cent bile.

Litmus milk: Acid, usually followed by curdling. Litmus reduced subsequent to curdling. No proteolysis.

Final pH in glucose broth, between 4.2 and 4.8.

Acid from glucose, maltose, sucrose and trehalose. Nearly all strains ferment lactose, although an occasional strain may fail to ferment or may lose its ability to ferment lactose. Salicin may or may not be fermented. Glycerol is fermented aerobically (Gunsalus and Sherman, Jour. Bact., *45*, 1943, 155), but rarely anaerobically. No acid from xylose, arabinose, raffinose, inulin, mannitol or sorbitol.

Starch not hydrolyzed; gelatin not liquefied.

Sodium hippurate hydrolyzed, but esculin not split.

Ammonia produced from arginine.

Erythrogenic toxin not produced.

Distinctive character: This species is distinctive among the pyogenic group by its ability to hydrolyze sodium hippurate.

Source: Isolated from milk and tissues from udders of cows infected with mastitis. Also reported to be associated with a variety of human infections, especially those of the urogenital tract.

Habitat: Udder of cows infected with mastitis.

9. Streptococcus acidominimus Ayers and Mudge, 1922. (Jour. Inf. Dis., *31*, 1922, 40; *ibid.*, *33*, 1923, 155.)

a.ci.do.mi'ni.mus. L. adj. *acidus* sour, acid; L. sup.adj. *minimus* very least; M.L. neut.n. *acidum* an acid; M.L. adj. *acidominimus* literally acid least, probably intended to mean that this organism produces the least amount of acid.

Description taken from Smith and Sherman (Jour. Inf. Dis., *65*, 1939, 301).

Spheres. Generally occur in short chains.

Serology: Does not belong to any established serological group.

Action on blood: Greening (alpha hemolytic). No soluble hemolysin produced.

Temperature relations: No growth at 10° or 45° C. Some strains are reported to produce feeble growth at 45° C. Does not survive 60° C. for 30 minutes.

Tolerance tests: Growth in broth containing 2 per cent NaCl but not 6.5 per cent NaCl. No growth at pH 9.6 or in milk containing 0.01 per cent methylene blue.

Litmus milk: Little or no visible change.

Final pH in glucose broth, between 6.5 and 5.6. Most strains fail to lower the pH below 6.0.

Acid from glucose, lactose and sucrose. The majority of strains ferment maltose and trehalose. Mannitol may or may not be fermented. A few cultures ferment sorbitol and salicin. Arabinose, xylose, raffinose, inulin and glycerol not fermented. The fermentation tests are difficult to perform with accuracy because of the high limiting pH.

Starch and gelatin not hydrolyzed.

Sodium hippurate hydrolyzed slowly. Esculin not split by most strains.

Ammonia not produced from arginine.

Distinctive characters: This species may be confused with *Streptococcus agalactiae* because of its ability to hydrolyze sodium hippurate, but it can be differentiated easily by its low acid production in glucose broth, by its inability to produce ammonia from arginine and by its inability to ferment glycerol.

Source: Originally isolated from freshly drawn milk. Occurs abundantly in the bovine vagina. Also found on the skin of calves.

Habitat: The bovine vagina.

10. Streptococcus salivarius Andrewes and Horder, 1906. (Lancet, *2*, 1906, 712.)

sa.li.va'ri.us. L. adj. *salivarius* salivary, slimy.

Description based on studies by Sherman, Niven and Smiley (Jour. Bact., *45*, 1943, 249).

Spherical or ovoid cells 0.8 to 1.0 micron in diameter. Chain length may vary from short to very long. Gram-positive.

Serology: No group-specific antigen has been demonstrated. Serological types I and II have been established based upon the presence of capsular antigens (Sherman, Niven and Smiley, *loc. cit.*). Several additional serological types are known to exist. A cross reaction occurs between type I and *Streptococcus* MG (Mirick *et al.*, Jour. Exp. Med., *80*, 1944, 431).

Action on blood: Indifferent (gamma reaction of Brown, Rockefeller Inst. Med. Res., Monograph 9, 1919, 8) on horse blood agar. Rare strains produce weak greening. No soluble hemolysin is produced.

Both smooth and rough variants are observed as detected by colony forms and growth characteristics in broth. Rough variants often revert to smooth upon subculture in broth. Notwithstanding rather vigorous growth in culture media, cultures die out rapidly.

Temperature relations: Optimum temperature, approximately 37° C. Growth at 45° C. but no growth at 10° C. No growth at 47° C. Does not survive 60° C. for 30 minutes.

Tolerance tests: No growth in broth containing 6.5 per cent NaCl. No growth at pH 9.6, on 30 per cent bile blood agar or in milk containing 0.1 per cent methylene blue.

Litmus milk: Acidified and curdled promptly by all lactose-fermenting strains. Litmus completely reduced after curdling. No digestion.

Final pH in glucose broth, between 4.0 and 4.4.

Produces large, mucoid colonies on agar medium containing 5 per cent sucrose or raffinose similar to those produced by *Leuconostoc* species. The polysaccharides produced are a soluble, serologically active levan (not related to type specificity on other media) and an insoluble dextran. Colonies on sucrose agar may vary from "smooth" to "rough" depending upon the relative proportions of the two polysaccharides synthesized. These variations are not related to the smooth-rough variants observed in other media.

Acid from glucose, maltose, sucrose, raffinose, inulin and salicin. No acid from glycerol, mannitol, sorbitol, arabinose or xylose. Trehalose and lactose usually fermented. Some strains ferment only the terminal fructofuranose portion of the raffinose molecule, thus leaving melibiose as a metabolic product.

Starch, sodium hippurate and gelatin not hydrolyzed. Esculin split.

Ammonia is not produced from arginine.

Distinctive character: Members of this species are most easily identified by their characteristic colonies produced on agar media containing 5 per cent sucrose.

Source: Saliva, sputum and intestinal tract of the human. Not pathogenic.

Habitat: Human mouth, throat and nasopharynx.

11. **Streptococcus mitis** Andrewes and Horder, 1906. (Lancet, *2*, 1906, 712.)

mi′tis. L. adj. *mitis* mild.

Description based on studies by Sherman, Niven and Smiley (Jour. Bact., *45*, 1943, 249).

Spherical or ellipsoidal cells 0.6 to 0.8 micron in diameter. Long axis of cell coincides with long axis of chain. Chain length may vary from moderately long to very long. Gram-positive.

Serology: No group-specific antigen has been demonstrated. A very large number of serological types exists as determined by the precipitin and agglutinin reactions. Serological typing is of little or no value in the identification of this species.

Action on blood: Produces pronounced green zones (alpha hemolytic) of varying intensities on blood agar. No soluble hemolysin produced.

Both smooth and rough variants are observed as detected by colony forms and growth characteristics in broth. Rough variants often revert to smooth upon subculture in broth. Cultures tend to die out rapidly in artificial media.

Temperature relations: Optimum growth at approximately 37° C. Growth may or may not occur at 45° C. Does not survive 60° C. for 30 minutes.

Tolerance tests: No growth in broth containing 6.5 per cent NaCl. No growth at pH 9.6, and only a minority of the strains grow on 10 per cent bile blood agar. No growth in litmus milk containing 0.01 per cent methylene blue.

Litmus milk: Acidified and usually curdled promptly by the lactose-fermenting strains. Litmus reduced after curdling. No digestion.

Final pH in glucose broth, between 4.2 and 5.8, usually about 4.5.

Only rare strains produce large, mucoid colonies on 5 per cent sucrose agar. Some strains produce colonies on sucrose agar resembling small bits of broken glass.

Acid from glucose, maltose, sucrose and usually from lactose and salicin. A minority of the strains ferment raffinose and trehalose. No acid from inulin, mannitol, sorbitol, glycerol, arabinose or xylose.

Sodium hippurate and gelatin not hydrolyzed. Esculin is split by a minority of the strains. Starch may be hydrolyzed feebly by some strains.

Ammonia may or may not be produced from arginine.

Some strains oxidize butyric acid with the production of hydrogen peroxide and acetic acid (Wolin, Evans and Niven, Jour. Bact., *64*, 1952, 531).

Comments: This species comprises the heterogeneous group of greening streptococci associated with the human respiratory tract. It has no unique identifiable characteristic, and some non-hemolytic varieties of the pyogenic group may be confused with it. The species may yield to more incisive methods of segregation and more accurate characterization of its constituent units.

Source: Saliva, sputum and intestinal tract of the human. Ordinarily not considered pathogenic but may be recovered from ulcerated teeth and sinuses and from the blood and heart lesions in subacute endocarditis cases.

Habitat: Human mouth, throat and nasopharynx.

12. **Streptococcus bovis** Orla-Jensen, 1919, *emend.* Sherman, 1937. (Orla-Jensen, The Lactic Acid Bacteria, 1919, 137; Sherman, Bacteriological Reviews, *1*, 1937, 57.)

bo'vis. L. noun *bos* a cow; L. gen.noun *bovis* of a cow.

Spherical or ovoid cells, 0.8 to 1.0 micron in diameter, occurring in pairs and chains. Some occur in long chains. Gram-positive.

Serology: This species is serologically heterogeneous. Many serological types are known to occur. Some strains cross-react with group D sera (Sherman, Jour. Bact., *35*, 1938, 81). Shattock (Jour. Gen. Microbiol., *3*, 1949, 80) claims that by special methods of preparing the cellular extracts, the group D antigen can be demonstrated.

Action on blood: The changes exhibited

vary from strong greening (alpha hemolytic) to no observable change (gamma hemolytic). No soluble hemolysin produced.

Generally uniform turbidity with some sediment produced in broth cultures. Some strains tend to die out rapidly in artificial media.

Temperature relations: Growth at 45° but not at 10° C. Survives 60° C. for 30 minutes.

Tolerance tests: No growth in broth containing 6.5 per cent NaCl. No growth at pH 9.6. May tolerate 0.01 per cent, but not 0.1 per cent, methylene blue in milk. Growth occurs on blood agar containing 40 per cent bile.

Litmus milk: Acid; usually curdles with litmus reduction after curdling. No digestion.

Final pH in glucose broth, between 4.0 and 4.5.

Some strains synthesize a dextran from sucrose resulting in the production of large, mucoid colonies on agar media containing 5 per cent sucrose.

Acid from glucose, fructose, mannose, galactose, maltose, lactose, sucrose, raffinose and salicin; sometimes from xylose, arabinose, trehalose, inulin, mannitol and sorbitol. No acid from glycerol.

Starch is hydrolyzed. Occasional strains hydrolyze sodium hippurate. Gelatin not hydrolyzed. Esculin split.

Ammonia is not produced from arginine.

Distinctive characters: This species is characterized by its temperature limits of growth, its bile tolerance and its ability to hydrolyze starch. A significant proportion of the strains from bovine sources do not, however, fit the above description. Further study of the streptococci from bovine sources is indicated.

Source: Alimentary tract of the cow. Sometimes found in large numbers in human feces. May be encountered in blood and heart lesions of certain cases of subacute endocarditis (Niven, Washburn and White, Jour. Bact., *55*, 1948, 601).

Habitat: Bovine alimentary tract.

13. **Streptococcus equinus** Andrewes and Horder, 1906. (Lancet, *2*, 1906, 712.)

e.qui'nus. L. adj. *equinus* pertaining to a horse.

Spheres, occurring in moderately long chains. Some cultures show very long chains in broth.

Serology: No group-specific antigen has been demonstrated.

Action on blood: Usually weak greening. No soluble hemolysin produced.

Temperature relations: Growth at 45° but not at 50° C. No growth at 10° C. Occasional strains survive 60° C. for 30 minutes.

Tolerance tests: Growth in broth containing 2 per cent NaCl but not in 6.5 per cent NaCl. No growth at pH 9.6 or in milk containing 0.1 per cent methylene blue. Growth on 40 per cent bile blood agar.

Litmus milk: No visible change.

Final pH in glucose broth, between 4.0 and 4.5.

No polysaccharide synthesized from sucrose.

Acid from glucose, fructose, galactose, maltose and usually from sucrose and salicin. Raffinose and inulin are seldom fermented. No acid from arabinose, xylose, lactose, mannitol or glycerol.

Starch is hydrolyzed on a favorable medium. Sodium hippurate and gelatin not hydrolyzed. Esculin split.

Ammonia not produced from arginine.

Distinctive character: This species is ordinarily differentiated from the other viridans streptococci by its inability to ferment lactose. However, occasional strains in other species of this group also fail to ferment this sugar, thus necessitating the determination of the tolerance to bile, of the ability to hydrolyze starch and of other tests for final identification.

Source and habitat: Predominating streptococcus in the alimentary tract of the horse.

14. Streptococcus thermophilus Orla-Jensen, 1916. (Maelkeri-Bacteriologi, 1916, 37; The Lactic Acid Bacteria, 1919, 136.)

ther.mo'phil.us. Gr. noun *therme* heat; Gr. adj. *philus* dear, loving; M.L. adj. *thermophilus* heat-loving.

Spherical or ovoid cells, 0.7 to 0.9 micron in diameter, occurring in pairs to long chains. Gram-positive.

Serology: No group-specific antigen has been demonstrated.

Action on blood: Most strains produce a weak greening reaction.

Temperature relations: Optimum, between 40° and 45° C. Grows at 50° but not at 53° C. No growth below 20° C. Survives 65° C. for 30 minutes.

Tolerance tests: Very sensitive to salt as indicated by no growth in broth containing 2 per cent NaCl. No growth in milk containing 0.01 per cent methylene blue nor on 10 per cent bile blood agar.

Litmus milk: Acid, curdled, followed by reduction of the litmus. No digestion.

Final pH in glucose broth, between 4.0 and 4.5. Members of this species preferentially ferment the disaccharides sucrose and lactose and, therefore, may show a lower final pH from fermenting these sugars than from fermenting glucose.

No polysaccharide is synthesized from sucrose.

Acid from glucose, fructose, lactose and sucrose; seldom ferments the pentoses or raffinose. No acid from trehalose, maltose, inulin, glycerol, mannitol, sorbitol or salicin.

Starch may be hydrolyzed on a favorable medium. Sodium hippurate and gelatin not hydrolyzed. Esculin not split.

Ammonia not produced from arginine.

Distinctive characters: This species may be easily recognized by its high temperature range for growth, its thermal tolerance, its extreme sensitivity to salt and its inability to ferment maltose.

Source: Milk and milk products. Employed as a starter for Swiss cheese.

Habitat: Unknown.

15. Streptococcus uberis Diernhofer, 1932. (Diernhofer, Milchw. Forsch., *13*, 1932, 368; "Group III" non-hemolytic streptococci, Edwards, Jour. Comp. Path. Therap., *45*, 1932, 43.)

u'ber.is. L. noun *uber* udder, teat; L. gen.noun *uberis* of an udder.

Description taken from Seeley (Jour. Bact., *62*, 1951, 107).

Spheres, occurring in pairs or chains of moderate length.

Serology: A group-specific and distinctive antigen has been reported to exist among the strains tested (Seeley, *loc. cit.*), but the status of this species with respect to its serology remains doubtful. Members of this species have been related to group E (Little, Thirteenth Ann. Report, N. Y. State Assoc. Dairy Milk Insp., 1939, 35; Jacob, Thesis, Univ. Reading, 1947). Plastridge and Williams (Jour. Bact., *38*, 1939, 352) established 11 serological types.

Action on blood: Slight greening (alpha hemolytic) or indifferent (gamma hemolytic).

Temperature relations: Growth at 10° and 45° C. Some variation occurs among the individual strains at both extremes of temperature, depending, however, upon the previous history of the method for handling the culture. Most strains survive 60° C. for 30 minutes.

Tolerance tests: Growth in broth containing 4.0 per cent NaCl but not in 6.5 per cent NaCl. Growth in milk containing 0.01 per cent methylene blue but not in 0.1 per cent methylene blue. No growth at pH 9.6. Most strains fail to grow on 10 per cent bile blood agar but a few strains are able to tolerate as much as 40 per cent bile.

Litmus milk: Freshly isolated strains may acidify and curdle milk with reduction of litmus after curdling. Old laboratory strains tend to lose their ability to curdle milk. No digestion.

Final pH in glucose broth, between 4.6 and 4.9.

No polysaccharide synthesis from sucrose.

Acid from glucose, fructose, maltose, lactose, sucrose, trehalose, mannitol, sorbitol and salicin. Most strains ferment inulin but fail to ferment raffinose. Xylose, arabinose and melibiose not fermented. Glycerol fermented aerobically but not anaerobically.

Starch hydrolyzed by a minority of the strains. Gelatin not liquefied. Sodium hippurate hydrolyzed, though slowly, by some strains. Esculin split.

Ammonia produced from arginine. Tyrosine not decarboxylated.

Relationships: This species represents an important group commonly associated with bovine mastitis. Its temperature limits of growth and its ability to ferment the higher alcohols tend to relate this species to the enterococci. However, other characteristics, including its nutritional requirements, clearly differentiate this species from the enterococci and would tend to place it among the viridans streptococci.

Source: From raw milk and from freshly drawn milk of cows affected with mastitis.

Habitat: Found in bovine udder infections.

16. **Streptococcus faecalis*** Andrewes and Horder, 1906. (*Micrococcus ovalis* Escherich, Die Darmbakterien des Säuglings und ihre Beziehungen zur Physiologie der Verdauung. Stuttgart, 1886, 89; reclassified as a streptococcus by Escherich in Jahrb. f. Kinderheilk., *49*, 1899, 161; Entérocoque, Thiercelin, Compt. rend. Soc. Biol., Paris, *54*, 1902, 1082; *Enterococcus proteiformis* Thiercelin and Jouhaud, Compt. rend. Soc. Biol., Paris, *55*, 1903, 686; Andrewes and Horder, Lancet, *2*, 1906, 708; *Streptococcus ovalis* Lehmann and Neumann, Bakt. Diag., 7 Aufl., *2*, 1927, 209 and 230.)

fae.cal′is. L. adj. *faex, faecis* dregs; M.L. adj. *faecalis* relating to feces.

Ovoid cells elongated in direction of the chain; 0.5 to 1.0 micron in diameter. Occur mostly in pairs or short chains. Gram-positive.

Serology: Belongs to Lancefield's group D. Many serological types and sub-types are known to exist (Takedo, Zeit. Immunforsch., *86*, 1935, 341; Shigeno, *ibid.*, *90*, 1937, 323). Sharpe and Shattock (Jour. Gen. Microbiol., *6*, 1952, 150) established 24 serological types based upon agglutinin and precipitin tests. Some cultures of *Streptococcus faecalis* and *Streptococcus lactis* appear to contain identical type-specific antigens, although they belong to different serological groups (Niven, Thesis, Cornell Univ., 1939; Sharpe, Jour. Gen. Microbiol., *7*, 1952, 192).

---

* Although the specific epithet *ovalis* has priority, the species name *Streptococcus faecalis* is being retained here because of its widespread usage and because of the more complete description given by Andrewes and Horder (*op. cit.*, 1906, 708).

Action on blood: Greening (alpha hemolytic) to indifferent (gamma hemolytic).

Abundant growth in broth media containing fermentable carbohydrate with the production of uniform turbidity and heavy sediment.

Some strains are actively motile (Levensen, Ann. Inst. Past., *60*, 1938, 99; Bruner, Edwards, Doll and Moran, Cornell Veterinarian, *38*, 1948, 313; Auerbach and Felsenfeld, Jour. Bact., *56*, 1948, 587).

A few strains are reported that are yellow pigmented (Hannay, Jour. Gen. Microbiol., *4*, 1950, 294).

Not fibrinolytic.

Temperature relations: Growth at 10° and 45° C. Survives 60° C. for 30 minutes.

Tolerance tests: Growth in broth containing 6.5 per cent NaCl. Growth at pH 9.6 (Sherman and Stark, Jour. Dairy Sci., *17*, 1934, 525; Shattock and Hirsch, Jour. Path. Bact., *59*, 1947, 495). Growth in milk containing 0.1 per cent methylene blue. Growth on 40 per cent and higher concentrations of bile in blood agar.

Litmus milk: Acidified, usually curdled with complete reduction of litmus before curdling. Some cultures do not reduce litmus before curdling.

Final pH in glucose broth, between 4.0 and 4.4.

Acid from glucose, maltose, lactose, trehalose and salicin. All cultures ferment glycerol, although this substance may be fermented only under aerobic conditions by some strains (Gunsalus and Sherman, Jour. Bact., *45*, 1943, 155). Mannitol and sorbitol are fermented with only occasional exceptions. Arabinose and sucrose may or may not be fermented. Inulin and raffinose are seldom fermented.

Some strains are able to ferment citric acid in the absence of any fermentable carbohydrate with the production of acetic acid, carbon dioxide, formic acid and lactic acid (Campbell and Gunsalus, Jour. Bact., *48*, 1944, 71).

No polysaccharide is synthesized from sucrose.

Starch and gelatin not hydrolyzed. Sodium hippurate may or may not be hydrolyzed. Esculin split.

Ammonia produced from arginine.

Tyrosine is decarboxylated with the production of tyramine and carbon dioxide.

Distinctive characters: This species and the other members of the enterococcus group are easily distinguished from the other *Streptococcus* species by their wide temperature limits of growth, their salt tolerance and their ability to initiate growth at pH 9.6. They are also considerably more tolerant to penicillin than the other streptococci, most strains being able to grow in the presence of 0.5 to 1.0 unit of this antibiotic per ml. All enterococci are distinctive in their ability to decarboxylate tyrosine.

Source: Human feces and the intestine of many warm-blooded animals. Occasionally encountered in urinary infections and in the blood stream and heart lesions in subacute endocarditis cases. Associated with European foul-brood of bees; found in milk and dairy products. Has been associated with mild outbreaks of food poisoning.

Habitat: Intestines of humans and many other warm-blooded animals.

16a. *Streptococcus faecalis* var. *liquefaciens* (Sternberg, 1893, *emend.* Orla-Jensen, 1919) Mattick, 1947. (*Streptococcus liquefaciens* Sternberg*, Manual of Bacteriology, 1893, 613; Orla-Jensen, The Lactic Acid Bacteria, 1919, 142; Mattick, Proc. Fourth Internat. Cong. for Microbiology, Copenhagen, 1947, 519.)

li.que.fa′ci.ens. L. part.adj. *liquefaciens* liquefying.

This variety was regarded as a separate species, *Streptococcus liquefaciens*, in the Manual, 6th ed., 1948, 326, but it is believed that the differences are not sufficient to warrant species distinction. This variety possesses the same characteristics as *Streptococcus faecalis* except as given below. It is a member of the enterococcus group and Lancefield's group D. It can not be dis-

---

* *Streptococcus liquefaciens* Frankland and Frankland, 1888 (Phil. Trans. Roy. Soc. London, *178*, B, 1888, 264), may have been an organism identical with Sternberg's; it was described as producing a yellow pigment, as do certain strains of *Streptococcus faecalis*.

tinguished from *Streptococcus faecalis* by serological type-specificity.

Litmus milk: Acidified, curdled and peptonized. The proteolysis of the milk is usually characteristic in showing digestion down one side of the tube. Litmus completely reduced before curdling. Old laboratory strains tend to lose their ability to peptonize milk.

Gelatin liquefied.

16b. *Streptococcus faecalis* var. *zymogenes* (MacCallum and Hastings, 1899) Mattick, 1947. (*Micrococcus zymogenes* MacCallum and Hastings, Jour. Exp. Med., *4*, 1899, 521; *Streptococcus zymogenes* Holland, Jour. Bact., *5*, 1920, 226; Mattick, Proc. Fourth Internat. Cong. for Microbiology, Copenhagen, 1947, 519.)

zy.mo'ge.nes. Gr. noun *zyme* leaven, ferment; Gr. v. *gennaio* to produce; M.L. adj. *zymogenes* ferment-producing.

This variety was regarded as a separate species, *Streptococcus zymogenes*, in the Manual, 6th ed., 1948, 327, but it is believed that the differences are not sufficient to warrant species distinction. This variety possesses the same characteristics as *Streptococcus faecalis* except as given below. It is a member of the enterococcus group and Lancefield's group D. It can not be distinguished from *Streptococcus faecalis* by serological type-specificity.

Action on blood: Broad zoned hemolysis (beta hemolytic). An acid-labile soluble hemolysin is produced, but it is difficult to demonstrate under the usual conditions of testing.

Litmus milk: Acidified, usually curdled, with complete reduction of the litmus before curdling. May or may not peptonize. The proteolytic strains show changes in litmus milk similar to those effected by *Streptococcus faecalis* var. *liquefaciens*.

Gelatin may or may not be liquefied.

17. **Streptococcus durans** Sherman and Wing, 1937. (Jour. Dairy Sci., *20*, 1937, 165.)

du'rans. L. part.adj. *durans* hardening, resisting.

Spherical to ovoid cells elongated in direction of the chain, 0.5 to 1.0 micron in diameter. Occur mostly in pairs or short chains.

Serology: Belongs to Lancefield's group D. Many serological types are known to exist. No distinctive separation of the serological types from those of *Streptococcus faecalis* and its varieties, although some broad divisions can be made (Sharpe and Shattock, Jour. Gen. Microbiol., *6*, 1952, 150).

Action on blood: Hemolytic (beta), but the zones of hemolysis are generally less extensive than those produced by *Streptococcus faecalis* var. *zymogenes*. Soluble hemolysin difficult to demonstrate.

Abundant growth with the production of uniform turbidity and heavy sediment in broth media containing fermentable carbohydrate.

Not fibrinolytic.

Temperature relations: Growth at 10° and 45° C. Survives 60° C. for 30 minutes.

Tolerance tests: Same as for *Streptococcus faecalis*.

Litmus milk: Acidified, usually curdled, with litmus reduction after curdling. No proteolysis.

Final pH in glucose broth, between 4.0 and 4.5.

Acid from glucose, maltose and lactose. Trehalose and salicin may or may not be fermented. Ferments glycerol only aerobically. Sucrose and mannitol rarely fermented. Arabinose, raffinose, inulin and sorbitol not fermented.

No polysaccharide synthesized from sucrose.

Starch or gelatin not hydrolyzed. Sodium hippurate may or may not be hydrolyzed. Esculin split.

Ammonia produced from arginine.

Tyrosine is decarboxylated to yield tyramine and carbon dioxide.

Distinctive characters: As a member of the enterococcus group, this species is closely related to *Streptococcus faecalis* and its varieties. Other than its hemolytic properties, this species may be difficult to distinguish from some cultures now classified as *Streptococcus faecalis*. However, in contrast to the typical *Streptococcus faecalis*, this species fails to reduce litmus before curdling milk, fails to ferment sorbitol, rarely ferments mannitol or sucrose and ferments glycerol only aerobically. Skadhauge (Studies on Enterococci with Special Reference to Their Serological Properties, A Monograph, Copenhagen, 1950) reports that this species does not tolerate 1/2500 potassium tellurite in a medium, which is in contrast to the typical *Streptococcus faecalis* and its varieties.

Source: Originally isolated from spray dried milk powder. Found in milk and dairy products and in the human intestine.

Habitat: Intestines of humans and other warm-blooded animals.

18. **Streptococcus lactis** (Lister, 1873) Löhnis, 1909. (*Bacterium lactis* Lister, Quart. Jour. Micro. Sci., *13*, 1873, 380; also see *ibid.*, *18*, 1878, 177; Löhnis, Cent. f. Bakt., II Abt., *22*, 1909, 553.)

lac'tis. L. noun *lac* milk; L. gen.noun *lactis* of milk.

Ovoid cells elongated in direction of the chain; 0.5 to 1.0 micron in diameter. Occur mostly in pairs or short chains. Some cultures produce long chains. Gram-positive.

Serology: A group-specific antigen has been demonstrated (Sherman, Smiley and Niven, Jour. Dairy Sci., *23*, 1940, 529; Seeleman and Nottbohm, Zent. f. Bakt., I Abt., Orig., *146*, 1940, 142; Shattock and Mattick, Jour. Hyg., *43*, 1943, 173). The serological group has been designated by Shattock and Mattick (*loc. cit.*) as group N. Many serological types are known to exist.

Action on blood: Slight greening (alpha hemolytic) to indifferent (gamma hemolytic).

Temperature relations: Growth at 10° but not at 45° C. May survive 60° C. for 30 minutes.

Tolerance tests: Growth in broth containing 4 per cent NaCl but not in 6.5 per cent NaCl. Growth initiated at pH 9.2 but not at pH 9.6. Growth in milk containing 0.3 per cent methylene blue. Growth on 40 per cent bile blood agar.

Litmus milk: Acidified, curdled, litmus completely reduced before curdling. Old laboratory strains may lose the ability to curdle milk. No digestion.

Final pH in glucose broth, between 4.0 and 4.5.

Acid from glucose, maltose and lactose. May or may not ferment xylose, arabinose, sucrose, trehalose, mannitol and salicin. No acid from raffinose, inulin, glycerol or sorbitol. Strains have been isolated from plants that fail to ferment lactose (Yawger and Sherman, Jour. Dairy Sci., *20*, 1937, 83). Orla-Jensen and Hansen (Zent. f. Bakt., II Abt., *86*, 1932, 6) described certain strains that ferment raffinose.

Starch and gelatin not hydrolyzed. Sodium hippurate and esculin may or may not be split.

Ammonia produced from arginine. Tyrosine not decarboxylated.

This species is of great economic importance in the dairy industry. Certain strains are employed as starter cultures in preparing cheeses and cultured milk drinks. Some strains are capable of fermenting citric acid when incorporated with a fermentable sugar with the production of carbon dioxide, acetic acid and diacetyl. (See discussion and reference citations of citrate-fermenting strains by Swartling, Jour. Dairy Res., *18*, 1951, 256.) For a recent discussion of the relationships of *Streptococcus lactis* to *S. cremoris* and other lactic acid streptococci, see Sherman (Jour. Dairy Sci., *38*, 1955, 1184).

Some cultures of this species synthesize a powerful antibiotic, nisin, that inhibits the growth of a wide variety of other Grampositive microorganisms (Mattick and Hirsch, Nature, *154*, 1944, 551; Hirsch, Jour. Gen. Microbiol., *5*, 1951, 208).

Distinctive characteristics: Growth at 10° or below and at 40° but not at 45° C.; rapid and complete reduction of litmus before curdling milk; growth in the presence of 4 per cent but not in 6.5 per cent NaCl; ammonia produced from arginine; growth at pH 9.2 but not at pH 9.6; tyrosine not decarboxylated.

Source: A common contaminant in milk and dairy products.

Habitat: Probably of plant origin (Stark and Sherman, Jour. Bact., *30*, 1935, 639).

19. **Streptococcus cremoris** Orla-

Jensen, 1919. (*Streptococcus hollandicus* Weigmann, quoted from Kramer, Die Bakteriologie in ihren Beziehungen zur Landwirtschaft und den Landw. Technischen Gewerben, Wien, 1890; Orla-Jensen, The Lactic Acid Bacteria, 1919, 132; *Streptococcus lactis* B, Ayers, Johnson and Mudge, Jour. Inf. Dis., *34*, 1934, 29.)

cre.mo'ris. L. noun *cremor* juice; cream; L. gen.noun *cremoris* of cream.

Spheres or ovoid cells elongated in direction of the chain; 0.6 to 1.0 micron in diameter (often larger than *Streptococcus lactis*); form long chains, especially in milk, but some cultures occur predominantly as pairs. Gram-positive.

Serology: Possesses group-specific antigen (group N) of *Streptococcus lactis* (Sherman, Smiley and Niven, Jour. Dairy Sci., *23*, 1940, 529; Swartling, Jour. Dairy Res., *18*, 1951, 256; Briggs and Newland, Jour. Dairy Res., *19*, 1952, 160). Many serological types are known to exist.

Action on blood: Slight greening (alpha hemolytic) to indifferent (gamma hemolytic).

Temperature relations: Growth at 10° and below but not at 40° C. Optimum, below 30° C. May survive 60° C. for 30 minutes.

Tolerance tests: No growth in broth containing 4 per cent NaCl. Growth not initiated in broth adjusted to pH 9.2. No growth in milk containing 0.3 per cent methylene blue. Growth on 40 per cent bile blood agar.

Litmus milk: Acidified, curdled, litmus completely reduced before curdling. No digestion.

Final pH in glucose broth, between 4.0 and 4.6.

Acid from glucose and lactose. May or may not ferment trehalose and salicin. Rarely ferments maltose, sucrose, raffinose or mannitol. Arabinose, xylose, inulin, glycerol and sorbitol not fermented.

Starch, gelatin and sodium hippurate not hydrolyzed. Esculin may or may not be split.

Ammonia not produced from arginine.

Comments: Members of this species are commonly employed in commercial dairy starters. Like *Streptococcus lactis*, some strains ferment citric acid when incorporated with a fermentable sugar with the production of carbon dioxide, acetic acid and diacetyl.

Some cultures produce an antibiotic-like substance that is active against other lactic acid bacteria. This substance is distinct from nisin, the antibiotic from *Streptococcus lactis* (Oxford, Biochem. Jour., *38*, 1944, 178).

Related species: Although closely related, this species can be distinguished readily from *Streptococcus lactis* by its inability to grow at 40° C., in a 4 per cent NaCl broth or in a medium adjusted to pH 9.2. Also, it fails to produce ammonia from arginine, and the majority of the strains fail to ferment maltose.

Source: Raw milk and milk products; commercial starters for butter and cheese manufacture.

Habitat: Probably of plant origin.

Addendum: *Species incertae sedis.* Descriptions of species to which no name has been given or of poorly defined species, the taxonomic relationships of which are not clear:

1. *Streptococcus sp.* Serological group E. (Brown, Frost and Shaw, Jour. Inf. Dis., *38*, 1926, 381; Lancefield, Jour. Exp. Med., *57*, 1933, 571.)

Spherical or ovoid cells occurring in pairs or chains of medium length.

Serology: Constitutes Lancefield's group E. Several serological types are known to occur. May cross react with group C.

Action on blood: Strongly hemolytic (beta). Some non-hemolytic strains have been reported. The streptolysin produced is very acid-stable (Todd, Jour. Path. Bact., *39*, 1934, 299).

Not fibrinolytic.

Temperature relations: No growth at 10° or at 45° C. Does not survive 60° C. for 30 minutes.

Tolerance tests: Does not grow in broth containing 6.5 per cent NaCl or at pH 9.6. No growth in 0.1 per cent methylene blue milk or in 10 per cent bile blood agar.

Litmus milk: Acid, but not curdled. No digestion.

Final pH in glucose broth, between 4.2 and 4.8.

Acid from glucose, lactose, trehalose and sorbitol. May or may not ferment sucrose, glycerol, mannitol and salicin. No acid from arabinose, raffinose or inulin.

Gelatin not liquefied. Sodium hippurate not hydrolyzed. Some strains may hydrolyze starch or split esculin.

Ammonia produced from arginine.

Not pathogenic.

Source: Isolated from raw milk and the bovine udder.

Habitat: Unknown.

2. *Streptococcus sp.* Lancefield and Hare. (Large colony group G, Lancefield and Hare, Jour. Exp. Med., *60*, 1934, 633; Lancefield, The Harvey Lectures, Series XXXVI, 1940–1941, 251.)

Spherical or ovoid cells 0.6 to 1.0 micron in diameter; occur in medium-sized or long chains.

Serology: Belongs to Lancefield's group G. At least three serological types of the large-colony group G streptococci have been established (Simmons and Koegh, Austral. Jour. Exp. Biol. Med. Sci., *18*, 1940, 151). May contain a common protein antigen with *Streptococcus equisimilis* which sometimes gives rise to confusing cross-reactions. Griffith's type 16 belongs to this species.

Action on blood: Broad-zone beta hemolysis on blood agar. Area of hemolysis may be much larger than that produced by *Streptococcus pyogenes*. Soluble hemolysin produced that is identical to streptolysin O.

Colony form: Matt colonies similar to those of *Streptococcus pyogenes* and *Streptococcus equisimilis* are produced characteristically.

May or may not be fibrinolytic (Sherman, Bact. Rev., *1*, 1937, 1).

Temperature relations: No growth at 10° and, with few exceptions, no growth at 45° C. Does not survive 60° C for 30 minutes.

Tolerance tests: Fails to grow in presence of 6.5 per cent NaCl or in skim milk containing 0.1 per cent methylene blue. Generally more tolerant to methylene blue than *Streptococcus pyogenes*. No growth in broth adjusted to pH 9.6 or on blood agar containing 40 per cent bile.

Litmus milk: Acid, some strains curdle; litmus not reduced before curdling.

Final pH in glucose broth, between 4.8 and 5.2.

Acid produced from glucose, lactose, sucrose and trehalose. Glycerol is fermented when incubated aerobically. Salicin may or may not be fermented. Inulin fermented by a few strains. No acid from raffinose, mannitol or sorbitol.

Starch may be hydrolyzed by some strains. Gelatin not liquefied.

Sodium hippurate not hydrolyzed. Esculin usually split.

Ammonia produced from arginine.

Source: Obtained from the human throat, nose, skin, vagina and feces. Also found in the throat of a number of domestic animals, especially the dog. May be associated with a variety of animal diseases.

Habitat: Human respiratory tract and vagina; throats of domestic animals.

This group of streptococci deserves species recognition, but no suitable name has been proposed. More than one variety or species may be included among these large-colony group G streptococci (Sherman, Bact. Rev., *1*, 1937, 1). Some strains, especially those that are fibrinolytic, are very difficult to differentiate from *Streptococcus pyogenes* by means other than serological methods.

3. *Streptococcus sp.* Hare. (Group K, Hare, Jour. Path. Bact., *41*, 1935, 499.)

Spherical cells in medium-sized to long chains. Gram-positive.

Serology: Established as group K.

Action on blood: Small, incomplete zones of hemolysis on 8 per cent blood agar. No soluble hemolysin produced.

Colony forms: Moist and transparent with crenated edges; 0.8 to 1.3 mm in diameter after 48 hours.

Not fibrinolytic.

Tolerance test: Does not grow on 10 per cent bile blood agar.

Final pH in glucose broth, between 5.1 and 5.4.

Acid from glucose and generally from lactose. May or may not ferment salicin. Acid generally not produced from trehalose, mannitol or sorbitol.

Sodium hippurate not hydrolyzed.

Source: Normal human throat. Not considered to be pathogenic.

Habitat: Human throat.

4. *Streptococcus sp.* Fry. (Group L, Hare and Fry, Vet. Rec., *1*, 1938, 1537.) Additional information from Laughton, Jour. Path. Bact., *60*, 1948, 471.

Spherical or ovoid cells in long chains. Gram-positive.

Serology: Established as group L.

Action on blood: Surface and submerged colonies are beta hemolytic. Most strains do not produce a demonstrable soluble hemolysin.

Colony forms: Glossy, matt and intermediate types observed on blood agar.

Final pH in glucose broth, between 4.7 and 5.2.

Acid produced from maltose, lactose, sucrose, trehalose and salicin. May or may not ferment glycerol and sorbitol.

Sodium hippurate not hydrolyzed.

Source: Isolated from miscellaneous infections of the dog.

Habitat: Probably the throat and genital tract of the dog.

5. *Streptococcus sp.* Fry. (Group M, Hare and Fry, Vet. Rec., *1*, 1938, 1537.) Additional information from Laughton, Jour. Path. Bact., *60*, 1948, 471.

Spherical or ovoid cells in long chains. Gram-positive.

Serology: Established as group M. At least two serological types are known.

Action on blood: Surface and submerged colonies are beta hemolytic. A weak, slow acting soluble hemolysin produced by some strains; other strains appear to be negative.

Colony forms: Glossy, matt and intermediate types observed on blood agar.

Final pH in glucose broth, between 4.6 and 6.9.

Acid produced from maltose, lactose, sucrose and usually from trehalose. May or may not ferment glycerol and salicin. Sorbitol not fermented.

Sodium hippurate not hydrolyzed.

Source: Isolated from the urethra, the vagina and the tonsillar area of dogs. Prob-

ably not associated with any canine disease.

Habitat: Probably the dog.

6. *Streptococcus sp.* Boissard and Wormald. (Hitherto undescribed serological group O, Boissard and Wormald, Jour. Path. Bact., *62*, 1950, 37.)

Spherical or ovoid cells occurring in very long chains in broth culture.

Serology: Belongs to a new serological group for which "group O" is proposed.

Action on blood: Hemolysis on blood agar ranges from frank green to a moderately wide zone of beta hemolysis similar to that produced by *Streptococcus pyogenes*. Growth under anaerobic conditions reduces or completely inhibits the beta hemolysis. No soluble hemolysin detected.

Colony forms: Surface colonies on blood agar 0.4 to 0.8 mm in diameter after 18 hours at 37° C. with flattened margin and raised center. The margin is radically striated and has a beaded or pleated edge. Colony has rubbery and coherent consistency.

Not fibrinolytic.

Temperature relations: Does not survive 60° C. for 30 minutes.

Tolerance tests: May or may not grow on blood agar containing 10 per cent bile. No growth on 40 per cent bile blood agar.

Final pH in glucose broth, between 4.5 and 5.1.

Acid produced from glucose and lactose. May or may not ferment trehalose and salicin. No acid from mannitol or sorbitol.

Sodium hippurate not hydrolyzed.

Not pathogenic for mice.

Source: Nasopharynx of normal humans; occasionally from throats of individuals suffering from tonsilitis.

Habitat: Probably the human nasopharynx.

7. *Streptococcus* MG. Mirick, Thomas, Curnen and Horsfall. (Jour. Exp. Med., *80*, 1944, 391, 407 and 431.)

Spherical or ovoid cells occurring in pairs or short chains. Gram-positive.

Serology: No group-specific antigen has been demonstrated. All strains belong to one serological type due to the presence of a type-specific capsular antigen shown to be a nitrogen-containing polysaccharide. Reciprocal cross-reactions occur between this group and type I *Streptococcus salivarius*, thus indicating a similarity in their capsular antigens. Capsular swelling can be demonstrated in the presence of homologous immune serum. Rough variants lacking the capsular antigen can be induced by culturing in the presence of homologous immune sera.

Action on blood: Greening (alpha hemolytic) or indifferent (gamma hemolytic). The reaction is variable depending upon the type of blood employed. No soluble hemolysin is produced.

Temperature relations: No growth at 10° or at 45° C. Does not survive 56° C. for 30 minutes.

Tolerance tests: No growth in broth containing 6.5 per cent NaCl. No growth at pH 9.6. Growth in milk containing 0.005 per cent methylene blue but not in 0.02 per cent methylene blue. Growth on 10 per cent bile blood agar. May or may not grow on 40 per cent bile blood agar.

Litmus milk: Acidified and curdled with reduction of litmus after curdling. No digestion.

Final pH in glucose broth, between 4.3 and 5.6.

Produces small colonies on 5 per cent sucrose agar that are fluorescent under ultraviolet light.

Acid from glucose, maltose, lactose, sucrose and salicin. May or may not ferment trehalose. No acid from xylose, arabinose, raffinose, inulin, glycerol, mannitol or sorbitol.

Starch, sodium hippurate and gelatin not hydrolyzed. Esculin split.

Ammonia produced from arginine.

Comments: This group of streptococci is of particular interest because of its association with primary atypical pneumonia. Patients recuperating from this disease develop precipitins and agglutinins in their blood against this streptococcus, as well as against *Streptococcus salivarius* type I. In contrast with other viridans streptococci, this group appears to be particularly resistant to the sulfonamides.

Source: Saliva, sputum and lung cultures from cases of primary atypical pneumonia. Also found in the respiratory tract of normal individuals.

Genus III. **Pediococcus** *Balcke, 1884,* **emend.** *Mees, 1934.**

(Balcke, Wochnschr. f. Brauerei, *1*, 1884, 257; Mees, Onderzoekingen over de Biersarcina. Thesis, Delft, 1934, 92.)

Pe.di.o.coc'cus. Gr. noun *pedium* a plane; Gr. noun *coccus* a berry, sphere; M.L. mas.n. *Pediococcus* plane coccus.

Cocci occurring singly, as tetrads, pairs or even short chains. Although these organisms are frequently called sarcinae in the literature, packets of eight cells, if they occur at all, are very rare. Non-motile. Gram-positive. Microaerophilic, showing poor surface growth. Generally catalase-negative in sugar media. Homofermentative, producing optically inactive lactic acid from carbohydrates. Nitrites not produced from nitrates. Produce acidification and more or less clouding of wort and beer. Saprophytes in fermenting vegetable juices.

The type species is *Pediococcus cerevisiae* Balcke.

Key to the species of genus **Pediococcus.**

I. Optimum temperature, between 25° and 32°C. Grows in wort, hopped wort and beer.
　　　　　　　　　1. *Pediococcus cerevisiae.*
II. Optimum temperature, about 40°C. Grows in unhopped wort but not in beer.
　　　　　　　　　2. *Pediococcus acidilactici.*

---

* Prepared by Prof. Carl S. Pederson, New York State Experiment Station, Geneva, New York, September, 1954.

1. **Pedicoccus cerevisiae** Balcke, 1884. (Ferment No. 7, Pasteur, Études sur la bière. Paris, 1876, 4; *Sarcina* from beer, Hansen, Compt. rend. Trav. Lab. Carlsberg, *1*, 1879, 234 and 288; Balcke, Wochnschr. f. Brauerei, *1*, 1884, 257.)

ce.re.vi'si.ae. L. noun *cerevisia* beer; L. gen.noun *cerevisiae* of beer.

Spheres, 1.0 to 1.3 microns in diameter, occurring singly, in pairs or in tetrads. In acid media the latter prevail. Non-motile. Gram-positive.

No growth in alkaline media.

Peptone, meat-extract gelatin colonies: White becoming yellowish to yellowish brown. No liquefaction.

Wort gelatin with calcium carbonate: White colonies, 2 to 3 mm; carbonate dissolved.

Meat extract gelatin stab: Growth along stab; white, raised surface growth. No liquefaction.

Wort and beer: Slight to moderately turbid growth, strong development on bottom of the flask. Hop-sensitive, but may develop in heavily hopped beers under special conditions.

Litmus milk: Usually no growth; a few strains may show acid and may curdle the milk.

Potato: Scant growth.

Acid from glucose, fructose, mannose, galactose and maltose; usually from arabinose, sucrose, lactose, raffinose, salicin and amygdalin; sometimes from xylose and rhamnose. No acid from mannitol, alpha-methyl glucoside, inulin, dextrin or starch (Pederson, Bact. Rev., *13*, 1949, 228). Optically inactive lactic acid, as well as traces of acetic acid and carbon dioxide, is produced.

Diacetyl is produced, apparently from the oxidation of acetylmethylcarbinol; diacetyl is the substance responsible for the "sarcina odor" of spoiled beer and the aroma of fresh butter (Shimwell and Kirkpatrick, Jour. Inst. Brewing, *45* (N.S. *36*), 1939, 141).

L-tryptophane, L-cystine, DL-threonine, DL-valine, DL-leucine, DL-isoleucine, L-histidine, DL-phenylalanine, L-tyrosine, L-proline, glycine, DL-alanine, L-arginine, DL-serine, L-glutamic acid, L-aspartic acid and asparagine are required for growth. Aspartic acid can completely replace asparagine, whereas asparagine can only partially replace aspartic acid. DL-methionine and possibly DL-lysine are stimulatory (Jensen and Seeley, Jour. Bact., *67*, 1954, 486).

Purine and pyrimidine requirements vary considerably with the strain: some strains require neither of these compounds; other strains, requiring both purines and pyrimidines, exhibit greatest growth with either xanthine or guanine, whereas uracil and thymine are least effective; still other strains require uracil (Jensen and Seeley, *loc. cit.*).

Leucovorin (citrovorum factor), niacin and pantothenic acid are absolute vitamin requirements, whereas biotin and pyridoxine are merely stimulatory; a few strains require riboflavin in addition (Jensen and Seeley, *loc. cit.*).

Urea not utilized.

Nitrites not produced from nitrates.

Usually catalase-negative; may be weakly positive in media low in sugar content (Felton, Evans and Niven, Jour. Bact., *65*, 1953, 481).

Microaerophilic.

Optimum temperature, between 25° and 32° C. Growth range, 7° to 45° C. Killed at 60° C. in 8 minutes.

Source: Originally isolated from sarcina-sick beer and for many years known only as found in beer yeasts, spoiled wort and beer. More recently this species has been recognized in various types of fermenting vegetable juices (Pederson, *op. cit.*, 1949, 228; also see Wallerstein Lab. Communications, *17*, 1954, 10).

Habitat: Widely distributed in fermenting materials such as beer, sauerkraut and pickles.

2. **Pediococcus acidilactici** Lindner, 1887. (Lindner, Wochnschr. f. Brauerei, *3*, No. 23, 1887; see Cent. f. Bakt., *2*, 1887, 342; also see Die Sarcina-Organismen der Gährungsgewerbe. Lindner, Inaug. Diss., Berlin, 1888, 26, and Cent. f. Bakt., *4*, 1888, 427.)

a.ci.di.lac.ti'ci. M.L. noun *acidum lacti-*

cum lactic acid; M.L. gen.noun *acidi lactici* of lactic acid.

Original description supplemented by material from Shimwell (Jour. Inst. Brewing, *54* (N.S. *45*), 1948, 103).

Cocci, 0.6 to 1.0 micron in diameter, occurring singly, in pairs and tetrads or even in short chains. Gram-positive.

Gelatin colonies: Small; no liquefaction.

Gelatin streak: Growth grayish white, moist, iridescent, thin; smooth edges.

Gelatin stab: Growth along stab; white, leafy surface growth.

Growth in unhopped wort but not in beer. Produces much acid from maltose and wort. Cultures that do not produce acid from maltose are regarded by some (see Shimwell, *loc. cit.*) as forming a distinct species as they produce slight or no acid in unhopped wort.

Catalase-negative.

Optimum temperature, 41° C. Killed in a short time at 60° C.

Source: Isolated from spoiled mash.

Habitat: Found in mash and unhopped wort.

Genus IV. Leuconostoc *van Tieghem*, emend. *Hucker and Pederson, 1930.**

(Van Tieghem, Ann. Sci. Nat., *6*, Sér. 7, 1878, 170; *Betacoccus* Orla-Jensen, The Lactic Acid Bacteria. Mem. Acad. Sci. Danemark, Sec. d. Sci., *5*, Sér. 8, 1919, 146; Hucker and Pederson, New York Agr. Exp. Sta. Tech. Bul. 167, 1930, 66.)

Leu.co.nos'toc. Gr. *leucus* clear, light; M.L. neut.n. *Nostoc* algal generic name; M.L. neut.n. *Leuconostoc* colorless *Nostoc*.

Cells normally spherical. Under certain conditions, such as in acid fruits and vegetables, the cells may lengthen and become pointed or even elongated into a rod. Certain types grow with a characteristic slime formation in sucrose media. Grow on ordinary culture media, but growth is enhanced by the addition of yeast, tomato or other vegetable extracts. Generally, a limited amount of acid is produced, consisting of lactic and acetic acids; alcohol is also formed, and about one-fourth of the fermented glucose is changed to CO_2. Levo rotatory lactic acid is always produced, and sometimes dextro rotatory lactic acid also. Milk is rarely curdled. Fructose is reduced to mannitol. Found in milk and in plant juices.

The type species is *Leuconostoc mesenteroides* (Cienkowski) Van Tieghem.

Key to the species of genus Leuconostoc.

I. Acid from sucrose.
  A. Acid from pentoses.

                  1. *Leuconostoc mesenteroides.*

  B. No acid from pentoses.

                  2. *Leuconostoc dextranicum.*

II. No acid from sucrose.

                  3. *Leuconostoc citrovorum.*

1. **Leuconostoc mesenteroides** (Cienkowski, 1878) van Tieghem, 1878. (*Ascococcus mesenteroides* Cienkowski, Arb. d. Naturf. Gesellsch. a. d. Univ. a. Charkoff, 1878, 12; van Tieghem, Ann. Sci. Nat., *6*, Sér. 7, 1878, 170.)

me.sen.te.ro.ï'des. Gr. noun *mesenterium* the mesentery; Gr. noun *eidus* form, shape; M.L. adj. *mesenteroïdes* mesentery-like.

Spheres, 0.9 to 1.2 microns in diameter, occurring in pairs and short or long chains. In sucrose solutions the chains are usually surrounded by a thick, gelatinous, colorless membrane consisting of dextran. Gram-positive.

---

* Revised by Prof. G. J. Hucker and Prof. Carl S. Pederson, New York State Experiment Station, Geneva, New York, September, 1938; further revision, December, 1943, and August, 1954.

Glucose gelatin colonies: Small, white to grayish white, raised, nodular.

Glucose gelatin stab: Growth along entire stab. No liquefaction.

Sucrose broth: Usually produces slime from sucrose; slime most pronounced in sucrose gelatin stab. Niven, Castellani and Allanson (Jour. Bact., *58*, 1949, 633) have described types from meat products that do not produce slime. Pederson and Ward (New York State Agr. Exp. Sta. Tech Bull. 288, 1949) have described similar types from high-salt cucumber brines. Pederson and Albury (Jour. Bact., *70*, 1955, 702) have induced such types to produce typical slime by repeated transfers in sucrose solutions.

Potato: No visible growth.

Indole not produced.

Acid from glucose, fructose, galactose, mannose, xylose, arabinose, sucrose and generally from lactose, raffinose, salicin and mannitol. Rarely acid from dextrin, starch, inulin, sorbitol, rhamnose or glycerol. Mc-Cleskey, Faville and Barnett (Jour. Bact., *54*, 1947, 697) recognize four colonial types which differ somewhat in fermentation reactions.

Nitrites not produced from nitrates.

Microaerophilic, facultatively anaerobic.

Optimum temperature, between 21° and 25° C.

Distinctive characters: Usually active slime producer in sucrose solutions. Mc-Cleskey, Faville and Barnett (*op. cit.* 1947, 697) recognized four colonial types, A, B, C and F, which differ in amounts of gum, acid and gas produced and in temperature and pH requirements for growth. McCleskey and Barnett (Proc. Louisiana Acad of Sci., *12*, 1949, 38) have correlated these with nutritional requirements and Leiva-Quiros and McCleskey (Jour. Bact., *54*, 1947, 709) with serological relationships.

Source: Isolated from slime in a sugar factory.

Habitat: Most active species of the genus. Encountered in fermenting vegetable and other plant materials and in prepared meat products. Frequently isolated from slimy sugar solutions.

2. Leuconostoc dextranicum (Bei-

jerinck, 1912) Hucker and Pederson, 1930. (*Lactococcus dextranicus* Beijerinck, Folia Microbiologica, Delft, 1912, 377; Hucker and Pederson, New York Agr. Exp. Sta. Tech. Bull, 167, 1930, 67.)

dex.tra′ni.cum. L. adj. *dexter* right; M.L. noun *dextranum* dextran; M.L. adj. *dextranicus* related to dextran.

Spheres, 0.6 to 1.0 micron in diameter, occurring in pairs and in short chains. Gram-positive.

Gelatin stab: Gray filiform growth in stab.

Agar colonies: Small, gray, circular, slightly raised, entire.

Glucose broth: Slight grayish sediment.

Litmus milk: Acid, coagulation. Frequently shows slight reduction of litmus in bottom of tube.

Potato: No visible growth.

Indole not produced.

Produces slime from sucrose in rapidly growing cultures.

Acid from glucose, fructose, galactose, maltose, sucrose and generally from lactose and mannose. No acid from xylose, arabinose, glycerol, rhamnose, sorbitol, mannitol or starch; rarely from raffinose, inulin or dextrin.

Nitrites not produced from nitrates.

Microaerophilic, facultatively anaerobic.

Optimum temperature, between 21° and 25° C.

Distinctive characters: Produces a moderate amount of slime in sucrose solutions.

Source: Isolated from dairy starters.

Habitat: Found in plant materials and in milk products.

3. Leuconostoc citrovorum (Hammer, 1920) Hucker and Pederson, 1930. (*Streptococcus citrovorus* Hammer, Iowa Agr. Exp. Sta. Research Bull. No. 63, 1920; Hucker and Pederson, New York Agr. Exp. Sta. Tech. Bull. 167, 1930, 67.)

cit.ro′vo.rum. L. noun *citrus* the citron tree; M.L. noun *citrus* the lemon, here referring to citric acid; L. v. *voro* to devour; M.L. adj. *citrovorus* citrate-utilizing.

Spheres, 0.6 to 1.0 micron in diameter, occuring in pairs and chains. Gram-positive.

Gelatin stab: Filiform growth in stab. No liquefaction.

Agar colonies: Small, gray, entire, slightly raised.

Agar slant: Small, gray, discrete colonies.

Glucose broth: Slight gray sediment.

Litmus milk: Slightly acid with partial reduction of litmus.

Potato: No visible growth.

Indole not produced.

Grows poorly on ordinary media without the addition of yeast extract or other growth-accessory substance.

Acid from glucose, fructose, galactose and lactose. Generally does not form acid from mannose, sucrose, maltose, xylose, arabinose, rhamnose, raffinose, glycerol, dextrin, inulin, starch, salicin, mannitol or sorbitol.

Uses citric acid in milk.

Nitrites not produced from nitrates.

Microaerophilic, facultatively anaerobic.

Optimum temperature, between 20° and 25° C.

Distinctive character: Non-slime producer.

Source: Isolated from dairy products.

Habitat: Found in milk and dairy products.

Genus V. **Peptostreptococcus** *Kluyver and van Niel, 1936.**

(Zent. f. Bakt., II Abt., *94*, 1936, 391, 395 and 401.)

Pep.to.strep.to.coc'cus. Gr. v. *pepto* to cook, digest; M.L. mas.n. *Streptococcus* a generic name; M.L. mas.n. *Peptostreptococcus* the digesting streptococcus.

Spherical cells which occur in pairs or in chains. Non-motile. Gram-positive. Chemoheterotrophic, fermenting protein decomposition products, organic acids and usually carbohydrates with the production of carbon dioxide, hydrogen and other products. Anaerobic. Found in septic and gangrenous conditions in man and other animals and as part of the normal bacterial flora of respiratory and digestive tracts. May be pathogenic.

The present classification of the species in this genus is based on morphological and various physiological characters. However, recent work has shown that the presence of fatty acids and sulfur compounds exerts a marked influence on the morphology and/or biochemical behavior of these organisms; consequently, in choosing criteria for the classification of the species in this genus, it seems exigent to use those obtained with standardized media. With the use of rather ill-defined media, at least thirty anaerobic cocci have been recognized and described; however, with standardized media, Hare and his associates have divided a very large number of anaerobic cocci into only nine groups. Thus, future work may show that some or even many of the species here regarded as distinct are, in reality, identical with one another. (See Hare, Wildy, Billett and Twort, Jour. Hyg., *50*, 1952, 295; Hare, Atti del VI Congresso Internaz di. Microbiologia, Roma, *1*, 1953, 55; and Thomas and Hare, Jour. Clin. Path., *7*, 1954, 300.)

The type species is *Peptostreptococcus anaerobius* (Krönig *emend.* Natvig) Kluyver and van Niel.

Key to the species of genus **Peptostreptococcus.**

I. Cells occur in chains.
    A. Strict anaerobes.
        1. Gas and fetid odor produced.
            a. No general turbidity in broth.
                b. Acid from maltose.
                    1. *Peptostreptococcus anaerobius.*
                bb. No acid from maltose.
                    2. *Peptostreptococcus foetidus.*
            aa. Turbidity in broth.

* Revised by Dr. Louis DS. Smith, Montana Agricultural Experiment Station, Bozeman, Montana, February, 1955.

b. No gas in peptone broth.
  c. Milk unchanged. No gas in semisolid agar.
                     3. *Peptostreptococcus putridus.*
  cc. Milk slowly coagulated.
                     4. *Peptostreptococcus productus.*
  bb. Gas produced in peptone broth. Abundant gas in semisolid agar.
                     5. *Peptostreptococcus lanceolatus.*
2. No gas or fetid odor produced.
  a. Milk not coagulated.
                     6. *Peptostreptococcus micros.*
  aa. Milk coagulated.
    b. Viscous sediment in broth. Semisolid agar colonies blacken with age.
                     7. *Peptostreptococcus parvulus.*
    bb. No viscous sediment in broth. Semisolid agar colonies do not blacken with age.
                     8. *Peptostreptococcus intermedius.*
B. Strictly anaerobic on isolation, later becomes aerotolerant.
                     9. *Peptostreptococcus evolutus.*
II. Cells normally occur in pairs although short chains may occur.
  A. Greater than 1 micron in diameter.
    1. Carbohydrates not attacked.
                  10. *Peptostreptococcus magnus.*
  B. Not greater than 1 micron in diameter.
    1. Acid from glucose and lactose.
      a. Encapsulated. Pathogenic.
               11. *Peptostreptococcus paleopneumoniae.*
      aa. Not encapsulated. Non-pathogenic.
               12. *Peptostreptococcus plagarumbelli.*
    2. Acid from glucose but not from lactose. No growth on ordinary culture media.
               13. *Peptostreptococcus morbillorum.*

1. **Peptostreptococcus anaerobius** (Krönig, 1895, *emend.* Natvig, 1905) Kluyver and van Niel, 1936. (*Streptococcus anaerobius* Krönig, Zent. f. Gyn., *19*, 1895, 409; Natvig, Arch. f. Gyn., 1905, 724; Kluyver and van Niel, Zent. f. Bakt., II Abt., *94*, 1936, 391, 395 and 401.)

an.a.e.ro.bi′us. Gr. pref. *an-* not; Gr. noun *aër* air; Gr. noun *bius* life; M.L. adj. *anaerobius* not living in air, anaerobic.

Description taken from Prévot (Ann. Sci. Nat., Sér. Bot., *15*, 1933, 180).

Spheres, averaging 0.8 micron in diameter, occurring in chains. Non-motile. Gram-positive.

Gelatin: No liquefaction.

Semi-solid agar (Veillon): After 48 hours, colonies 1 to 2 mm in diameter, very regular, lenticular; gas is produced; agar slightly acidified.

Martin broth: Rapid growth; no turbidity; sediment in 24 hours; medium slightly acidified; feeble production of gas; slight fetid odor.

Martin glucose broth: Very abundant growth; gas fetid, inflammable; no hydrogen sulfide; very marked acidification.

Peptone broth: Abundant, flocculent growth; gas produced at expense of peptone; medium not acidified; neither indole nor hydrogen sulfide is produced.

Meat and liver broth: Very abundant growth; much gas produced which contains CO_2 and H_2.

Milk: No acid; no coagulation.

Cooked protein (egg white, meat, liver, fibrin and serum) not attacked. Fresh fibrin and fresh organs partially disintegrated with blackening, abundant gas and a very fetid odor due in part to hydrogen sulfide.

Serum broth: Abundant gas and fetid odor.

Acid from glucose, fructose, galactose, sucrose and maltose. Mannitol and arabinose are sometimes fermented. Fermentation products include formic and acetic acids (Prévot, Ann. Inst. Past., *67*, 1941, 88).

Neutral red broth: Changed to fluorescent yellow.

Anaerobic.

Temperature relations: Optimum, between 36° and 38° C. Grows at 26° but not below 22° C. Survives 5 minutes at 60° C. or two minutes at 80° C. Killed in ten minutes at 80° C.

Optimum pH, between 6.0 and 8.0.

Some strains are pathogenic.

Distinctive characters: Very peptolytic; gas produced in peptone water with destruction of the peptone. Differs from *Peptostreptococcus foetidus* by being morphologically like a typical streptococcus. Differs from *Peptostreptococcus putridus* by its physiology, by its bread-crumb-like growth and by the production of gas in all media.

Source: Isolated in cases of putrefactive gangrene; war wounds; uterus, lochia and blood in puerperal infections; appendicitis; pleurisy; and amniotic fluid.

Habitat: Found in the mouth and intestines; also from the cavities of man and animals, especially the vagina. Can invade all tissues.

2. **Peptostreptococcus foetidus** (Veillon, 1893) Smith, *comb. nov.* (*Micrococcus foetidus* Veillon, Compt. rend. Soc. Biol., Paris, *45*, 1893, 867; not *Micrococcus foetidus* Flügge, Die Mikroorganismen, 2 Aufl., 1886, 172; not *Micrococcus foetidus* Klamann, Allgem. med. Centralzeitung, 1887, 1344; *Streptococcus foetidus* Prévot, Ann. Sci. Nat., Sér. Bot., *15*, 1933, 189; not *Streptococcus foetidus* Migula, Syst. d. Bakt., *2*, 1900, 38.) foe'ti.dus. L. adj. *foetidus* stinking.

Large spheres, 0.8 to 1.0 micron in diameter, occurring normally in short chains; also in tetrads and double or zig-zag chains. Nonmotile. Gram-positive.

Gelatin: No liquefaction.

Semi-solid agar (Veillon): Slow growth; at first punctiform. Small colonies, $\frac{1}{4}$ to $\frac{1}{2}$ mm in diameter, which grow 1 to 2 cm below the surface, regular, thick, lenticular, opaque. Gas bubbles are produced.

Blood agar colonies: 0.5 to 1.0 mm in diameter, convex, grayish, entire margin. Small, brownish hemopeptic zone around colonies. No true hemolysis.

Martin broth: Poor growth; no turbidity; flakes form on wall of tube but rapidly settle to the bottom; little or no gas is produced; very faint, fetid odor.

Martin glucose broth: Good growth; no turbidity; gas fetid, inflammable.

Meat and liver broth: Rapid, abundant growth; abundant gas; strong, fetid odor.

Milk: No acid; no coagulation.

Peptone broth: Gas production is feeble. Indole not produced.

Fresh organs become green, then blacken. Much gas is produced which contains hydrogen sulfide; later the organs are gradually disintegrated; partial bioproteolysis and hydrogen sulfide formation.

Coagulated protein is not attacked.

Acid and gas from glucose, fructose, galactose and sucrose. No acid from lactose, maltose, arabinose, glycerol, mannitol, dulcitol or starch.

Neutral red broth: Changed to fluorescent yellow.

Anaerobic.

Temperature relations: Optimum, between 36° and 38° C. Feeble growth at 26° C. No growth below 22° C. Killed in one hour at 60° C. or in ten minutes at 80° C.

Optimum pH, between 6.5 and 8.0.

Some strains are pathogenic.

Comment: A variety of this species, which differs from the parent strain in being smaller in size and in producing more gas in carbohydrate media, has been reported by Prévot (*ibid.*, 193).

Source: First isolated from a fatal case of Ludwig's angina; also from perinephritic phlegmon, the fetid pus from Bartholin's gland, gangrene of the lung and appendicitis.

Habitat: Found in the mouth, intestines and vagina of man and animals. Common in fetid suppurations and autogenous gangrenous processes.

3. **Peptostreptococcus putridus** (Schottmüller, 1910, *emend.* Prévot, 1933) Smith, *comb. nov.* (*Streptococcus putridus* Schottmüller, Mitteil. a. d. Grenzgeb. d.

Med. Chirurg., *21*, 1910, 450; Prévot, Ann. Sci. Nat., Sér. Bot., *15*, 1933, 170 and 184.) pu′tri.dus. L. adj. *putridus* rotten, decayed.

Spheres, averaging 0.8 micron in diameter, occurring in chains. Gram-positive.

Gelatin: No liquefaction.

Semi-solid agar (Veillon) colonies: More or less lenticular; 1 to 2 mm in diameter; no gas produced.

Blood agar colonies: 2 mm in diameter; become brownish, sometimes blackish on aging. Surrounded by a brownish hemopeptic zone.

Martin broth: In 6 to 8 hours there is a uniform turbidity which does not precipitate completely; no gas; little odor.

Martin glucose broth: Rapid, abundant growth; uniform turbidity; sediment; no gas; slight fetid odor; black pigment in the sediment.

Meat and liver broth: Very abundant growth; very marked putrid odor; incomplete sedimentation.

Peptone broth: Sparse growth; neither gas, odor, hydrogen sulfide nor indole is produced.

Milk: No acid; no coagulation.

Coagulated protein is not attacked.

Deep blood agar: Agar is broken by the gas (hydrogen sulfide).

Fresh-blood broth: Abundant gas which contains a large amount of hydrogen sulfide is produced; blood blackens rapidly and has typical putrid odor.

Fresh fibrin broth: The fibrin is broken up and partially digested.

Lead media are blackened.

Acid from glucose, fructose and maltose. Acid sometimes produced from sucrose, mannitol and galactose. Fermentation products include valerianic, butyric and acetic acids (Prévot, Ann. Inst. Past., *67*, 1941, 88).

Neutral red is changed to fluorescent yellow.

Anaerobic.

Temperature relations: Optimum, between 36° and 38° C. Growth feeble at 28° C. No growth below 22° C. Killed in ten minutes at 80° C.

Optimum pH, between 7.0 and 8.5.

Rare strains are pathogenic for laboratory animals.

Distinctive characters: Putrescence but absence of gas in ordinary media; presence of gas and hydrogen sulfide in media with fresh tissue or body fluids.

Comments: Thomas and Hare (Jour. Clin. Path., *7*, 1954, 302) divide certain of the anaerobic cocci into nine groups and state that Group I is essentially *Streptococcus putridus*. This group is described as including Gram-positive, anaerobic spheres, 0.6 to 0.8 micron in diameter, which grow in the form of chains and which, in media containing 0.01 per cent sodium oleate, 0.1 per cent sodium thioglycollate and 1.0 per cent of the substance tested, produce acid and gas from glucose, fructose and maltose and gas from pyruvate; galactose, sucrose, malate, citrate, tartrate and lactate are not attacked. Gas is produced in ordinary media if sulfur compounds are present.

Source: Isolated from normal and fetid lochia; blood in puerperal fever; gangrenous appendicitis; gangrene of the lung; gas gangrene; gangrenous metastases; war wounds; osteomyelitis and from amniotic fluid. Found in sea water by Montel and Mousseron (Paris Médical, 1929).

Habitat: Found in the human mouth and intestines and especially in the vagina.

4. **Peptostreptococcus productus** (Prévot, 1941) Smith, *comb. nov.* (*Streptococcus productus* Prévot, Compt. rend. Soc. Biol., Paris, *135*, 1941, 105.)

pro.duc′tus. L. adj. *productus* lengthened.

Large spheres, 0.7 to 1.2 microns in diameter, occurring in chains which contain 6 to 20 cells. Gram-positive.

Gelatin: No liquefaction.

Gas and odor produced.

Deep agar colonies: Lens-shaped; slight gas.

Glucose broth: Homogeneous turbidity; viscid; mucoid, coherent sediment; slight gas; hydrogen sulfide is produced.

Peptone broth: Homogeneous turbidity; no gas; indole not produced.

Milk: Slowly coagulated (8 to 10 days). Coagulated proteins not attacked.

Acid and gas from glucose, fructose, xylose, arabinose, sorbose and lactose. Fermentation products include ammonia, hydrogen sulfide, acetic and propionic acids and traces of lactic acid and acetylmethylcarbinol.

Neutral red reduced.

Nitrites not produced from nitrates.

Anaerobic.

Optimum temperature, between 30° and 37° C.

Optimum pH, between 6.5 and 8.2.

Non-pathogenic for guinea pigs, rabbits and mice.

Comments: A hemolytic variety of this organism has been reported by Beeuwkes and Aladame (Ann. Inst. Past., *75*, 1948, 390).

Source: Isolated from a subacute case of pulmonary gangrene.

Habitat: Found in the natural cavities of man, especially the respiratory.

5. **Peptostreptococcus lanceolatus** (Prévot, 1933) Smith, *comb. nov. (Coccus lanceolatus anaerobius* Tissier, Compt. rend. Soc. Biol., Paris, *94*, 1926, 447; *Streptococcus lanceolatus* Prévot, Ann. Sci. Nat., Sér. Bot., *15*, 1933, 173 and 193; not *Streptococcus lanceolatus* Gamaleïa, Ann. Inst. Past., *2*, 1888, 440.)

lan.ce.o.la′tus. L. adj. *lanceolatus* lancet-shaped.

Large, ovoid cells, 1.2 to 1.4 microns in diameter, with pointed ends, occurring in short chains in culture and in pairs in exudates. Non-motile. Gram-positive.

Gelatin: No liquefaction.

Deep agar colonies: Very large, lenticular; abundant gas produced which breaks up the medium.

Peptone broth: Uniform turbidity; granular, viscous sediment.

Peptone broth: Good growth; gas produced.

Milk: No change.

Coagulated protein not attacked.

Hydrolyzed albumen reduced to CO_2, $(NH_4)_2CO_3$ and NH_3.

Acid from glucose, sucrose and starch. No acid from lactose. Butyric, valerianic and acetic acids are produced, in the proportions 2:1:trace, from glucose and sucrose.

Anaerobic.

Optimum temperature, 37° C.

Non-pathogenic for laboratory animals.

Distinctive characters: Proteolytic and saccharolytic; produces ammonia from hydrolyzed proteins; butyric, valerianic and acetic acids are produced from certain carbohydrates. No hydrogen sulfide is produced.

Source: Isolated from human feces in a case of diarrhoea.

Habitat: Found in putrefying materials.

6. **Peptostreptococcus micros** (Prévot, 1933) Smith, *comb. nov. (Streptococcus anaerobius micros* Lewkowicz, Arch. Méd. Exp., *13*, 1901, 645; *Streptococcus micros* Prévot, Ann. Sci. Nat., Sér. Bot., *15*, 1933, 193.)

mi′cros. Gr. adj. *micrus* small.

Very small spheres, 0.2 to 0.4 micron in diameter, occurring in long chains or in pairs. Non-motile. Gram-positive.

Gelatin: Poor growth. No liquefaction.

Semi-solid agar (Veillon): Slow growth; colonies at first punctiform, becoming lenticular and later forming processes into the medium. Average size, 0.5 to 1.0 mm in diameter; some reach 2 to 3 mm, growing 2 or 3 cm below the surface.

Blood agar: No hemolysis. No hemopeptolysis.

Martin broth: Slight, particulate turbidity which slowly settles.

Meat and liver broth: Rapid growth; abundant sediment.

Peptone broth: Powdery sediment; medium not acidified; no indole is produced.

Milk: Grows with difficulty; no acid; no coagulation.

Coagulated protein not attacked.

Acid from glucose, fructose, galactose, sucrose and maltose. Fermentation products include propionic, formic and lactic acids (Prévot, Man. d. Classif. et d. Déterm. d. Bact. Anaérobies, 2ᵉ ed., 1948, 59).

Neutral red broth is changed to fluorescent yellow.

Anaerobic.

Optimum temperature, between 36° and 38° C. No growth at 22° C. Killed in 15 minutes at 60° C.

Optimum pH, about 7.0.

Non-pathogenic for mice.

No toxin and no hemolysin.

Distinctive characters: Neither gas nor fetid odor produced; small size.

Source: Isolated from gangrene of the lung, from lochia and uterus in puerperal sepsis and from cases of appendicitis.

Habitat: Found in the mouth and intestine of man and other animals.

7. Peptostreptococcus parvulus (Weinberg et al., 1937) Smith, comb. nov. (Streptococcus parvulus non liquefaciens Repaci, Compt. rend. Soc. Biol., Paris, 68, 1910, 528; Streptococcus parvulus Weinberg, Nativelle and Prévot, Les Microbes Anaérobies, 1937, 1011; not Streptococcus parvulus Levinthal, Cent. f. Bakt., I Abt., Orig., 106, 1928, 195.)

par'vu.lus. L. dim.adj. parvulus somewhat small.

Small spheres which average 0.3 to 0.4 micron in diameter and which occur in short chains, sometimes in pairs. Non-motile. Gram-positive.

Gelatin: At 37° C., slow growth; culture at bottom of tube; no gas. No liquefaction.

Deep glucose agar colonies: After 48 hours, very tiny, lenticular, whitish. Old colonies become blackened. No gas is produced.

Broth: Rapid turbidity; sediment forms in 5 or 6 days as a whitish, mucous mass which clears the fluid; no gas; faint, disagreeable odor.

Milk: Coagulation in 24 hours.

Indole not produced.

Coagulated proteins not attacked.

Glucose and lactose are feebly attacked. Does not attack sucrose, galactose or dextrin. Fermentation products include acetic, propionic and lactic acids (Prévot, Man. d. Classif. et d. Déterm. d. Bact. Anaérobies, 2ᵉ ed., 1948, 59).

Anaerobic.

Optimum temperature, 37° C. No growth at room temperature. Will grow at 41° C. Non-pathogenic.

Distinctive characters: Differs from Peptostreptococcus micros by its black colonies, its coagulation of milk and by its feeble saccharolytic power. Differs from Peptostreptococcus intermedius by its black colonies, the smallness of its elements, its feeble saccharolytic power and by the viscous sediment it forms in broth.

Relationship to other species: Veillon and Repaci identified this organism as Streptococcus micros, but Weinberg, Nativelle and Prévot consider it as a distinct species, although rare.

Source: Isolated from the respiratory tract.

Habitat: Unknown.

8. Peptostreptococcus intermedius (Prévot, 1925) Smith, comb. nov. (Streptococcus intermedius Prévot, Ann. Inst. Past., 39, 1925, 439.)

in.ter.me'di.us. L. adj. intermedius intermediate.

Description taken in part from Prévot (Ann. Sci. Nat., Sér. Bot., 15, 1933, 197).

Spheres, 0.5 to 0.7 micron in diameter, occurring in very long chains in culture. Non-motile. Gram-positive.

Gelatin: Poor growth.

Semi-solid agar (Veillon): After 24 hours, colonies 1 to 2 mm in diameter, regular, lenticular, sometimes with complex processes.

Blood agar: No change or slight greening.

Martin broth: Rapid growth; uniform turbidity which slowly settles.

Martin glucose broth: Abundant growth; abundant sediment; medium strongly acidified.

Peptone broth: Particulate sediment.

Milk: Very acid; coagulated in 24 hours without retraction of clot; not peptonized.

Serum broth (1:2): Rapid growth; coagulation by acidification.

Indole not produced.

Coagulated proteins not attacked.

Acid from glucose, fructose, galactose, maltose and lactose. Fermentation products include formic, propionic and lactic acids (Prévot, Man. d. Classif. et d. Déterm. d. Bact. Anaérobies, 2ᵉ ed., 1948, 60).

Neutral red broth is changed to fluorescent yellow.

Anaerobic.

Temperature relations: Optimum, between 36° and 38° C. Poor growth at 26° C. No growth below 22° C. Killed in 30 minutes at 70° C. or in ten minutes at 80° C.

Optimum pH, between 6.0 and 8.5.

Some strains are pathogenic for guinea pigs and mice, causing small abscesses; sometimes kill in 48 hours.

No toxin and no hemolysin.

Distinctive characters: Strongly acidifies media; coagulates milk.

Source: Isolated from lochia and uterus in puerperal sepsis; also from cases of gangrene of the lung, pleurisy, bronchiectasis and appendicitis.

Habitat: Found in the human respiratory and digestive tracts and in the vagina.

9. **Peptostreptococcus evolutus** (Prévot, 1924) Smith, *comb. nov.* (*Streptococcus Sch.* (Schwarzenbek), Gräf and Wittneben, Cent. f. Bakt., I Abt., Orig., *44*, 1907, 97; *Streptococcus evolutus* Prévot, Thès. Méd., Paris, 1924; *Streptococcus Schwarzenbeck* (sic) Ford, Textb. of Bact., 1927, 455: also see Weiss and Mercado, Jour. Inf. Dis., *62*, 1938, 181.)

e. vo.lu′tus. L. part.adj. *evolutus* unrolled.

Description taken in part from Prévot (Ann. Sci. Nat., Sér. Bot., *15*, 1933, 199).

Spheres, 0.7 to 1.0 micron in diameter, averaging 0.7 micron, occurring in pairs or in short and long chains. Pleomorphic. Often appear as short, ovoid rods with rounded ends. Gram-positive.

Gelatin: Liquefaction.

Deep agar colonies: Lenticular or rosettes. Growth occurs about one cm beneath the surface; after a transfer the second generation may show a ring of growth in the middle of this sterile zone. This is the characteristic alternate zones appearance. Successive generations may grow fully when exposed to the air. Colonies usually become brownish with age.

Glucose broth: Abundant growth resembling bread crumbs. Medium strongly acidified (pH 5). A small quantity of lactic acid is produced.

Peptone broth: Rapid growth; no general turbidity; precipitating, flocculent growth on the wall of the tube; indole not produced.

Blood agar: No change, sometimes greening.

Litmus milk: Acid; curdled in 24 hours; clot retracts and fragments; slight peptonization with some strains.

Coagulated protein not attacked.

Acid from glucose, fructose, galactose, sucrose, lactose and maltose. Arabinose sometimes fermented.

Anaerobic, becoming aerotolerant with subsequent transfers. Viability is short aerobically and several months anaerobically.

Optimum temperature, between 36° and 38° C. No growth below 22° C.

Optimum pH, between 6.0 and 8.5.

Pathogenicity: Most strains are not pathogenic; some produce slight local swelling subcutaneously with little pus in guinea pigs and mice.

Distinctive characters: Growth in alternate zones in agar; strict anaerobe at first, later aerotolerant.

Source· Isolated from skin abscesses and from cases of appendicitis, synergistic gangrene and endocarditis.

Habitat: Found in the respiratory tract, mouth and vagina.

10. **Peptostreptococcus magnus** (Prévot, 1933) Smith, *comb. nov.* (*Diplococcus magnus anaerobius* Tissier and Martelly, Ann. Inst. Past., *16*, 1902, 885; *Diplococcus magnus* Prévot, Ann. Sci. Nat., Sér. Bot., *15*, 1933, 140.)

mag′nus. L. adj. *magnus* large.

Large spheres, 1.5 to 1.8 microns in diameter, usually in pairs, sometimes occurring singly, in small clumps or in very short chains. Gram-positive.

Gelatin: Growth slow, scant. No liquefaction.

Deep agar colonies: After 24 hours at 37° C., lenticular, whitish, granular; margin finely cut. No gas produced.

Broth: Turbid, clearing in 4 or 5 days resulting in a viscous mass similar to the zoogloea which *Clostridium bifermentans* forms.

Peptone broth: Slight turbidity; indole not produced.

Milk: Unchanged.

Carbohydrates not attacked.

Fibrin not digested.

Sterilized urine: Turbid in 3 to 4 days. The urea is attacked forming $(NH_4)_2CO_3$.

Proteoses: Digested and disintegrated forming $(NH_4)_2CO_3$ with the liberation of NH_3.

Anaerobic.

Temperature relations: Optimum, 37° C. Grows from 18° to 37° C. Killed in five minutes on boiling or in half an hour at 60° C. Optimum pH, 7.0. Limits of pH, 5.5 to 8.5

Non-pathogenic.

Distinctive characters: Large size; very marked alkalinizing power.

Source: Isolated from putrefying butcher's meat (Tissier and Martelly) and from a case of acute appendicitis (Prévot).

Habitat: Unknown.

11. Peptostreptococcus paleopneumo niae (Prévot, 1930) Smith, *comb. nov.* (An anaerobic pseudopneumococcus, Études bact. sur les infections d'origine otique, Rist, Thèse méd., Paris, 1898; also see Compt. rend. Soc. Biol., Paris, *52*, 1902, 305; Der Fränkelsche Diplococcus, Bolognesi, Cent. f. Bakt., I Abt., Orig., *43*, 1907, 113; *Diplococcus paleopneumoniae* Prévot, Ann. Sci. Nat., Sér. Bot., *15*, 1933, 143.)

pa.le.o.pneu.mo'ni.ae. Gr. adj. *palaeus* old; Gr. noun *pneumon* the lungs; M.L. noun *pneumonia* pneumonia; M.L. fem.gen.n. *paleopneumoniae* of old pneumonia.

Spheres, about 0.7 to 1.0 micron in diameter, occurring in pairs, rarely singly or in very short chains. Encapsulated. Gram-positive.

Gelatin: No liquefaction.

Deep agar colonies: Lenticular.

Blood agar colonies: Round, raised, transparent, dew drop. No hemolysis.

Broth: Opalescent turbidity which settles as a rather abundant, powdery, flocculent precipitate. No gas produced.

Glucose or lactose broth: Rapid, abundant growth.

Peptone broth (2 per cent): Very slow development; after 4 or 5 days at 37° C., growth very poor.

Milk: Good growth; partial coagulation.

Blood agar: Very rapid, abundant growth.

Coagulated protein not attacked.

Acid from glucose and lactose.

Anaerobic. Some strains become aerotolerant (Smith, Brit. Jour. Exp. Path., *17*, 1936, 329).

Temperature relations: Optimum, 37° C. No growth at 20° nor at 42° C. Killed at 55° C.

Pathogenic for mice.

Distinctive characters: Resembles *Diplococcus pneumoniae* but is a strict anaer obe; highly pathogenic.

Source: Isolated from an osseous abscess (Rist), from lesions of pleuropneumonia (Bolognesi) and from bronchitis and pneumonia (Smith).

Habitat: Found in the buccal-pharyngeal cavity of man and rodents.

12. Peptostreptococcus plagarumbelli (Prévot, 1933) Smith, *comb. nov.* (*Diplococcus* from septic wounds, Adamson, Jour. Path. Bact., *22*, 1919, 393; *Diplococcus plagarumbelli* Prévot, Ann. Sci. Nat., Sér. Bot., *15*, 1933, 157.)

pla.ga.rum.bel'li. L. noun *plaga* injury, plague; L. noun *bellum* war; M.L. gen.noun *plagarumbelli* of the plagues of war.

Spheres, 0.6 to 1.0 micron in diameter, occurring in pairs of unequal size or in short chains. Gram-positive.

Gelatin: No liquefaction.

Deep agar colonies: Appear after 24 to 48 hours, gradually increasing in size to to 2 mm in diameter; lenticular, regular, almost transparent. Gas is not produced, even in glucose agar.

Broth: Growth precipitates in 5 or 6 days: no gas is produced.

Milk: Strongly acidified and coagulated in 2 to 3 days.

Coagulated proteins not digested.

Indole not produced.

Acid but no gas from glucose, maltose, lactose and sucrose.

Anaerobic.

Temperature relations: Optimum, 37° C. Not always killed in 30 minutes at 80° C.

Non-pathogenic.

Source: Sixteen strains were isolated from fifty-one cases of septic war wounds.

Habitat: Common in septic wounds.

13. Peptostreptococcus morbillorum (Prévot, 1933) Smith, *comb. nov.* (Diplococci from cases of measles, Tunnicliff, Jour. Amer. Med. Assoc., *68*, 1917, 1028; *Diplococcus rubeolae* Tunnicliff, Jour. Inf. Dis., *52*, 1933, 39; *Diplococcus morbillorum* Prévot, Ann. Sci. Nat., Sér. Bot., *15*, 1933,

148; original name withdrawn by Tunnicliff, Jour. Inf. Dis., *58*, 1936, 1.)

mor.bil.lo'rum. L. noun *morbus* disease; M.L. dim.noun *morbillus* little disease; pl. *morbilli* measles; M.L. gen.noun *morbillorum* of measles.

Spheres, 0.6 to 0.8 micron in diameter, occurring in short chains, rarely in small masses. Gram-positive.

This organism does not develop on ordinary culture media; the addition of fresh serum or ascitic fluid is necessary.

Gelatin: No liquefaction.

Serum agar colonies: Very small, punctiform, appearing after 5 to 22 days. No gas is produced.

Glucose agar containing ascitic fluid and blood: Colonies are slightly larger and appear more rapidly than those on serum agar; greenish.

Blood agar colonies: Surrounded by a greenish halo. May be large and moist. Gas is not produced.

Broth: Very poor growth.

Hemolysed blood broth: Growth flocculent, leaving the liquid clear.

Milk: Unchanged by most strains. Acidified and coagulated by some strains.

Indole not produced.

Insoluble in bile.

Acid from glucose, sucrose and maltose.

Anaerobic; most strains become aerotolerant with transfers.

Temperature relations: Optimum, 37° C. Killed in 45 minutes at 57° C. Withstands −2° C. for two weeks.

Distinctive characters: Greenish colonies on blood media; poor growth on ordinary media.

Comments: Certain strains of this organism become aerotolerant upon repeated transfers; these aerotolerant strains are regarded as varieties of this species by Prévot (*op. cit.*, 1933, 152).

Source: Isolated from the throat and blood in cases of measles.

Habitat: Found in the nose, throat, eyes, ears, mucous secretions and blood from cases of measles.

TRIBE II. LACTOBACILLEAE WINSLOW ET AL., 1920.

(Winslow, Broadhurst, Buchanan, Krumwiede, Rogers and Smith, Jour. Bact., *5*, 1920, 211.)

Lac.to.ba.cil'le.ae. M.L. mas.n. *Lactobacillus* type genus of the tribe; -*eae* ending to denote a tribe; M.L. fem.pl.n. *Lactobacilleae* the *Lactobacillus* tribe.

Straight or curved rods usually occurring singly or in chains, sometimes in filaments; so-called false branching may also occur. Usually non-motile but may be motile, the motile species possessing peritrichous flagella. Gram-positive. Gelatin may be liquefied, but only by the strict anaerobes. Carbohydrates are usually attacked, the end-products of fermentation including either one or a number of the following: formic, acetic, propionic, butyric, lactic and valerianic acids, alcohol and carbon dioxide. Microaerophilic to anaerobic. Catalase-negative. May or may not be pathogenic. Found in fermenting animal and plant products; also found in the intestinal tracts and in lesions of various warm-blooded animals, including man.

The physiologies of the strictly anaerobic species included in this tribe have not been completely elucidated; future work may show that some of these species should be placed in *Propionibacterium* Orla-Jensen or in *Butyribacterium* Barker and Haas.

Key to the genera of tribe Lactobacilleae.

I. Microaerophilic to anaerobic. Glucose fermented with the production of lactic acid (subgenus *Lactobacillus* Beijerinck) or with the production of lactic and acetic acids, alcohol and carbon dioxide (subgenus *Saccharobacillus* van Laer).

Genus I. *Lactobacillus*, p. 542.

II. Strictly anaerobic.
  A. Non-motile.
    1. Cells do not show so-called false branching.
      a. Cells do not occur in long chains and/or filaments.
              Genus II. *Eubacterium*, p. 552.
      aa. Cells occur in long chains and/or filaments.
              Genus III. *Catenabacterium*, p. 560.
    2. Cells show so-called false branching.
              Genus IV. *Ramibacterium*, p. 563.
  B. Motile.
              Genus V. *Cillobacterium*, p. 566.

Genus I. **Lactobacillus** *Beijerinck, 1901.**

(Arch. néerl. d. sci. exact. et nat., Haárlem, Sér. 2, *7*, 1901, 212.)

Lac.to.ba.cil′lus. L. noun *lac, lactis* milk; L. dim.noun *bacillus* a small rod; M.L. mas.n. *Lactobacillus* milk rodlet.

Rods, often long and slender. Non-motile. Gram-positive. Pigment production rare; when present, yellow or orange to rust or brick-red. Gelatin is not liquefied. Growth on potato is poor or absent. Glucose and similar aldehydic hexoses, carbohydrates which yield these simple sugars, and polyhydroxy alcohols are changed either by homofermentation to lactic acid or by heterofermentation to lactic and acetic acids, alcohol and carbon dioxide. Nitrates are not reduced except under certain conditions with *Lactobacillus plantarum*. Several species grow at relatively high temperatures. Poor surface growth because these bacteria are generally microaerophilic or anaerobic. Do not produce catalase. Found in fermenting animal (especially dairy) and plant products.

Many taxonomists continue to recognize three subdivisions of the lactic acid rods described here as belonging to the genus *Lactobacillus* Beijerinck: *Thermobacterium* Orla-Jensen (The Lactic Acid Bacteria, 1919, 160) and *Streptobacterium* Orla-Jensen (*ibid*, 166) for the homofermentative species, and *Betabacterium* Orla-Jensen (*ibid.*, 175) for the heterofermentative types. Two of these generic names are illegitimate homonyms: *Streptobacterium* apparently was first used by Maggi (Jour. Micrographie, *10*, 1886, 84) to designate a growth form of *Bacterium aceti* Zopf; Billet (Bull. Sci. de la France et de la Belgique, Paris, 1890, 23) used it as a form genus to designate rod-shaped organisms which occur in chains; Jacqué and Masay (Cent. f. Bakt., I Abt., Orig., *62*, 1912, 180) defined it as a genus, including *Streptobacterium foetidum* as a species in the genus; this organism was similar to if not identical with one of the species placed in the genus *Proteus* Hauser. *Betabacterium*, as a name for the heterofermentative types, is antedated by *Saccharobacillus* van Laer, type species *Saccharobacillus pastorianus* van Laer. There seems to be no more reason for separating the high temperature, homofermentative lactic rods from the species that grow at ordinary temperatures than there is for making a similar subdivision of the homofermentative lactic streptococci. *Thermobacterium* is therefore regarded as a synonym in part of *Lactobacillus* Beijerinck. *Lactobacterium* as used by some recent authors (e.g. Krassilnikov, Guide to the Bacteria and Actinomycetes, Izd. Akad. Nauk, U.S.S.R., Moskau, 1949, 208) as a substitute for *Lactobacillus* Beijerinck is invalid. *Lactobacterium* was proposed by van Steenberge (Ann. Inst. Past., *34*, 1920, 803) for lactobacilli in beer and beer wort; it is a synonym of *Lactobacillus* Beijerinck. At the same time when Beijerinck proposed *Lactobacillus* and van Laer proposed *Saccharobacillus*, the generic name *Bacillus* was generally accepted as applying to any large, rod-shaped bacterium whether it did or did not form spores, and this interpretation is in accord with the classical meaning of bacillus. In other

*Completely revised by Prof. Carl S. Pederson, New York State Experiment Station, Geneva, New York, October, 1954.

words, the use of *Bacillus* for spore-forming rods at a later period cannot be properly interpreted as rendering generic names of non-spore-forming rods with the suffix *-bacillus* illegitimate. Stability in bacteriological nomenclature can, it is believed, be best brought about by observing the rules of the internationally accepted Bacteriological Code. Under this Code no one has authority to reject, change or modify a name because in his judgment another name is preferable. Exceptions to rules should be internationally approved.

The type species is *Lactobacillus caucasicus* Beijerinck.

It is impossible to make an entirely satisfactory differentiation of the species in the genus *Lactobacillus* due to the inadequacy of comparative data. The end-products of fermentation, utilization of carbon compounds and temperatures of growth are the criteria relied upon at present. It is quite possible that when more comparative information is made available in regard to nutritional patterns in defined media, serological reactions and variations in sugar fermentations, a more satisfactory arrangement of species may be effected. See Rogosa, Wiseman, Mitchell, Disraely and Beaman (Jour. Bact., *65*, 1953, 681), Tittsler, Geib and Rogosa (Jour. Bact., *54*, 1947, 12), Williams (Jour. Inf. Dis., *82*, 1948, 31) and Orland (Jour. Inf. Dis., *86*, 1950, 63).

Key to the species of genus **Lactobacillus.**

I. Homofermentative, producing only traces of end-products other than lactic acid from glucose. Sub-genus *Lactobacillus* Beijerinck (Arch. néerl. d. sci. exact. et nat., Haárlem, Sér. 2, *7*, 1901, 212).
  A. Optimum temperature, between 37° and 60° C. or higher.
    1. Produce acid from lactose.
      a. Optimum temperature, between 37° and 45° C.
        b. Produce levo rotatory lactic acid.
            1. *Lactobacillus caucasicus.*
            2. *Lactobacillus lactis.*
        bb. Produce optically inactive or dextro rotatory lactic acid.
          c. Microaerophilic.
            3. *Lactobacillus helveticus.*
            4. *Lactobacillus acidophilus.*
          cc. Anaerobic in freshly isolated cultures.
            5. *Lactobacillus bifidus.*
      aa. Optimum temperature, between 45° and 62° C.; usually no acid from maltose.
            6. *Lactobacillus bulgaricus.*
            7. *Lactobacillus thermophilus.*
    2. Does not produce acid from lactose.
            8. *Lactobacillus delbrueckii.*
  B. Optimum temperature, between 28° and 32° C.
    1. Produce optically active lactic acid.
      a. Produces dextro rotatory lactic acid. Often prefers lactose to sucrose and maltose.
            9. *Lactobacillus casei.*
      aa. Produces levo rotatory lactic acid.
           10. *Lactobacillus leichmannii.*
    2. Produces optically inactive lactic acid.
          11. *Lactobacillus plantarum.*
II. Heterofermentative, producing considerable amounts of end-products other than lactic acid from glucose (carbon dioxide, alcohol and acetic acid; mannitol from fructose). Sub-genus *Saccharobacillus* van Laer (Contributions à l'Histoire des Ferments des Hydrates de Carbone. Mém. Acad. Royale de Belgique, *47*, 1892, 5).
  A. Optimum temperature, between 28° and 32° C. Usually ferment arabinose.

1. Ferment raffinose, sucrose and lactose.
   12. *Lactobacillus pastorianus.*
   13. *Lactobacillus buchneri.*
2. Does not ferment raffinose and often does not ferment sucrose or lactose.
   14. *Lactobacillus brevis.*

B. Optimum temperature, between 35° and 40° C. or higher. Usually does not ferment arabinose.

15. *Lactobacillus fermenti.*

1. **Lactobacillus caucasicus** (Beijerinck, 1889) Beijerinck, 1901. (*Bacillus caucasicus* Beijerinck, Arch. néerl. d. sci. exact. et nat., *23*, 1889, 428; Beijerinck, *ibid.*, Sér. 2, *7*, 1901, 212; not *Bacillus caucasicus* von Freudenreich, Cent. f. Bakt., II Abt., *3*, 1897, 54 and 135.)

cau.ca'si.cus. Gr. noun *Caucasia* region of the Caucasus; M.L. adj. *caucasicus* of the Caucasus.

Description taken from the reports of Beijerinck cited above.

Rods, thin and variable in size, occurring singly or in filaments. Non-motile. Gram-positive (not recorded in early descriptions).

Gelatin: No liquefaction.

Wort gelatin: Small, white colonies.

Agar colonies: Small.

Broth: Carbohydrates necessary for growth.

Milk: Rapid acid production with coagulation; no action on casein.

Utilizes animal peptones with difficulty; utilizes vegetable peptones more readily.

Acid from glucose, sucrose, maltose and lactose. No action on starch. Action on other carbohydrates not studied. Lactose in milk converted to levo rotatory lactic acid with little carbon dioxide.

Microaerophilic.

Optimum temperature, between 40° and 44° C. Temperature range, 25° to 45° C.

Source: Isolated from kefir and from cheese.

Habitat: Occurs symbiotically with yeast in kefir.

Prototype: *Dispora caucasica* Kern, 1882. (Biol. Zent., *2*, 1882, 135; later in Bull. de la Soc. Imp. des Naturalistes de Moscow, *56*, 1882, 168.)

The description by Kern of an organism from kefir grains is confused probably because the organism (a spore former) which he isolated by the use of Cohn's solution was not the same as the presumably granulated lactobacillus he saw in microscopical preparations of kefir. Beijerinck was apparently the first to have isolated a lactobacillus from kefir in pure culture and to have given a sufficiently complete description to make reidentification possible. It should be noted that from the characters given, this could not have been the same species as that isolated later from kefir by von Freudenreich (*op. cit.*, 1897, 54 and 135) and Orla-Jensen (The Lactic Acid Bacteria, 1919, 175).

2. **Lactobacillus lactis** (Orla-Jensen, 1919) Holland, 1920. (*Bacillus lactis acidi* Leichmann, Cent. f. Bakt., II Abt., *2*, 1896, 779; also see Milch. Zeitung, *25*, 1896, 67; *Thermobacterium lactis* Orla-Jensen, The Lactic Acid Bacteria, 1919, 164; Holland, Jour. Bact., *5*, 1920, 223.)

lac'tis. L. noun *lac* milk; *lactis* of milk.

Rods, appearing as long forms with a tendency to grow into threads, often strongly curling, occurring singly or in pairs in young vigorous cultures. Generally contain volutin grains. Gram-positive (not recorded in original description).

Milk: Acid produced followed by coagulation in one to four days. 1.7 per cent acid produced.

Acid from fructose, glucose, mannose, galactose, sucrose, maltose, lactose, raffinose and dextrin. Glycerol, xylose, arabinose, rhamnose, sorbitol, mannitol, inulin and starch not fermented. Salicin may or may not be fermented.

Forms levo rotatory lactic acid with only a trace of other products.

Temperature relations: Optimum, 40° C. Minimum, between 18° and 22° C. Maximum, 50° C.

Source: Isolated from milk and cheese.

Habitat: Undoubtedly widely distributed in milk or milk products.

3. Lactobacillus helveticus (Orla-Jensen, 1916) Holland, 1920. (Bacillus ε, von Freudenreich, Cent. f. Bakt., II Abt., *1*, 1895, 173; also see Landw. Jahrb. d. Schweiz, 1895, 211; *Bacillus casei* ε, von Freudenreich and Thöni, Landw. Jahrb. d. Schweiz, 1904, 526; *Thermobacterium helveticum* Orla-Jensen, Maelkeri-Bakteriologie, 1916, 35; also see The Lactic Acid Bacteria, 1919, 164; Holland, Jour. Bact., *5*, 1920, 223.)

hel.ve′ti.cus. L. adj. *Helveticus* Swiss.

Rods, 0.7 to 0.9 by 2.0 to 6.0 microns, occurring singly and in chains. Non-motile. Gram-positive.

Whey gelatin colonies: Does not grow readily at temperatures required for incubation of gelatin.

Lactose agar colonies: Small, grayish, viscid.

Milk: Acid, with coagulation; may become slimy.

Acid from glucose, fructose, galactose, mannose, maltose and lactose; smaller amounts are produced from dextrin. The lactic acid produced is optically inactive.

Nitrites not produced from nitrates.

Microaerophilic.

Temperature relations: Optimum, between 40° and 42° C. Minimum, between 20° and 22° C. Maximum, 50° C.

Source: Isolated from sour milk and cheese.

Habitat: Widely distributed in dairy products.

4. Lactobacillus acidophilus (Moro, 1900) Holland, 1920. (*Bacillus acidophilus* Moro, Wiener klin. Wochnschr., *13*, 1900, 114; also see Jahrb. f. Kinderheilkunde, *52*, 1900, 38; Holland, Jour. Bact., *5*, 1920, 215.)

a.ci.do′phi.lus. L. adj. *acidus* sour; M.L. neut.n. *acidum* acid; Gr. adj. *philus* loving; M.L. adj. *acidophilus* acid-loving.

Description of Moro supplemented by material from Kulp and Rettger (Jour. Bact., *9*, 1924, 357), Curran, Rogers and Whittier (Jour. Bact., *25*, 1933, 595) and Rettger, Levy, Weinstein and Weiss (*Lactobacillus acidophilus*, Yale Univ. Press, New Haven, 1935).

Rods, 0.6 to 0.9 by 1.5 to 6.0 microns, occurring singly, in pairs and in short chains with rounded ends. Non-motile. Dimensions variable (Kulp and Rettger), (Curran, Rogers and Whittier). Gram-positive; old cultures often Gram-negative (Moro).

Gelatin: No growth at 20° C. No liquefaction.

Wort-agar (Moro) or tomato agar (Kulp and Rettger) plates. Surface colonies: peripheries a capilliform maze of long, delicate, twisted, fuzzy projections; center appears as a thick, dark, felt-like mass. Deep colonies: small, irregularly shaped, with fine radiate or ramified projections.

Wort-agar slants: Growth scant, limited, dry, veil-like.

Wort-broth: After 48 hours, fine, flocculent sediment. Other acid broths sediment whitish, slight turbidity.

Milk: Slow growth with small inoculum. Coagulates from the bottom up.

Potato: No growth.

Acid but no gas from glucose, sucrose and lactose (Moro). Acid from glucose, fructose, galactose, mannose, maltose, lactose and sucrose. Some cultures ferment raffinose and trehalose and have slight action on dextrin. Xylose, arabinose, rhamnose, glycerol, mannitol, sorbitol, dulcitol and inositol not fermented (Kulp and Rettger). Optically inactive lactic acid and volatile acids formed from sugars (Curran, Rogers and Whittier).

No visible growth in carbohydrate-free media (Rettger, Levy, Weinstein and Weiss).

Microaerophilic.

Temperature relations: Optimum, 37° C. No growth between 20° and 22° C. (Moro). Maximum, between 43° and 48° C. (Curran, Rogers and Whittier).

Not pathogenic for laboratory animals.

Distinctive characters: Grows in acid media. Unless frequent transfers are made, organism may become Gram-negative and rapidly develop characteristic degeneration forms (Moro). The so-called original strains of *Bacillus acidophilus* from the Král collection, described and called *Microbacterium lacticum* by Orla-Jensen, do not have the characteristics given by Moro.

Comments: Crecelius and Rettger (Jour.

Bact., *46*, 1943, 12) describe a variety of this species from the feces and intestinal contents of guinea pigs.

Source: Isolated from the feces of milk-fed infants. Also found in the feces of older persons on high milk-, lactose- or dextrin-containing diets.

Habitat: Same as for the source.

5. Lactobacillus bifidus (Tissier, 1900) Holland, 1920. (*Bacillus bifidus communis* and *Bacillus bifidus* Tissier, Recherches sur la flore intestinal des nourrissons, Paris, 1900, 85; Holland, Jour. Bact., *5*, 1920, 223.)

bi'fi.dus. L. adj. *bifidus* cleft, divided.

Description supplemented from Weiss and Rettger (Jour. Bact., *28*, 1934, 501).

Small, slender rods, the average length of which is 4.0 microns, 0.5 to 0.7 by 2 to 8 microns (Weiss and Rettger), occurring singly or in pairs and short chains, parallel to each other, very variable in appearance. Branched and club forms develop in some cultures. Non-motile. Gram-positive but stains irregularly in old cultures (Tissier).

Little or no growth in ca/bohydrate-free agar (Weiss and Rettger).

Deep sugar-agar colonies: After 3 days, solid with slightly irregular edge, whitish. Grow up to 3 cm from the surface forming a ring. Average diameter 3 mm. No gas.

Sugar broth: Good growth. Turbid within 3 days. Clears with flocculent precipitate.

Milk: Good growth with large inoculum. No coagulation (Tissier). May or may not coagulate milk (Weiss and Rettger).

Acid but no gas from glucose (Tissier). Acid from glucose, fructose, galactose, sucrose, inulin and usually from dextrin, starch, maltose, raffinose and trehalose. A few strains form acid from lactose and salicin. The acid consists of optically inactive lactic acid and 18 to 25 per cent of volatile acid (Weiss and Rettger). Orla-Jensen (The Lactic Acid Bacteria, 1919, 192), Eggerth (Jour. Bact., *30*, 1935, 295) and Weiss and Rettger (Jour. Bact., *35*, 1938, 17; Jour. Inf. Dis., *62*, 1938, 115) describe a more anaerobic variety of this species which produces more volatile acid as well as dextro rotatory lactic acid and which ferments arabinose, xylose and melezitose but not mannose.

Strict anaerobe (Tissier). Strict anaerobe in primary culture, becoming microaerophilic (Weiss and Rettger).

Optimum temperature, 37° C. May show slight growth at 20° C. Killed at 60° C. in 15 minutes.

Non-pathogenic for mice or guinea pigs.

Distinctive characters: Bifurcations and club-shaped forms (Tissier), particularly in infant feces and in primary culture (Weiss and Rettger).

Comment: A variety of this species that grows more readily in human than in cow's milk is discussed by György and Rose (Jour. Bact., *69*, 1955, 483) and in papers listed in the bibliography of this report. This difference appears to be due to a specific growth factor, the so-called bifidus factor.

Source: Isolated from feces of nursing infants.

Habitat: Very common in the feces of infants. May constitute almost the entire intestinal flora of breast-fed infants. Also present in smaller numbers with bottle-fed infants. Possibly more widely distributed than indicated in the intestines of warm-blooded animals.

6. Lactobacillus bulgaricus (Luerssen and Kühn, 1907) Holland, 1920. (*Bacillus A*, Grigoroff, Revue Méd. Suisse romande, *25*, 1905; *Bacillus bulgaricus* Luerssen and Kühn, Cent. f. Bakt., II Abt., *20*, 1907, 241; Holland, Jour. Bact., *5*, 1920, 215.)

bul.ga'ri.cus. M.L. adj. *bulgaricus* Bulgarian.

Description of Luerssen and Kühn supplemented by Grigoroff (*op. cit.*, 1905), Cohendy (Compt. rend. Soc. Biol. Paris, *58*, 1906, 364), Kuntze (Cent. f. Bakt., II Abt., *21*, 1908, 737), Bertrand and Duchacek (Ann. Inst. Past., *23*, 1909, 402), White and Avery (Cent. f. Bakt., II Abt., *25*, 1910, 161), Rahe (Jour. Bact., *3*, 1918, 420), Orla-Jensen (The Lactic Acid Bacteria, 1919, 164), Kulp and Rettger (Jour. Bact., *9*, 1924, 357) and Sherman and Hodge (Jour. Dairy Sci., *19*, 1936, 494).

Slender rods with rounded ends, often in chains. Non-motile. Gram-positive, older cultures showing unstained portions (Luerssen and Kühn).

Whey gelatin: No liquefaction (White and Avery).

Colonies: Flat, yellowish white, 2 to 3 mm in diameter. Old cultures have dark centers. Deep colonies globular (Luerssen and Kühn).

Whey agar colonies: Circular to irregular (White and Avery).

Milk: Coagulation at 37° C. No gas. No decomposition of casein.

Potato: Yellow-white colonies (Luerssen and Kühn). No growth (Grigoroff), (Cohendy), (White and Avery).

Indole not produced (Grigoroff), (White and Avery).

Results on acid production from sugars vary. Glucose, lactose and galactose are apparently always fermented while xylose, arabinose, sorbose, rhamnose, dulcitol, mannitol, dextrin, inulin and starch are never fermented. Early workers (Gigoroff) (Cohendy) noted fermentation of fructose, maltose and sucrose. Later workers (Bertrand and Duchacek), (Orla-Jensen), (Rahe), (Kulp and Rettger), (Sherman and Hodge) noted variable or negative results on sucrose, maltose and unheated fructose.

Forms high acidity in milk. The lactic acid is optically inactive (Grigoroff), (Bertrand and Duchacek), (White and Avery) or levo rotatory (White and Avery), (Orla-Jensen) with small quantities of volatile acid (White and Avery).

Nitrites not produced from nitrates.

Aerobic or anaerobic (Luerssen and Kühn). Microaerophilic (White and Avery). Anaerobic in fresh isolation (Sherman and Hodge).

Temperature relations: Optimum, between 45° and 50° C. Minimum, 22° C. (Luerssen and Kühn).

Distinctive characters: This species at present is regarded as including the high-temperature organisms isolated from milk with difficulty. These ferment glucose, galactose and lactose but usually do not ferment sucrose, maltose or unheated fructose when freshly isolated.

Source: Originally isolated from yogurt.

Habitat: Probably present in many milk products if held at high temperature.

7. **Lactobacillus thermophilus** Ayers and Johnson, 1924. (Jour. Bact., *9*, 1924, 291.)

ther.mo'phi.lus. Gr. noun *therme* heat; Gr. adj. *philus* loving; M.L. adj. *thermophilus* heat-loving.

Description of Ayers and Johnson supplemented by material from Charlton (Jour. Dairy Sci., *15*, 1932, 393).

Rods 0.5 by 3.0 microns. Non-motile (Charlton). Stain irregularly. Gram-positive.

Gelatin stab: No liquefaction.

Agar plate: Small colonies.

Agar slant: Slight, translucent growth (Charlton).

Broth: Turbid (Charlton).

Litmus milk: Acid.

Acid from glucose, lactose, sucrose, starch and trace from glycerol; no acid from salicin, mannitol, raffinose or inulin (Ayers and Johnson). Acid from fructose, galactose, mannose, maltose, raffinose and dextrin; no acid from arabinose, xylose, glycerol, rhamnose, salicin, inulin or mannitol. Dextro rotatory lactic acid formed (Charlton).

Nitrites not produced from nitrates (Charlton).

Facultatively anaerobic. Grows best aerobically.

Temperature relations: Optimum, between 50° and 62.8° C. Minimum, 30° C. Maximum, 65° C. Thermal death point, 71° C. for 30 minutes or 82° C. for 2½ minutes.

This is the thermophilic lactobacillus obtained from pasteurized milk which causes pin-point colonies on agar plates.

Source: Isolated from pasteurized milk.

Habitat: Known only from pasteurized milk.

8. **Lactobacillus delbrueckii** (Leichmann, 1896) Beijerinck, 1901. (*Bacillus delbrückii* Leichmann, Cent. f. Bakt., II Abt., *2*, 1896, 284; Beijerinck, Arch. néerl. d. sci. exact. et nat., Haárlem, Sér. 2, *7*, 1901, 212.)

del.bruec'ki.i. M.L. gen.noun *delbrueckii* of Delbrück; named for Prof. M. Delbrück, a German bacteriologist.

Description of Leichmann supplemented by material from Henneberg (Cent. f. Bakt., II Abt., *11*, 1903, 154).

Rods, 0.5 to 0.8 by 2.0 to 9.0 microns (Henneberg), occurring singly and in short chains. Non-motile. Gram-positive.

Gelatin colonies: Small, gray, circular, not liquefied.

Agar colonies: Small, flat, crenated.

Agar slant: Narrow, translucent, soft, grayish streak.

Broth: Slightly turbid.

Milk: Unchanged.

Acid from maltose and sucrose (Leichmann) and glucose, fructose, galactose and dextrin. No acid from xylose, arabinose, rhamnose, lactose, raffinose, trehalose, inulin, starch, mannitol or α-methyl-glucoside (Henneberg). Levo rotatory lactic acid is formed. Forms 1.6 per cent acid in mash.

Nitrites not produced from nitrates.

Microaerophilic.

Optimum temperature, 45° C.

This is the high-temperature organism of fermenting mashes. In fresh isolations it apparently has a higher optimum temperature than when held in pure culture.

Source: Isolated from sour potato mash in a distillery.

Habitat: Fermenting vegetable and grain mashes.

9. Lactobacillus casei (Orla-Jensen, 1919) Holland, 1920. (*Bacillus α*, von Freudenreich, Ann. d. Microg., *2*, 1890, 266; also see Landw. Jahrb. d. Schweiz, 1891, 20; *Bacillus casei α*, von Freudenreich and Thöni, Landw. Jahrb. d. Schweiz, 1904, 526; *Caseobacterium vulgare* Orla-Jensen, Maelkeri-Bakteriologie, 1916, 35; *Streptobacterium casei* Orla-Jensen, The Lactic Acid Bacteria, 1919, 166; Holland, Jour. Bact., *5*, 1920, 221.)

ca′se.i. L. noun *caseus* cheese; L. gen.noun *casei* of cheese.

Short or long rods occurring in short or long chains. Non-motile. Gram-positive.

Milk: Acid with coagulation in 3 to 5 days or longer, may become slimy. Forms about 1.5 per cent lactic acid.

Utilizes casein and therefore important in cheese ripening.

Acid from glucose, fructose, mannose, galactose, maltose, lactose, mannitol and salicin. May or may not ferment sucrose. Mostly dextro rotatory lactic acid produced though a small amount of levo rotatory lactic acid may be formed. Only lactic acid

is produced with a trace of other end-products.

Microaerophilic.

Temperature relations: Optimum, 30° C. Minimum, 10° C. Maximum, between 37° and 40° C.; with some strains, 45° C.

Relationship to other species: This is the more common lactic acid rod found in milk and milk products. Orla-Jensen distinguishes it from *Lactobacillus plantarum* Holland in that it produces dextro rotatory lactic acid and usually ferments lactose more readily than sucrose or maltose.

Comments: Rogosa, Wiseman, Mitchell, Disraely and Beaman (Jour. Bact., *65*, 1953, 688) recognize three varieties of this species based on the ability to ferment lactose and/or rhamnose.

Source: Isolated from milk and cheese.

Habitat: Probably more widely distributed than indicated by isolations.

10. Lactobacillus leichmannii Bergey et al., 1925. (*Bacillus leichmanni I*, Henneberg, Ztschr. f. Spiritusindustrie, *26*, 1903, 22; also see Cent. f. Bakt., II Abt., *11*, 1903, 163; Bergey et al., Manual, 2nd ed., 1925, 180.)

leich.man′ni.i. M.L. gen.noun *leichmannii* of Leichmann; named for Prof. G. Leichmann, a German bacteriologist.

Rods, 0.6 by 2.0 to 4.0 microns, occurring singly and in short chains. The cells show two or more deeply staining granules. Non-motile. Gram-positive.

Gelatin stab: No liquefaction.

Agar colonies: Small, clear with white centers.

Agar slant: Limited, grayish streak, better growth in stab.

Broth: Turbid.

Acid from glucose, fructose, maltose, sucrose and trehalose; slight amounts from galactose, mannitol and α-methyl-glucoside. Lactose, raffinose, arabinose, rhamnose, dextrin and inulin not fermented. Forms 1.3 per cent lactic acid in mash. Produces levo rotatory lactic acid, according to Rogosa et al. (Jour. Bact., *65*, 1953, 686).

Nitrites not produced from nitrates.

Microaerophilic.

Temperature relations: Optimum, 36° C. Maximum, between 40° and 46° C.

Relationship to other species: This species is apparently similar to *Lactobacillus delbrueckii* but has a lower optimum temperature.

Source: Isolated from compressed yeast and from fermenting milk.

Habitat: Dairy and plant products.

11. Lactobacillus plantarum (Orla-Jensen, 1919) Holland, 1920. (*Streptobacterium plantarum* Orla-Jensen, The Lactic Acid Bacteria, Copenhagen, 1919, 174; Holland, Jour. Bact., *5*, 1920, 225.)

Probable synonyms: *Lactobacillus pentosus* Fred, Peterson and Anderson, Jour. Biol. Chem., *48*, 1921, 410; *Lactobacillus arabinosus* Fred, Peterson and Anderson, *loc. cit.*

plan.ta'rum. L. fem.n. *planta* a sprout; M.L. *planta* a plant; M.L. gen.pl.noun *plantarum* of plants.

Description from Orla-Jensen supplemented by material from Pederson (Jour. Bact., *31*, 1936, 217).

Rods, ordinarily 0.7 to 1.0 by 3.0 to 8.0 microns, occurring singly or in short chains, with rounded ends. Under favorable growth conditions these organisms tend to be short rods. Under adverse conditions they tend to be longer; for example, in tomato juice agar at 45° C. (Pederson, N. Y. Agr. Exp. Sta. Tech. Bull. 150, 1929). In fermenting vegetables, the organisms tend to become longer as the acidity becomes greater. The organisms are usually longer in milk than in broths. Differences in morphology are well illustrated by Orla-Jensen. Non-motile. A motile strain of this organism has been described by Harrison and Hansen (Jour. Bact., *59*, 1950, 444). Gram-positive.

Gelatin-yeast extract-glucose stab: Filiform growth. No liquefaction.

Agar slant: Growth, if any, is very faint.

Broth: Turbid, clearing after a few days. A few strains flocculate.

Litmus milk: Acid, usually coagulated.

The majority of strains produce acid from glucose, fructose, mannose, galactose, arabinose, sucrose, maltose, lactose, raffinose, salicin and, to a lesser extent, from sorbitol, mannitol, dextrin, glycerol and xylose. Rhamnose, starch and inulin usually not fermented.

Lactic acid (usually optically inactive), with only small quantities of acetic acid and carbon dioxide, is produced in the fermentation of hexose sugars. Acetic and lactic acids are produced from the pentoses. Produces up to 1.2 per cent acid in broth.

Nitrites not produced from nitrates in ordinary broth. In special media, some strains produce nitrites from nitrates (Costilow and Humphreys, Science, *121*, 1955, 168).

Microaerophilic.

Temperature relations: Optimum, 30° C. Minimum, 10° C. Maximum, 40° C. Thermal death point, 65° to 75° C. for 15 minutes.

Salt tolerance: Usually grows in salt up to 5.5 per cent.

Relationship to other species: This species is the optically inactive lactic acid-producing rod from fermenting materials but is closely related to *Lactobacillus casei*. It ferments sucrose and maltose as readily as lactose.

Comments: Breed and Pederson (Jour. Bact., *36*, 1938, 667; also see New York Agr. Exp. Sta. Tech. Bull. 259, 1941, 15 pp.) have described a chromogenic variety of this species which causes rusty spots in cheese.

Source: Isolated from cheese, butter, kefir, feces, fermenting potatoes, beets, corn, chard, bread dough, sauerkraut, cucumber pickles, tomato pickles, cauliflower pickles and spoiled tomato products.

Habitat: Widely distributed in nature, particularly in fermenting plant and animal products.

12. Lactobacillus pastorianus (van Laer, 1892) Bergey et al., 1923. (*Saccharobacillus pastorianus* van Laer, Contributions à l'Histoire des Ferments des Hydrates de Carbone. Mém. Acad. Royale de Belgique, *47*, 1892, 5; Bergey et al., Manual, 1st ed., 1923, 246.)

pas.tor.i.an'us. L. mas.n. *pastor* a shepherd, the Latin rendition of Pasteur; M.L. adj. *pastorianus* pertaining to Pasteur; named for Louis Pasteur, French chemist and bacteriologist.

Description supplemented by material from Henneberg (Cent. f. Bakt., II Abt., *8*, 1902, 184), Shimwell (Jour. Inst. Brewing,

41, 1935, 481) and Pederson (Jour. Bact., *35*, 1938, 107).

Rods, 0.5 to 1.0 by 7.0 to 35.0 microns, occurring singly and in chains. Non-motile. Gram-positive.

Wort gelatin: Surface colonies are rhizoid and slightly spreading. Submerged colonies are round with smooth edges, yellowish by transmitted light and rarely exceed 0.3 mm in diameter.

Wort gelatin slant: Growth is narrow (about 1 mm wide), flat, translucent and rhizoid, becoming dry.

Wort gelatin stab: A luxuriant, arborescent form is produced in 7.5 per cent gelatin. With 10 per cent gelatin the growth spreads less vigorously, and in 15 per cent gelatin the stab is no longer arborescent but becomes beaded.

Wort agar colonies: Appear as irregular masses of threads radiating from a central nucleus; grayish white by reflected light.

Wort agar slant: Growth same as for wort gelatin slant. However, at higher temperatures (32° C.) the rhizoid form becomes obscure, and the growth develops into a beaded, raised, grayish white streak about 2 mm in width.

Broth: Produces a silky turbidity in unhopped beer and wort. Good growth in yeast extract; turbid.

Litmus milk: Acid.

Acid from arabinose, glucose, fructose, galactose, maltose, sucrose, dextrin, raffinose, trehalose and mannitol; slight acid from lactose and starch. No acid from xylose, rhamnose or inulin. Forms 1.5 per cent acid in mash. Also forms CO_2 and alcohol, lactic, formic and acetic acids.

This species includes the ordinarily long rod types from spoiled beers. Apparently the same variations in regard to sugar fermentation may be found as are noted for similar species.

Nitrites not produced from nitrates.

Microaerophilic.

Temperature relations: Optimum, between 29° and 33° C. Minimum, 11° C. Maximum, 37° C.

Optimum pH for initial growth, 8.0; growth shows signs of inhibition at pH 9.0.

Comment: A slime-producing variety, differing from the parent strain in sugar fermentations, has been described by Shimwell (Jour. Inst. Brewing, *55* (N.S. *46*), 1949, 26).

Source: Isolated from sour beer and from distillery yeast.

Habitat: Probably more widely distributed than indicated by isolations.

13. **Lactobacillus buchneri** (Henneberg, 1903) Bergey et al., 1923. (*Bacillus buchneri* Henneberg, Cent. f. Bakt., II Abt., *11*, 1903, 163; Bergey et al., Manual, 1st ed., 1923, 251.)

buch'ner.i. M.L. gen.noun *buchneri* of Buchner; named for Prof. E. Buchner, a German bacteriologist.

Description supplemented by material from Pederson (Jour. Bact., *35*, 1938, 107).

Rods, 0.35 by 0.7 to 4.0 microns, occurring singly, in pairs and chains or in filaments 25 microns or longer. Non-motile. Gram-positive.

Agar colonies: White to yellowish, adherent.

Agar slant: Growth, if any, faint.

Broth: Turbid, clearing after a few days.

Litmus milk: Usually unchanged but may be slightly acid with no reduction.

Acid usually from arabinose, xylose, glucose, fructose, galactose, mannose, sucrose, lactose, maltose and raffinose. Mannitol, sorbitol, glycerol, rhamnose, salicin, inulin, dextrin and starch fermented by a few strains.

Lactic acid produced usually optically inactive. Acetic acid, ethyl alcohol and carbon dioxide formed in the fermentation of aldohexoses. Mannitol produced from fructose. Acetic and lactic acids from pentoses. Forms 1.3 per cent lactic acid in mash and 2.7 per cent alcohol.

Nitrites not produced from nitrates.

Temperature relations: Optimum, between 32° and 37° C. Minimum, between 10° and 15° C. Maximum, between 44° and 48° C.

Relationship to other species: Strains of this species might be considered intermediates between *Lactobacillus brevis* and *Lactobacillus fermenti*.

Source: Isolated from sour mash, pressed yeast, molasses, wine, catsup and sauerkraut.

Habitat: Widely distributed in fermenting substances.

14. Lactobacillus brevis (Orla-Jensen, 1919) Bergey et al., 1934. (*Bacillus* γ, von Freudenreich, Landw. Jahrb. d. Schweiz, 1891, 22; *Bacillus casei* γ, von Freudenreich and Thöni, Landw. Jahrb. d. Schweiz, 1904, 526; *Betabacterium breve* Orla-Jensen, The Lactic Acid Bacteria, 1919, 175; Bergey et al., Manual, 4th ed., 1934, 312.)

bre'vis. L. adj. *brevis* short.

Description supplemented by material from Pederson (Jour. of Bact., *35*, 1938, 105).

Rods, 0.7 to 1.0 by 2.0 to 4.0 microns, with rounded ends, occurring singly, in short chains and occasionally in long filaments which may show granulation. Non-motile. Gram-positive.

Gelatin: No liquefaction.

Agar slant: Growth, if any, faint.

Broth: Turbid, clearing after a few days.

Milk: Acid produced but no clot except with some freshly isolated strains.

Does not attack casein as a rule.

Utilizes calcium lactate as a source of carbon.

Acid from arabinose, xylose, glucose, fructose, galactose and maltose. Strains vary in fermentation of lactose, sucrose, mannose and raffinose. Salicin, mannitol, glycerol, rhamnose, dextrin, inulin and starch seldom fermented. Usually shows a particularly vigorous fermentation of arabinose.

Lactic acid produced usually optically inactive; acetic acid, ethyl alcohol and carbon dioxide formed in fermentation of aldohexoses. Mannitol produced from fructose. Acetic and lactic acids produced from the pentoses.

Temperature relations: Optimum, 30° C. Growth poor below 15° and above 37° C. Maximum, 38° C.

This species includes the large group of gas-producing lactic acid rods ordinarily characterized by a marked fermentation of pentoses, particularly arabinose. They usually also ferment fructose more readily than glucose.

Comment: A chromogenic variety which causes the production of rusty spot in cheese has been described by Davis and Mattick

(Proc. Soc. Agr. Bact., 1936, 3) and by Breed and Pederson (Jour. Bact., *36*, 1938, 667; also see New York Agr. Exp. Sta. Tech. Bull. 259, 1941, 15 pp.).

Source: Isolated from milk, kefir, cheese, feces, fermenting sauerkraut, ensilage, manure, soils, sour dough and spoiled tomato products.

Habitat: Widely distributed in nature, particularly in plant and animal products.

15. Lactobacillus fermenti Beijerinck, 1901. (Arch. néerl. d. sci. exact. et nat., Sér. 2, *7*, 1901, 212.)

fer.men'ti. L. neut.n. *fermentum* ferment yeast; L. gen.noun *fermenti* of yeast.

Description supplemented by material from Smit (Ztschr. f. Gärungsphysiol., *5*, 1916, 273) and Pederson (Jour. Bact., *35*, 1938, 106).

Rods, variable in size, usually short (Beijerinck), 0.5 to 1.0 by 3.0 to 15.0 microns (Smit), sometimes in pairs or chains. Non-motile. Gram-positive (Smit).

Yeast extract-glucose-gelatin: Filiform, no liquefaction (Pederson).

Agar colonies: Flat, circular, small, translucent like droplets of water.

Agar slant: Growth, if any, scant.

Broth: Turbid, clearing after a few days.

Milk: Unchanged or slightly acid.

Reduction of litmus, methylene blue, indigo carmine, sodium thiosulfate. Na_2SO_3 is reduced to H_2S (Smit).

Acid usually from glucose, fructose, maltose, sucrose and lactose (Beijerinck) and mannose, galactose and raffinose; some strains ferment xylose; usually does not ferment arabinose, rhamnose, sorbitol, mannitol, inulin, dextrin, starch or salicin (Pederson).

Lactic acid produced usually optically inactive; acetic acid, ethyl alcohol and carbon dioxide are formed in the fermentation of aldohexoses (Smit), (Pederson). Mannitol is formed in the fermentation of fructose (Beijerinck), (Smit). Acetic acid and lactic acid are produced from pentoses if they are fermented (Pederson).

These are the higher temperature gas-producing rods. They usually do not ferment the pentoses, but when they do the fermentation is seldom as active as that produced by strains of *Lactobacillus brevis*.

Nitrites not produced from nitrates.

Microaerophilic.

Temperature relations: Optimum, between 41° and 42° C. Minimum, between 15° and 18° C. Maximum, between 48° and 50° C.

Source: Isolated from yeast, milk products, fermenting dough, potatoes or vegetables, tomato products and wine.

Habitat: Widely distributed in nature, particularly in fermenting plant or animal products.

Genus II. **Eubacterium** *Prévot, 1938.**

(Prévot, Ann. Inst. Past., *60*, 1938, 294; not Subgenus *Eubacterium* Janke, Zent. f. Bakt., II Abt., *80*, 1930, 490.)

Eu.bac.te′ri.um. Gr. prefix *eu-* true; Gr. neut.dim.n. *bacterium* a small rod; M.L. neut.n. *Eubacterium* true *Bacterium*.

Straight or curved rods which usually occur singly, in pairs or in very short chains. Never show branching. Non-motile. Gram-positive. Carbohydrates are usually attacked, the end-products of fermentation including some of the following: formic, acetic, propionic, butyric and lactic acids. Anaerobic. May be pathogenic. Found in the intestinal tracts of vertebrates.

The descriptions of the species in *Eubacterium, Catenabacterium, Ramibacterium* and *Cillobacterium* which appeared prior to 1948 have been supplemented by material taken from Prévot (Man. d. Classif. et d. Déterm. d. Bact. Anǎerobies, Paris, 1948, 95–105).

The type species is *Eubacterium foedans* (Klein) Prévot.

Key to the species of genus **Eubacterium.**

I. Gas produced in culture media.
  A. Produce a fetid odor.
    1. Not proteolytic. Gelatin not liquefied.
      a. Milk not coagulated. Not pathogenic.
                    1. *Eubacterium foedans.*
      aa. Milk is coagulated.
        b. Presumably not hemolytic. Effect on carbohydrates not recorded. Pathogenic.
                    2. *Eubacterium niosii.*
        bb. Hemolytic. Carbohydrates are attacked.
          c. Pathogenic. Effect on gelatin not recorded.
                    3. *Eubacterium obstii.*
          cc. Not pathogenic.
                    4. *Eubacterium rectale.*
    2. Proteolytic. Gelatin is liquefied. Milk is digested. Pathogenic.
                    5. *Eubacterium quartum.*
  B. Do not produce a fetid odor.
    1. Elements occur in twisted chains.
      a. Gelatin is liquefied.
                    6. *Eubacterium pseudotortuosum.*
      aa. Gelatin not liquefied.
                    7. *Eubacterium tortuosum.*
    2. Elements do not occur in twisted chains.
      a. Gelatin is liquefied.

---

*Arranged by Mrs. Eleanore Heist Clise and Mr. Erwin F. Lessel, Jr., Cornell University, Geneva, New York, March, 1955.

      b. Milk coagulated then digested.
                8. *Eubacterium quintum.*
    bb. Milk not attacked.
                9. *Eubacterium limosum.*
  aa. Gelatin not liquefied.
     b. Milk is coagulated.
       c. Ethanol produced as a principal end-product of fermentation.
                10. *Eubacterium ethylicum.*
      cc. Ethanol not produced.
        d. Nitrites produced from nitrates.
                11. *Eubacterium ureolyticum.*
        dd. Nitrites not produced from nitrates.
                12. *Eubacterium biforme.*
    bb. Milk not coagulated.
      c. Nitrites produced from nitrates.
                13. *Eubacterium nitritogenes.*
      cc. Nitrites not produced from nitrates.
                14. *Eubacterium aerofaciens.*
II. Gas not produced in culture media.
  A. Carbohydrates are attacked.
    1. Neutral red reduced.
      a. Phenosafranin reduced.
                15. *Eubacterium parvum.*
      aa. Phenosafranin not reduced.
                16. *Eubacterium crispatum.*
    2. Neutral red not reduced.
                17. *Eubacterium disciformans.*
  B. Carbohydrates not attacked.
    1. Pathogenic. Action on milk not recorded.
                18. *Eubacterium minutum.*
    2. Not pathogenic. Milk not coagulated.
                19. *Eubacterium lentum.*
  C. Effect on carbohydrates not recorded. No growth in milk. Pathogenic.
                20. *Eubacterium poeciloides.*

1. Eubacterium foedans (Klein, 1908) Prévot, 1938. (*Bacillus foedans* Klein, Lancet, *1*, 1908, 1832; Prévot, Ann. Inst. Past., *60*, 1938, 294.)

foe′dans. L. part.adj. *foedans* making foul or filthy.

Straight or curved rods, 0.4 by 3.0 to 5.0 microns, occurring in short chains or sometimes in filaments. Non-motile. Gram-positive.

Gas and fetid odor produced in culture media.

Glucose gelatin: Colonies cloudy. No liquefaction.

Deep agar colonies: Lenticular, becoming floccose and arborescent.

Glucose broth: Growth occurs as a viscid, semifluid mass. Alkaline reaction. Gas and fetid odor produced.

Milk: No change. Fetid odor produced. Coagulated proteins not attacked.

Hydrogen sulfide is produced.

Acid from glucose, fructose, maltose and galactose.

Ammonia, acetylmethylcarbinol, volatile amines, alcohol, ketone and formic, propionic and lactic acids are produced.

Nitrites produced from nitrates.

Neutral red not reduced.

Phenosafranine reduced.

Anaerobic.

Optimum temperature, between 20° and 37° C.

Not pathogenic.

Source: Isolated from a spoiled, salted ham; also from soil from Equatorial Africa.

Habitat: Probably decomposing organic material.

2. Eubacterium niosii (Hauduroy et al., 1937) Prévot, 1938. (Anaerobe Bacillus, Niosi, Cent. f. Bakt., I Abt., Orig., *58*, 1911, 193; *Bacteroides niosii* Hauduroy et al., Dict. d. Bact. Path., 1937, 65; Prévot, Ann. Inst. Past., *60*, 1938, 294.)

ni.o'si.i. M.L. gen.noun *niosii* of Niosi; named for F. Niosi, the bacteriologist who first isolated this organism.

Short, thick rods, 0.8 to 1.2 by 1.0 to 1.5 microns, with rounded ends, occurring singly, in pairs, in V-formation, in short chains and in clumps. Non-motile. Gram-positive in pus and in young cultures.

Gas and fetid odor produced in culture media.

Gelatin: No growth.

Deep agar colonies: Small, lenticular, becoming mulberry-like. Gas is produced.

Glucose broth: Turbid. Gas and fetid odor produced.

Tarozzi broth: Abundant turbidity. Very fetid odor.

Milk: Coagulated in 5 days; curd digested.

Indole not produced.

Anaerobic.

Optimum temperature, between 20° and 37° C.

Pathogenic for rabbits and guinea pigs.

Source: Isolated from a case of suppurative pleurisy.

Habitat: Respiratory tract. Uncommon.

3. Eubacterium obstii Prévot, 1938. (Bacillus B, Obst, Jour. Inf. Dis., *24*, 1919, 159 and 168; *Eubacterium obsti* (sic) Prévot, Ann. Inst. Past., *60*, 1938, 294.)

ob'sti.i. M.L. gen.noun *obstii* of Obst; named for M. Obst, the bacteriologist who first isolated this organism.

Short, straight rods. Non-motile. Gram-positive.

Gas produced in culture media.

Deep agar colonies: Discoid. Gas is produced.

Blood agar colonies: Discoid. Hemolysis.

Blood media: Abundant growth. Fetid gas produced.

Indole not produced.

Acid and gas from glucose.

Ammonia, amines and nitrogen are produced.

Anaerobic.

Optimum temperature, 37.5° C. Killed at 65° C.

Pathogenic for mice, guinea pigs and marine fish, causing death.

Source: Isolated from the intestines of copepods, schizopods and shrimp.

Habitat: Found in sea water and in the intestines of marine fish. Rather common.

4. Eubacterium rectale (Hauduroy et al., 1937) Prévot, 1938. (Un bacille anaérobie, Grootten, Compt. rend. Soc. Biol., Paris, *102*, 1929, 43; *Bacteroides rectalis* Hauduroy et al., Dict. d. Bact. Path., 1937, 72; Prévot, Ann. Inst. Past., *60*, 1938, 294.)

rec'ta.le. L. part.adj. *rectus* straight; M.L. neut.n. *rectum* the straight bowel, rectum; M.L. adj. *rectalis* rectal.

Straight or curved rods, 0.8 by 3.0 microns, with rounded ends; sinuous filaments up to 20.0 microns in length may also occur. Non-motile. Gram-positive.

Gas produced in culture media.

Gelatin: No liquefaction.

Deep agar colonies: Spherical, 1 to 2 mm in diameter, arborescent. Medium broken by gas.

Glucose broth: Abundant turbidity which precipitates. Fetid gas produced.

Blood broth: Hemolysis in 24 hours.

Milk: Acidified; coagulated in 3 weeks. Gas is produced.

Coagulated proteins not attacked.

Hydrogen sulfide is produced.

Acid and gas from glucose, maltose and lactose.

Neutral red reduced in 24 hours.

Anaerobic.

Optimum temperature, 37° C. Killed at 56° C.

Source: Isolated in association with a rectal ulcer.

Habitat: Found in the rectum. Very uncommon.

5. Eubacterium quartum Prévot, 1938. (Anaerob No. IV, Rodella, Ztschr. f. Hyg.,

41, 1902, 474; Prévot, Ann. Inst. Past., *60*, 1938, 294.)

quar'tum. L. adj. *quartus* fourth.

Thick rods, with rounded ends, which vary in length. Non-motile. Gram-positive.

Gas and fetid odor produced in culture media.

Gelatin: Liquefaction in 6 to 9 days. Sediment.

Deep agar colonies: Small, round, arborescent.

Glucose broth: Turbid. Abundant gas. Sediment.

Milk: Digested in 3 to 5 days. Cheese-like odor produced.

Coagulated serum not liquefied.

Hydrogen sulfide is produced.

Acid from glucose, fructose, maltose and glycerol.

Ammonia, volatile amines, alcohol and formic, butyric and lactic acids are produced.

Nitrites not produced from nitrates.

Neutral red and safranin are reduced.

Anaerobic.

Optimum temperature, 37° C. Killed at 70° C.

Pathogenic. Guinea pigs killed in 24 hours by intraperitoneal inoculation.

Source: Isolated from feces in cases of infantile diarrhea; also from soil from French West Africa.

Habitat: Found in intestines of children. Rather uncommon.

6. Eubacterium pseudotortuosum Prévot, 1947. (Ann. Inst. Past., *73*, 1947, 409.)

pseu.do.tor.tu.o'sum. Gr. adj. *pseudes* false; L. adj. *tortuosus* full of windings, a specific epithet; M.L. adj. *pseudotortuosum* not the true (*Eubacterium*) *tortuosum*.

Straight or curved rods, 0.4 to 0.5 by 3.0 to 4.0 microns, occurring in twisted chains or wavy filaments. Non-motile. Gram-positive (decoloring easily).

Gas but no odor produced in culture media.

Gelatin: Liquefaction in 3 days.

Deep agar colonies: Lenticular. Gas is produced.

Glucose broth: Abundant turbidity and gas.

Peptone broth: Turbid.

Milk: No coagulation.

Coagulated proteins not attacked.

Hydrogen sulfide is produced.

Acid from glucose, fructose, maltose, sucrose, lactose, galactose, sorbitol and starch.

Ammonia, formic, butyric and lactic acids, volatile amines, alcohol, aldehyde, ketone and acetylmethylcarbinol are produced.

Nitrites produced from nitrates.

Neutral red and safranin are reduced.

Anaerobic.

Optimum temperature, 37° C.

Optimum pH, 7.4.

Not pathogenic for guinea pigs or mice.

Source: Isolated from a case of purulent, acute appendicitis.

Habitat: Found in human intestines. Uncommon.

7. Eubacterium tortuosum (Debono, 1912) Prévot, 1938. (*Bacillus tortuosus* Debono, Cent. f. Bakt., I Abt., Orig., *62*, 1912, 233; Prévot, Ann. Inst. Past., *60*, 1938, 295.)

tor.tu.o'sum. L. adj. *tortuosus* full of windings.

Straight rods of medium size, with rounded ends, occurring in twisted chains. Non-motile. Gram-positive.

Slight gas production in culture media.

Gelatin: Granular growth. No liquefaction.

Deep agar colonies: Small, lenticular or irregular, grayish. Little gas produced.

Glucose broth: Uniform turbidity. Viscous, coherent sediment. Gas produced.

Milk: Acidified; no coagulation.

Coagulated proteins not digested.

Indole not produced.

Hydrogen sulfide not produced.

Acid and gas from glucose, lactose, sucrose, galactose, fructose, maltose, mannitol and starch.

Ammonia, acetylmethylcarbinol and formic, propionic and lactic acids are produced.

Nitrites not produced from nitrates.

Neutral red reduced.

Anaerobic.

Not pathogenic.

Source: Isolated from human feces.

Habitat: Found in the human intestine. Rather uncommon.

8. **Eubacterium quintum** Prévot, 1940. (Anaerob No. V, Rodella, Ztschr. f. Hyg., *41*, 1902, 475; Prévot, Man. d. Classif. et d. Déterm. d. Bact. Anaérobies, 1940, 65.)

quin'tum. L. adj. *quintus* fifth.

More or less thick rods, of variable length, with rounded ends. Non-motile. Gram-positive.

Gas but no odor produced in culture media.

Gelatin: Liquefaction in 5 to 7 days.

Deep agar colonies: Opaque centers. Gas is produced.

Glucose broth: Rapid turbidity.

Milk: Digested in 2 to 3 days after coagulation.

Coagulated serum slowly digested.

Anaerobic.

Pathogenic. Guinea pigs killed in 48 hours after subcutaneous injection.

Source: Isolated from cases of infantile diarrhea.

Habitat: Found in the intestines of children. Uncommon.

9. **Eubacterium limosum** (Eggerth, 1935) Prévot, 1938. (*Bacteroides limosus* Eggerth, Jour. Bact., *30*, 1935, 290; Prévot, Ann. Inst. Past., *60*, 1938, 295.)

li.mo'sum. L. adj. *limosus* full of slime, slimy.

Rods, 0.5 to 1.5 by 1.0 to 5.0 microns; the average length is 3.0 to 4.0 microns. Pleomorphic. Occur as short ovoids and as wedge-shaped bacilli; curved, hooked and bifid forms are numerous. Metachromatic granules are absent. Non-motile. Gram-positive.

Gas but no odor produced in culture media.

Gelatin: Slow liquefaction.

Glucose agar and blood agar colonies: 2 to 4 mm in diameter, raised, cream-colored, mucoid, adherent. No hemolysis on blood agar.

Glucose broth: Cloudy with a heavy, mucoid sediment; the pH reaches 4.8.

Milk: Unchanged.

Coagulated proteins not attacked.

Indole not produced.

Hydrogen sulfide not produced.

Acid and gas from glucose, fructose, mannitol, adonitol, erythritol, dextrin and tre-

halose. A slight acidity (pH 6.0 to 6.5) develops without detectable gas in aesculin, cellobiose, glucosamine, inulin, glycogen, maltose, mannose, methylmannoside, raffinose, salicin, starch and sucrose. No acid from amygdalin, arabinose, dulcitol, galactose, glycerol, inositol, lactose, melezitose, methylglucoside, rhamnose, sorbitol or xylose.

Gas and volatile acid, of which butyric acid is a main component, are produced from glucose; traces of lactic acid are also produced (Pederson, Jour. Bact., *50*, 1945, 478).

Nitrites not produced from nitrates.

Anaerobic.

Optimum temperature, 37° C.

Non-pathogenic for white mice and rabbits.

Relationship to other species: A culture of this organism supplied to Dr. H. A. Barker has been carefully studied. Barker (personal communication, November, 1955) states that acetic and n-butyric acids are produced from glucose and lactate and that this organism should be transferred to the genus *Butyribacterium*.

Source: One strain, obtained as a single-cell culture, was isolated from human feces.

Habitat: Found in human feces and presumably in the feces of other warm-blooded animals.

10. **Eubacterium ethylicum** Prévot, 1938. (*Bacillus gracilis ethylicus* Achalme and Rosenthal, Compt. rend. Soc. Biol., Paris, *58*, 1906, 1025; Prévot, Ann. Inst. Past., *60*, 1938, 295.)

e.thy'li.cum. Gr. noun *ethēr* ether; M.L. neut.n. *ethyl* the ethyl radical; M.L. adj. *ethylicus* pertaining to ethyl.

Slender, straight or curved rods occurring singly, in pairs or in short chains. Granular. Non-motile. Gram-positive.

Gas but no odor produced in culture media.

Gelatin: No liquefaction.

Deep agar colonies: At first punctiform, spreading to 2 mm in diameter; irregular.

Glucose broth: Flocculent growth which precipitates, leaving the medium clear. Ammonia is produced.

Peptone broth: Same as for glucose broth.

Milk: Coagulated in 5 days, followed by digestion. Gas produced.

Indole not produced.

Glucose, fructose, sucrose, lactose, mannitol, starch and glycerol are fermented with the production of gas, acid (acetic and butyric) and ethanol.

Anaerobic.

Optimum temperature, 37° C.

Pathogenic for rabbits and guinea pigs, which are killed after subcutaneous inoculation.

Source: Isolated from a case of gastritis.

Habitat: Found in the human stomach. Uncommon.

11. Eubacterium ureolyticum Huet and de Cadore, 1954. (Ann. Inst. Past., *86*, 1954, 242.)

u.re.o.ly'ti.cum. M.L. fem.n. *urea* urea; Gr. adj. *lyticus* dissolving; M.L. adj. *ureolyticus* urea-digesting.

Large rods, 0.8 by 3.0 microns. Non-motile. Gram-positive.

Gas produced in culture media.

Gelatin: No liquefaction.

Deep agar colonies: Irregular, snowflake-like.

Glucose broth: Abundant growth. Gas is produced.

Peptone broth: Poor growth.

Milk: Coagulated.

Proteins not attacked.

Hydrogen sulfide produced abundantly.

Acid from lactose, maltose, fructose, glucose and galactose.

Volatile amines, aldehydes and butyric, acetic and lactic acids, but not alcohol or ketones, are produced.

Nitrites produced from nitrates.

Produces an extremely active urease.

Neutral red, safranin and phenosafranin are reduced.

Anaerobic.

Source: Isolated from feces from a sheep.

Habitat: Unknown.

12. Eubacterium biforme (Eggerth, 1935) Prévot, 1938. (*Bacteroides biformis* Eggerth, Jour. Bact., *30*, 1935, 283; Prévot, Ann. Inst. Past., *60*, 1938, 295.)

bi.for'me. L. adj. *biformis* two-formed.

Short, ovoid rods, 0.7 by 1.5 microns, occurring singly, in pairs or in short chains. Non-motile. Gram-positive.

Gas produced in culture media.

Gelatin: No liquefaction.

Deep agar colonies: Lenticular, 2 to 3 mm in diameter.

Glucose broth: Turbid. Acidified.

Milk: Acidified and coagulated.

Coagulated proteins not attacked.

Indole not produced.

Hydrogen sulfide not produced.

Acid and abundant gas from glucose, fructose, maltose, galactose, mannose, lactose and dextrin.

Nitrites not produced from nitrates.

Anaerobic.

Pathogenic for rabbits but not for mice.

Relationship to other species: Pederson (personal communication, March, 1945) points out that this organism may have been a *Lactobacillus*, but that its relationships are not definitely known.

Source: Isolated from human feces.

Habitat: Found in the human intestine. Uncommon.

13. Eubacterium nitritogenes Prévot, 1940. (Compt. rend. Soc. Biol., Paris, *134*, 1940, 353.)

ni.tri.to'ge.nes. M.L. neut.n. *nitritum* nitrite; Gr. v. *gennaio* to produce; M.L. adj. *nitritogenes* nitrite-producing.

Straight, thick rods, 1.0 by 2.5 to 4.0 microns, with rounded ends. Non-motile. Gram-positive.

Gas but no odor produced in culture media.

Gelatin: No liquefaction.

Deep agar colonies: Lenticular. Gas produced.

Glucose broth: Abundant turbidity and gas.

Peptone broth: Turbid; gas is produced.

Milk: No coagulation.

Coagulated proteins not attacked.

Indole not produced.

Hydrogen sulfide not produced.

Acid from glucose and fructose; sucrose and lactose are very weakly fermented.

Ammonia, volatile amines and propionic, butyric and lactic acids are produced. Acetylmethylcarbinol not produced.

Nitrites produced from nitrates.

Neutral red reduced.

Anaerobic.

Optimum temperature, 37° C.

Optimum pH, between 6.5 and 7.8. Acid-tolerant but not acidophilic.

Not pathogenic for guinea pigs or mice.

Source: Isolated from a peptic digest of meat in an acid medium.

Habitat: Unknown.

14. Eubacterium aerofaciens (Eggerth, 1935) Prévot, 1938. (*Bacteroides aerofaciens* Eggerth, Jour. Bact., *30*, 1935, 282; Prévot, Ann. Inst. Past., *60*, 1938, 295.)

a.e.ro.fa′ci.ens. Gr. mas.n. *aër* air, gas; L. v. *facio* to make, produce; M.L. part.adj. *aerofaciens* gas-producing.

Ovoid rods, 0.4 to 2.0 by 2.0 to 3.0 microns, with rounded or pointed ends, occurring in chains of two to ten elements. Non-motile. Gram-positive.

Gas produced in culture media.

Gelatin: No liquefaction.

Deep agar colonies: 1 to 2 mm in diameter, coherent.

Glucose broth: Slightly turbid.

Milk: Acidified; not coagulated.

Coagulated proteins not attacked.

Indole not produced.

Hydrogen sulfide not produced.

Acid and gas from glucose, maltose, fructose, galactose, sucrose and lactose.

Nitrites not produced from nitrates.

Anaerobic.

Pathogenic for mice.

Source: Isolated from human feces.

Habitat: Found in the human intestine. Rather uncommon.

15. Eubacterium parvum Prévot, 1938. (*Coccobacillus anaerobicus parvus* Choukévitch, Ann. Inst. Past., *25*, 1911, 256; Prévot, Ann. Inst. Past., *60*, 1938, 295.)

par′vum. L. adj. *parvus* small.

Small, ovoid rods, 0.5 by 1.0 to 1.5 microns, occurring singly or in pairs; filamentous forms may occur. Non-motile. Gram-positive.

Gas not produced in culture media.

Gelatin: No liquefaction.

Deep agar colonies: Small, lenticular.

Glucose broth: Abundant turbidity and sediment.

Milk: Coagulated in 20 to 25 days; some strains coagulate more rapidly; no digestion.

Coagulated proteins not attacked.

Acid from glucose, fructose, maltose, galactose and lactose.

Ammonia, aldehydes, alcohols, ketones, acetylmethylcarbinol and formic, butyric and lactic acids are produced.

Nitrites not produced from nitrates.

Neutral red and phenosafranin reduced.

Anaerobic.

Optimum temperature, 37° C.

Not pathogenic for laboratory animals.

Source: Isolated from the large intestine of a horse; also from a case of acute appendicitis.

Habitat: Found in the intestines of foals and of man. Uncommon.

16. Eubacterium crispatum Brygoo and Aladame, 1953. (Ann. Inst. Past., *84*, 1953, 640.)

cris.pa′tum. L. part.adj. *crispatus* curled, crisped.

Straight or slightly curved rods, 1.0 by 3.0 microns, occurring sometimes singly but usually in rather long chains having a twisted appearance and numerous loops; the length of each chain varies from 20 to 40 microns. Non-motile. Gram-positive.

Gas not produced in culture media.

Gelatin: No liquefaction.

Deep agar colonies: Punctiform.

Glucose broth: Abundant, uniform turbidity.

Peptone broth: Slightly turbid.

Milk: Slowly coagulated; partially digested.

Coagulated proteins not attacked.

Indole not produced.

Hydrogen sulfide not produced.

Acid from glucose, fructose, maltose, sucrose, lactose, galactose and starch. No acid from glycerol.

Acetic acid and traces of lactic acid, but not amines, aldehydes, ketones or acetone, are produced.

Nitrites not produced from nitrates.

Sulfites not produced from sulfates.

Neutral red reduced. Safranin and phenosafranin not reduced.

Anaerobic.

Not pathogenic for guinea pigs or mice.

Source: Isolated from pus from a dental abscess.

Habitat: Unknown.

17. Eubacterium disciformans (Massini, 1913) Prévot, 1938. (*Bacillus disciformans* Massini, Ztschr. f. gesammte Exp. Med., *2*, 1913, 81; Prévot, Ann. Inst. Past., *60*, 1938, 295.)

dis.ci.for'mans. Gr. noun *discus* a disc; L. part.adj. *formans* forming; M.L. adj. *disciformans* disc-forming.

Small, ovoid rods, 0.3 to 0.7 by 0.5 to 0.7 micron, with rounded ends, occurring singly, in pairs and in small masses. Non-motile. Gram-positive (decolorizing easily).

Gas not produced in culture media.

Gelatin: No growth.

Deep lactose agar colonies: Punctiform, then lenticular, forming a disc of colonies in the upper part of the medium. No gas produced.

Glucose broth agar: Acidified.

Glucose broth: Fine, flaky growth which precipitates, leaving the medium clear.

Milk: Slowly coagulated.

Indole not produced.

Acid but no gas from glucose, fructose, maltose, lactose, sucrose, galactose, arabinose, mannitol and starch.

Ammonia and formic, acetic and propionic acids are produced.

Nitrites not produced from nitrates.

Neutral red not reduced.

Anaerobic.

Optimum temperature, 37° C. Killed at 56° C.

Pathogenic for man, rabbit, guinea pig and mouse.

Source: Isolated from cases of fetid suppurations in empyema, pulmonary gangrene, liver abscess and dermatosis.

Habitat: Found in the respiratory system, the liver and the skin. Common.

18. Eubacterium minutum (Hauduroy et al., 1937) Prévot, 1938. (*Bacillus anaerobicus minutus* Tissier, Recherches sur la flore intestinale des nourissons, Paris, 1900; *Bacteroides minutus* Hauduroy et al., Dict. d. Bact. Path., 1937, 64; Prévot, Ann. Inst. Past., *60*, 1938, 295.)

mi.nu'tum. L. part.adj. *minutus* small (literally, diminished).

Very slender, straight rods, 2.0 to 4.0 microns in length, with rounded ends, occurring singly or in pairs. Non-motile. Gram-positive.

Gas not produced in culture media.

Deep agar colonies: Delicate, irregular, ovoid.

Glucose broth: Poor growth. Slightly turbid.

Anaerobic.

Optimum temperature, 37° C.

Pathogenic for mice.

Source: Isolated from a case of diarrhea in an infant.

Habitat: Found in the intestines of breast-fed infants. Uncommon.

19. Eubacterium lentum (Eggerth, 1935) Prévot, 1938. (*Bacteroides lentus* Eggerth, Jour. Bact., *30*, 1935, 280; Prévot, Ann. Inst. Past., *60*, 1938, 295.)

len'tum. L. adj. *lentus* slow.

Short, ovoid rods, 0.5 to 1.5 by 2.0 to 3.0 microns, occurring in chains. Pleomorphic, occurring as coccoid forms and as spindles up to 6.0 microns in length. Non-motile. Gram-positive.

Gas not produced in culture media.

Gelatin: No liquefaction.

Deep blood agar colonies: Small, 0.25 to 0.75 mm in diameter. Not hemolytic.

Milk: No coagulation.

Coagulated proteins not attacked.

Indole not produced.

Hydrogen sulfide produced in trace amounts.

Carbohydrates not attacked.

Anaerobic.

Optimum temperature, 37° C.

Not pathogenic.

Source: Isolated from human feces.

Habitat: Found in normal human feces. Common.

20. Eubacterium poeciloides (Roger and Garnier, 1906) Prévot, 1938. (*Bacillus poeciloides* Roger and Garnier, Bull. et Mem. Soc. Méd. des Hôpitaux Paris, *2*, 1906, 870; Prévot, Ann. Inst. Past., *60*, 1938, 295.)

poe.ci.lo′i.des. Gr. adj. *poecilus* many-colored, spotted; Gr. noun *eidus* shape, form; M.L. adj. *poeciloides* variegated.

Straight or curved rods, 0.8 by 3.0 microns, with rounded ends, occurring singly, in pairs or in V- or L-shaped groups, sometimes tapered. Non-motile. Gram-positive.

Gas not produced in culture media.

Gelatin: No liquefaction.

Deep agar colonies: Small, punctiform, becoming confluent.

Glucose broth: Turbidity which finally precipitates.

Milk: No growth.

Potato: No growth.

Anaerobic.

Optimum temperature, between 37° and 38° C.

Pathogenic for guinea pigs and rabbits.

Source: Isolated from a case of intestinal occlusion.

Habitat: Found in human intestines. Uncommon.

Genus III. **Catenabacterium** *Prévot, 1938.*[*]

(Ann. Inst. Past., *60*, 1938, 294.)

Ca.te.na.bac.te′ri.um. L. fem.n. *catena* a chain; Gr. dim.n. *bacterium* a small rod; M.L. neut.n. *Catenabacterium* chain rodlet.

Straight or curved rods which usually occur in long chains or filaments. No branching. Non-motile. Gram-positive. Carbohydrates are attacked, the end-products of fermentation including some of the following: formic, acetic, propionic, butyric and lactic acids. Anaerobic. May be pathogenic. Found in the intestinal tracts and in lesions of warm-blooded animals.

The type species is *Catenabacterium helminthoides* (Lewkowicz) Prévot.

Key to the species of genus **Catenabacterium.**

I. Gas produced in culture media.
   A. Liquefies gelatin.
      1. *Catenabacterium helminthoides.*
   B. Do not liquefy gelatin.
      1. Milk is coagulated.
         2. *Catenabacterium filamentosum.*
      2. Milk not coagulated.
         3. *Catenabacterium contortum.*
II. Gas not produced in culture media.
   A. Do not require serum or ascitic fluid for growth.
      1. Liquefies gelatin.
         4. *Catenabacterium lottii.*
      2. Do not liquefy gelatin.
         a. No turbidity in glucose broth. No fetid odor. Agar colonies do not turn black.
            5. *Catenabacterium catenaforme.*
         aa. Slight turbidity in glucose broth. Very fetid odor. Agar colonies turn black.
            6. *Catenabacterium nigrum.*
   B. Requires serum or ascitic fluid for growth.
      7. *Catenabacterium leptotrichoides.*

1. Catenabacterium helminthoides (Lewkowicz, 1901) Prévot, 1938. (*Bacillus helminthoides* Lewkowicz, Arch. de Méd. Exp., *13*, 1901, 631; Prévot, Ann. Inst. Past., *60*, 1938, 295.)

hel.min.tho.i′des. Gr. adj. *helminthoides* worm-like.

Straight or curved rods, with rounded ends, occurring as S-shaped forms and as long filaments, 0.7 to 1.0 by 3.0 to 20.0 mi-

* Arranged by Mrs. Eleanore Heist Clise and Mr. Erwin F. Lessel, Jr., Cornell University, Geneva, New York, March, 1955.

crons; possess fusiform or spherical swellings. Non-motile. Gram-positive.

Gas produced in culture media.

Gelatin: Liquefaction.

Deep agar colonies: Large (3 to 5 mm in diameter), flocculent, arborescent. Medium broken by gas. Rancid odor. Acidified.

Glucose broth: Turbid. Flaky sediment. Abundant gas. Rancid odor. Acidified.

Milk: Acidified; not coagulated. Gas is produced. Rancid odor.

Coagulated proteins not attacked.

Hydrogen sulfide is produced.

Acid from glucose, maltose, sucrose, sorbitol, mannitol and glycerol.

Ammonia, alcohols, acetylmethylcarbinol and formic, butyric and lactic acids are produced.

Nitrites not produced from nitrates.

Neutral red and phenosafranin not reduced.

Anaerobic.

Optimum temperature, 37° C. Killed at 60° C.

Not pathogenic or only slightly so; causes minor abscesses in rabbits.

Source: Isolated from the mouth of a breast-fed infant; also from pond mud.

Habitat: Unknown.

2. **Catenabacterium filamentosum** Prévot, 1938. (Jungano, Compt. rend. Soc. Biol., Paris, *66*, 1909, 112 and 122; Prévot, Ann. Inst. Past., *60*, 1938, 295.)

fi.la.men.to'sum. L. noun *filum* a thread; M.L. noun *filamentum* a filament; M.L. adj. *filamentosus* full of filaments.

Large rods with rounded ends. Pleomorphic, occurring either as short and swollen or long and curved forms. Bifurcation. Non-motile. Gram-positive.

Slight amount of gas produced (on agitation) in culture media.

Gelatin: No liquefaction.

Deep agar colonies: Rather large, white, lenticular. Slight gas.

Glucose broth: Turbid. Slight gas.

Peptone broth: Slight turbidity.

Milk: Coagulated.

Coagulated proteins not attacked.

Indole not produced.

Acid from glucose, fructose, maltose, galactose, lactose and sucrose.

Ammonia, volatile amines, alcohol, acetylmethylcarbinol, acetic and lactic acids and traces of formic and propionic acids are produced.

Nitrites not produced from nitrates.

Neutral red reduced.

Anaerobic.

Optimum temperature, 37° C.

Not pathogenic for guinea pigs or mice.

Source: Isolated from the intestine of a rat; also from cases of acute appendicitis, lung abscess, putrid pleurisy and uterine suppuration.

Habitat: Found in the intestine of the rat and in the natural cavities of man. Common.

3. **Catenabacterium contortum** Prévot, 1947. (Ann. Inst. Past., *73*, 1947, 414.)

con.tor'tum. L. adj. *contortus* twisted.

Rods, 0.5 to 0.7 by 3.0 to 4.0 microns, occurring in long, twisted chains of 30 to 50 or more elements. Non-motile. Gram-positive.

Gas but no odor produced in culture media.

Gelatin: No liquefaction.

Deep agar colonies: Lenticular. Gas is produced.

Peptone broth: Little or no growth.

Glucose broth: Slowly turbid; growth occurs as a viscid, semifluid mass. Gas is produced.

Milk: No coagulation.

Coagulated proteins not attacked.

Indole is produced.

Acid and gas from glucose, fructose, maltose, galactose, sucrose, xylose and arabinose.

Ammonia, formic, propionic and lactic acids, volatile amines, aldehydes, alcohols and acetylmethylcarbinol are produced.

Nitrites not produced from nitrates.

Neutral red reduced.

Anaerobic.

Optimum temperature, 37° C.

Neither toxin nor hemolysin is produced.

One strain pathogenic for guinea pigs, causing death in 48 hours.

Source: Isolated from two cases of putrid, gangrenous appendicitis.

Habitat: Found in human intestines. Uncommon.

4. **Catenabacterium lottii** Prévot, 1938. (Bacillo γ, Lotti, Ann. Ig. Sper., *19*, 1909, 101; Prévot, Ann. Inst. Past., *60*, 1938, 296.)

lot'ti.i. M.L. gen.noun *lottii* of Lotti; named for C. Lotti, the bacteriologist who first isolated this organism.

Straight, slender rods, 3 to 4 microns long, occurring in chains of 3 to 4 elements and in very long filaments. Non-motile. Gram-positive.

Gas not produced in culture media.

Gelatin: Liquefaction.

Deep agar colonies: Lenticular, white.

Glucose broth: Turbid; viscous sediment; acidified. No odor.

Milk: Coagulated.

Coagulated proteins not attacked.

Indole produced in trace amounts.

Acid from glucose and lactose.

Anaerobic.

Optimum temperature, 37° C. No growth at 22° C. Killed in 3 minutes at 70° C.

Pathogenic for guinea pigs, causing fatal abscesses.

Source: Isolated from a case of appendicitis.

Habitat: Found in the human appendix and intestines.

5. **Catenabacterium catenaforme** (Eggerth, 1935) Prévot, 1938. (*Bacteroides catenaformis* Eggerth, Jour. Bact., *30*, 1935, 286; Prévot, Ann. Inst. Past., *60*, 1938, 296.)

ca.te.na.for'me. L. fem.n. *catena* a chain; L. noun *forma* shape; M.L. adj. *catenaformis* chain-like.

Rods, 0.3 to 0.5 by 2.0 to 3.5 microns, occurring in long chains (20 to 100 elements) which are filamentous-like and non-segmented; possess globular swellings 2.0 to 3.0 microns in diameter. Non-motile. Gram-positive.

Gas not produced in culture media.

Gelatin: No liquefaction.

Deep agar colonies: 2 to 3 mm in diameter, irregular.

Glucose broth: Viscous zoogloeae at the bottom of the tube; no turbidity; acidified.

Milk: Not coagulated.

Coagulated proteins not digested.

Indole not produced.

Hydrogen sulfide produced in trace amounts.

Acid from glucose, maltose, fructose, galactose, lactose, dextrin, sucrose, glycerol and starch.

Ammonia and formic, butyric and lactic acids are produced.

Nitrites not produced from nitrates.

Neutral red and phenosafranin not reduced.

Anaerobic.

Optimum temperature, 37° C.

Not pathogenic.

Source: Isolated from feces; also from a case of putrid pleurisy.

Habitat: Found in human intestines and pulmonary cavity.

6. **Catenabacterium nigrum** Prévot, 1938. (*Streptobacillus gangrenae pulmonaris* Repaci, Compt. rend. Soc. Biol., Paris, *61*, 1910, 410; Prévot, Ann. Inst. Past., *60*, 1938, 296.)

ni'grum. L. adj. *niger* black.

Pleomorphic rods, sometimes occurring as short rods in chains of 10 to 14 elements, each measuring 0.6 by 1.0 to 2.0 microns, at other times occurring in very long and flexuous chains. Non-motile. Gram-positive.

Gas not produced in culture media.

Gelatin: No liquefaction.

Deep agar colonies: Delicate, lenticular, becoming blackened.

Glucose broth: Slight, uniform turbidity; whitish mass of agglutinated filaments. Very fetid odor.

Coagulated proteins not attacked.

Indole not produced.

Glucose feebly fermented.

Anaerobic.

Optimum temperature, 37° C.

Pathogenic for guinea pigs, causing death.

Source: Isolated from a gangrenous lung abscess.

Habitat: Unknown.

7. **Catenabacterium leptotrichoides** Prévot, 1938. (*Leptothrix sp.* Jay, no reference given; *Catenabacterium leptothricoides* (sic) Prévot, Ann. Inst. Past., *60*, 1938, 296.)

lep.to.tri.cho.i'des. Gr. adj. *leptus* fine, thin; Gr. fem.n. *thrix*, *trichis* thread, hair; Gr. noun. *eidus* shape, form; M.L. adj. *leptotrichoides* like a fine thread.

Long rods, 0.3 by 8.0 microns, with tapered, rounded or swollen ends, often occurring in short chains or in very long filaments. Non-motile. Gram-positive.

Requires serum or ascitic fluid for growth. Gas not produced in culture media.

Blood agar colonies: Arborescent. Not hemolytic.

Acid from glucose, fructose, mannose, lactose, sucrose, arabinose, xylose, mannitol, dulcitol, sorbitol and inositol.

Anaerobic.

Optimum temperature, between 37° and 40° C.

Not pathogenic.

Source: Isolated from a case of dental caries.

Habitat: Found in the human mouth. Common.

Genus IV. **Ramibacterium** *Prévot, 1938.**

(Ann. Inst. Past., *60*, 1938, 294.)

Ra.mi.bac.te′ri.um. L. mas.n. *ramus* a branch; Gr. neut.dim.n. *bacterium* a rodlet; M.L neut.n. *Ramibacterium* branched rodlet.

Straight or curved rods which show so-called false branching. Non-motile. Gram-positive. Carbohydrates are attacked, the end-products of fermentation including some of the following: formic, acetic, propionic, butyric, lactic and valerianic acids. Anaerobic. May be pathogenic. Found in the intestinal tracts and in lesions of warm-blooded animals, especially man.

The type species is *Ramibacterium ramosum* (Veillon and Zuber) Prévot.

Key to the species of genus **Ramibacterium.**

I. Indole not produced.
  A. Milk coagulated.

          1. *Ramibacterium ramosum.*

  B. Milk not coagulated.

          2. *Ramibacterium pleuriticum.*

II. Indole produced.
  A. Milk coagulated slowly.
    1. Produces acetic and propionic acids. Pathogenic.

          3. *Ramibacterium ramosoides.*

    2. Produces formic and valerianic acids and traces of lactic acid. Not pathogenic.

          4. *Ramibacterium pseudoramosum.*

  B. Milk not coagulated.
    1. Neutral red reduced.

          5. *Ramibacterium dentium.*

    2. Neutral red not reduced.

          6. *Ramibacterium alactolyticum.*

1. **Ramibacterium ramosum** (Veillon and Zuber, 1898) Prévot, 1938. (*Bacillus ramosus* Veillon and Zuber, Arch. méd. exp. et anat. path., *10*, 1898, 542; *Fusiformis ramosus* Topley and Wilson, Princ. Bact., and Immun., 2nd ed., 1936, 358; Prévot, Ann. Inst. Past., *60*, 1938, 296.)

ra.mo′sum. L. adj. *ramosus* much-branched.

Straight, slender rods, 0.3 to 0.4 by 2.0 to 3.0 microns, which are sometimes undulating and sometimes filamentous; form acute, V- and Y-shaped angles, thus giving the appearance of false branching. Possess spherical swellings. Non-motile. Gram-positive.

Gas produced in moderate amounts in culture media.

---

* Arranged by Mrs. Eleanore Heist Clise and Mr. Erwin F. Lessel, Jr., Cornell University, Geneva, New York, March, 1955.

Gelatin: No liquefaction.

Deep agar colonies: Lenticular. Some gas bubbles are produced.

Blood media: No hemolysis.

Glucose broth: Turbid. Acidified. Gas. Rancid odor.

Peptone broth: Very poor growth.

Milk: Coagulated. No digestion.

Coagulated proteins not attacked.

Indole not produced.

Acid and gas from glucose, maltose, galactose, sucrose, lactose and mannitol.

Ammonia, acetylmethylcarbinol and formic and acetic acids are produced.

Nitrites not produced from nitrates.

Neutral red reduced temporarily. Safranin not reduced.

Anaerobic.

Grows at temperatures from 22° to 37° C. Killed at 56° C.

Optimum pH, between 7.0 and 8.0.

Toxin, but no hemolysin, is produced.

Pathogenic. Fatal for guinea pigs and rabbits.

Comments: Prévot (*loc. cit.*) recognizes two varieties of this species which differ from the parent strain with respect to certain cultural and biochemical characters.

Source: Isolated in association with mastoiditis, otitis, pulmonary gangrene, putrid pleurisy, appendicitis, intestinal infections, balanitis, liver abscess, osteomyelitis, septicemia, urinary infections, etc.

Habitat: Found in the natural cavities of man and animals; also found in sea water. Very common.

2. **Ramibacterium pleuriticum** Prévot et al., 1947. (Prévot, Raynaud and Digeon, Ann. Inst. Past., *73*, 1947, 481.)

pleu.ri'ti.cum. Gr. fem.n. *pleura* a rib; M.L. adj. *pleuriticus* pertaining to pleurisy.

Rods resemble those found in *Ramibacterium ramosum*; the Y-shaped forms predominate. Non-motile. Gram-positive.

Gas but no odor produced in culture media.

Gelatin: No liquefaction.

Deep agar colonies: Lenticular. Gas is produced.

Glucose broth: Abundant turbidity. Rather coherent, viscous sediment. Gas is produced.

Peptone broth: Slightly turbid. Gas is produced.

Milk: No coagulation.

Coagulated proteins not attacked.

Indole not produced.

Acid from glucose and galactose. One strain ferments sucrose and maltose.

Ammonia, traces of hydrogen sulfide, alcohol, ketones, volatile amines and acetic, valerianic and lactic acids are produced.

Acetylmethylcarbinol not produced.

Nitrites not produced from nitrates.

Neutral red and safranin reduced.

Anaerobic.

Optimum temperature, 37° C.

Optimum pH, 7.8.

Not pathogenic for guinea pigs or mice.

Source: Isolated from two cases of fetid, purulent pleurisy.

Habitat: Found in the natural cavities of man, especially the respiratory tract. Not common.

3. **Ramibacterium ramosoides** (Runeberg, 1908) Prévot, 1938. (*Bacillus ramosoides* Runeberg, Arb. a. d. path. Inst. d. Univ. Helsingfors, *2*, 1908, 271; see Cent. f. Bakt., I Abt., Ref., *43*, 1909, 665; Prévot, Ann. Inst. Past., *60*, 1938, 296.)

ra.mo.so.i'des. L. mas.n. *ramus* a branch; L. adj. *ramosus* full of branches; Gr. noun *eidus* form, shape; M.L. adj. *ramosoides* branch-like.

Cells occur either as ovoids in small chains or as long elements showing what appears to be false branching; sometimes spherical. Non-motile. Gram-positive.

Gas produced in moderate amounts in culture media.

Gelatin: No liquefaction.

Deep agar colonies: Lenticular. Some gas is produced.

Brain media: Fetid odor produced.

Blood media: Hemolysis. Fetid odor produced.

Glucose broth: Turbid. Viscous, glairy sediment. Acidified. Gas is produced.

Peptone broth: Moderate growth.

Milk: Coagulation in 8 days.

Coagulated proteins not attacked.

Indole is produced.

Acid from glucose, maltose and lactose.

Ammonia and acetic and propionic acids are produced.

Anaerobic.

Optimum temperature, 37° C.

Pathogenic for mice, guinea pigs and rabbits.

Source: Isolated from cases of appendicitis and various suppurations (dacryocystitis, tubercular tissues).

Habitat: Found in the appendix, lacrymal sac and lungs. Common.

4. **Ramibacterium pseudoramosum** (Distaso, 1912) Prévot, 1938. (*Bacillus pseudoramosus* Distaso, Cent. f. Bakt., I Abt., Orig., *62*, 1912, 441; Prévot, Ann. Inst. Past., *60*, 1938, 296.)

pseu.do.ra.mo'sum. Gr. adj. *pseudés* false; L. adj. *ramosus* much-branched; M.L. adj. *pseudoramosus* false (*Ramibacterium*) *ramosum*.

Cells similar to those of *Ramibacterium ramosum* but slightly smaller and flexuous; occur in angles and in short chains. Non-motile. Gram-positive.

Gas produced in slight amounts in culture media.

Gelatin: No liquefaction.

Deep agar colonies: Lenticular. Gas is produced.

Glucose broth: Turbid. Whitish precipitate.

Milk: Slowly coagulated.

Coagulated proteins not attacked.

Indole is produced.

Acid and gas from glucose, fructose, galactose, lactose and trehalose.

Ammonia, traces of hydrogen sulfide, aldehyde, ketone, formic and valerianic acids and traces of lactic acid are produced.

Nitrites not produced from nitrates.

Neutral red reduced temporarily.

Anaerobic.

Optimum temperature, 37° C.

Not pathogenic.

Source: Isolated from human feces.

Habitat: Found in human intestines. Very common.

5. **Ramibacterium dentium** Vinzent and Reynes, 1947. (Ann. Inst. Past., *73*, 1947, 594.)

den'ti.um. L. mas.n. *dens* tooth; L. gen. pl.noun *dentium* of teeth.

Straight, slender rods, 0.3 to 0.4 by 2.0 to 3.0 microns, resembling those of *Ramibacterium ramosum;* occur in short chains and in clumps; Y-shaped forms occur as the result of what appears to be false branching. Non-motile. Gram-positive.

Gas but no odor produced in culture media.

Gelatin: Abundant growth. No liquefaction.

Deep agar colonies: Punctiform, becoming cotton-like in appearance. Develop slowly.

Glucose broth: Produces a viscid, semifluid mass which precipitates. Gas is produced.

Peptone broth: Growth poor; produces a viscid, semifluid mass.

Milk: No coagulation.

Coagulated proteins not attacked.

Indole is produced.

Acid from glucose, fructose and mannitol.

Ammonia, acetylmethylcarbinol and butyric and valerianic acids are produced.

Nitrites not produced from nitrates.

Neutral red and safranin are reduced.

Anaerobic.

Optimum temperature, 37° C. Grows at 26° C. Killed at 65° C.

Optimum pH, between 7.0 and 8.0.

Neither toxin nor hemolysin is produced.

Not pathogenic for guinea pigs or mice.

Source: Isolated from dental tartar.

Habitat: Found in the human mouth. Not common.

6. **Ramibacterium alactolyticum** Prévot and Taffanel, 1942. (Ann. Inst. Past., *68*, 1942, 259.)

a.lac.to.ly'ti.cum. Gr. pref. *a* not; L. noun *lac, lactis* milk; Gr. adj. *lyticus* dissolving; M.L. adj. *alactolyticus* non-milk-dissolving.

Straight rods occurring either in sinuous, short chains or in zigzags; Y-shaped forms occur as the result of what appears to be false branching. Non-motile. Gram-positive.

Gas but no odor produced in culture media.

Gelatin: No liquefaction.

Deep agar colonies: Lenticular. Slight amount of gas is produced.

Glucose broth: Abundant turbidity. Acidified. Gas is produced.

Peptone broth: Very poor growth.

Milk: No coagulation.

Coagulated proteins not attacked.

Indole is produced.

Acid from glucose, fructose, galactose, arabinose and xylose.

Ammonia, hydrogen sulfide, aldehydes, volatile amines, acetylmethylcarbinol and acetic, butyric and lactic acids are produced.

Nitrites not produced from nitrates.

Neutral red not reduced; phenosafranin reduced temporarily.

Anaerobic.

Optimum temperature, between 33° and 37° C.

Optimum pH, between 6.0 and 8.0.

Not pathogenic for guinea pigs or mice.

Source: Isolated from dental suppurations and from cases of purulent pleurisy.

Habitat: Found in the human mouth. Rather common.

Genus V. **Cillobacterium** *Prévot, 1938.**

(Ann. Inst. Past., *60*, 1938, 294.)

Cil.lo.bac.te′ri.um. L. v. *cillo* to move, to put in motion; Gr. neut.dim.n. *bacterium* a small rod; M.L. neut.n. *Cillobacterium* motile rodlet.

Straight or curved rods. Motile by means of peritrichous flagella. Gram-positive. Carbohydrates are attacked, the end-products of fermentation including some of the following: formic, acetic, butyric, lactic and valerianic acids. Anaerobic. May be pathogenic. Found in the intestinal tracts and in lesions of warm-blooded animals; also found in soil.

The type species is *Cillobacterium moniliforme* (Repaci) Prévot.

Key to the species of genus **Cillobacterium.**

I. Does not liquefy gelatin.

          1. *Cillobacterium moniliforme.*

II. Liquefy gelatin.

  A. Milk not coagulated.

    1. Neutral red not reduced.

          2. *Cillobacterium endocarditidis.*

    2. Neutral red reduced.

          3. *Cillobacterium meningitidis.*

  B. Milk coagulated and digested.

    1. Acid and gas produced from glucose.

      a. Deep agar colonies circular with small amount of gas produced.

          4. *Cillobacterium tenue.*

     aa. Deep agar colonies lenticular with abundant amount of gas produced.

          5. *Cillobacterium multiforme.*

    2. Carbohydrates not attacked.

          6. *Cillobacterium combesii.*

1. **Cillobacterium moniliforme** (Repaci, 1910) Prévot, 1938. (*Bacillus moniliformis* Repaci, Compt. rend. Soc. Biol., Paris, *61*, 1910, 216; Prévot, Ann. Inst. Past., *60*, 1938, 296.)

mo.ni.li.for′me. L. noun *monile* a necklace; L. noun *forma* shape; M.L. adj. *moniliformis* necklace-shaped.

Straight rods, 0.7 by 3.0 to 4.0 microns, occurring singly or in pairs. Possess spindle-shaped swellings and metachromatic granules. Motile. Gram-positive.

---

* Arranged by Mrs. Eleanore Heist Clise, Geneva, New York, March, 1955.

Gas produced in culture media.

Gelatin: No liquefaction.

Deep agar colonies: Lenticular, 2 to 3 mm in diameter. Abundant gas is produced. Aromatic odor.

Glucose broth: Flaky growth which precipitates forming a viscous mass. Gas is produced.

Milk: No coagulation.

Coagulated proteins not attacked.

Indole produced in trace amounts.

Acid and gas from glucose, fructose, galactose and lactose.

Ammonia, alcohol, acetone, acetylmethylcarbinol and formic, butyric and lactic acids are produced.

Nitrites not produced from nitrates.

Neutral red reduced.

Anaerobic.

Optimum temperature, between 37° and 41° C.

Pathogenic for guinea pigs, causing death in 8 days.

Source: Isolated from a case of pulmonary gangrene; also from soil from Equatorial Africa.

Habitat: Found in the human respiratory system. Uncommon.

2. Cillobacterium endocarditidis Prévot, 1938. (Bacille BG, Routier and Braunberger, Compt. rend. Soc. Biol., Paris, *115*, 1934, 611; *Cillobacterium endocarditis* (sic) Prévot, Ann. Inst. Past., *60*, 1938, 296.)

en.do.car.di'ti.dis. Gr. pref. *endo* within; Gr. noun *cardia* heart; Gr. suffix *-itis* disease of; M.L. noun *endocardium* heart lining; M.L. gen.n. *endocarditidis* of endocarditis.

Pleomorphic rods. Actively motile. Grampositive.

Gas produced in culture media.

Gelatin: Liquefaction in 2 to 5 days.

Deep agar colonies: Lenticular. Gas is produced.

Glucose broth: Turbid. Sediment. Gas is produced.

Peptone broth: Poor growth.

Milk: No change.

Coagulated proteins not attacked.

Acid and gas from glucose, fructose, maltose, sucrose and arabinose.

Neutral red not reduced.

Anaerobic.

Optimum temperature, 37° C.

Toxin is produced.

Pathogenic for guinea pigs, causing death in 2 to 6 days.

Source: Isolated from the blood in a case of febrile endocarditis.

Habitat: Probably the natural body cavities of man. Uncommon.

3. Cillobacterium meningitidis Prévot, 1938. (Stamm S.V., Ghon, Mucha and Müller, Cent. f. Bakt., I Abt., Orig., *41*, 1906, 145 and 693; *Cillobacterium meningitis* (sic) Prévot, Ann. Inst. Past., *60*, 1938, 297.)

me.nin.gi'ti.dis. Gr. fem.n. *meninx, meningis* the membrane enclosing the brain; M.L. fem.n. *meningitis* inflammation of the meninges; fem.gen.n. *meningitidis* of meningitis.

Pleomorphic rods, occurring sometimes as ovoids, 1.5 to 3.5 microns long, with rounded ends, and at other times as filaments with spindle-shaped swellings. Actively motile. Show bipolar staining. Grampositive.

Gas produced in culture media.

Gelatin: Cloudy turbidity. Slow liquefaction. Gas is produced.

Deep agar colonies: Mulberry-like, surrounded by small, satellite colonies. Gas is produced.

Glucose broth: Turbid. Flaky sediment. Gas is produced.

Peptone broth: Turbid. Flaky sediment.

Milk: No coagulation. Gas is produced.

Coagulated proteins not attacked.

Indole is produced.

Hydrogen sulfide is produced.

Ethanol and butyric, acetic and lactic acids are produced.

Neutral red reduced.

Anaerobic.

Grows at temperatures from 22° to 37° C.

Grows at pH 7.8 to 8.5.

Pathogenic for guinea pigs and rabbits.

Source: Isolated from a fatal case of purulent meningitis of otic origin.

Habitat: Unknown.

4. Cillobacterium tenue (Bergey et al., 1923) Clise, *comb. nov.* (*Bacillus tenuis spatuliformis* Distaso, Cent. f. Bakt., I Abt.,

Orig., *59*, 1911, 101; *Bacteroides tenuis* Bergey et al., Manual, 1st ed., 1923, 263; *Cillobacterium spatuliforme* Prévot, Ann. Inst. Past., *60*, 1938, 297.)

te′nu.e. L. adj. *tenuis* slender.

Straight or curved rods with square ends; one of the ends is usually enlarged, thus giving the cells the appearance of spatulas. Motile. Gram-positive.

Gas produced in culture media.

Gelatin: Liquefaction.

Deep agar colonies: Circular. Small amount of gas is produced.

Milk: Coagulated then digested.

Coagulated protein is attacked.

Indole is produced.

Acid and gas from glucose.

Anaerobic.

Optimum temperature, 37° C.

Pathogenicity unknown.

Source: Isolated from feces from a dog.

Habitat: Unknown.

5. Cillobacterium multiforme (Distaso, 1911) Prévot, 1938. (*Bacillus multiformis* Distaso, Cent. f. Bakt., I Abt., Orig., *59*, 1911, 101; not *Bacillus multiformis* van Senus, Dissert., Leiden, 1890; Prévot, Ann. Inst. Past., *60*, 1938, 297.)

mul.ti.for′me. L. adj. *multus* much, many; L. noun *forma* shape; M.L. adj. *multiformis* many-shaped.

Straight or curved, thick, pleomorphic rods, 3 microns long. Motile. Gram-positive.

Gas and odor produced in culture media.

Gelatin: Liquefaction.

Deep agar colonies: Lenticular. Abundant gas is produced.

Glucose broth: Turbid. Gas is produced. Putrid odor.

Milk: Coagulated then digested.

Coagulated protein is attacked. Fibrin and coagulated serum are digested.

Indole is produced in trace amounts.

Acid and gas from glucose, lactose, fructose, maltose, galactose, sorbitol, mannitol and glycerol.

Ammonia, hydrogen sulfide and formic, butyric and lactic acids are produced.

Nitrites not produced from nitrates.

Neutral red reduced.

Anaerobic.

Optimum temperature, 37° C.

Neither toxin nor hemolysin is produced.

Not pathogenic for guinea pigs.

Source: Isolated from the feces of a dog; also from soil from Equatorial Africa.

Habitat: Unknown.

6. Cillobacterium combesii Prévot and Laplanche, 1947. (Ann. Inst. Past., *73*, 1947, 687.)

com.be′si.i. M.L. gen.noun *combesii* of Combes; named after Combes.

Straight rods, 0.7 by 3.0 to 4.2 microns, with square ends, occurring singly or in pairs, more often in chains of 3 to 10 elements. Motile by means of slow undulations. Gram-positive.

Gas and odor produced in culture media.

Gelatin: Liquefaction in 5 days.

Deep agar colonies: Irregular; arborescent or like tufts of cotton. Gas is produced.

Glucose broth: Abundant turbidity which forms a viscous, zoogloea-like mass. Fetid gas is produced.

Peptone broth: Turbid.

Milk: Coagulated in 8 days, then digested.

Coagulated proteins not attacked.

Carbohydrates not attacked.

Ammonia, hydrogen sulfide, alcohol, traces of acetylmethylcarbinol and formic, butyric and valerianic acids are produced.

Nitrites not produced from nitrates.

Neutral red and safranin are reduced.

Anaerobic.

Optimum temperature, 37° C.

Toxin not produced.

Not pathogenic for guinea pigs or mice.

Source: Isolated from forest soil from French West Africa.

Habitat: Unknown.

FAMILY XI. PROPIONIBACTERIACEAE DELWICHE, Fam. Nov.*

Pro.pi.on.i.bac.te.ri.a'ce.ae. M.L. neut.n. *Propionibacterium* the type genus of the family; *-aceae* ending to denote a family; M.L. fem.pl.n. *Propionibacteriaceae* the *Propionibacterium* family.

Irregularly shaped rods which tend toward bending or terminal swelling (in *Butyribacterium*) or pleomorphism (in *Propionibacterium*). Non-motile. Gram-positive. Colonial development on semi-solid media is slow, visible colonies seldom being discernible before two days. Where pigment is produced, it is brownish red. Non-proteolytic; usually saccharolytic. Ferment carbohydrates, usually *lactic acid* and, in some cases, polyhydroxy alcohols with the production of saturated aliphatic carboxylic acids. With *Propionibacterium*, extensive carbon dioxide production occurs with some substrates. Lactic acid usually does not accumulate. Anaerobic to aerotolerant, many strains of *Propionibacterium* being readily adapted to growth under aerobic conditions, with the actual utilization of oxygen. Generally catalase-positive when subjected to the usual laboratory test, but exceptions exist, particularly in *Butyribacterium*. Inhabitants of the intestinal tracts of animals; also occur in materials outside the body where suitable foodstuffs are found.

Key to the genera of family **Propionibacteriaceae.**

I. Ferment carbohydrates and lactic acid.
    A. Produce propionic and acetic acids and carbon dioxide.
                    Genus I. *Propionibacterium*, p. 569.
    B. Produce butyric and acetic acids and carbon dioxide.
                    Genus II. *Butyribacterium*, p. 577.
II. Carbohydrates are fermented. Glucose is converted mainly to ethanol and carbon dioxide, with small amounts of acetic and other acids. Lactic acid is not fermented.
                    Genus III. *Zymobacterium*, p. 577.

Genus I. **Propionibacterium** *Orla-Jensen, 1909.*†

(Cent. f. Bakt., II Abt., *22*, 1909, 337.)

Pro.pi.on.i.bac.te'ri.um. Gr. pref. *pro-* before, priority in order; Gr. neut.n. *pium (pion)* fat; M.L. adj. *propionicus* propionic, referring to priority in the fatty acid series of compounds as in *acidum propionicum* propionic acid; Gr. dim.noun *bacterium* a small rod; M.L. neut.n. *Propionibacterium* propionic bacterium.

Non-motile, non-sporeforming, Gram-positive bacteria which grow under anaerobic conditions in neutral media as short, diphtheroid rods which sometimes resemble streptococci in appearance; under aerobic conditions and with a heavy inoculum, they grow as long, irregular, club-shaped and branched cells. Metachromatic granules are demonstrable with Albert's stain. Ferment lactic acid, carbohydrates and polyhydroxy alcohols with the production of propionic and acetic acids and carbon dioxide. As a rule, strongly catalase-positive, sometimes weakly so. There is a strong tendency towards anaerobiosis; development is slow, macroscopically visible colonies generally not discernible in less than five to seven days.‡ Nutritional requirements complex. Development best in yeast extract media with the addition of lactates or simple carbohydrates. Vitamin B requirements are relatively

---

* Proposed by Prof. E. A. Delwiche, Cornell University, Ithaca, New York, November, 1954.

† Revised by Prof. C. B. van Niel, Hopkins Marine Station, Pacific Grove, California, January, 1944.

‡ In an atmosphere containing 5 per cent carbon dioxide, growth is enhanced both aerobically and anaerobically. Contrary to the claim made by Krebs and Eggleston (Biochem. Jour., *35*, 1941, 676), a differential effect of carbon dioxide tension on aerobic and anaerobic development has never been observed.

simple: practically all, if not all, of the species require pantothenic acid, and the majority require biotin; a few species require either thiamine or para-aminobenzoic acid in addition. Optimum temperature, 30° C. Found in dairy products, especially hard cheeses.

The type species is *Propionibacterium freudenreichii* van Niel.

Key to the species of genus **Propionibacterium.**

I. Little surface growth on yeast-agar-lactate stab. Short chains of small, spherical cells occur in yeast extract-glucose media. Sucrose and maltose not fermented.

A. Lactose not fermented.

   1. *Propionibacterium freudenreichii.*

B. Lactose fermented.

   2. *Propionibacterium shermanii.*

II. Distinct surface growth on yeast-agar-lactate stab. Growth in yeast extract-glucose media does not occur in the form of small, spherical cells in short chains. Sucrose and maltose are fermented.

A. Typical short rods of diphtheroid appearance are produced in yeast extract-glucose media.

   1. Brownish red growth in yeast-agar-lactate stab.

      a. Raffinose and mannitol, but not sorbitol, are fermented.

         3. *Propionibacterium rubrum.*

      aa. Sorbitol, but not raffinose or mannitol, is fermented.

         4. *Propionibacterium thoenii.*

   2. Cream-colored growth in yeast-agar-lactate stab.

      a. Cream-colored surface growth.

         5. *Propionibacterium zeae.*

      aa. Yellow to orange surface growth.

         b. Dextrin, glycogen and starch fermented.

            6. *Propionibacterium technicum.*

         bb. Dextrin, glycogen and starch not fermented.

            c. Cellobiose fermented.

               7. *Propionibacterium raffinosaceum.*

            cc. Cellobiose not fermented.

               d. Growth in liquid media flocculent, as if agglutinated. Acid from salicin.

                  8. *Propionibacterium peterssonii.*

               dd. Growth in liquid media dispersed and smooth. No acid from salicin.

                  9. *Propionibacterium jensenii.*

B. Growth in yeast extract-glucose media occurs as highly irregular cells which give the appearance of involution forms.

   1. Involution forms occur as large, swollen spheres. Surface growth on yeast-agar-lactate stab is orange-yellow. Xylose and rhamnose not fermented.

      10. *Propionibacterium arabinosum.*

   Involution forms occur as long, irregular rods. Surface growth on yeast-agar-lactate stab is cream-colored. Xylose and rhamnose are fermented.

      11. *Propionibacterium pentosaceum.*

1. **Propionibacterium freudenreichii** van Niel, 1928. (*Bacterium acidi propionici a*, von Freudenreich and Orla-Jensen, Cent. f. Bakt., II Abt., *17*, 1906, 532; van Niel, The Propionic Acid Bacteria, Haarlem, 1928, 162.)

freu.den.reich′i.i. M.L. gen.noun *freudenreichii* of Freudenreich; named for Eduoard von Freudenreich, the Swiss bacteriologist who isolated this species.

Description taken from van Niel (*loc. cit.*) and from Werkman and Brown (Jour. Bact., *26*, 1933, 397).

Small, spherical cells, 0.5 to 0.6 micron in diameter, occurring mostly in pairs and short chains. Little difference in morphology between growth from anaerobic solid media and neutral or acid liquid media. Aerobic growth irregular, club-shaped and branched, long rods. Non-motile. Show metachromatic granules. Gram-positive.

Yeast-gelatin-lactate stab: No liquefaction.

Yeast-agar-lactate stab: Dirty, grayish-creamy development in stab; very slight surface growth of same color.

Liquid media: Distinctly turbid with grayish-creamy, ropy sediment.

Litmus milk: Slight development; faint reduction; not coagulated.

Indole not produced.

Ferments lactic and pyruvic acids, glycerol, dihydroxyacetone, glucose, fructose, mannose and galactose with the production of chiefly propionic and acetic acids and carbon dioxide.

Acid from erythritol, adonitol, inositol and esculin. No acid from amygdalin, d- and l-arabinose, dextrin, dulcitol, glycogen, inulin, lactose, maltose, mannitol, melezitose, melibiose, perseitol, raffinose, rhamnose, sucrose or xylose.

Pantothenic acid, but not thiamine or para-aminobenzoic acid, is required for growth; a few strains require biotin (Delwiche, Jour. Bact., *58*, 1949, 396).

Nitrites not produced from nitrates.

Catalase-positive.

Anaerobic to aerotolerant.

Distinctive character: Inability to ferment any of the disaccharides when inoculated into yeast extract-sugar media.

Source: Isolated from dairy products; also from raw market milk and Swiss cheese.

Habitat: Dairy products.

2. **Propionibacterium shermanii** van Niel, 1928. (*Bacterium acidi propionici d,* Sherman, Jour. Bact., *6*, 1921, 387; van Niel,

The Propionic Acid Bacteria, Haarlem, 1928, 163.)

sher.man′i.i. M.L. gen.noun *shermanii* of Sherman; named for J. M. Sherman, the American bacteriologist who isolated this species.

Description taken from van Niel (*loc. cit.*) and from Werkman and Brown (Jour. Bact., *26*, 1933, 400).

Small, spherical cells, 0.5 to 0.6 micron in diameter, occurring mostly in pairs and short chains. Little difference in morphology between growth from anaerobic solid media and neutral or acid liquid media. Aerobic growth occurs as irregular, club-shaped and branched rods. Non-motile. Show metachromatic granules. Gram-positive.

Yeast-gelatin-lactate stab: No liquefaction.

Yeast-agar-lactate stab: Dirty, grayish creamy development in stab; very slight surface growth of same color.

Liquid media: Distinctly turbid with grayish-creamy, ropy sediment.

Litmus milk: Acid coagulation.

Indole not produced.

Ferments lactic and pyruvic acids, glycerol, dihydroxyacetone, glucose, fructose, mannose, galactose and lactose with the production of chiefly propionic and acetic acids and carbon dioxide. Occasionally arabinose is fermented.

Acid from erythritol, adonitol, arabitol, inositol and esculin. No acid from amygdalin, dextrin, dulcitol, glycogen, inulin, maltose, mannitol, melezitose, melibiose, perseitol, raffinose, rhamnose, salicin, sorbitol, sucrose, starch, trehalose or xylose.

Pantothenic acid and biotin, but not para-aminobenzoic acid, are required for growth; some strains require thiamine, others do not, and still others find this vitamin stimulating but not required for growth (Delwiche, Jour. Bact., *58*, 1949, 396).

Nitrites not produced from nitrates.

Catalase-positive.

Anaerobic to aerotolerant.

Distinctive characters: Resembles *Propionibacterium freudenreichii* in every respect, but differs in its ability to ferment lactose.

Source: Isolated from dairy products; also from Swiss cheese and buttermilk.

Habitat: Dairy products.

3. Propionibacterium rubrum van Niel, 1928. (*Bacterium acidi propionici* var. *rubrum* Thöni and Allemann (in part), Cent. f. Bakt., II Abt., *25*, 1910, 8; van Niel, The Propionic Acid Bacteria, Haarlem, 1928, 164.)

rub'rum. L. adj. *ruber* red.

Medium sized, stoutish rods to elongated diplococci, 0.8 by 1.2 microns, occurring singly or in pairs, resembling diphtheroids rather than streptococci. Somewhat more slender in media without fermentable carbohydrate. Aerobic growth occurs as irregular, club-shaped and branched rods. Nonmotile. Show metachromatic granules. Gram-positive.

Yeast-gelatin-lactate stab: No liquefaction.

Yeast-agar-lactate stab: Brownish red development in stab, with appreciable dome-shaped surface growth of same color. (Also see Margolena and Hansen, Cent. f. Bakt., II Abt., *99*, 1938, 107.)

Liquid media: Turbidity in early stages; sediment red and smooth.

Litmus milk: Acid coagulation.

Indole not produced.

Ferments lactic and pyruvic acids, glycerol, dihydroxyacetone, glucose, fructose, mannose, galactose, sucrose, maltose, lactose, raffinose and mannitol with the production of chiefly propionic and acetic acids and carbon dioxide.

Acid from erythritol, adonitol, arabitol, amygdalin, esculin, salicin, melezitose and trehalose. No acid from d- and l-arabinose, dextrin, dulcitol, glycogen, inulin, melibiose, perseitol, rhamnose, sorbitol, starch or xylose.

Pantothenic acid and biotin are required for growth; para-aminobenzoic acid is required by some strains and stimulating for others; thiamine, although not required, is stimulating for growth (Delwiche, Jour. Bact., *58*, 1949, 396).

Nitrites not produced from nitrates.

Catalase-positive; very weakly so for aerobically grown cells.

Less anaerobic than *Propionibacterium*

freudenreichii and *Propionibacterium shermanii*.

Distinctive characters: Production of brownish red pigment under anaerobic and aerobic conditions. Fermentation of raffinose and mannitol, but not of sorbitol.

Source: Isolated from various dairy products.

Habitat: Dairy products.

4. Propionibacterium thoenii van Niel, 1928. (*Bacterium acidi propionici* var. *rubrum* Thöni and Allemann (in part), Cent. f. Bakt., II Abt., *25*, 1910, 8; van Niel, The Propionic Acid Bacteria, Haarlem, 1928, 164.)

thoe'ni.i. M.L. gen.noun *thoenii* of Thöni; named for J. Thöni, the Swedish bacteriologist who isolated this organism.

Description taken from van Niel (*loc. cit.*) and from Werkman and Brown (Jour. Bact., *26*, 1933, 412).

Medium sized, stoutish rods to elongated diplococci, 1.0 by 1.5 microns, occurring singly or in pairs, resembling diphtheroids. In media without fermentable carbohydrate, small, spherical cells occur in short chains. Aerobic growth occurs as irregular, club-shaped and branched rods. Non-motile. Shows metachromatic granules. Gram-positive.

Yeast-gelatin-lactate-stab: No liquefaction.

Yeast-agar-lactate-stab: Brownish red growth throughout stab with appreciable dome-shaped surface growth of same color.

Liquid media: Turbidity in early stages; sediment smooth and red.

Litmus milk: Mostly acid coagulation.

Indole not produced.

Ferments lactic and pyruvic acids, glycerol, dihydroxyacetone, glucose, fructose, mannose, galactose, sucrose, maltose, lactose and sorbitol with the production of propionic and acetic acids and carbon dioxide.

Acid from adonitol, arabitol, erythritol, esculin, salicin and trehalose. No acid from amygdalin, arabinose, dextrin, dulcitol, glycogen, inulin, mannitol, melezitose, melibiose, perseitol, pectin, raffinose, rhamnose, starch or xylose.

Domke (Milchwirtsch. Forsch., *15*, 1933,

480) reports that this species may or may not ferment lactose and may or may not produce acid from esculin and salicin.

Pantothenic acid and biotin, but not para-aminobenzoic acid, are growth requirements; thiamine is required by some strains, but other strains, while not requiring this vitamin, find it stimulating for growth (Delwiche, Jour. Bact., *58*, 1949, 396).

Nitrites not produced from nitrates.

Catalase-positive.

Less anaerobic than *Propionibacterium freudenreichii* and *Propionibacterium shermanii*.

Distinctive characters: Closely resembles *Propionibacterium rubrum* in morphology and in the production of brownish red pigment under aerobic and anaerobic conditions. Differs from this species in its inability to ferment raffinose and mannitol, whereas fermentation of sorbitol occurs.

The biochemical characteristics of a ten-year-old stock culture have remained unchanged.

Source: Isolated from cheese and buttermilk.

Habitat: Dairy products.

5. Propionibacterium zeae Hitchner, 1932. (Jour. Bact., *23*, 1932, 40; also see *ibid.*, *28*, 1934, 473.)

ze'ae. Gr. fem.n. *zia* spelt; M.L. fem.n. *Zea* generic name of maize; M.L. gen.noun *zeae* of maize.

Cells in neutral lactate media spherical, 0.8 micron in diameter, usually occurring in short chains. In carbohydrate media which turn acid during development, the cells are distinctly rod-shaped, 0.8 by 2.0 to 3.0 microns, with a slight tendency towards the formation of club-shaped forms. Appearance typically diphtheroid. Aerobic growth occurs as irregular, club-shaped and branched rods. Non-motile. Show metachromatic granules. Gram-positive.

Yeast-gelatin-lactate-stab: No liquefaction.

Yeast-agar-lactate-stab: Cream-colored growth in stab with distinct surface growth of same color.

Liquid media: Distinctly turbid; cream-colored; smooth sediment; very ropy.

Litmus milk: Coagulated; acid.

Indole not produced.

Ferments lactic and pyruvic acids, glycerol, dihydroxyacetone, l-arabinose, rhamnose, glucose, fructose, mannose, galactose, sucrose, cellobiose, maltose, lactose and mannitol with the production of propionic and acetic acids and carbon dioxide.

Acid from salicin. No acid from d-arabinose, dextrin, dulcitol, glycogen, inulin, starch or xylose.

Pantothenic acid and biotin are required for growth; thiamine and para-aminobenzoic acid, although not required, are growth-stimulating (Delwiche, Jour. Bact., *58*, 1949, 396).

Nitrites not produced from nitrates.

Catalase-positive, especially when grown in neutral media.

Less anaerobic than *Propionibacterium freudenreichii* and *Propionibacterium shermanii*.

Distinctive characters: Cream-colored surface growth and ability to ferment l-arabinose and rhamnose but not d-arabinose or xylose.

Source: Not definitely recorded, but probably isolated from silage.

Habitat: Dairy products.

6. Propionibacterium technicum van Niel, 1928. (The Propionic Acid Bacteria, Haarlem, 1928, 164.)

tech'ni.cum. Gr. adj. *technicus* technical.

In neutral media spherical cells, 0.8 micron in diameter, occur in pairs and in short chains. In acid media short rods, 0.6 by 1.0 to 1.5 microns, occur, often in pairs, with a typical diphtheroid appearance. Aerobic growth occurs in the form of irregular, long rods, swollen and branched. Non-motile. Show metachromatic granules. Gram-positive.

Yeast-gelatin-lactate-stab: No liquefaction.

Yeast-agar-lactate-stab: Cream-colored development in stab with distinct yellow surface growth.

Liquid media: Turbid in early stages; cream-colored, somewhat flocculent sediment.

Litmus milk: Coagulation, acid.

Indole not produced.

Ferments lactic and pyruvic acid, glycerol, dihydroxyacetone, arabinose, glucose, galactose, fructose, mannose, lactose, maltose, sucrose, raffinose, dextrin, glycogen and starch with the production of propionic and acetic acids and carbon dioxide.

Acid from esculin, salicin and mannitol. No acid from dulcitol, inulin or xylose.

Nitrites not produced from nitrates.

Catalase-positive.

Anaerobic, but less so than *Propionibacterium freudenreichii.*

Distinctive character: The ability to ferment the polysaccharides dextrin, glycogen and starch.

Source: Isolated from Edam and Tilsit cheeses.

Habitat: Dairy products.

7. Propionibacterium raffinosaceum

Werkman and Kendall, 1931. (*Propionibacterium jensenii* var. *raffinosaceum* van Niel, The Propionic Acid Bacteria, Haarlem, 1928, 162; Werkman and Kendall, Iowa State Coll. Jour. Sci., *6*, 1931, 17.)

raf.fi.no.sa'ce.um. Fr. v. *raffiner* to refine; M.L. neut.n. *raffinosum* raffinose, a sugar secured by refining beet sugar molasses; M.L. adj. *raffinosaceum* relating to raffinose.

Description taken from van Niel (*op. cit.*, 1928, 162) and from Werkman and Brown (Jour. Bact., *26*, 1933, 402).

Cells in neutral media spherical to short, rod-shaped cells, 0.8 by 0.8 to 1.5 microns, of typical diphtheroid appearance. In media in which acid is produced, the cells are somewhat longer rod-shaped, to 2 microns in length. Aerobic growth occurs as irregular, long rods, swollen and branched. Non-motile. Show metachromatic granules. Gram-positive.

Yeast-gelatin-lactate-stab: No liquefaction.

Yeast-agar-lactate-stab: Cream-colored growth in stab; distinct, orange-yellow surface growth.

Liquid media: Turbid in early stages; cream-colored, smooth sediment.

Litmus milk: Coagulated, acid.

Indole not produced.

Ferments lactic and pyruvic acids, glycerol, dihydroxyacetone, glucose, fructose, mannose, galactose, cellobiose, maltose, lactose, sucrose, raffinose and mannitol with the production of propionic and acetic acids and carbon dioxide.

Acid from adonitol, amygdalin, arabitol, erythritol, esculin, inositol, melezitose, salicin and trehalose. No acid from d- and l-arabinose, dextrin, dulcitol, glycogen, inulin, melibiose, perseitol, pectin, rhamnose, sorbitol, starch or xylose.

Nitrites not produced from nitrates.

Catalase-positive; only very slightly so when grown aerobically.

Less anaerobic than *Propionibacterium freudenreichii.*

Distinctive characters: Differs from *Propionibacterium jensenii* in its somewhat greater length and in its ability to ferment cellobiose and salicin; the behaviour of *Propionibacterium jensenii* towards raffinose and mannitol is not constant and hence cannot be used as a differential character. Werkman and Kendall have reported different agglutination reactions for *Propionibacterium jensenii* and *Propionibacterium raffinosaceum.*

Source: Isolated from buttermilk.

Habitat: Dairy products.

8. Propionibacterium peterssonii

van Niel, 1928. (*Bacterium acidi propionici c*, Troili-Petersson, Cent. f. Bakt., II Abt., *24*, 1909, 333; van Niel, The Propionic Acid Bacteria, Haarlem, 1928, 163.)

pe.ters.so'ni.i. M.L. gen.noun *peterssonii* of Petersson; named for Gerda Troili-Petersson, the Swedish bacteriologist who isolated this organism.

Description taken from van Niel (*loc. cit.*) and from Werkman and Brown (Jour. Bact., *26*, 1933, 406).

Cells in neutral media spherical, 0.8 micron in diameter, occurring in clumps of short chains. In carbohydrate media which turn acid during development, rod-shaped cells, 0.8 by 1.5 to 2.0 microns, also occur in clumps. Aerobic growth occurs as heavily swollen and branched rods. Non-motile. Show metachromatic granules. Gram-positive.

Yeast-gelatin-lactate stab: No liquefaction.

Yeast-agar-lactate stab: Cream-colored

growth, dry and wrinkled, resembling that of *Mycobacterium spp.*

Liquid media: No turbidity; sediment a coherent layer, cream-colored.

Litmus milk: Acid coagulation.

Indole not produced.

Ferments lactic and pyruvic acids, glycerol, dihydroxyacetone, glucose, fructose, mannose, galactose, sucrose, maltose and lactose with the production of propionic and acetic acids and carbon dioxide.

Acid from esculin and salicin. No acid from d- and l-arabinose, cellobiose, dextrin, dulcitol, glycogen, inulin, perseitol, pectin, raffinose, rhamnose, sorbitol, starch or xylose.

Pantothenic acid, biotin and para-aminobenzoic acid are required for growth; thiamine, while not required, is stimulating for growth (Delwiche, Jour. Bact., *58*, 1949, 396).

Nitrites not produced from nitrates.

Catalase-positive; aerobically developed growth very slightly so.

Less anaerobic than *Propionibacterium freudenreichii* and *Propionibacterium shermanii*.

Distinctive character: Growth in liquid media in clumps, giving the cultures the appearance of agglutinated bacteria. So far as known, the only species among the propionic acid bacteria possessing this characteristic.

Source: Isolated from cheese and soil.

Habitat: Dairy products.

9. **Propionibacterium jensenii** van Niel, 1928. (*Bacterium acidi propionici b*, von Freudenreich and Orla-Jensen, Cent. f. Bakt., II Abt., *17*, 1906, 532; van Niel, The Propionic Acid Bacteria, Haarlem, 1928, 163.)

jen.se′ni.i. M.L. gen.noun *jensenii* of Jensen; named for Prof. S. Orla-Jensen, the Danish bacteriologist who isolated this organism.

Description taken from van Niel (*loc. cit.*) and from Werkman and Brown (Jour. Bact., *26*, 1933, 404).

In neutral media spherical to short rod-shaped cells, 0.8 by 0.8 to 1.5 microns, occur, often in pairs or short chains; possess typical diphtheroid appearance. Morphology little influenced by developing acidity. Aerobic growth occurs as irregular long rods, swollen and branched. Non-motile. Show metachromatic granules. Gram-positive.

Yeast-gelatin-lactate stab: No liquefaction.

Yeast-agar-lactate stab: Cream-colored growth in stab; orange-yellow, dome-shaped surface growth.

Liquid media: Turbid in early stages; cream-colored, smooth sediment.

Litmus milk: Coagulated, acid.

Indole not produced.

Ferments lactic and pyruvic acids, glycerol, dihydroxyacetone, glucose, fructose, mannose, galactose, sucrose, maltose, lactose and sometimes raffinose and mannitol with the production of propionic and acetic acids and carbon dioxide.

Acid from adonitol, arabitol, erythritol. esculin, inositol and trehalose. No acid from arabinose, cellobiose, dextrin, dulcitol, glycogen, inulin, perseitol, pectin, rhamnose, salicin, sorbitol, starch or xylose.

Pantothenic acid and biotin are growth requirements; some strains require para-aminobenzoic acid, others do not, and still others find this vitamin stimulating but not required for growth; thiamine, although not required, is growth-stimulating (Delwiche, Jour. Bact., *58*, 1949, 396).

Nitrites not produced from nitrates.

Strongly catalase-positive.

Less anaerobic than *Propionibacterium freudenreichii.*

Distinctive characters: Morphologically similar to *Propionibacterium rubrum* and *Propionibacterium thoenii* from which it is distinguished chiefly by the failure to produce a red pigment under anaerobic conditions. The yellow surface growth distinguishes *Propionibacterium jensenii* from *Propionibacterium zeae*, as does also the inability of the former to ferment l-arabinose and rhamnose.

Source: Isolated from cheese and butter.

Habitat: Dairy products.

10. **Propionibacterium arabinosum** Hitchner, 1932. (Jour. Bact., *23*, 1932, 40; also see *ibid.*, *28*, 1934, 473.)

a.ra.bi.no′sum. Gr. noun *Arabia* Arabia;

M.L. neut.n. *arabinosum* arabinose, a pentose sugar derived from gum arabic.

Cells in neutral lactate media spherical, 0.8 micron in diameter, occurring in pairs and short chains. In acid media swollen spheres and ellipsoidal cells occur, mostly 2.0 by 3.0 to 3.5 microns, often in pairs and short chains. Non-motile. Show metachromatic granules. Gram-positive.

Yeast-gelatin-lactate-stab: No liquefaction.

Yeast-agar-lactate-stab: Cream-colored growth in stab with distinct orange-yellow surface growth.

Liquid cultures: Turbid in early stages; cream-colored, smooth sediment.

Litmus milk: No coagulation.

Indole not produced.

Ferments lactic and pyruvic acids, glycerol, dihydroxyacetone, d- and l-arabinose, glucose, galactose, fructose, mannose, cellobiose, maltose, sucrose, raffinose and mannitol with the production of propionic and acetic acids and carbon dioxide.

Acid from sorbitol. No acid from dulcitol, xylose, rhamnose, salicin or inulin.

Pantothenic acid and biotin, but not para-aminobenzoic acid, are required for growth; thiamine, although not required, is growth-stimulating (Delwiche, Jour. Bact., *58*, 1949, 396).

Nitrite production not recorded.

Very slightly catalase-positive.

Anaerobic, but less so than *Propionibacterium freudenreichii*.

Distinctive characters: The development of spherical involution forms in acid media, the almost complete absence of catalase and the ability to ferment both d- and l-arabinose but not xylose or rhamnose.

Note: The strain obtained from Dr. E. B. Fred produced only minute amounts of acid from lactose and starch; it is questionable whether these carbohydrates are fermented.

Source: Not definitely stated.

Habitat: Dairy products.

11. **Propionibacterium pentosaceum** van Niel, 1928. (*Bacillus acidi propionici* von Freudenreich and Orla-Jensen, Cent. f. Bakt., II Abt., *17*, 1906, 532; van Niel, The Propionic Acid Bacteria, Haarlem, 1928, 163.)

pen.to.sa′ce.um. Gr. pl.adj. *pente* five; M.L. neut.n. *pentosum* a pentose sugar; M.L. adj. *pentosaceus* relating to a pentose.

Description taken from van Niel (*loc. cit.*) and from Werkman and Brown (Jour. Bact., *26*, 1933, 408).

In neutral lactate media cells spherical, 0.8 micron in diameter, occurring in pairs and short chains. In media developing acidity, long, irregular rods, swollen and branched, 3 to 4 microns in length, occur. Aerobic growth occurs as irregular, swollen and branched, long rods. Non-motile. Show metachromatic granules. Gram-positive.

Yeast-gelatin-lactate stab: No liquefaction.

Yeast-agar-lactate stab: Cream-colored development in stab with abundant, cream-colored surface growth.

Liquid media: Turbid in early stages; smooth, creamy sediment; ropy.

Litmus milk: Coagulated, acid.

Indole not produced.

Ferments lactic and pyruvic acids, glycerol, dihydroxyacetone, d- and l-arabinose, xylose, rhamnose, glucose, galactose, fructose, mannose, cellobiose, lactose, maltose, sucrose, raffinose, mannitol and sorbitol with the production of propionic and acetic acids and carbon dioxide.

Acid from adonitol, arabitol, erythritol, esculin, inositol, salicin and trehalose. No acid from dextrin, dulcitol, glycogen, inulin, perseitol or pectin.

Pantothenic acid and biotin, but not para-aminobenzoic acid, are growth requirements; although thiamine is not required, it is stimulating for growth (Delwiche, Jour. Bact., *58*, 1949, 396).

Nitrites and free nitrogen produced from nitrates.

Slightly catalase-positive.

Anaerobic, but less so than any of the other species of the genus.

Distinctive characters: The formation of long, rod-shaped involution forms in acid media, the absence of pigment production, and the ability to ferment d- and l-arabinose, rhamnose and xylose.

Source: Isolated from Emmental cheese.

Habitat: Dairy products.

Genus II. **Butyribacterium** *Barker and Haas, 1944.**

(Jour. Bact., *47*, 1944, 301.)

Bu.ty.ri.bac.te′ri.um. Gr. noun *butyrum* butter; M.L. adj. *butyricus* butyric; Gr. dim. noun *bacterium* a little rod; M.L. neut.n. *Butyribacterium* the butyric bacterium.

Straight or slightly curved rods. Non-motile. Gram-positive. Anaerobic to microaerophilic. Ferment carbohydrates and lactic acid, forming acetic and butyric acids and carbon dioxide. Generally catalase-negative but sometimes weakly positive. From the intestinal contents of vertebrates so far as known.

The type species is *Butyribacterium rettgeri* Barker and Haas.

1. Butyribacterium rettgeri Barker and Haas, 1944. (Strain 32, Lewis and Rettger, Jour. Bact., *40*, 1940, 298; Barker and Haas, Jour. Bact., *47*, 1944, 303.)

ret′tge.ri. M.L. gen.noun *rettgeri* of Rettger; named for L. F. Rettger, one of the bacteriologists who first isolated this organism.

Rods straight or slightly curved, 0.7 by 2.3 microns, occurring singly, in pairs and in short chains. Non-motile. Not encapsulated. No branched cells observed, but some cells have swollen club-shaped ends. Gram-positive.

Glucose-cysteine agar colonies: Circular, translucent, often with opaque center, grayish white with yellowish tinge, convex when small, later umbonate, glistening, smooth, finely granular, edges entire or finely irregular; develop slowly, attaining a diameter of 1.5 mm in 7 days.

Tryptone-yeast extract-lactate agar colonies: Similar to those described above except larger (2 mm in 4 days at 37° C.); pulvinate rather than umbonate in cross sections.

Glucose-cysteine broth: Abundant turbidity and sediment; no pellicle.

Agar stab (King and Rettger's medium, Jour. Bact., *44*, 1942, 302): Heavy growth in 2 days. Gas production often causes slight splitting of agar.

Acetic and butyric acids and carbon dioxide produced from glucose and maltose; occasionally a small amount of visible gas is produced. Lactic acid fermented readily without visible gas. Arabinose, xylose, lactose, sucrose, trehalose, rhamnose, mannitol, sorbitol, dulcitol and glycerol are not fermented.

Not proteolytic.

Indole not produced.

Hydrogen sulfide not produced.

Generally catalase-negative.

Anaerobic.

Temperature relations: Optimum, 37° C. Minimum, 15° C. Maximum, between 40° and 45° C.

Source: Isolated from the intestinal contents of a white rat.

Habitat: Presumably found generally in the intestines of mammals.

Genus III. **Zymobacterium** *Wachsman and Barker, 1954.†*

(Jour. Bact., *68*, 1954, 400.)

Zy.mo.bac.te′ri.um. Gr. noun *zyme* leaven, ferment; Gr. dim.neut.n. *bacterium* a small rod; M.L. neut.n. *Zymobacterium* ferment rodlet.

Rods which occur singly or in chains. Non-motile. Gram-positive. Anaerobic or microaerophilic. Catalase-negative. Carbohydrates are utilized, glucose being converted mainly to ethanol and carbon dioxide with small amounts of acetic and possibly lactic and formic acids.

The type species is *Zymobacterium oroticum* Wachsman and Barker.

---

* Prepared by Prof. H. A. Barker, University of California, Berkeley, California, November, 1954.

† Prepared by Prof. H. A. Barker, University of California, Berkeley, California, November, 1954.

1. **Zymobacterium oroticum** Wachsman and Barker, 1954. (Jour. Bact., *68*, 1954, 400.)

o.ro'ti.cum. M.L. noun *acidum oroticum* orotic acid; M.L. adj. *oroticus* orotic.

Rods, 0.35 to 0.60 by 1.2 to 2.0 microns, with tapering ends, usually occurring in long, intertwined chains. Non-motile. Gram-positive.

Gelatin: No liquefaction.

Tryptone-glucose-yeast extract agar colonies: Small, round, convex.

Tryptone-glucose-yeast extract broth: In young cultures the cells are characteristically short rods with tapering ends, becoming ovoid in old cultures.

Orotic acid-basal medium; Morphologically, the cells are similar to those described directly above.

Milk: No growth.

Indole not produced.

Acid and gas (in 3 to 5 days) from glucose, fructose, sucrose, lactose, maltose, arabinose, galactose and mannitol. Lactic and glutamic acids and glycerol not utilized.

Glucose fermentation yields predominantly ethanol (1.3 moles per mole of glucose) and carbon dioxide with small amounts of acetic and possibly lactic and formic acids. The maximum level of ethanol production has not yet been determined; however, the level must be quite low since glucose is fermented slowly, even under optimum conditions.

Orotic acid fermented with the production of ammonia.

Starch not hydrolyzed.

Nitrites not produced from nitrates.

Catalase-negative.

Anaerobic to microaerophilic.

Source: Isolated from bay mud.

Habitat: Unknown.

FAMILY XII. CORYNEBACTERIACEAE LEHMANN AND NEUMANN, 1907.*

(Bakt. Diag., 4 Aufl., *2*, 1907, 500.)

Co.ry.ne.bac.te.ri.a'ce.ae. M.L. neut.n. *Corynebacterium* type genus of the family; *-aceae* ending to denote a family; M.L. fem.pl.n. *Corynebacteriaceae* the *Corynebacterium* family.

Usually non-motile rods, frequently banded or beaded with metachromatic granules. May show marked diversity of form. Branching cells have been described in a few species, but these are very uncertain. Generally Gram-positive, some species being partially decolorized more easily than others. Where pigment is formed, it is grayish yellow or orange or pink. Gelatin may be liquefied. Nitrites may be produced from nitrates. Aerobic to microaerophilic; a few species are anaerobic. Animal and plant parasites and pathogens; also found in dairy products and soil.

Key to the genera of family **Corynebacteriaceae.**

I. Primarily pathogenic on animals and plants.
    A. Aerobic to anaerobic, pleomorphic rods that show the characteristic arrangement produced by snapping division.
        1. Animal species are non-motile, but some of the plant pathogens are motile.
                Genus I. *Corynebacterium*, p. 579.
        2. Animal species are motile by means of peritrichous flagella. Causes a monocytosis in warm-blooded animals, including man.
                Genus II. *Listeria*, p. 597.
    B. Microaerophilic rods to long filaments. Non-motile.
                Genus III. *Erysipelothrix*, p. 599.

* Definition and key with arrangement of genera in family prepared by Prof. Robert S. Breed, Cornell University, Geneva, New York, November, 1954.

II. Live primarily on decomposing organic matter. Saprophytic.
  A. Found primarily in dairy products. Acid production weak. Lactic acid is the principal acid produced. Non-motile.

                               Genus IV. *Microbacterium*, p. 600.

  B. Found primarily in soil.
    1. Decomposes cellulose. Motile and non-motile species.

                               Genus V. *Cellulomonas*, p. 601.

    2. Does not decompose cellulose. Generally non-motile. Gram-negative rods occur in young cultures, and coccoid, Gram-positive cells develop in older cultures.

                               Genus VI. *Arthrobacter*, p. 605.

Genus I. **Corynebacterium** *Lehmann and Neumann, 1896.**

(Bakt. Diag., 1 Aufl., *2*, 1896, 390.)

Co.ry.ne.bac.te′ri.um. Gr. noun *coryne* a club; Gr. noun *bacterium* a small rod; M.L. neut.n. *Corynebacterium* club bacterium.

Straight to slightly curved rods with irregularly stained segments, sometimes granules. Frequently show club-shaped swellings. Snapping division produces angular and palisade (picket fence) arrangements of cells. Non-motile with exceptions among the plant pathogens as stated in the text. Gram-positive, sometimes young cells and sometimes old cells losing the stain easily. Granules invariably Gram-positive. Generally quite aerobic, but micro-aerophilic or even anaerobic species occur. Catalase-positive. May or may not liquefy gelatin. May or may not produce nitrites from nitrates. May or may not ferment sugars, but seldom, if ever, is a high acidity produced. Many species oxidize glucose completely to CO_2 and H_2O without producing visible gas. Some pathogenic species produce a powerful exotoxin. This group is widely distributed in nature. The best known species are parasites and pathogens on man and domestic animals. Other species have been found in birds and even in invertebrate animals. Several species are well known plant pathogens while still other common species are found in dairy products.

The type species is *Corynebacterium diphtheriae* (Flügge) Lehmann and Neumann.

Key to the species of genus **Corynebacterium.**

1. AEROBIC TO FACULTATIVELY ANAEROBIC.

I. From animal sources.† Non-motile.
  A. From vertebrates.
    1. Acid from glucose.
      a. Attack man and frequently other animals.
        b. Nitrites produced from nitrates.
          c. Indole not produced.

                      1. *Corynebacterium diphtheriae.*

          cc. Indole produced.

                      2. *Corynebacterium enzymicum.*

---

* The human section of this genus was revised by Prof. E. G. D. Murray, University of Western Ontario, London, Canada, the animal section by Dr. E. V. Morse, Department of Microbiology and Public Health, College of Veterinary Medicine, Michigan State University, East Lansing, Michigan, the plant section by Prof. Walter H. Burkholder, Department of Plant Pathology, College of Agriculture, Cornell University, Ithaca, New York and the anaerobic section by Dr. H. Seeliger, Hygiene-Institut der Universität Bonn, Germany, November, 1954.

† Habitat relationships are used in this key because comparative studies of the species in these groups are still completely lacking.

bb. Nitrites not produced from nitrates.
 c. Grow on ordinary agar.
  d. Grows on potato.
   3. *Corynebacterium hoagii.*
  dd. Growth on potato doubtful if at all.
   e. Good growth on plain gelatin.
    4. *Corynebacterium striatum.*
   ee. Poor or slight growth on plain gelatin.
    f. Yellow growth on Loeffler's blood serum.
     5. *Corynebacterium pseudotuberculosis.*
    ff. Grayish growth on Loeffler's blood serum.
     6. *Corynebacterium xerosis.*
 cc. Does not grow on ordinary agar.
   7. *Corynebacterium pyogenes.*
aa. Not known to attack man.
 b. Do not attack seals. Pathogenic for mice.
  c. Grow on potato.
   d. Acid from lactose, sucrose and mannitol.
    8. *Corynebacterium murisepticum.*
   dd. No acid from lactose, sucrose or mannitol.
    9. *Corynebacterium renale.*
  cc. Does not grow on potato.
   10. *Corynebacterium kutscheri.*
 bb. Attacks seals.
   11. *Corynebacterium phocae.*
2. No acid from carbohydrates.
 a. Nitrites produced from nitrates.
  b. Creamy white growth on potato. From apparently normal human throats.
   12. *Corynebacterium pseudodiphtheriticum.*
  bb. Tan, yellow or pink growth on potato. From infectious pneumonia of foals.
   13. *Corynebacterium equi.*
 aa. Nitrites not produced from nitrates.
   14. *Corynebacterium bovis.*
B. From invertebrates. Non-motile.
 1. From insects. No acid from carbohydrates. Slow liquefaction of gelatin.
   15. *Corynebacterium paurometabolum.*
 2. From leeches. No acid from carbohydrates. No liquefaction of gelatin.
  a. Slender rods with no tendency to develop filamentous forms.
   16. *Corynebacterium nephridii.*
  aa. Slender rods that develop into filaments 30 or more microns in length.
   17. *Corynebacterium vesiculare.*
II. From plant sources.
 A. Non-motile.
  1. Nitrites not produced from nitrates.
   a. Colonies cream-colored.
    b. Slow liquefaction of gelatin.
     c. Bluish granules in growth on ordinary media. Attacks alfalfa.
      18. *Corynebacterium insidiosum.*
     cc. No bluish granules. Causes ring-rot of potatoes.
      19. *Corynebacterium sepedonicum.*
    bb. No liquefaction of gelatin.
     20. *Corynebacterium humiferum.*

aa. Colonies yellow. No liquefaction of gelatin. Causes a wilt and canker of tomatoes.
> 21. *Corynebacterium michiganense.*

2. Nitrites produced from nitrates. Slow or no liquefaction of gelatin.
a. Colonies yellow.
b. Slow liquefaction of gelatin. Attacks members of the grass family.
> 22. *Corynebacterium rathayi.*

bb. No liquefaction of gelatin. Attacks members of the grass family.
> 23. *Corynebacterium agropyri.*

aa. Colonies orange. Parasitic on sweet peas, etc.
> 24. *Corynebacterium fascians.*

B. Motile, usually by means of a single flagellum.
1. Non-chromogenic on beef extract agar media.
a. Colonies white on beef extract agar media.
> 25. *Corynebacterium hypertrophicans.*

aa. Colonies colorless and almost transparent on beef extract agar media. Salmon- to flesh-colored on potato glucose agar.
> 26. *Corynebacterium poinsettiae.*

2. Yellow colonies on beef extract agar.
a. Nitrites produced from nitrates.
> 27. *Corynebacterium tritici.*

aa. Nitrites not produced from nitrates.
> 28. *Corynebacterium flaccumfaciens.*

2. ANAEROBIC TO AEROTOLERANT.

I. Acid but no gas produced in glucose-agar shake media.
A. Gelatin liquefied.
> 29. *Corynebacterium acnes.*

B. Gelatin not liquefied.
1. Carbohydrates generally not attacked; slight acid from glucose. Pathogenic.
> 30. *Corynebacterium parvum.*

2. Carbohydrates attacked. Not pathogenic.
> 31. *Corynebacterium granulosum.*

II. Acid and gas produced in glucose-agar shake media.
A. Gelatin liquefied.
> 32. *Corynebacterium avidum.*

B. Gelatin not liquefied.
> 33. *Corynebacterium diphtheroides.*

1. **Corynebacterium diphtheriae** (Flügge, 1886) Lehmann and Neumann, 1896. (Die Klebs'schen Stäbchen, Löffler, Mitteil. a. d. kaiserl. Gesundheitsamte, *2*, 1884, 421; *Bacillus diphtheriae* Flügge, Die Mikroorganismen, 2 Aufl., 1886, 225; Lehmann and Neumann, Bakt. Diag., 1 Aufl., *2*, 1896, 350; *Corynebacterium ulcerans* Gilbert and Stewart, Jour. of Lab. and Clin. Med., *12*, 1927, 756.)

diph.the'ri.ae. Gr. noun *diphthera* leather, skin; M.L. fem.n. *diphtheria* diphtheria; M.L. gen.noun *diphtheriae* of diphtheria.

Common name: Diphtheria bacillus; Klebs-Loeffler bacillus.

Rods, varying greatly in dimensions, 0.3 to 0.8 by 1.0 to 8.0 microns, occurring singly. The rods are straight or slightly curved, frequently swollen at one or both ends. The rods do not, as a rule, stain uniformly with methylene blue but show alternate bands of stained and unstained material and in addition one or more metachromatic granules which are best shown by special stains. Non-motile. Gram-positive but not intensely so in older cultures.

Gelatin colonies: Slow development. Very small, grayish, lobulate.

Gelatin stab: Slight growth on surface and scant growth in stab. No liquefaction.

Agar slant: Scant, grayish, granular, translucent growth, with irregular margin.

Blood-tellurite media: Produces gray to black colonies.

Colony forms: Smooth (S) colony form: Round and umbonate or convex, with even margin and smooth surface. Opaque when viewed by transmitted light, glistening and somewhat moist in appearance when viewed by reflected light. Colonies about 1 to 3 mm in diameter. Growth frequently slowed or inhibited by the presence of potassium tellurite in the medium.

Rough (R) colony form: Flat, margin is very irregular. Surface is pitted and very uneven. Very little light reflected from surface. Translucent when viewed by transmitted light. Colonies about 1 to 5 mm in diameter.

Intermediate colony forms: Several colony forms are found in this group since the term includes all forms between the pure S form and the pure R form. Sr forms very nearly approach the S colonies and the sR forms nearly approach the pure R forms. The SR form shows properties distinct from either the S or R forms. The colonies are 3 to 5 mm in diameter. The margin usually shows indentations. The surface is raised but not convex; it may be nearly level or show a central elevation surrounded by a concentric depression and elevation.

Dwarf (D) colony form: Colonies very small, about 0.2 mm or less in diameter. Margin round and even. Surface convex.

All of the above colony forms have been isolated from cases of diphtheria (Morton, Jour. Bact., 40, 1940, 768 ff.).

Broth: Uniform turbidity produced by S form, pellicle produced by SR form, sediment produced by the R form.

Litmus milk: Unchanged.

Potato: No visible growth.

Blood serum: Growth grayish to cream-colored, moist, smooth, slightly raised, margin entire. May be bright yellow or occasionally reddish (Hill, Sci., 17, 1903, 375).

Indole not produced.

All strains produce acid from glucose and fructose; some strains also ferment galactose, maltose, sucrose, dextrin and glycerol.

Nitrites produced from nitrates.

Does not hydrolyze urea (Merkel, Zent. f. Bakt., I Abt., Orig., 147, 1941, 398).

A highly poisonous exotoxin is produced in fluid media. This toxin represents the principal disease-producing agency of the organism. Toxin production may fail in otherwise typical strains.

A highly potent antitoxin can be produced by repeated injection of toxin into experimental animals. The antitoxin possesses both curative and protective properties.

Serological types: In a study of 250 strains of *Corynebacterium diphtheriae*, Murray (Jour. Path. and Bact., 41, 1935, 439–45) was able to classify 228 strains into 11 serological types, and 22 strains remained unclassified (Morton, Bact. Rev., 4, 1940, 196).

McLeod et al. (Jour. Path. and Bact., 34, 1931, 667; *ibid.*, 36, 1933, 169; Lancet, 1, 1933, 293) describe three types which have been confirmed by other workers; these are distinguishable by colony form on McLeod's blood-tellurite medium, they are antigenically different with subtypes, there is some difference between their toxins (Etris, Jour. Inf. Dis., 50, 1934, 220) and the severity of disease is associated with the type.

Corynebacterium diphtheriae type *gravis* grows with dark gray, daisy-head colonies; ferments dextrin, starch and glycogen; is not hemolytic; has very few small metachromatic granules; forms a pellicle and a granular deposit, and there is an early reversal of pH in broth.

Corynebacterium diphtheriae type *mitis* grows in convex, black, shiny, entire colonies; no fermentation of starch and glycogen, and it is variable with dextrin; hemolytic; metachromatic granules are prominent; diffuse turbidity, infrequent pellicle, and there is a late reversal of pH in broth.

Corynebacterium diphtheriae type *intermedius* produces a small, flat, umbonate colony with a black center and slightly crenated periphery; not hemolytic; barring of bacilli is accentuated; there is no fermentation of starch and glycogen, and it is variable with dextrin; forms no pellicle but a fine granular deposit, and there is no reversal of pH in broth.

Ten years of observations in all parts of the world have shown (McLeod, Bact. Rev., *7*, 1943, 1) that a small percentage of strains does not correspond closely to any of these three types. Variant strains are found most frequently in regions where the diphtheria is of mild or moderate severity.

Aerobic, facultative.

Optimum temperature, between 34° and 36° C. Grows well at 37° C.

Relationship to other species: A comparison of cultures has shown *Corynebacterium ulcerans* Gilbert and Stewart to be identical with *C. diphtheriae* Lehmann and Neumann (Henriksen and Grelland, Jour. Path. and Bact., *64*, 1952, 509).

Source: Commonly from membranes in the pharynx, larynx, trachea and nose in human diphtheria; from the seemingly healthy pharynx and nose in carriers; occasionally from the conjunctiva and infected superficial wounds. Found occasionally infecting the nasal passages and wounds in horses; also reported from natural diseases in fowl.

Habitat: The cause of diphtheria in man. Pathogenic to guinea pigs, kittens and rabbits. For action on other animals see Andrewes et al. (Diphtheria. London, 1923, 170 ff.).

2. Corynebacterium enzymicum (Mellon, 1917) Eberson, 1918.

(An unusual diphtheroid bacillus, Mellon, Med. Record, New York, *81*, 1916, 240; *Bacillus enzymicus* Mellon, Jour. Bact., *2*, 1917, 297; Eberson, Jour. Inf. Dis., *23*, 1918, 29.)

en.zy'mi.cum. Gr. noun *zyme* leaven; M.L. noun *enzymum* enzyme; M.L. adj. *enzymicus* relating to enzyme.

Rods, beaded and club-shaped, definitely pleomorphic, showing coccoid forms. Nonmotile. Gram-positive.

Gelatin stab: Slight surface growth. No liquefaction.

Glucose agar: Bacillary form shows very small colorless colonies. Coccoid form shows heavy, yellowish white, moist growths.

Blood agar: Same as on glucose agar.

Loeffler's blood serum: Fine, moist, confluent growth.

Glucose broth: Bacillary form shows granular sediment. Coccoid form shows diffuse, luxuriant growth.

Litmus milk: Acid, coagulated.

Potato: No growth.

Indole production slight.

Acid from glucose, maltose, sucrose, dextrin and glycerol.

Slight production of nitrites from nitrates.

Aerobic, facultative.

Optimum temperature, 37° C.

Pathogenic for rabbits, guinea pigs and mice.

Source: Isolated from lungs, blood and joints.

Habitat: From human sources so far as known.

3. Corynebacterium hoagii (Morse, 1912) Eberson, 1918.

(Bacillus X, Hoag, Boston Med. and Surg. Jour., *157*, 1907, 10; *Bacillus hoagii* Morse, Jour. Inf. Dis., *11*, 1912, 284; Eberson, Jour. Inf. Dis., *23*, 1918, 10.)

hoa'gi.i. M.L. gen.noun *hoagii* of Hoag; named for Dr. Louis Hoag, the bacteriologist who first isolated this species.

Rods, 0.8 to 1.0 by 1.0 to 3.0 microns, occurring singly. Show polar staining in the shorter forms while the longer forms are barred and slightly club-shaped. Non-motile. Gram-positive.

Gelatin colonies: Small, dull, pale pink, entire.

Gelatin stab: Slight pink surface growth. No liquefaction.

Agar colonies: Small, pale pink, dull, granular, entire.

Agar slant: Filiform, dull, pink growth.

Broth: Turbid, with slight pink sediment.

Litmus milk: Slightly alkaline, with pink sediment.

Potato: Dull, filiform streak.

Indole not produced.

Acid from glucose and sucrose but not maltose.

Nitrites not produced from nitrates.

Blood serum: Dull, filiform, pink streak.

Aerobic.

Optimum temperature, 30° C.

Source: Isolated from the throat; also from air contamination of cultures.

Habitat: Unknown

4. Corynebacterium striatum (Chester, 1901) Eberson, 1918. (*Bacillus striatus flavus* and *Bacillus striatus albus* von Besser, Beitr. z. path. Anat. u. allgem. Path., *6*, 1888, 349; *Bacterium striatum* Chester, Man. Determ. Bact., 1901, 171; *Bacillus flavidus* Morse, Jour. Inf. Dis., *11*, 1912, 281; Eberson, Jour. Inf. Dis., *23*, 1918, 5 and 22; *Corynebacterium flavidum* Holland, Jour. Bact., *5*, 1920, 218.)

stri.a′tum. L. v. *strio* to groove; L. part. adj. *striatus* grooved.

Original description supplemented by material taken from Munch-Petersen (Austral. Jour. Exp. Biol. and Med. Sci., *32*, 1954, 367).

Pleomorphic rods, many of which are club-shaped, which measure 0.25 to 0.5 by 2.0 to 3.0 microns; coccoid and long, filamentous forms increase with the age of the culture. Possess fairly large metachromatic granules arranged so as to produce regular bars (striae or segments). Non-motile. Gram-positive.

Gelatin: Good growth. Many cultures liquefy gelatin slowly, while others do not liquefy even by 5 weeks.

Agar colonies: Visible after 48 hours; circular, 1.0 to 1.25 mm in diameter, white, smooth and entire by the fifth day.

Agar slants: Visible growth in 48 hours; discrete, white, entire, slightly moist, non-confluent growth in 3 days; profuse, slightly spreading, erose growth in 5 days.

Agar shakes: Excellent growth on surface and throughout the medium; similar to that on agar plates.

Chromogenesis: Some strains produce a yellowish green pigment soluble in the medium.

Citrate agar: Fair growth similar to that on agar.

Broth (with and without serum or glucose): Excellent growth visible in 24 hours; clear supernatant; finely granular, white sediment easily shaken up; no pellicle or growth on surface.

Loeffler's serum: Growth moderate, slightly raised, low convex, opaque, erose.

Litmus milk: No change in 5 days; reduction may occur in 3 weeks.

Potato: Very doubtful growth.

Indole not produced.

Hydrogen sulfide production slight, if at all.

Acid from glucose, fructose, mannose, trehalose, dextrin and glycogen; acid usually produced from galactose, lactose, maltose and starch; acid occasionally produced from sucrose, glycerol and mannitol. No acid from arabinose, xylose, rhamnose, raffinose, inulin, salicin, amygdalin, erythritol, adonitol, dulcitol, sorbitol or inositol.

Acetylmethylcarbinol not produced.

Methyl red test usually negative.

Nitrites not produced from nitrates.

Ammonia is not produced.

Aerobic.

Catalase-positive.

Methylene blue may or may not be reduced.

Thermal death point (24-hour broth cultures): 60° C. for 5 minutes.

Blood agar: Slight hemolysis around deep but not around surface colonies.

Pathogenicity: A 24-hour broth culture, when injected intramuscularly, proved fatal to all of the guinea pigs and to nearly all of the mice which were tested.

Comments: Eberson (*op. cit.*, 1918, 5) points out that the description of *Bacillus flavidus* Morse agrees with that of *Bacterium striatum* Chester; therefore with good reason he regards the two species as identical, and they are so regarded here. Munch-Petersen's description agrees, with minor exceptions, with that of *Corynebacterium flavidum* Holland as found in the Manual, 5th ed., 1939, 797. Investigators find no essential differences, other than chromogenesis, between the white and yellow strains of this species.

Source: Originally isolated from nasal mucus and from the throat; also found in the udders of cows with mastitis.

Habitat: Probably associated with the mucous membranes and skin glands of mammals, including man.

5. Corynebacterium pseudotuberculosis (Buchanan, 1911) Eberson, 1918. (Nocard, Bull. de la Soc. Centr. de méd. Vet., 1885, 207; Pseudotuberculose-Bakterien, Preisz, Cent. f. Bakt., *10*, 1891, 568; *Bacillus tuberculosis ovis* Lehmann and Neumann, Bakt. Diag., 1 Aufl., *2*, 1896, 362; *Bacillus* *pseudotuberculosis* Buchanan, Veter. Bact., Phila., 1911, 238; Eberson, Jour. Inf. Dis., *23*, 1918, 10.)

pseu.do.tu.ber.cu.lo'sis. Gr. adj. *pseudes* false; L. neut.n. *tuberculum* a little tubercle; M.L. fem.n. *tuberculosis* tuberculosis; M.L. gen.noun *pseudotuberculosis* of false tuberculosis.

Common name: Preisz-Nocard bacillus.

Slender rods, 0.5 to 0.6 by 1.0 to 3.0 microns, staining irregularly and showing clubbed forms. Non-motile. Gram-positive.

Gelatin colonies: Slight development.

Gelatin stab: No liquefaction.

Agar colonies: Thin, cream-colored to orange, folded, serrate, dry.

Loeffler's blood serum: Small, yellow, serrate colonies. No liquefaction.

Broth: No turbidity. Granular sediment. Pellicle formed (Carne, Jour. Path. and Bact., *49*, 1939, 316).

Litmus milk: Unchanged.

Potato: No growth.

Acid from glucose, fructose, galactose, mannose, sucrose, lactose, maltose and dextrin. Some strains attack xylose.

Nitrites not produced from nitrates.

Aerobic, facultative.

Optimum temperature, 37° C.

Causes caseous lymphadenitis in sheep and ulcerative lymphangitis in horses. Forms an exotoxin.

Shows a close serological relationship with *Corynebacterium renale* (Merchant, Jour. Bact., *30*, 1935, 109).

Source: Isolated from necrotic areas in the kidney of a sheep.

Habitat: Found in caseous lymphadenitis in sheep and ulcerative lesions in horses, cattle and other warm-blooded animals.

6. **Corynebacterium xerosis** Lehmann and Neumann, 1899. (Bacillus der xerose, Neisser and Kuschbert, Breslauer ärtzl. Ztschr., *5*, 1883, 42; Lehmann and Neumann, Bakt. Diag., 2 Aufl., *2*, 1899, 365 and 385.)

xe.ro'sis. Gr. fem.n. *xerosis* a parched skin, xerosis; M.L. gen.noun *xerosis* of xerosis.

An excellent historical discussion of this organism is given by Andrewes et al. (Diphtheria. London, 1923, 377–382).

Rods showing polar staining; occasionally club-shaped forms are seen. Non-motile. Gram-positive.

Plain gelatin colonies: Rarely develop.

Serum gelatin stab: No liquefaction.

Agar colonies: Minute, circular, almost transparent, raised, smooth, pearly white.

Agar slant: Thin, grayish, limited growth.

Loeffler's blood serum: Thin, grayish, adherent growth.

Broth: Clear, with slight, granular sediment.

Litmus milk: Unchanged.

Potato: No visible growth.

Indole not produced.

Acid from glucose, fructose, galactose, maltose and sucrose.

Nitrites not produced from nitrates.

Aerobic, facultative.

Optimum temperature, 37° C. Grows very slowly as low as 18° to 25° C. (Eberson, Jour. Inf. Dis., *23*, 1918, 3).

Not pathogenic.

Source: Isolated from normal and diseased conjunctiva. Kuschbert (Deutsche med. Wochnschr., *10*, 1884, 321 and 341) states that this species was originally isolated by Colomiatti.

Habitat: Probably identical with other species described from the skin and other parts of the body.

7. **Corynebacterium pyogenes** (Glage, 1903) Eberson, 1918. (*Bacillus liquefaciens pyogenes bovis* Lucet, Ann. Inst. Past., *7*, 1893, 327; *Bacillus pyogenes* Glage, Ztschr. f. Fleisch- u. Milchhyg., *13*, 1903, 166; Eberson, Jour. Inf. Dis., *23*, 1918, 5.)

py.o'ge.nes. Gr. noun *pyum* pus; Gr. v. *gennaio* to produce; M.L. adj. *pyogenes* pus-producing.

For a fuller description see Brown and Orcutt (Jour. Exp. Med., *32*, 1920, 244).

Rods 0.2 by 0.3 to 2.0 microns in length. Smallest forms appear as scarcely visible points (common in old abscesses). Chains formed. Club forms may be present. Non-motile. Gram-positive.

Serum gelatin: Liquefaction.

No growth on ordinary agar.

Serum agar: Minute colonies after 36 to 48 hours. Surface colonies may increase to 3 mm in diameter. Colonies smoky brown by transmitted light and bluish white by reflected light.

Bovine blood serum slants: Pit-like or more general areas of liquefaction.

Serum bouillon: Cloudy with fine flocculent grayish flakes that form a sediment like a streptococcus culture.

Milk: Coagulation after 48 hours at 37° C., with acid at bottom of tube. Separation of whey and peptonization.

Indole not produced.

Acid produced in serum bouillon from glucose, sucrose, lactose and xylose but not from raffinose, inulin, mannitol or salicin.

Nitrites not produced from nitrates (Merchant, Jour. Bact., *30*, 1935, 108).

Beta hemolytic; not hemoglobinophilic, though growth is favored by proteins as egg albumen, serum or blood (Brown and Orcutt, *op. cit.*, 1920, 244).

Aerobic as well as anaerobic growth.

Optimum temperature, 37° C. Growth range, 20° to 40° C.

Intravenous injection of rabbits and mice usually fatal.

Toxin and a heat-labile hemolysin are produced (Lovell, Jour. Path. and Bact., *45*, 1937, 339).

Source: Isolated from bovine pus (Lucet, *op. cit.*, 1893, 327); also isolated from pathological processes in man (Forgeot, Halbron and Levy-Bruhl, Ann. Inst. Past., *65*, 1940, 326; also see Ballard, Upsher and Seeley, Amer. Jour. Clin. Path., *27*, 1947, 209).

Habitat: Found in abscesses in cattle, swine and other warm-blooded animals, including man.

8. Corynebacterium murisepticum von Holzhausen, 1927. (Cent. f. Bakt., I Abt., Orig., *105*, 1927, 94.)

mu.ri.sep'ti.cum. L. noun *mus, muris* a mouse; Gr. adj. *septicus* septic; L. adj. *murisepticus* mouse-poisoning (-infecting).

Slender rods, 1.2 to 1.5 microns in length, with polar granules. Grow out into long filaments. Non-motile. Gram-positive.

Gelatin stab: Feeble growth, with fimbriate outgrowth along line of puncture.

Egg glycerol broth: Good growth.

Loeffler's blood serum: Good growth.

Broth: Turbid.

Litmus milk: Acid. No coagulation.

Potato: Good growth.

Indole not produced.

Hydrogen sulfide produced.

Acid from glucose, fructose, galactose, maltose, lactose, sucrose, inulin and mannitol. Arabinose and isodulcitol are not attacked.

Action on nitrates not reported.

Aerobic, facultative.

Optimum temperature, 37° C.

Pathogenic for mice.

Habitat: Septicemia in mice.

9. Corynebacterium renale (Migula, 1900) Ernst, 1905. (*Bacillus renalis bovis* Bollinger, in Enderlen, Zeit. f. Tiermed., *17*, 1890, 346; *Bacterium renale* Migula, Syst. d. Bakt., *2*, 1900, 504; Ernst, Cent. f. Bakt., I Abt., Orig., *40*, 1905, 80.)

re.na'le. L. adj. *renalis* pertaining to the kidneys.

Description taken mainly from Jones and Little (Jour. Exp. Med., *44*, 1926, 11).

Rods, 0.7 by 2.0 to 3.0 microns, occurring usually in masses, rarely singly. Non-motile. Bacteria from tissues not so pleomorphic as those from the earlier transfer cultures, although many show polar granules or swollen ends. Cultures grown in broth show coccoid forms and beaded rods with swollen ends. Gram-positive.

Gelatin: Grows poorly if at all. No liquefaction.

Agar: Small, punctiform colonies.

Agar slants: Raised, grayish white and dry growth (Jones and Little). Others say cream-colored and moist.

Blood serum slants: Fine, gray, punctiform colonies in 24 hours at 37° C. which are a little larger than those on agar. Streak scarcely 1 mm in width. Glistening and slimy in fresh cultures. No liquefaction.

Litmus milk: Reduction and coagulation from the bottom. Slow digestion, becoming alkaline.

Broth: Sediment at end of 2 days with clear bouillon above.

Potato: Growth grayish white, later becoming a dingy yellow, turning the potato brown.

Acid from glucose. No acid from lactose, sucrose, maltose or mannitol. Some strains ferment fructose and mannose (Merchant, Jour. Bact., *30*, 1935, 109).

Aerobic, facultatively anaerobic.

Optimum temperature, 37° C.

Pathogenic for mice (Lovell and Cotchin, Jour. Comp. Path. and Therap., *56*, 1946, 205) and for rabbits (Feenstra, Thorp and Gray, Amer. Jour. Vet. Res., *10*, 1949, 12).

No toxin produced.

Shows a close serological relationship with *Corynebacterium psuedotuberculosis* (Merchant).

Source: Isolated from pyelonephritis in cattle.

Habitat: Occurs in purulent infections of the urinary tract in cattle, sheep, horses and dogs.

10. Corynebacterium kutscheri (Migula, 1900) Bergey et al., 1925. (*Bacillus pseudotuberculosis murium* Kutscher, Ztschr. f. Hyg., *18*, 1894, 338; *Bacterium kutscheri* Migula, Syst. d. Bakt., *2*, 1900, 372; Bergey et al., Manual, 2nd ed., 1925, 395.)

kut'scher.i. M.L. gen.noun *kutscheri* of Kutscher; named for Kutscher, the bacteriologist who first isolated this species.

Rods, with pointed ends, staining irregularly. Non-motile. Gram-positive.

Gelatin colonies: Small, white, translucent.

Gelatin stab: No growth on surface. White, filiform growth in stab. No liquefaction.

Agar colonies: Small, thin, yellowish white, translucent, serrate.

Agar slant: Thin, white, translucent.

Loeffler's blood serum: Abundant growth. Not peptonized.

Broth: Slight turbidity. Crystals of ammonium magnesium phosphate are produced.

Litmus milk: Unchanged.

Potato: No growth.

Indole not produced.

Nitrites not produced from nitrates.

Aerobic, facultative.

Optimum temperature, 37° C.

Source: Isolated from a cheesy mass in the lung of a mouse.

11. Corynebacterium phocae Svenkerud et al., 1951. (Svenkerud, Rosted and Thorshang, Nord. Vet. Med., *3*, 1951, 168.)

pho'cae. M.L. noun *Phoca* a generic name of seals; M.L. gen.noun *phocae* of *Phoca*.

Description prepared by Prof. E. G. D. Murray from the original publication by Svenkerud et al. and from a study of cultures supplied by these investigators.

Rods, 0.4 to 0.6 by 0.7 to 2.0 microns, occurring in frequently flexed chains of 3 to 7 or more cells, in linear, end to end pairs or in pairs lying at an obtuse angle to each other; occasionally single cells and very long rod-shaped forms, 10 to 15 microns in length, may occur, the latter sometimes being curved. Non-motile. Gram-positive.

Gelatin: No liquefaction.

Agar colonies: Small (0.1 mm), circular, smooth, moderately elevated, entire; at first (24 hours) transparent and colorless, later (48 hours) becoming enlarged (0.5 to 1.0 mm), opalescent and slightly white.

Potassium tellurite medium: No growth.

Peptone broth: Poor growth at 37° C. and room temperature.

Pneumo broth: Good growth at 37° C. and room temperature; slight growth in 3 to 4 days at 4° C., becoming progressively heavier and producing a turbidity in the lower portion of the medium, thus leaving a clear supernatant several mm in depth.

Coagulated blood serum: No liquefaction.

Litmus milk: No change.

Indole not produced.

Hydrogen sulfide not produced.

Carbohydrate fermentation determinations (except those of esculin, arbutin and alpha-methyl-glucoside) performed in Hiss serum sugar water. Acid from glucose, fructose, sucrose, maltose, trehalose and salicin. Slight acid from xylose, galactose, lactose, inulin, glycerol, inositol and mannitol. Acid occasionally produced from rhamnose and dextrin. No acid from arabinose, dulcitol, sorbitol or arbutin. Glucose, fructose, sucrose and salicin cause clotting of the medium in 24 hours at 37° C. as does trehalose in 48 hours; dextrin causes clotting by one week.

Starch, aesculin and alpha-methyl-glucoside are hydrolyzed.

Methyl red test positive.

Acetylmethylcarbinol produced.

Citrate not utilized.

Sodium oleate severely inhibits growth.

Nitrites not produced from nitrates.

Urease not produced.

Blood agar colonies: 0.7 mm in diameter, smooth, glistening, moderately elevated, entire, transparent, slightly white; later (48 hours) becoming enlarged (1.0 mm in diameter) and white with opaque centers. No hemolysis.

Catalase-negative.

Aerobic, facultative.

Comment: Svenkcrud ct al. raise the question whether this species should be placed in *Corynebacterium, Erysipelothrix* or *Listeria*. However, the further cultural and serological studies that have been made of their cultures show that this species is properly placed in the genus *Corynebacterium*.

Source: Isolated from an erysipelas occurring in the transition between the corium and blubber of seals (*Phoca groenlandica, P. hispida, Cristophara cristata* and *Erignathus barbatus*).

12. Corynebacterium pseudodiphtheriticum Lehmann and Neumann, 1896. (Bacillus der pseudodiphtherie, Loeffler, Cent. f. Bakt., *2*, 1887, 105; G. von Hofmann-Wellenhof, Wien. med. Wochenschr., *38*, 1888, 65; Lehmann and Neumann, Bakt. Diag., 1 Aufl., *2*, 1896, 361.)

pseu.do.diph.the.ri'ti.cum. Gr. adj. *pseudes* false; M.L. fem.n. *diphtheria* diphtheria; M.L. adj. *diphtheriticus* diphtheritic; M.L. adj. *pseudodiphtheriticus* relating to false diphtheria.

Common name: Pseudodiphtheria bacillus or Hofmann's bacillus.

Excellent historical discussions of this and related organisms are given by Bergey (Comparative Studies upon the Pseudodiphtheria or Hofmann's Bacillus, the Xerosis Bacillus, and the Loeffler Bacillus. Contrib. from Lab. of Hyg., Univ. of Penn., No. 2, 1898, 19–54) and by Andrewes et al. (Diphtheria. London, 1923, 382–388).

Rods, with rounded ends, 0.3 to 0.5 by 0.8 to 1.5 microns, fairly uniform in size, without swollen ends. Not barred but even staining interrupted by transverse, medial unstained septum; granules usually absent. Non-motile. Gram-positive.

Gelatin colonies: Small, grayish to cream-colored, smooth, homogeneous, entire.

Gelatin stab: Slight surface growth with little growth in stab. No liquefaction.

Agar colonies: Opaque, grayish to cream-colored, smooth, homogeneous, entire.

Agar slant: Moist, smooth, white to cream-colored, entire growth.

Loeffler's blood serum: Same as on agar.

Broth: Slightly turbid with slight, grayish sediment.

Litmus milk: Unchanged.

Potato: Slight, creamy white, smooth, entire growth.

Indole not produced.

No acid from carbohydrate media.

Nitrites produced from nitrates.

Hydrolyzes urea (Merkel, Zent. f. Bakt., I Abt., Orig., *147*, 1941, 398).

Aerobic, facultative.

Optimum temperature, 37° C.

Not pathogenic.

Source: From the oral cavity of 26 out of 45 control cases.

Habitat: Normal throats.

13. Corynebacterium equi Magnusson, 1923. (Arch. f. wiss. prakt. Tierheilk., *50*, 1923, 22.)

e'qui. L. noun *equus* horse; L. gen.noun *equi* of the horse.

Description taken from Dimock and Edwards (Kentucky Agr. Exp. Sta. Bull. 333, 1932), Bruner and Edwards (Kentucky Agr. Exp. Sta. Bull. 414, 1941), Merchant (Jour. Bact., *30*, 1935, 95) and Brooks and Hucker (Jour. Bact., *48*, 1944, 309).

Rods variable according to medium. Coccoid and ellipsoidal cells to rather long, curved and sometimes clubbed forms. The latter are especially apt to occur in liquid media. Non-motile. Gram-positive.

Gelatin stab: Good growth. No liquefaction.

Agar colonies: Usually moist, smooth and glistening, tan to yellow (Brooks and Hucker, *ibid.*, 300) or pink to red chromogenesis (Merchant, *op. cit.*, 1935, 107).

Agar slant: Moist heavy growth which may run down the slant (Dimock and Edwards, *op. cit.*, 1932, 322).

Broth: Turbid with no pellicle and little sediment (Dimock and Edwards, *loc. cit.*).

Pellicle, and final pH alkaline (Brooks and Hucker, *op. cit.*, 1944, 309). Branched cells occur in 6- to 8-hour cultures in broth.

Loeffler's blood serum: Good growth with tan to yellow chromogenesis. No liquefaction.

Coagulated egg yolk: Vigorous salmon-pink growth. Dryer than on agar, resembling wrinkled growth of tubercle bacillus after two weeks.

Litmus milk: No change to slightly alkaline.

Potato: Abundant growth, usually tan, yellow or pink.

Indole not produced.

Hydrogen sulfide produced on appropriate media.

No acid from carbohydrate media. However, glucose stimulates growth.

Nitrites produced from nitrates. No ammonia produced.

Sodium hippurate: Not hydrolyzed.

Esculin: Not hydrolyzed.

No exotoxin demonstrated in filtrate of broth cultures.

No or slight hemolysis of horse blood.

Aerobic.

Temperature relations: Optimum, between 25° and 37° C. Minimum, between 7° and 18° C. Maximum, between 37° and 45° C.

Not pathogenic for laboratory animals.

Source: Originally isolated from infectious pneumonia of foals.

Habitat: Found in spontaneous pneumonia of foals and in other infections of horses. Also found in swine, cattle and buffaloes.

14. **Corynebacterium bovis** Bergey et al., 1923. (*B. pseudodiphtheria*, Bergey, The Source and Nature of Bacteria in Milk. Penn. Dept. Agr. Bull. 125, 1904, 11; Bergey et al., Manual, 1st ed., 1923, 388.)

bo'vis. L. noun *bos* the ox; L. gen.noun *bovis* of the ox.

Slender rods, 0.5 to 0.7 by 2.5 to 3.0 microns, which are barred and clubbed. Nonmotile, Gram-positive.

Gelatin stab: Slight, gray, flat surface growth.

Agar colonies: Circular, gray, slightly raised, radiate, undulate, dry.

Agar slant: Thin, gray, filiform, dry growth.

Broth: Slight, granular sediment.

Litmus milk: Slowly becomes deeply alkaline.

Potato: No growth.

Indole not produced.

No acid from carbohydrate media.

Nitrites not produced from nitrates.

No growth on agar containing asparagine as a sole source of nitrogen (Evans, Jour. Inf. Dis., *18*, 1916, 461).

Coagulated blood serum: Thin, gray, filiform growth.

Blood serum (10 per cent) and bile (5 per cent) enhance growth, especially the former (Evans, *ibid.*, 459).

Causes rancidity in cream. Weakly lipolytic on tributyrin agar (Black, Jour. Bact., *41*, 1941, 99).

Optimum temperature, 37° C.

Not pathogenic for guinea pigs (Evans, Jour. Inf. Dis., *22*, 1918, 579).

Comments: Miss Alice Evans (personal communication) states that the organism from the udder which she described as *Bacterium lipolyticus* (sic) (*ibid.*, 576) was probably a *Corynebacterium*. This is also regarded as probable by Steck (Die latente Infektion der Milchdrüse, Hannover, 1930) and by Hendrixen (Ztschr. f. Infektionskrankh. d. Haustier., *43*, 1933, 106). Miss Evans also indicates that it is probable that the organism described by Bergey first in 1904 (*op. cit.*, 1904, 11) and later in the first edition of the MANUAL as *Corynebacterium bovis* was the same organism; this is further confirmed by Black (*op. cit.*, 1941, 99). In his unpublished manuscript, Black reports that he found no essential differences between his cultures isolated from milk (53 cultures) and those described by Bergey except for action on litmus milk. Black reports no action on litmus milk.

Source: Isolated from fresh milk drawn directly from the cow's udder.

Habitat: Found rather commonly in freshly drawn milk.

15. **Corynebacterium paurometabolum** Steinhaus, 1941. (Jour. Bact., *41*, 1941, 763 and 783.)

pau.ro.me.ta'bo.lum. Gr. adj. *paurus*

little; Gr. adj. *metabolus* changeable; M.L. adj. *paurometabolus* little changeable, probably intended to mean producing little change.

Rods, 0.5 to 0.8 by 1.0 to 2.5 microns, occurring singly, in pairs and in masses. Metachromatic granules present. Non-motile. Gram-positive.

Gelatin stab: Slow liquefaction at surface.

Agar colonies: White to gray, entire, circular, small, dry, somewhat granular.

Agar slant: Filiform to arborescent, thick, granular growth.

Broth: Abundant, granular sediment but no turbidity. Pellicle.

Litmus milk: Alkaline.

Potato: Thick, raised, dry, granular, profuse, gray to light cream-colored growth.

Indole not produced.

Slight production of hydrogen sulfide.

No action on the following carbohydrates: glucose, lactose, sucrose, maltose, fructose, mannitol, galactose, arabinose, xylose, dextrin, salicin, raffinose, trehalose, sorbitol, inulin, dulcitol, glycerol, rhamnose, adonitol, mannose, esculin and inositol.

Nitrites not produced from nitrates.

Aerobic.

Slight alpha hemolysis.

Non-pathogenic for guinea pigs.

A special semi-solid medium, the main nutritive constituents of which were proteose peptone, rabbit serum, gelatin, minced rabbit kidney and carbohydrates, was used for the original isolation. An incubation period of 4 to 7 days at 26° C. was necessary for the initial isolation. Subsequent transfers to ordinary beef-infusion agar grew out in 24 to 48 hours.

Source: Isolated from media inoculated with the mycetome and ovaries of the bedbug, *Cimex lectularius* L. A very similar diphtheroid strain was isolated from the alimentary tract of the bagworm, *Thyridopteryx ephemeraeformis* Haw.

Habitat: Distribution in nature unknown.

16. **Corynebacterium nephridii** Büsing et al., 1953. (Büsing, Döll and Freytag, Arch. f. Mikrobiol., *19*, 1953, 77.)

neph.ri′di.i. Gr. adj. *nephridius* of the kidney; M.L. noun *nephridium* a nephri-

dium, a little kidney; M.L. gen.noun *nephridii* of a nephridium.

Description taken from Büsing and Freytag (Zent. f. Bakt., I Abt., Orig., *160*, 1954, 582).

Slender rods, 0.4 to 0.5 by 1.0 to 2.0 microns, with no tendency toward filamentous forms or chains; occasionally occur in a palisade arrangement. Non-motile. Gram-positive.

Growth occurs on common culture media on primary isolation.

Gelatin: No liquefaction.

Agar colonies: 1.5 mm in diameter, round, smooth, moist, slimy, gray.

Broth: Uniformly turbid; later becoming slimy with a gray pellicle with stalactite-like growths; sediment.

Coagulated blood serum: No liquefaction.

Litmus milk: Distinctly alkaline in 10 days.

Indole not produced.

Hydrogen sulfide not produced.

No acid from carbohydrate media.

Acetylmethylcarbinol not produced.

Nitrites not produced from nitrates.

Ammonia produced in peptone media.

Urea not hydrolyzed.

Blood agar: No hemolysis.

Aerobic.

Optimum temperature range, 15° to 37° C.

Optimum pH range, 6.2 to 7.2.

Source: Isolated from the medicinal leech (*Hirudo medicinalis*).

17. **Corynebacterium vesiculare** Büsing et al., 1953. (Büsing, Döll and Freytag, Arch. f. Mikrobiol., *19*, 1953, 76.)

ve.si.cu.la′re. M.L. adj. *vesicularis* pertaining to a vesicle.

Description taken from Büsing and Freytag (Zent. f. Bakt., I Abt., Orig., *160*, 1954, 579).

Slender, pleomorphic rods 0.4 by 3.0 to 8.0 microns; filamentous forms 30 microns or more in length may also occur. Non-motile. Gram-positive.

Primary isolation accomplished on "fungus" medium, but this species can be adapted to grow on common culture media.

Gelatin: No liquefaction.

Agar colonies: After 2 days, 1 to 2 mm in

diameter, round, smooth, moist, slimy, orange to rust-red.

Coagulated blood serum: No liquefaction.

Litmus milk: Distinct alkalinity after 10 days.

Indole not produced.

Hydrogen sulfide not produced.

No acid from carbohydrate media.

Starch not hydrolyzed.

Acetylmethylcarbinol not produced.

Nitrites not produced from nitrates.

Ammonia produced in peptone media.

Urea not hydrolyzed.

Blood agar: No hemolysis.

Aerobic.

Optimum temperature range, 15° to 22° C.

Optimum pH, 6.4.

Source: Isolated from the medicinal leech (*Hirudo medicinalis*).

18. Corynebacterium insidiosum (McCulloch, 1925) Jensen, 1934. (*Aplanobacter insidiosum* McCulloch, Phytopath., *15*, 1925, 497; also see Jour. Agr. Res., *33*, 1926, 502; Jensen, Proc. Linnean Soc. New So. Wales, *59*, 1934, 41.)

in.si.di.o'sum. L. adj. *insidiosus* deceitful, insidious.

Rods, 0.4 to 0.5 by 0.7 to 1.0 micron. Encapsulated. Non-motile. Gram-positive.

Gelatin: Slow liquefaction.

Beef agar colonies: Pale yellow, circular, smooth, shining; edges entire; viscid. Blue granules found on the medium.

Milk: Coagulated after 16 to 20 days. No digestion. An apricot-yellow sediment is deposited on the walls of the tube.

Indole not produced.

Hydrogen sulfide not produced.

Acid from glucose, sucrose, lactose and glycerol.

Moderate diastatic action.

Nitrites not produced from nitrates.

Grows in 5 per cent salt.

Aerobic.

Optimum temperature, 23° C. Maximum, 31° C.

Distinctive character: Bluish granules produced in culture.

Comments: Jensen (*ibid.*, 42) reports that he has found a non-infectious variety of this species in grass land soil in Australia.

Source: Isolated from diseased alfalfa plants.

Habitat: Vascular pathogen of alfalfa, *Medicago sativa*.

19. Corynebacterium sepedonicum (Spieckermann and Kotthoff, 1914) Skaptason and Burkholder, 1942. (*Bacterium sepedonicum* Spieckermann (*nomen nudum*), Ill. Landw. Zeitung, *33*, 1913, 680; *Bacterium sepedonicum* Spieckermann and Kotthoff, Landw. Jahr., *46*, 1914, 674; Skaptason and Burkholder, Phytopath., *32*, 1942, 439.)

se.pe.do'ni.cum. Gr. adj. *sepedonicus* leading to decay.

Description taken from Stapp (Ztschr. f. Par., *5*, 1930, 756).

Rods 0.3 to 0.4 by 0.8 to 1.0 micron. Pleomorphic. Non-motile. Gram-positive.

Gelatin: Liquefaction slight.

Agar colonies: Thin, smooth, translucent, glistening, whitish, 2 to 3 mm in diameter.

Broth: Weak growth. No pellicle. Light sediment.

Litmus milk: Little change in 6 weeks, after which litmus is reduced.

Indole not produced.

Hydrogen sulfide production feeble, if at all.

Glucose, galactose, fructose, arabinose, xylose, mannitol, glycerol and dulcitol are utilized.

Starch hydrolysis light.

Grows in 4 per cent salt.

Temperature relations: Optimum, between 20° and 23° C. Minimum, 4° C. Maximum, 31° C.

Distinctive characters: Differs from *Corynebacterium michiganense* in that it is white to cream-colored on various media and has a lower optimum temperature. *Corynebacterium michiganense* does not infect potatoes.

Source: Stapp used 17 cultures isolated from diseased potatoes.

Habitat: Causes ring rot of potato tubers in Germany.

20. Corynebacterium humiferum Seliskar, 1952. (Colorado Farm and Home Research, *2*, 1952, 9.)

hu.mi'fer.um. L. noun *humus* soil; L. v. *fero* to bear; M.L. adj. *humiferus* soil-borne.

Pleomorphic rods, 0.4 to 0.7 by 0.7 to 2.8 microns, occasionally club-shaped, occurring singly and in an angular arrangement due to the snapping division of the cells. Non-motile. Gram-positive.

Gelatin: No liquefaction.

Nutrient-glucose agar colonies: White to cream, circular, smooth, entire, convex, translucent, 1 to 2 mm in diameter.

Broth: Turbid in 36 to 48 hours; no pellicle; light sediment.

Litmus milk: Slow reduction of litmus, but no other change.

Acid but no gas from glucose, mannitol and glycerol. No growth in lactose or raffinose.

Starch not hydrolyzed.

No growth in Koser citrate medium.

Nitrites not produced from nitrates.

Growth in 3 per cent salt.

Catalase-positive.

Aerobic to slightly microaerophilic.

Temperature relations: Optimum, between 24° and 28° C. Minimum, 6° C. Maximum, between 34° and 36° C.

Source: Isolated from wet wood of Lombardy poplar (*Populus nigra* var. *italica*).

Habitat: Pathogenic on *Populus nigra* var. *italica* and on *P. tremuloides*.

21. **Corynebacterium michiganense** (Erw. Smith, 1910) Jensen, 1934. (*Bacterium michiganense* (Erw. Smith, Science, *31*, 1910, 794; Jensen, Proc. Linnean Soc. New So. Wales, *59*, 1934, 47.)

mi.chi.ga.nen'se. M.L. adj. *michiganensis* pertaining to Michigan.

Description taken from Bryan (Jour. Agr. Res., *41*, 1930, 825).

Rods 0.6 to 0.7 by 0.7 to 1.2 microns. Characteristic angular growth with branching and club-shaped cells (Jensen, *op. cit.*, 1934, 47). Encapsulated. Non-motile. Gram-positive.

Beef agar colonies: Growth slow, mustard-yellow, smooth, glistening, butyrous.

Chromogenesis: Develops yellowish brown, light ochre-yellow to sepia-brown colors on suitable media (Jensen, *loc. cit.*).

Gelatin: Slow liquefaction.

Broth: Turbidity slow and moderate.

Milk: Slow coagulation. No peptonization.

Indole not produced.

Hydrogen sulfide not produced.

Acid from glucose, sucrose, galactose, fructose, maltose, and slight acid from lactose, glycerol and mannitol.

Starch: Very weak diastatic action.

Nitrites not produced from nitrates.

Utilizes peptone but not ammonia, nitrite, nitrate, tyrosine, asparagine or glutamic acid (Mushin, Austral. Jour. Exp. Biol. and Med., *16*, 1938, 326).

No growth in 3 per cent salt.

Aerobic.

Temperature relations: Optimum, between 25° and 27° C. Minimum, 1° C. Maximum, 33° C.

Comments: A non-pathogenic variety of this species has been reported by Jensen (*op. cit.*, 1934, 48); it grows more rapidly with more moist growth, has a higher maximum temperature and has a stronger proteolytic activity than does the pathogenic strain.

Source: Isolated from the bacterial canker of tomato.

Habitat: Pathogenic on tomato.

22. **Corynebacterium rathayi** (Erw. Smith, 1913) Dowson, 1942. (*Aplanobacter rathayi* Erw. Smith, Science, *38*, 1913, 926; also see Bact. in Rel. to Plant Dis., *3*, 1914, 155; Dowson, Trans. Brit. Myc. Soc., *25*, 1942, 313.)

ra.thay'i. M.L. gen.noun *rathayi* of Rathay; named for E. Rathay, an Austrian plant pathologist who was the first to isolate this species.

Rods 0.6 to 0.75 by 0.75 to 1.5 microns. Encapsulated. Non-motile. Not acid-fast. Gram-positive.

Gelatin: Slow liquefaction after 7 weeks.

Agar colonies: Small, yellow, slow-growing.

Milk: Growth slow. Yellow ring.

Litmus milk: Alkaline and reduced.

Potato plugs: Good, yellow, viscid growth.

Acid but no gas from glucose, sucrose and lactose.

Nitrites produced from nitrates.

Cohn's solution: No growth.

Heavy inoculum necessary in media.

Source: Isolated from slimy heads of *Dactylis glomerata*.

Habitat: Pathogenic on *Dactylis glomerata*.

23. Corynebacterium agropyri (O'-Gara, 1916) Burkholder, 1948. (*Aplanobacter agropyri* O'Gara, Phytopath., *6*, 1916, 343; Burkholder, in Manual, 6th ed., 1948, 395.)

ag.ro.py'ri. Gr. noun *agrus* field; Gr. noun *pyrus* wheat; M.L. neut.n. *Agropyron* generic name of a grass; M.L. gen.noun *agropyri* of *Agropyron*.

Rods 0.4 to 0.6 by 0.6 to 1.1 microns. Encapsulated. Non-motile. Gram-variable.

Gelatin: No liquefaction.

Nutrient agar slant: Meager, yellow, very viscid growth.

Broth: Light clouding with yellow precipitate.

Milk: Little-changed. Yellow sediment formed.

Acid but no gas from glucose, lactose, sucrose and glycerol.

Starch: Hydrolysis feeble.

Nitrites produced from nitrates.

Optimum temperature, between 25° and 28° C.

This species is very similar to and may be identical with *Corynebacterium rathayi* Dowson.

Source: Isolated from slimy heads of wheat grass.

Habitat: Found on wheat grass, *Agropyron smithii*.

24. Corynebacterium fascians (Tilford, 1936) Dowson, 1942. (*Phytomonas fascians* Tilford, 54th Rept. Ohio Agr. Exp. Sta. Bull. 561, 1936, 39; also see Jour. Agr. Res., *53*, 1936, 393; Dowson, Trans. Brit. Myc. Soc., *25*, 1942, 313.)

fas'ci.ans. L. part.adj. *fascians* banding, binding.

Rods 0.5 to 0.9 by 1.5 to 4.0 microns. Non-motile. Gram-positive.

Gelatin: No liquefaction.

Potato-glucose agar colonies: Light cream-colored colonies appear after 72 hours. Punctiform, circular, later cadmium-yellow to deep chrome.

Nutrient agar slant: After one week streak is filiform, flat, dull to glistening, smooth, opaque, cream-colored and butyrous.

Broth: Slightly turbid. Fragile pellicle with distinct rim.

Milk: Litmus becomes blue. Other changes slight.

Indole not produced.

Hydrogen sulfide produced.

Acid but no gas from glucose, galactose, fructose, mannose, arabinose, xylose, maltose, sucrose, glycerol, mannitol and dextrin. No acid from rhamnose, lactose, raffinose or inulin.

Starch not hydrolyzed.

Nitrites produced from nitrates.

Grows in 8 per cent salt.

Aerobic.

Optimum temperature, between 25° and 28° C.

Source: Described from 15 single-cell isolates from fasciated growths on sweet peas.

Habitat: Pathogenic on sweet pea, chrysanthemum, geranium, petunia, tobacco, etc.

25. Corynebacterium hypertrophicans (Stahel, 1933) Burkholder, 1948. (*Pseudomonas hypertrophicans* Stahel, Phyt. Ztschr., *6*, 1933, 445; Burkholder, in Manual, 6th ed., 1948, 398.)

hy.per.tro'phi.cans. Gr. pref. *hyper* very; Gr. adj. *trophicus* well-fed, stout, overgrown; M.L. adj. *hypertrophicans* becoming overgrown, producing a hypertrophy.

Rods 0.6 to 0.8 by 1.2 to 2.8 microns. Motile by means of a single polar flagellum. Bipolar staining. Gram-positive.

Gelatin: No growth.

Agar colonies: Slow growing, circular, raised, wet-shining, white.

Broth plus sucrose: Growth good. No pellicle.

Milk: No visible change.

Indole not produced.

Hydrogen sulfide not produced.

Acid but no gas from glucose, fructose and sucrose. No acid from lactose and glycerol. The acids from sucrose are lactic and formic.

Nitrites not produced from nitrates.

Aerobic.

Source: Isolated from witches' brooms.

Habitat: Pathogenic on *Eugenia latifolia*.

26. Corynebacterium poinsettiae Starr

and Pirone, 1942. (Phytopath., *32*, 1942, 1080.)

poin.set'ti.ae. M.L. fem.n. *Poinsettia* name of a genus of flowering plants; M.L. gen.noun *poinsettiae* of *Poinsettia*.

Rods which average 0.3 to 0.8 by 1.0 to 3.0 microns. Pleomorphic, with some cells 8.5 microns in length. Encapsulated. Granules present. Motile by means of a single (rarely 2) polar or lateral flagellum. Gram-positive.

Gelatin: Liquefaction.

Loeffler's blood-serum: Liquefaction.

Beef-extract agar colonies: Round, slightly convex, 0.1 to 1.0 mm in diameter, entire, smooth, non-viscid, colorless and almost transparent.

Potato glucose agar slants: Moderate growth, filiform, glistening, non-viscid, salmon- to flesh-colored.

Beef-extract broth: Turbid in 24 hours; abundant, pale salmon sediment. No pellicle.

Milk: Slight acidity but no other visible change for 2 weeks, then a soft curd, reduction of litmus and complete peptonization.

Indole not produced.

Hydrogen sulfide not produced.

Sodium hippurate not hydrolyzed.

Moderate to abundant acid, but no gas, from glucose, fructose, mannose, galactose, sucrose, maltose, cellobiose, melibiose, raffinose, glycerol, erythritol, salicin and amygdalin; weak acid from arabinose, xylose, lactose, trehalose, dextrin and adonitol; no acid from rhamnose, fucose, inulin, glycogen, mannitol, dulcitol, sorbitol or inositol.

Acetylmethylcarbinol not produced.

Methyl red test negative.

Starch hydrolyzed.

No action on cellulose.

Non-lipolytic.

Tellurite reduced.

Nitrites not produced from nitrates.

Asparagine not utilized as carbon-nitrogen source. Uric acid not utilized; urea not hydrolyzed.

Aerobic.

Growth occurs after 24 hours from 15° to 36° C.; after 48 hours from 7° to 12° C. No growth above 36° or below 7° C. at the end of a week.

Source: Fourteen cultures isolated from diseased stems of poinsettia, *Euphorbia pulcherrima*.

Habitat: Causes a canker of stems and spots on leaves of the poinsettia.

27. Corynebacterium tritici (Hutchinson, 1917) Burkholder, 1948. (*Pseudomonas tritici* Hutchinson, India Dept. of Agr., Bact. Ser., *1*, 1917, 174; Burkholder, in Manual, 6th ed., 1948, 400.)

tri'ti.ci. L. noun *triticum* wheat; M.L. neut.n. *Triticum* generic name of wheat; L. gen.noun *tritici* of wheat.

Rods 0.8 by 2.4 to 3.2 microns. Motile by means of a single polar flagellum. Gram-positive.

Gelatin: No liquefaction.

Agar colonies: Bright yellow becoming orange, glistening, moist, entire. Agar brownish.

Broth: Turbid. Thin pellicle.

Milk: Yellow surface and yellow precipitate. Little change.

Hydrogen sulfide not produced.

Acid but no gas from glucose and lactose.

Nitrites produced from nitrates.

This species is very similar to and may be identical with *Corynebacterium rathayi* Dowson.

Source: Isolated from slimy heads of wheat in India.

Habitat: Pathogenic on wheat, *Triticum aestivum*.

28. Corynebacterium flaccumfaciens (Hedges, 1922) Dowson, 1942. (*Bacterium flaccumfaciens* Hedges, Science, *55*, 1922, 433; also see Phytopath., *16*, 1926, 20; Dowson, Trans. Brit. Myc. Soc., *25*, 1942, 313.)

flac.cum.fa'ci.ens. L. adj. *flaccus* flabby; L. part.adj. *faciens* making; M.L. part.adj. *flaccumfaciens* wilt-making.

Rods 0.3 to 0.5 by 0.6 to 3.0 microns. Motile by means of a single polar flagellum; also non-motile (Adams and Pugsley, Jour. Dept. Agr. Victoria, *32*, 1934, 306). Gram-positive.

Gelatin: Liquefaction feeble.

Beef agar slants: Rather moderate growth, glistening, flat, smooth, viscid and yellow.

Broth: Moderate turbidity in 24 hours. Pellicle formed.

Milk: Acid curd and slow peptonization.

Indole not produced.

Hydrogen sulfide not produced.

Acid from glucose, lactose, sucrose and glycerol.

Starch not hydrolyzed.

Nitrites not produced from nitrates.

Slight growth in 5 per cent salt.

Optimum temperature, 31° C. Maximum temperature, between 36° and 40° C.

Distinctive character: A strict vascular parasite of the bean.

Source: Isolated from wilted bean plants from South Dakota.

Habitat: Causes a wilt of beans and related plants.

29. Corynebacterium acnes (Gilchrist, 1901) Eberson, 1918. (*Bacillus acnes* Gilchrist, Johns Hopkins Hosp. Repts., *9*, 1901, 425; *Bacillus parvus liquefaciens* Jungano, Compt. rend. Soc. Biol., Paris, *65*, 1908, 618; Eberson, Jour. Inf. Dis., *23*, 1918, 10; *Corynebacterium liquefaciens* Prévot, Ann. Inst. Past., *60*, 1938, 304; not *Corynebacterium liquefaciens* Andrewes et al., Diphtheria, London, 1923, 408; not *Corynebacterium liquefaciens* Jensen, Proc. Linn. Soc. New So. Wales, *59*, 1934, 49; *Propionibacterium acnes* Douglas and Gunter, Jour. Bact., *52*, 1946, 22.)

ac'nes. Gr. noun *acme* a point; incorrectly transliterated as M.L. noun *acne* acne; M.L. gen.noun *acnes* of acne.

Original description supplemented by material from more recent authors.

Rods varying in dimensions, usually 0.4 to 0.5 by 0.8 to 0.9 micron, occasionally slightly club-shaped; under aerobic conditions the cells are quite long and are swollen or club-shaped, sometimes possessing what appears to be rudimentary branching (Douglas and Gunter, *ibid.*, 17 and 18). Show alternate bands of stained and unstained material. Non-motile. Gram-positive.

Aerobic growth in culture media is very feeble; anaerobic growth is excellent. Best growth occurs in shake cultures with soft, slightly acid, glucose agar.

Gelatin: Liquefaction (Douglas and Gunter, *ibid.*, 19).

Agar colonies: Circular, 1.5 to 4.0 mm in diameter, raised, smooth, glistening, entire, slightly pink, later becoming a pale salmon-pink (Douglas and Gunter, *ibid.*, 18).

Agar slant: Very small, circular, transparent colonies which may later become rose-colored.

Loeffler's blood serum: Small, grayish colonies which may later become rose-colored,

Broth: Clear.

Litmus milk: Soft coagulum.

Potato: No growth in aerobic cultures, but pink streak in anaerobic cultures.

Indole may or may not be produced (Douglas and Gunter, *ibid.*, 19). Indole produced (Seeliger, personal communication, 1955).

Acid from glucose, sucrose (slight), maltose, mannitol and inulin (Eberson, *op. cit.*, 1918, 23). Produces propionic acid; lactic acid not fermented (Douglas and Gunter, *op. cit.*, 1946, 22).

Nitrites produced from nitrates.

Anaerobic to aerotolerant.

Catalase-positive.

Optimum temperature, between 35° and 37° C.

Blood agar: Beta hemolysis (Douglas and Gunter, *ibid.*, 19).

Pathogenic for mice, giving rise to characteristic lesions (Eberson, *op. cit.*, 1918, 23).

Serology: See Linzenmeier (Ann. Inst. Past., *87*, 1954, 572).

Comments: Even before 1901 several authors reported finding bacteria in acne pustules which were evidently diphtheroid in nature. Unna (Monatshefte f. prakt. Derm., *13*, 1891, 232) found an organism in acne pustules for which he gave the name Flaschenbacillus. Hodara (Monatshefte f. prakt. Derm., *18*, 1894, 586) reported the presence of two types of bacteria in acne lesions, the second of which he called Flaschenkugelbacillus. Sabouraud (Ann. Inst. Past., *11*, 1897, 134) gave a more accurate description of these diphtheroids which he reported to need an acid medium for growth; he called this bacterium "bacille de séborrhée grasse".

Relationship to *Corynebacterium liquefaciens*: Seeliger (Arch. f. Hyg. u. Bakt.,

137, 1953, 1–10) found a culture of this organism isolated from a submandibular abscess to be identical with *C. liquefaciens* as recognized by Prévot and also identical with cultures of *C. acnes* as isolated and identified by Lentze (Zent. f. Bakt., I Abt., Orig., *155*, 1950, 290). Since that time, Seeliger (personal communication, December, 1954) has had opportunity to study the cultures of *C. acnes* found in both the National Collection of Type Cultures (London) and the American Type Culture Collection (Washington), all isolated from acne pustules, and he has found all of them to be identical. At the same time he finds these cultures to be the same as the cultures that he examined in 1953. All cultures agree with the brief but characteristic description of *C. acnes* as given by Gilchrist. As the name *C. acnes* has priority and as the name *C. liquefaciens* is an illegitimate homonym, the former binomial is used here.

Source: Originally isolated from acne pustules. The specific epithet "acnes" was given by Gilchrist to indicate the source of this culture, and it should not be interpreted as meaning that this species is the cause of acne.

Habitat: While this species appears to be an organism commonly found in acne pustules, it also occurs in other types of lesions in the human body or even as a saprophyte in the intestine, in skin, in hair follicles and in sewage. It probably also occurs in domestic and wild animals.

30. **Corynebacterium parvum** Prévot, 1940. (*Corynebacterium parvum infectiosum* Mayer, Cent. f. Bakt., I Abt., Orig., *98*, 1926, 370; Prévot, Man. de Class. et Déterm. des Bactéries Anaérobies. Monographie, Inst. Past., Paris, 1940, 202.)

par′vum. L. adj. *parvus* small.

Small, slightly curved, club-shaped rods, usually 0.3 by 1.4 microns, occurring in pairs in which the cells are either parallel to each other or in an angular arrangement due to snapping division. Non-motile. Gram-positive.

Gelatin: No liquefaction.

Nutrient broth: Slightly turbid.

Carbohydrates generally not attacked; slight acid from glucose.

Neutral red not reduced.

Blood serum agar: Numerous, porcelain-white colonies.

Obligately anaerobic.

Pathogenic to white mice.

Serology: See Linzenmeier (Ann. Inst. Past., *87*, 1954, 572).

Source: Isolated from blood from a woman with a postnatal fever. Also found in various infections of the female urogenital organs.

Habitat: Found in female urogenital organs so far as known.

31. **Corynebacterium granulosum** Prévot, 1938. (Bacille granuleux, Jungano, Compt. rend. Soc. Biol., Paris, *66*, 1909, 123; Prévot, Ann. Inst. Past., *60*, 1938, 304.)

gra.nu.lo′sum. L. noun *granula* a little grain; L. adj. *granulosus* full of granules.

Slender, medium-sized rods resembling those of *Corynebacterium diphtheriae*. Non-motile. Show bipolar staining and metachromatic granules. Gram-positive.

Gas not produced in culture media.

Gelatin: No liquefaction.

Agar stab: Round colonies; no gas.

Glucose broth: Turbid; no gas.

Milk: Not coagulated.

Coagulated egg white: Not attacked.

Glucose and galactose are acidified.

Anaerobic.

Optimum temperature, 37° C.

Not pathogenic.

Serology: See Linzenmeier (Ann. Inst. Past., *87*, 1954, 572).

Source: Isolated from the intestines of white rats.

32. **Corynebacterium avidum** (Eggerth, 1935) Prévot, 1938. (*Bacteroides avidus* Eggerth, Jour. Bact., *30*, 1935, 289; Prévot, Ann. Inst. Past., *60*, 1938, 304.)

a′vi.dum. L. adj. *avidus* greedy, voracious.

Rods, 0.5 to 1.0 by 1.0 to 2.5 microns, with pointed or rounded ends, frequently slightly curved, occasionally branched. Non-motile. Gram-positive.

Gelatin liquefied.

Glucose agar colonies: 2 to 3 mm in diameter, raised, yellowish white, smooth.

Glucose broth: Turbid; acidified (final pH, 4.8).

Milk: Acid; coagulated; partially digested.

Indole production weak, if at all.

Hydrogen sulfide irregularly produced.

Acid and gas from glucose, fructose, galactose, sucrose, maltose, trehalose, melezitose, glycerol, mannitol, inositol, erythritol, adonitol, dextrin and starch. Lactose, raffinose, inulin and glucosamine slowly acidified (in 20 to 40 days). No acid or gas from xylose, rhamnose, arabinose, aesculin, amygdalin, salicin, cellobiose, dulcitol, mannitol, sorbitol, methyl glucoside or methyl mannoside.

Nitrites not produced from nitrates.

Coagulated egg albumen: Not digested away but becomes transparent.

Blood agar colonies: 2 to 3 mm in diameter, raised, yellowish white, smooth; no hemolysis.

Anaerobic.

Optimum temperature, 37° C.

Non-pathogenic for rabbits or white mice.

Linzenmeier (Ann. Inst. Past., *87*, 1954, 572) states that serologically *Corynebacterium avidum* is closely related to *C. acnes*.

Comments: Pederson (Jour. Bact., *50*, 1945, 478) secured a culture of this species from Eggerth and found that it ferments glucose with the production of higher fatty (mainly butyric) acids and lactic acid; he further states that this species appears to be closely related to *Butyribacterium rettgeri* Barker and Haas.

Source: Isolated from feces.

Habitat: From the human intestinal tract so far as known.

33. **Corynebacterium diphtheroides** Prévot, 1938. (Bacille diphtéroïde, Jungano, Compt. rend. Soc. Biol., Paris, *66*, 1909, 112; *Corynebacterium diphteroides* (sic) Prévot, Ann. Inst. Past., *60*, 1938, 304.)

diph.the.ro.i'des. Gr. noun *diphthera* leather, skin; M.L. fem.n. *diphtheria* diphtheria; Gr. *eidus* form, shape; M.L. adj. *diphtheroides* resembling diphtheria.

Medium-sized (0.3 to 0.4 by 3.0 to 4.0 microns), straight or curved, club-shaped rods resembling those of *Corynebacterium diphtheriae* and occurring singly, in pairs or in clumps or angularly arranged due to snapping division. Non-motile. Gram-positive.

Gelatin: No liquefaction.

Glucose agar stab: Colonies round; gas is produced.

Glucose broth: Turbid with the production of gas.

Milk: Not coagulated.

Indole is produced.

Acid and gas from glucose.

Non-proteolytic.

Anaerobic.

Optimum temperature, 37° C.

Non-pathogenic.

Serology: See Linzenmeier (Ann. Inst. Past., *87*, 1954, 572).

Source: Isolated from the intestine of a white rat. Also found in a case of fibrous osteitis (Beerens).

Habitat: Unknown except as stated above.

Genus II. **Listeria** *Pirie, 1940.**

(*Listerella* Pirie, Publ. So. African Inst. for Med. Res., *3*, 1927, 163; not *Listerella* Jahn, Ber. d. deutsch. Bot. Ges., *24*, 1906, 538; not *Listerella* Cushman, Contr. Cushman Lab. Foram., Sharon, Mass., *9*, 1933, 32; Pirie, Science, *91*, 1940, 383; also see Seeliger, Listeriosis. Beitr. z. Hyg. u. Epidemiol., Barth, Leipzig, Heft 8, 1955, 143 pp.)

Lis.te'ri.a. M.L. fem.n. *Listeria* named for Joseph Lister, an English surgeon and bacteriologist.

Small rods. Motile by means of peritrichous flagella. Gram-positive. Grow freely on ordinary media. Acid but no gas from glucose and a few additional carbohydrates. Esculin is hydrolyzed. Catalase-positive. Aerobic. Pathogenic parasites. Parasitic in warm-blooded animals.

The type species is *Listeria monocytogenes* (Murray et al.) Pirie.

---

* Revised by Prof E. G. D Murray, McGill University, Montreal, P.Q., Canada, June, 1955.

1. **Listeria monocytogenes** (Murray et al., 1926) Pirie, 1940. (*Bacterium monocytogenes* Murray, Webb and Swann, Jour. Path. and Bact., *29*, 1926, 407; Pirie, Science, *91*, 1940, 383.)

mo.no.cy.to'ge.nes. Gr. adj. *monus* alone, single; Gr. noun *cytus* a hollow, a vessel; M.L. noun *cytus* a cell; M.L. noun *monocytum* a blood cell, monocyte; Gr. v. *gennaio* to produce; M.L. adj. *monocytogenes* monocyte-producing.

Small rods, 0.4 to 0.5 by 0.5 to 2.0 microns, with rounded ends, slightly curved in some culture media, occurring singly and in V-shaped or parallel pairs. Motile by means of peritrichous flagella (Paterson, Jour. Path. and Bact., *48*, 1939, 25) at 2.5° C. to room temperatures with a tendency to reduced motility in time at 37° C. (Griffin, Jour. Bact., *48*, 1944, 114). Not acid-fast. Gram-positive.

Gelatin: Growth is confined to the needle track. No liquefaction.

In 0.25 per cent agar, 8.0 per cent gelatin, 1.0 per cent glucose semisolid medium, growth along the stab in 24 hours at 37° C. followed by irregular, cloudy extensions into the medium; growth spreads slowly through the entire medium. This is characteristic (Seastone, Jour. Exp. Med., *62*, 1935, 203).

Sheep liver extract agar colonies: Circular, smooth, butyrous, slightly flattened, transparent by transmitted and milky by reflected light.

Sheep liver extract agar slant: Confluent, flat, transparent, butyrous growth.

Peptone agar: Growth is thinner than on liver extract agar.

Blood agar: Improved growth with zone of hemolysis around colonies varying with the species of blood.

Peptone broth: Turbid; flocculent sediment.

Litmus milk: Slightly acid, decolorized. No coagulation.

Glycerol-potato: No apparent growth.

Inspissated ox serum: Grows as a very thin, transparent film.

Dorsett's egg medium: Very thin film.

Indole not produced.

Hydrogen sulfide not produced.

Acid but no gas from glucose, salicin and trehalose promptly, more slowly or variable from maltose, lactose, dextrin, sucrose, rhamnose, melezitose, soluble starch and glycerol. Tends to be negative on arabinose and galactose. No action on xylose, mannitol, dulcitol, inulin or inositol.

Esculin hydrolyzed in 24 hours (Sohier, Ann. Inst. Past., *74*, 1948, 57).

All cultures give off a penetrating, rather acid smell.

Nitrites not produced from nitrates.

Catalase-positive.

Aerobic, facultatively anaerobic.

Optimum temperature, 37° C.; grows at all temperatures down to 2.5° C. Thermal death point, 58° to 59° C. in 10 minutes. Survives eight weeks in 20 per cent NaCl at 4° C. (Wramby, Skandinavisk Vetinartidskriften, *34*, 1944, 279).

Animal inoculations: Intravenous or intraperitoneal injection of rabbits with cultures results in a very marked increase in monocytes circulating in the blood. This is the most striking character of the organism, and it is exhibited by strains derived from all sources. Monocytosis is induced by extracted chloroform-soluble lipid (Stanley, Australian Jour. Exp. Biol. and Med., *27*, 1949, 123). Infection is characterized by necrotic or granulomatous foci in various organs. Causes conjunctivo-keratitis when instilled into the conjunctiva of rabbits and guinea pigs (Anton, Zent. f. Bakt., I Abt., Orig., *131*, 1934, 89; also see Julianelle, Proc. Exp. Biol. and Med., *40*, 1939, 362); also produces this effect in the horse and hamster.

Serological characters: Paterson (Jour. Path. and Bact., *51*, 1940, 427) and Seeliger and Linzenmeier (Ztschr. f. Hyg., *136*, 1953, 335) conclude from studies of the flagellar and somatic antigens that four types may be recognized in this species; these do not bear any relation to the host species or to the geographical area from which they were isolated.

Relationships to other species: Possibly identical with *Bacterium hepatis* Hülphers (Sven. Vet. Tidskrift, *2*, 1911, 271) according to Nyfeldt (Sven. Vet. Tidskrift, *30*, 1940, 280). Further comparative studies are needed, however, before this can be determined definitely, as *Bacterium hepatis* does not ferment lactose, rhamnose, sucrose or salicin while it does ferment xylose. Failure to infect guinea pigs and chickens also indicates a possible difference between the two species. There may also be other species (Sohier, Benazet and Piéchaud, Ann. Inst. Past., *74*, 1948, 54).

Source and habitat: Isolated from lesions in organs, from meconium, and from blood and cerebrospinal fluid of man and at least twenty-six species of other mammals and

of birds, in all of which disease occurs. Many cases have proved fatal. Suggested as a cause of infectious mononucleosis in man by Anton, Nyfeldt and others (see Girard and Murray, Amer. Jour. Med. Sci., *221*, 1951, 343). "Granulomatosis infantiseptica" of Potel (Ztschr. f. Kinderheilk., *73*, 1953, 113; also see Wissensch. Ztschr. der Martin-Luther Univ., *3*, 1953, 341). Isolated from ferrets (Morris and Norman, Jour. Bact., *59*, 1950, 313) without apparent disease. In some species it causes metritis and abortion.

Genus III. **Erysipelothrix** *Rosenbach, 1909*.*

(Ztschr. f. Hyg., *63*, 1909, 367.)

E. ry.si.pe′lo.thrix. Gr. neut.n. *erysipelas* erysipelas; Gr. fem.n. *thrix* hair; M.L. fem.n. *Erysipelothrix* erysipelas thread.

Rod-shaped organisms with a tendency to form long filaments. The filaments may also thicken and show characteristic granules. Non-motile. Gram-positive, older cultures having a tendency to become Gram-negative. Acid but no gas from glucose and from certain other carbohydrates. Catalase-negative. Esculin not hydrolyzed. Facultatively anaerobic. Parasitic on mammals, birds and fish.

The type species is *Erysipelothrix insidiosa* (Trevisan) Langford and Hansen.

1. **Erysipelothrix insidiosa** (Trevisan, 1885) Langford and Hansen, 1953. (Bacillus der Septicämie bei Mäusen, Koch, Aetiologie der Wundinfektionskrankheiten, Leipzig, 1878, 43; *Bacillus insidiosus* Trevisan, Caratteri di alcuni nuovi generi di Batteriacee. Atti della Acad. Fisio-Medico-Statistica, Milano, Ser. 4, *3*, 1885, 100; Bacillus des Schweinerotlaufs, Loeffler, Arb. a. d. k. Gesundheitsamte, *1*, 1886, 46; *Erysipelothrix porci* Rosenbach, Ztschr. f. Hyg., *63*, 1909, 367; *Erysipelothrix Erysipeloides* (sic) Rosenbach, *loc. cit.*; *Erysipelothrix murisepticus* (sic) Rosenbach, *loc. cit.*; *Erysipelothrix rhusiopathiae* Winslow et al., Jour. Bact., *5*, 1920, 198; Langford and Hansen, Riassunti delle Comunicazioni, VI Congresso Internaz. di Microbiol., Roma, *1*, 1953, 18; also see Antonie van Leeuwenhoek, *20*, 1954, 87; and Atti del VI Congresso Internaz. di Microbiol., Roma, *1*, (1953) 1955, 21.)

in.si.di.o′sa. L. adj. *insidiosus* deceitful, dangerous.

Description taken in part from Langford

(Thesis, Univ. of Maryland, 1952) and Byrne, Connell, Frank and Moynihan (Can. Jour. Comp. Med. and Vet. Sc., *16*, 1952, 129).

Cells in smooth colonies are slender rods, 0.2 to 0.4 by 0.5 to 2.5 microns. Cells in rough and in some smooth colonies vary from short forms to long filamentous structures. Thick rods may be present singly, in chains or in entangled masses. Non-motile. Predominantly Gram-positive, although some Gram-negative cells may be found, particularly in old cultures or in unfavorable media.

Gelatin colonies: Hazy, bluish gray, racemose.

Gelatin stab: Filiform at first; most strains develop, in less than 48 hours, lateral, radiating projections resulting in the typical "test-tube brush" appearance. No spreading on the surface. No liquefaction.

Agar colonies: Pinpoint and transparent in 24 hours at 33° C. increasing to about 1.0 to 1.5 mm in 48 to 72 hours. Fully devel-

---

* Revised by Dr. G. C. Langford, University of Florida, Gainsville, Florida, U. S. A., and Prof. P. Arne Hansen, University of Maryland, College Park, Maryland, September, 1953.

oped colonies are transparent with a bluish sheen by reflected light, circular and entire.

Tellurite agar colonies: Grayish and pinpoint in 24 hours, later increasing in size and becoming jet black.

Broth: Slight turbidity with scant, grayish sediment.

Litmus milk: No change.

Indole not produced.

Hydrogen sulfide produced.

Blood serum shows scant growth.

No gas from carbohydrates.

Acid from glucose, galactose, fructose and lactose. When the basic medium is very favorable, acid may be produced from xylose, arabinose, mannose, maltose, cellobiose and melibiose. Usually no acid from glycerol, sorbitol, mannitol, inositol, rhamnose, sucrose, trehalose, melezitose, raffinose, starch, inulin or salicin. The addition of yeast autolysate to media for fermentation studies is recommended.

Esculin not hydrolyzed.

Final pH in yeast extract trypticase-glucose broth usually about 6.

Blood agar: On prolonged incubation there is at first a greening and then a slight but definite clearing around the colonies.

Nitrites not produced from nitrates.

Catalase-negative.

Facultatively anaerobic.

Temperature range of growth, 16° to 41° C. The fastest growth rate is at about 37° C. The maximum cell crop is obtained near 33° C.

Optimum pH, between 7.4 and 7.8.

Tolerates phenol in concentrations to 0.2 per cent and potassium tellurite in concentrations to 0.05 per cent.

Source: Isolated from cases of swine erysipelas, human erysipeloid and mouse septicemia; also isolated from infections in birds, e.g. turkeys and ducks. Transmissible to a large number of experimental animals: pigeons and mice are susceptible to experimental infection, but rabbits are less susceptible, and guinea pigs are quite resistant; inoculation in man has been successful; susceptibility of swine is very variable. Fish handlers are especially subject to erysipeloid infections derived from fish (Bedford and Leeds, Brit. Jour. Dermat. and Syph., *44*, 1932, 368; Niewiarowski, see Biol. Abst., *27*, 1953, No. 17069).

Habitat: This organism is widely distributed in nature as indicated above.

Genus IV. **Microbacterium** *Orla-Jensen, 1919.**

(The Lactic Acid Bacteria, 1919, 179.)

Mic.ro.bac.te′ri.um. Gr. adj. *micrus* small; Gr. neut.dim.n. *bacterium* a small rod; M.L. neut.n. *Microbacterium* a small rodlet.

Small rods with rounded ends; vary in length from 0.5 to 30 microns. Non-motile. Granulations demonstrable with methylene blue stain. Gram-positive. Good surface growth on media supplemented with milk or yeast extract. Acid production weak with principally L (+)- lactic acid produced from fermented carbohydrates. Catalase-positive. Optimum temperature, 32° C. Thermoduric saprophytes found chiefly in dairy products and on utensils.

The type species is *Microbacterium lacticum* Orla-Jensen.

Key to the species of genus **Microbacterium.**

I. Hydrolyzes starch; produces acid from maltose.
1. *Microbacterium lacticum.*
II. Does not hydrolyze starch; acid not produced from maltose.
2. *Microbacterium flavum.*

1. **Microbacterium lacticum** Orla-Jensen, 1919. (The Lactic Acid Bacteria, 1919, 179.)

lac′ti.cum. L. mas.n. *lac, lactis* milk; M.L. adj. *lacticus* pertaining to milk, lactic.

Small, diphtheroid rods, 0.4 to 0.7 by 1.0

* Revised by Dr. R. N. Doetsch, University of Maryland, College Park, Maryland, April, 1953.

to 2.0 microns, with rounded ends. Occasionally coccobacillary. Granulations demonstrable with methylene blue stain. Angular and pallisade arrangements of cell masses are typical. Non-motile. Gram-positive.

Gelatin stab: No liquefaction.

Milk agar: Surface colonies are smooth, convex, entire, pearl-gray and finely amorphous; 0.5 to 1.5 mm in diameter after 3 days at 32° C.

Agar slant: Pearl-gray to pale greenish yellow pigment. Grows as a thin butyrous film, occasionally firmly adherent.

Litmus milk weakly acid; occasionally acid coagulation.

Indole not produced.

Hydrogen sulfide not produced.

Acid but no gas from glucose, fructose, mannose, galactose, maltose and lactose. No acid from melibiose, glycerol or dulcitol.

Starch hydrolyzed.

Non-lipolytic.

Ammonia not produced from peptone or arginine.

Catalase-positive.

Survives 72° C. for 30 minutes in skim milk.

Comment: Doetsch and Rakosky (Proc. 50th Gen. Meeting Soc. Amer. Bact., Baltimore, 1950, 38) report a gelatin-liquefying variety of this species.

Source: Isolated from pasteurized milk, non-fat dry milk solids, cheese and dairy utensils.

2. **Microbacterium flavum** Orla-Jensen, 1919. (The Lactic Acid Bacteria, 1919, 181.)

fla'vum. L. adj. *flavus* yellow.

Rods, 0.7 to 0.9 by 1.0 to 3.0 microns, with rounded ends. Non-motile. Granulations demonstrable with methylene blue stain. Gram-positive.

Gelatin stab: No liquefaction.

Milk agar: Surface colonies are smooth, convex, entire, cream to canary-yellow; 2 to 3 mm in diameter after 3 days at 32° C.

Agar-slant: Cream to canary-yellow pigment. Growth moderate to heavy, butyrous but occasionally adherent.

Litmus milk: No change or slight reduction.

Indole not produced.

Hydrogen sulfide not produced.

Acid but no gas from glucose, fructose or mannose. No acid from maltose, lactose or dextrin.

Starch not hydrolyzed.

Non-lipolytic.

Ammonia not produced from peptone or arginine.

Catalase-positive.

Survives 72° C. for 15 minutes in skim milk.

Source: Isolated from cheese and butter. Under conditions used by several workers in recent extensive investigations, occurrence reported as rare.

Genus V. **Cellulomonas** *Bergey et al., 1923,* **emend.** *Clark, 1952.**

(Bergey et al., Manual, 1st ed., 1923, 154; Clark, Internat. Bull. Bact. Nomen. and Taxon., *2*, 1952, 50.)

Cel.lu.lo.mo'nas. M.L. noun *cellulosa* cellulose; Gr. noun *monas* a unit, monad; M.L. fem.n. *Cellulomonas* cellulose monad.

Small, pleomorphic rods, straight to angular or slightly curved with occasional beaded, clubbed, branched or coccoid cells, the number of such cells depending on the age and condition of the subculture. Motile by means of one or a few peritrichous flagella; some species are non-motile. If only a single flagellum is present, it is usually polar. Gram-variable. Growth on ordinary culture media often not vigorous; otherwise, growth on solid media usually soft and smooth and, in broth, turbid. Yellow, non-water-soluble pigmentation common; other pigments also occur. Gelatin slowly hydrolyzed. Catalase-positive. Acid but no gas from carbohydrates; cellulose commonly attacked. Typically of soil or plant origin.

The type species is *Cellulomonas biazotea* (Kellerman et al.) Bergey et al.

---

* Completely revised by Dr. Francis E. Clark, Agricultural Research Service, Soil Research Branch, U. S. Dept. Agr., Beltsville, Maryland, January, 1954.

Key to the species of genus **Cellulomonas.**

I. Motile by means of one or a few peritrichous flagella.
  A. Nitrites produced from nitrates.
    1. Xylose and arabinose not fermented.
      a. Ammonia not produced.
        b. Yellow chromogenesis on nutrient agar.
            1. *Cellulomonas biazotea.*
        bb. White, grayish or ivory growth on agar.
            2. *Cellulomonas cellasea.*
      aa. Ammonia produced.
        b. Yellow chromogenesis on nutrient agar.
            3. *Cellulomonas aurogena.*
        bb. Grayish white or ivory growth on agar.
            4. *Cellulomonas pusilla.*
    2. Xylose and arabinose fermented.
        5. *Cellulomonas fimi.*
  B. Nitrites not produced from nitrates.
    1. Yellow chromogenesis on nutrient agar.
        6. *Cellulomonas galba.*
    2. Grayish white or ivory growth on agar.
        7. *Cellulomonas gelida.*
II. Non-motile.
  A. Nitrites produced from nitrates.
    1. Yellow chromogenesis on nutrient agar.
        8. *Cellulomonas flavigena.*
    2. Grayish white or ivory growth on agar.
        9. *Cellulomonas uda.*
  B. Nitrites not produced from nitrates.
      10. *Cellulomonas acidula.*

1. Cellulomonas biazotea (Kellerman et al., 1913) Bergey et al., 1923. (*Bacillus biazoteus* Kellerman, McBeth, Scales and Smith, Cent. f. Bakt., II Abt., *39*, 1913, 506; Bergey et al., Manual, 1st ed., 1923, 158.)

bi.az.o′te.a. L. prefix *bi*-two; Gr. *azous* without life; Fr. noun *azote* nitrogen; M.L. adj. *biazoteus* denoting two nitrogen sources utilized (*i.e.*, organic and inorganic).

Small, angular rods 0.5 by 0.8 to 1.5 microns, occasionally branched, beaded, clubbed or curved. Motile by means of one or a few peritrichous flagella. Gram-variable, appearing most commonly as Gram-negative.

Gelatin agar: Gelatin hydrolyzed.

Gelatin stab: Slow, crateriform liquefaction in 10 days.

Agar slant: Moderate, smooth, opaque, yellow growth.

Broth: Uniformly turbid.

Filter paper in 0.5 per cent peptone broth:

Paper strip reduced to a pulpy mass or weakened sufficiently so that the fibers separate on slight agitation.

Potato: Smooth, yellow growth.

Acid from glucose, lactose, maltose, sucrose and glycerol; no acid from mannitol.

Acetylmethylcarbinol not produced.

Starch is hydrolyzed.

Nitrites produced from nitrates.

Ammonia not produced.

Aerobic, facultatively anaerobic.

Optimum temperature, between 28° and 33° C.

Source: Isolated from soil from Utah.

Habitat: Soil. Probably widely distributed in soil and in decomposing plant residues.

2. Cellulomonas cellasea (Kellerman et al., 1913) Bergey et al., 1923. (*Bacillus cellaseus* Kellerman, McBeth, Scales and Smith, Cent. f. Bakt., II Abt., *39*, 1913, 508;

Bergey et al., Manual, 1st ed., 1923, 158.)

cel.la'se.a. M.L. adj. *cellaseus* pertaining to cellulose.

Angular rods, 0.4 to 0.5 by 0.8 to 2.0 microns, occasionally clubbed, curved or branched. Motile by means of one or a few peritrichous flagella. Gram-variable, appearing most commonly as Gram-negative.

Gelatin agar: Gelatin hydrolyzed.

Gelatin stab: Very scant crateriform liquefaction in 10 days.

Agar slant: Moderate, smooth, glistening, white or ivory-colored growth; lacks deep yellow pigmentation.

Broth: Uniformly turbid.

Filter paper in 0.5 per cent peptone broth: Paper strip reduced to a pulpy mass or weakened sufficiently so that the fibers separate on slight agitation.

Potato: Smooth, opaque, cream-colored growth; freshly isolated strains may fail to grow on potato.

Acid from glucose, maltose, lactose, sucrose and starch; usually no acid from glycerol or mannitol.

Acetylmethylcarbinol not produced.

Starch is hydrolyzed.

Nitrites produced from nitrates.

Ammonia not produced.

Optimum temperature, between 28° and 33° C.

Source: Isolated from soil from Utah.

Habitat: Probably widely distributed in soil.

3. Cellulomonas aurogena (Kellerman et al., 1913) Bergey et al., 1923. (*Bacillus aurogenus* Kellerman, McBeth, Scales and Smith, Cent. f. Bakt., II Abt., *39*, 1913, 505; *Cellulomonas aurogenes* (sic) Bergey et al., Manual, 1st ed., 1923, 157.)

au.ro'ge.na. L. noun *aurum* gold; L. v. *gigno* to produce; M.L. adj. *aurogenus* gold (color)-producing.

Cells 0.5 by 1.4 microns. Motile by means of one to three peritrichous flagella. Gram-negative.

Gelatin stab: Slow liquefaction, usually not apparent until 7 to 10 days.

Agar slant: Scant to abundant, flat, yellow growth.

Cellulose agar: Variable enzymatic zones surround colonies.

Broth: Turbid.

Potato: Scant to abundant, yellow growth.

Acid from glucose, maltose, lactose, sucrose, starch and glycerol.

Nitrites produced from nitrates.

Ammonia produced.

Aerobic, facultatively anaerobic.

Optimum temperature, between 28° and 33° C.

Comment: A non-chromogenic variety of this species has been described by Kellerman et al. (Cent. f. Bakt., II Abt., *39*, 1913, 506).

Source: Isolated from soil from Louisiana and Maine.

Habitat: Soil.

4. Cellulomonas pusilla (Kellerman et al., 1913) Bergey et al., 1923. (*Bacillus pusilus* (sic) Kellerman, McBeth, Scales and Smith, Cent. f. Bakt., II Abt., *39*, 1913, 512; *Cellulomonas pusila* (sic) Bergey et al., Manual, 1st ed., 1923, 161.)

pu.sil'la. L. dim.adj. *pusillus* very small.

Cells 0.4 to 0.6 by 0.8 to 1.5 microns. Motile by means of one to three peritrichous flagella. Gram-negative.

Gelatin stab: Slow liquefaction, usually becoming apparent after 15 days.

Agar slant: Scant, grayish white growth.

Cellulose agar: Variable enzymatic zones around colonies.

Broth: Turbid.

Potato: Scant growth when heavily inoculated.

Acid from glucose, maltose, lactose, sucrose, starch and glycerol; no acid from mannitol.

Nitrites produced from nitrates.

Ammonia produced.

Aerobic, facultatively anaerobic.

Optimum temperature, between 28° and 33° C.

Source: Isolated from soil from the District of Columbia and from South Carolina.

Habitat: Soil.

5. Cellulomonas fimi (McBeth and Scales, 1913) Bergey et al., 1923. (*Bacterium fimi* McBeth and Scales, U. S. Dept. Agr. Plant Ind. Bull. 266, 1913, 30; *Cellulomonas fima* (sic) Bergey et al., Manual, 1st ed.,

1923, 166; *Corynebacterium fimi* Jensen, Proc. Linnean Soc. New So. Wales, *59*, 1934, 48.)

fi'mi. L. noun *fimus* dung; L. gen.noun *fimi* of dung.

Angular rods, 0.4 to 0.5 by 1.2 to 2.5 microns, occasionally clubbed, curved or branched. Feebly motile by means of one or a few peritrichous flagella. Gram-variable.

Gelatin agar: Gelatin hydrolyzed.

Gelatin stab: Slow, infundibuliform liquefaction.

Agar slant: Smooth, glistening, opaque, yellow growth.

Broth: Uniformly turbid; scant, soft, cream-colored to yellow sediment.

Filter paper in 0.5 per cent peptone broth: Paper strip reduced to a pulpy mass or weakened sufficiently so that the fibers separate on slight agitation.

Potato: Cream-colored to yellow growth.

Acid from glucose, fructose, arabinose, xylose, maltose, sucrose, lactose, raffinose, melezitose, dextrin, starch, salicin and glycerol; no acid from mannitol or dulcitol.

Acetylmethylcarbinol not produced.

Starch is hydrolyzed.

Nitrites usually produced from nitrates.

Ammonia production scant if at all.

Aerobic, facultatively anaerobic.

Optimum temperature, between 28° and 33° C.

Source: Isolated from soil.

Habitat: Soil.

6. Cellulomonas galba (Kellerman et al., 1913) Bergey et al., 1923. (*Bacillus galbus* Kellerman, McBeth, Scales and Smith, Cent. f. Bakt., II Abt., *39*, 1913, 509; Bergey et al., Manual, 1st ed., 1923, 157.)

gal'ba. L. adj. *galbus* yellow.

Cells 0.4 by 1.0 micron. Motile by means of one to three peritrichous flagella. Gram-positive.

Gelatin stab: Liquefaction slow, usually appearing only after 10 days.

Agar slant: Moderate, raised, canary-yellow growth.

Cellulose agar: Narrow enzymatic zone around colonies.

Broth: Turbid.

Potato: Scant yellow growth.

Acid from glucose, maltose, lactose, sucrose, starch and glycerol; no acid from mannitol.

Nitrites not produced from nitrates.

Aerobic, facultatively anaerobic.

Optimum temperature, between 28° and 33° C.

Source: Isolated from soil from Louisiana.

Habitat: Soil.

7. Cellulomonas gelida (Kellerman et al., 1913) Bergey et al., 1923. (*Bacillus gelidus* Kellerman, McBeth, Scales and Smith, Cent. f. Bakt., II Abt., *39*, 1913, 510; Bergey et al., Manual, 1st ed., 1923, 162.)

ge'li.da. L. adj. *gelidus* cold.

Small, angular rods, 0.4 to 0.6 by 0.8 to 2.0 microns, sometimes curved, clubbed or branched. Motile by means of one or a few peritrichous flagella. Gram-variable.

Gelatin agar: Gelatin hydrolyzed.

Gelatin stab: Liquefaction very slow if at all.

Agar slant: Moderate, flat, grayish white growth.

Broth: Uniformly turbid.

Filter paper in 0.5 per cent peptone broth: Paper strip reduced to a pulpy mass or weakened sufficiently so that the fibers separate on slight agitation.

Potato: Good growth.

Acid from glucose, maltose, lactose, sucrose, starch and glycerol; no acid from mannitol.

Acetylmethylcarbinol not produced.

Starch is hydrolyzed.

Nitrites not produced from nitrates.

Ammonia occasionally produced.

Aerobic, facultatively anaerobic.

Optimum temperature, between 28° and 33° C.

Source: Isolated from soil from Connecticut.

Habitat: Soil.

8. Cellulomonas flavigena (Kellerman and McBeth, 1912) Bergey et al., 1923. (*Bacillus flavigena* (sic) Kellerman and McBeth, Cent. f. Bakt., II Abt., *34*, 1912, 488; Bergey et al., Manual, 1st ed., 1923, 165.)

fla.vi'ge.na. L. noun *flavus* yellow; L. v. *gigno* to produce; M.L. adj. *flavigenus* yellow-producing.

Angular rods, 0.4 to 0.6 by 0.7 to 1.8 microns, occasionally curved, clubbed or branched. Non-motile. Gram-variable.

Gelatin agar: Gelatin hydrolyzed.

Gelatin stab: Slow liquefaction.

Agar slant: Smooth, glistening, opaque, yellow growth.

Broth: Uniformly turbid.

Filter paper in 0.5 per cent peptone broth: Paper strip reduced to a pulpy mass or weakened sufficiently so that the fibers separate on slight agitation.

Potato: Smooth, creamy yellow growth.

Acid from glucose, lactose, sucrose, maltose and starch.

Acetylmethylcarbinol not produced.

Starch is hydrolyzed.

Nitrites produced from nitrates.

Ammonia not produced.

Aerobic, facultatively anaerobic.

Optimum temperature, between 28° and 33° C.

Source: Isolated from a mixed culture and from soil.

Habitat: Widely distributed in soil.

9. **Cellulomonas uda** (Kellerman et al., 1913) Bergey et al., 1923. (*Bacterium udum* Kellerman, McBeth, Scales and Smith, Cent. f. Bakt., II Abt., *39*, 1913, 514; Bergey et al., Manual, 1st ed., 1923, 166.)

u'da. L. adj. *udus* moist, wet.

Cells 0.5 by 1.0 to 1.5 microns. Non-motile. Gram-negative.

Gelatin agar: Gelatin hydrolyzed.

Gelatin stab: Slow liquefaction.

Agar slant: Moderate, flat, grayish white growth.

Broth: Uniformly turbid.

Filter paper in 0.5 per cent peptone broth:

Paper strip reduced to a pulpy mass or weakened sufficiently so that the fibers separate on slight agitation.

Potato: Good growth.

Acid from glucose, fructose, maltose, lactose, sucrose and starch; acid production variable with xylose and arabinose.

Acetylmethylcarbinol not produced.

Starch is hydrolyzed.

Nitrites produced from nitrates.

Aerobic, facultatively anaerobic.

Optimum temperature, between 28° and 33° C.

Source: Isolated from compost from Virginia.

Habitat: Soil.

10. **Cellulomonas acidula** (Kellerman et al., 1913) Bergey et al., 1923. (*Bacterium acidulum* Kellerman, McBeth, Scales and Smith, Cent. f. Bakt., II Abt., *39*, 1913, 513; Bergey et al., Manual, 1st ed., 1923, 167.)

a.ci'du.la. L. dim.adj. *acidulus* somewhat sour.

Cells 0.3 to 0.4 by 1.0 to 1.3 microns. Non-motile. Gram-negative.

Gelatin stab: Growth scant; liquefaction usually not apparent.

Agar slant: Slight to moderate or abundant grayish growth.

Cellulose agar: Variable enzymatic zones around colonies.

Broth: Slightly turbid.

Potato: No apparent growth.

Acid from glucose; other sugars weakly or variably fermented.

Nitrites not produced from nitrates.

Ammonia not produced.

Aerobic, facultatively anaerobic.

Optimum temperature, between 28° and 33° C.

Source: Isolated from soil from Utah.

Habitat: Soil.

Genus VI. **Arthrobacter** *Conn and Dimmick, 1947.**

(Jour. Bact., *54*, 1947, 300.)

Ar.thro.bac'ter. Gr. noun *arthrus* a joint; M.L. mas.n. *bacter* the masculine equivalent of the Gr. neut.n. *bactrum* a rod; M.L. mas.n. *Arthrobacter* a jointed rod.

Buchanan, Cowan and Wikén (Internat. Bull. Bact. Nomen. and Taxon., *5*, 1955, 83)

---

* Prepared by Dr. A. G. Lochhead, Department of Agriculture, Ottawa, Canada, July, 1954.

regard *Arthrobacter* Fischer (Jahrb. f. wissen. Bot., *27*, 1895, 141) as a *nomen dubium*, no species having been named as belonging to the genus by Fischer. Under these circumstances *Arthrobacter* Fischer would appear to be illegitimate. Conn and Dimmick (*op. cit.*, 1947, 300) revived Fischer's name for the organisms they describe as they feel it to be an appropriate name. Fischer defined *Arthrobacter* as including all non-flagellate, rod-shaped bacteria which produce "arthrospores" as recognized by De Bary. While the real meaning of arthrospores is somewhat uncertain, it sometimes has been used for the coccoid bodies developed by the species placed in *Arthrobacter* as defined here.

In young cultures the cells appear as rods which may vary in size and shape from straight to bent, curved, swollen or club-shaped forms; snapping division may show angular cell arrangement. Short filament formation with rudimentary budding may occur, especially in richer liquid media. Gram-negative or Gram-variable. Coccoid cells are characteristically observed in cultures after one or more days; these coccoid cells persist as the predominant form in older cultures and are Gram-negative to Gram-positive. Larger coccoid cells (cystites), which give rise to one or more rod-shaped cells on fresh transfer, also occur. Generally non-motile. Growth on solid media soft or viscous; growth in liquid media generally not profuse. Most species liquefy gelatin. Little or no acid from carbohydrates. Nitrites generally produced from nitrates. Indole not produced. Aerobic. Most species show little or no growth at 37°C. Typically soil organisms.

The type species is *Arthrobacter globiformis* (Conn) Conn and Dimmick.

Key to the species of genus **Arthrobacter.**

I. Utilize nitrates or ammonium salts as a sole source of nitrogen; utilize citrate as a sole organic nutrient.
   A. Non-chromogenic.
      1. Starch hydrolyzed; little or no growth at 37° C.
         a. Growth not viscous in liquid or on solid media; moderate growth on asparagine agar.
                   1. *Arthrobacter globiformis.*
         aa. Growth viscous in most liquid or solid media; profuse growth on asparagine agar.
                   2. *Arthrobacter pascens.*
      2. Starch not hydrolyzed; grows well at 37° C.
                   3. *Arthrobacter simplex.*
   B. Chromogenic.
      1. Starch hydrolyzed; nitrites produced from nitrates.
         a. Grows profusely on nicotine agar producing a diffusible blue pigment; some strains produce yellow pigment on plain agar.
                   4. *Arthrobacter oxydans.*
         aa. Poor growth on nicotine agar, and no blue pigment is produced; yellow pigment on plain agar.
                   5. *Arthrobacter aurescens.*
      2. Starch not hydrolyzed; nitrites not produced from nitrates; yellow pigment on plain agar.
                   6. *Arthrobacter ureafaciens.*
II. Do not utilize nitrates or ammonium salts as a sole source of nitrogen; citrates not utilized.
   A. Non-chromogenic; weak diastatic action; agar colonies punctiform.
                   7. *Arthrobacter tumescens.*
   B. Chromogenic; no diastatic action; agar colonies 1 to 2 mm in diameter.
      1. Yellow pigment produced on plain agar; gelatin liquefied; grows at 10° C.
                   8. *Arthrobacter citreus.*

2. No growth on plain agar; brownish yellow pigment produced on soil-extract agar; gelatin not liquefied; no growth at 10° C.

9. *Arthrobacter terregens.*

1. Arthrobacter globiformis (Conn, 1928) Conn and Dimmick, 1947. (*Bacterium globiforme* Conn, New York Agr. Exp. Sta. Tech. Bull. 138, 1928, 3; also see Conn and Darrow, *ibid.*, 172, 1930, 3; *Arthrobacter globiforme* (sic) Conn and Dimmick, Jour. Bact., *54*, 1947, 295, Fig. 1, and 301.)

glo.bi.for'mis. L. noun *globus* ball, globe; L. noun *forma* shape; M.L. adj. *globiformis* spherical.

Rods, irregular in shape and size, generally 0.5 to 0.7 by 1.0 to 3.0 microns, occurring in an angular arrangement. Cells may be curved, slightly bent or, frequently, swollen; rudimentary branching may occur in liquid media. Coccoid cells, 0.6 to 0.8 micron in diameter, develop in older cultures; larger coccoid cells (cystites) occur which give rise to rod forms by germination on transfer to fresh media. Non-motile. Gram-negative in young cultures; coccoid forms prevailingly Gram-positive.

Gelatin stab: Slow crateriform liquefaction, becoming stratiform; liquid clear; abundant sediment.

Agar colonies: Circular, up to 1.5 mm in diameter, slightly raised, cream-colored, waxy luster.

Agar slant: Growth filiform, flat, smooth, cream-colored, soft glistening with metallic sheen.

Soil extract agar slant: Growth filiform, flat, pale cream-colored, surface slightly rippled, soft, translucent, glistening, no sheen, lobate edge.

Asparagine agar slant: Filiform, flat, smooth, whitish, dull, soft.

Broth: Slightly turbid; little or no surface growth; slight sediment.

Potato: Growth abundant, pale brown, glistening, soft.

Milk: Slow clearing (2 to 3 weeks) without coagulation; alkaline.

Indole not produced.

Hydrogen sulfide produced in small amounts in cysteine medium.

Slight acid but no gas from glucose, sucrose, mannitol and arabinose; no acid or gas from lactose or glycerol.

Acetylmethylcarbinol not produced.

Starch is hydrolyzed.

Nitrites produced from nitrates.

Urease not produced.

Utilizes nitrates and ammonium salts as nitrogen sources; citrates utilized as sole source of carbon.

Of 19 amino acids tested, none was required for growth; preformed growth factors also were not required (Campbell and Williams, Food Research, *16*, 1951, 506).

Ammonium chloride and the 19 amino acids which were tested may serve as sources of nitrogen; the amino acids may also be utilized as carbon sources (Campbell and Williams, *loc. cit.*).

Inorganic sulfur may serve as a source of sulfur (Campbell and Williams, *loc. cit.*).

Catalase-positive.

Aerobic.

Temperature relations: Optimum, about 25° C.; good growth from 20° to 32° C.; slight growth at 10° C.; no growth at 37° C.

Source: Isolated from soil.

Habitat: Widely distributed in soil.

2. Arthrobacter pascens Lochhead and Burton, 1953. (Can. Jour. Botany, *31*, 1953, 7.)

pas'cens. L. part.adj. *pascens* nourishing.

Rods, generally 0.6 to 0.8 by 1.0 to 4.0 microns, occurring in an angular arrangement as a result of snapping division. The cells vary in size and shape according to the culture medium: irregular forms, curved, swollen or club-shaped, may be noted as well as a tendency to form short filaments with rudimentary budding, especially in liquid media. Coccoid cells occur by the process of fragmentation, usually within two days. On solid media the cocci are 0.5 to 0.7 micron in diameter, and 0.7 to 0.9 microns in diameter in semisolid or liquid media. On fresh transfer, the large coccoid cells (cystites) germinate and give rise to two or more rod forms. Non-motile. Gram-negative.

Gelatin stab: White, viscous surface growth followed by slow liquefaction which becomes stratiform; liquid flaky; abundant sediment.

Agar colonies: Circular, entire, creamy white, glistening, translucent, viscous.

Agar slant: Growth filiform, flat, smooth, viscous, cream-colored, glistening with a copper sheen.

Soil extract agar slant: Growth filiform, flat, smooth, cream-colored, glistening, slightly metallic, soft.

Asparagine agar: Abundant, filiform, cream-colored, very viscous growth; edge wrinkled, surface smooth and glistening.

Broth: Moderately turbid; no surface growth; whitish, viscous sediment.

Potato: Pale brown, glistening, viscous.

Milk: Slow clearing after 1 week without coagulation; abundant, white surface growth; reaction becoming alkaline.

Indole not produced.

Hydrogen sulfide produced in cysteine medium.

Slight acid but no gas from glucose and sucrose.

Acetylmethylcarbinol not produced.

Starch is hydrolyzed.

Nitrites produced from nitrates.

Urease not produced.

Utilizes nitrates and ammonium salts as nitrogen sources; citrates utilized as sole source of carbon.

Catalase-positive.

Aerobic, facultatively anaerobic.

Temperature relations: Optimum, between 20° C. and 26° C.; growth range, 10° to 35° C.; no growth at 37° C.

Source: Isolated from soil.

Habitat: Soil.

3. **Arthrobacter simplex** (Jensen, 1934) Lochhead, *comb. nov.* (*Corynebacterium simplex* Jensen, Proc. Linn. Soc. New So. Wales, *59*, 1934, 43.)

sim'plex. L. adj. *simplex* simple.

Rods which vary in size with the culture medium, generally 0.4 to 0.5 by 1.0 to 3.0 microns; occasionally cells may attain a length of 6.0 microns. In older cultures the cells are shorter and become very small rods or cocci, measuring 0.4 to 0.5 by 0.5 to 0.8 micron. Though curved or swollen rods generally tend to be inconsistent in form, the tendency is less pronounced with this species. Generally non-motile; motile strains have been reported (Clark and Carr, Jour. Bact., *62*, 1951, 3 and 4). Gram-variable; coccoid cells are Gram-variable with a predominance of Gram-positive cells.

Gelatin stab: Saccate liquefaction (2 to 4 days) becoming stratiform; slight surface growth; considerable sediment; liquid clear.

Agar colonies: Circular, 1.0 to 1.5 mm in diameter, slightly raised, cream-colored, smooth, glistening.

Agar slant: Growth filiform, cream-colored, smooth, glistening, soft; lobate edge.

Soil extract agar slant: Growth filiform, flat, pale cream-colored, smooth, glistening, translucent, soft.

Asparagine agar slant: Growth filiform, flat, pale cream-colored, smooth, glistening, soft.

Broth: Moderately turbid; no surface growth; moderate, stringy sediment.

Potato: Growth abundant, light brown, moist, glistening, membranous.

Milk: Slow clearing (7 to 10 days) without coagulation, becoming alkaline.

Indole not produced.

Hydrogen sulfide produced in cysteine and thiosulfate media.

Sugar media: Slight alkaline reaction; no gas produced.

Acetylmethylcarbinol not produced.

Starch not hydrolyzed.

Nitrites produced from nitrates.

Urease not produced.

Utilizes nitrates and ammonium salts as nitrogen sources; citrates utilized as sole carbon source.

Catalase-positive.

Aerobic.

Temperature relations: Optimum, between 26° and 37° C.; no growth at 10° or 45° C.

Source: Isolated from Australian soil.

Habitat: Soil.

4. **Arthrobacter oxydans** Sguros, 1954. (Proc. 54th Gen. Meeting, Soc. Amer. Bact., Pittsburgh, 1954, 21.)

ox'y.dans. Gr. adj. *oxys* sharp; M.L. adj. *oxydans* oxidizing.

Complete description furnished by Dr. P. L. Sguros.

Rods, 0.5 to 1.0 by 1.0 to 4.0 microns, which may be curved or club-shaped; occasionally rudimentary filamentous forms may occur, although branching is infrequent. The longer forms fragment into short rods and cocci. Cells in older cultures are almost exclusively coccoid and vary from 1.0 to 3.0 microns in diameter. When transferred to fresh media, the larger coccoid cells (cystites) germinate, giving rise to one or two rod-shaped cells (Sguros, Jour. Bact., *69*, 1955, 28). Non-motile. Gram-negative; the cystites are Gram-negative and usually possess a Gram-positive granule.

Gelatin stab: Slow, crateriform liquefaction.

Agar colonies: Punctiform or circular, convex, opaque, smooth, glistening; viscid or butyrous varieties may occur.

Agar slant: Growth abundant, filiform, opaque, smooth, glistening; yellow and pearl-gray strains occur, the former being viscid and the latter butyrous in consistency.

Asparagine agar: Growth filiform, opaque, smooth, glistening; development of chromogenesis retarded.

Nicotine agar: Abundant growth with the production of a diffusible, deep blue pigment which turns reddish to yellowish brown with age.

Broth: Abundant growth; surface ring; viscid sediment.

Potato: Abundant growth, yellow to gray varying with the strain.

Milk: Slow peptonization and reduction of litmus; reaction alkaline.

Indole not produced.

Hydrogen sulfide not produced.

Acid but no gas from fructose and sucrose; acid in glucose broth weak and transient; with other carbohydrates, reaction alkaline.

Acetylmethylcarbinol not produced.

Starch is hydrolyzed.

Nitrites produced from nitrates.

Utilizes nitrates and ammonium salts as nitrogen sources; citrates utilized as sole source of carbon.

Catalase-positive.

Aerobic.

Optimum temperature, 25° C.

Comment: Yellow-viscid and pearl-white-butyrous biotypes of this species have been recognized (Sguros, *loc. cit.*).

Source: Isolated from tobacco leaves.

Habitat: Probably soil.

5. Arthrobacter aurescens (Clark, 1951) Phillips, 1953. (*Arthrobacter globiforme* var. *aurescens* Clark, Proc. Soil Sci. Soc. Amer., *15*, 1951, 180; Phillips, Iowa State Coll. Jour. Sci., *27*, 1953, 240.)

au.res'cens. L. v. *auresco* to become golden; L. part.adj. *aurescens* becoming golden.

Rods which vary in shape and size according to the nature of the culture medium: 0.5 by 1.0 to 3.0 microns on plain agar and 0.6 to 0.8 by 1.0 to 6.0 microns on enriched solid media; the cells may be straight, curved or swollen or may show rudimentary branching, especially in enriched liquid media. In older cultures the cells become coccoid, measuring 0.6 micron in diameter. Non-motile. Gram-variable; the cocci are generally Gram-negative although the larger coccoids (cystites) are usually Gram-positive.

Gelatin stab: Stratiform liquefaction; yellowish surface growth; moderate sediment; liquid very turbid.

Agar colonies: Circular, up to 2 mm in diameter, convex, yellow, opaque, smooth, glistening.

Agar slant: Growth abundant, filiform, opaque, smooth, creamy lemon-yellow, soft, waxy luster with a metallic sheen.

Soil-extract agar slant: Growth filiform, smooth, cream-colored becoming pale yellow, glistening, soft.

Asparagine agar slant: Growth filiform, lemon-yellow, soft, waxy luster; surface uneven; edge finely indented.

Nicotine agar: Growth slow and sparse, flat, translucent, colorless.

Broth: Moderately turbid; no surface growth; considerable cream-colored sediment.

Potato: Growth moderate, brownish yellow, dull, cheesy in consistency.

Milk: Pale yellow surface and ring growth; clearing (3 to 4 days) without coagulation; cream-colored sediment.

Indole not produced.

Hydrogen sulfide produced in cysteine and thiosulfate media.

Sugar media: Very slight acidity from glucose and sucrose; no gas from carbohydrates.

Acetylmethylcarbinol not produced.

Starch is hydrolyzed.

Nitrites produced from nitrates.

Urease not produced.

Utilizes nitrates and ammonium salts as nitrogen sources; citrates utilized as sole carbon source.

Catalase-positive.

Aerobic, facultatively anaerobic.

Temperature relations: Optimum, between 20° and 32° C.; slight growth at 10° and at 37° C.; no growth at 45° C.

Source: Isolated from soil by Conn and Dimmick (Soil Sci., *65*, 1948, 349). Cultures of yellow forms were labelled *Arthrobacter aurescens* and were distributed to other investigators under this name.

Habitat: Soil.

6. Arthrobacter ureafaciens (Krebs and Eggleston, 1939) Clark, 1955. (Culture NC, Dubos and Miller, Jour. Biol. Chem., *121*, 1937, 431; Krebs and Eggleston, Enzymologia, *7*, 1939, 310; *Corynebacterium creatinovorans*, name used by Dubos on Culture NC (ATCC No. 7562) as sent to Amer. Type Culture Coll., December, 1941, and used in the Catalogue of Cultures, 1949, and later in the literature by various authors such as Kalinsky, Proc. Soc. Exp. Biol. and Med., *74*, 1950, 767, and Barron, Ardac and Hearson, Arch. Biochem., *29*, 1950, 130; Clark, Internat. Bull. of Bact. Nomen. and Taxon., *5*, 1955, 111; also see Bact. Rev., *19*, 1955, 273.)

u.re.a.fa′ci.ens. Gr. noun *urum* urine; M.L. noun *urea* urea; L. v. *facio* to make, produce; M.L. part.adj. *ureafaciens* urea-producing.

Rods which vary in shape and size according to the nature of the culture medium: in young cultures, 0.5 by 1.0 to 3.0 microns on plain agar and 0.7 by 2.0 to 7.0 microns on richer media; the cells are irregular and may be curved, bent or swollen. In older cultures the cells are cocci and coccoid rods, measuring 0.6 by 0.8 micron. Non-motile. The rods and cocci are Gram-negative.

Gelatin stab: Stratiform liquefaction; cream-colored surface growth; liquid slightly turbid and flaky. Sediment is abundant.

Agar colonies: Circular, 1.5 to 2.0 mm in diameter, convex, yellow, smooth, glistening.

Agar slant: Growth moderate, filiform, yellow, glistening with a metallic sheen, soft; surface uneven, becoming wrinkled.

Soil-extract agar slant: Growth filiform, pale gray becoming yellow, glistening, soft; surface uneven; edge finely wrinkled.

Asparagine agar slant: Growth filiform, lemon-yellow, glistening, soft; surface uneven; edge becoming wrinkled.

Broth: Moderately turbid; no surface growth; cream-colored sediment.

Potato: Growth moderate, raised, yellowish brown, dull, cheesy in consistency.

Milk: Flaky, yellowish surface growth; clearing without coagulation; cream-colored sediment.

Indole not produced.

Hydrogen sulfide produced in cysteine media.

Sugar media: Little or no acidity; no gas.

Acetylmethylcarbinol not produced.

Starch is not hydrolyzed.

Nitrites not produced from nitrates.

Urea produced from creatine, creatinine and uric acid.

Urease not produced.

Utilizes nitrates and ammonium salts as nitrogen sources.

Catalase-positive.

Aerobic.

Temperature relations: Optimum, 32° C. No growth at 10° or at 45° C. Good growth between 25° and 37° C.

Source: Isolated from soil.

Habitat: Soil.

7. Arthrobacter tumescens (Jensen, 1934) Conn and Dimmick, 1947. (*Corynebacterium tumescens* Jensen, Proc. Linn. Soc. New So. Wales, *59*, 1934, 45; Conn and Dimmick, Jour. Bact., *54*, 1947, 295, Fig. 3, and 302.)

tu.mes′cens. L. part.adj. *tumescens* swelling up.

Rods, 0.5 to 0.8 by 2.0 to 6.0 microns, occurring in an angular arrangement and showing pronounced cytomorphosis. The cells are curved or swollen and often possess rudimentary branches as well as deeply staining granules. Older cultures contain many small cocci, 0.5 to 0.6 micron in diameter, which arise from the fragmentation of the longer rods. After two to three days, many spherical cells (cystites), up to 3.0 microns in diameter, occur from which one to four rod forms may arise by germination. Non-motile. Gram-negative with Gram-positive granules; coccoid forms are Gram-negative to Gram-positive.

Gelatin stab: Saccate liquefaction (4 to 5 days), becoming stratiform; cream-colored surface growth and sediment; liquid finely flocculent.

Agar colonies: Punctiform, grayish cream-colored, flat, translucent.

Agar slant: Growth scant, filiform, flat, grayish cream-colored, translucent.

Soil extract agar slant: Growth moderate, filiform, whitish, opaque, dull, soft.

Asparagine agar slant: Growth scant, filiform, thin, flat, colorless.

Broth: Slightly turbid; no surface growth; slight sediment; faintly acid.

Potato: Growth abundant, pale brown, glistening, membranous.

Milk: Soft coagulation (10 to 12 days) followed by slow digestion; no change in reaction.

Indole not produced.

Hydrogen sulfide not produced.

Slight or no acid produced in sugar broth; no gas produced.

Acetylmethylcarbinol not produced.

Starch weakly hydrolyzed.

Nitrites produced from nitrates.

Urease not produced.

Unable to utilize nitrates or ammonium salts as nitrogen source, or citrates as sole carbon source.

Catalase-negative.

Aerobic.

Optimum temperature, between 30° and 32° C.; poor growth at 20° and 37° C.; no growth at 10° C.

Source: Isolated from Australian soils.

Habitat: Soil.

8. **Arthrobacter citreus** Sacks, 1954. (Jour. Bact., *67*, 1954, 342.)

cit′re.us. L. adj. *citreus* pertaining to the citrus tree; M.L. adj. *citreus* lemon-colored.

Rods, usually 0.8 by 2.0 to 5.0 microns, which occur in V-shaped pairs as a result of snapping division. The individual cells are irregular, curved or swollen and show a slight tendency to branch. The rods rapidly undergo fragmentation, usually within 24 hours, to give rise to forms indistinguishable from true cocci; these forms measure 0.7 micron in diameter. Feebly motile. Gram-variable.

Gelatin stab: Slow, crateriform liquefaction, becoming stratiform; moderate surface growth; considerable yellowish sediment; liquid turbid.

Agar colonies: Circular, entire, low convex, lemon-yellow, glistening.

Agar slant: Growth abundant, filiform, flat, lemon-yellow, smooth, glistening, soft.

Soil extract agar slant: Growth moderate, filiform, flat, yellow, glistening, soft; surface has a fine "ground glass" appearance.

Asparagine agar: Growth scant, filiform, thin, colorless.

Broth: Slightly turbid; no surface growth; slight sediment; reaction unchanged.

Potato: Growth scant, slightly raised, dull, yellow.

Milk: No change.

Indole not produced.

Hydrogen sulfide not produced.

Little or no acid produced from carbohydrates.

Acetylmethylcarbinol not produced.

Starch not hydrolyzed.

Nitrites produced from nitrates.

Urease not produced.

Unable to utilize nitrates or ammonium salts as nitrogen source, or citrates as sole carbon source.

Catalase-positive.

Aerobic.

Optimum temperature, between 25° and 30° C.; grows well at 20° to 32° C.; fair growth at 10° but little or none at 37° C.

Source: Isolated from chicken feces.

Habitat: Soil.

9. **Arthrobacter terregens** Lochhead and Burton, 1953. (Can. Jour. Botany, *31*, 1953, 7.)

ter're.gens. L. noun *terra* soil; L. part.adj. *egens* requiring; M.L. part.adj. *terregens* soil-requiring.

Rods, 0.6 to 0.8 by 1.0 to 5.0 microns, usually occurring in V-shaped pairs as a result of snapping division. The cells vary in shape from short, straight rods to irregular, curved or swollen forms; some of the longer rods show rudimentary budding. In older cultures (usually after 3 days), coccoid cells, formed by the fragmentation of long rods, predominate. The cocci vary in size according to the medium: on soil extract agar the cells measure 0.6 to 0.7 micron, and on richer media containing yeast extract, they are 0.8 to 0.9 micron in diameter. When freshly transferred, the larger coccoids (cystites) may germinate rod forms, up to three in number. Gram-negative; the coccoid cells are Gram-variable, usually Gram-negative.

Requires a growth factor, 'terregens factor' (TF), present in soil extract or in culture filtrates of *Arthrobacter pascens*. No growth in standard media; these may be rendered suitable for growth by addition of soil extract or culture filtrate of *A. pascens*.

Gelatin stab: Yellowish growth, best at surface; no liquefaction.

Agar colonies: Circular, 1.0 to 2.5 mm in diameter, entire, convex, yellowish brown, glistening.

Agar slant: Growth filiform, flat, pale brown, glistening.

Soil extract agar slant: Growth filiform, flat, yellowish brown, glistening, soft; surface finely roughened.

Broth: Moderately turbid; no surface growth; stringy, yellowish sediment.

Potato: Slight or no growth.

Milk: No change after 6 weeks.

Indole not produced.

Hydrogen sulfide not produced.

Slight acid from glucose and sucrose; trace or no acid from other sugars; no gas produced.

Acetylmethylcarbinol not produced.

Starch not hydrolyzed.

Nitrites produced from nitrates.

Urease not produced.

Unable to utilize nitrates or ammonium salts as nitrogen source, or citrates as sole carbon source, even in presence of growth factor.

Catalase-positive.

Aerobic.

Optimum temperature, between 20° and 26° C.; grows from 15° to 35° C.; no growth at 10° or 37° C.

Source: Isolated from soil.

Habitat: Soil.

FAMILY XIII. BACILLACEAE FISCHER, 1895.

(Jahrb. f. wiss. Bot., *27*, 1895, 139.)

Ba.cil.la'ce.ae. M.L. noun *Bacillus* type genus of the family; *-aceae* ending to denote a family; M.L. fem.pl.n. *Bacillaceae* the *Bacillus* family.

Rod-shaped cells capable of producing endospores which are cylindrical, ellipsoidal or spherical, and which are located in the center of the cell, subterminally or terminally. Sporangia do not differ from the vegetative cells except when bulged by spores larger than the cell diameter; such sporangia are spindle-shaped when spores are central and wedge- or drumstick-shaped when spores are terminal. Motile by means of peritrichous flagella or non-motile. Usually Gram-positive. Pigment formation is rare. Gelatin is frequently hydrolyzed. Sugars are generally fermented, sometimes with the production of visible gas. Aerobic, facultatively anaerobic; anaerobic; or anaerobic, aerotolerant. Some species are capable of growth at 55° C. Mostly saprophytes, commonly found in soil; a few are animal or insect parasites or pathogens.

Key to the genera of family **Bacillaceae.**

I. Aerobic or facultatively anaerobic; catalase-positive.
>Genus I. *Bacillus*, p. 613.

II. Anaerobic or aerotolerant; catalase not known to be produced.
>Genus II. *Clostridium*, p. 634.

Genus I. **Bacillus Cohn, 1872.***

(Beiträge z. Biol. d. Pflanzen, *1*, Heft 2, 1872, 146 and 175.)

Ba.cil'lus. L. dim.noun *bacillum* a small rod; M.L. noun *Bacillus* a rodlet.

Rod-shaped cells, sometimes in chains, capable of producing endospores. Sporangia do not differ from the vegetative cells except when bulged by spores larger than the cell diameter; such sporangia are spindle-shaped when the spores are central and wedge- or drumstick-shaped when the spores are terminal. Motile by means of peritrichous flagella or non-motile. Gram-positive, some species being Gram-variable or Gram-negative. Some species usually occur in the rough stage, forming a pellicle on broth, whereas other species are smooth and the rough stage is rarely seen. Usually proteins are decomposed with the production of ammonia. Carbohydrates are generally fermented with the production of more or less acidity; a few also produce visible gas. Catalase-positive. Aerobic or facultatively anaerobic. Maximum temperatures for growth vary greatly, not only between species but also between strains of the same species. Variations in other characters frequently occur within a species. Mostly saprophytes, commonly found in soil; a few are animal, especially insect, parasites or pathogens.

The type species is *Bacillus subtilis* Cohn *emend.* Prazmowski.

Key to the species of genus **Bacillus.**

I. Sporangia not definitely swollen.† Spores ellipsoidal to cylindrical, central to terminal. Spore walls thin and not easily stained. Gram-positive.

---

* Revised by Dr. Nathan R. Smith, St. Armands Key, Sarasota, Florida, and Dr. Ruth E. Gordon, N. J. Agricultural Experiment Station, New Brunswick, N. J., September, 1954. The arrangement and the descriptions of the species, unless otherwise noted, have been taken from the work of Smith, Gordon and Clark (Agricultural Monograph 16, U. S. Department of Agriculture, 1952).

† Nearly 50 per cent of the strains of *Bacillus coagulans* studied by Smith, Gordon and Clark (*op. cit.*, 1952) had definitely swollen sporangia; the species was placed in group I because of other characteristics.

A. Protoplasm of young cells grown on glucose agar vacuolated if lightly stained. Diameter of vegetative rods is 0.9 micron or more.
  1. Acid from mannitol with ammonium salts as source of nitrogen. Acetylmethylcarbinol not produced.
                        1. *Bacillus megaterium.*
  2. No acid from mannitol with ammonium salts as source of nitrogen. Acetylmethylcarbinol produced.
      a. Saprophytic, certain strains weakly pathogenic.
        b. Growth on agar not rhizoid. Usually motile.
                        2. *Bacillus cereus.*
        bb. Growth on agar rhizoid. Usually non-motile.
                        2a. *Bacillus cereus* var. *mycoides.*
      aa. Pathogenic.*
        b. Causative agent of anthrax. Non-motile.
                        3. *Bacillus anthracis.*
        bb. Cause of disease in certain insects. Usually motile.
                        4. *Bacillus thuringiensis.*
B. Protoplasm of young cells grown on glucose agar not vacuolated if lightly stained. Diameter of vegetative rods is less than 0.9 micron.
  1. Growth on glucose agar as good as or better than on agar. Good growth on soybean agar.
      a. Growth in 7 per cent NaCl broth.†
        b. Starch hydrolyzed. Nitrites produced from nitrates.
          c. Good growth under anaerobic conditions in glucose broth; pH of cultures is 5.2 or below. Gas produced from nitrates under alkaline, anaerobic conditions.
                        5. *Bacillus licheniformis.*
          cc. Scant if any growth in glucose broth under anaerobic conditions; pH of cultures is higher than 5.2. No gas produced from nitrates under alkaline, anaerobic conditions.
                        6. *Bacillus subtilis.*
          d. Black pigment on carbohydrate media only.
                        6a. *Bacillus subtilis* var. *aterrimus.*
          dd. Black pigment on tyrosine media only.
                        6b. *Bacillus subtilis* var. *niger.*
        bb. Starch not hydrolyzed. Nitrites not produced from nitrates.
                        7. *Bacillus pumilus.*
      aa. No growth in 7 per cent NaCl broth.
        b. Glucose utilized. Weak, if any, hydrolysis of gelatin.
                        8. *Bacillus coagulans.*

---

* Smith et al. (*loc. cit.*) pointed out that pathogenicity is a variable character in these two species and that academically they should be classified as variants of *Bacillus cereus*, the stable parent form. From the practical standpoint and to avoid complications that would arise as to priority, it has been thought best to retain these as separate species in the Manual until more work has been done.

† Gordon and Smith (Jour. Bact., *58*, 1949, 327) recommended the use of 5 per cent NaCl. Ford et al. (Bact. Proc., 1952, 18), however, found that certain strains of *Bacillus coagulans* would grow in 5 per cent broth, thus rendering this character useless as a means of separating *Bacillus coagulans* from *Bacillus subtilis*. Since then the writers have obtained growth in 7 per cent NaCl broth by all strains of *Bacillus licheniformis*, *Bacillus subtilis* (one exception) and its varieties and *Bacillus pumilus*. The use of the higher percentage of NaCl is, therefore, recommended to overcome the objection of Ford and his co-workers. (Also see Smith, Gordon and Clark, *op. cit.*, 1952.)

bb. Glucose not utilized. Strong hydrolysis of gelatin.
9. *Bacillus badius.*
2. Growth on glucose agar definitely not so good as on agar. Scant, if any, growth on soybean agar.
a. Casein hydrolyzed. Urease not produced.
10. *Bacillus firmus.*
aa. Casein not hydrolyzed. Urease produced.
11. *Bacillus lentus.*
II. Sporangia definitely swollen. Spores ellipsoidal, rarely cylindrical, central to terminal. Spore wall thick and easily stained. Remnants of sporangium sometimes adhering. Gram-variable.
A. Gas from carbohydrates.
1. Acetylmethylcarbinol produced. Crystalline dextrins not produced from starch.
12. *Bacillus polymyxa.*
2. Acetylmethylcarbinol not produced. Crystalline dextrins produced from starch.
13. *Bacillus macerans.*
B. Gas not produced from carbohydrates.
1. Saprophytic. Grow on ordinary media.
a. Starch hydrolyzed.
b. Indole and acetylmethylcarbinol produced.
14. *Bacillus alvei.*
bb. Indole and acetylmethylcarbinol not produced.
c. Grows at 65° C.
15. *Bacillus stearothermophilus.*
cc. Does not grow at 65° C.
16. *Bacillus circulans.*
aa. Starch not hydrolyzed.
b. pH of glucose broth cultures is less than 8.0. Grow in glucose broth under anaerobic conditions.
c. Indole produced. Acid from glucose and mannitol with ammonium salts as source of nitrogen.
17. *Bacillus laterosporus.*
cc. Indole not produced. Does not grow on carbohydrates with ammonium salts as source of nitrogen.
18. *Bacillus pulvifaciens.*
bb. pH of glucose broth cultures is 8.0 or higher. Does not grow in glucose broth under anaerobic conditions.
19. *Bacillus brevis.*
2. Parasitic. Do not grow on ordinary media.
a. Cause of American foulbrood of honey bees.
20. *Bacillus larvae.*
aa. Cause of the milky disease of Japanese beetles.
Type A. 21. *Bacillus popilliae.*
Type B. 22. *Bacillus lentimorbus.*
III. Sporangia definitely swollen. Spores spherical or nearly so. Gram-variable.
A. Grow on ordinary media at pH 6.0. Urea or alkaline conditions not necessary for growth.
1. Starch hydrolyzed. Grows in 10 per cent NaCl broth.
23. *Bacillus pantothenticus.*
2. Starch not hydrolyzed. Does not grow in 10 per cent NaCl broth.
24. *Bacillus sphaericus.*
B. Does not grow on ordinary media at pH 6.0. Urea or alkaline conditions necessary for growth.
25. *Bacillus pasteurii.*

1. **Bacillus megaterium** de Bary, 1884. (DeBary, Vergleichende Morph. und Biol. der Pilze, 1884, 499; *Bacillus megatherium* (sic) Schroeter, in Cohn, Kryptogamen-Flora v. Schlesien, *3*, 1, 1886 (1889), 160.)

me.ga.te'ri.um. Gr. adj. *mega* large; Gr. noun *teras, teratis* monster, beast; M.L. noun *megaterium* big beast. The second stem has been claimed to be a faulty transliteration of the Gr. noun *therium* an animal. The Judicial Commission of the International Committee on Bacteriological Nomenclature has ruled, however, that the original spelling is to be preferred (Internat. Bull. Bact. Nomen. and Taxon., *1*, 1951, 35).

Rods, 1.2 to 1.5 by 2.0 to 4.0 microns, with rounded ends, occurring singly or in short chains. When lightly stained, protoplasm granular or foamy. Occasional shadow- or ghost-forms. Motile. Gram-positive. Variations: 0.9 to 2.2 by 1.0 to 5.0 microns, occurring in filaments or long and tangled chains. Ends square. Protoplasm evenly stained. Many shadow-forms. Buds at end or side of rods. Non-motile. Gram-variable.

On glucose agar, rods are usually larger, longer and more vacuolated because of numerous, large, fat globules, sometimes irregular in shape with pointed ends or corkscrew-shaped (in wet mount).

Spores, 1.0 to 1.2 by 1.5 to 2.0 microns, ellipsoidal, central to para-central. Thin-walled. Many formed in 48 hours. Variations: Diameters 0.8 to 1.4 microns. Shapes are irregular, reniform, oviform, almost spherical and cylindrical. Lateral. Only a few are formed in 3 to 6 days.

Sporangia not distinctly swollen.

Gelatin stab: Slow liquefaction.

Gelatin agar streak plate: Wide zone of hydrolysis.

Agar colonies: Large, smooth, soft, glistening, round, convex, entire, non-spreading, dense, creamy white to yellow. Variations: Rough, concentrically or radially ridged, thin edged.

Agar slants: Growth abundant, smooth, soft to butyrous, opaque, glistening, slightly spreading, non-adherent, creamy white to yellow. Some browning with pellucid dots on aging. Variations: Rough, slightly wrinkled, tough, adherent, non-spreading.

Glucose agar slants: Growth usually more abundant and softer (somewhat slimy) than on agar. Variations: Gummy, coarsely wrinkled. Pellucid dots more distinct than on agar.

Glucose nitrate agar slants: Growth very heavy, raised.

Soybean agar slants: Growth abundant. Better sporulation and fewer shadow-forms than on agar.

Tyrosine agar slants: Deep black pigment by few strains.

Broth: Turbidity medium to heavy, uniform, with or without abundant sediment. No pellicle. Variations: Turbidity flocculent or granular. Pellicle thin and friable. Broth clear with flocculent sediment.

Milk: Peptonized.

Milk agar streak plate: Wide zone of hydrolysis of the casein.

Potato: Growth abundant, smooth, soft to slimy, glistening, spreading, creamy white, pale to lemon-yellow or pink. Variations: Rough, wrinkled. Potato blackened or orange-colored. No growth.

Acid but no gas (with ammonium salts as source of nitrogen) from glucose, sucrose and mannitol. Acid usually produced from arabinose, xylose and glycerol. Acid production variable from lactose.

Starch hydrolyzed.

Acetylmethylcarbinol not produced.

Citrates utilized as sole source of carbon.

Nitrites usually not produced from nitrates. No gas from nitrates under anaerobic conditions.

Growth factors not essential.[*]

Lecithinase not produced.[†]

Aerobic. No growth in glucose broth under anaerobic conditions.

Temperature relations: Optimum, be-

---

[*] Information on the nutritional requirements of this as well as of the succeeding species was supplied by Knight and Proom (Jour. Gen. Microbiol., *4*, 1950, 508).

[†] The lecithinase reaction of this and succeeding species was reported by Colmer (Jour. Bact., *55*, 1948, 777), McGaughey and Chu (Jour. Gen. Microbiol., *2*, 1948, 334) and Knight and Proom (*op. cit.*, 1950, 508).

tween 28° and 35° C. Maximum, usually between 40° and 45° C.

Source: Isolated from cooked cabbage.

Habitat: Widely distributed in soil, water, dust and decomposing materials.

2. **Bacillus cereus** Frankland and Frankland, 1887. (Philosoph. Trans. Roy. Soc. London, *178*, B, 1887, 279.)

ce're.us. L. adj. *cereus* wax-colored, waxen.

Rods, 1.0 to 1.2 by 3.0 to 5.0 microns, with square ends, usually occurring in short to long, tangled chains. When lightly stained, protoplasm granular or foamy. No shadow-forms. Not encapsulated. Motile. Gram-positive. Variations: 0.8 to 1.3 by 2.0 to 6.0 microns. Filaments. Ends rounded. Encapsulated. Non-motile. Protoplasm stains uniformly. Gram-variable.

On glucose agar, rods are larger and more vacuolated and contain many, large, fat globules. Variation: Sometimes contain only a few, small, fat globules but always vacuolated when lightly stained.

Spores, 1.0 to 1.5 microns, ellipsoidal, central or para-central. Thin-walled. Many formed in 18 to 24 hours. Variations: 0.5 to 1.2 by 1.3 to 2.5 microns. Few or none at 48 hours or longer.

Sporangia not appreciably swollen.

Gelatin stab: Rapid liquefaction.

Gelatin agar streak plate: Wide zone of hydrolysis.

Agar colonies: Large, rough, flat, irregular with whip-like outgrowths. Whitish with characteristic mottled appearance by transmitted light (resembling galvanized iron or moiré silk). Variations: Thin and spreading, rough and arborescent, smooth and dense.

Agar slants: Growth abundant, rough, opaque, whitish, non-adherent, spreading. Edge irregular with whip-like outgrowths. Variations: Relatively smooth. Very rough extending into the agar. Greenish yellow, diffusing pigment.

Glucose agar slants: Growth abundant, heavier and softer than on agar.

Glucose nitrate agar slants: Scant, if any, growth.

Broth: Heavy, uniform turbidity with soft, easily dispersed sediment, with or without soft ring pellicle. Variations: Flocculent growth. Firm pellicle.

Milk: Rapid peptonization, with or without slight coagulation.

Milk agar streak plate: Wide zone of hydrolysis of the casein.

Potato: Growth abundant, thick, spreading, soft, creamy white, sometimes with pinkish tinge. Variations: Growth restricted, thin, folded, dry or slimy. Potato darkened or orange-colored.

Acid but no gas (with ammonium salts as source of nitrogen*) from glucose; also usually from sucrose, glycerol and salicin. No acid from arabinose, xylose or mannitol. Usually no acid from lactose.

Starch hydrolyzed.

Acetylmethylcarbinol produced.

Citrates usually utilized as sole source of carbon.

Nitrites usually produced from nitrates. Gas usually produced from nitrates under anaerobic conditions.

Amino acids necessary for growth.

Lecithinase produced.

Aerobic, facultatively anaerobic. Growth in glucose broth under anaerobic conditions; pH usually below 5.2.

Temperature relations: Optimum about 30° C. Maximum, between 37° and 48° C.

Pathogenicity: Large doses of 24-hour broth cultures fatal to guinea pigs (Clark, Jour. Bact., *33*, 1937, 435).

Source: Isolated from dust.

Habitat: Widely distributed in soil, dust, milk and on plant surfaces.

2a. *Bacillus cereus* var. *mycoides* (Flügge, 1886) Smith et al., 1946. (*Bacillus mycoides* Flügge, Die Mikroorganismen, 2 Aufl., 1886, 324; Smith, Gordon and Clark, U. S. Dept. Agr. Misc. Pub. 559, 1946, 54.)

my.co.i'des. Gr. noun *myces* fungus; Gr. noun *eidus* form, shape; M.L. adj. *mycoides* fungus-like.

Bacillus cereus var. *mycoides* is identical in all respects with *Bacillus cereus* except in the following characters:

---

* A major portion of the investigations of carbohydrate utilization reported by Smith et al. (*op. cit.*, 1952) was made with crude agar. Later, when refined agar was used, 0.02 per cent yeast extract was incorporated in the ammonium salts medium.

Rods, usually slightly thinner, in long chains twisted together to form strands.

Agar colonies: Grayish, thin, widely spreading by means of long, twisted chains of cells, turning to the left or right (sinistral or dextral). The sinistral form occurs more often in soil (Gause, Mikrobiologia, *18*, 1949, 154).

Agar slants: Growth thin, rhizoid, grayish, widely spreading, adhering to or growing into the agar. With aging, growth becomes thicker and softer.

Gordon (Jour. Bact., *39*, 1940, 98) and Smith, Gordon and Clark (*op. cit.*, 1952) showed that *Bacillus mycoides* lost its rhizoid character if grown from a small inoculum in flasks containing 100 ml of broth and plated on agar after 3 to 30 days. The resulting non-rhizoid cultures could not be differentiated from *Bacillus cereus*. Dissociation occurred under other conditions, but not so rapidly or completely. Reversion to the rhizoid state was not observed, although the dissociants were grown under a variety of conditions intended to induce such reversion.

Source: Isolated from soil.

Habitat: Widely distributed in soil.

3. Bacillus anthracis Cohn, 1872, *emend.* Koch, 1876. (Les infusories de la maladie charbonneuse, Davaine, Compt. rend. Acad. Sci., Paris, *69*, 1864, 393; Cohn, Beiträge z. Biol. d. Pflanzen, *1*, Heft 2, 1872, 177; Koch, *ibid.*, *2*, Heft 2, 1876, 279; Bactéridie des charbon, Pasteur and Joubert, Compt. rend. Acad. Sci., Paris, *84*, 1877, 900.)

an'thra.cis. Gr. noun *anthrax* charcoal, a red precious stone, a carbuncle; M.L. noun *anthrax* the disease anthrax; M.L. gen.noun *anthracis* of anthrax.

Rods, 1.0 to 1.3 by 3.0 to 10.0 microns, with square or concave ends, occurring in long chains; resemble *Bacillus cereus*. When lightly stained, protoplasm granular or foamy. Encapsulated. Non-motile. Grampositive.

Spores ellipsoidal to cylindrical, 0.8 to 1.0 by 1.3 to 1.5 microns, central or paracentral, often in chains. Germination polar.

Sporangia ellipsoidal to cylindrical, not definitely swollen, in chains.

Gelatin stab: Arborescent in depth, inverted pine tree. Liquefaction crateriform becoming stratiform.

Gelatin agar streak plate: Wide zone of hydrolysis.

Agar colonies: Large, dense, irregular, composed of parallel chains of cells giving a curled or combed appearance; similar to certain strains of *Bacillus cereus*.

Agar slants: Growth abundant, spreading, dense, grayish, with irregular borders.

Blood hemolysis: Variable (Bekker, Zent. f. Bakt., I Abt., Orig., *147*, 1941, 451; also see *ibid.*, *150*, 1943, 326).

Broth: Little or no turbidity; thick pellicle.

Milk: Coagulated, slightly acid, peptonized.

Milk agar streak plate: Wide zone of hydrolysis of the casein.

Potato: Growth abundant, spreading, white to creamy.

Acid but no gas (with ammonium salts as source of nitrogen) from glucose, fructose, sucrose, maltose, trehalose and dextrin. Late and slight acidity from glycerol and salicin by some strains. No acid from arabinose, rhamnose, mannose, galactose, lactose, raffinose, inulin, mannitol, dulcitol, sorbitol, inositol or adonitol.

Starch hydrolyzed.

Acetylmethylcarbinol produced.

Nitrites produced from nitrates.

Amino acids are necessary for growth.

Lecithinase produced.

Aerobic, facultatively anaerobic.

Temperature relations: Optimum, about 35° C. Maximum, about 43° C.

Pathogenicity: Cause of anthrax in man, cattle, swine, sheep, rabbits, guinea pigs, mice, etc. (Smith, Gordon and Clark (*op. cit.*, 1952) considered *Bacillus anthracis* as a pathogenic variety of *Bacillus cereus* because certain strains of the two were in close agreement in all characters except pathogenicity. As strains of *Bacillus anthracis* may become avirulent, and as certain strains of *Bacillus cereus* may be lethal in massive dosages (Clark, Jour. Bact., *33*, 1937, 435), the relationship is closer than most investigators realize.)

Source: Isolated from the blood of infected animals.

Habitat: Man and animals with anthrax.

4. Bacillus thuringiensis Berliner, 1915. (Ztschr. f. angew. Ent., Beihefte *2*, 1915, 29.) thur.in.gi.en'sis. M.L. gen.noun *thuringiensis* of Thuringia; named for Thuringia, a German province.

Rods same as those of *Bacillus cereus*.

Spore size and shape the same as in *Bacillus cereus*.

Sporangia not definitely swollen. Spores tend to lie obliquely in the sporangium; after aging, a knob of protoplasm remains at each end. These so-called crystalline inclusion bodies are described in greater detail by Steinhaus (Hilgardia, *23*, 1954, 1) and by Hannay (Nature, *172*, 1953, 1004). The significance of the crystals has not been determined.

Other cultural and biochemical characters are the same as for *Bacillus cereus*.

As in the case of *Bacillus anthracis*, Smith et al. considered *Bacillus thuringiensis* as a pathogenic variety of *Bacillus cereus*. From the practical standpoint, it seems best to retain it as a separate species in the MANUAL.

Pathogenicity: Cause of death of larvae of certain insects.

Source: Isolated from the larvae of the flour moth (*Ephestia kuehniella* Zell).

Habitat: Diseased insects.

5. Bacillus licheniformis (Weigmann, 1898) Chester, 1901, *emend.* Gibson, 1937. (*Clostridium licheniforme* Weigmann, Cent. f. Bakt., II Abt., *4*, 1898, 820; *Bacillus licheniformis* Chester, Man. Determ. Bact., 1901, 287; Gibson, Soc. Agr. Bact., Abs. Proc., 1937; also see Jour. Dairy Res., *13*, 1944, 248.)

li.che.ni.for'mis. Gr. noun *lichen* a tree moss, lichen; L. noun *forma* shape; M.L. adj. *licheniformis* lichen-shaped.

Rods, 0.6 to 0.8 by 1.5 to 3.0 microns, stain uniformly, not in chains. Not encapsulated. Motile. Gram-positive. Variations: Rods, 0.5 to 0.9 by 1.2 microns, to long filaments. Encapsulated. Shadow-forms. Non-motile.

Spores, 0.6 to 0.9 by 1.0 to 1.5 microns, ellipsoidal to cylindrical, central or para-

central, thin-walled. Many formed in 48 hours at 37° C. Variations: Slightly smaller or larger. Only a few are formed in 2 or 3 weeks.

Spore germination is equatorial without splitting of the spore coat along transverse axis (Lamanna, Jour. Bact., *44*, 1942, 611; Burdon and Wende, Bact. Proc., 1952, 46).

Sporangia not definitely swollen; frequently resemble rods with bipolar staining.

Gelatin stab: Rapid crateriform to stratiform liquefaction.

Gelatin agar streak plate: Wide zone of hydrolysis.

Agar colonies: Large, spreading; surface rough or rugose; hairy outgrowths. Offwhite. Variations: Smooth, entire or lobate.

Agar slants: Growth abundant, rough, opaque, adherent, spreading, with hairy outgrowths. Matt surface. Variations: Smooth, thin, non-adherent, rugose.

Glucose agar slants: Growth heavy, rugose, often with extruded droplets or mucoid vesicles on surface. Usually hairy outgrowths from line of inoculation. Sometimes gas produced at 37° C.

Glucose nitrate agar slants: Growth slow, scant to abundant, with hairy outgrowths. Offwhite to brownish red. Sometimes gas is produced.

Soybean agar slants: Growth softer and more abundant than on agar. Brownish to reddish, often purplish at the bottom. Droplets extruded. Variations: Matt surface. Folded growth.

Tyrosine agar slants: Same as agar slants.

Broth: Clear with heavy, wrinkled, tough pellicle. Variations: Flocculent or uniform turbidity, with or without fragile pellicle.

NaCl broth: Good growth in 5 to 8 per cent NaCl, inhibition with higher concentrations. In a few cases, growth in 12 per cent.

Milk agar streak plate: Usually narrow zone of hydrolysis of the casein.

Potato: Growth heavy, spreading, wrinkled, warty, with extruded droplets. Pink. Submerged portion of potato red to violet. Variations: Soft. Offwhite.

Acid but no gas (with ammonium salts as source of nitrogen) from arabinose, xylose, glucose, sucrose and mannitol. Acid production variable from lactose.

Starch hydrolyzed.

Acetylmethylcarbinol produced (37° C. better incubation temperature than 32° C.).

pH of glucose broth cultures is 5.2 to 8.2 in 7 days.

Citrates utilized.

Nitrites produced from nitrates. Gas produced from nitrates under anaerobic conditions.

Growth factors not essential.

Lecithinase not produced.

Aerobic, facultatively anaerobic. Growth in glucose broth under anaerobic conditions; pH is 5.2 or lower at 14 days. Usually a small amount of gas is produced.

Temperature relations: Optimum, between 32° and 45° C. Maximum, between 50° and 56° C. (in water bath).

Antibiotics obtained from cultures of certain strains are bacitracin (Johnson, Anker and Meleney, Science, *102*, 1945, 376) and licheniformin (Callow and Hart, Nature, *157*, 1946, 334).

Source: Isolated from cheese.

Habitat: Widely distributed in soil and food; also common as a laboratory contaminant.

6. **Bacillus subtilis** Cohn, 1872, *emend.* Prazmowski, 1880. (Cohn, Beitr. z. Biol. d. Pflanzen, *1*, Heft 2, 1872, 174; also see Heft 3, 1875, 188; and *2*, Heft 2, 1876, 249; Prazmowski, Untersuchungen über die Entwicklungsgeschichte und Fermentwirkung einigen Bakterien-Arten. Inaug. Diss., Leipzig, 1880.)

sub'ti.lis. L. adj. *subtilis* slender.

The identity of this species has been the subject of considerable controversy owing to the great variations in cultural characters exhibited by various strains, to the distribution of mislabeled cultures and to confusion with *Bacillus cereus*. In cases in which an organism is said to be "anthrax-like" or "similar to the anthrax bacillus," it should be remembered that these terms apply to *Bacillus cereus* and not to *Bacillus subtilis*. Conn (Jour. Inf. Dis., *46*, 1930, 341) concluded that the so-called Marburg strain fitted the earliest recognizable descriptions of this species. His interpretation was accepted by the International Committee on Bacteriological Nomenclature (Jour. Bact., *33*, 1937, 445).

Rods, 0.7 to 0.8 by 2.0 to 3.0 microns, not in chains, uniformly stained. Not encapsulated. No shadow-forms. Motile. Gram-positive. Variations: Rods, 0.6 to 1.0 by 1.3 to 6.0 microns, or filaments. Long chains. Encapsulated. Shadow-forms. Budding from end of cells. Occasionally non-motile. Rarely Gram-variable.

Spores, 0.6 to 0.9 by 1.0 to 1.5 microns, ellipsoidal to cylindrical, central or para-central, thin-walled. Many are formed in 48 hours. Variations: 0.5 to 1.0 by 1.0 to 2.0 microns. Few are formed in 15 to 21 days.

Sporulation poor on media made with highly refined agar; much better when crude agar is used or when soil extract is added to the refined agar (Smith and Gordon, unpublished data).

Spore germination is equatorial with splitting of the spore coat along the transverse axis (Lamanna, Jour. Bact., *44*, 1942, 611; Burdon and Wende, Bact. Proc., 1952, 46).

Sporangia not definitely swollen; frequently show bipolar staining.

Gelatin stab: Liquefaction crateriform to stratiform.

Gelatin agar streak plate: Wide zone of hydrolysis.

Agar colonies: Rough, opaque, dull, spreading, offwhite. Variations: Smooth to slimy, soft, thin, translucent, dendroid. Yellow, orange or brown.

Agar slants: Growth abundant, rough, opaque, dull, waxy, spreading. Cream-colored to light brown. Variations: Smooth, slimy, thin, translucent, dendroid. Yellow or orange (some strains show a greenish yellow, diffusing pigment when incubated at 45° C.).

Glucose agar slants: Growth heavier and softer than on agar, sometimes pink or brown.

Glucose asparagine agar slants: Growth abundant. Variation: Scant growth.

Glucose nitrate agar: Usually abundant, cream-colored growth.

Soybean agar slants: Growth more abundant and softer than on agar.

Tyrosine agar slants: Growth same as on agar.

Broth: Clear with heavy, wrinkled, waxy, tough pellicle. Variations: Flocculent or uniform turbidity with or without fragile pellicle.

NaCl broth: Good growth up to a concentration of 7 per cent NaCl; growth in a few cases in 10 or 12 per cent.

Milk: Slowly peptonized, usually becoming alkaline.

Milk agar streak plate: Usually there is a wide zone of hydrolysis of the casein.

Potato: Growth heavy, wrinkled to coarsely folded, spreading. Offwhite, yellow, pink or brown. Variations: Slimy, soft, thin, warty.

Acid but no gas (with ammonium salts as source of nitrogen) from arabinose, xylose, glucose, sucrose and mannitol. Usually no acid produced from lactose.

Starch is hydrolyzed.

Acetylmethylcarbinol produced (37° C. better incubation temperature than 32° C.).

pH of glucose broth cultures is 5.0 to 8.6 in 7 days.

Citrates utilized.

Nitrites produced from nitrates. No gas produced from nitrate broth under anaerobic conditions.

Aerobic, certain strains facultatively anaerobic. Growth scant, if any, in glucose broth under anaerobic conditions; pH of 14-day cultures is 5.5 or higher.

Temperature relations: Optimum growth temperatures lie between 28° and 40° C. The maximum temperature for growth is usually 50° C., but some cultures find 40° too warm for growth while still others will grow even up to 55° C.

Accessory growth factors not essential.

Lecithinase not produced.

Antibiotics obtained from cultures of certain strains are subtilin (Jansen and Hirschmann, Arch. Biochem., 4, 1944, 297), bacillin (Foster and Woodruff, Jour. Bact., 51, 1945, 363), subtenolin (Hirschhorn, Bucca and Thayer, Proc. Soc. Exp. Biol. and Med., 67, 1948, 429), bacillomycin (Landy, Warren, Rosenman and Colio, Proc. Soc. Exp. Biol. and Med., 67, 1948, 539) and others.

Source: Isolated from infusions of lentils, cheese, white beets and hay (Cohn).

Habitat: Widely distributed in soil and decomposing organic matter; also common as a laboratory contaminant.

6a. *Bacillus subtilis* var. *aterrimus* (Lehmann and Neumann, 1896) Smith et al., 1946. (Potato bacillus, Biel, Cent. f. Bakt., II Abt., 2, 1896, 137; *Bacillus aterrimus* Lehmann and Neumann, Bakt. Diag., 1 Aufl., 2, 1896, 303; Smith, Gordon and Clark, U. S. Dept. Agr. Misc. Pub. 559, 1946, 64.)

a.ter′ri.mus. L. sup.adj. *aterrimus* very black.

The description of *Bacillus subtilis* will serve for var. *aterrimus* with the additional statement that a blue-black to black pigment is formed on media containing a carbohydrate utilized by the organism. The ability to form black pigments, however, may be lost and the cultures stabilized in the colorless condition (Smith et al., *ibid.*, 9; also see *op. cit.*, 1952, 29); they are then indistinguishable from cultures of *Bacillus subtilis*.

Source: Isolated from rye bread in a moist chamber used for growing aspergilli (Biel).

Habitat: Widely distributed in soil, air and decomposing carbonaceous materials.

6b. *Bacillus subtilis* var. *niger* (Migula, 1900) Smith et al., 1946. (*Bacillus lactis niger* Gorini, Gior. d. Reale Soc. Ital. d'Ig., 16, 1894, 9; also see Cent. f. Bakt., I Abt., Orig., 20, 1896, 94; *Bacillus niger* Migula, System der Bakterien, 2, 1900, 636; Smith et al., U. S. Dept. Agr. Misc. Pub. 559, 1946, 66.)

ni′ger. L. adj. *niger* black.

The characterization of *Bacillus subtilis* will serve for var. *niger* by adding the statement that media containing tyrosine are blackened. The ability to form black pigment, however, may be lost and the cultures stabilized in the colorless condition; then they cannot be distinguished from *Bacillus subtilis*.

Source: Isolated from milk.

Habitat: Widely distributed in soil, dust and decomposing materials.

7. Bacillus pumilus Gottheil, 1901. (Cent. f. Bakt., II Abt., **7**, 1901, 681.)

pu'mi.lus. L. adj. *pumilus* little, diminutive.

Rods, 0.6 to 0.7 by 2.0 to 3.0 microns, not in chains. Stain uniformly. Not encapsulated. Motile. Gram-positive. Variations: Chains and filaments. Encapsulated. Gram-variable.

Spores, 0.5 by 1.0 micron, ellipsoidal to cylindrical, central or para-central, thin-walled. Readily formed. Variations: 0.6 to 0.8 by 0.8 to 1.5 microns. Sporulation slow (certain strains sporulate best on soybean agar).

Sporulation in certain strains poor on media made with highly refined agar; much better when crude agar is used or when soil extract is added to the refined agar (Smith and Gordon, unpublished data).

Sporangia not definitely swollen.

Gelatin stab: Slow liquefaction.

Gelatin agar streak plate: Wide zone of hydrolysis.

Agar colonies: Smooth, thin, flat, spreading, dendroid, translucent. Variations: Small to pinpoint, nonspreading, dense.

Agar slants: Growth smooth, thin, glistening, spreading, non-adherent. Frequently yellowish. Variations: Rough, dull, tough or wrinkled.

Glucose agar slants: Growth usually the same as on agar, sometimes heavier or scantier.

Glucose asparagine agar slants: Growth abundant. Variations: Scant or no growth.

Glucose nitrate agar slants: Growth usually scant.

Soybean agar slants: Growth more abundant than on agar, soft, yellow. Variations: Rough, red or colorless.

Tyrosine agar slants: Same as agar slants.

Broth: Turbidity uniform, with or without ring or fragile pellicle. Variations: Turbidity flocculent. Broth clear with rough pellicle.

NaCl broth: Growth in 7 per cent NaCl; in a few cases growth in 10 per cent.

Milk: Peptonized, sometimes coagulated.

Milk agar streak plate: Usually there is a wide zone of hydrolysis of the casein.

Potato: Growth smooth, thin, soft, spreading, moist to slimy, yellow to brown. Potato darkened. Variations: Rough, dry, wrinkled, pink or red.

Acid but no gas (with ammonium salts as source of nitrogen) from arabinose, xylose, glucose, sucrose and mannitol. Usually no acid from lactose.

Starch not hydrolyzed.

Acetylmethylcarbinol is produced.

pH of glucose broth cultures is 5.0 to 8.4.

Citrates utilized as sole source of carbon.

Nitrites not produced from nitrates. No gas produced in nitrate broth under anaerobic conditions.

Biotin essential for growth.

Lecithinase not produced.

Aerobic, certain strains facultatively anaerobic. Growth scant, if any, in glucose broth under anaerobic conditions; pH is 5.5 or higher at 14 days.

Temperature relations: Optimum, between 28° and 40° C. Maximum, between 45° and 50° C.

Source: Isolated from plants.

Habitat: Widely distributed in soil, dust and cheese; also common as a laboratory contaminant.

8. Bacillus coagulans Hammer, 1915. (Iowa Agr. Exp. Station, Research Bull. 19, 1915, 129; also see Sarles and Hammer, Jour. Bact., *23*, 1932, 301.)

co.a'gu.lans. L. part.adj. *coagulans* curdling, coagulating.

Rods, 0.6 to 1.0 by 2.5 to 5.0 microns, not in chains. Stain uniformly. Motile. Gram-positive. Variations: Rods, 0.5 to 1.2 by 2.0 to 6.0 microns, to filaments. Gram-variable.

Spores, 0.9 to 1.0 by 1.2 to 1.5 microns, ellipsoidal, thin-walled, subterminal to terminal. Variations: 0.8 to 1.1 by 1.2 to 2.0 microns. Kidney-shaped or cylindrical.

Sporulation poor when highly refined agar is used in the medium; much better with crude agar or when soil extract is added to the refined agar (Smith and Gordon, unpublished data).

Sporangia definitely swollen in some cases, not swollen in others.

Gelatin agar streak plate: Zone of hydrolysis small, if any.

Agar colonies: Usually small, round, opaque, not distinctive.

Agar slants: Growth scant to moderate, flat, smooth to rough, translucent to opaque.

Glucose agar slants: Growth soft, moist and usually more abundant than on agar.

Glucose asparagine agar slants: Growth scant, if any.

Proteose-peptone acid agar slants: Good growth, better than on agar.

Soybean agar slants: Growth usually more abundant than on agar.

Stock culture agar slants: Growth as good as or better than on agar.

Broth: Moderate uniform turbidity followed by clearing and formation of sediment.

NaCl broth: No growth in 7 per cent NaCl.

Milk agar streak plate: Zone of hydrolysis of the casein narrow, if any.

Potato: Growth erratic, not distinctive.

Acid but no gas (with peptone as source of nitrogen) from glucose. Acid production variable from arabinose, xylose, lactose, sucrose, glycerol and mannitol.

Starch is hydrolyzed.

Acetylmethylcarbinol usually produced.

pH of glucose broth is 5.0 or less in 7 days.

Citrates not utilized.

Tomato yeast milk curdled in 1 to 3 days at 45° C.

Nitrites usually not produced from nitrates. No gas in nitrate broth under anaerobic conditions.

Amino acids, biotin and thiamine are essential for growth; perhaps also nicotinic acid.

Lecithinase not produced.

Aerobic, facultatively anaerobic. Growth in glucose broth under anaerobic conditions; pH is less than 5.2 in 7 days (some strains are inhibited by the alkalinity of the medium as generally prepared; for this species, therefore, a neutral or slightly acid medium is recommended).

Temperature relations: Optimum, between 33° and 45° C. Maximum, between 55° and 60° C. for the majority of the strains. Poor growth, if any, at 28° C.

Source: Isolated from evaporated milk and tomato juice.

Habitat: Widely distributed in spoiled food, cream, cheese and silage.

9. **Bacillus badius** Batchelor, 1919, *emend*. Saghafi and Appleman, 1953. (Batchelor, Jour. Bact., *4*, 1919, 25; Saghafi and Appleman, Jour. Bact., *65*, 1953, 220.)

ba'di.us. L. adj. *badius* brown.

Rods, 0.8 to 1.0 by 2.5 to 5.0 microns, occurring usually singly or in short chains; long chains on certain media. Stain uniformly. Motile. Gram-positive.

Spores, 0.8 to 0.9 by 1.2 to 1.5 microns, cylindrical or ellipsoidal, terminal to subterminal. Thin-walled. Resemble those of *Bacillus coagulans*.

Sporangia usually not definitely swollen, in some cases slightly swollen.

Gelatin stab: Rapid crateriform liquefaction.

Gelatin agar streak plate: Wide zone of hydrolysis.

Agar colonies: Large, dense, rough, opaque, with hairy outgrowths, resemble those of *Bacillus cereus*.

Agar slants: Abundant, grayish white (brown, Batchelor), with outgrowths. Fecal odor.

Glucose agar slants: Same as on agar.

Glucose nitrate agar slants: No growth.

Soybean agar slants: Growth slow, becoming moderate. Edges hairy.

Broth: Uniform turbidity. Fecal odor. (Medium becomes very brown, Batchelor.)

NaCl broth: No growth in 7 per cent NaCl.

Milk: No change (peptonization, Batchelor).

Milk agar streak plate: Moderate zone of clearing of the casein.

Potato: Scant, soft, spreading, slightly brownish.

Indole not produced.

No acid or gas (with either ammonium salts, peptone or yeast extract as source of nitrogen) from arabinose, xylose, glucose, lactose, sucrose and mannitol. Slight acid production from glycerol with yeast extract (Smith and Gordon, unpublished data).

Starch not hydrolyzed.

Acetylmethylcarbinol not produced.

pH of glucose broth is 7.6 to 8.0 in 10 days.
Citrates not utilized.

Nitrites not produced from nitrates. No gas produced in nitrate broth under anaerobic conditions.

Urease not produced.

Aerobic. No growth in glucose broth under anaerobic conditions.

Temperature relations: Optimum, between 35° and 40° C. Maximum, 52° C.

Source: Isolated from an infant's stool (Batchelor), from macerated figs (Saghafi and Appleman) and from the surface of an orange (Smith and Gordon, unpublished data).

Habitat: Uncertain. Probably associated with decomposing materials.

10. **Bacillus firmus** Werner, 1933. (Cent. f. Bakt., II Abt., *87*, 1933, 470.)

fir'mus. L. adj. *firmus* strong, firm.

Rods, 0.6 to 0.9 by 1.5 to 4.0 microns, with ends poorly rounded, occurring singly or in pairs. Stain uniformly. Motile. Gram-positive.

Spores, 0.7 to 0.9 by 1.0 to 1.4 microns, ellipsoidal, central to subterminal. Usually form in 48 hours and more numerous on agar without the beef extract.

Sporangia only slightly swollen if at all.

Gelatin stab: Slow crateriform liquefaction.

Gelatin agar streak plate: Wide zone of hydrolysis.

Agar colonies: Small, round, smooth, dense, whitish, rarely pink.

Agar slants: Growth moderate, flat, smooth, opaque, whitish, rarely pink.

Glucose agar slants: Growth very scant, inhibited by the acid produced from the glucose.

Glucose nitrate agar slants: No growth.

Soybean agar slants: Scant, if any, growth.

Broth: Turbidity light, uniform or flocculent.

NaCl broth: Usually there is growth in 5 per cent NaCl; no growth in 10 per cent.

Milk agar streak plate: Moderate to wide zone of hydrolysis of the casein.

Potato: No growth.

Indole not produced.

Slight acid but no gas (with peptone as source of nitrogen) from glucose.

Starch hydrolyzed.

Ammonium salts not utilized as source of nitrogen.

Acetylmethylcarbinol not produced.

pH of glucose broth is not less than 6.2 in 7 days; very little growth.

Citrates not utilized.

Nitrites produced from nitrates. No gas produced in nitrate broth under anaerobic conditions.

Urease not produced.

Accessory growth substances essential.

Lecithinase not produced.

Aerobic. No growth in glucose broth under anaerobic conditions.

Temperature relations: Optimum, between 28° and 33° C. No growth at 50° C.

Source: Isolated from soil.

Habitat: Soil and decomposing materials; also found as a laboratory contaminant.

11. **Bacillus lentus** Gibson, 1935. (Zent. f. Bakt., II Abt., *92*, 1935, 368.)

len'tus. L. adj. *lentus* slow.

Rods, 0.6 to 0.9 by 1.5 to 4.0 microns, with ends poorly rounded, occurring singly or in pairs. Stain uniformly. Motile. Gram-positive.

Spores, 0.7 to 0.9 by 1.0 to 1.4 microns, ellipsoidal, central to subterminal. Usually form in 48 hours and are more numerous on agar without the beef extract.

Sporangia only slightly swollen if at all.

Gelatin stab: No liquefaction.

Gelatin agar streak plate: No zone of hydrolysis.

Agar colonies: Small, round, smooth, dense, whitish, not distinctive.

Agar slants: Growth slow, thin, translucent becoming opaque, whitish.

Glucose agar slants: Growth scant, not so good as on agar because of the acid produced from the glucose.

Glucose nitrate agar slants: No growth.

Soybean agar slants: Very scant, if any, growth.

Broth: Faint, uniform turbidity; granular sediment.

NaCl broth: Growth in 4 per cent, none in 5 per cent NaCl.

Milk: Unchanged.

Milk agar streak plate: Casein not hydrolyzed.

Potato: No growth.

Indole not produced.

Acid but no gas (with peptone as source of nitrogen) from arabinose, xylose and glucose. Ammonium salts not utilized as source of nitrogen.

Starch is hydrolyzed.

Acetylmethylcarbinol not produced.

pH of glucose broth cultures is not less than 6.2.

Citrates not utilized.

Nitrites not produced from nitrates. No gas produced in nitrate broth under anaerobic conditions.

Accessory growth factors essential.

Lecithinase reaction doubtful.

Urease produced.

Aerobic. No growth in glucose broth under anaerobic conditions.

Temperature relations: Optimum, between 28° and 33° C. No growth at 45° C.

Source: Isolated from soil.

Habitat: Probably common in soil.

12. **Bacillus polymyxa** (Prazmowski, 1880) Migula, 1900. (*Clostridium polymyxa* Prazmowski, Inaug. Diss., Leipzig, 1880, 37; Migula, Syst. d. Bakt., *2*, 1900, 638.)

po.ly.my′xa. Gr. pref. *poly-* much, many; Gr. noun *myxa* slime or mucus; M.L. *polymyxa* much slime.

Rods, 0.6 to 1.0 by 2.0 to 7.0 microns, not in chains. Motile. Gram-variable.

Spores, 1.2 to 1.5 by 1.5 to 2.5 microns, ellipsoidal, central to sub-terminal. Spore wall usually thick and easily stained. Freely formed.

Sporangia definitely bulged, spindle-shaped or clavate.

Gelatin stab: Slow liquefaction.

Gelatin agar streak plate: Usually there is a wide zone of hydrolysis (in the case of widely spreading cultures, the zone of hydrolysis sometimes extends only slightly beyond the limits of growth).

Agar colonies: Usually thin, translucent, spreading, lobate or fimbriate. Rough stage small, round, whitish, sometimes adherent.

Agar slants: Growth scant to moderate, restricted or spreading, indistinct to whitish.

Glucose agar slants: Growth usually much thicker than on agar, raised, glistening, gummy, with production of gas. Variation: Growth thin and not gummy.

Glucose nitrate agar slants: Usually good growth, gummy.

Proteose-peptone acid agar slants: Good growth, usually no gas.

Soybean agar slants: Good growth, usually with the production of gas.

Stock culture agar slants: Slightly heavier growth than on agar. No gas.

Broth: Turbidity uniform to granular. Gummy sediment. Sometimes a pellicle is formed.

NaCl broth: No growth in 5 per cent NaCl.

Milk: Usually coagulated with the production of gas.

Milk agar streak plate: Casein hydrolyzed.

Potato: Growth moderate to abundant, slimy, whitish to light tan. Potato decomposed with the production of gas. Growth of rough strains thicker and heaped up.

Indole not produced.

Acid and usually gas and gum (with ammonium salts as source of nitrogen) from arabinose, xylose, rhamnose, glucose, lactose, mannitol and sorbitol (the production of gas can best be demonstrated by growing the cultures on one of the following media: agar plus 1 per cent potato starch, potato plugs or wheat mash as used for the production of crystalline dextrins).

Starch hydrolyzed. Crystalline dextrins not produced from starch.

Hemicellulose and pectin attacked (Ankersmit, Cent. f. Bakt., I Abt., Orig., *40*, 1905, 100).

Acetylmethylcarbinol is produced. Ethanol, butylene-glycol and small amounts of acetone and butanol are also produced.

pH of glucose broth cultures is 4.8 to 7.2.

Citrates usually not utilized.

Methylene blue reduced; not reoxidized in 21 days.

Nitrites produced from nitrates. No gas produced in nitrate broth under anaerobic conditions.

Biotin necessary for growth.

Lecithinase reaction variable.

Aerobic, facultatively anaerobic. Growth with vigorous production of gas in glucose broth under anaerobic conditions.

Temperature relations: Optimum, between 28° and 35° C. Maximum, for the majority of the strains, 40° C. No growth at 45° C.

Antibiotic substance (polymyxin) obtained from cultures of a certain strain (Stansly, Shepherd and White, Bull. Johns Hopkins Hosp., 81, 1947, 43; also see Stansly and Schlosser, Jour. Bact., 54, 1947, 549).

Source: Isolated from grain, soil and pasteurized milk.

Habitat: Widely distributed in soil, water, milk, feces and decaying vegetables.

13. **Bacillus macerans** Schardinger, 1905. (Rottebazillus 1, Schardinger, Wien. Klin. Wochnschr., 17, 1904, 207; Schardinger, Cent. f. Bakt., II Abt., 14, 1905, 772.)

ma'ce.rans. L. part.adj. *macerans* to soften by steeping, to ret.

Rods, 0.5 to 0.7 by 2.5 to 5.0 microns, not in chains. Motile. Gram-variable.

Spores, 1.0 to 1.5 by 1.2 to 2.5 microns, ellipsoidal, subterminal to terminal. Spore wall thick and easily stained.

Sporangia definitely swollen, clavate.

Gelatin stab: Liquefaction variable owing to the low temperature.

Gelatin agar streak plate: Fair to good zone of hydrolysis.

Agar colonies: Thin, transparent to whitish, spreading, irregular. Rough stage small and compact.

Agar slants: Growth thin, spreading or restricted, inconspicuous to whitish.

Glucose agar slants: Growth heavier than on agar, usually with the production of gas.

Glucose nitrate agar slants: Very scant, if any, growth.

Proteose-peptone acid agar slants: No growth.

Soybean agar slants: Growth usually as good as or better than on agar; sometimes gas is produced.

Stock culture agar slants: Growth generally better than on agar. Usually no gas.

Broth: Turbidity light, uniform to granular, with or without flocculent sediment.

NaCl broth: No growth in 5 per cent NaCl.

Milk: Acid and gas. No visible peptonization.

Milk agar streak plate: Very small, if any, zone of hydrolysis of the casein.

Potato: Inconspicuous or scant growth with the production of much gas and decomposition of the potato.

Indole not produced.

Acid and usually gas (with ammonium salts as source of nitrogen) from arabinose, rhamnose, xylose, glucose, sucrose, lactose, mannitol and sorbitol (the production of gas can best be demonstrated by growing the cultures at 37° C. on the following media: agar plus 1 per cent potato starch, potato plugs or wheat mash as used for the production of crystalline dextrins).

Starch hydrolyzed. Crystalline dextrins produced from starch.

Acetylmethylcarbinol not produced. Acetone and ethanol produced.

pH of glucose broth cultures is 5.0 or lower.

Citrates not utilized.

Methylene blue reduced and then completely reoxidized.

Nitrites produced from nitrates. No gas produced in nitrate broth under anaerobic conditions.

Biotin and thiamine are essential for growth.

Lecithinase reaction negative or faint.

Aerobic, facultatively anaerobic. Usually there is growth with the production of gas in glucose broth under anaerobic conditions (neutral broth is better than the alkaline broth generally prepared for this test).

Temperature relations: Optimum, between 28° and 40° C. Maximum, usually between 45° and 50° C.

Source: Isolated from vats in which flax was retting.

Habitat: Widely distributed in soil, water, decomposing starchy materials, retting flax, etc.

14. **Bacillus alvei** Cheshire and Cheyne,

1895. (Jour. Roy. Microscop. Soc., Ser. II, *5*, 1895, 592.)

al've.i. L. noun *alveus* a beehive; L. gen. noun *alvei* of a beehive.

Rods, 0.5 to 0.8 by 2.0 to 5.0 microns, frequently occurring side by side in long rows. Motile. Gram-variable. Variation: Non-motile and with capsular material (Clark, Jour. Bact., *38*, 1939, 491).

Spores, 0.8 to 1.0 by 1.2 to 2.0 microns, ellipsoidal, central to terminal. Spore wall thick and easily stained. Free spores frequently in parallel arrangement like that of the rods.

Sporangia distinctly bulged, spindle-shaped to clavate.

Gelatin stab: Slow liquefaction.

Gelatin agar streak plate: Good zone of hydrolysis.

Agar colonies: Thin, smooth, translucent, quickly spreading as a thin layer over entire plate. Variation: Round and rather gummy.

Giant colonies: Motile, bullet-shaped, micro-colonies moving in large arcs from point of inoculation, usually covering the plate in 1 day (agar plates should stand a couple days in order to dry the surface somewhat before using).

Agar slants: Growth thin, flat, spreading over the surface. Migrating colonies on the upper, drier part of the slant. Variation: Growth thick and gummy.

Glucose agar slants: Growth thinner or thicker than on agar.

Glucose nitrate agar slants: Scant, if any, growth.

Proteose-peptone acid agar slants: No growth.

Soybean agar slants: Growth, if any, scant, thin and spreading. Variation: Abundant, dense, wrinkled.

Broth: Turbidity uniform, light to moderate.

NaCl broth: No growth in 5 per cent NaCl.

Milk: Usually coagulated; little or no acid; peptonized.

Milk agar streak plate: Wide zone of hydrolysis of the casein.

Potato: Growth, if any, inconspicuous to moderate, spreading, yellowish.

Indole is produced.

Acid but no gas (with ammonium salts as source of nitrogen) from glucose; acid usually produced from sucrose. Generally no acid from lactose or mannitol. No acid from arabinose or xylose.

Starch is hydrolyzed.

Acetylmethylcarbinol is produced.

pH of glucose broth is usually 4.8 to 5.6.

Citrates not utilized.

Methylene blue reduced; reoxidation variable.

Nitrites not produced from nitrates. No gas produced in nitrate broth under anaerobic conditions.

Urease not produced.

Thiamine is essential for growth.

Lecithinase reaction negative or restricted.

Aerobic, facultatively anaerobic. Growth in glucose broth under anaerobic conditions, often with a few bubbles of gas.

Temperature relations: Optimum, about 30° C. Maximum, between 43° and 45° C.

Source: Isolated from the larvae of the honey bee infected with European foulbrood.

Habitat: Widely distributed in soil and bee-hives.

15. Bacillus stearothermophilus Donk, 1920. (Jour. Bact., *5*, 1920, 373.)

ste.a.ro.ther.mo'phi.lus. Gr. noun *stear* fat; Gr. noun *thermus* heat; Gr. adj. *philus* loving; M.L. adj. *stearothermophilus* (presumably intended to mean) heat- and fat-loving.

Rods, 0.6 to 1.0 by 2.0 to 5.0 microns, sometimes occurring in filaments. Motile. Gram-variable.

Spores, 1.0 to 1.2 by 1.5 to 2.2 microns, characteristically variable in size, ellipsoidal, terminal to subterminal. Spore wall thick and easily stained.

Sporangia definitely swollen and racket-shaped.

Gelatin stab: No liquefaction (temperature too low).

Gelatin agar streak plate: Usually there is a wide zone of hydrolysis.

Agar colonies: Not distinctive, pinpoint to small, round to irregular, translucent to opaque, rough to smooth.

Agar slants: Growth variable, ranging from thin, scant, rough and non-spreading to good, opaque, smooth and spreading.

Glucose agar slants: Growth usually less than on agar.

Glucose asparagine agar slants: Growth variable.

Proteose-peptone acid agar slants: No growth.

Soybean agar slants: Growth, if any, less than on agar.

Stock culture agar slants: Growth usually less than on agar.

Broth: Turbidity usually uniform.

NaCl broth: Scant, if any, growth in 3 per cent NaCl.

Milk agar streak plate: Hydrolysis of casein variable.

Tomato yeast milk: Not coagulated in 3 days at 45° to 50° C. (Gordon and Smith, Jour. Bact., 58, 1949, 327). Coagulated at 65° C. (Stark and Tetrault, Sci. Agr., 32, 1952, 81).

Potato: Scant, if any, growth.

Indole not produced.

Acid but no gas (with peptone as source of nitrogen) from glucose. Acid production variable from arabinose and xylose. With ammonium salts as a source of nitrogen, acid production is variable from glucose.

Starch is hydrolyzed.

Acetylmethylcarbinol not produced.

pH of glucose broth cultures is 4.5 to 6.6.

Citrates usually not utilized.

Nitrites usually produced from nitrates. Nitrites not produced from nitrates (Donk). Usually no gas produced in nitrate broth under anaerobic conditions.

Aerobic, facultatively anaerobic. Usually there is growth in glucose broth under anaerobic conditions.

Temperature relations: Optimum, between 50° and 65° C. Growth variable at 70° C. and 37° C. No growth at 28° C.

Source: Isolated from spoiled canned corn and string beans.

Habitat: Widely distributed in soil and spoiled food products.

16. **Bacillus circulans** Jordan, 1890, *emend.* Ford, 1916. (Jordan, Mass. State Board of Health, Exp. Invest., pt. 2, 1890, 831; Ford, Jour. Bact., 1, 1916, 519.)

cir'cu.lans. L. part.adj. *circulans* circling, making round.

Rods, 0.5 to 0.7 by 2.0 to 5.0 microns, some slightly bent, with ends rounded or pointed, usually not in chains. Usually actively motile. Gram-negative. Variations: 0.4 to 0.9 by 1.5 to 5.0 microns. Contain metachromatic granules. Encapsulated.

Spores, 0.8 to 1.4 by 1.1 to 2.4 microns, ellipsoidal, terminal to sub-terminal. Spore wall thick and easily stained. Variations: Kidney-shaped or cylindrical. Lateral or central. Thin-walled.

Sporangia definitely swollen and clavate.

Gelatin stab: Slow, cone-shaped liquefaction, liquefied portion evaporating (Jordan); no liquefaction (Ford).

Gelatin agar streak plate: Usually a zone of hydrolysis is visible.

Agar colonies: Thin, spreading, translucent to transparent, sometimes barely visible or small to medium in size, opaque, entire.

Giant colonies: Sometimes there are motile micro-colonies which move from the point of inoculation in a rotating pattern, eventually covering the entire plate (poured agar plates should be allowed to stand 2 or 3 days at room temperature in order to dry the surface somewhat before using).

Agar slants: Growth scant, thin, spreading, often indistinct. Variations: Growth moderate, entire, dense, coherent.

Beef extract agar slants (without peptone): Sporulation usually better than on agar.

Glucose agar slants: Growth usually heavier than on agar. Variations: Very gummy, opaque. Less growth than on agar.

Proteose-peptone acid agar slants: Usually no growth.

Soybean agar slants: Growth, if any, less than on agar.

Broth: Turbidity light to fair. Sediment flocculent to slimy. No growth by a few strains.

NaCl broth: No growth by some strains in 2 per cent NaCl. Growth by other strains in 5 per cent. No growth in 7 per cent.

Milk: Usually acid; slowly coagulated.

Milk agar streak plate: Usually scant, if any, hydrolysis of the casein.

Potato: Usually no visible growth. Variations: Growth scant to abundant, yellowish to brownish. Gummy.

Indole not produced.

Acid but no gas (with ammonium salts as source of nitrogen) from glucose; acid usually produced from arabinose, xylose and sucrose.

Starch is hydrolyzed. Crystalline dextrins produced from starch by some strains.

Acetylmethylcarbinol not produced.

pH of glucose broth cultures is usually less than 5.5.

Citrates usually not utilized.

Methylene blue usually reduced; reoxidized in few days.

Nitrites may or may not be produced from nitrates. Usually no gas produced in nitrate broth under anaerobic conditions.

Urease usually not produced.

Thiamine and biotin are essential for growth.

Lecithinase not produced.

Aerobic, usually facultatively anaerobic. Usually there is growth in glucose broth under anaerobic conditions, pH 4.8 to 6.0.

Temperature relations: Optimum, about 30° C. Maximum, usually between 40° and 45° C.; with some strains, between 50° and 55° C.

Source: Isolated from tap water.

Habitat: Widely distributed in soil, water and dust; also found as a laboratory contaminant.

17. **Bacillus laterosporus** Laubach, 1916. (Jour. Bact., *1*, 1916, 511.)

la.te.ros'po.rus. L. noun *latus, lateris* the side or flank; Gr. noun *spora* seed; M.L. noun *spora* a spore; M.L. adj. *laterosporus* with lateral spore.

Rods, 0.5 to 0.8 by 2.0 to 5.0 microns, sometimes slightly smaller or larger in width, with ends poorly rounded or pointed. Motile. Gram-variable.

Spores, 1.0 to 1.3 by 1.2 to 1.5 microns, ellipsoidal, central, formed at one side of the rod. Spore wall thick and easily stained. Remnants of sporangium adhering to ma-

ture spore thicker on one side of the spore than on the other.

Sporangia definitely bulged and spindle-shaped.

Gelatin stab: Slow liquefaction.

Gelatin agar streak plate: Visible zone of hydrolysis.

Agar colonies: Thin, translucent, spreading, irregular. Variations: Small, round, rough, opaque.

Agar slants: Growth thin, flat, spreading, translucent. Variations: Growth abundant or restricted. Opaque.

Glucose agar slants: Growth heavier than on agar, dense and wrinkled.

Soybean agar slants: Growth variable.

Broth: Turbidity uniform to granular.

NaCl broth: Usually there is growth in 2 per cent NaCl; no growth in 5 per cent.

Milk: Usually curdled, peptonized.

Milk agar streak plate: Usually there is a wide zone of hydrolysis of the casein.

Potato: Growth scant to abundant, spreading, gray, pink or brown.

Indole usually produced.

Acid but no gas (with ammonium salts as source of nitrogen) from glucose and mannitol; acid usually produced from sucrose. No acid from arabinose or xylose.

Starch not hydrolyzed.

Acetylmethylcarbinol not produced.

pH of glucose broth cultures is 6.0 to 7.4.

Citrates not utilized.

Nitrites produced from nitrates. Usually a few bubbles are produced in nitrate broth under anaerobic conditions.

Urease not produced.

Aerobic, facultatively anaerobic. Growth in glucose broth under anaerobic conditions, pH 4.8 to 5.8.

Temperature relations: Optimum, between 28° and 37° C. No growth at 45° C.

Source: Isolated from water.

Habitat: Widely distributed in soil, water and dust.

18. **Bacillus pulvifaciens** Katznelson, 1950. (Jour. Bact., *59*, 1950, 153.)

pul.vi.fa'ci.ens. L. noun *pulvus* dust; L. v. *facio* to make; M.L. part.adj. *pulvifaciens* dust-producing.

Rods, 0.3 to 0.6 by 1.5 to 3.0 microns,

with rounded ends, not in chains. Motile. Gram-positive.

Spores, 0.8 to 1.0 by 1.3 to 1.5 microns, ellipsoidal, central to terminal; spore wall thick and easily stained (sporulation variable on most media; best on potato).

Sporangia definitely swollen; spindle-shaped to clavate.

Gelatin agar streak plate: Visible zone of hydrolysis.

Glucose agar colonies: Small, round, smooth, dense, orange to colorless.

Agar slants: Growth scant to fair, flat, smooth, translucent to opaque, pink to orange or brownish, rapidly dissociating to the colorless stage.

Glucose agar slants: Growth heavier than on agar. Many needle-, boat- and bayonet-shaped microcrystals are present in the growth after 6 days.

Soybean agar slants: Growth scant to fair, pink to orange, rapidly dissociating to the colorless stage. Many microcrystals.

Tyrosine agar slants: Same as on agar.

Broth: Poor to fair uniform turbidity.

NaCl broth: Growth in 5 per cent NaCl. No growth in 8 per cent.

Milk agar streak plate: Wide zone of hydrolysis of the casein.

Potato: Growth moderate, spreading, thin, orange (sporulation and pigment formation may be maintained by transferring every 2 months on potato plugs; incubation temperature, 37° C.; storage at 28° C.).

Indole not produced.

Acid but no gas (with agar as the base medium) from glucose, glycerol and mannitol. No acid (no growth) with ammonium salts as source of nitrogen.

Starch not hydrolyzed.

Acetylmethylcarbinol not produced.

pH of glucose broth cultures is 5.0 to 5.8.

Citrates not utilized.

Methylene blue usually reduced and re-oxidized.

Nitrites produced from nitrates. No gas produced in nitrate broth under anaerobic conditions.

Urease not produced.

Aerobic, facultatively anaerobic. Growth in glucose broth under anaerobic conditions, pH 5.2 to 5.6.

Temperature relations: Optimum, about 37° C. Maximum, 45° C. No growth at 50° C. Poor growth and less pigmentation at 28° C.

Pathogenicity: Possible cause of death of honey bee larvae.

Source: Isolated from dry, powdery, light-brown scales of dead larvae of the honey bee.

Habitat: Probably same as the source.

19. **Bacillus brevis** Migula, 1900, *emend.* Ford, 1916. (Bacillus No. I, Flügge, Ztschr. f. Hyg., *17*, 1894, 294; *Bacillus lactis* No. I, Kruse, in Flügge, Die Mikroorganismen, 3 Aufl., *2*, 1896, 208; Migula, Syst. d. Bakt., *2*, 1900, 583; not *Bacillus brevis* Lustig, Diagnostica dei batteri delle acque, Torino, 1890, 52; Ford, Jour. Bact., *1*, 1916, 522.)

bre'vis. L. adj. *brevis* short.

Rods, 0.6 to 0.9 by 1.5 to 4.0 microns, with ends poorly rounded or pointed, not in chains. Protoplasm finely granular. Motile. Gram-variable, usually Gram-negative. Variations: Slightly smaller or larger in diameter. Rarely encapsulated.

Spores, 1.0 to 1.3 by 1.3 to 2.0 microns, ellipsoidal, central to sub-terminal. Spore wall usually thick and easily stained. Variation: Spores lateral in few cases, like those of *Bacillus laterosporus*.

Sporulation in some strains poor on media made with highly refined agar; much better when crude agar is used or when soil extract is added to the refined agar (Smith and Gordon, unpublished data).

Sporangia definitely bulged; spindle-shaped to clavate.

Gelatin stab: Slow, crateriform liquefaction.

Gelatin agar streak plate: Wide zone of hydrolysis.

Agar colonies: Thin, smooth, translucent, quickly spreading over entire plate. Variations: Small, round, opaque, non-spreading.

Agar slants: Growth thin, smooth, spreading or non-spreading, translucent, becoming opaque and creamy with age.

Glucose agar slants: Growth usually more abundant than on agar, wrinkled, spreading.

Soybean agar slants: Growth usually abundant, dense, spreading.

Broth: Turbidity usually heavy, uniform, with or without fragile pellicle.

NaCl broth: Usually no growth in 2 per cent NaCl.

Milk agar streak plate: Wide zone of hydrolysis of the casein.

Potato: Growth scant to moderate, flat, spreading, creamy, pink or brownish. Frequently resembles growth of *Bacillus pumilus*.

Indole not produced.

Acid but no gas (with ammonium salts as source of nitrogen) from glucose and sucrose; acid usually produced from mannitol. No acid from arabinose, xylose or lactose. (A few strains are not able to use ammonia. Organic nitrogen cannot be substituted because of the strong proteolytic activity of the organism.)

Starch not hydrolyzed.

Acetylmethylcarbinol not produced.

pH of glucose broth cultures is 8.0 to 8.6.

Citrate utilization variable.

Methylene blue reduced and not reoxidized in 21 days.

Nitrites may or may not be produced from nitrates. A few strains produce gas in nitrate broth under anaerobic conditions.

Urease not produced.

Growth factors not essential.

Lecithinase not produced.

Aerobic, rarely facultatively anaerobic. No growth in glucose broth under anaerobic conditions.

Temperature relations: Optimum, between 28° and 40° C. Maximum, usually between 45° and 55° C.

The antibiotics gramicidin and tyrocidin are obtained from certain strains (Dubos and Hotchkiss, Jour. Exp. Med., *73*, 1941, 629; also see Hotchkiss and Dubos, Jour. Biol. Chem., *141*, 1941, 155), while gramicidin S is obtained from other strains (Gause and Brazknikova, Lancet, *247*, 1944, 715).

Source: Isolated from milk (Flügge); milk, soil and dust (Ford).

Habitat: Widely distributed in soil, air, dust, milk and cheese; also common as a laboratory contaminant.

20. **Bacillus larvae** White, 1905. (Bacterium X, Moore and White, N. Y. State Dept. Agr., 11th Ann. Rept. Comm. Agr. for 1903, 1904, 111; Bacillus X, Moore and White, *ibid.*, Rept. for 1904, 1905, 106; White, Thesis, Cornell Univ., Ithaca, N. Y., 1905; White, U. S. Dept. Agr. Bur. Entomol., Tech. Ser. Bull. 14, 1906, 32; White, U. S. Dept. Agr. Bull. 809, 1920, 13.)

lar'vae. L. noun *larva* a ghost, mask; M.L. noun *larva* a larva; M.L. gen.noun *larvae* of a larva.

Description taken from Lochhead (Sci. Agr., *9*, 1928, 84).

Rods, 0.5 to 0.8 by 2.5 to 5.0 microns, occurring singly and in chains. Motile. Gramvariable.

Spores ellipsoidal, central to subterminal. Sporangia swollen and spindle-shaped.

Gelatin stab: No growth.

Carrot gelatin: Slow liquefaction.

Yeast carrot agar colonies: Small, whitish, somewhat transparent, smooth, slightly glistening.

Agar slants: No growth. With addition of carrot extract, there is noticeable growth along the line of inoculation. More abundant growth with the further addition of yeast extract.

Yeast carrot broth: Fungoid in appearance, floating masses breaking up on shaking to produce uniform clouding.

Carrot milk: Acid with curdling. No peptonization.

Potato: No growth.

Indole not produced (Stoilova, Zent. f. Bakt., II Abt., *99*, 1938, 124).

Acid but no gas (in yeast extract peptone broth) from xylose, glucose, fructose, galactose and salicin; slight acid produced by some strains from lactose and sucrose. No acid from mannitol or dulcitol.

Starch not hydrolyzed (carrot starch agar).

Nitrites produced from nitrates (Lochhead, Can. Jour. Research, C, *15*, 1937, 79).

Purine bases are necessary for growth (Katznelson and Lochhead, Jour. Bact., *55*, 1948, 763).

Thiamine replaces the growth factor in vegetable or yeast extract, etc. (Lochhead, Jour. Bact., *44*, 1942, 185).

Growth, as well as spore-formation, in complex organic media enhanced by treatment with activated charcoal or soluble starch (Foster et al., Jour. Bact., *59*, 1950, 463).

Temperature relations: Optimum, about 37° C. Maximum, about 45° C.

Pathogenicity: Cause of American foulbrood of honey bees.

Source: Isolated from scales of dead larvae.

Habitat: Diseased broods.

21. **Bacillus popilliae** Dutky, 1940. (Jour. Agr. Research, *61*, 1940, 59.)

po.pil'li.ae. M.L. noun *Popillia* generic name of the Japanese beetle; M.L. gen.noun *popilliae* of *Popillia*.

Description taken from Dutky (*loc. cit.*).

Rods, unstained, 0.9 by 5.2 microns. Stained by crystal violet after fixing in Schaudinn's solution, 0.3 by 3.5 microns. Non-motile. Gram-positive.

Spores, 0.9 by 1.8 microns, cylindrical, central. No free spores observed. Spores formed on artificial media (Steinkraus and Tashiro, Science, *121*, 1955, 873).

Sporangia swollen and spindle-shaped (contain a refractile body, about half the size of the spore, at the broader pole of the cell; this body reacts similarly to spores with respect to stains).

Unheated egg yolk beef infusion agar slants: Small, discrete colonies.

Aerobic, facultatively anaerobic.

Temperature relations: Optimum, about 30° C. Maximum, about 36° C.

Pathogenicity: Cause of type A milky disease of Japanese beetle (*Popillia japonica* Newm.).

Source: Isolated from infected larvae.

Habitat: Diseased larvae in soil.

22. **Bacillus lentimorbus** Dutky, 1940. (Jour. Agr. Research, *61*, 1940, 65.)

len.ti.mor'bus. L. adi. *lentus* slow; L. noun *morbus* disease; M.L. noun *lentimorbus* the slow disease.

Description taken from Dutky (*loc. cit.*).

Rods, unstained, 1.0 by 5.0 microns. Stained by crystal violet after fixing in Schaudinn's solution, 0.5 by 4.0 microns.

Spores formed on artificial media (Steinkraus and Tashiro, Science, *121*, 1955, 873).

Grows on artificial media (Dutky, Jour.

Bact., *54*, 1947, 267; also see Steinkraus and Tashiro, *op. cit.*, 1955, 873).

Aerobic, facultatively anaerobic.

Temperature relations: Optimum, about 25° C. Maximum, about 30° C.

Pathogenicity: Cause of type B milky disease of Japanese beetle (*Popillia japonica* Newm.).

Source: Isolated from infected beetles.

Habitat: Diseased larvae in soil.

23. **Bacillus pantothenticus** Proom and Knight, 1950. (Jour. Gen. Microbiol., *4*, 1950, 539.)

pan.to.then'ti.cus. M.L. adj. *acidum pantothenicum* pantothenic acid; M.L. adj. *pantothenticus* (probably intended to mean) related to pantothenic acid.

Rods, 0.4 to 0.7 by 1.2 to 3.5 microns, not in chains. Stain evenly. Motile. Gram-positive.

Spores, 0.8 to 1.0 by 0.8 to 1.3 microns, round to ellipsoidal, terminal. Spore wall thin and not easily stained. (Round spores are smaller than the ellipsoidal.)

Sporangia definitely swollen; drumstick- to racket-shaped.

Gelatin agar streak plate: Wide zone of hydrolysis.

Agar colonies: Small, round, translucent to dense, granular to moiré, smooth to rough. Embedded colonies lenticular or irregular and hairy.

Agar slants: Growth moderate, thick, not spreading, whitish.

Glucose agar slants: Growth scant, less than on agar.

Proteose-peptone acid agar slants: No growth.

Soybean agar slants: No growth.

Broth: Light to moderate uniform turbidity.

NaCl broth: Growth in 10 per cent NaCl; marked stimulation by a 5 per cent concentration.

Milk agar streak plate: Wide zone of hydrolysis of the casein.

Potato: No growth.

Indole not produced.

Acid but no gas (with ammonium salts as source of nitrogen) from glucose and sucrose. Acid production variable from arabinose. No acid from xylose or mannitol. With organic basal medium (Proom and Knight), acid from arabinose and xylose.

Starch hydrolyzed. Crystalline dextrins not produced from starch.

Acetylmethylcarbinol not produced.

pH of glucose broth cultures is 5.8 to 6.0.

Citrate utilization variable.

Methylene blue reduction variable.

Nitrites may or may not be produced from nitrates. Usually no gas produced in nitrate broth under anaerobic conditions.

Urease not produced.

Pantothenic acid, biotin and thiamine are essential for growth.

Lecithinase reaction positive though restricted.

Aerobic, facultatively anaerobic. Scant growth in glucose broth under anaerobic conditions, pH 5.4 to 6.4.

Temperature relations: Optimum, between 33° and 40° C. Maximum, between 45° and 50° C. Slow growth at 28° C.

Source: Isolated from soils of Southern England.

Habitat: Probably widely distributed in soil.

24. Bacillus sphaericus Neide, 1904. (Cent. f. Bakt., II Abt., *12*, 1904, 350.)

sphae′ri.cus. Gr. adj. *sphaericus* spherical.

Rods, 0.6 to 1.0 by 1.0 to 7.0 microns, with ends rounded or pointed, occurring singly or in short chains. Motile. Gram-variable, often Gram-negative with Gram-positive granules.

Spores, 0.7 to 1.2 microns in diameter, round, terminal to subterminal. Spore wall usually thick and easily stained. Remnants of the sporangium often adhere making the surface rough and spiny. Immature spores sometimes ellipsoidal, becoming round. Sporulation variable, best on soybean agar.

Sporangia, definitely swollen; usually drumstick-shaped.

Gelatin stab: Growth scant; no liquefaction.

Gelatin agar streak plate: Usually there is a visible zone of hydrolysis.

Agar colonies: Thin, smooth, translucent, rapidly spreading over entire plate. Variations: Small, round or irregular.

Giant agar colonies: Usually motile mi-cro-colonies of various shapes move in large arcs from the point of inoculation and cover the plate in 1 day (the surface of poured agar plates should be dried by holding at room temperature for 2 or 3 days before use).

Agar slants: Growth thin, smooth, translucent, spreading. Variations: Rough, restricted, opaque, wrinkled.

Agar slants at pH 6.0: Growth same as at pH 7.0.

Glucose agar slants: Same as on agar.

Glucose nitrate agar slants: Scant, if any, growth.

Soybean agar slants: Growth heavier and sporulation much better than on agar.

Broth: Turbidity heavy, uniform to granular. Sometimes a fragile pellicle is formed.

NaCl broth: Usually there is growth in 4 per cent NaCl. No growth in higher concentrations.

Milk: No change.

Milk agar streak plate: Hydrolysis of the casein is variable.

Potato: Growth thin, soft, spreading, gray, usually becoming brownish with age.

Indole not produced.

No acid from carbohydrates.

Starch not hydrolyzed.

Acetylmethylcarbinol not produced.

pH of glucose broth cultures is 7.8 to 8.2.

Citrates usually not utilized.

Methylene blue reduced; not reoxidized in 21 days.

Nitrites not produced from nitrates. No gas produced in nitrate broth under anaerobic conditions.

Urease production variable.

Usually thiamine and sometimes also biotin are essential for growth.

Lecithinase not produced.

Aerobic. No growth in glucose broth under anaerobic conditions.

Temperature relations: Optimum, between 28° and 35° C. Maximum, between 40° and 45° C.

Not pathogenic for guinea pigs.

Source: Isolated from mud from a pond; also from rotting cypress and oak wood and soil.

Habitat: Widely distributed in nature.

25. Bacillus pasteurii (Miquel, 1889) Migula, 1900. (*Urobacillus pasteurii* Miquel,

Ann. de Micrographie, *1*, 1889, 552; Migula, Syst. d. Bakt., *2*, 1900, 726.)

pas.teur'i.i. M.L. gen.noun *pasteurii* of Pasteur; named for Louis Pasteur, a French chemist and bacteriologist.

Description taken from Löhnis and Kuntze (Cent. f. Bakt., II Abt., *20*, 1908, 684), Gibson (Jour. Bact., *28*, 1934, 295 and 313; also see *ibid.*, *29*, 1935, 491) and Smith, Gordon and Clark (*op. cit.*, 1952).

Rods, 0.6 to 0.9 by 1.5 to 3.5 microns (1.0 to 1.5 by 4.0 to 5.0 microns, Löhnis and Kuntze), with rounded ends, usually not in chains. Motile. Gram-variable.

Spores, 1.0 to 1.2 microns in diameter, round, terminal to subterminal.

Sporangia usually bulged and clavate.

Urea gelatin stab: Slow, crateriform liquefaction.

Urea gelatin streak plate: Visible zone of hydrolysis.

Urea agar colonies: Small, round, not distinctive.

Urea agar slants: Growth thin, restricted, translucent.

Urea agar slants with pH 6.0 or less: No growth.

Urea soybean agar slants: Good growth, heavier than on agar.

Urea broth: Turbidity uniform, moderate to heavy.

NaCl urea broth: Growth in 10 per cent NaCl.

Urea milk agar streak plate: Hydrolysis of the casein is variable.

No acid from carbohydrates with agar plus urea as base medium.

Starch not hydrolyzed.

Acetylmethylcarbinol not produced (urea added).

Nitrites produced from nitrates in urea nitrate broth. Gas production variable under anaerobic conditions.

Urease produced.

Thiamine plus biotin or nicotinic acid are essential for growth. Alkaline reaction and usually ammonia or urea are also essential.

Aerobic, facultatively anaerobic. Growth in urea glucose broth under anaerobic conditions.

Temperature relations: Optimum, between 28° and 35° C. Maximum, between 37° and 40° C.

Source: Isolated from decomposing urine.

Habitat: Widely distributed in soil, manure and sewage.

Genus II. **Clostridium** *Prazmowski, 1880.**

(Untersuchungen über die Entwickelungsgeschichte und Fermentwirkung einiger Bacterien-Arten, Inaug. Diss., Leipzig, 1880, 23.)

Clos.tri'di.um. Gr. noun *closter* a spindle; M.L. dim.noun *clostridium* a small spindle.

Rods, often swollen at sporulation, producing clostridial, plectridial, clavate or navicular forms. Motile by means of peritrichous flagella; occasionally non-motile. Generally Gram-positive. Many species are saccharolytic and fermentative, producing various acids (generally butyric and acetic), gases (CO_2, H_2 and, at times, CH_4) and variable amounts of neutral products, i.e. alcohols and acetone. Other species are proteolytic, some being capable of attacking native and coagulated proteins with putrefaction or more complete proteolysis. Several species are active in the fixation of free nitrogen. Strictly anaerobic or anaerobic, aerotolerant. Catalase is lacking except in small amounts in certain aerotolerant forms. A few species are obligately thermophilic. Exotoxins are sometimes produced. Commonly found in soil and in the intestinal tracts of man and other animals.

The type species is *Clostridium butyricum* Prazmowski.

---

* Revised by Prof. R. S. Spray, School of Medicine, West Virginia University, Morgantown, West Virginia, May, 1942. Further revision by Prof. L. S. McClung, Department of Bacteriology, Indiana University, Bloomington, Indiana, and Prof. Elizabeth McCoy, Department of Bacteriology, College of Agriculture, University of Wisconsin, Madison, Wisconsin, September, 1955.

Key to the species of genus **Clostridium.**

I. Strictly anaerobic.*
  A. Cellulose not typically fermented.
    1. Distinctive pigments not characteristically produced.
      a. Central or eccentric to subterminal spores.
        b. Ovoid spores.
          c. Rods distinctly swollen at sporulation.
            d. Motile.
              e. Gelatin and/or glucose-gelatin may or may not be liquefied.
                f. Gelatin and/or glucose-gelatin not liquefied.
                  g. Glucose fermented.
                    h. Coagulated albumin not liquefied.
                      i. Milk coagulated.
                        j. Stormy fermentation or at least active coagulation of milk.
                          k. Glycerol may or may not be fermented.
                            l. Glycerol not fermented. Mannitol fermented.
                              m. Starch, lactose and sucrose fermented.
                                n. Starches of potato and of maize mash are fermented.
                        1. *Clostridium butyricum.*
                                nn. Starch of potato mash but not of maize mash is fermented.
                        2. *Clostridium butylicum.*
                            mm. Starch not fermented. Lactose and sucrose fermented.
                      3. *Clostridium beijerinckii.*
                          ll. Glycerol fermented.
                            m. Hemolytic on blood agar.
                    4. *Clostridium multifermentans.*
                            mm. Non-hemolytic on blood agar.
                    5. *Clostridium iodophilum.*
                      kk. Action on glycerol not recorded. Colonies rubbery mucoid.
                  6. *Clostridium gummosum.*
                  jj. Milk slowly coagulated, not stormily. Glycerol and mannitol not fermented.
                7. *Clostridium fallax.*
              ii. Milk not coagulated.
                j. Salicin fermented.
                8. *Clostridium difficile.*
                jj. Salicin not fermented.
                  k. Calcium lactate fermented.

---

* Those unfamiliar with anaerobic techniques should consult L. Ds. Smith, Introduction to the Pathogenic Anaerobes, University of Chicago Press, 1955, 253 pp.

         9. *Clostridium tyrobutyricum.*

        kk. Calcium lactate not fermented.

        10. *Clostridium pasteurianum.*

     hh. Action on coagulated albumin not recorded.

       i. Milk coagulated without gas production.

         j. Digestion of milk not recorded. Milk acid-coagulated.

         11. *Clostridium toanum.*

         jj. Digestion of milk slight, if at all. Milk slowly acid-coagulated.

         12. *Clostridium amylosaccharobutylpropylicum.*

       ii. Milk coagulated with gas production; no digestion.

        j. Hydrogen sulfide produced.

         13. *Clostridium madisonii.*

        jj. Hydrogen sulfide not produced.

         14. *Clostridium muelleri.*

   gg. Glucose not fermented.

    h. Hydrogen sulfide not produced.

     15. *Clostridium amylolyticum.*

    hh. Hydrogen sulfide produced.

     16. *Clostridium nigrificans.*

  ff. Gelatin and/or glucose-gelatin liquefied.

   g. Glucose fermented.

    h. Coagulated albumin may or may not be liquefied.

     i. Coagulated albumin not liquefied.

      j. Milk not digested.

       k. Milk slowly coagulated. Clot not digested.

        l. Glycerol and mannitol not fermented.

         m. Lactose fermented. Pathogenic.

          n. Sucrose not fermented. Salicin fermented.

       17. *Clostridium septicum.*

          nn. Sucrose fermented. Salicin not fermented.

       18. *Clostridium chauvoei.*

         mm. Lactose not fermented. Nonpathogenic.

       19. *Clostridium nauseum.*

        ll. Glycerol fermented.

       20. *Clostridium haemolyticum.*

       kk. Milk acidified but not coagulated. Mannitol not fermented.

        l. Lactose, sucrose and salicin not fermented. Exotoxin (atoxic strains possible) produced which is toxic on injection but not on feeding. Colonies on egg yolk agar produce intense precipitate and luster zone in regular circle.

m. Exotoxin is produced.

n. Produces hemolytic lecithinase (gamma).

21. *Clostridium novyi* (Type A).

nn. Produces hemolytic lecithinase (beta).

21a. *Clostridium novyi* (Type B).

mm. Non-toxic.

21b. *Clostridium novyi* (Type C).

ll. Lactose, sucrose and salicin not
fermented. Exotoxin (atoxic strains
possible) produced which is toxic
on injection and feeding. Colonies
on egg yolk agar produce precipitation zone in regular circle and
narrow luster zone following contour of colony.

m. Adonitol fermented (Type B).

22. *Clostridium botulinum*.

mm. Adonitol not fermented.

22a. *Clostridium botulinum* (Type C).

22b. *Clostridium botulinum* (Type D).

22c. *Clostridium botulinum* (Type E).

jj. Milk digested.

23. *Clostridium limosum*.

ii. Coagulated albumin slowly to rapidly liquefied.

j. Stormy fermentation or at least active
coagulation of milk; slow digestion.

k. Pectin not fermented. Inulin and mannitol fermented.

24. *Clostridium acetobutylicum*.

kk. Pectin fermented. Inulin and mannitol
not fermented.

25. *Clostridium laniganii*.

jj. Milk slowly and softly coagulated, not
stormily. Clot slowly to rapidly digested.

k. Glycerol may or may not be fermented.

l. Glycerol and mannitol not fermented. Action on starch not recorded.

m. Lactose fermented.

26. *Clostridium aerofoetidum*.

mm. Lactose not fermented.

27. *Clostridium sporogenes*.

ll. Glycerol fermented. Mannitol not
fermented. Exotoxin produced
which is toxic on injection and on
feeding.

28. *Clostridium parabotulinum* (Types A and
B).

kk. Action on glycerol not recorded. Mannitol not fermented.
29. *Clostridium caproicum*.
hh. Action on coagulated albumin not recorded.
30. *Clostridium saccharoacetoperbutylicum*.
gg. Glucose not fermented (carbohydrates not fermented).
h. Coagulated albumin not digested. Lab-coagulation of milk; increasing alkalinity. Clot digested.
31. *Clostridium hastiforme*.
hh. Action on coagulated albumin not recorded.
Slow, mildly acid coagulation of milk. Clot digested.
32. *Clostridium subterminale*.
ee. Action on gelatin and glucose-gelatin not recorded.
f. Glucose fermented.
g. Raffinose, sorbitol and dulcitol fermented.
33. *Clostridium lactoacetophilum*.
gg. Raffinose, sorbitol and dulcitol not fermented.
34. *Clostridium kaneboi*.
ff. Glucose not fermented.
35. *Clostridium propionicum*.
dd. Non-motile.
e. Gelatin and glucose-gelatin not liquefied. Glucose fermented.
36. *Clostridium setiense*.
ee. Gelatin liquefied.
f. Indole produced.
g. Milk coagulated and later digested.
37. *Clostridium tale*.
gg. Milk digested without coagulation.
38. *Clostridium mangenotii*.
ff. Indole not produced.
39. *Clostridium lituseburense*.
cc. Rods not swollen at sporulation.
d. Motile.
e. Gelatin and/or glucose-gelatin liquefied. Glucose fermented.
Coagulated albumin liquefied. Milk slowly coagulated. Clot
slowly digested. Some strains produce exotoxin.
40. *Clostridium bifermentans*.
ee. No growth on iron-gelatin (Spray).
41. *Clostridium cylindrosporum*.
dd. Non-motile. Gelatin and/or glucose-gelatin liquefied. Glucose
fermented. Coagulated albumin not liquefied. Milk stormily fermented. Clot not digested. Glycerol fermentation variable. Mannitol not fermented. Starch, lactose and sucrose fermented.
Salicin rarely fermented. Types identified by specific toxin-
antitoxin neutralization.
42. *Clostridium perfringens* (Types A, B, C,
D, E and F).
bb. Spherical spores.
c. Rods distinctly swollen at sporulation. Motile. Gelatin and/or glucose-gelatin not liquefied. Glucose fermented. Coagulated albumin
not liquefied.

    d. Milk acidified.

        e. Milk slowly and softly coagulated, not stormily. Clot not digested.

            43. *Clostridium sphenoides.*

        ee. Milk not coagulated.

            44. *Clostridium innominatum.*

    dd. Milk neither acidified nor coagulated.

            45. *Clostridium microsporum.*

  cc. Rods not swollen at sporulation. Non-motile. Gelatin and/or glucose-gelatin not liquefied. Glucose fermented. Coagulated albumin not liquefied. Milk acidified but not coagulated.

            46. *Clostridium filiforme.*

aa. Terminal spores.

  b. Distinctly ovoid to ellipsoid spores. Rods distinctly swollen at sporulation.

    c. Motile.

      d. Gelatin and/or glucose-gelatin not liquefied.

        e. Glucose fermented. Coagulated albumin not liquefied.

          f. Milk slowly coagulated. Clot not digested. Glycerol not fermented.

            g. Mannitol fermented.

              47. *Clostridium sartagoformum.*

            gg. Mannitol not fermented.

              48. *Clostridium paraputrificum.*

          ff. Milk unchanged.

            49. *Clostridium indologenes.*

        ee. Glucose not fermented.

          f. Coagulated albumin not liquefied. Milk unchanged.

            50. *Clostridium cochlearium.*

          ff. Action on coagulated albumin not recorded. No growth on milk or on iron-milk (Spray). Carbohydrates not fermented.

            g. Ethyl alcohol fermented chiefly to caproic acid.

              51. *Clostridium kluyveri.*

            gg. Ethyl alcohol not fermented to caproic acid. Requires uric acid or other purines as primary source of carbon and energy

              52. *Clostridium acidiurici.*

    dd. Gelatin and/or glucose-gelatin liquefied. Glucose fermented.

        e. Coagulated albumin liquefied.

          f. Milk often, but not always, coagulated. Clot, if produced, not digested.

            53. *Clostridium capitovale.*

          ff. Milk partially coagulated, later partially digested.

            54. *Clostridium cadaveris.*

        ee. Coagulated albumin not liquefied.

            55. *Clostridium saprogenes.*

    cc. Non-motile.

            56. *Clostridium perenne.*

  bb. Spores spherical, or nearly so.

    c. Rods distinctly swollen at sporulation.

      d. Motile.

        e. Action on gelatin definitely established.

f. Gelatin and/or glucose-gelatin not liquefied.
g. Glucose fermented. Coagulated albumin not liquefied.
h. Action on milk recorded.
i. Milk not alkalinized.
j. Milk slowly coagulated, not stormily. Clot not digested.
k. Indole not produced.
57. *Clostridium thermosaccharolyticum.*
kk. Indole produced.
58. *Clostridium indolis.*
jj. Milk not coagulated; unchanged.
59. *Clostridium caloritolerans.*
ii. Milk slowly alkalinized. Casein slowly separated.
60. *Clostridium tetanoides.*
hh. Action on milk not recorded.
61. *Clostridium tartarivorum.*
gg. Glucose not fermented.
62. *Clostridium sporosphaeroides.*
ff. Gelatin and/or glucose-gelatin liquefied. Glucose not fermented. Coagulated albumin slowly liquefied.
g. Milk may show soft lab-coagulation. Clot not definitely digested.
63. *Clostridium tetani.*
gg. Milk shows soft lab-coagulation. Clot slowly digested.
64. *Clostridium lentoputrescens.*
ee. Records on action on gelatin at variance. Glucose fermented. Coagulated albumin not liquefied. Milk not coagulated; unchanged.
65. *Clostridium tetanomorphum.*
dd. Non-motile. Gelatin and/or glucose-gelatin liquefied. Glucose fermented. Coagulated albumin liquefied.
66. *Clostridium putrefaciens.*
cc. Rods slightly swollen at sporulation.
67. *Clostridium thermoaceticum.*
2. Pigments of varied colors are characteristically produced. Rods distinctly swollen at sporulation.
a. Central or eccentric to subterminal, ovoid spores. Motile.
b. Gelatin and/or glucose-gelatin not liquefied.
c. Violet pigment produced in potato mash. Indole produced.
68. *Clostridium belfantii.*
cc. Red pigment produced.
d. Milk coagulated.
69. *Clostridium venturellii.*
dd. Milk not coagulated.
70. *Clostridium saturnirubrum.*
bb. Gelatin and/or glucose-gelatin liquefied.
c. Reddish pigments produced.
d. Red to orange-red pigment produced, especially in starchy media. Indole not produced.
e. Stormy fermentation of milk. Clot slowly softened.
71. *Clostridium roseum.*

ee. Milk not fermented stormily.
  f. Slow, spongy coagulation of milk. Clot slowly digested.
    72. *Clostridium chromogenes*.
  ff. Milk coagulated rapidly. Clot not digested.
    73. *Clostridium corallinum*.
dd. Pink to orange-red pigment produced in maize mash. Nitrites not produced from nitrates.
    74. *Clostridium aurantibutyricum*.
cc. Yellowish pigments produced.
  d. Yellow-orange pigment produced in various media. Indole not produced. Milk actively coagulated but not stormily. Clot not digested.
    75. *Clostridium felsineum*.
  dd. Canary-yellow pigment produced in various media.
    76. *Clostridium flavum*.
aa. Terminal spores.
  b. Ovoid spores.
    c. Non-motile. Gelatin and/or glucose-gelatin not liquefied. Deep red pigment produced on potato slants.
      77. *Clostridium carbonei*.
    cc. Motile.
      78. *Clostridium haumanii*.
  bb. Spherical spores. Produces a soluble, green pigment.
      79. *Clostridium virens*.
B. Cellulose typically fermented. Terminal spores. Rods distinctly swollen at sporulation.
  1. Distinctive pigments not characteristically produced.
    a. Distinctly ovoid to ellipsoid spores.
      b. Motile.
        c. A variety of carbohydrates, other than cellulose, are fermented after prolonged incubation.
          80. *Clostridium spumarum*.
        cc. Carbohydrates, other than cellulose, not fermented.
          81. *Clostridium werneri*.
      bb. Non-motile.
          82. *Clostridium leptinotarsae*.
    aa. Spores spherical, or nearly so.
      b. Non-motile. Glucose not fermented.
          83. *Clostridium cellulosolvens*.
      bb. Motile.
        c. Glucose fermented.
          84. *Clostridium cellobioparum*.
        cc. Glucose not fermented.
          85. *Clostridium omelianskii*.
  2. Distinctive pigments characteristically produced in certain media.
    a. Distinctly ovoid to ellipsoid spores.
      b. Non-motile.
          86. *Clostridium dissolvens*.
      bb. Motile.
          87. *Clostridium thermocellum*.
    aa. Spores spherical, or nearly so. Thermophilic. Glucose fermented.
          88. *Clostridium thermocellulaseum*.

II. Anaerobic, aerotolerant (grow customarily as anaerobes but are able to produce scant, sometimes atypical, growth on aerobic agar slants). Cellulose not typically fermented. Distinctive pigments not characteristically produced.
  A. Central or eccentric to subterminal, ovoid spores. Rods distinctly swollen at sporulation. Motile.
    1. Gelatin and/or glucose-gelatin not liquefied.
                             89. *Clostridium carnis.*
    2. Gelatin and/or glucose-gelatin liquefied.
      a. Carbohydrates not fermented.
                             90. *Clostridium histolyticum.*
      aa. Carbohydrates fermented.
                             91. *Clostridium lacunarum.*
  B. Terminal, distinctly ovoid to ellipsoid spores. Rods distinctly swollen at sporulation. Motile.
    1. Gelatin and/or glucose- gelatin not liquefied.
                             92. *Clostridium tertium.*
    2. Gelatin liquefied.
                             93. *Clostridium pectinovorum.*

1. **Clostridium butyricum** Prazmowski, 1880. (Untersuchungen über die Entwickelungsgeschichte und Fermentwirkung einiger Bacterien-Arten, Inaug. Diss., Leipzig, 1880, 23.)

bu.ty'ri.cum. Gr. noun *butyrum* butter; M.L. adj. *butyricus* relating to butter; M.L. noun *acidum butyricum* butyric acid.

Original description supplemented by material taken from Adamson (Jour. Path. and Bact., *22*, 1919, 371) and from Hall (Jour. Inf. Dis., *30*, 1922, 467).

Straight or slightly curved rods, 0.7 by 5.0 to 7.0 microns, with rounded ends, occurring singly, in pairs, in short chains and occasionally in long filaments. Spores are oval and eccentric to subterminal, swelling the cells to clostridial forms. Motile. Granulose-positive in the clostridial stage (blue color with iodine). Gram-positive, becoming Gram-negative.

Gelatin and glucose-gelatin: No liquefaction.

Glucose agar surface colonies (anaerobic): Circular or slightly irregular, slightly raised, moist, creamy white.

Glucose agar deep colonies: Biconvex, dense, yellowish white, entire. Agar fragmented early by abundant gas.

Plain agar slant (anaerobic): Little or no growth.

Plain broth: Little or no growth.

Glucose broth: Abundant, diffuse turbidity; much gas.

Litmus milk: Acid and early coagulation. Litmus is reduced. Stormy fermentation; clot fragmented but not digested.

Indole not produced.

Acid and gas from xylose, glucose, lactose, sucrose, starch, salicin, esculin and mannitol. Amygdalin, pectin, cellulose, glycerol and Ca-lactate not fermented.

Fermentation products include butyl, ethyl and iso-propyl alcohols, acetone, organic acids, H_2 and CO_2.

Nitrites not produced from nitrates.

Atmospheric nitrogen is fixed, though less actively than by *Clostridium pasteurianum* Winogradsky (Rosenblum and Wilson, Jour. Bact., *57*, 1949, 413).

Coagulated albumin: No liquefaction.

Blood agar: No hemolysis.

Blood serum: No liquefaction.

Brain medium: No blackening or digestion.

Anaerobic.

Grows well between 30° and 37° C.

Not pathogenic for guinea pigs or rabbits.

Source: Originally isolated from cheese. Commonly encountered in naturally soured milk, in naturally fermented starchy plant substances and in soil.

Habitat: Probably rather widely dispersed in soils rich in humus.

2. **Clostridium butylicum** (Beijerinck, 1893) Donker, 1926. (*Granulobacter butylicum* Beijerinck, Verhandl. d. K. Akad. v. We-

tensch., Amsterdam, Tweedie Sectie, Deel I, 1893, 3; Donker, Thesis, Delft, 1926, 149; also see Sjolander and McCoy, Zent. f. Bakt., II Abt., *97*, 1937, 314.)

bu.ty'li.cum. M.L. adj. *butylicus* pertaining to the butyl radical.

Rods. Large, ovoid spores swelling the cells. Clostridia freely formed. Motile. Granulose-positive in young cultures. Gram-positive.

Gelatin: No liquefaction.

Glucose agar colonies: Moist, circular to irregular, raised, creamy.

Milk: Stormy fermentation.

Xylose, glucose, sucrose, lactose, mannitol, salicin, esculin and maize starch are fermented. Glycerol, amygdalin, pectin, cellulose and Ca-lactate are not fermented.

Products of glucose fermentation, in addition to acetic and butyric acids, are isopropyl, butyl and ethyl alcohols and acetone.

Ferments starch of potato mash; maize mash starch not fermented due to inadequate growth.

Nitrites not produced from nitrates.

Atmospheric nitrogen fixed, though less actively than by *Clostridium pasteurianum* Winogradsky (Rosenblum and Wilson, Jour. Bact., *57*, 1949, 413).

Coagulated albumin: Action not recorded; assumed negative.

Blood agar: No hemolysis.

Anaerobic.

Optimum temperature, 30° C.

Source: Isolated from soil.

Habitat: Soil.

3. **Clostridium beijerinckii** Donker, 1926. (Donker, Thesis, Delft, 1926, 145; also see Sjolander and McCoy, Zent. f. Bakt., II Abt., *97*, 1937, 314.)

bei.jer.inck'i.i. M.L. gen.noun *beijerinckii* of Beijerinck; named for Prof. M. W. Beijerinck of Delft, Holland.

Large rods, sometimes occurring in chains. Sporulation free, forming clostridia; spores measure 1.5 by 2.0 microns. Motile by means of peritrichous flagella. Granulose-positive in young clostridia. Gram-positive.

Gelatin: No liquefaction.

Glucose agar colonies: Moist, circular to irregular, raised, white to creamy.

Milk: Stormy fermentation.

Glucose, fructose, lactose, galactose, maltose, sucrose, xylose, mannitol, sorbitol, inositol, inulin, salicin and esculin are fermented. Glycerol, dextrin, glycogen, dulcitol, amygdalin, starch, pectin, cellulose and Ca-lactate are not fermented.

Nitrites not produced from nitrates.

Atmospheric nitrogen fixed, though less actively than by *Clostridium pasteurianum* Winogradsky (Rosenblum and Wilson, Jour. Bact., *57*, 1949, 413).

Coagulated albumin: Action not recorded; assumed negative.

Blood agar: No hemolysis.

Anaerobic.

Optimum temperature, 30° C.

Distinctive character: Starch not fermented.

Source: Isolated from soil and from fermenting plant tissues.

Habitat: Apparently widely distributed in agricultural soils.

4. **Clostridium multifermentans** Bergey et al., 1923. (*Bacillus multifermentans tenalbus* Stoddard, Lancet, *1*, 1919, 12; Bergey et al., Manual, 1st ed., 1923, 324.)

mul.ti.fer.men'tans. L. adj. *multus* much, many; L. part.adj. *fermentans* fermenting; M.L. part.adj. *multifermentans* many (sugars)-fermenting.

Slender rods, with rounded ends, occurring singly or in short chains. Ovoid spores, subterminal or central, are freely formed and swell the cells. Motile, though sometimes non-motile forms occur in glucose broth. Granulose-positive (Hill, Jour. Bact., *10*, 1925, 413). Gram-positive in very young cultures, quickly becoming Gram-negative.

Gelatin: No liquefaction (Hill, *loc. cit.*).

Glucose agar surface colonies: Grayish, opaque, 2 to 3 mm in diameter, raised, with sharp edges and irregular outline. Older colonies white and rubbery mucoid.

Glucose agar deep colonies: Lenticular, often with horn-like projections. Gas production common.

Carbohydrate-free medium: No growth.

Glucose broth: Heavy, flocculent growth with extensive gas production.

Milk: Gas and acid production with coagulation; no digestion.

Indole not produced.

Glucose, lactose, sucrose, maltose, glycerol, raffinose and salicin fermented. No action on dulcitol or mannitol. Action on inulin variable.

Starch agar: Strong diastatic action.

Coagulated albumin: No digestion.

Blood agar surface colonies: Similar to those on glucose agar; definite hemolytic zone (Stoddard, Lancet, *1*, 1919, 12).

Chopped meat medium: Extensive gas production without change in color or without digestion.

Anaerobic.

Optimum temperature, 37° C.

Apparently not pathogenic for rabbits except in combination with *Clostridium sporogenes*.

Source: Isolated from a human muscle infected with gas gangrene (Stoddard, Lancet, *1*, 1919, 12), from fermented olives (Gililland and Vaughn, Jour. Bact., *46*, 1943, 315) and from spoiled chocolate candy (Hill, *op. cit.*, 1925, 413).

Habitat: Unknown.

5. Clostridium iodophilum Svartz, 1935. (*Clostridium butyricum iodophilum* Svartz, Jour. Inf. Dis., *47*, 1930, 149; Svartz, Acta Med. Scand., Supp., *78*, 1935, 434; also see Sjolander and McCoy, Zent. f. Bakt., II Abt., *97*, 1937, 314.)

i.o.do'phi.lum. Gr. noun *ium* the violet; M.L. noun *iodinum* iodine; Gr. adj. *philus* loving; M.L. adj. *iodophilum* iodine-loving.

Rods, 0.5 to 0.8 by 3.0 to 6.0 microns, with rounded ends. Ovoid spores, eccentric to subterminal, swell the cells. Clostridia measure 1.5 by 4.0 microns. Motile. Granulose-positive. Gram-positive.

Gelatin: No liquefaction.

Glucose calcium carbonate agar colonies: Lens- or star-shaped, white, small, gummy.

Glucose blood agar surface colonies: Round or slightly angular, brown to grayish white, shiny. No hemolysis.

Agar slants: Sparse growth.

Milk: Rapid curdling; stormy fermentation.

Fructose, galactose, salicin, sucrose, lactose, arabinose, glucose, glycerol, esculin, maize starch and pectin are fermented. Dulcitol, cellulose, amygdalin and Ca-lactate

are not fermented. Fermentation variable for inulin and mannitol.

Fermentation of glucose yields, in addition to acetic and butyric acids, butyl and ethyl alcohols and acetone but not isopropyl alcohol.

Nitrites not produced from nitrates.

Coagulated albumin: Action not recorded; assumed negative.

Brain media: No blackening.

Anaerobic.

Optimum temperature, 37° C.

Source: Isolated from the feces of man and from fertile soil.

Habitat: Found in the intestinal tract of man.

6. Clostridium gummosum Spray, 1947. (Jour. Bact., *54*, 1947, 15; also see *ibid.*, *55*, 1948, 841.)

gum.mo'sum. L. adj. *gummosus* full of gum, gummy.

Rods, 0.8 to 1.0 by 4.0 to 8.0 microns, occurring singly and in pairs but not in chains. Sporulation active at 24 to 48 hours; spores are eccentric to chiefly subterminal, large, ovoid to elongate, markedly swelling the cells. Moderately motile, increasing in activity up to 48 hours. Gram reaction not recorded; implied positive.

Gelatin (or iron-gelatin): No liquefaction or blackening at 19 days.

Agar surface colonies (anaerobic): Large, round, convex, entire, very glistening, mucoid.

Agar deep colonies: Large lenticular to buckwheat. White to creamy; very viscid to rubbery mucoid; entire colony dissected from the medium or dragged unbroken by needle through 2 per cent agar (subsurface colonies).

Milk (with iron-strip): Slow fermentation, with a stream of fine gas bubbles; coagulation at 18 to 20 hours, with the coagulum torn and forced to the surface. No digestion or blackening even upon prolonged incubation.

Indole not produced.

Hydrogen sulfide not produced in lead acetate agar or peptone iron agar.

Acid and gas from glucose, maltose, galactose and mannitol. Lactose more slowly fermented. Sucrose, salicin, dulcitol and inositol not attacked.

Nitrites not produced from nitrates.

Coagulated albumin: No liquefaction.

Blood agar: No hemolysis.

B ood serum: No liquefaction.

Brain medium (Hibler): No blackening or digestion even in the presence of an iron strip.

Anaerobic.

Optimum temperature not determined. Grows well both at 37° C. and at room temperature.

Not pathogenic for white mice, guinea pigs or rabbits.

Distinctive character: Submerged colonies extremely gummatous.

Source: Isolated once from gaseous gangrene and twice from normal human feces (adult and infant).

Habitat: Decomposing organic matter, so far as known.

7. Clostridium fallax (Weinberg and Séguin, 1915) Bergey et al., 1923. (Bacille A, Weinberg and Séguin, Compt. rend. Soc. Biol., Paris, *78*, 1915, 277; *Bacillus fallax* Weinberg and Séguin, *ibid.*, 686; Bergey et al., Manual, 1st ed., 1923, 325; *Clostridium pseudo-fallax* Prévot and Loth, Ann. Inst. Past., *67*, 1941, 244.)

fal'lax. L. adj. *fallax* deceptive, false.

Rods, 0.6 by 1.2 to 5.0 microns, occurring singly or rarely in pairs. Spores, rarely observed, are ovoid, eccentric to subterminal and swell the cells. Encapsulated in body fluids. Motile by means of peritrichous flagella. Gram-positive.

Gelatin: No liquefaction.

Glucose agar surface colonies (anaerobic): Circular, flat; transparent, crenated margin.

Glucose agar deep colonies: Lenticular, bean-shaped, irregular, smooth.

Agar slant (anaerobic): Grayish film.

Broth: Poor growth; slight, diffuse turbidity.

Glucose broth: Abundant turbidity and gas. Clearing by sedimentation.

Litmus milk: Acid; slowly coagulated. Litmus reduced. Clot channeled by gas but not digested.

Indole not produced (Duffett, Jour. Bact., *29*, 1935, 576).

Acid and gas from glucose, galactose, fructose, maltose, lactose, sucrose, inulin, salicin and starch. Glycerol and mannitol not fermented. Records vary in regard to action on lactose, inulin and salicin.

Coagulated albumin: No liquefaction.

Blood serum: No liquefaction.

Brain medium: No blackening or digestion.

Meat medium: Reddened; no blackening or digestion.

Anaerobic.

Optimum temperature, not recorded. Grows well at 37° C.

A weak exotoxin is produced.

Pathogenicity for guinea pig variable and commonly lost in cultivation.

Source: Isolated from war wounds, appendicitis and once from black-leg of sheep.

Habitat: Presumably widely distributed.

8. Clostridium difficile (Hall and O'Toole, 1935) Prévot, 1938. (*Bacillus difficilis* Hall and O'Toole, Amer. Jour. Dis. Child., *49*, 1935, 390; *Clostridium difficilis* (sic) Prévot, Ann. Inst. Past., *61*, 1938, 84.)

dif.fi'ci.le. L. adj. *difficilis* difficult.

Heavily bodied rods. Spores elongated and subterminal, slightly swelling the cells. Actively motile. Gram-positive.

Gelatin: No liquefaction.

Agar deep colonies: Minute, flat, opaque discs, becoming lobate.

Egg yolk agar surface colonies: Irregular, flattened, dry, roughened, somewhat granular, with little or no color. No precipitate in the agar nor luster on the colony.

Milk: Poor growth. Gas produced in traces, but milk unchanged.

Acid and gas from glucose, fructose, mannitol, salicin and xylose. Traces of gas but no acid from galactose, maltose, sucrose, lactose, raffinose, inulin and glycerol.

Nitrites produced from nitrates (Reed, Jour. Bact., *44*, 1942, 425).

Coagulated albumin: No liquefaction.

Blood agar surface colonies (anaerobic): Irregular, flat; no hemolysis.

Blood serum: No liquefaction.

Brain medium with iron: Moderately blackened. Digestion not recorded.

Anaerobic.

Grows well at 37° C.

Toxicity: Glucose broth culture filtrates kill guinea pigs and rabbits in 24 to 36 hours.

Pathogenic for guinea pigs and rabbits. Subcutaneous inoculation induces marked edema. Death may occur in from 1 to 9 days.

Source: Isolated from the feces of newborn infants.

Habitat: Presumably widely distributed.

9. **Clostridium tyrobutyricum** van Beynum and Pette, 1935. (Zent. f. Bakt., II Abt., *93*, 1935, 208; also see Bryant and Burkey, Jour. Bact., *71*, 1955, 43).

ty.ro.bu.ty′ri.cum. Gr. noun *tyrus* cheese; M.L. noun *acidum butyricum* butyric acid; M.L. adj. *tyrobutyricus* (probably intended to mean) the butyric acid-producing organism from cheese.

Large rods, 0.8 to 1.2 by 2.0 to 15.0 microns. Subterminal, ovoid spores swelling the cells. Motile. Gram-positive.

Gelatin: No liquefaction.

Tomato juice agar surface colonies: Entire, opaque, slightly convex, cream-colored.

Tomato juice agar deep colonies: Lenticular.

Milk: No change.

Indole not produced.

Hydrogen sulfide not produced.

Glucose, calcium lactate, fructose and arabinose are fermented. Sucrose, maltose, starch, inulin, raffinose, salicin, dextrin, mannose, dulcitol, sorbitol and rhamnose are not fermented. Galactose, xylose, lactose, mannitol and glycerol are variably fermented.

Nitrites may or may not be produced from nitrates.

Coagulated albumin: Action not recorded; assumed negative.

Anaerobic.

Distinctive character: Fermentation of lactate.

Source: Isolated from silage and from cheese.

Habitat: Decomposing organic matter, so far as known.

10. **Clostridium pasteurianum** Wino-

gradsky, 1895. (Winogradsky, Arch. Sci. Biol. (Russ.), *3*, 1895, 330; *Clostridium pastorianum* (sic) Winogradsky, Cent. f. Bakt., II Abt., *9*, 1902, 43; also see McCoy, Fred, Peterson and Hastings, Jour. Inf. Dis., *46*, 1930, 118.)

pas.teu.ri.a′num. M.L. adj. *pasteurianus* pertaining to Pasteur; named for Louis Pasteur, French chemist and bacteriologist.

Large rods, 0.9 to 1.7 by 3.5 to 4.7 microns, sometimes occurring in chains. Spores large, 1.5 by 2.0 microns, each retained in a characteristic "capsule" (a portion of the clostridial cell). Motile by means of peritrichous flagella. Granulose-positive. Gram-positive.

Gelatin: No liquefaction.

Beef-peptone-glucose agar surface colonies: Round, slightly raised, moist, creamy yellow; granular structure; dense centers; entire edges.

Beef-peptone-glucose agar deep colonies: Small, woolly, biconvex, dense.

Milk: Little change.

Indole not produced.

Hydrogen sulfide not produced in brain mash, with or without iron.

Glucose, fructose, maltose, sucrose, arabinose, xylose (possibly variable), galactose, mannose, trehalose, raffinose, soluble starch, melezitose, inulin (possibly variable), alpha-methyl-glucoside, glycerol, inositol, mannitol and sorbitol are fermented. Rhamnose, lactose, maize starch, dextrin, glycogen, amygdalin, salicin, esculin, erythritol, dulcitol, quercitol, pectin, cellulose and calcium lactate are not fermented.

More tolerant of high concentrations of glucose and sucrose than are other butyric-acid-producing species (Spiegelberg, Food Research, *5*, 1940, 115).

Nitrites not produced from nitrates.

Atmospheric nitrogen is fixed.

Coagulated egg albumin: No digestion.

Blood agar: No hemolysis.

Coagulated blood serum: No change in color or texture.

Anaerobic.

Optimum temperature, 25° C.

Distinctive characters: Prolonged retention of the spore within a peculiar, brushlike spore-capsule; starch and lactose not fermented. More active in the assimilation of free atmospheric nitrogen than are other butyric-acid-producing species.

Source: Isolated from soil and from acid-canned fruit.

Habitat: Soil.

11. Clostridium toanum Baba, 1943. (Jour. Agr. Chem. Soc. Japan, *19*, 1943, 207.)

to.a′num. Etymology Japanese, meaning unknown.

Large rods, 1.04 by 5.47 microns, occurring singly or in short chains, becoming spindle-shaped in 48 hours; average size then is 1.91 by 7.35 microns. Spores ovoid, 1.4 to 2.1 microns, central to subterminal. Encapsulated. Actively motile in young cultures. Granulose-positive. Gram-positive, becoming Gram-negative.

Gelatin: No liquefaction.

Glucose meat infusion agar slant (anaerobic, 35° C., 3 days): Fairly good growth. Moist, glistening, irregular, milky white colonies. Gas splits agar.

Glucose meat infusion agar stab: Growth good; sticky; gas is produced.

Tryptone agar slant: Poor growth.

Meat infusion: Poor growth.

Glucose meat infusion: Good growth; viscous precipitate; butanol odor.

Milk: Coagulated.

Potato slant (anaerobic, 35° C., 3 days): Colonies island-like, moist, dull glistening, milky white, bubbling. After 7 days, growth heavier with strong butanol odor.

Potato or maize mash: Good growth; "head" formation; clear fermentation liquid.

Indole not produced.

Hydrogen sulfide not produced.

Glucose, l-arabinose, fructose, mannose, galactose, sucrose, maltose, trehalose, alpha-methyl-glucoside, dextrin, soluble starch and glycogen are vigorously fermented. Less vigorously fermented are raffinose, salicin, mannitol and beta-cellobiose. Xylose, lactose, pectin and calcium lactate are weakly fermented. Fermentation questionable for amygdalin. Adonitol, l-rhamnose, inulin, glycerol, dulcitol, d-sorbitol, inositol and quercitol not attacked.

Fermentation products are butanol, isopropanol, acetone, ethanol and butyric acid.

Nitrites produced from nitrates.

Serum: Poor growth; liquefaction very weak.

Catalase-negative.

Anaerobic.

Temperature relations: Optimum, 33° C. Optimum fermentation, between 35° C. and 37° C.

Chemical tolerance: Fermentation occurs between pH 5.8 and 6.5. Growth occurs between pH 6.0 and 7.0, 6.2 affording the best growth.

Source: Not indicated.

Habitat: Unknown.

12. Clostridium amylosaccharobutylpropylicum Beesch and Legg, 1947. (*Clostridium amylo-saccharo-butylpropylicum* (sic) Beesch and Legg, U. S. Letters Pat., 2,420,998, May 27, 1947.)

a.my.lo.sac.char.o.bu.tyl.pro.pyl′i.-cum. L. noun *amylum* starch; Gr. noun *saccharum* sugar; M.L. adj. *butylicus* pertaining to the butyl radical; M.L. adj. *propylicus* pertaining to the propyl radical; M.L. adj. *amylosaccharobutylpropylicum* (probably intended to mean) the organism which ferments starch and sugar with the production of butyl and propyl alcohols.

Short and long rods, 0.6 to 2.8 by 2.5 to 12.0 microns, with rounded ends, occurring singly or in chains. Sporangia are spindle-shaped and clavate. Spores cylindrical to ovoid, measuring 0.5 to 2.0 by 0.8 to 2.8 microns, subterminal to terminal. Motile by means of peritrichous flagella. Granulose-positive. Gram-positive, but variable after 24 hours.

Gelatin stab: Growth best below surface to bottom line of puncture. No liquefaction.

Agar colonies: Circular with spreading tendency, smooth, pearly luster to surface, entire, convex. Colonies appear opalescent with dark centers, finely granular, light tan.

Agar slant: Growth abundant, spreading, glistening, light cream-colored to tan, viscid with a butylic odor.

Broth: No surface growth; slight clouding; no odor.

Litmus milk: Acid curd produced in 10 days; slight, if any, peptonization at 15 days.

Potato: Abundant, spreading, glistening,

viscid, light cream-colored to yellow growth with a butylic odor. Medium liquefied slightly, if at all.

Indole not produced.

Hydrogen sulfide produced in trace amounts, if at all, on lead acetate agar.

Acid and gas from esculin, trehalose, arabinose, xylose, glucose, fructose, galactose, mannose, lactose, sucrose, maltose, maize starch, soluble starch, inulin, dextrin, glycogen, salicin and alpha-methyl-glucoside. Rhamnose, raffinose, melezitose, glycerol, erythritol, mannitol, sorbitol, dulcitol, inositol and melibiose not attacked.

Nitrites not produced from nitrates.

Anaerobic.

Optimum fermentation temperature, between 29° and 32° C.

Optimum pH, between 5.4 and 5.8.

Source: Isolated from soil.

Habitat: Soil.

13. **Clostridium madisonii** McCoy, 1946. (U. S. Letters Pat., 2,398,837, April 23, 1946.)

mad.i.son′i.i. M.L. gen.noun *madisonii* of Madison.

Short to long rods, 0.5 to 1.0 by 3.0 to 5.8 microns, with rounded ends, occurring singly or in short chains. Spores abundant, cylindrical to ellipsoidal, 0.7 to 1.3 by 1.3 to 2.4 microns, subterminal to terminal. Sporangia elongated, spindle-shaped. Actively motile in young cultures. Granulose-positive in young cells. Gram-positive, becoming negative in old cultures.

Gelatin: No liquefaction.

Molasses-glucose agar colonies: Dark cream, round, entire, viscid, raised to convex.

Molasses-glucose agar slant: Moderate, glistening, confluent growth.

Litmus milk: Reduced before curdling; moderate gas production; soft acid curd with turbid pink whey, white crystals develop in old cultures. No digestion of casein.

Indole not produced.

Hydrogen sulfide production is positive by strip test when thiosulfate brain mash, sulfite brain mash or oatmeal (5 per cent) mash is used. Negative with other media tried.

Acid and gas from glucose, mannose, fruc-

tose, sucrose, maltose, lactose, trehalose, alpha-methyl-glucoside, mannitol, arabinose, xylose, galactose, melezitose, soluble starch, maize starch, dextrin, inulin, glycogen, esculin, sorbitol, raffinose, salicin, amygdalin and inositol. Rhamnose, glycerol, erythritol, quercitol, dulcitol and cellulose not attacked.

Nitrites not produced from nitrates.

Atmospheric nitrogen fixed, though not as actively as by *Clostridium pasteurianum* Winogradsky (Rosenblum and Wilson, Jour. Bact., *57*, 1949, 413).

Blood agar (glucose agar plus 10 per cent defibrinated horse blood): Good growth; no hemolysis, but some surrounding colonies discolored by acid.

Von Hibler brain (plain or with iron): Growth with gas production and sporulation but no blackening or digestion.

Temperature relations: Growth between 8° and 42° C. Optimum fermentation, between 29° and 33° C.

Chemical tolerance: Growth between pH 4.3 and 7.6; apparent optimum for fermentation, between pH 5.0 and 6.0, preferably about 5.5.

Anaerobic.

Source: Original strain isolated from field soil collected near Madison, Wisconsin.

Habitat: Probably soil.

14. **Clostridium muelleri** McClung and McCoy, *comb. nov.* (*Clostridium granulobacter acetobutylicum* Müller, U. S. Letters Pat., 2,195,629, April 2, 1940.)

muel′le.ri. M.L. gen.noun *muelleri* of Müller; named for Müller, the bacteriologist who first isolated this species.

Short rods, 0.5 to 1.4 by 3.0 to 10.0 microns, the majority of the cells measuring 1.0 by 5.0 microns, with rounded ends, occurring in chains. Sporangia spindle-shaped, clavate, 1.0 to 2.3 by 6.0 to 10.0 microns, the majority measuring 1.5 by 8.0 microns; spores terminal to subterminal. Motile. Gram-positive.

Gelatin: No liquefaction.

Agar surface colonies: Smooth surface, raised to convex, dull luster, round, granular internal structure; good growth.

Agar + 2 per cent glucose slant: Moderate, slightly spreading, opaque growth with a dull luster, a contoured surface, a butyrous consistency and an odor of butyl alcohol.

Milk: Acid and gas; slight coagulation, no peptonization.

Litmus milk: Acid, gas, coagulation, reduction in bottom of tube; no digestion.

Potato slant: No visible growth, but a butyl alcohol odor, as well as gas, is present in the substended liquid.

Broth: No growth.

Indole not produced.

Hydrogen sulfide not produced.

Acid and gas from glucose, sucrose, lactose, maltose, inulin, starch, salicin, dextrin, mannitol and galactose. Glycerol is not fermented.

Nitrites not produced from nitrates.

Optimum temperature, between 28° and 33° C.

Anaerobic.

Source: Isolated from an ear of sugar maize.

Habitat: Probably soil.

15. Clostridium amylolyticum Prévot and Saissac, 1950. (Ann. Inst. Past., *79*, 1950, 331.)

a.my.lo.ly'ti.cum. Gr. noun *amylum* fine meal, starch; Gr. adj. *lyticus* loosening, dissolving; M.L. adj. *amylolyticus* starch-dissolving.

Straight rods, 0.8 to 1.0 by 4.0 to 5.0 microns. Spores ovoid and subterminal, swelling the cells. Motile. Strongly Gram-positive.

Non-fetid gas and a pronounced butyric odor are produced in culture media.

Gelatin: No liquefaction.

Bean or potato agar deep colonies: Small, woolly, irregular, white, opaque. Gas is produced.

Milk: Acid coagulation without retraction or digestion of clot.

VF glucose (or without glucose) broth: No growth.

Peptone solution (2 per cent): No growth in autoclaved medium; in filtered broth, growth abundant.

Potato mash: Growth rapid, abundant, very gaseous, acidified (pH 4.5 after 4 days of incubation). Very pronounced butyric odor. Mash disintegrated, liquefied, ropy.

Indole not produced.

Hydrogen sulfide not produced.

Spontaneously, only starch and lactose are fermented; pectin not fermented. The following carbohydrates are fermented (tested in filtered peptone solution): glucose, fructose, galactose, maltose, sucrose and mannitol.

Nitrites produced from nitrates in the presence of starch.

Sulfites reduced slowly only in the presence of starch.

Coagulated proteins not attacked.

Anaerobic.

Optimum temperature, between 33° and 37° C.

Hemolysin not produced.

Toxin not produced.

Not pathogenic for guinea pigs or mice.

Source: Isolated from soil.

Habitat: Presumably soil.

16. Clostridium nigrificans Werkman and Weaver, 1927. (Werkman and Weaver, Iowa State Coll. Jour. Sci., *2*, 1927–28, 63; also see Werkman, Iowa State Coll. Research Bull. 117, 1929, 165.)

nig.ri'fi.cans. L. part.adj. *nigrificans* blackening.

Rods, 0.3 to 0.5 by 3.0 to 6.0 microns, with rounded ends. Spores ovoid and subterminal, slightly swelling the cells. Motile. Gram-positive.

Gelatin: No liquefaction.

Agar deep colonies: Blackening of medium around colonies. Black increased by adding 0.1 per cent ferric chloride to medium.

Milk: Action not recorded.

Indole not produced.

Hydrogen sulfide produced from cystine.

Glucose and other carbohydrates not fermented.

Nitrites not produced from nitrates.

Coagulated albumin: No liquefaction.

Blood serum: No liquefaction.

Brain medium: Blackening but no digestion.

Anaerobic.

Temperature relations: Optimum, 55° C. Thermophilic, growing between 65° and 70° C.

Not pathogenic for man, guinea pig, mouse, rat or rabbit.

Distinctive character: Black colonies in

agar media due to extensive hydrogen sulfide production.

Source: Isolated from canned corn showing sulfur stinker spoilage; also occasionally isolated from soil and manure.

Habitat: Presumably soil, although detected with great difficulty.

17. Clostridium septicum (Macé, 1888) Ford, 1927.

(Vibrion septique, Pasteur and Joubert, Compt. rend. Acad. Sci., Paris, *85*, 1877, 113; also see Bull. Acad. Med., 2° Ser., *6*, 1877, 794; *Vibrio pasteurii* Trevisan, Reale Ist. Lombardo d. Sci. e Lett., Rendiconti, Ser. 2, *12*, 1879, 147; *Bacillus septicus* Macé, Traité Prat. d. Bact., 1st ed., 1888, 455; Ford, Textbook of Bact., 1927, 726.)

sep'ti.cum. Gr. adj. *septicus* putrefactive, septic.

Description taken from Weinberg and Séguin (La Gang. Gaz., Paris, 1918, 79) and from Hall (Jour. Inf. Dis., *30*, 1922, 486).

Rods, 0.6 to 0.8 by 3.0 to 8.0 microns, with rounded ends, occurring singly, in pairs and in short chains in cultures; long chains and filaments commonly predominate in body exudates. Spores ovoid, eccentric to subterminal, swelling the cells. Motile by means of peritrichous flagella. Gram-positive.

Gelatin: Liquefaction with gas bubbles.

Agar surface colonies (anaerobic): Small, transparent, variable in shape.

Agar deep colonies: Variable; usually finely filamentous, cottony, spherical.

Egg yolk agar surface colonies: Irregular, flat, moist, somewhat roughened, colorless, without precipitate or luster, often having a tendency to spread.

Broth: Slight, diffuse turbidity, with clearing.

Litmus milk: Litmus reduced; slow coagulation and moderate gas production. Clot not digested.

Indole not produced.

Acid and gas from glucose, fructose, galactose, maltose, lactose and salicin. Sucrose, inulin, mannitol and glycerol not fermented (Hall, *ibid.*, 489).

Nitrites produced from nitrates.

Coagulated albumin: No liquefaction.

Blood agar surface colonies (anaerobic): Delicate, flat, leaf-like, irregular. Hemolytic.

Blood serum: No liquefaction.

Brain medium: No blackening or digestion.

Meat medium: Reddened; no blackening or digestion.

Anaerobic.

Optimum temperature, about 37° C.

An exotoxin is produced which is lethal and hemolytic (van Heyningen, Bacterial Toxins, C. C Thomas, Springfield, 1950, 43).

Pathogenic for guinea pigs, rabbits, mice and pigeons.

Source: Originally isolated from animals inoculated with soil; later from malignant edema of animals, from human war wounds and from cases of appendicitis.

Habitat: Found in animal intestines and in manured soils.

18. Clostridium chauvoei (Arloing et al., 1887) Holland, 1920.

(*Bacterium chauvoei* Arloing, Cornevin and Thomas, Le charbon symptomatique du boeuf, Paris, 2nd ed., 1887, 82; *Clostridium chauvei* (sic) Holland, Jour. Bact., *5*, 1920, 217.)

chau.voe'i. M.L. gen.noun *chauvoei* of Chauveau; named for J. B. A. Chauveau, a French scientist.

Rods, 1.0 by 3.0 to 8.0 microns, occurring singly, in pairs and in short chains. Usually show a dark chromatic point near each end. Spores ovoid, eccentric to subterminal, swelling the cells. Motile by means of peritrichous flagella. Gram-positive.

Gelatin: Liquefaction with gas bubbles.

Agar surface colonies (anaerobic): Small, grayish, semi-opaque, filamentous.

Agar slant (anaerobic): Grayish, spreading growth.

Egg yolk agar surface colonies: Circular to slightly irregular, moist, relatively smooth to somewhat roughened, colorless; no precipitate or luster.

Broth: Turbid; slightly peptolytic.

Litmus milk: Acid; slowly coagulated. Gas may be produced. Clot not digested.

Indole not produced (early studies record only a trace).

Acid and gas from glucose, fructose, galactose, maltose, lactose and sucrose. Inulin, salicin, mannitol, glycerol and dextrin not fermented (Hall, Jour. Inf. Dis., *30*, 1922, 486).

Coagulated albumin: No liquefaction.

Blood serum: No liquefaction.

Brain medium: No blackening or digestion.

Egg-meat medium: Small gas bubbles in 8 hours. Meat becomes pinkish and the liquid slightly turbid. No blackening or digestion.

Anaerobic.

Optimum temperature, 37° C. Growth occurs at 50° C.

An exotoxin is produced.

Pathogenic for guinea pigs, mice and rabbits. Also pathogenic for hamsters (Ryff and Lee, Science, *101*, 1945, 361).

Source: The cause of black leg, black quarter or symptomatic anthrax in cattle and other animals.

Habitat: Probably soil, especially where heavily manured.

19. Clostridium nauseum Spray, 1947. (Jour. Bact., *54*, 1947, 15; also see *ibid.*, *55*, 1948, 839.)

nau'se.um. Gr. noun *nausea* sea sickness; M.L. adj. *nauseus* nauseous, sickening.

Rods, 0.8 to 1.1 by 6.0 to 12.0 microns, with rounded ends, occurring singly, in pairs and in short chains of 4 to 6 cells. Spores ellipsoidal to elongate, subterminal, distinctly swelling the cells, often becoming apparently terminal at maturation. Actively motile, especially in young cultures in semisolid medium, by means of numerous peritrichous flagella. Gram-positive in early vegetative stage, but Gram-negative at sporulation.

Gelatin (or iron-gelatin): Very slow liquefaction; softened at 14 days; complete liquefaction at 30 days; not blackened even in the presence of an iron strip.

Agar surface colonies (anaerobic): Minute, transparent, flat, slightly lobate.

Agar deep colonies: Minute, lenticular, entire, whitish to creamy.

Milk (with iron strip): Solidly coagulated at 4 to 5 days; clot shrinks slowly, but without gas, blackening or digestion. Evidently a rennet curdling, since the whey reaction is neutral to litmus.

Indole production is questionable; if positive, it is obscured by an abundance of skatole. Mercaptan is produced together with other aromatic, putrid, nitrogenous compounds not yet identified.

Lead acetate agar or peptone iron agar (Difco): Blackened in 24 hours.

Acid and gas from glucose, fructose and maltose. Sucrose, lactose, inulin, mannitol, sorbitol, glycerol and inositol are not attacked.

Nitrites not produced from nitrates.

Coagulated albumin: No liquefaction.

Blood agar: No hemolysis.

Blood serum: No liquefaction.

Brain medium (Hibler): Blackened but not visibly digested.

Anaerobic.

Optimum temperature not determined, but grows well at both 37° C. and at room temperature.

Not pathogenic for white mice, guinea pigs or rabbits.

Distinctive character: Extremely nauseous, fecal odor, due apparently to some presently unidentified aromatic nitrogenous compound.

Source: Isolated three times from soil.

Habitat: Presumably from soil.

20. Clostridium haemolyticum (Hall, 1929) Hauduroy et al., 1937. (*Clostridium hemolyticus bovis* (sic) Vawter and Records, Jour. Amer. Vet. Med. Assoc., *68* (N.S. *21*), 1925–26, 512; *Bacillus hemolyticus* (sic) Hall, Jour. Inf. Dis., *45*, 1929, 156; *Clostridium hemolyticum* (sic) Hauduroy et al., Dict. d. Bact. Path., 1937, 125.)

hae.mo.ly'ti.cum. Gr. noun *haema* blood; Gr. adj. *lyticus* dissolving; M.L. adj. *haemolyticus* blood-dissolving.

Rods, 1.0 to 1.3 by 3.0 to 5.6 microns, with rounded ends, occurring singly, in pairs and in short chains. Spores ovoid to elongate, subterminal, swelling the cells. Motile by means of long, peritrichous flagella. Gram-positive.

Gelatin: Liquefaction.

Agar deep colonies: At first lenticular, becoming densely woolly masses with short, peripheral filaments. Little or no gas produced.

Egg yolk agar surface colonies: Punctiform, surrounded by a wide area of precipitation (McClung and Toabe, Jour. Bact., *53*, 1947, 139).

Broth plus liver: Luxuriant, diffuse turbidity followed by agglutinative clearing. Moderate gas production.

Milk: Acid; slow coagulation. Clot not digested.

Indole is produced (Records and Vawter, Nevada Agr. Exp. Sta. Bull. 173, 1945, 30).

Hydrogen sulfide is produced (Records and Vawter, *loc. cit.*).

Acid and gas from glucose, fructose, galactose and glycerol. Lactose, maltose, sucrose, raffinose, arabinose, xylose, inulin, salicin, mannitol and dulcitol not fermented. Subsequent studies have shown that pure galactose is not fermented (Records and Vawter, *loc. cit.*).

Acetylmethylcarbinol not produced (Records and Vawter, *loc. cit.*).

Methyl red test is negative (Records and Vawter, *loc. cit.*).

Nitrites not produced from nitrates (Records and Vawter, *loc. cit.*).

Coagulated albumin: No liquefaction.

Blood agar surface colonies (anaerobic): Light, diffuse growth. Blood hemolyzed.

Blood serum: No liquefaction.

Brain medium: No blackening or digestion.

Meat medium: Reddened; no blackening or digestion.

Anaerobic.

Grows well at 37° C.

Somatic antigen not common with that of *Clostridium novyi* (Turner and Eales, Austral. Jour. Exp. Biol. and Med. Sci., *21*, 1943, 79; also see Smith, Jour. Bact., *65*, 1953, 222).

Pathogenic and toxic for guinea pigs and rabbits. Effect due to an unstable, hemolytic, lethal toxin which is a lecithinase (McClung and Toabe, *op. cit.*, 1947, 255). Toxin also contains (in common with the toxin of *Clostridium novyi* Type B) lysolecithin (Bard and McClung, Indiana Acad. Sci., Proc., *57*, 1948, 43).

Source: Isolated from the blood and from other tissues of cattle dying of icterohemoglobinuria.

Habitat: Not determined. Thus far isolated only from animals.

21. **Clostridium novyi** (Migula, 1900) Bergey et al., 1923. (*Bacillus oedematis ma-*

ligni No. II, Novy, Ztschr. f. Hyg., *17*, 1894, 212; *Bacillus oedematis thermophilus* Kruse, in Flügge, Die Mikroorganismen, 3 Aufl., *2*, 1896, 242; *Bacillus novyi* Migula, Syst. d. Bakt., *2*, 1900, 872; Bergey et al., Manual, 1st ed., 1923, 326; *Clostridium novyi* Type A, Scott, Turner and Vawter, Proc. 12th Internat. Vet. Cong., N. Y., *2*, 1934, 175.)

no'vy.i. M.L. gen.noun *novyi* of Novy; named for F. G. Novy, the American bacteriologist who first isolated this organism.

The descriptions of this and the following types were compiled from Keppie (A study of the Antigens and Toxins of *Clostridium oedematiens* and *C. gigas* by *in-vitro* and *in-vivo* methods. Thesis, Cambridge, 1943), McClung and Toabe (Jour. Bact., *53*, 1947, 139), Oakley, Warrack and Clarke (Jour. Gen. Microbiol., *1*, 1947, 91), Spray (in Manual, 6th ed., 1948, 777) and Turner (Black Disease (Infectious Necrotic Hepatitis) of Sheep in Australia. Counc. Sci. and Ind. Res., Australia, Bull. 46, 1930).

Clostridium novyi Type A.

Rods, 0.8 to 0.9 by 2.5 to 5.0 microns, occurring singly and in pairs, not in chains. Spores large, ovoid, usually subterminal, slightly swelling the cells. Motile by means of peritrichous flagella. Gram-positive.

Iron gelatin (Spray): Liquefaction.

Glucose blood agar surface colonies: Large, 3.0 to 4.0 mm in diameter, compact, raised; finely granular surface; edges coarsely indented; center raised and dense. Usually hemolytic.

Egg yolk agar surface colonies: Smooth; irregular edge; precipitation zone under colony and around colony in a regular circle to a radial distance of about 4 mm. The intense zone of precipitation is sharply defined. Characteristically, an iridescent luster area marked by radial linear striations covers the colony and extends beyond the colony in a regular circular zone to a radial distance of about 2 mm, only partially covering the precipitation zone.

Broth: Turbid; flocculent sediment.

Litmus milk: Acid; no coagulation. Litmus reduced.

Indole not produced.

Glucose and fructose are fermented. Action on glycerol and maltose variable. No action on lactose, sucrose, mannitol or salicin.

Nitrates rapidly reduced; nitrites absent (Reed, Jour. Bact., *44*, 1942, 425).

Coagulated albumin: No liquefaction.

Blood serum: No liquefaction.

Brain medium: No blackening or digestion.

Anaerobic, although less strict than Types B and C.

Optimum temperature, between 35° and 38° C.

Produces an exotoxin which is toxic on injection but not on feeding. Four antigenic components have been recognized in toxic filtrates (Oakley, Warrack and Clarke, Jour. Gen. Microbiol., *1*, 1947, 91; also see van Heyningen, Bacterial Toxins, C. C Thomas, Springfield, 1950, 42). These include: alpha, classical lethal toxin; gamma, hemolytic lecithinase; delta, oxygen-labile hemolysin; and epsilon, probably pearly-layer-agent in egg-agar. Production of gamma toxin differentiates Type A from Types B and C.

Produces a species-specific hemolysin for human red blood cells which is neutralized by selected antisera; differentiated from *Clostridium septicum* on this character.

Pathogenic for guinea pigs, rabbits, mice, rats and pigeons.

Comment: Some authors regard *Clostridium hemolyticum* Hauduroy et al., which produces a hemolytic lecithinase, as belonging to this species.

Source: Isolated from a guinea pig inoculated with peptonized casein; later from a human case of gaseous gangrene. Also isolated from human necrotic hepatitis (Mollaret, Prévot and Guéniot, Ann. Inst. Past., *75*, 1948, 195).

Habitat: Probably widely distributed in manured soil.

21a. *Clostridium novyi* Type B, Scott et al., 1934. (*Bacillus gigas* Zeissler and Rassfeld, Arch. Wiss. u. Prakt. Tierheilk., *59*, 1929, 419; Scott, Turner and Vawter, Proc. 12th Internat. Vet. Cong., N. Y., *2*, 1934, 175.)

Large rods, 1.2 to 2.0 by 10.0 to 14.0 microns, occurring singly, in pairs or in chains of 3 to 4 elements. Spores ovoid, most frequently subterminal, only slightly swelling

the cells. Motile by means of peritrichous flagella. Gram-positive.

Gelatin: Good growth. No liquefaction.

Glucose-gelatin: Good growth. Liquefaction after two weeks of incubation.

Glucose blood agar surface colonies: Delicate, thin, flat plaques of fine filaments, dull surface, scarcely raised above surface of medium. Hemolysis variable.

Egg yolk surface colonies: Small, irregular, transparent, producing a wide (8 mm in diameter), regular, sharply defined circle of precipitation, without luster, under and beyond the colony.

Agar deep colonies: Lenticular or biconvex disc, sometimes with outgrowths or filamentous, woolly colonies with opaque center or bursting-grenade colony type.

Glucose broth: Abundant growth with gas; flocculent sediment.

Meat infusion broth: Growth less abundant than in glucose broth; little or no gas; sediment.

Cooked meat medium: Good growth; gas; meat not blackened.

Milk: Reports variable; little action long delayed, possibly late coagulation without digestion.

Glucose, galactose and fructose are fermented. Action on glycerol and maltose variable. No action on lactose, sucrose, rhamnose, dulcitol, mannitol, inulin or salicin.

Coagulated egg albumin: No digestion.

Brain medium: No blackening unless iron-nail added.

Strictly anaerobic.

Optimum temperature, apparently 37° C.; growth occurs between 24° and 43° C.

An exotoxin is produced which is toxic on injection but not on feeding. Three antigenic components have been recognized in toxic filtrates (Oakley, Warrack and Clarke, Jour. Gen. Microbiol., *1*, 1947, 91). These include: alpha, classical lethal toxin; beta, hemolytic lecithinase; and zeta, oxygen-stable hemolysin. Production of beta toxin differentiates Type B from Types A and C.

Pathogenic for sheep, cows, horses, pigs, fowls, rabbits, guinea pigs, rats and mice.

Source: Isolated from black disease (infectious necrotic hepatitis) of sheep in Australia. Also isolated from similar diseases in New Zealand, France, Germany, Chile and England.

21b. *Clostridium novyi* Type C, Scott et al., 1934. (Non-pathogenic bacillus of osteomyelitis of water buffalo, Kraneveld, Nederl. Ind. Bl. Diergeneesk., *42*, 1930, 564; Scott, Turner and Vawter, Proc. 12th Internat. Vet. Cong., N. Y., *2*, 1934, 175; *Clostridium bubalorum* Prévot, Ann. Inst. Past., *61*, 1938, 82; *Bacillus osteomyelitis bubalorum* Prévot, Man. d. Class. et d. Detérm. d. Bact., 1940, 123).

Large rods, 1.5 to 2.0 by 8.0 to 10.0 microns, occurring singly, in pairs and in chains. Spores ovoid, swelling the cells only slightly if at all. Motile by means of peritrichous flagella. Gram-positive.

Glucose blood agar surface colonies: No growth without further enrichment with 30 per cent serum; thin delicate cords of filaments, dull surface, scarcely raised above medium surface.

Strictly anaerobic.

Non-toxic. Lack of toxin differentiates Type C from Types A and B.

Not pathogenic for experimental animals.

Source: Isolated from bacillary osteomyelitis of water buffaloes in Java.

Habitat: Not determined other than this single isolation.

22. Clostridium botulinum (van Ermengem, 1896) Holland, 1920. (*Bacillus botulinus* van Ermengem, Cent. f. Bakt., I Abt., *19*, 1896, 443; also see Ztschr. f. Hyg., *26*, 1897, 48; Holland, Jour. Bact., *5*, 1920, 217.)

bo.tu.li′num. L. noun *botulus* a sausage; M.L. adj. *botulinus* pertaining to sausage.

The original van Ermengem strain is not available, and the description by van Ermengem is inadequate for classification purposes. Description taken from Bengtson (U. S. Public Health Serv., Hyg. Lab. Bull. 136, 1924, 33), who used Lister Institute Strain No. 94 (Brit. Med. Res. Counc., Spec. Rept. Ser. No. 12, 1917, 29; and *ibid.*, Spec. Rept., Ser. No. 39, 1919, 26) as a type culture.

Clostridium botulinum Type B.

Rods, 0.5 to 0.8 by 3.0 to 8.0 microns, with rounded ends, occurring singly, in pairs and in short to occasionally long chains. Spores ovoid, central, subterminal, terminal at maturation, swelling the cells. Motile by means of peritrichous flagella. Gram-positive.

Gelatin: Liquefaction.

Liver agar surface colonies (anaerobic): No perceptible growth.

Liver agar deep colonies: Fluffy with dense center.

Egg yolk agar surface colonies: (Type B) Flat, spreading, with irregular edges and a luster which extends in a regular circle slightly beyond the colony edge. An area of precipitation lies under the colony and to the edge of the luster zone. The reaction zones tend to be wider than those of *Clostridium parabotulinum* Types A and B.

Broth: Scant growth, if at all.

Liver broth: Luxuriantly turbid; considerable gas.

Milk: Slowly increasing acidity. No coagulation. No gas.

Acid and gas from glucose, fructose, maltose, dextrin, glycerol, adonitol and inositol. Galactose, sucrose, lactose, raffinose, inulin, dulcitol, mannitol, xylose, arabinose, rhamnose and salicin not fermented (Bengtson, *op. cit.*, 1924, 22–25).

Coagulated albumin: No liquefaction.

Blood serum: No liquefaction.

Brain medium: No blackening or digestion.

Strictly anaerobic.

Optimum temperature, between 20° and 30° C. (van Ermengem, *op. cit.*, 1897, 42); 30° C. (van Ermengem, Arch. d. Pharmacodyn., *3*, 1897, 213 and 499; also see Williams and Reed, Jour. Inf. Dis., *71*, 1942, 227). Growth usually earlier at 37° C. (Starin, Jour. Inf. Dis., *38*, 1926, 103).

A powerful exotoxin is produced which is neurotoxic both on injection and on feeding. Toxin is neutralized by *Clostridium parabotulinum* Type B antitoxin. Toxin production probably best around 28° C.

Pathogenic for animals.

Comments: *Clostridium botulinum* Holland comprises a number of toxic types, conveniently divided by Bengtson (*op. cit.*, 1924, 33), by Meyer and Gunnison (Jour. Inf. Dis., *45*, 1929, 96 and 108) and by Gunnison and Meyer (Jour. Inf. Dis., *45*, 1929, 130) into a non-ovolytic (*Clostridium botu-*

linum) and an ovolytic (*Clostridium para-botulinum*) group. Authorities are not yet in agreement on fermentations and on variant sub-types, and the present groupings are only tentative and are subject to revision. Meyer and Gunnison cite some 15 sub-types on the basis of toxicity, agglutination and fermentation. Many authors have ignored the Bengtson system of classification and thus have referred incorrectly to *Clostridium botulinum* in reporting data for the ovolytic types.

Source: Unknown. Culture received through Reddish from Robertson as *Bacillus botulinus* No. 94, Strain A, Institute of Infectious Diseases at Berlin. Similar strains have been isolated from canned foods.

Habitat: Probably occurs in soil.

22a. Clostridium botulinum Type C, Spray, 1948. (Toxin-producing anaerobe, Bengtson, U. S. Public Health Repts., *37*, 1922, 164 and 2252; *Bacillus botulinus* Type C, Bengtson, *ibid.*, 38; also see U. S. Public Health Serv., Hyg. Lab. Bull. 136, 1924, 7; *Clostridium luciliae* Bergey et al., Manual, 1st ed., 1923, 336; Spray, in Manual, 6th ed., 1948, 779.)

Rods, 0.5 to 0.8 by 3.0 to 6.0 microns, commonly slightly curved.

Agar surface growth (anaerobic): Very scant, thin.

Glucose agar deep colonies: Fluffy, without central nucleus. Gas not produced.

Liver agar deep colonies: Lenticular, becoming loosely fluffy. Gas is produced.

Agar stab: Slight growth. No gas.

Broth: Scant growth.

Milk: Slowly increasing acidity; no coagulation; no digestion.

Acid and gas from glucose, fructose, galactose, maltose, glycerol and inositol. Dextrin is weakly fermented. Sucrose, lactose, raffinose, inulin, adonitol, dulcitol, mannitol, xylose, arabinose, rhamnose and salicin not fermented.

Strictly anaerobic.

Grows well at 37° C.

A powerful exotoxin is produced which is neurotoxic both on injection and feeding. Toxin is neutralized by homologous (Type Cα) antitoxin, but not by *Bacillus parabotulinus* Seddon (Type Cβ) antitoxin, al-though Seddon-toxin is neutralized by Type Cα antitoxin (Pfenninger, Jour. Inf. Dis., *35*, 1924, 347).

Pathogenic for animals.

Comments: *Clostridium botulinum* Type C may be regarded as a variety of *Clostridium botulinum* as it has morphological and cultural characters very similar to those of the van Ermengem strain. Only divergent or additional characters are recorded here.

Source: Isolated from the larvae of the blue-bottle fly (*Lucilia caesar*). Produces limberneck in chickens.

Habitat: Not determined.

22b. Clostridium botulinum Type D Meyer and Gunnison, 1928. (*Clostridium parabotulinus bovis* Theiler, Viljoen, Green, Du Toit, Meier and Robinson, Union So. Africa, Dept. Agr., 11th and 12th Repts. of the Dir. Vet. Educ. and Res., Part II, 1927, 1202; Meyer and Gunnison, Proc. Soc. Exp. Biol. and Med., *26*, 1928–29, 88; not *Clostridium botulinum* Type D, Weinberg and Ginsbourg, Données Recentes sur les Microbes Anaér., Paris, 1927; not *Clostridium botulinum* Type D, Willems, Acta Biol. Belg., *1*, 1941, 353; also see Meyer and Gunnison, Jour. Inf. Dis., *45*, 1929, 106; and Eales and Turner, Austral. Jour. Exp. Biol. and Med. Sci., *30*, 1952, 295.)

Straight rods, 0.9 to 2.0 by 3.0 to 9.0 microns, with rounded ends, sometimes pleomorphic with curved or bent forms mixed with large, thick, straight forms, occurring singly, in pairs or in short chains. Large, ovoid, terminal or subterminal spores, slightly distending the cells. Motile, probably by means of peritrichous flagella, in young cultures examined anaerobically. Gram-positive.

Iron-gelatin (Spray) or gelatin in peptic digest broth: Liquefaction.

Glucose rabbit blood agar surface colonies: Round, slightly granular, lobulate, faintly gray, glistening; possess blunt processes and fine outgrowths with thicker nodes at intervals; no hemolysis.

Liver agar deep colonies: Large, fluffy with dense centers.

Beef heart broth: Good growth with moderate gas production. Rapid sedimentation of cells. Meat reddened but not softened. Butyric odor.

Milk (plain): Unchanged.

Iron milk (Spray): Clotted and peptonized.

Indole production slight, if at all.

Hydrogen sulfide produced in bismuth carbonate agar.

Acid but no gas from glucose, fructose, maltose, inositol and galactose. Arabinose, xylose, rhamnose, trehalose, raffinose, inulin, glycogen, erythritol, adonitol, mannitol, dulcitol, sorbitol, amygdalin and salicin not fermented. Results with different base media vary with lactose, sucrose and dextrin.

Nitrites not produced from nitrates.

Coagulated serum: No clearing.

Coagulated egg albumin: Cleared but not dissolved.

Brain medium with iron: No blackening.

Strictly anaerobic.

Optimum temperature, 37° C.

Exotoxin produced in beef heart mash which is toxic by injection or feeding. Toxin neutralized by type D antitoxin but not by types A, B, C or E. Mice, guinea pigs and rabbits are susceptible to toxin on injection or feeding. Monkeys are susceptible on injection but are resistant to feeding. Chickens not susceptible on injection. Non-toxic substrains are frequently encountered.

Source: Isolated from South African "Lamziekte" of cattle and from Australian soil.

Habitat: Probably soil.

22c. Clostridium botulinum Type E, Gunnison et al., 1936. (Gunnison, Cummings and Meyer, Proc. Soc. Exp. Biol. and Med., *35*, 1936, 278.)

Description taken from Gunnison, Cummings and Meyer (*loc. cit.*), Hazen (Proc. Soc. Exp. Biol. and Med., *50*, 1942, 112), Dolman and Kerr (Canad. Jour. Pub. Health, *38*, 1947, 48) and Dolman, Chang, Kerr and Shearer (Canad. Jour. Pub. Health, *41*, 1950, 215).

Rods, 4.0 to 6.0 microns in length, with rounded ends, often vacuolated. Spores large, ovoid, subterminal, very slightly swelling the cells. Motile. Gram-positive.

Gelatin: Liquefaction (probably slowly and not completely).

Peptone beef infusion broth with ground meat: Slightly turbid, clearing on continued incubation; gas production marked in young cultures; meat not digested.

Milk: No change or slightly acid without action on casein.

Acid and gas from glucose, fructose, sucrose, maltose, adonitol, sorbitol and inositol. Lactose, raffinose, rhamnose, galactose, mannitol, inulin and dulcitol are not fermented. Reports vary on arabinose, xylose, glycerol, salicin and dextrin.

Coagulated egg medium: No digestion.

Coagulated serum: No digestion on original isolation.

Human or sheep blood agar surface colonies: Small, flat, translucent, faintly gray, with smooth or irregular edges. Sometimes with slightly raised centers. Tendency to form film on moist agar. Reports on hemolysis vary.

Brain medium: No blackening or digestion.

Strictly anaerobic.

Optimum temperature, probably between 25° and 30° C.

Produces an exotoxin potent by injection or feeding. Toxin neutralized by type E antitoxin but not by types A, B, C or D. Mice, guinea pigs, rabbits and kittens susceptible on injection. Susceptibility of chickens varies with the strain.

Source: Isolated from Russian sturgeon, German canned sprats, Nova Scotian smoked salmon, canned California mushrooms, Canadian canned salmon, canned salmon eggs, Canadian pickled herring, canned chicken, soil contaminated with chicken feces, mud and sand.

Habitat: Not determined.

23. **Clostridium limosum** Prévot, 1948. (Ann. Inst. Past., *74*, 1948, 165.)

li.mo′sum. L. adj. *limosus* full of mud or slime, slimy; (probably intended to mean) from mud.

Rods, 0.7 by 3.0 microns, with rounded ends, occurring singly, in pairs and occasionally in short chains. Spores subterminal, clostridial. Motile. Gram-positive.

Gelatin: Liquefaction.

Agar deep colonies: Lenticular, small.

Milk: Digested in four days.

VF glucose broth: Abundantly turbid; sediment; weakly acid.

Indole and skatole not produced.

Hydrogen sulfide produced in small amounts.

Glucose and galactose weakly fermented.

Nitrites not produced from nitrates.

Coagulated proteins: Not attacked.

Strictly anaerobic.

Optimum temperature, 37° C.

Not pathogenic for guinea pigs.

Source: Isolated from mud from an African lagoon.

Habitat: Presumably soil.

24. Clostridium acetobutylicum Mc-Coy et al., 1926. (McCoy, Fred, Peterson and Hastings, Jour. Inf. Dis., *39*, 1926, 483; also see *ibid.*, *46*, 1930, 118.)

a.ce.to.bu.ty'li.cum. L. noun *acetum* vinegar; Gr. noun *butyrum* butter; M.L. adj. *butylicum* butylic, having the butyl radical, as in butyl alcohol; M.L. adj. *acetobutylicus* acetic acid and butyl alcohol (-producing).

Straight rods, with rounded ends, occurring singly and in pairs but not in chains. The vegetative cells measure 0.6 to 0.72 by 2.6 to 4.7 microns, the clostridia, 1.3 to 1.6 by 4.7 to 5.5 microns. Spores ovoid, eccentric to subterminal, swelling the cells to clostridia. Not encapsulated. Motile by means of peritrichous flagella. Granulose-positive in clostridial stage. Gram-positive, becoming Gram-negative.

Glucose-gelatin: Liquefaction.

Glucose agar surface colonies (anaerobic): Compact, raised, fairly regular.

Glucose agar deep colonies: Compact, typically lenticular and smooth. Agar fragmented early by abundant gas.

Pigmentation: None. Colonies creamy white, opaque.

Plain broth: No growth.

Glucose broth: Abundantly and uniformly turbid; much gas produced.

Litmus milk: Acid and active, often stormy, coagulation. Litmus reduced. Clot fragmented by gas but not visibly digested. Proteolysis demonstrable, however, on milk agar.

Potato: Creamy yellow growth. Potato digested to a yellow slime.

Maize mash: Much gas with butylic odor. Indole not produced.

Hydrogen sulfide produced from thiosulfate or sulfite; generally negative from proteinaceous sources.

Acid and gas from arabinose, xylose, rhamnose, glucose, galactose, mannose, fructose, sucrose, maltose, lactose, raffinose, melezitose, starch, dextrin, inulin, glycogen, d-mannitol, alpha-methyl-glucoside and salicin. Esculin, amygdalin and trehalose are weakly fermented. Melibiose, dulcitol, d-arabitol, perseitol, lactositol, sorbitol, erythritol, adonitol, inositol, quercitol, glycerol, pectin and cellulose are not fermented.

Fermentation products include acetone, butyl and ethyl alcohols, butyric and acetic acids, H_2 and CO_2 .

Acetylmethylcarbinol produced from many carbohydrates.

Nitrites not produced from nitrates. Nitrites reduced to ammonia.

Atmospheric nitrogen is fixed, though less actively than by *Clostridium pasteurianum* Winogradsky (Rosenblum and Wilson, Jour. Bact., *57*, 1949, 413).

Coagulated albumin cubes: Softened and browned by slow digestion.

Blood agar: No hemolysis.

Blood serum: No liquefaction.

Brain medium: No blackening or digestion.

Anaerobic.

Optimum temperature, probably about 37° C. Grows between 20° and 47° C.

Not pathogenic for guinea pigs or rabbits.

Source: Isolated from maize, molasses, potatoes and garden soil.

Habitat: Widely, but apparently sparsely, dispersed in agricultural soils.

25. Clostridium laniganii McClung and McCoy, *nom. nov.* (Type II of retting clostridia, Lanigan, Austral. Jour. Sci. Research, Ser. B, Biol. Sci., *4*, 1951, 474.)

la.ni.gan'i.i. M.L. gen.noun *laniganii* of Lanigan; named for Lanigan, the first to isolate this species.

Medium-sized rods with markedly incomplete fission at 24 hours; by 48 hours the chains and filaments disappear. Straight to slightly curved rods, 0.6 to 0.8 by 2.0 to 7.0 microns, with rounded ends. Elliptical, terminal spores (arise subterminally), 1.1 by 1.8 to 2.0 microns. Motile. Gram-positive in young cultures.

Glucose-gelatin: Liquefaction within seven to twenty-one days.

Agar slant: Little or no growth.

Glucose yeast agar surface colonies: Irregular outline with woolly or myceloid margin. On moist agar there is a marked tendency to spread forming effuse, amoeboid projections. Center of colony grayish white, opaque, low convex with an effuse translucent marginal zone.

Glucose yeast agar deep colonies: Spherical, woolly balls, 1.0 mm in diameter; medium split by gas evolved.

Glucose yeast agar slant: Abundant growth; filiform on dry slants; spreading, with finger-like projections on moist medium. Slightly raised, smooth, glistening with butyrous center.

Glucose yeast broth: Heavily turbid; heavy, amorphous deposit; much gas. Distinct odor of butanol.

Litmus milk: Acid; reduction; gas and clot; frequently stormy coagulation; no digestion.

Potato mash: Active fermentation with "head"; complete diastatic action.

Indole not produced.

Hydrogen sulfide produced in small to moderate amounts in glucose yeast agar in three to seven days.

Acid and gas from glucose, galactose, maltose, sucrose, lactose, starch and pectin. Inulin, mannitol, glycerol and calcium lactate not attacked.

Active retting of flax sterilized in yeast water.

Nitrites not produced from nitrates. Nitrites reduced, presumably to ammonia, in two to three days.

Coagulated egg albumin: No visible effect but, after several days, slight softening is usually detected by probing.

Brain medium: Some gas; no blackening or digestion.

Anaerobic.

Grows well between 30° and 37° C.

Source: Isolated from Australian flax.
Habitat: Presumably soil.

26. **Clostridium aerofoetidum** (Weinberg and Séguin, 1916) Bergey et al., 1923. (Bacille D, Weinberg, Compt. rend. Soc. Biol., Paris, *79*, 1916, 117; *Bacillus aerofoetidus* Weinberg and Séguin, *ibid.*, 1028; Bergey et al., Manual, 1st ed., 1923, 327.)

a.e.ro.foe'ti.dum. Gr. noun *aer* air, gas; L. adj. *foetidus* with a bad odor, fetid; M.L. adj. *aerofoetidus* with bad-smelling gas.

Rods, 0.4 to 0.6 by 3.0 to 5.0 microns, occurring singly, in pairs and in short chains. Spores rare, ovoid, subterminal, slightly swelling the cells. Motile by means of peritrichous flagella. Gram-positive.

Gelatin: Rapid liquefaction.

Agar surface colonies (anaerobic): Circular, transparent, with faint, bluish tint, fimbriate.

Agar deep colonies: Lenticular, becoming indented and lobate.

Egg yolk agar surface colonies: Irregular, flat, somewhat moist, slightly rough, colorless, without precipitate or luster.

Glucose broth: Turbid; sediment.

Litmus milk: Acid; slow coagulation followed by slow peptonization. Gas is produced.

Acid and gas from glucose, fructose, galactose, mannose, maltose, lactose, xylose, amygdalin, salicin, esculin and glycogen. Sucrose, inulin, glycerol and mannitol not fermented.

Nitrites produced from nitrates (Reed, Jour. Bact., *44*, 1942, 425).

Coagulated albumin: Slow liquefaction.

Blood agar: No hemolysis.

Blood serum: Liquefaction.

Brain medium: Blackened and digested.

Meat medium: Reddened, then blackened and slowly digested.

Anaerobic.

Optimum temperature, between 30° and 35° C.

Slightly pathogenic for guinea pigs.

Source: Isolated from gaseous gangrene and from feces.

Habitat: Not determined. Probably occurs in soil.

27. Clostridium sporogenes (Metchnikoff, 1908) Bergey et al., 1923. (*Bacillus sporogenes* var. *A*, Metchnikoff, Ann. Inst. Past., *22*, 1908, 944; not *Bacillus sporogenes* Migula, Syst. d. Bakt., *2*, 1900, 560; Bergey et al., Manual, 1st ed., 1923, 329; not *Clostridium sporogenes* Holland, Jour. Bact., *5*, 1920, 220.)

spo.ro'ge.nes. Gr. noun *sporus* seed; M.L. noun *spora* a spore; Gr. v. *gennaio* to produce; M.L. adj. *sporogenes* spore-producing.

Rods, 0.6 to 0.8 by 3.0 to 7.0 microns, with rounded ends, occurring singly, in pairs or, less frequently, in short to long chains and filaments. Spores ovoid, eccentric to subterminal, swelling the cells. Motile by means of peritrichous flagella. Gram-positive.

Gelatin: Liquefaction and blackening.

Agar surface colonies (anaerobic): Small, irregular, transparent, becoming opaque, yellowish white, fimbriate.

Agar deep colonies: Woolly balls with dense, nodular centers.

Egg yolk agar surface colonies: Irregular, roughened, dry, cream-colored, with precipitate under colony and rarely spreading beyond. A slight luster covers the colony but does not extend beyond.

Agar slant (anaerobic): Grayish, opaque, spreading growth.

Broth: Turbid; gas is produced; putrid odor.

Litmus milk: Softly coagulated. Litmus reduced. Slow peptonization, leaving a dark, amber-colored liquid.

Indole not produced (Hall, Jour. Inf. Dis., *30*, 1922, 482). Skatole produced.

Acid and gas from glucose, fructose, galactose and maltose. Lactose, sucrose, salicin, glycerol, mannitol and inulin not fermented. (Records vary on many sugars.)

Nitrates rapidly reduced; nitrites absent (Reed, Jour. Bact., *44*, 1942, 425).

Atmospheric nitrogen not fixed (Rosenblum and Wilson, Jour. Bact., *57*, 1949, 413).

Coagulated albumin: Liquefaction.

Blood agar: Hemolysis.

Blood serum: Liquefied to a dark, putrid liquid.

Brain medium: Blackened and digested. Foul odor.

Meat medium: Reddened, then blackened and digested with foul odor. Gas is produced.

Anaerobic.

Optimum temperature, 37° C. Growth occurs at 50° C.

Filtrate is non-toxic on injection or on feeding.

Not pathogenic for guinea pigs or rabbits other than producing a slight, temporary, local tumefaction.

Source: Isolated from intestinal contents, gaseous gangrene and from soil.

Habitat: Common in soil, especially where heavily manured.

28. Clostridium parabotulinum Bengtson, 1924. (Bengtson, U. S. Public Health Serv., Hyg. Lab. Bull. 136, 1924, 32; Types A and B, Burke, Jour. Bact., *4*, 1919, 556; *Clostridium botulinum* Types A and B, Bergey et al., Manual, 1st ed., 1923, 328.)

pa.ra.bo.tu.li'num. Gr. pref. *para* beside, by; M.L. noun *botulinum* a specific epithet; M.L. adj. *parabotulinus* (*Clostridium*) *botulinum*-like.

Rods, 0.5 to 0.8 by 3.0 to 8.0 microns, with rounded ends, occurring singly, in pairs and in short chains. Spores ovoid, subterminal, distinctly swelling the cells. Motile by means of peritrichous flagella. Gram-positive.

Gelatin: Liquefaction.

Liver agar surface growth (anaerobic): Profuse, moist.

Liver agar deep colonies: Type A tend to be restricted to compact discs, with sharp outline and small, opaque nucleus at periphery. Type B tend rather to form loose, woolly colonies (indicative only).

Egg yolk agar surface colonies: (Types A and B) Raised, irregularly edged, covered with a luster which extends in a regular circle slightly beyond the colony edge and area of precipitation under the colony and luster zone. Radial striations not so marked as with *Clostridium novyi* Bergey et al.

Broth: Fairly abundant, diffuse turbidity. Many strains spontaneously agglutinate.

Liver broth: Luxuriantly turbid. Profuse gas.

Milk: Slight acidity; slow, curdling precipitation with subsequent digestion and darkening.

Acid and gas from glucose, fructose, maltose, dextrin, glycerol and salicin. Galactose, sucrose, lactose, rhamnose, raffinose, inulin, adonitol, dulcitol, mannitol, xylose, arabinose and inositol not fermented (Bengtson, *op. cit.*, 1924, 22–25). Fermentation records are variable.

Coagulated albumin: Liquefaction. Action of Type B usually more marked than that of Type A.

Blood serum: Liquefaction.

Brain medium: Blackened and digested with putrefactive odor.

Meat medium: Blackened and digested. Putrefactive odor. Tyrosine crystals not observed.

Anaerobic.

Optimum temperature, between 35° and 37° C.

A powerful exotoxin is produced which is neurotoxic both on injection and on feeding and which is neutralized only by the homologous type antitoxin. Toxin production best at about 28° C.

Pathogenic for animals.

Distinctive characters: This group comprises the putrefactive (ovolytic) species, including strains commonly referred to as *Memphis* and *Canton* (Type A), and *Nevin* (Type B). Growth of these types is more easily obtained than with the *Clostridium botulinum* strains, and the reactions are more obvious. Types are identified chiefly by protection tests with known-type antitoxin and, to a lesser extent, by agglutination.

Comments: Many authors have ignored the Bengtson system of classification and thus have referred incorrectly to *Clostridium botulinum* (*q.v.*, comments) in reporting data for the ovolytic types. Gunnison and Meyer (Jour. Inf. Dis., *45*, 1929, 130) propose an intermediate group between *Clostridium botulinum* and *Clostridium parabotulinum* which they call *Clostridium metabotulinum*. Such a group would provisionally include certain European Type B strains, the Australian Type C strain, certain American Type C strains and the South African Type D strain.

Source: Isolated chiefly from spoiled, non-acid, canned goods, from soil and from silage.

Habitat: Found rather widely dispersed in soil.

29. **Clostridium caproicum** Prévot, 1938. (*Bacillus anaerobicus* der Capronsäuregruppe, Rodella, Cent. f. Bakt., II Abt., *16*, 1906, 58; Prévot, Ann. Inst. Past., *61*, 1938, 84; *Bacillus anaerobicus caproicus* Prévot, Man. d. Class. et d. Déterm. d. Bact. Anaérob., 1940, 140.)

ca.pro'i.cum. M.L. noun *acidum caproicum* caproic acid; M.L. adj. *caproicus* pertaining to caproic acid.

Straight rods, 3.0 to 8.0 microns, with square ends. Spores ovoid, clostridial. Motile. Gram-positive.

Gelatin: Liquefaction in 48 hours.

Agar deep colonies: Woolly, arborescent.

Liquid media: Filamentous growth with viscous sediment. Gas produced with a fetid odor.

Milk: Digested in two to three days.

Indole produced in small amounts.

Hydrogen sulfide produced.

Glucose, fructose, maltose and sorbitol fermented. Lactose, galactose, sucrose, mannitol, inulin and starch not attacked.

Nitrites not produced from nitrates.

Coagulated egg albumin: Slowly attacked but not completely digested.

Fibrin incompletely digested.

Coagulated serum: Digested in three to eight days.

Anaerobic.

Distinctive characters: Produces caproic and acetic acids. Differs from *Clostridium kluyveri* Barker and Taha, which does not grow in the usual media.

Source: Isolated from cheese.

Habitat: Mud (Prévot, Zimmès, Peyré and Lanthiez, Ann. Inst. Past., *73*, 1947, 222).

30. **Clostridium saccharoacetoperbutylicum** Beesch, 1948. (*Clostridium saccharo-acetoperbutylicum* (sic) Beesch, U. S. Letters Pat., 2,439,791, April 20, 1948.)

sac.char.o.a.ce.to.per.bu.tyl'i.cum. Gr. noun *saccharum* sugar; L. noun *acidum aceticum* acetic acid; L. pref. *per* much, exceedingly; L. adj. *butylicus* pertaining to the butyl radical; M.L. adj. *saccharoacetoperbutylicus* (probably intended to mean) the organism which ferments sugar with the production of acetic acid and an abundance of butyl alcohol.

Short and long rods, 0.7 to 3.8 by 2.3 to 12.8 microns, the majority measuring 1.6 by 5.3 microns, with rounded ends, occurring singly, in pairs or in chains. Sporangia are spindle-shaped, clavate. Spores cylindrical with rounded ends or ovoid, the majority measuring 1.1 by 2.6 microns, subterminal to terminal. Motile by means of peritrichous flagella. Granulose-positive when stained with iodine. Gram-positive.

Gelatin: Liquefaction.

Agar surface colonies: Circular to irregular, both rough and smooth, entire and lobar-lobulate edges, convex, translucent to opaque.

Agar slant: Growth abundant, scattered to spreading, glistening, non-pigmented to a light cream color; butylic odor; viscid consistency.

Broth: No growth.

Litmus milk: Acid reaction with an acid curd in 15 days. Slight peptonization.

Potato slant: Growth spreading, glistening, abundant, non-pigmented to light cream color; butylic odor; viscid consistency.

Indole not produced.

Hydrogen sulfide produced in trace amounts, if at all.

Acid and gas from arabinose, xylose, glucose, fructose, galactose, mannose, lactose, sucrose, maltose, raffinose, maize starch, soluble starch, inulin, glycogen, salicin, alpha-methyl-glucoside, melibiose and dextrin. Trehalose, inositol, rhamnose, melezitose, glycerol, erythritol, mannitol, sorbitol, dulcitol and esculin not attacked.

Nitrites not produced from nitrates.

Optimum temperature, between 29° and 31° C.

Optimum pH, between 5.5 and 6.3.

Anaerobic.

Source: Isolated from maize husk.

Habitat: Probably soil.

31. Clostridium hastiforme MacLennan, 1939. (A4, Cunningham, Zent. f. Bakt., II Abt., *82*, 1930–31, 487; B4a, Cunningham,

ibid., *83*, 1931, 11; MacLennan, Jour. Path. and Bact., *49*, 1939, 543.)

has.ti.for'me. L. noun *hasta* a spear; L. noun *forma* shape, form; M.L. adj. *hastiformis* spear-shaped.

Slender rods, 0.3 to 0.6 by 2.0 to 6.0 microns, with rounded ends, occurring singly, in pairs and rarely in short chains. Filaments not observed. Spores ellipsoidal, subterminal, swelling the cells. Polar-cap of protoplasm remains long attached to free spores. Motile by means of delicate, peritrichous flagella; motility persists even after sporulation. Gram-positive.

Gelatin: Rapid liquefaction. Blackening not recorded.

Plain agar surface colonies (anaerobic): Minute, translucent dots, becoming irregularly round, granular, grayish white, with opaque center and delicate, translucent border.

Plain agar deep colonies: Small, irregularly round with coarsely filamentous border. A little gas is occasionally produced.

Broth: Transient, uniform turbidity, quickly settling as a heavy, white, flocculent deposit. Culture assumes a cheesy odor.

Milk: Abundant growth with lab-coagulation in 2 to 3 days. No increase in acidity, becoming slightly alkaline. Clot completely digested in 10 to 14 days, leaving a white, semi-translucent fluid of cheesy odor.

Indole not produced.

Hydrogen sulfide not produced.

Glucose and other carbohydrates not fermented.

Ammonia not produced.

Egg medium: No digestion or other visible change.

Coagulated albumin: No digestion or blackening.

Blood agar surface colonies (anaerobic): Same as on plain agar, but larger and more opaque. Old colonies show grayish pigmentation. No hemolysis.

Blood serum: No digestion or blackening.

Meat medium: No digestion or blackening, even in the presence of metallic iron. Meat particles slightly reddened.

Brain medium: No digestion or blackening.

Anaerobic.

Grows well between 22° and 37° C.

Not pathogenic for guinea pigs on subcutaneous inoculation (Cunningham, *op. cit.*, 1931, 12).

Source: Originally isolated by Cunningham as a dissociant from a culture of *Bacillus saccharobutyricus* von Klecki. Later isolated by MacLennan, 1 strain from a culture of *Clostridium sporogenes* and 2 strains from street dust.

Habitat: Not determined.

32. Clostridium subterminale (Hall and Whitehead, 1927) Spray, 1948. (*Bacillus subterminalis* Hall and Whitehead, Jour. Inf. Dis., *41*, 1927, 66; Spray, in Manual, 6th ed., 1948, 786.)

sub.ter.mi.na'le. L. pref. *sub* under; L. adj. *terminalis* terminal; M.L. adj. *subterminalis* near the end or tip, subterminal.

Rods occurring singly, in pairs and rarely in short chains. Spores ovoid, subterminal, swelling the cells. Motile. Gram-positive.

Gelatin: Slow liquefaction with slight turbidity and black sediment.

Agar deep colonies: Opaque, compact, biconvex or lobate discs.

Agar slant (anaerobic): No surface growth.

Glucose broth: Turbid; no acid or gas produced.

Milk: Slowly coagulated (2 to 3 days), with mild acidity and gas. Slow but complete digestion of casein (8 to 18 days).

Indole not produced.

Glucose, fructose, galactose, maltose and lactose not fermented.

Blood agar surface colonies (anaerobic): Delicate. At first mildly, later actively, hemolytic.

Brain medium: Slightly turbid in supernatant fluid. Slight gas production and slow digestion.

Iron brain medium: Blackening in 2 to 3 days.

Tyrosine crystals not observable.

Anaerobic.

Grows well at 37° C.

Not pathogenic for guinea pigs on subcutaneous injection.

Source: Isolated from an African arrowhead.

Habitat: Not determined.

33. Clostridium lactoacetophilum Bhat and Barker, 1947. (Jour. Bact., *54*, 1947, 384.)

lac.to.a.ce.to'phi.lum. L. noun *lactosum* lactose; L. noun *acidum aceticum* acetic acid; Gr. adj. *philus* loving; M.L. adj. *lactoacetophilus* loving a combination of lactate and acetate.

Rods, 0.7 to 0.9 by 3.0 to 8.0 microns, occurring singly, in pairs and occasionally in short chains. Spores ovoid, 1.1 by 1.5 microns, subterminal, swelling the cells. Not encapsulated. Motile by means of peritrichous flagella. Gram-positive, becoming Gram-negative.

Colonies: Generally compact, fluffy, dark gray spheres composed of filamentous outgrowths; coarsely lobed, rough-edged, eventually reaching a diameter of 1 to 2 mm. Colonies rubbery mucoid.

Iron-milk: Slightly acidified without clotting; little gas produced.

Indole not produced.

Hydrogen sulfide produced in slight amounts.

Glucose, fructose, galactose, mannose, xylose, arabinose, rhamnose, lactose, sucrose, maltose, trehalose, raffinose, dextrin, glycogen, starch, xylan, mannitol, inositol, inulin, sorbitol and dulcitol are readily fermented (yeast autolysate basal medium). Glycerol and lactate not attacked in basal medium unless 0.8 per cent sodium acetate is added.

Nitrites not produced from nitrates.

Atmospheric nitrogen fixed, though not as actively as by *Clostridium pasteurianum* Winogradsky (Rosenblum and Wilson, Jour. Bact., *57*, 1949, 413).

Anaerobic.

Optimum temperature, approximately 39° C.; growth range, 16° to 46° C.

Chemical tolerance: Optimum pH, between 6.2 and 7.4; pH range, 5.6 to 8.4.

Distinctive character: Ferments lactate, producing butyric acid.

Source: Isolated from soil.

Habitat: Soil.

34. Clostridium kaneboi Nakahama and Harada, 1949. (Jour. Agr. Chem. Soc. Japan, *23*, 1949, 178.)

ka.ne'bo.i. Etymology Japanese, meaning unknown.

Straight rods, 0.3 to 0.8 by 2.0 to 7.0 microns, with rounded ends, occurring singly or in chains of two to four cells. Sporangia spindle-shaped, 1.2 to 1.5 by 5.0 to 7.0 microns. Spores ovoid, 1.1 to 1.5 by 1.9 to 2.4 microns, central to subterminal. Motile. Gram-positive.

Sugar agar surface colonies: Circular, 2 to 5 mm in diameter, raised, moist, smooth edges, pale yellow-white, odor of solvents. Subsurface colonies: Spherical, smooth, gummy, splitting the agar.

Cane sugar broth: Good growth; turbid; slight acidity; rich sporulation; abundant slime; liquid is yellow-white, milky, semi-translucent with a fragrant odor.

Maize, cut yam, soybean mash: Good growth; turbid, with slime.

Litmus milk: Good growth; gas; acid coagulation.

Potato slants (anaerobic, 5-day incubation at 37° C.): Colonies yellow-brown, 2 mm in diameter, moist, irregular.

Indole not produced.

Hydrogen sulfide is produced.

Xylose, l-arabinose, glucose, fructose, mannose, galactose, sucrose, maltose, lactose, alpha-methyl-d-glucoside, starch, dextrin, inulin, glycogen, mannitol and salicin are fermented. Trehalose and pectin weakly fermented. Rhamnose, raffinose, glycerol, dulcitol, calcium lactate, melibiose and sorbitol not attacked.

Products of carbohydrate fermentation are acetone, butanol and ethanol.

Nitrites not produced from nitrates.

Anaerobic.

Optimum temperature, 37° C.; no growth at 45° C.

Optimum pH, between 5.6 and 6.7; growth range, pH 4.2 to 9.1.

Source: Isolated from soil and from sugar cane plant.

Habitat: Probably soil.

35. Clostridium propionicum Cardon and Barker, 1946. (Jour. Bact., *52*, 1946, 631.)

pro.pi.o'ni.cum. M.L. noun *acidum pro-pionicum* propionic acid; M.L. adj. *propionicus* pertaining to propionic acid.

Spindle-shaped rods, 0.8 by 3.0 microns, occurring singly or more commonly in pairs. Spores ovoid, terminal or subterminal, slightly swelling the cells; separate from sporangium soon after being formed. Spores do not form readily. Motile by means of peritrichous flagella. Gram-negative.

Complex nitrogenous or carbohydrate-containing medium without added alanine: No growth.

Alanine peptone yeast extract agar deep colonies: Lens-shaped with smooth edges.

Liquid medium: Uniformly turbid with gradual clearing in three to four days.

Glucose not attacked.

Alanine and other fermentations yield propionic acid.

Catalase-negative.

Anaerobic.

Optimum temperature, between 28° and 37° C.

Optimum pH, between 7.0 and 7.4. Growth range, pH 5.8 to 8.6.

Source: Isolated from black mud from San Francisco Bay.

Habitat: Presumably mud.

36. Clostridium setiense (Prévot and Raynaud, 1944) McClung and McCoy, *comb. nov.* (*Inflabilis setiensis* Prévot and Raynaud, Ann. Inst. Past., *70*, 1944, 51.)

se.ti.en'se. M.L. adj. *setiensis* (probably intended to mean) pertaining to Setia, Italy.

Rods, 0.7 by 1.5 to 2.0 microns. Spores subterminal, clostridial. Non-motile. Gram-positive.

Gelatin: No liquefaction.

Agar deep colonies: Lenticular; gas.

Glucose broth: Turbid; non-fetid gas.

Peptone broth: Poor growth.

Milk: Not coagulated.

Indole not produced.

Hydrogen sulfide not produced.

Glucose, fructose, galactose, lactose, maltose, sucrose, xylose, arabinose and glycerol fermented.

Nitrites not produced from nitrates.

Coagulated proteins: Not attacked.

Anaerobic.

Optimum pH, between 7.3 and 8.8.

Not pathogenic for guinea pigs.
Source: Isolated from oysters.
Habitat: Found in oysters so far as known.

37. **Clostridium tale** (Prévot et al., 1947) McClung and McCoy, *comb. nov.* (*Inflabilis talis* Prévot, Digeon, Peyré, Pantaléon and Senez, Ann. Inst. Past., *73*, 1947, 416.)

ta'le. L. adj. *talis* such, so great, so excellent.

Straight rods, 0.7 to 0.8 by 3.0 to 5.0 microns. Spores subterminal, swelling the cells. Not encapsulated. Non-motile. Gram-positive.

Gelatin: Liquefaction.

Agar deep colonies: Lenticular with tendency to become irregular, evolving putrid gas.

Peptone broth: Slightly turbid.

VF glucose broth: Abundantly turbid; much gas; marked putrid odor.

Milk: Coagulated in one to several days, then digested.

Indole produced in trace amounts.

Glucose, fructose, galactose, sucrose, sorbitol and glycerol fermented with the production of gas.

Nitrites produced from nitrates (in presence of maltose) by one strain.

Coagulated protein: Slowly and partially attacked.

Anaerobic.

Pathogenicity variable. One strain is pathogenic for guinea pigs without producing local lesions but with hepatic degeneration and pulmonary congestion. Toxin, on intravenous injection, kills mouse in several seconds.

Agglutination: Sera are strain-specific.

Source: Isolated from an acute appendix and from canned fish.

Habitat: From decomposing organic matter, so far as known.

38. **Clostridium mangenotii** (Prévot and Zimmès-Chaverou, 1947) McClung and McCoy, *comb. nov.* (*Inflabilis mangenoti* (sic) Prévot and Zimmès-Chaverou, Ann. Inst. Past., *73*, 1947, 603.)

man.ge.no'ti.i. M.L. gen.noun *mangenotii* of Mangenot; named for Prof. Mangenot,

director of the Institut intercolonial d'Adiopodoumé.

In liquid media, short, very thick rods, 1.6 to 1.8 by 3.0 to 4.0 microns, often ovoid, with rounded ends, occurring most often in chains. On agar the rods are longer, 6.0 to 8.0 microns, often occurring in chains or filaments. Clostridial spores are formed. Non-motile. Gram-positive.

Gelatin: Liquefaction in 24 hours.

Agar deep colonies: Irregular, with woolly edges, sometimes arborescent; little gas.

Glucose broth: Abundant, flocculating growth depositing a viscous mass. Foul odor.

Milk: Digested in 24 hours.

Indole and a little skatole are produced.

Hydrogen sulfide abundantly produced.

Glucose and maltose are fermented. Lactose, galactose, arabinose and starch are not attacked.

Nitrites not produced from nitrates.

Coagulated serum, fibrin and coagulated egg white are slowly attacked and become transparent but are not liquefied.

Anaerobic.

Optimum temperature, 37° C.

Not pathogenic for guinea pigs.

Source: Isolated from African soil.

Habitat: Soil.

39. **Clostridium lituseburense** (Prévot, 1948) McClung and McCoy, *comb. nov.* (*Inflabilis litus-eburense* (sic) Prévot, Ann. Inst. Past., *74*, 1948, 167.)

li.tus.e.bu.ren'se. L. noun *litus* coast; L. noun *ebur* ivory; M.L. adj. *lituseburensis* pertaining to the Ivory Coast.

Straight rods, 1.0 by 4.0 to 6.0 microns, with rounded ends, occurring in short chains. Subterminal, clostridial spores. Non-motile. Gram-positive.

Gelatin: Complete liquefaction in 24 hours.

Agar deep colonies: Woolly; gas is produced.

Peptone broth: Slightly turbid; gas.

VF glucose broth: Abundantly turbid; gas; foul odor; non-coherent, slimy sediment.

Milk: Coagulated with rapid digestion.

Indole and skatole not produced.

Hydrogen sulfide produced.

Glucose, fructose, maltose, galactose and sorbitol are fermented.

Nitrites not produced from nitrates.

Coagulated serum: Partially digested.

Coagulated egg white: Not attacked.

Fibrin: Digested.

Anaerobic.

Optimum temperature, 37° C.

Not pathogenic for guinea pigs or mice.

Source: Isolated from soil and from humus from Africa.

Habitat: Soil.

40. Clostridium bifermentans (Weinberg and Séguin, 1918) Bergey et al., 1923. (*Bacillus bifermentans sporogenes* Tissier and Martelly, Ann. Inst. Past., *16*, 1902, 894; *Bacillus bifermentans* Weinberg and Séguin, La Gangrène Gazeuse, Paris, 1918, 128; Bergey et al., Manual, 1st ed., 1923, 323.)

bi.fer.men'tans. L. pref. *bis* twice; L. part.adj. *fermentans* fermenting; M.L. adj. *bifermentans* doubly fermenting.

Rods, 0.8 to 1.0 by 5.0 to 6.0 microns, occurring singly, in pairs and in short chains. Spores ovoid, central to eccentric, not distinctly swelling the cells. Motile in very young cultures only (less than 24 hours old). Gram-positive.

Gelatin: Liquefaction.

Agar surface colonies (anaerobic): Circular, crenated to amoeboid.

Agar deep colonies: Biconvex to multiplanate discs.

Blood agar surface colonies (anaerobic): Small, transparent, becoming opaque, yellowish, spreading. Hemolysis.

Egg yolk agar surface colonies: Small to medium-sized, slightly raised, sometimes shiny, edges rough or entire. Colony surrounded by wide zone of white precipitate, but no luster is produced. Colony usually chalky white in contrast to colony of *Clostridium perfringens* Holland which is creamy white. Differentiation between these two species, which give similar characteristics on egg yolk agar, is easily done on the basis of iron milk, carbohydrate fermentations and indole production (McClung and Toabe, Jour. Bact., *53*, 1947, 139).

Broth: Turbid; gas produced. Thick, mucoid sediment.

Liquid cultures (particularly those of toxic strains) often have a pronounced valeric odor (Vawter, Amer. Jour. Vet. Research, *3*, 1942, 382).

Iron-milk (Spray): Inactive, gaseous fermentation; more or less rapid digestion of soft semi-coagulum; blackening.

Indole is produced.

Hydrogen sulfide is produced.

Acid and gas from glucose, fructose, mannose and maltose. Galactose, arabinose, xylose, lactose, sucrose, inulin and dulcitol not fermented. Records suggest variability in glycerol and salicin fermentation.

Nitrites not produced from nitrates.

Coagulated albumin: Rapid liquefaction and blackening.

Blood serum: Liquefaction and blackening.

Brain medium: Digestion and blackening.

Egg-meat medium: Digestion and blackening. Tyrosine crystals in 8 to 10 days.

Anaerobic.

Optimum temperature, between 30° and 37° C. Growth occurs at 50° C.

Toxicity varies from acute to none.

Pathogenicity varies with the strain: some kill rabbits in 24 hours, others produce only slight edema, while some show no effect.

Comment: Varying degrees of virulence and toxicity occur in this species. The more toxic and virulent strains are commonly referred to as *Clostridium sordelli*.

Source: Originally isolated from putrid meat; subsequently from gaseous gangrene.

Habitat: Occurs commonly in feces, soil and sewage. Widely distributed in nature.

41. Clostridium cylindrosporum Barker and Beck, 1941. (Jour. Biol. Chem., *141*, 1941, 3.)

cy.lin.dro'spo.rum. Gr. noun *cylindrus* a cylinder; Gr. noun *sporus* a seed; M.L. noun *spora* a spore; M.L. adj. *cylindrosporus* cylinder-spored.

Straight rods, 1.0 by 4.0 to 7.0 microns. Spores elongate to cylindrical, 1.0 to 1.1 by 1.7 to 3.0 microns, central, subterminal to terminal, with little or no swelling of the cells. Motile by means of peritrichous flagella. Gram-negative.

Iron-gelatin (Spray): No growth.

Plain agar deep: No growth.

Uric acid agar deep colonies: Whitish, compact, lobate, 1 to 2 mm in diameter, with irregular edges, surrounded by a zone of precipitated ammonium ureate which gradually disappears.

Plain broth: No growth.

Glucose broth: No growth.

Iron-milk (Spray): No growth.

Indole production not recorded (probably negative).

Glucose and other carbohydrates not fermented.

Cellulose not fermented.

Nitrite production not recorded (probably negative).

Coagulated albumin: No liquefaction.

Blood serum: No liquefaction.

Brain medium: No digestion or blackening.

Anaerobic.

Optimum temperature, about 35° C.

Optimum reaction, about pH 7.5; lower limit for growth, pH 6.5.

Distinctive characters: Requires uric acid or certain other purines as a primary source of carbon and energy. The purines are converted into ammonia, CO_2, acetic acid and a little glycine. This organism is physiologically similar to *Clostridium acidiurici* but may be readily distinguished from the latter by its morphology.

Source: A single strain was isolated from soil.

Habitat: Probably soil, although only this single isolation is recorded.

42. **Clostridium perfringens** (Veillon and Zuber, 1898) Holland, 1920.* *Clostridium perfringens* Type A, Spray, 1948. (*Bacillus aerogenes capsulatus* Welch and Nuttall, Johns Hopkins Hosp. Bull. 3, 1892, 81; *Bacillus phlegmones emphysematosae* Fraenkel, Ueber Gasphlegmonen, Leipzig, 1893, 47; *Bacillus emphysematosus* Kruse, in Flügge,

Die Mikroorganismen, 3 Aufl., *2*, 1896, 242; *Bacillus perfringens* Veillon and Zuber, Arch. Méd. Exp. et Anat. Path., *10*, 1898, 539; Holland, Jour. Bact., *5*, 1920, 219; *Clostridium welchii* Holland, *ibid.*, 221; *Bacillus welchii* Type A, Wilsdon, Univ. Cambridge, Inst. Animal Path., 2nd Rept. of Dir., 1931, 72; Spray, in Manual, 6th ed., 1948, 789.)

per.frin'gens. L. part.adj. *perfringens* breaking through.

Short, thick rods, 1.0 to 1.5 by 4.0 to 8.0 microns, occurring singly and in pairs, less frequently in short chains. Spores ovoid, central to eccentric, not swelling the cells. Encapsulated. Non-motile. Gram-positive.

Gelatin: Liquefaction and blackening.

Agar surface colonies (anaerobic): Circular, moist, slightly raised, opaque center, entire.

Egg yolk agar surface colonies: Circular to somewhat irregular, smooth (rough variants excepted), surrounded by a wide zone of opaque precipitate without luster over colony or zone. The reaction is given by all colony types, although there is some variation in the size of the zone of precipitation.

Broth: Turbid; peptolytic. Clearing with viscid sediment.

Litmus milk: Acid; coagulated. Clot torn with profuse gas production but not digested.

Potato: Thin, grayish white streak; gas in subtended liquid.

Indole not produced.

Acid and gas from glucose, fructose, galactose, mannose, maltose, lactose, sucrose, xylose, trehalose, raffinose, starch, glycogen and inositol. Salicin rarely fermented. Mannitol not fermented. Action on glycerol and inulin variable.

Nitrites produced from nitrates.

Atmospheric nitrogen not fixed (Rosenblum and Wilson, Jour. Bact., *57*, 1949, 413).

Coagulated albumin: No liquefaction.

Blood serum: No liquefaction.

Brain medium: No blackening or digestion.

Egg-meat medium: Profuse gas produc-

---

* Because of use of the specific epithet *perfringens* by the Permanent Standards Commission of the Health Organization of the League of Nations (Report of the Permanent Commission on Biological Standardization, London, June 23, 1931), the use of this epithet has been continued, although it is antedated by a valid binomial (*Bacillus emphysematosus* Kruse).

tion in 8 hours. The meat is reddened, and the liquid becomes turbid. No digestion.

Anaerobic.

Optimum temperature, between 35° and 37° C. Growth occurs at 50° C.

An exotoxin is produced for which an antitoxin can be prepared.

Pathogenic for guinea pigs, pigeons and mice.

Distinctive characters: Stormy fermentation of milk; non-motile.

Comments: Within this species group there exist several types established primarily on the basis of the variety and nature of the toxins shown to be present in culture filtrates. Some variation is reported concerning the morphological and physiological characteristics of this species. For a review of the characteristics of toxins, see van Heyningen (Bacterial Toxins., C. C Thomas, Springfield, 1950, 133 pp.) and Smith (Introduction to the Pathogenic Anaerobes, University of Chicago Press, Chicago, 1955, 253 pp.). For a method of routine typing, see Oakley and Warrack (Jour. Hyg., 51, 1953, 102). Type A is the classic human gas gangrene organism; Type B, lamb dysentery; Type C, "struck" of sheep; Type D, enterotoxemia, or "pulpy kidney" in lambs and grass sickness in horses; Type E, enterotoxemia of animals; Type F, hemorrhagic enteritis and enteritis necroticans, or "Darmbrand," of humans.

Source: Isolated from cases of gaseous gangrene and from feces, milk and soil.

Habitat: Widely distributed in feces, sewage and soil.

43. Clostridium sphenoides (Bulloch et al., 1919) Bergey et al., 1923. (*Bacillus sphenoides* Bulloch, Bullock, Douglas, Henry, McIntosh, O'Brien, Robertson and Wolf, Med. Res. Counc., Spec. Rept. Ser. No. 39, 1919, 43; Bergey et al., Manual, 1st ed., 1923, 331.)

sphe.no.i'des. Gr. adj. *sphenoides* wedge-shaped.

Original description supplemented by material taken from Hall (Jour. Inf. Dis., 30, 1922, 502).

Small, fusiform rods in the vegetative state, occurring singly, in pairs and occasionally in short chains. Sporulating cells cuneate. Spores spherical, subterminal, becoming terminal on maturation, swelling the cells. Motile. Gram-positive only in young cultures.

Gelatin: No liquefaction.

Agar surface colonies (anaerobic): Circular or slightly irregular, entire.

Agar deep colonies: Minute, opaque, smooth discs.

Egg yolk agar surface colonies: Irregular, moist, relatively smooth to somewhat roughened, colorless, without precipitate or luster.

Blood agar surface colonies (anaerobic): Minute dew-drops, becoming whitish, opaque. Hemolysis.

Broth: Turbid.

Litmus milk: Acid; slowly and softly coagulated. Clot not digested.

Indole not produced. Indole produced by Tholby strain (Stanley and Spray, Jour. Bact., 41, 1941, 256).

Acid and gas from glucose, galactose, maltose, lactose and salicin. Inulin, glycerol and dulcitol not fermented. Strains are apparently variable on mannitol, sucrose, dextrin and starch fermentation.

Nitrates reduced slowly, if at all; nitrites absent (Reed, Jour. Bact., 44, 1942, 425).

Coagulated albumin: No liquefaction.

Blood serum: No liquefaction.

Brain medium: No blackening or digestion.

Anaerobic.

Optimum temperature not determined. Grows well between 30° and 37° C.

Not pathogenic for guinea pigs or rabbits.

Source: Isolated from gangrenous war wounds.

Habitat: Not determined.

44. Clostridium innominatum Prévot, 1938. (*Bacillus E*, Adamson, Jour. Path, and Bact., 22, 1918–19, 391; Prévot, Ann. Inst. Past., 61, 1938, 85.)

in.no.mi.na'tum. L. adj. *innominatus* unnamed.

Very small, thick rods, tapering at one or both ends, occurring singly, in pairs, in chains and in filaments. Involution forms abundant on glucose agar. Spores small, spherical, subterminal, swelling the cells.

Motile. Gram-positive, quickly becoming Gram-negative.

Gelatin: No liquefaction.

Plain agar surface colonies (anaerobic): Small, circular, entire, whitish translucent, becoming yellowish opaque with age.

Glucose agar surface colonies (anaerobic): Two forms are produced: a) circular, entire, opaque; b) diffuse, spreading, irregular and translucent.

Plain broth: Moderately turbid; clears by sedimentation in 3 to 4 days.

Glucose broth: Abundantly turbid; slight gas production.

Milk: Slowly acidified but not clotted. No further change.

Acid and gas from glucose, maltose, lactose and mannitol. Sucrose not fermented.

Coagulated albumin: No digestion or blackening.

Blood serum: No digestion or blackening.

Meat medium: No digestion or blackening.

Brain medium: No digestion or blackening.

Anaerobic.

Grows well at 37° C.

Not pathogenic (Prévot, *loc. cit.*).

Source: Isolated from septic and gangrenous war wounds.

Habitat: Not determined.

45. Clostridium microsporum Spray, 1947. (Jour. Bact., *54*, 1947, 15; also see *ibid.*, *55*, 1948, 840.)

mic.ro'spo.rum. Gr. adj. *micrus* small; Gr. noun *sporus* seed; M.L. noun *spora* a spore; M.L. adj. *microsporus* small-spored.

Rods, 0.8 by 2.0 to 4.0 microns, occurring singly and in pairs but not in long chains, occasionally long, pleomorphic filaments, distinctly vacuolate, especially in old cultures. Organisms navicular and sharply pointed at both ends. Spores tiny, spherical, central to slightly eccentric, slightly swelling the cells. Actively motile, particularly by means of a spinning movement with little progressive motion. Presence, number and position of flagella not detected.

Gelatin (or iron-gelatin): No liquefaction or blackening.

Agar surface colonies (anaerobic): Tiny, almost imperceptible, transparent dew-drop

colonies, very slightly raised, with entire edges; visible only after some 48 hours' incubation.

Agar deep colonies: Tiny, 0.5 to 1.0 mm; lenticular with smooth, entire edges; whitish translucent (smaller and less opaque than those of *Clostridium tertium* Bergey et al.). Growth perceptible only after some 72 hours' incubation.

Milk (with iron strip): Fine and constant evolution of gas bubbles for many days, but no coagulation after 22 days' incubation. Medium slowly grayed but not blackened.

Indole not produced.

Lead acetate agar or peptone iron agar: No blackening.

Acid and gas from glucose, maltose and galactose. Lactose, trehalose, rhamnose, raffinose, dulcitol and inositol are not attacked.

Nitrites not produced from nitrates.

Coagulated albumin: No liquefaction.

Blood agar: No hemolysis.

Blood serum: No liquefaction.

Brain medium (Hibler): No blackening or digestion, even in the presence of an iron strip.

Anaerobic.

Optimum temperature not determined. Growth better at 37° C. than at room temperature.

Not pathogenic for white mice, guinea pigs or rabbits.

Distinctive characters: Minute size and navicular pointed form of the cells, and the tiny, spherical, central to eccentric spores.

Source: Isolated only once from the abdominal contents of a fatal case of peritonitis.

Habitat: From human sources, so far as known.

46. Clostridium filiforme Bergey et al., 1923. (*Bacillus regularis filiformis* Debono, Cent. f. Bakt., I Abt., Orig., *62*, 1912, 234; Bergey et al., Manual, 1st ed., 1923, 331.)

fi.li.for'me. L. adj. *filiformis* thread-like.

Slender rods, 0.5 to 0.8 by 3.0 to 5.0 microns, occurring singly, in pairs, in chains and in filaments. Spores very small, spherical, subterminal or occasionally terminal, not swelling the cells. Non-motile. Gram-positive.

Gelatin: No liquefaction.

Gelatin deep colonies: Small, gray, filamentous.

Agar deep colonies: Irregular, gray, translucent, filamentous.

Broth: Uniformly turbid.

Litmus milk: Acid, but no further change.

Potato: Gray, filamentous growth; substance not digested.

Acid and gas from glucose and lactose. Acid but no gas from sucrose and dulcitol. Starch not fermented.

Coagulated albumin: No liquefaction.

Anaerobic.

Growth occurs at 22° C. in gelatin.

Source: Isolated from human feces.

Habitat: Not determined.

47. Clostridium sartagoformum Partansky and Henry, 1935. (Jour. Bact., *30*, 1935, 570.)

sar.ta.go.for'mum. L. noun *sartago, -inis* a frying pan; L. noun *forma* shape; L. adj. *formus* warm; M.L. adj. *sartagoformum* (probably intended to mean) shaped like a frying pan.

Slender, curved rods, 0.3 to 0.5 by 3.5 to 6.0 microns, with rounded ends, occurring singly. Spores ovoid, terminal, swelling the cells. Motile. Gram-positive.

Gelatin: No liquefaction.

Agar surface colonies (anaerobic): Convex, discrete, circular, transparent to white and opaque. Surface moist and smooth.

Agar deep colonies: Regular, lenticular, smooth.

Broth: No growth. Clear.

Glucose broth: Turbid; gas bubbles.

Litmus milk: Acid; slowly coagulated with some gas production. Clot not digested.

Potato: Very scant growth. No gas in surrounding liquid.

Indole not produced.

Acid and gas from xylose, glucose, fructose, galactose, sucrose, lactose, maltose, raffinose, inulin, salicin, mannitol, acetate and butyrate. Starch, ethanol, glycerol and dulcitol not fermented.

Nitrites not produced from nitrates.

Coagulated albumin: No liquefaction.

Blood agar: No hemolysis.

Blood serum: No liquefaction. Scant growth.

Brain medium: No blackening or digestion. Some gas is produced.

Anaerobic.

Optimum temperature, 37° C.

Distinctive character: Ferments sulfitewaste liquor in 40 per cent concentration, producing butyric and acetic acids, H_2 and CO_2.

Source: Isolated from garden soil and from stream and lake mud.

Habitat: Presumably soil.

48. Clostridium paraputrificum (Bienstock, 1906) Snyder, 1936. (Art V, Bienstock, Fortschr. d. Med., *1*, 1883, 612; *Bacillus diaphthirus* Trevisan, I generi e le specie delle Batteriacee, 1889, 15; *Bacillus paraputrificus* Bienstock, Ann. Inst. Past., *20*, 1906, 413; also see Strassburger Med. Zeit., *3*, 1906, 111; Snyder, Jour. Bact., *32*, 1936, 401.)

pa.ra.pu.tri'fi.cum. Gr. pref. *para* beside, by; M.L. noun *putrificum* a specific epithet; M.L. adj. *paraputrificus* resembling (*Clostridium*) *putrificum*.

Description taken from Hall and Synder (Jour. Bact., *28*, 1934, 181).

Straight or slightly curved rods, 0.3 to 0.5 by 2.0 to 6.0 microns, with rounded ends, occurring singly, in pairs or in short chains. Spores ovoid, terminal, swelling the cells. Motile by means of peritrichous flagella. Gram-positive.

Gelatin: No liquefaction. Gas is produced.

Agar deep colonies: Small, irregular, opaque, dense, cottony masses. Gas is produced.

Blood agar surface colonies (anaerobic): Delicate, irregular, round-topped dewdrops. No hemolysis.

Broth: Diffuse turbidity.

Milk: Usually coagulated in from 6 to 10 days. Abundant gas, but no peptonization.

Indole not produced.

Acid and gas from glucose, fructose, galactose, maltose, lactose, sucrose, raffinose, dextrin, soluble starch, amygdalin and salicin. Xylose, inulin, mannitol and glycerol not fermented.

Nitrates reduced (Reed, Jour. Bact., *44*, 1942, 425).

Coagulated albumin: No liquefaction.

Blood serum: No liquefaction or discoloration.

Brain medium: No blackening or digestion. Non-proteolytic.

Anaerobic.

Grows well at 37° C.

Not pathogenic for guinea pigs or rabbits.

Source: Isolated from feces and gaseous gangrene and from post-mortem fluid and tissue cultures.

Habitat: Presumably occurs commonly in the intestinal canals of human beings.

49. Clostridium indologenes (Prévot, 1948) McClung and McCoy, *comb. nov.* (*Plectridium indologenes* Prévot, Ann. Inst. Past., *74*, 1948, 165.)

in.do.lo'ge.nes. M.L. neut.n. *indolum* indole; Gr. v. *gennaio* to produce; M.L. adj. *indologenes* indole-producing.

Straight rods, 0.6 by 3.0 to 4.0 microns, occurring singly or in pairs. Spores rare, ovoid, large-sized and distinctly terminal. Motile in very young cultures. Gram-positive.

Gelatin: No liquefaction.

Agar deep colonies: Lenticular with secondary off-shoots; little gas produced, if any.

Peptone broth: Turbid.

Glucose broth: Abundantly turbid; viscous sediment; putrid odor.

Milk: No change.

Indole produced.

Hydrogen sulfide produced.

Glucose, lactose and galactose are fermented.

Nitrites not produced from nitrates.

Coagulated proteins: Not attacked.

Anaerobic.

Optimum temperature, 37° C.

Optimum pH, 7.8.

Not pathogenic for guinea pigs.

Source: Isolated from a sample of "poto-poto" in Africa.

Habitat: Not determined.

50. Clostridium cochlearium (Bulloch et al., 1919) Bergey et al., 1923. (*Bacillus* Type IIIc, McIntosh, Med. Res. Counc., Spec. Rept. Ser. No. 12, 1917, 20; *Bacillus cochlearius* Bulloch, Bullock, Douglas, Henry, McIntosh, O'Brien, Robertson and Wolf, Med. Res. Counc., Spec. Rept. Ser.

No. 39, 1919, 40; Bergey et al., Manual, 1st ed., 1923, 333.)

coch.le.a'ri.um. L. noun *coclear* (*cochlear*) a spoon; M.L. adj. *cochlearius* spoon-like.

Straight, slender rods, occurring chiefly singly and infrequently in pairs or short chains. Spores ovoid, terminal, swelling the cells. Motile by means of peritrichous flagella. Weakly Gram-positive.

Gelatin: No liquefaction.

Agar surface colonies (anaerobic): Circular, clear, entire or crenated.

Agar deep colonies: Lenticular, entire.

Broth: Turbid.

Litmus milk: Unchanged.

Glucose and other carbohydrates not fermented.

Coagulated albumin: No liquefaction.

Blood serum: No liquefaction.

Brain medium: No blackening or digestion.

Meat medium: Slightly reddened. No blackening or digestion. Little gas produced of non-putrefactive odor.

Anaerobic.

Optimum temperature, between 30° and 35° C.

Not pathogenic.

Source: Isolated from human war wounds and septic infections.

Habitat: Not determined. Probably occurs in soil.

51. Clostridium kluyveri Barker and Taha, 1942. (*Clostridium kluyverii* (sic) Barker and Taha, Jour. Bact., *43*, 1942, 347.)

kluy've.ri. M.L. gen.noun *kluyveri* of Kluyver; named for Prof. A. J. Kluyver of Delft, Holland, in whose laboratory this organism was discovered.

Straight to slightly curved rods, 0.9 to 1.1 by 3.0 to 11.0 microns, usually occurring singly and in pairs, occasionally in long chains. Spores ovoid, 1.3 by 1.8 microns, terminal, swelling the cells. Motile by means of peritrichous flagella. Generally Gram-negative; some strains are weakly Gram-positive when young.

Iron-gelatin (Spray): No growth.

Agar surface colonies (anaerobic): Growth slow and restricted by residual traces of oxygen. Rough and smooth colonies are produced.

Agar deep colonies (yeast autolysate and C_2H_5OH): Small, 1 to 3 mm in diameter after 2 to 3 days; two types are formed: a) fluffy spheres with dense nuclear centers and filamentous peripheries; b) compact, lenticular colonies. Little gas is produced.

Plain broth: No growth.

Glucose broth: No growth.

Milk or iron-milk (Spray): No growth.

Indole production not recorded (probably negative).

Ethanol is converted to caproic acid.

Glucose and other carbohydrates not fermented.

Cellulose not fermented.

Nitrite production not recorded (probably negative).

Atmospheric nitrogen fixed, though less actively than by *Clostridium pasteurianum* Winogradsky (Rosenblum and Wilson, Jour. Bact., *57*, 1949, 413).

Coagulated albumin: No liquefaction.

Blood serum: No liquefaction.

Brain medium: No digestion or blackening.

Anaerobic.

Optimum temperature, about 34° C. Grows between 19° and 37° C.

Chemical tolerance: Optimum pH, about 6.8. Range for growth, pH 6.0 to 7.5.

Probably not pathogenic.

Distinctive characters: Large size of cells and slow growth, accompanied by nonputrefactive odor of caproic acid and of higher alcohols. Growth is exceptionally favored by synergistic association with *Methanobacterium omelianskii* Barker. In pure culture a high concentration of yeast autolysate is required. Caproic acid is produced from ethanol.

Source: Isolated from black mud of fresh water and of marine origin.

Habitat: Not determined. Presumably widely dispersed in nature.

52. Clostridium acidiurici (Liebert, 1909) Barker, 1938. (*Bacillus acidi urici* Liebert, Koninkl. Akad. v. Wetensch., Proc. Sect. Sci., Amsterdam, *12*, 1909, 55; Barker, Jour. Bact., *36*, 1938, 323.)

a.ci.di.u'ri.ci. L. adj. *acidus* sour; M. L. noun *acidum* acid; Gr. noun *urum* urine; M.L. adj. *uricus* pertaining to urine; M.L. *acidum uricum* uric acid; M.L. gen.noun *acidiurici* of uric acid.

Straight rods, 0.5 to 0.7 by 2.5 to 4.0 microns. Spores ovoid, 0.9 by 1.1 microns, terminal, swelling the cells. Motile by means of peritrichous flagella. Most strains are Gram-negative; a few strains are weakly Gram-positive, quickly becoming Gram-negative.

Iron-gelatin (Spray): No growth.

Plain deep agar: No growth.

Uric acid agar surface colonies (anaerobic): Variable with the strain and with the moisture of the medium. Colonies, 1 to 2 mm in diameter, opaque, white, raised, round, smooth edged, with concentric surface markings and of rubbery consistency. Other colonies may be very thin, soft, transparent, with fimbriate projections, spreading to cover almost the entire plate. Intermediate colony types also observed.

Uric acid agar deep colonies: Whitish, compact, lobate, 1 to 2 mm in diameter, with irregular edge; surrounded by a temporary zone of precipitated ammonium ureate which gradually disappears.

Yeast autolysate tryptone glucose semisolid agar: No growth (Barker and Beck, Jour. Bact., *43*, 1942, 291).

Plain broth: No growth.

Glucose broth: No growth.

Iron-milk (Spray): No growth.

Indole production not recorded (probably negative).

Glucose and other carbohydrates not fermented.

Cellulose not fermented.

Nitrite production not recorded (probably negative).

Atmospheric nitrogen not fixed (Rosenblum and Wilson, Jour. Bact., *57*, 1949, 413).

Coagulated albumin: No liquefaction.

Blood serum: No liquefaction.

Brain medium: No digestion or blackening.

Anaerobic.

Optimum temperature, about 35° C.

Optimum reaction, about pH 7.5; lower limit for growth, about pH 6.5.

Probably not pathogenic.

Distinctive characters: Requires uric acid or certain other purines as a primary source of carbon and energy. The purines are converted mainly into ammonia, CO_2 and acetic acid. During growth the medium tends to become alkaline (pH 8.0 to 8.5); there is no visible evolution of gas.

Source: Isolated from soils and muds of diverse origin.

Habitat: Evidently widely dispersed in soils. Present in fecal material of the yellow-shafted flicker (*Colaptes auratus*).

53. Clostridium capitovale (Snyder and Hall, 1935) Snyder, 1936. (*Bacillus capitovalis* Snyder and Hall, Zent. f. Bakt., I Abt., Orig., *135*, 1935, 290; *Clostridium capitovalis* (sic) Snyder, Jour. Bact., *32*, 1936, 401.)

ca.pi.to.va'le. L. noun *caput, capitis* head; M.L. adj. *ovalis* oval; M.L. adj. *capitovalis* with an oval head.

Slender, commonly curved rods, 0.5 to 0.8 by 2.0 to 2.5 microns, with rounded ends, occurring singly, in pairs and rarely in short chains. Spores ovoid, terminal, swelling the cells. Motile by means of long, peritrichous flagella. Gram-positive.

Gelatin: Liquefaction.

Agar deep colonies: Small, opaque, lenticular to heart-shaped.

Egg yolk agar surface colonies: Vary from circular to somewhat irregular, moist to only slightly so, smooth to somewhat roughened, somewhat flattened with no precipitate or luster.

Blood agar surface colonies (anaerobic): Tiny, transparent, round or irregular dewdrops, becoming opaque. No hemolysis.

Tryptone broth: Turbid. Gas is produced.

Milk: Often but not invariably clotted. Acid is produced. Clot, when formed, is not digested.

Indole not produced.

Acid and gas from glucose, fructose and galactose. Maltose, lactose, sucrose, raffinose, xylose, inulin, dextrin, starch, cellulose, amygdalin, salicin, mannitol and glycerol not fermented.

Nitrites not produced from nitrates. Nitrates reduced (Reed, Jour. Bact., *44*, 1942, 425).

Coagulated albumin: Liquefaction.

Blood serum: Slowly softened and partially liquefied. No blackening. Mildly proteolytic.

Brain medium: Blackening; slightly softened but not conspicuously liquefied.

Anaerobic.

Grows at 37° C.

Pathogenic for guinea pigs, which may show slight, subcutaneous edema; usually no effect. Not pathogenic for rabbits.

Source: Isolated from human feces, cases of gaseous gangrene and septicemia.

Habitat: Not determined.

54. Clostridium cadaveris (Klein, 1899) McClung and McCoy, *comb. nov.* (*Bacillus cadaveris sporogenes* (*anaerobicus*) Klein, Cent. f. Bakt., I Abt., *25*, 1899, 279; *Bacillus cadaveris* Klein, *ibid.*, 280; not *Bacillus cadaveris* Sternberg, Researches relating to the etiology and prevention of yellow fever, Washington, 1891, 212; *Bacillus cadaveris sporogenes* Klein, *op. cit.*, 1899, 282; *Plectridium cadaveris* Prévot, Ann. Inst. Past., *61*, 1938, 88; also see Saissac and Andre, Ann. Inst. Past., *73*, 1947, 936.)

ca.dav'er.is. L. noun *cadaver* the dead body of man or other animals, cadaver; L. gen.noun *cadaveris* of a cadaver.

Straight or curved rods, 0.4 to 0.5 by 4.0 to 5.0 microns, generally occurring singly. Spores terminal and ovoid, swelling the cells. Motile. Gram-positive.

Gelatin: Liquefaction in 4 days.

Agar deep colonies: Lenticular, later woolly, centers becoming brownish. Abundant gas is produced.

Peptone broth: Turbid; black deposit.

Glucose broth: Turbid; non-viscous sediment; fetid odor, with hydrogen sulfide.

Milk: Partially coagulated, later partially digested.

Indole produced; skatole not produced.

Glucose actively fermented. Fructose and sucrose slightly fermented. Arabinose, galactose, lactose, maltose, mannitol, glycerol and starch not attacked.

Nitrites not produced from nitrates.

Coagulated serum, egg, fibrin, liver and brain: Digestion begins in four to five days.

Anaerobic.

Optimum temperature, 37° C. Grows well at room temperature.

Neither toxin nor hemolysin produced.

Not pathogenic for guinea pigs or rabbits.

Source: Isolated from a human cadaver and from the peritoneum of a rabbit.

Habitat: Not determined.

55. Clostridium saprogenes (Salus, 1904) McClung and McCoy, *comb. nov.*

(*Bacillus saprogenes carnis* Salus, Arch. f. Hyg., *51*, 1904, 114; *Bacillus saprogenes* Salus, *ibid.*, 115; *Plectridium saprogenes* Prévot, Ann. Inst. Past., *61*, 1938, 87; also see Prévot and Weislitz, Ann. Inst. Past., *72*, 1946, 444.)

sap.ro'ge.nes. Gr. adj. *saprus* rotten; Gr. v. *gennaio* to produce; M.L. part.adj. *saprogenes* rot-producing.

Rods, 1.5 by 8.0 microns, curved, in chains and filaments. Spores ovoid, terminal. Motile. Gram-positive.

Gelatin: Slow liquefaction.

Agar deep colonies: Lenticular or spherical; gas is produced.

Liquid media: Gas production; disagreeable odor.

Glucose broth: Turbid; sediment; penetrating, putrid odor due in part to hydrogen sulfide.

Milk: Coagulated with a disagreeable odor.

Glucose, fructose, maltose, galactose, sucrose, lactose, arabinose, xylose, sorbitol, dulcitol, inulin and starch are fermented. Glycerol and mannitol are slightly attacked.

Nitrites not produced from nitrates.

Coagulated egg, serum, fibrin and brain: Not attacked.

Anaerobic.

Optimum temperature, 37° C.

Not pathogenic.

Source: Isolated from spoiled meat and from an industrial fermentation sample.

Habitat: Probably soil.

56. Clostridium perenne (Prévot, 1940) McClung and McCoy, *comb. nov.* (*Acuformis perennis* Prévot, Compt. rend. Soc. Biol., Paris, *133*, 1940, 576.)

per.en'ne. L. adj. *perennis* lasting through the year or through many years, perennial.

Straight rods, 0.3 to 0.4 by 1.6 to 3.0 microns for non-sporulating cells and 0.5 by 3.0 to 5.0 microns for sporulating cells, with rounded ends, occurring in pairs or in chains of 3 to 16 cells. Spores ovoid, terminal, measuring 0.6 by 1.0 micron. Nonmotile. Gram-positive.

Gelatin: No liquefaction.

Agar deep colonies: Lenticular, whitish, 1 to 2 mm in diameter. Agar is split by gas.

Glucose broth: Abundantly turbid; gas liberated has a slight, but not disagreeable, odor of volatile acids.

Peptone broth: Abundantly turbid; no gas.

Milk: Rapidly acidified, then coagulated with liberation of gas and retraction of clot.

Indole not produced.

Hydrogen sulfide not produced.

Glucose, fructose, maltose, galactose, sucrose, arabinose and lactose are strongly fermented.

Nitrites not produced from nitrates.

Anaerobic.

Optimum temperature, between 33° and 37° C.

Optimum pH, about 7.0.

Not pathogenic for guinea pigs, mice or rabbits.

Source: Isolated from a case of chronic appendicitis.

Habitat: Not determined.

57. Clostridium thermosaccharolyticum McClung, 1935. (Jour. Bact., *29*, 1935, 200.)

ther.mo.sac.cha.ro.ly'ti.cum. Gr. adj. *thermus* hot; Gr. noun *saccharum* sugar; Gr. adj. *lyticus* dissolving; M.L. adj. *thermosaccharolyticus* (presumably intended to mean) thermophilic and sugar-fermenting.

Slender, granulated rods, 0.4 to 0.7 by 3.5 to 7.5 microns, occurring singly and in pairs, not in chains. Spores spherical, terminal, swelling the cells. Motile by means of peritrichous flagella. Gram-negative.

Gelatin: No liquefaction.

Pea-infusion agar surface colonies (anaerobic): Granular, grayish white, raised center, feathery edges.

Glucose-tryptone agar deep colonies: Small, lenticular, smooth.

Liver-infusion broth over liver meat: Turbid; gas produced.

Litmus milk: Litmus reduced. Acid and slow but firm coagulation; coagulum split with gas. Clot not digested.

Indole not produced.

Acid and gas from arabinose, fructose, galactose, glucose, mannose, xylose, cellobiose, lactose, maltose, sucrose, trehalose, dextrin, glycogen, maize starch, amygdalin, esculin, alpha-methyl-glucoside and salicin. Raffinose weakly fermented. Rhamnose, inulin, pectin, erythritol, inositol, mannitol, glycerol, quercitol and Ca-lactate not fermented. Sorbitol and dulcitol not fermented (Mercer and Vaughn, Jour. Bact., *62*, 1951, 27).

Cellulose not fermented.

Nitrites not produced from nitrates.

Coagulated albumin: No liquefaction.

Blood serum: No liquefaction.

Brain medium: No blackening or digestion.

Meat medium: No blackening or digestion.

Anaerobic.

Optimum temperature, between 55° and 62° C. Thermophilic.

Not pathogenic on feeding to white rats or on injection to rabbits.

Distinctive character: Differentiated from *Clostridium tartarivorum* Mercer and Vaughn by not fermenting tartrate.

Source: Isolated from hard-swell of canned goods and from soil.

Habitat: Not determined.

58. Clostridium indolis McClung and McCoy, *nom. nov.** (*Terminosporus indologenes* Bezjak, Ann. Inst. Past., *82*, 1952, 101.)

in′do.lis. M.L. neut.n. *indolum* indole; M.L. gen.noun *indolis* of indole.

Straight to slightly curved rods, 0.6 by 3.0 to 4.0 microns. Spores terminal, round, measuring 1.0 to 1.5 microns. Motile. Gram-negative.

Gelatin: No growth.

Veillon agar colonies: Small, lenticular; no gas.

Blood agar colonies: After 3 days incubation, 2 mm in diameter, moist, grayish, round, irregular; there is also a spreading tendency.

Glucose broth: Uniformly turbid.

Milk: Acid and coagulated in 2 days; gas.

Indole is produced.

Hydrogen sulfide is produced.

Acid and gas from glucose, sucrose, maltose and lactose. Mannitol not fermented.

Coagulated proteins: Not attacked.

Anaerobic.

Grows well at 37° C. but not at ordinary temperatures nor at 46° C.

Pathogenicity: Mice injected peritoneally show no effects.

Source: Isolated from a patient operated on for cancer of the large intestine.

Habitat: Probably the human intestine.

59. Clostridium caloritolerans Meyer and Lang, 1926. (Jour. Inf. Dis., *39*, 1926, 321.)

ca.lo.ri.to′le.rans. L. noun *calor* heat; L. part.adj. *tolerans* tolerating; M.L. *caloritolerans* heat-tolerating.

Rods, 0.5 to 0.8 by 8.0 to 10.0 microns, with rounded ends, occurring singly, in pairs, in chains and in curved filaments. Spores spherical or pear-shaped, terminal, swelling the cells. Motile by means of peritrichous flagella. Gram-positive.

Gelatin: No liquefaction.

Liver agar deep colonies: Small, flat, transparent discs with large, polar tufts. Some colonies become fluffy.

Glucose blood agar surface colonies (anaerobic): Small, flat, grayish, rhizoidal. No hemolysis.

Broth: Slightly turbid.

Glucose broth: Abundantly turbid; clearing by sedimentation; gas is produced.

Brom cresol purple milk: No change.

Indole not produced.

Acid and gas from glucose, galactose and maltose. Fructose feebly fermented. Lactose, sucrose, raffinose, inulin, salicin, mannitol, inositol and glycerol not fermented.

---

*The specific epithet *indolis* is used here in lieu of *indologenes* because the latter is preoccupied in the genus *Clostridium* for an earlier-described organism (see species number 49, *Clostridium indologenes* McClung and McCoy).

Coagulated albumin: No liquefaction.

Blood serum: No liquefaction.

Brain medium: No blackening or digestion.

Beef-heart mash medium: Reddened; no blackening or digestion.

Anaerobic.

Optimum temperature not determined. Grows at 37° C.

Not pathogenic for mice, guinea pigs or rabbits.

Source: Isolated from an old culture of *Clostridium parabotulinum* Type A.

Habitat: Not determined.

60. **Clostridium tetanoides** (Adamson, 1918) Hauduroy et al., 1937. (Unnamed anaerobe, Adamson and Cutler, Lancet, *1*, 1917, 688; *Bacillus tetanoides* (*A*) Adamson, Jour. Path. and Bact., *22*, 1918-19, 382; Hauduroy et al., Dict. d. Bact. Path., 1937, 140.)

te.ta.no.i'des. M.L. noun *tetani* a specific epithet; Gr. noun *eidus* shape, form; M.L. adj. *tetanoides* (*Clostridium*) *tetani*-like.

Rods, 1.0 to 2.0 by 4.0 to 12.0 microns (averaging 1.0 to 1.5 by 6.0 to 7.0 microns), with rounded to slightly tapered ends, occurring singly, in pairs and in chains of 3 to 5 cells but not in filaments. Spores large, spherical, terminal, swelling the cells. Motile only in young cultures. Gram-positive in young cultures, soon becoming Gram-negative.

Gelatin: No liquefaction.

Plain agar surface colonies (anaerobic): Confluent, becoming an opaque film. Isolated colonies are circular to slightly irregular. Dendritic branching and mucoid tendency less evident than on glucose agar.

Glucose agar surface colonies (anaerobic): Circular, regular, opaque, bluish gray, moist, shining, thick, raised. Surface flat, becoming conical in center with age. On moist medium, shows radiating dendritic branching. Growth becomes tenacious-mucoid.

Glucose agar stab: Thick growth along stab, starting 0.5 cm below surface. No gas or splitting of medium.

Neutral-red glucose agar: Reduced to orange by transmitted, and to greenish fluorescent by reflected light.

Plain broth: Early, slight turbidity; clearing and mucoid sedimentation.

Glucose broth: Abundantly turbid; profuse, mucoid sediment.

Milk: Slight and slowly increasing alkalinity; slow separation of casein. No further change.

Indole produced in trace amounts in broth.

Acid but no gas from glucose and maltose. Lactose, sucrose, mannitol, starch and cellulose not fermented.

Coagulated albumin: No digestion or blackening.

Blood serum: No digestion or blackening.

Meat medium: No digestion or blackening.

Brain medium: No digestion or blackening.

Anaerobic.

Optimum temperature not recorded. Grows well at 37° C.

Not pathogenic for guinea pigs or rabbits.

Source: Isolated from war wounds, from postmortem blood cultures and from garden soil.

Habitat: Not determined.

61. **Clostridium tartarivorum** Mercer and Vaughn, 1951. (Jour. Bact., *62*, 1951, 36.)

tar.ta.ri'vo.rum. M.L. noun *acidum tartaricum* tartaric acid; L. v. *voro* to devour; M.L. adj. *tartarivorus* tartrate-destroying.

Long, uniformly slender, granulated rods; older cells are slightly curved. Cells, usually measuring 0.4 to 0.6 by 5.0 to 6.8 microns, vary in size depending on the growth medium. Occur singly or in pairs. Spores large (0.7 to 2.0 microns), ellipsoidal to spherical and generally terminal. Sluggishly motile by means of peritrichous flagella. Gram-negative.

Gelatin: No liquefaction.

Green pea agar surface colonies: Large (10.5 to 12.0 mm in diameter), grayish cream in color. Colonies on tartrate agar are smaller.

Indole not produced.

Hydrogen sulfide not produced from tryptone (peptone); production variable from sodium thiosulfate.

L-arabinose, d-xylose, glucose, fructose, galactose, mannose, maltose, lactose, sucrose, trehalose, cellobiose, alpha-methyl-glucoside, esculin, amygdalin, salicin, mannitol, sorbitol, dextrin, glycogen and potato starch are fermented. Raffinose, melibiose, adonitol, erythritol, glycerol, inositol, cellulose and pectin not fermented. Rhamnose and dulcitol may or may not be fermented.

Nitrites not produced from nitrates.

Sodium sulfate and sulfite not reduced.

Egg albumin: No growth.

Beef heart infusion: No growth.

Brain medium: Slow growth; slight gas production; no blackening nor digestion.

Blood agar: No growth.

Anaerobic.

Temperature relations: Optimum, between 55° and 60° C. Grows between 37° and 67° C.

Optimum pH, between 6.2 and 7.2.

Distinctive character: Differentiated from *Clostridium thermosaccharolyticum* McClung by the fermentation of tartrate.

Source: Isolated from crude tartrates, grape pomace and other industrial samples containing crude tartrate; also isolated from vineyard soils.

Habitat: Found in soil and in natural substances containing tartrate.

62. Clostridium sporosphaeroides Soriano and Soriano, 1948. (Rev. Asoc. Argentina Dietol., *6*, 1948, 36.)

spo.ro.sphae.ro'i.des. Gr. noun *sporus* seed; M.L. noun *spora* spore; Gr. adj. *sphaeroides* globular; M.L. adj. *sporosphaeroides* spheroidal-spored.

Rods, 0.6 to 0.7 by 5.0 to 8.0 microns. Sporulation after 48 hours, forming plectridia with a terminal spore that is spherical and about 0.7 to 0.9 micron in diameter. Motile.

Gelatin: No liquefaction.

Yeast autolysate glucose agar colonies: Lenticular with smooth edges.

Milk: At the beginning there is very little production of gas with no apparent change in the medium. After one week, partial coagulation commences, forming then a soft clot with a small amount of gas.

Meat broth with meat: Slightly turbid; gas is produced. After several days a very scant sediment forms, and there is fairly good sporulation.

Heart broth: Good growth with good sporulation and good production of gas. In several days the medium turns viscous.

Liver broth: Good growth but little sporulation.

Indole not produced.

Hydrogen sulfide not produced.

Glucose, fructose, arabinose, xylose, galactose, mannose, rhamnose, sucrose, maltose, lactose, glycerol, mannitol, dulcitol, salicin, inulin, dextrin and starch not fermented.

Nitrites not produced from nitrates.

Coagulated egg albumin: Not attacked.

Brain medium: Good growth with good production of gas. In brain medium with iron filings added, there is no blackening.

Von Hibler's medium: Good growth, but the culture medium is not blackened.

Anaerobic.

Not pathogenic upon inoculation into a small rat.

Source: Isolated from a tin of spoiled sardines.

Habitat: Not determined.

63. Clostridium tetani (Flügge, 1886) Holland, 1920. (Tetanusbacillen and Tetanuserreger, Nicolaier, Deutsch. med. Wochnschr., *10*, 1884, 843; *Bacillus tetani* Flügge, Die Mikroorganismen, 2 Aufl., 1886, 274; Holland, Jour. Bact., *5*, 1920, 220.)

te'ta.ni. Gr. noun *tetanus* tetanus; M.L. gen.noun *tetani* of tetanus.

Rods, 0.4 to 0.6 by 4.0 to 8.0 microns, with rounded ends, occurring singly, in pairs and often in long chains and filaments. Spores spherical, terminal, swelling the cells. Motile by means of peritrichous flagella. Gram-positive.

Gelatin: Slow liquefaction and blackening.

Agar deep colonies: Fluffy, cottony spheres, usually without visible, central nucleus.

Egg yolk agar surface colonies: Irregular, somewhat dry, somewhat roughened, without precipitate or luster.

Serum agar surface colonies (anaerobic):

Small, transparent; villous to fimbriate margin.

Broth: Slightly turbid. Gas is produced. Some strains clear quickly by sedimentation.

Litmus milk: Slow precipitation of casein or soft clotting. Clot slowly softened but not definitely digested. Little gas is produced.

Indole not produced (Reed, Jour. Bact., 44, 1942, 425).

Glucose and other carbohydrates not fermented.

Nitrates rapidly reduced; nitrites absent (Reed, loc. cit.).

Coagulated albumin: Slow liquefaction.

Blood agar: Hemolysis.

Blood serum: Slowly softened; feeble digestion.

Brain medium: Blackening and slow digestion. Not actively proteolytic.

Strictly anaerobic.

Optimum temperature, 37° C.

A potent exotoxin is produced for which an antitoxin is prepared. Toxin intensely toxic on injection but not on feeding.

Pathogenic and toxic.

Source: Originally isolated from animals inoculated with garden-soil extract. Isolated from wounds in human tetanus.

Habitat: Common in soils and in human and horse intestines and feces.

64. Clostridium lentoputrescens Hartsell and Rettger, 1934. (Jour. Bact., 27, 1934, 39 and 497.)

len.to.pu.tres'cens. L. adj. lentus slow; L. part.adj. putrescens decaying; M.L. adj. lentoputrescens slow-rotting.

Rods, 0.4 to 0.6 by 7.0 to 9.0 microns, with rounded ends, occurring singly, in pairs and in chains. Spores spherical, terminal, swelling the cells. Motile by means of peritrichous flagella. Weakly Gram-positive, becoming Gram-negative.

Gelatin: Liquefaction.

Agar surface colonies (anaerobic): Small, circular, flat; edge crenated to filamentous spreading. Develop a ground-glass appearance.

Agar deep colonies: Fluffy spheres with fibrils radiating from central nuclei.

Egg yolk agar surface colonies: Irregular, somewhat dry, slightly roughened, colorless, no precipitate or luster.

Litmus milk: Slow, soft coagulation or flocculent precipitation. Casein is slowly digested.

Indole is produced (Hall, Jour. Inf. Dis., 30, 1922, 141). Indole not produced (Hartsell and Rettger, op. cit., 1934, 509).

Hydrogen sulfide produced in egg-meat medium.

Carbohydrates not fermented. Glucose slightly attacked without distinct acid production (Hartsell and Rettger, ibid., 508)

Nitrites not produced from nitrates.

Coagulated albumin: Slow liquefaction and blackening.

Blood agar: Hemolysis.

Blood serum: Liquefaction. Gas is produced.

Brain medium: Slow blackening and digestion.

Egg-meat medium: Slightly turbid liquid. Meat reddened in 7 to 10 days, then digested with a foul odor.

Anaerobic.

Grows well at 37° C.

Filtrate is non-toxic on injection or feeding.

Not pathogenic for white mice, guinea pigs or rabbits.

Source: Isolated from putrefying meat.

Habitat: Found in the intestinal canals of humans. Widely dispersed in soil.

65. Clostridium tetanomorphum (Bulloch et al., 1919) Bergey et al., 1923. (Bacillus pseudo-tetanus, Type No. IX,—Tetanuslike Bacillus (Pseudotetanus Bacillus), McIntosh and Fildes, Med. Res. Counc., Spec. Rept. Ser. No. 12, 1917, 11 and 32; Bacillus tetanomorphus Bulloch, Bullock, Douglas, Henry, McIntosh, O'Brien, Robertson and Wolf, Med. Res. Counc., Spec. Rept. Ser. No. 39, 1919, 41; Bergey et al., Manual, 1st ed., 1923, 330.)

te.ta.no.mor'phum. Gr. noun tetanus tetanus; Gr. noun morphe shape; M.L. adj. tetanomorphus (presumably intended to mean) (Clostridium) tetani-shaped.

Slender rods, with rounded ends, occurring singly and in pairs, not in chains. Spores spherical, or nearly so, terminal, swelling the cells. Motile by means of peritrichous flagella. Gram-positive.

Gelatin: No liquefaction. Gelatin is liquefied (Hall, Jour. Inf. Dis., *30*, 1922, 501).

Agar surface colonies (anaerobic): Small, flat, irregularly circular, translucent, crenated.

Agar deep colonies: Small, opaque, irregular; not woolly or branched.

Agar slant (anaerobic): Grayish, translucent growth.

Broth: Turbid.

Litmus milk: Unchanged or occasionally slight reduction of litmus.

Indole not produced.

Acid and gas from glucose and maltose. Fructose, galactose, lactose, sucrose, salicin, inulin, mannitol and glycerol not fermented.

Nitrates rapidly reduced; nitrites absent (Reed, Jour. Bact., *44*, 1942, 425).

Atmospheric nitrogen is fixed, though not as actively as by *Clostridium pasteurianum* Winogradsky (Rosenblum and Wilson, Jour. Bact., *57*, 1949, 413).

Coagulated albumin: No liquefaction.

Blood serum: No liquefaction.

Brain medium: No blackening or digestion.

Egg-meat medium: Slight gas production in 48 hours. White crystals are deposited.

Anaerobic.

Grows at 30° and at 37° C.

Not pathogenic for guinea pigs or rabbits.

Source: Isolated from war wounds and from soil.

Habitat: Not determined. Probably rather common in soil.

66. Clostridium putrefaciens (McBryde, 1911) Sturges and Drake, 1927. (*Bacillus putrefaciens* McBryde, U.S.D.A., Bur. An. Ind., Bull. 132, 1911, 6; Sturges and Drake, Jour. Bact., *14*, 1927, 175.)

pu.tre.fa'ci.ens. L. part.adj. *putrefaciens* putrefying.

Rods, 0.5 to 0.7 by 3.0 to 15.0 microns, with rounded ends, occurring singly, in pairs and in chains and filaments. Spores spherical, terminal, swelling the cells. Non-motile. Gram-positive.

Gelatin: Liquefaction.

Agar surface colonies (anaerobic): Small, filamentous.

Agar slant (anaerobic): Scanty, white, beaded, glistening growth.

Broth: Moderately turbid; heavy, flocculent sediment.

Litmus milk: Rennet coagulation; peptonized. Litmus reduced.

Indole not produced.

Hydrogen sulfide produced in slight amounts.

Acid and gas from glucose. Lactose, sucrose, maltose and starch not fermented.

Nitrites not produced from nitrates.

Coagulated albumin: Liquefaction.

Blood serum: Liquefaction.

Brain medium: Blackening and slow digestion.

Minced pork medium: Slight disintegration; sour, putrefactive odor.

Anaerobic.

Temperature relations: Optimum, between 20° and 25° C. Slow growth at 0° C.; no visible growth at 37° C.

Not pathogenic.

Source: Isolated from muscle tissues of hogs at slaughter.

Habitat: Not determined.

67. Clostridium thermoaceticum Fontaine et al., 1942. (Fontaine, Peterson, McCoy, Johnson and Ritter, Jour. Bact., *43*, 1942, 705.)

ther.mo.a.ce'ti.cum. Gr. adj. *thermus* hot; M.L. noun *acidum aceticum* acetic acid; M.L. adj. *thermoaceticus* (probably intended to mean) producing acetic acid under thermophilic conditions.

Rods, 0.4 by 2.8 microns. Spores terminal, very nearly round, slightly swelling the cell. Gram-positive.

Gelatin: No liquefaction.

Agar colonies: Circular, smooth, opaque.

Litmus milk: Slight reduction of litmus.

Glucose, fructose and xylose are readily fermented. Lesser fermentation of galactose, mannose, d-arabinose, d-lactic acid, gluconic acid and esculin.

Nitrites produced from nitrates.

Coagulated egg albumin: Not attacked.

Brain medium: Not attacked.

Anaerobic.

Temperature relations: Optimum, between 55° and 60° C. Minimum, about 45° C. Maximum, about 65° C.

Distinctive characters: No gas produced in carbohydrate fermentation; acetic acid is the principal fermentation product.

Source: Isolated from horse manure.

Habitat: Found in fecal matter.

68. Clostridium belfantii (Carbone and Venturelli, 1925) Spray, 1939. (*Bacillus belfantii* Carbone and Venturelli, Boll. Ist. Sieroter., Milan, *4*, 1925, 59; Spray, in Manual, 5th ed., 1939, 759.)

bel.fan′ti.i. M.L. gen.noun *belfantii* of Belfant; named for Belfant, an Italian bacteriologist.

Thick, straight rods, 0.4 to 0.6 by 1.5 to 7.0 microns, occurring singly, in pairs and in short chains. Spores large, ovoid, central to subterminal, swelling the cells. Motile. Granulose-negative. Usually Gram-negative, occasional cells are Gram-positive.

Gelatin: No liquefaction.

Plain agar surface colonies (anaerobic): Large, round, opaque, with filamentous edge.

Agar deep colonies: Arborescent along the stab. Gas is produced.

Plain broth: Diffuse turbidity, clearing by precipitation. No pigmentation. Gas is produced.

Potato mash: Forms a foam which becomes violet in 24 to 48 hours and which persists 3 to 6 days, disappearing on exposure to air.

Potato slant: Grayish pellicle, becoming violet in 24 to 48 hours. Gas of alcoholic odor is produced. No acetone.

Glycerinated potato: Thin, grayish pellicle, not becoming violet.

Milk: Coagulated in 24 to 48 hours. Clot broken by gas.

Milk agar: Abundant growth. Gas of butyric odor is liberated.

Indole is produced.

Hydrogen sulfide not produced.

Acid and gas from glucose, fructose, maltose, sucrose, lactose and mannitol. Starch and inulin weakly fermented.

Coagulated albumin: No liquefaction.

Blood serum: No liquefaction.

Anaerobic.

Grows well at 37° C.

Specifically agglutinated only by homologous antiserum.

Source: Isolated from retting beds and from air.

Habitat: Not determined.

69. Clostridium venturellii (de Tomasi, 1925) Spray, 1939. (*Bacillus venturelli* (sic) de Tomasi, Boll. Ist. Sieroter. Milan., *4*, 1925, 203; Spray, in Manual, 5th ed., 1939, 769.)

ven.tu.rel′li.i. M.L. gen.noun *venturellii* of Venturelli; named for Venturelli, an Italian bacteriologist.

Pleomorphic, fusiform to straight or slightly curved rods, 0.5 to 0.8 by 2.5 to 8.0 and up to 20.0 microns, the size varying with the medium, with rounded ends, occurring singly, in pairs, in chains or frequently in parallel groupings. Spores ovoid, central to eccentric, swelling the cells. Encapsulated. Motile. Granulose-positive, showing violet granules with iodine. Gram-negative.

Gelatin: No growth. No liquefaction.

Glucose agar surface colonies (anaerobic): Round, becoming rose-colored.

Plain agar slant (anaerobic): No growth.

Maltose agar stab: Colonies lenticular, yellowish, turning rose. Odor of acetone.

Plain broth: No growth.

Milk with $CaCO_3$: Coagulated, becoming yellow, then pale rose. Amylic odor.

Potato slant (anaerobic): Becomes mucilaginous. Bubbles of gas of amylic odor.

Potato mash: Very abundant growth; rose-colored with red spots.

Acid and gas from glucose, maltose, sucrose, fructose, lactose, inositol, dextrin and starch. Arabinose, glycerol, mannitol and inulin not fermented (Weinberg et al., Les Microb. Anaérob., 1937, 800).

Fermentation products include especially acetone and amyl alcohol with smaller amounts of propyl, butyl and iso-butyl alcohols and acetic acid.

Coagulated albumin: No digestion.

Blood serum: No liquefaction; produces a small amount of yellowish liquid.

Anaerobic.

Optimum temperature, between 18° and 20° C. Inhibition of growth and pigmentation above 25° C.

Distinctive character: Produces a rose·

colored pigment which is soluble in alcohol but not in water, ether or chloroform.

Source: Isolated from potato.

Habitat: Not determined.

70. Clostridium saturnirubrum Prévot, 1946. (*Clostridium saturni-rubrum* (sic) Prévot, Compt. rend. Acad. Sci., Paris, *223*, 1946, 1037.)

sa.tur.ni.rub'rum. L. noun *Saturnus* the planet Saturn; L. adj. *ruber* red; M.L. adj. *saturniruber* Saturn-red, a color in the universal color code.

Straight rods, 0.8 by 4.0 to 5.0 microns, with rounded ends, occurring singly, in pairs or in chains. Spores very rare, subterminal, ovoid, clostridial. Weakly motile. Granulose-positive. Gram-positive.

Gelatin: No liquefaction.

VF glucose agar deep colonies (26° C.): Irregular with woolly outline, rapidly becoming yellow then turning red (Saturn-red according to the universal color code); abundant gas production splitting the agar. No pigment produced at 37° C., and strains cultivated at this temperature lose their chromogenic power.

Milk: Not coagulated.

Peptone water: Poor growth; slight gas.

VF glucose broth: Rapidly turbid; abundant gas; red-lead-colored sediment.

Indole and skatole not produced.

Hydrogen sulfide not produced.

Glucose, fructose, maltose, galactose, lactose, sucrose, arabinose, mannitol and starch are energetically fermented.

Nitrites not produced from nitrates.

Coagulated proteins: Not attacked.

Anaerobic.

Optimum temperature, 26° C.

Probably not pathogenic.

Source: Isolated from African soils.

Habitat: Presumably soil.

71. Clostridium roseum McCoy and McClung, 1935. (Arch. f. Mikrobiol., *6*, 1935, 237.)

ro'se.um. L. adj. *roseus* rosy.

Rods, 0.7 to 0.9 by 3.2 to 4.3 microns, occurring singly, in pairs and in short chains. Spores ovoid, subterminal, swelling the cells to clostridia. Motile by means of peritrichous flagella. Granulose-positive in clostridial stage. Gram-positive, becoming Gram-negative.

Glucose gelatin: Liquefaction.

Plain agar slant (anaerobic): Surface growth scant, scarcely perceptible.

Glucose agar surface colonies (anaerobic): Raised, smooth, edges slightly irregular. Pink to orange pigment.

Glucose agar deep colonies: Compact, lenticular, pink to red-orange.

Pigmentation (anaerobic): Colonies red-orange, becoming purplish black on aeration.

Plain broth: No growth.

Glucose broth: Abundant, uniform turbidity; much gas.

Litmus milk: Stormy coagulation. Litmus reduced but obscured by pink pigment. Clot slowly softened. Proteolysis demonstrable on milk agar.

Potato: Rapid digestion to a clear, yellow fluid and bluish sediment. Much gas with butylic odor.

Maize mash: Resembling the reaction of *Clostridium acetobutylicum* McCoy et al., but with flesh-orange pigment becoming slowly purple at surface on ageing.

Indole not produced.

Hydrogen sulfide produced from thiosulfate and sulfite.

Acid and gas from xylose, arabinose, glucose, mannose, fructose, galactose, lactose, maltose, sucrose, raffinose, starch, dextrin, glycogen, inulin, pectin and salicin. Esculin and amygdalin weakly fermented. Mannitol, erythritol, glycerol, alpha-methyl-glucoside, Ca-lactate and cellulose not fermented.

Ammonia produced from nitrates and from nitrites.

Coagulated albumin cubes: Softened and yellowed by slow digestion.

Blood agar: No hemolysis.

Blood serum: No liquefaction.

Brain medium: No blackening or digestion.

Anaerobic.

Optimum temperature, about 37° C. Growth occurs from 8° to 62° C.

Not pathogenic for guinea pigs or rabbits.

Distinctive characters: Differentiated from *Clostridium acetobutylicum* McCoy et al. by the fermentation of pectin and by pigment production. Differs from *Clos-*

tridium felsineum Bergey et al. in that it oxidizes pigment to purplish brown.

Source: Isolated from German maize.

Habitat: Probably occurs in soil.

72. Clostridium chromogenes Prévot, 1938. (Chromogenic anaerobe, Ghon and Mucha, Cent. f. Bakt., I Abt., Orig., *42*, 1906, 406; *Bacillus anaerobius chromogenes* LeBlaye and Guggenheim, Man. Prat. d. Diag. Bact., 1914, 321; Prévot, Ann. Inst. Past., *61*, 1938, 85.)

chro.mo′ge.nes. Gr. noun *chroma* color; Gr. v. *gennaio* to produce; M.L. adj. *chromogenes* color-producing.

Straight to slightly curved, coccoid to elongated rods, moderately sized, with rounded to slightly pointed ends, occurring singly, in pairs, in short chains and in long, curved to coiled filaments. Spores abundant, ovoid, central, subterminal, apparently terminal at maturation, swelling the cells to clubs and clostridia. Encapsulated, especially in serum media. Motile by means of many peritrichous flagella. Granulose-negative with iodine solution. Gram-positive.

Gelatin: Liquefaction in 48 hours. Diffuse turbidity; clearing with abundant, whitish gray sediment which later becomes red to violet-red. Upper (1 cm) layer shows diffuse, red pigment.

Plain agar (without peptone): Deep growth is sparse. Pigment not produced in absence of peptone.

Glucose agar surface colonies (anaerobic): Same as for blood agar. Growth slightly less profuse.

Glucose agar deep colonies: Grayish white, multi-lobate; dense centers and dendritic, tufted edges. Growth begins about 1 cm below surface. Gas abundantly produced. Diffuse, red pigment appears in superficial layers after 4 to 5 days.

Blood agar surface colonies (anaerobic): Grayish, moist, shining, flat; edges lobate with finely dendritic-tufted edges. Hemolysis.

Glucose meat-infusion broth: Abundant, diffuse turbidity with much gas. Gradual, profuse sedimentation, but with prolonged turbidity.

Peptone water: Growth variable; some-

times fails. At best, moderate turbidity and sediment. No gas.

Synthetic fluid media (Uschinsky, etc.): No growth (unless peptone is added). Growth is proportionate to added peptone.

Milk: Spongy coagulation after 3 to 4 days. Abundant gas. Turbid, yellowish whey is expressed. Casein clot gradually digested in 4 to 5 weeks. Fecal odor.

Potato slant (anaerobic): Growth delicate, shining, grayish yellow. Fecal odor.

Indole not produced.

Hydrogen sulfide abundantly produced.

Acid and gas from sucrose, lactose, fructose, maltose, galactose and mannitol (Prévot, Man. d. Class. et d. Déterm. d. Bact. Anaér. 1948, 191).

Coagulated albumin, hydrocoele and ascitic-fluids: Digestion and blackening, with moderate gas production with fecal odor. When covered with agar, the agar plug shows diffuse, red pigmentation.

Anaerobic.

Grows well at 21° and at 37° C.

Weakly pathogenic for white mice and guinea pigs. Produces hemorrhagic serous peritonitis after intraperitoneal inoculation. Death due apparently to a weak toxin. Virulence increased by animal passage.

Distinctive character: Produces a red pigmentation which is increased on addition of chlorine- or of bromine-water. Although produced by an anaerobe, the pigment appears only in the aerated zone and depends on the peptone content of the medium.

Source: Isolated from the pus of a human perinephritic abscess.

Habitat: Not determined.

73. Clostridium corallinum Prévot and Raynaud, 1944. (Ann. Inst. Past., *70*, 1944, 184.)

co.ral.li′num. L. adj. *corallinus* coral-red.

Long rods, 0.8 by 3.0 to 4.0 microns, with rounded ends, occurring singly, in pairs or in short chains. Subterminal spores, 1.0 by 1.5 to 2.0 microns, swelling the cells. Motile by means of peritrichous flagella. Gram-positive.

Gelatin: Liquefaction in 48 hours.

Glucose agar deep colonies: Woolly or

arborescent, with coral-red pigment. Colonies near aerobic layer are more pigmented.

Agar slants (in vacuum): Round colonies with irregular edges, non-pigmented. Colonies become coral-colored if air is introduced into the tube.

Peptone broth: Slightly turbid; colorless sediment; pigment develops on addition of glucose.

Glucose broth: Abundantly turbid; gas liberated; no pigment produced under anaerobic conditions.

Milk: Coagulated in 24 hours, clot not digested (Prévot and Raynaud, *ibid.*, 183); coagulation with digestion (Prévot and Sansonnens, Ann. Inst. Past., *73*, 1947, 1044).

Indole and skatole not produced.

Hydrogen sulfide produced.

Glucose, fructose, maltose, galactose, sucrose, lactose, arabinose, xylose, mannitol, sorbitol, dulcitol, glycerol, starch and inulin are fermented.

Pectin not attacked (Prévot and Raynaud, *op. cit.*, 1944, 183); pectin attacked (Prévot and Raynaud, Compt. rend. Acad. Sci., Paris, *222*, 1946, 1531).

Produces butyric and formic acids; lactic acid not produced (Prévot and Raynaud, *op. cit.*, 1944, 183); fermentation type: formic-butyric-lactic with alcohol and acetone or acetic-isobutyric-lactic with acetone (Prévot and Sansonnens, *op. cit.*, 1947, 1044); acetic, butyric and formic acids, ethyl and butyl alcohols and acetone (Prévot and Raynaud, *op. cit.*, 1946, 1531).

Acetylmethylcarbinol not produced.

Nitrites not produced from nitrates.

Coagulated serum: Not attacked.

Anaerobic.

Not pathogenic for mice or guinea pigs.

Source: Isolated from the serum from a mouse inoculated with Paris street dust (Prévot and Raynaud, *op. cit.*, 1944, 182) and from African soil (Prévot and Sansonnens, *op. cit.*, 1947, 1044).

Habitat: Soil.

74. **Clostridium aurantibutyricum** Hellinger, 1944. (Commemorative Vol. to Dr. Ch. Weizmann's 70th Birthday, Nov., 1944, 46; also see Jour. Gen. Microbiol., *1*, 1947, 203.)

au.ran.ti.bu.ty'ri.cum. M.L. noun *au-*

rantium the orange; M.L. noun *acidum butyricum* butyric acid; M.L. adj. *aurantibutyricus* (probably intended to mean) the golden organism producing butyric acid.

Straight rods, 0.5 by 4.7 microns at 30° to 0.5 by 9.4 microns at 37° C. Spores subterminal and ovoid (0.9 by 2.1 microns), swelling the cells. Spore-bearing cells are motile and mostly spindle-shaped. Motile by means of peritrichous flagella. Clostridia are granulose-positive. Gram-positive.

Gelatin: Liquefaction.

Glucose yeast agar surface colonies: Slightly granular with orange-red pigment; sometimes pink, deepening to pale orange on continued anaerobic incubation.

Potato slant: Not disintegrated.

Carrot slant: Softening and rotting within 48 hours.

Maize mash: Active gas production with distinct pink coloration; good but incomplete diastatic action.

Acid and gas from xylose, galactose, glucose, sucrose, lactose, maltose, pectin and starch. Cellulose, inulin, mannitol, glycerol and sorbitol not fermented.

Products of maize (starch) and glucose fermentation: Main products are acetic and butyric acids. Acetone, butanol, ethanol, acetone and iso-propanol are formed in lesser amounts. Lactic and formic acids and acetylmethylcarbinol produced only in slight or negligible amounts.

Nitrites not produced from nitrates.

Anaerobic.

Optimum temperature, 30° C.

Distinctive characters (differentiation from *Clostridium felsineum* Bergey et al. and *C. roseum* McCoy and McClung): Partial diastatic action in maize mash; lower yield of neutral fermentation products from carbohydrates; inability to ferment inulin; failure to digest potato tissue; inability to reduce nitrates; optimum temperature, 30° C.

Source: Isolated from stems of South African hibiscus and from English flax.

Habitat: Soil.

75. **Clostridium felsineum** (Carbone and Tombolato, 1917) Bergey et al., 1930. (*Bacillus felsineus* Carbone and Tombolato, Le Staz. Sper. Agrar., Ital., *50*, 1917, 563;

Clostridium felsinus (sic) Bergey et al., Manual, 3rd ed., 1930, 453.)

fel.si'ne.um. L. noun *Felsinea* the Latin name for Bologna, Italy; M.L. adj. *felsineus* pertaining to Felsinea.

Description taken from Ruschmann and Bavendamm (Cent. f. Bakt., II Abt., *64*, 1925, 340), from the Kluyver strain used by van der Lek (Thesis, Delft, 1930) and from McCoy and McClung (Arch. f. Mikrobiol., *6*, 1935, 230).

Rods, 0.3 to 0.4 by 3.0 to 5.0 microns, occurring singly, in pairs and in short chains. Spores ovoid, subterminal, swelling the cells to clostridia. Motile by means of peritrichous flagella. Granulose-positive in the clostridial stage. Gram-positive, becoming Gram-negative.

Glucose-gelatin: Liquefaction.

Glucose agar surface colonies (anaerobic): Raised, smooth, slightly irregular, yellow-orange.

Glucose agar deep colonies: Compact, lenticular, opaque, yellow.

Plain agar slant (anaerobic): Surface growth scant, scarcely perceptible.

Pigmentation (anaerobic): Yellow-orange, ageing to brownish. No change on aeration.

Plain broth: No growth.

Glucose broth: Abundant, uniform turbidity; much gas. Yellow, slimy sediment.

Litmus milk: Acid and coagulation. Litmus reduced. Clot torn and yellowed. No visible digestion.

Potato: Digested to a yellow slime. Much gas with butylic odor.

Maize mash: Resembling reaction of *Clostridium acetobutylicum* McCoy et al., but with flesh-colored to orange pigment.

Indole not produced.

Acid and gas from arabinose, xylose, glucose, mannose, fructose, galactose, lactose, maltose, sucrose, raffinose, starch, dextrin, inulin, glycogen, pectin and salicin. Mannitol, erythritol, glycerol, Ca-lactate and cellulose not fermented.

Fermentation products include butyl and ethyl alcohols, acetone, organic acids (probably butyric and acetic), H_2 and CO_2.

Ammonia produced from nitrates and nitrites.

Atmospheric nitrogen fixed (Rosenblum and Wilson, Jour, Bact., *57*, 1949, 413).

Coagulated albumin cubes: Softened and yellowed by slow digestion.

Blood agar: No hemolysis.

Blood serum: No liquefaction.

Brain medium: No blackening or digestion.

Anaerobic.

Grows at 37° C.

Not pathogenic for guinea pigs or rabbits.

Source: Isolated from retting flax; also found in soil in Italy, in Argentina and in the United States.

Habitat: Not determined.

76. Clostridium flavum McClung and McCoy, *nom. nov.* (Type IV of retting clostridia, Lanigan, Austral. Jour. Sci. Research, Ser. B, Biol. Sci., 4, 1951, 475.)

fla'vum. L. adj. *flavus* yellow.

Slender, straight to slightly curved rods, 0.4 by 2.0 to 7.0 microns, with rounded ends, occurring singly, in pairs, end to end and in small clusters with some palisade formation; short filaments occasionally occur. Subterminal spores, elliptical or bean-shaped, 0.8 by 2.5 to 2.7 microns. Sporulation occurs early and freely. Cell distended at sporulation by an elongated, subterminal spore with pronounced terminal "cap". Motile. Gram-positive in young cultures.

Glucose-gelatin: Liquefaction in 7 to 11 days.

Nutrient agar: No growth.

Glucose yeast agar surface colonies: Circular, 1.0 to 1.5 mm in diameter, entire, low-convex or umbilicate, smooth and glistening, opaque, canary-yellow by reflected light, viscid consistency.

Glucose yeast agar deep colonies: Biconvex discs, 1 mm in diameter, canary-yellow in color; medium disrupted by gas.

Glucose yeast agar slant: Good, filiform growth; smooth and glistening surface; canary-yellow, non-diffusible pigment; soft butyrous to viscid consistency.

Glucose yeast peptone broth: Heavy, uniform turbidity; much gas; pale yellow viscid deposit. Marked odor of butanol.

Litmus milk: Acid and gas; reduction; coagulation; usually a stormy clot within two to four days. No digestion of curd.

Indole not produced.

Hydrogen sulfide produced in trace amounts on glucose yeast agar.

Potato mash: Active fermentation with "head"; pale canary-yellow pigment; complete diastatic action.

Acid and gas from glucose, galactose, maltose, sucrose, lactose, starch and pectin. Inulin, mannitol, glycerol and calcium lactate not fermented.

Flax sterilized in yeast infusion: Active retting.

Nitrites not produced from nitrates. Nitrites reduced, presumably to ammonia.

Coagulated egg albumin: No visible change, but after several days softening can be detected by probing.

Brain medium: Slight gas; no blackening or digestion.

Anaerobic.

Grows well at 37° and well but more slowly at 30° C.

Distinctive characters: Non-diffusible, canary-yellow pigment; active retting of flax.

Source: Isolated from Australian flax.

Habitat: Presumably soil.

77. Clostridium carbonei Arnaudi, 1936. (Soc. Intern. Microbiol., Boll. Sez. Ital., *8*, 1936, 251; also see Boll. Ist. Sieroter, Milano, *16*, 1937, 650.)

car.bo'ne.i. M.L. gen.noun *carbonei* of Carbone; named for Carbone, an Italian bacteriologist.

Rods, 0.8 to 1.0 by 3.5 to 4.5 microns, with ends slightly tapered. Spores ovoid, 0.8 to 1.0 by 1.0 to 1.75 microns, terminal, swelling the cells. Non-motile. Strongly granulose-positive with iodine solution. Gram-positive.

Gelatin: No growth.

Glucose- and lactose-gelatin: No growth.

Plain agar surface colonies (anaerobic): Flat, shining, colorless, with irregular edges.

Malt agar surface colonies (anaerobic): Creamy to slightly reddish; irregular edges.

Plain agar stab: Only traces of growth along stab.

Glucose and maltose agar stab: No growth.

Plain broth: Very slight, colorless, diffuse turbidity.

Glucose broth: Very slight turbidity.

Maltose broth: Intensely turbid; profuse, reddish yellow sediment.

Tarozzi broth: Slight, diffuse turbidity.

Coagulated egg-yolk broth: Slightly turbid; no digestion.

Coagulated egg-albumin broth: Slightly turbid; no digestion.

Milk: Soft coagulation; slight, fine, reddish flocculence. Whey turbid and colorless. Reaction acid. Clot not digested.

Digest-milk (optimum medium): Very abundantly turbid; bright red, flocculent sediment, diffusing uniformly on shaking.

Roux-potato slant (anaerobic): Punctiform, raised, opaque, deep red colonies, becoming almost violet.

Indole not produced.

Hydrogen sulfide not produced.

Glucose, maltose, sucrose, galactose, fructose and raffinose are weakly fermented. Lactose is slowly and partially fermented (only in acidified medium). Starch slightly fermented.

Cellulose not attacked. Hemp is not retted.

Fermentation products include H_2, CO_2, CH_4, butyric acid and traces of ethyl alcohol.

Coagulated serum (Loeffler, anaerobic): Poor growth; flat, red surface colonies. No digestion.

Brain medium: Action not recorded.

Anaerobic.

Temperature relations: Optimum, 37° C. Grows slowly between 25° and 30° C. Growth ceases at 40° C.

Chemical tolerance: Optimum pH, between 7.0 and 7.2. Minimum pH, 6.0. Maximum pH, 8.0.

Not pathogenic for sheep, rabbits, guinea pigs or white mice.

Distinctive character: Production of a brilliant red pigment which is soluble in amyl alcohol, petrol-ether, xylol and aniline oil and partly soluble in ether, chloroform and acetone; pigment very stable in light.

Source: Isolated from raw potato infusion.

Habitat: Not recorded.

78. Clostridium haumanii (Soriano, 1930) Prévot, 1938. (Unnamed plectridium, Sordelli and Soriano, Compt. rend. Soc.

Biol., Paris, *99*, 1928, 1517; Plectridio amarillo, Soriano, Tomo commemorativo del XXV aniversario de la fundación de la Facultad de Agronomia y Veterinaria, Buenos Aires, 1929 (?); *Bacillus haumani* (sic) Soriano, Rev. Inst. Bact., Buenos Aires, *5*, 1930, 743; *Plectridium amarillum* Stampa, Ann. Brass. et Distill., *29*, 1930–31, (253, 271 and 302?); *Clostridium haumanni* (sic) Prévot, Ann. Inst. Past., *61*, 1938, 81; *Clostridium felsineum* var. *haumanni* (sic) Heyn, Verhand. d. k. Akad. v. Wetensch., Amsterdam, Tweedie Reeks, *48*, 1951, 29.)

hau.man'i.i. M.L. gen.noun *haumanii* of Hauman; named for Prof. Lucien Hauman, Microbiologist of the University of Buenos Aires.

Rods, averaging 0.7 to 0.8 by 4.0 to 10.0 microns, occurring singly or in short chains. Terminal, ovoid spores, 1.6 by 3.0 microns, with spore cap. Actively motile. Granulose-negative. Gram-positive, becoming Gram-negative.

Gelatin: No liquefaction.

Carrot agar deep colonies: Lenticular with smooth edges. Gas production disrupts agar. Intense canary-yellow pigment diffuses in medium.

Carrot juice: Uniformly turbid.

Potato mash: Produces good growth with slow gas and with yellow pigment production. No head formation as with *Clostridium felsineum* Bergey et al.

Acid and gas from amygdalin, salicin, mannitol, arabinose, xylose, glucose, fructose, mannose, galactose, sucrose, maltose, lactose, pectin and rhamnose. Arabitol, dulcitol, sorbitol, inositol, raffinose, inulin and starch not fermented.

Retting action: Positive in three days.

Anaerobic.

Optimum temperature, 37° C.

Source: Isolated from retting liquid from Argentina.

Habitat: Found in decomposing plant materials.

79. Clostridium virens (Prévot, 1946) McClung and McCoy, *comb. nov.* (*Plectridium virens* Prévot, Ann. Inst. Past., *72*, 1946, 665.)

vi'rens. L. v. *vireo* to be green; L. part. adj. *virens* becoming green.

Straight rods, 0.6 to 0.8 by 3.0 to 4.0 microns. Terminal, spherical spores, 1 micron in diameter. Gram-positive in young cultures.

Gelatin: No growth.

Glucose agar deep colonies: Colonies appear slowly in 5 to 8 days; transparent, large, woolly colonies with green, fluorescent coloration. Sometimes colonies are smaller, opaque, irregular-edged and green-pigmented. Pigment is soluble and diffuses completely into the agar but stops at the level of the aerobic zone.

VF glucose broth: Slow growth at 26° C. in 8 to 10 days; after 15 days the broth is colored green; no gas.

Milk: No growth.

Indole not produced.

Potato mash: Strongly colored green in 2 days; marked production of gas.

Lactose and galactose are strongly fermented. Fructose is more weakly fermented, while glucose, maltose, sucrose, sorbitol, mannitol and starch are not fermented.

Cellulose is not attacked (Prévot, Man. d. Class. et d. Déterm. d. Bact. Anaérob., 2ᵉ ed., 1948, 210).

Propionic and formic acids are produced.

Nitrites produced from nitrates.

Coagulated egg white: No growth.

Liver, brain and fibrin: No growth.

Anaerobic.

Temperature relations: Optimum, 26° C. Weak growth at 18° and no growth above 30° C. Inhibition of pigment production in second-generation cultures at 30° C.

Not pathogenic for experimental animals.

Source: Isolated from pond and river muds.

Habitat: Presumably mud.

80. Clostridium spumarum (Prévot and Pochon, 1939) Spray, 1948. (*Plectridium spumarum* Prévot and Pochon, Compt. rend. Soc. Biol., Paris, *130*, 1939, 966; Spray, in Manual, 6th ed., 1948, 808.)

spu.ma'rum. L. noun *spuma* foam, froth; L. gen.pl. noun *spumarum* of foams.

Rods, 0.5 by 4.0 microns. Spores are ovoid and terminal, swelling the cells. Motile. Gram-positive.

Gelatin: Liquefaction in 15 days.

Agar deep colonies: Small, cottony; a few gas bubbles are produced.

Peptone water: Turbid; slight sediment.

Milk: Coagulated in 5 days, but clot is not digested.

Indole is produced.

Hydrogen sulfide is produced (medium not stated).

Glucose, fructose, galactose, maltose, arabinose, xylose, sucrose, mannitol and starch slowly fermented after 1 month of cultivation. Inulin not fermented. Carbohydrates not attacked immediately after isolation.

Cellulose (in synthetic medium) is fermented chiefly to acetic and butyric acids together with inflammable gas and traces of ethyl alcohol.

Coagulated albumin: Not attacked.

Brain medium: No blackening.

Anaerobic.

Optimum temperature, around 37° C. Not thermophilic.

Distinctive characters: Does not produce pigment; ferments a variety of carbohydrates.

Source: Isolated from the scum of sugar-refining vats.

Habitat: Not determined.

81. Clostridium werneri Bergey et al., 1930. (*Bacillus cellulosam fermentans* Werner, Cent. f. Bakt., II Abt., *67*, 1926, 297; Bergey et al., Manual, 3rd ed., 1930, 452.)

wer'ne.ri. M.L. gen.noun *werneri* of Werner; named for Erich Werner, the German bacteriologist who first isolated this organism.

Rods, 0.5 to 0.7 by 1.5 to 7.0 microns, occurring singly and in pairs but not in chains. Spores ovoid, terminal, swelling the cells. Motile by means of peritrichous flagella. Gram-negative.

Agar slant (anaerobic): No growth.

Cellulose agar slant (anaerobic): Growth only in contact with cellulose. Growth grayish black; agar is darkened. Gas is produced.

Broth: No growth.

Broth with filter paper: Poor growth; cellulose weakly attacked.

Omelianski solution with filter paper: Abundant growth; cellulose digested with the production of H_2 and CO_2.

Hydrogen sulfide is produced in the Omelianski medium, presumably from the $(NH_4)_2SO_4$ and $MgSO_4$.

Glucose and carbohydrates other than cellulose not fermented.

Anaerobic.

Optimum temperature, between 33° and 37° C.

Not pathogenic for mice.

Relationship to other species: Probably closely related to *Clostridium omelianskii* Spray.

Source: Isolated from the larvae of the rose-leaf beetle (*Potosia cuprea*).

Habitat: Found in soil and in the feces of herbivorous animals.

82. Clostridium leptinotarsae Sartory and Meyer, 1941. (Compt. rend. Acad. Sci., Paris, *212*, 1941, 819.)

lep.ti.no.tar'sae. M.L. noun *Leptinotarsa* a genus of insects; M.L. gen.noun *leptinotarsae* of *Leptinotarsa*.

Straight or curved rods, 0.5 to 0.7 by 1.5 to 4.0 microns, frequently occurring in pairs. Terminal, ovoid spores, 0.6 to 0.7 by 1.0 to 1.8 microns. Non-motile. Gram-negative (Prévot, Man. d. Class. et Déterm. d. Bact. Anaérob., 2ᵉ ed., 1948, 201).

Gelatin: No liquefaction.

Peptone broth: Turbid.

Milk: Coagulated then digested.

Indole is produced.

Celulose readily attacked. Glucose, galactose, mannitol, maltose, sucrose and lactose are fermented; fructose is only moderately fermented.

Lactic and butyric acids, carbon dioxide and hydrogen are produced.

Nitrites not produced from nitrates (Prévot, *loc. cit.*).

Anaerobic.

Optimum temperature, between 27° and 37° C.

Source: Isolated from the intestines of a potato beetle.

Habitat: Decomposing organic matter.

83. Clostridium cellulosolvens Cowles and Rettger, 1931. (Jour. Bact., *21*, 1931, 167.)

cel.lu.lo.sol'vens. M.L. noun *cellulosum* cellulose; L. part.adj. *solvens* dissolving; M.L. adj. *cellulosolvens* cellulose-dissolving.

Rods, 0.5 by 2.0 to 6.0 microns, commonly curved, occurring singly and in pairs, not in chains. Spores spherical, terminal, swelling the cells. Non-motile. Gram stain uncertain; usually Gram-negative.

Grows in routine media only when cellulose or a certain few carbohydrates are added.

Surface colonies on dextrin-cysteine meat infusion agar (anaerobic): Tiny, round, transparent dew-drops; finely granular; smooth edge.

Acid and gas from cellulose, dextrin, arabinose, xylose and soluble starch. Glucose, fructose, mannose, lactose, maltose, sucrose, melezitose, raffinose, inulin, salicin, amygdalin, adonitol, dulcitol, erythritol, glycerol, inositol, mannitol, sorbitol and gum arabic not fermented.

Cellulose decomposed to H_2, CO_2 and organic acids.

Anaerobic.

Grows at 37° C.

Source: Isolated from horse feces.

Habitat: Probably widely dispersed in manured soils.

84. Clostridium cellobioparum Hungate, 1944. (*Clostridium cellobioparus* (sic) Hungate, Jour. Bact., *48*, 1944, 503.)

cel.lo.bi·o′pa.rum. M.L. noun *cellobiosum* cellobiose; L. v. *pario* to bear, produce; L. verb.adj.suffix *parus* producing; M.L. adj. *cellobioparus* cellobiose-producing.

Slightly curved rods, 0.3 to 0.4 by 3.0 to 5.0 microns, occurring singly or as two cells attached. Spores are terminal and spherical, 0.9 micron in diameter, swelling the cells; spores rarely remain attached to the cells. Motile by means of 1 to 4 peritrichous flagella. Gram-negative.

Glucose agar deep colonies: Disc-shaped and compact, older colonies become more complex in shape, often by growth of daughter discs at right angles to the original one; pigmentation not reported, presumed negative.

Cellulose agar deep colonies: Irregular in shape, even when small.

Acid and gas readily produced from glucose, fructose, xylose, arabinose, mannose, cellobiose, melibiose, maltose and a hemicellulose from birch. Galactose, sucrose,

lactose, raffinose, mannitol and dextrin less readily fermented. Melezitose, trehalose, salicin, inulin, soluble starch, glycerol and rhamnose not fermented.

Fermentation products are acetic, formic and lactic acids, ethyl alcohol, carbon dioxide, hydrogen and other products not identified. Cellobiose is the chief product of digestion of cellulose; no glucose is produced.

Ferrous sulfate not reduced.

Biotin and carbohydrates are required in inorganic media.

Strictly anaerobic.

Temperature relations: Optimum, 38° C. Growth is slow at 25° C. Growth inhibited at 18° and at 45° C.

Distinctive characters: Distinguished from *Clostridium cellulosolvens* Cowles and Rettger by the fermentation of glucose, fructose, mannose and maltose, from *C. dissolvens* Bergey et al. by spore shape and fermentation of mono- and di-saccharides and from *C. werneri* Bergey et al. by spore shape and fermentation of glucose (Hungate, Jour. Bact., *48*, 1944, 499).

Source: Isolated from the rumina of cattle.

Habitat: Found in the rumina of ruminants, so far as known.

85. Clostridium omelianskii (Henneberg, 1922, *emend.* Clausen, 1931) Spray, 1948. (Bacillus hydrogénique, Omeliansky, Arch. Sci. Biol. (Russ.), *9*, 1902–03, 263 (Wasserstoffbacillus, Omeliansky, Cent. f. Bakt., II Abt., *8*, 1902, 262), and Bacille formenique, Omeliansky, *op. cit.*, 1902–03, 263 (Methanbacillus, Omeliansky, Cent. f. Bakt., II Abt., *11*, 1903–04, 370); *Bacillus omelianskii* Henneberg, Cent. f. Bakt., II Abt., *55*, 1922, 276; Clausen, Cent. f. Bakt., II Abt., *84*, 1931, 40 and 54; Spray, in Manual, 6th ed., 1948, 809.)

o.me.li.an′ski.i. M.L. gen.noun *omelianskii* of Omeliansky; named for Prof. W. Omeliansky, the Russian bacteriologist who was the first to observe this organism.

Straight to slightly curved rods, 0.5 to 0.7 by 5.0 to 15.0 microns, the length varying with the medium, occurring chiefly singly, occasionally in pairs, frequently parallel in groups, never in chains or filaments. Spores, 1.0 to 1.5 microns in diameter, the size varying with the medium, spherical, terminal, swelling the cells. Young cells are motile, the motility disappearing with sporulation; flagella not demonstrable. Young vegetative cells are colored wine-red with iodine solution. Gram-positive, becoming Gram-labile on sporulation.

Gelatin (plus asparagine): Liquefaction in 6 to 10 days. Medium remains perfectly clear.

Asparagine agar deep colonies: Grayish white, delicate, cottony, with fine radial outgrowths.

Asparagine agar surface colonies (anaerobic): Poor, delicate, translucent, filmy, scarcely discernible growth.

Cellulose-liver broth: Solution remains visibly clear and does not darken with age. Occasionally, large gas bubbles arise.

Milk: Soft coagulation in 24 hours. Amorphous clot shrinks and settles, forming a yellowish red to orange sediment with turbid supernatant whey.

Indole not produced.

Hydrogen sulfide produced in trace amounts in inorganic solutions.

Maltose, mannitol, lactose, glucose, sucrose, galactose, fructose, starch, salicin, glycerol and inulin not attacked.

Cellulose, apparently the primary carbon source, is only weakly attacked by pure cultures with the production of hydrogen and carbon dioxide. Yellow pigment not observed in the presence of cellulose (see *Clostridium dissolvens*).

Nitrites not produced from nitrates.

Ammonia not produced.

Brain medium: No digestion or blackening. No visible evidence of growth.

Non-pathogenic for mice; effect on other animals not recorded.

Anaerobic. Grows at 25 to 30 mm mercury pressure.

Optimum temperature, between 37° and 42° C.

Optimum reaction, between pH 7.0 and 7.4. Grows between pH 6.0 and 8.4.

Distinctive characters: Ability to liquefy gelatin (with asparagine added), to coagulate milk, producing an orange sediment, and to grow in media containing asparagine without requiring the presence of cellulose.

Spores resist heating at 100° C. for 90 minutes.

Comments: This species was apparently first isolated and studied in pure culture by Clausen (*op. cit.*, 1931, 40 and 54). From his studies he concluded that Omeliansky's Wasserstoffbacillus and Methanbacillus are but a single species and that the gaseous fermentation products are H_2 and CO_2, not methane; the production of methane observed by Omeliansky was effected by the symbiotic forms or other contaminants always present in Omeliansky's cultures. Clausen's evidence is quite convincing, and the organism is presented here from his description.

Source: Isolated from human, cow and horse excreta, from the stomach contents of cows, from cheese and from soil.

Habitat: Found in the intestinal canals of animals and presumably thence widely disseminated in soil.

86. **Clostridium dissolvens** Bergey et al., 1925. (*Bacillus cellulosae dissolvens* Khouvine, Ann. Inst. Past., *37*, 1923, 711; Bergey et al., Manual, 2nd ed., 1925, 344.)

dis.sol′vens. L. part.adj. *dissolvens* dissolving.

Slender rods, ranging from 2.5 to 12.5 microns in length, occurring singly and occasionally in pairs, but not in chains. Spores ovoid, terminal, swelling the cells. Nonmotile. Gram-negative.

Cellulose is digested by the formation of an endocellulase which acts only when the bacteria are attached to the cellulose. Saccharides and CO_2, H_2, ethyl alcohol and acetic, lactic and butyric acids are produced from cellulose.

A yellow pigment is produced in the presence of cellulose.

Glucose and carbohydrates other than cellulose not fermented.

Anaerobic.

Grows between 35° and 51° C. without a definite optimum. For the thermophilic strain of Khouvine, see *Clostridium thermocellum* Viljoen et al.

Not pathogenic for guinea pigs.

Distinctive character: Grows only in media containing cellulose, in the presence of which it produces a yellow pigment.

Source: Isolated from human feces.

Habitat: Intestinal canal of man.

87. Clostridium thermocellum Viljoen et al., 1926. (Viljoen, Fred and Peterson, Jour. Agr. Sci. (London), *16*, 1926, 7; *Terminosporus thermocellus* Prévot, Ann. Inst. Past., *61*, 1938, 86; *Plectridium snieszkoi* Prévot, Man. d. Class. et Déterm. d. Bact. Anaérob., 1940, 154; also see McBee, Jour. Bact., *67*, 1954, 505; and Bact. Rev., *14*, 1950, 51.)

ther.mo'cel.lum. Gr. adj. *thermus* hot; M.L. noun *cellulosum* cellulose; M.L. adj. *thermocellus* (probably intended to mean) a thermophilic organism that digests cellulose.

Vegetative cells are straight or slightly curved rods, 0.6 to 0.7 by 2.5 to 3.5 microns, usually occurring as individuals but occasionally forming long chains in liquid media. Terminal, ovoid spores, about 1.2 by 1.6 microns, swelling the cells. Motile by means of peritrichous flagella. Gram-negative.

Cellulose-gelatin: Cellulose digested, but gelatin not liquefied.

Cellobiose agar surface colonies (anaerobic): Watery, slightly convex, translucent with a bluish fluorescence.

Cellulose agar surface colonies (anaerobic): As above but with an insoluble, yellowish orange pigment frequently produced. Cellulose digested in an area surrounding the colony.

Cellulose agar deep colonies: Lenticular, becoming lobate in old cultures. Colonies may be white or produce a yellowish orange pigment which is more intense in some strains than in others. Cellulose surrounding the colony is digested.

Nutrient broth (anaerobic): No growth.

Glucose broth (anaerobic): No growth.

Indole not produced.

Hydrogen sulfide not produced.

Acid and gas from cellulose, cellobiose, xylose and hemicelluloses. Glucose, fructose, mannose, galactose, arabinose, sucrose, lactose, maltose, melibiose, trehalose, inulin, salicin, dextrin, soluble starch, inositol, sorbitol, dulcitol, mannitol, glycerol, pectin and gum arabic not fermented.

Fermentation products include CO_2, H_2,

formic, acetic, lactic and succinic acids and ethyl alcohol.

Acetylmethylcarbinol not produced.

Nitrites not produced from nitrates.

Anaerobic.

Optimum temperature, about 60° C. Grows between 50° and 68° C.

Comment: A thermophilic strain of *Bacillus cellulosae dissolvens* Khouvine is regarded as identical with this species.

Source: Isolated from horse manure, human feces, soil and marine mud.

Habitat: Probably widely dispersed in soils.

88. Clostridium thermocellulaseum Enebo, 1951. (Physiol. Plantarum, *4*, 1951, 653.)

ther.mo.cel.lu.la'se.um. Gr. adj. *thermos* hot; M.L. noun *cellulosum* cellulose; M.L. adj. *thermocellulaseus* (probably intended to mean) a thermophilic organism that digests cellulose.

Slender rods, 0.35 to 0.45 by 2.0 to 4.8 microns, with rounded ends, occurring singly or in pairs. Terminal spores, about 1.0 to 1.25 microns in size, soon separate from the sporangia, which are rapidly dissolved. Often times a small amount of the vegetative cell remains attached to the spore. Motile by means of very few peritrichous flagella. Gram-negative.

Gelatin: No liquefaction at 55° C.

Cellulose agar colonies: Minute, colorless, translucent, convex surface colonies; subsurface colonies are minute, faintly yellow and lens-shaped. Colonies are surrounded by clear, circular, decomposition zones.

Nutrient and starch agar: No growth (Enebo, Studies on Cellulose Decomposition by an Anaerobic Thermophilic Bacterium and Two Associated Non-cellulolytic Species, Stockholm, 1954).

Litmus milk: Not coagulated; acid not produced.

Indole not produced.

Acid and gas from glucose, fructose, mannose (weakly), maltose (weakly), cellobiose, arabinose and xylose. Galactose, rhamnose, sucrose, lactose, melibiose, trehalose, raffinose, glycerol, mannitol, dulcitol, sorbitol and starch not fermented.

Cellulose is hydrolyzed to low-molecular

carbohydrates, especially cellobiose and glucose. Higher saccharides are also formed. Decomposition of cellulose is immediately followed by the appearance of reducing sugars and cellulase in the medium.

Products of hydrolysis are partly fermented with the production of ethanol, formic, acetic, lactic and succinic acids, carbon dioxide and hydrogen. Methane is not produced. Acetaldehyde (traces), malic and fumaric acids and glycerol are also produced (Enebo, *op. cit.*, 1954).

Neither nitrites nor ammonia produced from nitrates.

Catalase-negative.

Strictly anaerobic.

Temperature relations: Optimum, between 55° and 60° C. Slow growth at 37° C. No growth below 30° or above 65° C.

Optimum initial pH for fermentation, about 8.0.

Not pathogenic for mice or guinea pigs.

Source: Isolated from decaying grass and leaves.

Habitat: Found in decomposing plant materials.

89. **Clostridium carnis** (Klein, 1904) Spray, 1939. (Art V, von Hibler, Cent. f. Bakt., I Abt., *25*, 1899, 515; *Bacillus carnis* Klein, Cent. f. Bakt., I Abt., Orig., *35*, 1904, 459; also see Trans. Path. Soc., London, *55*, 1904, 74; Art VI, von Hibler, Untersuch. ü. d. Path. Anaer., 1908, 3 and 406; Spray, in Manual, 5th ed., 1939, 750.)

car′nis. L. noun *caro* flesh; L. gen.noun *carnis* of flesh.

Description taken from Hall and Duffett (Jour. Bact., *29*, 1935, 269).

Rods, 0.5 to 0.7 by 1.5 to 4.5 microns, occurring singly and in pairs, rarely in chains of 3 to 4 cells. Spores ovoid to elongate, subterminal, slightly swelling the cells. Motile by means of peritrichous flagella. Gram-positive.

Gelatin: No liquefaction or blackening.

Agar surface colonies (aerobic): Minute, transparent dew-drops, becoming flat and lobate.

Blood agar surface colonies (aerobic): Similar to those on plain agar. Slight hemolysis.

Agar deep colonies: Lenticular, becoming nodular to arborescent.

Milk: Abundant gas, but no coagulation or other change.

Indole not produced.

Acid and gas from glucose, galactose, fructose, maltose, lactose, sucrose, amygdalin, salicin and dextrin. Trehalose, raffinose, xylose, arabinose, starch, inulin, mannitol, dulcitol, sorbitol, glycerol and inositol not fermented.

Nitrites produced from nitrates (Sompolinsky, Ann. Inst. Past., *79*, 1950, 204).

Coagulated albumin: No liquefaction.

Blood serum: No liquefaction.

Brain medium: No blackening or digestion.

Anaerobic, aerotolerant, growing delicately on aerobic agar slants.

Grows well at both 37° C. and at room temperature.

An exotoxin of moderate intensity is produced which causes edema, necrosis and death on sufficient dosage.

Pathogenic for guinea pigs, white rats and rabbits.

Source: Originally isolated from a rabbit inoculated with garden soil (von Hibler); isolated from contaminated beef infusion (Klein).

Habitat: Probably occurs in soil.

90. **Clostridium histolyticum** (Weinberg and Séguin, 1916) Bergey et al., 1923. (*Bacillus histolyticus* Weinberg and Séguin, Compt. rend. Acad. Sci., Paris, *163*, 1916, 449; Bergey et al., Manual, 1st ed., 1923, 328.)

his.to.ly′ti.cum. M.L. noun *histus* tissue; Gr. adj. *lyticus* dissolving; M.L. adj. *histolyticus* tissue-dissolving.

Rods, 0.5 to 0.7 by 3.0 to 5.0 microns, occurring singly and in pairs. Spores ovoid, subterminal, swelling the cells. Motile by means of peritrichous flagella. Gram-positive.

Gelatin: Complete liquefaction in 24 hours.

Agar deep colonies: Vary from lenticular, lobate to fluffy, according to the agar concentration.

Agar slant (aerobic): Grows aerobically

in a barely perceptible film or in tiny, smooth, discrete colonies.

Egg yolk agar surface colonies: Small, circular to slightly irregular, moist, smooth, creamy white, without precipitate or luster.

Blood agar surface colonies (aerobic): Minute, round dew-drops. Hemolysis.

Broth: Turbid; slight precipitate.

Litmus milk: Softly coagulated, then slowly digested. Little gas is produced.

Indole not produced.

Carbohydrates not fermented.

Nitrites not produced from nitrates.

Coagulated albumin: Slow liquefaction.

Blood serum: Slow liquefaction with darkened, putrid fluid.

Brain medium: Blackening and digestion; putrefactive odor.

Egg-meat medium: Little gas is produced. Meat first reddened then darkened in 3 days. Digestion apparent in about 24 hours. Nauseous odor. Tyrosine crystals are abundant after about a week.

Anaerobic, aerotolerant, growing feebly on aerobic agar slant.

Grows well at 37° C.

A cytolytic exotoxin is produced which causes extensive local necrosis and sloughing on injection. Not toxic on feeding.

Produces at least three antigenic components in toxic culture filtrates: (1) *alpha*, lethal and necrotizing toxin, (2) *beta*, collagenase, and (3) cysteine-activated proteinase which attacks altered collagen (hidepowder or azocoll) but not native collagen (Oakley and Warrack, Jour. Gen. Microbiol., *4*, 1950, 365). Produces an oxygenlabile hemolysin (Howard, Brit. Jour. Exp. Path., *34*, 1953, 564).

Pathogenic for small laboratory animals.

Source: Originally isolated from war wounds, where it induces active necrosis of tissue. Found occasionally in feces and soil.

Habitat: Not determined. Apparently widely but sparsely dispersed in soil.

91. Clostridium lacunarum Prévot, 1948. (Ann. Inst. Past., *74*, 1948, 166.)

la.cu.na'rum. L. fem.n. *lacuna* a ditch, pit or hole, especially one in which water is apt to collect, a lagoon; L. fem.gen.pl.n. *lacunarum* of lagoons.

Straight or curved rods, 0.9 by 4.0 microns, with rounded ends, occurring singly, in pairs or in short chains. Subterminal, ovoid, clostridial spores, 1.5 by 2.0 microns. Encapsulated. Weakly motile. Gram-positive.

Gelatin: Liquefaction.

Agar deep colonies: Lenticular; gas is produced.

Peptone broth: Slightly turbid.

VF glucose broth: Abundantly turbid; abundant sediment.

Milk: Not coagulated; not changed.

Indole and skatole not produced.

Hydrogen sulfide produced.

Glucose, fructose, maltose, lactose, galactose and sucrose are strongly fermented. Mannitol weakly fermented.

Nitrites produced from nitrates in the presence of mannitol.

Coagulated proteins: Not attacked.

Anaerobic, aerotolerant.

Optimum temperature, 37° C.

Not pathogenic for guinea pigs.

Source: Isolated from mud from an African lagoon.

Habitat: Presumably mud.

92. Clostridium tertium (Henry, 1916) Bergey et al., 1923. (*Bacillus tertius* Henry, Jour. Path. and Bact., *21*, 1916, 347; Bergey et al., Manual, 1st ed., 1923, 332.)

ter'ti.um. L. adj. *tertius* third.

Rods, 0.4 to 0.6 by 3.0 to 6.0 microns, occurring singly and in pairs, not in chains. Spores ovoid, terminal, swelling the cells. Motile. Gram-positive.

Gelatin: No liquefaction.

Agar surface colonies (aerobic): Circular with opalescent, crenated margin.

Agar deep colonies: Small, lenticular, regular, smooth.

Agar slant (aerobic): Grayish, filmy, opalescent growth.

Broth: Turbid; sediment.

Litmus milk: Acid; coagulated; some gas is produced. Clot not digested.

Indole not produced.

Acid and gas from glucose, fructose, galactose, mannose, lactose, maltose, sucrose, arabinose, xylose, trehalose, melezitose, soluble starch, esculin, mannitol, inositol and salicin. Inulin and glycerol not fermented.

Nitrites produced from nitrates.

Coagulated albumin: No liquefaction.

Blood agar: Hemolysis.

Blood serum: No liquefaction.

Brain medium: No blackening or digestion.

Meat medium: Reddened; acid and gas produced. Meat neither blackened nor digested. Non-putrefactive.

Anaerobic, aerotolerant, growing feebly on aerobic agar slant.

Optimum temperature, between 30° and 35° C. Growth occurs at 50° C.

Not pathogenic for guinea pigs or rabbits.

Source: Isolated from gangrenous wounds and from feces.

Habitat: Widely distributed in soil, feces and sewage.

93. **Clostridium pectinovorum** (Störmer, 1903) Donker, 1926. (*Plectridium pectinovorum* Störmer, Mitteil. d. deutsch. Landwirts. Gesellsch., *18*, 1903, 195; not *Granulobacter pectinovorum* Beijerinck and van Delden, Arch. néerl. d. Sci. Exact. et. Nat., Ser. II, *9*, 1904, 423; Donker, Thesis, Delft, 1926, 149.)

pec.ti.no'vo.rum. Gr. adj. *pecticus* congealing or hardening; M.L. noun *pectinum* pectin; L. v. *voro* to devour; M.L. adj. *pectinovorus* pectin-destroying.

For additional descriptive characters see Störmer (Cent. f. Bakt., II Abt., *13*, 1904, 35), McCoy, Fred, Peterson and Hastings (Jour. Inf. Dis., *46*, 1930, 118), Weizmann and Hellinger (Jour. Bact., *40*, 1940, 665), Weizmann and Hellinger (Palestine Jour. Bot., Rehovot Ser., *4*, 1944, 51), Hellinger (Bul. Research Council Israel, *2*, 1952, 225) and Hellinger (Jour. Applied Bact., *17*, 1954, 6).

Long and short rods, slender, 0.5 to 0.6 by 3.8 to 4.2 microns, somewhat curved with rounded ends, occurring singly or in short chains. Large, ovoid, terminal spores, swelling the cells; plectridial sporangia, spatulate to capitate. Spores, 1.4 by 2.3 microns; plectridia, 0.7 to 1.4 by 6.0 to 10.0 microns. Motile by means of peritrichous flagella. Granulose-positive in young plectridial stage. Gram-positive.

Glucose-gelatin: Liquefaction (active growth of sporulating cultures necessary).

Agar slant (aerobic): Minute, translucent colonies, containing long rods and thread-like forms without spores.

Glucose yeast agar surface colonies: Large, 1 to 5 mm in diameter, rounded or irregular, raised, smooth or crested, often star-shaped, somewhat hard, compact, glutinous, wax-like. Whole colony removed intact when fished with needle.

Milk: Stormy fermentation with some peptonization.

Hydrogen sulfide produced in yeast glucose agar tested with lead acetate paper. Negative in brain media with or without iron.

Maize or potato mash: Rapid fermentation with abundant gas production and partial diastatic action. Butyric odor. Head collapses on continued incubation leaving clear supernatant above coarse sediment.

Glucose, fructose, galactose, maltose, mannose, soluble starch, maize starch, dextrin, glycogen, salicin and mannitol are fermented. Glycerol, pectin, rhamnose, raffinose, melezitose and alpha-methylglucoside are slightly attacked, if at all. Reports variable on arabinose, lactose, sucrose, xylose and inulin. Trehalose, amygdalin, esculin, erythritol, sorbitol, dulcitol, quercitol and cellulose not fermented.

Products of glucose fermentation, in addition to butyric, acetic and lactic acids and ethyl alcohol, include negligible yields of acetone and butyl and iso-propyl alcohols.

Nitrites not produced from nitrates.

Atmospheric nitrogen fixed, though not as actively as by *Clostridium pasteurianum* Winogradsky (Rosenblum and Wilson, Jour. Bact., *57*, 1949, 413).

Egg albumin: Digestion.

Brain medium: No blackening.

Blood agar: No hemolysis.

Blood serum: No liquefaction.

Catalase-negative reaction obtained on anaerobic cultures on glucose yeast agar; results on aerobic cultures not recorded.

Anaerobic, aerotolerant.

Temperature relations (for fermentation): Optimum, 27° C. Range, 20° to 45° C.

Source: Isolated from soil, hemp and jute.

Habitat: Found in soil and in naturally retting plant materials.

Note: *Species incertae sedis.* The relationships of *Methanobacterium soehngenii* Barker and *Methanobacterium omelianskii* Barker to other species of bacteria are not entirely clear. *M. soehngenii*, a non-motile, nonsporeforming, Gram-negative species, has tentatively been placed in the family *Spirillaceae.* While *M. omelianskii* was described for some time as being non-motile and nonsporeforming, it was later found to be definitely motile at times, to form spores and to be Gram-variable. As an anaerobe, it should be placed in the genus *Clostridium.* If, however, it were placed in the genus *Clostridium*, it could not bear the specific epithet *omelianskii*, as this epithet is preempted by the cellulose-fermenting *Clostridium omelianskii* (Henneberg, *emend.* Clausen) Spray, a different organism. While awaiting a better determination of the relationships of *Methanobacterium omelianskii*, this organism has been placed here.

1.   **Methanobacterium omelianskii** Barker, 1936. (Bacille de la décomposition méthanique de l'alcohol ethylique, Omeliansky, Ann. Inst. Past., *30*, 1916, 56; Barker, Arch. f. Mikrobiol., *7*, 1936, 436; also see Antonie van Leeuwenhoek, *6*, 1940, 201; and Jour. Biol. Chem., *137*, 1941, 153.)

o.me.li.an'ski.i. M.L. gen.noun *omelianskii* of Omeliansky; named for Prof. W. Omeliansky, the Russian bacteriologist who was the first to observe this organism.

Rods, 0.6 to 0.7 by 1.5 to 10.0 microns, usually 3.0 to 6.0 microns in length. Originally described as non-sporeforming (Omeliansky, *op. cit.*, 1916, 60; Barker, *op. cit.*,

1936, 437), this organism was later found to form spores of low heat resistance which are spherical and terminal and which swell the cells (Barker, *op. cit.*, 1940, 207). Initially reported as non-motile (Barker, *op. cit.*, 1936, 437) but later observed to be occasionally and feebly motile, the type of flagellation not determined (Barker, *op. cit.*, 1940, 207). At first described as Gram-negative (Barker, *op. cit.*, 1936, 437), the cells were later reported to be Gram-variable (Barker, *op. cit.*, 1940, 208).

Primary alcohols, including ethanol, propanol, n-butanol and n-amyl alcohol, are oxidized to the corresponding fatty acids. Secondary alcohols, including isopropanol and sec-butanol, are oxidized to the corresponding ketones. Hydrogen is oxidized.

Ethanol is utilized the best of all organic compounds.

Carbon dioxide is utilized and converted to methane. Growth and alcohol oxidation are directly proportional to the carbon dioxide supply, at low concentrations.

Fatty and hydroxy acids, glucose and other polyhydroxy alcohols and amino acids are not attacked.

Ammonia is utilized as a nitrogen source.

Nitrate, sulfate and oxygen cannot be used as oxidizing agents.

Obligate anaerobe.

Optimum temperature, between 37° and 40° C. Maximum, between 46° and 48° C.

Growth limits, pH 6.5 and 8.1.

Source: Isolated from soil, fresh-water and marine muds, rabbit feces and sewage. Pure cultures were isolated from fresh-water and marine muds (Barker, *op. cit.*, 1940, 201).

Habitat: Found wherever organic matter is decomposing in an anaerobic, approximately neutral environment.

ORDER V. ACTINOMYCETALES BUCHANAN, 1917.*

(Jour. Bact., *2*, 1917, 162.)

Ac.ti.no.my.ce.ta′les. M.L. mas.n. *Actinomyces* type genus of the order; -*ales* ending to denote an order; M.L. pl.f.n. *Actinomycetales* the *Actinomyces* order.

Organisms forming elongated cells which have a definite tendency to branch. These hyphae do not exceed 1.5 microns and are mostly about 1.0 micron or less in diameter. In some species the cells are acid-fast. In the *Mycobacteriaceae* the mycelium is rudimentary or absent; no spores are formed. The *Actinomycetaceae, Streptomycetaceae* and *Actinoplanaceae* usually produce a characteristic branching mycelium and multiply by means of special spores (oidiospores, conidia or sporangiospores) or combinations of these spores. Special spores are formed by fragmentation of the plasma within straight or spiral-shaped, spore-bearing hyphae; the oidiospores are formed by segmentation or by transverse division of hyphae, similar to the formation of oidia among the true fungi; the conidia are produced singly, at the end of simple or branching conidiophores; the sporangiospores are borne in spherical or variously shaped sporangia. A few species in *Nocardia* are reported to be motile. In *Actinoplanes* the sporangiospores have polar flagella and swim; in *Streptosporangium* the spores are non-motile. The cell structure is like that of the bacteria proper. The cell wall substance is neither chitin nor cellulose (Avery and Blank, Can. Jour. Microbiol., *1*, 1954, 140). Thus it differs from the cell wall substance of the true fungi, another indication of a closer relationship with the bacteria than with the fungi. Only a few species are pathogenic. The majority are found in soil or less commonly in fresh water.

Among the recent systems of classification of this order it is sufficient to mention the following: Baldacci (Mycopath., *2*, 1939, 84; and *ibid.*, *4*, 1947, 60) divided the order *Actinomycetales* into two families: (a) *Mycobacteriaceae* Chester with two subfamilies, *Leptotrichioideae* Baldacci and *Proactinomycoideae* Baldacci, each with five genera, and (b) *Actinomycetaceae* Buchanan, with two genera, *Micromonospora* and *Actinomyces*. Krassilnikov (Ray fungi and related organisms, Izd. Akad. Nauk, Moskau, 1938) divided the order into (a) *Actinomycetaceae*, with four genera, *Actinomyces, Proactinomyces, Mycobacterium* and *Mycococcus*, and (b) *Micromonosporaceae*, with one genus, *Micromonospora*. Waksman (Jour. Bact., *39*, 1940, 549) divided the order into four families: *Mycobacteriaceae, Proactinomycetaceae, Actinomycetaceae* and *Micromonosporaceae*. Later, Waksman and Henrici (Jour. Bact., *48*, 1943, 339) arranged these organisms into three families: *Mycobacteriaceae, Actinomycetaceae* and *Streptomycetaceae*. This was the arrangement used in the Manual, 6th ed., 1948, 875. Later Couch (Trans. N. Y. Acad. Sci., *16*, 1954, 315) added the family of water-inhabiting species (*Actinoplanaceae*) to this grouping.

Key to the families of order **Actinomycetales.**

I. Mycelium rudimentary or absent; no spores formed.

Family I. *Mycobacteriaceae*, p. 695.

II. A true mycelium produced.

---

* The general arrangement of the families in this Order follows that developed by Prof. S. A. Waksman, New Jersey Experiment Station, New Brunswick, New Jersey, and Prof. A. T. Henrici, University of Minnesota, Minneapolis, Minnesota, as supplemented more recently by the work of Prof. J. N. Couch, University of North Carolina, Chapel Hill, North Carolina, May, 1955.

A. Spores formed, but not in sporangia.
　1. Spores formed by fragmentation of the mycelium.
　　　　　　　　Family II. *Actinomycetaceae*, p. 713.
　2. Vegetative mycelium normally remains undivided.
　　　　　　　　Family III. *Streptomycetaceae*, p. 744.
B. Spores formed in sporangia.
　　　　　　　　Family IV. *Actinoplanaceae*, p. 825.

FAMILY I. MYCOBACTERIACEAE CHESTER, 1901.

(Chester, Man. Determ. Bact., 1901, 349; *Proactinomycetaceae* Lehmann and Haag, in Lehmann and Neumann, Bakt. Diag., 7 Aufl., *2*, 1927, 674.)

My.co.bac.te.ri.a′ce.ae. M.L. neut.n. *Mycobacterium* type genus of the family; -*aceae* ending to denote a family; M.L. pl.f.n. *Mycobacteriaceae* the *Mycobacterium* family.

Cells spherical to rod-shaped; branching not evident on ordinary media. No conidia. Aerobic. Mesophilic. Gram-positive. Found in soil, dairy products and as parasites on animals, including man.

Key to the genera of family **Mycobacteriaceae.**

I. Cells usually acid-fast. Rod-shaped cells that do not branch under ordinary cultural conditions.
　　　　　　　　Genus I. *Mycobacterium*, p. 695.
II. Non-acid-fast cells so far as observed. Cells generally spherical, occurring singly, in short chains or in clumps.
　　　　　　　　Genus II. *Mycococcus*, p. 707.

Genus I. **Mycobacterium** *Lehmann and Neumann, 1896.**

(*Coccothrix* Lutz,† Zur Morphologie des Mikroorganismus der Lepra. Dermatologische Studien, Heft 1, 1886, 22; *Sclerothrix* Metchnikoff, Arch. f. path. Anat. u. Physiol., *113*, 1888, 70; not *Sclerothrix* Kuetzing, Species Algarum, 1849, 319; Lehmann and Neumann, Bakt. Diag., 1 Aufl., *2*, 1896, 108.)

My.co.bac.te′ri.um. Gr. noun *myces* a fungus; Gr. neut.dim.n. *bacterium* a small rod; M.L. neut.n. *Mycobacterium* a fungus rodlet.

Acid-fast, slender rods, straight or slightly curved, occasionally slender filaments, but branched forms rarely occur. No conidia. Non-motile. Aerobic. Two species are obligate parasites and have not been cultivated apart from living cells; other species grow slowly on all media, species pathogenic for higher animals requiring two to several weeks, other species requiring two to several days. Saprophytic species are not so strongly acid-fast as are the parasitic species. Nearly all acid-fast bacteria treated with carbol-auramin and decolorized with NaCl-HCl-ethyl alcohol fluoresce when they are irradiated by long wavelength

---

* Completely revised by Dr. Ruth Gordon (saprophytic species and those affecting cold-blooded animals), Institute of Microbiology, Rutgers University, New Brunswick, New Jersey, Dr. G. B. Reed (species affecting warm-blooded animals except those causing leprosy), Queens University, Kingston, Ontario, Canada, and Dr. John H. Hanks (species causing leprosy), Harvard Medical School, Brookline, Massachusetts, July, 1953.

† The name *Coccothrix* has priority over *Mycobacterium* as the name for this genus but it has never come into general use. A recommendation has been made to the Judicial Commission that the name *Coccothrix* be placed in the list of rejected generic names. Until an Opinion has been issued, the MANUAL will continue to recognize *Mycobacterium*.

ultraviolet light (Richards, Chapter on Fluorescent Microscopy, in Analytical Cytology, ed. by R. C. Mellors, New York, 1953).

The members of this genus are arranged as a natural spectrum, starting with the saprophytes (some of which may be potentially parasitic) and proceeding through the tubercle bacilli to the highly host-dependent leprosy bacilli.

The type species is *Mycobacterium tuberculosis* (Zopf) Lehmann and Neumann.

Key to the species of genus **Mycobacterium.**

I. Saprophytes, including potential parasites; grow rapidly on most media at 28° C. Strains recovered from tuberculosis of cold-blooded animals and from ulcers, skin lesions and other infections in mammals tend, after artificial cultivation, to be indistinguishable from the saprophytes found in soil, water, plants, etc. Cells acid-fast when grown under proper conditions.
  A. Growth at 45° C.*
    1. Growth at 52° C.; no acid from rhamnose or inositol.
                          1. *Mycobacterium phlei.*
    2. No growth at 52° C.; acid from rhamnose and inositol.
                       2. *Mycobacterium smegmatis.*
  B. No growth at 45° C.
                       3. *Mycobacterium fortuitum.*
                       4. *Mycobacterium marinum.*
                       5. *Mycobacterium thamnopheos.*
                       6. *Mycobacterium platypoecilus.*
II. Parasites on warm-blooded animals. Cells usually acid-fast.
  A. Growth on ordinary or special media.
    1. No growth at temperatures above 33° C.; not pathogenic for guinea pigs or rabbits, experimentally produces cutaneous lesions in rats and mice; causes ulcerous lesions on the lower extremities of man.
                       7. *Mycobacterium ulcerans.*
    2. Growth at 37° C.
      a. Slow growth on all media.
        b. Experimentally produces generalized tuberculosis in guinea pigs.
          c. Experimentally does not produce generalized tuberculosis in rabbits or fowls. Growth enhanced by the addition of glycerol to most media. Generally pale yellow to orange pigmentation, especially on media containing serum.
                       8. *Mycobacterium tuberculosis.*
          cc. Experimentally produces generalized tuberculosis in rabbits but not in fowls. Growth not enhanced by the addition of glycerol to media. Not pigmented.
                       9. *Mycobacterium bovis.*
       bb. Experimentally does not produce generalized tuberculosis in guinea pigs.
          c. Experimentally produces generalized tuberculosis in voles, but not in rabbits or fowls.
                    10. *Mycobacterium microti.*
          cc. Experimentally produces generalized tuberculosis in fowls.
                    11. *Mycobacterium avium.*
    aa. Growth in primary cultures only when heat-killed, acid-fast bacteria or extracts of acid-fast bacteria are added to the media. Experimentally fails to infect guinea pigs or fowls.
                    12. *Mycobacterium paratuberculosis.*

---

* All temperatures above 37° C. are water-bath temperatures.

B. Have not been grown on non-living culture media.
    1. Occurs in man. Has not been transmitted experimentally to any other species of animal.

                      13. *Mycobacterium leprae.*

    2. Occurs in wild rats and mice. Experimentally transmissible to rats, mice and hamsters.

                      14. *Mycobacterium lepraemurium.*

1. Mycobacterium phlei Lehmann and Neumann, 1899, pro parte. (Timotheebacillus or Grasbacillus I, Moëller, Therapeutischen Monatsch., *12*, 1898, 607; Moëller, Deutsch. med. Wochnschr., *24*, 1898, 376; Lehmann and Neumann, Bakt. Diag., 2 Aufl., *2*, 1899, 411.)

phle′i. Gr. noun *phleus* a flowering reed; M.L. neut.n. *Phleum* a grass genus, timothy; M.L. gen. noun *phlei* of timothy.

Description taken from Gordon and Smith (Jour. Bact., *66*, 1953, 43).

Rods, 1.0 to 2.0 microns in length after cultivation for 48 hours on glycerol agar at 37° C., coccoid forms to short rods; those of a few cultures longer, averaging 2.5 to 3.0 microns. Non-motile. Some with irregularly and some with uniformly staining protoplasm. Filaments and branching rarely, if ever, seen. Acid-fastness after incubation for 5 days at 28° C. from 5 to 100 per cent.

Gelatin: Variable, limited hydrolysis by Frazier method.

Bennett's and soil extract agar colonies: Dense with smooth edges, dense with fringe of filaments, or filamentous. Filaments fragmenting into short rods.

Glycerol agar slants: Growth at 2 to 4 days usually rough, thin, dry, spreading, pale yellow; at 10 to 14 days, thick, waxy, coarsely wrinkled, deep yellow to orange. Growth of a few cultures smooth, soft, spreading, butyrous, deep yellow to orange.

Milk agar plate: No hydrolysis of casein.

Indole not produced (Penso, Ortali, Gaudiano, Princivalle, Vella and Zampieri, Rend. dell'Istituto Superiore di Sanità, *14*, 1951, 855).

Acid from glucose, mannitol and sorbitol (with ammoniacal nitrogen); usually from mannose and arabinose. Variable reaction on xylose, trehalose, maltose and galactose. No acid from rhamnose, inositol, dulcitol, lactose or raffinose.

Starch is hydrolyzed.

Citrate, succinate and malate usually used as sole sources of carbon.

Tyrosine not decomposed (Gordon and Smith, Jour. Bact., *69*, 1955, 503).

Benzoate not utilized (Gordon and Smith, *loc. cit.*).

Nitrites produced from nitrates.

Temperature relations: Growth at 28° to 52° C. inclusive; variable at 55° and 15° C.; negative at 10° C. Survives 60° C. for 4 hours.

Optimum pH, 6.0; range, 5.5 to 8.8 (Penso et al., *op. cit.*, 1951, 855).

Salt tolerance: Scant, if any, growth in glycerol broth containing 5 per cent NaCl.

Pathogenicity: Not pathogenic for mouse, rat, guinea pig, rabbit, chicken, frog or carp (Penso et al., *loc. cit.*).

Source: Originally isolated from hay and grass.

Habitat: Widely distributed in soil, dust and on plants.

2. Mycobacterium smegmatis (Trevisan, 1889) Lehmann and Neumann, 1899. (Smegma bacillus, Alvarez and Tavel, Arch. phys. norm. et path., *21*, (sér. 3, *6*), 1885, 303; *Bacillus smegmatis* Trevisan, I generi e le specie delle Batteriacee, 1889, 14; Lehmann and Neumann, Bakt. Diag., 2 Aufl., *2*, 1899, 403; *Mycobacterium lacticola* Lehmann and Neumann, *ibid.*, 408.)

smeg′ma.tis. Gr. neut.n. *smegma* an ungent or ointment, a detergent, in Modern Latin sebaceous humor; M.L. gen.n. *smegmatis* of smegma.

Description taken from Gordon and Smith (Jour. Bact., *66*, 1953, 45).

Rods, 3.0 to 5.0 microns in length after 48-hours cultivation on glycerol agar at 37° C., slender, of varying lengths, often filamentous, sometimes branched, curved and beaded, occasionally swollen with ovoid, deeper staining bodies. Acid-fastness after incubation for 5 days at 28° C. on glycerol agar from 10 to 80 per cent.

Gelatin: Usually no hydrolysis by Frazier method.

Bennett's and soil extract agar colonies: Dense with smooth edges, dense with fringe of filaments, or filamentous. Filaments fragmenting into short rods.

Glycerol agar slants: Growth at 2 to 3 days usually, rough, good, spreading, finely wrinkled, creamy white; at 14 days, abundant, spreading, finely wrinkled, waxy, cream-yellow to orange. Growth of cultures in smooth stage abundant, glistening, butyrous and sometimes nodular.

Milk agar plate: No hydrolysis of casein.

Acid from glucose, rhamnose, xylose, arabinose, sorbitol, inositol, mannose, mannitol, trehalose and galactose (with ammoniacal nitrogen); usually from dulcitol. No acid from lactose and usually none from raffinose. Acid not produced from maltose by a majority of the cultures.

Starch is hydrolyzed.

Citrate, succinate and malate used as sole sources of carbon.

Tyrosine not decomposed (Gordon and Smith, Jour. Bact., 69, 1955, 504).

Benzoate utilized (Gordon and Smith, loc. cit.).

Oxalate is decomposed by strains isolated from the intestines of earthworms (Khambata and Bhat, Jour. Bact., 69, 1955, 227). Khambata and Bhat identified their strains as Mycobacterium lacticola Lehmann and Neumann; however, an earlier study by Gordon and Smith (op. cit.., 1953, 44) has shown that M. lacticola is identical with M. smegmatis Lehmann and Neumann, the latter name having priority.

Nitrites usually produced from nitrates.

Temperature relations: Growth at 28° to 45° C. inclusive; scant, if any, at 50° C.; none at 52° C. Does not survive 60° C. for 4 hours.

Salt tolerance: Usually growth in glycerol broth containing 5 per cent NaCl; usually none in 7 per cent.

Source: Isolated from smegma.

Habitat: Widely distributed in soil, dust and water.

3. **Mycobacterium fortuitum** Cruz,

1938. (Strains of Mycobacterium from cows 18, 19, 70 and 75, Minett, Jour. Comp. Path. and Ther., 45, 1932, 317; Cruz, Acta Med. Rio de Janeiro, 1, 1938, 298; Mycobacterium giae Darzins, Arquiv. Inst. Brasil. Invest. Tuberc., 9, 1950, 29; Mycobacterium minetti Penso, Castelnuovo, Gaudiano, Princivalle, Vella and Zampieri, Rend. dell'Istituto Superiore di Sanità, 15, 1952, 491.)

for.tu'i.tum. L. adj. fortuitus casual, accidental.

Description taken from Cruz (op. cit., 1938, 298), Penso et al. (op. cit., 1952, 491) and Gordon and Smith (Jour. Bact., 69, 1955, 502).

Rods, 1.0 to 3.0 microns in length after cultivation for 72 hours on glycerol agar at 28° C., the largest number from 2.0 to 2.2 microns in length. Coccoid and short forms, to long, slender rods, occasionally beaded or swollen with an ovoid, non-acid-fast body at one end. In pus, long and filamentous forms with definite branching (Penso et al.). Acid-fastness after incubation for 5 days at 28° C. on glycerol agar 10 to 100 per cent. In the majority of cultures, 70 to 100 per cent of cells were acid-fast. Non-motile. Gram-positive.

Gelatin: No hydrolysis by Frazier method (Gordon and Smith).

Gelatin stab: Heavy growth on surface and along stab. No liquefaction.

Agar colonies: After 3 or 4 days of incubation, dense colonies with smooth edges, dense colonies fringed with short filaments and/or filamentous colonies. On further incubation the filaments usually fragment into short rods (Gordon and Smith).

Glycerol agar: Growth at 2 to 3 days at 28° C. scant to fair, soft and butyrous or waxy and nodular, off-white to cream-colored; at 14 days, abundant, spreading, butyrous and glistening or dull, rough and waxy, often very nodular, off-white to cream to beige in color (Gordon and Smith).

Yeast extract agar: Growth moderate to heavy, spreading, butyrous or dry and waxy, usually nodular, sometimes finely wrinkled, off-white to cream to beige (Gordon and Smith).

Glucose asparagine agar: At 2 weeks, moderate, spreading, soft, and glistening or dull and waxy, off-white to cream-colored (Gordon and Smith).

Glycerol potato: Poor growth.

Broth: Thin ring pellicle; broth clear.

Milk not coagulated.

Milk agar plate: No hydrolysis of casein (Gordon and Smith).

Indole not produced.

Hydrogen sulfide not produced (Penso et al.). Hydrogen sulfide production variable (Gordon and Smith, unpublished data).

Acid from glucose, mannose, trehalose and occasionally mannitol. No acid from rhamnose, xylose, arabinose, galactose, sorbitol, inositol, dulcitol, lactose or raffinose. Maltose hydrolyzed by only one culture (Gordon and Smith).

Starch is hydrolyzed (Gordon and Smith).

Succinate and malate used as sole sources of carbon; citrate used by all but one culture (Gordon and Smith).

Tyrosine not decomposed (Gordon and Smith).

Benzoate not utilized (Gordon and Smith).

Nitrites usually produced from nitrates.

Temperature relations: Growth at 28° to 35° C.; variable at 10° C.; most cultures grow at 40° C.; growth, if any, scant at 45° C. Does not survive 60° C. for 4 hours (Gordon and Smith).

Salt tolerance: Usually growth in broth containing 5 per cent NaCl; usually none in 7 per cent (Gordon and Smith).

Pathogenicity: Guinea pigs, rabbits and mice resistant to massive doses of young cultures (Cruz). Local lesions produced in lymph glands and kidneys of mice, guinea pigs, rabbits, monkeys and calves (Penso et al.).

Source: Several strains were isolated from lymph glands of cattle by F. D. Minett, from human abscesses by Cruz, from a systemic, nodular infection of Gia by Darzins.

Habitat: Found in soil and infections of humans, cattle and cold-blooded animals.

4. Mycobacterium marinum Aronson, 1926. (Jour. Inf. Dis., *39*, 1926, 315.)

ma.ri′num. L. adj. *marinus* of the sea, marine.

In lesions, short, thick, uniformly staining organisms are seen frequently occurring in clumps, while long, thin, beaded or barred rods are scattered more discretely. In cultures the organisms have the same appearance. Non-motile. Acid-fast and acid-alcohol-fast. Gram-positive.

Gelatin: No liquefaction.

Agar slant (slightly acid): In five to seven days, moist, glistening, elevated colonies, becoming lemon-yellow.

Agar colonies: In 5 to 7 days, smooth, moist, slimy, lemon-yellow, later orange-colored.

Glycerol agar colonies: In 14 to 18 days, grayish white, moist, elevated with irregular margins. Old growths lemon-yellow and still later orange-colored.

Dorset's and Petroff's egg media: Similar to growth on glycerol agar but more luxuriant.

Broth and glycerol broth: Growth is diffuse; no pellicle formed.

Litmus milk: Acidified and coagulated.

Indole not produced.

Arabinose and fructose are utilized; sorbitol and galactose are not utilized (Gordon, Jour. Bact., *34*, 1937, 617)

Nitrites not produced from nitrates.

Aerobic, facultatively anaerobic.

Optimum temperature, between 18 and 20° C. Fails to survive 60° C. for 1 hour; fails to grow at 45° C. (Gordon, Jour. Bact., *34*, 1937, 617).

Pathogenicity: Experimentally infects salt-water fish, goldfish, frogs, mice and pigeons but not rabbits or guinea pigs.

Source: Isolated from areas of focal necrosis of the liver of sergeant majors (*Abudefduf mauritii*), croakers (*Micropogon undulatus*) and sea bass (*Centropristes striatus*).

Habitat: Causes spontaneous tuberculosis in salt-water fish.

5. Mycobacterium thamnopheos Aronson, 1929. (Jour. Inf. Dis., *44*, 1929, 215.)

tham.no′phe.os. Gr. noun *thamnus* a bush; Gr. noun *ophis, opheos* a snake; M.L. mas.n. *Thamnophis* bush snake, a genus of snakes; M.L. gen.noun *thamnopheos* of the bush snake.

Original description supplemented by material taken from Bynoe (Thesis, McGill University, Montreal, 1931).

Slender rods, 0.5 by 4 to 7 microns, frequently slightly curved, beaded and barred forms often occur. Non-motile. Acid-fast in cultures of 4 days or older, in younger cultures some organisms are not acid-fast. Not alcohol-fast. Gram-positive.

Gelatin stab: Growth occurs along the line of inoculation. No liquefaction.

Agar colonies: 0.5 to 1 mm in diameter, irregular, raised, moist and glistening.

Glycerol agar: Spreading, raised, dry, pale pink to buff growth.

Glycerol broth: A thin pellicle appears in 5 to 6 days, gradually becomes thicker and falls as a sediment.

Dorset's egg medium: Raised, moist, pinkish growth after 10 days, later becoming salmon-colored.

Loeffler's serum: Small, raised, convex, dry growth.

Litmus milk: Alkaline.

Glycerol potato: Raised, hemispherical, dry and granular growth.

Indole not produced.

Fructose, mannitol and trehalose are utilized; arabinose, sucrose, galactose and sorbitol not utilized (Gordon, Jour. Bact., 34, 1937, 617).

Nitrates reduced by 1 strain but not by 2 strains tested (Aronson). Nitrates slightly reduced (Gordon). Nitrates not reduced (Bynoe).

Temperature relations: Fails to survive 60° C. for 1 hour, fails to grow at 45° C. (Gordon); good growth at 25° C., no growth at 37° C. (Aronson); optimum for growth, 25° C., range, 10° to 35° C. (Bynoe).

Range of pH, 6.6 to 7.8 (Aronson); optimum, between 7.3 and 8.0, range 5.0 to 11.0 (Bynoe).

Pathogenicity: Experimentally produces generalized tuberculosis in snakes, frogs, lizards and fish but not pathogenic for guinea pigs, rabbits or fowls.

Variation: According to Bynoe and Wyckoff (Amer. Rev. Tub., 29, 1934, 389), S and R forms may be distinguished by colony structure and individual cell arrangement.

Source: Isolated from the lungs and livers of garter snakes (Thamnophis sirtalis).

Habitat: Present as a parasite in the garter snake and possibly other cold-blooded vertebrates.

6. **Mycobacterium platypoecilus** Baker and Hagan, 1942. (Jour. Inf. Dis., 70, 1942, 248.)

pla.ty.poe'ci.lus. M.L. mas.n. Platypoecilus a genus of platyfishes.

Rods resembling those of the tubercle bacillus; not usually pleomorphic. Strongly acid-fast.

Glycerol egg medium: Primary growth on this medium only after 3 weeks of incubation at 25° C. Smooth, moist colonies becoming dry, wrinkled, grayish white and waxy with age. Cultures grown in the presence of light are deep orange in color.

Glycerol phosphate agar: Growth of subcultures slow. Appearance same as on glycerol egg medium.

Söhngen's medium: No growth.

Temperature relations: Optimum, 25° C. No growth at 37° C.

Source: Isolated from the organs of a small, tropical platyfish, Platypoecilus maculatus.

Habitat: Found in skin ulcers, liver, spleen, gills and kidneys of diseased platyfish.

7. **Mycobacterium ulcerans** MacCallum, 1950. (A new mycobacterial infection of man, MacCallum, Tolhurst, Buckle and Sissons, Jour. Path. and Bact., 60, 1948, 93; MacCallum, in Fenner, Med. Jour. Austral., 2, 1950, 817; also see Fenner and Leach, Austral. Jour. Exp. Biol. and Med. Sci., 30, 1952, 1; and Fenner, ibid., 11.)

ul'ce.rans. L. part. adj. ulcerans making sore, causing to ulcerate.

Description taken from MacCallum et al. (op. cit., 1948, 93).

Rods, 0.2 by 1.5 to 3.0 microns from cultures, somewhat longer from tissues. Acid-fast and acid-alcohol-fast, frequently beaded.

Egg yolk agar colonies: Primary cultures after 9 weeks are 2 to 3 mm in diameter, round, smooth, low convex, opaque white to pale cream-colored. Subcultures appear in 2 to 3 weeks, the colonies similar to those of the primary culture.

Petragnani's medium: Primary growth visible in 4 weeks as minute, transparent, dome-shaped colonies; in older cultures colonies are low convex to flat with irregular outline and rough surface, lemon to mustard-yellow.

Dorset's egg medium: Scanty growth, the colonies resembling those on Petragnani's medium, but there is little or no pigment.

Glycerol broth: Growth only when colony fragments are used as the inoculum, forming white, irregular, floating balls; no pellicle formed.

Glycerol: Low concentrations in most media enhance growth, especially in the later stages of growth.

Optimum temperature, between 30° and 33° C. Very limited growth at 25° and 37°, and no growth at 41° C.

Pathogenicity: Causes skin ulcers in man which are characterized by indolent extension from areas of inconspicuous induration to involve large areas. Rats and mice are infected experimentally; guinea pigs, rabbits, fowls and lizards are resistant. Experimentally inoculated rats develop hemorrhagic necrotic lesions surrounded by zones of cellular accumulations consisting of leucocytes, lymphocytes and macrophages. There are no giant cells. The necrotic and cellular zones show large clumps of acid-fast bacilli in the extra-cellular spaces and in macrophages.

Antigenic structure: In complement fixation tests with sera of rabbits immunized with human, bovine and murine types of tubercle bacilli, *Mycobacterium ranae* and *M. phlei*, the heat-killed, washed bacilli serving as antigens, *M. ulcerans* was found to be antigenically distinct from the other pathogenic species of *Mycobacterium* tested. This conclusion was supported by skin sensitivity reactions in guinea pigs (Fenner and Leach, *op. cit.*, *30*, 1952, 1; and Fenner, *op. cit.*, *30*, 1952, 11).

Distinctive characters: Acid-fast bacilli; grows at 33° but not at 37° C.; produces necrotic and ulcerative lesions in man, rats and mice without giant-cell formation; antigenically distinct from the other pathogenic species of *Mycobacterium*.

Source: Isolated from ulcerative skin infections in man.

Habitat: The apparent cause of skin ulcers in man. Transmissible to rats and mice.

8. **Mycobacterium tuberculosis** (Zopf, 1883) Lehmann and Neumann, 1896. (Tuberkelbacillen, Koch, Berl. klin. Wochnschr., *19*, 1882, 225; *Bacterium tuberculosis* Zopf, Die Spaltpilze, 1 Aufl., 1883, 67; Tuberkelbacillen, Koch, Mitteil. a. d. kaiserl. Gesundheitsamte, *2*, 1884, 6; *Bacillus tuberculosis* Schroeter, in Cohn, Kryptogamen-Flora v. Schlesien, *3*, 1886, 164; Human tubercle bacilli, Th. Smith, Trans. Assoc. Am. Phys., *11*, 1896, 75; Lehmann and Neumann, Bakt. Diag., 1 Aufl., *2*, 1896, 363; *Mycobacterium tuberculosis* typus *humanus* Lehmann and Neumann, *ibid.*, 4 Aufl., *2*, 1907, 550; *Mycobacterium tuberculosis* var. *hominis* Bergey et al., Manual, 4th ed., 1934, 536.)

tu.ber.cu.lo'sis. L. dim.noun *tuberculum* a small swelling, tubercle; Gr. suffix *-osis* characterized by; M.L. fem.gen.n. *tuberculosis* of tuberculosis.

Common name: Human tubercle bacillus.

Original description supplemented by material taken from Topley and Wilson (Princip. of Bact. and Immun., London, 2nd ed., 1936, 315).

Rods, ranging in size from 0.3 to 0.6 by 0.5 to 4.0 microns, straight or slightly curved, occurring singly and in occasional threads. Sometimes swollen, clavate or even branched. Stain uniformly or irregularly, showing banded or beaded forms. Acid-fast and acid-alcohol-fast. Gram-positive. Growth in all media is slow, requiring several weeks for development.

This bacterium contains mycolic acid (Stodola, Lesuk and Anderson, Jour. Biol. Chem., *126*, 1938, 505). The acid-fast mycolic acid combines more firmly with carbolauramin than with carbol-fuchsin, and this apparently accounts for the increased sensitivity of fluorescence microscopy for this bacterium (Richards, Science, *93*, 1941, 190; Richards, Kline and Leach, Amer. Rev. Tuberc., *44*, 1941, 255).

Glycerol agar colonies: Raised, thick,

cream-colored, with a nodular or wrinkled surface and irregular thin margin.

Nutrient broth without glycerol: No growth.

Dorset's egg, Lowenstein, Petragnani, Woolsey colonies: Similar to those on glycerol agar, but growth is more rapid and luxuriant.

Variation in colony structure of the human and the bovine species has been described by several authors, e.g. Petroff et al. (Jour. Exp. Med., 60, 1934, 515), Birkhaug (Ann. Inst. Past., 57, 1933, 428), Kahn et al. (Jour. Bact., 25, 1933, 157), Uhlenhuth and Sieffert (Zeit. Immun., 59, 1930, 187), Reed and Rice (Canad. Jour. Res., 5, 1931, 111), Smithburn, (Jour. Exp. Med., 63, 1936, 95) and Shaffer (Jour. Path. and Bact., 40, 1935, 107). Several of these authors have found associated variation in cell structure and in virulence, though Boquet (Compt. rend. Soc. Biol., Paris, 103, 1930, 290), Birkhaug (Ann. Inst. Past., 49, 1932, 630) and others have failed to find differences in virulence. Reed and Rice (Jour. Immunol., 23, 1932, 385) found the S form to contain an antigenic substance lacking in the R form.

Glycerol broth: After 6 to 8 weeks, thick white to cream-yellow, wrinkled pellicle extending up the sides of the flask; no turbidity; granular or scaly deposit.

Dubos' tween-albumin broth: Diffuse growth visible in a few days and extensive in 7 to 10 days. In undisturbed cultures growth tends to settle but is readily dispersed. Virulent strains tend to grow in serpentine, cord-like forms in which the bacilli show a parallel orientation. A virulent forms show a more uniformly diffuse growth (Dubos and Middlebrook, Amer. Rev. Tuberc., 56, 1947, 334).

Glucose, fructose, arabinose and galactose are utilized; sucrose and lactose are not utilized (Merrill, Jour. Bact., 20, 1930, 235, based on the examination of one strain).

Optimum temperature, 37° C.

Optimum pH, between 7.4 and 8.0 (Ishimori, Ztschr. f. Hyg., 102, 1924, 329); between pH 6.0 and 6.5 (Dernby and Naslund, Biochem. Zeit., 132, 1922, 392).

Pathogenicity: Produces tuberculosis in man, monkey, dog and parrot. Experimentally, it is highly pathogenic for guinea pigs but not for rabbits, cats, goats, oxen or domestic fowls.

Antigenic structure: By agglutination, absorption of agglutinins and complement fixation, a distinction may be made between the human and bovine species and *Mycobacterium avium*, but it has been impossible to distinguish by these means between the two mammalian species (Tullock et al., Tubercle, 6, Oct.-Dec., 1924, 18, 57 and 105; Wilson, Jour. Path. and Bact., 28, 1925, 69; Griffith, Tubercle, 6, May, 1925, 417; Rice and Reed, Jour. Immunol., 23, 1932, 385; Kauffman, Ztschr. f. Hyg., 114, 1932, 121). Tuberculins prepared from the human and the bovine species are ordinarily indistinguishable in their action, but Lewis and Seibert (Jour. Immunol., 20, 1931, 201) detected a difference by cross anaphylactic reactions.

Distinctive characters: *Mycobacterium tuberculosis* produces generalized tuberculosis in experimentally inoculated guinea pigs but not in rabbits, voles or fowls. *Mycobacterium bovis* produces generalized tuberculosis in guinea pigs, rabbits and voles but not in fowls. *Mycobacterium microti* produces generalized tuberculosis in voles but not in guinea pigs, rabbits or fowls. *Mycobacterium avium* produces generalized tuberculosis in fowls but not in guinea pigs or voles. Growth of the human form is enhanced by the addition of glycerol to most media. Growth of the bovine and murine forms is not enhanced by glycerol. The human form generally develops a creamy to yellow or faint red pigment especially on media containing serum; the bovine and murine forms are not pigmented.

Comments: Griffith (Lancet, 1, 1916–17, 721; Jour. Path. and Bact., 21, 1924, 54) has found aberrant mammalian types, particularly in skin lesions of both man and ox, which are, in certain characteristics, intermediate between the human and the bovine species. He finds no evidence, however, that the one species may change into the other.

Source: Isolated from tuberculous lesions in man.

Habitat: The cause of tuberculosis in man.

9. Mycobacterium bovis Bergey et al.,

1934. (Bovine tubercle bacilli, Th. Smith, Trans. Assoc. Am. Phys., *11*, 1896, 75; also see *ibid.*, *13*, 1898, 417; and Jour. Exp. Med., *3*, 1898, 451; *Mycobacterium tuberculosis* typus *bovinus* Lehmann and Neumann, Bakt. Diag., 4 Aufl., *2*, 1907, 550; *Mycobacterium tuberculosis* var. *bovis* Bergey et al., Manual, 4th ed., 1934, 537.)

bo'vis. L. noun *bos* the ox; L. gen.noun *bovis* of an ox.

Common name: Bovine tubercle bacillus.

Original description supplemented by material taken from Topley and Wilson (Princip. of Bact. and Immun., London, 2nd ed., 1936, 315).

Rods which are shorter and plumper than those of the human species. Range in size from 1.0 to 1.5 microns. Very short forms are frequently intermixed with somewhat larger forms. Stain regularly or irregularly. Acid-fast and acid-alcohol-fast. Gram-positive.

Less easily cultivated than is the human species.

Glycerol agar colonies: Small, irregular, with granular surface; no pigment.

Dorset's egg, Lowenstein, Petragnani, Woolsey colonies: Similar to those on glycerol agar, but growth is more rapid and colonies are somewhat larger.

For variation in colony structure, see *Mycobacterium tuberculosis*.

Glycerol broth: After 8 weeks, thin, gray-white film, slightly nodular; no turbidity; slight, granular deposit.

Dubos' tween-albumin broth: Growth similar to that of *M. tuberculosis*.

Optimum temperature, 37° C.

Optimum pH, between 5.8 and 6.9 (Ishimori, Ztschr. f. Hyg., *102*, 1924, 329); between 6.0 and 6.5 (Dernby and Naslund, Biochem. Ztschr., *132*, 1922, 392).

Pathogenicity: Produces tuberculosis in ox, man, monkey, goat, sheep, pig, cat, parrot, cockatoo and possibly some birds of prey. Experimentally it is highly pathogenic for rabbits and guinea pigs, slightly pathogenic for dogs, horses, rats and mice; not pathogenic for fowls.

Antigenic structure: See *M. tuberculosis*.

Source: Isolated from tubercles in cattle.

Habitat: The cause of tuberculosis in cattle. Transmissible to man and domestic animals. More highly pathogenic for animals than is the human species.

10. **Mycobacterium microti** Reed, *nom. nov.* (Vole bacillus, Wells, Lancet, *1*, 1937, 1221; *Mycobacterium tuberculosis* var. *muris* Brooke, Amer. Rev. Tuberculosis, *43*, 1941, 806; Vole tubercle bacillus, Griffith, Jour. Hyg., *42*, 1942, 527; *Mycobacterium muris* Smith et al., in Zinsser's Textb. of Bact., 9th ed., 1948, 483; not *Mycobacterium muris* Simmons, Jour. Inf. Dis., *41*, 1927, 13.)

mic.ro'ti. M.L. mas.n. *Microtus* a genus that includes the vole; M.L. gen.noun *microti* of *Microtus*.

Common name: Vole bacillus.

Description taken from Brooke (*op. cit.*, 1941, 806).

Rods in cultures average 0.4 by 2.5 microns and in tissues, 0.4 by 3.6 microns. Ovoid to spherical forms occasionally occur among the rods. In infected lymph nodes, rods 8 to 10 microns long are occasionally seen. Therefore resembles other mammalian acid-fast species, but in general longer and thinner. Irregular shapes are frequently found in tissues: S-shaped, hook-shaped, semicircular or circular. Acid-fast and acid-alcohol-fast.

Growth in all media is slow; requires 4 to 5 weeks on favorable media before colonies are visible to the naked eye.

Whole egg medium colonies: After 4 to 6 weeks, small, granular, with irregular margins; on further growth the colonies become larger and more irregular. On moist media the consistency is creamy and on dry media, butyrous to friable.

Egg yolk-saline medium (3:1): Growth on this medium is superior to that on Lowenstein's, Dorset's egg or Dorset's egg plus extract of *M. phlei*. Growth is enhanced by the addition of 10 per cent CO_2 to the atmosphere.

Nutrient broth without glycerol: Film-like colonies on the surface: fine deposit.

Glycerol: Primary growth does not occur on any media containing glycerol. On subculture, growth occurs but is not enhanced by the presence of glycerol.

Distinctive characters: Slow growth, slower than that of the human or bovine forms; growth in nutrient broth without glycerol; experimentally produces generalized tuberculosis in voles but not in guinea pigs or rabbits.

Source: Isolated from naturally occurring tuberculosis in the field vole, *Microtus agrestis*, and the bank vole, *Clethrionomys glareolus*.

Habitat: The cause of generalized tuberculosis in voles; transmissible to guinea pigs, rabbits and calves, causing localized infections.

11. **Mycobacterium avium** Chester, 1901. (Tuberculose des oiseaux, Strauss and Gamaléia, Arch. Méd. exp. et Anat. path., 1891; Bacillus der Hühnertuberculose, Maffucci, Ztschr. f. Hyg., *11*, 1892, 449; *Bacillus tuberculosis gallinarum* Sternberg, Man. of Bact., 1893, 392; *Mycobacterium tuberculosis avium* Lehmann and Neumann, Bakt. Diag., 1 Aufl., *1*, 1896, 370; Chester, Man. Determ. Bact., 1901, 357; *Mycobacterium tuberculosis typus gallinaceus* Lehmann and Neumann, Bakt. Diag., 4 Aufl., *2*, 1907, 553.)

a'vi.um. L. noun *avis* a bird; L. gen.pl. noun *avium* of birds.

Common name: Avian tubercle bacillus.

Original description supplemented by material from Topley and Wilson (Princip. of Bact. and Immun., London, 2nd ed., 1936, 315).

Rods resembling those of the bovine type of tubercle organism.

Agar: After 4 weeks, slight, effuse, translucent growth with fine, granular surface.

Glycerol agar colonies: After 3 to 4 weeks, raised, regular, hemispherical, creamy or white colonies.

Dorset's egg slants: After 4 weeks, confluent, slightly raised growth with smooth, regular surface.

Glycerol egg slants: After 4 weeks, luxuriant, raised, confluent, creamy to yellow growth with perfectly smooth surface.

Winn and Petroff (Jour. Exp. Med., *57*, 1933, 239), Kahn and Schwartzkopf (Jour. Bact., *25*, 1933, 157), Birkhaug (Ann. Inst. Past., *54*, 1935, 19), Reed and Rice (Canad. Jour. Res., *5*, 1931, 111) and others have shown variation to follow the course described for many species. Winn and Petroff have separated four colonial types: smooth, flat smooth, rough, deep yellow smooth.

These also differ in chemical and physical properties. The smooth form exhibited the greatest degree of virulence, the flat smooth a lower virulence, while the chromogenic smooth and the rough were relatively benign. Some authors have failed to demonstrate this difference in virulence. The above description applies primarily to the smooth form.

Broth: After 4 weeks, very slight viscous to granular bottom growth; no pellicle, no turbidity.

Glycerol broth: After 4 weeks, diffuse, turbid growth with a viscous to granular deposit.

Coagulated beef serum: After 4 weeks, thin, effuse, grayish yellow growth with smooth surface.

Glycerol beef serum: After 4 weeks, luxuriant, raised, confluent, yellow to orange-yellow or occasionally pale pink growth with a smooth glistening surface.

Glycerol potato: After 4 weeks, luxuriant, raised, confluent growth with smooth to nodular surface.

Litmus milk: Growth, but no change in the milk.

Fructose, arabinose and sucrose are utilized; glucose is slightly utilized; galactose and lactose are not utilized (Merrill, Jour. Bact., *20*, 1930, 235, based on the examination of one strain).

Optimum temperature, 40° C.; range 30° to 44° C. (Bynoe, Thesis, McGill University, Montreal, 1931).

Optimum pH, between 6.8 and 7.3 (Bynoe, *loc. cit.*).

Pathogenicity: Produces tuberculosis in domestic fowls and other birds. In pigs it produces localized and sometimes disseminated disease. Experimentally in the rabbit, guinea pig, rat and mouse it may proliferate without producing macroscopic tubercles—tuberculosis of the Yersin type. Man, ox, goat, cat, horse, dog and monkey are not infected.

Antigenic structure: By agglutination, absorption of agglutinins and complement fixation, *Mycobacterium avium* may be distinguished from other members of the genus (Tullock et al., Tubercle, *6*, 1924, 18, 57 and 105; Wilson, Jour. Path. and Bact., *28*, 1925, 69; Mudd, Proc. Soc. Exp. Biol. and

Med., *23*, 1925, 569; and others). Furth (Jour. Immunol., *12*, 1926, 273) and Shaffer (Jour. Path. and Bact., *40*, 1935, 107) on this basis divided *Mycobacterium avium* into 1 or 2 subgroups.

Distinctive characters: Tubercle bacilli pathogenic for fowls but not for guinea pigs or rabbits; culturally distinguished from the mammalian types by the absence of pellicle formation in fluid media and the habit of growth on most solid media; antigenically distinguished from other species.

Source: Isolated from tubercles in fowls; widely distributed as the causal agent of tuberculosis in birds and less frequently in pigs.

Habitat: The cause of tuberculosis in chickens. Transmissible to pigeons, other birds, mice, rabbits and pigs.

12. Mycobacterium paratuberculosis Bergey et al., 1923. (Darmtuberculose bacillen, Johne and Frothingham, Deutsch. Ztschr. f. Tiermed., *21*, 1895, 438; Pseudotuberkulose bacillen, Bang, Berl. tierärztl. Wochschr., *22*, 1906, 759: Bacillus of Johne's Disease, M'Fadyean, Jour. Comp. Path., *20*, 1907, 48; also see Twort, Proc. Roy. Soc., B, *83*, 1910, 156; Bergey et al., Manual, 1st ed., 1923, 374; *Mycobacterium enteritidis* Lehmann and Neumann, Bakt. Diag., 7 Aufl., *2*, 1927, 755; *Bacterium paratuberculosis* Meissner and Berge, in Kolle and Wasserman, Handbuch d. path. Mikroorganismen, 3 Aufl., *6*, 1927–29, 788; *Mycobacterium johnei* Francis, Jour. Comp. Path., *53*, 1943, 140.)

pa.ra.tu.ber.cu.lo′sis. Gr. pref. *para* beside, related; M.L. noun *tuberculosis* tuberculosis; M.L. fem.n. *paratuberculosis* tuberculosis-like, paratuberculosis.

Common name: Johne's bacillus.

Description taken from M'Fadyean (*op. cit.*, 1907, 48) and Twort and Ingram (A Monograph on Johne's Disease, London, 1913).

Plump rods, 1 to 2 microns in length, staining uniformly, but occasionally the longer forms show alternately stained and unstained segments. Non-motile. Acid-fast.

This organism is difficult to cultivate, and, in primary cultures, it has been grown only in media containing dead tubercle ba-

cilli or other dead acid-fast bacteria (Boquet, Ann. Inst. Past., *37*, 1928, 495). In a few instances cultures have been acclimatized to a synthetic medium free from added dead bacteria (Dunkin, Jour. Comp. Path. and Therap., *46*, 1933, 159; Watson, Canad. Pub. Health Jour., *26*, 1935, 268).

Colonies on glycerol agar containing heat-killed *Mycobacterium phlei*: After 4 to 6 weeks, just distinguishable, dull-white, raised, circular.

Colonies on Dorset's glycerol egg medium containing heat-killed *M. phlei*: After 4 to 6 weeks, minute, dull-white, raised, circular, with a thin, slightly irregular margin. Older colonies become more raised, radially striated or irregularly folded and dull yellowish white.

Dorset's glycerol egg medium containing sheep's brain and heat-killed *M. phlei*: Growth slightly more luxuriant than that described immediately above.

Glycerol broth containing heat-killed *M. phlei*: Thin surface pellicle which later becomes thickened and folded.

Dorset's synthetic fluid containing heat-killed *M. phlei*: Growth as in glycerol broth with *Mycobacterium phlei*.

Pathogenicity: Produces Johne's disease, chronic diarrhoea, in cattle and sheep. Experimentally produces a similar disease in bovine animals, sheep and goats. Guinea pigs, rabbits, rats and mice are not affected. Very large doses in laboratory animals produce slight nodular lesions comparable with those produced by *M. phlei*.

Antigenic structure: Johnin, prepared as is tuberculin, gives positive reactions in cattle with Johne's disease. According to M'Fadyean et al. (Jour. Comp. Path. and Therap., *29*, 1916, 62), tuberculous animals may also give a reaction. Plumb (Den Kong. Vet. Landbohøjskole Arssk., 1925, 63) has shown that a reaction may be produced in animals sensitized to avian tuberculin and that avian tuberculin causes a reaction in some animals infected with Johne's bacillus.

Distinctive characters: Small acid-fast bacilli which produce characteristic lesions in cattle; grow only in the presence of dead acid-fast bacilli.

Comment: The organism isolated from a similar disease in sheep is probably identical with this species, although it is more difficult to cultivate (Dunkin and Balfour-Jones, Jour. Comp. Path., *48*, 1935, 236).

Source: Isolated from the intestinal mucous membrane of cattle suffering from chronic diarrhoea. Apparently an obligate parasite.

Habitat: The cause of Johne's disease, a chronic diarrhea in cattle. Found in the intestinal mucosa.

13. **Mycobacterium leprae** (Hansen, 1874) Lehmann and Neumann, 1896. (*Bacillus leprae* Hansen, Norsk. Mag. Laegevidensk., *9*, 1874, 1; also see Arch. f. path. Anat. u. Physiol., *79*, 1879, 32; Nord. Med. Ark., *12*, 1880, 1; and Quart. Jour. Micro. Sci., *20*, 1880, 92; Lehmann and Neumann, Bakt. Diag., 1 Aufl., *2*, 1896, 372).

lep'rae. Gr. noun *lepra* leprosy; M.L. gen.noun *leprae* of leprosy.

Common name: Leprosy bacillus or Hansen's bacillus.

Though not yet cultivated *in vitro*, these bacilli were the first to be recognized as a cause of human disease (Hansen, *op. cit.*, 1874). The bacilli occur in enormous numbers in lepromatous (nodular) cases of leprosy (Hansen's disease) and very sparsely in the tuberculoid or neural forms. Bacteriological identification depends on: (a) acid-fast staining and (b) failure of the organism to multiply in bacteriological media or in laboratory animals. Heated suspensions of the bacilli (obtained from nodules) produce a positive lepromin reaction in 75 to 97 per cent of normal persons and of tuberculoid cases of leprosy but usually produce no reaction in lepromatous individuals (Mitsuda: See Hayashi, Int. Jour. Leprosy, *1*, 1933, 31–38). The failure of lepromatous persons to respond to injected leprosy bacilli constitutes a criterion for testing the validity of the acid-fast microorganisms which can at times be recovered from leprous tissues by inoculation of bacteriological media.

Many organisms have been isolated from leprous tissues, some of which are acid-fast and which have been styled *Mycobacterium leprae*. The strains which have been adequately studied have proven to fall into the saprophytic groups. Hanks (Int. Jour. Lep-

rosy, *9*, 1941, 275) found that acid-fast cultures of this type were recoverable only from lesions located proximally with respect to open ulcers in the skin.

Description of organisms seen in leprosy tissue from Hansen (*op. cit.*, 1874, 1) and Topley and Wilson (Princip. Bact. and Immun., London, 2nd ed., 1936, 316).

Rods, 0.3 to 0.5 by 1.0 to 8.0 microns, with parallel sides and rounded ends, staining evenly or at times beaded. When numerous, as from lepromatous cases, they are generally arranged in clumps, rounded masses or in groups of bacilli side by side. Strongly acid-fast. Gram-positive.

Pathogenicity: The communicability of leprosy from man to man is accepted (Rogers and Muir, Leprosy, 2nd ed., Baltimore, 1940, 260 pp.). Experimental transmission to humans or to animals has not been successful.

Source: Found in human leprous lesions. In the lepromatous form of the disease, bacilli are so abundant as to produce stuffed-cell granulomas; in the tuberculoid and neural lesions they are rare.

Habitat: Obligate parasite in man. Confined largely to the skin (especially to convex and exposed surfaces), testes and to peripheral nerves. Probably do not grow in the internal organs.

14. **Mycobacterium lepraemurium** Marchoux and Sorel, 1912. (Bacillus der Rattenlepra, Stefansky, Cent. f. Bakt., I Abt., Orig., *33*, 1903, 481; *Mycobacterium leprae murium* (sic) Marchoux and Sorel, Ann. Inst. Past., *26*, 1912, 700.)

lep.rae.mu'ri.um. Gr. noun *lepra* leprosy; L. noun *mus* the mouse; L. gen.noun *muris* of the mouse; M.L. noun *lepramuris* leprosy of the mouse; M.L. gen.pl.noun *lepraemurium* of leprosy of mice.

Common name: Rat leprosy bacillus.

Rods, 3 to 5 microns in length, with slightly rounded ends. When stained, the cells often show an irregular appearance. Strongly acid-fast. Gram-positive.

Like the human leprosy bacillus, this organism has not been cultivated *in vitro*, but it can be passed experimentally through rats, mice and hamsters.

Distinctive characters: The heat-killed

cells produce lepromin reactions in lepromatous humans. The bacilli from lesions are not bound together in clumps, rounded masses and palisades as in human lesions. For further details, see review by Lowe (Internat. Jour. Leprosy, *5*, 1937, 310 and 463).

Comment: Nodular diseases of the skin of other animals have been described, e.g. a disease of the buffalo in India and of the frog in South America, which are caused by leprosy-like acid-fast bacilli that have not yet been cultivated on artificial media.

Source: An endemic disease of rats in various parts of the world, having been found in Odessa, Berlin, London, New South Wales, Hawaii, San Francisco and elsewhere.

Habitat: The natural disease occurs chiefly in the skin and lymph nodes, causing induration, alopecia (loss of hair) and eventually ulceration.

Genus II. **Mycococcus** *Krassilnikov, 1938.**

(Krassilnikov, Microbiologia (Russian), *7*, Part I, 1938, 335; also see Ray Fungi and Related Organisms, Izd. Akad. Nauk, U.S.S.R., Moskau, 1938, 121, Guide to the Actinomycetes, Izd. Akad. Nauk, U.S.S.R., Moskau, 1941, 122, and Guide to the Bacteria and Actinomycetes, Izd. Akad. Nauk, U.S.S.R., Moskau, 1949, 198; not *Mycococcus* Bokor, Arch. f. Mikrobiol., *1*, 1930, 1.)

My'co.coc.cus. Gr. noun *myces* a fungus; Gr. noun *coccus* a berry, a sphere; M.L. mas.n. *Mycococcus* coccus-shaped fungus.

Cells generally spherical, occurring singly, in short chains or in clumps; rod-shaped cells also occur, particularly in potato and liquid media. The spherical cells are quite variable in size and shape, the smaller cocci measuring 0.2 to 0.5 micron in diameter, and the larger cells (involution forms) measuring 0.7 to 1.0 micron in diameter; occasional cells are angular or ameboid in shape. The length of the rod-shaped cells ordinarily does not exceed twice the width. Multiplication is by fission, constriction or bud formation. Resting cells, which are produced from vegetative, coccus-like cells, germinate in a manner analogous to that of the spores of the *Actinomycetes*, forming one to three germ tubes on their surface. Not acid-fast. Gram-positive. Grow well on ordinary culture media. Gross appearance of colonies similar to those of the genus *Mycobacterium;* red, yellow-green or orange pigments are produced. Aerobic. Found widely distributed in soils.

The type species is *Mycococcus albus* Krassilnikov.

Key to the species of genus **Mycococcus.†**

I. Non-chromogenic.
    A. Proteolytic property strong. Milk coagulated and peptonized.
           1. *Mycococcus albus.*
    B. Proteolytic property weak.
        1. Milk slowly coagulated, becoming slightly alkaline; weakly peptonized.
              1a. *Mycococcus albus* subsp. *albidus.*
        2. Milk rapidly coagulated, becoming slightly acid; not peptonized.
              1b. *Mycococcus albus* subsp. *lactis.*
II. Chromogenic.
    A. Chromogenesis red, orange or rust.
        1. Colonies with dough-like consistency.
           a. Cells occur singly, in pairs or in chains 3 to 4 microns in length.
              2. *Mycococcus ruber.*

---

* Prepared by Miss Lois Nellis, Hobart College, Geneva, New York, from a translation made by Prof. S. A. Waksman, Rutgers University, New Brunswick, New Jersey, December, 1954.

† Key based on a table by Krassilnikov, Guide to the Actinomycetes, Izd. Akad. Nauk, U.S.S.R., Moskau, 1941, 123.

　　　aa. Cells frequently united into groups of four.
　　　　　　　　　　　　　　2a. *Mycococcus ruber* subsp. *tetragenus*.
　　2. Colonies mucoid and spreading.
　　　a. Cells occur singly or in short chains; surrounded by a thick, slimy capsule.
　　　　　　　　　　　　　　3. *Mycococcus capsulatus*.
　　　aa. Cells occur in groups of four; surrounded by a thin, slimy capsule.
　　　　　　　　　　　　　　3a. *Mycococcus capsulatus* subsp. *mucosus*.
　B. Chromogenesis yellow.
　　1. Colonies bright yellow or brownish yellow.
　　　a. Colonies bright yellow; fermentative capacity weak.
　　　　　　　　　　　　　　4. *Mycococcus luteus*.
　　　aa. Colonies brownish yellow; fermentative capacity strong.
　　　　　　　　　　　　　　5. *Mycococcus flavus*.
　　2. Colonies yellow-green or lemon-yellow.
　　　　　　　　　　　　　　6. *Mycococcus citreus*.

1. Mycococcus albus Krassilnikov, 1938. (Microbiologia (Russian), 7, Part I, 1938, 350.)

al'bus. L. adj. *albus* white.

Original description supplemented by material from Krassilnikov (Guide to the Actinomycetes, Izd. Akad. Nauk, U.S.S.R., Moskau, 1941, 124).

Cells round or slightly ovoid, 0.7 to 1.0 micron in diameter. On some media, such as salt agar, are found rod-shaped cells, 0.7 by 1.0 to 1.2 microns, with wide branches. In 2- to 5-day-old cultures there are found large, spherical and lemon-shaped cells up to 1.5 microns in diameter; these frequently form on the surface of the medium when the culture has been seeded upon a fresh substrate. There are marked differences between the daughter and mother cells. In old cultures many cells are changed into resting forms. Not acid-fast. Gram-positive.

Gelatin: Rapid liquefaction.

Colonies: Well developed on all media; large, moist and shiny.

Malt agar: Excellent growth; colonies pasty.

Synthetic agar with sucrose: Excellent growth.

Glycerol agar: Excellent growth.

Potato: Good growth by some strains.

Milk: Coagulated and peptonized.

Acetic acid and citric acid media: Good growth.

Sucrose is inverted.

Acid from glucose and fructose.

Starch: Good growth; hydrolysis.

No growth on paraffin.

Comment: Krassilnikov (*loc. cit.*) recognizes two subspecies: *Mycococcus albus* subsp. *albidus*, distinctive because of its weak ability to attack substances, and *Mycococcus albus* subsp. *lactis*, distinctive because of the way in which it coagulates milk.

Source: Isolated from soil at Yershovo Station, Russia.

Habitat: Infrequently found in soil.

1a. *Mycococcus albus* subsp. *albidus* Krassilnikov, 1941. (Guide to the Actinomycetes, Izd. Akad. Nauk, U.S.S.R., Moskau, 1941, 124.)

al'bi.dus. L. adj. *albidus* white.

Cells rounded or slightly angular, usually 0.6 to 0.7 micron in diameter, occurring singly or in short chains of 3 to 5 cells. Rod-shaped forms and enlarged forms have not been observed. Resting forms, 0.8 micron in diameter, are found in old cultures.

Gelatin: Weak liquefaction.

Colonies on solid nutrient media poorly developed; they are white and are smaller, flatter, smoother, more shiny and of a more compact consistency than those of *Mycococcus albus*.

Protein media: Good growth.

Synthetic agar with sucrose: Good growth.

Milk: Slow coagulation; weak peptonization; slightly alkaline.

No acid from glucose, sucrose or lactose.

Starch: Hydrolysis slow, forming a narrow zone of not more than 2 mm around the colony.

Nitrites rapidly produced from nitrates. Proteolytic action weak.

Comment: One culture (No. 25), after a

month's cultivation, dissociated into a stable mycobacterial culture which was distinct from the original culture in structure and size of cells. After one day's growth, cells were rod-shaped, 0.6 to 0.7 by 2.0 to 3.5 microns; they curved slightly and had irregular contours; on salt agar and especially in liquid media and peptone broth, cells up to 5 microns were found, often exhibiting branching. Krassilnikov regarded the history of the development of this strain to be the same as that of typical mycobacteria, since these rods became shorter and changed into a coccus-like stage. Resting forms then developed, completing the cycle. Cultural and physiological properties were not different from those of the original culture. In view of the morphological characteristics and the cycle of development, this culture was referred to as *Mycobacterium albus* Krassilnikov (1916) under the name *Micrococcus candicans*; this organism formed rod-shaped cells with side branches under certain conditions (Löhnis and Smith, Jour. Agr. Res., *6*, 1916, 675–702). Spassky (Zent. f. Bakt., I Abt., Orig., *128*, 1933, 245) described a streptococcus which gave rise to a mycobacterial strain in the process of dissociation. Krassilnikov suggests that the original culture of both these organisms belonged to the genus *Mycococcus*.

Source: Isolated from soil.

Habitat: Infrequently found in soil.

1b. *Mycococcus albus* subsp. *lactis* Krassilnikov, 1941. (Guide to the Actinomycetes, Izd. Akad. Nauk, U.S.S.R., Moskau, 1941, 125.)

lac'tis. L. noun *lac* milk; L. gen.noun *lactis* of milk.

Morphological and cultural characteristics are the same as those of *Mycococcus albidus*.

Gelatin: No liquefaction (two months).

Milk: Acid; rapid coagulation. No peptonization within 30 days. Coagulation apparently takes place through the production of acid in a manner similar to that of the lactic acid bacteria.

Sucrose is inverted.

Acid from glucose and lactose; slight acid from sucrose.

Starch weakly hydrolyzed.

Comment: Krassilnikov regards as closely related to this species a culture described by Lieberman (1935) under the name *Streptococcus lactis*.

Source: Isolated from soil.

Habitat: Infrequently found in soil.

2. **Mycococcus ruber** Krassilnikov, 1938. (Microbiologia (Russian), *7*, Part I, 1938, 349.)

ru'ber. L. adj. *ruber* red.

Original description supplemented by material from Krassilnikov (Guide to the Actinomycetes, Izd. Akad. Nauk, U.S.S.R., Moskau, 1941, 125).

Cells spherical, irregularly rounded, slightly compressed, somewhat angular, 0.5 to 0.9 micron in diameter. In liquid cultures there are occasionally found short rods, 0.7 by 0.8 to 1.0 micron, with branches; enlarged cells of different shapes are also found. In old cultures are found resting cells which germinate in a manner similar to that of the spores of actinomycetes.

Not acid-fast. Gram-positive.

Gelatin: No liquefaction.

Colonies: Dough-like consistency; smooth; weak shine. Colonies dark brown, rose, red-orange or, frequently, orange. A culture may show different pigmentation on different media. Pigment not soluble.

Milk: No coagulation or peptonization.

Sucrose not inverted.

Sucrose and organic acids (acetic and citric) are utilized as sources of carbon.

Starch: No hydrolysis or weak hydrolysis with a clear zone only under the colonies.

Nitrites not produced from nitrates.

Nitrates and ammonium salts are readily utilized as sources of nitrogen.

Some strains produce good growth on paraffin.

Some strains grow well in high concentrations of salts, such as 10 per cent NaCl and 10 to 20 per cent sodium sulfate.

Resistant to desiccation.

Comments: Krassilnikov isolated several strains which could be distinguished on the basis of shades of pigmentation of the colony and by the size of the cells. Strains Nos. 3 and 5 were blood-red on all media; cells 0.6 to 0.9 micron, frequently 1.0 micron, in diameter. Strain No. 45 was rose-red, red or orange, depending on the medium; cells 0.3 to 0.9 micron in diameter.

After one year of cultivation in peptone broth, strains Nos. 43 and 45 dissociated to form mycobacterial strains which were closely related to each other. Cells were rod-shaped, 0.8 by 0.5 to 2.5 microns, curving and branching, changing to cocci in 3 to 5 days. Enlarged cells were formed on certain media. These showed no differences in fermentative capacity as compared with the original culture. Krassilnikov regards these organisms as closely related to *Mycobacterium brevicale* on the basis of appearance of cells, pigmentation of colonies and physiological properties. Krassilnikov (*loc. cit.*) recognizes as a subspecies *Mycococcus tetragenus*.

Source: Isolated from soil at Yershovo Station, Russia.

Habitat: Infrequently found in soil.

2a. *Mycococcus ruber* subsp. *tetragenus* Krassilnikov, 1938. (Ray Fungi and Related Organisms, Izd. Akad. Nauk, U.S.S.R., Moskau, 1938, 121.)

tet.ra'ge.nus. Gr. pref. *tetra* four; Gr. v. *gennaio* to produce; M.L. adj. *tetragenus* produced in fours.

Original description supplemented by material from Krassilnikov (Guide to the Actinomycetes, Izd. Akad. Nauk, U.S.S.R., Moskau, 1941, 126).

Cells coccoid, occurring in tetrads formed by the multiplication of two different branches; occasionally combined into parallel chains. Both types are consistently found on synthetic agar.

Colonies: Red; slightly enlarged; weak shine.

Physiological and cultural characteristics are, in general, not different from those of *Mycococcus ruber*.

Comment: Krassilnikov regards this organism as a form of *Mycococcus ruber*. Two strains have been isolated.

Source: Isolated from soil.

Habitat: Infrequently found in soil.

3. **Mycococcus capsulatus** Krassilnikov, 1938. (Microbiologia (Russian), 7, Part 1, 1938, 349.)

cap.su.la'tus. L. noun *capsula* a small chest; M.L. adj. *capsulatus* encapsulated.

Original description supplemented by material from Krassilnikov (Guide to the Actinomycetes, Izd. Akad. Nauk, U.S.S.R., Moskau, 1941, 127).

Cells rounded, irregular in size, 0.7 to 1.0 micron in diameter, frequently occurring in short chains of 3 to 7 cells. Cells surrounded by a thick, slimy capsule. Chains sometimes form side branches. Not acid-fast. Gram-positive.

Colonies: Rose or pale rose, slimy, spreading. No soluble pigment.

Physiological properties and fermentative capacity are not different from those of *Mycococcus ruber*.

Comment: One of the two strains isolated, No. 53, dissociated into strains with smooth colonies and rod-shaped cells, 0.7 by 1.5 to 5.5 microns, without a slimy capsule. Fermentative capacity no different from that of the original culture. Krassilnikov regards this strain as closely related to *Mycobacterium planum* on the basis of its cultural, morphological and physiological properties.

Krassilnikov (*loc. cit.*) regards this organism as a subspecies of *Mycococcus mucosus*.

Source: Isolated from soil.

Habitat: Infrequently found in soil.

3a. *Mycococcus capsulatus* subsp. *mucosus* Krassilnikov, 1938. (Ray Fungi and Related Organisms, Izd. Akad. Nauk, U.S.S.R., Moskau, 1938, 349.)

mu.co'sus. L. adj. *mucosus* slimy, mucous.

Original description supplemented by material from Krassilnikov (Guide to the Actinomycetes, Izd. Akad. Nauk, U.S.S.R., Moskau, 1941, 127).

Cells occur in tetrads in one plane, occasionally forming short, parallel chains and joining chains, surrounded by a thin, slimy capsule. There are also cells which form individual cases of branching rods. Resting cells are found.

Cultural and physiological characters are not different from those of *Mycococcus capsulatus*.

Comment: Krassilnikov regards this or

ganism as a member of the genus *Mycococcus* on the basis of the resting cells and branching rods; it resembles a tetracoccus on the basis of the characteristic cell groupings. It differs from *Mycococcus capsulatus* in that the capsules form on practically all media.

Source: Isolated from soil of the Quybishev Agricultural Institute.

Habitat: Infrequently found in soil.

4. **Mycococcus luteus** Krassilnikov, 1938. (Microbiologia (Russian), 7, Part I, 1938, 349.)

lu'te.us. L. adj. *luteus* yellow.

Original description supplemented by material from Krassilnikov (Guide to the Actinomycetes, Izd. Akad. Nauk, U.S.S.R., Moskau, 1941, 217).

Cells coccoid, ovoid or irregular, 0.5 to 0.8 micron in diameter, united somewhat into short rods. After 5 to 7 days there are found enlarged, lemon-shaped, spherical cells up to 1.5 microns in diameter; they are later destroyed and disappear. In old cultures there are resting cells with thicker protoplasm; they reproduce like the spores of an actinomycete. In liquid media, some strains form individual short rods, 0.7 by 1.0 micron, which branch infrequently.

Gelatin: No liquefaction by two strains, weak liquefaction by one.

Colonies: Bright yellow, sometimes golden or brown. No soluble pigment.

Milk: No coagulation; no peptonization.

Sucrose is weakly inverted.

Acid from glucose and fructose; no acid from sucrose.

Citric and acetic acids are not utilized as sources of carbon.

No growth on paraffin.

Source: Isolated from soil.

Habitat: Infrequently found in soil.

5. **Mycococcus flavus** Krassilnikov, 1941. (Guide to the Actinomycetes, Izd. Akad. Nauk, U.S.S.R., Moskau, 1941, 127.)

fla'vus. L. adj. *flavus* yellow.

Morphology same as that of *Mycococcus luteus*.

Gelatin: Rapid liquefaction.

Colonies: Brownish yellow; no soluble pigment.

Milk: Coagulation and peptonization.

Acid from glucose.

Starch: No hydrolysis.

Citric and acetic acids are utilized as sources of carbon.

Source: Isolated from soil of Zabolgia, Russia.

Habitat: Infrequently found in soil.

6. **Mycococcus citreus** Krassilnikov, 1938. (Microbiologia (Russian), 7, Part I, 1938, 349.)

cit're.us. L. adj. *citreus* of the citrus tree; M.L. adj. *citreus* lemon-yellow.

Original description supplemented by material from Krassilnikov (Guide to the Actinomycetes, Izd. Akad. Nauk, U.S.S.R., Moskau, 1941, 127).

Cells extremely variable in size: in the same culture are found cells from 0.2 micron and smaller up to 1.0 micron in diameter. Cells are frequently round, single or united into short chains of two or three cells. Protoplasm is light and uniform. Rod forms up to 1.5 microns in length are occasionally seen in liquid media; branched forms are observed in hanging drop preparations. Resting forms are found in old cultures.

Gelatin: Rapid liquefaction.

Colonies: Yellow-green and lemon-colored; smooth; waxy.

Milk: Peptonization and coagulation.

Sucrose is inverted.

Acid from glucose, fructose and sucrose.

Nitrites produced from nitrates by most strains.

Starch: Active hydrolysis.

No growth on organic acids.

No growth on paraffin.

Comment: Ten cultures were isolated, all of which differed from each other in intensity of pigment and in certain physiological properties. Krassilnikov regards these differences as insufficient to separate them into distinct species or even strains. One culture, isolated in the Institute of Microbiology of the Academy of Sciences under the name *Micrococcus*, was found to be *Mycococcus citreus*.

Source: Isolated from soil.

Habitat: Found in soil rather frequently.

Note: Krassilnikov (Guide to the Bacteria and Actinomycetes, Izd. Akad. Nauk, U.S.S.R., Moskau, 1949, 123) states that probably a considerable number of previously described species placed in the genus *Micrococcus* really belong in the genus *Mycococcus* as he has described it. Inasmuch as Hucker (personal communication, 1955) has always felt that the two species of red micrococci recognized by him (Hucker, N. Y. State Exp. Sta. Tech. Bull. 135, 1938, 33 pp.) as *Micrococcus cinnabareus* Flügge and as *M. rhodochrous* Migula were not typical micrococci, further studies of cultures of these coral-red to cinnabar-red species have been made by Dr. Ruth Gordon and by Dr. A. G. Lochhead. These investigators are in agreement that these species may well be mycococci or nocardias. For this reason the descriptions of the two species under consideration have been removed from the section in which micrococci are described and are given in this note. It is of interest in this connection that Hucker (N. Y. State Exp. Sta. Tech. Bull. 102, 1924, 26) lists nearly a dozen named and described (sometimes very poorly) species of red micrococci that may be identical with one or the other of the two species described below.

1. **Micrococcus cinnabareus** Flügge, 1886. (Die Mikroorganismen, 2 Aufl., 1886, 174.)

cin.na.ba're.us. Gr. noun *cinnabari* cinnabar, vermilion; M.L. adj. *cinnabareus* of the color of vermilion.

Spheres, 1.0 micron in diameter, occurring singly and in pairs. Non-motile. Gram-variable.

Gelatin colonies: Small, circular, bright red, becoming cinnabar-red.

Gelatin stab: Thick, raised, rose- to cinnabar-red growth on surface. No liquefaction. White colonies along stab.

Agar slant: A carmine-red streak. Slow growth.

Broth: Turbid.

Litmus milk: Slightly alkaline to slightly acid.

Potato: Slowly developing vermilion-red streak.

Indole not produced.

Small amount of acid from sugars.

Starch not hydrolyzed.

Nitrites produced from nitrates.

Does not utilize $NH_4H_2PO_4$ as a source of nitrogen.

Aerobic.

Optimum temperature, 25° C.

Saprophytic.

Source: Found as contamination of cultures.

Habitat: Usually found as a dust contamination.

2. **Micrococcus rhodochrous** (Zopf, 1891) Migula, 1900. (*Rhodococcus rhodochrous* Zopf, Berichte d. deutsch. bot. Gesellsch., *9*, 1891, 22; Migula, Syst. d. Bakt., *2*, 1900, 162.)

rho.do'chro.us. Gr. noun *rhodum* the rose; Gr. noun *chroa* color, complexion; M.L. adj. *rhodochrous* rose-colored.

Spheres, 0.5 to 1.0 micron in diameter, occurring singly. Non-motile. Gram-variable.

Gelatin colonies: Small, circular, glistening, raised, entire, dark, reddish brown.

Gelatin stab: Dark, carmine-red, dry surface growth. Slight growth in stab. No liquefaction.

Agar slant: Carmine-red streak, becoming brick-red in color.

Broth: Thick, rose-red pellicle with red, flocculent sediment.

Litmus milk: Slightly alkaline.

Potato: Carmine-red streak.

Acid from glucose. No acid from lactose, sucrose, glycerol or mannitol (Hucker, 1923, retest of original culture).

Nitrites produced from nitrates (Hucker, 1923, retest of original culture).

Aerobic.

Optimum temperature, 25° C.

Saprophytic.

Comments: In the description of this organism given by Migula, which is taken from Zopf's original description, emphasis is laid on the arrangement of the cells in tetrads or occasionally as diplococci. Mention is made of short chains, but again emphasis is laid on the fact that these are not formed by division in planes parallel with each other, as are the chains of streptococci, but rather by an accidental rearrangement of tetrads, the cells dividing in two planes perpendicular to each other. It is noteworthy that two of the red chromogenic species of *Mycococcus* described above show a tetrad arrangement of cells.

Gordon (personal communication, 1954) reports that she finds an apparently authentic culture of *Rhodococcus rhodochrous* Zopf to be identical with *Nocardia corallina* Waks-man and Henrici. This culture was secured by Breed from the Král collection in 1923 and differs from a culture (No. 2682) carried for a time in the Nat. Coll. Type Cultures in London that came from the Amer. Mus. Nat. Hist. Coll. (Culture 184), origin unknown.

Habitat: Water.

FAMILY II. ACTINOMYCETACEAE BUCHANAN, 1918.*

(Jour. Bact., *3*, 1918, 403.)

Ac.ti.no.my.ce.ta'ce.ae. M.L. mas.n. *Actinomyces* type genus of the family; *-aceae* ending to denote a family; M.L. pl.noun *Actinomycetaceae* the *Actinomyces* family.

Mycelium is non-septate during the early stages of growth but later may become septate and break up into short segments, rod-shaped or spherical in shape, or the mycelium may remain non-septate and produce spores on aerial hyphae. The organisms in culture media are either colorless or produce various pigments. Some species are partially acid-fast. This family is distinguished from the previous one by the formation of a true mycelium. As compared with the next family, it is characterized by the manner of spore formation.

Key to the genera of family **Actinomycetaceae.**

I. Obligately aerobic. The colonies are bacteria-like in nature, smooth, rough or folded, of a soft to a dough-like consistency, sometimes compact and leathery in young stages. Most forms do not produce any aerial mycelium; a few produce a limited mycelium, the branches of which also break up into oidiospores or segmentation spores. Some species are partially acid-fast.

Genus I. *Nocardia*, p. 713.

II. Anaerobic or microaerophilic; parasitic; non-acid-fast, non-proteolytic and non-diastatic.

Genus II. *Actinomyces*, p. 742.

Genus I. **Nocardia** *Trevisan*, 1889.

(Trevisan, I generi e le specie delle Batteriacee, 1889, 9; *Proactinomyces* Jensen, Proc. Linn. Soc. New So. Wales, *56*, 1931, 345; *Asteroides* Puntoni and Leonardi, Boll. e. Atti d. R. Accad. Med., *61*, 1935, 90.)

No.car'di.a. M.L. fem.n. *Nocardia* named for Prof. Edmund Nocard, who first described the type species of this genus.

Slender filaments or rods, frequently swollen and occasionally branched, forming a mycelium which, after reaching a certain size, assumes the appearance of bacterium-like growths. Shorter rods and coccoid forms are found in older cultures. Conidia not formed. Stain readily, occasionally showing a slight degree of acid-fastness. Non-motile.† No endo-

---

* Completely revised by Prof. S. A. Waksman, Rutgers University, New Brunswick, New Jersey, March, 1953.

† H. L. Jensen (Symposium on Actinomycetales, VI Internat. Cong. Microbiol., Rome, 1953, Istituto Superiore di Sanita) comments on motility in nocardias as follows (unimportant editorial changes have been made in the text, such as the use of the term "nocardias" for "proactinomycetes"):

"Motility in the nocardias seems first to have been alleged in *Nocardia asteroides* by Ep-

spores. Aerobic. Gram-positive. The colonies are similar in gross appearance to those of the genus *Mycobacterium*. Paraffin, phenol and m-cresol are frequently utilized as a source of energy.

In their early stages of growth on culture media (liquid or solid), the structure of nocardias is similar to that of actinomycetes in that they form a typical mycelium; hyphae branch abundantly, the branching being true. The diameters of the hyphae vary between 0.5 and 1 micron, usually 0.7 to 0.8 micron, according to the species. The mycelium is not septate. However, the further development of nocardias differs sharply from that of actinomycetes: the filaments soon form transverse walls and the whole mycelium breaks up into regularly cylindrical short cells, then into coccoid cells. On fresh culture media, the coccoid cells germinate into mycelia. The whole cycle in the development of nocardias continues for 2 to 7 days. Most frequently the coccoid cells are formed on the third to fifth day, but in certain species (e.g., *Nocardia rubra*) they can be found on the second day.

Numerous chlamydospores may be found in older cultures of nocardias. They are formed in the same way as the chlamydospores in true fungi: the plasma inside the filaments of

---

pinger (Beitr. Path. Anat. u. Allg. Path., *9*, 1891, 287–328) whose observation has not been corroborated. Nocardia-like motile organisms were later mentioned by Rullman (quoted by von Magnus, Undersgelser over en Gruppe Actinomyceter isolerede fra Mennskets Svaelg., Thesis, 1936, Univ. Copenhagen), Schurmayer (Cent. f. Bakt., I Abt., Orig., *27*, 1900, 49–61, 101–106), Luginger (Montash. f. Prakt. Tierheilk., *15*, 1904, 289–336) and Huntemüller (Beitr. Path. Anat. u. Allg. Path., *69*, 1921, 110–121). Luginger's observation is particularly interesting because it refers to a microaerophilic organism. In no case was the presence of flagella demonstrated, and the statements seem to have attracted little attention. Colien (Jour. Bact., *30*, 1935, 301–322) saw a stage of cocci motile by a single flagellum in what appears to have been a non-acid-fast *Nocardia*, and Topping (Zent. f. Bakt., II Abt., *97*, 1937, 289–304) and Ørskov (Zent. f. Bakt., II Abt., *98*, 1938, 344–357) found instances of motility among nocardias as well as coryneform bacteria from soil. The forty strains studied by Topping included acid-fast as well as non-acid-fast forms and showed both granular and turbid growth in liquid media. Stained preparations showed the presence of flagella: polar or short and lateral on longer branched cells.

One of Ørskov's motile strains was examined by Jensen and was found to agree essentially with *Nocardia citrea* (Krassilnikov) Waksman and Henrici. It produced a soft, lemon-yellow growth on nutrient agar and a diffuse turbidity in broth. The cells were Gram-positive but not acid-fast (fully decolorized by 5 per cent sulfuric acid in 10 seconds). Nitrate was reduced to nitrite, starch was hydrolyzed, gelatin was slowly liquefied and casein was very slowly digested. Direct microscopic examination showed well developed initial mycelia with mere traces of aerial hyphae. The mycelial structure persisted for a considerable time below the agar surface, but after 24 to 40 hours some of the surface hyphae began to divide into rod-shaped cells that were very actively motile; this was best seen when a drop of water and a coverslip were placed on top of the agar colonies. In broth cultures the motility was much less obvious. Staining of the motile cells showed one to four (or more) stout flagella. Single flagella were often attached to the corner of the cell. Rods with both polar and lateral flagella were sometimes seen, but not branched flagellated filaments as pictured by Topping.

Motility may not be common among the nocardias (it was not observed in the numerous strains studied by von Magnus (*op. cit.*, 1936), Krassilnikov (Proaktinomitseti., Bull. Acad. Sci., U.S.S.R., Sér. Biol. No. 1, 1938, 138–182), Erikson (Ann. Rev. Microbiol., *3*, 1948, 23–54) or previously by the present writer), but its existence, at least in *Nocardia*, is indisputable and this really is not surprising in view of the numerous observations on motility in the closely related coryneform bacteria (Jensen, Ann. Rev. Microbiol., *6*, 1952, 77–90). The species in the order *Actinomycetales* cannot any longer be regarded as constantly non-motile."

the mycelium condenses into elongated portions. In older cultures of nocardias many coccoid cells are changed into resistant cells. The latter are larger than the vegetative coccoid cells; the plasma of these cells is thicker than the plasma of vegetative cells; on fresh media they germinate like the spores of actinomycetes; they form 2 to 3 germ tubes. Besides the cells mentioned, numerous involution forms can often be found in older cultures of nocardias; the cells are thin, regularly cylindrical or coccoid and are often transformed into a series of spherical or elliptical ampules and a club-like form (2 to 3 microns and more).

The multiplication of nocardias proceeds by fission and budding; occasionally they form special spores. Budding occurs often. The buds are formed on the lateral surface of the cells; when they have reached a certain size, they fall off and develop into rod-shaped cells or filaments. The spores are formed by the breaking up of the cell plasm into separate portions usually forming 3 to 5 spores; every portion becomes rounded, covered with a membrane and is transformed into a spore; the membrane of the mother cell dissolves and disappears. The spores germinate in the same way as those of actinomyces. They form germ tubes which develop into a mycelium.

The colonies of nocardias have a paste-like or mealy consistency and can easily be taken up with a platinum loop; they spread on glass and occasionally render the broth turbid. The surface colonies are smooth, folded or wrinkled. Typical nocardias never form an aerial mycelium, but there are cultures whose colonies are covered with a thin coating of short aerial hyphae which break up into cylindrical oidiospores.

Examination by fluorescent microscopy after treatment with carbol-auramin and decolorizing with NaCl-HCl-ethyl alcohol can reveal acid-fast species or their exudates (Richards, Stain Technol., *18*, 1943, 91).

Many species of nocardias form pigments; their colonies are of a blue, violet, red, yellow or green color; more often the cultures are colorless. The color of the culture serves as a stable character.

Krassilnikov (Ray fungi and related organisms, Izd. Akad. Nauk, U.S.S.R., Moskau, 1938) divides the genus into two groups: 1) Well developed aerial mycelium; substrate mycelium seldom produces cross-walls; the threads break up into long, thread-like rods; branches of the aerial mycelium produce segmentation spores and oidiospores; the latter are cylindrical with sharp ends; no spirals or fruiting branches. This group is the same as group B of Jensen (*op. cit.*, 1931, 345). 2) Typical forms; mycelium develops only at early stages of growth, then breaks up into rod-shaped and coccoid bodies; smooth and rough colonies, dough-like consistency; never form an aerial mycelium; similar to bacterial colonies; aerial mycelium may form around colonies. This genus can also be divided, on the basis of acid-fastness, into two groups: Group 1) Partially acid-fast organisms which are non-proteolytic, non-diastatic and utilize paraffin; usually yellow, pink, or orange-red in color. Group 2) Non-acid-fast organisms which are diastatic, largely proteolytic and do not utilize paraffin; yellow, orange to black in color.

The type species is *Nocardia farcinica* Trevisan.

Key to the species of genus **Nocardia**.

I. Partially acid-fast* organisms with strongly refractive cells; non-proteolytic and generally non-diastatic; constantly capable of utilizing paraffin.
　　A. Initial mycelium fully developed, well branching, dividing into rods and generally into cocci.
　　　　1. Vegetative mycelium soft, without macroscopically visible aerial mycelium.
　　　　　　a. Vegetative mycelium yellow, orange or red.
　　　　　　　　b. Pathogenic.

---

* Acid-fastness is not marked in cultures, is apparent in infected tissues and is pronounced in sputum or other exudates.

c. Vegetative mycelium white, buff or pale yellow.
1. *Nocardia farcinica.*
cc. Vegetative mycelium yellow to red.
2. *Nocardia asteroides.*
bb. Not pathogenic.
3. *Nocardia polychromogenes.*
aa. Vegetative mycelium white to pink.
b. Gelatin not liquefied.
c. Growth on nutrient agar opaque, cream-colored; coccoid forms in broth.
4. *Nocardia opaca.*
cc. Growth on nutrient agar watery; no coccoid forms in broth.
5. *Nocardia erythropolis.*
ccc. Growth on nutrient agar pink.
d. Aerial mycelium on milk white.
6. *Nocardia leishmanii.*
dd. Pellicle on milk pink.
7. *Nocardia caprae.*
ddd. Pellicle on milk yellow.
8. *Nocardia pretoriana.*
dddd. Causes galls on blueberry plants.
9. *Nocardia vaccinii.*
bb. Gelatin liquefied.
10. *Nocardia pulmonalis.*
2. Vegetative mycelium hard, yellow, with white, aerial mycelium; hyphae divide into chains of acid-fast cocci.
11. *Nocardia paraffinae.*
B. Initial mycelium very short, rapidly dividing into rods and cocci.
1. Slowly growing organisms; cells 0.5 to 0.7 micron in diameter.
12. *Nocardia minima.*
2. Rapidly growing organisms; cells 1.0 to 1.2 microns in diameter.
a. Growth pink.
b. No cystites (swollen cells) formed.
c. No indigotin from indole.
13. *Nocardia corallina.*
cc. Indigotin from indole.
14. *Nocardia globerula.*
bb. Cystites formed.
15. *Nocardia salmonicolor.*
aa. Growth coral-red.
16. *Nocardia rubropertincta.*
aaa. Growth dark red.
17. *Nocardia rubra.*
aaaa. Growth white.
b. No aerial mycelium.
18. *Nocardia coeliaca.*
bb. Aerial mycelium.
19. *Nocardia transvalensis.*
II. Non-acid-fast organisms with weakly refractive cells; diastatic.
A. Parasitic or soil forms. Not known to digest agar.
1. Not proteolytic.
a. Growth on agar pale cream.
20. *Nocardia mesenterica.*

  b. Growth on agar whitish.

          21. *Nocardia albicans.*

  c. Growth on agar yellow.

          22. *Nocardia flava.*

  d. Growth on agar green.

          23. *Nocardia viridis.*

  e. Growth on agar yellow-green.

          24. *Nocardia citrea.*

  f. Growth on agar pink to crimson.

          25. *Nocardia madurae.*

  g. Growth on agar dark brown and even black.

          26. *Nocardia nigra.*

  h. Growth consistency soft; aerial mycelium sparse.

          27. *Nocardia lutea.*

  i. Growth consistency medium; aerial mycelium profuse.

          28. *Nocardia blackwellii.*

  j. Good action on milk; growth consistency firm; aerial mycelium liberal.

          29. *Nocardia cuniculi.*

  k. Pigment on protein media deep brown.

          30. *Nocardia rangoonensis.*

  l. Pigment on protein media light brown.

          31. *Nocardia caviae.*

2. Proteolytic.

  a. Growth on nutrient agar with rapid formation of unbranched, diphtheroid-like rods; no typical cystites; broth turbid.

          32. *Nocardia actinomorpha.*

  b. Growth white, shiny or pale; dough-like consistency; breaks up into short rods.

          33. *Nocardia alba.*

  c. Growth on nutrient agar with extensive mycelium; simple unbranched rods not formed; cystites present. Broth clear.

          34. *Nocardia flavescens.*

  d. Growth cream-colored.

          35. *Nocardia gibsonii.*

  e. Growth rose-colored to bright red or red-orange.

          36. *Nocardia fructifera.*

  f. Growth pink.

   a. Gelatin not liquefied.

          37. *Nocardia africana.*

   aa. Gelatin liquefied, at first slowly, then completely.

          38. *Nocardia pelletieri.*

  g. Colonies orange-yellow to orange-red, which may change to black.

          39. *Nocardia maculata.*

  h. Pigment on protein media light brown.

          40. *Nocardia rhodnii.*

  i. Pigment on protein media green to greenish brown.

          41. *Nocardia gardneri.*

  j. Growth yellowish to golden brown.

          42. *Nocardia fordii.*

  k. Growth yellow to reddish brown; soluble pigment brown to red.

          43. *Nocardia kuroishi.*

B. Marine species. Digest agar.

1. Growth on agar lemon-yellow.

     44. *Nocardia marina.*

2. Growth on agar orange-yellow.

     45. *Nocardia atlantica.*

1. Nocardia farcinica Trevisan, 1889. (Bacille du farcin, Nocard, Ann. Inst. Past., *2*, 1888, 293; Trevisan, I generi e le specie delle Batteriacee, Milan, 1889, 9.)

far.ci'ni.ca. L. v. *farcio* to stuff; L. noun *farciminum* a disease of horses; Fr. *farcin* farcy or glanders; M.L. adj. *farcinicus* relating to farcy.

This description is based on a study of a culture believed to be Prof. Nocard's original culture (American Type Culture Collection No. 3318). This culture agrees in its characteristics with those of a second culture isolated and identified by Dr. C. P. Fitch at the New York State Veterinary College, Ithaca, New York (ATCC No. 3399).

Branched filaments, 0.25 micron in diameter. Markedly acid-fast.

Gelatin colonies: Small, circular, transparent, glistening.

Gelatin stab: No liquefaction.

Agar colonies: Yellowish white, irregular, refractive, filamentous.

Agar slant: Grayish to yellowish white growth, surface roughened.

Broth: Clear; granular sediment, often with gray pellicle.

Litmus milk: Unchanged.

Potato: Abundant, dull, crumpled, whitish yellow growth.

No soluble pigment formed.

Proteolytic action absent.

Starch not hydrolyzed.

Aerobic, facultatively anaerobic.

Nitrites not produced from nitrates.

Optimum temperature, 37° C.

Source: Isolated from cases of bovine farcy.

Habitat: Associated with a disease in cattle resembling chronic tuberculosis. Transmissible to guinea pigs, cattle and sheep but not to rabbits, dogs, horses or monkeys.

2. Nocardia asteroides (Eppinger, 1891) Blanchard, 1895. (*Cladothrix asteroides* Ep-

pinger, Beitr. z. path. Anat., *9*, 1891, 287; Blanchard, in Bouchard, Traité Path. Gén., *3*, 1895, 811.)

as.ter.o.i'des. Gr. adj. *asteroides* starlike.

Straight, fine mycelium, 0.2 micron in diameter, which breaks up into small, coccoid conidia. Acid-fast.

Gelatin stab: Yellowish surface growth. No growth in stab. No liquefaction.

Synthetic agar: Thin, spreading, orange growth. No aerial mycelium.

Starch agar: Restricted, scant, orange growth.

Plain agar: Much folded, light yellow growth, becoming deep yellow to yellowish red.

Glucose broth: Thin, yellowish pellicle.

Litmus milk: Orange-colored ring. No coagulation. No peptonization.

Potato: Growth much wrinkled, whitish becoming yellow to almost brick-red.

No soluble pigment formed.

Proteolytic action doubtful.

Starch not hydrolyzed.

Nitrites produced from nitrates.

Aerobic.

Optimum temperature, 37° C.

Transmissible to rabbits and guinea pigs but not to mice.

Comment: A number of strains of acid-fast actinomycetes isolated from human lesions have deviated in certain particulars from the description of *Nocardia asteroides*, but not sufficiently to warrant separation as species. Baldacci, e.g., recognizes and names three varieties of this species (Mycopathologia, *1*, 1938, 68).

Source: Isolated from a cerebral abscess in man.

Habitat: Also found in conditions resembling pulmonary tuberculosis.

3. Nocardia polychromogenes (Vallée, 1903) Waksman and Henrici, 1948. (*Streptothrix polychromogenes* Vallée, Ann. Inst. Past., *17*, 1903, 288; *Proactinomyces poly-*

chromogenes Jensen, Proc. Linnean Soc. New So. Wales, *56*, 1931, 79 and 363; Waksman and Henrici, in Manual, 6th ed., 1948, 897.)

po.ly.chrom.o'ge.nes. Gr. adj. *poly* many; Gr. noun *chromus* color; Gr.v. *gennaeo* to produce; M.L.adj. *polychromogenes* producing many colors.

Description taken from Jensen (*op. cit.*, 1931).

Long, wavy filaments, 0.4 to 0.5 by 70 to 100 microns, extensively branched but without septa. Older cultures consist entirely of rods 4 to 10 microns in length, frequently in V, Y or smaller forms. Still older cultures consist of shorter rods and coccoid forms. Gram-positive, frequently showing bands and granules.

Gelatin stab: Thin, yellowish growth along the stab with thin, radiating filaments. Surface growth flat, wrinkled, red. No liquefaction.

Nutrient agar: Scant, orange-red growth.

Glucose agar: After 3 to 4 days, raised, flat, glistening, rose-colored growth. After 1 to 3 weeks, becoming folded and coral-red.

Glucose broth: After 3 to 4 days, turbid; after 2 to 3 weeks an orange, flaky, sediment. No surface growth.

Milk: Growth starts as small orange-colored surface granules. After 1 to 2 weeks a thick, soft, orange-colored sediment forms.

Optimum temperature, between 22° and 25° C.

Distinctive characters: Differs from *Nocardia corallina* in the formation of very long filaments and in filiform growth in gelatin stabs.

Source: Isolated from the blood of a horse and from soil in France and Australia.

Habitat: Soil.

4. **Nocardia opaca** (den Dooren de Jong, 1927) Waksman and Henrici, 1948. (*Mycobacterium opacum* den Dooren de Jong, Cent. f. Bakt., II Abt., *71*, 1927, 216; *Proactinomyces opacus* Jensen, Proc. Linn. Soc. New So. Wales, *57*, 1932, 369; Waksman and Henrici, in Manual, 6th ed., 1948, 897.)

o.pa'ca. L.adj. *opacus* shaded, dark.

Description taken from Gray and Thornton (Cent. f. Bakt., II Abt., *73*, 1928, 86),

Bynoe (Thesis, McGill University, Montreal, 1931), Jensen (*op. cit.*, 1932, 369) and Erikson (Jour. Gen. Microbiol., *3*, 1949, 363).

Long, curved, irregular and branching filaments or rods, 0.8 to 1.0 by 2 to 16 microns, or occasionally longer. Few chains or clumps are formed. In older cultures shorter rods or cocci are generally formed. Readily stained. Not acid-fast. Acid-fast cell elements predominate during periods of maximum growth and free air supply (Erikson). Gram-positive.

Gelatin colonies: Round, convex, whitish, smooth, shining, edges slightly arborescent. Deep colonies: Burrs, with slightly irregular processes.

Gelatin stab: Convex, whitish, smooth, resinous, filiform, erose.

Nutrient agar: Soft cream to pink growth (Erikson).

Synthetic agar: Growth colorless and thin, producing an initial mycelium, the hyphae dividing rapidly into short rods; addition of 0.01 per cent $MnSO_4$ stimulates production of pale pink pigment (Erikson).

Broth: Turbid with broken white scum or clear with granular suspension.

Dorset's egg medium: Spreading, smooth, moist, salmon-colored growth.

Loeffler's medium: Scant, smooth, moist, light buff-colored growth.

Glycerol potato: Dry, rough, crumpled, pink to buff-colored growth.

Litmus milk: Grayish pellicle; slightly alkaline.

No acid from sucrose, lactose, maltose or glucose.

Phenol and naphthalene are utilized as sources of energy.

Nitrites produced from nitrates.

Optimum temperature, 30° C.

Optimum pH, between 6.8 and 7.3.

Distinctive characters: Differs from *Nocardia corallina* and *Nocardia polychromogenes* in that the cells are much longer than those of the former and much shorter than those of the latter. Grows in smooth convex surface colonies and burr-like deep colonies.

Source: Twenty-four strains were isolated from soils in Great Britain.

Habitat: Probably sparingly distributed in soils.

5. Nocardia erythropolis (Gray and Thornton, 1928) Waksman and Henrici, 1948. (*Mycobacterium erythropolis* Gray and Thornton, Cent. f. Bakt., II Abt., *73*, 1928, 87; *Proactinomyces erythropolis* Jensen, Proc. Linn. Soc. New So. Wales, *57*, 1932, 371; Waksman and Henrici, in Manual, 6th ed., 1948, 898.)

e.ry.thro′po.lis. Gr. adj. *erythrus* red; Gr.noun *polis* a city; M.L.noun *erythropolis* red city.

Original description supplemented by material taken from Bynoe (Thesis, McGill University, Montreal, 1931).

Long, uneven-sided rods and filaments, curved and branching, 0.8 by up to 11.0 microns. Coccoid forms not formed. Stains readily. Not acid-fast. Gram-positive.

Gelatin colonies: After 12 days, round, flat, white, shining; edge entire. Deep colonies: Round, smooth.

Gelatin stab: After 8 to 14 days, growth convex, white, smooth, shining; radiate from center; borders cleft. Line of puncture filiform, erose.

Agar colonies: Round, 2 to 3 mm in diameter, convex, watery white; edge entire. Deep colonies: Lens-shaped.

Agar slant: Filiform, flat, watery growth; edge undulate.

Broth: Growth slight; turbid.

Dorset's egg medium: After 2 weeks, growth raised, moist, finely granular, flesh-colored; irregular margin.

Loeffler's medium: After 7 days growth as on Dorset's egg medium, but pink.

Glycerol potato: After 7 days, flat, dry, rough, orange-colored.

Litmus milk: Pale pink pellicle.

No acid from glucose, lactose, sucrose or glycerol.

Nitrites not produced from nitrates.

Phenol is utilized.

Optimum temperature, 25° C.

Optimum pH, between 6.8 and 8.0.

Distinctive characters: Differs from *Nocardia coeliaca* and *Nocardia actinomorpha* in the filiform growth and absence of liquefaction of gelatin. Long rods and filaments.

Source: Six strains were isolated from soils in Great Britain.

Habitat: Presumably soil.

6. Nocardia leishmanii Chalmers and Christopherson, 1916. (A new acid-fast streptothrix, Birt and Leishman, Jour. Hyg., *2*, 1902, 120; Chalmers and Christopherson, Ann. Trop. Med. and Parasit., *10*, 1916, 255.)

leish.ma′ni.i. M.L. gen.noun *leishmanii* of Leishman; named for W. B. Leishman, one of the two who first isolated this organism.

Description taken from Erikson (Med. Res. Council Spec. Rept. Ser. 203, 1935, 27).

Initial cells frequently swollen, large and irregular, aggregated in short chains and then branching out into regular, narrow filaments; at margin of colony on synthetic glycerol agar may be seen comparatively long, thick segments with accompanying fringe of normal hyphae; later, entire colonies asteroid in appearance, very fine and close, angular branching, with aerial hyphae situated singly; aerial mycelium generally abundant with irregularly cylindrical conidia. Slightly acid-fast. The latter property must have been attenuated during artificial cultivation, for the organism is reported as markedly acid-fast by the original isolators.

Gelatin: Small, pink colonies in depths of stab. No liquefaction.

Glucose agar: Rounded, elevated colonies with paler frosting of aerial mycelium; growth becoming piled up; aerial mycelium sparse.

Glycerol agar: Small, round, pink colonies, tending to be umbilicated and piled up; stiff, white aerial spikes.

Coon's agar: Small, round, colorless colonies; stiff white aerial spikes; later a pink tinge.

Potato agar: Minute, colorless, round colonies; small raised patches of white aerial mycelium.

Dorset's egg medium: Colorless, confluent growth studded with little wart-like projections bearing stiff aerial spikes; growth becomes pinkish with a white aerial mycelium; later, growth drab gray; medium discolored.

Serum agar: Minute, round, colorless colonies with pinkish tinge in confluent, raised patch.

Inspissated serum: Small, round, pale pink colonies; umbilicated and raised up.

Broth: Liberal growth, white flocculent colonies; later pink surface colonies.

Synthetic sucrose solution: Colorless, flocculent sediment; thin, colorless pellicle.

Milk: Surface growth; white aerial mycelium; solid coagulum; later partly peptonized with pink aerial mycelium.

Litmus milk: Pink surface growth; aerial mycelium; milky opaque after 40 days.

Carrot plug: Small, irregularly round, raised colonies, colorless, covered with stiff aerial spikes; later buff-colored, convoluted and ribbed growth with small patches of white, aerial mycelium; aerial mycelium pink in two months.

Source: Isolated from a fatal case of lung disease and pericarditis in man.

Habitat: Human infections so far as known.

7. **Nocardia caprae** (Silberschmidt, 1899) Waksman and Henrici, 1948. (*Streptothrix caprae* Silberschmidt, Ann. Inst. Past., *13*, 1899, 841; Waksman and Henrici, in Manual, 6th ed., 1948, 899.)

cap'rae. L. noun *capra* a she-goat; L. gen. noun *caprae* of a she-goat.

Description taken from Erikson (Med. Res. Council Spec. Rept. Ser. 203, 1935, 26).

Initial cells only slightly enlarged; early development of aerial hyphae while substratum threads are still short; frequent slipping of branches; aerial mycelium abundant on all media with tendency to form coherent spikes; mycelium not very polymorphous, but occasional, thicker segments appear. Slightly acid-fast.

Gelatin: Extensive dull growth with small, raised patches of pink, aerial mycelium; later ribbon-like, depressed. No liquefaction.

Glucose agar: Irregular, bright pink growth tending to be heaped up; later abundant masses frosted over with thin, white, aerial mycelium.

Glycerol agar: Abundant growth; small round pink colonies partly covered with white aerial mycelium.

Potato agar: Extensive, thin growth, pink in raised patches, covered by white, aerial mycelium; later aerial mycelium also becomes pink.

Starch agar: Minute, colorless colonies covered by white, aerial mycelium.

Blood agar: Minute, round, colorless colonies aggregated in broad, pink zones; paler aerial mycelium. No hemolysis.

Dorset's egg medium: Few, colorless colonies, some pink; white aerial mycelium; later, growth becoming dull pink, irregular, with scant white aerial mycelium.

Ca-agar: Minute, colorless colonies; white aerial mycelium; later a pinkish tinge.

Serum agar: Small, round, pink colonies frosted over with thin, white, aerial mycelium.

Inspissated serum: No growth.

Broth: Superficial pellicle composed of pink colonies with white aerial mycelium; moderate, flocculent sediment.

Glucose broth: Small sediment of fine flocculi; later pellicle composed of small pink colonies; superficial skin entire and salmon-colored in 16 days.

Synthetic glycerol solution: Round, pink, disc-like colonies on surface and tenuous, white, wispy growth in suspension and sediment; after 20 days, surface colonies bearing white aerial mycelium extending 2 cm up tube.

Synthetic sucrose solution: Minute, white colonies in suspension and sediment in 3 days; thin, dust-like pellicle in 10 days; some surface colonies with white aerial mycelium in 17 days.

Milk: Red surface skin; solid coagulum.

Litmus milk: Red surface growth; no change in liquid; after 4 weeks, liquid decolorized, opaque.

Potato plug: Abundant growth; small colonies, mostly confluent, entirely covered with pale pink aerial mycelium; growth becomes membranous, considerably buckled; later superficial colonies with pink aerial mycelium on liquid at base of tube; bottom growth of round white colonies.

Starch not hydrolyzed.

Source: Isolated from lesions in goats.

Habitat: Found in infections of goats so far as known.

8. Nocardia pretoriana Pijper and Pullinger, 1927. (Jour. Trop. Med. and Hyg., *30*, 1927, 153.)

pre.to.ri.a'na. M.L. adj. *pretorianus* pertaining to Pretoria; named for Pretoria, South Africa.

Description taken from Erikson (Med. Res. Council Spec. Rept. Ser. 203, 1935, 30).

Minute, flat colonies are formed consisting of angularly branched filaments and bearing a few short, straight aerial hyphae; later the growth becomes spreading and extensive, the slipping of the branches is well marked and the aerial hyphae are divided into cylindrical conidia. Slightly acid-fast.

Gelatin: A few, colorless flakes. No liquefaction.

Glucose agar: Pale buff, umbilicated and piled up colonies.

Glycerol agar: Piled up pink mass; very scant, white aerial mycelium at margin.

Ca-agar: Yellowish, wrinkled, coherent growth with white aerial mycelium on apices and at margin.

Coon's agar: Colorless, mostly submerged growth; scant white aerial mycelium.

Dorset's egg medium: A few, round, colorless colonies in 3 days; after 3 weeks, irregular, raised, pink mass; warted appearance; moderate degree of liquefaction.

Serum agar: Raised, convoluted, slightly pinkish growth.

Inspissated serum: No growth.

Broth: Moderate quantity of flakes and dust-like surface growth.

Synthetic sucrose solution: A few colorless flakes on the surface; lesser bottom growth.

Milk: Yellowish surface growth; solid coagulum in one month; later, partly digested, pale pink growth up the wall of the tube.

Litmus milk: Colorless surface growth; liquid blue; becomes hydrolyzed and decolorized.

Potato plug: Small, raised, pale pink colonies with white aerial mycelium; after 2 months, plug and liquid discolored, growth dull buff, dry and convoluted at base, round and zonate at top of slant, white aerial mycelium, surface and bottom growth on liquid.

Source: Isolated from a case of mycetoma of the chest wall in a South African native.

Habitat: Found in human infections so far as known.

9. Nocardia vaccinii Demaree and Smith, 1952. (*Actinomyces sp.* Demaree, Phytopath., *37*, 1947, 438; Demaree and Smith, Phytopath., *42*, 1952, 249.)

vac.cin'i.i. M.L. noun *Vaccinium* generic name of the blueberry; M.L. gen.noun *vaccinii* of *Vaccinium*.

Rods and filaments, 0.4 to 0.8 micron in diameter, granular when stained, eventually breaking up into bacillary forms. A few cells are acid-fast. Presence of fat was demonstrated by staining with Sudan black B.

Gelatin: Dry, ribbon growth; no hydrolysis.

Agar: Poor, slow, granular, gray growth which is sometimes pinkish in old cultures.

Synthetic agar: Scant, gray growth.

Starch agar: Dry, ribbon, pinkish to orange growth.

Potato-yeast-mannitol agar: Abundant, fluffy, gray to orange growth.

Milk: Dry, raised, gray growth with orange spots. Casein not hydrolyzed.

Potato: Slow, spreading, raised, gray growth.

On a basal agar with ammonia as a source of nitrogen, acid was produced from glucose, sucrose, glycerol and mannitol; reactions variable with arabinose and xylose; no growth on lactose or sorbitol.

Starch is hydrolyzed.

Citrates utilized to a limited extent.

Paraffin is utilized.

Nitrites slowly produced from nitrates.

Optimum temperature, between 25° and 28° C.; inhibited at 32° C.; no growth or very scant growth at 37° C.

Antagonistic properties: None.

Distinctive characters: Resembles *Nocardia minima* but differs from it in the following respects: utilizes glycerol and mannitol and sometimes arabinose and xylose; reduces nitrates to nitrites; utilizes citrates and causes formation of bud-proliferating galls on blueberry plants.

Source: Original isolate, BG 19, came from a bud-proliferating gall on a blueberry plant.

Habitat: Found on blueberry plants so far as known.

10. Nocardia pulmonalis (Burnett, 1910) Waksman and Henrici, 1948. (*Actinomyces pulmonalis* Burnett, Ann. Rept. N. Y State Vet. Coll., 1909–1910, 167; Waksman and Henrici, in Manual, 6th ed., 1948, 901.)

pul.mo.na'lis. L. noun *pulmo* the lung; L. gen.noun *pulmonis* of the lung; M.L. adj. *pulmonalis* pertaining to the lung.

Gram-positive mycelium breaking up readily into oval-shaped conidia. Acid-fast, especially in early stages of growth.

Gelatin: Small, whitish, spherical colonies, edges of colony becoming chalky white. Limited liquefaction.

Agar: Moist, raised growth in the form of small, spherical colonies.

Glucose agar: Dull, whitish, convoluted growth.

Broth: Delicate, translucent film on surface, becoming corrugated with some whitish, spherical colonies in medium.

Milk: Colonies on the surface of the medium; milk is coagulated in a few days, later digested.

Potato: Luxuriant growth in the form of small, translucent, round colonies which become lemon-yellow; later, growth becomes convoluted or folded with chalky white aerial mycelium, color of plug brownish.

Non-pathogenic for rabbits or guinea pigs.

Aerobic.

Source: Isolated from the lungs of a cow.

Habitat: Found in bovine infections so far as known.

11. Nocardia paraffinae (Jensen, 1931) Waksman and Henrici, 1948. (*Proactinomyces paraffinae* Jensen, Proc. Linn. Soc. New So. Wales, *56*, 1931, 362; Waksman and Henrici, in Manual, 6th ed., 1948, 901; also see Erikson, Jour. Gen. Microbiol., *3*, 1949, 366.)

pa.raf.fi'nae. M.L. noun *paraffina* paraffin; M.L. gen.noun *paraffinae* of paraffin.

In agar media the organism initially forms an extensive mycelium of long, richly-branching hyphae, 0.4 to 0.5 micron in diameter. After 5 to 6 days at room temperature, numerous end-branches swell to about double thickness, become more refractive, exhibit fine incisions along their external contours and divide into ovoid, spore-like elements, 0.8 to 1.0 by 1.2 to 1.5 microns. This process of division starts at the tips of the swollen branches and proceeds basipetally until most of the hyphae appear divided. Primary septa have not been seen in the hyphae. A similar process of division takes place in liquid media, where also the filaments often fall into fragments of variable length. The spore-like elements, but not the undivided filaments, are markedly acid-fast. Acid-fastness is observed in certain stages, notably in the early stages of growth and in the coccus forms (Erikson, *loc. cit.*). The aerial mycelium consists of rather short, straight, not very much branched hyphae, 0.4 to 0.6 micron in diameter, which never show any differentiation into spores.

Gelatin: No liquefaction.

Sucrose agar: Very scant growth. Thin, colorless veil, sometimes with a trace of white aerial mycelium.

Glucose agar: Fair growth. Vegetative mycelium flat, growing into medium; pale ochre-yellow to orange, with raised outgrowths on the surface. Growth of a crumbly consistency. Scant, white, aerial mycelium.

Nutrient agar: Slow but good growth. Vegetative mycelium superficial, somewhat raised, ochre-yellow, hard, but with a loose, smeary surface. Aerial mycelium scant, small white tufts. No pigment.

Liquid media (milk, broth, synthetic solutions): Small, round granules of various yellow to orange colors, firm, but can be crushed into a homogeneous smear. In old broth cultures a thick, hard, orange to brownish surface pellicle is formed.

Milk: No coagulation or digestion.

Potato: Fair growth. Vegetative mycelium granulated, first pale-yellow, later deep ochre-yellow to orange. Scant, white, aerial mycelium. No diffusible pigment.

Sucrose not inverted.

Starch not hydrolyzed.

Cellulose not decomposed.

Nitrites not produced from nitrates.

Final reaction in glucose NH₄Cl solution, between pH 4.6 and 4.4.

All strains show a marked power of utilizing paraffin wax as a source of energy.

Source: Isolated from a soil from Rothamsted, England.

Habitat: Soil.

12. Nocardia minima (Jensen, 1931) Waksman and Henrici, 1948. (*Proactinomyces minimus* Jensen, Proc. Linn. Soc. New So. Wales, *56*, 1931, 365; Waksman and Henrici, in Manual, 6th ed., 1948, 902.)

mi′ni.ma. L. sup.adj. *minimus* least, very small.

Filaments and rods, 0.4 to 0.6 by 2.0 to 10.0 microns. In older cultures mostly short rods, frequently V, Y, swollen forms or cocci. Irregularly stained with ordinary dyes, generally show bars and bands. Generally a few cells from cultures are acid-fast, most are not acid-fast. Gram-positive.

Gelatin stab: Filiform, granulated, cream-colored growth. No liquefaction.

Agar: Slow growth, raised, folded, with finely myeloid margins. At first colorless, after 6 to 8 weeks flesh-pink or coral-pink.

Potato: Growth slow, after 6 to 8 weeks abundant, spreading, much raised, finely wrinkled, coral-pink.

Paraffin is utilized.

Optimum temperature, between 22° and 25° C.

Distinctive characters: Closely resembles *Nocardia corallina* but differs in the much slower growth and the smaller size of the cells.

Source: Isolated from soil in Australia.

Habitat: Soil.

13. Nocardia corallina (Bergey et al., 1923) Waksman and Henrici, 1948. (*Bacillus mycoides corallinus* Hefferan, Cent. f. Bakt., II Abt., *11*, 1904, 459; *Serratia corallina* Bergey et al., Manual, 1st ed., 1923, 93; *Mycobacterium agreste* Gray and Thornton, Cent. f. Bakt., II Abt., *73*, 1928, 84; *Proactinomyces agrestis* Jensen, Proc. Linn. Soc. New So. Wales, *56*, 1931, 345; *Proactinomyces corallinus* Jensen, *ibid.*, *57*, 1932, 364; Waksman and Henrici, in Manual, 6th ed., 1948, 902.)

co.ral.li′na. L. adj. *corallinus* coral-red.

Description taken from Gray and Thornton (*op. cit.*, 1928, 84), Jensen (*op. cit.*, 1931, 345) and Bynoe (Thesis, McGill University, Montreal, 1931).

Branching rods, generally curved, 1.0 to 1.5 by 3.0 to 10.0 microns. In older cultures generally shorter rods and cocci. Nonmotile. Not acid-fast. Gram-positive.

Gelatin colonies: Round, convex, smooth, pink, shining; edge filamentous. Deep colonies: Burrs.

Gelatin stab: Nailhead; line of stab arborescent. No liquefaction.

Agar colonies: Round, convex or umbonate, smooth, pink, shining or matte; border lighter; edge filamentous or with arborescent projections. Deep colonies: Burrs or lens-shaped, with arborescent projections. In their very early stages, colonies consist of branching, filamentous rods. As the colony grows, the cells in the interior break up into short rods and cocci which eventually form the mass of the colony. Cells on the outside remain filamentous, giving the colony a burr-like appearance and often forming long arborescent processes.

Agar slant: Filiform, convex, smooth, pink, shining or matte growth; arborescent or with projections from undulate border.

Litmus milk: Alkaline. Reddish pellicle.

Glycerol potato: Filiform, raised, dry, wrinkled, yellowish brown to coral-red.

Broth: Usually turbid. Pink scum.

Dorset's egg medium: Filiform, raised, dry, wrinkled, orange growth.

Loeffler's medium: Similar to growth on Dorset's egg medium, but pink.

Acid from glycerol and glucose by some strains. No acid or gas from sucrose, maltose or lactose.

Phenol and m-cresol are utilized. Some strains utilize naphthalene (Gray and Thornton). Some strains utilize phenol or m-cresol (Jensen).

Nitrites produced from nitrates.

Optimum temperature, between 22° and 25° C.

Optimum pH, between 6.8 and 8.0.

Distinctive characters: Soil organism forming *Mycobacterium*-like colonies after 2 to 4 days on simple media; pale pink chromogenesis; nailhead growth in gelatin stab; branching rods and short filaments.

Source: Seventy-four strains were isolated from soils in Great Britain and Australia.

Habitat: Soil.

14. Nocardia globerula (Gray, 1928) Waksman and Henrici, 1948. (*Mycobacterium globerulum* Gray, Proc. Roy. Soc. London, B, *102*, 1928, 265; *Proactinomyces globerulus* Reed, in Manual, 5th ed., 1939, 838; Waksman and Henrici, in Manual, 6th ed., 1948, 903.)

glo.be′ru.la. L. noun *globus* a globe; M.L. dim.adj. *globerulus* globular.

Original description supplemented by material taken from Bynoe (Thesis, McGill University, Montreal, 1931).

Curved rods and filaments, 1 by 2 to 9 microns, with many coccoid cells, especially in old cultures. Rods and filaments are frequently irregularly swollen. Capsules may be present. Not acid-fast. Gram-positive.

Gelatin: After 19 days, surface colonies irregularly round, 1 to 2 mm in diameter, convex, light buff, smooth, shining; edge entire. Deep colonies: Round, with entire edge.

Gelatin stab: After 8 days, nailhead, irregularly round, convex, pinkish white, smooth, shining growth; line of stab erose.

Agar: After 4 days surface colonies irregularly round, 3 to 5 mm in diameter, convex, white, smooth, shining; edge undulate, erose. After 7 days, more convex and of a watery appearance. Deep colonies: After 4 days, lens-shaped.

Agar slant: After 3 days, filiform, flat, watery; edge irregular.

Dorset's egg medium: After 2 weeks, spreading, raised, moist, orange-colored growth.

Loeffler's medium: Growth as on Dorset's egg medium, but salmon-colored.

Nutrient and peptone broth: Turbid with viscous suspension.

Litmus milk: Alkaline.

Glycerol potato: After 24 hours, filiform, moist, smooth, pale pink growth.

Indole not produced.

Indole agar: Blue crystals of indigotin formed.

No acid from glucose, lactose, maltose, sucrose or glycerol.

Phenol is utilized.

Nitrites not produced from nitrates.

Optimum temperature, between 25° and 28° C.

Optimum pH, between 6.8 and 7.6.

Distinctive characters: This organism resembles most closely *Nocardia corallina*. It is distinguished by producing a more watery type of surface growth, more nearly entire deep colonies and more particularly by the production of indigotin from indole.

Source: Isolated from soil in Great Britain.

Habitat: Presumably soil.

15. Nocardia salmonicolor (den Dooren de Jong, 1927) Waksman and Henrici, 1948. (*Mycobacterium salmonicolor* den Dooren de Jong, Cent. f. Bakt., II Abt., *71*, 1927, 216; *Proactinomyces salmonicolor* Jensen, Proc. Linn. Soc. New So. Wales, *57*, 1932, 368; Waksman and Henrici, in Manual, 6th ed., 1948, 904; also see Erikson, Jour. Gen. Microbiol., *3*, 1949, 364.)

sal.mo.ni′co.lor. L. noun *salmo* salmon; L. gen.noun *salmonis* of a salmon; M.L. adj. *salmonicolor* salmon-colored.

On glucose-asparagine-agar after 18 to 24 hrs., long branching rods are formed, 1.0 to 1.3 microns in diameter, with small refractive granules of aerial mycelium, sometimes stretching into quite long filaments; after 2 to 3 days small definite mycelia are present, and after 5 to 6 days these have largely divided into short rods and cocci; the colonies have the same burr-like appearance as those of *Nocardia corallina*. Many cells at the edge of the colonies show, after 3 to 4 days, club- or pear-shaped swellings, up to 2.5 to 3.0 microns in diameter; after 5 to 6 days, many of these swollen cells are seen to germinate with the formation of two more slender sprouts. On some media a few short, undivided aerial hyphae appear which may actually form a thin white frosting over the pink growth. Acid-fastness is found among the earlier stages of growth in some of the strains on some media.

Gelatin: At 20° to 22° C., scant, arborescent growth in stab; small, wrinkled orange, surface colony. No liquefaction.

Glucose-asparagine-agar: Good growth, restricted, rather flat; edges lobate; surface warty, glistening, at first pale orange, later ochre-yellow; consistency crumbly. After 5 to 6 weeks the growth is paler with many small, round, raised, yellow, secondary colonies.

Agar: Rich, salmon-pink to yellow, soft growth.

Glucose-nutrient agar: Excellent growth, spreading, flat, dense; edges lobate; surface folded, glistening, yellow, gradually changing to deep orange-red.

Nutrient broth: Fair growth; thin pellicle; granular sediment, at first cream-colored, later red; broth clear at first, slightly turbid after 3 weeks.

Milk: Good growth; pellicle of small, cream-colored granules after 2 days; later a thick orange sediment. Not coagulated but appears slightly cleared after 5 weeks, the reaction becoming alkaline.

Potato. Good growth, raised, warty, crumbly, glistening, at first buff, changing to orange and finally to almost blood-red.

Indole not produced.

No acid from glucose or glycerol.

Sucrose not inverted, although it is readily utilized with sodium nitrate as a source of nitrogen.

Starch not hydrolyzed.

Paraffin readily utilized as a source of carbon.

Phenol not utilized.

Nitrites produced from nitrates.

Nitrate, ammonium salts, asparagine and peptone are utilized almost equally well with glucose as source of carbon, although the growth is most rapid with peptone.

No growth in oxygen-free atmosphere.

Relationships to other species: Closely related to *Nocardia corallina*.

Source: Isolated from soil from Rothamsted, England, by means of an ethylamine-enriched medium, at 37° C.

Habitat: Probably soil.

16. **Nocardia rubropertincta** (Hefferan, 1904) Waksman and Henrici, 1948. (Butterbacillus, Grassberger, Münch. med. Wochnschr., *46*, 1899, 343; *Bacillus rubropertinctus* Hefferan, Cent. f. Bakt., II Abt., *11*, 1904, 460; *Proactinomyces rubropertinctus* Reed, in Manual, 5th ed., 1939, 835; Waksman and Henrici, in Manual, 6th ed., 1948, 904.)

rub.ro.per.tinc'ta. L. adj. *ruber* red; L. prefix *per* very; L. part.adj. *tinctus* dyed, colored; M.L. adj. *rubropertinctus* heavily dyed red.

Original description supplemented by material taken from Hefferan (*op. cit.*, 1904, 460) and from Jensen (Proc. Linn. Soc. New So. Wales, *49*, 1934, 32).

Small rods, 0.3 to 0.9 by 1.5 to 3.0 microns. Cells in 18- to 24-hour agar culture in beautiful angular arrangement, after 2 to 3 days nearly coccoid, 0.6 by 0.8 micron. Tendency for branching on glycerol agar after 2 to 3 days, but branching does not occur commonly though granules of aerial mycelium are sometimes seen (Jensen). Nonmotile. Not acid-fast (Grassberger). Acid-fast (Hefferan). Variable (Jensen). Gram-positive.

Gelatin colonies: Irregular with crenate margin and folded surface. Coral-red.

Gelatin stab: Surface growth like the colonies. Growth in stab at first thin, then granular to arborescent with chromogenesis. No liquefaction.

Agar colonies: Small, granular, becoming pink to red depending on composition of agar.

Agar slant: Dry, lustreless (R) to glistening (S), pink to vermilion-red.

Broth: Faint, uniform turbidity with salmon-pink pellicle (in scales) which is renewed on surface as it settles to form a red sediment (Hefferan, Jensen).

Litmus milk: Thick, fragile, dull coral-red surface scales and sediment. Unchanged (Hefferan) to alkaline and somewhat viscid after 3 to 4 weeks (Jensen).

Potato: Slow but excellent intensive red growth becoming dull orange (Jensen).

Benzine, petroleum, paraffin oil and paraffin are utilized as sources of energy; no action on manganese dioxide (Söhngen, Cent. f. Bakt., II Abt., *40*, 1914, 554).

Nitrites not produced from nitrates; nitrates, ammonia and asparagine are almost as good sources of nitrogen as peptone (Jensen).

Aerobic to facultatively anaerobic.

Grows well between 20° and 37° C. (Jensen).

Optimum pH, between 6.8 and 7.2. Growth stops at pH 4.9.

Distinctive characters: *Mycobacterium*-like colonies with coral to vermilion-red chromogenesis on asparagine agar, potato, gelatin and other media; short rods, seldom forms filaments; generally not acid-fast.

Comments: Gordon (personal communication, 1954) reports that she finds that a culture isolated and identified by Ford (Textb. of Bact., 1927, 255) as this species is identical with *Nocardia corallina* Waksman and Henrici.

Source: Six cultures were isolated from butter (Grassberger). Several cultures were isolated from soil in Holland (Söhngen) and Australia (Jensen). Two cultures were isolated as contaminants in tuberculin flasks (Hagan and Breed, personal communications).

Habitat: Probably widely distributed in soil.

17. **Nocardia rubra** (Krassilnikov, 1938) Waksman and Henrici, 1948. (*Proactinomyces ruber* Krassilnikov, Bull. Acad. Sci., U.S.S.R., No. 1, 1938, 139; also see Krassilnikov, Guide to the Actinomycetes, Izd. Akad. Nauk, U.S.S.R., Moskau, 1941, 81; Waksman and Henrici, in Manual 6th, ed., 1948, 905.)

rub′ra. L. adj. *ruber* red.

Threads at first filamentous, developing into a unicellular mycelium; after a few days, frequent septa are produced and the mycelium breaks up into short, rod-shaped, and later coccoid elements. These grow into a mycelium on a fresh substrate. No aerial mycelium produced in nutrient media. Not acid-fast. Gram-positive.

Gelatin: No liquefaction.

Colonies usually rough; some are smooth, dry, powdery or of dough-like consistency. Part of mycelium grows into substrate. Colonies bright red. Pigment not dissolved into medium; weakly soluble in ether, alcohol and acetic acid; well soluble in chloroform; belongs to the carotenoids.

Agar: Poor growth.

Synthetic agar: Good, typical growth.

Broth: Sediment and surface ring; medium clear.

Milk: No change.

Potato: Good, typical growth.

Sucrose not inverted.

Starch not hydrolyzed.

Cellulose not attacked.

Readily assimilates fats, paraffin and, to a less extent, wax.

Nitrites not produced from nitrates.

Distinctive characters: Grows well in high salt concentrations (5 to 10 per cent NaCl).

Various strains of this organism may vary considerably from the type strain.

Source: Isolated from soil.

Habitat: Soil.

18. **Nocardia coeliaca** (Gray and Thornton, 1928) Waksman and Henrici, 1948. (*Mycobacterium coeliacum* Gray and Thornton, Cent. f. Bakt., II Abt., *73*, 1928, 88; *Proactinomyces coeliacus* Reed, in Manual, 5th ed., 1939, 836; Waksman and Henrici, in Manual, 6th ed., 1948, 906.)

coe.li′a.ca. Gr. adj. *coeliacus* suffering in the bowels; L. adj. *coeliacus* relating to the bowels.

Original description supplemented by material taken from Jensen (Proc. Linn. Soc. New So. Wales, *56*, 1931, 201).

Short, curved, uneven-sided rods, 0.8 by 5 microns with occasional filaments up to 10 to 12 microns long, frequently beaded, occasionally swollen or branched. Coccoid forms 0.8 to 1.2 microns in diameter are common, especially in older cultures. Stain readily. Not acid-fast or occasionally slightly acid-fast. Gram-positive.

Gelatin colonies: After 12 days, irregular, raised, white, rugose, dull, entire. Deep colonies: Irregular, smooth or slightly broken.

Gelatin stab: Convoluted, buff-white to yellowish, dull; below surface the growth forms many irregular hollow lobes, giving a glistening appearance, to a depth of 3 to 4 mm.

Agar colonies: After 11 days, less than 1 mm in diameter, round or irregular, raised, white, resinous, irregular, burred. Deep colonies: Irregularly round or ovoid; edge slightly broken.

Agar slant: Filiform, convex, white, rugose, resinous, undulate growth.

Dorset's egg medium: Raised, smooth, moist, verrucose, buff-colored growth.

Loeffler's medium: After 10 days, slight growth, dry, granular, pale buff-colored.

Broth: Turbid.

Litmus milk: Slightly alkaline after 5 to 7 days.

Glycerol potato: After 2 days, dry, crumpled, orange, becoming brown after about 10 days.

No acid from glucose, lactose, sucrose or glycerol.

Phenol is utilized.

Nitrites not produced from nitrates.

Optimum temperature, between 22° and 25° C.

Optimum pH, between 7.6 and 8.0.

Distinctive characters: Differs from the previously described members of the genus in the absence of chromogenesis. Forms hollow lobes in deep gelatin cultures. Cells are rods, seldom filaments.

Source: Isolated from soil in Great Britain and Australia.

Habitat: Presumably soil.

19. **Nocardia transvalensis** Pijper and Pullinger, 1927. (Jour. Trop. Med. Hyg., *30*, 1927, 153.)

trans.va.len'sis. M.L. adj. *transvalensis* pertaining to the Transvaal; named for Transvaal, South Africa.

Description taken from Erikson (Med. Res. Council Spec. Rept. Ser. 203, 1935, 28).

Initial mycelium unicellular, but with the central branch frequently broader and showing dense, granular refractile contents; small colonies quickly covered with aerial mycelium, the straight aerial hyphae in some cases becoming clustered into irregular spikes; colorless drops are exuded and a pink coloration produced in the densest part of the growth on synthetic glycerol agar. Angular branching with division of the substratum filaments can be seen, the aerial hyphae also being irregularly segmented. Acid-fast.

Gelatin: Poor growth; there are a few irregular colorless flakes. No liquefaction.

Agar: No growth.

Glucose agar: Raised, granular, pink colonies with white aerial mycelium.

Glycerol agar: Small, pink, coiled masses with thin, white, aerial mycelium.

Potato agar: No growth.

Coon's agar: Colorless growth with liberal, white, aerial mycelium.

Dorset's egg medium: Small, irregularly raised and coiled dull pink mass.

Serum agar: Very poor growth.

Inspissated serum: Scant, colorless, flaky growth; later a minute tuft of pale pink, aerial mycelium.

Broth: Moderate, flaky growth.

Synthetic sucrose solution: Poor growth, a few flakes on the surface and a few at the bottom.

Milk: No change.

Potato plug: Dry, raised, convoluted, pink growth with white aerial mycelium in one month; dull, pink, brittle surface colonies with paler aerial mycelium floating coherently on liquid at base in 2 months.

Starch not hydrolyzed.

Source: Isolated from a case of mycetoma of the foot in South Africa.

Habitat: Found in human infections so far as known.

20. **Nocardia mesenterica** (Orla-Jensen, 1919) Waksman and Henrici, 1948. (*Microbacterium mesentericum* Orla-Jensen, The Lactic Acid Bacteria, 1919, 181; *Proactinomyces mesentericus* Jensen, Proc. Linnean Soc. New So. Wales, *57*, 1932, 373; Waksman and Henrici, in Manual, 6th ed., 1948, 907.)

me.sen.te'ri.ca. Gr.noun *mesenterium* the mesentery; M.L. adj. *mesentericus* pertaining to the mesentery.

Extensive mycelium composed of richly branching hyphae of a somewhat variable diameter, 0.4 to 0.8 micron; no aerial hyphae are seen. With increasing age the hyphae divide into fragments of varying size and shape, partly diphtheroid rods, but no real cocci. There is, particularly in richer media, a tendency to form large, swollen, fusiform to almost spherical cells, up to 3.5 microns in diameter. These may stain intensely with carbol fuchsin; when transferred to fresh media, they germinate and produce a new mycelium.

Gelatin: Good growth; finely arborescent, cream-colored growth in the stab; raised, folded, pale-yellow, surface colony. No liquefaction.

Glucose-asparagine-agar: Fair growth, narrow, raised, granular, very pale yellow, glistening; condensation water clear, with small granules. At 30° C. there is only scant growth consisting of small, irregular, white granules growing deeply down into the agar.

Glucose-nutrient-agar: Good growth, restricted, with undulate edges, surface with high transverse folds, cream-colored; the consistency is firm and cartilaginous after 2 days, later looser and more brittle. Growth at 28° to 30° C. rather scant; smooth, soft, glistening; cream-colored smear.

Sabouraud's agar: Excellent growth, spreading, at first flat and smooth, pale straw-yellow, perfectly hard and cartilaginous, later raised and strongly folded, of a loose, curd-like consistency, bright lemon-yellow. Growth at 28° to 30° C. only fair, restricted, folded, cream-colored, soon becoming soft and smeary.

Broth: Good growth; voluminous, flaky, whitish sediment; broth clear.

Potato: Scant growth; restricted, soft, cream-colored smear.

Milk: At 28° to 30° C., small cream-colored granules along the tube; the milk undergoes no visible changes within 4 weeks. No proteolytic action.

Indole not produced.

Sucrose is inverted.

Starch is hydrolyzed.

Cellulose not decomposed.

Nitrites produced from nitrates.

No growth in oxygen-free atmosphere.

Nitrogen is utilized as sodium nitrate, ammonium phosphate and asparagine, although these are inferior to peptone as sources of nitrogen.

Source: Isolated from fermented beets.

Habitat: Found in fermented vegetable materials.

21. **Nocardia albicans** (Krassilnikov, 1941) Waksman, 1953. (*Proactinomyces albicans* Krassilnikov, Guide to the Actinomycetes, Izd. Akad. Nauk, U.S.S.R., Moskau, 1941, 71; Waksman, in Waksman and Lechevalier, Actinomycetes and Their Antibiotics, Baltimore, 1953, 146.)

al'bi.cans. L. part.adj. *albicans* white-making.

On solid media the hyphae break up into rod-shaped cells 0.6 to 0.7 by 12 to 25, sometimes up to 50, microns. Cells straight or slightly curved and branching. No aerial mycelium observed except surface layer of sporophores, which produce a velvety appearance. Multiplication is by fission, seldom by budding. Gram-positive.

Gelatin: No liquefaction.

Agar colonies: Smooth, shiny; good growth.

Broth: Poor growth; faintly turbid; settles on bottom and leaves a surface ring. No true mycelium produced. Cells rod-shaped, 5 to 10, seldom 15 to 20, microns.

Milk: No change.

Sucrose inverted.

Starch hydrolyzed.

No growth on cellulose.

Utilizes glycerol well but not paraffin.

Nitrites not produced from nitrates.

Nitrate utilized as a source of nitrogen.

Source: Isolated from soil.

Habitat: Soil.

22. **Nocardia flava** (Krassilnikov, 1938) Waksman and Henrici, 1948. (*Proactinomyces flavus* Krassilnikov, Bull. Acad. Sci. U.S.S.R., No. 1, 1938, 139; Waksman and Henrici, in Manual, 6th ed., 1948, 908.)

fla'va. L. adj. *flavus* yellow.

Cells at first filamentous, 0.7 to 0.8 micron in diameter; after 2 to 3 days, cells broken into long rods and then into cocci 0.7 micron in diameter. No spores, although some strains form chlamydospores. Cell multiplication is by fission, cross-wall formation and rarely by budding. Not acid-fast. Gram-positive.

Gelatin: No liquefaction.

Agar colonies: Pigment bright yellow or gold-colored on synthetic media, dirty yellow on meat peptone media. Pigment not soluble in medium. Surface of colony somewhat shiny or rough and folded, of a dough-like consistency.

Synthetic agar colonies: Bright yellow or gold.

Meat peptone media: Dirty yellow pigmentation.

Milk: No peptonization or coagulation.

Sucrose weakly inverted.

Starch is hydrolyzed.

Does not grow on paraffin or wax but produces weak growth on fat.

Source: Isolated from soil.

Habitat: Soil; not common.

23. Nocardia viridis (Krassilnikov, 1938) Waksman and Henrici, 1948. (*Proactinomyces viridis* Krassilnikov, Bull. Acad. Sci. U.S.S.R., No. 1, 1938, 139; Waksman and Henrici, in Manual, 6th ed., 1948, 908.)

vi'ri.dis. L. adj. *viridis* green.

Mycelial cells often branching, 0.7 to 0.8 micron in diameter with cross-wall; after 5 to 7 days the cells break up into rods 5 to 15 microns long. Cocci not observed. Cells multiply by fission, seldom by budding. Spores not formed. Not acid-fast. Cells Gram-positive.

Gelatin: No liquefaction.

Colonies colored dark green. Pigment not soluble in medium, in water or in organic solvents. Surface of colony somewhat shiny. On potato, rough, much folded, broken up into small colonies.

Milk: No peptonization or coagulation.

Sucrose readily inverted.

Starch weakly hydrolyzed.

Grows well on fats and paraffin and less on wax.

Source: Isolated from soil.

Habitat: Soil.

24. Nocardia citrea (Krassilnikov, 1938) Waksman and Henrici, 1948. (*Proactinomyces citreus* Krassilnikov, Bull. Acad. Sci. U.S.S.R., No. 1, 1938, 139; Waksman and Henrici, in Manual, 6th ed., 1948, 908.)

cit're.a. L. adj. *citreus* of or pertaining to the citrus tree; M.L. adj. *citreus* lemon-yellow.

Mycelium in young cultures consists of very fine threads, 0.3 to 0.5 micron in diameter. After several days the cells break up into short rods, 0.5 by 1.5 to 5.0 microns, and into cocci, 0.3 to 0.5 micron in diameter. Multiplies by fission and bud formation; spores not formed. Not acid-fast.

Gelatin: Liquefaction.

Colonies: Yellow-green, usually rough and folded.

Milk: Coagulation and peptonization.

Sucrose is inverted.

Starch is hydrolyzed.

Weak growth on fat. No growth on paraffin or wax.

Source: Isolated from soil and water.

Habitat: Soil.

25. Nocardia madurae (Vincent, 1894) Blanchard, 1896. (*Streptothrix madurae* Vincent, Ann. Inst. Past., *8*, 1894, 129; Blanchard, in Bouchard, Traité Path. Gén., *2*, 1896, 868.)

ma'du.rae. M.L. gen.noun *madurae* of Madura; named for Madura, India.

In tissues, growth in form of granules consisting of radiating actinomycosis. In cultures, initial branched mycelium fragmenting into rod-shaped and coccoid bodies. No aerial mycelium or spores. Not acid-fast.

Gelatin: Growth scant, whitish; no liquefaction.

Gelatin colonies: Round, glistening, at first white, then buff to rose or crimson. Pigment production is irregular and unpredictable. Occasionally a red, soluble pigment is produced. Growth eventually wrinkled. No aerial mycelium.

Broth: Growth occurs as a floccular sediment.

Milk: No change or slight, slow peptonization.

Potato: Wrinkled, friable growth; buff-colored, sometimes red.

Diastatic action questionable.

Not pathogenic for the usual laboratory animals; pathogenic for monkeys (Musgrave and Clegg, Philippine Jour. Sci., Ser. B., Med. Sci., *3*, 1908, 470).

Source: Isolated from a case of Madura foot.

Habitat: Cause of some cases of Madura foot.

26. Nocardia nigra (Krassilnikov, 1941) Waksman, 1953. (*Proactinomyces niger* Krassilnikov, Guide to the Actinomycetes, Izd. Akad. Nauk, U.S.S.R., Moskau, 1941, 89; Waksman, in Waksman and Lechevalier, Actinomycetes and Their Antibiotics, Baltimore, 1953, 149; not *Nocardia nigra* Castellani and Chalmers, Man. Trop. Med., 3rd ed., 1919, 1062.)

nig'ra. L. adj. *niger* black.

Colonies rough, folded, shiny, of dough-like consistency. Growth at first colorless or brownish, gradually becoming darker and, after 10 to 15 days, dark brown and even black. Pigment, similar to melanin, not soluble in the medium. Hyphae are thread-like, breaking up into rods, 0.7 by 2.0 to 10.0 microns, and cocci, 0.6 to 0.8 micron. Aerial mycelium not formed.

Gelatin: No growth or liquefaction.

Agar: Poor growth.

Synthetic agar: Poor growth. Many cells are swollen to 3.0 microns in diameter.

Broth: Small sediment produced. Medium clear.

Milk: No change.

Potato: Good growth.

Cellulose: No growth.

Source: Isolated from soil.

Habitat: Soil. Rarely found. Growth rapidly disappears on continued cultivation.

27. Nocardia lutea Christopherson and Archibald, 1918. (Lancet, *2*, 1918, 847).

lu'te.a. L. adj. *luteus* yellow.

Description taken from Erikson (Med. Res. Council Spec. Rept. Ser. 203, 1935, 30).

Initial elements swollen and segmented, giving rise to irregular, spreading, polymorphous colonies composed of cells of all shapes and sizes with markedly granular contents; later more monomorphous, the filaments being arranged in angular apposition. Sometimes (e.g., on synthetic glycerol agar) the segments are so granular as to appear banded. On potato agar, small, filamentous colonies are formed with irregular, angular branching, and which bear a few isolated short straight aerial hyphae.

Gelatin: Pale pink wrinkled growth on wall of tube; colorless, punctiform colonies and stellate colonies are in the medium; no liquefaction.

Agar: Abundant, coherent, moist, pink, membranous growth with round, discrete colonies at margin; after 3 weeks, colorless, fringed margin, round confluent portion.

Glucose agar: Scant, reddish, smeary growth.

Glycerol agar: Yellowish pink, wrinkled membrane.

Potato agar: Coherent, pink, moist growth, centrally embedded with small, round, discrete colonies at margin.

Dorset's egg medium: Poor growth, dull pink, spreading.

Serum agar: Confluent, granular, pink membrane.

Broth: Pink flakes and surface growth.

Inspissated serum: Raised, convoluted, pink mass; becoming orange and much wrinkled with a scalloped margin.

Synthetic sucrose solution: Red granules and abundant, minute, colorless colonies at bottom; in 2 weeks a colorless, dust-like surface pellicle.

Glucose broth: Abundant, pinkish, flaky surface growth, breaking up easily and sinking to bottom.

Potato plug: Carrot-red, moist, thick, granular growth in bands, partly raised, and with discrete round colonies; sparse, colorless, very thin aerial mycelium at top of slant in 2 months.

Litmus milk: Orange-red surface and bottom growth; liquid blue.

Source: Isolated from actinomycosis of the lachrymal gland.

Habitat: Unknown.

28. Nocardia blackwellii (Erikson, 1935) Waksman and Henrici, 1948. (*Actinomyces blackwellii* Erikson, Med. Res. Council Spec. Rept. Ser. 203, 1935, 37; Waksman and Henrici, in Manual, 6th ed., 1948, 910.)

black.wel'li.i. M.L. gen.noun *blackwellii* of Blackwell; named for Blackwell.

Description taken from Erikson (*op. cit.*, 1935, 32).

Initial elements short and rod-like, growing out into sparsely branching longer forms; small, radiating colonies are produced with short, straight aerial mycelia; frequently large, round or ovoid cells are interposed in the irregularly segmented chains of cells, being sometimes isolated in company with 2 or 3 short filaments and sometimes terminal.

Gelatin: Few, colorless, minute colonies along line of inoculation; after 30 days abundant, colorless colonies to 10 mm below surface, larger pink-yellow surface colonies with white aerial mycelium; no liquefaction.

Agar: Confluent, wrinkled growth with

small, round, pinkish, discrete colonies at margin.

Glucose agar: Abundant, pale pink growth; small conical colonies, piled up, convoluted.

Glycerol agar: Extensive, granular, irregular, thin, pinkish growth; after 40 days, a few discrete colonies with depressed margins, center piled up, pink.

Serum agar: Smooth, cream, umbilicated colonies with submerged growth extending into medium in scallops 5 to 8 mm deep; a pale pink mass in 2 weeks.

Potato agar: Small, round, colorless colonies covered with white aerial mycelium; after 2 weeks colonies dull pink; submerged margins; few aerial spikes; moderate aerial mycelium at top of slant.

Broth: Flakes, later innumerable, minute colonies, some adhering to wall just above liquid level.

Synthetic sucrose solution: Delicate, round, white colonies; later abundant minute colonies in suspension; thick cream pellicle on surface and pink grains in sediment.

Milk: Heavy, convoluted, bright yellow surface pellicle; no coagulation.

Litmus milk: Yellow surface growth; milky sediment; liquid unchanged.

Carrot plug: Small, round, smooth, cream-colored, elevated colonies in 10 days; sparse, stiff, colorless aerial spikes in 16 days; abundantly piled up, convoluted, ochreous growth in 25 days.

Source: Isolated from the hock joint of a foal.

Habitat: Unknown.

29. Nocardia cuniculi Snijders, 1924. (Geneesk. Tijdsch. Ned. Ind., *64*, 1924, 47 and 75.)

cu.ni'cu.li. L. noun *cuniculus* a rabbit; L. gen.noun *cuniculi* of a rabbit.

Description taken from Erikson (Med. Res. Council Spec. Rept. Ser. 203, 1935, 31).

Large, swollen cells giving rise to ramifying filaments or to small chains of short, thick segments which branch out into more regular hyphae; sometimes the irregular elements are beset with spiny processes before giving rise to typical long branching filaments; later the picture becomes more monomorphous, and short, straight aerial hyphae are borne which presently exhibit irregular segmentation.

Gelatin: Few flakes. No liquefaction.

Agar: Small, round, elevated, cream-colored colonies, umbilicated and radially wrinkled.

Glucose agar: Minute, colorless colonies; becoming dull pink, partly confluent and piled up; few stiff pink aerial spikes.

Glycerol agar: Small, round, elevated, cream-colored colonies; margins depressed; becoming smooth, discrete, yellowish.

Dorset's egg medium: Scant, pinkish, smeary growth.

Serum agar: Small, raised, cream-colored colonies, becoming confluent and piled up.

Inspissated serum: Thick, colorless, ribbed membrane; no liquefaction.

Broth: Small and larger cream-colored, scale-like surface colonies; abundant, flocculent bottom growth.

Synthetic sucrose solution: Thin surface pellicle; small colorless flakes; minute particles at bottom; scant growth.

Milk: Heavy yellow growth attached to walls; solid coagulum in 1 month.

Litmus milk: Yellow surface growth; liquid unchanged.

Potato plug: Coral-pink, dry, granular growth covered to a considerable extent with white aerial mycelium, piled up in center, discrete colonies at margin, pink surface pellicle on liquid and colorless colonies at base.

Source: Isolated from infected rabbits.

Habitat: Unknown.

30. Nocardia rangoonensis (Erikson, 1935) Waksman and Henrici, 1948. (*Actinomyces rangoon* Erikson, Med. Res. Council Spec. Rept. Ser. 203, 1935, 37; Waksman and Henrici, in Manual, 6th ed., 1948, 911.)

ran.goo.nen'sis. M.L. adj. *rangoonensis* pertaining to Rangoon; named for Rangoon, Burma.

Swollen, round initial cells, giving rise to branching hyphae which segment and present slipping and angular arrangement; few short straight aerial hyphae, which later develop into a profusely branching, long waving aerial mycelium. Non-acid-fast.

Gelatin: Abundant, minute colonies in depths and larger cream-colored ones on surface with white aerial mycelium; brown pigment surrounding growth. No liquefaction.

Agar colones: Round, lobate, umbilicated, raised up, cream-colored to pale pink; later, medium discolored dark brown, colonies colorless.

Glucose agar: Convoluted, coherent, cream-colored growth; medium discolored. After 23 days, wrinkled, biscuit-colored growth; colorless margin; border white aerial mycelium; medium dark brown.

Glycerol agar: Dull, mealy, pink, wrinkled growth; scant white aerial mycelium at top; medium slightly discolored.

Coon's agar: Minute, colorless colonies in streaks.

Potato agar: Small, round, lemon-colored colonies, partly confluent, with white aerial mycelium; later medium discolored light brown; submerged growth greenish.

Dorset's egg medium: Extensive, colorless growth, pale pink aerial mycelium in center; later covered with a powdery, pinkish white aerial mycelium.

Serum agar colonies: Irregular, small, elevated, cream-colored, frequently umbilicated.

Inspissated serum: Poor growth; small piled up pink mass.

Broth: Abundant colorless growth; flocculent mass at bottom and pellicle at surface; medium slightly discolored.

Synthetic sucrose solution: Small, white colonies with pinkish tinge on surface; lesser bottom growth.

Milk: Coagulation; yellow surface ring; becoming partly peptonized; liquid discolored dark brown; brownish growth up side of tube.

Litmus milk: Colorless growth; liquid partly decolorized; coagulation; later partly digested.

Carrot plug: Small, round, colorless colonies; velvety white aerial mycelium; in 2 months, piled up, pink, granular mass with warted prominences; marginal zone white aerial mycelium and thin all-over central aerial mycelium.

Source: Isolated from a human pulmonary case of streptothricosis.

Habitat: Unknown.

31. **Nocardia caviae** Snijders, 1924. (Geneesk. Tijdschr. Ned. Ind., *64*, 1924, 47 and 75.)

ca'vi.ae. M.L. noun *Cavia* generic name of the cavy, or guinea pig.

Description taken from Erikson (Med. Res. Council Spec. Rept. Ser. 203, 1935, 32).

Initial segmentation, producing elements of approximately even diameter arranged in angular apposition, and later long profusely ramifying threads with strongly refractile protoplasm. Aerial mycelium straight and branching, the aerial hyphae with occasional coiled tips divided into cylindrical conidia.

Gelatin: A few colorless flakes. No liquefaction.

Glucose agar: Piled up, convoluted, cream-colored to pale pink growth; white aerial mycelium.

Glycerol agar: Scant growth.

Coon's agar: Colorless, scant growth, partly submerged, white aerial mycelium.

Potato agar: Colorless, spreading growth with dense white aerial mycelium.

Dorset's egg medium: Heavily corrugated pale pink growth with submerged margin and dense white aerial mycelium in center; after 3 weeks, colorless, transpired drops.

Serum agar: Pale pink, wrinkled growth, partly submerged; after 4 weeks, piled up with scant white aerial mycelium; medium discolored reddish brown.

Inspissated serum: Pale pink, raised growth; coiled, white aerial mycelium.

Broth: Cream-colored, wrinkled surface pellicle extending up wall and breaking easily; moderate bottom growth, flaky; medium discolored.

Synthetic sucrose solution: Round, white colonies in suspension and attached to one side of tube; pink surface colonies with white aerial mycelium.

Milk: Colorless surface growth; white aerial mycelium; coagulation.

Litmus milk: Liquid blue, surface growth; after 1 month, white aerial mycelium, colorless sediment, liquid still blue.

Potato plug: Small, colorless colonies;

white powdery aerial mycelium; later abundant, raised, pale pink, confluent growth, discolored plug; after 2 months, raised, buckled, pink colonies with white aerial mycelium floating on liquid at base.

Source: Isolated from infected guinea pigs in Sumatra.

Habitat: Unknown.

32. Nocardia actinomorpha (Gray and Thornton, 1928) Waksman and Henrici, 1948. (*Mycobacterium actinomorphum* Gray and Thornton, Cent. f. Bakt., II Abt., *73*, 1928, 88; *Proactinomyces actinomorphus* Jensen, Proc. Linn. Soc. New So. Wales, *56*, 1931, 363; Waksman and Henrici, in Manual, 6th ed., 1948, 912.)

ac.ti.no.mor'pha. Gr. noun *actis, actinis* a ray; Gr. noun *morphe* shape; M.L. adj. *actinomorphus* ray-shaped.

Original description supplemented by material taken from Jensen (*op. cit.*, 1931, 363) and Bynoe (Thesis, McGill University, Montreal, 1931).

Long branching filaments and rods, 0.5 to 0.8 by up to 10 microns. In older cultures rods 2 to 3 microns long generally predominate. On some media, extensively branching hyphae occur. Readily stained. Not acid-fast. Gram-positive.

Gelatin colonies: After 12 days, round, saucer-like, white, raised rim, edges burred. Deep colonies: Burrs. Liquefaction.

Gelatin stab: After 8 to 14 days, saccate liquefaction, 5 to 8 mm.

Agar colonies: After 11 days, round, 1 mm in diameter, convex, white, granular or resinous; long, arborescent processes from the edge. Deep colonies: Arborescent burrs; processes about equal to diameter of colony.

Agar slant: Filiform, raised to convex, white, rugose, dull growth; edge undulate, with strong tufted projections below surface.

Broth: Turbid or clear with white scum.

Dorset's egg medium: After 2 weeks, raised, dry, smooth, salmon-buff growth.

Loeffler's medium: After 2 days, smooth, moist, warty, salmon-colored growth.

Litmus milk: Alkaline after 5 to 7 days.

Glycerol potato: After 2 days, dry, wrinkled, pink to orange growth.

No acid from glucose, lactose, sucrose or glycerol.

Nitrites produced from nitrates.

Phenol and naphthalene are utilized.

Optimum temperature, between 25° and 30° C.

Optimum pH, between 7.8 and 8.5.

Distinctive characters: Differs from *Nocardia coeliaca* in saccate liquefaction of gelatin. Long rods and filaments.

Source: A few strains have been isolated from soil in Great Britain and Australia.

Habitat: Presumably soil.

33. Nocardia alba (Krassilnikov, 1938) Waksman, 1953. (*Proactinomyces albus* Krassilnikov, Bull. Acad. Sci., U.S.S.R., No. 1, 1938, 139; Waksman, in Waksman and Lechevalier, Actinomycetes and Their Antibiotics, Baltimore, 1953, 153.)

al'ba. L. adj. *albus* white.

Colonies white, never pigmented, of dough-like consistency; smooth or folded growth; shiny or pale. True substrate mycelium produced at first, then breaking up into short rods, 0.7 to 0.8 by 2.7 microns, later changing into a mass of coccus-like cells, 0.7 to 1.0 micron in diameter. Many cells are swollen, others form side buds. No aerial mycelium produced on nutrient media. Not acid-fast. Gram-positive.

Gelatin: Liquefaction.

Agar: Good growth.

Synthetic agar: Inorganic sources of nitrogen are used, and sugar, starch or organic acids serve as sources of carbon.

Milk: Coagulated and peptonized.

Sucrose inverted.

Starch rapidly hydrolyzed.

Cellulose: No growth.

Nitrites not produced from nitrates.

Comment: Krassilnikov (*op. cit.*, 1941, 73) recognizes several subspecies.

Source: Isolated from soil.

Habitat: Soil.

34. Nocardia flavescens (Jensen, 1931) Waksman and Henrici, 1948. (*Proactinomyces flavescens* Jensen, Proc. Linn. Soc. New So. Wales, *56*, 1931, 361; Waksman and Henrici, in Manual, 6th ed., 1948, 913.)

fla.ves'cens. L. part.adj. *flavescens* becoming gold-colored.

On media where a firm growth is produced, the vegetative mycelium appears as long, branched, non-septate hyphae, 0.4 to 0.6 micron in diameter. In other media, as on nutrient agar and potato, septa are formed, and the mycelium appears in preparations as fragments of very variable size, partly resembling highly branched mycobacteria. In several cases—for instance on nutrient agar at 28° to 30° C., in 5 to 6 weeks-old cultures in glucose broth and in glucose NH₄Cl solution—short elements assume swollen, fusiform to lemon-shaped forms. The aerial mycelium consists of fairly long hyphae of the same diameter as the vegetative hyphae, not very much branched, without spirals, often clinging together in wisps. A differentiation into spores is never visible by direct microscopic examination. Neither is this the case in stained preparations: here the aerial hyphae break up into fragments of quite variable length, from 1.2 to 1.5 up to 10 to 12 microns, showing an irregular, granulated staining.

Gelatin: Slow liquefaction.

Sucrose agar: Good growth. Vegetative mycelium superficially spreading, much raised and wrinkled, cracking, white to cream-colored, of a dry, but loose and crumbly, consistency. Aerial mycelium scant, thin, white. Faint yellow, soluble pigment after 2 to 3 weeks.

Glucose agar: Good growth. Vegetative mycelium superficial, wrinkled, honey-yellow, of a hard and cartilaginous consistency. Aerial mycelium thin, smooth, white. Yellow, soluble pigment.

Nutrient agar: Good growth. Vegetative mycelium raised and much wrinkled, first dirty cream-colored, later dark yellowish gray, of a soft, moist, curd-like consistency. No aerial mycelium. No pigment.

Glucose broth: Rather scant growth. Granulated, yellowish sediment; no surface growth. Broth clear. No pigment. No acidity.

Milk: Coagulated and slowly redissolved with acid reaction.

Potato: Good to excellent growth. Vegetative mycelium much raised and wrinkled, first cream-colored, later yellowish brown, soft and smeary. No aerial mycelium; no pigment.

Sucrose is inverted.

Starch is hydrolyzed.

Cellulose not decomposed.

Nitrates are reduced slightly or not at all with various sources of energy.

Final reaction in glucose-NH₄Cl solution, pH 3.9 to 3.6.

No growth under anaerobic conditions.

Source: Isolated from soil.

Habitat: Soil.

35. **Nocardia gibsonii** (Erikson, 1935) Waksman, 1953. (*Actinomyces gibsonii* Erikson, Med. Res. Council Spec. Rept. Ser. 203, 1935, 36; *Streptomyces gibsonii* Waksman and Henrici, in Manual, 6th ed., 1948, 963; Waksman, in Waksman and Lechevalier, Actinomycetes and Their Antibiotics, Baltimore, 1953, 155.)

gib.so'ni.i. M.L. gen.noun *gibsonii* of Gibson; named for Prof. Gibson of Oxford.

Young, growing mycelium branches profusely at short intervals; later grows out into long, frequently wavy filaments; twisted hyphae also seen on water agar. Power of producing aerial mycelium apparently lost.

Gelatin: Dull white flakes sinking as the medium liquefies; liquefaction complete in 12 days.

Agar: Small, cream-colored, depressed, partly confluent colonies, becoming an extensive, wrinkled, cream-colored skin.

Glucose agar: Cream-colored, wrinkled, membranous growth.

Potato agar: Wrinkled, glistening, membranous growth.

Serum agar: Small, moist, cream-colored colonies growing into medium.

Dorset's egg medium: Small, round, smooth, colorless colonies with conically elevated centers.

Inspissated serum: Innumerable colorless, pinpoint colonies with scant white aerial mycelium at top; after 8 days, a coherent wrinkled skin with brownish red discoloration at reverse, medium becoming transparent; completely liquefied, pigmented brown in 15 days.

Blood agar: Yellowish, confluent bands,

irregularly wrinkled, with small discrete colonies; clear hemolytic zone.

Broth: Sediment of flocculi; some round and fan-shaped colonies.

Synthetic sucrose solution: Very delicate, white flocculi.

Milk: Coagulated; partly peptonized.

Potato plug: No growth.

Starch not hydrolyzed.

Tyrosine agar: Negative reaction.

Source: Isolated from the spleen in a case of acholuric jaundice. Injected into a monkey from which it was then reisolated.

Habitat: Found in human infections so far as known.

36. Nocardia fructifera (Krassilnikov, 1941) Waksman, 1953. (*Proactinomyces fructiferi* (sic) Krassilnikov, Guide to the Actinomycetes, Izd. Akad. Nauk, U.S.S.R., Moskau, 1941, 78; Waksman, in Waksman and Lechevalier, Actinomycetes and Their Antibiotics, Baltimore, 1953, 155.)

fruc.ti'fe.ra. L. part.adj. *fructiferus* fruit-bearing.

Mycelium septate, hyphae breaking up into rods and in some cultures into cocci. Aerial mycelium well developed, whitish to rose-colored. Sporophores long. Straight or weakly wavy, but not spiral-shaped. Oidiospores cylindrical, elongated, 0.7 by 1.5 microns. Not acid-fast. Gram-positive.

Colonies not compact, mostly dough-like in consistency, smooth or rough.

Gelatin: Slow liquefaction.

Agar: Aerial mycelium weakly developed or entirely absent.

Synthetic agar: Rose-colored to bright red and even red-orange growth. Pigment not soluble in medium.

Milk: Coagulated and weakly peptonized.

Sucrose is inverted.

Starch weakly hydrolyzed.

Cellulose: Poor growth.

Fats: Good growth.

Comment: This species is considered as a typical transition point between *Streptomyces ruber* and *Nocardia rubra* (Krassilnikov, *op. cit.*, 1941, 78).

Source: One strain was obtained as a mutant of *Nocardia rubra*. Another strain was changed, after 8 months of cultivation, into a typical *Streptomyces*.

Habitat: Unknown.

37. Nocardia africana Pijper and Pullinger, 1927. (Pijper and Pullinger, Jour. Trop. Med. and Hyg., *30*, 1927, 153; *Streptomyces africanus* Waksman and Henrici, in Manual, 6th ed., 1948, 959.)

af.ri.ca'na. L. adj. *africanus* pertaining to Africa.

Description taken from Erikson (Med. Res. Council Spec. Rept. Ser. 203, 1935, 18).

Unicellular, branching mycelium forming small, dense, pink colonies with short, straight, sparse, white aerial mycelium.

Gelatin: Irregular pink flakes. No liquefaction.

Agar: A few, flat, pink, discoid colonies.

Glucose agar: Minute, red, discrete, round colonies and piled up, paler pink mass with thin white aerial mycelium.

Glycerol agar: After 2 weeks, small, heaped-up, colorless masses with pink tinge around the colorless colonies; margin depressed; after 3 weeks, abundant, piled up, pale pink growth.

Ca-agar: After 1 week, small, round, colorless colonies with red centers; margins submerged; after 2 weeks, growth bright cherry-red, confluent, with colorless margin.

Dorset's egg medium: Small, colorless blister colonies, partly confluent; become wrinkled and depressed into medium; slight liquefaction.

Serum agar: Irregularly round, raised, wrinkled, colorless colonies; becoming dry, pink and flaky; later piled up, brownish, friable.

Inspissated serum: After one week, smooth, round, colorless colonies with submerged margin, in confluent patches pink and pitted into medium; after 2 weeks, medium broken up, slight liquefaction; after 3 weeks, liquid dried up, colonies umbilicated, raised, dry and friable.

Broth: Small pink colonies embedded in coherent flocculent mass.

Synthetic sucrose solution: Small pink granules in sediment after 1 week; colonies of medium size, coherent, after 3 weeks.

Potato agar: Bright red growth, small round colonies with colorless submerged margins and piled up patches with stiff, sparse, white aerial mycelium.

Litmus milk: Bright red surface growth; liquid unchanged after one month; liquid opaque reddish purple after 2 months; hydrolyzed, clear wine-red after 3 months.

Antagonistic properties: Positive.

Source: Isolated from a case of mycetoma of a foot in South Africa.

Habitat: Unknown.

38. **Nocardia pelletieri** (Laveran, 1906) Pinoy, 1912. (*Micrococcus pelletieri* Laveran, Compt. rend. Soc. Biol., Paris, *61*, 1906, 340; *Oospora pelletieri* Thiroux and Pelletier, Bull. Soc. path. exot., *5*, 1912, 588; Pinoy, in Thiroux and Pelletier, *ibid.*, 589; *Streptomyces pelletieri* Waksman and Henrici, in Manual, 6th ed., 1948, 960.)

pel.le.ti.e′ri. M.L. gen.noun *pelletieri* of Pelletier; named for M. Pelletier, the first to isolate this species.

Description taken from Erikson (Med. Res. Council Spec. Rept. Ser. 203, 1935, 21).

Mycelium composed of slender, straight and not very long filaments, forming small, dense, pink colonies with a few short, straight, isolated aerial branches.

Gelatin: Slight liquefaction; few pink flakes; later almost completely liquefied.

Agar: Minute, colorless colonies and piled-up, pale pink masses.

Glucose agar: Poor growth; a few minute pink colonies.

Glycerol agar: Poor growth; a few moist pink colonies.

Ca-agar: Colorless, small colonies; after 1 week, confluent skin, pink, buckled; medium discolored later.

Coon's agar: Poor growth, cream-colored with pink center, mostly submerged.

Potato agar: Colorless blister colonies; after 3 weeks, colonies larger, showing concentric zones, submerged margins and occasional zone or tuft of white aerial mycelium, pinkish coloration.

Dorset's egg medium: Abundant, wrinkled, pink skin with small discrete colonies at margin in six days; later surface rough, mealy; considerable liquefaction in 17 days.

Serum agar: Moist, cream-colored growth tending to be heaped up; discrete colonies at margin; becoming umbilicated.

Inspissated serum: Round, moist, colorless colonies.

Blood agar: At first a few pinhead, cream-colored colonies, no hemolysis; later colonies dense, button-shaped, with narrow fringed margin.

Broth: Small, minute, pink, clustered colonies.

Synthetic sucrose solution: Small, pink colonies in sediment; later minute colonies adhering to side of tube.

Milk: Soft curd; half-digested; peptonization complete in 20 days.

Litmus milk: Pink surface growth, semi-solid, no color change; after 20 days, coagulum cleared, liquid purple.

Potato plug: After one month growth sparse, yellowish pink, irregularly piled up, portions with scant white aerial mycelium; after 6 months abundant, highly piled-up, small, rounded pink masses; scant white aerial mycelium persistent.

Relationships to other species: Thiroux and Pelletier (Bull. Soc. path. exot., *5*, 1912, 585) considered that their cultures resembled *Nocardia madurae*, but they grew the organism only on Sabouraud's gelatin, on which it appeared in a constantly red, easily detachable form. *Nocardia indica* was regarded as identical by Pinoy, although in the original description by Laveran the organism was called *Micrococcus pelletieri*, owing to the fact that no mycelium was seen, merely coccoid bodies. *Nocardia genesii* Froes (Bull. Inst. Past., *29*, 1931, 1158) is described as closely allied, the distinction being founded upon the fact that the red grains were smaller in size and much more numerous, but no cultural details are given.

Source: Isolated from a case of crimson-grained mycetoma in Nigeria (E. C. Smith, Trans. R. Soc. Trop. Med. Hyg., *22*, 1928, 157).

Habitat: Unknown.

39. **Nocardia maculata** (Millard and Burr, 1926) Waksman and Henrici, 1948. (*Actinomyces maculatus* Millard and Burr, Ann· Appl. Biol., *13*, 1936, 580; *Proactinomyces maculatus* Umbreit, Jour. Bact., *38*, 1939, 84; Waksman and Henrici, in Manual, 6th ed., 1948, 913.)

ma.cu.la′ta. L. part.adj. *maculatus* spotted.

Filamentous organisms possessing a tough, shiny colony which is cartilaginous, rarely producing an aerial mycelium, though in certain strains it may occur frequently. Retains the mycelium form for long periods. Not acid-fast.

Gelatin: Liquefaction.

In the young colony an orange-yellow to orange-red, intercellular pigment is produced on all media, which may or may not change to black as the culture ages.

Milk: No digestion.

Starch is hydrolyzed.

Paraffin not utilized.

Source: Isolated from soil.

Habitat: Soil.

40. Nocardia rhodnii (Erikson, 1935) Waksman and Henrici, 1948. (*Actinomyces rhodnii* Erikson, Med. Res. Council Spec. Rept. Ser. 203, 1935, 37; Waksman and Henrici, in Manual, 6th ed., 1948, 914.)

rhod'ni.i. M.L. mas.n. *Rhodnius* generic name of an insect; M.L. gen.noun *rhodnii* of *Rhodnius*.

In early stages, the minute colonies are composed of hyphal segments arranged in angular apposition, the aerial mycelium being short and straight. Later the growth becomes extensive and spreading, made up partly of long, genuinely branching filaments and partly of short segments exhibiting slipping branching, each giving rise to aerial hyphae. After 2 weeks the angular branching is very marked, delicate spreading herring-bone patterns being formed.

Gelatin: Rapid liquefaction; pale pink colonies in superficial pellicle and sediment.

Coon's agar: Colorless, pinpoint colonies.

Czapek's agar: Minute, colorless, round colonies.

Glucose agar: Abundant, coral-pink, convoluted, piled-up growth.

Glycerol agar: Extensive growth, dull pink colonies round and umbilicated, becoming piled-up and deeper coral; later partly submerged.

Dorset's egg medium: Salmon-pink, granular membrane; later piled up.

Serum agar: Extensive, reddish, confluent mass, granular, tending to be piled up; the medium around the growth shows reddish coloration in 2 weeks.

Inspissated serum: Smooth, round, pale pink colonies, centrally depressed and irregularly coiled larger mass; no liquefaction.

Broth: Salmon-pink flakes in sediment and colonies on surface; after 2 weeks, abundant growth and discoloration of medium.

Glucose broth: Thin, pink, superficial pellicle, easily breaking up, and small flakes in sediment; after 2 weeks abundant growth extending up tube.

Synthetic sucrose solution: Colorless to pink colonies in superficial pellicle and minute, round, white colonies coherent in loosely branching mass in sediment.

Milk: Bright orange growth; medium unchanged.

Potato agar: Abundant, pink growth, piled up; scant stiff white aerial mycelium at top of slant.

Source: Isolated from the reduvid bug, *Rhodnius prolixus*.

Habitat: Presumably insects.

41. Nocardia gardneri (Waksman, 1942) Waksman and Henrici, 1948. (Actinomycete, Gardner and Chain, Brit. Jour. Exp. Path., *23*, 1942, 123; *Proactinomyces gardneri* Waksman, in Waksman, Horning, Welsch and Woodruff, Soil Sci., *54*, 1942, 289; Waksman and Henrici, in Manual, 6th ed., 1948, 914.)

gard'ne.ri. M.L. gen.noun *gardneri* of Gardner; named for Prof. A. D. Gardner, one of the two who first isolated this organism.

Branching mycelium. Gram-positive.

Gelatin: Cream-colored surface ring. Rapid liquefaction. Green to greenish brown soluble pigment gradually diffuses through the liquefied portion.

Nutrient agar: Cream-colored, elevated, lichenoid growth, soft, not leathery; no aerial mycelium; very faint brownish pigment.

Glucose agar: Brownish, lichenoid growth, with wide, cream-colored edge; white to grayish aerial mycelium gradually covering surface. Reverse of growth yellowish; no soluble pigment.

Glucose-asparagine agar: Aerial mycelium develops slowly.

Tryptone broth: Growth occurs as small pellets at the base of the flask; later, a thin surface pellicle appears which consists of a branching mycelium. Black pigment slowly produced.

Litmus milk: Unchanged.

Potato: Barnacle-like, brownish, spreading growth; no aerial mycelium. Medium brownish around growth.

Indole not produced.

No acid from glucose, lactose, maltose, mannitol, sucrose or dulcitol.

Good growth at 25° C. Slow growth at 37° C.

Distinctive character: Produces an antibiotic substance (proactinomycin) upon synthetic and organic media which is primarily active against various Gram-positive bacteria.

Source: Isolated as an air contaminant at Oxford, England.

Habitat: Unknown.

42. **Nocardia fordii** (Erikson, 1935) Waksman, 1953. (*Actinomyces fordii* Erikson, Med. Res. Council Spec. Rept. Ser. 203, 1935, 15 and 36; *Streptomyces fordii* Waksman and Henrici, in Manual, 6th ed., 1948, 958; Waksman, in Waksman and Lechevalier, Actinomycetes and Their Antibiotics, Baltimore, 1953, 159.)

for'di.i. M.L. gen.noun *fordii* of Ford; presumably named for the surgeon who first secured the culture.

Filaments of medium length, no spirals or markedly wavy branches. Short, straight, sparse aerial mycelium. Small ovoid conidia on potato agar and starch agar.

Gelatin: No visible growth, slight softening in 20 days; half-liquefied after 40 days.

Agar: Small, creamy golden, ring-shaped colonies and heaped-up patches, becoming golden brown in color and convoluted.

Glycerol agar: Extensive, golden brown, convoluted, thin layer.

Serum agar: Golden brown, ring-shaped and coiled smooth colonies; no liquefaction.

Ca-agar: Yellow, scale-like, closely adherent colonies; scattered white aerial mycelium.

Blood agar: Innumerable, small, yellowish, ring-shaped colonies; no hemolysis.

Broth: Few flakes at first; later abundant, coherent, puffball growth.

Synthetic sucrose solution: Moderate sediment of minute round white colonies.

Synthetic glycerol solution: Light white fluffy colonies, minute and in clusters.

Inspissated serum: Innumerable, colorless, pinpoint colonies; scant white aerial mycelium; after 15 days colonies large, hollow on reverse side; margin depressed; no liquefaction.

Dorset's egg medium: Minute, cream-colored, elevated colonies, becoming golden brown, raised, convoluted.

Milk: Coagulated; brownish surface ring.

Litmus milk: No change in reaction.

Potato plug: Yellowish growth in thin line, terminal portion tending to be piled up; scant white aerial mycelium at top of slant; after 12 days, growth abundant, golden brown, confluent, partly honeycombed, partly piled up.

Starch not hydrolyzed.

Tyrosine agar: Reaction negative.

Source: Isolated from a human spleen in a case of acholuric jaundice.

Habitat: Unknown.

43. **Nocardia kuroishi** Uesaka, 1952. (Jour. Antibiotics (Japanese), *5*, 1952, 75.)

ku.ro.i'shi. Etymology Japanese, meaning uncertain.

Mycelium gives a weak acid-fast reaction, but the separated cells, 0.8 by 1.3 microns, are not acid-fast.

Aerial mycelium: Abundant, branching hyphae slightly curved at first, later turning around each other; cells refractive. Granules soon become visible.

Gelatin: Yellowish brown growth sinking into medium. No aerial mycelium. Yellowish brown, soluble pigment. No liquefaction.

Synthetic glycerol agar: Thin, pale yellow growth, partly covered with punctiform, white aerial mycelia. Yellow pigment.

Agar: Wrinkled, grayish yellow colonies. No aerial mycelium. Faint, grayish brown, soluble pigment.

Glucose agar: Abundant growth, at first yellowish brown then reddish brown. Scant white aerial mycelium at margin of colonies. Red to wine-colored, soluble pigment.

Synthetic solution: White, minute colonies on surface. Medium becomes brown.

Glucose broth: Red colonies, forming a

pellicle. Abundant, flocculent sediment. Dark brown, soluble pigment.

Milk: No coagulation; slow liquefaction. Brown pigment.

Potato: Moderate growth, at first red or brownish red, later dark brown. Aerial mycelium grayish white. Dark brown pigment.

Lactose is an excellent source of carbon.

Starch is hydrolyzed.

Nitrites not produced from nitrates.

Antagonistic properties: Produces an antibiotic substance, neonocardin.

Source: Isolated from soil.

Habitat: Soil.

44. **Nocardia marina** (Krassilnikov, 1949) Waksman, *nom. nov.* (*Proactinomyces flavus* Humm and Shepard, Duke Univ. Marine Sta. Bull., *3*, 1946, 76; not *Proactinomyces flavus* Krassilnikov, Bull. Acad. Sci., U.S.S.R., No. 1, 1938, 139; *Proactinomyces citreus* subsp. *marinae* (sic) Krassilnikov, Guide to the Bacteria and Actinomycetes, Izd. Akad. Nauk, U.S.S.R., Moskau, 1949, 141.)

ma.ri'na. L. adj. *marinus* of the sea, marine.

Vegetative growth: Young colonies composed of slender rods and filaments of various lengths up to 5.0 microns or more, some of which are branched. Filaments 0.5 to 0.8 micron in diameter. Older colonies composed of coccoid elements only, about 0.6 micron in diameter, occurring singly or variously grouped. Non-motile. Not acid-fast. Gram-positive.

Gelatin: Liquefaction crateriform or napiform at first, becoming infundibuliform and, after ten days or more, stratiform. Usually complete after three or four weeks at 20° to 23° C.

Agar colonies: Bright lemon-yellow, flat or slightly raised, the margin growing outward just beneath the surface of the agar with center somewhat raised. Margin undulate or crenate. Older colonies exhibit characteristic division into segments. Thickly seeded colonies apparently antagonistic toward each other; their margins never grow together. Surface smooth, usually rather dull. Consistency thick-butyrous. No soluble pigments. Pungent, rather pleasant, fruity odor characteristically produced.

Agar slant: Filiform, flattened, lemon-yellow streak with undulate margin which usually spreads slowly just beneath the agar surface.

Broth: Turbid; no pellicle. Yellow ring sometimes formed. Broth may remain clear with yellow granular growth adherent to sides of tube.

Milk: Alkaline after a week or more. Peptonization; no coagulation.

Indole not produced but slowly utilized. Indigotin not produced from indole.

Hydrogen sulfide produced very slowly.

Acid from arabinose, rhamnose, xylose, galactose, glucose, fructose, mannose, cellobiose, lactose, maltose, sucrose, salicin, glycerol, mannitol and gum arabic. No acid from inulin, dulcitol, inositol, sorbitol, ethyl alcohol or ethylene glycol.

Acetic, butyric and lactic acids are utilized. Citric, gluconic, malic, malonic, maleic, oxalic, propionic, succinic, tartaric and iso-valeric acids are not utilized.

d-Arginine utilized as a source of both nitrogen and carbon. Aspartic acid, cystine, glycine, glutamic acid, l-leucine and tyrosine utilized only as nitrogen sources. dl-Alanine, creatine and dl-β-phenylalanine not utilized.

Acetylmethylcarbinol not produced.

Starch is hydrolyzed.

Cellulose, chitin and alginic acid are attacked.

Seaweed gels: Agar slowly digested. Colonies on agar containing added nitrate usually form a slight, narrow depression. On nutrient agar, agar digestion is not visible except with iodine test. Gelase field narrow, fading margin. Acid and reducing sugar produced from agar and from Irish moss gel. Gels from Agardhiella and Hypnea slowly utilized.

Nitrites not produced from nitrates.

Nitrite or ammonia utilized as nitrogen source. Ammonia produced from nitrite, nitrate, urea, asparagine and peptone (sparingly). Urea used as nitrogen source.

Catalase-positive.

Aerobic.

Optimum temperature, between 25° and 30° C.

Good growth in media prepared with distilled water and in all salinities through 6 per cent (sea salt), but slightly less vigorous in concentrations above 5 per cent. Pigmentation and morphological characteristics apparently the same at all salinities.

Source: Isolated frequently from intertidal marine sediments and beach sand in North Carolina and Florida.

Habitat: Found in marine sediments of the South Atlantic coast of the United States.

45. Nocardia atlantica (Humm and Shepard, 1946) Waksman, *comb. nov.* (*Proactinomyces atlanticus* Humm and Shepard, Duke Univ. Marine Sta. Bull., *3*, 1946, 78.)

at.lan'ti.ca. M.L. adj. *atlanticus* pertaining to the Atlantic Ocean.

Vegetative growth: Young colonies composed of slender filaments of various lengths, occasionally branched. Diameter of filaments 0.4 to 0.6 micron. Older colonies composed entirely of coccoid cells 0.5 to 0.7 micron in diameter, occurring singly or variously grouped. Non-motile. Not acid-fast. Gram-positive.

Gelatin: Liquefaction crateriform at first, becoming stratiform after about one week at 20° to 23° C.

Agar colonies: Orange-yellow on all media. No variant colonies observed on poured or streaked plates. Colonies flat with slightly raised center, the margin undulate or crenate and growing slowly outward just beneath the surface of the agar. Older colonies become characteristically divided into sectors. Thickly seeded colonies exhibit a mutual antagonism so that their margins do not grow together. No soluble pigments.

Agar slant: Orange-yellow, filiform streak, margin slowly spreading just beneath surface of agar. Surface of growth rather dull, consistency butyrous. Old slants may develop sectored appearance.

Broth: Usually clear with yellow, granular growth adherent to sides of tube. Heavy growth ring may develop at surface, flocculent sediment. Pellicle usually lacking, though thin, fragile, surface film may develop.

Milk: Rapid coagulation, acid; slow peptonization.

Indole not produced. Indigotin not produced from indole.

Hydrogen sulfide not produced.

Acid from arabinose, xylose, rhamnose, raffinose, fructose, galactose, glucose, mannose, cellobiose, maltose, sucrose, salicin, gum arabic and Karaya gum. No acid from lactose, dulcitol, mannitol or sorbitol. Sorbitol slowly utilized without acid production.

Gluconic, lactic and malonic acids utilized. Acetic, butyric, citric, malic, maleic, oxalic, propionic and iso-valeric acids not utilized.

d-Arginine and glutamic acid utilized as sources of both nitrogen and carbon. dl-Alanine, aspartic acid, cystine, glycine, l-leucine, dl-β-phenylalanine (slowly), l-proline and tyrosine utilized only as nitrogen source. Creatine not utilized. Glucosamine-HCl utilized with acid production.

Acetylmethylcarbinol not produced.

Starch is hydrolyzed.

Cellulose, chitin and alginic acid are attacked.

Seaweed gels: Agar slowly digested; softened, not liquefied, evident only by means of the iodine test. Gelase field narrow, margin fading. Irish moss gel also slowly attacked.

Nitrites vigorously produced from nitrates.

Ammonia, nitrite or nitrate slowly utilized as nitrogen sources. Ammonia produced slowly from nitrite, nitrate, asparagine and peptone. Urea utilized as a nitrogen source, but ammonia does not accumulate.

Catalase-positive.

Aerobic.

Optimum temperature, between 28° and 30° C.

Good growth in media prepared with distilled water and in all salinities through 6 per cent (sea salt). Pigmentation and morphological characteristics apparently the same at all salinities.

Source: Isolated from seaweed.

Habitat: Probably marine algae and marine sediments of the South Atlantic coast of the United States.

Genus II. Actinomyces Harz, 1877.

(Harz, in Bollinger, Cent. f. med. Wissensch., *15*, 1877, 485; also see Jahresber. d. Münch. Thierarzeneischule für 1877–78, 1879, 125; not *Actinomyce* Meyen, Linnaea, *2*, 1827, 442; *Cohnistreptothrix* Pinoy (in part), 1911, see Pinoy, Bull. Inst. Past., *11*, 1913, 929.)

Ac.ti.no.my′ces. Gr. noun *actis, actinis* ray; Gr. noun *myces* fungus; M.L. mas.n. *Actinomyces* ray-fungus.

True mycelium produced. The vegetative mycelium fragments into elements of irregular sizes and may exhibit angular branching. No conidia produced. Not acid-fast. Anaerobic to microaerophilic. Pathogenic for man and other animals.

The type species is *Actinomyces bovis* Harz.

Key to the species of genus Actinomyces.

I. Colonies soft, smooth, uniform, not adherent to medium. No aerial hyphae.
                         1. *Actinomyces bovis.*
II. Colonies tough in texture and warted in appearance, adherent to medium. Scant aerial growth of hyphae.
     A. Hyphae in pus granules stain with acid stains.
                         2. *Actinomyces israelii.*
     B. Hyphae in pus granules stain with basic stains.
                         3. *Actinomyces baudetii.*

1. **Actinomyces bovis** Harz, 1877. (Harz, in Bollinger, Cent. f. med. Wissensch., *15*, 1877, 485; also see Jahresber. d. Münch. Thierarzeneischule für 1877–78, 1879, 781.)

bo′vis. L. noun *bos* the ox; L. gen.noun *bovis* of the ox.

Description taken from Erikson (Med. Res. Council, London, Spec. Rept. Ser. 240, 1940, 63 pp.).

No aerial hyphae. Radiate, sulfur-colored granules occur in the pus found in cases of actinomycosis. Large club-shaped hyphae are seen in morbid tissues. Mycelium undergoes fragmentation very rapidly, extensive branching being rare. Hyphae less than 1 micron in diameter. Non-motile. Not acid-fast. Gram-positive.

Colonies: Smoother and softer in consistency and more uniform than those of the following species. The colonies are not adherent to the medium, and growth is scantier.

Semi-solid media: Excellent growth, especially with paraffin seal.

Gelatin: Occasionally scant, flaky growth. No liquefaction.

Liquid media: Occasionally turbid with a light, flocculent growth.

Acid from glucose, sucrose and maltose. No acid from salicin or mannitol.

Pigments: No soluble pigments produced on protein media. No insoluble pigments produced by growth.

Egg or serum media: No proteolytic action.

Litmus milk: Becomes acid but usually no coagulation, no peptonization. Sometimes no growth.

No hemolysis in blood broth or blood agar.

Anaerobic to microaerophilic. Bovine strains are more oxygen-tolerant on egg or serum media than strains of human origin belonging to the following species.

Optimum temperature, 37° C.

Serology: No cross agglutination between five bovine strains and human strains of *Actinomyces israelii*. No cross reactions with representative aerobic strains.

Comments: As pointed out by Lignières and Spitz (Bull. Soc. cent. Méd. vet., *20*, 1902, 487 and 546) and others, distinction should be made between the infections produced by *Actinomyces bovis* and those produced by the Gram-negative *Actinobacillus* now known as *Actinobacillus lignieresii*. These infections frequently occur in mixed form and are also frequently complicated by the presence of pyogenic cocci (Magnussen, Acta path. Microbiol. Scand., *5*, 1928, 170; and others).

Relationships to other species: This and the following species are sometimes regarded as being identical (see Emmons, Public Health Repts., U.S.P.H.S., *53*, 1935, 1967; Rosebury, Bact. Rev., *8*, 1944, 190; and others).

Source: Originally found in lumpy jaw of cattle.

Habitat: Frequently found in and about the mouths of cattle and probably other animals. Lesions may also be produced in the livers, udders or other organs of cattle and hogs. Possibly also found in human mouths (Naeslund, Acta path. Microbiol. Scand., *2*, 1925, 110).

2. Actinomyces israelii (Kruse, 1896) Lachner-Sandoval, 1898. (Strahlenpilz, Wolff and Israel, Arch. f. path. Anat., *126*, 1891, 11; *Streptothrix israeli* (sic) Kruse, in Flügge, Die Mikroorganismen, 3 Aufl., *2*, 1896, 56; *Actinomyces israeli* (sic) Lachner-Sandoval, Inaug. Diss., Strassburg, 1898, 64.)

is.ra.e'li.i. M.L. gen.noun *israelii* of Israel; named for Prof. James Israel, one of the original isolators of this organism.

Description taken from Erikson (Med. Res. Council, London, Spec. Rept. Ser. 240, 1940, 63 pp.).

Erect aerial hyphae are produced in an atmosphere of reduced oxygen tension. These hyphae are occasionally septate, but no definite spores are formed. One micron or more in diameter. The hyphae stain with acid stains. Large club-shaped forms, greater than 5 microns in diameter, are seen in morbid tissues. Substrate mycelium is initially unicellular, and the branches may extend into the medium in long filaments or may, more or less quickly, exhibit fragmentation and characteristic angular branching. The latter resembles the similar phenomenon found in *Corynebacterium*. Non-motile. Not acid-fast. Gram-positive.

Colonies: These exhibit a considerable degree of polymorphism, but no stable variants have been established. Tougher in texture than those of *Actinomyces bovis*. Old colonies warted in appearance. Adherent to the medium.

Gelatin: Occasionally scant, flaky growth. No liquefaction.

Liquid media: Usually clear.

Acid from sugars: According to Slack

(Jour. Bact., *43*, 1941, 193–209), acid from glucose, maltose, mannitol, sucrose and lactose; according to Negroni and Bonfiglioli (Physics, *15*, 1939, 159), acid from glucose, galactose, lactose, fructose, maltose, raffinose, sucrose and xylose.

Pigments: No soluble pigments on protein media. No insoluble pigments produced by growth.

Egg or serum media: No proteolytic action.

Litmus milk: Becomes acid but usually does not clot. No peptonization. Frequently no growth.

No hemolysis.

Anaerobic to microaerophilic.

Optimum temperature, 37° C.

Serology: No cross agglutination between 12 human strains and bovine strains of *Actinomyces*. No cross reactions with representative aerobic strains.

Source: Isolated from two cases of human actinomycosis: 1) a retromaxillary tumor, 2) actinomycosis of lung and breast (Wolff and Israel).

Habitat: From human sources (mouth, tonsillar crypts, etc.).

3. Actinomyces baudetii Brion, 1942. (*Actinomyces du chien et du chat*, Brion, Rev. de Méd. Vétér., March, 1939; *Actinomyces baudeti* (sic) Brion, Rev. de Méd. Vétér., *91*, 1942, 157; *Actinobacterium baudeti* Prévot, Goret, Joubert, Tardieux and Aladame, Ann. Inst. Past., *81*, 1951, 85.)

bau.de'ti.i. M.L. gen.noun *baudetii* of Baudet; named for Dr. E. Baudet, an early student of this organism.

Description taken from Brion, Goret and Joubert (Proc. VI Congress Internacional de Patol. Comp., Madrid, 4–11 Mayo, 1952, i. 48).

Granules from histological preparations appear as tangled, radiating hyphae; the ends of the hyphae are rounded and ovoid, forming a crown. These club-shaped ends are not more than 5 microns in diameter. The hyphae take basic stains. Mycelia possess slender hyphae (0.2 to 0.4 micron) with irregular diameters. Non-septate. The ends are swollen and rounded. Copious branching. In artificial media the hyphae are frequently short, rarely exceeding 20 microns in length. Gram-positive.

Best growth is obtained in an atmosphere of low oxygen tension.

Gelatin: No liquefaction.

Agar colonies: Dull, whitish granules adhering slightly to the medium.

Liquid media: A sediment of white granules is produced.

Loeffler's blood serum: In 4 to 5 days the surface is covered with white granules which are the size of a pin head.

Serum media: No proteolytic action.

Brain extract favors growth in some media.

Indole production slight.

Acid from glucose, sucrose and starch.

Anaerobic to microaerophilic.

Optimum temperature, 37° C.

Pathogenic when inoculated into dogs, rabbits and guinea pigs where it forms subcutaneous abscesses.

Distinctive characters: For some years this organism was regarded as identical with *Actinomyces israelii*. However, recent work by Brion et al. (*loc. cit.*), Brion (*op. cit., 91*, 1942, 157), Prévot et al. (*op. cit., 81*, 1951, 85) and Guyard (Thesis, Fac. de Méd. et de Pharm. de Lyon, No. 34, Année Scolaire 1951–1952) has shown that these two organisms can be differentiated as follows: *A. israelii* is pathogenic for man and cattle, and the club-shaped bodies at the ends of the hyphae in the pus granules stain with acid stains while those found in *A. baudetii* absorb basic stains.

Source: Isolated from various types of lesions in cats and dogs.

Habitat: Cause of actinomycosis in cats and dogs.

FAMILY III. STREPTOMYCETACEAE WAKSMAN AND HENRICI, 1943.*

(Jour. Bact., *46*, 1943, 339.)

Strep.to.my.ce.ta′ce.ae. M.L. mas.n. *Streptomyces* type genus of the family; -*aceae* ending to denote a family; M.L. fem.pl.n. *Streptomycetaceae* the *Streptomyces* family.

Vegetative mycelium does not fragment into bacillary or coccoid forms. Conidia borne on sporophores. Primarily soil forms, sometimes thermophilic in rotting manure. A few species are parasitic.

Key to the genera of family **Streptomycetaceae**.

I. Conidia produced in aerial hyphae in chains.

    Genus I. *Streptomyces*, p. 744.

II. Conidia produced terminally and singly on short conidiophores.

    A. No growth between 50° and 65°C.

    Genus II. *Micromonospora*, p. 822.

    B. Growth occurs between 50° and 65°C.

    Genus III. *Thermoactinomyces*, p. 824.

Genus I. **Streptomyces** *Waksman and Henrici, 1943*.

(*Streptothrix* Cohn, Beitr. zur Biol. der Pflanzen, I, Heft 3, 1875, 186; not *Streptothrix* Corda, Prachtflora Europaescher Schimmelbildung, 1839; Waksman and Henrici, Jour. Bact., *46*, 1943, 339.)

Strep.to.my′ces. Gr. adj. *streptus* pliant, bent; Gr. noun *myces* fungus; M.L. mas.n. *Streptomyces* pliant fungus.

Grow in the form of a much-branched mycelium with a typical aerial mycelium. Conidio-

---

* Completely revised by Prof. S. A. Waksman, Rutgers University, New Brunswick, New Jersey, March, 1953.

spores are formed in chains. Aerobic. Saprophytic soil forms, less commonly parasitic on plants or animals.

This genus can be divided, on the basis of the structure of the sporulating hyphae, into five groups:

Group 1. Straight, sporulating hyphae, monopodial branching, never producing regular spirals.

Group 2. Spore-bearing hyphae arranged in clusters.

Group 3. Spiral formation in aerial mycelium; long, open spirals.

Group 4. Spiral formation in aerial mycelium; short, compact spirals.

Group 5. Spore-bearing hyphae arranged on mycelium in whorls or tufts.

The type species is *Streptomyces albus* (Rossi-Doria *emend.* Krainsky) Waksman and Henrici.

Key to the species of genus **Streptomyces**.

I. Saprophytes; psychrophilic to mesophilic.
  A. Soluble pigment on organic media absent or faint brown, pink, purple, golden yellow or blue.
    1. Pigment absent, or only faint brown pigment produced in protein media.
        a^1. Aerial mycelium abundant, white.
          b^1. Spirals formed; spores spherical to ellipsoidal.
            1. *Streptomyces albus*
          b^2. Long, open spirals; spores cylindrical.
            2. *Streptomyces longisporus.*
          b^3. Straight sporophores, forming broom-shaped clusters; spores spherical to ellipsoidal.
            3. *Streptomyces globisporus.*
        a^2. Aerial mycelium whitish to light gray, in concentric zones.
            4. *Streptomyces anulatus.*
        a^3. Aerial mycelium on synthetic sucrose agar sandy lavender of dark gray.
            5. *Streptomyces rochei.*
    2. Aerial mycelium gray to blue-gray; soluble pigment blue.
        a^1. Strongly proteolytic.
          b^1. Spirals formed.
            c^1. Pigment at first red, changing to blue.
              6. *Streptomyces coelicolor.*
            c^2. Pigment at first yellow-red, changing to blue or bluish green.
              7. *Streptomyces pluricolor.*
            c^3. Pigment unchanged with acidity.
              8. *Streptomyces cyaneus.*
          b^2. No spirals formed.
              9. *Streptomyces vinaceus.*
        a^2. Weakly proteolytic; aerial mycelium poorly developed.
            10. *Streptomyces violaceus.*
    3. Pigment at first green, becoming brown.
        a^1. Aerial mycelium usually absent.
            11. *Streptomyces verne.*
        a^2. Aerial mycelium dark gray, olive-colored or gray-green.
            12. *Streptomyces viridans.*
    4. Growth pink on synthetic media, yellowish on organic media; no soluble pigment.
            13. *Streptomyces californicus.*

5. Growth yellow to greenish or orange-colored; soluble pigment yellow to golden yellow.
    a^1. Growth yellow to green; pigment insoluble.
        14. *Streptomyces virgatus.*
    a^2. Growth sulfur-yellow; soluble pigment yellow.
        b^1. Conidia ellipsoidal.
            c^1. Aerial mycelium white.
                15. *Streptomyces flaveolus.*
            c^2. Aerial mycelium light yellow.
                16. *Streptomyces parvus.*
            c^3. Aerial mycelium white to gray to reddish gray.
                17. *Streptomyces xanthophaeus.*
        b^2. Conidia spherical; cellulose decomposed.
            18. *Streptomyces cellulosae.*
    a^3. Growth reddish brown to orange-colored to cinnamon-drab, covered with white to gray aerial mycelium; soluble pigment on synthetic media yellowish.
        b^1. Soluble pigment yellow. No liquefaction of gelatin.
            19. *Streptomyces rimosus.*
        b^2. Faint yellowish coloration of liquefied gelatin. Milk rapidly peptonized.
            20. *Streptomyces griseoflavus.*
        b^3. Soluble pigment golden yellow.
            21. *Streptomyces aureofaciens.*
    a^4. Growth cream-colored to brown; aerial mycelium white to yellowish.
        b^1. Soluble pigment yellow to yellow-orange.
            22. *Streptomyces albidoflavus.*
        b^2. Soluble pigment yellowish to yellow-green.
            c^1. Aerial mycelium white to yellow.
                23. *Streptomyces lieskei.*
            c^2. Aerial mycelium gray.
                d^1. Growth on synthetic agar yellowish green.
                    24. *Streptomyces flavovirens.*
                d^2. Growth on synthetic agar yellow; produces soluble yellow pigment on Ca-malate-glycerol agar.
                    25. *Streptomyces celluloflavus.*
                d^3. Growth on glucose-asparagine agar yellow, becoming black.
                    26. *Streptomyces limosus.*
6. Growth cream-colored; soluble pigment yellowish brown to reddish brown.
        27. *Streptomyces griseoluteus.*
7. Growth coral-red; aerial mycelium scant, white; soluble pigment brown.
    a^1. Gelatin rapidly liquefied.
        28. *Streptomyces bobiliae.*
    a^2. Gelatin slowly liquefied.
        29. *Streptomyces aurantiacus.*
8. Growth on synthetic media mouse-gray; aerial mycelium white to gray
    a^1. Sporophores straight.
        30. *Streptomyces griseolus.*
    a^2. Sporophores broom-shaped.
        31. *Streptomyces fasciculus.*

9. Growth cream-colored to yellowish to red; aerial mycelium white to gray.

a^1. Growth becoming red; aerial mycelium white.

32. *Streptomyces erythraeus.*

a^2. Growth yellow; aerial mycelium mouse-gray to drab.

33. *Streptomyces flavogriseus.*

10. Soluble pigment on potato plug brown to brownish red to reddish purple.

a^1. Growth on potato greenish-colored; spirals formed.

34. *Streptomyces diastaticus.*

a^2. Growth on potato gray; no spirals formed.

35. *Streptomyces canescens.*

a^3. Growth on potato yellowish-colored.

b^1. Greenish tinge produced.

36. *Streptomyces fimicarius.*

b^2. Pigment reddish brown.

37. *Streptomyces felleus.*

b^3. Soluble brown pigment on synthetic agar.

38. *Streptomyces achromogenes.*

a^4. Growth on potato pink to reddish purple; spirals produced.

39. *Streptomyces noursei.*

B. Soluble pigment on organic media brown.

1. Pigment deep brown (chromogenic types).

a^1. Aerial mycelium thin, rose-colored.

b^1. Spirals produced.

40. *Streptomyces roseochromogenes.*

b^2. No spirals formed.

41. *Streptomyces cinnamonensis.*

a^2. Aerial mycelium gray to brown to reddish.

b^1. Growth on organic media greenish to black.

42. *Streptomyces olivochromogenes.*

b^2. Growth dark brown.

43. *Streptomyces resistomycificus.*

a^3. Aerial mycelium cottony, dark brown; rapid liquefaction of gelatin.

44. *Streptomyces diastatochromogenes.*

a^4. Colonies yellow; aerial mycelium white to gray.

45. *Streptomyces flavochromogenes.*

a^5. Growth white to gray; aerial mycelium white to gray.

46. *Streptomyces bikiniensis.*

a^6. Growth white, fluffy; sporulating hyphae straight.

47. *Streptomyces mirabilis.*

a^7. Growth cream-colored to brown; aerial mycelium gray; sporophores in clusters.

48. *Streptomyces antibioticus.*

a^8. Aerial mycelium white, turning light pink on certain media; sporophores straight, no spirals.

49. *Streptomyces griseocarneus.*

a^9. Aerial mycelium greenish yellow, turning gray; sporophores produced in tufts or whorls.

50. *Streptomyces viridoflavus.*

2. Growth on synthetic agar dark brown.

a^1. Aerial mycelium dark gray; spores globose.

51. *Streptomyces globosus.*

a². Aerial mycelium white; spores cylindrical.

52. *Streptomyces cylindrosporus.*

3. Growth on synthetic agar dark green; aerial mycelium white to light green.

53. *Streptomyces viridochromogenes.*

4. Pigments on synthetic agar deep brown to black.

a¹. Growth on potato orange to orange-red; growth on synthetic agar brown to purplish; no aerial mycelium.

54. *Streptomyces purpureochromogenes.*

a². Growth on potato brown to black.

b¹. Aerial mycelium on synthetic agar white to brownish.

55. *Streptomyces phaeochromogenes.*

b². Growth on synthetic media colorless to light orange; aerial mycelium gray to cinnamon-drab.

56. *Streptomyces aureus.*

5. Growth on synthetic agar grayish yellow; light yellow soluble pigment.

57. *Streptomyces tanashiensis.*

6. Soluble pigment on synthetic media red to rose-red.

a¹. Soluble pigment on potato black.

58. *Streptomyces erythrochromogenes.*

a². No soluble pigment on potato.

59. *Streptomyces collinus.*

7. Aerial mycelium lavender to light tan or pink.

a¹. Aerial mycelium cottony white, lavender to vinaceous-lavender colored.

60. *Streptomyces lavendulae.*

a². Aerial mycelium light tan to pink.

61. *Streptomyces venezuelae.*

a³. Aerial mycelium grayish pink to lavender.

62. *Streptomyces virginiae.*

8. Aerial mycelium forms whorls.

a¹. Growth gray-colored to brownish.

b¹. Spores spherical.

63. *Streptomyces reticuli.*

b². Spores cylindrical.

64. *Streptomyces netropsis.*

a². Growth dark gray to gray-green; spores cylindrical.

65. *Streptomyces verticillatus.*

a³. Spores produced in spirals; spores cylindrical, weakly proteolytic.

66. *Streptomyces circulatus.*

a⁴. Whorls in secondary branches; growth yellowish red to pink.

67. *Streptomyces rubrireticuli.*

9. Growth on potato greenish to black.

a¹. Growth on synthetic agar yellow to sulfur-yellow.

68. *Streptomyces flavus.*

a². Growth on synthetic agar red to orange.

69. *Streptomyces ruber.*

a³. Growth on synthetic agar black.

70. *Streptomyces niger.*

a⁴. Growth on synthetic agar white.

71. *Streptomyces alboniger.*

10. Growth on synthetic and organic media yellow; sporophores straight.

72. *Streptomyces abikoensis.*

11. Soluble brown pigment only occasionally produced; growth usually colorless; odor very strong.
> 73. *Streptomyces odorifer.*

C. No soluble pigment produced in organic media.
  1. Proteolytic action strong.
        a¹. Growth yellowish to orange-brown.
              b¹. Aerial mycelium white to rose-colored.
              > 74. *Streptomyces roseoflavus.*
              b². Growth only on potato and serum yellowish; aerial mycelium white.
              > 75. *Streptomyces putrificus.*
        a². Growth yellowish green to citron-yellow; aerial mycelium white to yellow to pinkish.
        > 76. *Streptomyces citreus.*
        a³. Growth golden yellow to orange-colored; soluble pigment yellow to orange; growth may also be red-brown and pigment orange.
        > 77. *Streptomyces fulvissimus.*
        a⁴. Growth colorless to cream-colored; aerial mycelium scant, white.
        > 78. *Streptomyces chrysomallus.*
              b¹. Pigment on nutrient agar faint yellowish.
              > 79. *Streptomyces gougerotii.*
              b². No soluble pigment; forms oidiospores.
              > 80. *Streptomyces farinosus.*
              b³. Pigment on synthetic media yellowish.
              > 81. *Streptomyces albidus.*
        a⁵. Growth white to cream-colored; aerial mycelium flesh-colored to light cinnamon-colored.
        > 82. *Streptomyces cinnamoneus.*
        a⁶. Growth on synthetic media dark to black to almost bluish black; aerial mycelium white to gray.
              b¹. Soluble pigment produced on autolysis.
              > 83. *Streptomyces violaceoniger.*
              b². No soluble pigment.
              > 84. *Streptomyces gedanensis.*
        a⁷. Growth colorless to yellowish to olive-buff; aerial mycelium water-green.
        > 85. *Streptomyces griseus.*
        a⁸. Growth bright orange to golden red; aerial mycelium white to yelow.
        > 86. *Streptomyces longissimus.*
        a⁹. Growth yellow to olive-ocher; aerial mycelium mouse-gray.
        > 87. *Streptomyces olivaceus.*
        a¹⁰. Growth yellow; aerial mycelium scant or rose-yellow.
        > 88. *Streptomyces microflavus.*
        a¹¹. Growth yellowish to brown to reddish brown. Aerial mycelium white to mouse-gray.
        > 89. *Streptomyces cacaoi.*
        a¹². Aerial mycelium white; conidia gray to dark gray.
        > 90. *Streptomyces marinus.*
  2. Proteolytic action limited.
        a¹. Soluble pigment produced on synthetic agar.

b¹. Pigment purple.
> 91. *Streptomyces novaecaesareae.*

b². Pigment brown to black.
> c¹. Growth on potato gray to brown.
>> 92. *Streptomyces exfoliatus.*
>
> c². Growth on potato greenish to black.
>> 93. *Streptomyces gelaticus.*
>
> c³. Aerial mycelium pigmented green.
>> 94. *Streptomyces glaucus.*

a². No soluble pigment on synthetic agar.
> b¹. Growth dark brown to almost black; aerial mycelium white to gray.
>> c¹. Abundant spirals in aerial mycelium.
>>> d¹. Conidia spherical to ellipsoidal.
>>>> 95. *Streptomyces rutgersensis.*
>>>
>>> d². Conidia ellipsoidal to cylindrical.
>>>> 96. *Streptomyces halstedii.*
>>
>> c². No spirals produced on synthetic agar.
>>> d¹. Spores cylindrical; growth on synthetic agar dark brown.
>>>> 97. *Streptomyces fumosus.*
>>>
>>> d². Spores ellipsoidal. Growth on synthetic agar light brown.
>>>> 98. *Streptomyces lipmanii.*
>
> b². Growth cream-colored to yellow or yellow-orange.
>> c¹. Aerial mycelium on certain media white, moist with dark, glistening patches; spores ellipsoidal.
>>> 99. *Streptomyces hygroscopicus.*
>>
>> c². Aerial mycelium white-yellow to brownish yellow; spores cylindrical.
>>> 100. *Streptomyces longisporoflavus.*
>>
>> c³. Aerial mycelium white; spores cylindrical.
>>> 101. *Streptomyces candidus.*
>>
>> c⁴. Aerial mycelium powdery white with yellow tinge.
>>> 102. *Streptomyces alboflavus.*
>>
>> c⁵. Growth cream-colored; aerial mycelium cottony white; pigment in milk and on potato rose to yellowish.
>>> 103. *Streptomyces flocculus.*
>>
>> c⁶. Aerial mycelium gray; slight darkening of potato plug.
>>> 104. *Streptomyces antimycoticus.*
>
> b³. Growth orange or red.
>> c¹. Growth yellowish to orange; aerial mycelium sea-shell-pink.
>>> 105. *Streptomyces fradiae.*
>>
>> c². Growth rose to red; aerial mycelium white.
>>> d¹. Growth on gelatin yellow to red; slow liquefaction.
>>>> 106. *Streptomyces albosporeus.*
>>>
>>> d². Growth light brown; rapid liquefaction.
>>>> 107. *Streptomyces purpurascens.*
>>
>> c³. Growth light rose to purple-red; aerial mycelium

whitish to rose-white; pigment dissolves in fat-containing media.
>   108. *Streptomyces longispororuber.*

   c⁴. Growth pale rose to red; aerial mycelium weakly developed, velvety, rose-white.
>   109. *Streptomyces oidiosporus.*

   c⁵. Growth red; aerial mycelium black.
>   110. *Streptomyces melanocyclus.*

3. Proteolytic action very weak.
   a¹. Growth colorless; aerial mycelium whitish; acid-resistant.
>   111. *Streptomyces acidophilus.*

   a². Growth becoming salmon-pink; acid-sensitive.
>   112. *Streptomyces rubescens.*

   a³. Growth green to dark green; aerial mycelium whitish to grayish; no soluble pigment.
>   113. *Streptomyces viridis.*

II. Saprophytes; thermophilic.
  A. Growth on potato yellowish; diastatic.
    1. No aerial mycelium.
>   114. *Streptomyces thermophilus.*

    2. Aerial mycelium light gray.
>   115. *Streptomyces thermodiastaticus.*

  B. Growth on potato abundant, dark colored; non-diastatic.
>   116. *Streptomyces thermofuscus.*

  C. Thermotolerant cultures.
>   117. *Streptomyces casei.*

III. Plant parasites or cultures isolated from diseased plants or from soil in which diseased plants were grown (after Millard and Burr).
  A. Isolated from potato scab or from soil in which scabby potatoes were grown.
    1. Star-like colonies in glycerol synthetic solution.
      a¹. Deep pigment produced in nearly all media; tyrosinase-positive.
>   118. *Streptomyces clavifer.*

      a². Deep pigment produced in protein media only; tyrosinase-positive.
>   119. *Streptomyces fimbriatus.*

      a³. Pale pigment produced in nearly all media; tyrosinase-negative.
>   120. *Streptomyces carnosus.*

      a⁴. No soluble pigment (or only trace) produced; minute craters produced on sucrose and glucose media.
>   121. *Streptomyces craterifer.*

    2. Surface growth heavy on glycerol synthetic solution with abundant aerial mycelium.
      a¹. Aerial mycelium on nutrient potato agar limited, pale gray.
>   122. *Streptomyces gracilis.*

      a². Aerial mycelium on nutrient potato agar abundant, white; gelatin liquefaction stratiform; no soluble pigment.
>   123. *Streptomyces praecox.*

      a³. Gelatin liquefaction stratiform; soluble pigment produced.
>   124. *Streptomyces setonii.*

      a⁴. Abundant aerial mycelium on nearly all media; pigment on Camalate-glycerol agar carnelian red.
>   125. *Streptomyces praefecundus.*

3. Surface growth fair on glycerol synthetic solution with some aerial mycelium.

    a^1. Soluble pigment (often green) produced on all solid media.

        126. *Streptomyces viridogenes.*

    a^2. Soluble pigment (yellow) produced on all synthetic media.

        127. *Streptomyces loidensis.*

    a^3. Soluble pigment none or only poor; decided clot produced in milk.

        128. *Streptomyces wedmorensis.*

4. Surface growth scant or none, but some bottom growth on glycerol synthetic solution.

    a^1. Color changes produced in brom-cresol milk.

        b^1. Tyrosinase-positive; no aerial mycelium on nutrient potato agar.

            129. *Streptomyces scabies.*

        b^2. Tyrosinase-negative; aerial mycelium produced on all solid media.

            c^1. Aerial mycelium on synthetic sucrose agar abundant.

                d^1. Growth good on egg-albumen agar with abundant aerial mycelium.

                130. *Streptomyces tenuis.*

                d^2. Growth poor on egg-albumen agar with scant aerial mycelium.

                131. *Streptomyces marginatus.*

            c^2. Aerial mycelium on synthetic sucrose agar scant; no true aerial mycelium produced on any medium; colonies often show dark centers.

            132. *Streptomyces salmonicolor.*

    a^2. No color changes produced in brom-cresol milk.

        b^1. Facultatively anaerobic; no true aerial mycelium, or only trace, produced on any medium; colonies frequently show dark centers.

            133. *Streptomyces maculatus.*

        b^2. Obligately aerobic; aerial mycelium arises centripetally on the colonies.

            134. *Streptomyces coroniformis.*

5. No growth on glycerol synthetic solution; starch not hydrolyzed. Growth in brom-cresol milk good; characteristic color changes.

        135. *Streptomyces spiralis.*

6. Other organism isolated from potato scab.

        136. *Streptomyces sampsonii.*

B. Grow on or isolated from sweet potatoes.

        137. *Streptomyces intermedius.*

1. Growth on synthetic agar olive-yellow; no aerial mycelium; no soluble pigment on potato.

        138. *Streptomyces ipomoeae.*

2. Growth on synthetic agar cream-colored; growth on potato reddish brown with soluble pigment purple; aerial mycelium white.

        139. *Streptomyces poolensis.*

C. Attack or isolated from scab of mangels and sugar beets.

        140. *Streptomyces tumuli.*

IV. Isolated from animal tissues; in the animal body, hyphae often show clavate enlargements at the ends.

A. Limited proteolytic action in gelatin, milk, coagulated egg-albumin or fibrin.
    1. Vegetative growth white.
        a^1. No soluble pigment in organic media.
            141. *Streptomyces listeri.*
        a^2. Soluble pigment in organic media brown to brown-red.
            142. *Streptomyces galtieri.*
    2. Vegetative growth cream-colored; aerial mycelium scant, white.
            143. *Streptomyces upcottii.*
    3. Growth very limited on various media, except on potato plug; no liquefaction of gelatin.
            144. *Streptomyces hortonensis.*
B. Strong proteolytic action in gelatin and milk.
    1. Growth on potato plug moist, membranous.
        a^1. Pigment deep brown.
            145. *Streptomyces beddardii.*
        a^2. Pigment faint brown.
            146. *Streptomyces kimberi.*
    2. Growth on potato plug abundant, becoming black; aerial mycelium white-gray; plug discolored.
            147. *Streptomyces somaliensis.*
    3. Growth on some media pink.
            148. *Streptomyces panjae.*
    4. Aerial mycelium on most media profuse, white; spiral formation.
            149. *Streptomyces willmorei.*
V. No aerial mycelium.
            150. Sterile (non-conidia-forming) species.

1. **Streptomyces albus** (Rossi-Doria, 1891, *emend.* Krainsky, 1914) Waksman and Henrici, 1943. (*Streptotrix* (sic) *alba* Rossi-Doria, Ann. d'Ist. d'Ig. sper. d. Univ. di Roma, *1*, 1891, 399; *Actinomyces albus* Krainsky, Cent. f. Bakt., II Abt., *41*, 1914, 662; Waksman and Henrici, Jour. Bact., *46*, 1943, 339.)

al'bus. L. adj. *albus* white.

The description of this species by Rossi-Doria is incomplete. The characters given below are taken from Krainsky (*op. cit.*, 1914, 662) with some supplementary information from later authors. Other descriptions which may vary from this in certain details are given by Waksman and Curtis (Soil Sci., *1*, 1916, 117), Bergey et al. (Manual, 1st ed., 1923, 367), Duché (Les actinomyces du groupe albus, Paris, 1934, 257) and Baldacci (Mycopathologia, *2*, 1940, 156).

Vegetative growth: Hyphae branched, 1 micron in diameter.

Aerial mycelium: Abundant, white. Hyphae 1.3 to 1.7 microns in diameter with ellipsoidal spores (1 micron long) in coiled chains on lateral branches of the aerial hyphae.

Gelatin: Rapid liquefaction. Gray colonies. No soluble pigment.

Agar: No aerial mycelium, but a chalky white deposit forms on old colonies.

Ca-malate agar: Colonies of medium size; the center only is covered with a white aerial mycelium.

Starch agar: White aerial mycelium covering the whole surface.

Glucose agar: Gray aerial mycelium becoming brownish.

Broth: Flaky growth on bottom with surface pellicle in old cultures. White aerial mycelium.

Milk: Rapidly peptonized after coagulation. Reaction becomes alkaline (Duché). Cream-colored surface ring. White aerial mycelium.

Potato: White aerial mycelium. Growth folded, cream-colored.

Carrots and other vegetables: Excellent growth (Duché).

No hydrolysis of starch in some cultures; rapid hydrolysis in others.

No growth on cellulose.

Actively proteolytic.

Nitrites produced from nitrates.

Odor: Earthy or musty.

Aerobic.

Antagonistic properties: Usually none. Some strains produce actinomycetin. Some produce thiolutin or endomycin.

Comment: Because of the wide distribution of this species and the ease of its superficial identification, numerous strains with varying physiological properties have been reported.

Source: Isolated from air and soil (Rossi-Doria); from garden soil (Krainsky).

Habitat: Dust, soil, grains and straw. Widely distributed.

2. **Streptomyces longisporus** (Krassilnikov, 1941) Waksman, 1953. (*Actinomyces longisporus* Krassilnikov, Guide to the Actinomycetes, Izd. Akad. Nauk, U.S.S.R., Moskau, 1941, 47; Waksman, in Waksman and Lechevalier, Actinomycetes and Their Antibiotics, Baltimore, 1953, 39.)

lon.gi'spo.rus. L. adj. *longus* long; Gr. fem.n. *spora* a seed; M.L. noun *spora* a spore; M.L. adj. *longisporus* long-spored.

Vegetative growth: Colorless colonies. Some strains produce a brown substance in protein media.

Aerial mycelium: White. Long sporophores with many curls, weak spirals, occasionally forming small brooms. Spores cylindrical, with sharply cut ends, 0.6 to 0.8 by 1.0 to 1.7 microns; later spores may become ellipsoidal, 0.5 to 0.8 by 0.9 to 1.0 micron.

Gelatin: Rapid liquefaction.

Milk: Rapidly coagulated and peptonized.

Starch is actively hydrolyzed.

Fair to good growth on cellulose.

Nitrate reduction variable.

Antagonistic properties: None.

Distinctive characters: Distinguished from *Streptomyces albus* in that its spores are never spherical.

Source: Isolated from soil.

Habitat: Soil.

3. **Streptomyces globisporus** (Krassilnikov, 1941) Waksman, 1953. (*Actinomyces globisporus* Krassilnikov, Guide to the Actinomycetes, Izd. Akad. Nauk, U.S.S.R., Moskau, 1941, 48; Waksman, in Waksman and Lechevalier, Actinomycetes and Their Antibiotics, Baltimore, 1953, 39.)

glo.bi'spo.rus. L. mas.n. *globus* a round body; Gr. fem.n. *spora* seed; M.L. noun *spora* a spore; M.L. adj. *globisporus* round-spored.

Vegetative growth: Flat, colorless colonies. No diffusible pigment.

Aerial mycelium: Well developed, powdery, white. Sporophores straight, frequently forming brooms. Spores ellipsoidal and spherical, 0.8 micron in diameter.

Gelatin: Rapid liquefaction.

Agar: Grayish, smooth or lichenoid colonies. Aerial mycelium poorly developed.

Synthetic agar: Abundant growth, giving flat, colorless colonies, not coloring medium. Aerial mycelium well developed, powdery, white with trace of yellow.

Milk: Rapidly peptonized; not coagulated.

Potato: No aerial mycelium or trace; faint brown color of plug.

Sucrose not inverted.

Starch hydrolyzed slowly.

Good growth on cellulose.

Antagonistic properties: None or weak.

Distinctive characters: Waksman (*loc. cit.*) regards this species as distinct from *Streptomyces griseus* (No. 85) on the basis of a white aerial mycelium, lack of ability to coagulate milk and slow hydrolysis of starch. Further studies have indicated that these variations may not be sufficient to justify the separation into two species. (Also see comment following description of *S. griseus*.)

Comment: Krassilnikov distinguishes this species from *S. griseus* primarily upon the fact that the sporophores of the latter species, as originally described by Krainsky (1914), exhibited spiral formation. The streptomycin-producing culture, isolated by Waksman et al. (1943) and identified as *Streptomyces griseus*, exhibited no spiral formation and is therefore regarded by Krassilnikov (Izd. Akad. Nauk, U.S.S.R., Moskau, 1949, 100) as a subspecies of *Actinomyces globisporus* named *Actinomyces globisporus streptomycini*. Krassilnikov recognizes several substrains of the species *Streptomyces globisporus* on the basis of milk coagulation, proteolysis and pigmentation of aerial mycelium.

Source: Isolated from soil.

Habitat: Soil.

4. Streptomyces anulatus (Beijerinck, 1912, *emend*. Krassilnikov, 1941) Waksman, 1953. (*Streptothrix annulatus* (sic) Beijerinck, Folia Microbiologica, *1*, 1912, 4; *Actinomyces annulatus* (sic) Krassilnikov, Guide to the Actinomycetes, Izd. Akad. Nauk, U.S.S.R., Moskau, 1941, 40; Waksman, in Waksman and Lechevalier, Actinomycetes and Their Antibiotics, Baltimore, 1953, 40.)

a.nu.la'tus. L. adj. *anulatus* furnished with a ring.

Aerial mycelium: Whitish or light gray. Sphorophores produce spirals with 3 to 7 turns (sinistrorse); spores spherical, 0.7 micron in diameter.

Gelatin: Slow liquefaction.

Agar: White aerial mycelium, concentric rings less marked than those on synthetic agar.

Synthetic agar: Colorless, flat growth, penetrating deep into agar. White, velvety aerial mycelium growing in the form of concentric rings.

Milk: Coagulated, slowly peptonized.

Sucrose is inverted.

Starch is hydrolyzed.

Good growth on cellulose.

Odor: Strong, earthy.

Antagonistic properties: Highly antagonistic against mycobacteria and Grampositive bacteria; some strains are active against fungi.

Source: Isolated from soil.

Habitat: Soil.

5. Streptomyces rochei Waksman, 1953. (*Streptomyces rochei* Berger, Jampolsky and Goldberg (*nomen nudum*), Arch. of Biochem., *22*, 1949, 477; Waksman, in Waksman and Lechevalier, Actinomycetes and Their Antibiotics, Baltimore, 1953, 40.)

ro'che.i. M.L. gen.noun *rochei* of Roche.

Description prepared by Julius Berger for use in Waksman and Lechevalier, Actinomycetes and Their Antibiotics, Baltimore, 1953.

Vegetative growth: Vegetative mycelium characteristically fine, 0.8 to 1.5 microns in diameter, with short branches on synthetic (calcium malate) and non-synthetic (peptone-tomato paste) agars.

Aerial mycelium: Sporogenous hyphae 1.5 microns in diameter, often spirally twisted; spirals usually short and loose with rarely more than 2 to 3 coils. Spores ellipsoidal, sometimes spherical, 0.8 to 1.5 by 1.3 to 2.8 microns.

Gelatin: Cream-colored surface ring, covered with white aerial mycelium. Rapid liquefaction. Faint yellow soluble pigment.

Agar: Cream-colored growth. White aerial mycelium. No soluble pigment.

Synthetic agar: Thin, colorless growth, covered with sandy lavender to dark gray aerial mycelium. Reverse light gray, later becoming grayish yellow. No soluble pigment.

Ca-malate-glycerol agar: Abundant growth, raised in center. Gray aerial mycelium, buff around the edges, having a fuzzy appearance. Medium is cleared directly under the growth.

Starch agar: Brownish growth. Mousegray aerial mycelium. Reverse shows slight purple pigmentation in four days.

Glucose agar: Smooth, yellowish growth, covered with white to gray aerial mycelium. Yellowish soluble pigment.

Ca-citrate-glycerol broth: Growth at surface forming a thin mat of partially sporulated, discrete, grayish white colonies. From the mat, soft, round, fuzzy, gray colonies drop into the medium.

Milk: Ring at the surface cream-colored to brownish. Coagulated; rapidly peptonized.

Potato: Abundant, lichenoid, cream-colored growth. Abundant, cottony, white to gray aerial mycelium. Color of plug becomes reddish tan.

Strong diastatic action.

Antagonistic properties: On certain complex nitrogenous media such as those containing soybean flour or distillers' dried solubles, the organism produces a wide range of antimicrobial activity. Part of this is attributable to a specific antibiotic known as borrelidin.

Comment: Morphologically the culture resembles some species in the *Streptomyces albus* group, such as *Streptomyces albido-*

flavus, Streptomyces californicus and *Streptomyces lipmanii*, but it is not believed to be identical with any of them.

Source: Isolated from soil.

Habitat: Soil.

6. Streptomyces coelicolor (Müller, 1908) Waksman and Henrici, 1948. (*Streptothrix coelicolor* Müller, Cent. f. Bakt., I Abt., Orig., *46*, 1908, 197; Waksman and Henrici, in Manual, 6th ed., 1948, 935.)

coe.li'co.lor. L. noun *coelum* heaven, sky; L. noun *color* color; M.L. adj. *coelicolor* sky-colored.

Description by Müller except as noted.

Morphology of *Streptomyces coelicolor* has not been fully described. According to Waksman and Curtis, who described *Actinomyces violaceus-ruber*, this is as follows: straight filaments with open, dextrorse spirals. Conidia ellipsoidal or rod-shaped, 0.7 to 1.0 by 0.8 to 1.5 microns.

Gelatin: Good growth. No pigment formation. Liquefaction fairly rapid, beginning in 4 to 7 days.

Agar: Good growth. Pigment lacking or faint blue (J. E. Conn, Jour. Bact., *46*, 1943, 133).

Synthetic agar: Thin, spreading, colorless at first, becoming red, then blue. Aerial mycelium thin, white, powdery, becoming mouse-gray.

Asparagine agar: With glycerol as source of carbon, good growth, violet to deep blue, with pigment diffusing through medium; final H-ion concentration, about pH 7.0 to 8.0. With glucose as source of carbon, poorer growth, red, no diffusion of pigment; final H-ion concentration, about pH 6.0 to 5.0 (Conn).

Broth: Good growth. Cretaceous layer around edge.

Milk: No change at 25° C. (Conn). At 37° C., coagulation. Peptonization beginning in 3 to 5 days.

Potato: Strong pigment production, sometimes greenish blue or violet, but usually sky-blue, diffusing through medium and coloring water at base of tube.

Blood agar: Hemolysis showing on 4th day.

Müller reports no acid from carbohydrates on organic media. In synthetic liquid media, acid production from glucose is pronounced; pyruvic and succinic acids have been identified (Cochrane and Dimmick, Jour. Bact., *58*, 1949, 723).

Nitrites produced from nitrates.

Pigment: The most striking characteristic of this organism is a litmus-like pigment, usually produced on potato or synthetic media, which is deep blue and water-soluble at alkaline reactions (beyond pH 8.0), violet around neutrality, and red (insoluble in water) at about pH 6.0. Conn points out that the primary pigment has a spectrophotometric curve almost identical with that of azolitmin but that there are undoubtedly other pigments produced, especially in the case of the strains believed to be typical of *Actinomyces violaceus-ruber* (as previously pointed out by Waksman and Curtis).

Aerobic.

Good growth at room temperature and at 37° C.

Antagonistic properties: Some strains produce coelicolorin and mycetin.

Distinctive character: Litmus-like pigment.

Comments: Because of the numerous colors and shades shown by the pigment according to final H-ion concentration and other less understood factors, this species may have been described under various names. On the other hand, it is entirely possible, as pointed out by J. E. Conn (*op. cit.*, 1943, 133), that careful study of the pigments may show that more than one species is actually involved.

Relationships to other species: Regarded by Waksman and Henrici (in Manual, 6th ed., 1948, 935) as the same as *Actinomyces violaceus* Waksman and Curtis, Soil Science, *1*, 1916, 110 (*Actinomyces violaceus-ruber* Waksman and Curtis, *ibid.*, 127) and *Actinomyces tricolor* Wollenweber, Arbeiten d. Forschungsinstitut für Kartoffelbau, 1920, 13. It is however, pointed out by Conn (*op. cit.*, 1943, 133) that certain differences between the descriptions of Waksman and Curtis and that of Müller may correspond to actual chemical differences in the pigments produced and that the organism of Waksman and Curtis may be a separate species.

Source: Dust contamination on a potato slant.

Habitat: Soil and plant surfaces. Very abundant.

7. Streptomyces pluricolor (Berestnew, 1897, *emend.* Krassilnikov, 1941) Waksman, 1953. (*Actinomyces pluricolor diffundens* Berestnew, Inaug. Diss., Moskow, 1897; see Cent. f. Bakt., I Abt., *24*, 1898, 708; *Actinomyces pluricolor* Krassilnikov, Guide to the Actinomycetes, Izd. Akad. Nauk, U.S.S.R., Moskau, 1941, 17; not *Actinomyces pluricolor* Terni, quoted from Gasperini, Cent. f. Bakt., *15*, 1894, 684; Waksman, in Waksman and Lechevalier, Actinomycetes and Their Antibiotics, Baltimore, 1953, 42.)

plu.ri'co.lor. L. comp.adj. *plus, pluris* more, many; L. mas.n. *color* color; M.L. adj. *pluricolor* many-colored, variegated.

Aerial mycelium: Well-developed, white-gray. Sporophores produce numerous spirals with 3 to 5 turns (sinistrorse). Spores ellipsoidal, 0.7 by 0.9 micron.

Gelatin: Rapid liquefaction.

Synthetic agar: At first red-yellow growth, changing to blue or blue-green. The blue pigment dissolves into medium.

Broth: Green, fluorescent pigment produced.

Milk: Peptonized without coagulation.

Potato: Sharp blue growth and soluble pigment.

Sucrose is inverted.

Starch is hydrolyzed.

No growth on cellulose.

Antagonistic properties: None.

Source: Isolated from air.

Habitat: Unknown.

8. Streptomyces cyaneus (Krassilnikov 1941) Waksman, 1953. (*Actinomyces cyaneus* Krassilnikov, Guide to the Actinomycetes, Izd. Akad. Nauk, U.S.S.R., Moskau, 1941, 14; Waksman, in Waksman and Lechevalier, Actinomycetes and Their Antibiotics, Baltimore, 1953, 42.)

cy.an'e.us. Gr. adj. *cyaneus* dark blue.

Vegetative growth: Blue, diffusible pigment, remaining blue at both acid and alkaline reactions.

Aerial mycelium: Sporophores produce open spirals (sinistrorse) with 2 to 3 turns in each. Spores ellipsoidal, seldom spherical, 0.6 by 0.6 to 0.8 micron.

Gelatin: Rapid liquefaction, completed in 5 to 6 days.

Synthetic agar: Colonies at first smooth, becoming lumpy, leathery-compact and covered with well developed blue-gray aerial mycelium.

Milk: Peptonized after coagulation.

Sucrose not inverted.

Starch is weakly hydrolyzed.

No growth on cellulose.

Nitrites not produced from nitrates.

Antagonistic properties: Weak.

Source: Isolated from soil.

Habitat: Soil.

9. Streptomyces vinaceus Mayer et al., 1951. (Mayer, Crane, DeBoer, Konopka, Marsh and Eisman, XIIth Intern. Congr. Pure and Appl. Chem., 1951, 283.)

vi.na'ce.us. L. adj. *vinaceus* of or belonging to wine or the grape.

Aerial mycelium: No spirals. Spores nearly spherical, 1.0 to 1.5 microns.

Gelatin: Sparse, tan-white growth. No soluble pigment. Ready liquefaction.

Agar: Rough, dry, off-white growth with reverse blue-red. No soluble pigment. Several strains produce concentric growth rings.

Synthetic agar: Rough, off-white growth with reverse purple-red. Soluble, blue-red pigment upon extended incubation.

Starch agar: Rough, dry, elevated, spreading, off-white growth.

Glucose agar: Rough, dry, off-white growth with reverse dark red-blue. Soluble red-blue pigment only on extended incubation.

Potato: Rough, slightly moist, off-white growth. No soluble pigment.

Starch is hydrolyzed.

Optimum temperature, between 22° and 28° C.

Antagonistic properties: Produces vinactin, an antibiotic similar in many respects to viomycin.

Distinctive character: Soluble red-blue pigment produced in certain media, particularly in glucose-peptone broth by shake culture.

Source: Presumably soil.
Habitat: Soil.

10. **Streptomyces violaceus** (Rossi-Doria, 1891, *emend*. Krassilnikov, 1941) Waksman, 1953. (*Streptotrix* (sic) *violacea* Rossi-Doria, Ann. d. Inst. d'Ig. sper. d. Univ. di Roma, *1*, 1891, 411; *Actinomyces violaceus* Gasperini, Cent. f. Bakt., *15*, 1894, 684; Krassilnikov, Guide to the Actinomycetes, Izd. Akad. Nauk, U.S.S.R., Moskau, 1941, 15; Waksman, in Waksman and Lechevalier, Actinomycetes and Their Antibiotics, Baltimore, 1953, 43.)

vi.o.la'ce.us. L. adj. *violaceus* violet-colored.

Vegetative growth: Well developed, nonseptated; readily breaks up in old cultures. Lichenoid colonies at first red, then becoming dark blue and finally purple-violet. Some cultures produce fat droplets in the colony, pigmented red or purple.

Aerial mycelium: Produced only poorly or not at all; some substrates, such as cellulose, paraffin or fats, favor its formation. Aerial hyphae long, straight, seldom branching and also short-branched. Sporophores forming open spirals, sinistrorse curvatures.

Spores spherical and ellipsoidal.

Gelatin: Slow liquefaction.

Synthetic agar: Diffusible pigments which become purple-violet to dark violet.

Milk: Not coagulated; slowly peptonized.

Sucrose rapidly inverted.

Starch is weakly hydrolyzed.

Poor or no growth on cellulose.

No evidence of nitrate reduction by most strains; a few strains give a positive nitrite reaction.

Optimum temperature, between 25° and 30° C.

Antagonistic properties: Exerts strong antagonistic effect upon various bacteria.

Source: Isolated from air and water.

Habitat: Unknown.

11. **Streptomyces verne** (Waksman and Curtis, 1916) Waksman and Henrici, 1948. (*Actinomyces verne* Waksman and Curtis, Soil Sci., *1*, 1916, 120; Waksman and Henrici, in Manual, 6th ed., 1948, 936.)

ver'ne. Etymology uncertain.

Filaments with close branching of the hyphae. Capacity to produce aerial mycelium lost on cultivation.

Gelatin stab: Small, cream-colored colonies. Rapid liquefaction.

Agar: Small, grayish colonies with depressed center, becoming wrinkled.

Synthetic agar: Abundant, spreading, wrinkled, elevated, glossy, yellowish growth, becoming brownish, lichenoid margin.

Starch agar: Scant, brownish, restricted growth.

Glucose agar: Abundant, much folded growth, center raised, gray with purplish tinge, entire.

Glucose broth: Slightly flaky sediment.

Litmus milk: Pinkish brown ring; coagulated; peptonized, with alkaline reaction.

Potato: Cream-colored growth, becoming gray, wrinkled.

Soluble brown pigment formed. Soluble green pigment produced when freshly isolated.

Starch is hydrolyzed.

Nitrites produced from nitrates.

Aerobic.

Optimum temperature, 37° C.

Antagonistic properties: Limited activity against some bacteria.

Source: Isolated once from upland California soil.

Habitat: Soil.

12. **Streptomyces viridans** (Krassilnikov, 1941) Waksman, 1953. (*Actinomyces viridans* Krassilnikov, Guide to the Actinomycetes, Izd. Akad. Nauk, U.S.S.R., Moskau, 1941, 33; Waksman, in Waksman and Lechevalier, Actinomycetes and Their Antibiotics, Baltimore, 1953, 44.)

vi'ri.dans. L. part.adj. *viridans* green-making.

Vegetative growth: Green to brown-green colonies.

Aerial mycelium: Dark gray, olive-colored or gray-green, velvety, covering the whole colony. Sporophores long, spiral-shaped. Spores cylindrical.

Gelatin: Rapid liquefaction.

Agar: Brown-green growth. Soluble brown substance produced.

Synthetic agar: Green colonies. Soluble green pigment produced.

Milk: Coagulated and rapidly peptonized.
Sucrose rapidly inverted.
Starch is rapidly hydrolyzed.
Poor growth on cellulose.
Nitrites actively produced from nitrates.
Antagonistic properties: None; some strains are weakly active.
Source: Isolated from soil.
Habitat: Soil.

13. Streptomyces californicus (Waksman and Curtis, 1916) Waksman and Henrici, 1948. (*Actinomyces californicus* Waksman and Curtis, Soil Sci., *1*, 1916, 122; Waksman and Henrici, in Manual, 6th ed., 1948, 936.)

ca.li.for'ni.cus. M.L. adj. *californicus* pertaining to California; named for California, U.S.A.

Aerial mycelium: Filaments with long, narrow, open spirals. Spherical to ellipsoidal conidia.

Gelatin stab: Gray, moist, abundant surface growth. Liquefaction in 30 days. No soluble pigment.

Agar: Thin, restricted, yellowish to cream-colored growth.

Synthetic agar: Spreading, vinaceous-colored growth. Aerial mycelium powdery, thin, light neutral gray. No soluble pigment.

Starch agar: Growth spreading, pink center with colorless to gray margin.

Glucose agar: Restricted, much folded, cream-colored growth with sulfur-yellow tinge.

Glucose broth: Solid, cream-colored mass on surface, with pink tinge.

Litmus milk: Faint, brownish surface growth; coagulated; peptonized in 40 days.

Potato: Glossy, yellow to red growth, turning red-brown.

Starch is hydrolyzed.

Nitrites produced from nitrates.

Aerobic.

Optimum temperature, 37° C.

Antagonistic properties: Limited. Some strains produce viomycin.

Source: Isolated once from California sandy loam.

Habitat: Soil.

14. Streptomyces virgatus (Krassilnikov, 1941) Waksman, 1953. (*Actinomyces*

virgatus Krassilnikov, Guide to the Actinomycetes, Izd. Akad. Nauk, U.S.S.R., Moskau, 1941, 32; Waksman, in Waksman and Lechevalier, Actinomycetes and Their Antibiotics, Baltimore, 1953, 45.)

vir.ga'tus. L. adj. *virgatus* of twigs, rod-shaped.

Vegetative growth: Yellow-green to citron-yellow or pure yellow colonies; pale green on some media. Pigment insoluble in substrate. Some strains produce brown substance in protein media.

Aerial mycelium: Weakly developed, white or pale yellow. Sporophores produced in form of tufts. Oidiospores cylindrical, elongated; in some strains round-ellipsoidal.

Gelatin: Rapid liquefaction.

Milk: Rapidly coagulated and peptonized.

Starch is rapidly hydrolyzed.

No growth on cellulose.

Nitrites actively produced from nitrates.

Antagonistic properties: None.

Source: Isolated from soil.

Habitat: Soil.

15. Streptomyces flaveolus (Waksman, 1923) Waksman and Henrici, 1948. (Actinomyces 168, Waksman, Soil Sci., *8*, 1919, 134; *Actinomyces flaveolus* Waksman, in Manual, 1st ed., 1923, 368; Waksman and Henrici, in Manual, 6th ed., 1948, 936.)

fla.ve'o.lus. L. adj. *flavus* golden yellow; M.L. dim.adj. *flaveolus* somewhat yellow.

Aerial mycelium: Numerous closed and open spirals on all media. Conidia ellipsoidal.

Gelatin stab: Liquefied; abundant, yellowish, spreading pellicle.

Agar: White, glistening, wrinkled growth.

Synthetic agar: Growth light sulfur-yellow turning to cadmium-yellow, penetrating deep into medium. Aerial mycelium white to ash-gray patches.

Starch agar: White, spreading growth.

Glucose agar: Restricted growth, surface folded, raised.

Glucose broth: Thin, yellow pellicle.

Litmus milk: Sulfur-yellow ring; coagulated; peptonized, with faintly alkaline reaction.

Potato: Abundant, wrinkled, cream-colored growth.

Starch is hydrolyzed.

Soluble empire-yellow pigment formed.

Nitrites produced from nitrates.

Aerobic.

Optimum temperature, 25° C.

Antagonistic properties: Some strains produce actinomycin.

Source: Isolated from soil.

Habitat: Soil.

16. Streptomyces parvus (Krainsky, 1914) Waksman and Henrici, 1948. (*Actinomyces parvus* Krainsky, Cent. f. Bakt., II Abt., *41*, 1914, 622; Waksman and Henrici, in Manual, 6th ed., 1948, 939.)

par′vus. L. adj. *parvus* small.

Vegetative growth: Golden yellow to brick-red, depending on composition of medium.

Aerial mycelium: Poorly developed, rose-white. Sporophores produce spirals. Spores spherical to ellipsoidal, 0.9 to 1.3 by 1.2 to 1.8 microns.

Gelatin: Yellow colonies. Slow liquefaction.

Ca-malate agar: Small, yellow colonies with light yellow aerial mycelium.

Starch agar: Same as on Ca-malate agar.

Glucose agar: Same as on Ca-malate agar.

Glucose broth: Hemispherical colonies in bottom of tube.

Litmus milk: Rapidly coagulated and peptonized.

Diastatic action good.

Good growth on cellulose.

Nitrites weakly produced from nitrates.

Aerobic.

Optimum temperature, 25° C.

Antagonistic properties: Produces actinomycin.

Source: Isolated from garden soil.

Habitat: Soil.

17. Streptomyces xanthophaeus Lindenbein, 1952. (Arch. f. Mikrobiol., *17*, 1952, 378.)

xan.tho.phae′us. Gr. adj. *xanthophaes* golden, gleaming; M.L. adj. *xanthophaeus* shining like gold.

Gelatin: Leathery, brown, abundant growth. Aerial mycelium velvety, ash-gray. Soluble yellow-brown pigment. Rapid liquefaction.

Agar: Abundant, diffuse, smooth growth

with light brown reverse. Aerial mycelium powdery ash-gray to white. Yellow to yellow-brown soluble pigment.

Synthetic agar: Abundant, crumb-like, smooth, brownish growth. Aerial mycelium cottony white, later grayish or even reddish gray. Soluble light brown pigment, later yellow-brown.

Glucose asparagine agar: Abundant, diffuse, colorless growth with light yellow reverse. Aerial mycelium powdery white. Soluble light yellow pigment.

Ca-malate agar: Abundant, crumb-like growth with yellowish red reverse. Aerial mycelium velvety, white-gray or reddish gray. Soluble dark red-yellow pigment.

Starch agar: Abundant, lichenoid growth. Aerial mycelium velvety, violet-gray. Soluble dark brown pigment.

Glucose agar: Abundant, diffuse, colorless growth with light yellow reverse. Aerial mycelium abundant, powdery, seldom velvety, light brown. Soluble yellow pigment.

Glucose broth: Very good, colorless surface growth, later producing heavy sediment. Abundant flocculent particles. Aerial mycelium cottony, grayish white, tending later to disappear. Soluble light yellow pigment, becoming orange-yellow.

Milk: Abundant, lichenoid growth. Aerial mycelium gray to violet. Soluble dark brown pigment. Actively peptonized.

Potato: Abundant, lichenoid growth. Aerial mycelium powdery gray. No soluble pigment.

Starch is rapidly hydrolyzed.

No growth on cellulose.

Antagonistic properties: Produces antibiotics.

Source: Isolated from soil.

Habitat: Soil.

18. Streptomyces cellulosae (Krainsky, 1914) Waksman and Henrici, 1948. (*Actinomyces cellulosae* Krainsky, Cent. f. Bakt., II Abt., *41*, 1914, 662; Waksman and Henrici, in Manual, 6th ed., 1948, 938.)

cel.lu.lo′sae. M.L. noun *cellulosa* cellulose; M.L. gen.noun *cellulosae* of cellulose.

Vegetative growth: Yellow, producing soluble yellow pigment. No soluble brown pigment.

Aerial mycelium: Well developed, gray to

white-gray. Spores almost spherical, 1.3 microns in diameter, often arranged in chains.

Gelatin colonies: Circular, yellowish.

Gelatin stab: Liquefaction.

Agar: White aerial mycelium.

Ca-malate agar: Yellowish colonies; gray aerial mycelium. Soluble yellow pigment formed.

Starch agar: Abundant growth; gray aerial mycelium. Soluble yellow pigment.

Glucose agar: Same as for starch agar.

Glucose broth: Coarse, flaky growth. Yellow pigment.

Litmus milk: Rapidly coagulated and peptonized.

Potato: Colorless growth; aerial mycelium gray.

Strong diastatic action.

Esculin is hydrolyzed.

Cellulose is decomposed.

Nitrates show slight reduction.

Aerobic.

Optimum temperature, between 30° and 35° C.

Antagonistic properties: Positive.

Source: Isolated from soil.

Habitat: Soil.

19. **Streptomyces rimosus** Sobin et al., 1950. (Sobin, Finlay and Kane, U. S. Pat. 2,516,080, July 18, 1950.)

ri.mo′sus. L. adj. *rimosus* full of cracks.

Vegetative growth: Flat, smooth colonies with irregular edge; yellow pigment.

Aerial mycelium: Limited, ocher-colored in center, colonial-buff at edge; spirals numerous; conidia 0.6 to 0.7 by 0.8 to 1.4 microns, cylindrical.

Gelatin: Aerial mycelium white. No soluble yellow pigment. No liquefaction.

Agar: Poor growth, no aerial mycelium; faint yellowish pigment.

Czapek's synthetic agar: Produces very limited growth which is colorless and submerged. No aerial mycelium and no soluble pigment.

Asparagine agar: Aerial mycelium white to pallid quaker-drab; faint yellow soluble pigment.

Starch agar: Poor, thin growth; aerial mycelium limited; cinnamon-drab colonies.

Glucose agar: Growth with dry, cracked surface; aerial mycelium mouse-gray; yellowish brown pigment.

Milk: Thick pellicle, aerial mycelium grayish white; not peptonized; no change in pH.

Potato: Moderate, wrinkled growth; aerial mycelium white to dark; yellowish brown pigment.

Starch is weakly hydrolyzed.

Cellulose not decomposed.

Nitrites actively produced from nitrates.

Odor: Earthy.

Antagonistic properties: Produces oxytetracycline, an amphoteric substance active against various bacteria, rickettsiae and the larger viruses; also produces rimocidin, an antifungal agent.

Source: Isolated from soil. Cultural characteristics described are those of isolate No. S3279. A culture has been deposited with the Fermentation Division of the Northern Regional Research Laboratory, Peoria, Illinois, permanent collection number NRRL-2234.

Habitat: Soil.

20. **Streptomyces griseoflavus** (Krainsky, 1914) Waksman and Henrici, 1948. (*Actinomyces griseoflavus* Krainsky, Cent. f. Bakt., II Abt., *41*, 1914, 662; Waksman and Henrici, in Manual, 6th ed., 1948, 948.)

gri.se.o.fla′vus. M.L. adj. *griseus* gray; L. adj. *flavus* yellow; M.L. adj. *griseoflavus* grayish yellow.

Vegetative growth: Thin, cream-colored, later becoming much folded or lichenoid.

Aerial mycelium: Powdery, white, appearing first on drier edges of growth. Sporophores straight, abundantly branched; no curvatures and no spirals produced.

Gelatin: Cream-colored to brownish growth, covered with white aerial mycelium. Slow liquefaction, with faint yellowish coloration of the liquefied zone.

Agar: Cream-colored growth, covered with white aerial mycelium; no soluble pigment.

Synthetic agar: Reddish brown to orange growth, covered with white aerial mycelium; faint yellowish soluble pigment.

Ca-malate agar: Large colonies covered with yellow to greenish gray aerial mycelium.

Starch agar: Cream-colored growth with brownish center; no aerial mycelium.

Glucose agar: White aerial mycelium is slowly formed.

Yeast-glucose agar: Lichenoid, cream-colored to brownish growth; white to grayish aerial mycelium; soluble yellowish pigment.

Glucose broth: Flaky growth.

Milk: Cream-colored to yellowish growth; aerial mycelium thin, white. Rapidly peptonized without previous coagulation.

Potato: Lichenoid, cream-colored to brownish growth, later becoming reddish brown; aerial mycelium powdery white to gray; no soluble pigment.

Starch is weakly hydrolyzed.

Esculin is attacked.

Good growth on cellulose.

Nitrites produced from nitrates.

Aerobic.

Optimum temperature, 35° C.

Antagonistic properties: Strongly antagonistic.

Source: Isolated from soil.

Habitat: Soil.

21. **Streptomyces aureofaciens** Duggar, 1948. (Ann. N. Y. Acad. Sci., *51*, 1948, 177; U. S. Patent 2,482,055, Sept. 13, 1949.)

au.re.o.fa'ci.ens. L. neut.n. *aurum* gold; L. part.adj. *faciens* producing; M.L. part. adj. *aureofaciens* golden-making.

Vegetative growth: Mycelium hyaline, becoming yellow in 2 to 3 days, later golden tan to tawny.

Aerial mycelium: White, becoming brownish gray to dark, drab-gray in 5 to 10 days. Sporophores straight, flexuous; no spirals. Spores spherical to ellipsoidal, longest diameter 1.5 microns.

Gelatin: No liquefaction.

Agar: Good, light brownish growth. No aerial mycelium. No soluble pigment.

Asparagine-meat extract glucose agar: Hyaline growth changing to orange-yellow. Aerial mycelium abundant, white, changing to deep gray or dark gray with tawny reverse. Faint yellowish soluble pigment.

Milk: Limited, yellow-brown growth. No coagulation or peptonization.

Potato: Wrinkled, orange-yellow growth. Color of plug unchanged.

Antagonistic properties: Produces chlortetracycline, an amphoteric compound containing both nitrogen and non-ionic chlorine, active against various bacteria, rickettsiae and the larger viruses.

Comments: The numerous natural and induced variants of *S. aureofaciens* display wide variations in color of vegetative growth ranging from pale yellow to reddish brown and even occasionally greenish depending upon the composition of the nutrient substrates and environmental conditions. The color of aerial mycelia is influenced by sporulation. Yellowish, soluble pigment often not discernible. Loose spirals are infrequently encountered.

Source: Isolated from soil.

Habitat: Presumably soil.

22. **Streptomyces albidoflavus** (Rossi-Doria, 1891) Waksman and Henrici, 1948. (*Streptotrix* (sic) *albido-flava* Rossi-Doria, Ann. d. Ist. d'Ig. sper. d. Univ. di Roma, *1*, 1891, 407; Waksman and Henrici, in Manual, 6th ed., 1948, 949.)

al.bi.do.fla'vus. L. adj. *albidus* white; L. adj. *flavus* yellow; M.L. adj. *albidoflavus* whitish yellow.

Description taken from Duché (Encyclopédie Mycologique, Paris, *6*, 1934, 294).

Gelatin: Punctiform colonies with white aerial mycelium on surface of liquid; no soluble pigment; rapid liquefaction.

Agar: Cream-colored growth covered with fine white aerial mycelium; yellow soluble pigment.

Synthetic asparagine agar: Growth becomes rapidly covered with white aerial mycelium, later becoming whitish yellow; brown on reverse side; yellowish soluble pigment.

Tyrosine agar: Fine growth with orange-yellow on reverse side; medium becomes colored yellowish to yellowish rose.

Synthetic asparagine solution: Long branching filaments, 0.6 micron in diameter. Thicker aerial mycelium producing irregular spores; flaky growth dropping to bottom of tube. Surface growth becomes covered with yellowish white aerial mycelium; brownish on reverse side; soluble pigment yellowish.

Peptone solution: Rapid, much folded

growth, partly covered with white mycelium on surface of medium; soluble yellow-ochre pigment.

Milk: Rapid growth becoming covered with whitish aerial mycelium; never fully covering the surface; no coagulation; peptonization begins slowly and is completed in 13 days, liquid becoming colored yellowish orange.

Coagulated serum: Cream-colored growth of surface becoming covered with white aerial mycelium; rapid liquefaction of serum.

Starch medium: Cream-colored growth rapidly colored with yellow aerial mycelium; after 20 days growth becomes much folded; greenish on reverse side; slightly amber-colored in medium.

Antagonistic properties: Positive.

Comments: This species is closely related to *Streptomyces albus*. Develops poorly on synthetic media without asparagine.

Source: Isolated from dust.

Habitat: Unknown.

23. **Streptomyces lieskei** (Duché, 1934) Waksman and Henrici, 1948. (*Actinomyces lieskei* Duché, Encyclopédie Mycologique, Paris, *6*, 1934, 289; Waksman and Henrici, in Manual, 6th ed., 1948, 950.)

lies'ke.i. M.L. gen.noun *lieskei* of Lieske; named for Prof. Rudolf Lieske of Leipzig.

Gelatin: Cream-colored growth becoming covered with white aerial mycelium; no soluble pigment. Rapid liquefaction.

Agar: Cream-colored growth becoming covered with white aerial mycelium; yellowish soluble pigment.

Synthetic agar: Cream-colored growth with delayed white aerial mycelium growing from the edge toward the center; mycelium later yellowish. Reverse of growth yellowish to green. Dirty yellow to yellow-green soluble pigment.

Synthetic solution: Long branching filaments 0.7 micron in diameter. Yellowish white aerial mycelium does not readily produce spores; flakes drop to the bottom of the tube.

Peptone solution: Cream-colored colonies on surface with flakes in the liquid dropping to the bottom of the tube. Liquid becomes yellowish in color.

Tyrosine medium: Rapid growth on surface with whitish yellow aerial mycelium; yellowish to orange-yellow soluble pigment.

Milk: Cream-colored growth; colorless on reverse side; no aerial mycelium. Peptonization without coagulation. After 20 days the whole milk becomes a clear yellowish liquid.

Coagulated serum: Clear-colored growth. Rapid liquefaction.

Relationship to other species: Culture related to *Streptomyces alboflavus* and *Streptomyces albidoflavus*.

Source: Culture secured from the collection of Prof. R. Lieske.

Habitat: Unknown.

24. **Streptomyces flavovirens** (Waksman, 1923) Waksman and Henrici, 1948. (Actinomyces 128, Waksman, Soil Sci., *8*, 1919, 117; *Actinomyces flavovirens* Waksman, in Manual, 1st ed., 1923, 352; Waksman and Henrici, in Manual, 6th ed., 1948, 940.)

fla.vo.vi'rens. L. adj. *flavus* yellow; L. p.adj. *virens* being green; M.L. adj. *flavovirens* being yellow-green.

Aerial mycelium: Large masses of minute tufts; the hyphae coarse, straight, short, relatively unbranched, beaded; open spirals may be produced in certain substances. Conidia spherical, ellipsoidal to rod-shaped, 0.75 to 1.0 by 1.0 to 1.5 microns.

Gelatin stab: Yellowish green surface pellicle, consisting of a mass of small colonies, on the liquefied medium.

Agar: Yellowish growth; the reverse dark in center with yellowish zone and outer white zone.

Synthetic agar: Growth spreading deep into the substratum, yellowish with greenish tinge. Aerial mycelium gray, powdery.

Starch agar: Greenish yellow, spreading growth, developing deep into the medium.

Glucose agar: Restricted growth, developing only to a very small extent into the medium, yellow, turning black, edge entire.

Glucose broth: Thick, sulfur-yellow pellicle or ring.

Litmus milk: Cream-colored to brownish ring; coagulated; peptonized, becoming faintly alkaline.

Potato: Sulfur-yellow, wrinkled growth. Starch is hydrolyzed.

Greenish yellow soluble pigment formed. Only a trace of nitrite is produced from nitrates.

Aerobic.

Optimum temperature, 25° C.

Antagonistic properties: Active against fungi.

Source: Isolated from soil.

Habitat: Soil.

25. Streptomyces celluloflavus Nishimura et al., 1953. (Nishimura, Kimura and Kuroya, Jour. Antibiotics (Japanese), 6, 1953, 57.)

cel.lu.lo.fla'vus. L. dim.n. *cellula* a small room; M.L. n. *cellulosum* cellulose; L. adj. *flavus* yellow; M.L. adj. *celluloflavus* cellulose-yellow (probably intended to mean turning cellulose yellow).

Aerial mycelium: A few imperfect spirals. Almost spherical spores, 0.9 by 1.0 micron.

Gelatin: Ivory-yellow to olive-buff colonies on surface of liquefied portion. No aerial mycelium. Faint brownish pigment. Rapid to medium liquefaction.

Agar: Olive-buff growth turning colorless. Scant, cottony, white to grayish aerial mycelium. Soluble yellow pigment with tinge of green to old gold.

Synthetic agar: Glossy growth, developing deep into medium, later becoming marguerite-yellow. Faint sulfur-yellow soluble pigment.

Ca-malate glycerol agar: Primrose-yellow growth, later turning white to pale olive-buff, with blackish center. Cottony aerial mycelium white with grayish patches, later turning olive-buff. Soluble citron-yellow pigment.

Glucose agar: Cream-colored to yellow growth. Scant cottony white to gray aerial mycelium. Soluble sulfur-yellow pigment.

Milk: Yellow to dark olive-buff growth. White aerial mycelium. Soluble reddish brown pigment. Coagulated and rapidly peptonized.

Potato: Wrinkled, spreading, deep olive-buff growth. Aerial mycelium white to olive-buff. Soluble deep olive-buff pigment.

Poor growth on cellulose with soluble, yellow pigment.

Tyrosine medium: Ivory-yellow to cream-buff growth. None to scant white aerial mycelium. Soluble greenish yellow pigment.

Antagonistic properties: Produces thiolutin.

Source: Isolated from soil.

Habitat: Soil.

26. Streptomyces limosus Lindenbein, 1952. (Arch. f. Mikrobiol., 17, 1952, 379.)

li.mo'sus. L. adj. *limosus* full of slime, slimy.

Vegetative growth: Crumb-like, yellowish, later becoming gray to coal-black; greenish yellow reverse.

Aerial mycelium: Powdery snow-white to gray, or completely lacking. Soluble greenish yellow to citron-yellow pigment.

Gelatin: Yellow-brown growth. No aerial mycelium. Soluble, dark brown pigment. Complete liquefaction.

Agar: Diffuse, colorless growth with light brown reverse. No aerial mycelium. Soluble pigment around bottom.

Synthetic agar: Diffuse, colorless growth, later becoming crumb-like, light yellow. No aerial mycelium. Soluble citron-yellow pigment.

Glucose asparagine agar: Crumb-like, light yellow growth, later becoming black with citron-yellow reverse. Aerial mycelium white, later ash-gray. Soluble citron-yellow pigment.

Ca-malate agar: Crumb-like growth with dark yellow reverse. Aerial mycelium powdery to velvety, white, later ash-gray. Soluble golden yellow pigment.

Starch agar: Small, yellowish colonies with brownish reverse. Aerial mycelium velvety, gray-white. Soluble light gray pigment.

Glucose agar: Good growth with yellow-brown reverse. Aerial mycelium velvety, white-gray to ash-gray. Soluble yellow-brown pigment.

Glucose broth: Growth in the form of sediment, white, later light yellow. No aerial mycelium. Soluble citron-yellow pigment.

Milk: Lichenoid, light yellow growth. Aerial mycelium powdery, gray-white. Soluble light brown pigment. Actively peptonized.

Potato: Moderate, brownish yellow to light brown growth. Aerial mycelium powdery, gray-white. Soluble citron-yellow to sulfur-yellow pigment.

Starch is rapidly hydrolyzed.

No growth on cellulose.

Source: Isolated from mud from the edge of a river.

Habitat: Unknown.

27. Streptomyces griseoluteus Umezawa et al., 1951. (Umezawa, Hayano, Maeda, Ogata and Okami, Jour. Antibiotics (Japanese), *4*, 1951, 34; also see Okami, Jour. Antibiotics (Japanese), *5*, 1952, 478.)

gri.se.o.lu'te.us. M.L. adj. *griseus* gray; *luteus* golden yellow; M.L. adj. *griseoluteus* grayish yellow.

Aerial mycelium: Hyphae branch monopodially and irregularly; conidia ellipsoidal to cylindrical, 1.0 to 1.2 by 1.8 to 2.2 microns.

Gelatin: No growth.

Agar: Wrinkled, transparent growth. Aerial mycelium thin, white, powdery. No soluble pigment or a yellowish brown pigment.

Synthetic agar: Thin, colorless to cream-colored growth. Margin plumose, penetrating into medium. Aerial mycelium powdery, grayish white to light drab. No soluble pigment or a yellowish brown pigment.

Glucose agar: Wrinkled, cream-colored growth. Aerial mycelium thin, white. Reddish brown pigment.

Glucose broth: Cream-colored to brown surface ring. Aerial mycelium powdery, white. Soluble reddish brown pigment weakly produced.

Milk: Cream-colored ring; white surface patches.

Potato: Abundant, wrinkled, cream-colored growth. Aerial mycelium dusty white, thin; plug becoming slightly brownish.

Starch is hydrolyzed.

Nitrites produced from nitrates.

Antagonistic properties: Produces griseolutein, a yellow antibiotic active against Gram-positive and Gram-negative bacteria.

Source: Isolated from the soil of a potato field in Tokyo.

Habitat: Soil.

28. Streptomyces bobiliae (Waksman and Curtis, 1916) Waksman and Henrici, 1948. (*Actinomyces bobili* Waksman and Curtis, Soil Sci., *1*, 1916, 121; Waksman and Henrici, in Manual, 6th ed., 1948, 937.)

bo.bi'li.ae. M.L. gen.noun *bobiliae* of Bobili; named for Bobili, a person's nickname.

Aerial mycelium: Few close spirals of a dextrorse type.

Gelatin: Dense, cream-colored to brownish surface growth. Rapid liquefaction.

Agar: Restricted, glossy, gray growth becoming brownish.

Synthetic agar: Abundant, glossy wrinkled, elevated, coral-red growth becoming deep red. Aerial mycelium scant, white.

Starch agar: Restricted, finely wrinkled, coral-red growth with hyaline margin.

Glucose broth: Round colonies in fluid; flaky sediment.

Milk: Dark brown ring; not coagulated; peptonized.

Potato: Thin, yellowish growth becoming red, dry and wrinkled.

Starch is hydrolyzed.

Nitrites produced from nitrates.

Soluble brown pigment formed.

Aerobic.

Optimum temperature, 37° C.

Antagonistic properties: Positive.

Source: Isolated once from adobe and from garden soils.

Habitat: Soil.

29. Streptomyces aurantiacus (Rossi-Doria, 1891, *emend.* Krassilnikov, 1941) Waksman, 1953. (*Streptotrix* (sic) *aurantiaca* Rossi-Doria, Ann. Inst. d'Ig. sper. d. Univ. di Roma, *1*, 1891, 417; *Actinomyces aurantiacus* Gasperini, Ann. Inst. d'Ig. sper. d. Univ. di Roma, *2*, 1892, 222; Krassilnikov, Guide to the Actinomycetes, Izd. Akad. Nauk, U.S.S.R., Moskau, 1941, 36; Waksman, in Waksman and Lechevalier, Actinomycetes and Their Antibiotics, Baltimore, 1953, 53.)

au.ran.ti'a.cus. L. neut.n. *aurum* gold; M.L. neut.n. *Aurantium* generic name of the orange; M.L. adj. *aurantiacus* orange-colored.

Vegetative growth: Lichenoid, dry, compact, bright orange or golden color which does not change on continued incubation. Pigment insoluble in medium but soluble in organic solvents. Produces an abundance of chlamydospores.

Aerial mycelium: Poorly developed or completely absent on many media; nonseptate. Sporophores form spirals with 3 to

5 turns. Spores spherical to ellipsoidal, 0.6 to 0.8 by 0.7 to 0.9 micron.

Gelatin: Slow liquefaction after 20 to 30 days' incubation.

Milk: Weakly peptonized, usually without previous coagulation.

Potato: Soluble brown pigment.

Sucrose not inverted.

Starch is slowly hydrolyzed.

No growth on cellulose.

Fats rapidly hydrolyzed and utilized.

Paraffin: Good growth with spiral-forming sporophores and spherical spores.

Nitrites not produced from nitrates.

Antagonistic properties: Strongly antagonistic.

Comment: This species represents a widely distributed group of organisms including such forms as *Actinomyces parvus* of Krainsky and others.

Source: Isolated from soil.

Habitat: Soil.

30. **Streptomyces griseolus** (Waksman, 1923) Waksman and Henrici, 1948. (Actinomyces 96, Waksman, Soil Sci., *8*, 1919, 121; *Actinomyces griseolus* Waksman, in Manual, 1st ed., 1923, 369; Waksman and Henrici, in Manual, 6th ed., 1948, 938.)

gri.se′o.lus. Old French adj. *gris* gray; Med.L. adj. *griseus* gray; M.L. dim.adj. *griseolus* somewhat gray.

Aerial mycelium: No spirals observed. Conidia spherical or ellipsoidal.

Gelatin stab: Liquefied with yellowish, flaky pellicle and sediment.

Agar: Brownish growth with smooth surface.

Synthetic agar: Colorless, thin, spreading growth, chiefly in the medium; surface growth limited almost entirely to the aerial mycelium. Aerial mycelium at first gray, later becoming pallid, neutral gray.

Starch agar: Grayish brown growth with dark ring.

Glucose agar: Spreading growth, both on the surface and into the medium; center raised, cream-colored, turning dark.

Glucose broth: Thick, brown ring.

Litmus milk: Abundant growth, pink pellicle; coagulated; peptonized, becoming alkaline.

Potato: Cream-colored growth, becoming black, spreading.

Starch is hydrolyzed.

Faint brownish soluble pigment formed.

Nitrites produced from nitrates.

Aerobic.

Optimum temperature, 25° C.

Antagonistic properties: Considerable activity against various bacteria; some of the strains show negative activity.

Source: Isolated from soil.

Habitat: Soil.

31. **Streptomyces fasciculus** (Krassilnikov, 1941) Waksman, 1953. (*Actinomyces fasciculus* Krassilnikov, Guide to the Actinomycetes, Izd. Akad. Nauk, U.S.S.R., Moskau, 1941, 51; Waksman, in Waksman and Lechevalier, Actinomycetes and Their Antibiotics, Baltimore, 1953, 54.)

fas.ci′cu.lus. L. mas.dim.n. *fasciculus* a small bundle.

Vegetative growth: Good growth, lichenoid, colorless, covered with dark gray, powdery or velvety aerial mycelium.

Aerial mycelium: Sporophores straight, short, arranged in broom-shaped bodies or fascicles. Spores oblong, 0.7 by 1.0 to 1.5 microns.

Gelatin: Liquefaction.

Agar: Aerial mycelium poorly developed, gray.

Synthetic agar: Typical vegetative growth.

Milk: Readily coagulated and peptonized.

Potato: Heavy, folded growth with well developed, dark gray aerial mycelium. Soluble brown pigment. Sporophores and spores same as on synthetic agar.

Sucrose is readily inverted.

Starch is rapidly hydrolyzed.

Good growth on cellulose.

Nitrites weakly produced from nitrates.

Antagonistic properties: Strongly antagonistic.

Relationship to other species: Related to *Streptomyces candidus*.

Source: Isolated from soil.

Habitat: Soil.

32. **Streptomyces erythraeus** (Waksman, 1923) Waksman and Henrici, 1948. (Actino-

myces 161, Waksman, Soil Sci., *8*, 1919, 112; *Actinomyces erythreus* (sic) Waksman, in Manual, 1st ed., 1923, 370; *Streptomyces erythreus* (sic) Waksman and Henrici, in Manual, 6th ed., 1948, 938.)

e.ryth'rae.us. Gr. adj. *erythraeus* red.

Vegetative growth: Growth spreading, with irregular margin, developing deep into the medium. Color at first white, later turning yellowish, agar around growth has a white, milky surface.

Aerial mycelium: Fine, branching; numerous open spirals formed as side branches of the main hyphae.

Gelatin stab: Abundant, dense, gray growth with pinkish tinge, chiefly on surface of liquefied medium.

Agar: Cream-colored growth.

Synthetic agar: Spreading growth with irregular margin, developing deep into the medium; color at first white, later turning yellowish; agar around growth has a white, milky surface. Aerial mycelium thick, solid, white.

Starch agar: Cream-colored, circular colonies, with faint greenish tinge.

Glucose agar: Abundant, spreading, cream-colored growth, later turning brown chiefly on surface; center raised, lobate margin.

Glucose broth: Abundant, cream-colored surface growth.

Litmus milk: Yellowish surface zone; coagulated; peptonized, becoming alkaline.

Potato: Wrinkled, cream-colored growth, becoming yellowish.

Starch is hydrolyzed.

Soluble purple pigment formed.

Nitrites produced from nitrates.

Aerobic.

Optimum temperature, 25° C.

Antagonistic properties: Marked. Produces erythromycin.

Distinctive character: Similar to *Streptomyces erythrochromogenes* except that no brown soluble pigment is formed.

Source: Isolated from Californian and Hawaiian soils.

Habitat: Soil.

33. **Streptomyces flavogriseus** (Duché, 1934) Waksman, 1953. (*Actinomyces flavo-*

griseus Duché, Encyclopédie Mycologique, Paris, *6*, 1934, 341; Waksman, in Waksman and Lechevalier, Actinomycetes and Their Antibiotics, Baltimore, 1953, 55.)

fla.vo.gri'se.us. L. adj. *flavus* yellow; M.L. adj. *griseus* gray; M.L. adj. *flavogriseus* yellowish gray.

Aerial mycelium: Long, straight hyphae producing a few curling tips. Spores spherical.

Gelatin: Flocculent growth throughout medium. No soluble pigment. Slow liquefaction.

Agar: Thin, cream-colored growth. Aerial mycelium thin, white. No soluble pigment.

Synthetic agar: Limited, yellowish growth with reverse turning black. Aerial mycelium thin, gray to mouse-gray.

Glucose peptone agar: Yellow surface growth with reverse tending to turn dark. Aerial mycelium abundant, mouse-gray to drab. No soluble pigment.

Starch agar: Very limited growth. Similar to that on synthetic agar.

Broth: Cream-colored surface growth in clumps. Aerial mycelium gray.

Milk: Cream-colored ring. No aerial mycelium. Very rapid peptonization.

Potato: Abundant, lichenoid growth. Abundant aerial mycelium, mouse-gray to drab with white edge. No soluble pigment.

Starch is hydrolyzed.

Source: Isolated from volcanic soils in Martinique.

Habitat: Presumably soil.

34. **Streptomyces diastaticus** (Krainsky, 1914) Waksman and Henrici, 1948. (*Actinomyces diastaticus* Krainsky, Cent. f. Bakt., II Abt., *41*, 1914, 662; also see Waksman and Curtis, Soil Sci., *1*, 1916, 116; Waksman and Henrici, in Manual, 6th ed., 1948, 939.)

di.a.sta'ti.cus. Gr. adj. *diastaticus* separative; M.L. n. *diastasum* the enzyme diastase, hence M.L. adj. *diastaticus* diastatic, starch-digesting.

Aerial mycelium: Filaments may show fine, long, narrow spirals. Conidia ellipsoidal, 1.0 to 1.2 by 1.1 to 1.5 microns.

Gelatin stab: Liquefaction with small, cream-colored flakes in liquid.

Agar: Cream-colored growth. Thin aerial mycelium.

Synthetic agar: Thin, gray, spreading growth. Aerial mycelium white, becoming drab gray.

Starch agar: Thin, colorless, spreading growth. Aerial mycelium gray.

Glucose agar: Yellowish, spreading growth. No aerial mycelium.

Glucose broth: Gray ring with grayish colonies in bottom of tube.

Litmus milk: Brownish ring; coagulated; peptonized in 25 to 30 days, becoming faintly alkaline.

Potato: Abundant, wrinkled, cream-colored growth with greenish tinge.

Starch is hydrolyzed.

Brown to dark brown soluble pigment formed.

Nitrites produced from nitrates.

Aerobic.

Optimum temperature, 37° C.

Antagonistic properties: Limited.

Source: Isolated from soil.

Habitat: Soil.

35. **Streptomyces canescens** Hickey et al., 1952. (*Streptomyces canescus* (sic) Hickey, Corum, Hidy, Cohen, Nager and Kropp, Antibiotics and Chemotherapy, *2*, 1952, 472.)

ca.nes'cens. L. part.adj. *canescens* becoming white, or hoary.

Aerial mycelium: At first white, becoming, on sporulation, gray-white to gray. Conidiophores straight or curved, not forming any spirals, richly septate. Spores globose, 1.0 to 1.3 by 1.3 to 2.6 microns.

Gelatin: Rapid liquefaction.

Sabouraud's agar: Growth first white, dull-shiny, spreading, translucent with tan reverse. After 7 days' incubation, growth beaded, slightly wrinkled at base of the slant, grayish white; reverse tan to amber. Amber pigment diffused throughout medium. After 14 days aerial mycelium faintly greenish.

Bennett's agar: Circular colonies, effuse to convex, edge filamentous; powdery; varying from gray-white to gray. Reverse brown. No soluble pigment.

Egg medium: Tan, very wrinkled surface growth. No sporulation observed after 10

days' incubation; small amount of white sporulation observed in 14 days. Soluble brown pigment. After 21 days, odor of hydrogen sulfide detected. Liquefaction after 28 days.

Ca-malate agar: Gray to rose-gray mycelium with yellow to tan reverse. Digestion of calcium malate slight at edge of colony. No soluble pigment.

Glucose, arabinose, trehalose, xylose, sucrose, maltose, galactose, dextrin, soluble starch, mannitol, glycerol and salicin are used as sole sources of carbon. No growth observed with sorbose, melezitose, dulcitol, rhamnose, sorbitol, melibiose, phenol, raffinose or lactose.

Milk: At 36° C., becomes alkaline (pH 8.4). Soft, rennet curd, formed after 48 hours, is completely peptonized in 12 days.

Potato: Light gray, spreading, wrinkled growth. Deep brown pigment diffused throughout.

Starch is actively hydrolyzed.

Nitrites not produced from nitrates.

Optimum temperature, 36° C.

Antagonistic properties: Produces ascosin.

Source: Isolated from a contaminated fungus plate.

Habitat: Unknown.

36. **Streptomyces fimicarius** (Duché, 1934) Waksman and Henrici, 1948. (*Actinomyces fimicarius* Duché, Encyclopédie Mycologique, Paris, *6*, 1934, 346; Waksman and Henrici, in Manual, 6th ed., 1948, 940.)

fi.mi.ca'ri.us. L. noun *fimus* dung, manure; L. adj. *carus* dear, loving; M.L. adj. *fimicarius* dung-loving.

Gelatin: Punctiform colonies with whitish aerial mycelium; reddish soluble pigment. Liquefaction.

Agar: Cream-colored growth with white aerial mycelium; reverse side, yellowish.

Asparagine agar: Cream-colored growth with whitish aerial mycelium; reverse side cream-colored to slight ochre.

Synthetic agar: Yellowish masses of growth with yellowish white aerial mycelium; reverse side orange-colored; faint yellowish soluble pigment.

Asparagine solution: Vegetative filaments 0.5 to 0.6 micron long; branching aerial mycelium, 0.8 to 1.0 micron, forming numerous conidia; flaky growth produced on bottom; surface growth becomes covered with a white aerial mycelium; reverse side, brownish red.

Synthetic solution: Cream-colored, punctiform growth with yellowish aerial mycelium; no soluble pigment.

Peptone solution: Whitish growth that flakes throughout liquid; yellowish pigment.

Tyrosine medium: White growth with yellowish reverse; yellowish soluble pigment.

Milk: Colorless growth becoming covered with whitish aerial mycelium; slow peptonization of milk which becomes rose-colored, finally changing to brownish red.

Potato: Cream-colored to yellowish growth with whitish aerial mycelium; reddish brown pigmentation of plug.

Coagulated serum: Cream-colored growth with whitish aerial mycelium; rapid liquefaction of serum.

Distinctive characters: Abundant growth upon neutral and acid media; whitish aerial mycelium; marked odor; soluble brownish red pigment.

Relationships to other species: This species seems to form the transition type between the *Streptomyces albus* group and the *Streptomyces chromogenes* group.

Source: Isolated from manure.

Habitat: Found abundantly in manure.

37. **Streptomyces felleus** Lindenbein, 1952. (*Streptomyces felleus* Brockmann and Henkel (*nomen nudum*), Chem. Ber., *84*, 1951, 284; Lindenbein, Arch. f. Mikrobiol., *17*, 1952, 374.)

fel'le.us. L. adj. *felleus* of gall, like gall.

Aerial mycelium: Hyphae long, straight, branching. Spores spherical.

Gelatin: Colorless growth. No aerial mycelium. No soluble pigment. No liquefaction.

Agar: Colorless diffuse growth with brownish yellow reverse. No aerial mycelium. Soluble light brownish yellow pigment.

Synthetic agar: Effused, smooth growth with yellow-brown reverse. Aerial mycelium velvety gray-white. Soluble yellowish brown pigment.

Ca-malate agar: Crumb-like, colorless to yellowish growth. Aerial mycelium powdery gray-white. Soluble yellowish brown pigment.

Glucose asparagine agar: Thin, colorless growth with yellowish reverse. Aerial mycelium powdery gray-white. Soluble brownish pigment.

Starch agar: Lichenoid, colorless growth. Aerial mycelium powdery white. No soluble pigment.

Glucose agar: Effused, crumb-like, yellowish brown growth. Aerial mycelium powdery gray-white. Soluble light brown pigment.

Glucose broth: Fine sediment with some flakes; later a colorless ring on surface. No aerial mycelium and no soluble pigment.

Milk: Brownish to orange growth. Aerial mycelium velvety gray-white. Peptonized.

Potato: Heavy, brownish yellow growth. Aerial mycelium powdery. Faint reddish pigment around growth.

Starch is actively hydrolyzed.

No growth on cellulose.

Odor: Typical earthy.

Antagonistic properties: Produces picromycin.

Source: Isolated from soil.

Habitat: Soil.

38. **Streptomyces achromogenes** Okami and Umezawa, 1953. (Okami and Umezawa, in Umezawa, Takeuchi, Okami and Tazaki, Jap. Jour. of Med. Sci. and Biol., *6*, 1953, 266.)

a.chro.mo'ge.nes. Gr. adj. *achromus* colorless; Gr. v. *gennaio* to produce; M.L. adj. *achromogenes* producing no color.

Aerial mycelium: Fine branching aerial hyphae, no spirals. Spores cylindrical.

Gelatin: Yellowish brown, restricted growth. No aerial mycelium. Soluble, slightly brown pigment. Very weak liquefaction.

Agar: Wrinkled, elevated, colorless to brownish growth. No aerial mycelium. No soluble pigment.

Glucose asparagine, agar: Yellowish brown, restricted growth with brown reverse. Scant yellowish white aerial mycelium. Slightly brown soluble pigment may be weakly produced.

Synthetic glycerol agar: Colorless to brownish, restricted growth. Scant white to dark grayish colored aerial mycelium. Soluble brown pigment.

Egg media: Reddish brown, wrinkled growth. No aerial mycelium. No soluble pigment.

Loeffler's blood serum: Elevated, wrinkled, colorless to brownish growth. No aerial mycelium. No soluble pigment. No liquefaction.

Blood agar: Brownish, wrinkled, poor growth. No aerial mycelium. No soluble pigment. No hemolysis.

Milk: Poor surface growth. No aerial mycelium. No soluble pigment. Coagulated and slowly peptonized.

Potato plug: Yellowish brown to brownish, fine, wrinkled growth. White, powdery aerial mycelium. No soluble pigment at first, later reddish brown.

Nitrites produced from nitrates.

Antagonistic properties: Produces an antiviral agent, achromoviromycin.

Distinctive characters: This species resembles Streptomyces diastaticus and Streptomyces fimicarius. This species differs from the former in spiral formation, hemolysis, liquefaction of gelatin and proteolytic action of milk. It differs from the latter in the liquefaction of coagulated serum. This species is characterized by the brown pigmentation on synthetic agar only.

Source: Isolated from garden soil at Suginami-ku, Tokyo.

Habitat: Soil.

39. **Streptomyces noursei** Brown et al., 1953. (A soil actinomycete, Hazen and Brown, Science, *112*, 1950, 423; *Streptomyces sp.* No. 48240, Hazen and Brown, Proc. Soc. Exp. Biol. and Med., *76*, 1951, 93; Brown, Hazen and Mason, Science, *117*, 1953, 609.)

nour'se.i. M.L. gen.noun *noursei* of Nourse; named for the owner of the farm where the soil sample was obtained from which this organism was isolated.

Description prepared by Hazen and Brown for use in Waksman and Lechevalier, Actinomycetes and Their Antibiotics, Baltimore, 1953.

Vegetative growth: Good growth, gray to brown, much folded on various organic and certain synthetic media. Soluble pink to purple pigment frequently produced.

Aerial mycelium: Well developed, white to shell-pink. Straight, curved and spiral-forming sporulating hyphae. Round to ellipsoidal spores.

Gelatin: Rapid liquefaction.

Synthetic agar: Scant, colorless, flat growth. No aerial mycelium.

Glucose asparagine agar: Wrinkled, tan growth with gray and white knob-like projections. Dark gray reverse. At 35° to 36°C., scant, shell-pink aerial mycelium; limited, shell-pink soluble pigment.

Starch agar: Good growth in form of discrete colonies with white aerial mycelium in center and periphery colorless and embedded.

Glucose agar: Good, folded growth. White aerial mycelium, turning gray. Reverse of growth brown, medium often becoming darkened throughout. Occasionally pomegranate-purple soluble pigment is formed.

Blood agar: Good growth, consisting of convex, lobate colonies with central perforation. Aerial mycelium heavy, chalky white. No hemolysis, but darkening of blood.

Honey broth: Heavy white ring on surface; flocculent sediment. Broth clear.

Milk: Coagulated then peptonized.

Potato: Good, folded growth with chalky white aerial mycelium. At 35° to 36° C., a reddish purple pigment is formed.

Starch is hydrolyzed.

Poor growth on cellulose.

Nitrites weakly produced from nitrates.

Antagonistic properties: Produces an antifungal agent, nystatin, which is active against various yeast-like and filamentous fungi, and an antibacterial agent, phalamycin.

Source: Isolated from soil from Fauquier County, Virginia.

Habitat: Soil.

40. **Streptomyces roseochromogenes** (Jensen, 1931) Waksman and Henrici, 1948. (*Actinomyces roseus* Krainsky, Cent. f. Bakt., II Abt., *41*, 1914, 662; also see Waksman and Curtis, Soil Sci., *1*, 1916, 125; and Waksman, Soil Sci., *8*, 1919, 148; not *Acti-*

nomyces roseus Namyslowski, Cent. f. Bakt.,
I Abt., Orig., *62*, 1912, 567; *Actinomyces
roseochromogenus* (sic) Jensen, Proc. Linnean Soc. New So. Wales, *56*, 1931, 359;
Streptomyces roseochromogenus (sic) Waksman and Henrici, in Manual, 6th ed., 1948,
937.)

ro.se.o.chro.mo'ge.nes. L. adj. *roseus*
rosy; Gr. noun *chroma* color; Gr. v.suffix
-genes producing; M.L. adj. *roseochromogenes* producing a red color.

Vegetative growth: Red to rose-colored
pigment; produces dark brown soluble substance.

Aerial mycelium: Well developed. Sporophores produce numerous open and closed
spirals. Spores 1.0 to 1.2 by 1.5 to 3.0 microns.

Gelatin stab: Liquefaction, with small,
cream-colored colonies in bottom of liquid.

Agar: White growth, becoming yellowish.

Synthetic agar: Thin, spreading, colorless growth. Aerial mycelium thin, pale,
brownish.

Starch agar: Colorless, spreading growth.

Glucose agar: Growth extensive, spreading, colorless, entire.

Glucose broth: Cream-colored ring; flaky
sediment.

Litmus milk: Brownish ring. Coagulation limited. Peptonized in 10 to 15 days,
becoming strongly alkaline.

Potato: Much wrinkled, brownish growth.

Purple pigment on egg media; brown on
gelatin.

Starch is hydrolyzed.

Nitrites produced from nitrates.

Aerobic.

Optimum temperature, 37° C.

Antagonistic properties: Active against
various bacteria; produces an antibiotic,
roseomycin.

Source: Isolated from soil.

Habitat: Soil.

41. Streptomyces cinnamonensis Okami, 1952. (Okami, in Maeda, Okami,
Kosaka, Taya and Umezawa, Jour. Antibiotics (Japanese), *5*, 1952, 572; also see
Okami, Maeda, Kosaka, Taya and Umezawa, Jap. Jour. Med. Sci. and Biol., *6*,
1953, 87.)

cin.na.mo.nen'sis. Gr. neut.n. *cinna-*

mum cinnamon; M.L. adj. *cinnamonensis*
relating to cinnamon.

Vegetative growth: Fine branching mycelium.

Aerial mycelium: 0.8 to 1.2 microns in
diameter; long filamentous mycelium; no
spirals. Spores ellipsoidal.

Gelatin: Colorless to dark brownish
growth. Aerial mycelium in form of white
patches. Soluble brown pigment. No liquefaction or very slow liquefaction.

Agar: Colorless to dark growth. No aerial
mycelium. Soluble, slightly brown pigment
may be produced.

Glucose asparagine agar: Colorless to
light cream-colored growth. White to white-
pinkish-cinnamon aerial mycelium with
light brownish-vinaceous tinge. No soluble
pigment.

Synthetic glycerol agar: Colorless,
spreading growth. Scant, white aerial mycelium or white with pale cinnamon-pinkish
to light brownish-vinaceous tinge. No soluble pigment.

Starch agar: Colorless, spreading growth.
Aerial mycelium white with pinkish tinge.
No soluble pigment.

Loeffler's blood serum: Colorless to dark
colored growth. No aerial mycelium. Soluble
brown pigment. No liquefaction.

Blood agar: Dark to brownish growth.
No aerial mycelium. Soluble brown pigment. No hemolysis.

Milk: Cream-colored to brownish surface
ring. No aerial mycelium or scant, white.
No soluble pigment or slightly brown. Not
coagulated; may be very slowly peptonized.

Potato plug: Light cream- to dark-colored
growth. No aerial mycelium. No soluble
pigment, later black pigment produced
around growth.

Starch is actively hydrolyzed.

Cellulose not decomposed.

Sucrose, mannose, dextrin, galactose,
glycerol, fructose, glucose, maltose, mannitol, xylose and sodium succinate are utilized
as carbon sources. Arabinose, esculin,
rhamnose, dulcitol, sodium acetate, inulin
and lactose are not utilized as carbon
sources. Salicin and raffinose are negative.

Nitrites not produced from nitrates.

Antagonistic properties: Produces an
antibiotic which is active against myco-

bacteria and which is identical with actithiazic acid or thiozolidone.

Relationships to other species: Resembles *Streptomyces roseochromogenes* in the color of the growth and in the slow or no liquefaction of coagulated serum or gelatin. *S. roseochromogenes* differs from this species in that it forms numerous open spirals and produces nitrite.

Source: Isolated as strain No. 154 T-3 from soil at Kanegasaki, Iwate Prefecture.

Habitat: Soil.

42. Streptomyces olivochromogenes

(Bergey et al., 1925) Waksman and Henrici, 1948. (*Actinomyces chromogenus 205*, Waksman, Soil Sci., *8*, 1919, 106; *Actinomyces olivochromogenus* (sic) Bergey et al., Manual, 2nd ed., 1925, 368; *Streptomyces olivochromogenus* (sic) Waksman and Henrici, in Manual, 6th ed., 1948, 941.)

o.li.vo.chro.mo'ge.nes. L. noun *oliva* an olive; Gr. noun *chroma* color; Gr. v.suffix *-genes* producing; M.L. adj. *olivochromogenes* producing an olive color.

Aerial mycelium: Filaments with numerous close spirals. Conidia ellipsoidal.

Gelatin stab: Cream-colored, spreading surface growth. Rapid liquefaction.

Agar: Wrinkled, brown growth, becoming gray-green.

Synthetic agar: White, spreading growth. Aerial mycelium ash-gray with brownish tinge.

Starch agar: Transparent, spreading growth.

Glucose agar: Abundant, natal-brown to almost black growth, entire margin.

Glucose broth: Thin, brown growth; flaky sediment.

Litmus milk: Dark brown ring; coagulated; peptonized, becoming alkaline.

Potato: Small, wrinkled, black colonies. Soluble brown pigment formed.

Starch is hydrolyzed.

Nitrites produced in trace amounts from nitrates.

Aerobic.

Optimum temperature, 37° C.

Antagonistic properties: Positive.

Source: Isolated from soil.

Habitat: Soil.

43. Streptomyces resistomycificus

Lindenbein, 1952. (*Streptomyces resistomycificus* Brockmann and Schmidt-Kastner (*nomen nudum*), Naturwiss., *38*, 1951, 479; Lindenbein, Arch. f. Mikrobiol., *17*, 1952, 376.)

re.sis.to.my.ci'fi.cus. L. v *resisto* to resist; Gr. mas.n. *myces* fungus; L. v. *facio* to make; L. comb.adj.ending *-ficus* producing; M.L. adj. *resistomycificus* making resistant to a fungus; producing resistomycin.

Aerial mycelium: Hyphae long with curling tips. Spores short, ellipsoidal. Pigment of mycelium becomes pink to pink-gray.

Gelatin: Dark brown growth. Aerial mycelium powdery, white-gray. Soluble chestnut-brown pigment. Liquefaction.

Agar: Crumb-like growth. Aerial mycelium powdery blue-gray. Soluble dark brown pigment.

Synthetic agar: Crumb-like, dark brown growth. Aerial mycelium velvety chalkwhite, later ash-gray. Soluble red-brown pigment.

Glucose asparagine agar: Crumb-like growth with light brown reverse. Aerial mycelium velvety ash-gray. Soluble yellowbrown pigment.

Ca-malate agar: Strong, crumb-like growth with dark brown reverse. Aerial mycelium velvety ash-gray. Soluble ashgray pigment.

Starch agar: Lichenoid growth with reddish brown reverse. Aerial mycelium velvety gray-white, later becoming red-gray. Soluble pigment lacking or uniformly reddish brown.

Glucose agar: Crumb-like growth with dark brown reverse. Aerial mycelium velvety chalk-white. Soluble reddish to dark brown pigment.

Glucose broth: Floating, large, light yellow colonies. Aerial mycelium cottony white to red. Soluble light yellow pigment.

Milk: Lichenoid growth with dark brown reverse. Aerial mycelium velvety chalkwhite, later yellowish red. Soluble dark brown pigment. Sometimes weakly peptonized.

Potato: Brownish black growth. Aerial mycelium powdery, reddish white. Soluble dark brown pigment.

Starch is actively hydrolyzed.

No growth on cellulose.

Antagonistic properties: Produces resistomycin, which is present in the mycelium and which is active against Gram-positive bacteria.

Source: Isolated from soil.

Habitat: Soil.

44. Streptomyces diastatochromogenes (Krainsky, 1914) Waksman and Henrici, 1948. (*Actinomyces diastatochromogenes* Krainsky, Cent. f. Bakt., II Abt., *41*, 1914, 662; Waksman and Henrici, in Manual, 6th ed., 1948, 941.)

di.a.sta.to.chro.mo'ge.nes. Gr. adj. *diastatus* split, divided; M.L. adj. *diastatus* diastatic; Gr. noun *chroma* color; Gr. v. suffix *-genes* producing; M.L. adj. *diastatochromogenes* producing diastatic color (presumably intended to mean producing diastase and color).

Aerial mycelium: Conidia spherical or ellipsoidal, about 1.2 microns.

Gelatin colonies: Light gray-colored. Soluble brown pigment formed.

Gelatin stab: Liquefaction.

Agar: Medium-sized colonies, colorless, with white to gray aerial mycelium.

Ca-malate agar: Medium-sized colonies, colorless, with gray aerial mycelium.

Glucose agar: Same as on Ca-malate agar.

Starch agar: Same as on Ca-malate agar.

Glucose broth: Flaky colonies in depth at first, later also over surface.

Potato: Light gray colonies; gray aerial mycelium; medium colored black.

Weakly diastatic.

No growth on cellulose.

Tyrosinase produced.

Aerobic.

Optimum temperature, 35° C.

Antagonistic properties: Very strong.

Source: Isolated from soil.

Habitat: Soil.

45. Streptomyces flavochromogenes (Krainsky, 1914) Waksman and Henrici, 1948. (*Actinomyces flavochromogenes* Krainsky, Cent. f. Bakt., II Abt., *41*, 1914, 662; Waksman and Henrici, in Manual, 6th ed., 1948, 941.)

fla.vo.chro.mo'ge.nes. L. adj. *flavus* yellow; Gr. noun *chroma* color; Gr. v.suffix *-genes* producing; M.L. adj. *flavochromogenes* producing yellow color.

Aerial mycelium: Conidia ellipsoidal, 1.7 microns.

Gelatin colonies: Yellowish.

Gelatin stab: Slight liquefaction.

Agar: Aerial mycelium formed late, at first white, later gray. Gray soluble pigment formed.

Ca-malate agar: Colonies yellow with white aerial mycelium forming late.

Glucose agar: Brown soluble pigment formed.

Starch agar: Yellow colonies, with white aerial mycelium.

Glucose broth: Fine flakes, with small spherical colonies adherent to glass. Medium colored brown.

Potato: Yellow colonies with white aerial mycelium.

Weakly diastatic.

Esculin is attacked.

Slow growth on cellulose.

Tyrosinase formed.

Nitrites produced from nitrates.

Aerobic.

Optimum temperature, 35° C.

Source: Isolated from soil.

Habitat: Soil.

46. Streptomyces bikiniensis Johnstone and Waksman, 1948. (Jour. Bact., *55*, 1948, 317.)

bi.ki.ni.en'sis. M.L. adj. *bikiniensis* pertaining to the Bikini Islands.

Aerial mycelium: Hyphae straight, branched heterogeneously. No spirals. Conidia ellipsoidal.

Gelatin: Slight liquefaction.

Agar: Luxuriant growth with a moderate amount of white aerial mycelium. Deep brown soluble pigment.

Synthetic agar: White growth becoming pallid neutral gray with white tinge. Aerial mycelium abundant. Light brown soluble pigment. Amber-colored superficial droplets.

Glucose-asparagine agar: Luxuriant growth. Aerial mycelium white to mouse-gray. Soluble light amber pigment.

Starch agar: Abundant growth. Aerial mycelium white, becoming gray.

Glucose agar: Aerial mycelium gray. Soluble deep brown pigment.

Broth: Abundant, white surface pellicle. Soluble deep brown pigment.

Milk: Patchy, white surface growth. Aerial mycelium gray. Gradual hydrolysis.

Potato: Wrinkled, raised, pale ocherous buff growth. Soluble pigment brown to black.

Starch is weakly hydrolyzed.

Antagonistic properties: Strongly antagonistic. Produces streptomycin.

Source: Isolated from soil from Bikini atoll.

Habitat: Soil.

47. Streptomyces mirabilis Ruschmann, 1952. (Die Pharmazie, 7, 1952, 542.)

mi.ra'bi.lis. L. adj. *mirabilis* miraculous, extraordinary.

Aerial mycelium: White fluffy layer consisting of abundant aerial mycelium and spores. Hyphae straight, without spirals or curvature; sporulation takes place after 6 to 7 days.

Gelatin: Good, flaky growth. Liquefaction rapid. Soluble dark brown to black pigment.

Agar: Poor growth with slimy surface, resembling that of bacteria. No sporulation.

Glucose agar: Grayish brown, slimy growth. No aerial mycelium even after 14 days. Soluble brown pigment.

Carrot juice agar: Good growth in form of round colonies covered with white aerial mycelium. Each colony produces 3 to 5 cracks or holes in center.

Czapek's solution: Limited growth in the form of a few surface colonies, sinking rapidly to the bottom.

Milk: Surface growth with white, fluffy aerial mycelium. Milk coagulated and peptonized. Liquefied portion colored black. Reaction of medium unchanged.

Potato: Good, lichenoid growth. Soluble dark brown to black pigment.

Fats are readily utilized.

Oxygen requirement: Quite considerable.

Optimum temperature, 29° C. No growth at 37° C.

Antagonistic properties: Produces miramycin. Antagonistic effect strongest in freshly isolated cultures. Property lost on cultivation; activity upon Gram-positive bacteria is lost first, then upon Gram-negative rods; cocci remain most sensitive.

Distinctive characters: Highly proteolytic and lipolytic. Grows best on complex organic media. Grows best at slightly acid reaction or pH 6.0 to 6.6.

Source: Presumably isolated from soil.

Habitat: Soil.

48. Streptomyces antibioticus (Waksman and Woodruff, 1941) Waksman and Henrici, 1948. (*Actinomyces antibioticus* Waksman and Woodruff, Jour. Bact., 42, 1941, 232 and 246; Waksman and Henrici, in Manual, 6th ed., 1948, 942.)

an.ti.bi.o'ti.cus. Gr. pref. *anti* against; Gr. noun *bius* life; M.L. adj. *antibioticus* against life, antibiotic.

Aerial mycelium: Spore-bearing hyphae produced in the form of straight aerial hyphae. The conidiophores are arranged in clusters; no spirals formed. The conidia are nearly spherical to somewhat ellipsoidal.

Gelatin: Dark brown growth on surface with patches of gray aerial mycelium. Dark pigment produced which gradually diffuses into the unliquefied part of the gelatin. Liquefaction at first very slow, later becoming rapid.

Agar: Production of dark pigment at early stage of growth is very characteristic. Growth brownish, thin, with a yellowish gray to yellowish green aerial mycelium.

Synthetic agar: Thin, whitish growth. Thin, gray aerial mycelium.

Litmus milk: Thick, brownish ring on surface of milk. Mouse-gray aerial mycelium with greenish tinge; growth becomes brown, especially in drier portions adhering to glass. No reaction change, no coagulation of milk, no clearing; whitish sediment at bottom of tube. Old cultures: heavy growth ring on surface of milk, heavy precipitation on bottom; liquid brownish to black in upper portion.

Potato plug: Folded, brown-colored growth with a thin black ring on plug, fading into a bluish tinge. No aerial mycelium.

Carrot plug: Cream-colored to faint brownish growth. No aerial mycelium. No pigment.

Odor: Very characteristic soil odor.

Antagonistic properties: Has a marked antagonistic effect on Gram-positive and Gram-negative bacteria, much more on the former than on the latter, as well as on actinomycetes. It is also active against fungi, which vary in degree of sensitivity. Produces actinomycin, a specific bacteriostatic and bactericidal substance (Waksman and Woodruff, Jour. Bact., *40*, 1940, 581).

Source: Isolated from soil on *Escherichia coli*-washed-agar plate, using living cells of *E. coli* as the only source of available nutrients.

Habitat: Soil.

49. **Streptomyces griseocarneus** Benedict et al., 1950. (*Streptomyces griseo-carneus* (sic) Benedict, Stodola, Shotwell, Borud and Lindenfelser, Science, *112*, 1950, 77; also see Benedict, Lindenfelser, Stodola and Traufler, Jour. Bact., *62*, 1951, 487; and Grundy, Whitman, Hanes and Sylvester, Antibiotics and Chemotherapy, *1*, 1951, 309.)

gri.se.o.car′ne.us. M.L. adj. *griseus* gray; L. adj. *carneus* pertaining to flesh, flesh-colored; M.L. adj. *griseocarneus* grayish flesh-colored.

Vegetative growth: Good, with monopodial branching.

Aerial mycelium: Two types: On some media, powdery, suggestive of sporulation, but no spores are produced; this type of mycelium usually becomes gray with continued incubation. On other media, the aerial mycelium forms a rather fluffy, white mat; it turns slightly pink when sporulation occurs. No spirals have been observed. None of the common media will induce sporulation. It occurs best after 10 to 14 days' incubation on a carbon-free salt agar to which 0.5 per cent soluble starch has been added. Inositol and mannose will also support sporulation, but they are not as satisfactory carbon sources for this purpose as starch. The only other medium on which spores are found is nitrogen-free synthetic

agar to which 0.2 per cent glycine or asparagine is added. The spores are coccoid to ellipsoidal, 0.7 to 1.1 by 1.1 to 1.6 microns.

Gelatin: Cream-colored to brown growth. Rapid liquefaction. Soluble dark brown pigment.

Agar: Moderate, cream-colored growth. No aerial mycelium. Soluble light yellow-brown pigment.

Synthetic agar: Sparse, white growth. Aerial mycelium white. No soluble pigment. No sporulation.

Glucose asparagine agar: Moderate growth. Aerial mycelium powdery white. No pigment. No sporulation.

Ca-malate agar: Moderate, white growth. Aerial mycelium white. No soluble pigment. No sporulation.

Oatmeal agar: Luxuriant, brown growth. Aerial mycelium abundant, fluffy, white. No soluble pigment. No sporulation.

Milk: Dark brown to black growth. Soluble brown pigment. Not coagulated; rapidly peptonized.

Potato: Luxuriant, spreading, cream-colored growth. Aerial mycelium gray. Soluble light brown pigment turning dark brown after 30 days' incubation.

Starch is hydrolyzed.

Glucose, dextrin, starch, glycerol, calcium malate and sodium succinate are rapidly utilized as carbon sources. Mannose, maltose, inositol and sodium acetate are assimilated slowly. Xylose, galactose, sorbose, sucrose, cellobiose, melibiose, lactose, mannitol, sorbitol, sodium citrate and potassium sodium tartrate are not utilized.

$(NH_4)_2HPO_4$, urea, asparagine, glycine and arginine are nitrogen sources which support moderate to rapid growth. Sodium nitrate supports slow growth. Tryptophane, tyrosine and methionine are not satisfactory nitrogen sources.

Nitrites not produced from nitrates.

Antagonistic properties: Produces hydroxystreptomycin.

Source: Simultaneously isolated from Japanese soil by Benedict and from soil from one of the gardens of Abbott Labs., North Chicago, Illinois.

Habitat: Soil.

50. **Streptomyces viridoflavus** Waksman and Taber, 1953. (Waksman and Taber, in Waksman and Lechevalier, Actinomycetes and Their Antibiotics, Baltimore, 1953, 66.)

vi.ri.do.fla′vus. L. adj. *viridis* green; L. adj. *flavus* yellow; M.L. adj. *viridoflavus* greenish yellow.

Vegetative growth: Abundant, lichenoid growth on most media, yellow-green, turning olive-green to almost brown. Soluble pigment variable. Hyphae on surface of agar 0.7 micron in diameter; in shake flasks, 0.7 to 0.8 micron; some submerged hyphae thicker, reaching 1.6 microns in diameter. Single spores formed at end of submerged sporulating lateral branches. Spores form early, germinate readily, even while apparently attached to hyphae.

Aerial mycelium: Hyphae formed in fascicles, greenish yellow, turning gray. Tends to lose ability to produce aerial mycelium. Tufts of hyphae with some curling of tips produced on certain media (glucose-asparagine agar). On glucose-asparagine agar, spores produced in chains in whorls. Spores not formed on nutrient or glucose-nutrient agar.

Gelatin: Limited growth in form of surface ring, canary-yellow. No pellicle. Soluble brown to dark brown pigment; ability to produce pigment may be lost on cultivation. Slight liquefaction.

Agar: Thin, moist, gray to light green, isolated colonies with green to almost bluish tinge at bottom of slant where colonies are confluent. White to gray, non-sporulating aerial mycelium appearing much later. No soluble pigment.

Synthetic agar: Limited, cream-colored to yellowish green growth. Generally no aerial mycelium. Hyphae penetrate deep into agar. No soluble pigment.

Glucose asparagine agar: Moist, flat, yellow to yellow-green colonies growing deep into medium. Aerial hyphae frequently abundant, grayish yellow to sulfur-yellow, later overgrown by white sporulating hyphae. May produce a soluble, faint yellow pigment.

Yeast-glucose agar: Heavy lichenoid growth, dark brown to olive-green. Aerial hyphae pale to grayish yellow to greenish yellow, becoming gray with age. Soluble grown pigment.

Glucose-nutrient agar: Heavy lichenoid growth, yellowish brown to olive-brown. Yellowish to gray aerial hyphae are abundant and appear later, covering the whole surface of growth with a mat. May produce a soluble brownish pigment.

Broth: Colorless clumps of growth on bottom of container. Soluble brown pigment; ability to produce pigment may be lost on cultivation.

Milk: Light yellow to brown surface ring. Not coagulated, gradually peptonized.

Potato: Lichenoid, brownish to greenish yellow to dark olive-green growth. Aerial hyphae absent or formed as thin, yellowish layer on drier portions of growth. May produce a soluble dark brown pigment.

Starch is actively hydrolyzed.

Limited growth on cellulose; cellulose not decomposed.

Carbon sources: With yeast extract-mineral agar there was no growth over control on sucrose, lactose or rhamnose; good growth on mannose and glucose.

Antagonistic properties: Produces antibiotic substances, one of which is candicidin-like material.

Comments: Several strains of this organism have been isolated. They differ in their pigmentation on gelatin and in the relative abundance of aerial mycelium.

Source: Isolated from soil.

Habitat: Soil.

51. **Streptomyces globosus** (Krassilnikov, 1941) Waksman, 1953. (*Actinomyces globosus* Krassilnikov, Guide to the Actinomycetes, Izd. Akad. Nauk, U.S.S.R., Moskau, 1941, 58; Waksman, in Waksman and Lechevalier, Actinomycetes and Their Antibiotics, Baltimore, 1953, 68.)

glo.bo′sus. L. adj. *globosus* round, spherical.

Vegetative growth: Dark brown colonies producing brown pigment which diffuses into medium.

Aerial mycelium: Dark gray, fine velvety. Sporophores straight, short. Spores spherical.

Gelatin: Weak liquefaction.

Milk: Peptonized.

Sucrose not inverted.

Starch is hydrolyzed.

Antagonistic properties: No activity against mycobacteria.

Source: Isolated from soil.

Habitat: Soil, food products and potatoes.

52. Streptomyces cylindrosporus

(Krassilnikov, 1941) Waksman, 1953. (*Actinomyces cylindrosporus* Krassilnikov, Guide to the Actinomycetes, Izd. Akad. Nauk, U.S.S.R., Moskau, 1941, 57; Waksman, in Waksman and Lechevalier, Actinomycetes and Their Antibiotics, Baltimore, 1953, 68.)

cy.lin.dro'spo.rus. Gr. mas.n. *cylindrus* a cylinder; Gr. fem.n. *spora* a seed; M.L. noun *spora* a spore; M.L. adj. *cylindrosporus* cylinder-spored.

Vegetative growth: Cultures readily lose capacity to produce spores.

Aerial mycelium: Well developed, cottony or velvety, grayish white. Sporophores straight; spores cylindrical, 0.7 by 1.0 to 1.7. microns.

Gelatin: Liquefaction.

Agar: Dark brown growth with white aerial mycelium.

Synthetic agar: Velvety, dark brown or chocolate colonies. White-gray aerial mycelium.

Milk: Slightly coagulated, weakly peptonized with milk becoming brown to almost black.

Sucrose not inverted.

Starch is weakly hydrolyzed.

No growth on cellulose.

Nitrites produced from nitrates.

Antagonistic properties: None.

Source: Isolated from soil.

Habitat: Soil.

53. Streptomyces viridochromogenes

(Krainsky, 1914) Waksman and Henrici, 1948. (*Actinomyces viridochromogenes* Krainsky, Cent. f. Bakt., II Abt., *41*, 1914, 662; Waksman and Henrici, in Manual, 6th ed., 1948, 942.)

vi.ri.do.chro.mo'ge.nes. L. adj. *viridis* green; Gr. noun *chroma* color; Gr. v.suffix -*genes* producing; M.L. adj. *viridochromogenes* producing green color.

Aerial mycelium: Hyphae with numerous open spirals, 3 to 5 microns in diameter, occurring as side branches; spores short, ellipsoidal or spherical, 1.25 to 1.50 microns.

Gelatin: Cream-colored surface growth, becoming greenish. Slow liquefaction.

Agar: Abundant, restricted, gray growth with greenish tinge.

Synthetic agar: Spreading growth, cream-colored with dark center, becoming dark green; reverse yellowish to light cadmium. Aerial mycelium abundant, spreading, white, becoming light green.

Starch agar: Circular, spreading, yellowish colonies.

Glucose agar: Abundant, spreading, wrinkled, gray growth, becoming black.

Glucose broth: Dense, solid ring, brownish, becoming dark green.

Litmus milk: Dark brown surface growth; coagulated; peptonized, with faintly alkaline reaction.

Potato: Abundant, gray-brown growth. Soluble brown pigment formed.

Starch is hydrolyzed.

Nitrites produced from nitrates.

Aerobic.

Optimum temperature, 37° C.

Antagonistic properties: Active upon fungi.

Source: Isolated from soil.

Habitat: Soil.

54. Streptomyces purpureochromogenes

(Waksman and Curtis, 1916) Waksman and Henrici, 1948. (*Actinomyces purpeochromogenus* (sic) Waksman and Curtis, Soil Sci., *1*, 1916, 113; *Streptomyces purpeochromogenus* (sic) Waksman and Henrici, in Manual, 6th ed., 1948, 943.)

pur.pur.e.o.chro.mo'ge.nus. L. adj. *purpureus* purple-colored; Gr. noun *chroma* color; Gr. v.suffix -*genes* producing; M.L. adj. *purpureochromogenes* producing purple color.

Aerial mycelium: Branching mycelium and hyphae with few imperfect spirals. Conidia spherical, 0.75 to 1.0 micron in diameter.

Gelatin stab: Slow, brownish surface growth. Slow liquefaction.

Agar: Gray to brownish growth, becoming dark brown, almost black.

Synthetic agar: Slow, restricted, smooth,

gray growth, becoming brown with purplish tinge; center raised. Margin yellow.

Starch agar: Small, dark brown colonies.

Glucose agar: Abundant, restricted, gray growth, becoming brown to dark brown.

Glucose broth: Slight, flaky sediment.

Litmus milk: Dark brown ring; coagulated; slowly peptonized, with faintly alkaline reaction.

Potato: Restricted, orange to orange- red growth.

Starch shows slight hydrolysis.

Soluble dark brown pigment formed.

Nitrites not produced from nitrates.

Aerobic.

Optimum temperature, 25° C.

Antagonistic properties: Active against various bacteria.

Source: Isolated once from Californian adobe soil.

Habitat: Soil.

55. Streptomyces phaeochromogenes (Conn, 1917) Waksman and Henrici, 1948.

(*Actinomyces pheochromogenus* (sic) Conn, N. Y. State Agr. Exp. Sta. Tech. Bull. No. 60, 1917, 16; *Streptomyces phaeochromogenus* (sic) Waksman and Henrici, in Manual, 6th ed., 1948, 943.)

phae.o.chro.mo′ge.nes. Gr. adj. *phaeus* brown; Gr. noun *chroma* color; Gr. v.suffix -*genes* producing; M.L. adj. *phaeochromogenes* producing brown color.

Aerial mycelium: Branching filaments and hyphae, spirals narrow, open, elongated, sinistrorse.

Gelatin stab: Abundant, spreading, cream-colored surface growth, becoming brown. Slow liquefaction.

Agar: Thin, cream-colored growth, becoming gray.

Synthetic agar: Colorless growth, becoming brown to almost black. Aerial mycelium abundant, white with brownish shade.

Starch agar: Spreading, brownish growth, becoming brown.

Glucose agar: Restricted, much folded, brown growth.

Glucose broth: Dense, wrinkled pellicle.

Litmus milk: Dark, almost black ring; coagulated, with slow peptonization; faintly alkaline reaction.

Potato: Brown to almost black growth.

Starch is hydrolyzed.

Soluble brown pigment formed.

Nitrites produced from nitrates.

Aerobic.

Optimum temperature, 25° C.

Antagonistic properties: Strong.

Comment: One strain produces an antibiotic, moldin (Maeda, Okami, Taya and Umezawa, Jap. Jour. Med. Sci. and Biol., *5*, 1952, 327).

Source: Isolated from soil.

Habitat: Soil.

56. Streptomyces aureus (Waksman and Curtis, 1916) Waksman and Henrici, 1948.

(*Actinomyces aureus* Waksman and Curtis, Soil Sci., *1*, 1916, 124; Waksman and Henrici, in Manual, 6th ed., 1948, 943.)

au′re.us. L. adj. *aureus* golden.

Aerial mycelium: Shows numerous spirals. Conidia spherical to ellipsoidal, 0.6 to 1.0 by 0.8 to 1.4 microns.

Gelatin stab: Fair, cream-colored surface growth, becoming brown, spreading. Liquefaction.

Agar: Restricted, gray growth.

Synthetic agar: Thin, spreading, colorless growth. Aerial mycelium thin, gray, powdery, becoming cinnamon-drab.

Starch agar: Thin, transparent, spreading growth.

Glucose agar: Spreading, light orange growth; raised center; hyaline margin.

Glucose broth: Thin, brownish ring; flaky sediment.

Litmus milk: Black ring. No coagulation. Peptonization doubtful.

Potato: Abundant, wrinkled, brown growth, becoming black.

Starch is hydrolyzed.

Soluble brown pigment formed.

Nitrites produced from nitrates.

Aerobic.

Optimum temperature, 25° C.

Antagonistic properties: Produces fungicidin, a substance active against various fungi. Some strains produce luteomycin.

Source: Isolated many times from a variety of soils.

Habitat: Soil.

57. Streptomyces tanashiensis Hata et al., 1952. (Hata, Ohki and Higuchi,

Jour. Antibiotics (Japanese), *5*, 1952, 529 and 313.)

ta.na.shi.en'sis. M.L. adj. *tanashiensis* pertaining to Tanash; named for Tanash, a place near Cairo, Egypt.

Aerial mycelium: Hyphae almost straight; lightly open spirals. Spores spherical to ellipsoidal, 1.0 by 1.2 microns.

Gelatin: Brown pigment. Rapid liquefaction.

Synthetic agar: Grayish yellow growth. Aerial mycelium white-gray turning brownish gray. Soluble, light yellow pigment.

Milk: Yellowish surface ring. Coagulated and peptonized.

Potato: Brown growth. Aerial mycelium dark gray to whitish gray. Soluble dark brown pigment.

Starch is hydrolyzed.

Carbon sources: Starch most suitable, followed by glycerol.

Nitrogen sources: Peptone and meat extract best.

Tyrosinase reaction: Positive.

Nitrites not produced from nitrates.

Optimum pH, between 5.8 and 6.5.

Antagonistic properties: Produces luteomycin.

Relationships to other species: Resembles *Streptomyces aureus* and *Streptomyces antibioticus*.

Source: Isolated from soil.

Habitat: Soil.

58. **Streptomyces erythrochromogenes** (Krainsky, 1914) Waksman and Henrici, 1948. (*Actinomyces erythrochromogenes* Krainsky, Cent. f. Bakt., II Abt., *41*, 1914, 662; also see Waksman and Curtis, Soil Sci., *1*, 1916, 112; Waksman and Henrici, in Manual, 6th ed., 1948, 944.)

e.ry.thro.chro.mo'ge.nes. Gr. adj. *erythrus* red; Gr. noun *chromus* color; Gr. v. suffix *-genes* producing; M.L. adj. *erythrochromogenes* producing red color.

Aerial mycelium: Conidia ellipsoidal, about 2.0 microns long.

Gelatin colonies: Slow growth.

Gelatin stab: Liquefied. A soluble brown pigment formed.

Agar: Brown soluble pigment. White aerial mycelium.

Ca-malate agar: Colonies circular, with grayish white margined aerial mycelium.

Glucose agar: Red pigment formed.

Starch agar: A soluble rose pigment on old cultures.

Glucose broth: Abundant growth. Floating colonies, later a pellicle is formed. Brown soluble pigment.

Potato: Gray aerial mycelium. Medium colored black.

Weakly diastatic.

No growth in cellulose.

No proteolytic enzyme formed.

Nitrates show slight reduction.

Aerobic.

Optimum temperature, 30° C.

Antagonistic properties: Active against various bacteria.

Source: Isolated from soil and from roots of *Alnus* (alder).

Habitat: Soil.

59. **Streptomyces collinus** Lindenbein, 1952. (Arch. f. Mikrobiol., *17*, 1952, 380.)

col.li'nus. L. adj. *collinus* hilly, mounded.

Aerial mycelium: Produces spirals. Abundant sedimentation producing ellipsoidal spores.

Gelatin: Dark brown growth. No aerial mycelium. Soluble dark brown pigment. Rapid liquefaction.

Agar: Crumb-like, dark brown growth. Aerial mycelium powdery gray-white. Soluble dark brown pigment.

Synthetic agar: Crumb-like growth with light brown to red-brown reverse. Aerial mycelium chalk-white. Soluble yellow-brown pigment, later becoming reddish brown.

Glucose asparagine agar: Crumb-like growth with reverse irregularly brown-purple to brown-yellow. Aerial mycelium chalk-white, later becoming ash-gray. Soluble carmine-red pigment, later brown-red.

Ca-malate agar: Crumb-like growth with yellow-brown to red reverse. Aerial mycelium velvety chalk-white. Soluble yellow-brown pigment.

Starch agar: Large, reddish colonies with reddish yellow reverse. Aerial mycelium velvety chalk-white.

Glucose agar: Good growth with yellow-brown and red reverse. Aerial mycelium velvety chalk-white. Soluble chestnut-brown pigment.

Glucose broth: Sedimentary light yellow growth. No aerial mycelium. Soluble brownish yellow pigment.

Milk: Good growth with dark brown reverse. Aerial mycelium chalk-white, later ash-gray. Soluble dark brown pigment. Not peptonized.

Potato: Good growth. Aerial mycelium chalk-white. No soluble pigment.

Starch is hydrolyzed.

Good growth on cellulose.

Source: Isolated from soil.

Habitat: Soil.

60. Streptomyces lavendulae (Waksman and Curtis, 1916) Waksman and Henrici, 1948. (*Actinomyces lavendulae* Waksman and Curtis, Soil Sci., *1*, 1916, 126; Waksman and Henrici, in Manual, 6th ed., 1948, 944.)

la.ven'du.lae. Med.L. noun *lavendula* lavender; Med.L. gen.noun *lavendulae* of lavender color.

Aerial mycelium: Hyphae coarse, branching. Spirals close, 5 to 8 microns in diameter. Conidia ellipsoidal, 1.0 to 1.2 by 1.6 to 2.0 microns.

Gelatin stab: Creamy to brownish surface growth. Liquefaction.

Agar: Gray, wrinkled growth.

Synthetic agar: Thin, spreading, colorless growth. Aerial mycelium cottony, white, becoming vinous-lavender.

Starch agar: Restricted, glistening, transparent growth.

Glucose broth: Abundant, flaky sediment.

Litmus milk: Cream-colored ring. No coagulation; peptonized, with strong alkaline reaction.

Potato: Thin, wrinkled, cream-colored to yellowish growth.

Starch is hydrolyzed.

Soluble brown pigment formed.

Nitrites produced from nitrates.

Aerobic.

Optimum temperature, 37° C.

Antagonistic properties: Certain strains of this organism produce antibiotics. One such antibiotic, designated as streptothricin, is active both *in vitro* and *in vivo* against various Gram-positive and Gram-negative bacteria, fungi and actinomycetes. Certain other strains produce an antiviral agent, ehrlichin.

Source: Isolated once from orchard soil.

Habitat: Soil.

61. Streptomyces venezuelae Ehrlich et al., 1948. (Streptomyces No. 844, Pridham and Gottlieb, Jour. Bact., *56*, 1948, 107; Ehrlich, Gottlieb, Burkholder, Anderson and Pridham, Jour. Bact., *56*, 1948, 467.)

ve.ne.zu.e'lae. M.L. noun *Venezuela* Venezuela; M.L. gen.noun *venezuelae* of Venezuela.

Vegetative growth: Hyphae colorless, monopodial branches, 0.9 to 1.8 microns in diameter.

Aerial mycelium: Straight or slightly and irregularly curved, 1.0 to 1.8 microns in diameter, lavender under microscope, gray to light tan or pink without magnification. Spores ellipsoidal to oblong, 0.4 to 0.8 by 0.7 to 1.6 microns.

Gelatin: Rapid liquefaction. Soluble dark pigment.

Synthetic agar: Light lavender-colored growth.

Starch agar: White to lavender growth.

Glucose agar: Soluble dark pigment.

Dorset's egg medium: White to gray growth.

Loeffler's serum: Dark brown growth.

Tyrosine agar: Reaction positive.

Xylose, arabinose, rhamnose, d-glucose, d-mannose, d-fructose, d-galactose, cellobiose, starch, dextrin, glycerol, acetate, citrate, succinate and salicin support good growth. Slight or no growth with d-ribose, sucrose, raffinose, inulin, erythritol, dulcitol, mannitol, sorbitol, inositol and malate. No growth with formate, oxalate, tartrate, salicylate, phenol, o-cresol, m-cresol or p-cresol.

Milk: Peptonized. Soluble dark pigment.

Potato: Abundant, gray growth.

Nitrites produced from nitrates.

Antagonistic properties: Produces chloramphenicol, a neutral compound active against various Gram-positive and Gram-negative bacteria, rickettsiae and the larger viruses.

Comment: The type culture of this species was found in the culture bureau of Parke, Davis and Company, Detroit, No. 04745. A culture of this organism described by Umezawa and Maeda as a variety of *Streptomyces phaeochromogenes* is regarded by Waksman as identical with this species. (See Waksman, in Waksman and Lechevalier, Actinomycetes and Their Antibiotics, Baltimore, 1953, 73.)

Source: Isolated from soil in mulched field near Caracas, Venezuela.

Habitat: Soil.

62. **Streptomyces virginiae** Grundy et al., 1952. (Grundy, Whitman, Rdzok, Hanes and Sylvester, Antibiotics and Chemotherapy, *2*, 1952, 399.)

vir.gi'ni.ae. M.L. noun *Virginia* Virginia; M.L. gen.noun *virginiae* of Virginia.

Vegetative growth: Cream-colored to light brown on complex media; soluble, light brown, diffusible pigment. On synthetic media white to cream-colored growth with pink or grayish lavender aerial mycelium. Undulating mycelium about 1 micron in diameter with short, thinner side branches.

Aerial mycelium: Long, grayish pink or lavender aerial hyphae. Most of the sporulating hyphae straight, occasionally a spiral is observed at or near the tip of the hypha. Spirals vary from tightly closed knots to loose, open spirals. Spores cylindrical, 0.75 to 1.0 by 1.1 to 1.5 microns.

Gelatin: Gray to brownish surface pellicle. Aerial mycelium thin, white. Soluble brown pigment extending as far as liquefied zone. Slow liquefaction.

Agar: Sparse, white growth, turning cream-colored. White aerial mycelium, turning light grayish lavender when sporulation occurs. No soluble pigment.

Synthetic glucose agar: Sparse, cream-colored growth. Aerial mycelium light grayish lavender. No soluble pigment.

Glucose asparagine agar: Sparse, cream-colored growth. No aerial mycelium. No sporulation. No pigmentation.

Ca-malate agar: Abundant, cream-colored growth. White aerial mycelium becoming tinged with grayish lavender. No soluble pigment.

Starch agar: Thin colorless growth with aerial mycelium rose- to lavender-colored.

Oatmeal agar: Abundant, cream-colored growth, turning golden brown. Abundant light rose aerial mycelium, turning lavender and gray. Soluble pale yellow pigment, turning light brown.

Broth: Thin, cream-colored surface ring; a few flakes on bottom. Soluble brownish pigment.

Milk: Brown growth. Milk becomes dark gray-brown or black. Not coagulated; slowly peptonized.

Potato: Abundant, spreading, brownish growth. Aerial mycelium grayish lavender. Browning of potato.

Starch is hydrolyzed.

Glucose, mannose, galactose, maltose, starch, glycerol, sodium acetate and sodium citrate are utilized. Xylose, lactose, sucrose, mannitol, sorbitol and potassium sodium tartrate are not utilized.

Nitrites weakly produced, if at all, from nitrates.

Optimum temperature, between 28° and 30° C.

Antagonistic properties: Produces actithiazic acid.

Source: Isolated from soil near Roanoke, Virginia.

Habitat: Soil.

63. **Streptomyces reticuli** (Waksman and Curtis, 1916) Waksman and Henrici, 1948. (*Actinomyces reticuli* Waksman and Curtis, Soil Sci., *1*, 1916, 118; Waksman and Henrici, in Manual, 6th ed., 1948, 944.)

re.ti'cu.li. L. dim.noun *reticulum* a small net; L. gen.noun *reticuli* of a small net.

Aerial mycelium: Whorls; spirals formed on glucose agar are sinistrorse. Conidia spherical, 1.0 to 1.4 microns in diameter.

Gelatin stab: Liquefaction, with small, brown flakes.

Agar: Gray, wrinkled growth, becoming brownish.

Synthetic agar: Colorless growth, with

yellowish tinge, becoming brownish, spreading. Aerial mycelium thin, white, cottony.

Starch agar: Brownish gray growth.

Glucose agar: Restricted, brownish growth; center raised.

Glucose broth: Sediment consisting of large colonies.

Litmus milk: Reaction unchanged; coagulated; peptonized.

Potato: Gray growth with black center.

Starch is hydrolyzed.

Dark brown pigment formed.

Nitrites produced from nitrates.

Aerobic.

Optimum temperature, 25° C.

Antagonistic properties: Some strains produce neomycin or a neomycin-like substance.

Source: Isolated from upland and adobe soils in California.

Habitat: Soil.

64. **Streptomyces netropsis** Finlay and Sobin, 1952. (U. S. Pat. 2,586,762, Feb. 19, 1952.)

ne.trop′sis. Gr. neut.n. *netrum* spindle; Gr. fem.n. *opsis* appearance of something; M.L. adj. *netropsis* spindle-like.

Vegetative growth: Slightly elevated with rough surface and smooth edge and with brown reverse.

Aerial mycelium: White. Sporophores on tips of short hyphae in form of whorls or terminal clusters of short hyphae. Conidia short, cylindrical, 0.7 by 1.3 microns.

Gelatin: Moderate surface growth. White aerial mycelium. Soluble dark brown pigment. No liquefaction.

Agar: Moderate to good light brown growth. White aerial mycelium. Soluble light brown pigment.

Synthetic agar: Thin, pale olive-buff growth. Aerial mycelium pale vinaceous fawn. No soluble pigment.

Glucose asparagine agar: Moderate, wrinkled growth. White aerial mycelium. Soluble brown pigment.

Ca-malate agar: Moderate, cream to buff growth. White aerial mycelium. No soluble pigment.

Starch agar: Moderate thin growth with pale olive-buff reverse. White aerial mycelium. No soluble pigment.

Glucose agar: Good, dark brown growth. White aerial mycelium. Soluble brown pigment.

Milk: Poor growth. Not peptonized.

Potato: Poor, waxy, wrinkled, brown growth. No aerial mycelium. Dark brown pigment.

Starch is actively hydrolyzed.

Nitrites not produced from nitrates.

Antagonistic properties: Produces a basic antibiotic, netropsin.

Source: Isolated from soil near Hudson, New York. Cultural characteristics described are those of isolate No. 2937-6. A culture has been deposited with the Fermentation Division of the Northern Regional Research Laboratory, Peoria, Illinois, permanent collection number NRRL-2268.

Habitat: Soil.

65. **Streptomyces verticillatus** (Kriss, 1938) Waksman, 1953. (*Actinomyces verticillatus* Kriss, Microbiologia, 7, 1938, 111; Waksman, in Waksman and Lechevalier, Actinomycetes and Their Antibiotics, Baltimore, 1953, 75.)

ver.ti.cil.la′tus. L. mas.n. *verticillus* a whorl; M.L. adj. *verticillatus* whorled.

Vegetative growth: Colorless or slightly brownish, smooth or rough colonies.

Aerial mycelium: Characteristic primary whorl; formation of straight sporophores. Spores cylindrical, oblong, 0.8 by 1.0 to 1.9 microns.

Gelatin: Rapid liquefaction.

Agar: Brown growth with no aerial mycelium. Soluble brown pigment.

Synthetic agar: Well developed, velvety aerial mycelium, at first white, later dark gray or gray-green.

Milk: Coagulated and peptonized.

Potato: Soluble brown pigment.

Sucrose is inverted.

Starch is hydrolyzed.

No growth on cellulose.

Nitrites rapidly produced from nitrates.

Antagonistic properties: Weak.

Relationships to other species: *Streptomyces verticillatus viridans* is described as a substrain.

Source: Isolated from rhizosphere of wheat, Transvolga region, U.S.S.R.

Habitat: Found in wheat soil so far as known.

66. Streptomyces circulatus (Krassilnikov, 1941) Waksman, 1953. (*Actinomyces circulatus* Krassilnikov, Guide to the Actinomycetes, Izd. Akad. Nauk, U.S.S.R., Moskau, 1941, 60; Waksman, in Waksman and Lechevalier, Actinomycetes and Their Antibiotics, Baltimore, 1953, 76.)

cir.cu.la'tus. L. part.adj. *circulatus* curled.

Vegetative growth: Better on synthetic media than on organic media.

Aerial mycelium: Spiral-producing sporophores formed in whorls. Spores cylindrical, oblong, 0.7 by 1.5 microns, some rounding up as culture ages.

Gelatin: Weak liquefaction.

Agar: Poor growth. No aerial mycelium.

Synthetic agar: Good growth, producing abundant, white aerial mycelium.

Milk: Not coagulated; slowly peptonized.

Sucrose not inverted.

Starch is weakly hydrolyzed.

No growth on cellulose.

Nitrites weakly produced from nitrates.

Antagonistic properties: Limited.

Source: Isolated from soil.

Habitat: Soil.

67. Streptomyces rubrireticuli Waksman and Henrici, 1948. (*Actinomyces reticulus-ruber* Waksman, Soil Sci., 8, 1919, 146; *Actinomyces reticulus* Bergey et al., Manual, 2nd ed., 1925, 373; Waksman and Henrici, in Manual, 6th ed., 1948, 945.)

ru.bri.re.ti'cu.li. L. adj. *ruber* red; L. noun *reticulum* a small net; M.L. gen.noun *rubrireticuli* of a small red net.

Aerial mycelium: Branching filaments with both primary and secondary whorl formation. Spirals formed on glucose agar. Conidia ellipsoidal.

Gelatin stab: Surface growth yellowish red to dragon-pink. Liquefaction.

Agar: Red growth, with yellowish margin becoming red.

Synthetic agar: Abundant, spreading growth, usually pink. Aerial mycelium thin, rose to pink.

Starch agar: White growth with red tinge.

Glucose agar: Abundant, spreading, rose-red, entire growth.

Glucose broth: Thin, flaky sediment.

Litmus milk: Abundant, red pellicle; coagulated; peptonized. Reaction unchanged.

Potato: Cream-colored growth, later pink to dark red.

Soluble dark brown pigment formed.

Starch is hydrolyzed.

Good growth on cellulose.

Nitrites produced from nitrates.

Aerobic.

Optimum temperature, 37° C.

Antagonistic properties: Certain strains of this organism produce an antibiotic, designated as streptin.

Source: Isolated from a New Jersey orchard and from California upland soils.

Habitat: Soil.

68. Streptomyces flavus (Krainsky, 1914) Waksman and Henrici, 1948. (*Actinomyces flavus* Krainsky, Cent. f. Bakt., II Abt., 41, 1914, 662; also see Waksman and Curtis, Soil Sci., 1, 1916, 118; not *Actinomyces flavus* Sanfelice, Cent. f. Bakt., I Abt., Orig., 36, 1905, 359; Waksman and Henrici, in Manual, 6th ed., 1948, 945.)

fla'vus. L. adj. *flavus* yellow.

Aerial mycelium: Coarse filaments with branching hyphae. Conidia formed by budding and breaking up of hyphae into ellipsoidal forms.

Gelatin stab: Small, yellowish masses on surface of liquefied medium.

Agar: Gray, spreading, folded growth.

Synthetic agar: Circular, yellow or sulfur-yellow colonies. Aerial mycelium straw-yellow.

Starch agar: Spreading, cream-colored growth, with pink tinge.

Glucose agar: Restricted, raised, folded, sulfur-yellow growth, center shading to brown.

Glucose broth: Small, white colonies in bottom of tube.

Litmus milk: Coagulated; peptonized, becoming distinctly alkaline.

Potato: Elevated, much wrinkled, greenish olive growth.

Soluble brown pigment formed.

Starch is hydrolyzed.

Nitrites produced in trace amounts from nitrates.

Aerobic.

Optimum temperature, 25° C.

Antagonistic properties: Weakly antagonistic. Some strains produce actinomycin.

Comment: Represents a large group of closely related forms.

Source: Isolated from soil.

Habitat: Soil.

69. **Streptomyces ruber** (Krainsky, 1914) Waksman and Henrici, 1948. (*Actinomyces ruber* Krainsky, Cent. f. Bakt., II Abt., *41*, 1914, 662; also see Waksman, Soil Sci., *8*, 1919, 149; not *Actinomyces ruber* Sanfelice, Cent. f. Bakt., I Abt., Orig., *36*, 1904, 355; Waksman and Henrici, in Manual, 6th ed., 1948, 946.)

ru'ber. L. adj. *ruber* red.

Aerial mycelium: Straight, branching, radiating. A few spirals may be formed.

Gelatin stab: Liquefaction, with yellow flakes.

Agar: Restricted, elevated, wrinkled, olive-green growth.

Synthetic agar: Abundant, spreading, red growth. Aerial mycelium abundant, cottony, chrome-orange.

Starch agar: Abundant, spreading, red growth.

Glucose agar: Restricted, abundant, entire, coral-red growth.

Glucose broth: Red ring, with spongy colonies on the surface.

Litmus milk: Dark ring with red tinge; coagulated; peptonized, with alkaline reaction.

Potato: Elevated, wrinkled, greenish growth.

Soluble brown pigment formed.

Starch is hydrolyzed.

Nitrites produced from nitrates.

Aerobic.

Optimum temperature, 37° C.

Antagonistic properties: Strongly effective against various bacteria.

Source: Isolated from soil.

Habitat: Soil.

70. **Streptomyces niger** (Rossi-Doria, 1891, *emend.* Krassilnikov, 1941) Waksman, 1953. (*Streptotrix* (sic) *nigra* Rossi-Doria,

Ann. d. Ist. d'Ig. sper. d. Univ. di Roma, *1*, 1891, 419; *Actinomyces niger* Krassilnikov, Guide to the Actinomycetes, Izd. Akad. Nauk, U.S.S.R., Moskau, 1941, 53; Waksman, in Waksman and Lechevalier, Actinomycetes and Their Antibiotics, Baltimore, 1953, 78.)

ni'ger. L. adj. *niger* black.

Vegetative growth: Not compact, of soft consistency, lumpy, dark colored. In old cultures, the mycelium is readily disintegrated into fine particles that can serve for reproduction.

Aerial mycelium: Produced only on potato and synthetic agar. Sporophores produced only seldom; form open spiral with 3 to 5 turns. Spores ellipsoidal.

Gelatin: No liquefaction in 30 days.

Agar: Black growth. Soluble brown pigment.

Synthetic agar: Black growth. Aerial mycelium dark gray. No soluble pigment.

Starch agar: No growth.

Sucrose not inverted.

Milk: No change.

No growth on cellulose.

Nitrites not produced from nitrates.

Optimum temperature, between 25° and 30° C.

Antagonistic properties: None.

Comment: This is a very unstable species and rapidly dies out. It easily mutates, giving rise to colorless cultures, producing no aerial mycelium.

Source: Isolated from soil.

Habitat: Soil.

71. **Streptomyces alboniger** Hesseltine et al., 1953. (Hesseltine, Porter, Deduck, Hauk, Bohonos and Williams, Mycologia, 1953; quoted from Waksman, in Waksman and Lechevalier, Actinomycetes and Their Antibiotics, Baltimore, 1953, 78.)

al.bo'ni.ger. L. adj. *albus* white; L. adj. *niger* black; M.L. adj. *alboniger* white-black.

Description prepared by Hesseltine et al. for use in Waksman and Lechevalier, Actinomycetes and Their Antibiotics, Baltimore, 1953.

Vegetative growth: Moist, colorless to yellowish, to dark brown or black.

Aerial mycelium: White to pale olive-buff. Irregularly branched sporophores, erect to flexuous. Spores catenulate, ellipsoidal, 0.8 by 1.25 microns.

Gelatin: Fair growth. White aerial mycelium. Soluble light yellow pigment. Liquefaction.

Agar: Poor, moist, smooth, colorless growth. No aerial mycelium.

Synthetic agar: Poor, white growth. White aerial mycelium. No soluble pigment.

Starch agar: Good growth. White to pale olive-buff aerial mycelium. Soluble black pigment.

Glucose agar: Blackish gray growth. White aerial mycelium. Soluble, blackish gray pigment.

Milk: White surface ring with yellow-green to light yellow-brown below surface. White aerial mycelium. Slowly peptonized.

Potato plug: Moist yellow growth. White aerial mycelium. Soluble, dark, greenish black pigment.

Starch is actively hydrolyzed.

No growth on cellulose.

Antagonistic properties: Produces puromycin, an antibiotic active against certain protozoa and certain Gram-positive bacteria.

Source: Isolated from soil.

Habitat: Soil.

72. Streptomyces abikoensis Umezawa et al., 1951. (*Streptomyces abikoensum* (sic) Umezawa, Tazaki and Fukuyama, Jap. Med. Jour., *4*, 1951, 331; also see Okami, Jour. Antibiotics (Japanese), *5*, 1952, 479.)

a.bi.ko.en'sis. M.L. adj. *abikoensis* pertaining to Abiko; named for Abiko, Japan.

Vegetative growth: In separate colonies with very thin yellow aerial mycelium. Submerged mycelium yellow or yellowish brown. Soluble yellowish brown pigment.

Aerial mycelium: Microscopically short, unbranched, bearing a straight conidia chain.

Gelatin: Cream or brown growth. Soluble brown pigment. Crateriform liquefaction.

Agar: Isolated colonies; growth cream, with triangular hole in the center. No aerial mycelium. Soluble brown pigment.

Loeffler's coagulated serum: Cream growth. No aerial mycelium. No hydrolysis. Brown pigment.

Blood agar: Dark cream-yellow growth. Hemolysis strong.

Glucose, maltose and glycerol are utilized. Arabinose, xylose, rhamnose, fructose, galactose, mannitol, sorbitol, lactose, sucrose, raffinose and inulin are not utilized.

Milk: Slight, brown growth. Aerial mycelium white: Soluble yellowish brown pigment. Peptonized.

Carrot: Slight, wrinkled, brownish cream growth. Aerial mycelium yellowish white. Brown pigment.

Egg: Greenish yellow growth, without aerial mycelium and with spreading reddish violet pigment.

Starch is hydrolyzed.

Tyrosinase not produced.

Nitrites not produced from nitrates.

Antagonistic properties: Produces an antiviral agent, abikoviromycin.

Source: Strain Z-1-6 was isolated from garden soil from Abiko, Chiba Prefecture.

Habitat: Found in garden soils.

73. Streptomyces odorifer (Rullmann, 1895, *emend.* Lachner-Sandoval, 1898) Waksman, 1953. (*Cladothrix odorifera* Rullmann, Inaug. Diss., Munich, 1895; see Cent. f. Bakt., I Abt., *17*, 1895, 884; and Cent. f. Bakt., II Abt., *2*, 1896, 116; *Actinomyces odorifer* Lachner-Sandoval, Ueber Strahlenpilze, 1898, 65; Waksman, in Waksman and Lechevalier, Actinomycetes and Their Antibiotics. Baltimore, 1953, 79.)

o.do'ri.fer. L. adj *odorifer* fragrant.

Vegetative growth: Colorless, folded.

Aerial mycelium: Well developed, white or light gray. Sporophores long, straight, branching. Spirals formed according to original report (none observed by Waksman, *loc. cit.*). Spores spherical.

Gelatin: Cream-colored surface ring. Aerial mycelium thin, white. No soluble pigment. Slow liquefaction.

Agar: Folded, brown growth. Aerial mycelium white around edge. Faint soluble brown pigment.

Synthetic agar: Cream-colored growth with trace of brown. Aerial mycelium heavy, cream-colored.

Starch agar: Cream-colored to brown growth. Aerial mycelium abundant, cream-colored to straw-colored. No soluble pigment.

Glucose agar: Cream-colored to brownish growth. Aerial mycelium abundant, cream-colored. Faint soluble brownish pigment.

Broth: Colorless surface film. Aerial mycelium heavy, cream-colored. No soluble pigment.

Milk: Colorless to brownish surface ring. No aerial mycelium. Not coagulated; peptonized.

Potato: Folded, brownish growth. Aerial mycelium cream-colored. Faint, soluble pigment.

Sucrose is inverted.

Starch is actively hydrolyzed.

Good growth on cellulose.

Paraffin and fats support good growth.

Nitrites produced from nitrates.

Odor: Strong, characteristic of soil.

Antagonistic properties: Some strains give positive effects, others are negative.

Source: Isolated from sputum in a case of chronic bronchitis.

Habitat: Unknown.

74. Streptomyces roseoflavus Arai, 1951. (Jour. Antibiotics (Japanese), *4*, 1951, 215; see Biol. Abst., *27*, 1953, No. 1867.)

ro.se.o.fla'vus. L. fem.n. *rosa* a rose; L. adj. *flavus* yellow; M.L. adj. *roseoflavus* rose-yellow.

Vegetative growth: Large, flat colonies; vegetative mycelium limited to medium.

Aerial mycelium: White to rose-colored, producing numerous spirals. Spores ellipsoidal to oblong, 0.8 to 1.0 by 1.0 to 1.8 microns.

Gelatin: Strong liquefaction. Orange-brown colonies at bottom of liquefied zone. No soluble pigment.

Agar: Much-folded, white-gray to golden yellow growth. White to rose-colored aerial mycelium, limited to center of colonies.

Synthetic agar: Colorless to yellowish growth, penetrating deep into medium. Powdery, white to yellow-rose aerial mycelium.

Starch agar: Golden yellow growth with whitish aerial mycelium.

Glucose agar: Colorless to yellowish white growth with rose-colored aerial mycelium.

Milk: Cream-colored surface ring. Rapidly coagulated and peptonized, the medium becoming strongly alkaline.

Potato: Yellow mass without aerial mycelium. No soluble pigment.

Fair growth on cellulose paper; cellulose is decomposed.

Nitrites produced from nitrates.

Antagonistic properties: Produces a basic antibiotic, flavomycin, similar to neomycin.

Comment: Culture similar to that of *Streptomyces microflavus*.

Source: Isolated from garden soil from Chiba and Hiroshima.

Habitat: Soil.

75. Streptomyces putrificus (Nicolaieva, 1915) Waksman, 1953. (*Actinomyces putrificus* Nicolaieva, Arch. Biol. Nauk, *18*, 1915, 240; *Streptomyces putrificans* (sic) Waksman, in Waksman and Lechevalier, Actinomycetes and Their Antibiotics, Baltimore, 1953, 81.)

pu.tri'fi.cus. L. v. *putrefacio* to make rotten; M.L. adj. *putrificus* making rotten.

Vegetative growth: Colorless.

Aerial mycelium: White.

Agar: Grayish growth covered with white aerial mycelium. No soluble pigment.

Loeffler's serum: Yellow growth. No aerial mycelium. Serum liquefied and colored yellowish brown.

Glucose broth: Yellow soluble pigment.

Milk: Heavy pellicle, covered with white aerial mycelium. Gradually peptonized without previous coagulation.

Potato: Folded, sulfur-yellow growth. Aerial mycelium chalk-white. No soluble pigment.

Proteins energetically decomposed with the production of bad-smelling products, hydrogen sulfide and ammonia.

Odor: Strong, putrefactive.

Relationships to other species: Similar to *Actinomyces albus* Krainsky but differs from it in that it putrefies proteins with the production of gases.

Source: Isolated from surface water near St. Petersburg.

Habitat: Unknown.

76. Streptomyces citreus (Krainsky, 1914) Waksman and Henrici, 1948. (*Actinomyces citreus* Krainsky, Cent. f. Bakt., II

Abt., *41*, 1914, 662; also see Waksman and Curtis, Soil Sci., *1*, 1916, 99; not *Actinomyces citreus* Gasperini, Cent. f. Bakt., *15*, 1894, 684; Waksman and Henrici, in Manual, 6th ed., 1948, 946.)

cit're.us. L. adj. *citreus* of the citrus tree; M.L. adj. *citreus* lemon-yellow.

Aerial mycelium: Filaments with long, narrow open spirals. Conidia spherical to ellipsoidal, 1.2 to 1.5 by 1.2 to 1.8 microns.

Gelatin stab: Yellowish, restricted surface growth. Liquefaction in 35 days.

Agar: Restricted, cream-colored growth.

Synthetic agar: Abundant, spreading, raised, wrinkled, citron-yellow growth. Aerial mycelium covering surface, citron-yellow.

Starch agar: Abundant, yellowish green growth.

Glucose agar: Extensive, glossy, olive-yellow, entire growth; center elevated.

Glucose broth: Thin, wide, yellow ring; flaky sediment.

Litmus milk: Cream-colored surface growth; coagulated; peptonized, becoming alkaline.

Potato: Yellowish growth, aerial mycelium white.

The pigment formed is not soluble.

Starch is hydrolyzed.

Nitrites produced in trace amounts from nitrates.

Aerobic.

Optimum temperature, 37° C.

Antagonistic properties: Negative.

Source: Isolated from soil.

Habitat: Soil.

77. Streptomyces fulvissimus (Jensen, 1930) Waksman and Henrici, 1948. (*Actinomyces fulvissimus* Jensen, Soil Sci., *30*, 1930, 66; Waksman and Henrici, in Manual, 6th ed., 1948, 946.)

ful.vis'si.mus. L. sup.adj. *fulvissimus* very yellow.

Vegetative growth: Mycelium without any special characteristics.

Aerial mycelium: Hyphae short, straight, often trifurcated, 1.0 to 1.2 microns broad; no spiral formation; branches of hyphae break up into conidia, 1.0 to 1.2 by 1.2 to 1.5 microns.

Gelatin: Vegetative mycelium narrow, smooth, yellowish brown to red-brown; no aerial mycelium; no pigment; gelatin completely liquefied in 10 to 12 days.

Agar: Good growth; vegetative mycelium raised, finely wrinkled, deep red-brown; no aerial mycelium; brownish yellow pigment.

Synthetic agar: Good growth (one strain very scant), vegetative mycelium flat, narrow, first light golden, later deep orange to red-brown; aerial mycelium scant, sometimes almost absent, first white, later light grayish brown; pigment very characteristic, bright golden to orange.

Glycerol agar: Good growth; vegetative mycelium narrow, raised, smooth, golden to dark bronze; aerial mycelium scant, in patches, white to light cinnamon-brown; pigment intensely golden to orange.

Starch-casein agar: Good growth; vegetative mycelium spreading, folded, yellowish brown; aerial mycelium abundant, smooth, lead-gray; pigment dull yellow to orange.

Potato: Good growth; vegetative mycelium raised, much wrinkled, rust-brown; aerial mycelium absent or traces of white; pigment gray to faint lemon-yellow.

Loeffler's blood serum: Vegetative mycelium red-brown; no aerial mycelium; yellowish pigment; no liquefaction.

Distinctive characters: The characteristic golden pigment is formed in nearly all media in which the organism grows, but it becomes most typical and attains its greatest brightness in synthetic agar media; it has indicator properties, turning red in strongly acid solutions. The species is easily recognized on agar plates by its bronze-colored colonies surrounded by haloes of bright yellow pigment.

Source: Very common in Danish soils.

Habitat: Soil.

78. Streptomyces chrysomallus Lindenbein, 1952. (*Streptomyces chrysomallus* Brockmann, Grubhofer, Kass and Kalbe (*nomen nudum*), Chem. Ber., *84*, 1951, 260; Lindenbein, Arch. f. Mikrobiol., *17*, 1952, 369.)

chry.so'mal.lus. Gr. adj. *chrysomallus* with golden wool.

Vegetative growth: Soft on all media. Long, branched hyphae with numerous staining granules.

Aerial mycelium: Hyphae long, sporulating, producing no spirals, Spores ellipsoidal or spherical.

Gelatin: Heavy, light to dark yellow surface growth. Aerial mycelium powdery, white. Soluble yellow-brown to deep brown pigment in liquefied portion. Strong liquefaction.

Agar: Poor, shiny, golden yellow growth. Aerial mycelium thin, powdery. Soluble golden yellow pigment.

Synthetic agar: Crumb-like, light yellow growth. Aerial mycelium powdery, white. Soluble golden yellow pigment.

Glucose asparagine agar: Smooth, almost colorless to yellowish growth. Aerial mycelium powdery, white. Soluble faint yellow pigment.

Ca-malate agar: Thin, smooth, colorless to faintly yellowish growth. Aerial mycelium powdery, grayish white.

Starch agar: Thin, colorless growth. Aerial mycelium powdery, white. No soluble pigment.

Glucose agar: Yellowish growth with tinge of orange. Aerial mycelium powdery, grayish white. Soluble light yellow to golden yellow pigment.

Glucose broth: Heavy yellowish surface growth; submerged flakes yellowish. Soluble golden yellow pigment.

Milk: Abundant, colorless growth with light yellow reverse. Aerial mycelium cottony, snow-white becoming yellowish. Actively peptonized. Slight acidity.

Potato: Heavy, yellow growth becoming brownish yellow or orange. Aerial mycelium cottony white to yellowish white.

Starch is actively hydrolyzed.

Poor growth on cellulose.

Antagonistic properties: Produces actinomycin C (actinochrysin).

Source: Isolated from soil.

Habitat: Soil.

79. Streptomyces gougerotii (Duché, 1934) Waksman and Henrici, 1948. (*Actinomyces gougeroti* (sic) Duché, Encyclopédie Mycologique, Paris, *6*, 1934, 272; *Streptomyces gougeroti* (sic) Waksman and Henrici, in Manual, 6th ed., 1948, 947.)

gou.ge.ro'ti.i. M.L. gen.noun *gougerotii* of Gougerot; named for Prof. Gougerot,

from whom the original culture was obtained.

Aerial mycelium: Hyphae short, gnarled. Spores ellipsoidal.

Gelatin: Heavy surface growth. Cream-colored colonies developing slowly with faint aerial mycelium; no pigment; liquefaction rapid.

Agar: Cream-colored growth forming concentric rings with age, with brownish reverse; faint yellow soluble pigment. Aerial mycelium thin, white.

Synthetic agar: Slow growth as punctiform colonies; cream-colored with smooth edge; no aerial mycelium; no soluble pigment.

Glucose agar: Colorless to yellowish growth. Aerial mycelium thin, white. No soluble pigment.

Peptone broth: Cream-colored ring on surface of medium with flakes throughout the medium; no soluble pigment. Aerial mycelium white.

Synthetic solution: Submerged mycelium in the form of flakes, later forming a surface pellicle; no soluble pigment.

Tyrosine medium: Good growth with white aerial mycelium; no soluble pigment.

Coagulated serum: Cream-colored growth covered with white aerial mycelium; rapid liquefaction of serum.

Milk: Cream-colored surface growth. Aerial mycelium white, thin. Rapidly peptonized.

Potato: Slow growth of a greenish tinge; Aerial mycelium thin, white. No soluble pigment.

Starch is rapidly hydrolyzed.

Nitrates not reduced.

Antagonistic properties: Active against fungi.

Relationships to other species: Intermediate between *Streptomyces albus* with its abundant aerial mycelium and *Actinomyces almquistii* with its very scant aerial mycelium.

Source: Culture obtained from the collection of Prof. Gougerot.

Habitat: Unknown.

80. Streptomyces farinosus (Krassilnikov, 1941) Waksman, 1953. (*Actinomyces farinosus* Krassilnikov, Guide to the Actinomycetes, Izd. Akad. Nauk, U.S.S.R., Moskau, 1941, 51; Waksman, in Waksman and Lechevalier, Actinomycetes and Their Antibiotics, Baltimore, 1953, 84.)

fa.ri.no'sus. L. adj. *farinosus* mealy.

Vegetative growth: Colorless, smooth or rough colonies.

Aerial mycelium: Powdery white on some media. Sporophores straight or wavy, singly or in clumps, forming no spirals. Organism produces segmented spores or oidiospores, cylindrical, 0.6 to 0.8 by 1.2 to 1.7 microns. Some form ellipsoidal or even spherical spores produced by swelling of cylindrical forms.

Gelatin: Liquefaction.

Synthetic agar: Aerial mycelium poorly developed and spotty.

Milk: Coagulated and rapidly peptonized.

Potato: Colorless growth. Aerial mycelium poorly developed.

Sucrose readily inverted by most strains.

Starch is actively hydrolyzed.

Some strains grow on cellulose.

Nitrites weakly produced from nitrates.

Antagonistic properties: None or very weak.

Source: Isolated from soil.

Habitat: Soil.

81. **Streptomyces albidus** (Duché, 1934) Waksman, 1953. (*Actinomyces albidus* Duché, Encyclopédie Mycologique, Paris, *6*, 1934, 266; Waksman, in Waksman and Lechevalier, Actinomycetes and Their Antibiotics, Baltimore, 1953, 84.)

al'bi.dus. L. adj. *albidus* white.

Aerial mycelium: Whitish but not snow-white. Sporophores long, open spirals. Spherical to ellipsoidal spores. Soluble pigment produced in synthetic and other media.

Gelatin: Cream-colored growth. No soluble pigment. Rapid liquefaction.

Agar: Colorless growth with slightly greenish reverse. Aerial mycelium white. Soluble yellowish pigment.

Synthetic agar: Colorless growth; some drops of colorless guttation. Aerial mycelium white. Yellowish pigment.

Milk: Cream-colored growth. Weakly coagulated, rapidly peptonized. Cheesy odor.

Potato: Flat, colorless growth. Aerial mycelium white. No soluble pigment.

Starch is actively hydrolyzed.

Good growth on cellulose.

Nitrites slowly produced from nitrates.

Odor: Strong, earthy.

Antagonistic properties: Strong.

Relationships to other species: Closely related to *Streptomyces albus* but differs from it by its more delicate growth and by its reverse that is often yellowish brown. Also related to *Streptomyces microflavus* Krainsky but differs from Krainsky's organism in that its growth is never rose-yellow and by its abundant growth on potato.

Source: The original culture was obtained under the name of *Actinomyces microflavus* (not *Actinomyces microflavus* Krainsky) from the Baarn Culture Collection.

Habitat: Unknown.

82. **Streptomyces cinnamoneus** Benedict, 1953. (*Streptomyces cinnamoneus* Benedict, Dvonch, Shotwell, Pridham and Lindenfelser (*nomen nudum*), Antibiotics and Chemotherapy, *2*, 1952, 591; Benedict, in Waksman and Lechevalier, Actinomycetes and Their Antibiotics, Baltimore, 1953, 85.)

cin.na.mo'ne.us. Gr. neut.n. *cinnamon* cinnamon; M.L. adj. *cinnamoneus* pertaining to cinnamon.

Description prepared by R. G. Benedict for use in Waksman and Lechevalier, Actinomycetes and Their Antibiotics, Baltimore, 1953.

Vegetative growth: Large colonies with irregular margins.

Aerial mycelium: White, gradually changing to flesh color. No spirals. Spores globose, 0.6 micron in diameter.

Gelatin: White flocculent growth. No aerial mycelium. No soluble pigment. Rapid liquefaction.

Agar: Cream to light lemon-yellow growth. No aerial mycelium.

Synthetic agar: Colorless to white to cream-colored growth. Aerial mycelium white to light cinnamon.

Starch: Colorless to brownish growth. Aerial mycelium white.

Glucose agar: Colorless growth with light greenish yellow to dull yellowish orange reverse. Aerial mycelium white to cinnamon.

Oatmeal agar: Tough, leathery, yellowish green to cream-yellow growth. Aerial mycelium floccose, pale violet to faint cinnamon. Tan to white exudate.

Glucose broth: White to lime-green ring. No aerial mycelium.

Milk: Light brown ring. Limited, white aerial mycelium. Rapidly peptonized with alkaline reaction.

Potato: Grayish white to yellow-green to light brown growth. Aerial mycelium light gray to gray. No soluble pigment.

Carrot: White to cream-colored growth. Aerial mycelium cretaceous. No soluble pigment.

Xylose, fructose, inositol, starch, dextrin, galactose and maltose are utilized. Arabinose, rhamnose, dulcitol and salicin not utilized.

Starch is hydrolyzed.

Nitrites not produced from nitrates.

Optimum temperature, between 25° and 37° C.

Antagonistic properties: Produces cinnamycin, a polypeptide antibiotic.

Relationships to other species: Resembles *Streptomyces griseocarneus*.

Source: Isolated from Japanese soil.

Habitat: Soil.

83. Streptomyces violaceoniger (Waksman and Curtis, 1916) Waksman and Henrici, 1948. (*Actinomyces violaceus-niger* Waksman and Curtis, Soil Sci., *1*, 1916, 111; Waksman and Henrici, in Manual, 6th ed., 1948, 947.)

vi.o.la.ce.o'ni.ger. L. adj. *violaceus* violet; L. adj. *niger* black; M.L. adj. *violaceoniger* violet-black.

Gelatin: Gray growth, with no production of aerial mycelium. Gelatin around colony rapidly liquefied, but without any change in color.

Synthetic agar: Colony at first dark gray, turning almost black, 2 to 4 mm in diameter. Surface glossy, much folded with a very thin gray margin. A white to gray aerial mycelium is produced after the colony has developed well. A bluish black pigment is produced at a later stage of its growth. The pigment slowly dissolves in the medium, turning almost black. Odor fairly strong. Microscopically, two types of mycelium are found: the thin, branching filaments of the substratum, and the thick filaments of the aerial mycelium. The aerial mycelium does not fragment very rapidly, producing a few conidia, spherical and ellipsoidal, 1.2 to 1.5 by 1.2 to 2.3 microns. These often occur in chains.

Synthetic solution: Colonies large, 2 to 3 mm in diameter, appearing at the bottom and surface of the solution, but none throughout the medium. Colonies bluish in color, with a regular margin. Medium not colored.

Potato plug: Growth at first very slight, but after 48 hours develops into a yellowish gray continuous thick smear which later turns brown, with a white aerial mycelium covering the growth. Medium not colored.

Antagonistic properties: None; certain strains show activity.

Source: Isolated once from the upland California soil.

Habitat: Soil.

84. Streptomyces gedanensis (Löhlein, 1909) Müller, 1950. (*Streptothrix gedanensis I*, Scheele and Petruschsky, Verhandl. d. Kongr. f. innere Med., 1897, 550; *Streptothrix gedanensis* Löhlein, Ztschr. f. Hyg., *63*, 1909, 11; Müller, Medizinische Mikrobiologie, 4 Aufl., 1950, 294.)

ge.da.nen'sis. M.L. neut.n. *Gedanum* the city of Danzig (Gdan'sk) on the Baltic Sea; M.L. adj. *gedanensis* pertaining to Danzig.

Aerial mycelium: Short, gnarled hyphae; spores short, ellipsoidal to spherical.

Gelatin: Thin, flaky growth. No soluble pigment. Rapid liquefaction.

Agar: Thin, colorless growth. No aerial mycelium. No soluble pigment.

Synthetic agar: Dark to almost black growth with dark reverse. Aerial mycelium abundant, mouse-gray. No soluble pigment.

Starch agar: Yellowish to cream-colored growth. Aerial mycelium light gray.

Glucose agar: Cream-colored growth becoming black with light margin. Aerial mycelium abundant, mouse-gray.

Broth: Flaky growth on bottom of tube.

Milk: Cream-colored surface ring. Not peptonized.

Potato: Lichenoid, cream-colored to brownish growth. No aerial mycelium. No soluble pigment.

Starch is actively hydrolyzed.

Nitrites not produced from nitrates.

Source: Isolated from the sputum of a patient with chronic lung disease.

Habitat: Unknown.

85. Streptomyces griseus (Krainsky, 1914) Waksman and Henrici, 1948. (*Actinomyces griseus* Krainsky, Cent. f. Bakt., II Abt., *41*, 1914, 662; Waksman and Henrici, in Manual, 6th ed., 1948, 948; also see Waksman, Reilly and Harris, Jour. Bact., *56*, 1948, 259.)

gri'se.us. M.L. adj. *griseus* gray.

Vegetative growth: Colonies smooth or folded, colorless, later turning olive-buff.

Aerial mycelium: Abundant, powdery, water-green. Sporophores produced in tufts. Spores spherical to ellipsoidal, 0.8 by 0.8 to 1.7 microns.

Agar: Abundant, cream-colored, almost transparent growth. Aerial mycelium powdery, white to light gray. No soluble pigment.

Gelatin stab: Greenish yellow or cream-colored surface growth with brownish tinge. Rapid liquefaction.

Synthetic agar: Thin, colorless, spreading growth, becoming olive-buff. Aerial mycelium thick, powdery, water-green.

Starch agar: Thin, spreading, transparent growth.

Glucose agar: Growth elevated in center, radiate, cream-colored to orange, erose margin.

Glucose broth: Abundant, yellowish pellicle with greenish tinge, much folded.

Litmus milk: Cream-colored ring; coagulated with rapid peptonization, becoming alkaline.

Potato: Yellowish, wrinkled growth covered with white, powdery aerial mycelium. The pigment formed is not soluble.

Starch is hydrolyzed.

Nitrites produced from nitrates.

Aerobic.

Optimum temperature, 37° C.

Antagonistic properties: Strongly antagonistic. Different strains of this organism produce different antibiotics. One of these, streptomycin, is active against a large number of bacteria and actinomycetes but not against fungi and viruses. Some strains produce grisein. Others form candicidin.

Distinctive characters: This species is distinguished by Waksman from *Streptomyces globisporus* (No. 3) primarily on the basis of the yellow-green to gray color of the aerial mycelium on most media, and on the ability to coagulate milk and to hydrolyze starch rapidly.

Comments: The original description of this organism by Krainsky (*op. cit.*, 1914, 662) mentions spiral formation in the sporophores; the cultures subsequently isolated and described by Waksman and Curtis (*op. cit.*, 1916, 119) and Waksman, Reilly and Harris (*op. cit.*, 1948, 259) were not shown to exhibit spiral forms. In other characteristics these cultures resembled the original description. The description of *Streptomyces griseus* presented here is based largely on the description of the culture isolated by Waksman and Curtis. Waksman does not feel that the differences among these various isolates are sufficient to justify separation into more than one species.

Krassilnikov (Guide to the Bacteria and Actinomycetes, Izd. Akad. Nauk, U.S.S.R., Moskau, 1949, 93 and 98) regards the organism isolated and described by Krainsky as different from the organisms isolated later by Waksman et al., the distinction being made on the appearance of the sporophores. Krassilnikov regards the organisms exhibiting spiral formation as *Actinomyces griseus* Krainsky; those without spiral formation as *Actinomyces globisporus* Krassilnikov. The streptomycin-producing strain is regarded as a subspecies of the latter species rather than of the former.

Source: Isolated from garden soil; later from soils, river muds and the throat of a chicken.

Habitat: Presumably soil.

86. Streptomyces longissimus (Krassilnikov, 1941) Waksman, 1953. (*Actinomyces longissimus* Krassilnikov, Guide to the Actinomycetes, Izd. Akad. Nauk, U.S.S.R., Moskau, 1941, 38; Waksman, in Waksman and Lechevalier, Actinomycetes and Their Antibiotics, Baltimore, 1953, 87.)

lon.gis′si.mus. L. sup.adj. *longissimus* longest, very long.

Vegetative growth: Bright orange or golden red colonies. No diffusible pigment.

Aerial mycelium: Weakly developed; absent on some media. Sporophores straight, short, single or branched. Spores elongated, 0.7 by 1.0 to 1.3 microns, cylindrical.

Gelatin: Rapid liquefaction.

Synthetic agar: Well developed, velvety, white-yellow aerial mycelium.

Potato: Well developed aerial mycelium of characteristic color.

Starch is actively hydrolyzed.

Good growth on cellulose.

Paraffin and waxes support good growth.

Antagonistic properties: Weakly antagonistic.

Relationships to other species: Similar to *Streptomyces fradiae.*

Source: Isolated from soil.

Habitat: Soil.

87. Streptomyces olivaceus (Waksman, 1923) Waksman and Henrici, 1948. (Actinomyces 206, Waksman, Soil Sci., 7, 1919, 117; *Actinomyces olivaceus* Waksman, in Manual, 1st ed., 1923, 354; Waksman and Henrici, in Manual, 6th ed., 1948, 950.)

o.li.va′ce.us. L.noun *oliva* the olive; M.L. adj. *olivaceus* olive-colored.

Aerial mycelium: Clumps small, with straight and branching hyphae. No spirals on most media. Conidia spherical and ellipsoidal, 0.9 to 1.1 by 0.9 to 2.0 microns.

Gelatin stab: Liquefaction with cream-colored, flaky, yellow sediment.

Agar: White, glistening growth.

Synthetic agar: Growth abundant, spreading, developing deep into medium, yellow to olive-ochre, reverse yellow to almost black. Aerial mycelium mouse-gray to light drab.

Starch agar: Thin, yellowish green, spreading growth.

Glucose agar: Growth abundant, restricted, entire, center raised.

Glucose broth: Sulfur-yellow ring.

Litmus milk: Faint, pinkish growth; coagulated; peptonized, becoming alkaline.

Potato: Growth abundant, much wrinkled, elevated, gray, turning sulfur-yellow on edge.

The pigment formed is not soluble.

Starch is hydrolyzed.

Nitrites produced from nitrates.

Aerobic.

Optimum temperature, 25° C.

Antagonistic properties: Positive.

Source: Isolated from soil.

Habitat: Soil.

88. Streptomyces microflavus (Krainsky, 1914) Waksman and Henrici, 1948. (*Actinomyces microflavus* Krainsky, Cent. f. Bakt., II Abt., *41*, 1914, 662; Waksman and Henrici, in Manual, 6th ed., 1948, 950.)

mic.ro.fla′vus. Gr. adj. *micrus* small; L. adj. *flavus* yellow; M. L. adj. *microflavus* somewhat yellow.

Aerial mycelium: Well developed, cottony, white. Spores spherical to rod-shaped, often in pairs or chains, 2.0 by 2.0 to 5.0 microns.

Gelatin colonies: Small, yellow.

Gelatin stab: Rapid liquefaction.

Agar: Yellow colonies with rose-yellow aerial mycelium in 3 to 4 weeks.

Ca-malate agar: Minute yellow colonies. No aerial mycelium.

Glucose agar: A rose-yellow aerial mycelium develops in about 12 days.

Starch agar: Same as on glucose agar.

Glucose broth: Small spherical colonies in depth.

Litmus milk: Rapidly coagulated and peptonized.

Potato: Yellow growth. No aerial mycelium.

Diastatic action strong.

Scant growth on cellulose.

Nitrites produced from nitrates.

Aerobic.

Optimum temperature, 25° C.

Antagonistic properties: Positive.

Source: Isolated from soil.

Habitat: Soil.

89. Streptomyces cacaoi (Waksman, 1932) Waksman and Henrici, 1948. (*Actinomyces cacaoi* Waksman, in Bunting, Ann. Appl. Biol., *19*, 1932, 515; Waksman and Henrici, in Manual, 6th ed., 1948, 951.)

ca.ca′o.i. Mexican Spanish *cacao* the cacao tree; M.L. gen.noun *cacaoi* of cacao.

Aerial mycelium: Long with considerable

spiral formation; spirals long and open, not compact.

Gelatin: Flocculent growth. No aerial mycelium. Rapid liquefaction. No pigment production.

Agar: Brown-colored growth covered with tiny patches of ivory-colored aerial mycelium.

Synthetic agar: Same as on glucose agar.

Potato: Abundant brownish growth with white to mouse-gray aerial mycelium.

Glucose agar: Thin yellowish growth, later turning reddish brown; no soluble pigment; light gray to mouse-gray mycelium with white edge. Typical odor of streptomyces.

Strong proteolytic enzymes acting on casein and gelatin.

Strong diastatic action; no sugar or dextrin left in 1 per cent starch solution after a few days.

Limited reduction of nitrate.

Antagonistic properties: Certain strains produce an antibiotic designated as cacaomycetin.

Source: Three strains were isolated from cacao beans in Nigeria. There were slight differences among the three strains; the above description is of Strain I.

Habitat: The cacao bean so far as known.

90. **Streptomyces marinus** (Humm and Shepard, 1946) Waksman, *comb. nov.* (*Actinomyces marinus* Humm and Shepard, Duke Univ. Marine Sta. Bull., *3*, 1946, 77.)

ma.ri′nus. L. adj. *marinus* marine, of the sea.

Vegetative growth: Mycelium sparingly branched, dense, entangled. Growth on agar moderately rapid, reaching a diameter of one cm or more after about ten days. Mycelium frequently forms concentric rings in response to alternate periods of light and darkness. No soluble pigments.

Aerial mycelium: White; conidia medium gray to dark gray. Aerial hyphae somewhat irregular in diameter, 0.8 to 1.4 microns. Conidia spherical to ellipsoidal, 0.8 to 1.2 microns in diameter, in chains, sometimes forming loose spirals. Conidia typically appear after three days as a dark gray area in center of each colony.

Gelatin: Growth arborescent. Stratiform liquefaction, beginning after about ten days at 20° to 23° C.

Broth: Strong white pellicle. White tufts may develop at sides of tube beneath surface of liquid.

Milk: Alkaline within one week; completely peptonized, usually within one month at 25° to 30° C.

Indole not produced. Indigotin not produced from indole.

Hydrogen sulfide vigorously produced.

Acid from galactose, glucose, fructose, mannose, cellobiose, lactose, maltose, sucrose and glycerol. Arabinose, xylose, rhamnose and sorbitol utilized without acid production. No growth in raffinose, salicin, inulin, dulcitol, inositol, ethyl alcohol or ethylene glycol.

Acetylmethylcarbinol not produced.

Starch vigorously hydrolyzed.

Cellulose not hydrolyzed.

Chitin and alginic acid are attacked.

Seaweed gells: Agar slowly digested; softened, not liquefied. Growth on agar in culture dish surrounded by rather wide, gently sloping depression. Gelase field relatively wide with distinct margin. Irish moss and Hypnea gels also slowly digested.

Acetic, citric, lactic, propionic, succinic and iso-valeric acids utilized. Butyric, gluconic, maleic, malonic and oxalic acids not utilized.

Aspartic acid, cystine, glutamic acid, glycine, l-leucine and tyrosine utilized as sources of both nitrogen and carbon. dl-Alanine and d-arginine utilized only as nitrogen sources. Creatine and dl-β-phenylalanine not utilized. Glucosamine-HCl utilized as source of nitrogen and carbon.

Ammonia, nitrite or nitrate utilized as nitrogen sources. Ammonia produced from nitrate, asparagine, peptone and glutamic acid. Urea used as nitrogen source with production of small amounts of ammonia.

Nitrites usually not produced from nitrates. In some media, slight nitrite is produced after ten days' incubation, especially if glucose is present.

Catalase-positive.

Aerobic.

Optimum temperature, between 25° and 30° C.

Good growth in media prepared with distilled water and in all salinities through 6 per cent (sea salt); optimum apparently about 3 per cent. Greater salinities inhibit development of aerial hyphae.

Source: Isolated from blackish sand from the intertidal zone of a beach in North Carolina.

Habitat: Found in marine sediments.

91. Streptomyces novaecaesareae Waksman and Henrici, 1948. (*Actinomyces violaceus-caeseri* Waksman and Curtis, Soil Sci., *1*, 1916, 111; Waksman and Henrici, in Manual, 6th ed., 1948, 951.)

no.vae.cae.sa're.ae. M.L. noun *Nova Caesarea* (the State of) New Jersey; M.L. gen.noun *novaecaesareae* of New Jersey.

Aerial mycelium: Filaments with both straight and spiral aerial hyphae; spirals dextrorse. Conidia ellipsoidal to elongate.

Gelatin stab: Small, cream-colored surface colonies with slow liquefaction.

Agar: Thin, cream-colored growth.

Synthetic agar: Gray growth, becoming bluish, glossy, much wrinkled. Aerial mycelium appears late; white.

Starch agar: Restricted, circular, bluish violet colonies.

Glucose agar: Restricted, gray growth, becoming red.

Glucose broth: Fine, colorless, flaky sediment.

Litmus milk: Gray ring; coagulated; slow peptonization, becoming faintly alkaline.

Potato: Growth cream-colored, wrinkled, turning yellowish.

Soluble purple pigment formed.

Starch is hydrolyzed.

Nitrites produced from nitrates.

Aerobic.

Optimum temperature, 37° C.

Antagonistic properties: Negative.

Source: Isolated once from upland California soil.

Habitat: Soil.

92. Streptomyces exfoliatus (Waksman and Curtis, 1916) Waksman and Henrici, 1948. (*Actinomyces exfoliatus* Waksman and Curtis, Soil Sci., *1*, 1916, 116; Waksman and Henrici, in Manual, 6th ed., 1948, 951.)

ex.fo.li.a'tus. L. part.adj. *exfoliatus* stripped of leaves.

Aerial mycelium: Slightly wavy filaments with tendency to form spirals. Conidia ellipsoidal, 1.0 to 1.5 by 1.2 to 1.8 microns.

Gelatin stab: Cream-colored surface growth. Liquefaction.

Agar: Grows only in depth of medium.

Synthetic agar: Colorless growth, becoming brown, smooth, glossy. Aerial mycelium in white patches over surface.

Starch agar: Restricted, gray growth, becoming brown.

Glucose broth: Small, grayish colonies in depth.

Litmus milk: Cream-colored ring, soft coagulum in 12 days; slow peptonization, becoming strongly alkaline.

Potato: Growth somewhat wrinkled, gray, becoming brown.

Brown, soluble pigment formed.

Starch is hydrolyzed.

Nitrites produced from nitrates.

Aerobic.

Optimum temperature, 37° C.

Antagonistic properties: Positive.

Source: Isolated several times from adobe and upland soils in California.

Habitat: Soil.

93. Streptomyces gelaticus (Waksman, 1923) Waksman and Henrici, 1948. (Actinomyces 104, Waksman, Soil Sci., *8*, 1919, 165; *Actinomyces gelaticus* Waksman, in Manual, 1st ed., 1923, 356; Waksman and Henrici, in Manual, 6th ed., 1948, 952.)

ge.la'ti.cus. L. part.adj. *gelatus* frozen, congealed, jellied; M.L. adj. *gelaticus* resembling hardened gelatin.

Aerial mycelium: Branching, with open spirals.

Gelatin stab: Liquefied with cream-colored flaky sediment.

Agar: Wrinkled, cream-colored growth only on the surface.

Synthetic agar: Colorless, spreading growth chiefly deep into the medium. Aerial mycelium thin, white, turning grayish.

Starch agar: Thin, spreading, cream-colored growth.

Glucose agar: Abundant, spreading, white growth.

Glucose broth: Thin, cream-colored pellicle; slight flaky sediment.

Litmus milk: Pinkish ring; coagulated; peptonized with distinctly alkaline reaction.

Potato: Abundant growth, much wrinkled, greenish, becoming black with yellowish margin.

Soluble brown pigment formed.

Starch is hydrolyzed.

Nitrites produced in slight amounts from nitrates.

Aerobic.

Optimum temperature, 25° C.

Antagonistic properties: Positive; some strains show no activity.

Source: Isolated from soil.

Habitat: Soil.

94. Streptomyces glaucus (Lehmann and Schütze, 1912, *emend*. Krassilnikov, 1941) Waksman, 1953. (*Actinomyces glaucus* Lehmann and Schütze, in Lehmann and Neumann, Bakt. Diag., 5 Aufl., *2*, 1912, 641; Krassilnikov, Guide to the Actinomycetes, Izd. Akad. Nauk, U.S.S.R., Moskau, 1941, 46; Waksman, in Waksman and Lechevalier, Actinomycetes and Their Antibiotics, Baltimore, 1953, 91.)

glau'cus. Gr. adj. *glaucus* bright bluish green or gray.

Aerial mycelium: Well developed, cottony, at first white then turning green, similar to green Penicillia. Sporophores form compact spirals with 3 to 5 turns. Spores ellipsoidal to spherical, 1.0 by 0.8 microns.

Gelatin: Slow liquefaction.

Agar: Heavy growth covered with green aerial mycelium.

Synthetic agar: Colorless growth. Soluble brown pigment.

Milk: Slowly peptonized, with prior coagulation by some strains.

Potato: Heavy growth, covered with velvety, green aerial mycelium.

Sucrose weakly inverted.

Starch is actively hydrolyzed.

Good growth on cellulose.

Paraffin: Good growth.

Nitrites produced from nitrates.

Antagonistic properties: All strains strongly antagonistic.

Source: Isolated from soil.

Habitat: Soil.

95. Streptomyces rutgersensis (Waksman and Curtis, 1916) Waksman and Henrici, 1948. (*Actinomyces rutgersensis* Waksman and Curtis, Soil Sci., *1*, 1916, 123; Waksman and Henrici, in Manual, 6th ed., 1948, 952.)

rut.ger.sen'sis. M.L. adj. *rutgersensis* pertaining to Rutgers; named for Rutgers University, New Brunswick, New Jersey.

Aerial mycelium: Branching filaments with abundant open and closed spirals; hyphae fine, long, branching. Conidia spherical and ellipsoidal, 1.0 to 1.2 microns, with tendency to bipolar staining.

Gelatin stab: Cream-colored, spreading surface growth. Liquefied.

Agar: Thin, wrinkled, cream-colored growth.

Synthetic agar: Growth thin, colorless, spreading, becoming brownish to almost black. Aerial mycelium thin, white, becoming dull gray.

Starch agar: Gray, spreading growth.

Glucose agar: Abundant, brown mycelium, becoming black with cream-colored margin.

Litmus milk: Cream-colored ring; coagulated; slow peptonization, becoming alkaline.

Potato: Abundant, white-gray, much folded growth.

The pigment formed is not soluble.

Starch is hydrolyzed.

Nitrites produced from nitrates.

Aerobic.

Optimum temperature, 37° C.

Antagonistic properties: Limited.

Source: Isolated many times from a variety of soils.

Habitat: Common in soil.

96. Streptomyces halstedii (Waksman and Curtis, 1916) Waksman and Henrici, 1948. (*Actinomyces halstedii* Waksman and Curtis, Soil Sci., *1*, 1916, 124; Waksman and Henrici, in Manual, 6th ed., 1948, 953.)

hal.ste'di.i. M.L. gen.noun *halstedii* of Halsted; named after Prof. Halsted of Rutgers University.

Aerial mycelium: Branching mycelium; hyphae with close spirals. Conidia ellipsoidal or rod-shaped, 1.0 to 1.2 by 1.2 to 1.8 microns.

Gelatin stab: Liquefaction, with small cream-colored masses in bottom of tube.

Agar: Restricted, wrinkled, cream-colored growth.

Synthetic agar: Growth abundant, heavy, spreading, raised, light, becoming dark, almost black. Aerial mycelium white, turning dull gray.

Starch agar: Abundant, brownish, glossy growth.

Glucose agar: Growth spreading, colorless, wrinkled, center elevated, edge lichenoid, becoming brown.

Glucose broth: Small, colorless colonies in bottom of tube.

Litmus milk: Cream-colored ring; coagulated; peptonized, becoming alkaline.

Potato: Growth abundant, moist, wrinkled, cream-colored with green tinge.

The pigment formed is not soluble.

Starch is hydrolyzed.

Nitrites produced from nitrates.

Aerobic.

Optimum temperature, 37° C.

Antagonistic properties: Strongly antagonistic; some strains show only antifungal activity; some strains produce magnamycin.

Source: Isolated many times from the deeper soil layers.

Habitat: Common in subsoil.

97. Streptomyces fumosus (Krassilnikov, 1941) Waksman, 1953. (*Actinomyces fumosus* Krassilnikov, Guide to the Actinomycetes, Izd. Akad. Nauk, U.S.S.R., Moskau, 1941, 58; Waksman, in Waksman and Lechevalier, Actinomycetes and Their Antibiotics, Baltimore, 1953, 92.)

fu.mo′sus. L. adj. *fumosus* full of smoke, smoky.

Aerial mycelium: Sporophores straight; spores cylindrical, 0.7 by 1.5 to 2.0 microns, later round.

Gelatin: Liquefaction.

Agar: Dark brown growth; aerial mycelium white. Medium brown-colored.

Synthetic agar: Dark brown growth. Pigment not soluble. Aerial mycelium well developed, cottony, dusty colored, occasionally gray-white.

Milk: Not coagulated; slowly liquefied with production of a dark brown to almost black pigment.

Potato: No growth, or only faint dark gray aerial mycelium.

Sucrose weakly inverted.

Starch is actively hydrolyzed.

No growth on cellulose.

Antagonistic properties: None.

Source: Isolated from soil.

Habitat: Soil.

98. Streptomyces lipmanii (Waksman and Curtis, 1916) Waksman and Henrici, 1948. (*Actinomyces lipmanii* Waksman and Curtis, Soil Sci., *1*, 1916, 123; Waksman and Henrici, in Manual, 6th ed., 1948, 952.)

lip.ma′ni.i. M.L. gen.noun *lipmanii* of Lipman; named for Prof. J. G. Lipman of the New Jersey Agr. Exp. Station.

Aerial mycelium: Straight, branching mycelium and hyphae. Conidia ellipsoidal, 0.8 to 1.1 by 1.0 to 1.5 microns.

Gelatin stab: Liquefaction, with cream-colored, flaky sediment.

Agar: Yellow, glossy, radiately wrinkled growth.

Synthetic agar: Growth abundant, raised, colorless, becoming light brown and wrinkled. Aerial mycelium white, turning gray.

Starch agar: Transparent growth, becoming dark with age.

Glucose agar: Light yellow, irregular, spreading growth.

Glucose broth: White ring, with abundant, colorless flaky sediment.

Litmus milk: Cream-colored ring; coagulated; peptonization with alkaline reaction.

Potato: Abundant, cream-colored, wrinkled growth.

The pigment formed is not soluble.

Starch is hydrolyzed.

Nitrites produced from nitrates.

Aerobic.

Optimum temperature, 25° C.

Antagonistic properties: Good, though some strains show no activity.

Source: Isolated many times from a variety of soils.

Habitat: Common in soil.

99. Streptomyces hygroscopicus (Jensen, 1931) Waksman and Henrici, 1948. (*Actinomyces hygroscopicus* Jensen, Proc.

Linn. Soc. New So. Wales, *56*, 1931, 257; Waksman and Henrici, in Manual, 6th ed., 1948, 953.)

hy.gro.scop'i.cus. Gr. adj. *hygrus* moist; Gr. noun *scopus* watcher; M.L. adj. *hygroscopicus* detecting moisture or covered with moisture.

Vegetative growth: Hyphae 0.6 to 0.8 micron in diameter.

Aerial mycelium: Hyphae long, tangled, branched, 0.8 to 1.0 micron in diameter. Spirals numerous, sinistrorse, narrow, usually short, only 1 or 2 turns, closed, typically situated as dense clusters on the main stems of the aerial hyphae. Spores ellipsoidal, 0.8 to 1.0 by 1.0 to 1.2 microns.

Gelatin: Slow liquefaction. No pigment produced.

Agar: Good growth; raised, wrinkled, glossy, cream-colored; later yellowish gray with yellowish brown reverse. Occasionally a scant white aerial mycelium.

Sucrose agar: Good to abundant growth. Vegetative mycelium heavy, superficially spreading, folded, glossy surface, white to cream-colored, later sulfur-yellow to yellowish gray, with golden to light orange reverse. Soluble pigment of the same color. Aerial mycelium scant, thin, white or absent.

Glucose agar: Good growth; granulated, cream-colored to straw-yellow, later dull chrome-yellow to brownish orange. Aerial mycelium thin, smooth, dusty, white to pale yellowish gray, after 1 or 2 weeks more or less abundantly interspersed with small, moist, dark violet-gray to brownish patches which gradually spread over the whole surface. Light yellow soluble pigment.

Potato: Fair growth. Vegetative mycelium raised, wrinkled, cream-colored, later yellowish gray to dull brownish. Aerial mycelium absent or trace of white.

Milk: Completely digested in 3 to 4 weeks at 30° C. without any previous coagulation. The reaction becomes faintly acid (pH 6.0 or less).

Sucrose is inverted.

Starch is hydrolyzed.

Cellulose is decomposed readily by some strains.

Nitrates not reduced with sucrose as source of energy.

Antagonistic properties: Positive.

Distinctive character: In this species, the aerial mycelium (which in other actinomycetes is strikingly hydrophobic) on certain media (glucose or glycerol asparagine agar) becomes moistened and exhibits dark, glistening patches. These patches, when touched with a needle, prove to be a moist, smeary mass of spores. This characteristic feature is not equally distinct in all strains.

Source: Seven strains were isolated from soils.

Habitat: Soil.

100. **Streptomyces longisporoflavus** (Krassilnikov, 1941) Waksman, 1953. (*Actinomyces longisporus flavus* Krassilnikov, Guide to the Actinomycetes, Izd. Akad. Nauk, U.S.S.R., Moskau, 1941, 30; Waksman, in Waksman and Lechevalier, Actinomycetes and Their Antibiotics, Baltimore, 1953, 94.)

lon.gi.spo.ro.fla'vus. L. adj. *longus* long; Gr. noun *spora* a seed; M.L. fem.n. *spora* a spore; L. adj. *flavus* yellow; M.L. adj. *longisporoflavus* long-spored, yellow.

Vegetative growth: Yellow, lemon-yellow or dirty yellow, seldom golden yellow colonies. Pigment not soluble. Some strains have a greenish tinge, depending on the composition of the medium.

Aerial mycelium: Well developed, velvety, whitish yellow to brownish yellow. Sporophores produce long, open spirals. Spores cylindrical or elongated, 1.0 to 1.5 by 0.7 microns; some with rounded ends and swollen in center.

Gelatin: Liquefaction in 10 to 15 days.

Milk: Coagulated; slowly peptonized.

Sucrose not inverted.

Starch is weakly hydrolyzed.

No growth on cellulose.

Nitrites actively produced from nitrates.

Antagonistic properties: Weakly antagonistic.

Source: Isolated from soil.

Habitat: Soil.

101. **Streptomyces candidus** (Krassilnikov, 1941) Waksman, 1953. (*Actinomyces candidus* Krassilnikov, Guide to the Actinomycetes, Izd. Akad. Nauk, U.S.S.R., Moskau, 1941, 49; Waksman, in Waksman and Lechevalier, Actinomycetes and Their

Antibiotics, Baltimore, 1953, 94; not *Streptothrix candida* Petruschky, Verhandl. d. Kongr. f. innere Med., 1898.)

can'di.dus. L. adj. *candidus* very white.

Vegetative growth; Organism grows well on various media.

Aerial mycelium: Sporophores long, straight or wavy, but never forming spirals. Spores cylindrical, elongated, 0.7 by 1.5 to 2.0 microns; on maturing, some become more rounded.

Gelatin: Slow liquefaction.

Agar: Lichenoid or smooth growth. Aerial mycelium whitish.

Synthetic agar: Well developed, colorless colonies. No soluble pigment. Aerial mycelium cottony white.

Milk: Weakly coagulated and peptonized.

Sucrose is inverted.

Starch is rapidly hydrolyzed.

Good growth on cellulose.

Nitrites produced from nitrates.

Antagonistic properties: Weak.

Source: Isolated from soil.

Habitat: Soil.

102. **Streptomyces alboflavus** (Waksman and Curtis, 1916) Waksman and Henrici, 1948. (*Actinomyces alboflavus* Waksman and Curtis, Soil Sci., *1*, 1916, 120; Waksman and Henrici, in Manual, 6th ed., 1948, 954.)

al.bo.fla'vus. L. adj. *albus* white; L. adj. *flavus* yellow; M.L. adj. *alboflavus* whitish yellow.

Aerial mycelium: Straight, branching mycelium, with very little tendency to form spirals. Very few ellipsoidal conidia formed.

Gelatin stab: Abundant, colorless surface growth. Liquefaction occurs in 35 days.

Agar: Restricted, cream-colored growth.

Synthetic agar: Growth glossy, colorless, spreading, becoming yellowish. Aerial mycelium white, powdery, with yellow tinge.

Starch agar: Thin, yellowish, spreading growth.

Glucose agar: Growth restricted, much-folded, creamy with sulfur-yellow surface.

Glucose broth: White, cylindrical colonies on surface, later flaky mass in bottom of tube.

Litmus milk: Pinkish ring. No coagulation. Peptonized, becoming alkaline.

Potato: Moist, cream-colored, wrinkled growth.

The pigment formed is not soluble.

Starch is hydrolyzed.

Nitrites produced from nitrates.

Aerobic.

Optimum temperature, 37° C.

Antagonistic properties: Positive.

Source: Isolated once from orchard soil.

Habitat: Soil.

103. **Streptomyces flocculus** (Duché, 1934) Waksman and Henrici, 1948. (*Actinomyces flocculus* Duché, Encyclopédie Mycologique, Paris, *6*, 1934, 300; Waksman and Henrici, in Manual, 6th ed., 1948, 955.)

floc'cu.lus. L. noun *floccus* a flock of wool; M.L. dim.adj. *flocculus* somewhat like a flock of wool.

Vegetative growth: Velvety surface with cottony or floccose edge.

Gelatin: Very limited growth. Slow liquefaction.

Agar: Cream-colored growth, later covered with white aerial mycelium; no soluble pigment.

Glucose asparagine agar: Weak growth; limited cream-colored colonies hardly raised above the surface of the medium; occasionally abundant growth is produced with white aerial mycelium and colorless on reverse side.

Synthetic agar: Cream-colored growth, later covered with white aerial mycelium; no soluble pigment.

Glucose asparagine solution: Branching, immersed filaments, 0.8 micron in diameter; aerial mycelium 1.0 by 1.2 microns with numerous conidia; flakes settle to the bottom of the tube.

Peptone solution: Pointed colonies; cream-colored on surface of medium.

Tyrosine medium: Whitish growth without any pigment.

Milk: Rose-colored growth; slow peptonization.

Potato: Punctiform growth covered with white aerial mycelium; faint yellowish pigment.

Coagulated serum: Cream-colored

growth; fine white aerial mycelium; slow liquefaction of serum.

Source: Culture obtained from Mr. Malençon, an inspector in Morocco.

Habitat: Unknown.

104. Streptomyces antimycoticus Waksman, *nom. nov.* (*Streptomyces sp.,* Leben, Stessel and Keitt, Mycologia, *44,* 1952, 159.)

an.ti.my.co'ti.cus. Gr. pref. *anti* against; Gr. noun *myces* fungus; M.L. adj. *antimycoticus* against-fungus.

Vegetative growth: On most media early growth at first white and later gray; the color change appears to be associated with the development of dense masses of spores.

Aerial mycelium: Spirals situated typically in dense groups along the main portions of aerial hyphae, especially toward the center of the colony. In early formation of sporing hyphae, spirals tend to be open; they become closed and compact, however, prior to the formation of spores. In late stages these fruiting structures tend to appear ball-like rather than spiral. Spores ellipsoidal, hyaline and 0.6 to 1.3 by 0.7 to 2.0 microns; diameter of spore spirals, 4 to 8 microns.

Gelatin: Vegetative mycelium translucent, cream-colored; sparse, white aerial mycelium. Liquefaction slight at 15 days, moderate at 30 days. No soluble pigment.

Agar: Shiny, cream-colored vegetative mycelium; moderate, pebbly, white aerial mycelium. No soluble pigment.

Synthetic agar: Abundant, pebbly, light neutral gray aerial mycelium. No soluble pigment.

Glucose asparagine agar: Same as on synthetic agar.

Glucose peptone agar: Same as on synthetic agar.

Ca-malate-glycerol agar: Abundant, pebbly, light neutral gray aerial mycelium. Faint green soluble pigment.

Potato glucose agar: Abundant, pebbly, light neutral gray aerial mycelium. Faint brown soluble pigment.

Yeast extract agar: Same as on synthetic agar.

Starch: Abundant, pebbly, white to neutral gray aerial mycelium. No soluble pigment.

Glucose broth: Surface colonies coalescing, white, powdery. Liquid clear, not pigmented. Small amount of flaky sediment present.

Milk: Cream-colored ring. Coagulated; peptonized in 15 to 30 days, becoming slightly alkaline. Yellowish orange serum, slightly turbid.

Potato: Finely wrinkled, cream-colored growth with sparse, white aerial mycelium. Plug darkened slightly.

Diastatic action weak to moderate.

Nitrites weakly produced from nitrates.

Antagonistic properties: Produces an antifungal agent, helixin.

Source: Isolate A 158 from compost soil.

Habitat: Soil.

105. Streptomyces fradiae (Waksman and Curtis, 1916) Waksman and Henrici, 1948. (*Actinomyces fradii* (sic) Waksman and Curtis, Soil Sci., *1,* 1916, 125; Waksman and Henrici, in Manual, 6th ed., 1948, 954.)

fra'di.ae. M.L. gen.noun *fradiae* of Fradia; named for a person, Fradia.

Aerial mycelium: Straight, branching filaments and hyphae. No spirals. Conidia rod-shaped or ellipsoidal, 0.5 by 0.7 to 1.25 microns.

Gelatin stab: Cream-colored to brownish, dense growth on liquid medium.

Agar: Yellowish growth, becoming orange-yellow, restricted. No soluble pigment.

Synthetic agar: Smooth, spreading, colorless growth. Aerial mycelium thick, cottony mass covering surface, sea-shell pink.

Starch agar: Spreading, colorless growth.

Glucose agar: Growth restricted, glossy, buff-colored, lichenoid margin.

Glucose broth: Dense, narrow, orange-colored ring; abundant, flaky, colorless sediment.

Litmus milk: Faint, cream-colored ring; coagulated; peptonized, becoming alkaline.

Potato: Restricted, orange-colored growth.

The pigment formed is not soluble.

Starch is hydrolyzed.

Nitrites not produced from nitrates.

Aerobic.

Optimum temperature, 25° C.

Antagonistic properties: Highly antagonistic. Produces an antibacterial agent, neomycin, and an antifungal agent, fradicin.

Source: Isolated once from adobe soil in California.

Habitat: Soil.

106. **Streptomyces albosporeus** (Krainsky, 1914) Waksman and Henrici, 1948. (*Actinomyces albosporeus* Krainsky, Cent. f. Bakt., II Abt., *41*, 1914, 649; also see Waksman and Curtis, Soil Sci., *1*, 1916, 99; Waksman and Henrici, in Manual, 6th ed., 1948, 954.)

al.bo.spo're.us. L. adj. *albus* white; Gr. noun *spora* a seed; M.L. noun *spora* a spore; M.L. adj. *albosporeus* white-spored.

Aerial mycelium: Hyphae straight, branching, with occasional spirals. Spores spherical or ellipsoidal, 0.8 to 1.2 by 1.0 to 1.8 microns.

Gelatin stab: Yellow growth, changing to red, with hyaline margin. Liquefaction in 35 days.

Agar: Minute, cream-colored colonies.

Synthetic agar: Spreading growth, colorless with pink center, becoming brownish. Aerial mycelium white, covering the whole surface. No soluble pigment.

Starch agar: Growth thin, spreading, transparent, with red tinge.

Glucose agar: Growth spreading, red, wrinkled, radiate, entire.

Glucose broth: Pinkish surface ring.

Litmus milk: Scant, pink ring. Not coagulated, not peptonized.

Potato: Growth thin, spreading, wrinkled, gray, becoming brown with greenish tinge.

The pigment formed is not soluble.

Starch is hydrolyzed.

Nitrites produced from nitrates.

Aerobic.

Optimum temperature, 37° C.

Antagonistic properties: Positive.

Source: Isolated from soil.

Habitat: Soil.

107. **Streptomyces purpurascens** Lindenbein, 1952. (*Streptomyces purpurascens* Brockmann, Bauer and Borchers (*nomen nudum*), Chem. Ber., *84*, 1951, 700; Lindenbein, Arch. f. Mikrobiol., *17*, 1952, 371.)

pur.pur.as'cens. L. part.adj. *purpurascens* making purple.

Vegetative growth: Usually heavy, red to carmine-red to almost purple.

Aerial mycelium: Cottony, white. Spirals observed in 6 days, but they may be lacking altogether.

Gelatin: Heavy, light brown surface growth. Aerial mycelium cottony, white. Soluble red-brown pigment. Rapid liquefaction.

Agar: Light brown growth with dark brown reverse. Aerial mycelium velvety, gray.

Synthetic agar: Typical carmine-red growth. Aerial mycelium cottony, chalk-white. Soluble brown-red pigment.

Glucose asparagine agar: Carmine-red growth. Aerial mycelium cottony, white. Soluble orange pigment.

Ca-malate agar: Carmine-red growth. Aerial mycelium chalk-white. Soluble brick-red pigment.

Starch agar: Lichenoid, light carmine-colored growth. Aerial mycelium white. No soluble pigment.

Glucose agar: Lichenoid, red to red-brown growth. Aerial mycelium cottony, chalk-white. Soluble light brown pigment.

Glucose broth: Heavy pellicle with limited bottom growth, carmine-red, later copper-red. Aerial mycelium powdery, chalk-white. Soluble carmine-red pigment.

Milk: Lichenoid, red to dark brown growth. Aerial mycelium velvety to cottony, white. No proteolysis.

Potato: Very good, brownish to reddish growth. Aerial mycelium velvety, white. No soluble pigment.

Starch is actively hydrolyzed.

Very good, white to red growth on cellulose.

Antagonistic properties: Produces rhodomycin.

Comment: On continued growth on synthetic media, the culture may lose the property to produce the typical pigment; it can be regained, however, by growing on organic media.

Source: Isolated from soil.

Habitat: Soil.

108. Streptomyces longispororuber (Krassilnikov, 1941) Waksman, 1953. (*Actinomyces longisporus ruber* Krassilnikov, Guide to the Actinomycetes, Izd. Akad. Nauk, U.S.S.R., Moskau, 1941, 22; Waksman, in Waksman and Lechevalier, Actinomycetes and Their Antibiotics, Baltimore, 1953, 99.)

lon.gi.spo.ro.ru′ber. L. adj. *longus* long; Gr. noun *spora* a seed; M.L. noun *spora* a spore; L. adj. *ruber* red; M.L. adj. *longispororuber* long-spored, red.

Vegetative growth: Dark red to purple-red to light rose colonies. Little pigment diffuses into media except those containing fat. Certain strains secrete a soluble brown substance in protein-containing media.

Aerial mycelium: Weakly developed, whitish to rose-white. Sporophores in some strains well developed, velvety, long, straight, seldom forming open spirals. Spores cylindrical to elongated, 0.7 by 1.0 to 1.5 microns, with sharply cut ends; a few are slightly swollen, becoming ellipsoidal or spherical, 1 micron in diameter.

Gelatin: Liquefaction.

Synthetic agar: Light red to pale rose growth. Pigment not soluble.

Milk: Weakly coagulated; peptonized.

Starch is hydrolyzed, sometimes slowly.

No growth on cellulose by some strains; others grow weakly.

Nitrites produced from nitrates by some strains.

Antagonistic properties: Strongly antagonistic to a number of bacteria.

Comment: This organism is very variable, especially regarding the production of aerial mycelium.

Relationships to other species: Related to *Streptomyces ruber*, except for the cylindrical spores.

Source: Isolated from soil.

Habitat: Soil.

109. Streptomyces oidiosporus (Krassilnikov, 1941) Waksman, 1953. (*Actinomyces oidiosporus* Krassilnikov, Guide to the Actinomycetes, Izd. Akad. Nauk, U.S.S.R., Moskau, 1941, 23; Waksman, in Waksman and Lechevalier, Actinomycetes and Their Antibiotics, Baltimore, 1953, 99.)

o.i.di.o′spo.rus. Gr. neut.n. *oum* egg; M.L. neut.dim.n. *oidium* a small egg, a type of fungus spore; Gr. noun *spora* a seed; M.L. noun *spora* a spore; M.L. adj. *oidiosporus* oidium-spored.

Vegetative growth: Red or rose to pale rose colonies. Pigment not soluble.

Aerial mycelium: Poorly developed, covering medium with velvety rose-white color. Sporophores straight or wavy, never forming spirals; they are short or long, frequently forming broom-shaped structures. Oidiospores produced by segmentation of sporophores. Spores 1.0 by 1.0 to 1.8 microns, frequently appearing as double cocci.

Gelatin: Weakly developed aerial mycelium, frequently lacking. Hyphae short, covering colony like a rose-white velvet; frequently occurs in spots or is absent. Weak liquefaction.

Milk: Not coagulated; peptonized.

Starch is actively hydrolyzed.

No growth on cellulose.

Nitrites produced from nitrates.

Antagonistic properties: None.

Relationships to other species: Resembles *Streptomyces ruber* and *Streptomyces longispororuber*.

Source: Some strains were obtained as variants of *Nocardia rubra*.

Habitat: Presumably soil.

110. Streptomyces melanocyclus (Merker, 1911) Waksman and Henrici, 1948. (*Micrococcus melanocyclus* Merker, Cent. f. Bakt., II Abt., *31*, 1911, 589; Waksman and Henrici, in Manual, 6th ed., 1948, 956.)

me.la.no.cy′clus. Gr. adj. *melas, melanis* black; Gr. noun *cyclus* a circle; M.L. noun *melanocyclus* the black circle.

Vegetative growth: Much-folded.

Aerial mycelium: Dark brown. Spores spherical, 0.9 micron in diameter. Produces red pigment as well as soluble brown substance, as a result of which culture and substrate become red-brown to almost black with a shade of red.

Gelatin colonies: Growth poor.

Gelatin stab: Rapid liquefaction.

Ca-malate agar: Colonies small, flat, orange-red. Aerial mycelium black, occurring along the edges.

Glucose agar: Same as on Ca-malate agar.

Starch agar: Same as on Ca-malate agar.

Glucose broth: Colorless, spherical colonies.

Litmus milk: Peptonized.

Sucrose is inverted.

Starch is actively hydrolyzed.

Cellulose is decomposed.

Nitrites produced from nitrates.

Aerobic.

Optimum temperature, 25° C.

Antagonistic properties: Strong effect upon various bacteria; some strains show no activity.

Source: Isolated from soil.

Habitat: Soil.

111. Streptomyces acidophilus (Jensen, 1928) Waksman and Henrici, 1948. (*Actinomyces acidophilus* Jensen, Soil Sci., *25*, 1928, 226; Waksman and Henrici, in Manual, 6th ed., 1948, 956.)

a.ci.do'phi.lus. L. adj. *acidus* sour; M.L. noun *acidum* an acid; Gr. adj. *philus* loving; M.L. adj. *acidophilus* acid-loving.

Vegetative growth: Mycelium profusely branched, hyphae 0.6 to 0.8 micron in diameter with homogeneous protoplasm and no visible septa.

Aerial mycelium: Hyphae 1.0 to 1.2 microns in diameter, somewhat branched, forming either very few or very numerous sinistrorse spirals. Ellipsoidal conidia 1.0 to 1.2 by 1.2 to 1.5 microns.

Gelatin: After 10 days, growth very scant, thin, colorless, semi-transparent. Slow liquefaction.

Agar: No growth.

Synthetic agar: No growth.

Glucose agar: Good growth at 25° C. Substratum mycelium raised, somewhat wrinkled, colorless in young cultures. Aerial mycelium thin, white at first, later gray or yellowish brown.

Starch agar: Good growth at 25° C. Substratum mycelium flat, smooth, colorless. Aerial mycelium abundant, smooth, white.

Broth: No growth.

Milk: No growth.

Potato: Growth good, raised, folded. No discoloration.

Sucrose not inverted.

Diastatic.

Weakly proteolytic.

Nitrites not produced from nitrates except a trace in two strains.

Antagonistic properties: Strongly positive.

Distinctive character: Ability to live in acid media only.

Source: Four strains were isolated from three acid humus soils.

Habitat: Found in acid humus soils.

112. Streptomyces rubescens (Jarach, 1931) Waksman and Henrici, 1948. (*Strepto thrix rubescens* Jarach, Boll. Sez. Ital. Soc. Intern. Microb., *3*, 1931, 43; Waksman and Henrici, in Manual, 6th ed., 1948, 956.)

ru.bes'cens. L. part.adj. *rubescens* becoming red.

Original description supplemented by material taken from Umezawa, Tazaki and Fukuyama (Jour. Antibiotics (Japanese), *5*, 1952, 469).

Aerial mycelium: Powdery, white. Microscopically, aerial mycelium short, curved, well branched, bearing spherical or ellipsoidal conidia in chains. No spirals.

Gelatin: Coral-pink surface growth. No liquefaction and no pigmentation of medium.

Agar: Submerged mycelium at first white, changing to salmon-pink after about 10 days' incubation. No soluble pigment. Reverse of growth changes to salmon-pink.

Synthetic agar: Same as on plain agar.

Glucose agar: Large number of small round colonies raised in the center and growing together as well as deep into the medium; whitish opalescent color.

Milk agar medium: Rose-coral-colored, thin growth with edge entire.

Loeffler's coagulated serum: Same as on plain agar. No hydrolysis.

Blood agar: After 10 days' incubation, mycelium becomes salmon-pink and bears powdery white aerial mycelium. No soluble pigment. No hemolysis.

Broth: Minute flakes, the liquid later becoming reddish colored.

Glucose broth: Surface growth with white powdery aerial mycelium becomes salmon-pink or coral-pink. The liquid later becomes coral-red.

Milk: Coral-pink growth; aerial mycelium

powdery and white. No coagulation and no digestion. Sometimes slightly reddish soluble pigment.

Potato: Coral-pink growth; aerial mycelium powdery, white. Plug changes slightly to brown. No soluble pigment.

Carrot: Dark reddish orange growth; aerial mycelium powdery, white. Plug changes very slightly to dark color.

Egg: Colorless growth, changing to coral-pink. Aerial mycelium powdery, white.

Glycerol and glucose, but not other carbohydrates, are utilized.

Tyrosinase not produced.

Starch is not hydrolyzed.

Nitrates not reduced.

Antagonistic properties: Produces an antiviral agent, abikoviromycin.

Source: Isolated from soil.

Habitat: Soil.

113. **Streptomyces viridis** (Lombardo-Pellegrino, 1903, *emend.* Krassilnikov, 1941) Waksman, 1953. (*Streptothrix viridis* Lombardo-Pellegrino, Riforma Med., *19*, 1903, 1065; also see Cent. f. Bakt., I Abt., Ref., *35*, 1904, 761; *Actinomyces viridis* Sanfelice, Cent. f. Bakt., I Abt., Orig., *36*, 1904, 355; Krassilnikov, Guide to the Actinomycetes, Izd. Akad. Nauk, U.S.S.R., Moskau, 1941, 34; Waksman, in Waksman and Lechevalier, Actinomycetes and Their Antibiotics, Baltimore, 1953, 101.)

vi′ri.dis. L. adj. *viridis* green.

Vegetative growth: Green to dark green on all media. No soluble pigment.

Aerial mycelium: Well developed on all media, cottony, whitish to grayish. Sporophores long or short, straight, forming no spirals but frequently producing broom-shaped clumps. Spores cylindrical, 0.7 to 0.8 by 1.0 to 1.5 microns.

Gelatin: No liquefaction in 13 to 15 days.

Milk: Not coagulated; not peptonized.

Starch is not hydrolyzed.

No growth on cellulose.

Nitrites weakly produced from nitrates.

Antagonistic properties: None; certain strains give positive activity.

Comments: According to Krassilnikov (*op. cit.*, 1941, 34), *Streptomyces lipmanii* and *Streptomyces verne* represent strains of this species; *Streptomyces viridis sterilis* is also listed as a strain that lost the capacity to produce aerial mycelia.

Source: Isolated from soil.

Habitat: Soil.

114. **Streptomyces thermophilus** (Gilbert, 1904) Waksman and Henrici, 1948. (*Actinomyces thermophilus* Gilbert, Ztschr. f. Hyg., *47*, 1904, 383; not *Actinomyces thermophilus* Berestnew, Inaug. Diss., Moskow, 1897; Waksman and Henrici, in Manual, 6th ed., 1948, 956.)

ther.mo′phi.lus. Gr. noun *therme* heat; Gr. adj. *philus* loving; M.L. adj. *thermophilus* heat-loving.

Description taken from Waksman, Umbreit and Cordon (Soil Sci., *47*, 1939, 49).

Aerial mycelium: Hyphae straight, conidia formed.

Gelatin: Liquefaction. No pigment.

Agar: No pigment formed.

Synthetic agar: At 28° C., deep colorless growth, thin white aerial mycelium; no soluble pigment.

Starch agar: Yellowish growth with white-gray, powdery aerial mycelium.

Milk: Proteolysis.

Potato plug: Yellowish growth with no aerial mycelium, the plug usually being colored brown.

Starch is hydrolyzed.

Aerobic.

Temperature relations: Optimum, 50° C. Good growth at 28° C. Usually no growth at 60° C. Some strains are incapable of growing at 28° whereas others seem to grow well even at 65° C.

Antagonistic properties: Some strains produce the antibiotic thermomycin.

Source: Unknown.

Habitat: Found in soil, hay and composts.

115. **Streptomyces thermodiastaticus** (Bergey et al., 1923) Waksman, 1953. (Var. a, Bergey, Jour. Bact., *4*, 1919, 301; *Actinomyces thermodiastaticus* Bergey et al., Manual, 1st ed., 1923, 370; Waksman, in Waksman and Lechevalier, Actinomycetes and Their Antibiotics, Baltimore, 1953, 102.)

ther.mo.di.a.sta′ti.cus. Gr. fem.n. *therme* heat; Gr. adj. *diastaticus* diastatic; M.L. adj. *thermodiastaticus* (probably intended to mean) thermophilic and diastatic.

Aerial mycelium: Well developed, white. Sporophores produce spirals; spores spherical to ellipsoidal.

Gelatin: Slow liquefaction.

Synthetic agar: Colorless growth. Aerial mycelium well developed, white.

Milk: Not coagulated; not peptonized.

Potato: Brownish growth. Aerial mycelium light gray.

Sucrose is inverted.

Starch is actively hydrolyzed.

Good growth on cellulose.

Nitrites produced from nitrates.

Optimum temperature, 65° C.

Source: Isolated from the stomach contents of a rabbit.

Habitat: Unknown.

116. **Streptomyces thermofuscus** (Waksman et al., 1939) Waksman and Henrici, 1948. (*Actinomyces thermofuscus* Waksman, Umbreit and Cordon, Soil Sci., *47*, 1939, 49; Waksman and Henrici, in Manual, 6th ed., 1948, 957.)

ther.mo.fus′cus. Gr. noun *therme* heat; L. adj. *fuscus* dark, dusky; M.L. adj. *thermofuscus* (probably intended to mean) thermophilic and dusky.

Aerial mycelium: Hyphae spiral-shaped; conidia produced.

Gelatin: Liquefaction. At 50° C. a grayish ring is produced and soluble pigment is formed. At 28° C. growth, with no soluble pigment.

Synthetic agar: Poor growth at 28° C., deep gray, with but little aerial mycelium. At 50° C., growth dark to violet, with gray to lavender aerial mycelium and soluble brown pigment.

Milk: Proteolysis.

Potato: Abundant, dark colored growth, no aerial mycelium, or few white patches, dark soluble pigment.

Starch is hydrolyzed.

Temperature relations: Good growth at 50° and 60° C. Will grow at 65° C. Faint growth at 28° C.

Aerobic.

Distinctive characters: This species is distinguished from *Streptomyces thermophilus* by the brown-colored aerial mycelium on synthetic media, spiral-shaped hyphae and ability to grow readily at 65° C.

Source: Unknown.

Habitat: Found in soils and composts.

117. **Streptomyces casei** (Bernstein and Morton, 1934) Waksman, 1953. (*Actinomyces casei* Bernstein and Morton, Jour. Bact., *27*, 1934, 625; Waksman, in Waksman and Lechevalier, Actinomycetes and Their Antibiotics, Baltimore, 1953, 103.)

ca′se.i. L. mas. n. *caseus* cheese; L. gen. noun *casei* of cheese.

Vegetative growth: Colorless to white.

Aerial mycelium: White, 0.5 to 0.7 micron; no spirals.

Gelatin: Complete liquefaction.

Milk: Coagulated and peptonized.

Starch is not hydrolyzed.

Nitrates not produced from nitrates.

Optimum temperature, between 40° and 60° C. Highly resistant to higher temperatures and to disinfectants. Thermal death point, 100°C.

Relationships to other species: Krassilnikov places this organism in the same group with *Actinomyces invulnerabilis* Acosta and Rossi (Cent. f. Bakt., *14*, 1893, 14), the latter being even more resistant to high temperatures and to disinfectants.

Source: Isolated from pasteurized cheese.

Habitat: Found in cheese so far as known.

118. **Streptomyces clavifer** (Millard and Burr, 1926) Waksman, 1953. (*Actinomyces clavifer* Millard and Burr, Ann. Appl. Biol., *13*, 1926, 601; Waksman, in Waksman and Lechevalier, Actinomycetes and Their Antibiotics, Baltimore, 1953, 103.)

cla′vi.fer. L. adj. *clavifer* club-bearing.

Vegetative growth: Yellow to yelloworange. Soluble yellow-brown pigment.

Aerial mycelium: Sporophores long, straight, some terminating in club-shaped structures. Spores cylindrical, 1.0 by 1.5 microns.

Gelatin: Gray to buff growth. White aerial mycelium. Soluble, yellow to reddish yellow pigment. Liquefaction.

Synthetic sucrose agar: Gray to brick-red growth. Aerial mycelium white, sprinkled with light cinnamon-drab. Yellowish to brown soluble pigment.

Synthetic glucose agar: Gray to brown

growth. Aerial mycelium white to drab. Soluble, cinnamon-buff to brown pigment.

Nutrient potato agar: Wrinkled, gray to grayish-olive growth. Trace of aerial mycelium. Soluble, deep golden brown pigment.

Glycerol synthetic solution: Growth in form of compact colonies at bottom and along sides of tube with some on surface, colored salmon to brown. Scant drab aerial mycelium. Soluble, buff to golden pigment.

Glucose broth: Sponge-like growth at bottom of tube. Soluble deep, golden brown pigment.

Potato: Wrinkled, gray to orange to brown growth. Aerial mycelium gray to olive-buff. Plug gray to brown.

Starch is hydrolyzed.

Tyrosinase reaction: Positive.

Nitrites not produced from nitrates.

Fair growth at 37.5° C.

Source: Isolated from limed soil and from the common scab of a potato.

Habitat: Soil and potatoes so far as known.

119. **Streptomyces fimbriatus** (Millard and Burr, 1926) Waksman, 1953. (*Actinomyces fimbriatus* Millard and Burr, Ann. Appl. Biol., *13*, 1926, 601; Waksman, in Waksman and Lechevalier, Actinomycetes and Their Antibiotics, Baltimore, 1953, 104.)

fim.bri.a'tus. L. adj. *fimbriatus* fibrous, fringed.

Vegetative growth: Chocolate-colored.

Aerial mycelium: Mouse-gray. Sporophores form spirals with 3 or more turns. Spores cylindrical to ellipsoidal, 0.9 by 0.9 to 1.2 microns.

Gelatin: Good growth with white aerial mycelium. Soluble reddish pigment. Slow liquefaction.

Synthetic sucrose agar: Gray growth. Aerial mycelium abundant, white to gray, with a few specks of white. Soluble, cream-colored pigment.

Synthetic glucose agar: Very good growth. Aerial mycelium white to mouse-gray.

Nutrient potato agar: Gray to blackish, flat colonies with raised center; a few specks of white aerial mycelium. Soluble, golden brown pigment.

Glycerol synthetic solution: Numerous colonies covering surface of medium and throughout medium; aerial mycelium scant, white.

Glucose broth: Flocculated growth, mostly at bottom. No aerial mycelium. Soluble golden brown pigment.

Milk: Good growth. Not coagulated and not hydrolyzed.

Potato: Mouse-gray growth. Aerial mycelium on dried portions of growth scant, white to mouse-gray. Black pigment around growth.

Starch is hydrolyzed.

Tyrosinase reaction: Strongly positive.

Nitrites produced from nitrates.

Source: Isolated from a small, partly ruptured potato scab.

Habitat: Found in potatoes so far as known.

120. **Streptomyces carnosus** (Millard and Burr, 1926) Waksman, 1953. (*Actinomyces carnosus* Millard and Burr, Ann. Appl. Biol., *13*, 1926, 601; Waksman, in Waksman and Lechevalier, Actinomycetes and Their Antibiotics, Baltimore, 1953, 105.)

car.no'sus. L. adj. *carnosus* pertaining to flesh.

Vegetative growth: Good, wrinkled growth on synthetic and organic media.

Aerial mycelium: White to gray. Spores cylindrical, 0.75 by 1.0 micron.

Gelatin: Growth covered with aerial mycelium, white in center, gray in margin. Rapid liquefaction.

Synthetic sucrose agar: Pale smoke-gray growth, covered with abundant, gray aerial mycelium. Colorless guttation drops appear over the whole surface.

Synthetic glucose agar: Pale olive-gray growth, covered with abundant, white to gray aerial mycelium. Soluble, ivory-yellow to cartridge-buff pigment.

Nutrient potato agar: Heavy, lichenoid, gray-colored growth. Aerial mycelium scant, white to gray; property lost on cultivation. Light golden to brown pigment.

Glycerol synthetic solution: Whitish to gray, discrete colonies, clinging to side or bottom of tube. Aerial mycelium scant, pale gray.

Glucose broth: Whitish, sponge-like masses, sinking to bottom of tube.

Milk: Good surface growth. No aerial

mycelium. Coagulated, followed by liquefaction.

Potato: Good, lichenoid growth, covered with gray to brownish aerial mycelium with white spots. The plug becomes covered gray to black.

Starch is hydrolyzed.

Tyrosinase reaction: Negative.

Nitrites produced from nitrates.

Source: Isolated from a small, unruptured potato scab.

Habitat: Found in potatoes so far as known.

121. **Streptomyces craterifer** (Millard and Burr, 1926) Waksman, 1953. (*Actinomyces craterifer* Millard and Burr, Ann. Appl. Biol., *13*, 1926, 601; Waksman, in Waksman and Lechevalier, Actinomycetes and Their Antibiotics, Baltimore, 1953, 105.)

cra.te'ri.fer. Gr. mas.n. *crater* a cup-shaped hollow; L. v. *fero* to bear; M.L. adj. *craterifer* cup (crater)-bearing.

Aerial mycelium: Much branched; terminal branches dichotomously forked. Spores rectangular, 0.8 to 1.0 by 0.9 to 1.3 microns.

Gelatin: Wrinkled surface growth. Aerial mycelium white. No soluble pigment. Rapid liquefaction.

Agar: Colorless growth; scant, white aerial mycelium. No soluble pigment.

Synthetic agar: Lichenoid, abundant, colorless growth. Aerial mycelium mouse-gray. Numerous guttation drops, which leave blackish craters behind.

Starch: Spreading, thin, colorless growth. No aerial mycelium.

Glycerol synthetic solution: Good growth on surface of medium; numerous star-like colonies throughout medium. Aerial mycelium scant, white to mouse-gray.

Glucose broth: Limited growth. Aerial mycelium white to gray.

Milk: Cream-colored surface growth. Not coagulated; rapidly peptonized.

Potato: Good, cream-colored growth. Aerial mycelium white to mouse-gray. Color of plug unchanged.

Starch is hydrolyzed.

Tyrosinase reaction: Negative.

Nitrites produced from nitrates.

Only slight growth at 37.5° C.

Source: Isolated from a large, raised, smooth potato scab.

Habitat: Found in potatoes so far as known.

122. **Streptomyces gracilis** (Millard and Burr, 1926) Waksman, 1953. (*Actinomyces gracilis* Millard and Burr, Ann. Appl. Biol., *13*, 1926, 601; Waksman, In Waksman and Lechevalier, Actinomycetes and Their Antibiotics, Baltimore, 1953, 106.)

gra'ci.lis. L. adj. *gracilis* slender.

Vegetative growth: On synthetic media, dark brown, producing a soluble brown substance.

Aerial mycelium: Dark olive. Spiral-forming sporophores. Spores ellipsoidal or spherical, 0.8 by 0.8 to 0.9 micron.

Gelatin: Gray growth, covered with white aerial mycelium. Soluble, pink to dark golden brown pigment. Rapid liquefaction.

Synthetic sucrose agar: Fern-like, pale gray growth covered with scant, gray to buff aerial mycelium. Soluble cream-colored pigment.

Synthetic glucose agar: Smooth, pale olive-gray growth. Aerial mycelium abundant, white, smooth. Soluble cream-colored pigment.

Nutrient potato agar: Vinaceous, buff to dark brown or almost black growth. Aerial mycelium gray. Soluble light golden brown pigment.

Glycerol synthetic solution: Good growth on surface and throughout medium. Abundant aerial mycelium, white to olive-buff.

Glucose broth: Good growth on surface and on bottom. Aerial mycelium abundant, olive-buff. Soluble, light golden brown pigment.

Milk: Good surface growth. Aerial mycelium white in the form of a ring and specks on surface. Slowly coagulated, followed by rapid peptonization.

Potato: Good, echinate growth covered with abundant olive-gray to buff aerial mycelium. Plug light brown.

Starch is hydrolyzed.

Tyrosinase reaction: Negative.

Nitrites produced from nitrates.

Good growth at 37.5° C.

Comment: According to Krassilnikov,

Streptomyces poolensis and *Streptomyces tumuli* belong to this group.

Source: Isolated from a small, unruptured potato scab.

Habitat: Found in potatoes so far as known.

123. Streptomyces praecox (Millard and Burr, 1926) Waksman, 1953. (*Actinomyces praecox* Millard and Burr, Ann. App. Biol., *13*, 1926, 601; Waksman, in Waksman and Lechevalier, Actinomycetes and Their Antibiotics, Baltimore, 1953, 107.)

prae'cox. L. adj. *praecox* premature, precocious.

Vegetative growth: Raised, colorless.

Aerial mycelium: Well developed, gray with greenish tinge. Sporophores produce open spirals. Spores spherical or ellipsoidal, 0.8 micron in diameter.

Gelatin: Good growth. Abundant, white aerial mycelium. Liquefaction.

Agar: Thin, colorless growth. Aerial mycelium thin, white.

Synthetic agar: Thin, powdery growth. Aerial mycelium white to olive-buff.

Synthetic glucose agar: Flat growth with radiating margins. Aerial mycelium white to olive-colored. On cultivation, aerial mycelium is only white.

Starch agar: Thin, cream-colored growth. Aerial mycelium abundant, white with greenish tinge.

Broth: Cream-colored surface pellicle. Aerial mycelium thin, white. No soluble pigment.

Glycerol synthetic solution: Heavy surface growth. Aerial mycelium abundant, powdery, white. Pale yellow soluble pigment.

Glucose broth: Flocculated growth at bottom and heavy, wrinkled growth at surface. Aerial mycelium abundant, white.

Milk: Cream-colored surface growth in form of a ring. Aerial mycelium white. Actively coagulated; rapidly peptonized.

Potato: Good, cream-colored to light brown growth. Aerial mycelium white to olive-buff. Plug olive-buff to drab. On cultivation, no soluble pigment produced.

Starch is hydrolyzed.

Tyrosinase reaction: Negative.

Nitrate reduction variable.

Odor: Very strong.

Grows well at 37.5° C.

Antagonistic properties: Represses growth of *Streptomyces scabies*.

Relationship to other species: Krassilnikov regards this species as being related to *Streptomyces griseus* Krainsky.

Source: Isolated from a large, knob-like, unruptured potato scab.

Habitat: Found in potatoes so far as known.

124. Streptomyces setonii (Millard and Burr, 1926) Waksman, 1953. (*Actinomyces setonii* Millard and Burr, Ann. Appl. Biol., *13*, 1926, 601; Waksman, in Waksman and Lechevalier, Actinomycetes and Their Antibiotics, Baltimore, 1953, 107.)

se.to'ni.i. M.L. gen.noun *setonii* of Seton; named for a person, Seton.

Vegetative growth: Golden yellow on synthetic media.

Aerial mycelium: Well developed, cottony, dark gray to dark olive. Sporophores straight, forming few spirals. Spores ellipsoidal, 0.6 to 0.8 by 0.85 micron.

Gelatin: Gray surface growth covered with white aerial mycelium. Soluble brownish pigment. Rapid liquefaction.

Agar: Good, colorless growth covered with white, smooth aerial mycelium. Soluble brownish pigment.

Synthetic agar: Abundant, smooth growth. Aerial mycelium covering the whole surface, gray to olive-buff. Soluble, faint yellowish pigment.

Starch agar: Cream-colored growth. Aerial mycelium patchy, white.

Glucose agar: Good, lichenoid, gray to brown growth. Aerial mycelium abundant, white to olive-buff. Soluble, golden brown pigment.

Glycerol synthetic solution: Flaky, white growth. Aerial mycelium abundant, olive-buff. Soluble greenish pigment.

Glucose broth: Growth on surface and in liquid good. Aerial mycelium abundant, olive-buff. Soluble, light golden brown pigment.

Milk: Good surface growth covered with ring of white aerial mycelium. Coagulated, followed by rapid digestion.

Potato: Heavy, wrinkled growth covered

with abundant, white to green to olive-buff aerial mycelium. Soluble, brownish to black pigment.

Nitrites produced from nitrates.

Starch is hydrolyzed.

Grows well at 37.5° C.

Comment: According to Krassilnikov, *Streptomyces flavus*, *Streptomyces marginatus*, *Streptomyces praefecundus*, *Streptomyces tenuis* and *Streptomyces loidensis* represent merely strains of this species.

Source: Isolated from a small, unruptured potato scab.

Habitat: Found in potatoes so far as known.

125. Streptomyces praefecundus (Millard and Burr, 1926) Waksman, 1953. (*Actinomyces praefecundus* Millard and Burr, Ann. Appl. Biol., *13*, 1926, 601; Waksman, in Waksman and Lechevalier, Actinomycetes and Their Antibiotics, Baltimore, 1953, 108.)

prae.fe.cun′dus. L. adj. *praefecundus* very fruitful.

Aerial mycelium: Spores ellipsoidal, 0.8 by 0.85 micron.

Gelatin: Good surface growth covered with aerial mycelium. Light pink to dark golden brown soluble pigment. Rapid liquefaction.

Synthetic sucrose agar: Good, cream-colored growth covered with abundant, cottony, olive-buff aerial mycelium. Soluble cream-colored pigment.

Synthetic glucose agar: Pale olive-gray growth covered with abundant, smooth, olive-buff aerial mycelium. Soluble, light golden to buff pigment.

Potato agar: Lichenoid, gray growth. Aerial mycelium smooth, white to yellowish. Soluble golden brown pigment.

Glycerol synthetic solution: Heavy surface growth covered with white to olive-buff aerial mycelium. Soluble pigment none or very slightly green.

Glucose broth: Masses throughout medium flaky, whitish. Aerial mycelium abundant, pale olive-buff. Soluble, light golden brown pigment.

Milk: Good surface growth covered with scant, white aerial mycelium. Coagulation followed by peptonization.

Potato: Good, wrinkled growth covered with abundant, white to yellowish to olive-buff aerial mycelium. Soluble, gray to brown pigment.

Starch is hydrolyzed.

Tyrosinase reaction: Negative.

Nitrites produced from nitrates.

Grows well at 37.5° C.

Source: Isolated from a large, ruptured potato scab.

Habitat: Found in potatoes and soil so far as known.

126. Streptomyces viridogenes Waksman, 1953. (*Actinomyces viridis* Millard and Burr, Ann. Appl. Biol., *13*, 1926, 601; not *Actinomyces viridis* Sanfelice, Cent. f. Bakt., I Abt., Orig., *36*, 1904, 355; Waksman, in Waksman and Lechevalier, Actinomycetes and Their Antibiotics, Baltimore, 1953, 109.)

vi.ri.do′ge.nes. L. adj. *viridis* green; Gr. v.suffix -*genes* producing; M.L. adj. *viridogenes* green-producing.

Aerial mycelium: Long, straight filaments. Spores spherical, 0.9 micron.

Gelatin: Grayish growth with scant, white to gray, aerial mycelium. Soluble light golden brown pigment. Rapid liquefaction.

Agar: Lichenoid, cream-colored growth. No aerial mycelium. No soluble pigment.

Synthetic sucrose agar: Abundant growth covered with olive-grayish aerial mycelium. Soluble greenish yellow to blackish green pigment.

Synthetic glucose agar: Smooth, raised, olive-buff growth. Abundant aerial mycelium, light gray to deep mouse-gray. Soluble yellowish to greenish yellow pigment.

Glucose agar: Gray to black growth. Aerial mycelium gray. Soluble dark brown pigment.

Starch agar: Gray to brown growth. Aerial mycelium thin, white.

Broth: Thin surface growth and flaky, cream-colored growth in bottom. No soluble pigment.

Glycerol synthetic solution: Flaky, white to vinaceous growth in medium and on surface. Aerial mycelium gray.

Glucose broth: Growth on surface and at base good, flaky. Aerial mycelium gray to mouse-gray. Soluble vinaceous to cinnamon-colored pigment.

Milk: Good surface growth; growth in medium cloudy. Aerial mycelium scant, white. Rapidly coagulated and gradually peptonized.

Potato: Gray to olive-gray growth. Aerial mycelium either absent or white, turning gray. Soluble brown pigment.

Starch is hydrolyzed.

Tyrosinase reaction: Negative.

Nitrites usually produced from nitrates.

Optimum temperature 37.5° C.

Source: Isolated from ruptured, pitted type potato scab.

Habitat: Soil.

127. Streptomyces loidensis (Millard and Burr, 1926) Waksman, 1953. (*Actinomyces loidensis* Millard and Burr, Ann. Appl. Biol., *13*, 1926, 601; Waksman, in Waksman and Lechevalier, Actinomycetes and Their Antibiotics, Baltimore, 1953, 110.)

lo.i.den'sis. M.L. adj. *loidensis* pertaining to Loidy; named for Loidy, a place in Siberia.

Aerial mycelium: Spores cylindrical to spherical, 0.9 to 0.95 by 0.9 to 1.0 micron.

Gelatin: Gray growth with scant, white aerial mycelium. Soluble yellow pigment. Rapid liquefaction.

Synthetic sucrose agar: Thin, flat, gray to yellowish olive growth. Aerial mycelium scant, olive-colored. Soluble yellow pigment.

Synthetic glucose agar: Thin, grayish olive growth. Aerial mycelium olive-buff. Soluble, light golden to yellowish pigment.

Potato agar: Good, gray growth. Aerial mycelium olive-buff. Soluble, golden brown pigment.

Glycerol synthetic solution: Flaky growth, mostly at bottom. Aerial mycelium scant, buff-colored.

Glucose broth: Growth on surface and at bottom good, gray to golden brown. Aerial mycelium olive-buff. Soluble, golden brown pigment.

Milk: Excellent surface growth covered with white aerial mycelium. Coagulated; rapidly peptonized.

Starch is hydrolyzed.

Tyrosinase reaction: Negative.

Nitrites not produced from nitrates.

Grows well at 37.5° C.

Source: Isolated from a medium-sized ruptured potato scab.

Habitat: Found in potatoes so far as known.

128. Streptomyces wedmorensis (Millard and Burr, 1926) Waksman, 1953. (*Actinomyces wedmorensis* Millard and Burr, Ann. Appl. Biol., *13*, 1926, 601; Waksman, in Waksman and Lechevalier, Actinomycetes and Their Antibiotics, Baltimore, 1953, 110.)

wed.mo.ren'sis. M.L. adj. *wedmorensis* pertaining to Wedmore; named for Wedmore, a city in England.

Aerial mycelium: Sporophores simple, straight, branched, closely septated. Spores ellipsoidal to cylindrical, 0.6 to 0.8 by 0.8 to 0.9 micron.

Gelatin: Fair growth. No aerial mycelium. Liquefaction.

Synthetic sucrose agar: Flat, thin, grayish growth covered with white to gray aerial mycelium.

Synthetic glucose agar: Good, grayish growth with crater-like dark spots. Moderate amount of gray aerial mycelium.

Potato agar: Wrinkled, good, grayish growth. No aerial mycelium.

Glycerol synthetic solution: Good growth in form of spongy masses at bottom and numerous colonies throughout medium; surface growth granular. Aerial mycelium gray, flecked with white.

Glucose broth: Small flakes and minute colonies at bottom and at surface.

Milk: Greenish surface growth. Coagulated; slowly peptonized.

Potato: Wrinkled, grayish growth covered with white aerial mycelium. Plug pigmented drab.

Starch is hydrolyzed.

Tyrosinase reaction: Negative.

Nitrites produced from nitrates.

Grows well at 37.5° C.

Source: Isolated from peat soil.

Habitat: Soil.

129. Streptomyces scabies (Thaxter, 1891) Waksman and Henrici, 1948. (*Oospora scabies* Thaxter, Ann. Rept. Conn. Agr. Exp. Sta., 1891, 153; Waksman and Henrici, in Manual, 6th ed., 1948, 957.)

sca′bi.es. L. noun *scabies* scab.

Vegetative growth: Folded, compact yellowish to yellow-brown; soluble, brown pigment.

Aerial mycelium: White, cottony or velvety; wavy or slightly curved hyphae show a few spirals. Spores cylindrical, 0.8 to 1.0 by 1.2 to 1.5 microns.

Gelatin stab: Cream-colored surface growth, becoming brown. Slow liquefaction. Yellowish soluble pigment.

Agar: Circular, entire colonies, smooth, becoming raised, lichenoid, wrinkled, white to straw-colored, opalescent to opaque. No aerial mycelium. Deep golden brown soluble pigment.

Synthetic agar: Abundant, cream-colored, wrinkled, raised growth. Aerial mycelium white, scarce.

Starch agar: Thin, transparent, spreading growth.

Glucose agar: Restricted, folded, cream-colored, entire growth.

Glucose broth: Ring in form of small colonies, settling to the bottom.

Litmus milk: Brown ring with greenish tinge; coagulated; peptonized with alkaline reaction.

Potato: Gray, opalescent growth, becoming black, wrinkled. Brown plug.

Brown soluble pigment formed.

Starch is hydrolyzed.

Strong tyrosinase reaction.

Nitrites produced from nitrates.

Aerobic.

Optimum temperature, 37° C.

Antagonistic properties: Certain strains give positive effects, others negative.

Comments: The potato scab organism, like other acid-fast organisms, can be selectively impregnated with carbol-auramin and when exposed to ultraviolet radiation fluoresces bright yellow. This technic confirms Lutman's conclusion that the hyphae are intercellular and grow within the middle lamellae (Richards, Stain Tech., *18*, 1943, 91–94).

Relationships to other species: *Streptomyces clavifer, Streptomyces spiralis, Streptomyces carnosus, Streptomyces sampsonii* and many other species or strains are closely related to this organism.

Source: Isolated from potato scab lesions.

Habitat: Cause of potato scab; found in soil.

130. **Streptomyces tenuis** (Millard and Burr, 1926) Waksman, 1953. (*Actinomyces tenuis* Millard and Burr, Ann. Appl. Biol., *13*, 1926, 601; Waksman, in Waksman and Lechevalier, Actinomycetes and Their Antibiotics, Baltimore, 1953, 111.)

te′nu.is. L. adj. *tenuis* slender.

Aerial mycelium: Irregularly branched. Spores cylindrical, 0.82 by 0.87 micron.

Gelatin: Pale gray growth covered with scant, white aerial mycelium. Soluble yellow pigment. Rapid liquefaction.

Synthetic sucrose agar: Growth penetrates deep into substratum. Thin, flat, yellowish drab surface growth. Aerial mycelium deep olive-buff. Soluble, pale orange-yellow pigment.

Synthetic glucose agar: Thin, flat growth covered by olive-buff aerial mycelium. Soluble green pigment.

Potato agar: Wrinkled, grayish growth. Aerial mycelium white to vinaceous-fawn-colored. Soluble, golden brown pigment.

Glycerol synthetic solution: White, flaky growth mostly at bottom. Aerial mycelium scant, olive-buff.

Glucose broth: Whitish surface and bottom growth. Aerial mycelium abundant, wrinkled, olive-buff. Soluble, golden brown pigment.

Milk: Good growth covered with white aerial mycelium. Coagulated, followed by incomplete peptonization.

Potato: Good growth covered with deep olive-buff aerial mycelium. Soluble, gray to olive to black pigment.

Starch is hydrolyzed.

Tyrosinase reaction: Negative.

Nitrites not produced from nitrates.

Source: Isolated from medium-sized, ruptured potato scab.

Habitat: Found in potatoes so far as known.

131. **Streptomyces marginatus** (Millard and Burr, 1926) Waksman, 1953. (*Actinomyces marginatus* Millard and Burr,

Ann. Appl. Biol., *13*, 1926, 601; Waksman, in Waksman and Lechevalier, Actinomycetes and Their Antibiotics, Baltimore, 1953, 112.)

mar.gi.na′tus. L. part.adj. *marginatus* margined.

Aerial mycelium: Abundant, gray to yellow to olive-buff. Sporophores simple. Spores spherical, 0.8 by 0.87 micron.

Gelatin: Thin, pale olive-gray growth covered with abundant, pale gray to olive-buff aerial mycelium. Soluble buff pigment.

Synthetic sucrose agar: Thin, echinate growth covered with abundant, olive-buff aerial mycelium. Cream-colored pigment.

Synthetic glucose agar: Thin, yellowish growth covered with white to buff aerial mycelium. Soluble buff pigment.

Potato agar: Heavy, gray growth covered with white to whitish yellow aerial mycelium. Soluble, light, golden brown to deep golden brown pigment.

Glycerol synthetic solution: Flaky growth at base and on surface. Aerial mycelium scant, olive-buff.

Glucose broth: White, spongy mass at surface and on bottom, covered with white to yellow aerial mycelium. Soluble, light golden brown pigment.

Milk: Good, flocculated growth. Aerial mycelium white. Coagulation followed by peptonization.

Potato: Good, raised growth covered with abundant, buff to olive-buff aerial mycelium. Plug at first gray, later becoming black.

Starch is hydrolyzed.

Tyrosinase reaction: Negative.

Nitrites produced from nitrates.

Grows well at 37.5° C.

Source: Isolated from a small, unruptured potato scab.

Habitat: Potato so far as known.

132. Streptomyces salmonicolor (Millard and Burr, 1926) Waksman, 1953. (*Actinomyces salmonicolor* Millard and Burr, Ann. Appl. Biol., *13*, 1926, 601; Waksman, in Waksman and Lechevalier, Actinomycetes and Their Antibiotics, Baltimore, 1953, 113.)

sal.mo.ni′co.lor. L. mas.n. *salmo* salmon;

L. gen.noun *salmonis* of a salmon; L. fem.n. *color* color; M.L. adj. *salmonicolor* salmon-colored.

Vegetative growth: Hyphae minute.

Aerial mycelium: Poorly developed or absent entirely. Sporophores straight or form open spirals. Spores spherical or ellipsoidal, 0.4 to 0.8 by 0.5 to 0.8 micron.

Gelatin: Poor growth. Slow liquefaction.

Synthetic sucrose agar: Minute, gray to pinkish colonies. No aerial mycelium. No soluble pigment.

Synthetic glucose agar: Gray to purplish growth. No aerial mycelium. Faint, golden soluble pigment.

Potato agar: Wrinkled, pinkish growth.

Glycerol synthetic solution: Poor, flaky growth at bottom of tube.

Glucose broth: Growth in form of sponge-like mass.

Milk: Fair surface growth. Coagulated; slowly peptonized.

Potato: Restricted, wrinkled, raised, ocher-red to brown growth. Plug pigmented drab-gray.

Starch is hydrolyzed.

Tyrosinase reaction: Negative.

Nitrites produced from nitrates.

Grows well at 37.5° C.

Source: Isolated from sour soil.

Habitat: Soil.

133. Streptomyces maculatus (Millard and Burr, 1926) Waksman, 1953. (*Actinomyces maculatus* Millard and Burr, Ann. Appl. Biol., *13*, 1926, 601; Waksman, in Waksman and Lechevalier, Actinomycetes and Their Antibiotics, Baltimore, 1953, 113.)

ma.cu.la′tus. L. part.adj. *maculatus* spotted.

Vegetative growth: Dark green. Hyphae extremely fine.

Aerial mycelium: Poorly developed; only on certain media as a fine gray cover. Sporophores short, straight. Spores spherical, 0.5 to 0.6 micron. Chlamydospores produced.

Gelatin: Poor growth. Slow liquefaction.

Synthetic sucrose agar: Round, flat, pale gray to pinkish colonies, later showing dark green centers. No aerial mycelium.

Synthetic glucose agar: Thin, flat, almost black growth with greenish tinge.

Potato agar: Vinaceous, tawny colored growth producing a vinaceous tawny soluble pigment.

Glycerol synthetic solution: Poor, flaky growth at bottom.

Glucose broth: Numerous minute, whitish colonies at bottom of container.

Milk: Very slight growth. Not coagulated; not peptonized.

Potato: Restricted, raised, pinkish growth. Aerial mycelium scant, white. Soluble, gray to brown pigment.

Starch is hydrolyzed.

Tyrosinase reaction: Negative.

Nitrites not produced from nitrates.

Grows well under anaerobic conditions.

Grows well at 37.5° C.

Source: Isolated from sour soil.

Habitat: Soil.

134. Streptomyces coroniformis (Millard and Burr, 1926) Waksman, 1953. (*Actinomyces coroniformis* Millard and Burr, Ann. Appl. Biol., *13*, 1926, 601; Waksman, in Waksman and Lechevalier, Actinomycetes and Their Antibiotics, Baltimore, 1953, 114.)

co.ro.ni.for'mis. L. fem.n. *corona* crown; L. fem.n. *forma* form; M.L. adj. *coroniformis* crown-shaped.

Aerial mycelium: Simple branching. Spores ellipsoidal, 0.6 by 0.8 micron.

Gelatin: Fair growth. Weak or no liquefaction.

Synthetic sucrose agar: Gray to greenish discrete colonies partially coalescing. White aerial mycelium covering edges of growth.

Synthetic glucose agar: Grayish discrete colonies growing into medium weakly produced. No aerial mycelium.

Potato agar: Wrinkled, grayish growth. No aerial mycelium.

Glycerol synthetic solution: Very poor growth in form of small flakes at bottom.

Glucose broth: Fair growth at bottom.

Milk: A few colonies on surface. Not coagulated; weakly peptonized.

Potato: Raised, grayish growth. Aerial mycelium white. Plug pigmented brownish around and under growth.

Starch may be weakly hydrolyzed.

Tyrosinase reaction: Negative.

Nitrites weakly produced from nitrates.

Fair growth at 37.5° C.

Source: Isolated from peat soil.

Habitat: Soil.

135. Streptomyces spiralis (Millard and Burr, 1926) Waksman, 1953. (*Actinomyces spiralis* Millard and Burr, Ann. Appl. Biol., *13*, 1926, 601; Waksman, in Waksman and Lechevalier, Actinomycetes and Their Antibiotics, Baltimore, 1953, 114.)

spi.ra'lis. Gr. fem.n. *spira* a spiral; M.L. adj. *spiralis* like a spiral.

Vegetative growth: Lichenoid, smooth, yellowish golden growth. No soluble pigment.

Aerial mycelium: Sporophores straight or spiral-forming. Spores cylindrical, 0.9 by 1.0 to 1.7 microns.

Gelatin: Limited, gray growth. Aerial mycelium scant, white. Rapid liquefaction.

Synthetic sucrose agar: Rough or granular growth. Aerial mycelium vinaceous buff to dark grayish olive. Soluble, pale vinaceous-fawn-colored pigment.

Synthetic glucose agar: Fairly rough, pale gray growth. Aerial mycelium scant, white. Soluble, yellowish to pink pigment.

Potato agar: Granular, gray growth. Aerial mycelium abundant, white to olive-buff. Soluble, light golden brown pigment.

Glycerol synthetic solution: No growth.

Glucose broth: Minute compact colonies at bottom and on surface. Aerial mycelium scant, white.

Milk: Good surface growth covered with abundant, white aerial mycelium. Coagulated, rapidly peptonized.

Potato: Poor, wrinkled, grayish vinaceous growth. Aerial mycelium white to grayish vinaceous. Plug colored brown around and below growth.

Starch is not hydrolyzed.

Tyrosinase reaction: Negative.

Nitrites not produced from nitrates.

Does not grow at 37.5° C.

Source: Isolated from a heap of decaying grass.

Habitat: Found in grass compost so far as known.

136. Streptomyces sampsonii (Millard

and Burr, 1926) Waksman, 1953. (*Actinomyces sampsonii* Millard and Burr, Ann. Appl. Biol., *13*, 1926, 601; Waksman, in Waksman and Lechevalier, Actinomycetes and Their Antibiotics, Baltimore, 1953, 115.)

samp.so'ni.i. M.L. gen.noun *sampsonii* of Sampson; named for a person, Sampson.

Original description supplemented by observations made by Waksman and Gordon.

Aerial mycelium: Long branching aerial hyphae. Spores cylindrical, 0.5 by 0.8 to 1.0 micron. Spores ellipsoidal to spherical (Waksman and Gordon).

Gelatin: Scant, gray surface growth. A trace of whitish aerial mycelium. Rapid liquefaction.

Synthetic sucrose agar: Good, wrinkled, pale gray to white growth. Aerial mycelium very scant, white. Soluble, green to buff pigment.

Synthetic glucose agar: Good, wrinkled, white to gray growth. Aerial mycelium scant, white. Soluble, yellow to brownish pigment.

Glycerol synthetic solution: No growth.

Glucose broth: Good surface and bottom growth as well as many colonies clinging to side of tube. Aerial mycelium white.

Milk: Good, whitish surface growth. No aerial mycelium. Not coagulated; not peptonized. Rapid peptonization (Waksman and Gordon).

Potato: Wrinkled, grayish growth. Aerial mycelium white. Soluble, golden brown pigment. None observed (Waksman and Gordon).

Starch is not hydrolyzed. Starch is rapidly hydrolyzed (Waksman and Gordon).

Tyrosinase reaction: Negative.

Nitrites produced from nitrates.

Optimum temperature, 28° C.

Source: Isolated from a medium-sized, ruptured potato scab.

Habitat: Unknown.

137. **Streptomyces intermedius** (Krüger, 1890, *emend.* Wollenweber, 1920) Waksman, 1953. (*Oospora intermedia* Krüger, Berichte der Versuchsstat. f. Zuckerrohrs, Kergok-Legal, 1890; *Actinomyces intermedius* Wollenweber, Arb. d. Forschungs-

inst. für Kartoffelbau, 1920, 16; Waksman, in Waksman and Lechevalier, Actinomycetes and Their Antibiotics, Baltimore, 1953, 116.)

in.ter.me'di.us. L. adj. *intermedius* intermediate.

Vegetative growth: Green-colored colonies. Soluble green pigment. On continued cultivation, green color tends to become cream-colored to brownish.

Aerial mycelium: Light gray to gray. Sporophores straight, frequently arranged in clumps. Spores elongated, 0.7 by 0.9 to 1.0 micron.

Gelatin: Thin, colorless to faintly brown growth, dropping to bottom. No soluble pigment. Slow liquefaction.

Agar: Much-folded, cream-colored growth. Aerial mycelium in upper portion of slant white. Soluble, faintly golden pigment.

Synthetic agar: Slightly folded, cream-colored to brown growth. Aerial mycelium thin, white.

Starch agar: Same as on synthetic agar.

Glucose agar: Good, brownish growth. Aerial mycelium heavy, cream-colored. No soluble pigment.

Broth: Thin, colorless film dropping to bottom. No aerial mycelium. No soluble pigment.

Milk: Heavy, cream-colored surface growth. No aerial mycelium. Not coagulated; slowly peptonized.

Potato: Folded, brown growth. Trace of white aerial mycelium in upper, drier portions of growth. No soluble pigment.

Sucrose slowly inverted.

Starch is actively hydrolyzed.

Nitrites weakly produced from nitrates.

Antagonistic properties: Positive.

Source: Isolated from the soil of potato fields near Berlin.

Habitat: Soil.

138. **Streptomyces ipomoeae** (Person and Martin, 1940) Waksman and Henrici, 1948. (*Actinomyces ipomoea* (sic) Person and Martin, Phytopath., *30*, 1940, 313; Waksman and Henrici, in Manual, 6th ed., 1948, 958.)

i.po.moe'ae. ML. noun. *Ipomoea* generic

name of the sweet potato; M.L. gen.noun *ipomoeae* of *Ipomoea*.

Conidia on glucose-casein agar: Ellipsoidal to elliptical, 0.9 to 1.3 by 1.3 to 1.8 microns.

Gelatin: After 25 days at 20° C., scant growth, no aerial mycelium; no soluble pigment; liquefaction.

Agar: Moderate growth in the form of small, shiny, crinkled colonies both on the surface and imbedded in the medium, silver-colored.

Synthetic agar: Abundant growth, mostly on surface of medium, moderately wrinkled, olive-yellow.

Starch agar: Growth moderate, smooth, deep in medium, ivory-colored. Aerial mycelium white with patches of bluish green. No soluble pigment. Complete hydrolysis after 12 days.

Milk: Growth in form of ring; hydrolysis, without visible coagulation.

Potato: Growth moderate, light brown, shiny, wrinkled. No aerial mycelium. No soluble pigment.

Starch is hydrolyzed.

No growth on cellulose.

Nitrites are produced from nitrates.

Antagonistic properties: Positive.

Source: Isolated from diseased sweetpotato (*Ipomoea sp.*) tubers and small rootlets from several localities in Louisiana.

Habitat: Found in sweet potatoes so far as known.

139. **Streptomyces poolensis** (Taubenhaus, 1918) Waksman and Henrici, 1948. (*Actinomyces poolensis* Taubenhaus, Jour. Agr. Res., *13*, 1918, 446; Waksman and Henrici, in Manual, 6th ed., 1948, 949.)

poo.len'sis. M.L. adj. *poolensis* pertaining to Poole; named for Prof. R. F. Poole, a plant pathologist.

Description taken from Waksman (Soil Sci., *8*, 1919, 140).

Aerial mycelium: Fine, branching; spirals usually not seen. Conidia ellipsoidal.

Gelatin stab: Liquefaction, with small, brownish flakes in fluid.

Agar: Yellowish, translucent growth.

Synthetic agar: Thin, colorless, spreading growth. Aerial mycelium white to gray.

Starch agar: Restricted, cream-colored growth.

Glucose agar: Growth abundant, light brown, glossy, raised center, entire.

Glucose broth: Thin, brownish ring.

Litmus milk: Brownish ring; coagulated; peptonized, with strongly alkaline reaction.

Potato: Thin, reddish brown; medium becomes purplish.

Faint trace of soluble brown pigment.

Starch not hydrolyzed.

Nitrites produced from nitrates.

Aerobic.

Optimum temperature, 37° C.

Antagonistic properties: Positive.

Source: Isolated from a sweet potato "pox."

Habitat: Unknown.

140. **Streptomyces tumuli** (Millard and Beeley, 1927) Waksman, 1953. (*Actinomyces tumuli* Millard and Beeley, Ann. Appl. Biol., *14*, 1927, 296; Waksman, in Waksman and Lechevalier, Actinomycetes and Their Antibiotics, Baltimore, 1953, 117.)

tu'mu.li. L. mas.n. *tumulus* a mound; L. gen.noun *tumuli* of a mound.

Gelatin: Beaded growth. No aerial mycelium. No soluble pigment. Rapid liquefaction.

Agar: Good, lustrous, slimy, gray growth. No aerial mycelium. No soluble pigment.

Synthetic agar: Gray growth penetrating into the medium, later becoming darkly opaque. Aerial mycelium arises on center of growth, at first white, later becoming pale gray. Surface of growth covered with colorless drops leaving small, black craters. No soluble pigment.

Glucose agar: Wrinkled, pale gray growth. White aerial mycelium arising in concentric rings around a dark bare center. Soluble, olive-colored pigment.

Broth: Large, spherical, white colonies. No soluble pigment.

Milk: Good growth. No aerial mycelium. Coagulated; slightly peptonized.

Potato: Heavy, slimy, black growth. No aerial mycelium. Plug becoming grayish brown.

Starch is hydrolyzed.

Nitrites produced from nitrates.

Grows well at 37° C.

Source: Isolated from a mound scab of mangels.

Habitat: Mangels, so far as known.

141. Streptomyces listeri (Erikson, 1935) Waksman and Henrici, 1948. (*Actinomyces listeri* Erikson, Med. Res. Council Spec. Rept. Ser. 203, 1935, 36; Waksman and Henrici, in Manual, 6th ed., 1948, 961.)

lis'te.ri. M.L. gen.noun *listeri* of Lister; named for Dr. Joseph Lister, father of antiseptic surgery.

Vegetative growth: Long slender filaments, many loosely wavy, forming a dense spreading mycelium which rapidly grows into a membrane on most media.

Aerial mycelium: Very slow and inconstant in appearance, short and straight; conidia ellipsoidal.

Gelatin: Slight liquefaction; round white surface colonies; after 45 days, confluent skin, almost completely liquefied.

Agar: Smooth, round, moist, cream-colored, margin depressed, center elevated, closely adherent; becoming umbilicated, with a myceloid margin.

Glucose agar: Cream-colored, glistening, pinpoint colonies; later aggregated in convoluted skin.

Glycerol agar: Abundant, moist, cream-colored growth, colonies elevated, piled up; powdery white aerial mycelium. After 20 days, skin deeply buckled; colorless with exuded drops.

Ca-agar: Poor growth, a slight biscuit-colored membrane.

Potato agar: After one week, extensive growth, colorless submerged colonies, warted surface; dirty pink coloration after 2 weeks; scant white aerial mycelium after 4 months.

Dorset's egg medium: No growth.

Blood agar: Small, round, cream-colored colonies, smooth translucent surface; no hemolysis.

Serum agar: Small, irregular, moist, cream-colored colonies, tending to be heaped up; later somewhat transparent.

Inspissated serum: Abundant growth, colorless shiny colonies, centrally elevated, becoming confluent.

Broth: Small, round, white colonies in sediment.

Glucose broth: Small, white, nodular colonies; later abundant flocculi.

Synthetic sucrose solution: Delicate white colonies in suspension and in sediment.

Litmus milk: Coagulation. No change in reaction.

Potato plug: Abundant, dull, brownish, wrinkled skin with white aerial mycelium; large, stellate, fluffy, white colonies in liquid at base.

Source: Isolated from human material. Strain from Lister Collection.

Habitat: Unknown.

142. Streptomyces galtieri Goret and Joubert, 1951. (Ann. Parasitol. Hum. et Comp., *26*, 1951, 118.)

gal.ti.e'ri. M.L. gen.noun *galtieri* of Galtier; named for Prof. Galtier of the Veterinary School, Lyons, France.

Vegetative growth: Wavy mycelium branched in a monopodial form, 1 micron in diameter. On agar, two types of colonies are produced: one is small, flat, regular and white; the other large, thick, irregular and yellowish.

Aerial mycelium: Producing spirals. Conidia ellipsoidal, 0.8 by 0.8 to 1.5 microns.

Gelatin: Poor, flaky, white growth. Limited liquefaction.

Agar: Poor, thin, yellowish growth. Aerial mycelium powdery, white. Soluble brown pigment.

Synthetic agar: Small colonies. Aerial mycelium powdery, white. No soluble pigment.

Peptone agar: Limited, cream-colored growth. Aerial mycelium powdery, white. Reddish brown soluble pigment weakly produced.

Starch: Thin colonies. Aerial mycelium powdery, white. No soluble pigment.

Glycerol potato: Reddish orange punctiform colonies growing together. A thick crust. Limited white aerial mycelium appearing very slowly. No soluble pigment.

Glucose-peptone medium: Numerous colonies covering surface. Soluble brownish pigment weakly produced.

Milk: Slow growth. Aerial mycelium white. No soluble pigment. At 25° C., not coagulated; at 37° C., coagulated after 20 days. Not peptonized. No change in reaction.

Nitrites produced from nitrates.

Proteolysis: No action on coagulated serum.

Pathogenicity: Pathogenic for guinea pigs and rabbits. Not pathogenic for dogs after laboratory growth.

Source: Isolated from cases of dog septicemia (thoracic, abdominal and brain lesions).

Habitat: Found in dogs, guinea pigs and rabbits so far as known.

143. **Streptomyces upcottii** (Erikson, 1935) Waksman and Henrici, 1948. (A new pathogenic form of *Streptothrix*, Gibson, Jour. Path. and Bact., *23*, 1920, 357; *Actinomyces upcottii* Erikson, Med. Res. Council Spec. Rept. Ser. 203, 1935, 36; Waksman and Henrici, in Manual, 6th ed., 1948, 961.)

up.cot′ti.i. M.L. gen.noun *upcottii* of Upcott; named for Dr. Harold Upcott, the surgeon who first secured this organism.

Description taken from Erikson (*op. cit.*, 1935, 22).

Vegetative growth: Filaments characteristically long, straight, much interwoven and ramified; typical unicellular mycelium, usually forming medium to large heavy cartilaginous colonies.

Aerial mycelium: A very slight transient aerial mycelium appeared on one agar slope, but this has not been repeated on any slide microculture on any medium. Slightly acid-fast.

Gelatin: Abundant flocculent growth along streak, round cream-colored colonies on surface. Partly liquefied in 14 days; complete liquefaction in 2 months.

Agar: Smooth, shining, round, cream-colored colonies, margin submerged, scant white aerial mycelium in one week; colonies large (up to 10 mm in diameter), centers elevated, greenish tinge, very sparse aerial mycelium in two weeks; the aerial mycelium

disappears and large radial grooves appear in most colonies in 3 weeks.

Glucose agar: Smooth, round, cream-colored colonies, margin depressed, centers elevated, hollow on reverse side; later a coherent membranous growth, piled up, yellowish.

Glycerol agar: Small, round, cream-colored, glistening colonies, heavy texture, margins submerged; later, colonies umbilicated, tending to be piled up; after 6 weeks, growth very much convoluted and raised, broad submerged margin, slightly reddish medium.

Coon's agar: Small, radiating, white colonies, growth mostly submerged.

Ca-agar: Small, colorless membranous growth with undulating margin; later, centrally depressed into medium.

Potato agar: Poor growth, small, colorless blister colonies, medium slightly discolored.

Dorset's egg medium: Round, flat, colorless, scale-like colonies, some marked by concentric rings and slightly hollowed in center; growth becomes yellow-brown.

Serum agar: Large colonies (3 to 4 mm in diameter), colorless, granular, centrally elevated, depressed at margin, resembling limpets.

Blood agar: Large drab heavily textured colonies; no aerial mycelium; no hemolysis.

Broth: Large coherent mass composed of fluffy colonies.

Synthetic sucrose solution: Fair growth, minute white colonies.

Carrot plug: Colorless, spreading, moist, wrinkled growth in six weeks; later a dull greenish brown, moist, very much wrinkled and depressed skin.

Source: Isolated from the spleen in a case of acholuric jaundice.

Habitat: Unknown.

144. **Streptomyces hortonensis** (Erikson, 1935) Waksman and Henrici, 1948. (*Actinomyces horton* (sic) Erikson, Med. Res. Council Spec. Rept. Ser. 203, 1935, 36; Waksman and Henrici, in Manual, 6th ed., 1948, 962.)

hor.to.nen′sis. M.L. adj. *hortonensis* pertaining to Horton; named for the Horton War Hospital, Epsom, England.

Vegetative growth: Typical germination into very slow-growing unicellular mycelium composed of long, slender, straight, branching filaments.

Aerial mycelium: Very sparse, straight aerial mycelium produced only once on potato. Non-acid-fast.

Gelatin: Round cream-colored colonies on surface and a few mm below. No liquefaction.

Agar: Very slow growth, a few smooth cream-colored coiled colonies in 19 days; after 2 months, liberal, irregular, convoluted growth.

Glucose agar: Coiled and heaped up cream-colored translucent masses; after 2 months, growth rounded, elevated, ridged outwards from hollow center.

Glycerol agar: Coiled, colorless, lustrous patches, isolated colony with central depression.

Serum agar: Poor growth, small amorphous cream-colored mass.

Inspissated serum: Intricately coiled cream-colored growth. No liquefaction.

Broth: Flakes.

Synthetic sucrose solution: Poor growth, a few flakes.

Synthetic glycerol solution: Delicate white flocculi at base.

Litmus milk: Green surface growth, liquid hydrolyzed, partly clear purple; later decolorized, brown.

Potato agar: Colorless blister colonies in one week; dull green heaped and coiled mass after 3 weeks; medium becomes slightly discolored.

Potato plug: After 3 weeks, abundant, colorless, umbilicated, round colonies, some coiled in raised masses; later, liberal olive-green growth, piled up, dense, velvety gray green aerial mycelium at top of slant, small round fluffy white colonies in liquid at base.

Source: Isolated from pus containing typical actinomycotic granules from parotid abscess.

Habitat: Found in human infections so far as known.

145. **Streptomyces beddardii** (Erikson, 1935) Waksman and Henrici, 1948. (*Actinomyces beddardii* Erikson, Med. Res. Council Spec. Rept. Ser. 203, 1935, 36; Waksman and Henrici, in Manual, 6th ed., 1948, 963.)

bed.dar'di.i. M.L. gen.noun *beddardii* of Beddard; presumably named for the surgeon who first secured this organism.

Vegetative growth: Rapidly growing, dense, spreading mycelium composed of very long, slender filaments, many wavy or closely coiled, particularly on glucose agar; spirals less marked or lacking on poorer nutritive media like synthetic glycerol agar or water agar.

Aerial mycelium: Sparse, short, straight on synthetic glycerol agar, much slower and more plentiful on glucose agar; later shows long, very fine spirals breaking up into small ellipsoidal conidia; aerial hyphae straighter and more branched with shorter conidiophores on starch agar. Non-acid-fast.

Gelatin: Dull white flakes sinking to bottom as medium liquefies; liquefaction complete in 8 days.

Agar: Colorless, coherent, wrinkled, membranous growth with submerged margin; after 3 months, medium discolored, scant white aerial mycelium at top.

Glucose agar: Wrinkled membranous growth; after 2 months, scant white aerial mycelium.

Glycerol agar: Small, cream-colored, discrete colonies becoming confluent, under surface much buckled.

Potato agar: Moist, cream-colored skin, convoluted, closely adherent.

Ca-agar: Extensive, moist, cream-colored, wrinkled, membranous growth.

Coon's agar: Scant, cream-colored, membranous growth.

Starch agar: Spreading, colorless growth, considerable white aerial mycelium.

Blood agar: Hemolysis. Growth in uniformly striated colorless bands, occasional round colonies at margin.

Dorset's egg medium: Extensive, very wrinkled, membranous growth, surface bright yellow. After 2 months, considerable liquefaction.

Serum agar: Wrinkled, glistening, cream-colored, membranous growth.

Inspissated serum: Colorless smeary growth, reverse becoming transparent, starting to liquefy at base; completely liquefied and brown in 12 days.

Broth: Suspended and sedimented colorless flocculi, some small round colonies.

Synthetic sucrose solution: Abundant white colonies in coherent mass near bottom of tube; large shell-shaped masses.

Synthetic glycerol solution: At first, a few round white colonies in suspension; later, large branched feathery mass at bottom.

Milk: Coagulated; later peptonized.

Litmus milk: Medium deep blue, becoming hydrolyzed to clear purple.

Potato plug: Colorless moist membranous growth with scant white aerial mycelium at top of plug.

Starch is hydrolyzed.

Tyrosine agar: Reaction negative.

Source: Isolated from human spleen in a case of splenic anemia.

Habitat: Unknown.

146. **Streptomyces kimberi** (Erikson, 1935) Waksman and Henrici, 1948. (*Actinomyces kimberi* Erikson, Med. Res. Council Spec. Rept. Ser. 203, 1935, 36; Waksman and Henrici, in Manual, 6th ed., 1948, 964.)

kim'be.ri. M.L. gen.noun *kimberi* of Kimber; presumably named for the surgeon who first secured this organism.

Vegetative growth: Mycelium of long, straight, profusely branching filaments forming circumscribed colonies on all media.

Aerial mycelium: Abundant production of short, straight and branched aerial mycelium; small round conidia. Non-acid-fast.

Gelatin: Liquefaction. Smooth shining colonies becoming powdery white with aerial mycelium, floating on liquefied medium. No pigmentation.

Agar: Smooth round moist cream-colored colonies, 1 mm in diameter; after 17 days, white powdery aerial mycelium.

Glucose agar: Discrete cream-colored colonies becoming confluent, white aerial mycelium.

Glycerol agar: Moist cream-colored colonies becoming confluent, white aerial mycelium.

Potato agar: Extensive growth covered by white powdery aerial mycelium; large colorless exuded droplets.

Wort agar: Heavy brownish lichenoid colony; after 30 days, a white aerial mycelium.

Ca-agar: Dull cream-colored scaly growth, covered by chalky white aerial mycelium.

Coon's agar: Extensive growth, white aerial mycelium in annular arrangement.

Synthetic agar: Small colonies covered with white aerial mycelium.

Blood agar: Many large colonies, cream-colored, tough, smooth, glistening, with margin depressed; no hemolysis.

Serum agar: Moist, cream-colored honeycombed skin, scant white aerial mycelium.

Dorset's egg medium: Closely adherent scale-like colonies, centrally elevated, with white aerial mycelium.

Inspissated serum: Rapid spreading growth, discrete round colonies at margin, completely covered with white aerial mycelium, colorless transpired drops; slight softening at base.

Broth: Small round colonies in sediment in 2 days; supernatant colonies with white aerial mycelium and large hollow flakes in sediment in 15 days; occasional reddish brown coloration.

Synthetic sucrose solution: Round white colonies at bottom; later small stellate colonies in suspension and a few supernatant with white aerial mycelium.

Synthetic glycerol solution: Round white colonies at bottom; later coherent mulberry-like mass composed of fluffy round portions; after 15 days, irregular wispy flocculi and large coherent mass.

Milk: Coagulation; no peptonization; initial pinkish brown ring descends until medium is dark brown throughout (2 months).

Litmus milk: Blue coloration, hydrolyzed to clear purple in 2 months.

Starch not hydrolyzed.

Tyrosine agar: Reaction negative.

Source: Isolated from a blood culture of a woman with acholuric jaundice.

Habitat: Unknown.

147. Streptomyces somaliensis (Brumpt, 1906) Waksman and Henrici, 1948.

(*Indiella somaliensis* Brumpt, Arch. Parasit., Paris, *10*, 1906, 489; Waksman and Henrici, in Manual, 6th ed., 1948, 965.)

so.ma.li.en'sis. M.L. adj. *somaliensis* pertaining to Somali; named for Somali, an East African people living in Somaliland.

Description taken from Erikson (Med. Res. Council Spec. Rept. Ser. 203, 1935, 17).

Vegetative growth: Simple branching, unicellular mycelium with long, straight filaments, forming circumscribed colony crowned with aerial mycelium.

Aerial mycelium: Short, straight.

Gelatin: Cream-colored colonies, medium pitted; complete liquefaction in 10 days; hard black mass at bottom.

Agar: Abundant yellowish granular growth with small discrete colonies at margin; later growth colorless, colonies umbilicated.

Glucose agar: Poor growth, moist cream-colored elevated patch.

Glycerol agar: Abundant growth, minute round to large convoluted and piled up masses, colorless to dark gray and black.

Ca-agar: Round cream-colored colonies, depressed, umbilicated, piled up, thin white aerial mycelium; colonies become pale brown.

Potato agar: Small round colorless colonies, zonate margin depressed, confluent portion dark greenish black.

Blood agar: Small dark brown colonies, round and umbilicated, piled up confluent bands, reverse red-black; hemolysis.

Dorset's egg medium: Extensive colorless growth, partly discrete; becoming opaque, cream-colored, very wrinkled; later rough, yellow, mealy, portion liquid.

Serum agar: Spreading yellow-brown skin, intricately convoluted.

Inspissated serum: Cream-colored coiled colonies, medium pitted, transparent and slightly liquid.

Broth: A few round white colonies at surface, numerous fluffy masses in sediment; later large irregular mass breaking into wisps.

Synthetic sucrose solution: Minute round white fluffy colonies in sediment; after 17 days, scant wispy growth.

Milk: Soft semi-liquid coagulum which undergoes digestion; heavy wrinkled surface pellicle, completely liquefied in 12 days.

Litmus milk: Soft coagulum, partly digested, blue surface ring; clear liquid in 12 days.

Potato plug: Abundant growth, colonies round and ellipsoidal, partly piled up in rosettes, frosted with whitish gray aerial mycelium, plug discolored; after 16 days, aerial mycelium transient, growth nearly black.

Antagonistic properties: Positive.

Comments: Although *Streptomyces somaliensis* has been known for a long time, there have been, until recently, no detailed descriptions of the organism beyond the fact that it possesses a distinctly hard sheath around the grain which is insoluble in potash and eau de javelle. The rare occurrence of septa and occasional intercalary chlamydospores is reported by Brumpt (Arch. Parasit., *10*, 1905, 562), but has not been confirmed by Erikson. Chalmers and Christopherson (Ann. Trop. Med. Parasit., *10*, 1916, 223) merely mentioned the growth on potato as yellowish white and lichenoid without describing any aerial mycelium. Balfour in 1911 reported a case but gave no data, and Fülleborn limited his description to the grain (Arch. Schiffs. Trop. Hyg., *15*, 1911, 131). This species was first placed in *Indiella*, a genus of fungi, by Brumpt (1906). Later Brumpt (1913) proposed a new genus or subgenus, *Indiellopsis*, containing the single species *Indiellopsis somaliensis*.

Source: Isolated from a case of yellow-grained mycetoma, Khartoum (Balfour, 4th Rept. Wellcome Trop. Res. Lab., A. Med., London, 1911, 365).

Habitat: This condition has been observed by Baufford in French Somaliland, by Balfour in the Anglo-Egyptian Sudan, by Fülleborn in German So. West Africa and by Chalmers and Christopherson in the Sudan.

148. Streptomyces panjae (Erikson, 1935) Waksman and Henrici, 1948. (*Actino-*

myces panja (sic) Erikson, Med. Res. Council Spec. Rept. Ser. 203, 1935, 36; Waksman and Henrici, in Manual, 6th ed., 1948, 966.)

pan'jae. M.L. gen.noun *panjae* of Panja; named for Dr. Panja, who first secured this organism.

Vegetative growth: Unicellular mycelium with slender, branching filaments; very small, round colonies.

Aerial mycelium: No aerial mycelium visible on any medium, but occasional isolated aerial branches. Non-acid-fast.

Gelatin: Complete liquefaction in 4 days.

Agar: Colorless irregularly piled up convoluted growth; after 1 month, easily detachable, brownish.

Glucose agar: Small colorless coiled mass in 1 week; heaped up green growth in 2 weeks.

Glycerol agar: Poor growth, scant colorless patch.

Ca-agar: Colorless to pink spreading growth with minute discrete colonies at margin; after 2 weeks, bright red mass, buckled and shining, colorless submerged margin.

Coon's agar: Small submerged colorless growth.

Potato agar: Small elevated convoluted colorless masses with purple tinge in center.

Dorset's egg medium: Small round tough colorless colonies, margin well embedded; after 3 weeks, colonies elevated, warted, darkened, medium discolored and broken; slight degree of liquefaction, medium dark brown.

Serum agar: Colorless, glistening, piled up, convoluted mass.

Inspissated serum: Small round blister colonies and irregularly convoluted patches deeply sunk in pitted medium; after 2 weeks, medium transparent, slight degree of liquefaction.

Broth: Flakes and minute colorless colonies.

Glucose broth: Poor growth, scant flakes, pinkish.

Synthetic sucrose solution: Pinkish flocculi; after 3 weeks, moderate growth, minute colorless colonies.

Milk: Coagulation; pale green surface growth; mostly digested in 2 weeks.

Litmus milk: Soft coagulum, color unchanged; after 2 months, mostly digested, residue coagulum light purple.

Source: Isolated from an ulcer of the abdominal wall from a patient in Calcutta.

Habitat: Unknown.

149. **Streptomyces willmorei** (Erikson, 1935) Waksman and Henrici, 1948. (*Actinomyces willmorei* Erikson, Med. Res. Council Spec. Rept. Ser. 203, 1935, 36; Waksman and Henrici, in Manual, 6th ed., 1948, 966.)

will.mo're.i. M.L. gen.noun *willmorei* of Willmore; named for the surgeon who first secured this organism.

Vegetative growth: Germination usual, but growing unicellular mycelium frequently branches at very short intervals, presenting peculiar clubbed and budding forms with occasional separate round swollen cells which may represent the cystites of other writers. The filaments are characteristically long, homogeneous, and much interwoven.

Aerial mycelium: Profuse in most media, with a marked tendency to produce loose spirals (water and synthetic glycerol agar) with chains of ellipsoidal conidia. Thick aerial clusters may also be formed.

Gelatin: Minute colorless colonies; liquefaction.

Agar: Heavy folded colorless lichenoid growth, rounded elevations covered with white aerial mycelium; later, submerged margin, round confluent growth, aerial mycelium marked in concentric zones.

Glucose agar: Colorless wrinkled confluent growth with smooth entire margin, large discrete colonies like flat rosettes; after 4 months, scant white aerial mycelium.

Glycerol agar: Round smooth cream-colored colonies, heavy texture, margin submerged, stiff sparse aerial spikes; after 3 weeks, colonies large (up to 10 mm in diameter).

Ca-agar: Spreading colorless growth, pitting medium, submerged undulating margin; very scant white aerial mycelium.

Coon's agar: Opaque white growth extending irregularly (up to 3 mm) into medium, margin smooth and submerged, center raised, greenish tinge covered with white aerial mycelium; after 3 weeks, margin green, central mass covered by gray aerial mycelium.

Potato agar: Fair growth, partly submerged, covered with grayish white aerial mycelium; medium becomes discolored.

Blood agar: Heavily textured small drab colonies, aerial mycelium microscopical; no hemolysis.

Dorset's egg medium: Large, round, colorless, scale-like colonies, radially wrinkled; growth brownish, medium discolored in 2 weeks.

Serum agar: Smooth colorless discoid colonies; marked umbilication after 2 weeks.

Broth: Large fluffy white hemispherical colonies, loosely coherent.

Synthetic sucrose solution: A few large round white colonies with smooth partly zonate margins, lightly coherent in sediment; later smaller colonies in suspension attached to side of tube.

Milk: Coagulation; one-third peptonized.

Carrot plug: Colorless raised colonies with powdery white aerial mycelium; after 1 month, very much piled up, aerial mycelium gray; after 2 months, superabundant growth around back of plug, confluent, greatly buckled, all-over gray aerial mycelium.

Antagonistic properties: Positive.

Source: Isolated from a case of streptothricosis of liver (Willmore, Trans. Roy. Soc. Trop. Med. Hyg., *17*, 1924, 344).

Habitat: Unknown.

150. Sterile (non-conidia-forming) species.

In view of the fact that various species of *Streptomyces* are able to lose the capacity to produce aerial mycelium, either on continued cultivation or by a sort of mutation, cultures are obtained which may be mistaken for nocardias. They can be recognized, however, by the structure of their vegetative mycelium and by their cultural and physiological properties, such as formation of soluble pigments, liquefaction of gelatin, hydrolysis of starch, inversion of sucrose, coagulation and peptonization of milk. Occasionally some are able to revert to the typical streptomycete condition or

to regain the capacity to produce aerial mycelium.

Such cultures represent many species. Their growth is more commonly colorless, but sometimes pigmented, smooth or lichenoid, leathery, compact, with shiny surface. Some produce a soluble brown pigment. This was recognized by Krassilnikov, who designated such cultures as *Actinomyces albus sterilis* and *A. viridis sterilis*, similar to the formation of *Fungus sterilis*. He isolated from the soil about 100 such cultures. These were divided into three groups:

1. Strongly proteolytic cultures capable of liquefying gelatin in 3 to 5 days, of peptonizing milk in 6 to 10 days, with or without preliminary coagulation, of hydrolyzing starch with varying degrees of rapidity, of inverting sugar. No growth on cellulose. Strongly antagonistic.

2. Gelatin slowly liquefied, in 15 to 30 days, or not at all in that time; milk coagulated and peptonized simultaneously; starch hydrolyzed with varying degrees of rapidity or not at all. No growth on cellulose. Weak antagonistic properties.

3. Milk coagulated, due to acidification, but not peptonized. No antagonistic effects.

Waksman (in Waksman and Lechevalier, Actinomycetes and Their Antibiotics, Baltimore, 1953, 20) has used for these groups such names as *Streptomyces sterilis albus*, *Streptomyces sterilis ruber*, *Streptomyces sterilis viridis*, *Streptomyces sterilis flavus*, etc. to designate variant forms of cultures which have lost the capacity to produce aerial mycelium. In his collection many of the cultures that originally produced aerial mycelium have lost this capacity and could, therefore, no longer be considered as typical. For example *Streptomyces griseus*, a vigorously growing culture capable of producing streptomycin, yielded a mutant which no longer produces aerial mycelium, nor is it able to produce streptomycin.

On the other hand, certain nocardia-like organisms have been isolated from natural substrates which, on continued cultivation on artificial media, gave rise to variants which produced sporulating aerial hyphae. This is true, for example, of the culture designated by Gause as *Proactinomyces cyaneus-antibioticus* and thought to be identical with Beijerinck's *Actinococcus cyaneus*. Beijerinck believed in a close relationship between his cultures and that of *Streptomyces coelicolor* Müller. Whether these cultures are naturally occurring sterile forms of *Streptomyces*, whether they are natural mutants, or whether, as Gause believed, *Streptomyces* can be a mutant of *Nocardia* (*Proactinomyces*), remains to be determined.

Genus II. **Micromonospora** Orskov, 1923.

(Investigations into the Morphology of the Ray Fungi. Copenhagen, 1923, 147.)

Mic.ro.mo.no′spo.ra. Gr. adj. *micrus* small; Gr. adj. *monus* single, solitary; Gr. noun *spora* a seed; M.L. noun *spora* a spore; M.L. fem.n. *Micromonospora* the small, single-spored (organism).

Well developed, fine, non-septate mycelium, 0.3 to 0.6 micron in diameter. Grow well into the substrate. Do not form at any time a true aerial mycelium. Multiply by means of conidia which are produced singly at the ends of special conidiophores on the surface of the substrate mycelium. Conidiophores are short and either simple, branched or clustered. Not acid-fast. Gram-positive. Strongly proteolytic and diastatic. Aerobic. Grow readily between 35° and 37° C. Usually saprophytic. Occur mostly in dust, soil and lake bottoms.

The type species is *Micromonospora chalcea* (Foulerton) Ørskov.

Key to the species of genus **Micromonospora.**

I. Grow vigorously; copious spore formation on glucose-asparagine agar.
  A. Vegetative mycelium pale pink to deep orange; no typical soluble pigment.
                    1. *Micromonospora chalcea.*
  B. Vegetative mycelium orange, changing to brownish black; soluble pigment brown.
                    2. *Micromonospora fusca.*
II. Grow slowly and feebly; scant spore formation on glucose-asparagine agar; no soluble pigment.
  A. Vegetative mycelium not blue.
    1. Vegetative mycelium pale pink to pale orange.
                    3. *Micromonospora parva.*
    2. Vegetative mycelium yellow to orange-red.
                    4. *Micromonospora globosa.*
  B. Vegetative mycelium blue.
                    5. *Micromonospora coerulea.*

1. **Micromonospora chalcea** (Foulerton, 1905) Ørskov, 1923. (*Streptothrix chalcea* Foulerton, Lancet, *1*, 1905, 1200; Ørskov, Thesis, Copenhagen, 1923, 156.)

chal′ce.a. Gr. adj. *chalceus* copper, bronze.

Vegetative growth: Grows rapidly on all nutrient media, especially on glucose-asparagine agar. Growth heavy, compact, raised, pale pink to deep orange, not spreading much into the medium. Long, thin, branching, non-septate hyphae. Surface of growth smooth or folded, dull or shining. No soluble pigment.

Aerial mycelium: None. Well developed spore layer, moist and glistening, brownish black to greenish black, this color sometimes spreading through the whole mass of growth. Ellipsoidal or spherical conidia formed individually on relatively non-branching conidiophores.

Gelatin: Liquefaction.

Milk: Peptonized, occasionally coagulated.

Sucrose is inverted.

Starch is hydrolyzed.

Cellulose rapidly decomposed.

Proteolytic action seems stronger in this than in the other species of this genus.

Nitrites produced from nitrates.

Aerobic.

Optimum temperature for growth, between 30° and 35° C. Thermal death point of mycelium, 70° C. in 2 to 5 minutes. Spores resist 80° C. for 1 to 5 minutes.

Source: Isolated from the air.

Habitat: Found in soil, lake mud and other substrates.

2. Micromonospora fusca Jensen, 1932. (Proc. Linn. Soc. New So. Wales, *57*, 1932, 178.)

fus'ca. L. adj. *fuscus* dark, tawny.

Vegetative growth: On glucose-aspara-gine agar, heavy, compact, orange, rapidly changing to deep brown and nearly black. Deep brown soluble pigment.

Aerial growth: Moist, glistening, grayish to brownish black spore layer.

Gelatin: Weak liquefaction. Soluble pig-ment very slight.

Grows in liquid media as small, brown granules and flakes.

Milk: Slowly digested; not coagulated; slight grayish brown discoloration.

Sucrose is inverted.

Starch is hydrolyzed.

Cellulose is attacked to a slight extent.

Nitrate reduction variable.

Aerobic.

Antagonistic properties: Produces micro-monosporin.

Source: Isolated from soil.

Habitat: Found in soil.

3. Micromonospora parva Jensen, 1932. (Proc. Linn. Soc. New So. Wales, *57*, 1932, 177.)

par'va. L. adj. *parvus* small.

Vegetative growth: Scant growth on glu-cose-asparagine agar; vegetative mycelium thin, spreading widely into the agar, almost colorless to pale pink or orange.

Aerial growth: Sporulation scant, giving rise to thin, grayish, moist crusts on the surface. Spores ellipsoidal, occurring in a gray-colored mass.

Gelatin: Liquefaction.

Milk: Unchanged; may be coagulated then slowly redissolved with a faintly acid reaction.

Sucrose not inverted.

Starch is hydrolyzed.

Cellulose not decomposed.

Nitrites not produced from nitrates.

Aerobic.

Source: Isolated from soil.

Habitat: Found in soil.

4. Micromonospora globosa Krassil-nikov, 1938. (Ray Fungi and Related Organ-isms. Izd. Akad. Nauk, U.S.S.R., Moskau, 1938, 134; also see Microbiology, U.S.S.R., *8*, 1939, 179.)

glo.bo'sa. L. adj. *globosus* spherical, glo-bose.

Vegetative growth: Rugose, at first very compact, later acquiring a pasty consis-tency, adhering but slightly to the medium. The color of the cultures varies from light yellow to orange-red. During fruit-bearing, the colonies are covered with a brownish black tarnish of conidia.

Aerial growth: Conidia are formed at the ends of short branches, one on each branch. Individual branches with conidia resemble grape vines. The conidia are spherical, 1.0 to 1.3 microns; they arise by the swelling of the branch tips. The swellings become round, acquire the shape of spheres which, as the formation of the conidia proceeds, are divided from the branch by a transverse septum.

Gelatin: Liquefaction.

Milk: Coagulated, peptonized.

Sucrose is inverted.

Starch is hydrolyzed.

Cellulose not decomposed.

Nitrites produced from nitrates.

Aerobic.

Source: Isolated from soil.

Habitat: Soil.

5. Micromonospora coerulea Jensen, 1932. (Proc. Linn. Soc. New So. Wales, *57*, 1932, 177.)

coe.ru'le.a. L. adj. *coeruleus* dark blue, azure.

Vegetative growth: Slow growth on glu-cose-asparagine agar. Mycelium dense, greenish blue. Insoluble pigment. Colonies pigmented only on free admission of oxygen. Surface of colonies hard and glossy.

Aerial growth: Thin, white veil on surface resembling aerial mycelium but without aerial spores.

Aerial mycelium: None. Spherical conidia produced on branching, short conidiophores. Conidia blue.

Liquid media: Growth at bottom forms firm, round, white to pink granules.

Gelatin: Rapid liquefaction.

Milk: May be coagulated, but digestion very slight.

Sucrose not inverted.

Starch is hydrolyzed.

Cellulose not decomposed.

Nitrites not produced from nitrates.

Aerobic.

Source: Isolated from soil.

Habitat: Occurs infrequently in soil.

Genus III. **Thermoactinomyces** *Tsiklinsky, 1899.*

(Ann. Inst. Past., *13*, 1899, 501; also see *ibid.*, *17*, 1903, 206.)

Ther.mo.ac.ti.no.my'ces. Gr. noun *thermus* heat; Gr. noun *actis, actinis* a ray; Gr. noun *myces* fungus; M.L. mas.n. *Thermoactinomyces* heat (-loving) ray fungus.

The genus *Thermoactinomyces* is, in some respects, similar to *Micromonospora*, especially in its ability to produce single conidia at the tips of simple or branching conidiophores, which may be so short that they often appear to be produced directly on the mycelium. In other respects, notably in appearance and in ability to produce a true aerial mycelium, this genus resembles *Streptomyces*. It comprises, so far, only forms capable of growing between 50° and 65° C. Some have their optimum temperature at 60° C. Three species have been recognized so far.

The type species is *Thermoactinomyces vulgaris* Tsiklinsky.

Key to the species of genus **Thermoactinomyces.**

I. Aerial mycelium white.
   A. No soluble pigment produced.
      1. *Thermoactinomyces vulgaris.*
   B. Soluble wine-colored to rose pigment produced in certain media.
      2. *Thermoactinomyces thalpophilus.*

II. Aerial mycelium grayish green.
      3. *Thermoactinomyces monosporus.*

1. **Thermoactinomyces vulgaris** Tsiklinsky, 1899. (Thermophile *Cladothrix*, Kedzior, Arch. f. Hyg., *27*, 1896, 328; Tsiklinsky, Ann. Inst. Past., *13*, 1899, 501; *Micromonospora vulgaris* Waksman, Umbreit and Gordon, Soil Sci., *47*, 1939, 51.)

vul.ga'ris. L. adj. *vulgaris* common.

Vegetative growth: Grows well on organic and synthetic media. Mycelium 0.5 micron in diameter. No soluble pigment.

Aerial mycelium: White, powdery. Spherical and ellipsoidal spores are borne singly at the end of short branches from which they are easily broken.

Gelatin: Liquefaction.

Agar: Grows well, produces aerial mycelium.

Synthetic agar: Colorless growth, covered with white aerial mycelium. Sporophores very short, not exceeding 2 microns in length, often only 0.5 to 1.0 micron. Spores ellipsoidal or spherical, often appear to sit directly on mycelium.

Broth: Growth in form of white pellicle and often as compact balls on bottom of culture.

Milk: Coagulated and peptonized.

Potato: Grows well.

Sucrose not inverted.

Starch is hydrolyzed.

Cellulose not decomposed.

Optimum temperature, 57° C. Grows between 48° and 68° C.

Source: Isolated from compost.

Habitat: Found in human and animal excreta, high-temperature composts, self-heated hay and soil.

2. **Thermoactinomyces thalpophilus** Waksman and Corke, 1953. (Jour. Bact., *66*, 1953, 377.)

thal.po'phi.lus. Gr. noun *thalpus* warmth,

heat; Gr. adj. *philus* loving; M.L. adj. *thalpophilus* warmth-loving.

Vegetative growth: Grows well on organic and synthetic media, except on potato, at 50° C. Growth is colorless with yellow pigmentation in edges; color changes to orange with age of culture. Soluble, wine-colored to light rose pigment produced in yeast-glucose agar.

Aerial mycelium: Well developed, white, powdery, with tendency to form "fairy rings" on some media. Sporulating hyphae very short, 0.6 to 1.0 micron in length. Spherical conidia, 0.8 to 1.5 microns in diameter, are produced singly on the short sporophores or are entirely sessile.

Gelatin: Liquefaction.

Synthetic sucrose agar: Abundant, colorless growth. Powdery white to light gray aerial mycelium.

Glucose-asparagine agar: Colorless growth with reverse white to yellow to light brown. White, powdery aerial mycelium. Considerable development of "fairy rings" in aerial mycelium.

Glycerol agar: Cream-colored vegetative growth; white aerial mycelium.

Yeast-glucose agar: Good, colorless growth, pigmented yellow at edges, color turning orange in older cultures. Lichenoid, white aerial mycelium. Soluble, wine to rose pigment.

Potato agar: Limited vegetative growth, penetrating deep into medium. Limited, powdery, white aerial mycelium.

Milk: Coagulated with limited peptonization.

Starch is rapidly hydrolyzed.

Nitrites weakly produced from nitrates.

No growth at 28° C.; good growth in 4 days at 37° C.; excellent growth in 2 days at 50° C.

Source: Isolated from soil and high-temperature composts.

Habitat: Presumably widely distributed in soil.

3. **Thermoactinomyces monosporus** (Lehmann and Schütze, 1908) Waksman, 1953. (*Actinomyces monosporus* Lehmann and Schütze, in Schütze, Arch. f. Hyg., *67*, 1908, 50; *Thermoactinomyces monospora* (sic) Waksman, in Waksman and Lechevalier, Actinomycetes and Their Antibiotics, Baltimore, 1953, 130.)

mo.no'spo.rus. Gr. adj. *monus* single; Gr. fem.n. *spora* a seed; M.L. fem.n. *spora* a spore; M.L. adj. *monosporus* single-spored.

Vegetative growth: Grows well in various media. Growth yellowish, compact, smooth or lichenoid. Hyphae about 1.0 micron in diameter.

Aerial mycelium: Well developed, covering the whole growth, grayish green. Good sporulation on hay infusion-peptone agar; somewhat less on glycerol-peptone and lactose-peptone agars; none on peptone-glucose agar. Ellipsoidal spores, 1.0 to 1.4 by 1.5 to 1.8 microns; produced singly on simple, short sporophores.

Gelatin: Liquefaction.

Blood serum: Good, smooth growth. Serum liquefied.

Milk: Not coagulated.

Potato: No growth.

Optimum temperature, between 37° and 55° C.; grows poorly at 27° and not at all at 60° C.

Source: Isolated from self-heated hay.

Habitat: Presumably soil.

FAMILY IV. ACTINOPLANACEAE COUCH, 1955.*

(*Actinosporangiaceae* Couch, Jour. Elisha Mitchell Scientific Soc., *71*, 1955, 149; Couch, *ibid.*, 269.)

Ac.ti.no.pla.na'ce.ae. M.L. noun *Actinoplanes* type genus of the family; *-aceae* ending to denote a family; M.L. fem.pl.n. *Actinoplanaceae* the *Actinoplanes* family.

* Prepared by Prof. John N. Couch, Department of Botany, University of North Carolina, Chapel Hill, North Carolina, January, 1955. The investigational work was supported by a grant from the National Science Foundation. The author gratefully acknowledges the assistance of Dr. E. K. Goldie-Smith.

The vegetative mycelium, usually inconspicuous, is formed in water on a variety of plant and animal parts. The aerial mycelium is lacking as a rule; it is formed in certain species and then much as in *Streptomyces*. Reproduction is by spores formed in sporangia, the spores in *Actinoplanes* possessing flagella and being motile, and those in *Streptosporangium* possessing no flagella and being non-motile; conidia are formed in many species. Culturable on a variety of artificial media and then resembling, in vegetative characters, certain species of *Nocardia*, *Micromonospora* or *Streptomyces*. Widely distributed in soil and fresh water.

Key to the genera of family **Actinoplanaceae**.

I. Aerial mycelium usually not formed; coiled conidiophores lacking; sporangiospores motile.

Genus I. *Actinoplanes*, p. 826.

II. Aerial mycelium abundant; coiled conidiophores as well as sporangia are formed in some species; sporangiospores non-motile.

Genus II. *Streptosporangium*, p. 828.

Genus I. **Actinoplanes** *Couch, 1950.*

(Couch, Jour. Elisha Mitchell Scientific Society, *66*, 1950, 87; also see *ibid.*, *71*, 1955, 148; *Myceliochytrium fulgens* Johanson, in part, Torreya, *45*, 1945, 104.)

Ac.ti.no.pla′nes. Gr. noun *actis, actinis* a ray, beam; Gr. noun *planes* a wanderer; M.L. noun *Actinoplanes* literally, a ray wanderer; intended to signify an actinomycete with swimming spores.

On sterilized leaves in water, a very inconspicuous mycelium which branches throughout the leaf tissue is formed, the external hyphae being scattered or in tufts on the leaf surface and forming a fringe around the edge of the leaf; aerial mycelium is lacking or sparingly formed as a rule. The mycelium is usually pinkish to reddish, sometimes hyaline, on leaves, frequently decolorizing the green leaf and giving it a pinkish or reddish color. Hyphae are slightly to considerably branched, irregularly coiled, twisted or straight, sparingly septate and 0.2 to 2.6 microns in diameter. Sporangia of varied sizes and shapes are usually abundant on leaves and are formed only when the leaf is at or close to the surface of the water, *i.e.*, they are formed typically only in air; owing to refraction, they appear black under the low power of the microscope. The spores are in coils, nearly straight chains or are irregularly arranged in the sporangia; they are 1.0 to 1.5 microns in diameter, globose or subglobose, usually slightly angular, possess one to several shiny bodies and several polar flagella and are motile. Germination is by a minute germ tube which branches to form a mycelium. Sporangial wall evanescent or persistent. Usually not acid-fast. Gram-positive. Gelatin is liquefied. On various nutrient agars a brilliantly colored, toughish to pasty growth is usually formed; surface very variable; growth smooth and even with the agar or elevated, bumpy, convoluted, ridged, folded, cracked, etc.; usually moist and shiny, rarely pulverulent. The hyphae are of two or more distinct forms, the submerged and the surface hyphae, the latter usually more or less vertical, in some species forming a compact "palisade." Sporangia are abundant on some agars and are usually formed at the surface. Conidia formed by some species. On certain agars, the mycelium of some species breaks up, when crushed, into irregular pieces of hyphae, rods and coccoid bodies. Some isolates produce a distinctive pleasant or slightly unpleasant odor, while others are odorless. Aerobic. Saprophytic in a variety of soils and in fresh water; world-wide in distribution.*

The above description is based not only on the type species, *Actinoplanes philippinensis*, but also on over a hundred and twenty isolates representing a number of species groups.

The genus is readily distinguished from *Streptosporangium*. On leaves the latter produces a conspicuous aerial mycelium which resembles that produced by most species of *Strep-*

---

* For methods of collection and isolation, see Couch, Trans. New York Acad. Sci., Ser. II, *16*, 1954, 315.

tomyces, whereas, as a rule, no such mycelium is found in the isolates of *Actinoplanes*. As a whole, the isolates of *Actinoplanes* grow much more vigorously on agar than do those of *Streptosporangium*. The most striking difference is that in *Actinoplanes* the sporangiospores are motile, whereas in *Streptosporangium* they are non-motile.

Under certain conditions of culture, some species of *Actinoplanes* resemble some species of *Micromonospora*. Indeed, a non-sporangial strain of *Actinoplanes* might easily be confused with certain micromonosporas. The spores of *Micromonospora*, however, are formed singly or in grape-like clusters but never in chains, whereas in *Actinoplanes* they are formed singly and also in chains but not in grape-like clusters. Furthermore, none of the cultures of *Micromonospora* so far tested forms sporangia. Another striking difference is that, with most species of *Micromonospora*, on certain agars, the sporulating surface turns black, whereas this change does not occur in *Actinoplanes*. In general, the species of *Micromonospora* are less vigorous in growth than those of *Actinoplanes*.

Several species of *Actinoplanes*, when grown on potato-glucose and certain other agars, will form a small, pasty culture which, when mounted and crushed under a coverslip, breaks up into minute spheres, irregular rods and short, branched, hyphal segments, much as in *Nocardia*. Such growth, however, is not the normal condition for any species of *Actinoplanes*. None of the twenty-five species of *Nocardia* from Baarn and from the American Type Culture Collection formed sporangia when grown either on any of the agars most favorable for sporangial formation or on *Paspalum* leaves in water.

The type species is *Actinoplanes philippinensis* Couch.

1. **Actinoplanes philippinensis** Couch, 1950. (Jour. Elisha Mitchell Scientific Soc., *66*, 1950, 87.)

phil.ip.pi.nen′sis. M.L. adj. *philippinensis* pertaining to the Philippines.

The mycelium on sterile *Paspalum* grass in water forms a very delicate, hyaline to pinkish buff internal mycelium and an inconspicuous external fringe of threads around the entire edge of the leaf; compact mounds or tufts of hyphae which are scattered over the top surface giving the leaf a speckled or finely powdery appearance are also sometimes formed. The hyphae are 0.5 to 1.5 microns wide, branched and sparingly septate. Sporangia are usually abundantly formed on grass after about ten days, usually on long unbranched stalks; they are mostly spherical when mature and measure 8.4 to 22.0 microns, most of them being about 12.0 microns in diameter on grass. At maturity the spores are arranged in coils or are irregularly placed in the sporangium; they are about 1.0 to 1.2 microns in diameter and are discharged through a pore or by the partial dissolution of the sporangial wall, swimming vigorously.

Czapek agar: Growth at room temperature poor to fair, rarely good; flat or slightly elevated; sometimes in two distinct planes; one within the agar, the other at the surface. Margin smooth or scalloped. Light buff to tawny, changing in some old cultures to Mars brown with a lighter margin (colors as in Ridgway, Color Standards and Color Nomenclature, Washington, D. C., 1912). Sectoring frequent. In section, the growth consists of a compact surface layer, made up mostly of distinct palisades, and a submerged region of loosely arranged hyphae; the surface region is frequently stratose in old cultures with narrow, orange-colored layers. Sporangia are fairly abundant in some cultures and are not formed in others; they are spherical to irregular, frequently occurring beneath the surface in old cultures owing to overgrowth by palisade hyphae; sometimes a new layer of sporangia is formed over the first layer. Odor slightly fragrant. The agar is usually colored pale yellow.

Peptone Czapek agar: Growth good to very good, consisting of heaped convolutions in the center, becoming concentric rings of narrow ridges with narrow radial grooves, towards the outside, usually with an elevated or radially ridged-and-grooved margin. Surface shiny. Color brilliant, near apricot-orange or orange-chrome. Sporangia absent to very rare. Palisades not formed. Smaller hyphae form vast numbers of bacteroid spheres and rods which, when the material is crushed, break off and resemble *Nocardia*. Odor as on Czapek agar.

Potato glucose agar: Growth good to very good. Central area with coarse convolutions or large bumps and irregular ridges separated by radial grooves which slope to the smooth distinct margin. Surface glossy. Apricot-orange to russet, becoming bay in old cultures. Produces a diffusible pigment which darkens the agar. Sporangia are formed on the margin of some cultures but are absent in most of them. Palisades are formed.

Nutrient agar: Growth fair. Center slightly elevated and with a wide flat margin. Color ochraceous orange to cinnamon-rufous. Sporangia very rarely formed. Palisade hyphae usually not distinct.

Krainsky's glucose asparagine agar: Growth good to very good, consisting of a central area of elevated, fine convolutions, radial ridges or bumps and a smooth area with radial grooves gradually sloping into the submerged margin. Surface moist-appearing and glossy. Color of center apricot-orange to Sayal brown surrounded by an ochraceous salmon or light ochraceous salmon margin. Sporangia are usually on the smooth areas, none being found on the elevated parts; they are formed on palisade hyphae.

Distinctive characters: This species is characterized by the predominantly spherical sporangia usually on long unbranched stalks, the rather poor and usually flat growth on Czapek agar, and the very distinct palisade hyphae on this medium. The dark brown diffusible pigment on potato glucose agar is also characteristic.

Source: Isolated from a small pinch of dry soil (coll. no. P15) collected by Lieutenant W. Lane Barksdale in the Philippine Islands, 1945.

Genus II. **Streptosporangium** *Couch, 1955.*

(Jour. Elisha Mitchell Scientific Soc., *71*, 1955, 148.)

Strep.to.spo.ran'gi.um. Gr. adj. *streptus* pliant, twisted; Gr. noun *spora* seed; M.L. noun *spora* spore; Gr. noun *angium* a vessel; M.L. neut.n. *Streptosporangium* pliant sporangium.

On sterilized leaves of *Paspalum* grass in water, an inconspicuous mycelium which overgrows the leaves and an aerial mycelium which grows in scattered or concentrically arranged tufts are formed. Aerial mycelium white to pinkish on leaves; the hyphae are much branched, sparingly septate and about 0.5 to 1.2 microns in diameter. Sporangia are formed abundantly on the aerial mycelium on leaves; spores are abundant in the sporangia and are without flagella and non-motile. Growth poor to good on a variety of semi-solid media; aerial mycelium absent to abundant; sporangia and conidia are formed on some nutrient agars.

This genus is represented by four isolates representing three distinct species. Two of the species were isolated from soil by the soil dilution method used by Jensen (Proc. Linn. Soc. New So. Wales, *55*, 1930–31, 238), and the third one was isolated from dog dung collected in New York City by Dr. L. S. Olive.

For a comparison of this genus with *Actinoplanes*, see under the latter.

The type species is *Streptosporangium roseum* Couch.

1. **Streptosporangium roseum** Couch, 1955. (Jour. Elisha Mitchell Scientific Soc., *71*, 1955, 148.)

ro'se.um. L. adj. *roseus* rose-colored.

On sterile leaves, either in soil water or on damp sterile soil, a vegetative mycelium is formed which spreads over the surface of the leaf, not penetrating or decolorizing it, and also over the soil; an aerial reproductive mycelium which is white at first but which soon changes to pale pink is also formed. The aerial mycelium appears as single hyphae or as minute tufts which grow to form mounds, up to 2 mm in diameter, arranged more or less in concentric circles; the mounds usually become minutely pockmarked. Sporangia first appear on scattered single hyphae, apical on the main thread.

or on short lateral branches, a few to many sporangia on one hypha; they are formed in the hyphal tufts and mounds until the latter may be almost solid masses of sporangia. The sporangia are white in small groups, pink in large masses and spherical, measuring 7 to 19 microns in diameter on leaves, most measuring 8 to 9 microns. Shortly after their formation, spores are visible as a single coil in each sporangium; when completely formed, they are irregularly arranged. Immersion of the mature sporangium in water brings about the swelling of an intersporal substance; this swelling causes the wall and the spores to push out on one side forming a cone-shaped projection about half as long as the diameter of the sporangium. The spores are forcibly ejected through an opening in the cone; they are spherical, 1.8 to 2.0 microns in diameter, possess a shiny globule and are non-motile. The sporangial wall persists for several hours after spore discharge. In addition to sporangia, conidia are formed in coils somewhat as in *Streptomyces*, though the coils are much less conspicuous.

Czapek agar: Growth fair, about 0.7 to 1.2 cm in diameter after 6 weeks; usually flat, level with agar surface; concentric zonation distinct or absent; central region usually compact with a broad fringed border and a tasseled edge. Surface glossy or powdery. Color usually white, sometimes pinkish buff or cream-buff. Sporangia, absent to fairly abundant, are always formed some distance above the surface of the agar. In some cultures coils are formed which break up into conidia as in *Streptomyces*. Palisades are absent.

Peptone Czapek agar: Growth good, about 1.5 to 2.0 cm in diameter after 6 weeks; flat or with a few low radial or irregular ridges and grooves; margin fringed or entire; aerial hyphae often formed in white concentric rings, sometimes as a white border and sometimes giving a powdery appearance to the normally glossy surface. Olive-buff to deep olive-buff. Sporangia very rare.

Potato glucose agar: Growth usually good, 1.0 to 1.8 cm in diameter after 2 months; center elevated with irregular bumps and ridges; margin flat and even with surface of agar. Color at first creamy, becoming tawny and then Carob brown or Kaiser brown, after which white floccose spots of hyphae appear, usually spreading to cover the entire culture. Sporangia are usually formed in vast numbers, the white areas becoming rosy pink as the sporangia mature; the pinkish areas are frequently minutely pocked. Surface moist at first, appearing dry and floccose as aerial hyphae and sporangia are formed. Agar colored reddish brown with a vinaceous tinge.

Agar: Growth fair, 0.7 to 1.3 cm in diameter after 2 months; central region elevated into irregular ridges which merge, towards the outside, into radial ridges and grooves sloping abruptly to the narrow, flat border; margin lobed. Usually cream-buff, rarely buffy brown. Surface usually glossy, sometimes powdery with aerial hyphae which may be united to form many upright fascicles. Sporangia absent.

Krainsky's glucose asparagine agar: Growth poor, 0.3 to 0.7 cm in diameter; slightly elevated and minutely ridged, sloping to the fimbriate margin. Surface of central region minutely powdery with aerial hyphae. White. Sporangia absent.

Emerson's agar: Growth good, about 2 cm in diameter after 6 weeks, composed of a whitish central area, 4 to 6 mm wide, made up of elevated, irregular bumps and ridges which abruptly change into radial ridges and grooves sloping down to a flat, white border, 1 to 2 mm wide and composed of minute, concentric circles of white hyphae. Ridges and grooves vinaceous brown, sometimes covered with a whitish down. Margin smooth or scalloped, ending abruptly. Surface dry. Sporangia formed abundantly, appearing first in the center as the white changes to pink. Agar colored pale vinaceous brown.

Habitat: Found in vegetable garden soil, Chapel Hill, North Carolina.

ORDER VI. CARYOPHANALES PESHKOFF, 1940.*

(Jour. Gen. Microbiol. (Russian), *1*, 1940, 611 and 616.)

Ca.ry.o.pha.na′les. M.L. neut.n. *Caryophanon* type genus of the order; *-ales* ending to denote an order; M.L. fem.pl.n. *Caryophanales* the *Caryophanon* order.

Bacteria which occur as trichomes (many-celled filaments) or as shorter structures which function as hormogonia. The individual cells are characterized by the presence of a central body or ring-like nucleus which frequently assumes the form of a disc; these bodies are clearly visible in the living cells. The nuclear elements give a clear-cut Feulgen reaction. The trichomes are not enclosed in sheaths. Colorless. Each trichome consists of cylindrical or discoidal cells enclosed in a continuous wall. Gonidia are sometimed formed. Found in water, the intestines of arthropods and vertebrates and in decomposing organic materials.

Key to the families of order Caryophanales.

I. Do not form spores so far as observed. Trichomes frequently motile.
Family I. Caryophanaceae, p. 830.

II. Form spores.
  A. Actively motile trichomes; found in the intestines of vertebrates.
Family II. Oscillospiraceae, p. 834.

  B. Non-motile trichomes; spores form in the distal ends of the trichomes; found in the intestines of millipeds, cockroaches and toads.
Family III. Arthromitaceae, p. 835.

FAMILY I. CARYOPHANACEAE PESHKOFF, 1940.

(Jour. Gen. Biol. (Russian), *1*, 1940, 611 and 616.)

Ca.ry.o.pha.na′ce.ae. M.L. neut.n. *Caryophanon* type genus of the family; *-aceae* ending to denote a family; M.L. fem.pl.n. *Caryophanaceae* the *Caryophanon* family.

Large trichomes and bacillary structures which do not form spores. Motile with peritrichous flagella or non-motile. The organisms are found on the mucous membranes of the oral cavity of man and various other animals, in the alimentary tract of ruminants and in decomposing organic materials.

Key to the genera of family Caryophanaceae.

I. Trichomatous bacteria that are actively motile by means of peritrichous flagella.
  A. Unstained trichomes show alternating light and dark bands, the dark bands being internal crosswalls.
Genus I. Caryophanon, p. 831.

  B. Trichomes show coenocytic structure. Divide by constriction.
Genus II. Lineola, p. 832.

---

* Revised by Prof. Robert S. Breed, Cornell University, Geneva, New York, May, 1955; revision based on a manuscript supplied by Prof. Michael A. Peshkoff, Institute of Cytology, Acad. of Sci., Moscow, U.S.S.R., April, 1947.

II. Non-motile trichomes. Found in the buccal cavities of vertebrates.
Genus III. *Simonsiella*, p. 833.

Genus I. **Caryophanon** *Peshkoff, 1940.*

(Jour. Gen. Biol. (Russian), *1*, 1940, 611 and 616.)

Ca.ry.o'pha.non. Gr. noun *caryum* nut, kernel, nucleus; Gr. adj. *phanus* bright, conspicuous; M.L. neut.n. *Caryophanon* that which has a conspicuous nucleus.

During active growth, the large filamentous and bacillary structures are essentially trichomes containing packed, discoid, protoplasmic units separated by internal crosswalls. The unstained trichome has the appearance of alternating light and dark bands. Trichomes may form long, unsheathed filaments. Spherical, single-celled structures are commonly seen. Kelley (Thesis, Ohio State Univ., 1952) states that the internal crosswalls are complete and that the chromatinic material is either disc-shaped or spherical depending upon the shape of the cell. Found in fresh cow dung.

The type species is *Caryophanon latum* Peshkoff.

1. **Caryophanon latum** Peshkoff, 1940. (Compt. rend. (Doklady) Acad. Sci., U.R.S.S., Nouvelle Sér. *25*, 1939, 244; Jour. Gen. Biol. (Russian), *1*, 1940, 527; Microbiology (Russian), *15*, 1946, 189.)

la'tum. L. adj. *latus* broad.

Additional descriptive material taken from Pringsheim and Robinow (Jour. Gen. Microbiol. (London), *1*, 1947, 267), Weeks and Kelley (Bact. Proc., Soc. Amer. Bact., 1951, 39) and Kelley (Thesis, Ohio State University, 1952).

Trichomes measure 3 or more microns by 6 to 20 microns. The bacillary unit or trichome shows alternating light and dark bands completely traversing the structure. The ends of the trichomes are rounded. The light bands seen in the unstained, fresh, wet mounts are the basic, discoid protoplasmic units; the dark bands are internal crosswalls. Each protoplasmic unit may extend from 0.6 to 1.8 microns along the longitudinal axis of the trichome, the crosswalls occupying from 0.15 to 0.3 micron of the same dimension. The number of discoid protoplasmic units per trichome varies from 4 to 22 depending on the length and age of the trichome and upon the cultural conditions. Trichomes divide transversely. Older populations (24 hours to 4 days), or cultures growing under unfavorable conditions, contain, or show exclusively, spherical cells 3 microns in diameter, each containing a single protoplasmic unit. Nuclear structures of discoid cells are disc-shaped, of spherical cells, rounded (Kelley). Trichomes may form unsheathed filaments up to 200 microns

in length. The diameters of trichomes and spherical cells may lessen as much as 50 per cent on cultivation for a year or more in the laboratory.

Motility: Trichomes show active motility even when they grow out into long filaments. The spherical units are less active. Peritrichous flagella.

Agar colonies: Colonies are 1 to 2 mm in diameter with entire or slightly undulating margins. Original isolations usually develop smooth colonies. Rough colonies predominate during laboratory cultivation. Long filaments tend to occur in the rough colonies; short, individual trichomes occur in the smooth colonies. The colonies appear in 6 to 8 hours on peptone-yeast extract-sodium acetate agar (Pringsheim and Robinow). Irregular giant forms may develop from older cultures (Peshkoff).

Rapid growth on peptone-yeast extract-sodium acetate agar, pH 7.6 to 7.8. Also on cow dung extract agar, pH 7.8 to 8.0. Growth at pH 7.0 produces spherical units. No growth on nutrient agar (Pringsheim and Robinow); poor growth (Kelley).

Poor growth in liquid media; added colloids result in the growth of long filaments. The organism survives for long periods in liquid media.

Aerobic.

Not known to be pathogenic.

Source: Isolated from 20 to 30 per cent of samples of fresh cow dung. Isolated at least 20 times in Moscow (U.R.S.S.) and its vicinity by Peshkoff. Isolated and cultivated in England by Pringsheim and Robinow and in Idaho (U. S. A.) by Weeks and Kelley.

Habitat: Apparently widely distributed in fresh cow dung and presumably found in the dung of other herbivorous mammals.

2. Caryophanon tenue Peshkoff, 1940. (Compt. rend. (Doklady) Acad. Sci., U.R.S.S., Nouvelle Sér. *25*, 1939, 244; Jour. Gen. Biol. (Russian), *1*, 1940, 597.)
ten'u.e. L. adj. *tenuis* slender.

Similar to the species described above, but more slender. Diameter, 1.5 microns. This species may be a variety of *Caryophanon latum* as the trichomes of the latter are frequently no broader than 1.5 microns after cultivation on artificial media.

Growth on cow manure extract agar and yeast extract agar at pH 7.8 to 8.0.

Source: Isolated from fresh cow manure.

Habitat: Apparently widely distributed in fresh cow dung and presumably found in the dung of other herbivorous mammals.

Genus II. **Lineola** *Pringsheim, 1950.**

(Jour. Gen. Microbiology, 4, 1950, 198.)

Long (often 20 to 50 microns), peritrichous rods, coenocytic in nature, which subdivide by constriction; the constrictions later develop into cross-walls and thus form new cells. Trichomes motile and frequently branched, attaining a length of up to several hundred microns. Very long, non-motile trichomes may occur. Non-sporeforming. Gram-negative. The rods do not break up into smaller units at the conclusion of the life cycle, as in other filamentous bacteria, but divide into two by constriction and fission. The absence of fatty acids in the culture media precludes multiplication. Found in cow dung and in nature where plant material is decaying.

The type species is *Lineola longa* Pringsheim.

1. Lineola longa Pringsheim, 1950. (*Lineola longa* Pringsheim and Robinow (*nomen provisorium*), Jour. Gen. Microbiology, *1*, 1947, 267; Pringsheim, *ibid.*, *4*, 1950, 198.)
lon'ga. L. adj. *longus* long.

Rods, 1.4 to 1.6 by 10 to 50 (mostly 25 to 40) microns, containing Feulgen-positive bodies which impart a coenocytic appearance to the cells. Peritrichous. Trichomes are motile, quite rigid, slightly and irregularly curved and may be more than 200 microns long; non-motile trichomes of much greater length may be found. All but the shortest trichomes are subdivided by constrictions which later develop into cross-walls, consequently forming new cells. Multiplication does not occur in the absence of fatty acids. Branching is infrequent and consists of two, three or even more single rods or short chains attached near the site of constriction. Although the branches are seemingly unconnected to the main axis,

no analogy can be drawn to false branching. Non-sporeforming. Gram-negative.

Acetate peptone yeast extract agar colonies: Large, flat, patch-like, irregularly shaped, semi-confluent; edges fringed. Small, medusa-head colonies form from single organisms; later these colonies become bluish white against a dark background and produce a watered silk effect. Young growths appear as parallel and straight threads which later break up to form bundles. Through intercalary elongation, isolated trichomes form coiled aggregations connected by almost straight sections.

Agar stab: Growth on or near the surface.

Broth: Liquid media support growth only when supplemented with extracts of dung, soil or other growth-promoting substances. Non-motile growth quite evident near the surface. If growth is not too meager, a ring is formed just below the meniscus; this ring

---

* Prof. Peshkoff has concluded (March, 1957) that the genus *Lineola* shows so many differences from the other genera of the order *Caryophanales* that it should be placed elsewhere, perhaps in a new order.

is easily detached and falls to the bottom at the slightest disturbance. When growth is rapid and motility strong, a homogeneous turbidity is produced.

Growth not appreciably quicker at 25° to 27° C. than at 18° to 20° C.; growth retarded at 32° C.

Source: Isolated from an infusion of cow dung from Cambridge, England.

Habitat: Found in cow dung and decaying plant material.

2. **Lineola articulata** Pringsheim, 1950. (*Lineola articulata* (*nomen nudum*) Pringsheim, Bact. Rev., *13*, 1949, 72; Pringsheim, Jour. Gen. Microbiology, *4*, 1950, 198.)

ar.ti.cu.la′ta. L. part.adj. *articulatus* jointed.

Rods 1.4 to 1.6 by 10 to 50 (mostly 30 to 40) microns, coenocytic in appearance. Peritrichous. Trichomes are motile, flexuous at the joints connecting the individual rods and attain a length of up to 160 microns. Branching is rather frequent, the branches being at times so long as to be indistinguishable from the main trichome. The branches appear to be unattached to the main axis and no more than two are found at one joint. Cell division occurs by constriction with a subsequent formation of cross-walls. In the absence of fatty acids multiplication does not occur. Non-sporeforming. Gram-negative.

Acetate peptone yeast extract agar colonies: Large and curly with wavy or lobed edges. Small colonies are iridescent, resembling mother-of-pearl. Young growths appear as irregularly undulating, snake-like threads which develop into small, narrow, elongated colonies; later these become V-, X- or Y-shaped and develop into increasingly regular patches.

Agar stab: Growth on or near the surface.

Broth: Usually filled with evenly distributed, rarely non-motile trichomes; settling occurs only in ageing cultures.

Growth not appreciably quicker at 25° to 27° C. than at 18° to 20° C.; growth not retarded at 32° C.

Source: Isolated from water with plant debris from the New Forest.

Habitat: Found in water and in nature where plant material is decaying.

Genus III. **Simonsiella** *Schmid, 1922.*

(Schmid, in Simons, Cent. f. Bakt., I Abt., Orig., *88*, 1922, 504.)

Si.mon.si.el′la. Named for Hellmuth Simons, who studied the species in this genus; M.L. dim. ending *-ella*; M.L. fem.n. *Simonsiella* a generic name.

Cells occur in short to long chains which are usually divided into segments. Each segment normally contains four cells or four cell pairs, occasionally double this number. The end cells are small and rounded. Non-motile. Harmless saprophytes in the buccal cavities of healthy persons and domestic animals.

The type species is *Simonsiella muelleri* Schmid.

1. **Simonsiella muelleri** Schmid, 1922. (Scheibenbakterien, Müller, München. med. Wochnschr., *58*, 1911, 227; *Simonsiella Mülleri* (sic) Schmid, in Simons, Cent. f. Bakt., I Abt., Orig., *88*, 1922, 504.)

muel′le.ri. M.L. gen.noun *muelleri* of Müller; named for Reiner Müller, a German bacteriologist.

Cells, 0.4 to 0.7 by 2.0 to 3.0 microns, arranged side by side in chains. Chains, 2.0 to 3.2 by 3.0 to 16.0 microns, with rounded ends, divided into segments which contain four cells or four cell pairs, sometimes double this number. Müller (*op. cit.*, 1911, 227) reported dark granules in the middle of each segment, but Simons (*op. cit.*, 1922, 507) maintains that these "granules" are merely artifacts. Non-motile. Stains very weakly with safranin.

Saprophytic.

Habitat: Found in normal buccal cavities.

2. **Simonsiella crassa** Schmid, 1922. (Schmid, in Simons, Cent. f. Bakt., I Abt., Orig., *88*, 1922, 509.)

cras′sa. L. adj. *crassus* thick.

Similar in morphology to *Simonsiella muelleri* but broader.

Habitat: Found on the mucous membranes of the oral cavities of domestic animals.

3. Simonsiella filiformis Schmid, 1922. (Schmid, in Simons, Cent. f. Bakt., I Abt., Orig., *88*, 1922, 509.)

fi.li.for'mis. L. noun *filum* thread; L. noun *forma* shape; M.L. adj. *filiformis* filiform.

Cells occur in long, pointed chains which vary in width at several places along their lengths.

Habitat: Found in mucus from the oral cavities of domestic animals.

FAMILY II. OSCILLOSPIRACEAE PESHKOFF, 1940.

(Jour. Gen. Biol. (Russian), *1*, 1940, 611 and 616.)

Os.cil.lo.spi.ra'ce.ae. M.L. neut.n. *Oscillospira* type genus of the family; *-aceae* ending to denote a family; M.L. fem.pl.n. *Oscillospiraceae* the *Oscillospira* family.

Cells occur in trichomes of varying lengths. The trichomes are partitioned to form narrow cells, each containing a central chromatin body (disc-like nucleus); these bodies give a clear Feulgen reaction and are embedded in hyaline protoplasm. Spores are formed by a fusion of the protoplasms of two to three neighboring cells. Actively motile by means of peritrichous flagella; non-motile strains may occur. Parasitic in the intestinal tracts of vertebrates.

There is a single genus, *Oscillospira*.

Genus I. **Oscillospira** *Chatton and Pérard, 1913.*

(Chatton and Pérard, Compt. rend. Soc. Biol., Paris, *65*, 1913, 1159; also see Pringsheim, Bact. Rev., *13*, 1949, 75 and 76.)

Os.cil.lo.spi'ra. L. neut.n. *oscillum* a swing; Gr. noun *spira* a spiral; M.L. fem.n. *Oscillospira* the oscillating spiral.

These bacteria occur as trichomes of varying lengths which contain a limited number of discoid cells which are usually biconcave and end cells which are approximately hemispherical. Cell division is by a diaphragm-like ingrowth of the trichome wall. Spores, usually one, rarely two, are formed which resemble endospores; they are too large to be accommodated by a single cell, and therefore several cells in a trichome break down to form a spore chamber. Motile by means of peritrichous flagella, although non-motile strains may occur. Anaerobic or, more probably, microaerophilic. Found in the alimentary tracts of animals, especially in the rumina of ruminants and the caeca of guinea pigs.

The type species is *Oscillospira guilliermondii* Chatton and Pérard.

1. Oscillospira guilliermondii Chatton and Pérard, 1913. (Compt. rend. Soc. Biol., Paris, *65*, 1913, 1159.)

guil.lier.mon'di.i. M.L. gen.noun *guilliermondii* of Guilliermond; named for Prof. A. Guilliermond, a French biologist.

Sturdy trichomes with a diameter of 5 microns and a length which never exceeds 100 microns. The extremities are rounded with approximately hemispherical end-cells. The biconcave, discoid cells within the trichomes are 1 to 2 microns long and

homogeneous or finely granular in appearance. Spores, which average 2.5 by 4.0 microns, are ellipsoidal and are oriented lengthwise on the long axis of the trichome or are very slightly inclined on this axis. Because the spore chamber is formed by the breakdown of several cells, it is considerably longer and slightly wider than the remaining cells. Sporulating trichomes, which contain one, rarely two spores, are infrequently found; the spores are located at various loci on the long axes of the trichomes. Motile strains possess peritrichous flagella.

Anaerobic, although probably microaerophilic (see Simons, Zent. f. Bakt., I Abt., Orig., *88*, 1922, 508 and 509; and Hocquette, Compt. rend. Soc. Biol., Paris, *113*, 1933, 779).

Habitat: Found in the alimentary tracts of various animals.

FAMILY III. ARTHROMITACEAE PESHKOFF, 1940.

(Jour. Gen. Biol. (Russian), *1*, 1940, 611 and 616.)

Ar.thro.mi.ta'ce.ae. M.L. mas.n. *Arthromitus* type genus of the family; *-aceae* ending to denote a family; M.L. fem.pl.n. *Arthromitaceae* the *Arthromitus* family.

Trichomes probably divided into cells although septa (protoplasmic?) disappear during sporulation. Disc-like nuclei alternate with thin protoplasmic segments (septa). Spores form in the distal ends of trichomes. Non-motile. The trichomes are attached by a spherical body in groups to the intestinal walls of insects, crustaceans and tadpoles.

Genus I. Arthromitus *Leidy, 1849.*

(Proc. Acad. Nat. Sci., Philadelphia, *4*, 1849, 227.)

Ar.thro.mi'tus. Gr. noun *arthrus* a joint; Gr. noun *mitus* a thread; M.L. mas.n. *Arthromitus* jointed thread.

Characters as for the family. Although the descriptions are worded somewhat differently, there does not seem to be any essential difference between this and the following genus.

The type species is *Arthromitus cristatus* Leidy.

1. **Arthromitus cristatus** Leidy, 1849. (Proc. Acad. Nat. Sci., Phila., *4*, 1849, 227; also see Jour. Acad. Nat. Sci., Phila., *8*, 1881, 443.)

cris.ta'tus. L. adj. *cristatus* crested.

Cells short, cylindrical and uniform with no trace of interior structure, 0.6 by 2.75 microns. Trichomes delicate, straight or inflected, growing in tufts usually of moderate density, from minute, attached, yellowish, rounded or ovoid bodies. Breadth of trichome, 0.6 micron; length, 67 to 543 microns.

Source: Found in the intestines of the milliped (*Julus marginatus*) and the termite (*Reticulitermes flavipes*). Also found on the mucous membrane of the small intestine of *Julus marginatus*, occasionally on the same surface at the commencement of the large intestine, on any part of the exterior surface of protozoa infesting these cavities and also on any part of the surface of *Enterobryus elegans*.

2. **Arthromitus intestinalis** (Valentin, 1836) Peshkoff, 1940. (*Hygrocrocis intes-* *tinalis* Valentin, Repert. f. Anat. u. Phys., *1*, 1836, 110; Peshkoff, Jour. Gen. Biol. (Russian), *1*, 1940, 597.)

in.tes.ti.na'lis. L. pl.noun *intestinae* intestines; M.L. adj. *intestinalis* pertaining to the intestines.

Cells are somewhat variable in size; however, generally speaking, they are approximately as wide as they are long. Trichomes are long, non-motile and grow indefinitely. In the spore regions of these trichomes there is a spore per cell; these sporogenous cells exhibit no hypertrophy. According to Leidy (Proc. Acad. Nat. Sci., Phila., *4*, 1849, 227) these trichomes attach themselves to the intestinal wall by means of a sort of globular, common holdfast.

Source: Found in the intestine of the cockroach (*Blatta orientalis*).

Habitat: Found in the intestines of certain insects.

3. **Arthromitus nitidus** Leidy, 1852. (Smithsonian Contributions to Knowledge, *5*, 1852, 35.)

ni'ti.dus. L. adj. *nitidus* shining, glittering.

Cells very distinct, the length equal to the breadth of the trichome. Trichomes very long, transparent, usually grow in twos or fours, pointed at the origin, rounded at the termination, 5 by 2083 microns. Sporelike bodies, formed within the cells, are usually solitary, oblique, oval and amorphous, 2.0 by 3.5 microns.

Source: Found in the intestine of the milliped (*Julus marginatus*).

Habitat: Found in considerable quantity with a profusion of *Enterobryus elegans* from the mucous membrane of the posterior portion of the rectum of *Julus marginatus*.

4. **Arthromitus batrachorum** Collin, 1913. (Arch. Zool. Expér. et Gén., *51*, 1913, 63.)

ba.tra.cho'rum. Gr. noun *batrachus* frog; L. gen.pl.noun *batrachorum* of frogs.

Cells colorless, granular, 2.0 to 3.0 by 3.5 microns. Trichomes are non-branching and grow indefinitely. At various places in the trichomes some cells are thicker than others, and occasionally debris is seen alongside the trichomes, resulting from the rupture thereof. Each cell has a spore, round to ellipsoidal, obliquely situated within the cell. At first the spores are quite small and stain intensely by cold staining techniques. Later the spores become more voluminous and, when completely mature, are no longer stained without heat. The sporulation of a given cell occurs independently of that of any other cell in the same trichome.

Source: Found in the rectum of a frog tadpole (*Alytes sp.*) and from the alimentary tracts of toad tadpoles (*Bufo calamita*).

Habitat: Found in the intestinal tract of amphibians so far as is known.

Genus II. **Coleomitus** Duboscq and Grassé, 1930.

(Arch. Zool. Expér. et Gén., *70*, 1930, Notes et Revue, 28.)

Co.le.o.mi'tus. Gr. noun *coleus* sheath; Gr. noun *mitus* thread; M.L. mas.n. *Coleomitus* sheathed thread.

Long trichomes, divided by partitions. Bacillary elements in basal region. Ovoid or ellipsoidal spores in other parts of the trichome originate by transformation from these bacillary elements through sporoblasts.

The type species is *Coleomitus pruvotii* Duboscq and Grassé.

1. **Coleomitus pruvotii** (Duboscq and Grassé, 1929) Duboscq and Grassé, 1930. (*Coleonema pruvoti* (sic) Duboscq and Grassé, Arch. Zool. Expér. et Gén., *68*, 1929, Notes et Revue, 14; *Coleomitus pruvoti* (sic) Duboscq and Grassé, *ibid.*, *70*, 1930, N. et R., 28.)

pru.vo'ti.i. M.L. gen.noun *pruvotii* of Pruvot; named for Pruvot.

Trichomes, with hyaline sheath, 1.3 microns wide, length variable, up to 320 microns. Bacillary elements are 3 to 4 microns long; elements up to 6 microns long with a chromatic granule or disc in the middle of the body also occur. Spores ellipsoidal, 0.8 to 0.9 by 1.7 to 2.0 microns, all containing an eccentrically placed granule of volutin.

Source: Found in the intestine of a termite (*Kalotermes sp.*) from the Loyalty Islands.

ORDER VII. BEGGIATOALES BUCHANAN, Ordo Nov.*

Beg.gi.a.to.a′les. M.L. fem.n. *Beggiatoa* type genus of the order; *-ales* ending to denote an order; M.L. fem.pl.n. *Beggiatoales* the *Beggiatoa* order.

Cells occur mostly in trichomes in three of the families and singly in the fourth family. When in contact with a substrate, the motile organisms glide over the surface or show a slow, rolling, jerky type of motion. No flagella or other organs of locomotion are known. Non-motile trichomes may also occur. The trichomes may show bending and flexing. With respect to gliding and oscillating, the trichomes function as distinct units except in the genus *Bactoscilla*, where the trichomes show bending at the joints between the cells. Multiplication is by transverse fission throughout the entire length of the trichomes or of the singly occurring cells; gonidia occur in one family, *Leucotrichaceae*. Do not possess chlorophyll or phycocyanin. Under favorable environmental conditions, sulfur globules, sometimes in accompaniment with calcium carbonate crystals, may be found in or on the cells. Found in fresh-water (with or without hydrogen sulfide) and marine habitats, in soil and in decomposing organic matter, especially algae.

Key to the families of order **Beggiatoales.**

I. Cells occur in trichomes.
    A. Trichomes motile by means of a gliding type of motility when in contact with a substrate.
        1. Cells, when growing in the presence of hydrogen sulfide, contain granules of sulfur.
                Family I. *Beggiatoaceae*, p. 837.
        2. Cells do not contain granules of sulfur, even when growing in the presence of hydrogen sulfide.
                Family II. *Vitreoscillaceae*, p. 844.
    B. Trichomes non-motile, although gonidia (single-celled, gliding, reproductive cells) occur.
                Family III. *Leucotrichaceae*, p. 850.
II. Cells occur singly and show a rolling, jerky type of motility when in contact with a substrate.
                Family IV. *Achromatiaceae*, p. 851.

FAMILY I. BEGGIATOACEAE MIGULA, 1894.†

(Migula, Arb. Bakt. Inst. Karlsruhe, *1*, 1894, 238; in part, *Leuco-Thiobacteria* Bavendamm, Die farblosen und roten Schwefelbakterien, Pflanzenforschung, Heft 2, 1924, 102.)

Beg.gi.a.to.a′ce.ae. M.L. fem.n. *Beggiatoa* type genus of the family; *-aceae* ending to denote a family; M.L. fem.pl.n. *Beggiatoaceae* the *Beggiatoa* family.

---

* Prepared by Prof. R. E. Buchanan, Iowa State College, Ames, Iowa, October, 1955.
† Prepared by Prof. R. E. Buchanan, Iowa State College, Ames, Iowa, October, 1955.

The individual cells, generally not visible without staining, occur in trichomes; within the trichomes the cells are arranged in chains. The trichomes show a gliding motion when in contact with a substrate; they also show flexing movements. When grown in the presence of hydrogen sulfide, the trichomes contain sulfur globules. The structure of these organisms is very similar to that of the *Oscillatoriaceae*, but the cells are devoid of chlorophyll and phycocyanin. Special reproductive structures are unknown.

In proposing the family name *Beggiatoaceae* for the two genera of this subgroup known in 1894, Migula (*op. cit.*, 1894, 238) remarked that "it would be best to combine them with the *Oscillatoriaceae* and classify them among the *Schizophyceae*". The same authority (in Engler and Prantl, Die natürl. Pflanzenfam., *1*, 1a, 1895, 41) has stated: "Also in view of their internal structure the species of *Beggiatoa* are so similar to those in the genus *Oscillaria* that they can hardly be separated generically". Since then, the close relationship between the colorless sulfur bacteria occurring in trichomes and the blue-green algae of the family *Oscillatoriaceae* has become even clearer. A particularly important line of evidence is supplied by the discovery of sulfur bacteria paralleling each of the major genera of the *Oscillatoriaceae*. Taxonomically these organisms could readily be classified as colorless members of the class *Schizophyceae*, for many species of *Oscillatoria* live in the same environments as do those of *Beggiatoa*, and some grow in the presence of hydrogen sulfide and contain sulfur granules. However, the *Beggiatoaceae* are, in this MANUAL, retained with the bacteria (*Schizomycetes*) for practical reasons: they have been so included in the past, they are not included in modern treatises on the blue-green algae, they show close kinship to other organisms commonly included in the bacteria, and they grow under natural conditions in close association with such organisms.

Studies on the physiologies of the organisms of this family and of the related *Oscillatoriaceae* are needed.

Key to the genera of family **Beggiatoaceae.**

I. Trichomes are free and motile and are not attached to a substrate.
   A. Trichomes occur singly and are not embedded in a common slime-sheath.
      1. Trichomes straight or somewhat bent, not permanently coiled.
               Genus I. *Beggiatoa*, p. 838.
      2. Trichomes coiled or spirally wound.
               Genus II. *Thiospirillopsis*, p. 840.
   B. Trichomes occur in bundles and are surrounded by a slime-sheath.
               Genus III. *Thioploca*, p. 841.
II. Trichomes attached to substrate at one end; apical segments, when freed, are motile until attached.
               Genus IV. *Thiothrix*, p. 842.

Genus I. **Beggiatoa** *Trevisan, 1842.*

(Prospetto della Flora Euganea, 1842, 56.)

Beg.gi.a.to′a. M.L. fem.n. *Beggiatoa* a genus of bacteria; named for F. S. Beggiatoa, a physician of Vicenza.

Cells occur in unattached, motile, segmented trichomes; the trichomes occur singly or in white to creamy, felted masses in which the trichomes retain their individuality. Existence of a sheath not definitely established. Movements of the trichomes are dependent upon contact with a solid substratum over which they glide in the same manner as do species of *Oscillatoria*. The gliding movements are often accompanied by a rotation of the trichomes around the long axis. Reproduction is by transverse fission of the cells; the trichomes may also break up into smaller units, each continuing a separate existence. The latter mode of multiplication corresponds to that of the so-called motile gonidia or segments in *Thio-*

thrix. Found in both fresh-water and marine environments containing hydrogen sulfide or soluble sulfides.

In *Beggiatoa* the species so far recognized have been differentiated on the basis of the diameters of the trichomes. The range of sizes for the several species appears, in most cases, to be quite arbitrary, especially in view of the existence of practically all intermediate diameters. In previous editions of the MANUAL, certain fresh-water forms were sometimes regarded as distinct from the salt-water forms of the same size. However, as their habitats have been found to be not mutually exclusive (Bavendamm, Die farblosen und roten Schwefelbakterien, Pflanzenforschung, Heft 2, 1924, 104), these organisms are now regarded as a single species irrespective of their habitat. Pure-culture studies may establish more satisfactory methods of differentiation of the species of this genus.

The type species is *Beggiatoa alba* (Vaucher) Trevisan.

Key to the species of genus **Beggiatoa.**

I. Diameter of trichomes is less than 15 microns.
  A. Diameter of trichomes is greater than 2.5 microns.
    1. Diameter of trichomes is less than 5 microns.
        1. *Beggiatoa alba.*
    2. Diameter of trichomes is greater than 5 microns.
        2. *Beggiatoa arachnoidea.*
  B. Diameter of trichomes is less than 2.5 microns.
    1. Diameter of trichomes is greater than 1 micron.
        3. *Beggiatoa leptomitiformis.*
    2. Diameter of trichomes is less than 1 micron.
        4. *Beggiatoa minima.*
II. Diameter of trichomes is greater than 15 microns.
  A. Diameter of trichomes is greater than 25 microns.
        5. *Beggiatoa gigantea.*
  B. Diameter of trichomes is less than 25 microns.
        6. *Beggiatoa mirabilis.*

1. **Beggiatoa alba** (Vaucher, 1803) Trevisan, 1845. (*Oscillatoria alba* Vaucher, Histoire des Conferves d'eau douce, 1803, 198; *Beggiatoa punctata* Trevisan, Prospetto della Flora Euganea, 1842, 56; Trevisan, Nomenclator Algarum, 1845, 58.)

al'ba. L. adj. *albus* white.

Trichomes, 2.5 to 5.0 (most commonly 3.0) microns in diameter, of uniform width. The segments, 3.0 to 9.0 microns long, are practically square shortly after division; segmentation is difficult to detect in trichomes containing many sulfur globules. Terminal cells are rounded.

Habitat: Found in both fresh-water and marine environments containing hydrogen sulfide. Ubiquitous. Probably the most common of the sulfur bacteria which occur in trichomes.

2. **Beggiatoa arachnoidea** (Agardh, 1827) Rabenhorst, 1865. (*Oscillatoria arachnoidea* Agardh, Regensburger Flora, 1827, 634; Rabenhorst, Flora europaea algarum, 1865, 94.)

a.rach.no.i'de.a. Gr. adj. *arachnoides* cobweb-like; M.L. adj. *arachnoideus* cobweb-like.

Trichomes, 5 to 14 microns in diameter, of uniform width. Segments 5 to 7 microns in length; segmentation generally observable only after special staining or removal of sulfur globules. Terminal cells are rounded.

Habitat: Found in both fresh-water and marine environments containing hydrogen sulfide.

3. **Beggiatoa leptomitiformis** Trevisan, 1842. (Prospetto della Flora Euganea, 1842, 56.)

lep.to.mi.ti.for'mis. M.L. noun *Leptomitus* a genus of bacteria; L. noun *forma* shape; M.L. adj. *leptomitiformis Leptomitus*-like.

Trichomes, 1.0 to 2.5 microns in diameter, of uniform width. Segments 4.0 to 8.0 microns in length; segmentation observable only after removal of sulfur globules. Terminal cells are usually rounded.

Habitat: Found in fresh-water and marine environments containing hydrogen sulfide.

4. Beggiatoa minima Winogradsky, 1888. (Beitr. z. Morph. u. Physiol. d. Bacterien, I. Schwefelbacterien, 1888, 25.)

mi′ni.ma. L. sup.adj. *minimus* least, smallest.

Trichomes, less than 1 micron in diameter, of uniform width, normally appearing unsegmented. Segments about 1 micron in length.

Habitat: Found in fresh-water and marine environments containing hydrogen sulfide.

5. Beggiatoa gigantea Klas, 1937. (Klas, Arch. f. Mikrobiol., *8*, 1937, 318; includes the large forms of *Beggiatoa mirabilis* Cohn, Hedwigia, *4*, 1865, 81.)

gi.gan′te.a. Gr. adj. *giganteus* gigantic.

Trichomes 26.4 to 55.0 (average 35 to 40) microns in diameter. Klas (*op. cit.*, 1937, 318) gives 26.4 to 42.9 microns as the dimensions, which would exclude the largest forms of *Beggiatoa mirabilis* described by Hinze (Ber. d. deut. bot. Ges., *19*, 1901, 369). Since the proposal of a separate species for such organisms appears at present unjustified, the maximum diameter has here been increased. When the trichomes are in a healthy condition, they are of uniform width; bulging of the sides occurs under unfavorable conditions. Trichomes clearly segmented. Segments 5.0 to 13.0 (average, 8.5) microns in length. Terminal cells are rounded or tapered.

Habitat: Apparently restricted to marine environments containing hydrogen sulfide. Frequently found on decaying marine algae.

6. Beggiatoa mirabilis Cohn, 1865, *emend.* Klas, 1937. (Cohn, Hedwigia, *4*, 1865, 81; Klas, Arch. f. Mikrobiol., *8*, 1937, 318.)

mi.ra′bi.lis. L. adj. *mirabilis* marvelous.

Trichomes 15.0 to 21.5 (average, 17.0) microns in diameter. The so-defined species does not overlap with *Beggiatoa gigantea* according to Klas (*loc. cit.*). When the trichomes are in a healthy condition, they are of uniform width; an unfavorable environment induces bulging of the sides. Segments 5.0 to 13.0 (average, 8.5) microns in length; segmentation usually observable without special treatment. Terminal cells are rounded or tapered, sometimes bent.

Comment: Uphof (Arch. f. Hydrobiol., *18*, 1927, 83) has recognized a species, *Beggiatoa maxima*, which, on account of its diameter (10 to 20 microns), falls partly within the range of *Beggiatoa mirabilis* and partly within *Beggiatoa arachnoidea*. Since it was found in a fresh-water environment, the habitat of *Beggiatoa mirabilis* may not be restricted to marine media.

Habitat: Apparently restricted to marine environments containing hydrogen sulfide. Common on decaying marine algae.

Genus II. **Thiospirillopsis** *Uphof, 1927.*

(Arch. f. Hydrobiol., *18*, 1927, 81.)

Thi.o.spi.ril.lop′sis. M.L. neut.n. *Thiospirillum* a genus of bacteria; Gr. noun *opsis* appearance; M.L. fem.n. *Thiospirillopsis* that which has the appearance of *Thiospirillum*.

Colorless sulfur bacteria occurring in segmented and spirally wound trichomes. Exhibit a creeping motility combined with rotation so that the trichomes move forward with a corkscrew-like motion. The tips may oscillate. Resembles *Spirulina* among the *Oscillatoriaceae*.

The type species is *Thiospirillopsis floridana* Uphof.

1. Thiospirillopsis floridana Uphof, 1927. (Arch. f. Hydrobiol., *18*, 1927, 83.)

flo.ri.da′na. M.L. adj. *floridanus* pertaining to Florida.

Trichomes 2 to 3 microns in diameter. Segments about 3 to 5 microns long; segmentation difficult to observe without special precautions. The spiral windings are regular.

Comments: A very similar organism has been observed at Pacific Grove, California, in a marine aquarium where hydrogen sulfide had been generated by sulfate reduction. The genus *Thiospirillopsis* may, therefore, be more widespread than is generally believed.

Source: Found in sulfur spring water at Wekiwa Springs and Palm Springs, Florida.

Habitat: Probably widely distributed in water containing sulfur.

Genus III. **Thioploca** *Lauterborn, 1907.*

(Ber. d. deut. botan. Ges., *25*, 1907, 238.)

Thi.o.plo′ca. Gr. noun *thium* sulfur; Gr. noun *plocē* a twining, a braid or twist; M.L. fem.n. *Thioploca* sulfur-braid or -twist.

Trichomes are of *Beggiatoa*-like appearance but occur in parallel or braided bundles enclosed by a common, wide slime-sheath. The latter is frequently incrusted on the outside with detritus. Within the sheath the individual trichomes are motile in the manner of *Beggiatoa*; the trichomes are segmented, the terminal segments often tapering.

Closely resembles the genera *Hydrocoleus* and *Microcoleus* among the *Oscillatoriaceae*.

It is doubtful whether the members of the genus *Thioploca* are true colorless sulfur bacteria; most investigators of these forms have reported a greenish blue coloration of the trichomes. Only the regular occurrence of sulfur droplets in trichomes taken from their natural habitat stamps the organisms as sulfur bacteria. In view of the close relationship of the *Beggiatoaceae* to the blue-green *Oscillatoriaceae*, this is, however, a minor issue.

Four species have been described to date. Three correspond, with respect to the individual trichomes, to *Beggiatoa arachnoidea*, *Beggiatoa alba* and *Beggiatoa leptomitiformis* respectively; the fourth appears to be a combination of the first and third of the abovementioned species of *Beggiatoa* in a common sheath. This occurrence of two distinct species of *Beggiatoa* in a common sheath makes the genus a doubtful taxonomic entity.

The type species is *Thioploca schmidlei* Lauterborn.

Key to the species of genus **Thioploca.**

I. Trichomes of a fairly uniform diameter occur in a common sheath.
  A. Diameter of trichomes is 5 to 9 microns.
           1. *Thioploca schmidlei.*
  B. Diameter of trichomes is less than 5 microns.
    1. Diameter of trichomes is greater than 2 microns.
           2. *Thioploca ingrica.*
    2. Diameter of trichomes is less than 2 microns.
           3. *Thioploca minima.*
II. Trichomes of greatly differing diameters occur in a common sheath.
           4. *Thioploca mixta.*

1. **Thioploca schmidlei** Wislouch, 1912. (Ber. d. deut. bot. Ges., *30*, 1912, 470.)

schmid′le.i. M.L. gen.noun *schmidlei* of Schmidle.

Individual trichomes, 5 to 9 microns in diameter, occur in a common, mucilaginous sheath, 50 to 160 microns in diameter. The number of trichomes embedded in one sheath is variable. The trichomes are segmented, each segment measuring 5 to 8 microns in length.

Source: Identified from various localities in Central Europe.

Habitat: So far reported only in freshwater mud containing hydrogen sulfide and calcium carbonate.

2. **Thioploca ingrica** Wislouch, 1912. (Ber. d. deut. bot. Ges., *30*, 1912, 470.)

in'gri.ca. M.L. adj. *ingricus* pertaining to Ingria; named after Ingria, an ancient district of Leningrad, Russia.

Individual trichomes, 2.0 to 4.5 microns in diameter, occur in a mucilaginous sheath up to 80.0 microns in diameter. The number of trichomes embedded in one sheath is variable. The trichomes are segmented, each segment measuring 1.5 to 8.0 microns in length.

Source: Identified from various localities in Central Europe.

Habitat: Found in fresh-water and marine mud containing hydrogen sulfide.

3. **Thioploca minima** Koppe, 1923. (Arch. f. Hydrobiol., *14*, 1923, 630.)

mi'ni.ma. L. sup.adj. *minimus* least, smallest.

Individual trichomes, 0.8 to 1.5 microns in diameter, occur in a common, mucilaginous sheath up to 30.0 microns in diameter. The number of trichomes embedded in one sheath is variable. Segmentation is generally observable only after removal of the sulfur droplets; the segments are 1 to 2 microns long.

Source: Identified from various localities in Central Europe.

Habitat: Found in fresh-water and marine mud containing hydrogen sulfide.

4. **Thioploca mixta** Koppe, 1923. (Arch. f. Hydrobiol., *14*, 1923, 630.)

mix'ta. L. part.adj. *mixtus* mixed.

Individual trichomes of two clearly different sizes, the one 6 to 8 microns and the other about 1 micron in diameter, occur in a common, mucilaginous sheath usually about 50 microns thick. The number of trichomes embedded in one sheath is variable. The wider trichomes are clearly segmented, the segments measuring 5 to 8 microns in length; in the narrower trichomes, segmentation is visible only after removal of the sulfur droplets, each segment measuring 1 to 2 microns in length.

Source: Identified only from Lake Constance.

Habitat: Found in fresh-water mud containing hydrogen sulfide.

Genus IV. **Thiothrix** *Winogradsky, 1888.*

(Beitr. z. Morph. u. Physiol. d. Bakt., I, Schwefelbacterien, Leipzig, 1888, 39.)

Thi'o.thrix. Gr. noun *thium* sulfur; Gr. noun *thrix* hair; M.L. fem.n. *Thiothrix* sulfur hair.

Cells occur in non-motile, segmented trichomes which are differentiated into base and tip and surrounded by a delicate sheath. Trichomes grow attached at the base to solid objects by means of gelatinous hold-fasts. Reproduction is by transverse fission of the segments and by rod-shaped, so-called conidia which probably are the apical segments which become free. Temporarily, the conidia show creeping motility, become attached to solid objects and develop into new trichomes.

The following key to the species of the genus *Thiothrix* is based upon the diameters of the trichomes and their habitats, the only criteria used by previous authors for the differentiation of the seven recognized species. The validity of these distinguishing characteristics is, however, doubtful because their constancy has not been sufficiently established; so far the morphology of the species in *Thiothrix* has not been studied in pure cultures.

The type species is *Thiothrix nivea* (Rabenhorst) Winogradsky.

Key to the species of genus **Thiothrix.**

I. From fresh-water environments.
    A. Diameter of trichomes is greater than 0.5 micron.
        1. Diameter of trichomes about 2.0 (1.4 to 3.0) microns.
                    1. *Thiothrix nivea.*
        2. Diameter of trichomes about 1.0 micron.
                    2. *Thiothrix tenuis.*

B. Diameter of trichomes is less than 0.5 micron.
        3. *Thiothrix tenuissima.*
II. From marine environments.
  A. Diameter of trichomes is greater than 15 microns.
        4. *Thiothrix voukii.*
  B. Diameter of trichomes is less than 15 microns.
    1. Diameter of trichomes is greater than 1.8 microns.
      a. Segments about 25 microns long.
        5. *Thiothrix longiarticulata.*
      aa. Segments about 1 micron long.
        6. *Thiothrix anulata.*
    2. Diameter of trichomes is less than 1.8 microns.
        7. *Thiothrix marina.*

1. Thiothrix nivea (Rabenhorst, 1865) Winogradsky, 1888. (*Beggiatoa nivea* Rabenhorst, Flora europaea algarum, *2*, 1865, 94; Winogradsky, Beitr. z. Morph. u. Physiol. d. Bact., I, Schwefelbacterien, 1888, 39.)

ni've.a. L. adj. *niveus* snow-white.

Trichomes, 2.0 to 3.0 microns at the base, 1.7 microns in the middle and 1.4 to 1.5 microns at the tip, occurring within a thin sheath. Segmentation invisible as long as the trichomes contain sulfur globules; the segments measure 4 to 15 microns, the longer ones usually near the apex, the shorter ones near the base. Motile segments (so-called conidia) are mostly single, 8 to 15 microns long, sometimes occurring in short trichomes of 2 to 4 cells and measuring up to 40 microns long. These segments may settle and develop near the base of the parent trichome or on a trichome itself, forming verticillate structures.

Habitat: Found in fresh-water environments where hydrogen sulfide is present (sulfur springs, stagnant pools, submerged decaying vegetation, etc.).

2. Thiothrix tenuis Winogradsky, 1888. (*Beggiatoa alba* var. *uniserialis* Engler, Über die Pilz-Vegetation des weissen oder todten Grundes in der Kieler Bucht. Vierter Bericht der Commission zur wissenschaftlichen Untersuchung der deutschen Meere in Kiel für 1877 bis 1881, Abt. I, 1883, 187–193; Winogradsky, Beitr. z. Morph. u. Physiol. d. Bact., I, Schwefelbacterien, 1888, 40.)

te'nu.is. L. adj. *tenuis* slender.

Trichomes, about 1 micron in diameter, of nearly uniform width, often occurring in dense, felted masses. Segments 4 to 5 microns long.

Habitat: Found in fresh-water environments where hydrogen sulfide occurs. Also found in sea water, according to Bavendamm (Die farblosen und roten Schwefelbacterien, Pflanzenforschung, Heft 2, 1924, 107).

3. Thiothrix tenuissima Winogradsky, 1888. (Beitr. z. Morph. u. Physiol. d. Bact., I, Schwefelbacterien, 1888, 40.)

te.nu.is'si.ma. L. sup.adj. *tenuissimus* very slender.

Trichomes less than 0.5 micron in diameter, usually occurring in dense masses.

Habitat: Found in fresh-water environments where hydrogen sulfide occurs.

4. Thiothrix voukii Klas, 1936. (Arch. f. Protistenk., *88*, 1936, 123.)

vou'ki.i. M.L. gen.noun *voukii* of Vouk; named for Vouk, a Yugoslavian scientist.

Trichomes, 15 to 30, most frequently 17, microns in diameter, of rather uniform width. Segments visible without special treatment. Segments generally somewhat longer than wide, occasionally barrel-shaped, rarely square. Segments 15 to 30, mostly 19 to 23, microns in length. Motile segments not yet observed.

Comment: Apart from the lack of motility, this species closely resembles the motile *Beggiatoa mirabilis.*

Source: Described from the effluent of sulfur springs at the seashore near Split, Yugoslavia. So far reported only once.

Habitat: Found in marine environments containing hydrogen sulfide.

5. Thiothrix longiarticulata Klas, 1936. (Arch. f. Protistenk., *88*, 1936, 126.) lon.gi.ar.ti.cu.la′ta. L. adj. *longus* long; L. part.adj. *articulatus* jointed; M.L. adj. *longiarticulatus* long-jointed.

Trichomes, 3.3 to 6.6, most frequently 4.2, microns in diameter, of uniform width, occurring in dense, felted masses. The segments are long, measuring 19 to 33, mostly 26, microns in length. Motile segments not yet reported. Sulfur droplets usually absent in the proximity of cross-walls.

Source: Described only once from the effluent of sulfur springs at the seashore near Split, Yugoslavia.

Habitat: Found in marine environments containing hydrogen sulfide.

6. Thiothrix anulata Molisch, 1912. (*Thiothrix annulata* (sic) Molisch, Cent. f. Bakt., II Abt., *33*, 1912, 58.) a.nu.la′ta. L. adj. *anulatus* furnished with a ring.

Trichomes 3 to 4, occasionally up to 5, microns in diameter, being thinner at the base (2 microns) and at the tip (1.8 microns). The trichomes are very long and may reach a length of 5 mm or even longer; they are found attached to detritus in the sea water. The segments are only about 1 micron in length. The included sulfur granules are very small and numerous; in old trichomes the granules become so massed that they are no longer recognizable as distinct granules. Narrow bands which are free of sulfur are often found, thus giving a ringed appearance to the trichomes. Old trichomes may show special thickening and distortion, but this is not characteristic of the species.

Source: Described as white, floating specks in a glass jar containing sea water in which algae were rotting; the water was obtained from the harbor at Trieste.

Habitat: Found in sea water containing hydrogen sulfide and decomposing organic matter (algae).

7. Thiothrix marina Molisch, 1912. (Cent. f. Bakt., II Abt., *33*, 1912, 58.) ma.ri′na. L. adj. *marinus* marine.

The trichomes, about 1.0 (0.8 to 1.3) micron in diameter and of uniform width, are relatively slender and short in comparison with those of *Thiothrix anulata* Molisch; they measure from 130 to 300, rarely as much as 500, microns in length.

Comment: This may be the form of *Thiothrix tenuis* reported by Bavendamm (Die farblosen und roten Schwelfelbacterien, Pflanzenforschung, Heft 2, 1924, 107) as found in sea water.

Source: Found in a deep, cylindrical, glass vessel in which the aquatic phanerogam *Zostera sp.* was rotting. From the harbor at Trieste. The threads formed a felted film over the surface.

Habitat: Found in sea water containing hydrogen sulfide and decomposing organic matter.

FAMILY II. VITREOSCILLACEAE PRINGSHEIM, 1949.*

(Pringsheim, Bact. Rev., *13*, 1949, 70; also see Jour. Gen. Microbiol., *9*, 1951, 124.)

Vit.re.os.cil.la′ce.ae. M.L. fem.n. *Vitreoscilla* type genus of the family; -*aceae* ending to denote a family; M.L. fem.pl.n. *Vitreoscillaceae* the *Vitreoscilla* family.

Cells occur in colorless trichomes of varying degrees of flexibility. The trichomes show a gliding motion when in contact with a substrate, the speed of movement varying inversely with the width of the trichome. One end of a trichome may become attached to a surface, the other end then becoming free-swinging. Gram-negative. The gliding habit determines the nature of growth: on agar low in nutrients, wavy, curly or spiral colonies are produced;

---

* Prepared by Mr. Erwin F. Lessel, Jr., Cornell University, Geneva, New York. Reviewed by Prof. E. G. Pringsheim, Pflanzenphysiologisches Institut, Göttingen, Deutschland, October, 1955.

on rich media, drop-like colonies, resembling those of many bacteria, are formed. Do not possess chlorophyll or phycocyanin. Closely resemble some of the *Beggiatoaceae*, differing primarily in that they never contain sulfur granules even when growing in an environment conducive to the development of such granules in *Beggiatoa*. The trichomes resemble those of *Oscillatoria* but do not possess the pigments characteristic of members of that genus. Do not hydrolyze genuine proteins. Found on dung, in soil, in water with decaying plant material and almost regularly in myxophycean scum on the surfaces of quiet waters.

A number of the organisms in this family have been described from microscopic studies only, cultural investigations not having been made at the time. The true relationships of these organisms can be clarified only by further study.

Key to the genera of family **Vitreoscillaceae.**

I. Trichomes perceptibly septate.
  A. Trichomes divided into cells which are not separated by empty interspaces; the trichomes may bend anywhere along their length.
          Genus I. *Vitreoscilla*, p. 845.
  B. Trichomes divided into cells separated by empty interspaces; the trichomes bend only at these pliable joints.
          Genus II. *Bactoscilla*, p. 848.
II. Trichomes not perceptibly septate.
          Genus III. *Microscilla*, p. 849.

Genus I. **Vitreoscilla** *Pringsheim, 1949.*

(Bact. Rev., *13*, 1949, 70; also see Jour. Gen. Microbiol., *5*, 1951, 127 and 147.)

Vit.re.os.cil′la. L. adj. *vitreus* glassy, clear; L. noun *oscillum* a swing; M.L. fem.n. *Vitreoscilla* transparent oscillator.

Trichomes clearly divided into cells. Usually motile by means of gliding movements; one species is non-motile. Gram-negative. Reproduction is by hormogonium-like fragmentation of the trichomes. True proteins are not hydrolyzed. Found in fresh water, in soil and in decomposing organic materials.

The type species is *Vitreoscilla beggiatoides* Pringsheim.

Key to the species of genus **Vitreoscilla.**

I. Trichomes relatively slender, measuring 2.5 microns or less in diameter.
  A. Trichomes 2.0 microns or less in diameter.
    1. Trichomes motile. Cultivable on artificial media.
      a. Trichomes sluggishly motile.
        b. Trichomes about 2.0 microns in diameter.
            1. *Vitreoscilla beggiatoides.*
        bb. Trichomes less than 1.6 microns in diameter.
            2. *Vitreoscilla stercoraria.*
      aa. Trichomes actively motile.
        b. Trichomes 1.2 microns in diameter.
            3. *Vitreoscilla filiformis.*
        bb. Trichomes more than 1.2 microns in diameter.
          c. Cells of trichomes relatively short (3.0 to 4.0, sometimes 6.0, microns in length).
            4. *Vitreoscilla catenula.*
          cc. Cells of trichomes relatively long (30 to 70 microns).
            5. *Vitreoscilla paludosa.*
    2. Trichomes non-motile. Not cultivated in pure culture.
          6. **Vitreoscilla stricta.**

B. Trichomes more than 2.0 microns in diameter.
7. *Vitreoscilla moniliformis.*
II. Trichomes more than 2.5 microns in diameter. Not cultivated in pure culture.
A. Trichomes 4.0 microns in diameter. Sluggishly motile.
8. *Vitreoscilla conica.*
B. Trichomes more than 4.0 microns in diameter. Actively motile.
9. *Vitreoscilla major.*

1. Vitreoscilla beggiatoides Prings-heim, 1949. (Bact. Rev., *13*, 1949, 70; also see Jour. Gen. Microbiol., *5*, 1951, 127.)

beg.gi.a.to.i'des. M.L. fem.n. *Beggiatoa* a generic name; Gr. noun *eidus* shape, form; M.L. adj. *beggiatoides Beggiatoa*-like.

Cylindrical trichomes measuring about 2 microns in diameter, sometimes more or less; length almost unrestricted, but under less favorable environments the trichomes may be as short as 10 microns. The trichomes are composed of cylindrical units showing constrictions which indicate the locations of cell wall primordia. Motile. Gram-negative.

Gelatin: No liquefaction.

Agar: Growth in curls, spirals and waves with loose ends.

Liquid media: Growth in trichomes of low optical refraction.

Casein not digested.

Source: Isolated from a ditch with decaying water weeds on Coldham Common, Cambridge, where it occurred together with *Sphaerotilus discophorus, Beggiatoa alba* and many other organisms.

Habitat: Found in quiet waters rich in organic material and with black mud on the bottom.

2. Vitreoscilla stercoraria Pringsheim, 1951. (Jour. Gen. Microbiol., *5*, 1951, 136.)

ster.co.ra'ri.a. L. adj. *stercorarius* pertaining to dung.

Trichomes 1.2 to 1.5 microns in diameter, varying in length, measuring up to 100 microns. The trichomes may be composed of rods of considerable length (12 microns and more) or of cells which are not much longer than they are wide. Above a certain length the trichomes rarely remain straight but bend irregularly forming aggregates like curled hair. Motility is hesitant and slow. Gram-negative.

Gelatin: No liquefaction.

Agar: Colonies are very dense and are connected by a fine network; regular spirals are formed. On rich media the colonies become thicker and, after some time, yellowish to translucent owing to autolysis of cells.

Liquid media: Growth at first filamentous and loose; later becomes flocculent.

Casein not digested.

Distinctive character: Dense colonies on agar connected by a fine network.

Source: Isolated from dung.

Habitat: Found in decomposing organic material.

3. Vitreoscilla filiformis Pringsheim, 1951. (Jour. Gen. Microbiol., *5*, 1951, 130.)

fi.li.for'mis. L. noun *filum* a thread; L. noun *forma* shape; M.L. adj. *fiiliformis* thread-shaped.

Cylindrical trichomes, 1.2 microns in diameter, of unlimited length, although short trichomes are regularly present. Trichomes pronouncedly more elastic and of greater tensile strength than are those of the other species in this genus. Both long and short trichomes exhibit an active gliding and swinging of the free ends. Gram-negative.

Gelatin: No liquefaction.

Agar: Growth occurs in delicate, more or less circular whirls and loops.

Liquid media: Growth occurs near the bottom or in tufts on the walls of the containing vessel.

Casein not digested.

Distinctive characters: Trichomes slender and elastic. Growth on agar is in the form of neatly rounded arches and loops as in certain species of *Oscillatoria*.

Source: Isolated from a crude culture consisting of a grain of wheat covered with soil and water from the pond in the Cambridge Botanic Garden.

Habitat: Found in fertilized soil and in polluted water.

4. Vitreoscilla catenula Pringsheim, 1951. (Jour. Gen. Microbiol., *5*, 1951, 130.)

ca.te'nu.la. M.L. noun *catenula* a small chain.

Trichomes, 1.5 to 2.0 microns in diameter, may be cylindrical and of almost uniform width. Usually there are constrictions between the cells, which are then barrel-shaped. The cells generally measure 3.0 to 4.0, sometimes up to 6.0, microns in length. The trichomes may break up into short fragments or grow to some length. Motile. Gram-negative.

Gelatin: No liquefaction.

Agar: Growth in curls without loose ends, otherwise similar to that of *Vitreoscilla beggiatoides* Pringsheim.

Liquid media: Growth similar to that of *Vitreoscilla beggiatoides*.

Casein not digested.

Distinctive characters: The bead-like appearance of the cells is correlated with a greater tendency to break up into shorter lengths than is found in *Vitreoscilla beggiatoides*. Very long trichomes are rarely found.

Relationship to other species: Due to the constrictions between the cells, the trichomes resemble those found in the blue-green genus *Pseudanabaena*, especially *P. tenuis* Koppe.

Source: Isolated several times from ditches between meadows in Cherry Hinton, Cambridge; later isolated from an infusion of cow dung from the same meadow.

Habitat: Found in decomposing organic material.

5. Vitreoscilla paludosa Pringsheim, 1951. (Bact. Rev., *13*, 1949, 72; also see Jour. Gen. Microbiol., *5*, 1951, 133.)

pa.lu.do'sa. L. adj. *paludosus* boggy, marshy.

Trichomes 1.8 to 2.0 microns in diameter and very long, 300 and more microns in length. Subdivision occurs into cylindrical, often slightly curved, cellular sections, 30 to 70 microns in length, separated by deep constrictions at which they readily break. Branching sometimes occurs. Old cells con-

tain spherical granules or droplets. Very actively motile. Gram-negative.

Gelatin: No liquefaction.

Agar: Young aggregations, composed of parallel trichomes, grow to form elongated, slender, pointed, often Y-shaped colonies. Older colonies possess an inner concentric structure reminiscent of brain convolutions; flame-like processes at the edges grow out into long, curved and anastomosing tongues from which single trichomes emerge, commencing further systems of growth.

Liquid media: Trichomes form a film on the glass surface or produce cotton-like floccules; sediment eventually produced.

Casein not digested.

Distinctive characters: Grows well and rapidly in liquid media. Not fastidious in food requirements.

Relationship to other species: Growth on bacteriological agar is so luxuriant that it can scarcely be distinguished from that of *Escherichia coli* Castellani and Chalmers.

Source: Isolated from material from the mill pond above Flatford Mill Field Centre, England.

Habitat: Commonly found in decomposing organic material.

6. Vitreoscilla stricta Pringsheim, 1949. (Bact. Rev., *13*, 1949, 72; also see Jour. Gen. Microbiol., *5*, 1951, 139.)

stric'ta. L. part.adj. *strictus* drawn so as to have no slack.

Rigid trichomes, 1.6 to 1.8 microns in diameter, relatively short, measuring up to 30 microns in length. The cells are, on the average, one and one-half times as long as they are wide. Terminal cells are rounded at the tip. The trichomes bend slowly and only to a small extent; true locomotion has not been observed. Generally the trichomes adhere to a surface with one end while the free end slowly oscillates. Gram-negative.

Comment: This species has not been grown in pure culture.

Source: Found in a pond with water fowl and in a pond polluted by cattle, both bodies of water containing iron organisms and a multitude of pigmented flagellates.

Habitat: Found in fresh water containing decomposing organic material.

7. **Vitreoscilla moniliformis** Prings-heim, 1949. (Bact. Rev., *13*, 1949, 72; also see Jour. Gen. Microbiol., *5*, 1951, 132.)

mo.ni.li.for'mis. L. noun *monile* a neck-lace; L. noun *forma* shape; M.L. adj. *moniliformis* necklace-like.

On plates the trichomes are in the form of relatively large, streptococcus-like chains. In mounted preparations the trichomes measure up to 150 microns in length, although generally they are only 30 microns long. The trichomes are composed of a limited number of rod-shaped sections with rounded ends which often appear to be separated by short gaps; the trichomes, however, move as a whole. The sausage-shaped sections are mostly 2.2 to 2.5 microns wide and are not very regular in form, often inflated to a diameter of 2.8 to 3.0 microns, sometimes only a little longer than they are wide; sometimes they measure 15 microns in length and are elongated and cylindrical. The cells tend to separate from each other, and units of 4 to 5 cells are often found. Long before division, the cells are marked by constriction. Motility not very active. Gram-negative.

Gelatin: No liquefaction.

Agar: Growth rather diffuse; the edges, particularly on less rich media, are composed of tongue-like processes while rounded, twisted areas may be seen in the interior of large colonies.

Liquid media: Markedly turbid; later, a sediment is formed.

Casein not digested.

Distinctive characters: Growth more rapid and abundant than with the other species of this genus. Not fastidious in food requirements.

Source: Isolated by Dr. C. F. Robinow from cow dung.

Habitat: Found in decomposing organic materials.

8. **Vitreoscilla conica** Pringsheim, 1951. (Jour. Gen. Microbiol., *5*, 1951, 139.)

con'i.ca. Gr. adj. *conicus* conical.

Trichomes about 4 microns wide and generally 20 to 50 microns in length. The cells are slightly barrel-shaped and are filled with refractive pseudo-granules. The terminal cell is often longer than the other cells and is attenuated near the tip. Not actively motile. Gram-negative.

Comment: This species has not been grown in pure culture.

Source: Described from mud from a pond at Du Klip Vlei, Cape Flates, Cape Province, South Africa, which had dried out during the dry season and which was again moistened in the laboratory.

Habitat: Mud.

9. **Vitreoscilla major** Pringsheim, 1951. (Jour. Gen. Microbiol., *5*, 1951, 138.)

ma'jor. L. comp.adj. *major* larger.

Trichomes relatively long and colorless, 6 to 7 microns in diameter, composed of cells whose length (5 microns) is slightly less than their width. A few refractive granules are found near the septa. The terminal cells are in the form of flattened hemispheres. As observed from the tip, the trichomes rotate clockwise. Gram-negative.

Comment: This species has not been grown in pure culture.

Relationship to other species: Morphologically similar to the species in the genus *Thiothrix* from which, however, it is distinguished by its continuous, active bending and twisting.

Source: Found in half-dried mud from a ditch at Cherry Hinton, Cambridge, England.

Habitat: Mud.

Genus II. **Bactoscilla** *Pringsheim, 1949.*

(Bact. Rev., *13*, 1949, 72; also see Jour. Gen. Microbiol., *5*, 1951, 144.)

Bac.tos.cil'la. *Bact-* probably intended as a part of the stem of the Gr. noun *bactrum* a staff, rod; L. noun *oscillum* a swing; M.L. fem.n. *Bactoscilla* oscillating rod.

Very slender trichomes composed of rod-shaped cells apparently separated by empty interspaces. Motile by means of a gliding movement. There is a slow, pronounced bending of the trichomes at the joints, the individual cells remaining rigid. Gram-negative. Found in fresh water containing decomposing organic matter.

The type species is *Bactoscilla flexibilis* Pringsheim.

1. **Bactoscilla flexibilis** Pringsheim, 1949. (Pringsheim, Bact. Rev., *13*, 1949, 72; *Bactoscilla mobilis* Pringsheim, Jour. Gen. Microbiol., *5*, 1951, 144.)

flex.i.bil'is. L. adj. *flexibilis* flexible.

Short, slender trichomes, about 0.4 to 0.5 micron in diameter, composed of a number of slender, rod-shaped cells apparently separated by empty interspaces. The trichomes bend slowly and pronouncedly at the joints, the individual cells remaining straight. Motile. Gram-negative.

Relationship to other species: Structur-ally comparable to *Lineola articulata* which is, however, motile by means of peritrichous flagella.

Source: Found in scum composed mainly of *Myxophyceae* from the outlet of the 'Clay Pond' near the Freshwater Biological Association laboratory at Wray Castle, Ambleside, later in the surface film of water over black mud from Flatford Mill Field Centre and a third time in mixed material from a duck pond near Colchester, all in England.

Habitat: Found in fresh water containing decomposing organic material.

Genus III. **Microscilla** *Pringsheim, 1951.*

(*Microscilla* Pringsheim (*nomen nudum*), Bact. Rev., *13*, 1949, 72; Pringsheim, Jour. Gen. Microbiol., *5*, 1951, 127 and 140.)

Mic.ros.cil'la. Gr. adj. *micrus* small; L. noun *oscillum* a swing; M.L. fem.n. *Microscilla* the small oscillator.

Slender trichomes without perceptible septation. Motile by means of active, gliding movements. Gram-negative. Reproduction is by division into relatively long daughter trichomes. Found on fresh-water and marine algae.

The type species is *Microscilla marina* Pringsheim.

Key to the species of genus **Microscilla.**

I. From salt water. Sea water or artificial sea water required for growth.
   1. *Microscilla marina.*
II. From fresh water. Sea water or artificial sea water not required for growth.
   A. Trichomes possess a free-swinging end.
      2. *Microscilla flagellum.*
   B. Trichomes do not possess a free-swinging end.
      3. *Microscilla agilis.*

1. **Microscilla marina** Pringsheim, 1951. (*Vitreoscilla marina* Pringsheim (*nomen nudum*), Bact. Rev., *13*, 1949, 72; Pringsheim, Jour. Gen. Microbiol., *5*, 1951, 140.)

ma.ri'na. L. adj. *marinus* pertaining to the sea, marine.

Slender trichomes, 0.5 to 0.6 by up to 100 microns, apparently without septation. The gliding movement, active and quick, particularly in young cultures from liquid media, is not associated with rotation but with much bending and waving. Gram-negative.

Sea water is required for growth.

Sea-water agar: Growth barely perceptible as a grayish veil. Microscopically the veil is seen to consist of a delicate network of widely separated trichomes forming loops and meshes.

On a medium composed of sodium acetate (0.1 per cent), Difco yeast-extract (0.1 per cent), Bactotryptone (0.1 per cent), soil extract (5 per cent), artificial sea water (half concentrated) and agar (1 per cent) and neutralized with calcium carbonate, a thick, peach- to orange-colored layer is produced after 4 days; after one week, the rich orange growth disappears due to autolysis of the cells; smaller growths keep their filamentous appearance for several weeks.

Liquid media: Growth occurs in floating bundles of more or less parallel trichomes gliding along one another.

Source: Isolated from fragments of *Schizonema* (diatoms) filaments from Brighton, Sussex, England.

Habitat: Found on marine algae.

2. Microscilla flagellum (Pringsheim, 1949) Pringsheim, 1951. (*Vitreoscilla flagellum* Pringsheim, Bact. Rev., *13*, 1949, 72; Pringsheim, Jour. Gen. Microbiol., *5*, 1951, 143.)

fla.gel'lum. L. neut.dim.n. *flagellum* a whip, flagellum.

Slender trichomes, about 0.3 to 0.4 micron in diameter, varying greatly in length: the shortest do not exceed 10 microns, and the longest, so much curved and entangled so as not to be measurable, are at least 100 microns in length. The trichomes are attached at one end, the lively movements of the free ends giving the impression of a flagellum of *Euglena*. Gram-negative.

Source: Found in fresh water containing filamentous *Myxophyceae* such as *Oscillatoria amphibia*.

Habitat: Found in fresh water containing algae.

3. Microscilla agilis Pringsheim, 1949. (Jour. Gen. Microbiol., *5*, 1951, 142.)

a'gi.lis. L. adj. *agilis* agile.

Slender trichomes, 0.6 to 0.8 by 12.0 to 70.0 microns, with no apparent septation. Motile by means of gliding movements. Motility and flexibility are extraordinary, reminiscent of that of *Spirochaeta plicatilis* Ehrenberg. The trichomes always seem attached to the substrate along their entire length, no free-swinging ends being evident. Rotation is apparently lacking. Gram-negative.

Source: Found in a ditch in Coldham Common near Cambridge, England, containing decaying plant residue, a great variety of flagellates, *Cladophora* and *Chlorohydra*.

Habitat: Found in fresh water containing decaying plant material and protozoa.

FAMILY III. LEUCOTRICHACEAE BUCHANAN, Fam. Nov.*

Leu.co.tri.cha'ce.ae. M.L. fem.n. *Leucothrix* type genus of the family; *-aceae* ending to denote a family; M.L. fem.pl.n. *Leucotrichaceae* the *Leucothrix* family.

Short, cylindrical cells arranged in long, colorless, unbranched, non-motile trichomes tapering from the base to the apex. Sulfur granules may be found on the exterior of the cells under certain conditions. Trichomes commonly attached basally to solid substrates by an inconspicuous holdfast. Multiplication by means of gonidia (single, gliding cells which arise apically from the trichomes). The gonidia may aggregate to form rosettes containing up to 50 cells. The cells in the rosettes become non-motile, develop holdfasts and elongate to form trichomes; therefore mature trichomes are characteristically arranged in the form of radial colonies, although occasionally gonidia develop singly, forming isolated trichomes. Strictly aerobic. Resemble blue-green algae in many respects but differ from them in that they do not produce photosynthetic pigments. Found in fresh- and salt-water containing decomposing algal material.

There is a single genus, *Leucothrix* Oersted.

Genus I. **Leucothrix** *Oersted, 1844,* **emend.** *Harold and Stanier, 1955.*

(Oersted, De regionibus marinis, elementa topographiae historiconaturalis freti Oeresund. J. C. Scharling, Copenhagen, 1844, 44; *Pontothrix* Nadson and Krassilnikov, Compt. rend. Acad. Sci. de U.R.S.S., A. No. 1, 1932, 243; Harold and Stanier, Bact. Rev., *19*, 1955, 54.)

Leu'co.thrix. Gr. adj. *leucus* clear, light; Gr. noun *thrix, trichis* hair; M.L. fem.n. *Leucothrix* colorless hair.

Description as for the family.

The type species is *Leucothrix mucor* Oersted.

---

* Prepared by Prof. R. E. Buchanan, Iowa State College, Ames, Iowa, October, 1955.

1. **Leucothrix mucor** Oersted, 1844. (Oersted, De regionibus marinis, elementa topographiae historiconaturalis freti Oeresund. J. C. Scharling, Copenhagen, 1844, 44; *Chlamydothrix longissima* Molisch, Cent. f. Bakt., II Abt., *33*, 1912, 60; *Pontothrix longissima* Nadson and Krassilnikov, Compt. rend. Acad. Sci. de U.R.S.S., A. No. 1, 1932, 243; also see Harold and Stanier, Bact. Rev., *19*, 1955, 49.)

mu'cor. L. noun *mucor* mold; M.L. noun *Mucor* a genus of molds.

Cells short, 1 to 5 microns long, cylindrical. Sulfur granules are found only on the exterior, never in the interior, of the cells, and they occur only when the trichomes lie near the surface of the water where there is an abundance of oxygen. Trichomes are colorless, unbranched, non-motile, occasionally surrounded by a gelatinous sheath 2 to 6 microns wide, and very long, frequently reaching a length of 0.5 cm or more; they are either entwined about each other or occur in loosely arranged bundles of several hundred or more where they lie parallel to each other or twist like the individual strands of a rope. The trichomes remain in contact with the surface film or with solid particles by means of an inconspicuous holdfast; in young colonies the trichomes radiate from the solid particles in a manner similar to that of *Thiothrix sp.* Reproduction occurs by the fragmentation of the trichomes into gonidia.

A large variety of carbohydrates and other simple organic compounds may serve as sources of carbon and energy.

No growth factors are required.

Strictly aerobic.

Temperature relations: Optimum, 25° C. Maximum, 30° C.

Grows best at a salt concentration (synthetic sea water) of 16 grams per liter; a salt concentration of 3 grams per liter supports growth, but with abnormal morphology.

Source: Isolated from decaying algal infusions. Found in the harbor at Trieste. Nadson and Krassilnikov (*op. cit.*, 1932, 243) report this organism on *Zostera marina* in the Bay at Sebastopol on the Black Sea.

Habitat: Found in fresh- and salt-water containing decomposing algal material.

FAMILY IV. ACHROMATIACEAE MASSART, 1902.*

(Rec. Inst. Bot., Univ. Bruxells, *5*, 1902, 251.)

A. chro. ma. ti. a'ce. ae. M.L. neut.n. *Achromatium* type genus of the family; -*aceae* ending to denote a family; M.L. fem.pl.n. *Achromatiaceae* the *Achromatium* family.

Large, unicellular organisms which are spherical to ovoid or shortly cylindrical with hemispherical extremities. Movements, if any, are of a slow, rolling, jerky type and are dependent upon the presence of a substrate; no special organs of locomotion are known. Division of cells is by a constriction in the middle. Do not possess photosynthetic pigments. In their natural habitat, the cells contain sulfur droplets and sometimes additional inclusions, such as large spherules of calcium carbonate. Found in fresh-water and marine environments.

The organisms in the family *Achromatiaceae* have so far been studied exclusively as found in their natural habitats. Pure-culture studies are greatly needed; they may show that the peculiar calcium carbonate inclusions (not calcium oxalate as thought by Schewiakoff nor calcium thiosulfate as believed by Hannevart) occur only under special environmental conditions.

There is a single genus, *Achromatium* Schewiakoff.

---

* Revised by Prof. C. B. van Niel, Hopkins Marine Station, Pacific Grove, California, January, 1944; further revision, October, 1955.

Genus I. **Achromatium** *Schewiakoff, 1893.*

(Schewiakoff, Über einen neuen bacterienähnlichen Organismus des Süsswassers, Habilitationsschrift, Heidelberg, 1893; *Hillhousia* West and Griffiths, Proc. Roy. Soc., B, *81*, 1909, 389.)

A.chro.ma'ti.um. Gr. pref. *a* not; Gr. noun *chromatium* color, paint; M.L. neut.n. *Achromatium* (that which is) not colored.

Description as for the family.

It is not easy as yet to determine whether several species should be recognized in this genus. There appears to be some justification for differentiating between the forms which contain the characteristic and conspicuous calcium carbonate inclusions and those in which these large spherules are lacking. The former have been reported mostly from fresh- or brackish-water environments, while the characteristic habitat of the latter seems to be marine. It is, of course, probable that the internal deposition of calcium carbonate depends upon the composition of the environment, so that the distinction may prove arbitrary and non-specific.

Achromatium cells of widely different sizes have been described. Schewiakoff (*op. cit.*, 1893) mentions a variation of 9 to 22 microns in width and of 15 to 43 microns in length for *Achromatium oxaliferum*. Larger cells have been observed by Warming (Videnskab. Meddel. naturhistor. Foren., Kjöbenhavn, 1875, No. 20–28, 360; size to 85 microns) and by Virieux (Ann. Sci. Natur., Ser. 9, *18*, 1913, 265; size to 95 microns in length). Nadson (Bull. Jard. Imp. Botan., St. Pétersb., *13*, 1913, 106; also see Jour. Microb., St. Pétersb., *1*, 1914, 52) proposed the name *Achromatium gigas* for the larger organisms; also West and Griffiths (Ann. Bot., *27*, 1913, 83) created two species: *Hillhousia mirabilis*, with sizes of 20 to 33 by 42 to 86 microns, and *Hillhousia palustris*, measuring, on the average, 14 by 25 microns, for the same group of sulfur bacteria. However, Bersa (Sitzungsber. Akad. Wiss., Wien, Math-em-naturw. Kl., I, *129*, 1920, 233) observed so many intermediate sizes that he recognized only a single species. Nadson and Wislouch (Bull. Princ. Jard. Botan., Républ. Russe, *22*, 1923, Suppl. 1, 33) arrived at the same conclusion, and this view is accepted here.

The marine *Achromatium* types, which do not contain calcium carbonate crystals, have also been segregated into species on the basis of their size. Here again there does not seem to be any valid reason for maintaining several species as there is a continuous series of intermediate forms.

Thus the organisms previously described as *Achromatium oxaliferum, Achromatium gigas, Hillhousia mirabilis* and *Hillhousia palustris* are provisionally treated here as one species, while the marine counterpart, *Thiophysa volutans*, is combined with *Thiophysa macrophysa* and *Thiosphaerella amylifera*, all three being regarded as *Achromatium volutans*.

The type species is *Achromatium oxaliferum* Schewiakoff.

Key to the species of genus Achromatium.

I. Characteristically contains calcium carbonate crystals in the form of highly refractile, large spherules; occurs mostly in fresh-water and brackish muds.
1. Achromatium oxaliferum.

II. Occurs naturally without such calcium carbonate inclusions in marine mud.
2. Achromatium volutans.

1. **Achromatium oxaliferum** Schewiakoff, 1893. (Schewiakoff, Über einen neuen bacterienähnlichen Organismus des Süsswassers, Habilitationsschrift, Heidelberg, 1893; *Hillhousia mirabilis* West and Griffiths, Proc. Roy. Soc., B, *81*, 1909, 389; *Hillhousia palustris* West and Griffiths, Ann. Bot., *27*, 1913, 83; *Achromatium gigas* Nadson, Bull. Jard. Imp. Bot., St. Pétersb., *13*, 1913, 106.)

o.xa.li'fe.rum. Gr. noun *oxalis* sorrel, a sour plant; M.L. noun *oxalatum* oxalate; L. v. *fero* to carry; M.L. adj. *oxaliferus* oxalate-containing.

Unicellular organisms varying in shape from spherical or ovoid to shortly cylindrical with hemispherical extremities. Division by constriction in the middle. Cells vary in size from spheres of about 7 microns or even less in diameter to giant forms, 35 by 100 microns; the extremes are connected by a continuous series of intermediate sizes. May show motility of a jerky and rotating kind, always very slow and dependent upon a substrate. Typical organs of locomotion are absent. Normally contain small sulfur globules accompanied by much larger calcium carbonate crystals, the latter in the form of large, highly refractile spherules; under favorable environmental conditions, these may disappear before the sulfur globules. Cells with calcium carbonate inclusions have a very high specific gravity and therefore are found only in the bottom of pools, streams, etc., usually in the mud.

Strictly microaerophilic; apparently require hydrogen sulfide.

Source: Described from fresh-water and brackish mud containing hydrogen sulfide and calcium salts. According to Nadson and Wislouch (Bull. princip. Jard. bot., Républ. Russe, *22*, 1923, Suppl. 1, 33), found also in marine mud.

2. **Achromatium volutans** (Hinze, 1903) van Niel, 1948. (*Thiophysa volutans* Hinze, Ber. d. deut. bot. Ges., *21*, 1903, 309; *Thiophysa macrophysa* Nadson, Bull. Jard. Imp. Bot., St. Pétersb., *13*, 1913, 106; and Jour. Microb., St. Pétersb., *1*, 1914, 54; *Thiosphaerella amylifera* Nadson, Bull. Jard. Imp. Bot., St. Pétersb., *13*, 1913, 106; and Jour. Microb., St. Pétersb., *1*, 1914, 54; van Niel, in Manual, 6th ed., 1948, 999.)

vo′lu.tans. L. part.adj. *volutans* rolling.

Unicellular organisms which are spherical to ovoid in shape. Division by constriction in the middle. Size variable, ranging from spheres about 5 microns in diameter to ovals up to 40 microns in length. May show motility of a jerky and rotating kind, always very slow and dependent upon a substrate. Typical organs of locomotion are absent. Normally contain sulfur globules but lack large, internal, calcium carbonate deposits.

Microaerophilic; apparently require hydrogen sulfide.

Source: Described from marine mud containing hydrogen sulfide; also from decaying seaweeds.

ORDER VIII. MYXOBACTERALES JAHN, 1915.*

(*Myxobacteriaceae* (sic) Thaxter, Bot. Gaz., *17*, 1892, 394; *Myxobactrales* Clements, The genera of fungi. Minneapolis, 1909, 8; Jahn, Kryptogamenflora der Mark Brandenburg, V, Heft 1, 1915, 187.)

Myx.o.bac.te.ra′les. M.L. mas.n. *Myxobacter* name of the genus first described by Thaxter; *-ales* ending to denote an order; M.L. fem.pl.n. *Myxobacterales* the order based upon the type genus, *Myxobacter*.

Common or trivial name. The myxobacters.

Brief characterization of the order. The vegetative cells are flexible rods of low refractility which exhibit gliding movement on solid surfaces and which multiply by binary, transverse fission to produce a thin, flat, rapidly extending colony. Actively motile cells at the periphery of the colony commonly occur as groups of 2 or 3 to several hundred individuals in the form of tongue-like extensions or isolated islands whose presence is virtually diagnostic of the order. The moving cells may pave the substrate with a thin layer of slime on which they rest.

Resting cells are formed by all myxobacters except members of the genus *Cytophaga*. In the family *Myxococcaceae* the resting cell is a spherical or oval body, thick-walled and highly refractile; in the remaining groups it is merely a shortened vegetative cell. Except in the genus *Sporocytophaga*, resting cells are borne in or on spatially localized, larger structures known as fruiting bodies. In the simplest case, the fruiting body consists of a uniform mass of resting cells held together by slime. Some groups produce more complex fruiting structures: the resting cells may be enclosed in cysts and may be raised above the substrate on stalks, either simple or branched. Fruiting bodies are usually brightly colored and often sufficiently large to be visible to the naked eye.

The vegetative state. In the vegetative condition, myxobacters consist of unicellular rods which occur in two characteristic shapes. Members of the family *Sorangiaceae*, together with some representatives of the families *Archangiaceae* and *Polyangiaceae*, have cylindrical vegetative cells with blunt, rounded ends; in extreme cases the cell is broader at the tips than at the center. All other myxobacters, with the possible exception of some *Cytophaga* species, have vegetative cells which taper towards the tips. The cells are not surrounded by a demonstrable wall and, perhaps as a consequence, are flexible and very weakly refractile. Division is always by binary, transverse fission. Motility is universal. Movement occurs only in contact with a solid surface and is of the gliding type also found in the *Cyanophyta* and in filamentous, colorless organisms such as the *Beggiatoaceae* and *Vitreoscillaceae*. There are no demonstrable means of locomotion, and the actual physical mechanism of movement is not understood, although many authors have offered speculations, which were recently reviewed by Meyer-Pietschmann (Arch. Mikrobiol., *16*, 1951, 163). Discrete nuclear structures similar to those of true bacteria can be demonstrated by appropriate cytological procedures. Their appearance and behavior during division and formation of resting cells are described and illustrated by Badian (Acta Soc. Bot. Poloniae, *7*, 1930, 55), Krzemieniew-

---

*Revised by Professor R. Y. Stanier, Department of Bacteriology, University of California, Berkeley, California, March, 1953.

ska (Acta Soc. Bot. Poloniae, 7, 1930, 507), Beebe (Jour. Bact., 41, 1941, 214) and Klieneberger-Nobel (Jour. Gen. Microbiol., 1, 1947, 33).

The myxobacterial colony, also sometimes designated as a swarm or pseudoplasmodium,
consists characteristically of a flat, thin mass of vegetative cells which spreads rapidly over
the surface of the substrate as a result of active movement from the periphery. Frequently,
but not invariably, the cells lie on a thin membrane of slime. Colonies of a more compact
nature may be produced if movement is impeded by copious slime formation or unfavorable
nutrient conditions or if growth occurs on a gel of soft enough consistency (e.g., 1 per cent
agar) to allow penetration of the cells into the substrate. In fruiting species, the fruiting
bodies are formed characteristically in the older, central portion of the colony, often in a
series of successive, concentric rings.

Resting cells and fruiting bodies. Each resting cell is produced from a single, entire,
vegetative cell. In the families *Archangiaceae, Sorangiaceae* and *Polyangiaceae* there is little
structural change: the vegetative cell merely becomes somewhat shorter and thicker. In
the family *Myxococcaceae*, the vegetative cell becomes converted to a mature resting cell
which is spherical or ellipsoidal and which is surrounded by a refractile, deeply staining
wall; these structures are commonly referred to as microcysts. In some genera the resting
cells are borne in cysts, which enclose several hundred individual resting cells within a
common membrane. Studies on the survival of the resting cells are still fragmentary. They
do not appear to possess markedly greater thermal resistance than the vegetative cells
but can survive desiccation for many years. Jahn reports germination of *Polyangium fuscum*
after almost 6 years and of *Myxococcus fulvus* after 8 years.

Except in the genus *Sporocytophaga* and the amicrocystogenous family *Cytophagaceae*, the
resting cells are found in structures known as fruiting bodies, each formed by the aggrega-
tion and transformation of a large number of vegetative cells. Whereas the properties of the
vegetative cells vary little from group to group, fruiting bodies differ widely in shape, size,
structure and color; hence differentiation of families, genera and species is based largely
on this character. Unfortunately, there have been relatively few studies on the range of
variation of the fruiting structures under varying conditions of cultivation, so that the
validity of the differences which have been employed for taxonomic purposes is difficult
to assess.

Ecology. Many species of fruiting myxobacters have been described as occurring on
the dung of herbivores. The work of the Krzemieniewskis (Acta Soc. Bot. Poloniae, 5, 1927),
Mishustin (Mikrobiologia, 7, 1938, 427), Singh (Jour. Gen. Microbiol., 1, 1947, 1) and others
has shown, however, that they occur in soil and can probably be regarded as characteristic
members of the soil microflora. Their frequent occurrence on dung is simply a reflection of
the fact that this material provides an exceptionally favorable substrate for fructification.
No really satisfactory method of estimating their numbers is available; Singh (*loc. cit.*)
reported from 2,000 to 76,400 myxobacters per gram of soil, but this is undoubtedly an
underestimate. Two aquatic fruiting myxobacters are known: one is parasitic on an aquatic
alga (Geitler, Arch. f. Protistenk., 50, 1924, 67), and the other is an important pathogen of
fresh-water fishes (Ordal and Rucker, Proc. Soc. Exper. Biol. Med., 56, 1944, 15). Of the
non-fruiting myxobacters, some are common in soil and others are marine forms.

Nutrition and cultivation. The ability to decompose complex polysaccharides such as
cellulose, agar and chitin is characteristic of many species in the family *Cytophagaceae* and
the genus *Sporocytophaga*. A few species of fruiting myxobacters belonging to the genera
Sorangium, Polyangium and *Angiococcus* are known to be cellulose-decomposers. For all
these forms, the methods of isolation and cultivation are accordingly well-defined and relatively simple. Most of them can be enriched from natural sources by the use of a simple
mineral base supplemented with the appropriate polysaccharide and thereafter maintained
in pure culture on similar media (Krzemieniewska and Krzemieniewski, Bull. Int. Acad. Pol.
Sci. Lett., Classe Sci. Math. Nat., B, 15, 1937, 11; Stanier, Bact. Rev., 6, 1942, 143; Stanier,
Jour. Bact., 53, 1947, 297). A few species appear to have complex growth factor require-

ments, so far not analyzed, and their cultivation accordingly requires the addition of peptone or yeast extract to the medium containing the specific polysaccharide which they attack. The polysaccharide-decomposing myxobacteria are all mesophilic, strictly aerobic organisms and develop best in neutral or slightly alkaline media.

For the vast majority of the fruiting myxobacters, however, the nutrient requirements have not yet been analyzed, and cultivation of these organisms still remains a highly empirical affair. The technique of enrichment developed by the Krzemieniewskis (*op. cit.*, *5*, 1927) provides the best general method for obtaining them from natural sources. Soil is placed on blotting paper in a large Petri dish and covered with pellets of sterilized rabbit dung. The soil is moistened with water, and the plates are incubated at 26° to 30° C. After 5 to 10 days, fruiting bodies begin to form on the surface of the dung pellets, from which they can be picked and transferred to agar media for purposes of purification. Singh (*op. cit.*, *1*, 1947, 1) recommends enriching by the use of non-nutrient agar, on the surface of which a few loopfuls of the cells of a suitable true bacterium (*e.g.*, *Aerobacter sp.*) are spread in the form of a disc about 1 inch in diameter; this disc is then inoculated with soil, compost, or a soil suspension, and the plate is incubated at 25° C. for 1 to 3 weeks. The myxobacters develop at the expense of the eubacterial cells and form fruiting bodies on the surface of the agar. The technique of Singh is excellent for the enrichment of a few of the more common members of the *Myxococcaceae* but does not yield the wide diversity of forms obtainable by the Krzemieniewskis' method.

Following these methods of enrichment, pure cultures of some species can be obtained fairly readily by repeated transfer on solid media of various compositions. Dung extract agar, potato extract agar and peptone agar either with or without the addition of carbohydrates have proved satisfactory. Perhaps the best general method is the use of agar containing a suspension of the cells of true bacteria. Many of the fruiting myxobacters are capable of lysing the cells of true bacteria and other microorganisms and of developing at the expense of the materials so liberated (Beebe, Jour. Bact., *40*, 1940, 155; Snieszko, Hitchner and McAllister, Jour. Bact., *41*, 1941, 26). Although the vegetative development of myxobacters on bacterial agar is usually somewhat scanty, vigorous fructification occurs, whereas on many of the other complex media which have been employed, the ability to form fruiting bodies may be greatly reduced or lost completely. The nature of the materials liberated from lysed true bacteria which promote fructification has not been determined. Bacterial agar has the additional advantage for purposes of purification that the growth of true bacteria, fungi and protozoa, invariably present in the original enrichments, is much slighter than on other complex media.

By the use of the methods described in the preceding paragraph, certain fruiting myxobacters, particularly representatives of the *Myxococcaceae*, are readily isolated and maintained in pure culture. There are many species, however, which have not yet been obtained in pure culture despite considerable efforts by a number of investigators. For *Chondromyces crocatus*, the claim has been made (Pinoy, Ann. Inst. Past., *35*, 1921, 487; Kühlwein, Arch. f. Mikrobiol., *14*, 1948, 678) that growth occurs only in "symbiotic association" with other microorganisms; this may simply reflect the ability of the species in question to lyse other microorganisms and to obtain, thereby, nutrients not furnished by conventional complex media.

No precise quantitative studies on the nutrition of the fruiting myxobacters have been reported, apart from the work of the Krzemieniewskis (*op. cit.*, *15*, 1937, 11) on the cellulose-decomposing *Sorangium spp.* and that of Norén (Svensk. Bot. Tidskr., *46*, 1952, 324). The widespread ability of these forms to destroy and to develop at the expense of true bacteria and fungi suggests that their chief source of food in nature may be the cells of other microorganisms, even though growth on simpler media is sometimes possible with pure cultures.

Relationships of the myxobacters. Thaxter (*op. cit.*, *17*, 1892, 389), whose work laid the foundations for our knowledge of the fruiting myxobacters, regarded these organisms as representatives of the *Schizomycetes* on the basis of their vegetative morphology. Although the vegetative cells of myxobacters resemble those of rod-shaped true bacteria in size and general appearance, they are distinguishable both by their gliding movement and by their lack of a rigid cell wall, and most later authors have agreed that the relationship between true bacteria and myxobacters is not close. The remarkable life cycle that characterizes the fruiting myxobacters is paralleled only among the amoeboid protists, in slime molds belonging to the order *Acrasiales*; however, the differences between the two groups with respect to vegetative morphology are so great that this developmental parallel evidently represents a case of evolutionary convergence. The postulation of a relationship between myxobacters and blue-green algae, put forward by Jahn (*op. cit.*, 1924) and accepted by subsequent writers (Stanier and van Niel, Jour. Bact., *42*, 1941, 437; Pringsheim, Bact. Rev., *13*, 1949, 47) was based in the first instance on the similarity in the mechanism of locomotion. This phylogenetic assumption became more probable with the recognition of non-fruiting myxobacters, not characterized by the life cycle previously considered to be diagnostic of the group; physiology apart, there is little to distinguish the members of the genus *Cytophaga* from certain unicellular, rod-shaped, blue-green algae. In a recent analysis of the relationships between bacteria and blue-green algae, Pringsheim (*loc. cit.*) has expressed the view that the mechanism of movement is a basic character, upon which can be based a separation of microorganisms at this level of organization into "gliding" forms and "swimming" (*i.e.*, flagellated) forms. If this view is accepted, then the myxobacters, together with other non-photosynthetic gliding organisms, should be grouped taxonomically with the blue-green algae rather than with the true bacteria as constituting non-photosynthetic offshoots from various groups of blue-green algae. By long tradition, however, even colorless gliding organisms such as the *Beggiatoaceae*, which show very close morphological relationships to specific genera of blue-green algae, have been treated taxonomically as "bacteria," and for practical reasons a continuance of this policy may be deemed desirable, even if one accepts the plausibility of Pringsheim's phylogenetic views.

In recent years, many new colorless, gliding organisms have been discovered, and their relationships to the *Myxobacterales* require discussion. The non-fruiting myxobacters of the genera *Cytophaga* and *Sporocytophaga* show clear evidences of relationship to the fruiting forms, both in their vegetative morphology and in the nature of the life cycle evidenced by the members of the latter genus. When their inclusion in the order *Myxobacterales* was proposed (Stanier, Jour. Bact., *40*, 1940, 619), the only other colorless, gliding organisms known were the chemoautotrophs of the family *Beggiatoaceae*, whose filamentous structure related them to certain genera of blue-green algae in the family *Oscillatoriaceae*. Thus a wide and clear-cut gap between the *Beggiatoaceae* and the non-fruiting myxobacters seemed to exist. Soriano (Revista Argentina de Agronomia, *12*, 1945, 120; Antonie van Leeuwenhoek, *12*, 1947, 215) has described a number of nutritionally unspecialized, gliding organisms which he places in a new genus, *Flexibacter*. Some of these are morphologically very similar to the representatives of the genus *Cytophaga* while others have a filamentous structure. Furthermore, Pringsheim (Jour. Gen. Microbiol., *5*, 1951, 124) has described a wide variety of filamentous, gliding organisms, some of which closely resemble the *Beggiatoaceae* in structure but do not share the nutritional peculiarities of this family. It is accordingly apparent that an argument can be made for linking up the unicellular, non-fruiting myxobacters with the *Beggiatoaceae* and other non-fruiting, colorless, gliding organisms which show a more or less pronouncedly filamentous vegetative organization. In fact, Soriano (*op. cit.*, *12*, 1945, 120) has suggested uniting all these forms in an order *Flexibacteriales* and conserving the order *Myxobacterales* for organisms capable of forming fruiting bodies. This proposal has not been adopted in the present revision of the MANUAL; instead, unicellular, non-fruiting forms are retained in the order *Myxobacterales*, and the filamentous forms are placed in a new order, *Beggiatoales*.

Families of the Order Myxobacterales. Five families are recognized, of which four (*Archangiaceae*, *Sorangiaceae*, *Polyangiaceae* and *Myxococcaceae*) were originally proposed by Jahn (*op. cit.*, 1924). The definition of the family *Myxococcaceae* is now modified to permit inclusion of the non-fruiting genus *Sporocytophaga*, as proposed by Stanier (*op. cit., 6,* 1942, 143). The fifth family, *Cytophagaceae* (Stanier, *loc. cit.*), consists of myxobacters which produce neither fruiting bodies nor resting cells.

Key to the families of order **Myxobacterales.**

I. Neither fruiting bodies nor resting cells produced.

Family I. *Cytophagaceae*, p. 858.

II. Resting cells produced.

A. Resting cells cylindrical, not spherical or ellipsoidal. Fruiting bodies produced.

1. Resting cells not contained in cysts. Fruiting bodies consist of mesenteric masses or finger-like aggregations of resting cells.

Family II. *Archangiaceae*, p. 863.

2. Resting cells contained in cysts of definite shape borne on the fruiting bodies.

a. Cysts angular. Vegetative cells always thick and short, with blunt, rounded ends.

Family III. *Sorangiaceae*, p. 866.

aa. Cysts rounded. Vegetative cells usually long and thin, with tapering ends.

Family IV. *Polyangiaceae*, p. 870.

B. Resting cells (microcysts) spherical or ellipsoidal, surrounded by a distinct wall. Fruiting bodies formed except in the genus *Sporocytophaga*.

Family V. *Myxococcaceae*, p. 882.

FAMILY I. CYTOPHAGACEAE STANIER, 1940.

(Jour. Bact., *40*, 1940, 630.)

Cy.to.pha.ga′ce.ae. M.L. fem.n. *Cytophaga* type genus of the family; -*aceae* ending to denote a family; M.L. fem.pl.n. *Cytophagaceae* the *Cytophaga* family.

Flexible, sometimes pointed rods showing gliding motility. No fruiting bodies or resting cells (microcysts) are formed.

Genus I. **Cytophaga** *Winogradsky, 1929.*

(Winogradsky, Ann. Inst. Past., *43*, 1929, 578; includes *Promyxobacterium* Imšenecki and Solntzeva, Mikrobiologia, *14*, 1945, 220; and *Flexoscilla* Pringsheim, Jour. Gen. Microbiol., *5*, 1951, 145; in part *Flexibacter* Soriano, Revista Argentina de Agronomia, *12*, 1945, 120.)

Cy.to′pha.ga. Gr. noun *cytus* hollow place, vessel, cell; Gr. v. *phagein* to devour; M.L. fem.n. *Cytophaga* cell destroyer.

Description same as for the family.

The type species is *Cytophaga hutchinsonii* Winogradsky.

Key to the species of genus **Cytophaga.**

I. From soil. Not obligately halophilic.

A. Vigorous growth on cellulose. Starch not utilized.

1. Produce yellow pigment.

1. *Cytophaga hutchinsonii.*
2. *Cytophaga lutea.*

2. Produces orange pigment.

3. *Cytophaga aurantiaca.*

3. Produces pink pigment.

                             4. *Cytophaga rubra.*

4. Produces olive-green pigment.

                             5. *Cytophaga tenuissima.*

  B. Weak or no growth on cellulose. Starch utilized.

    1. Utilizes chitin.

                           6. *Cytophaga johnsonii.*

    2. Utilization of chitin not tested.

      a. Produces yellow to orange pigment on starch.

                        7. *Cytophaga deprimata.*

     aa. Produces cream to pale-yellow pigment on starch.

                        8. *Cytophaga albogilva.*

II. From seawater. Obligately halophilic, not growing in media without at least 0.5 per cent sodium chloride.

  A. Produces a diffusible black to brown pigment.

                        9. *Cytophaga krzemieniewskae.*

  B. Do not produce a diffusible black to brown pigment.

    1. Growth not inhibited by presence of 0.5 per cent peptone or 0.2 per cent glucose.

                    10. *Cytophaga diffluens.*

    2. Growth inhibited by presence of 0.5 per cent peptone or 0.2 per cent glucose.

                    11. *Cytophaga sensitiva.*

1. **Cytophaga hutchinsonii** Winogradsky, 1929. (Winogradsky, Ann. Inst. Past., *43*, 1929, 578; *Cytophaga* strain 8, Jensen, Proc. Linn. Soc. N. S. Wales, *65*, 1940, 547; not *Cytophaga hutchinsonii* Imšenecki and Solntzeva, Bull. Acad. Sci. U.S.S.R., Ser. Biol., No. 6, 1936, 1129.)

hut.chin.so'ni.i. M.L. gen.noun *hutchinsonii* of Hutchinson; named for H. B. Hutchinson.

Description from Stanier (Bact. Rev., *6*, 1942, 191).

Flexible, singly-occurring rods, 0.3 to 0.5 micron wide and 2.0 to 10.0 microns long, averaging 6.0 microns in length. Thread-like or coccoid involution forms may occur in old cultures. Gram-negative.

Produces bright yellow, glistening, mucilaginous patches on filter paper-silica gel or -agar plates after 3 to 5 days. The filter paper in these regions is eventually dissolved, and the colony becomes translucent.

Produces bright yellow, glistening, slimy, raised colonies on mineral glucose-agar plates. Little movement is evident, and the colonies usually remain compact.

Cellulose, cellobiose and glucose are utilized. Xylose, arabinose, mannose, galactose, fructose and mannitol are not utilized.

Ammonia, nitrate, aspartic acid, aspara-gine, peptone and yeast extract can serve as nitrogen sources.

Catalase-positive.

Aerobic.

Optimum temperature, 30° C.

Source: Isolated from soil.

Habitat: Soil.

2. **Cytophaga lutea** Winogradsky, 1929. (Ann. Inst. Past., *43*, 1929, 599.)

lu'te.a. L. adj. *luteus* yellow.

Dimensions of the cells approximately those of *Cytophaga aurantiaca* (see below) but rather larger and thinner and without marked central swelling. Gram-negative.

Produces a brilliant yellow pigment similar to that of *Cytophaga hutchinsonii.*

This species differs only in size from *Cytophaga hutchinsonii* and is probably a variety of it.

Source: Isolated from soil.

Habitat: Soil. Decomposes cellulose.

3. **Cytophaga aurantiaca** Winogradsky, 1929. (Winogradsky, Ann. Inst. Past., *43*, 1929, 597; probably *Mycococcus cytophagus* Bokor, Arch. Microbiol., *1*, 1930, 34.)

au.ran.ti'a.ca. L. part.adj. *aurans, aurantis* gilded; M.L. adj. *aurantiacus* orange-colored.

Cells 1.0 micron wide at the center by 6 to 8 microns long. Except for size, very similar to those of *Cytophaga hutchinsonii*. Gram-negative.

Produces orange, mucilaginous patches on filter paper-silica gel plates. Fibrolysis is very rapid and intense.

Source: Isolated from soil.

Habitat: Soil. Decomposes cellulose.

4. **Cytophaga rubra** Winogradsky, 1929. (Ann. Inst. Past., *43*, 1929, 598.)

ru′bra. L. adj. *ruber* red.

Description taken from Stanier (Bact. Rev., *6*, 1942, 192).

Flexible, singly occurring rods, 0.5 to 0.7 by 3.5 to 11.0 microns, averaging about 7.0 microns in length. Gram-negative.

Produces diffuse, bright pink, rapidly spreading patches on filter paper-silica gel or -agar plates after a few days. The patches are only slightly mucilaginous, and dissolution of the fibers always remains incomplete.

Produces small, pale pink, translucent colonies with hazily defined peripheries on mineral-glucose-agar plates. The maximum diameter is 2 mm, and the colonies are sunken in the medium.

Cellulose, cellobiose, glucose, mannose and xylose are utilized. Arabinose, galactose, fructose and mannitol are not utilized.

Ammonia, nitrate, aspartic acid, asparagine, peptone and yeast extract can serve as nitrogen sources.

Catalase-positive.

Strictly aerobic.

Optimum temperature, 30° C.

Source: Isolated from soil.

Habitat: Soil. Decomposes cellulose.

5. **Cytophaga tenuissima** Winogradsky, 1929. (Ann. Inst. Past., *43*, 1929, 599; incorrectly spelled *Cytophaga ternissima* in Bergey et al., Manual, 4th ed., 1934, 559.)

te.nu.is′si.ma. L. sup.adj. *tenuissimus* very slender.

Dimensions of cells not given, but described as being extremely slender. Gram-negative.

Produces mucilaginous, greenish to olive patches on filter paper-silica gel plates.

Source: Isolated from soil.

Habitat: Soil. Decomposes cellulose.

6. **Cytophaga johnsonii** Stanier, 1947. (Vegetative myxobacteria, Johnson, Jour. Bact., *24*, 1932, 340; Stanier, Jour. Bact., *53*, 1947, 306.)

john.so′ni.i. M.L. gen.noun *johnsonii* of Johnson; named for Miss Delia E. Johnson, the bacteriologist who first isolated this species.

Thin rods of even width and very variable length. Dimensions 0.2 to 0.4 by 1.5 to 15.0 microns. Long rods predominate in very young cultures, but in most strains they give place to shorter, sometimes almost coccoid, elements as cultures age. Gram-negative.

Growth on peptone agar is smooth, glistening, translucent and bright yellow. Colony form markedly modified by peptone concentration. With low concentrations, a characteristically myxobacterial colony: thin, flat and rapidly spreading; with more than 0.5 per cent peptone: raised, convex and confined, with entire edge.

Growth on chitin agar is flat, rapidly spreading, translucent, pale yellow, accompanied by dissolution of the suspended chitin.

Peptone gelatin: Scanty growth, followed by very slow liquefaction. Some strains do not grow.

Milk: Very slow peptonization.

Arabinose, xylose, glucose, galactose, mannose, lactose, sucrose, cellobiose, maltose, raffinose, starch, inulin and chitin are utilized. Cellulose, mannitol and dulcitol are not utilized. Peptone and other complex nitrogenous materials can serve as carbon sources in the absence of carbohydrates.

Nitrate, ammonia and peptone are suitable nitrogen sources.

Catalase not formed.

Indole not produced.

Nitrate usually not reduced. One variety is capable of denitrification with a vigorous gas production from nitrate.

Strictly aerobic.

Optimum temperature, between 25° and 30° C.

Source: Isolated from soil and mud.

Habitat: Soil. Decomposes chitin.

7. **Cytophaga deprimata** Fuller and Norman, 1943. (Jour. Bact., *45*, 1943, 566.) de.pri.ma'ta. L. part.adj. *deprimatus* depressed.

Rod, long and flexuous with pointed ends, 0.3 to 0.5 by 5.5 to 10 microns, arranged singly. Creeping motility on solid surfaces. Gram-negative.

Growth on starch agar is at first smoky to faint yellow becoming bright yellow later. Colonies are irregular and concave in elevation. The edge spreads indistinguishably into the surrounding medium, and shallow depressions develop around the colony. Small colonies give the plate a characteristic pitted appearance.

Growth on cellulose dextrin agar is milky white. Colonies are depressed in medium.

Gelatin is liquefied in 4 days.

Glucose, lactose, maltose, sucrose, pectin, starch, cellulose dextrin and hemicellulose are utilized. Very scant growth on cellulose may be found on first isolation.

Yeast extract, ammonium nitrate and peptone are suitable nitrogen sources.

Indole not produced.

Nitrites not produced from nitrates.

No visible change in litmus milk.

Highly aerobic.

Optimum temperature, between 25° and 30° C.

Source: Isolated from soil.

Habitat: Soil. Decomposes organic matter.

8. **Cytophaga albogilva** Fuller and Norman, 1943. (Jour. Bact., *45*, 1943, 566.) al.bo.gil'va. L. adj. *albogilvus* whitish yellow.

Long flexuous rods with pointed ends, 0.3 to 0.5 by 4.5 to 7.5 microns, arranged singly. Creeping motility on solid surfaces. Gram-negative.

Growth on starch agar is cream to pale yellow. Colonies are small, concave and irregularly round. Edge is entire and irregular.

Growth on cellulose dextrin agar is restricted. Colonies are pin-point, milky white in color, round and concave.

Gelatin is liquefied in 7 days.

Glucose, galactose, lactose, maltose, sucrose, gum arabic, pectin, starch, cellulose,

dextrin and hemicellulose are utilized. Very scant growth on cellulose may be found on first isolation.

Ammonia, nitrate and peptone are suitable nitrogen sources.

Indole not produced.

Nitrites not produced from nitrates.

No visible change in litmus milk.

Highly aerobic.

Optimum temperature, between 22° and 30° C.

Source: Isolated from soil.

Habitat: Soil. Decomposes organic matter.

9. **Cytophaga krzemieniewskae** Stanier, 1940. (Incorrectly spelled *Cytophaga krzemieniewskii* in Stanier, Jour. Bact., *40*, 1940, 623; Jour. Bact., *42*, 1941, 532.) krze.mi.en.i.ew'skae. M.L. gen.noun *krzemieniewskae* of Krzemieniewska; named for Helena Krzemieniewska.

Long, flexible rods, usually of even width with blunt ends, occasionally somewhat pointed and spindle-shaped, 0.5 to 1.5 by 5 to 20 microns. Star-shaped aggregates occur in liquid media. Creeping motility on solid surfaces, non-motile in liquids.

Growth on a sea-water-peptone agar plate begins as a smooth, thin, pale pink, rapidly spreading swarm. After a few days, the older portions of the swarm assume a warty appearance, due to the accumulation of cells in drop-like masses, resembling immature fruiting bodies but always containing normal vegetative cells. A diffusible brown to black pigment which masks the pink color of the swarm is produced after about a week. Agar is rapidly decomposed, and ultimately liquefaction becomes almost complete.

Sea-water-gelatin stab: Liquefaction.

Growth in liquid media is turbid and silky with a pink sediment; the medium turns dark brown or black after 1 or 2 weeks.

Xylose, glucose, galactose, lactose, maltose, cellobiose, cellulose, alginic acid, agar and starch are utilized, but not arabinose, sucrose or chitin.

Yeast extract and peptone are the only suitable nitrogen sources known.

Weakly catalase-positive.

Indole not produced.

Nitrites produced from nitrates.

Hydrogen sulfide not produced.

Salt concentration range: 1.5 to 5.0 per cent.

Strictly aerobic.

Optimum temperature, between 22° and 25° C.

Source: Isolated from sea water.

Habitat: Sea-water. Probably on decaying marine vegetation.

10. Cytophaga diffluens Stanier, 1940. (Jour. Bact., *40*, 1940, 623; Jour. Bact., *42*, 1941, 546.)

dif'flu.ens. L. part.adj. *diffluens* flowing away.

Pointed, sometimes spindle-shaped, flexible rods, 0.5 to 1.5 by 4 to 10 microns. In old cultures involution forms consisting of long, twisted, thin threads are found. Star-shaped aggregates of cells occur in liquid media. Creeping motility on solid surfaces, non-motile in liquids.

Growth on a sea-water-peptone agar plate begins as a thin, pink, rapidly spreading swarm which often covers the entire surface in a few days. The swarm gradually increases in thickness and develops an irregular, beaten-copper surface due to the liquefaction of the underlying agar. After 4 to 5 days the color becomes orange. Liquefaction of the agar is ultimately almost complete.

Sea-water-gelatin stab: Rapid liquefaction.

Growth in liquid media is turbid, often with suspended floccules and a heavy pellicle.

Xylose, glucose, galactose, lactose, maltose, cellobiose, cellulose, agar and alginic acid are utilized, but not arabinose, sucrose, chitin or starch.

Yeast extract and peptone are the only suitable nitrogen sources known.

Weakly catalase-positive.

Indole not produced.

Nitrites produced from nitrates.

Hydrogen sulfide not produced.

Salt concentration range: 1.5 to 5.0 per cent.

Strictly aerobic.

Optimum temperature, between 22° and 25° C.

Source: Isolated from sea water.

Habitat: Sea water. Probably on decaying marine vegetation.

11. Cytophaga sensitiva Humm, 1946. (Duke Univ. Marine Lab., North Carolina, Bull. 3, 1946, 64.)

sen.si.ti'va. L. noun *sensus* perception; M.L. adj. *sensitivus* sensitive.

Cells long, slender, flexuous rods, 0.8 to 1.0 by 7.0 to 20 microns. Cell ends not tapered or only slightly so. Gram-negative. Cells exhibit creeping motility on agar with ability to reverse direction of movement without turning. Bending movements occur in liquid media.

Colonies light orange, thin and shining. Irregular margin. Outer part composed of a single layer of cells, spreading rapidly, the center somewhat thicker and more or less opaque, sunken in the agar. Agar liquefied. Single colony may nearly cover the surface of the agar in the Petri dish within one week; center of colony sinks to the bottom of the dish and may develop vertical sides. Usually the colony begins to die after a week or ten days from the center outward, as shown by loss of pigment. Apparently no water-soluble pigment is produced. Colony 18 mm in diameter and gelase field 25 mm in diameter after three days on agar containing 0.8 per cent potassium nitrate and 0.8 per cent peptone (iodine stain).

Gelatin: No growth.

Milk: No growth.

Nitrite apparently not produced from nitrate (agar medium).

Optimum nitrate concentration of medium appeared to be 0.5 per cent. Fair growth on sea water plus agar only, and on agar containing 1.0 per cent potassium nitrate. Slight growth on 2.0 per cent nitrate agar.

Optimum peptone concentration appeared to be about 0.1 per cent; growth inhibited by concentrations of peptone exceeding 0.4 per cent.

No growth on agar media containing any one of the following substances in a concentration of 0.2 per cent: glucose, starch, ammonium sulfate. The basal medium, however, supported excellent growth.

Repeated efforts were made to obtain a pure culture by streaking plates and by pouring plates. These were finally successful by the use of an agar medium that contained 0.1 per cent peptone, 0.05 per cent beef extract, 0.05 per cent glucose and traces of yeast extract and ferric phosphate. Good growth on broth of this composition was also obtained. Apparently the yeast extract supplied necessary growth substances.

Source: Isolated by streaking a piece of *Dictyota dichotoma* on agar containing 0.2 per cent potassium nitrate.

Habitat: From seaweed. Beaufort, North Carolina.

NOTE: *Species incertae sedis.* In recent years at least fourteen additional species have been placed in the genus *Cytophaga* or in other genera that appear to duplicate this genus. For example Stapp and Bortels (Zent. f. Bakt., II Abt., *90*, 1934, 28) have described five new species of *Cytophaga* from the humus of forest soils. Similarly, the following authors have described unicellular species that apparently belong here, the majority of which attack cellulose: Verona (Rendiconti R. Accad. Naz. d. Lincei, *19*, Ser. 6a, 1934, 731), Imšenecki and Solntzeva (Bull. Acad. Sci., U.S.S.R., Ser. Biol., No. 6, 1936, 000), Verona and Baldacci (Myco-pathologia, *2*, 1939, 135; also see Boll. R. Ist. Patol. d. Libro, *1*, 1939, 8 pp.), Soriano (Rev. Argentina de Agronomia, *12*, 1945, 125), Pringsheim (Jour. Gen. Microbiol., *5*, 1951, 145) and Kadota (Bull. Japanese Soc. of Sci. Fisheries, *19*, 1953, 476). Some of the organisms described were found in soil or humus, while others were found to cause deterioration of paper or stored fish nets; still others were found in the intestines or feces of termites. Comparative studies must be made before the true relationships of these species can be determined.

FAMILY II. ARCHANGIACEAE JAHN, 1924.

(Beiträge zur bot. Protistologie. I, Die Polyangiden. Geb. Borntraeger, Leipzig, 1924.)

Ar.chan.gi.a'ce.ae. M.L. neut.n. *Archangium* type genus of the family; *-aceae* ending to denote a family; M.L. fem.pl.n. *Archangiaceae* the *Archangium* family.

The resting cells are shortened rods, never enclosed in larger cysts. The fruiting bodies are irregularly swollen or twisted, or are finger-like structures.

Key to the genera of family **Archangiaceae.**

I. Fruiting body depressed, usually irregularly delimited, the interior usually consisting of swollen or intestine-like twisted or inter-twined masses, whose windings may be constricted or may jut out (project) as free ends.

Genus I. *Archangium*, p. 863.

II. Fruiting body consists of single (separate) columnar or finger-like structures arising from the substrate.

Genus II. *Stelangium*, p. 866.

Genus I. **Archangium** *Jahn, 1924.*

(Beiträge zur bot. Protistologie. I, Die Polyangiden. Geb. Borntraeger, Leipzig, 1924, 67.)

Ar.chan'gi.um. Gr. noun *arche* from the first, beginning; Gr. noun *angium* a vessel, receptacle; M.L. neut.n. *Archangium* primitive vessel.

The mass of shortened rods embedded in slime forms a pad-shaped or more rounded, superficially swollen or tuberous fruiting body, even with horny divisions. The fruiting body has no membrane. In the interior can be seen a mass resembling coiled intestines. The windings of this coil may be uniform, or irregularly jointed, free or stuck together; the ends may be extended and horny. Instead of a membrane there may be loosely enveloping slime.

The type species is *Archangium gephyra* Jahn.

Key to the species of genus **Archangium.**

I. No slimy capsules.

A. Fruiting body usually wound, irregularly constricted, sometimes swollen and vesicular, appressed.

1. Fruiting body red.
   a. The shortened rods 2.5 to 3 microns.
       1. *Archangium gephyra.*
   aa. The shortened rods 4 to 6 microns.
       2. *Archangium primigenium.*
  2. Fruiting body yellow.
       3. *Archangium flavum.*
  B. Tube usually uniformly thick, loosely wound, often branched.
       4. *Archangium serpens.*
II. Fruiting body consisting of a reddish, coiled tube embedded in yellow slime.
       5. *Archangium thaxteri.*

1. **Archangium gephyra** Jahn, 1924. (*Chondromyces serpens* Quehl, Cent. f. Bakt., II Abt., *16*, 1906, 16; Jahn, Beiträge zur bot. Protistologie. I, Die Polyangiden. Geb. Borntraeger, Leipzig, 1924, 67.)

ge′phy.ra. Gr. noun *gephyra* a bridge (intermediate).

Swarm stage (pseudoplasmodium): Grows easily in manure decoction, forming a pseudoplasmodium and ring of fruiting bodies. The vegetative rods are about 10 microns long, 0.5 micron in diameter.

Fruiting bodies: Up to 1 mm in diameter, of irregular form and with swollen or padded surface. Average-sized fruiting bodies are a reddish flesh color by reflected light; smaller fruiting bodies, a light rose. On a dark background, large fruiting bodies, when fresh, appear bluish violet. By transmitted light the fruiting bodies appear yellowish to light red.

The inner structures are for the most part a mesenteric mass of tubes 40 to 60 microns wide, without any membrane and without any enclosing slime. The convolutions are often pressed together. On the inside of these tubes there appears definitely a septation by straight or slightly arched cross walls which, however, do not always cut entirely through the spore masses from one side of the tube to the other. Upon pressure, the fruiting body breaks up into a number of small fragments about 15 to 30 microns in diameter. Within these fragments the shortened rods lie parallel and in bundles.

The rods in the fruiting bodies are so shortened that they resemble the spores of the *Myxococcaceae*. The spores are 2.5 to 2.8 microns long and about 1.4 microns wide. Often they are somewhat bent so that they appear to be bean-shaped. In the smooth, transparent tips of fruiting bodies they stand closely parallel to each other, so that in transmitted light one sees only their cross section and is at first led to believe that he is dealing with one of the *Myxococcaceae*.

Source: Found in rabbit dung. Found frequently in the region of Berlin on the dung of deer, rabbits and hare, once also on old decaying lichens. Easily overlooked on account of its usual bluish color.

Habitat: Found on decaying organic matter in soil and in the dung of various animals. According to Krzemieniewski (Acta Soc. Bot. Poloniae, *5*, 1927), the most common of myxobacters in the soils of Poland.

Illustrations: Quehl (*op. cit.*, *16*, 1906, Pl. 1, Fig. 7), Jahn (*op. cit.*, 1924, Pl. 1, Fig. 5) and Krzemieniewski (Acta Soc. Bot. Poloniae, *4*, 1926, Pl. III, Figs. 25–26).

2. **Archangium primigenium** (Quehl, 1906) Jahn, 1924. (*Polyangium primigenium* Quehl, Cent. f. Bakt., II Abt., *16*, 1906, 16; Jahn, Beiträge zur bot. Protistologie. I, Die Polyangiden. Geb. Borntraeger, Leipzig, 1924.)

pri.mi.ge′ni.um. L. adj. *primigenius* primitive.

Swarm stage (pseudoplasmodium): In manure decoction, cysts germinate readily. Vegetative rods 4 to 8 microns in length.

Fruiting bodies: Up to 1 mm in diameter, sometimes larger, with irregularly padded swollen surface; when fresh, a lively red color is produced which is quite prominent, especially against a dark background; when dried, dark red. In transmitted light flesh-red to yellowish red.

In transmitted light one sees that the fruiting body is made up of numerous intestine-like convolutions closely appressed, not, however, always definitely delimited. These tubes usually have a diameter of from 70 to 90 microns, often constricted and attenuated. No membrane is present. The rods in the fruiting bodies are about 4 microns long and 0.8 micron wide. Upon pressure on the fruiting bodies, the rods remain together in small fragments of various sizes.

Habitat: Found on rabbit dung, sometimes on roe dung. According to Jahn (*loc. cit.*), not particularly common.

Illustrations: Quehl (Cent. f. Bakt., II Abt., *16*, 1906, 16, Pl. 1, Fig. 5), Jahn (Kryptogamenflora d. Mark Brandenburg, V, Pilze I, Lief. 2, 1911, 201, Pl. 1, Fig. 5), Jahn (*op. cit.*, 1924, Pl. 1, Fig. 4, also Fig. G, page 37) and Krzemieniewski (Acta Soc. Bot. Poloniae, *4*, 1926, Pl. II, Fig. 23; also see *op. cit.*, 1927, Pl. IV, Fig. 3, var. *assurgens* and Pl. IV, Figs. 1–2).

2a. *Archangium primigenium* var. *assurgens* Jahn, 1924. (Beiträge zur bot. Protistologie. I, Die Polyangiden. Geb. Borntraeger, Leipzig, 1924, 69.)

as.sur'gens. L. part.adj. *assurgens* rising up.

Size and color of the fruiting body as in the species, likewise the inner structure, size and arrangement of the rods. However, the tubules which together constitute the fruiting bodies are more or less free at their ends and stand up from the substrate. Their diameter is somewhat less (about 45 microns), they are often convoluted so that they many times appear to be constricted (like pearls).

Pronounced races of the species and of the variety are so different in habits that they may be regarded as distinct species. Jahn believes the presence of intermediate strains makes a separation difficult.

Habitat: Relatively rare, being found only three times on rabbit dung by Kofler (Sitzber. d. kais. Akad. wiss. Wien, math.-nat. Klasse, Abt. I, *122*, 1913). Very rare in Polish soils according to Krzemieniewski (Acta Soc. Bot. Poloniae, *5*, 1927, 95).

3. **Archangium flavum** (Kofler, 1913) Jahn, 1924. (*Polyangium flavum* Kofler, Sitzber. d. kais. Akad. wiss. Wien, math.-nat. Klasse, Abt. I, *122*, 1913, 864; Jahn, Beiträge zur bot. Protistologie. I, Die Polyangiden. Geb. Borntraeger, Leipzig, 1924, 71.)

fla'vum. L. adj. *flavus* yellow or golden.

Swarm stage (pseudoplasmodium): Not described.

Fruiting bodies: About 0.5 mm in diameter, yellow, spherical or ellipsoidal, with humped or padded surface. The mass of cells quite homogeneous; upon pressure under cover glass, single sections tend to adhere. No membrane, though the rods are so tightly linked that when cautiously placed under a cover glass, the form of the fruiting body is retained. Rods 2 to 4 microns.

Source: Found by Kofler (1924) on hare dung found in Danube meadows.

Habitat: Found on decaying organic matter in soil and in the dung of various animals. Reported as frequent in Polish soils by Krzemieniewski (1926, 1927).

Illustrations: Krzemieniewski (Acta Soc. Bot. Poloniae, *4*, 1926, Pl. II, Fig. 24; also see *ibid.*, 1927, Pl. IV, Figs. 4, 5 and 6).

4. **Archangium serpens** (Thaxter, 1892) Jahn, 1924. (*Chondromyces serpens* Thaxter, Bot. Gaz., *17*, 1892, 403; Jahn, Beiträge zur bot. Protistologie. I, Die Polyangiden. Geb. Borntraeger, Leipzig, 1924, 72.)

ser'pens. L. part.adj. *serpens* creeping.

Swarm stage (pseudoplasmodium): Rods cylindrical, 0.6 by 5 to 7 microns. Cultures on agar develop convoluted form.

Fruiting body: About 1 mm in diameter, recumbent, consisting of numerous loosely intertwined cysts, confluent in an anastomosing coil, flesh-colored, when dry dark red, 50 microns in diameter, bent, occasionally somewhat broadened or constricted, branched.

Source: Found on decaying lichens from Cambridge, Mass.

Habitat: Decaying lichens.

Illustrations: Thaxter (*op. cit.*, Pl. 24, Fig. 24).

5. **Archangium thaxteri** Jahn, 1924. (Beiträge zur bot. Protistologie. I, Die

Polyangiden. Geb. Borntraeger, Leipzig, 1924, 71.)

thax'te.ri. M.L. gen.noun *thaxteri* of Thaxter; named for Dr. Roland Thaxter.

Swarm stage (pseudoplasmodium): Vegetative stages not observed. Either no germination or prompt cessation of growth on dung extract. May be transferred on dung.

Fruiting body: Usually 0.25 to 0.5 mm, occasionally 0.75 mm in diameter. Irregularly rounded, superficially sulfur-yellow. Upon pressure numerous reddish convoluted tubules are observed embedded in a yellow slime. The average diameter of the tubules is about 50 microns. No membrane surrounds the tubes. They contain the shortened rods. Enveloping slime is variable. In well developed specimens the slime forms a stalk, giving the whole the appearance of a morel. In small specimens the rods are embedded in the slime. The fruiting bodies stand loosely separated on surface of dung, never in large groups. Shortened rods (spores) 0.5 micron by 3 microns, very slender.

Habitat: According to Jahn, found only rarely on rabbit dung; races with well developed stalks are even less common.

Illustrations: Jahn (*ibid.*, Pl. 1, Figs. 1–2) and Krzemieniewski (Acta Soc. Bot. Poloniae, *4*, 1926, Pl. II, Fig. 27).

Genus II. **Stelangium** *Jahn, 1915.*

(Kryptogamenflora der Mark Brandenburg, V, Pilze I, Lief 2, 1915, 205.)

Ste.lan'gi.um or Ste.lan.gi'um. Gr. noun *stele* pillar or column; Gr. noun *angium* vessel, container; M.L. neut.n. *Stelangium* columnar vessel.

Fruiting bodies are columnar or finger-like, sometimes forked, without a definite stalk, standing upright on the substrate.

The type species is *Stelangium muscorum* (Thaxter) Jahn.

1. **Stelangium muscorum** (Thaxter, 1904) Jahn, 1915. (*Chondromyces muscorum* Thaxter, Bot. Gaz., *37*, 1904, 411; Jahn, Kryptogamenflora d. Mark Brandenburg, V, Pilze I, Lief 2, 1915, 205.)

mus.co'rum. L. noun *muscus* moss; L. gen.pl.noun *muscorum* of mosses.

Swarm stage (pseudoplasmodium): Not described.

Fruiting body: Bright yellow-orange, 90 to 300 microns long, 10 to 50 microns wide, without differentiated stalk, simple or rarely furcate, upright, elongate, compact or slender, narrowed at tip. Rods (spores) 1 to 1.3 by 4 to 6 microns.

Source: Found on liverworts on living beech trunks in Indiana.

Illustrations: Thaxter (*op. cit.*, 1904, Pl. 27, Figs. 16–18).

FAMILY III. SORANGIACEAE JAHN, 1924.

(Beiträge zur bot. Protistologie. I, Die Polyangiden. Geb. Borntraeger, Leipzig, 1924, 73.)

So.ran.gi.a'ce.ae. M.L. neut.n. *Sorangium* type genus of the family; *-aceae* ending to denote a family; M.L. fem.pl.n. *Sorangiaceae* the *Sorangium* family.

The shortened rods of the fruiting body lie in angular, usually relatively small cysts of definite polygonal shape. Often many of these cysts are surrounded by a common membrane. The primary cyst may be differentiated from the angular or secondary cysts. No stalked forms are known.

Genus I. **Sorangium** *Jahn, 1924.*

(Beiträge zur bot. Protisitologie. I, Die Polyangiden. Geb. Borntraeger, Leipzig, 1924, 73.)

So.ran'gi.um. Gr. noun *sōrus* a heap; M.L. noun *sorus* a fungus spore pustule; Gr. noun *angium* a vessel; M.L. noun *Sorangium* heaped vessel.

Description as for the family. The cysts are united into rounded fruiting bodies. Eight species have been allocated to this genus.

The type species is *Sorangium schroeteri* Jahn.

Key to the species of genus **Sorangium**.

I. Fruiting bodies not black when ripe.
   A. Primary cysts absent; fruiting body shows only angular, spherical or ellipsoidal small cysts.
      1. Cysts angular.
         a. Fruiting body very small (50 to 80 microns), often irregularly cerebriform; the angular cysts often completely separated from each other and about 13 microns in diameter.
               1. *Sorangium schroeteri.*
        aa. Fruiting body composed of many small cysts.
           b. Cysts orange-red in color; over 5.0 microns in diameter.
               2. *Sorangium sorediatum.*
           bb. Rusty brown color; cysts less than 3.5 microns in diameter.
               3. *Sorangium cellulosum.*
      2. Cysts spherical or ellipsoidal.
               4. *Sorangium spumosum.*
   B. Both primary and secondary cysts present.
      1. Primary cysts small and numerous, about 20 microns, with definite membrane and few angular secondary cysts.
               5. *Sorangium septatum.*
      2. Primary cysts large, with delicate, often indefinite, membrane.
               6. *Sorangium compositum.*
II. Fruiting bodies black or brownish-black when ripe.
   A. Primary cysts generally not formed.
               7. *Sorangium nigrum.*
   B. Primary cysts generally formed.
               8. *Sorangium nigrescens.*

1. Sorangium schroeteri Jahn, 1924. (Beiträge zur bot. Protistologie. I, Die Polyangiden. Geb. Borntraeger, Leipzig, 1924, 73; regarded as a synonym of *Sorangium compositum* by Krzemieniewski, Acta Soc. Bot. Poloniae, *5*, 1927, 96.)

schroe'te.ri. M.L. gen.noun *schroeteri* of Schroeter; named for Julius Schroeter.

Vegetative cells: Not described.

Fruiting bodies: Very small, circular, swollen, often kidney-shaped with brain-like convolutions, usually 60 microns (occasionally 120 microns) in diameter, bright orange-red. Surrounded by a delicate slime membrane about 0.7 micron thick, apparent only with high magnifications. Divided secondarily into angular cysts by sutures extending inward which divide the mass regularly into well delimited portions, many angled, usually about 12 microns in diameter, and in other places into areas less well delimited and about 14 microns in diameter. Resembles gelatin which has dried in a sheet and cracked into regular areas. Rods in cysts 5 microns long. Cysts sometimes occur together in large numbers, covering an area to 0.5 mm.

Source: Found by Jahn (*op. cit.*, 1924, 73) five times on rabbit dung in the environs of Berlin.

Illustrations: Jahn (*ibid.*, Pl. 2, Fig. 22).

2. Sorangium sorediatum (Thaxter, 1904) Jahn, 1924. (*Polyangium sorediatum* Thaxter, Bot. Gaz., *37*, 1904, 414; Jahn, Beiträge zur bot. Protistologie. I, Die

Polyangiden. Geb. Borntraeger, Leipzig, 1924, 73.)

so.re.di.a'tum. Gr. noun *sorus* a heap; M.L. dim.noun *soredium* a little heap, a soredium; M.L. adj. *sorediatus* having little heaps.

Vegetative cells: Rods 0.8 by 3 to 5 microns. Attempts to cultivate have failed.

Fruiting body: Orange-red, irregularly lobed, consisting of a compact mass of small angular cysts. Average size of cysts, 6 to 7 microns; smallest, 3 microns, with thick and sharply defined edges. Rods 0.8 by 3 to 5 microns. The Krzemieniewskis (Acta Soc. Bot. Poloniae, 1927, 96) have described a variety, *Sorangium sorediatum* var. *macrocystum*, consisting of cysts 6 to 14 by 7 to 16 microns, about twice as large as those in the type species.

Source: Reported by Thaxter (*op. cit.*, 1904, 414) on rabbit dung from South Carolina.

Habitat: Found on decaying organic matter in soil and in the dung of various animals. Common in Polish soils (Krzemieniewski, *op. cit.*, 1927, 96).

Illustrations: Thaxter (*op. cit.*, 1904, Pl. 27, Figs. 22–24), Quehl (Cent. f. Bakt., II Abt., *16*, 1906, 9, Pl. 1, Fig. 2), Jahn (Kryptogamen-flora d. Mark Brandenburg, V, Pilze I, Lief 2, 1911, 202, Fig. 1) and Krzemieniewski (Acta Soc. Bot. Pol., *4*, 1926, Pl. IV, Figs. 39–41; also see *ibid.*, 1927, Pl. V, Fig. 17, var. *macrocystum*, Fig. 18).

3. Sorangium cellulosum Imšenecki and Solntzeva, 1937. (Microbiologia, *6*, 1937, 7.)

cel.lu.lo'sum. M.L. noun *cellulosum* cellulose.

Vegetative cells: Flexible and rod-shaped with rounded ends, 0.4 to 0.6 by 2.2 to 4.5 microns, occurring singly.

Fruiting body: Mature fruiting body rusty brown, 400 to 500 microns in diameter, sessile on layer of partially dried slime. No outer wall or limiting membrane. Composed of numerous cysts, irregular in shape, 1.6 to 3.2 microns in diameter, each containing less than ten shortened rods. No discernible cyst wall or membrane.

Resting cells: 0.3 by 1.5 to 2.0 microns (no other data).

Vegetative colony: No data.

Physiology: Good growth on starch and cellulose. Decomposes up to 24 per cent cellulose in ten days but does not form fruiting bodies. Very poor growth on arabinose with the formation of many involution forms including very much elongated cells. Fails to grow on nutrient agar, washed agar, potato, carrot or milk.

Source: Isolated from soil.

Habitat: Soil. Decomposes organic matter.

4. Sorangium spumosum Krzemieniewski and Krzemieniewska, 1927. (Acta Soc. Bot. Poloniae, *5*, 1927, 97.)

spu.mo'sum. L. adj. *spumosus* foamy or frothy.

Vegetative cells: Rods 0.7 to 0.9 by 2.6 to 5.2 microns.

Fruiting bodies: Consist of numerous cysts, spherical or ellipsoidal, not surrounded by a common membrane but united into bodies embedded in slime. Often in double or single rows. Cyst walls colorless, or slightly brownish, transparent, so that the characteristic arrangement of the rods may be seen within. Cysts 8 to 26 by 7 to 20 microns.

Source: From Polish soil; also isolated from rabbit dung.

Habitat: Found on decaying organic matter in soil and in the dung of various animals.

Illustrations: Krzemieniewski (*ibid.*, Pl. V, Fig. 19).

5. Sorangium septatum (Thaxter, 1904) Jahn, 1924. (*Polyangium septatum* Thaxter, Bot. Gaz., *37*, 1904, 412; Jahn, Beiträge zur bot. Protistologie. I, Die Polyangiden, Geb. Borntraeger, Leipzig, 1924, 75.)

sep.ta'tum. L. adj. *septatus* fenced, *i.e.*, divided by walls.

Vegetative cells: Rods 0.8 to 1.0 by 3.0 to 5.0 microns.

Fruiting bodies: Yellowish orange. When dried, dark orange-red, 50 microns to more than 100 microns in diameter, cysts rounded or ellipsoidal, angular or cylindrical, inner portion of the envelope divided into a variable number of secondary cysts. Cysts 18 to 22 by 12 to 22 microns in diameter. Secondary cysts 10 to 12 microns. The Krzemieniewskis (Acta Soc. Bot. Poloniae, 5, 1927, 96) recognize a variety, *Sorangium septatum* var. *microcystum*, which has secondary cysts with dimensions 3 to 8 by 4 to 10 microns.

Source: Collected twice from horse dung in Cambridge, Mass.

Habitat: Found on decaying organic matter in soil and in the dung of various animals. Reported by Krzemieniewski (*loc. cit.*) as common in Polish soil.

Illustrations: Thaxter (*op. cit.*, 1904, Pl. 27, Figs. 25–28), Jahn (Kryptogamen-flora d. Mark Brandenburg, V, Pilze I. Lief 2, 1911, 202, Fig. 2) and Krzemieniewski (Acta Soc. Bot. Poloniae, 4, 1926, Pl. 27, Figs. 27–38; also see *ibid.*, 1927, Pl. V, Fig. 15, var. *microcystum*, Fig. 16).

6. Sorangium compositum (Thaxter, 1904) Jahn, 1924. (*Polyangium compositum* Thaxter, Bot. Gaz., 37, 1904, 413; Jahn, Beiträge zur bot. Protistologie. I, Die Polyangiden. Geb. Borntraeger, Leipzig, 1924, 74; *Polyangium sorediatum* Quehl, Cent. f. Bakt., II Abt., 16, 1906, 17; not *Polyangium sorediatum* Thaxter, *op. cit.*, 1904, 414.)

com.pos'i.tum. L. adj. *compositus* compound.

Vegetative cells: Not described.

Fruiting bodies: Dull yellowish orange changing to dark red on drying. Rounded, small, 0.5 to 1 mm, usually as a whole or even in larger clumps surrounded by a delicate and evanescent membrane. In large fruiting bodies the cysts are bound together in balls, 70 to 90 microns in diameter, by a delicate membrane. The balls readily fall apart. Secondary cysts are angular, 7 by 11 microns, surrounded by a delicate orangered membrane about 0.4 micron in thickness. Length of rods in the cysts, 5 microns.

Source: Found on rabbit dung from South Carolina. Jahn (*op. cit.*, 1904) found it four times on rabbit dung near Berlin, twice on hare dung in Oberharg.

Habitat: Found on decaying organic matter in soil and in the dung of various animals. Common in soils of Poland according to Krzemieniewski (Acta Soc. Bot. Poloniae, 5, 1927).

Illustrations: Thaxter (*op. cit.*, 1904, Pl. 27, Figs. 29–30), Jahn (*op. cit.*, 1924, Pl. I,

Fig. 6) and Krzemieniewski (*op. cit.*, 4, 1926, Pl. III, Figs. 32–36; *ibid.*, 5, 1927, Pl. IV, Figs. 7–12; Pl. V, Figs. 13–14; Pl. VI, Fig. 36).

7. Sorangium nigrum Krzemieniewska and Krzemieniewski, 1937. (Bull. Int. l'Acad. Pol. Sci. et Lettres, Classe Sci. Math. et Nat., Sér. B, 15, 1937.)

ni'grum. L. adj. *niger* black.

Vegetative cells: 1.1 to 1.3 by 2.5 to 5.5 microns.

Fruiting body: Primary cysts generally not formed; when observed, appeared as smoke-colored slime envelope surrounding clumps of a few cysts. Secondary cysts usually arranged in rows within cellulose fibers, the material of the fiber forming a common sheath. Each individual cyst is enclosed by a cyst wall, clearly differentiated from the tubular-shaped cellulose fibers. Cysts measure 9 to 16 by 9 to 23 microns; average 10 by 18 microns. Cyst wall moderately thick, colorless, transparent, becoming light brown with age, and finally black.

Colonies: Young colonies are black in color. On filter paper a bright orange margin is noted, the vegetative cells of which cover the cellulose fibers. On cotton cloth the margin is bright, dirty yellow, tinged with pink. Under low-power magnification, center of the colony appears similar to matted fungal hyphae, due to characteristic compact accumulation of cysts and cellulose fibers.

Physiology: Cellulose fibers become swollen by the action of this organism and become gray-brown with a violet tinge. Fibers lose the properties of cellulose and give no characteristic reactions.

Source: Isolated from soil.

Habitat: Soil. Decomposes cellulose.

Illustrations: Krzemieniewskis (*ibid.*, Plate IV, Figs. 22–26).

8. Sorangium nigrescens Krzemieniewska and Krzemieniewski, 1937. (Bull. Int. l'Acad. Pol. Sci. et Lettres, Classe Sci. Math. et Nat., Sér. B, 15, 1937.)

ni.gres'cens. L. part.adj. *nigrescens* becoming black.

Vegetative cells: 1.2 to 1.4 by 2.5 to 6.4 microns. Younger cells somewhat shorter.

Fruiting body: Primary cysts vary in size up to 200 microns in diameter, are irregular in shape and are enclosed in a colorless slime envelope. Formed by an accumulation of secondary cysts. Secondary cysts at first colorless, transparent, later becoming brownish with a limiting membrane; the young cysts appear dirty yellow, the older ones grayish brown to black. Secondary cysts measure 5 to 12 by 6 to 15 microns; average 6 by 10 microns. On filter paper not only well formed primary cysts are formed but also free secondary cysts are noted embedded in the slime of the colony.

Vegetative colony: A mass of dark fruiting bodies develops at the center of the colony on filter paper; margin, grayish yellow. The cellulose fibers are covered with vegetative cells on the outside and contain many cells within.

Physiology: Destroys cellulose. Cultivated six years with cellulose as a carbon source.

Source: Isolated from sandy soil in pine woods in Poland.

Habitat: Soil. Decomposes cellulose.

Illustrations: Krzemieniewskis (*ibid.*, Pl. III, Figs. 17–21).

FAMILY IV. POLYANGIACEAE JAHN, 1924.

(Beiträge zur bot. Protistologie. I, Die Polyangiden. Geb. Borntraeger, Leipzig, 1924.)

Po.ly.an.gi.a′ce.ae. M.L. neut.n. *Polyangium* type genus of the family; *-aceae* ending to denote a family; M.L. fem.pl.n. *Polyangiaceae* the *Polyangium* family.

The resting cells are shortened and usually somewhat thickened rods which are always enclosed in cysts. The cysts may be sessile, occurring either singly or in groups and enveloped in a slime membrane, or they may be raised on stalks (cystophores) which can be either simple or branched. Cysts can occur either singly or in clusters at the tips of the stalks.

Key to the genera of family **Polyangiaceae.**

I. Cysts embedded in slime; sessile, occurring singly or as loose aggregates.
　　　　　　　Genus I. *Polyangium*, p. 870.
II. Cysts never embedded in slime; either borne on stalks or arranged in tight clusters joined together at the base.
　A. Many cysts united at base to form a large disc or rosette; either sessile or stalked.
　　　　　　　Genus II. *Synangium*, p. 877.
　B. Cysts not united at base; borne singly or in large numbers on stalks.
　　1. Cysts borne singly on a stalk.
　　　　　　　Genus III. *Podangium*, p. 877.
　　2. Numerous cysts on a stalk.
　　　　　　　Genus IV. *Chondromyces*, p. 879.

Genus I. **Polyangium** Link, 1809.

(Mag. d. Ges. Naturforsch. Freunde zu Berlin, *3*, 1809, 42.)

Po.ly.an′gi.um or Po.ly.an.gi′um. Gr. adj. *poly* many; Gr. noun *angium* vessel; M.L. neut.n. *Polyangium* many vessels.

Cysts rounded or coiled and surrounded by a well developed membrane; either free or embedded in a second slimy layer.

The type species is *Polyangium vitellinum* Link.

Key to the species of genus **Polyangium.**

I. Not parasitic on algae.
　A. Sorus not white or grayish in color.

1. Cysts rounded to spherical.
  a. Ripe cysts yellow, reddish yellow, orange or light red; not brown.
    b. Cysts several or numerous and small.
      c. Not closely appressed.
        d. Slime envelope transparent white or colorless.
          e. Usually 10 to 15 cysts. Rods in cysts, 3 microns long. Cysts 75 to 200 microns.
            1. *Polyangium vitellinum.*
          ee. Cysts numerous. Rods 1.3 to 2.0 microns long. Cysts 20 to 80 microns.
            2. *Polyangium minus.*
        dd. Slime envelope bright yellow.
            3. *Polyangium luteum.*
      cc. Closely appressed; often polygonal due to pressure.
        d. Bright yellow.
            4. *Polyangium morula.*
        dd. Orange.
            5. *Polyangium cellulosum.*
    bb. Cysts single, large.
      c. Large, 250 to 400 microns; reddish yellow.
          6. *Polyangium simplex.*
      cc. Smaller, 30 to 60 by 50 to 130 microns; orange to light red.
          7. *Polyangium ochraceum.*
  aa. Ripe cysts reddish brown to dark brown.
    b. Cysts lying free, covered by a more or less definite slime envelope.
      c. About 60 microns in diameter; slime envelope delicate and colorless.
          8. *Polyangium fuscum.*
      cc. About 35 microns in diameter; slime envelope yellow.
          9. *Polyangium aureum.*
    bb. Cysts rounded, in stellate arrangements on a slimy substrate.
          10. *Polyangium stellatum.*
2. Cysts elongate, coiled.
  a. Cysts brownish red.
          11. *Polyangium ferrugineum.*
  aa. Cysts bright orange-yellow.
          12. *Polyangium indivisum.*
B. Sorus white or gray in color.
  1. Hyaline slime envelope white, foamy in appearance; cysts average 28 by 34 microns.
          13. *Polyangium spumosum.*
  2. Sorus flat, crust-like, smoke-gray in color due to slime envelope; cysts average 36 by 44 microns.
          14. *Polyangium fumosum.*
II. Aquatic, parasitic on *Cladophora.*
          15. *Polyangium parasiticum.*

1. Polyangium vitellinum Link, 1809. (Link, Mag. d. Ges. Naturforschender Feunde zu Berlin, *3*, 1809, 42; *Myxobacter aureus* Thaxter, Bot. Gaz., *17*, 1892, 403.)

vi.tel.li′num. L. noun *vitellus* an egg yolk; M.L. adj. *vitellinus* like egg yolk.

Vegetative cells: When rising to form cysts, milky white. Rods large, cylindrical, rounded at either end, 0.7 to 0.9 by 4.0 to 7.0 microns.

Fruiting body: Cysts golden yellow, usually relatively spherical, 75 to 150 microns, occasionally 200 microns in diameter, almost always surrounded by a white, slimy envelope, about 10 to 15 cysts in a mass. Rods in the cysts about 3 microns in length.

Source: Isolated from very wet wood and bark in swamps in Maine and Belmont, Mass. (Thaxter, *loc. cit.*). Also found on old wood lying in moist ditches, on old poplar bark which was kept in a moist dish and on rabbit dung.

Habitat: Found on decaying organic matter in soil and in the dung of various animals. Jahn (Beiträge zur bot. Protistologie. I, Die Polyangiden. Geb. Borntraeger, Leipzig, 1924) states that it is not common.

Illustrations: Thaxter (*op. cit.*, *17*, 1892, Pl. 25, Figs. 34–36), Zukal (Ber. d. deutsch. Bot. Ges., *15*, 1897, 542, Pl. 27, Figs. 6–10) and Jahn (Kryptogamenflora d. Mark Brandenburg, V, Pilze I, Lief 2, 1911, 199, Fig. 3; also see *op. cit.*, 1924, 77 and Pl. II, Fig. 13).

2. Polyangium minus Krzemieniewski, 1926. (Acta Soc. Bot. Poloniae, *4*, 1926, 33.)

mi'nus. L. comp.adj. *minor* less, smaller.

Vegetative cells: Rods 0.4 to 0.6 by 3.0 to 7.0 microns.

Fruiting bodies: Cyst masses commonly cover the substrate to an area of 0.5 sq. mm. Cysts are spherical or ellipsoidal, small, 20 to 80 by 20 to 50 microns, light rose in color, becoming brownish, embedded in a transparent colorless slime. Cyst membrane light colored, relatively thick, 0.5 to 1.0 micron, transparent, revealing the contents. Rods in cyst 0.8 to 1.0 by 1.3 to 2.0 microns.

Source: Isolated from rabbit dung which was sterilized and placed on soil (Poland). Relatively slow in appearance, only after many days.

Habitat: Found on decaying organic matter in soil and in the dung of various animals. Rather rare.

Illustrations: Krzemieniewski (*ibid.*, Pl. IV, Fig. 47–48; Pl. V, Fig. 49).

3. Polyangium luteum Krzemieniewski, 1927. (Acta Soc. Bot. Poloniae, *5*, 1927, 98.)

lu'te.um. L. adj. *luteus* saffron- or golden yellow.

Vegetative cells: Not described.

Fruiting bodies: Golden yellow, consisting of a few cysts surrounded by a common, bright yellow, very thick slime wall. The

cysts have colorless, thin walls. Rods 0.7 to 0.8 by 3.8 to 5.8 microns.

Source: Grown from soil on rabbit dung.

Habitat: Found on decaying organic matter in soil and in the dung of various animals.

Illustrations: Krzemieniewski (*ibid.*, Pl. V, Figs. 22–23).

4. Polyangium morula Jahn, 1911. (Kryptogamenflora der Mark Brandenburg, V, Pilze I, 1911, 202.)

mo'ru.la. Gr. noun *mora* the black mulberry; L. dim.noun *morula* a small mulberry.

Vegetative cells: Not described.

Fruiting bodies: Cysts bright yellow, closely packed into a mulberry-shaped sorus; cysts with thick membrane (3 microns), often made polygonal by pressure, 20 to 35 microns, bound together by slime. The whole sorus is 100 to 200 microns broad. Rods in cysts about 3 microns in length. Jahn states he has not studied fresh cysts. In the older cysts the rods are difficult to observe.

Source: Observed only once on rabbit dung.

Illustration: Jahn (Beiträge zur bot. Protistologie. I, Die Polyangiden, Geb. Borntraeger, Leipzig, 1924, Pl. 2, Fig. 21).

5. Polyangium cellulosum Imšenecki and Solntzeva, 1936*. (On aerobic cellulose-decomposing bacteria. Akademiia Nauk, Leningrad, Isvestiia, 1936, 1115; English summary, 1168.)

cel.lu.lo'sum. M.L. noun *cellulosum* cellulose.

Vegetative cells: Thick, bent rods with rounded ends, 0.8 to 1.2 by 3.5 to 8.5 microns.

Fruiting body: Rods at center of the colony are non-motile, forming large orange aggregates, and are shorter than those at the margin: 0.7 to 0.9 by 3.4 to 5.6 microns. Later a concentration of cells occurs. The rods come closer together to form rounded or ellipsoidal aggregates from which cysts become delimited. The cysts are orange in color, 8 to 24 microns, average 20 to 25 microns in diameter. In addition to bacterial cells, droplets of fat, 1.5 to 3.5 microns, are

---

* Translated from the original by E. V. Prostov, Iowa State College Library, Ames, Iowa.

sometimes seen within the cyst. When treated with H_2SO_4, cysts are easily broken up under the cover glass. Fruiting bodies are composed of clumps of cysts. The fruiting bodies are ellipsoidal or pear-shaped, 40 to 55 by 110 to 160 microns, reddish brown; they are covered with a slime membrane (flakes of dried slime). Each is composed of 12 to 40 cysts which become polygonal from pressure. The cysts are sometimes arranged in chains.

Resting cells: 0.7 to 0.8 by 2.2 to 3.5 microns.

Vegetative colony: Cysts germinate on filter paper producing vegetative colonies. Colonies large, orange, moist, increasing in size. The older colonies have orange margins while the center is dark brown, corresponding to the color of the fruiting bodies. Often show several concentric rings.

Physiology: Rods cover cellulose fibers, partially or completely destroying them. Paper becomes transparent.

Optimum temperature, between 18° and 22° C. Very slow growth at 30° C.

Grows only on cellulose, not in ordinary media.

Aerobic.

Source: Isolated from soil.

Illustrations: Imšenecki and Solntzeva (*ibid.*, Table II, 2, Figs. 1–5).

5a. *Polyangium cellulosum* var. *ferrugineum* Mishustin, 1938. (Microbiologia, 7, 1938, 427.)

fer.ru.gi'ne.um. L. adj. *ferrugineus* of the color of iron rust.

Vegetative cells: Long, flexible cells, 0.8 to 1.2 by 3.0 to 5.0 microns. Become shortened and highly refractile during fruiting-body formation.

Fruiting body: Composed of numerous cysts having definite wall. Mass of rods has a yellowish tinge, and the cysts are colored reddish yellow. Color probably confined to the cyst walls. Cysts round or egg-shaped, or may be angular due to pressure. Each cyst contains numerous shortened rods. Cysts usually 12 to 40 microns in diameter. Numerous cysts grouped into fruiting bodies having bright red or drabbish red color when ripe. Form of fruiting body variable: most commonly rounded, ellipsoidal or biscuit-shaped, sometimes sausage-shaped. Cysts

confined by an orange-colored slime membrane or envelope. No cystophore present. Fruiting bodies not easily broken up. Vary in size from 80 to 240 microns.

Vegetative colony: On silica gel with cellulose, at first pale pink. After six days fruiting bodies of red color appear together with free cysts and many non-encysted shortened rods. Fruiting bodies numerous at center of colony and later form in concentric rings around center. Margin of colony composed of vegetative cells; periphery pink. Mature colonies 2 to 5 cm in diameter, bright red, becoming drabbish red; pigmentation appears to be confined to limited areas. Surface dull, moist. Margin not definite.

Physiology: The cellulose at the center of the colony is completely destroyed, whereas that under the remainder of the colony is not entirely broken down.

The author considers this a color variant of *Polyangium cellulosum* Imšenecki and Solntzeva.

Source: Isolated from the black soils of Eastern European Russia.

Habitat: Soil. Decomposes cellulose.

5b. *Polyangium cellulosum* var. *fuscum* Mishustin, 1938. (Microbiologia, 7, 1938, 427.)

fus'cum. L. adj. *fuscus* dark, tawny.

Vegetative cells: Identical with those of *Polyangium cellulosum* var. *ferrugineum*.

Fruiting body: Composed of individual cysts, each with a separate cyst wall, and held together by a common slime membrane or envelope. Shortened, rod-shaped spores enclosed within the cyst walls. Cysts forming outside the large walls. Cysts forming outside the large masses usually rounded; those within often polygonal or angular. Cysts 5 to 24 microns long, ellipsoidal or egg-shaped. Encysted cells give cysts granular appearance. Ripe cysts brown to light brown in color; immature, yellow to pink. Fruiting bodies pinkish yellow when young, becoming brown when ripened. Considerable variation in form: round, ellipsoidal or sausage-shaped, and from 50 to 80 microns up to several hundred microns. Outer slime envelope often indistinct; no dried slime noticeable between the cysts.

Vegetative colony: A faint yellow cast on cellulose-silica gel after 2 to 3 days. Becomes yellow-orange to yellow-pink after 6 to 8 days, while center is brownish gray. Margin pinkish to yellow-pink. Surface dull, moist. As fruiting bodies ripen, colony becomes darker, finally dark brown. Reaches diameter of 2 to 5 cm. Fruiting bodies often arranged in form of pigmented, closely set, concentric rings. Margin of colony not clearly defined. Usually regularly rounded or ellipsoidal. Cellulose completely destroyed only at center of colony.

Source: Found only once in podzol soils. Common in black soils of Sumy Experiment Station.

Habitat: Soil. Decomposes cellulose.

5c. *Polyangium cellulosum* var. *fulvum* Mishustin, 1938. (Microbiologia, *7*, 1938, 427.)

ful'vum. L. adj. *fulvus* reddish yellow.

Vegetative cells: 0.8 to 1.2 by 3.5 to 6.0 microns.

Fruiting body: Rose or pink in color, composed of numerous cysts. Young cysts yellow to yellow-orange, becoming pink, rose or red, or pinkish yellow. Cysts same shape as others of the species; 6 to 24 microns in diameter, average 10 to 12 microns; contain many short rods. Fruiting bodies vary in shape, often elongated, flagella(?)-shaped(columnar?), up to 20 to 25 by 350 to 450 microns. Also globular, mace-shaped, etc. Usually 25 to 40 by 50 to 80 microns. Cysts enclosed by outer common envelope or slime membrane. Easily broken up mechanically.

Vegetative colony: On cellulose-silica gel form a hardly visible white (colorless?) colony at 2 days. After 6 days becomes pink in color. Fruiting bodies first form near center. After 9 to 10 days central area reddish pink while periphery has yellowish cast. Mature colony 2.5 to 7.5 cm in diameter, pink-orange color, fairly regularly round or ellipsoidal in shape. Pigmented concentric rings of fruiting bodies.

Physiology: Cellulose entirely destroyed at center of colony and often at other points.

Source: Podzol soils of Timiriazev Agricultural Academy. Seldom in black soils of Sumy Experiment Station.

Habitat: Soil. Decomposes cellulose.

5d. *Polyangium cellulosum* var. *luteum* Mishustin, 1938. (Microbiologia, *7*, 1938, 427.)

lu'te.um. L. adj. *luteus* saffron-yellow.

Vegetative cells: Similar to others of the species.

Fruiting body: Poorly organized agglomerations of colorless to yellow cysts enclosing sporulated cells. Cysts regularly egg-shaped to ellipsoidal, 8 to 20 microns in diameter; predominantly 6 to 10 microns. Matured cysts loosely connected into rounded or elongate masses 40 to 80 by 100 to 150 microns. Ripe fruiting bodies easily pulled apart.

Vegetative colony: On cellulose, colonies regularly rounded or ellipsoidal, surface has moist appearance. Yellowish cast 2nd or 3rd day, becoming deeper yellow. Ochre-yellow formations resembling fruiting bodies by 5 to 6 days. Many free cysts at center of colony. Later colony becomes pale dirty yellow while periphery remains bright yellow. Sometimes one or two brightly pigmented rings consisting of agglomerations of fruiting bodies are found in older colonies. Mature colonies 1.5 to 3.0 cm in diameter.

Physiology: Filter paper completely destroyed at center of colony. Developed better below pH 7 (around pH 6) than others of the species.

Source: Isolated from soils of the Timiriazev Agricultural Academy. Common in podzol soils.

Habitat: Soil. Decomposes cellulose.

6. **Polyangium simplex** (Thaxter, 1893) Thaxter, 1904. (*Myxobacter simplex* Thaxter, Bot. Gaz., *18*, 1893, 29; Thaxter, *ibid.*, *37*, 1904, 414.)

sim'plex. L. adj. *simplex* simple.

Vegetative cells: Large, cylindrical rods, rounded at either end, 0.7 to 0.9 by 4.0 to 7.0 microns.

Fruiting bodies: Cysts single, very large, 250 to 400 microns, bright reddish yellow, irregularly rounded. Rods flesh-colored in mass. Upon pressure, adhere together in sheaves.

Source: Isolated from very wet wood and bark in swamps.

7. **Polyangium ochraceum** Krzemieniewski, 1926. (Acta Soc. Bot. Poloniae, *4*, 1926, 34.)

o.chra′ce.um. Gr. noun *ochra* yellow ochre; M.L. adj. *ochraceus* of the color of yellow ochre.

Vegetative cells: Not described.

Fruiting bodies: Orange to light red in the form of a single spherical or ellipsoidal cyst 60 to 80 by 50 to 130 microns, each with a thick, yellow-brown membrane. The cyst content often (particularly in the ellipsoidal cysts) is constricted by the membrane which penetrates deeply. From the side the cyst appears to be divided. Rods in cysts measure 0.5 by 4.0 to 8.0 microns.

Source: Grown on sterilized rabbit dung on soil (Poland).

Illustrations: Krzemieniewski (*ibid.*, Pl. V, Figs. 50–51).

8. **Polyangium fuscum** (Schroeter, 1886) Thaxter, 1904. (*Cystobacter fuscus* Schroeter, in Cohn, Kryptogamenflora v. Schlesien, *3*, 1, 1886, 170; Thaxter, Bot. Gaz., *37*, 1904, 414.)

fus′cum. L. adj. *fuscus* dark, tawny.

Vegetative cells: Rods slender, elongate, 0.6 by 5.0 to 12 microns. Grows readily on agar, also on dung agar. Baur states rods are 15 to 20 microns in length.

Fruiting bodies: Cysts flesh-colored when young, chestnut-brown when ripe, spherical, about 60 microns (Thaxter, 50 to 150 by 50 to 70 microns) in diameter, with definite membrane, lying in considerable numbers in large sori, usually 30 to 40 sometimes up to 100. The slime envelope is much more delicate and evanescent than that in *P. vitellinum*. Occasionally a form is found with cysts measuring 100 microns: under these often lie kidney-shaped cysts even 150 microns in length; apparently a variety. Rods in cysts about 0.8 to 1.5 by 3.0 to 3.5 microns. Cysts (Baur) on dung decoction break in 10 to 12 hours, and rods pour out, apparently passively at first.

P. fuscum var. *velatum* Krzemieniewski differs from the type in that the membrane is thin, separated from cysts and folded.

Source: Isolated from rabbit dung from southern California. Kofler (Sitzber. d. kais. Akad. wiss. Wien. math.-nat. Klasse, 122 Abt., 1913, 845) also found it on rabbit dung from Vienna. Jahn (Beiträge zur bot. Protistologie. I, Die Polyangiden. Geb. Borntraeger, Leipzig, 1924) states that it

is common on dung; it also occurs on decaying lichens and on poplar bark which is kept moist.

Habitat: Found on decaying organic matter in soil and in the dung of various animals. Quite common in Polish soils according to Krzemieniewski (Acta Soc. Bot. Poloniae, *5*, 1927).

Illustrations: Thaxter (Bot. Gaz., *23*, 1897, Pl. 31, Figs. 37–39), Baur (Arch. Protistenkunde, *5*, 1905, Pl. 4, Figs. 14, 15 and 17), Quehl (Cent. f. Bakt., II Abt., *16*, 1906, Pl. 1, Figs. 8 and 16), Jahn (*op. cit.*, 1924, Pl. 2, Fig. 12; also Fig. A, page 9) and Krzemieniewski (Acta Soc. Bot. Poloniae, *4*, 1926, 34, Pl. IV, Figs. 42–43; also var. *velatum*, Pl. IV, Figs. 44–46).

9. **Polyangium aureum** Krzemieniewska and Krzemieniewski, 1930. (Acta Soc. Bot. Poloniae, *7*, 1930, 255.)

au′re.um. L. adj. *aureus* golden.

Separated from *Polyangium morula* on the basis of pigmentation.

Vegetative cells: Straight rods of uniform diameter; rounded ends, 0.7 to 0.9 by 2.8 to 5.3 microns.

Fruiting body: Cysts reddish brown, variable in number, embedded in yellow slime to form a sorus with a common slime envelope. Cysts nearly spherical or slightly elongate, averaging 32 by 37 microns. Cyst wall orange-yellow, about 3 microns thick. Older cysts contain shortened rods, a granular mass and a colorless or yellowish oleaginous liquid.

Habitat: Soil.

Illustrations: Krzemieniewski (*ibid.*, Pl. XVII, Figs. 14–17).

10. **Polyangium stellatum** Kofler, 1913. (Sitzber. d. kais. Akad. wiss. Wien, math.-nat. Klasse, Abt. I, *122*, 1913, 19.)

stel.la′tum. L. part.adj. *stellatus* set with stars, stellate.

Vegetative cells: Not described.

Fruiting bodies: Cysts elongate, 80 to 120 by 160 to 200 microns, flesh-colored when young, brownish red when old; star-shaped with 2 to 9 rays fixed by the narrowed base upon a kind of hypothallus.

Source: Found on hare dung from Vienna.

Illustrations: Kofler (*ibid.*, Pl. ?, Fig. 6).

11. **Polyangium ferrugineum** Krzemieniewska and Krzemieniewski, 1927. (Acta Soc. Bot. Poloniae, *5*, 1927, 97.)

fer.ru.gi′ne.um. L. adj. *ferrugineus* of the color of iron rust.

Fruiting bodies: Irregular, branched and occasionally constricted coils. Branches of same diameter as the main tube. Cyst wall is brown-red. In the interior no differentiation is visible. Rods in cysts are relatively short and thick, 0.8 to 1.1 microns by 2 to 2.5 microns, not definitely arranged. Close to *Archangium gephyra*, but with cyst walls.

Source: From soil in Poland and from rabbit dung.

Habitat: Found on decaying organic matter in soil and in the dung of various animals.

Illustrations: Krzemieniewski (*ibid.*, Pl. V, Fig. 21).

12. **Polyangium indivisum** Krzemieniewska and Krzemieniewski, 1927. (Acta Soc. Bot. Poloniae, *5*, 1927, 97.)

in.di.vi′sum. L. adj. *indivisus* undivided.

Vegetative cells: Not described.

Fruiting bodies: Similar to those in *Polyangium ferrugineum*, but much smaller and bright orange-yellow. Enclosed in a similarly colored slime membrane. Interior of coils undifferentiated. Cyst rods 0.8 to 1.0 by 3 to 6 microns, straight and rounded on ends. Arranged perpendicularly to the wall, giving a netted appearance resembling *Melittangium*.

Source: From soils in Poland.

13. **Polyangium spumosum** Krzemieniewska and Krzemieniewski, 1930. (Acta Soc. Bot. Poloniae, *7*, 1930, 254.)

spu.mo′sum. L. adj. *spumosus* foamy or frothy.

Vegetative cells: Straight rods, uniformly thick, with rounded ends; 0.6 to 0.8 by 3.9 to 6.8 microns.

Fruiting body: Colorless sori embedded in hyaline slime forming a common envelope around the cysts. Surface white, foamy in appearance; cysts in irregularly rounded accumulations, 100 to 150 microns in diameter. Cysts usually spherical, sometimes elongate; 18 to 38 by 20 to 50 microns; average 28 by 34 microns. Cyst membrane colorless. Cysts contain bundles of shortened cells, a granular colorless mass and a clear oleaginous fluid.

Habitat: Soil.

Illustrations: Krzemieniewski (*ibid.*, Pls. XVI and XVII, Figs. 10–13).

14. **Polyangium fumosum** Krzemieniewska and Krzemieniewski, 1930. (Acta Soc. Bot. Poloniae, *7*, 1930, 253.)

fu.mo′sum. L. adj. *fumosus* smoky.

Vegetative cells: Long, straight, cylindrical, with rounded ends; 0.7 to 0.9 by 2.7 to 5.7 microns. Encysted cells similar.

Fruiting body: A flat, crust-like layer of 2 to 20 (or more) cysts arranged to form a sorus. Sori rounded, up to 90 microns in diameter, or irregularly shaped; often elongate up to 400 microns long. Smoky gray color due to surrounding slime walls. Outer profile of sheath (or cortex) irregular. Cyst wall 2.4 to 3.5 microns thick; cysts often nearly spherical, 13 to 48 microns in diameter, though frequently elongate. Average 36 by 44 microns. Colorless, single, enclosed in a transparent membrane.

Habitat: Soil.

Illustrations: Krzemieniewski (*ibid.*, Pl. XVI, Figs. 6–9).

15. **Polyangium parasiticum** Geitler, 1924. (Arch. f. Protistenkunde, *50*, 1924, 67.)

pa.ra.si′ti.cum. Gr. adj. *parasiticus* parasitic.

Vegetative cells: In water, on the surface of the alga *Cladophora*. Rods long, cylindrical, rounded at end and 0.7 by 4.0 to 7.0 microns. At first saprophytic, later entering and destroying the *Cladophora* cell.

Fruiting bodies: Sometimes single, usually 2 to 8, microscopically small, united in irregular masses, spherical or somewhat elongated. From 15 to 50 microns, usually 25 to 40 microns, with hyaline slime. When mature, red-brown in color with firm wall.

Source: Found on *Cladophora* (*fracta*?) in a pool at Vienna.

Illustrations: Geitler (*ibid.*, Figs. 1–10).

Genus II. **Synangium** *Jahn, 1924.*

(Beiträge zur bot. Protistologie. I, Die Polyangiden. Geb. Borntraeger, Leipzig, 1924, 79.)

Syn.an'gi.um. Gr. pref. *syn* together; Gr. noun *angium* vessel; M.L. neut.n. *Synangium* vessels together (clustered).

Cysts united at the base to form a large disc or rosette which is usually elevated above the substrate on a stalk. The individual cyst is equipped with an apical tuft of hairs.

The type species is *Synangium sessile* (Thaxter) Jahn.

1. **Synangium sessile** (Thaxter, 1904) Jahn, 1924. (*Chrondromyces sessilis* Thaxter, Bot. Gaz., *37*, 1904, 411; *Chrondromyces lanuginosus* Kofler, Sitzber. d. kais. Akad. wiss. Wien, math.-nat. Klasse, Abt. I, *122*, 1913, 861; *Chondromyces thaxteri* Faull, Bot. Gaz., *62*, 1916, 226; Jahn, Beiträge zur bot. Protistologie. I, Die Polyangiden. Geb. Borntraeger, Leipzig, 1924, 79; *Synangium lanuginosum* Jahn, *loc. cit.; Synangium thaxteri* Jahn, *loc. cit.*)

ses'si.le. L. adj. *sessilis* sessile, stalkless.

Vegetative cells: Cylindrical rods with blunt ends, 0.9 to 1.0 by 3.0 to 8.0 microns.

Fruiting body: The cysts are joined together at their bases to form discoid or spherical clusters containing up to 30 individual cysts, the whole being elevated on a stalk of variable height (up to 1 mm), which is usually unbranched and bears one or two clusters at its tip. Each cyst bears an apical tuft of hairs. The diameter of the cyst cluster is highly variable (40 to 250 microns), as is the length of the hairs in the apical tuft (7 to 30 microns). The individual resting cells within the cysts are 2.5 to 6.0 by 0.6 to 1.0 microns. The color of developing fruiting bodies is initially white, changing to yellow, light pink and eventually orange; the shade is greatly affected by environmental factors, notably humidity and temperature. Sometimes the cyst clusters give rise to secondary stalks which are much thinner and shorter than the primary ones and which are tipped with smaller clusters.

Varieties: Three varieties of this species have been named on the basis of the presence or absence of cyst-bearing stalks: one variety is described as sessile, and another as bearing a stalk of variable height (up to 1 mm) which is usually unbranched; the third variety is intermediate between these two. This differentiation in stalks is highly dependent upon environmental conditions.

Cultivation: Grown in laboratory culture on hay (Krzemieniewska and Krzemieniewski, Bull. Intern. Acad. Pol. Sci. Lettres, No. 1–10, Série B (I), 1946, 37). Pure cultures not obtained.

Source: Originally isolated from decaying wood from Florida (Thaxter, *op. cit.*, 1904, 411). Also found in the dung of herbivores from Canada (Faull, *op. cit.*, 1916, 226) and from Austria (Kofler, *op. cit.*, 1913, 861); from soil in Poland (Krzemieniewska and Krzemieniewski, *op. cit.*, 1946, 37).

Habitat: Found on the dung of herbivores and on decaying organic matter in soil.

Illustrations: Thaxter (*op. cit.*, 1904, Pl. 27, Figs. 14–15), Kofler (*op. cit.*, 1913, Pl. I, Figs. 1–3), Faull (*op. cit.*, 1916, Pls. 5 and 6), Jahn (*op. cit.*, 1924, Fig. X, page 80) and Krzemieniewska and Krzemieniewski (*op. cit.*, Pl. 1, Figs. 1–3).

Genus III. **Podangium** *Jahn, 1924.*

(*Cystobacter* Schroeter, in Cohn, Kryptogamenflora v. Schlesien, *3*, 1, 1886, 170; Jahn, Beiträge zur bot. Protistologie. I, Die Polyangiden. Geb. Borntraeger, Leipzig, 1924, 80.)

Po.dan'gi.um. Gr. noun *pus, podis* a foot; Gr. noun *angium* a vessel; M.L. neut.n. *Podangium* footed vessel.

Cysts chestnut-brown or red-brown, single on a more or less definite, white stalk.

The type species is *Podangium erectum* (Schroeter) Jahn.

Key to the species of genus **Podangium.**

I. Stalk scarcely definite, cysts short, appressed, if elongate then passing over from the white stem into the club-shaped cyst. Ripe cysts chestnut-brown.

1. *Podangium erectum.*

II. Stalk well differentiated.

A. Cysts spherical, often irregular, confluent.

2. *Podangium lichenicolum.*

B. Cysts not spherical, regular in shape, distinct.

1. Cysts lengthened, ellipsoidal.

3. *Podangium gracilipes.*

2. Cysts flattened, like cap of *Boletus.*

4. *Podangium boletus.*

1. Podangium erectum (Schroeter, 1886) Jahn, 1924. (*Cystobacter erectus* Schroeter, in Cohn, Kryptogamenflora v. Schlesien, *3*, 1, 1886, 170; *Chondromyces erectus* Thaxter, Bot. Gaz., *23*, 1897, 407; Jahn, Beiträge zur bot. Protistologie. I, Die Polyangiden. Geb. Borntraeger, Leipzig, 1924, 80.)

e.rec'tum. L. adj. *erectus* erect.

Swarm stage (pseudoplasmodium): Kofler states rods are 2 to 5 microns in length.

Fruiting bodies: Cysts usually short, almost spherical, compact, rounded above, orange-red changing to chestnut-brown, single on a white to yellow hypothallus constituted from the slime remaining behind. A definite "foot" of whitish slime is seldom observed. Fifty to hundreds together. Usually about 80 microns high and 40 to 50 microns broad above, smaller below, often spherical cysts 60 microns in diameter. Rods in cysts 0.6 by 4 microns.

Jahn believes the European form to be distinct from that described by Thaxter. Thaxter's form produces cystophores 60 to 300 microns long which wither at maturity so that cysts appear sessile.

Source: Isolated by Thaxter (*op. cit.*, 1897, 407) from horse dung in laboratory cultures, Massachusetts; also found on bark covered with lichens (Jahn, *op. cit.*, 1924, 80).

Habitat: Found on decaying organic matter in soil and in the dung of various animals.

Illustrations: Thaxter (*op. cit.*, Pl. 31, Figs. 16–19), Quehl (Cent. f. Bakt., II Abt., *16*, 1906, Pl. 1, Fig. 4), Jahn (*op. cit.*, 1924, Pl. 1, Figs. 7–9) and Krzemieniewski (Acta Soc. Bot. Poloniae, *4*, 1926, 1, Pl. V, Figs. 52–53).

2. Podangium lichenicolum (Thaxter, 1892) Jahn, 1924. (*Chondromyces lichenicolus* Thaxter, Bot. Gaz., *17*, 1892, 402; Jahn, Beiträge zur bot. Protistologie. I, Die Polyangiden. Geb. Borntraeger, Leipzig, 1924, 81.)

li.che.ni'co.lum. Gr. noun *lichen* a tree moss, lichen; L. v. *colo* to dwell; M.L. adj. *lichenicolus* lichen-dwelling.

Swarm stage: Reddish, rods cylindrical, tapering slightly, 0.6 by 5.0 to 7.0 microns. Germinate readily after drying for 18 months when sown on moist lichens.

Fruiting bodies: Cysts single, rounded or irregularly lobed, often confluent. Cystophore short, squarish, often lacking or misshapen. Cysts 28 to 35 microns, stem 7 to 8 by 10 microns.

Source: Isolated from lichens from New Haven, Conn.

Habitat: Found on lichens and algae as well as on wet boards.

Illustrations: Thaxter (*op. cit.*, 1892, Pl. 23, Figs. 20–23) and Quehl (Cent. f. Bakt., II Abt., *16*, 1906, 9, Pl. 1, Fig. 6).

3. Podangium gracilipes (Thaxter, 1897) Jahn, 1924. (*Chondromyces gracilipes* Thaxter, Bot. Gaz., *23*, 1897, 406; Jahn, Beiträge zur bot. Protistologie. I, Die Polyangiden. Geb. Borntraeger, Leipzig, 1924, 82; *Chondromyces minor* Krzemieniewski, Acta Soc. Bot. Poloniae, *7*, 1930, 265.)

gra.ci'li.pes. L. adj. *gracilipes* slender-footed.

Swarm stage: Rods 5 to 7 microns.

Fruiting bodies: Cysts bright orange-red or red, 25 by 35 microns, elongate, rounded, on a white pointed stalk, rigid and persistent on substratum, rods also in stalk. Shortened rods in cyst 3 to 5 microns. Cysts sometimes pear-shaped, caducous.

Source: Isolated from rabbit dung from Massachusetts.

Habitat: Found on decaying organic matter in soil and in the dung of various animals.

Note: A variety of this species was originally described as an independent species by the Krzemieniewskis (loc. cit.). However, further study of this organism by the same workers (Bull. Intern. Acad. Pol. Sci. Lettres, No. 1–10, Série B (I), 1946, 46) revealed that the stalks were composite. Since the cysts correspond exactly in shape, size and color to those of *Podangium gracilipes*, the organism is evidently a composite form of *P. gracilipes*, the stalks being partly fused.

Illustrations: Thaxter (op. cit., 1897, Pl. 31, Figs. 20–24), Quehl (Cent. f. Bakt., II Abt., 16, 1906, Pl. 1, Fig. 12), Jahn (op. cit., 1924, Pl. II, Figs. 19–20) and Krzemieniewski (Acta Soc. Bot. Poloniae, 4, 1926, Pl. V, Fig. 54).

4. **Podangium boletus** (Jahn, 1924) Krzemieniewska and Krzemieniewski, 1946. (*Melittangium boletus* Jahn, Beiträge zur bot. Protistologie. I, Die Polyangiden. Geb. Borntraeger, Leipzig, 1924, 78; Krzemie-

niewska and Krzemieniewski, Bull. Intern. Acad. Pol. Sci. Lettres, No. 1–10, Série B (I), 1946, 36.)

bo.le'tus. L. noun *boletus* a kind of mushroom.

Vegetative cells: No description.

Fruiting bodies: Cyst stalked, mushroom-like, white when immature then yellowish flesh-colored, finally yellowish brown to nut-brown; when dried, more reddish brown. Width of cyst about 100 microns, height 40 to 50 microns, length of white stalk about 40 microns. Sometimes the cyst is smaller and spherical (50 to 60 microns in diameter), sometimes there is a fusion of neighboring cysts, occasionally the stalk is abortive. The resting cells are 0.5 by 3.0 to 4.0 microns and are arranged within the cyst in a characteristic manner, standing at right angles to the membrane; on germination the membrane is left colorless and can be observed to have a honey-combed structure caused by the impingement of the tips of the oriented resting cells against it.

Source: From the dung of herbivores from Germany and Denmark.

Habitat: Found on decaying organic matter in soil and in the dung of various animals.

Illustrations: Jahn (op. cit., Pl. 2, Figs. 17–18; Fig. B, page 11; C–F, page 23; O–Q, page 43; T–U, page 55) and Krzemieniewska and Krzemieniewski (Acta Soc. Bot. Poloniae, 4, 1926, 1, Pl. V, Figs. 55–56).

Genus IV. Chondromyces *Berkeley and Curtis, 1874.*

(Berkeley and Curtis, in Berkeley, Introduction to Cryptogamic Botany, London, 1857, 313 (illustration but no description); Berkeley (description), Notes on North American Fungi, Grevillea, 3, 1874, 97; see Berkeley and Curtis, in Saccardo, Sylloge Fungorum, 4, 1886, 679.)

Chon.dro'my.ces or Chon.dro.my'ces. Gr. noun *chondrus* cartilage, gristle; Gr. noun *myces* fungus; M.L. masc.n. *Chondromyces* cartilaginous fungus.

Cysts compactly grouped at the end of a colored stalk (cystophore). Cystophore simple or branched.

The type species is *Chondromyces crocatus* Berkeley and Curtis.

Key to the species of genus **Chondromyces.**

I. Vegetative rods are even cylinders with blunt, rounded ends.
1. *Chondromyces crocatus.*
II. Vegetative rods of uneven width with tapering ends.
  A. Cysts not in chains.
    1. Ripe cysts not attached to stalk by pedicel or stipe.

    a. Cysts not pointed.
      b. Cysts rounded.
        c. Ripe cysts orange-red.
                2. *Chondromyces aurantiacus.*
        cc. Ripe cysts dark chestnut-brown.
                3. *Chondromyces brunneus.*
      bb. Cysts cylindrical.
                4. *Chondromyces cylindricus.*
    aa. Cysts pointed.
                5. *Chondromyces apiculatus.*
  2. Cysts attached to stalk by pedicel or stipe.
    a. Cysts with flattened tips.
                6. *Chondromyces pediculatus.*
    aa. Cysts rounded.
                7. *Chondromyces medius.*
  B. Cysts arranged in chains.
                8. *Chondromyces catenulatus.*

1. Chondromyces crocatus Berkeley and Curtis, 1874. (Berkeley and Curtis, in Berkeley, Introduction to Cryptogamic Botany, London, 1857, 313 (illustration but no description); Berkeley (description), Notes on North American Fungi, Grevillea, *3*, 1874, 64.)

cro.ca′tus. L. adj. *crocatus* saffron-yellow.

Vegetative cells: Cylindrical rods with blunt, rounded ends, 1.3 to 1.7 by 3.0 to 11.0 microns.

Fruiting body: The cysts are at first spindle-shaped, widening at the base to become almost conical in the mature state. Initially straw-colored, they finally turn golden yellow. When mature, they are attached to the stalk by the remains of pedicels. Cysts are borne in spherical groups at the tips of stalks which are almost always branched. The stalks are 600 microns or more in height, covered with longitudinal striations and sometimes spirally twisted. Originally orange in color, they eventually turn brown. Mature cysts are 9 to 16 by 15 to 37 microns; the resting cells within them are 1.0 to 1.2 by 2.4 to 3.8 microns.

Source: Isolated from a decayed gourd from South Carolina. Also found by Thaxter (Bot. Gaz., *17*, 1892) on melon rind from south Carolina and on old straw from Ceylon and Cambridge, Mass. Quehl (Cent. f. Bakt., II Abt., *16*, 1906) found it on dung from Java and on deer dung from Berlin.

Habitat: Found on decaying organic matter in soil and in the dung of various animals.

Illustrations: Berkeley (*op. cit.*, 1857, 313), Thaxter (*op. cit.*, 1892, 389, Pls. 22 and 23, Figs. 1–11), Quehl (*op. cit.*, 1906, 9, Pl. 1, Fig. 10) and Jahn (Kryptogamenflora der Mark Brandenburg, V, Pilze I, Lief 2, 1911, 199, Fig. 6; also see Beiträge zur bot. Protistologie. I, Die Polyangiden. Geb. Borntraeger, Leipzig, 1924, Pl. 2, Figs. 14–16).

2. Chondromyces aurantiacus (Berkeley and Curtis, 1874) Thaxter, 1892. (*Stigmatella aurantiaca* Berkeley and Curtis, in Berkeley, Introduction to Cryptogamic Botany, London, 1857, 313 (illustration but no description); Berkeley, (description), Notes on North American Fungi, Grevillea, *3*, 1874, 97; Thaxter, Bot. Gaz., *17*, 1892, 339.)

au.ran.ti′a.cus. M.L. adj. *aurantiacus* orange-colored.

Vegetative cells: Rods which taper towards the ends, 0.6 to 1.0 by 4.0 to 10.0 microns, flesh-colored in mass.

Fruiting bodies: Cysts ellipsoidal or spherical, 16 to 40 by 30 to 60 microns. Originally flesh-colored, they become a vivid orange-red during maturation; may turn chestnut-brown when kept for long periods in moist air. The stalk, 135 to 400 microns high, is usually nearly colorless, sometimes a light yellow-brown, and in most cases is unbranched. Resting cells in cysts are 0.8 to 1.0 by 2.5 to 3.5 microns.

Source: Isolated from a lichen. Berkeley and Broome (Jour. Linn. Soc., *14*, 1873, 96, see Saccardo, Sylloge Fungorum, *4*, 1886,

571) found it on rotten wood from Ceylon; also found by Thaxter (Bot. Gaz., *17*, 1892; *23*, 1897, 395) on old wood, fungi and on antelope dung from Africa. Quehl (Cent. f. Bakt., II Abt., *16*, 1906, 9) found it on dung from Java, and the Krzemieniewskis (Bull. Intern. Acad. Pol. Sci. Lettres, No. 1–10, Série B (I), 1946, 42) report it from decayed wood in Poland.

Illustrations: Berkeley and Broome (*op. cit.*, 1873, Pl. 4, Fig. 16), Kalchbrenner and Cooke (Australian Fungi, Grevillea, *9*, 1880, 23), Thaxter (*op. cit.*, 1892, Pls. 23 and 24, Figs. 12–19 and 25–28), Zukal (Ber. d. deutsch. bot. Ges., *14*, 1896, Pl. 20), Quehl (*op. cit.*, 1906, Pl. 1, Fig. 10), Jahn (Beiträge zur bot. Protistologie. I, Die Polyangiden. Geb. Borntraeger, Leipzig, 1924, Fig. V, page 57; Fig. W, page 59) and Krzemieniewski (Acta Soc. Bot. Poloniae, *4*, 1926, Pl. V, Figs. 57–60).

3. Chondromyces brunneus Krzemieniewska and Krzemieniewski, 1946. (*Chondromyces aurantiacus* var. *frutescens* Krzemieniewska and Krzemieniewski, Acta Soc. Bot. Poloniae, *5*, 1927, 96; Krzemieniewska and Krzemieniewski, Bull. Intern. Acad. Pol. Sci. Lettres, No. 1–10, Série B (I), 1946, 44.)

brun'ne.us. M.L. adj. *brunneus* dark, brown.

Vegetative cells: Rods 0.6 to 0.7 by 5.0 to 10.0 microns.

Fruiting bodies: The fruiting bodies develop out of a greenish, later yellowish, mass of rods in the form of a group of thick stalks with a common base, each stalk bearing numerous terminal cysts. The cysts are ellipsoidal or spherical, 28 to 83 by 37 to 102 microns. At first orange in color, the cysts rapidly turn dark chestnut-brown and, in the dried state, almost black. In some cases the stalks persist through maturation of the cysts; at other times they shrink as the cysts darken and eventually deposit the latter on the substrate. Resting cells in the cysts are 0.9 to 1.0 by 2.0 to 3.5 microns.

Source: Isolated from soil from Poland.

Habitat: Found on decaying organic matter in soil.

Illustrations: Krzemieniewska and Krzemieniewski (*op. cit.*, 1927, Pl. VI, Figs. 27–35; *op. cit.*, 1946, Pl. 1, Figs. 9 and 10).

4. Chondromyces cylindricus Krzemieniewska and Krzemieniewski, 1930. (Acta Soc. Bot. Poloniae, *7*, 1930, 260.)

cy.lin'dri.cus. Gr. adj. *cylindricus* cylindrical.

Vegetative cells: Rods with tapering ends, 0.5 to 0.8 by 6.0 to 11.0 microns.

Fruiting bodies: Numerous cysts in spherical clusters set on thick, straight stalks which, slightly towards the tip, are colorless or yellow-orange and which average 200 microns in height. The cysts are ellipsoidal or elongated, mostly thick cylinders with rounded ends; orange, later becoming orange-red in color. When young they are attached to the stalk by thin pedicels about 30 microns in length but later become sessile on the stalk. Cysts are 20 to 30 by 30 to 90 microns. The resting cells within them are 0.7 to 1.0 by 2.0 to 4.0 microns.

Cultivation: Maintained in culture by the Krzemieniewskis on boiled rabbit dung for fifteen years. Cysts capable of germination within a week, after maintenance in the resting state for eight years.

Source: Isolated from Polish soil.

Habitat: Found on decaying organic matter in soil.

Illustrations: Krzemieniewska and Krzemieniewski (*ibid.*, Pl. XVII, Fig. 18; also see Bull. Intern. Acad. Pol. Sci. Lettres, No. 1–10, Série B (I), 1946, Pl. 1, Figs. 18, 21 and 22).

5. Chondromyces apiculatus Thaxter, 1897. (Bot. Gaz., *23*, 1897, 405.)

a.pi.cu.la'tus. L. noun *apex, apicis* point, top, cap; M.L. adj. *apiculatus* having a small point.

Vegetative cells: Rods 1 by 3 to 20 microns. Does not grow as well on nutrient agar as *Chondromyces crocatus* and produces cysts and cystophores rarely. Cultivated on dung. Kofler states rods are 3 to 5 microns in length.

Fruiting bodies: Cysts of variable form, cylindrical to broadly turnip-shaped, usually with basal and apical appendages, the latter longer and pointed, bright orange, 28 by 35 microns. Cysts united in a single, spherical, terminal head about 200 microns in diameter. Stalk rigid, stiff, seldom branched, to 1 mm high, colorless, longitudinally striate.

Source: Isolated from antelope dung from Africa; found later by Thaxter on deer dung from the Philippines and Florida. Baur (Arch. f. Protistenkunde, 5, 1905) found it on rabbit dung near Berlin, and Kofler (Sitzber. d. kais. Akad. wiss. Wien, math.-nat. Klasse, Abt. I, 122, 1913) reports it from the same source near Vienna.

Habitat: Found on decaying organic matter in soil and in the dung of various animals.

Illustrations: Thaxter (*op. cit.*, 1897, Pl. 30, Figs. 1–15), Quehl (Cent. f. Bakt., II Abt., 16, 1906, Pl. 1, Figs. 13 and 14), Jahn (Beiträge zur bot. Protistologie. I, Die Polyangiden. Geb. Borntraeger, Leipzig, 1924, 199, Fig. 5) and Kühlwein (Arch. Mikrobiol., 17, 1952, 403 (best)).

6. Chondromyces pediculatus Thaxter, 1904. (Bot. Gaz., 37, 1904, 410.)

pe.di.cu.la′tus. L. dim.noun *pediculus* a small foot (stalk); M.L. adj. *pediculatus* having a small foot or stalk.

Vegetative cells: Rods 0.6 to 0.7 by 2.0 to 4.0 microns.

Fruiting bodies: Cysts rounded to bellshaped, truncate at distal end, orange-yellow; when dry, orange-red, 35 to 50 microns. Sessile on stalks 40 to 60 microns in length which are arranged as an umbel on the tip of the stalk. Stalk 300 to 700 microns in length, solitary, simple, usually rather slender and somewhat wrinkled.

Source: Isolated from goose dung from South Carolina.

Habitat: Found in the dung of various animals.

Illustrations: Thaxter (*ibid.*, Pl. 26, Figs. 7–13).

7. Chondromyces medius Krzemieniewski, 1930. (Acta Soc. Bot. Poloniae, 7, 1930, 263.)

me′di.us. L. adj. *medius* medial, moderate.

Vegetative cells: Tapering rods, 0.6 to 1.0 by 4.5 to 9.2 microns. Nearly colorless in mass.

Fruiting bodies: Reddish orange cysts becoming light brown, attached to the stalk by pedicles about 40 microns long. Cysts 28 to 87 by 32 to 94 microns, variable in shape, predominantly flattened at the base, sometimes narrowing and elongated. Resting cells in cysts 0.7 to 1.2 by 3.5 to 5.0 microns.

Source: Isolated from soil from Poland; also found on a fungus in Panama.

Illustrations: Krzemieniewska and Krzemieniewski (*ibid.*, Pl. XVII, Figs. 20–22; also see Bull. Intern. Acad. Pol. Sci. Lettres, No. 1–10, Série B (I), 1946, Pl. 1, Figs. 11–13).

8. Chondromyces catenulatus Thaxter, 1904. (Bot. Gaz., 37, 1904, 410.)

ca.te.nu.la′tus. L. noun *catena* chain; L. dim.noun *catenula* a small chain; M.L. adj. *catenulatus* having small chains.

Vegetative cells: Cultivated only on original substrate. Rods 1.0 to 1.3 by 4.0 to 6.0 microns.

Fruiting bodies: Cysts light yelloworange, 18 by 20 to 50 microns in rosary-like chains which may be branched once or twice, sessile on a short, compact stalk, cysts separated by shriveled isthmuses. Chains up to 300 microns. Stalk simple, 180 to 360 microns, cleft above and passing over into the chains, rather broad at the base and spreading somewhat on the substratum. The divisions of the stalk are pointed, short and slightly swollen.

Source: From decaying poplar wood from New Hampshire.

Illustrations: Thaxter (*ibid.*, Pl. 26, Figs. 1–5).

FAMILY V. MYXOCOCCACEAE JAHN, 1924.

(Beiträge zur bot. Protistologie. I, Die Polyangiden. Geb. Borntraeger, Leipzig, 1924, 84.)

Myx.o.coc.ca′ce.ae. M.L. mas.n. *Myxococcus* type genus of the family; -aceae ending to denote a family; M.L. fem.pl.n. *Myxococcaceae* the *Myxococcus* family.

The rods become shortened when fruiting occurs and develop into spherical or ellipsoidal microcysts. Definite fruiting bodies are produced in three of the genera. In *Sporocytophaga* the microcysts are produced from the vegetative cells without development of fruiting bodies.

Key to the genera of family **Myxococcaceae.**

I. Definite fruiting bodies formed.
  A. Microcysts not enclosed in larger cysts.
    1. Fruiting bodies deliquescent.
                    Genus I. *Myxococcus*, p. 883.
    2. Fruiting bodies firm, not deliquescent.
                    Genus II. *Chondrococcus*, p. 886.
  B. Microcysts enclosed in larger cysts.
                    Genus III. *Angiococcus*, p. 889.
II. No definite fruiting bodies formed.
                    Genus IV. *Sporocytophaga*, p. 890.

Genus I. **Myxococcus** *Thaxter, 1892.*

(Bot. Gaz., *17*, 1892, 403.)

Myx.o.coc'cus. Gr. noun *myxa* mucus, slime; Gr. noun *coccus* berry; M.L. mas.n. *Myxococcus* slime coccus.

Spherical spores in spherical or occasionally ellipsoidal upright fruiting bodies united by slime.

The type species is *Myxococcus fulvus* (Cohn *emend.* Schroeter) Jahn.

Key to the species of genus **Myxococcus.**

I. Stalk lacking or indicated only by a constriction.
  A. Spores average less than 1.4 microns in diameter.
    1. Fruiting body red or brownish flesh color.
              1. *Myxococcus fulvus.*
    2. Fruiting body light blood-red.
              2. *Myxococcus cruentus.*
  B. Spores average 2.0 microns in diameter.
    1. Fruiting body yellow to greenish yellow.
              3. *Myxococcus virescens.*
    2. Fruiting body yellow-orange to orange.
              4. *Myxococcus xanthus.*
II. Well developed stalk supporting spherical spore mass above.
  A. Spores spherical.
              5. *Myxococcus stipitatus.*
  B. Spores ellipsoidal.
              6. *Myxococcus ovalisporus.*

1. **Myxococcus fulvus** (Cohn, 1875, emend. Schroeter, 1886) Jahn, 1924. (*Micrococcus fulvus* Cohn?, Beiträge z. Biologie d. Pflanzen, *1*, Heft 3, 1875, 181; *Micrococcus fulvus* Schroeter *char. emend.*, in Cohn, Kryptogamenflora v. Schlesien, *3*, 1, 1886, 144; Jahn, Beiträge zur bot. Protistologie. I, Die Polyangiden, Geb. Borntraeger, Leipzig, 1924, 84.)

ful'vus. L. adj. *fulvus* reddish yellow.

Vegetative cells: Slender rods irregularly curved, 0.4 by 3.0 to 7.0 microns. Masses are light flesh-colored.

Fruiting bodies: Spherical or elongate, pear-shaped, constricted below, often with definite slimy stalk, flesh-red to brownish red; when dry, rust-red to brown, about 300 microns in diameter. Spores 1.0 to 1.2 microns. Jahn (*loc. cit.*) notes two varieties of this species, one white, the other cinnabar-red.

Gelatin is quickly liquefied, completely in 1 to 2 days, but no fruiting bodies are formed.

Kofler secured good growth on Hasting's milk agar and determined digestion of casein.

Source: Isolated by Thaxter (Bot. Gaz., *17*, 1892, 403) from various decaying substances such as lichens, paper, dung, etc. Found by Smith (Jour. Bot., *39*, 1901, 71) on rabbit dung from Wales, by Baur (Arch. f. Protistenkunde, *5*, 1905, 95) on cow and dog dungs, by de Kruyff (Cent. f. Bakt., II Abt., *21*, 1908, 386) on stable manure in Java, by Jahn (*op. cit.*, 1924, 84) on almost all specimens of dung, as well as on bark, decaying wood and lichens, by Krzemieniewski (Acta Soc. Bot. Poloniae, *5*, 1927) in Polish soil, and by Kofler (Sitzber. d. kais. Akad. wiss. Wien, math.-nat. Klasse, Abt. I, *122*, 1913) on the dung of rabbit, horse, goat, mouse, roe and deer and on the stem of clematis and decaying leaves and in bird nest.

Habitat: Found on decaying organic matter in soil and in the dung of various animals.

Illustrations: Cohn (*op. cit.*, 1875, Pl. 6, Fig. 18), Smith (*op. cit.*, 1901, Fig. 1), Baur (*op. cit.*, 1905, Figs. 1–3 and Pl. 4, Figs. 1–13, 16), Jahn (*op. cit.*, 1924, Figs. L–M, page 43; Fig. R, page 47), Krzemieniewski (*op. cit.*, *4*, 1926, Pl. 1, Figs. 7–8) and Kofler (*op. cit.*, 1913, 845, Pl. 2, Figs. 10 and 12).

2. Myxococcus cruentus Thaxter, 1897.

(Bot. Gaz., *23*, 1897, 395.)

cru.en'tus. L. adj. *cruentus* blood-red.

Vegetative cells: Rods 0.8 by 3.0 to 8.0 microns. Not cultivated.

Fruiting body: Regularly spherical, 90 to 125 microns, blood-red. Slime forms on the surface a more or less definite membrane in which the microcysts lie. Microcysts ellipsoidal or irregularly oblong, 0.9 to 1.0 by 1.2 to 1.4 microns.

Source: Isolated from cow dung from Tennessee.

Habitat: Found on decaying organic matter in soil and in the dung of various animals. Krzemieniewski (Acta Soc. Bot. Po-

loniae, *5*, 1927) states that it is rarely found in Polish soils.

Illustrations: Thaxter (*op. cit.*, 1897, Pl. 31, Figs. 28–29).

3. Myxococcus virescens Thaxter, 1892.

(Bot. Gaz., *17*, 1892, 404.)

vi.res'cens. L. part.adj. *virescens* becoming green.

Vegetative cells: Rod masses greenish yellow. Rods slender, irregularly curved, 0.4 by 3.0 to 7.0 microns. When cultivated on potato agar, they tend to lose their green color and become yellowish.

Fruiting body: Spherical, usually less rounded than other species of the genus, yellowish, occasionally greenish, in culture on artificial media, easily becoming white, 150 to 500 microns. The slime deliquesces in continued moisture. Microcysts large, about 2 microns.

Source: Isolated from hen and dog dungs from New England. Jahn (Beiträge zur bot. Protistologie. I, Die Polyangiden. Geb. Borntraeger, Leipzig, 1924) states that it is not very abundant on the dungs of rabbit, horse, stag and black cock.

Habitat: Found on decaying organic matter in soil and in the dung of various animals. Common in Polish soil, according to Krzemieniewski (Acta Soc. Bot. Poloniae, *5*, 1927).

Illustrations: Krzemieniewski (*op. cit.*, *4*, 1926, Pl. 1, Fig. 9) and Badian (Acta Soc. Bot. Poloniae, *7*, 1930, 55, Pl. 1, 8 Figures).

4. Myxococcus xanthus Beebe, 1941.

(Jour. Bact., *42*, 1941, 193.)

xan'thus. Gr. adj. *xanthus* orange, golden.

Vegetative cells: Large, flexible, single, Gram-negative rods with rounded ends. Vary in size from 0.5 to 1.0 by 4.0 to 10.0 microns; average, 0.75 by 5.0 microns.

Fruiting body: Spherical to subspherical, usually sessile but occasionally constricted at the base giving the appearance of a short stalk or foot. Mature fruiting body up to 300 to 400 microns in diameter, often slightly flattened on top or one side. Color varies from light yellowish orange when young to bright orange when mature; color constant, never tending toward greenish yellow. No outer cyst wall or limiting membrane discernible, the spores being imbedded in the slime holding the mass together. Usually single, though two or three fruiting bodies may become joined to form an irregular mass; each is attached to the substrate, however, and never bud one from another.

Microcysts: Spherical, with thick outer wall or membrane. Highly refractile. 2.0 microns in diameter, seldom larger.

Vegetative colony: Characteristics vary with the substrate.

On plain 1.5 per cent agar (no nutrients added): Very thin and transparent, often hardly visible except by transmitted light. Little or no pigmentation. Surface covered with fine, more or less regularly spaced ridges causing a dull macroscopic appearance without gloss or sheen. Margin very thin and quite regular.

On rabbit dung decoction agar: Colony thicker, the surface being broken by veins or ridges radiating from the center. Thick central area often smooth and glossy while margin much the same as that on plain agar. Veins or ridges extend outward from center in loose spiral, always in clock-wise direction. Pigmentation, yellow to pale orange, confined to thicker central portion, extends part way along veins to margin.

On nutrient agar: Growth poor. Colony thick, at first heavily veined, the veins later merging to form an irregular glossy surface. Colony remains small, pigmentation usually fairly heavy; margin thick, irregular to lobate.

Physiology: Grows well on mineral salt-agar to which has been added dulcitol, inulin, cellulose, reprecipitated cellulose or starch; hydrolyzes starch; does not destroy cellulose to any appreciable extent. Best growth on suspension of killed bacterial cells in agar; suspended cells in growth area lysed. Development completely inhibited by arabinose, largely by maltose and mannose.

Source: Isolated from dried cow dung, Ames, Iowa.

Habitat: Decomposed bacterial cells in dung.

Illustrations: Beebe (ibid., Figs. 1–28).

5. Myxococcus stipitatus Thaxter, 1897. (Bot. Gaz., *23*, 1897, 395.)

sti.pi.ta'tus. L. noun *stipes, stipitis* trunk, stalk; M.L. adj. *stipitatus* stalked.

Vegetative cells: Rods 0.5 to 0.7 by 2.0 to 7.0 microns or longer. Grows well on nutrient agar but does not fruit readily.

Fruiting body: Nearly spherical, 175 microns in diameter, deliquescent, sessile on a well developed, compact stalk, white to yellowish and flesh-colored. Microcysts 0.8 to 1.2 by 1.0 to 1.15 microns. Stalk 100 to 200 microns long, 30 to 50 microns wide.

Source: Isolated from dung in laboratory cultures at Cambridge, Mass., Maine and Tennessee.

Habitat: Found on decaying organic matter in soil and in the dung of various animals. Common in Polish soils, according to Krzemieniewski (Acta Soc. Bot. Poloniae, *5*, 1927).

Illustrations: Thaxter (*op. cit.*, Pl. 31, Figs. 30–33) and Krzemieniewski (*op. cit.*, *4*, 1926, Pl. II, Figs. 13–14).

6. Myxococcus ovalisporus Krzemieniewska and Krzemieniewski, 1926. (Acta Soc. Bot. Poloniae, *4*, 1926, 15.)

o.va.li'spo.rus. L. noun *ovum* egg; M.L. adj. *ovalis* oval; Gr. noun *spora* seed; M.L. noun *spora* a spore; M.L. adj. *ovalisporus* oval-spored.

Vegetative cells: Not described.

Fruiting bodies: Nearly spherical, characteristically shortened, ellipsoidal spore masses of light milky yellow color; these are often raised on a poorly developed stalk. This stalk always shows some bacterial cells remaining and, with respect to this and to color, is differentiated from *M. stipitatus*. From the base of the stalk or directly from the substrate, one or more small fruiting bodies develop. Microcysts are ellipsoidal, sometimes irregularly spherical, 1.0 to 1.4 by 1.3 to 1.9 microns. In culture it retains its differences from *M. stipitatus*. The latter sporulates best at room temperature, but *M. ovalisporus* sporulates best in an incubator (presumably at 37° C.).

Source: From soil from Poland.

Habitat: Found on decaying organic matter in soil.

Addendum: *Species incertae sedis.* As it stands now, the taxonomy of the genus

Myxococcus is not entirely satisfactory. A careful comparative study of many strains under a variety of cultural conditions is necessary in order to determine the validity of the morphological criteria currently employed for the delimitation of species. The three species described below may merit recognition pending exhaustive study of the whole genus:

1. *Myxococcus albus* Finck, 1950. (Arch. f. Mikrobiol., *15*, 1950, 382.)

al'bus. L. adj. *albus* white.

Vegetative cells: Rods approximately 1.2 by 6.5 to 9.1 microns.

Fruiting bodies: Dimensions not given. Roundish to lengthened, sometimes confluent, white to beige in color. Rapidly deliquescing at 30° C. to slime masses with the appearance of oil drops. Microcysts spherical, 2.0 to 2.5 microns in diameter.

Source: Isolated from soil from Germany.

Habitat: Found on decaying organic matter in soil.

Comments: Appears to be clearly distinguishable from the white variety of *Myxococcus fulvus* on the basis of the size of microcysts. Possibly a non-pigmented variety of *M. virescens* or *M. xanthus*.

2. *Myxococcus viperus* Finck, 1950. (Arch. f. Mikrobiol., *15*, 1950, 383.)

vi'pe.rus. L. noun *vipera* viper, snake; M.L. adj. *viperus* pertaining to a viper.

Vegetative cells: Rods 1.0 to 1.3 by 6.5 to 7.8 microns. Rod masses greenish yellow, becoming red on exposure to light.

Fruiting bodies: Dimensions not given. Convoluted or club-shaped, mesenteric, yellow to copper-red in color. Microcysts spherical, 2 microns in diameter.

Source: Isolated from soil from Germany.

Habitat: Found on decaying organic matter in soil.

Comments: Possibly a variety of *Myxococcus virescens*.

3. *Myxococcus brevipes* Finck, 1950. (Arch. f. Mikrobiol., *15*, 1950, 384.)

bre'vi.pes. L. adj. *brevis* short; L. noun *pes* foot; M.L. adj. *brevipes* short-footed.

Vegetative cells: Rods 1.0 by 6.5 to 8.0 microns.

Fruiting bodies: Pale red to bright red, generally raised from the substrate on a colorless foot of slime. Deliquescent. Microcysts irregular, mostly spherical, 1.3 to 1.8 microns in diameter.

Source: Isolated from the dung of herbivores from Germany.

Habitat: Found in the dung of various animals.

Genus II. Chondrococcus* *Jahn, 1924.*

(Jahn, Beiträge zur bot. Protistologie. I, Die Polyangiden. Geb. Borntraeger, Leipzig, 1924, 85; not *Chondrococcus* Kützing, Botanische Zeitung, *5*, 1847, 23.)

Chon.dro.coc'cus. Gr. noun *chondrus* cartilage; Gr. noun *coccus* a berry, sphere; M.L. mas.n. *Chondrococcus* cartilaginous sphere.

Spores embedded in a viscous slime which hardens. Fruiting bodies divided by joints or constrictions, often branched, usually relatively small. This genus is a segregate from *Myxococcus* Thaxter.

Seven species are included, of which the first described by Thaxter and the best described, *Chondrococcus coralloides* (Thaxter) Jahn, has subsequently been designated as the type by Buchanan (Manual, 4th ed., 1934, 614). The first species listed by Jahn is regarded as doubtful and should not be regarded as the type for there is no evidence that Jahn ever saw the species.

The type species is *Chondrococcus coralloides* (Thaxter) Jahn.

---

* In spite of the fact that *Chondrococcus* Jahn appears to be an illegitimate homonym of the algal genus *Chondrococcus* Kützing, the former name is retained in this edition because of general usage and because *Chondrococcus* Kützing is not, so far as has been determined, in current use by algologists.

Key to the species of genus **Chondrococcus.**

I. Not parasitic on fish.
  A. Erect, simple or somewhat branched fruiting bodies.
    1. Secondary fruiting bodies not produced.
      a. Fruiting bodies constricted or jointed.
                    1. *Chondrococcus coralloides.*
      aa. Fruiting body simple, columnar, club- or cushion-shaped.
        b. Fruiting body thick below, lesser above.
                    2. *Chondrococcus cirrhosus.*
        bb. Not as in b.
          c. Fruiting body cushion-shaped.
                    3. *Chondrococcus megalosporus.*
          cc. Fruiting body branched.
                    4. *Chondrococcus macrosporus.*
    2. Secondary fruiting bodies arise as bud-, finger- or coral-like growths from primary fruiting body.
                    5. *Chondrococcus blasticus.*
  B. Recumbent, simple swelling or cyst heap constituting the fruiting body.
                    6. *Chondrococcus cerebriformis.*
II. Parasitic on fish.
                    7. *Chondrococcus columnaris.*

1. Chondrococcus coralloides (Thaxter, 1892) Jahn, 1924. (*Myxococcus coralloides* Thaxter, Bot. Gaz., *17*, 1892, 404; Jahn, Beiträge zur bot. Protistologie. I, Die Polyangiden. Geb. Borntraeger, Leipzig, 1924, 85.)

co.ral.lo.i'des or co.ral.loi'des. Gr. noun *corallium* coral; Gr. noun *eidus* shape; M.L. adj. *coralloides* coral-like.

Vegetative cells: Rods slender and curved, 0.4 by 4.0 to 7.0 microns. Rod masses pale pinkish, thin. Readily cultivated on potato agar or peptone agar.

Fruiting bodies: Very variable in shape, usually with rounded coral-like processes, recumbent or upright, sometimes with finger-like outgrowths or rounded constrictions, usually small, about 50 microns in diameter, protuberances 20 to 30 microns wide, light rose to flesh color. Microcysts 1.0 to 1.2 microns. Jahn recognizes two varieties of this species: the one, isolated by Quehl (Cent. f. Bakt., II Abt., *16*, 1906, 18), has fruiting bodies simple or branched rather than constricted or jointed; the other, described by Kofler (Sitzber. d. kais. Akad. Wiss., Wien, math.-nat. Klasse, Abt. I, *122*, 1913, 865), has its fruiting bodies in the form of simple swellings or "cyst heaps"

instead of branches; the latter is also recumbent rather than erect. Krzemieniewski (Acta Soc. Bot. Poloniae, *4*, 1926, 46) regards a variety of this species as a distinct species.

Source: Isolated from lichens. Found by Jahn (*op. cit.*, 1924) on dung of rabbit, hare, horses and deer and on old bark and lichens; also found on goat dung from Lapland and Italy. Kofler (*op. cit.*, 1913, 865) reports it from the dung of field mice, horses, hares, goats, roe and deer.

Habitat: Found on decaying organic matter in soil and in the dung of various animals. Thaxter (*op. cit.*, 1892, 404) reports that it is common in Europe but uncommon in America. Common in Polish soil, according to Krzemieniewski (*op. cit.*, *5*, 1927).

Illustrations: Thaxter (*op. cit.*, 1892, Pl. 24, Figs. 29–33), Quehl (*op. cit.*, 1906, Pl. 1, Figs. 1 and 9), Kofler (*op. cit.*, 1913, Pl. 1, Fig. 4; Pl. 2, Fig. 9), Krzemieniewski (*op. cit.*, 1926, Pl. II, Figs. 15–18) and Jahn (*op. cit.*, 1924, Fig. Y, page 87).

2. Chondrococcus cirrhosus (Thaxter, 1897) Jahn, 1924. (*Myxococcus cirrhosus* Thaxter, Bot. Gaz., *23*, 1897, 409; Jahn, Beiträge zur bot. Protistologie. I, Die Polyangiden. Geb. Borntraeger, Leipzig, 1924, 200.)

cir.rho'sus. Gr. *cirrhus* tawny; M.L. adj. *cirrhosus* tawny.

Vegetative cells: Rods 0.8 by 2.0 to 5.0 microns.

Fruiting bodies: Elongate, upright, thickened below, slender above, extended to a rounded point, 50 to 100 microns long, 20 microns in diameter at base, light red to flesh-colored. Microcysts about 1 micron.

Source: Isolated once from grouse dung from Massachusetts.

Habitat: Found in the dung of various animals.

Illustrations: Thaxter (*op. cit.*, Pl. 31, Figs. 25–27).

3. Chondrococcus megalosporus Jahn, 1924. (Jahn, Beiträge zur bot. Protistologie. I, Die Polyangiden. Geb. Borntraeger, Leipzig, 1924, 86.)

me.ga.lo'spo.rus. Gr. adj. *megas, megale, mega* big; Gr. noun *spora* seed; M.L. noun *spora* spore; M.L. adj. *megalosporus* large-spored.

Vegetative cells: Not described.

Fruiting bodies: About 80 to 160 microns wide, rounded, cushion-shaped, dark flesh-colored. Microcysts 2 microns.

Source: Isolated from stag dung near Berlin.

Habitat: Found in the dung of various animals.

Illustrations: Jahn (*ibid.*, Fig. Y, i to k, page 87).

4. Chondrococcus macrosporus Krzemieniewski, 1926. (Acta Soc. Bot. Poloniae, 4, 1926.)

ma.cro'spo.rus. Gr. adj. *macrus* long, large; Gr. noun *spora* seed; M.L. noun *spora* spore; M.L. adj. *macrosporus* long- or large-spored.

Vegetative cells: Not described.

Fruiting bodies: Much like those in *Chondrococcus coralloides*, differing in color and in size of microcysts. Microcysts 1.6 to 2.0 microns. Fruiting body yellow or light brown color with long branches.

Source: Isolated first from leaves then from soil on rabbit dung.

Habitat: Found on decaying organic mat-

ter in soil and in the dung of various animals.

Illustrations: Krzemieniewska and Krzemieniewski (*ibid.*, Pl. II, Fig. 19).

5. Chondrococcus blasticus Beebe, 1941. (Iowa State Coll. Jour. Sci., 15, 1941, 310.)

blas'ti.cus. Gr. adj. *blasticus* budding.

Vegetative cells: Long, slender, flexible rods, straight or curved to bent, ends rounded to slightly tapered, Gram-negative. 0.5 to 0.6 by 3.0 to 5.0 microns.

Fruiting body: Primary: Spherical to subspherical, usually sessile but occasionally with a short stalk or foot; pale pink to bright salmon-pink; 300 to 600 microns in diameter. No outer wall or limiting membrane evident. Develops on sterilized rabbit dung in from 3 to 6 days at room temperature. Secondary: Arising as bud-like growth from the primary fruiting body. Develops into irregularly shaped, finger-, coral- or bud-like protuberance. Seldom branched; occasionally stalked but usually sessile on primary fruiting body until latter is utilized in formation of several secondary fruiting bodies. Deep pink to salmon-pink in color. Variable in size and shape; 50 to 150 by 75 to 225 microns. No outer wall or limiting membrane evident.

Microcysts: Spherical, thick-walled, highly refractile; 1.2 to 1.4 microns in diameter. Held together in the fruiting body by the mass of slime.

Vegetative colony: Thin, colorless, transparent at margin; surface broken by many small ridges or veins. Center smooth, slightly thicker, often showing pale pink color. Fruiting bodies first form at or near center, later distributed irregularly on other parts of colony. Margin composed of active vegetative cells.

Physiology: Good growth on mineral salt agar to which has been added such complex carbohydrates as dulcitol, inulin, cellulose, reprecipitated cellulose or starch; starch hydrolyzed, cellulose not destroyed appreciably. Can utilize agar as both C and N sources. Best growth on suspensions of killed bacterial cells in agar. Growth inhibited partially or entirely by arabinose, mannose or maltose.

Source: Isolated from goat dung and from soil from Ames, Iowa.

Habitat: Soil. Decomposes organic matter, especially bacterial cells in dung.

Illustrations: Beebe (*ibid.*, Pl. II, Figs. 5 and 6; Pl. IV, Fig. 18).

6. **Chondrococcus cerebriformis** (Kofler, 1913) Jahn, 1924. (*Myxococcus cerebriformis* Kofler, Sitzber. d. kais. Wiss. Wien, math.-nat. Klasse, Abt. I, *122*, 1913, 866; Jahn, Beiträge zur bot. Protistologie. I, Die Polyangiden. Geb. Borntraeger, Leipzig, 1924, 86.)

ce.reb.ri.for'mis. L. noun *cerebrum* brain; L. noun *forma* shape; M.L. adj. *cerebriformis* brain-like.

Vegetative cells: Rods 4 to 12 microns.

Fruiting bodies: About 1 mm long, clumped masses with swollen upper surface, brain-like, violet-rose, often lead-gray. Microcysts 1.1 to 1.6 microns. Jahn (*loc. cit.*) suggests that this may be *Archangium gephyra*.

Source: Isolated from hare dung in the vicinity of Vienna.

Habitat: Found in the dung of various animals.

Illustrations: Kofler (*op. cit.*, 1913, Pl. 2, Figs. 7 and 8).

7. **Chondrococcus columnaris** (Davis, 1923) Ordal and Rucker, 1944. (*Bacillus columnaris* Davis, Bull. U. S. Bur. Fisheries, *38*, 1923, 261; Ordal and Rucker, Proc. Soc. Exper. Biol. and Med., *56*, 1944, 18; also see Fish and Rucker, Trans. Amer. Fish. Soc., 73rd Annual Vol. for 1943, 1945, 32.)

co.lum.na'ris. L. adj. *columnaris* rising like a pillar.

Vegetative cells: Flexible, weakly refractive, Gram-negative rods, 0.5 to 0.7 by 4.0 to 8.0 microns. Creeping motion observed on solid media, and flexing movements observed in liquid media.

Microcysts: 0.7 to 1.2 microns, spherical to ellipsoidal.

Fruiting bodies: A peculiar type of fruiting body is formed in liquid media. Where organisms are in contact with infected tissues or with scales, columnar and sometimes branched fruiting bodies are produced in which typical microcysts develop in 7 to 10 days.

Physiology: Growth best on 0.5 to 0.9 per cent agar with 0.25 to 0.50 per cent Bactotryptone at pH 7.3. Colonies on tryptone agar are yellow, flat and irregular; edge uneven with swarming apparent. Gelatin liquefied rapidly. Indole not produced. Nitrites not produced from nitrates. Starch, cellulose and agar not attacked. Sugars not fermented, but glucose is oxidized.

Source: First described as the cause of a bacterial disease of warm-water fishes (Davis, *op. cit.*, 1923, 261), and later in fingerlings of the cold-water blue-black salmon (*Oncorrhynchus nerka*). Transmissible to salmonid fishes.

Genus III. **Angiococcus** *Jahn, 1924.*

(Beiträge zur bot. Protistologie. I, Die Polyangiden. Geb. Borntraeger, Leipzig, 1924, 89.)

An.gi.o.coc'cus. Gr. noun *angium* vessel; Gr. noun *coccus* a berry; M.L. mas.n. *Angiococcus* vessel coccus.

Fruiting body consists of numerous, round (disc-shaped) cysts; cyst wall thin, microcysts within.

The type species is *Angiococcus disciformis* (Thaxter) Jahn.

Key to the species of genus **Angiococcus.**

I. Cysts yellow to dark orange-yellow; disc-shaped; 35 microns in diameter.
1. *Angiococcus disciformis.*

II. Cysts colorless to yellow; round; up to 15 microns in diameter.
2. *Angiococcus cellulosum.*

1. **Angiococcus disciformis** (Thaxter, 1904) Jahn, 1924. (*Myxococcus disciformis* Thaxter, Bot. Gaz., *37*, 1904, 412; Jahn, Beiträge zur bot. Protistologie. I, Die Poly-

angiden, Geb. Borntraeger, Leipzig, 1924, 89.)

dis.ci.for'mis. Gr. noun *discus* a disc; L. noun *forma* form; M.L. adj. *disciformis* disc-shaped.

Vegetative cells: Rods 0.5 to 0.6 by 2.0 to 3.0 microns.

Fruiting bodies: Cysts disc-shaped, crowded, sessile, attached by a more or less ragged, scar-like insertion or in masses. Cysts yellowish when young, when old dark orange-yellow, about 10 by 35 microns. Cyst wall distinct, thin, becoming very slightly wrinkled. Microcysts irregularly spherical, embedded in viscous slime, difficult to see in the ripe cyst.

Source: Isolated from the dung of muskrat and deer from Massachusetts and New Hampshire.

Habitat: Found on decaying organic matter in soil and in the dung of various animals. Rare in Polish soils according to Krzemieniewski (Acta Soc. Bot. Poloniae, *5*, 1927).

Illustrations: Thaxter (*op. cit.*, 1904, Pl. 27, Figs. 19–21) and Krzemieniewski (*op. cit.*, *4*, 1926, Pl. II, Figs. 21 and 22).

2. **Angiococcus cellulosum** Mishustin, 1938. (Microbiologia, *7*, 1938, 427.)

cel.lu.lo'sum. M.L. noun *cellulosum* cellulose.

Vegetative cells: 0.4 to 0.5 by 1.5 to 2.0 microns.

Fruiting body: Regularly rounded (less frequently extended or angular), 20 to 150 microns in diameter; yellow or pink in color to drabbish when old. Encysted cells surrounded by a colorless cyst wall or envelope. Usually 1 to 3 short stalks, or cystophores, up to 10 microns high. Within the outer wall are numerous cysts containing microcysts. Cysts have regularly rounded form; unpigmented to yellow; 5 to 15 microns in diameter, average 6 microns. Number of cysts in fruiting body increases with age. Size of microcysts not given.

Vegetative colony: Fairly rapid growth on cellulose with silica gel. Colony has a yellowish cast. Reaches diameter of 1.5 to 2.0 cm after 6 days with center yellowish pink and margin tinged light pink. Surface moist. Fruiting bodies more numerous at center but distributed over entire area. Fruiting bodies do not noticeably protrude above the surface of the colony.

Physiology: Cellulose attacked but not completely destroyed.

Source: Isolated from soil.

Habitat: Found on decaying organic matter in soil.

Genus IV. **Sporocytophaga** *Stanier, 1940*.

(Jour. Bact., *40*, 1940, 629.)

Spo.ro.cy.to'pha.ga. Gr. noun *spora* seed; M.L. noun *spora* a spore; Gr. noun *cytus* hollow place, vessel, cell; Gr. v. *phagein* to devour; M.L. fem.n. *Cytophaga* generic name; M.L. fem.n. *Sporocytophaga* the sporing *Cytophaga*.

Spherical or ellipsoidal microcysts formed loosely in masses of slime among the vegetative cells. Fruiting bodies absent.

The type species is *Sporocytophaga myxococcoides* (Krzemieniewska) Stanier.

Key to the species of genus **Sporocytophaga.**

I. Microcysts spherical.

　A. Does not utilize starch.

　　　　1. *Sporocytophaga myxococcoides.*

　B. Utilizes starch.

　　　　2. *Sporocytophaga congregata.*

II. Microcysts ellipsoidal.

　　　　3. *Sporocytophaga ellipsospora.*

1. **Sporocytophaga myxococcoides** (Krzemieniewska, 1933) Stanier, 1940. (*Cytophaga myxococcoides* Krzemieniewska,

Arch. f. Mikrobiol., *4*, 1933, 400; Stanier, Jour. Bact., *40*, 1940, 630.)

myx.o.coc.co.i'des or myx.o.coc.coi'-

des. M.L. mas.n. *Myxococcus* a generic name; Gr. noun *eidus* shape; M.L. adj. *myxoccoides* resembling *Myxococcus*.

Vegetative cells: Flexible, singly occurring rods, 0.3 to 0.4 by 2.5 to 8.0 microns. Gram-negative. Young cells stain uniformly with basic dyes, but with the onset of microcyst formation, chromatin becomes concentrated in central bands or spots in the shortening rods.

Microcysts: Spherical, varying in size from 1.2 to 1.6 microns. Surrounded by a highly refractile wall.

Produces glistening, light yellow patches on filter paper-silica gel or -agar plates after 4 to 5 days. The central areas gradually become translucent owing to complete destruction of the cellulose. Old cultures assume a brownish tinge.

On mineral glucose agar plates, colonies are small, pale yellow and translucent; they may be round with even edges or flat and irregular. The agar under the colony becomes etched and sunken.

Cellulose, cellobiose and glucose are utilized. Mannose utilized by some strains (Kaars Sijpestein and Fahraeus, Jour. Gen. Microbiol., *3*, 1947, 232). Xylose, arabinose, galactose, fructose, mannitol and starch not utilized.

Ammonia, nitrate, urea, peptone and yeast extract can serve as nitrogen sources.

Catalase-positive.

Strictly aerobic.

Optimum temperature, 30° C.

Source: Isolated from soil.

Habitat: Soil. Decomposes cellulose.

2. Sporocytophaga congregata Fuller and Norman, 1943. (Jour. Bact., *45*, 1943, 567.)

con.gre.ga'ta. L. part.adj. *congregatus* assembled.

Vegetative cells: Long, flexuous rods with pointed ends, 0.5 to 0.7 by 5.5 to 8.0 microns.

Microcysts: Spherical, 0.7 to 1.1 microns in diameter. Usually occur in localized regions within the colony.

Growth on starch agar is smoky, later turning yellow. Colonies are irregularly round, slightly concave. Edge is smooth and entire at first, later becoming irregular. Marginal and internal swarming may be prominent. The vegetative cells gather into

groups, and in these regions a large number of spherical spores are found.

Growth on cellulose dextrin agar is pale; colonies are small and concave. Hollowing of the agar is limited to the area of colony growth.

Litmus milk: Growth, but no digestion or curd formation.

Indole not produced.

Glucose, galactose, lactose, maltose, sucrose, arabinose, calcium gluconate, starch, cellulose, dextrin, pectin and hemicellulose are utilized. Filter paper is not attacked.

Ammonium, nitrate and peptone are suitable nitrogen sources.

Nitrites not produced from nitrates.

Highly aerobic.

Optimum temperature, between 25° and 30° C.

Source: Isolated from soil.

Habitat: Soil. Decomposes organic matter.

3. Sporocytophaga ellipsospora (Imšenecki and Solntzeva, 1936) Stanier, 1942. (*Cytophaga ellipsospora* Imšenecki and Solntzeva, Bull. Acad. Sci. U.S.S.R., Ser. Biol., No. 6, 1936, 1137; Stanier, Bact. Rev., *6*, 1942, 153 and 190.)

el.lip.sos'po.ra. Gr. noun *ellipsis* ellipse; Gr. noun *spora* seed; M.L. noun *spora* spore; M.L. adj. *ellipsosporus* with elliptical spores.

Vegetative cells: Flexible, singly occurring rods, 0.4 microns wide at the center and tapering to both ends. Length, 7.5 microns. May be straight, bent U-shaped or S-shaped.

Microcysts: Ellipsoidal or somewhat elongated, 0.9 to 1.2 by 1.6 to 1.8 microns. Almost always situated in closely packed aggregates; isolated, individual microcysts rare. Germinate by elongation.

On mineral salts-silica gel plates covered with filter paper, orange, glistening, mucilaginous patches are produced. Ultimately the filter paper is completely dissolved, and the patches become translucent.

Ammonia, nitrate and peptone can serve as sources of nitrogen.

Strictly aerobic.

Optimum temperature, between 28° and 30° C.

Source: Isolated from soil.

Habitat: Soil. Decomposes cellulose.

ORDER IX. SPIROCHAETALES BUCHANAN, 1918.*

(Jour. Bact., *3*, 1918, 542.)

Spi.ro.chae.ta'les. M.L. fem.n. *Spirochaeta* type genus of the order; *-ales* ending to denote an order; M.L. fem.pl.n. *Spirochaetales* the *Spirochaeta* order.

Slender, flexuous bodies, 6 to 500 microns in length, in the form of spirals with at least one complete turn. Some forms may show an axial filament, a lateral crista, or ridge, or transverse striations; otherwise there is no significant protoplasmic pattern. Smaller forms may have a lower refractive index than that of true bacteria, and therefore they can be seen only with dark-field illumination. Some forms take aniline dyes with difficulty; Giemsa's stain is uniformly successful. Granules are formed in some species which are found in vector hosts. All forms are motile. In the true bacteria, motility is effected by flagella endowed with a lashing movement; however, no such structures exist among the spirochetes. Terminal projections, whether derived from the periplast or from the axial filament, may assist in the movements, and it is possible that the crista has a similar function, although neither of these structures can explain the violent motion of the spirochetes. This motility consists of a rapid whirling or spinning about the long axis, which activity drives the organism forward or backward, there being no anteroposterior polarity. In addition the spirochetes make violent, lashing movements, curling and uncurling their spirals. Multiplication is by transverse fission, no sexual cycle being known. Free-living, saprophytic and parasitic forms.

Key to the families of order **Spirochaetales.**

I. Spirals 30 to 500 microns in length, possessing definite protoplasmic structures.
Family I. *Spirochaetaceae*, p. 892.
II. Spirals 4 to 16 microns in length, possessing no obvious protoplasmic structure.
Family II. *Treponemataceae*, p. 896.

FAMILY I. SPIROCHAETACEAE SWELLENGREBEL, 1907.

(Ann. Inst. Past., *21*, 1907, 581.)

Spi.ro.chae.ta'ce.ae. M.L. fem.n. *Spirochaeta* type genus of the family; *-aceae* ending to denote a family; M.L. fem.pl.n. *Spirochaetaceae* the *Spirochaeta* family.

Coarse, spiral organisms, 30 to 500 microns in length, possessing definite protoplasmic structures. Found in stagnant, fresh or salt water and in the intestinal tracts of bivalve molluscs (*Lamellibranchiata*).

---

* Revised by Dr. G. H. Robinson, Wm. H. Singer Memorial Research Laboratory of the Allegheny General Hospital, Pittsburgh, Pa., September, 1943; further revision by Dr. Gordon E. Davis, Rocky Mountain Laboratory, U. S. Public Health Service, Hamilton, Montana, assisted by Mrs. Elsie Wattie Lackey (Family *Spirochaetaceae*), University of Florida, Gainesville, Florida, May, 1955.

Key to the genera of family **Spirochaetaceae.**

I. No obvious periplast membrane and no cross striations present.

Genus I. *Spirochaeta*, p. 893.

II. Periplast membrane present. Cross striations present in stained specimens.

A. Free-living in marine ooze.

Genus II. *Saprospira*, p. 894.

B. Parasitic on lamellibranch molluscs. Cristae are prominent.

Genus III. *Cristispira*, p. 895.

Genus I. **Spirochaeta** *Ehrenberg, 1833.*

(Ehrenberg, Abhandl. Berl. Akad., 1833, 313; *Spirochoeta* Dujardin, Hist. nat. des Zoophytes infusoires, Paris, 1841, 209; *Spirochaete* Cohn, Beitr. z. Biol. d. Pflanz., *1*, Heft 1, 1872, 180.)

Spi.ro.chae′ta. Gr. noun *spira* a coil, spiral; Gr. noun *chaete* hair; M.L. fem.n. *Spirochaeta* spiral hair.

Flexible, undulating, spiral-shaped rods with or without flagelliform, tapering ends. The protoplast is wound spirally around a well defined axial filament; there is no obvious periplast membrane and there are no cross striations. The primary spiral is permanent. Motility is by a creeping motion along the surface of supporting objects. Presumably Gram-negative. Non-parasitic. Found free-living in fresh- or sea-water slime, especially in the presence of hydrogen sulfide; common in sewage and foul waters.

The type species is *Spirochaeta plicatilis* Ehrenberg.

Key to the species of genus **Spirochaeta.**

I. Large spirals with rounded ends.

1. *Spirochaeta plicatilis.*
2. *Spirochaeta marina.*
3. *Spirochaeta eurystrepta.*

II. Smaller spirals with pointed ends.

4. *Spirochaeta stenostrepta.*
5. *Spirochaeta daxensis.*

1. **Spirochaeta plicatilis** Ehrenberg, 1838. (Die Infusionstierchen, 1838, 83.)

pli.ca′ti.lis. L. adj. *plicatilis* flexible.

Cylindrical, spiral-shaped rods, 0.5 to 0.75 by 100 to 500 microns, with blunt ends. There are several, large, inconstant, irregular waves. Spiral amplitude: 2.0 microns, regular; spiral depth: 1.5 microns, regular. A flexible, elastic, axial filament, consisting of chitin or of a cutin-like substance, is distinct in stained specimens; this filament is resistant to trypsin digestion. Multiplication is by transverse fission. Stain violet with Giemsa's stain and gray with iron-hemotoxylin. Cytoplasmic spirals stain with eosin, rubin, etc. Cells contain volutin granules and fat inclusions. Gram-negative (Dyar, Jour. Bact., *54*, 1947, 490).

Dyar (*ibid.*, 483), who used recent micro-scopic and staining techniques in her studies, questions the presence of axial filaments and the absence of distinct periplast membranes and of prominent cross striations in this species.

Although not cultivable on ordinary laboratory media, Dyar (*ibid.*, 483) succeeded in obtaining good growth of pure cultures on a blood-enriched agar medium which contained a dilute decoction of decaying leaves from a hydrogen sulfide spring; the hydrogen sulfide was found to be apparently unnecessary for growth.

Bile salts (10 per cent): Cells become shadowy and pale but do not dissolve.

Saponin (10 per cent): Cells live for 30 minutes; later they become shadowy but do not dissolve.

Grows best under low oxygen tension.

Optimum temperature, between 20° and 25° C.

Habitat: Found free-living in fresh or salt water.

2. Spirochaeta marina Zuelzer, 1912.
(*Spirochaeta plicatilis marina* Zuelzer, Arch. f. Protistenk., *24*, 1912, 17; Zuelzer, *ibid.*, 51.)

ma.ri′na. L. adj. *marinus* of the sea.

Probably a subspecies or variant of *Spirochaeta plicatilis*.

Cylindrical, spiral-shaped rods, 0.5 by 100 to 200 microns, with blunt ends. A flexible, elastic, axial filament is present. Multiplication is by transverse fission. The cytoplasmic spirals take stain. Contain smaller and more irregularly distributed volutin granules than those found in *Spirochaeta plicatilis*.

Grows best at low oxygen tension.

Optimum temperature, 20° C.

Habitat: Sea water.

3. Spirochaeta eurystrepta Zuelzer, 1912.
(*Spirochaeta plicatilis eurystrepta* Zuelzer, Arch. f. Protistenk., *24*, 1912, 17; Zuelzer, *ibid.*, 51.)

eu.ry.strep′ta. Gr. adj. *eurys* broad; Gr. adj. *streptus* easily twisted, pliant; M.L. adj. *eurystreptus* loosely coiled.

Probably a subspecies or variant of *Spirochaeta plicatilis*.

Cylindrical, spiral-shaped rods, 0.5 by 300 microns, with blunt ends. A flexible, elastic, axial filament is present. Spiral amplitude: more shallow than that of *S. plicatilis*. Multiplication is by transverse fission. The cytoplasmic spirals take stain. Cells contain fewer volutin granules than do those of *S. plicatilis*.

Optimum temperature, 20° C.

Habitat: Found in swamp water and in grossly polluted water containing hydrogen sulfide.

4. Spirochaeta stenostrepta Zuelzer, 1912. (Arch. f. Protistenk., *24*, 1912, 16.)

ste.no.strep′ta. Gr. adj. *stenus* narrow; Gr. adj. *streptus* easily twisted, pliant; M.L. adj. *stenostreptus* tightly coiled.

Cylindrical, spiral-shaped rods, 0.25 by 20 to 60, occasionally up to 200, microns, with pointed ends. A flexible, elastic, axial filament is present. Spiral amplitude: very narrow with steep windings. Multiplication is by transverse fission. The cytoplasmic spirals take stain. Cells contain fewer granules than do those of *Spirochaeta plicatilis*.

Optimum temperature, 20° C.

Habitat: Found in water containing hydrogen sulfide.

5. Spirochaeta daxensis Cantacuzène, 1910. (Compt. rend. Soc. Biol., Paris, *68*, 1910, 75.)

dax.en′sis. M.L. adj. *daxensis* pertaining to Dax; named for Dax, a watering place in France.

Large, spiral-shaped cells, 0.5 by 2.5 by 30 to 100 microns, possessing a longitudinal chromatin filament and tapering at the ends. The cells are flattened and exhibit a double series of curls, smaller waves being superimposed on larger undulations.

Optimum temperature, between 44° and 52° C.

Source: From water from a hot spring at Dax (52° to 56° C.).

Habitat: Found in hot springs.

Genus II. Saprospira Gross, 1911.

(Mittheil. Zool. Stat. zu Neapel, *20*, 1911, 190.)

Sap.ro.spi′ra. Gr. adj. *saprus* rotten, putrid; Gr. noun *spira* a spiral; M.L. fem.n. *Saprospira* rot-spiral.

Cells contain spiral protoplasm without an evident axial filament; transverse markings or septa (?) are observed in stained and unstained specimens. Possess a distinct periplast membrane. The spirals are rather shallow. Motility is active and rotating. Found free-living in marine ooze.

The type species is *Saprospira grandis* Gross.

1. **Saprospira grandis** Gross, 1911. (Mittheil. Zool. Stat. zu Neapel, *20*, 1911, 190.)

gran'dis. L. adj. *grandis* large.

Cylindrical, flexible, elastic, spiral-shaped rods, 1.2 by 80 microns, with obtuse ends. The waves are large, inconstant, shallow, irregular, 3 to 5 in number and sometimes almost straight. Spiral amplitude: 24 microns. There is no evident axial filament and no crista; cross striations are present. There is a distinct membrane but no terminal spiral filament and no highly motile end portion. Multiplication is by transverse fission. The cells undergo trypsin digestion.

Source: From the intestinal tract of an oyster.

Habitat: Found free-living in foraminiferous sand.

2. **Saprospira punctum** Dimitroff, 1926. (*Saprospira puncta* (sic) Dimitroff, Jour. Bact., *12*, 1926, 146.)

punc'tum. L. noun *punctum* a point.

Large spirals, 1 by 86 microns, with pointed ends. Spiral amplitude: 4 to 8 microns; average number of turns: 3. There is no evident axial filament; cross striations are present. There is a distinct membrane. Multiplication is by transverse fission.

Source: From oysters.

3. **Saprospira lepta** Dimitroff, 1926. (Jour. Bact., *12*, 1926, 144.)

lep'ta. Gr. adj. *leptus* fine, delicate.

Large spirals, 0.5 by 70 microns, with pointed ends. Spiral amplitude: ranges from 5 to 13 microns; spiral width: varies from 1.6 to 4.8 microns; average number of turns: 6. There is no evident axial filament; cross striations are present. There is a distinct membrane. Multiplication is by transverse fission.

Comments: A variety which differs from the parent strain in the shape of the ends of the cells has been reported by Dimitroff (*ibid.*, 145).

Source: From oysters from Baltimore, Maryland.

Genus III. **Cristispira** *Gross, 1910.*

(Mittheil. Zool. Stat. zu Neapel, *20*, 1910, 41.)

Cris.ti.spi'ra. L. noun *crista* a crest; Gr. noun *spira* a spiral; M.L. fem.n. *Cristispira* crested-spiral.

Flexuous cell bodies, in coarse spirals, 28 to 120 microns in length. Possess cross striations and a crista, or thin membrane of varying prominence, on one side of the body extending the entire length of the organism. Actively motile. Found in the intestinal tracts of molluscs.

The type species is *Cristispira balbianii* (Certes) Gross.

1. **Cristispira balbianii** (Certes, 1882) Gross, 1912. (*Trypanosoma balbianii* Certes, Bull. Soc. Zool. de France, *7*, 1882, 347; Gross, Cent. f. Bakt., I Abt., Orig., *65*, 1912, 90.)

bal.bi.a'ni.i. M.L. gen.noun *balbianii* of Balbiani; named for Balbiani.

Cylindrical, flexible, elastic, spiral-shaped rods, 1 to 3 by 40 to 120 microns, with obtuse ends. The waves are large, irregular, shallow and 2 to 5 in number, sometimes more. Spiral amplitude: 8 microns; spiral depth: 1.6 microns. There is no evident axial filament; cross striations are present. A crista, a ridge-like membrane, making one or two complete turns is present. There is a distinct membrane but no terminal spiral filament and no highly motile end portion. With respect to staining, the cell membrane behaves like chitin or cutin substance: it stains violet with Giemsa's solution and light gray with iron-hemotoxylin. The membrane is resistant to trypsin digestion, but the crista and the striations disappear.

Bile salt (10 per cent): Crista quickly dissolves.

Saponin (10 per cent): Crista becomes fibrillar then indistinct.

Source: From the crystalline styles of oysters.

Habitat: Parasitic in the alimentary tracts of shellfish.

2. **Cristispira anodontae** (Keysselitz, 1906) Gross, 1912. (*Spirochaeta anodontae* Keysselitz, Arb. a. d. kaiserl. Gesundheitsamte, *23*, 1906, 566; Gross, Cent. f. Bakt., I Abt., Orig., *65*, 1912, 900.)

a.no.don'tae. Gr. adj. *anodus, anodontis* toothless; M.L. noun *Anodonta* a genus of molluscs; M.L. gen.noun *anodontae* of *Anodonta*.

Large, spiral-shaped cells, 0.8 to 1.2 by 44 to 88 microns, with sharply pointed ends. Average spiral width: 2 microns; average wave length: 8 microns; average number of complete turns: from 5 to 11. The cells are flattened and possess an undulating membrane; the periplast is fibrillar in appearance, and there is a dark granule at each end of the undulating membrane. Chromatin material is distributed in the form of globules or elongated bands.

Habitat: Found in the crystalline styles of fresh-water mussels (*Anodonta cygnea*

and *A. mutabilis*); also found in the intestinal tracts of oysters.

3. **Cristispira pinnae** (Gonder, 1908) Zuelzer, 1912. (*Spirochaete pinnae* Gonder, Cent. f. Bakt., I Abt., Orig., *47*, 1908, 491; Zuelzer, Verhandl. d. VIII Internat. Zool.-Kongres. zu Graz (August, 1910), Jena, 1912 (January), 433.)

pin'nae. Gr. noun *pinna* a kind of mussel; M.L. fem.n. *Pinna* a genus of mussels; M.L. gen.noun *pinnae* of *Pinna*.

Spiral-shaped cells, 0.5 to 3.0 by 10 to 60 microns, with blunt ends, the one end being slightly more pointed than the other; round in section. A ridge or comb is evident along one side, but there are no terminal filaments; cross striations are distinct. Possess undulating membranes. Chromatin granules are grouped in fours.

Source: From the intestinal canal of a scallop (*Pecten jacobaeus*).

Habitat: Found in the crystalline styles of molluscs.

FAMILY II. TREPONEMATACEAE ROBINSON, 1948.

(*Treponemidae*, incorrectly attributed to Schaudinn by Castellani and Chalmers, Man. Trop. Med., 3rd ed., 1919, 454; *Microspirochaetaceae* Gieszczykiewicz, Bull. Acad. Polonaise Sci. et Lett., Sér. B (1), 1939, 24; *Treponemataceae*, incorrectly attributed to Schaudinn by Robinson, in Manual, 6th ed., 1948, 1058.)

Tre.po.ne.ma.ta'ce.ae. M.L. neut.n. *Treponema* type genus of the family; -*aceae* ending to denote a family; M.L. fem.pl.n. *Treponemataceae* the *Treponema* family.

Coarse or slender spirals, 4 to 16 microns in length; longer forms are due to incomplete or delayed division. The spirals are regular or irregular and flexible or comparatively rigid. The protoplasm possesses no obvious structural features. Some cells may show terminal filaments. Some cells are visible only with dark-field illumination. Many of these organisms can be cultivated. With few exceptions, parasitic in vertebrates. Some are pathogenic.

Key to the genera of family **Treponemataceae.**

I. Stains easily with ordinary aniline dyes.

Genus I. *Borrelia*, p. 897.

II. Stain with difficulty except with Giemsa's stain or silver impregnation.

A. Anaerobic.

Genus II. *Treponema*, p. 904.

B. Aerobic.

Genus III. *Leptospira*, p. 907.

Genus I. **Borrelia** *Swellengrebel, 1907.*

(Swellengrebel, Ann. Inst. Past., *21*, 1907 (June), 582; *Spiroschaudinnia* Sambon, in Manson, Tropical Diseases, 1907 (August), 833; *Spironema* Bergey et al., Manual, 1st ed., 1923, 424; not *Spironema* Vuillemin, Compt. rend. Acad. Sci., Paris, *140*, 1905, 1567.)

Bor.rel'i.a. M.L. fem.gen.n. *Borrelia* of Borrel; named for A. Borrel, a French scientist.

Cells, 8 to 16 microns in length, with coarse, shallow, irregular spirals, a few of which may be obtuse-angled. Generally taper terminally into fine filaments. Stain easily with ordinary aniline dyes. Refractive index approximately the same as that of true bacteria. Parasitic upon many forms of animal life. Some are pathogenic for man, other mammals or birds. Generally these organisms are hematophytic or are found on mucous membranes. Some are transmitted by the bites of arthropods.

The type species is *Borrelia anserina* (Sakharoff) Bergey et al.

Key to the species of genus **Borrelia.**

I. From birds.

  1. *Borrelia anserina.*

II. From animals other than birds.

  A. From man.

   1. Cause relapsing fever in man.

    a. Transmitted by arthropod vectors.

     b. Arthropod vector is the louse *Pediculus humanus* subsp. *humanus.*

      2. *Borrelia recurrentis.*

      3. *Borrelia berbera.*

      4. *Borrelia carteri.*

     bb. Arthropod vector is of the genus *Ornithodoros* (tick).

      c^1. Transmitted by *Ornithodoros erraticus* (large form).

       5. *Borrelia hispanica.*

      c^2. Transmitted by *Ornithodoros hermsi.*

       6. *Borrelia hermsii.*

      c^3. Transmitted by *Ornithodoros moubata.*

       7. *Borrelia duttonii.*

      c^4. Transmitted by *Ornithodoros parkeri.*

       8. *Borrelia parkeri.*

      c^5. Transmitted by *Ornithodoros rudis.*

       9. *Borrelia venezuelensis.*

      c^6. Transmitted by *Ornithodoros tholozani.*

       10. *Borrelia persica.*

      c^7. Transmitted by *Ornithodoros turicata.*

       11. *Borrelia turicatae.*

      c^8. Transmitted by *Ornithodoros verrucosus.*

       12. *Borrelia caucasica.*

    aa. Arthropod vector unknown.

      13. *Borrelia novyi.*

      14. *Borrelia kochii.*

   2. Do not cause relapsing fever in man.

    a. From the mouth and from the respiratory mucous membrane.

      15. *Borrelia buccalis.*

      16. *Borrelia vincentii.*

    aa. From the genital mucous membranes.

      17. *Borrelia refringens.*

  B. From animals other than man.

1. From insects or ticks.
    a. From the tse-tse fly (*Glossina palpalis*).
            18. *Borrelia glossinae.*
    aa. From ticks.
        b¹. From *Ornithodoros brasiliensis.*
            19. *Borrelia brasiliensis.*
        b². From *Ornithodoros dugesi.*
            20. *Borrelia dugesii.*
        b³. From *Ornithodoros graingeri.*
            21. *Borrelia graingeri.*
        b⁴. From *Ornithodoros tholozani* var. *babylonensis.*
            22. *Borrelia babylonensis.*
2. From animals other than insects or ticks.
    a. From rodents.
        b. From the shrew-mouse (*Crocidura stampflii*).
            23. *Borrelia crocidurae.*
        bb. From gerbilles.
            c. Transmitted by *Ornithodoros erraticus* (small form).
            24. *Borrelia dipodilli.*
            cc. Transmitted by *Ornithodoros tartakovskyi.*
            25. *Borrelia latyschewii.*
    aa. From animals other than rodents.
        b. From non-primates.
            c. From non-ruminants.
            26. *Borrelia hyos.*
            cc. From ruminants.
            27. *Borrelia theileri.*
        bb. From primates.
            28. *Borrelia harveyi.*

1. **Borrelia anserina** (Sakharoff, 1891) Bergey et al., 1925. (*Spirochaeta anserina* Sakharoff, Ann. Inst. Past., *5*, 1891, 564; *Spiroschaudinnia anserina* Castellani and Chalmers, Man. Trop. Med., 2nd ed., 1913, 403; Bergey et al., Manual, 2nd ed., 1925, 435.)

an.se.ri′na. L. adj. *anserinus* pertaining to geese.

Cells, 0.25 to 0.3 by 8.0 to 20.0 microns, averaging about one spiral per micron. Actively motile by means of lashing movements. Stain readily with aniline dyes and Giemsa's stain.

Growth occurs in Noguchi's ascitic fluid rabbit kidney medium.

Antigenically distinct from the species of this genus found in mammals.

Pathogenic for birds but not for mammals.

Transmitted by the bites of ticks (*Argas persicus, A. miniatus, A. reflexus* and *Ornithodoros moubata*).

Source: Isolated from the blood of infected geese, ducks, fowls and vector ticks.

Habitat: Found as the cause of spirochetosis of fowls.

2. **Borrelia recurrentis** (Lebert, 1874) Bergey et al., 1925. (See Obermeier, Berlin. klin. Wochnschr., 1873, 152; *Protomycetum recurrentis* Lebert, Ziemssen's Handbuch, *2*, 1874, 267; *Spiroschaudinnia recurrentis* Castellani and Chalmers, Man. Trop. Med., 2nd ed., 1913, 398; Bergey et al., Manual, 2nd ed., 1925, 433.)

re.cur.ren′tis. L. part.adj. *recurrens, recurrentis* recurring.

Cylindrical or slightly flattened cells, 0.35 to 0.5 by 8.0 to 16.0 microns, with pointed ends. Spirals are large, wavy, inconstant, about 5 in number. Spiral amplitude, 1.5 microns. Terminal, finely spiral filaments are present. Motile by means of an active, cork-screw motion without polarity. Lashing movements are common in drawn blood. Highly motile end portion absent. Stain with the common aniline dyes; violet with Giemsa's stain. Gram-negative.

Growth occurs in ascitic or hydrocoel fluid to which a piece of sterile rabbit kidney is added.

Bile salts (10 per cent): Disintegration of cells is complete.

Saponin (10 per cent): Cells are immobilized in 30 minutes, then broken up in a few hours. In some cases a skeletal structure remains.

Optimum pH, between 7.2 and 7.4.

Serum does not agglutinate *Borrelia duttonii*.

Disease in experimental animals (small rodents after monkey passage) is mild.

Transmission, accidental and experimental, is by conjunctival sac and skin abrasions.

Arthropod vector is the louse (*Pediculus humanus* subsp. *humanus*), which exhibits normal transmission from the 16th to the 28th day. Found in ticks but not transmitted by them. No evidence of hereditary transmission in the louse.

Habitat: Found as the cause of epidemic relapsing fever. Transmissible to man and monkeys and from monkeys to mice and rats.

3. **Borrelia berbera** (Sergent and Foley, 1910) Bergey et al., 1925. (*Spirochaeta berbera* Sergent and Foley, Ann. Inst. Past., *24*, 1910, 337; Bergey et al., Manual, 2nd ed., 1925, 435.)

ber'be.ra. M.L. adj. *berberus* pertaining to the Berbers; named for the Berbers, a North African tribe.

Cells are more tenuous than those of other relapsing-fever organisms, measuring 0.2 to 0.3 by 12 to 24 microns.

There is no record of cultivation.

Antigenically distinct from *Borrelia recurrentis*.

Pathogenicity: Virulent for monkeys; produces non-fatal infection in rats and mice.

Possibly carried by the louse (*Pediculus humanus* subsp. *humanus*).

Comment: Regarded by some investi-

gators as identical with *Borrelia recurrentis* Bergey et al.

Source: From cases of relapsing fever in Algiers, Tunis and Tripoli.

Habitat: Found as a cause of relapsing fever in North Africa.

4. **Borrelia carteri** (Mackie, 1907) Bergey et al., 1925. (*Spirochaeta carteri* Mackie, Ann. Trop. Med. and Parasitol., *1*, 1907, 157; also see Indian Med. Gazette, *44*, 1908, 370; Bergey et al., Manual, 2nd ed., 1925, 435.)

car'te.ri. M.L. gen.noun *carteri* of Carter; named for R. M. Carter, who, in 1879, described this organism in the blood of patients with Indian relapsing fever.

Morphologically similar to *Borrelia berbera*.

Cultivation not recorded.

Immunologically, this is probably a distinct species. A succession of distinct serological types occurs with the relapse in a single infection (Cunningham et al., Far Eastern Association of Tropical Medicine, Tokyo, 1925; also see Indian Journal of Medical Research, *22*, 1934–1935, 105 and 595; and *ibid.*, *24*, 1937, 571 and 581).

Carried by *Pediculus humanus* subsp. *humanus*.

Transmissible to monkeys, rabbits, rats and mice.

Comment: Regarded by some investigators as identical with *Borrelia recurrentis* Bergey et al.

Habitat: Found as the cause of Indian relapsing fever.

5. **Borrelia hispanica** (de Buen, 1926) Steinhaus, 1946. (*Spirochaeta hispanica* de Buen, Ann. de Parasitol., *4*, 1926, 185; Steinhaus, Insect Microbiology, 1946, 453.)

hi.spa'ni.ca. L. adj. *hispanicus* Spanish.

Transmitted by *Ornithodoros erraticus* (large form).

Pathogenicity: Pathogenic for small laboratory animals, especially the guinea pig.

Habitat: Found as a cause of relapsing fever in Spain, Portugal and northwest Africa.

6. **Borrelia hermsii** (Davis, 1942) Stein-

haus, 1946. (*Spirochaeta hermsi* Davis, Amer. Assoc. Adv. Sci., Pub. No. 18, 1942, 46; Steinhaus, Insect Microbiology, 1946, 453.)

herm'si.i. M.L. gen.noun *hermsii* the specific epithet of the tick vector of this species, *Ornithodoros hermsi*.

Investigations by Davis (*op. cit.*, 1942, 46) indicate that each species of *Ornithodoros* that is a relapsing-fever vector carries a spirochete that is tick-host-specific and that this host-specific relationship offers a more accurate approach to the differentiation of relapsing-fever spirochetes than any of the several criteria previously used. This was shown to be the case for *Borrelia hermsii* and *Borrelia parkeri*. For this reason no attempt is made to describe the morphology and other characters of the relapsing-fever spirochetes of North and South America.

Transmitted by *Ornithodoros hermsi*; not transmitted by other species of *Ornithodoros* from the Western Hemisphere.

Pathogenicity: Produces characteristic relapses in adult white mice and guinea pigs.

Habitat: Found as a cause of relapsing fever in British Columbia, Canada, California, Colorado, Idaho, Nevada, Oregon and Washington.

7. Borrelia duttonii (Novy and Knapp, 1906) Bergey et al., 1925.

(See Dutton and Todd, Brit. Med. Jour., *2*, 1905, 1259; *Spirillum duttoni* (sic) Novy and Knapp, Jour. Inf. Dis., *3*, 1906 (March), 296; *Spirochaeta duttoni* Breinl, Lancet, *1*, 1906 (June), 1691; Bergey et al., Manual, 2nd ed., 1925, 434.)

dut.to'ni.i. M.L. gen.noun *duttonii* of Dutton; named for J. E. Dutton, one of the bacteriologists who first described this species.

Morphologically similar to *Borrelia recurrentis*.

Growth occurs under anaerobic conditions in serum water, hydrocoele or ascitic fluid to which a piece of sterile rabbit kidney is added.

This organism is antigenically distinct from the other causes of relapsing fever.

Pathogenicity: Varies widely with the strain. Not pathogenic for the guinea pig, but most strains are pathogenic for white mice and white rats, especially for the newborn of these two species.

This species is transmitted to man through the bite of the tick (*Ornithodoros moubata*). There is hereditary transmission to at least the third generation of the tick. Not transmitted by the louse.

Habitat: Found as the cause of Central and South African relapsing fever; also found in Madagascar.

8. Borrelia parkeri (Davis, 1942) Steinhaus, 1946.

(*Spirochaeta parkeri* Davis, Amer. Assoc. Adv. Sci., Pub. No. 18, 1942, 46; Steinhaus, Insect Microbiology, 1946, 453.)

par'ker.i. M.L. gen.noun *parkeri* the specific epithet of the tick vector of this species, *Ornithodoros parkeri*.

Transmitted by *Ornithodoros parkeri*; not transmitted by other species of *Ornithodoros* from the Western Hemisphere.

Pathogenicity: Produces characteristic relapses in adult white mice and guinea pigs.

Source: From *Ornithodoros parkeri* from California, Idaho, Montana, Nevada, Oregon, Utah and Wyoming.

Habitat: Found as a cause of relapsing fever in the Western part of the U. S. A.

9. Borrelia venezuelensis (Brumpt, 1921) Brumpt, 1922.

(Spirochetes of relapsing fever in Panama, Bates, Dunn and St. John, Amer. Jour. Trop. Med., *1*, 1921, 183; *Treponema venezuelense* Brumpt, in Lavier, Les Parasites des Invertebres Hematophages. Thèse, Paris, 1921, 207 pp.; also see Brumpt, Nouveau Traité de Médecine, Paris, *4*, 1922, 492; Spirochete of Panama, St. John and Bates, Amer. Jour. Trop. Med., *2*, 1922, 262; Brumpt, *op. cit.*, 1922, 495; *Spirochaeta neotropicalis* Bates and St. John, Jour. Amer. Med. Assoc., *79*[1], 1922, 575; *Borrelia neotropicalis* Steinhaus, Insect Microbiology, 1946, 453.)

ve.ne.zue.len'sis. M.L. adj. *venezuelensis* the specific epithet of the tick vector of this species, *Ornithodoros rudis* (*O. venezuelensis*).

Transmitted by *Ornithodoros rudis* (*O. venezuelensis*).

Pathogenicity: White mice and white rats are susceptible, but the guinea pig, rabbit, dog and fowl are reported as refractory.

Comment: Brumpt (Précis de Parasitol., 3rd ed., Paris, 1936) regarded *Borrelia neotropicalis* Steinhaus as identical with *Borrelia venezuelensis* Brumpt; this has been confirmed by Davis (Internat. Bull. of Bact. Nomen. and Taxon., *5*, 1955, 107).

Habitat: Found as a cause of relapsing fever in Panama, Colombia, Venezuela and Ecuador.

10. **Borrelia persica** (Dschunkowsky, 1913) Steinhaus, 1946. (*Spirochaeta persica* Dschunkowsky, Deutsch. med. Wochnschr., *39*, 1913, 419; Steinhaus, Insect Microbiology, 1946, 453.)

per'si.ca. L. adj. *persicus* Persian.

Transmitted by *Ornithodoros tholozani*.

Pathogenicity: Varies considerably with the strain, but especially pathogenic for the guinea pig.

Habitat: Found as a cause of relapsing fever in Iran (Persia). The vector of this species has a wide distribution: it is known from the Egyptian Western Desert, Cyprus, Israel, Iraq and the U.S.S.R. to the western border of China, Afghanistan and Kashmir.

11. **Borrelia turicatae** (Brumpt, 1933) Steinhaus, 1946. (*Spirochaeta turicatae* Brumpt, Compt. rend. Soc. Biol., Paris, *113*, 1933, 1369; Steinhaus, Insect Microbiology, 1946, 453.)

tu.ri.ca'tae. M.L. gen.noun *turicatae* of turicata, a Mexican tick.

Transmitted by *Ornithodoros turicata*; not transmitted by other species of *Ornithodoros* from the Western Hemisphere.

Pathogenicity: Produces characteristic relapses in adult white mice and guinea pigs.

Habitat: Found as a cause of relapsing fever in Mexico, New Mexico, Kansas, Oklahoma and Texas.

12. **Borrelia caucasica** (Maruashvili, 1945) Davis, *comb. nov.* (*Spirochaeta caucasica* Maruashvili, Med. Parasit., Parasitic Dis., *14*, 1945, 24.)

cau.ca'si.ca. M.L. adj. *caucasicus* pertaining to the Caucasus.

Transmitted by *Ornithodoros verrucosus*.

Pathogenicity: Pathogenic for the guinea pig.

Source: From *Pallasinus erythourus caucasicus*, *Apodemus sylvaticus* and *Mus musculus*.

Habitat: Found as a cause of relapsing fever in the Caucasus.

13. **Borrelia novyi** (Schellack, 1907) Bergey et al., 1925. (Spirochaete from relapsing fever, Norris, Pappenheimer and Flournoy, Jour. Inf. Dis., *3*, 1906, 266; *Spirochaeta novyi* Schellack, Arb. kaiserl, Gesundheitsamte, *27*, 1907, 199 and 364; Bergey et al., Manual, 2nd ed., 1925, 434.)

no'vy.i. M.L. gen.noun *novyi* of Novy; named for F. G. Novy, an American bacteriologist.

Morphologically similar to *Borrelia recurrentis*.

Growth occurs under the same conditions as for *Borrelia recurrentis*.

Antigenically distinct from other relapsing-fever organisms.

Pathogenic for monkeys, white rats and white mice.

Arthropod vectors are unknown.

Source: From a patient in Bellevue Hospital, New York. Origin of infection unknown.

14. **Borrelia kochii** (Novy, 1907) Bergey et al., 1925. (*Spirochaeta kochi* (sic) Novy, Proc. Path. Soc. Philadelphia, *10* (N.S.), 1907, 1; Bergey et al., Manual, 2nd ed., 1925, 434.)

ko'chi.i. M.L. gen.noun *kochii* of Koch; named for Dr. Robert Koch, who was the first to observe spirochetes in East African relapsing fever.

Morphologically similar to *Borrelia recurrentis*.

Growth occurs under the same conditions as for *Borrelia recurrentis*.

Antigenically distinct from both *Borrelia recurrentis* and *B. duttonii*.

Pathogenic for mice and rats.

No record of an arthropod vector.

Comment: Regarded by some investigators as identical with *Borrelia duttonii* Bergey et al.

Habitat: Found as the cause of African relapsing fever.

15. Borrelia buccalis (Steinberg, 1862) Brumpt, 1922. (*Spirochaeta buccalis* Steinberg, 1862, according to Hoffman and von Prowazek, Cent. f. Bakt., I Abt., Orig., *41*, 1906, 819; Brumpt, Nouveau Traité de Médecine, Paris, *4*, 1922, 495.)

buc.ca'lis. L. adj. *buccalis* buccal.

Cells 0.4 to 0.9 by 7.0 to 20.0 microns. The largest of the mouth spirochetes. Sluggishly motile by means of serpentine, rotating and flexuous movements. Stains with aniline dyes; violet with Giemsa's stain.

Not obtained in pure culture and probably does not grow in any medium tried to date.

Habitat: Found in normal mouths; invades lesions formed on the respiratory mucous membrane.

16. Borrelia vincentii (Blanchard, 1906) Bergey et al., 1925. (*Spirochaeta vincenti* (sic) Blanchard, Arch. f. Protistenk., *10*, 1906, 129; Bergey et al., Manual, 2nd ed., 1925, 435.)

vin.cen'ti.i. M.L. gen.noun *vincentii* of Vincent; named for H. Vincent, a French bacteriologist.

Cells, 0.3 by 8.0 to 12.0 microns, with 3 to 8 irregular, shallow spirals. Motile with a rapid, progressive, vibratory motion. Stain easily with the common aniline dyes. Gramnegative.

Cultivation occurs under anaerobic conditions. Cultures may show long forms with only a writhing motion.

Not pathogenic for laboratory animals.

Habitat: Found on normal respiratory mucous membrane; associated with a fusiform bacillus (*Fusobacterium fusiforme* Hoffman) in cases of Vincent's angina.

17. Borrelia refringens (Schaudinn and Hoffmann, 1905) Bergey et al., 1925. (*Spirochaeta refringens* Schaudinn and Hoffmann, Arb. a. d. kaiserl. Gesundheitsamte, *22*, 1905, 528; Bergey et al., Manual, 2nd ed., 1925, 436.)

re.frin'gens. L. part.adj. *refringens* breaking up, refringent.

Cells, 0.5 to 0.75 by 6.0 to 20.0 microns, with coarse and shallow spirals. The spirals are generally smoothly rounded and regular, tapering towards the end into a fine projection. Motile with an active serpentine and rotating motion with marked flexion. Stain easily with the common dyes. In stained specimens, the spirals appear irregular.

Cultivation is uncertain.

Non-pathogenic.

Source: Isolated with *Treponema pallidum* in some cases of syphilis as originally described by Schaudinn.

Habitat: Found in genital mucous membranes and in uncleanly states or in necrotic lesions of the genitalia of man.

18. Borrelia glossinae (Novy and Knapp, 1906) Bergey et al., 1925. (*Spirillum glossinae* Novy and Knapp, Jour. Inf. Dis., *3*, 1906, 385; Bergey et al., Manual, 2nd ed., 1925, 435.)

glos.si'nae. M.L. fem.n. *Glossina* a genus of insects; M.L. gen.noun *glossinae* of *Glossina*.

Cells, 0.2 by 8.0 microns, occurring singly, sometimes in pairs. Generally there are 4 spirals. Shorter, narrower and with more turns than the cells of *Borrelia recurrentis*.

Habitat: Found in the stomach contents of the tse-tse fly (*Glossina palpalis*).

19. Borrelia brasiliensis Davis, 1952. (Jour. of Parasitol., *38*, 1952, 473.)

bra.si.li.en'sis. M.L. adj. *brasiliensis* the specific epithet of the tick vector of this species, *Ornithodoros brasiliensis*.

Transmitted by *Ornithodoros brasiliensis*.

Pathogenicity: Characteristic relapses are produced in white mice and guinea pigs.

Source: Isolated from *Ornithodoros brasiliensis* from the state of Rio Grande do Sul, Brazil.

20. Borrelia dugesii (Mazzotti, 1949) Davis, *comb. nov.* (*Spirochaeta dugesi* Mazzotti, Rev. Instit. Sal. y Enferm. Trop., *10*, 1949, 277.)

du.ge'si.i. M.L. gen.noun *dugesii* the specific epithet of the tick vector of this species, *Ornithodoros dugesi*.

Transmitted by *Ornithodoros dugesi*.

Pathogenicity: Pathogenic for white mice but not for guinea pigs.

Source: Isolated from *Ornithodoros dugesi* in Mexico.

21. Borrelia graingeri (Heisch, 1953) Davis, comb. nov. (*Spirochaeta graingeri* Heisch, Parasitology, *43*, 1953, 133.)

grain'ger.i. M.L. gen.noun *graingeri* the specific epithet of the tick vector of this species, *Ornithodoros graingeri*.

Transmitted by *Ornithodoros graingeri*.

Pathogenicity: White rats and mice are mildly susceptible. Guinea pigs, a monkey (*Cercopithecus aethiops*) and a young rabbit were not susceptible. Causes a persistent parasitemia in cases of general paralysis of man.

Source: Isolated from *Ornithodoros graingeri* from caves near Tiwi, about 20 miles south of Mombasa, Kenya.

22. Borrelia babylonensis (Brumpt, 1939) Davis, comb. nov. (*Spirochaeta babylonensis* Brumpt, Compt. rend. Acad. Sci., Paris, *208*, 1939, 2030.)

ba.by.lo.nen'sis. L. adj. *babylonensis* pertaining to Babylon.

Transmitted by *Ornithodoros tholozani* var. *babylonensis*.

Pathogenic for guinea pigs.

Comments: Originally reported as isolated from *Ornithodoros asperus*. Later it was found that the ticks were not *O. asperus* but *O. tholozani*. However, as this spirochete was transmitted only by *O. tholozani* collected near Babylon and not by *O. tholozani* from other areas, the spirochete was accorded specific rank and the tick was given a varietal status, *O. tholozani* var. *babylonensis*. (See Brumpt, Précis de Parasitol., *1*, 1949, 101.)

Source: Isolated from *Ornithodoros tholozani* var. *babylonensis* from a rodent burrow in the ruins of Kish near Babylon.

23. Borrelia crocidurae (Leger, 1917) Davis, comb. nov. (*Spirochaeta crocidurae* Leger, Bull. Soc. Path. Exot., *10*, 1917, 280.)

cro.ci.du'rae. M.L. gen.noun *crocidurae* of *Crocidura;* M.L. fem.n. *Crocidura* a genus of rodents.

Transmitted by *Ornithodoros erraticus* (small form).

Pathogenicity: Pathogenic for white mice but not for guinea pigs.

Source: Isolated from the shrew-mouse, *Crocidura stampflii*, in Senegal.

24. Borrelia dipodilli (Heisch, 1950) Davis, comb. nov. (*Spirochaeta dipodilli* Heisch, Ann. Trop. Med. and Parasit., *44*, 1950, 260.)

di.po.dil'li. M.L. gen.noun *dipodilli* of *Dipodillus;* M.L. mas.n. *Dipodillus* a genus of rodents.

Transmitted by *Ornithodoros erraticus* (small form).

There is no cross immunity against *Borrelia duttonii*, *B. harveyi*, *B. turicatae* or *B. crocidurae*.

Pathogenicity: Pathogenic for rats, mice, monkeys and young rabbits but not for guinea pigs; man is mildly susceptible.

Source: Isolated from the pigmy gerbille (*Dipodillus sp.*) from Crescent Island on the east shore of Lake Naivasha, Kenya.

25. Borrelia latyschewii (Soviev, 1941) Davis, 1948. (*Spirochaeta latyschewi* (sic) Soviev, Parasitic Diseases (U.S.S.R.), *10*, 1941, 267; Davis, Ann. Rev. Microbiology, *2*, 1948, 315.)

la.ty.sche'wi.i. M.L. gen.noun *latyschewii* of Latyschew; named for Latyschew.

Transmitted by *Ornithodoros tartakovskyi*.

Pathogenicity: Pathogenic for white mice and rabbits but not for white rats, guinea pigs or dogs.

Source: Isolated from the gerbilles *Rhombombys opimus* and *Gerbillus eversmanni* in Fergana, Usbekistan; also found in Iran.

26. Borrelia hyos (King and Drake, 1915) Bergey et al., 1925. (Hog cholera virus, King and Baeslack, Jour. Inf. Dis., *12*, 1913, 39; *Spirochaeta suis* King, Baeslack and Hoffmann, Jour. Inf. Dis., *12*, 1913, 235; not *Spirochaeta suis* Bosanquet, Spirochetes, Saunders, 1911; *Spirochaeta hyos* King and Drake, Jour. Inf. Dis., *16*, 1915, 54; Bergey et al., Manual, 2nd ed., 1925, 436.)

hy'os. L. noun *hys, hyos* the hog.

Cells 1 by 5 to 7 microns. Distinctly shorter and thicker than the other members of the genus. Motile with an active, spinning motion, the spirals being fixed.

Growth occurs under anaerobic conditions in the presence of tissue.

Habitat: Found in the blood and in intestinal ulcers and other lesions of hogs suffering from hog cholera.

27. Borrelia theileri (Laveran, 1903) Bergey et al., 1925. (*Spirochaeta theileri* Laveran, Compt. rend. Acad. Sci., Paris, *136*, 1903, 939; Bergey et al., Manual, 2nd ed., 1925, 435.)

thei'le.ri. M.L. gen.noun *theileri* of Theiler; named for A. Theiler, who discovered this organism in 1902 in Transvaal, South Africa.

Cells, 0.25 to 0.3 by 20.0 to 30.0 microns, with pointed ends.

Cultivation not recorded.

Immunologically distinct from the species of this genus which infect man.

Transmitted by the tick (*Rhipicephalus decoloratus*).

Source: From the blood of cattle.

Habitat: Found in the blood of cattle and other mammals in South Africa.

28. Borrelia harveyi (Garnham, 1947) Davis, 1948. (*Spirochaeta harveyi* Garnham, East African Med. Jour., *24*, 1947 (January), 47; Davis, Ann. Rev. Microbiology, *2*, 1948, 316.)

har'vey.i. M.L. gen.noun *harveyi* of Harvey; named for A. E. C. Harvey.

Arthropod vector is unknown; not transmitted by *Polyplax serrata*, *Pediculus humanus* or *Ornithodoros moubata*.

There is no cross immunity with *Borrelia duttonii* or *B. recurrentis*.

Pathogenicity: Pathogenic for rats, mice and monkeys but not for rabbits or guinea pigs. Produces a mild infection in man.

Source: From the blood of a grivet monkey (*Cercopithecus aethiops centralis*) captured in the forest of Southern Mau, Kenya Colony.

Genus II. **Treponema** Schaudinn, 1905.

(Schaudinn, Deutsche med. Wochnschr., *31*, 1905, 1728; *Spironema* Vuillemin, Compt. rend. Acad. Sci., Paris, *140*, 1905, 1567.)

Tre.po.ne'ma. Gr. v. *trepo* to turn; Gr. noun *nema* a thread; M.L. neut.n. *Treponema* a turning thread.

Cells, 3 to 18 microns in length, with acute, regular or irregular spirals; longer forms are due to incomplete division. Terminal filament may be present. Some species stain only with Giemsa's stain. Weakly refractive by dark-field illumination in living preparations. Cultivated under strictly anaerobic conditions. Some are pathogenic and parasitic for man and other animals. Generally produce local lesions in tissues.

The type species is *Treponema pallidum* (Schaudinn and Hoffmann) Schaudinn.

Key to the species of genus **Treponema.**

I. From human sources.
    A. Do not cause pinta (spotted sickness).
        1. Not normally found in the human mouth.
            a. Cause definite venereal diseases.
                b. Causes syphilis.
                        1. *Treponema pallidum.*
                bb. Causes yaws (tropica frambesia).
                        2. *Treponema pertenue.*
            aa. Do not cause definite venereal diseases.
                b. Cells possess deep spirals.
                        3. *Treponema calligyrum.*
                bb. Cells possess shallow spirals.
                        4. *Treponema genitalis.*
        2. Found in the human mouth.

a. From the normal mouth cavity.
> 5. *Treponema microdentium.*

aa. From mouths affected with pyorrhea alveolaris.
> 6. *Treponema mucosum.*

B. Causes pinta.
> 7. *Treponema carateum.*

II. From rabbits.
> 8. *Treponema cuniculi.*

1. **Treponema pallidum** (Schaudinn and Hoffmann, 1905) Schaudinn, 1905. (*Spiro-chaete pallida* Schaudinn and Hoffmann, Arb. a. d. kaiserl. Gesundheitsamte, *22*, 1905, 528; Schaudinn, Deutsche med. Wochnschr., *31*, 1905, 1728.)

pal'li.dum. L. adj. *pallidus* pale.

Cells occur as very fine protoplasmic spirals, 0.25 to 0.3 by 6.0 to 14.0 microns. Spiral amplitude, 1.0 micron, regular, fixed; spiral depth, 0.5 to 1.0 micron. A terminal spiral filament is present. Weakly refractive in the living state by dark-field illumination. May appear as a series of bright dots or as a string of radiant beads with poor dark-field illumination. Motile by means of a sluggish, drifting motion; stiffly flexible, rarely rotating. Stain with difficulty except with Giemsa's stain by which they appear pink or rose. Appear black with silver impregnation methods.

Cultivated with difficulty under strict anaerobiosis in ascitic fluid with the addition of fresh rabbit kidney.

Trypsin digestion: The cells are resistant for many days.

Bile salts (10 per cent): Disintegration of cells is complete.

Saponin (10 per cent): The cells are broken up in time.

Habitat: The cause of syphilis in man. Can be transmitted experimentally to anthropoid apes and to rabbits.

2. **Treponema pertenue** Castellani, 1905. (Jour. Trop. Med., *8*, 1905, 253.)

per.te'nu.e. L. adj. *pertenuis* very thin, slender.

Morphologically indistinguishable from *Treponema pallidum.*

Cultivable under anaerobic conditions in the same medium used for *Treponema pallidum.*

Habitat: The cause of yaws, tropica frambesia. Patients with the disease give a positive Wassermann test. Transmission by flies (*Hippelates pallipes*) in the West Indies (Kumm and Kumm et al.) and by flies (*Musca spectanda*) in Africa (Thomson and Lamborn) (for references, see Hill, Bull. World Health Organiz., *8*, 1953, 32 and 47).

3. **Treponema calligyrum** Noguchi, 1913. (Jour. Exp. Med., *17*, 1913, 96.)

cal.li.gy'rum. Gr. noun *callus* beauty; Gr. adj. *gyrus* round; M.L. adj. *calligyrus* beautifully rounded.

The cells measure 0.35 to 0.4 by 6.0 to 14.0 microns, averaging 9.0 to 12.0 microns. The spirals are regular and deep but are more rounded than those of *Treponema pallidum.* The cells are of uniform width until near the extremities, which end in sharp points with delicate projections. Actively motile, chiefly rotating. Stain reddish violet with Giemsa's stain.

Grows under anaerobic conditions.

Non-pathogenic for monkeys and rabbits.

Source: Isolated from smegma.

Habitat: Found in the lesions and membranes of the pudenda.

4. **Treponema genitalis** Noguchi, 1923. (*Treponema minutum* Noguchi, Jour. Exp. Med., *27*, 1918, 671; not *Treponema minutum* Dobell, Arch. f. Protistenk., *26*, 1912, 151; not *Treponema minutum* Castellani, 1916; Noguchi, Laboratory Diagnosis of Syphilis, New York, 1923, 260.)

ge.ni.ta'lis. L. adj. *genitalis* genital.

The cells measure 0.25 to 0.3 by 3.0 to 14.0 microns. The spirals are round, regular and shallow. The cells are smaller, and the spirals are closer together than those of *Treponema pallidum.* Actively motile.

Grows anaerobically and requires fresh tissue.

Non-pathogenic.

Habitat: Found on male and female genitalia.

5. Treponema microdentium Noguchi, 1912. (Jour. Exp. Med., *15*, 1912, 81.)

mic.ro.den'ti.um. Gr. adj. *micrus* small; L. noun *dens, dentis* tooth; M.L. gen.pl.noun *microdentium* of small teeth.

The cells are less than 0.25 micron in thickness in the middle and taper toward each extremity, which is pointed. The length varies with age, but the cells may reach 8 microns and may show an average of 14 curves. Sometimes a long, thin, flagella-like projection is observed at each extremity.

Growth occurs under anaerobic conditions in serum water medium containing fresh tissue. The serum is slightly coagulated and gives off a strong, fetid odor.

Habitat: Found in the normal oral cavity.

6. Treponema mucosum Noguchi, 1912. (Jour. Exp. Med., *16*, 1912, 194.)

mu.co'sum. L. adj. *mucosus* full of slime or mucus.

Spiral-shaped cells, 0.25 to 0.3 by 8.0 to 12.0 microns, the number of curves varying from 6 to 8. Both extremities are sharply pointed and often possess a minute, curved projection 8 to 10 microns long. Stain red with Giemsa's stain.

Cultivable under anaerobic conditions, forming mucin.

A strong, putrid odor is produced in cultures.

Strictly anaerobic.

Source: Isolated from the pus in a case of pyorrhoea.

Habitat: Found in pyorrhea alveolaris; possesses pyogenic properties.

7. Treponema carateum Brumpt, 1939. (Treponema de un caso de pinta, Saenz, Grau Triana and Alfonso, Arch. de Med. Int., Havana, *4*, 1938, 3; Brumpt, Compt. rend. Soc. Biol., Paris, *130*, 1939, 942; *Treponema herrejoni* León and Blanco, Rev. de Med. Trop. y Parasitol., Habana, *6*, 1940, 5; *Treponema pictor* Pardo-Castelló, Rev. de Med. Trop. y Parasitol., Habana, *6*, 1940, 117; *Treponema americanus* (sic) León, Rev.

de Med. Trop. y Parasit., *6*, 1940, 253–276; *Treponema pintae* Curbelo, Elementos de Bacteriología Médica, 1941, 34.)

ca.ra'te.um. M.L. noun *carate* name of a South American disease, pinta; M.L. adj. *carateus* of carate.

Description taken from León and Blanco (*op. cit.*, 1940, 5).

Cylindrical cells, 0.25 to 0.30 by 7.8 to 36.8 microns, averaging 17.8 microns in length, with sharp-pointed ends. Spiral amplitude, 1.0 micron, regular; spiral depth, 0.8 to 1.0 micron. Number of waves, 6 to 27, according to the length of the cell; 10 to 12 (Brumpt, *op. cit.*, 1939, 942). Actively motile; at times undulating or creeping movements are shown. Readily takes silver impregnations, Giemsa's stain, carbolfuchsin and gentian violet.

Not yet cultivated artificially. Experimental transmission unsuccessful so far.

Saponin (10 per cent): Cells disintegrate in six hours at room temperature. Same result with sodium taurocholate (10 per cent) and with bile.

Distilled water: Produces swelling of the cells.

Motility is lost on heating for 15 minutes at 50° C. or for 3 hours at 41° C.

Wassermann, Kahn and Meinicke reactions are positive.

Source: From the borders of cutaneous lesions of persons having pinta (spotted sickness).

Habitat: The cause of pinta, or carate. Common in Mexico and Colombia; also found in other northern countries of South America, in Central America and in the West Indies; rarely found in Cuba. Possibly found in other tropical regions of the world.

8. Treponema cuniculi Noguchi, 1921. (*Spirochaeta paraluis cuniculi* Jacobsthal, Dermatol. Wochnschr., *71*, 1920, 569; Noguchi, Jour. Amer. Med. Assoc., *77*, 1921, 2052; also see Jour. Exp. Med., *35*, 1922, 395.)

cu.ni'cu.li. L. noun *cuniculus* rabbit; L. gen.noun *cuniculi* of a rabbit.

Description taken from Noguchi (*loc. cit.*).

Aside from being longer, the cells closely resemble those of *Treponema pallidum*. 0.25

by 10.0 to 16.0 microns; long specimens up to 30.0 microns are frequent. The spirals, 8 to 12 in number, are regular and deep. Spiral amplitude, 1.0 to 1.2 microns; spiral depth, 0.6 to 1.0 micron. A delicate, terminal filament is present at one end, sometimes at both ends. Entangled masses of long threads often occur; sometimes occur in a stellate arrangement. Staining properties are the same as for *Treponema pallidum*: both are readily stained by ordinary basic aniline dyes when fixed in a buffered form-aldehyde solution or mordanted with $KMnO_4$.

Wassermann reaction is negative.

Pathogenicity: The disease is transmissible to healthy rabbits producing papular lesions in the genitoperineal region. Nonpathogenic for monkeys, mice and guinea pigs.

Source: From lesions in the genitoperineal regions of five rabbits.

Habitat: The cause of rabbit spirochetosis.

Genus III. Leptospira *Noguchi, 1917.**

(Jour. Exp. Med., *25*, 1917, 753.)

Lep.to.spi′ra. Gr. adj. *leptus* thin, small; Gr. noun *spira* a spiral; M.L. fem.n. *Leptospira* thin spiral.

Finely coiled organisms which measure 6 to 20 microns in length. The spirals measure 0.3 micron in depth and 0.4 to 0.5 micron in amplitude. In liquid media either one or both ends of the cells are bent into a semicircular hook, each involving $\frac{1}{10}$ to $\frac{1}{8}$ of the organism. Spinning movements occur in liquid media, and vermiform movements occur in semisolid agar, forward or backward. In living preparations the cells are observed most clearly with dark-field and much less clearly with phase-contrast microscopy; not visible with ordinary illumination. Stain with difficulty except with Giemsa's stain and silver impregnation. Axial filament can be demonstrated by electron microscopy. Require oxygen for growth.

The type species is *Leptospira icterohaemorrhagiae* (Inada and Ido) Noguchi.

Before any of the parasitic leptospires were known, Wolbach and Binger (Jour. Med. Res., *30*, 1914, 23) applied the name *Spirochaeta biflexa* to non-pathogenic leptospires isolated from stagnant fresh water; later, Noguchi (Jour. Exp. Med., *25*, 1917, 753) placed this species in a new genus, *Leptospira*. These water strains will grow in simple media such as hay infusions or in the feces medium recommended by Hindle (Brit. Med. Jour., *2*, 1925, 57); as parasitic leptospires will not grow in media of this type, a means of differentiating between saprophytic and parasitic leptospires is furnished. Babudieri and Archetti (Rend. Istit. Sup. di Sanitá, *10*, 1947, 962; Ann. Inst. Past., *75*, 1948, 552) examined a large series of strains of water leptospires and found them to be composed of a number of antigenic fractions. The apparently random distribution of the same or closely similar antigens among the different strains led to a wide variety of extremely complicated serological relationships. Satisfactory means of differentiating species of saprophytic leptospires have not been developed, so it has become a custom to identify the non-pathogenic leptospires found in stagnant water or similar materials as *Leptospira biflexa* Noguchi.

Pathogenic leptospires were first isolated from human cases of Weil's disease by Inada and Ido (Tokyo Ijishinshi, 1915, No. 1908), and, in the first record of their work published in English, the organisms were named *Spirochaeta icterohaemorrhagiae* by Inada, Ido, Hoki, Kaneko and Ito (Jour. Exp. Med., *23*, 1916, 377). Since that time other leptospires, serologically distinct from *Leptospira icterohaemorrhagiae*, have been recognized as causing disease in man and other animals and as having host-carrier relationships. As examples, *L. canicola* (dogs), *L. grippotyphosa* (voles) and *L. pomona* (pigs) may be mentioned, but knowledge of

---

* Completely revised by Prof Dr. J. W. Wolff, Koninklijk Instituut voor de Tropen, Afd: Instituut voor Tropische Hygiene en Geograph. Path., Amsterdam, Holland, and Dr J. C. Broom, The Wellcome Laboratories of Tropical Medicine, London, England.

this relationship is still incomplete for other serologically distinct strains of leptospires isolated from human and animal cases of leptospirosis.

Because leptospires cannot be satisfactorily studied by the methods used for the true bacteria or even for other spirochetes, it has proved difficult to apply the species concept to this important group. The differentiation of strains of leptospires is however of epidemiological importance as well as of academic interest. Various schemes of differentiation have been used, but at present the most satisfactory method is based on the antigenic constitution of the leptospires, which can be determined by agglutination-lysis and cross-absorption tests. Complement-fixation tests have not yet been developed as a means of typing, though they are probably of value in confirming a clinical diagnosis of leptospirosis. Neither has any system so far been evolved of cultural or biochemical tests which could be used as a basis for differentiation.

Building on and extending the work begun by Schüffner and his collaborators and continued by Borg-Petersen and many other workers in this field, Wolff and Broom (Documenta de Medicina Geographica et Tropica, 6, 1954, 78) compared the serological characters of a number of strains of leptospires whose origins and subsequent histories could be fully authenticated. These workers assembled into 'serogroups' (serological groups) serotypes which showed marked similarities in their serological reactions. These serological groupings quite probably have some relation to the differentiation of the organisms into species, but Wolff and Broom consider that knowledge of the bionomics of leptospires is not yet sufficiently far advanced to allow a decision to be taken regarding the criteria on which the subdivision of the genus should ultimately be made. Hence, for the time being, they propose that the term 'serotype' should be adopted to designate the basic taxon of a serological classification based on the agglutinogens of the leptospires.

In view of the tentative nature of this classification, Wolff and Broom have retained the specific epithets or place names which have been applied to various leptospires as a means of designating serotypes. In this way they follow much the same custom that has been followed by students of salmonellas.

The serological Table as prepared by Wolff and Broom is given here by permission of these authors; complete bibliography will be found in their original paper.

Serogroup	Serotype	Type Strain	Origin
icterohaem-orrhagiae	*icterohaemorrha-giae* (AB)	M 20[1]	1935, Man, Denmark
	icterohaemorrha-giae (A)	RGA[2]	1915, Man, France
	naam	Naam	1936, Man, Indonesia
	mankarso	Mankarso	1938, Man, Indonesia
javanica	*javanica*	Veldrat, Batavia 46	1938, *Rattus brevicaudatus* Indonesia
	poi	Poi	1941, Man, Italy
	sarmin	Sarmin	1930, Man, Indonesia
	schüffneri	Vleermuis 90 C	1938, *Cynopterus sp.*, Indonesia
	canicola	Hond Utrecht IV	1931, Dog, Netherlands
	benjamin	Benjamin	1937, Man, Indonesia
	ballum	Mus 127[3]	1943, *Mus musculus spicilegus*, Denmark
pyrogenes	*pyrogenes*	Salinem	1924, Man, Indonesia
	australis B	Zanoni (C.14)	1935, Man, Australia
	cynopteri	3522 C[4]	1938, *Cynopterus sp.*, Indonesia
	sentot	Sentot	1937, Man, Indonesia
autumnalis	*autumnalis* (AB)	Akiyami A	1925, Man, Japan
	autumnalis (A)	Rachmat	1923, Man, Indonesia
	bangkinang	Bangkinang I	1929, Man, Indonesia
	djasiman	Djasiman	1937, Man, Indonesia
australis A	*australis A*	Ballico	1937, Man, Australia
	muenchen	Muenchen 90 C	1942, Man, Germany
	pomona	Pomona	1937, Man, Australia
	grippotyphosa	Moscow V[5]	1928, Man, Russia
hebdomadis	*hebdomadis*	Hebdomadis	1918, Man, Japan
	medanensis	HC	1929, Dog, Indonesia
	wolffii	3705	1937, Man, Indonesia
	hardjo	Hardjoprajitno	1938, Man, Indonesia
	sejroe	M 84	1937, Man, Denmark
	saxkoebing	Mus 24	1942, *Apodemus flavicollis*, Denmark

List of recognized serotypes—Continued

Serogroup	Serotype	Type Strain	Origin
bataviae	*bataviae* *paidjan*	van Tienen[6] Paidjan	1932, Man, Indonesia 1939, Man, Indonesia
	semarang	R.S. 173	1937, *Rattus brevicaudatus*, Indonesia
	andaman A	CH 11	1931, Man, Andaman Isles
	hyos, syn. *mitis* Johnson	Mitis Johnson	1940, Man, Australia

[1] Strain "Wijnberg," isolated in 1926 from man in the Netherlands, is also *L. icterohaemorrhagiae* (AB).

[2] Strain "Kantorowicz," isolated in 1931 from man in the Netherlands, is also *L. icterohaemorrhagiae* (A).

[3] Strain "S102," isolated in 1941 from an albino mouse in the Netherlands, is also *L. ballum*.

[4] Strain "3868 C" was subsequently demonstrated to be indistinguishable from strain "3522 C."

[5] The bovine strain of Bernkopf and other strains of the grippotyphosa serogroup isolated in Israel are not yet definitely established as serotypes distinct from serotype *grippotyphosa*. The same applies to other strains of this serogroup isolated elsewhere.

[6] Strain "Swart," isolated by Walch, was lost after it was demonstrated to be indistinguishable from the strain "van Tienen."

Alphabetical list of recognized serotypes

Serotype	Synonyms	Common Name of disease	Important Carrier Hosts
andaman A[1]	Strain CH 11[1]	—	—
australis A[2]	Ballico strain[3]	Canefields fever	*R. rattus culmorum*
australis B[2]	Zanoni strain[2]	Canefields fever	*R. rattus*
autumnalis[4] divided into		Akiyami; Hasami-Netsu seven-day fever; autumnal fever; leptospirosis febrilis; Fort Bragg fever	*Microtus montebelloi; Apodemus speciosus speciosus*
subtype *autumnalis* (AB)[5]	Akiyami A group;[6] Andaman B group[1]		
subtype *autumnalis* (A)[5]	Rachmat strain[7]		
ballum[8]	—	—	*Mus musculus spicilegus; Mus musculus*
bangkinang[9]	—	—	—
bataviae[10]	Swart strain;[11] *mitis*;[12] *oryzeti*[13]	Indonesian Weil's disease; rice-field fever	*R. norvegicus; R. rattus brevicaudatus; Micromys minutus sorcinus*; dog; cat
benjamin[14]	Mukingilwa strain[15]	—	—
canicola[16]	—	Canicola fever (human) Stuttgart disease (dogs)	Dog
cynopteri[17]	3522 C strain;[18] 3868 C strain[18]	—	*Cynopterus sp.*
djasiman[17]	Djasiman strain[19]	—	—
grippotyphosa[20]	Nzirandukula strain;[15] Bovine strain;[21] *bovis*;[22] *geffeni*;[23] Duyster strain[24]	Mud fever; field-fever; Feldfieber A; Schlammfieber; fièvre des marais	*Microtus spp.*
hardjo[25]	—	—	—
hebdomadis[26]	Akiyami B group[6]	Nanukayami; Akiyami B; seven-day fever	*Microtus montebelloi*
hyos[27]	*mitis*[28]	Swineherds' disease	Pig
icterohaemorrhagiae[29, 30] divided into	See page 913	Weil's disease; leptospiral jaundice; infectious jaundice (human); yellows (dog)	*R. norvegicus;* other species of rats and mice
subtype *icterohaemorrhagiae* (AB)[31]	complete biotype[5]		
subtype *icterohaemorrhagiae* (A)[31]	incomplete biotype[5]		
javanica[32]	—	—	*R. brevicaudatus; R. exulans (= R. concolor)*
mankarso[33]	Marikini strain[15]	—	—
medanensis[17]	Dog HC strain[34]	—	—
muenchen[25]	—	—	—
naam[14]	—	—	—
paidjan[25]	—	—	—
poi[35]	—	Rice-field fever	—
pomona[36]	*Australis C*;[37] Mezzano type;[38] *suis*[27]	Swineherds' disease; pomona fever	Pig; cattle
pyrogenes[39]	Salinem strain	Leptospirosis febrilis	—
sarmin[19]	—	—	—
saxkoebing[40]	—	—	*Apodemus flavicollis; A. sylvaticus*
schuffneri[41]	90 C strain[42]	—	*Cynopterus sp.*
sejroe[31]	—	Feldfieber B	*Apodemus sylvaticus; Mus musculus spicilegus*
semarang[43]	—	—	*R. brevicaudatus*
sentot[14]	—	—	—
wolffii[17]	3705 strain[44]	—	—

[1] Taylor, J., and Goyle, A. N., Indian med. Research Mem., no. 20, 1931.

[2] Lumley, G. F., Med. Jour. Australia, *1*, 1937, 654.

[3] Cotter, T. J. P., and Sawers, W. C., Med. Jour. Australia, *2*, 1934, 597.

[4] Abe, T., Jap. Jour. Exp. Med., *12*, 1934, 255.

[5] Gispen, R., and Schüffner, W. A. P., Zent. f. Bakt., I Abt., Orig., *144*, 1939, 427.

[6] Koshina, M., Shiozawa, S., and Kitayama, K., Jour. Exp. Med., *42*, 1925, 873.

Alphabetical list of recognized serotypes—Continued

[7] Baermann, G., Geneesk. Tijdschr. Ned.-Ind., *63*, 1923, 885.

[8] Borg-Petersen, C., Acta Pathol. Microbiol. Scand., *21*, 1944, 504.

[9] Slot, G. A., and van der Walle, N., Geneesk. Tijdschr. Ned.-Ind., *72*, 1932, 1579.

[10] Esseveld, H., and Collier, W. A., Mededeel. Dienst Volksgezondheid Ned.-Ind., *27*, 1938, 250.

[11] Walch, E. W., Geneesk. Tijdschr. Ned.-Ind., *66*, 1926, 115.

[12] Mino, P., Intern. Congr. Trop. Med., 3. Amsterdam, Acta, *1*, 1938, 422.

[13] Babudieri, B., Policlinico, *45*, 1938, 1774.

[14] Walch-Sorgdrager, B., Bohlander, L., Schüffner, W. A. P., and Wolff, J. W., Geneesk. Tijdschr. Ned.-Ind., *80*, 1940, 578.

[15] van Riel, J., Ann. Soc. Belge Méd. Trop., *26*, 1946, 197.

[16] Schüffner, W., Trans. Roy. Soc. Trop. Med. Hyg., *28*, 1934, 7.

[17] Collier, W. A., Acta Trop., Basel, *5*, 1948, 135.

[18] Collier, W. A., and Mochtar, A., Geneesk. Tijdschr. Ned.-Ind., *79*, 1939, 226.

[19] Kotter, G. F., Ned. Tijdschr. Geneesk., *83*, 1939, 3590.

[20] Tarassoff, S., Ann. Inst. Pasteur, *46*, 1931, 222.

[21] Bernkopf, H., Harefuah, For. edn., *30*, 1946, 109.

[22] Btesh, S., Trans. Roy. Soc. Trop. Med. Hyg., *41*, 1947, 419.

[23] Olejnik, E., and Shneyerson, S., Trans. Roy. Soc. Trop. Med. Hyg., *46*, 1952, 165.

[24] Wolff, J. W., and Bohlander, H., Docum. Med. Geogr. Trop., *4*, 1952, 257.

[25] Wolff, J. W., Symposium on the Leptospiroses. Washington, D. C.: Army Medical Service Graduate School, 1953.

[26] Ido, Y., Ito, H., and Wani, H., Jour. Exp. Med., *28*, 1918, 435.

[27] Savino, E., and Rennella, E., Rev. Inst. Bact. Malbran, *13*, 1945/8, 62.

[28] Johnson, D. W., Med. Jour. Australia, *1*, 1942, 431.

[29] Inada, R., Ido, Y., Hoki, R., Kaneko, R., and Ito, H., Jour. Exp. Med., *23*, 1916, 377.

[30] Noguchi, H., Jour. Exp. Med., *25*, 1917, 755.

[31] Borg-Petersen, C., Intern. Cong. Trop. Med., 3. Amsterdam, Acta, *1*, 1938, 396.

[32] Esseveld, H., and Mochtar, A., Geneesk. Tijdschr. Ned.-Ind., *78*, 1938, 1513.

[33] Wolff, J. W., Advances in the Control of Zoonoses, 139. Geneva: World Health Organization: Monograph Series, 1953.

[34] Kouwenaar, W., and Wolff, J. W., Ned.-Ind. Bl. Diergeneesk., *41*, 1929, 457.

[35] Mino, P., Klin. Wochschr., *21*, 1942, 337.

[36] Derrick, E. H., Med. Jour. Australia, *1*, 1942, 431.

[37] Clayton, G. E. B., Derrick, E. H., and Cilento, R., Med. Jour. Australia, *1*, 1937, 647.

[38] Babudieri, B., Z. Immunitätsforsch., *99*, 1941, 442.

[39] Vervoort, H., Geneesk. Tijdschr. Ned.-Ind., *63*, 1923, 800.

[40] Borg-Petersen, C., Acta Pathol. Microbiol. Scand., *20*, 1943, 793.

[41] Collier, W. A., and Mochtar, A., Mededeel. Dienst Volksgezondheid Ned.-Ind., *28*, 1939, 356.

[42] Collier, W. A., and Esseveld, H., Mededeel. Dienst Volksgezondheid Ned.-Ind., *27*, 1938, 262.

[43] Sardjito, M., and Mochtar, A., Geneesk. Tijdschr. Ned.-Ind., *79*, 1939, 2520.

[44] Schüffner, W., Gispen, R., and Bohlander, H., Geneesk. Tijdschr. Ned.-Ind., *79*, 1939, 2470.

ADDENDUM

Details of the serological characteristics of the following were published while this section of the MANUAL was in press: *autumnalis*, Fort Bragg (Alexander, Evans Jeffries, Gleiser and Yager, Proc. Soc. Exp. Biol. and Med., *86*, 1954, 405); *malaya, wolffii A, grippotyphosa AB, borincana* and *alexi* (Alexander, Wetmore, Evans, Jeffries and Gleiser Amer. Jour. Trop. Med., *4*, 1955, 492); *ballum AB* (Babudieri, Rend. Istit. Sup. di Sanitá, *18*, 1955, 57); *mini AB* and *mini A* (Babudieri, Ztschr. f. Hyg., *143*, 1956, 121) and *celledoni* (Broom and Smith, Lancet, *2*, 1956, 866).

Cultures of the following are maintained at one or more of the Leptospirosis Reference Laboratories, but they are not included among the Recognized Serotypes because full details of their serological relationships have not yet been published: *bafani, kabura, ndambari, kamituga* and *butembo* (van Riel, Ann. Soc. Belge Méd. Trop., *26*, 1946, 197); *Robinson* and *Kremastos* (Smith, Brown, Tonge, Sinnamon, Macdonald, Ross and Doherty, Austral. Ann. Med., *3*, 1954, 98); *Leeds* (Czekalowski and McLeod, Jour. Path. Bact., *67*, 1954, 43); *hemolyticus* (Alexander, Smith, Hiatt and Gleiser, Proc. Soc. Exp. Biol. and Med., *91*, 1956, 205); *sorex* (Kmety, Zent. f. Bakt., I Abt., Orig., *161*, 1954, 382) and *jez* (Kmety, Čsl. Hyg., *3*, 1954, 41).

Key to the species of genus **Leptospira.**

I. Parasitic. Pathogenic for man and/or other animals. Requires serum for growth. Divided into numerous distinct serological types.

  1. *Leptospira icterohaemorrhagiae* and presumably other species.

II. Saprophytic. Grows in simple media. This species has not been further differentiated.

  2. *Leptospira biflexa* and presumably other species.

1. **Leptospira icterohaemorrhagiae** (Inada and Ido, 1916) Noguchi, 1917. (*Spirochaeta icterohaemorrhagica japonica* Inada and Ido, Tokyo Ijishinshi, 1915, No. 1908; *Spirochaeta ictero-haemorrhagiae japonica* Inada and Ido, *ibid.*, No. 1926; *Spirochaeta ictero-haemorrhagiae* Inada and Ido, Tokyo Ijishinshi, 1916, No. 1964; also see Inada, Ido, Hoki, Kaneko and Ito, Jour. Exp. Med., *23*, 1916, 377; Noguchi, Jour. Exp. Med., *25*, 1917, 755.)

ic.te.ro.hae.mor.rha'gi.ae. Gr. noun *icterus* jaundice; Gr. noun *haemorrhagia* hemorrhage; M.L. noun *icterohaemorrhagia* hemorrhagic jaundice; M.L. gen.noun *icterohaemorrhagiae* of hemorrhagic jaundice.

Cells measure 0.25 to 0.3 by 6.0 to 9.0 microns; occasionally measure 20.0 to 25.0 microns in length. Spiral amplitude, 0.4 to 0.5 micron, regular, rigid; spiral depth, 0.3 micron, regular. One or more gentle waves occur throughout the entire length. When in liquid media, one or both ends may be semicircularly hooked, while in semisolid media the organism appears serpentine, waved or bent. Very active flexibility. Axial filament does not extend beyond cell body; flagella are absent. Body stains reddish by Giemsa's stain.

Cultured easily in a medium containing 10 per cent rabbit serum, 0.2 per cent agar and a slight amount of hemoglobin in salt or in Ringer's solution. Does not grow in surface colonies.

Bile salts (10 per cent): The cells are easily dissolved.

Saponin (10 per cent): The cells are completely resistant.

Temperature range, 25° to 37°C. Remains alive longer at 25°C.

Pathogenic for guinea pigs, deer-mice, hamsters and meriones.

Comments: In general these characteristics apply to the other parasitic serotypes, although minor variations may occur in morphology and growth; there are also differences in the clinical symptoms (e.g. presence or absence of jaundice) of the diseases which they produce in man and other susceptible animals.

Source: Orginally isolated from cases of infectious jaundice (Weil's disease) in man.

Habitat: Found in kidneys and urines of wild rats. No insect vector is known. Survives possibly for weeks in water and in slime (in mines and sewers).

2. **Leptospira biflexa** (Wolbach and Binger, 1914) Noguchi, 1918. (*Spirochaeta biflexa* Wolbach and Binger, Jour. Med. Res., *30*, 1914, 23; Noguchi, Jour. Exp. Med., *27*, 1918, 585.)

bi.fle'xa. L. adj. *bis* twice; L. part.adj. *flexus* bent; M.L. adj. *biflexus* twice-bent.

Cells, 0.2 to 0.25 by 5.0 to 7.0 microns, with tapering ends. Spiral amplitude, 0.2 to 0.25 micron. There are 22 to 30 waves per cell. Pass through an L5 candle filter. Stains best with Giemsa's stain.

Growth occurs in simple media without serum.

Optimum temperature, 20°C.

Non-pathogenic.

Comment: Comprises a large variety of antigenic types not yet satisfactorily differentiated.

Source: Isolated from tap water, ponds and pools.

Habitat: Found in fresh water.

ORDER X. MYCOPLASMATALES FREUNDT, 1955.*

(*Borrelomycetales* Turner, Jour. Path. and Bact., *41*, 1935, 25; *Pleuropneumoniales* Tulasne and Brisou, Ann. Inst. Past., *88*, 1955, 237; Freundt, Internat. Bull. of Bact. Nomen. and Taxon., *5*, 1955, 71; *Mollicutales* Edward, Internat. Bull. of Bact. Nomen. and Taxon., *5*, 1955, 89.)

My.co.plas.ma.ta′les. M.L. neut.n. *Mycoplasma* type genus of the order; *-ales* ending to denote an order; M.L. fem.pl.n. *Mycoplasmatales* the *Mycoplasma* order.

Highly pleomorphic organisms which possess a peculiar mode of reproduction (according to some observers) characterized by the breaking up of filaments (with a more or less pronounced tendency to true branching) into coccoid, filterable elementary bodies. The cell bodies are soft and fragile; without special precautions they are often distorted or entirely destroyed in microscopical preparations. Non-motile. Typical endospores are never produced. Gram-negative. Growth occurs in agar media, although most of the species have exacting nutritional requirements. Pathogenic and saprophytic species occur.

FAMILY I. MYCOPLASMATACEAE FREUNDT, 1955.

(*Borrelomycetaceae* Turner, Jour. Path. and Bact., *41*, 1935, 25; *Pleuropneumoniaceae* Tulasne and Brisou, Ann. Inst. Past., *88*, 1955, 237; Freundt, Internat. Bull. of Bact. Nomen. and Taxon., *5*, 1955, 71; also see Edward, Internat. Bull. of Bact. Nomen. and Taxon., *5*, 1955, 89.)

My.co.plas.ma.ta′ce.ae. M.L. neut.n. *Mycoplasma* type genus of the family; *-aceae* ending to denote a family; M.L. fem.pl.n. *Mycoplasmataceae* the *Mycoplasma* family.

Characters as for the order.

Genus I. **Mycoplasma** *Nowak, 1929.*

(*Asterococcus* Borrel, Dujardin-Beaumetz, Jeantet and Jouan, Ann. Inst. Past., *24*, 1910, 179; not *Asterococcus* Scherffel, Ber. d. deutsch. Bot. Gesellsch., *26A*, 1908, 762; *Coccobacillus* Martzinovski, Ann. Inst. Past., *25*, 1911, 917; not *Coccobacillus* Gamaleïa, Cent. f. Bakt., *4*, 1888, 167; *Micromyces* Frosch, Arch. f. wissen. u. prakt. Tierheilk., *49*, 1923, 35 and 273; not *Micromyces* Dangeard, Le Botaniste, *1*, 1889, 55; Nowak, Ann. Inst. Past., *43*, 1929, 1349; *Asteromyces* Wroblewski, Ann. Inst. Past., *47*, 1931, 105; *Anulomyces* Wroblewski, *ibid.*, 111; *Borrelomyces* Turner, Jour. Path. and Bact., *41*, 1935, 25; *Bovimyces* Sabin, Bact. Rev., *5*, 1941, 57; *Pleuropneumonia* Tulasne and Brisou, Ann. Inst. Past., *88*, 1955, 237; see Freundt, Internat. Bull. of Bact. Nomen. and Taxon., *5*, 1955, 72; and Edward, Internat. Bull. of Bact. Nomen. and Taxon., *5*, 1955, 87.)

---

* Prepared by Dr. E. A. Freundt, Statens Seruminstitut, Copenhagen, Denmark, May, 1955.

My.co.plas'ma. Gr. mas.n. *myces* a fungus; Gr. neut.n. *plasma* something formed or molded, a form; M.L. neut.n. *Mycoplasma* fungus form.

It has proved difficult to interpret properly the significance of the morphological details and the mode of growth of these organisms. Elementary bodies have been observed both in fluid and solid media; these elementary bodies extrude one or more filaments of varying lengths that ramify to form an apparently unicellular, branching, mycelioid structure. At a later stage of growth tiny endomycelial corpuscles develop in the filaments by a process of successive condensations and constrictions, the formation of septa not being demonstrable. The homogeneous, coenocytic filaments thus become transformed into chains of close-set, spherical bodies which, upon fragmentation of the chains, are liberated as free elementary bodies. These elements are extremely plastic and, under certain growth conditions, may develop into peculiar forms, among which are the so-called "large bodies." Some workers claim to have observed various other deviating growth forms, including multiplication by simple budding. Granules may form in the large bodies and, according to some observers, after rupture of the membrane, begin the "life cycle" anew as elementary bodies. In contrast to this, however, there are others who regard the large bodies as representing a stage of involution and degradation. The basic reproductive units, the elementary bodies, are filterable and have a particle diameter of 125 to 250 millimicrons. Gram-negative. Stain poorly with the ordinary bacterial stains, but fairly well with that of Giemsa. Non-motile. Colonial growth on solid media is quite characteristic: the minute colonies have an opaque, granular, brown or yellowish central area growing down into the agar; the central area is surrounded by a translucent, flat zone of variable size. Certain species produce small, black dots consisting of deposits of calcium and magnesium soaps; these occur beneath and around the colonies together with a crinkled, grayish film. Growth in semi-solid or fluid media is granular or smooth and fluffy. With the exception of the saprophytic species, all species require enrichment with serum or ascitic fluid for growth on artificial media. Aerobic to facultatively anaerobic; certain species prefer anaerobic conditions. From human and animal sources; one saprophytic species is known.

The type species is *Mycoplasma mycoides* (Borrel et al.) Freundt.

Key to the species of genus **Mycoplasma.**

I. Parasitic to pathogenic.
  A. From animals other than man.
    1. From mammalian sources.
      a. From mammals other than rodents.
        b. From ruminants.
          c. Acid from glucose.
                1. *Mycoplasma mycoides.*
          cc. No acid from glucose.
            d. Growth occurs throughout semi-solid media.
                2. *Mycoplasma bovigenitalium.*
            dd. Growth preferably near the surface of semi-solid media.
                3. *Mycoplasma agalactiae.*
        bb. From non-ruminants.
          c. From carnivores.
             d. Film and spots not produced on horse-serum agar.
               e. Poor growth on rabbit-serum agar.
                  4. *Mycoplasma spumans.*
               ee. Good growth on rabbit-serum agar.
                  5. *Mycoplasma canis.*
            dd. Film and spots produced on horse-serum agar.
                6. *Mycoplasma maculosum.*
        cc. From omnivores.
             7. *Mycoplasma hyorhinis.*

aa. From rodents.
  b. Primarily from rats.
    c. Acid from glucose.

        8. *Mycoplasma pulmonis.*

    cc. No acid from glucose.

        9. *Mycoplasma arthritidis.*

  bb. Primarily from mice.

        10. *Mycoplasma neurolyticum.*

2. From avian sources.

        11. *Mycoplasma gallinarum.*

B. From human sources.
  1. No acid from glucose.
    a. Granular growth throughout semi-solid media.

        12. *Mycoplasma hominis.*

    aa. Smooth growth at bottom of semi-solid media.

        13. *Mycoplasma salivarium.*

  2. Acid from glucose.

        14. *Mycoplasma fermentans.*

II. Saprophytic.

        15. *Mycoplasma laidlawii.*

1. Mycoplasma mycoides (Borrel et al., 1910) Freundt, 1955. (Le microbe de la péripneumonie, Nocard and Roux, Ann. Inst. Past., *12*, 1898, 240; *Asterococcus mycoides* Borrel, Dujardin-Beaumetz, Jeantet and Jouan, Ann. Inst. Past., *24*, 1910, 179; *Coccobacillus mycoides peripneumoniae* Martzinovski, Ann. Inst. Past., *25*, 1911, 917; *Micromyces peripneumoniae bovis contagiosae* Frosch, Arch. f. wissensch. u. prakt. Tierheilk., *49*, 1923, 35 and 273; *Mycoplasma peripneumoniae* Nowak, Ann. Inst. Past., *43*, 1929, 1349; *Asteromyces peripneumoniae bovis* Wroblewski, Ann. Inst. Past., *47*, 1931, 105; *Borrelomyces peripneumoniae* Turner, Jour. Path. and Bact., *41*, 1935, 25; *Bovimyces pleuropneumoniae* Sabin, Bact. Rev., *5*, 1941, 57; *Pleuropneumonia bovis* Tulasne and Brisou, Ann. Inst. Past., *88*, 1955, 237; Freundt, Internat. Bull. of Bact. Nomen. and Taxon., *5*, 1955, 73; also see Edward, Internat. Bull. of Bact. Nomen. and Taxon., *5*, 1955, 89.)

my.co.i'des. Gr. mas.n. *myces* a fungus; Gr. noun *eidus* shape, form; M.L. adj. *mycoides* fungus-like.

The cultural and biochemical characteristics of this and of most of the other species of the genus are, to a wide extent, based on the work of Edward (Jour. Gen. Microbiol., *10*, 1954, 27).

Stable and richly branching mycelioid structure with long filaments which measure 40 to 50 microns in length, the maximum being about 100 to 150 microns (Ørskov, Ann. Inst. Past., *41*, 1927, 413; also see Acta Path. et Microbiol. Scand., *19*, 1942, 586; Nowak, *op. cit.*, 1929, 1330; Wroblewski, *op. cit.*, 1931, 94; Ledingham, Jour. Path. and Bact., *37*, 1933, 393; Klieneberger, Jour. Path. and Bact., *39*, 1934, 409; Tang, Wei, McWhirter and Edgar, Jour. Path. and Bact., *40*, 1935, 391; Turner, *op. cit.*, 1935, 1; Freundt, Acta Path. et Microbiol. Scand., *31*, 1952, 508). The filaments are regarded by other authors mainly as artifacts. Klieneberger and Smiles (Jour. of Hyg., *42*, 1942, 110) describe reproduction by multiplication of minute granules within large, irregularly round cells. Gram-negative.

Horse-serum agar: Neither film nor spots are produced.

Horse-blood agar: Alpha hemolysis.

Rabbit-serum agar: Poor growth.

Semi-solid media: Fluffy growth, preferably near the surface.

Broth: Rather strong, generalized opacity with a small deposit which produces silky swirls and threads on shaking. Cultures in broth without glucose remain viable for 45 to 60 days at 37°C. Filtrates of 6-day broth cultures discolor suspensions of horse erythrocytes, presumably due to the formation of methemoglobin.

Coagulated blood serum: Liquefaction.
Cell suspensions are bile-soluble.
Indole not produced.
Hydrogen sulfide not produced.

Acid from glucose, fructose, maltose, mannose, glycogen, dextrin and starch; slight acid by some strains from galactose, sucrose and trehalose. No acid from lactose, xylose, salicin, glycerol, mannitol or dulcitol.

Nitrites not produced from nitrates.
Slight production of ammonia.
Methylene blue is rapidly reduced.
Catalase-positive according to some investigators.
Aerobic; poor growth under anaerobic conditions.
Serologically distinct from the other members of the pleuropneumonia group.

Pathogenicity: Subcutaneous inoculation of infected lymph or of a virulent culture into cattle, goats and sheep causes a spreading, oedematous swelling accompanied by fever and other general symptoms; typical lung lesions are not produced by this route of infection, although positive blood cultures and arthritis do occur (Nocard and Roux, op. cit., 1898, 240; Dujardin-Beaumetz, Ann. Inst. Past., 20, 1906, 449; Tang, Wei, McWhirter and Edgar, Jour. Path. and Bact., 40, 1935, 391; Campbell et al., Counc. Sci. and Ind. Res. Bull. 97, 1936). The natural disease has been reproduced in cattle by intratracheal inoculation, by intrajugular injection of the organism included in emboli of 2 to 3 per cent agar (Daubney, Jour. Comp. Path., 48, 1935, 83; Campbell et al., op. cit., 1936) and by exposure to nebulized cultures (Campbell, Jour. Counc. Sci. Ind. Res. Austral., 11, 1938, 119). Mice, rats, guinea pigs and hamsters are not susceptible.

Comments: Two varieties of this species are recognized: the common, well known variety that causes bovine pleuropneumonia, and the variety described by Edward (Vet. Rec., 65, 1953, 873) which produces a similar infection in goats. Pleuropneumonia-like organisms have recently been isolated from cases of bronchopneumonia of cattle (Carter, Science, 120, 1954, 113); further study is needed before their relationships to this species and to *Myco-* *plasma bovigenitalium* Freundt can be determined.

Source: Isolated from cases of contagious pleuropneumonia in cattle.

Habitat: The etiological agent of contagious pleuropneumonia in cattle.

1a. *Mycoplasma mycoides* var. *mycoides* Freundt, 1955. (Internat. Bull. of Bact. Nomen. and Taxon., 5, 1955, 73.)

This is the common, well known variety which causes bovine pleuropneumonia and which is the type variety described above.

1b. *Mycoplasma mycoides* var. *capri* (Edward, 1953) Freundt, 1955. (*Borrelomyces peripneumoniae caprae* Longley, Colonial Research Publications No. 7, H. M. Stationery Office, London, 1951, 23; *Asterococcus mycoides* var. *capri* Edward, Vet. Rec., 65, 1953, 873; *Pleuropneumonia capri* Tulasne and Brisou, Ann. Inst. Past., 88, 1955, 238; Freundt, Internat. Bull. of Bact. Nomen. and Taxon., 5, 1955, 73; also see Edward, Internat. Bull. of Bact. Nomen. and Taxon., 5, 1955, 90.)

cap'ri. L. mas.n. *caper* goat; L. gen.noun *capri* of a goat.

Relatively stable mycelioid structure with filaments of moderate length (10 to 30 microns) (Freundt, unpublished observation). Short, filamentous forms and elementary bodies have been demonstrated in electron micrographs by Klieneberger-Nobel and Cuckow (Jour. Gen. Microbiol., 12, 1955, 95). Gram-negative.

Serum agar: Unusually large colonies (1.5 mm in diameter) after 3 days.

Horse-blood agar: Alpha hemolysis.

Rabbit-serum agar: Good growth.

Media devoid of serum: Slight growth.

Semi-solid media: Fluffy growth near the surface.

Broth: Strong opalescence.

Horse erythrocyte suspensions are decolorized.

Coagulated blood serum: Liquefaction.

Hydrogen sulfide production is slight.

Acid from glucose, fructose, maltose, mannose, dextrin, glycogen and starch. No acid from lactose, sucrose, galactose, salicin, mannitol or dulcitol.

Methylene blue is rapidly reduced.

Aerobic; poor growth under anaerobic conditions.

Serologically different from *Mycoplasma mycoides* var. *mycoides* and *M. agalactiae*.

Comments: A closely related organism was identified as the cause of an infectious and highly fatal oedema and cellulitis of goats (Melanidi, Bull. Office Internat. des Épizooties, Paris, *36*, 1951, 363; Edward, *op. cit.*, 1953, 873). An organism also closely related to *Mycoplasma mycoides* var. *capri* in cultural, physiological and serological respects was recently isolated as the etiological agent of a highly fatal disease, characterized by septicemia and arthritis, in a herd of dairy goats; clinically the outbreak was typical of neither contagious agalactia nor caprine pleuropneumonia (Cordy, Adler and Yamamoto, Cornell Vet., *45*, 1955, 50).

Source: Isolated from cases of contagious pleuropneumonia of goats.

Habitat: The etiological agent of contagious pleuropneumonia of goats.

2. **Mycoplasma bovigenitalium** Freundt, 1955. (P strains of the bovine genital tract, Edward, Jour. Gen. Microbiol., *4*, 1950, 4; *Pleuropneumonia bovigenitalis* Tulasne and Brisou, Ann. Inst. Past., *88*, 1955, 238; Freundt, Internat. Bull. of Bact. Nomen. and Taxon., *5*, 1955, 73; also see Edward, Internat. Bull. of Bact. Nomen. and Taxon., *5*, 1955, 90; *Borrelomyces bovigenitalium* Freundt, *op. cit.*, 1955, 74.)

bo.vi.ge.ni.ta'li.um. L. noun *bos, bovis* the ox; L. neut.adj. (used as a noun) *genitale* genital organ; L. pl.noun *genitalia* the genitalia; L. gen.pl.noun *genitalium* of genitalia; M.L. gen.pl.noun *bovigenitalium* of bovine genitalia.

Unstable, sparsely branching mycelioid structure with very short, almost bacillary filaments which usually measure 2 to 5 microns in length (Freundt, unpublished observation). Gram-negative.

Horse-serum agar: A film and spots are produced.

Horse-blood agar: Alpha hemolysis.

Rabbit-serum agar: Poor growth.

Semi-solid media: Fluffy growth throughout.

Broth: Dense, uniform opalescence.

Carbohydrates not attacked.

Methylene blue is reduced rather rapidly.

Aerobic, facultatively anaerobic.

Ten strains investigated serologically shared common antigens, but at least three different serological types appear to exist.

Pathogenicity: Suggested as a cause of inflammation of the genital tract, predisposing to infertility, although inoculation of cultures into the uteri of heifers has so far been unsuccessful.

Source: Isolated from the bovine genital tract.

Habitat: Frequent inhabitant of the bovine lower genital tract, both in males and females.

3. **Mycoplasma agalactiae** (Wroblewski, 1931) Freundt, 1955. (Le microbe de l'agalaxie contagieuse, Bridré and Donatien, Compt. rend. Acad. Sci., Paris, *177*, 1923, 841; also see Ann. Inst. Past., *39*, 1925, 925; *Anulomyces agalaxiae* (sic) Wroblewski, Ann. Inst. Past., *47*, 1931, 111; *Borrelomyces agalactiae* Turner, Jour. Path. and Bact., *41*, 1935, 25; *Capromyces agalactiae* Sabin, Bact. Rev., *5*, 1941, 57; *Pleuropneumonia agalactiae* Tulasne and Brisou, Ann. Inst. Past., *88*, 1955, 238; Freundt, Internat. Bull. of Bact. Nomen. and Taxon., *5*, 1955, 73; also see Edward, Internat. Bull. of Bact. Nomen. and Taxon., *5*, 1955, 90.)

a.ga.lac'ti.ae. Gr. noun *agalactia* want of milk, agalactia; M.L. gen.noun *agalactiae* of agalactia.

Relatively stable mycelioid structure with filaments of moderate length (10 to 30 microns) (Wroblewski, *op. cit.*, 1931, 94; Ledingham, Jour. Path. and Bact., *37*, 1933, 393; Ørskov, Acta Path. et Microbiol. Scand., *19*, 1942, 586; Freundt, unpublished observation). Round and oval elementary bodies and short filaments have been demonstrated in electron micrographs by Klieneberger-Nobel and Cuckow (Jour. Gen. Microbiol., *12*, 1955, 95). Gram-negative.

Horse-serum agar: A film and spots are produced by most strains.

Horse-blood agar: Alpha hemolysis.

Rabbit-serum agar: Poor growth.

Semi-solid media: Fluffy growth, preferably near the surface.

Broth: Generalized opacity. Filtrates of

broth cultures do not discolor suspensions of horse erythrocytes.

Coagulated blood serum: No liquefaction.

Hydrogen sulfide production is slight.

Carbohydrates not attacked.

Methylene blue is rapidly reduced.

Aerobic; poor growth under anaerobic conditions.

Serologically different from *Mycoplasma mycoides* var. *mycoides* and *M. mycoides* var. *capri*.

Pathogenicity: Goats are more susceptible than sheep to experimental infection by subcutaneous inoculation; the inflammatory lesions are localized in the udders of females and, in 10 to 20 per cent of the cases, in the joints. Non-pathogenic for mice and other laboratory animals.

Source: Isolated from cases of contagious agalactia of sheep and goats.

Habitat: The etiological agent of contagious agalactia of sheep and goats.

4. **Mycoplasma spumans** Edward, 1955. (α strains of dogs, Edward and Fitzgerald, Jour. Gen. Microbiol., *5*, 1951, 566; Edward, in Freundt, Internat. Bull. of Bact. Nomen. and Taxon., *5*, 1955, 73; see Edward, Internat. Bull. of Bact. Nomen. and Taxon., *5*, 1955, 90.)

spu'mans. L. part.adj. *spumans* foaming.

Unstable and sparsely branched mycelioid structure with very short, almost bacillary filaments which usually measure 2 to 5 microns in length (Freundt, unpublished observation). Gram-negative.

Horse-serum agar: Upon initial isolation and in early subcultures, the colonies are coarsely reticulated, and the centers contain large globules; colonial characteristics are lost on repeated subculture. Neither film nor spots are produced.

Horse-blood agar: Trace of hemolysis.

Rabbit-serum agar: Poor growth.

Semi-solid media: Growth throughout the medium is neither definitely smooth nor definitely granular.

Carbohydrates not attacked.

Methylene blue is slowly reduced.

Aerobic, facultatively anaerobic.

Serologically distinct from the other members of this genus by agglutinin adsorption and complement fixation tests.

Pathogenicity: Unknown.

Source: Isolated from the vagina and semen of dogs.

5. **Mycoplasma canis** Edward, 1955. (β strains of dogs, Edward and Fitzgerald, Jour. Gen. Microbiol., *5*, 1951, 566; Edward, in Freundt, Internat. Bull. of Bact. Nomen. and Taxon., *5*, 1955, 73; see Edward, Internat. Bull. of Bact. Nomen. and Taxon., *5*, 1955, 90.)

ca'nis. L. noun *canis* the dog.

Unstable and sparsely branched mycelioid structure with very short, almost bacillary filaments which usually measure 2 to 5 microns in length (Freundt, unpublished observation). Gram-negative.

Horse-serum agar: Relatively large colonies with poorly developed central spots in early subcultures. Neither film nor spots are produced.

Horse-blood agar: Pronounced alpha hemolysis.

Rabbit-serum agar: Good growth.

Semi-solid media: Growth throughout the medium is usually neither definitely smooth nor definitely granular; a few strains produce a typical smooth growth.

Carbohydrates not attacked.

Methylene blue is reduced rather rapidly.

Aerobic, facultatively anaerobic.

Serologically distinct from the other members of this genus.

Pathogenicity: Unknown.

Source: Isolated from the throats and genital tracts of dogs.

Habitat: Commonly found in the genital tract and throat of dogs.

6. **Mycoplasma maculosum** Edward, 1955. (γ strains of dogs, Edward and Fitzgerald, Jour. Gen. Microbiol., *5*, 1951, 566; Edward, in Freundt, Internat. Bull. of Bact. Nomen. and Taxon., *5*, 1955, 73; see Edward, Internat. Bull. of Bact. Nomen. and Taxon., *5*, 1955, 90.)

ma.cu.lo'sum. L. adj. *maculosus* spotted.

Unstable and sparsely branched mycelioid structure with very short, almost bacillary filaments which usually measure 2 to 5 microns in length (Freundt, unpublished observation). Gram-negative.

Horse-serum agar: A film and spots are produced.

Horse-blood agar: Slight hemolysis.

Rabbit-serum agar: Poor growth.

Semi-solid media: Growth throughout the medium is neither definitely smooth nor definitely granular.

Carbohydrates not attacked.

Methylene blue is slowly reduced.

Aerobic, facultatively anaerobic.

Serologically distinct from the other members of this genus.

Pathogenicity: Unknown.

Comments: Shoetensack (Kitasato Arch. Exp. Med., *11*, 1934, 277; also see *ibid.*, *13*, 1936, 175 and 269) isolated organisms of this genus from the tissues and nasal secretions of dogs suffering from distemper and regarded these organisms as comprising two distinct types, differing from each other in their cultural characteristics: *Asterococcus canis*, type I, Shoetensack (Shoetensack, *op. cit.*, 1936, 175; *Canomyces pulmonis* I, Sabin, Bact. Rev., *5*, 1941, 57; *Canomyces canis* I, Sabin, *ibid.*, 334) and *Asterococcus canis*, type II, Shoetensack (Shoetensack, *op. cit.*, 1936, 175; *Canomyces pulmonis* II, Sabin, *op. cit.*, 1941, 57; *Canomyces canis* II, Sabin, *ibid.*, 334). Klieneberger (Jour. Hyg., *38*, 1938, 458), furthermore, noted that type I differed serologically from type II. Type I apparently produced distemper in dogs on subcutaneous inoculation and was regarded by Shoetensack as the etiological agent of the disease; this organism is not now regarded as the cause of canine distemper. Shoetensack's organisms were lost and cannot, with certainty, be identified with any of the recently established species from dogs.

Source: Isolated from the vaginae and throats of dogs.

7. **Mycoplasma hyorhinis** Switzer, 1955. (Filterable agent of infectious, atrophic rhinitis of swine, Switzer, Jour. Amer. Vet. Med. Assoc., *123*, 1953, 45; also see Vet. Med., *48*, 1953, 392; Amer. Jour. Vet. Res., *16*, 1955, 540.)

hy.o.rhi'nis. Gr. noun *hys, hyos* a swine; Gr. noun *rhis, rhinis* nose; M.L. gen.noun *hyorhinis* of a hog's nose.

Elementary bodies appear as minute, coccoid rods 0.3 to 0.6 micron in size. Stain distinctly blue with Machiavello's stain. Gram-negative.

Serum agar colonies: 0.01 to 0.1 mm in diameter, smooth, glistening, entire; some of the colonies have a small central elevation; the central portions become granular as the colonies age.

Carbohydrates not attacked.

Withstands 56°C. for 30 but not for 60 minutes. Remains viable for 2 to 3 weeks at 4°C. and for more than 10 months at −40°C.

Pathogenicity: Produces an irregular mortality pattern when inoculated into chicken embryos. Heart and liver lesions are produced in the embryos, the outstanding lesion being a severe pericarditis which is usually present in those dead after the seventh day postinoculation. When inoculated intraperitoneally into pigs 6 weeks or less of age, the organism produces severe fibrinous pericarditis, moderate fibrinous pleuritis and mild peritonitis; from 5 to 20 per cent of the inoculated pigs usually develop arthritis. Similar lesions produced by this organism occur in swine under field conditions. Not pathogenic for mice or guinea pigs when inoculated intraperitoneally or for mice on intranasal instillation. Inoculation into the trachea, nasal cavity, infraorbital sinus or conjunctival sac of 10-day-old chickens fails to produce any symptoms.

Comment: Further studies are needed in order to determine the cultural and physiological characteristics of this species.

Source: Isolated from the nasal cavity of swine with infectious atrophic rhinitis; also found in apparently healthy pigs. Pleuropneumonia-like organisms were also isolated by Carter and McKay (Canad. Jour. Comp. Med., *17*, 1953, 413) and by Carter (Canad. Jour. Comp. Med., *18*, 1954, 246) from the nasal cavities of swine with atrophic rhinitis and from the tissues of pigs suffering from an infectious condition (Glasser's disease) similar to that reported by Switzer; young pigs inoculated intraperitoneally with secondary cultures developed typical lesions.

Habitat: Found in the nasal cavity of swine. The etiological agent of a generalized infection in swine involving the serous membranes of the thoracic and abdominal cavity. The relationship of this organism to atrophic rhinitis seems to require further study.

8. **Mycoplasma pulmonis** (Sabin, 1941) Freundt, 1955. (L₃ , Klieneberger and Steabben, Jour. Hyg., *37*, 1937, 143; *Murimyces pulmonis* Sabin, Bact. Rev., *5*, 1941, 57; Freundt, Internat. Bull. of Bact. Nomen. and Taxon., *5*, 1955, 73; also see Edward, Internat. Bull. of Bact. Nomen. and Taxon., *5*, 1955, 91.)

pul.mo′nis. L. noun *pulmo* the lung; L. gen.noun *pulmonis* of the lung.

Unstable, sparsely branched mycelioid structure with very short, almost bacillary filaments which usually measure 2 to 5 microns in length (Ørskov, Acta Path. et Microbiol. Scand., *19*, 1942, 575; Freundt, unpublished observation). Elementary bodies and short rods have been demonstrated in electron micrographs by Klieneberger-Nobel and Cuckow (Jour. Gen. Microbiol., *12*, 1955, 95). Gram-negative.

Horse-serum agar: A film and spots are produced. Central spot of the colonies is less marked than those of most of the other species in this genus; rough surface.

Horse-blood agar: Alpha hemolysis.

Rabbit-serum agar: Poor growth.

Semi-solid media: Granular growth, preferably near the surface.

Broth: Granular growth.

Acid from glucose, mannose, maltose, glycogen, dextrin and starch. No acid from fructose, galactose, sucrose, lactose, salicin, mannitol or dulcitol.

Methylene blue is slowly reduced.

Aerobic; very poor growth under anaerobic conditions.

Serologically different from *Mycoplasma arthritidis* Freundt.

Pathogenicity: Produces suppuration in mice when injected along with agar. Not pathogenic for rats in artificial infection. Sometimes found in young rats without definite lung lesions, while in older rats a close connection has been demonstrated between the presence of this organism and bronchiectatic pulmonary disease; however,

the etiological significance of this organism to this condition seems obscure. Experiments reported by Klieneberger-Nobel and Cheng (Jour. Path. and Bact., *70*, 1955, 245) suggest that the role of this organism may be that of a secondary invader.

Comment: The isolation of closely related organisms from mice with infectious catarrh has been reported by Edward (Jour. Gen. Microbiol., *10*, 1954, 27).

Source: Isolated from the lungs of laboratory rats, most of which had bronchiectasis although some were without lesions; also isolated from a wild rat.

Habitat: From the normal and diseased lungs of rats so far as definitely known.

9. **Mycoplasma arthritidis** (Sabin, 1941) Freundt, 1955. (L₄ , Klieneberger, Jour. Hyg., *38*, 1938, 458; *Murimyces arthritidis* Sabin, Bact. Rev., *5*, 1941, 57; *Pleuropneumonia arthritidis muris* Tulasne and Brisou, Ann. Inst. Past., *88*, 1955, 238; Freundt, Internat. Bull. of Bact. Nomen. and Taxon., *5*, 1955, 73; also see Edward, Internat. Bull. of Bact. Nomen. and Taxon., *5*, 1955, 91.)

ar.thri′ti.dis. Gr. noun *arthritis* gout, arthritis; M.L. gen.noun *arthritidis* of arthritis.

Unstable to relatively stable mycelioid structure; filaments vary from short, almost bacillary forms (usually 2 to 5 microns in length) to moderately long structures (10 to 30 microns) (Preston, Jour. Inf. Dis., *70*, 1942, 180; Freundt, unpublished observation). Gram-negative.

Horse-serum agar: Neither film nor spots are produced.

Horse-blood agar: Alpha hemolysis.

Rabbit-serum agar: Good growth.

Semi-solid media: Fluffy growth throughout.

Broth: Slight, uniform opalescence.

Carbohydrates not attacked.

Methylene blue is slowly reduced.

Aerobic, facultatively anaerobic.

Serologically distinct from *Mycoplasma pulmonis* Freundt.

Pathogenicity: When injected together with agar intravenously or into the pads of rats and mice, the organism appears to have a predilection for the joints. Subcutaneous injection produces diffuse abscesses. Intracerebral inoculation causes encephalitis in mice but usually no cerebral symptoms in rats. Intranasal instillation causes pneumonia in mice. Non-pathogenic for monkeys, rabbits or guinea pigs.

Comments: The description of this species is based on a strain isolated by Preston (Jour. Inf. Dis., *70*, 1942, 180) from infected joints of rats. Preston's organism is generally believed to be identical with Klieneberger's L_4, although it was not typed serologically. Moreover, L_4 is identical with the pyogenic virus of Woglom and Warren (Jour. Exp. Med., *68*, 1938, 513), with L_7 of Findlay, MacKenzie, MacCallum and Klieneberger (Lancet, *237*, 1939, 7) and probably also with the organisms isolated by Beeuwkes and Collier (Jour. Inf. Dis., *70*, 1942, 1).

Source: Isolated from the submaxillary gland of a laboratory rat with eye, ear and lung infections (Klieneberger, *op. cit.*, 1938, 458); also isolated from a contaminated transmissible sarcoma (Klieneberger, Jour. Hyg., *39*, 1939, 260) and from outbreaks of spontaneous polyarthritis in laboratory rats (Findlay et al., *op. cit.*, 1939, 7; Preston, *op. cit.*, 1942, 180).

Habitat: From various infected lesions of rats so far as known.

10. **Mycoplasma neurolyticum** (Sabin, 1941) Freundt, 1955. (A filterable, transmissible agent with "neurolytic" properties, Sabin, Science, *88*, 1938, 189; also see *ibid.*, 575; L_5, Findlay, MacKenzie, MacCallum and Klieneberger, Lancet, *235*, 1938, 1511; *Musculomyces neurolyticus*, type A, Sabin, Bact. Rev., *5*, 1941, 24 and 57; *Pleuropneumonia cerebri-muris* Tulasne and Brisou, Ann. Inst. Past., *88*, 1955, 238; Freundt, Internat. Bull. of Bact. Nomen. and Taxon., *5*, 1955, 73; also see Edward, Internat. Bull. of Bact. Nomen. and Taxon., *5*, 1955, 91.)

neu.ro.ly'ti.cum. Gr. noun *neuron* nerve; Gr. adj. *lyticus* able to loose; M.L. adj. *neurolyticus* nerve-destroying.

Unstable to relatively stable mycelioid structure, the filaments varying from short, almost bacillary forms (usually 2 to 5 microns in length) to moderately long structures (10 to 30 microns) (Freundt, unpublished observation). Gram-negative.

Horse-serum agar: Neither film nor spots are produced.

Horse-blood agar: Alpha hemolysis.

Rabbit-serum agar: Poor growth.

Semi-solid media: Smooth or granular growth, preferably near the surface.

Broth: Generalized opalescence.

Acid from glucose, mannose, maltose, dextrin, glycogen and starch. No acid from fructose, galactose, sucrose, lactose, salicin, mannitol or dulcitol.

Methylene blue is slowly reduced.

Aerobic; poor growth under anaerobic conditions.

A thermolabile exotoxin, which causes acute necrosis of the posterior pole of the cerebellum in mice, is produced *in vivo* and *in vitro* by the American strains.

Serologically distinct from the other members of this genus. The American and English strains of this species appear to be serologically and immunologically identical.

Pathogenicity: American strains of this organism produce "rolling disease" and other nervous symptoms in young mice after intracerebral, intraabdominal or intrathoracal injection; older mice sometimes develop a transient, non-destructive polyarthritis after intravenous injection. The English strains are less virulent, and "rolling disease" develops only if the organisms are injected together with agar or a neurotropic virus. Other animals, with the exception of the field-vole, are not susceptible.

Source: Isolated from the brain of mice that had developed "rolling disease" during the course of intracerebral passage of various agents: *Toxoplasma* (Sabin, *op. cit.*, 1938, 189 and 575), lymphocytic choriomeningitis and probably also yellow fever virus (Findlay et al., *op. cit.*, 1938, 1511). Later isolated on a few occasions from the brain of normal mice and almost regularly from the conjunctiva and nasal mucosa of carriers, and from pneumonic foci of mouse lungs after nasal instillation of various materials (Sabin, Science, *90*, 1939, 18; also see *op. cit.*, 1941, 24; Sabin and Johnson, Proc. Soc. Exp. Biol. and Med., *44*, 1940, 569, and Sullivan and Dienes, *ibid.*, *41*, 1939, 620).

Habitat: From normal and diseased mice so far as known.

11. Mycoplasma gallinarum Freundt, 1955. (A pleuropneumonia-like organism isolated from the upper respiratory tract of a fowl, Edward, Jour. Gen. Microbiol., *10*, 1954, 52 and 53; Freundt, Internat. Bull. of Bact. Nomen. and Taxon., *5*, 1955, 73; *Borrelomyces gallinarum* Freundt, *ibid.*, 75.)

gal.li.na'rum. L. fem.n. *gallina* a hen; L. fem.gen.pl.n. *gallinarum* of hens.

Morphological characters not recorded for the type strain (cf. *Comments*). Gram-negative.

Horse-serum agar: A film and spots are produced.

Horse-blood agar: Hemolysis.

Rabbit-serum agar: Good growth.

Semi-solid media: Smooth growth throughout.

No acid from glucose.

Methylene blue is reduced rather rapidly.

Aerobic, facultatively anaerobic.

Pathogenicity: Not tested for the representative strain.

Comments: The coccobacillary bodies of fowl coryza described by Nelson were probably pleuropneumonia-like organisms (Nelson, Science, *82*, 1935, 43; also see Jour. Exp. Med., *63*, 1936, 509 and 515; and *ibid.*, *69*, 1939, 199). Herick and Eaton (Jour. Bact., *50*, 1945, 47) isolated a pleuropneumonia-like organism as a contaminant of a pneumonia virus which was being passaged in chick embryos; broth cultures agglutinated chicken erythrocytes as well as those of other animals; hemagglutination inhibition tests with sera of chickens from the hatchery that had furnished the eggs showed an appreciable antibody level to the organism in a fairly high percentage of the chickens. Report of pleuropneumonia-like organisms from egg-passage material of the agent(s) of a chronic respiratory disease (CRD) of chickens and of turkey sinusitis (TS), which were originally regarded as viruses by van Roekel, Olesiuk and Peck (Amer. Jour. Vet. Res., *13*, 1952, 252), was made by Markham and Wong (Poult. Sci., *31*, 1952, 902); following a series of thirteen successive subcul-

tures in artificial media, the organisms produced mortality and microscopic findings in embryonated eggs that were typical for the above agents, and suspensions prepared from yolk sacs harvested from these embryos caused sinusitis in turkeys. Lecce and Sperling (Vet. Ext. Quart., Univ. of Pennsylvania, No. 134, 1954, 96) were able to cultivate pleuropneumonia-like organisms from the tracheae of chickens which had long since recovered from symptoms of CRD and from asymptomatic chickens that had been in contact with sick birds, but they were not able to cultivate these organisms from normal birds obtained from flocks that had never been associated with CRD. They also showed (Cornell Vet., *44*, 1954, 441) that pleuropneumonia-like organisms were more commonly found in the tracheae than in the lungs and air sacs of sick chickens. White, Wallace and Alberts (Poult. Sci., *33*, 1954, 500) studied two strains of the CRD agent and one strain of the TS agent obtained from van Roekel. Broth cultures from the 22nd serial transfer in an artificial medium were inoculated into the infraorbital sinuses and into the tracheae of 10-week-old chickens and turkeys. The latter developed sinusitis 9 to 12 days after exposure, and at necropsy performed one month after exposure, tracheitis and signs of inflammation of the thoracic and abdominal air sacs were demonstrated. In the chickens, a catarrhal inflammation of the nasal membranes and tracheae was observed, while there were no external symptoms of sinusitis and no gross pathological changes in the air sacs. Hemagglutination tests with broth cultures and chicken and turkey erythrocytes were positive and were inhibited both by homologous and heterologous sera of the infected birds. Sera from apparently normal birds showed a slight inhibition. Structures similar to those characteristic of the pleuropneumonia group were demonstrated in electron micrographs prepared from broth cultures: single elementary bodies varying from 0.1 to 0.5 micron, and large and small filaments, some of which contained close-set spherical bodies that were about the size of single cells. Strains from chickens and turkeys could not be distinguished morphologically. Morton, Lecce, Oskay and Coy (Jour. Bact., 68, 1954, 697) failed to demonstrate anything but single spherical bodies in electron micrographs of two other strains of pleuropneumonia-like organisms also obtained from van Roekel. Further comparative studies are needed before the relationships of the fowl pleuropneumonia-like organisms isolated from different sources and in various laboratories can be determined. Edward, in preliminary investigations, found more than one species represented in strains isolated from fowls; at least three species would appear to be represented among strains isolated from the continent of America (Edward, personal communication, 1955). Strains described by Tahey and Crawley (Canad. Jour. Comp. Med., 18, 1954, 67) and by Gianforte, Fungherr and Jacobs (Poult. Sci., 34, 1955, 662) differed from *Mycoplasma gallinarum* Freundt by fermenting glucose and other sugars.

Source: Isolated from the upper respiratory tract of a fowl.

Habitat: Found in the normal and diseased upper respiratory tract of fowls. Other strains of pleuropneumonia-like organisms from fowls that may or may not belong to this species have been shown to be etiologically implicated in a chronic respiratory disease of chickens and of turkey sinusitis.

12. **Mycoplasma hominis** (Freundt, 1953) Edward, 1955. (Human types 1 and 2, Nicol and Edward, Brit. Jour. Vener. Dis., 29, 1953, 146 and 147; also see Edward, Jour. Gen Microbiol., 10, 1954, 54 and 55; *Micromyces hominis*, group I, Freundt, Acta Path. et Microbiol. Scand., 32, 1953, 471; also see Atti del VI Congresso Internazionale di Microbiologia, Roma, 1, 1953, 138; and Acta Path. et Microbiol. Scand., 34, 1954, 143; Edward, in Freundt, Internat. Bull. of Bact. Nomen. and Taxon., 5, 1955, 73; see Edward, Internat. Bull. of Bact. Nomen. and Taxon., 5, 1955, 90.)

ho'mi.nis. L. noun *homo* man; L. gen.noun *hominis* of man.

Unstable and sparsely branched mycelioid structure with very short, almost bacillary filaments which usually measure 2 to 5 microns in length (Freundt, *op. cit.*, 1954, 127). Spherical elementary bodies have been demonstrated in electron micrographs by Morton, Lecce, Oskay and Coy (Jour. Bact., 68, 1954, 697). Slender, branching filaments and strings of minute cocci have been reported in a non-classified strain of human origin by Beveridge (Med. Jour. of Australia, 2, 1943, 479). Gram-negative.

Horse-serum agar: Neither film nor spots are produced.

Horse-blood agar: Very slight hemolysis, if any.

Rabbit-serum agar: Good growth.

Semi-solid media: Usually granular growth throughout the medium.

Broth: Very faint generalized opacity, if any; small sediment.

Carbohydrates not attacked.

Reduction of methylene blue is slow and variable.

Tetrazolium salts are reduced under anaerobic conditions.

Aerobic, facultatively anaerobic.

Serologically there are two distinct types (Nicol and Edward, *op. cit.*, 1953, 145).

Pathogenicity: Type 1 is not pathogenic for mice. Local abscesses are produced in mice on subcutaneous inoculation of type 2 strains.

Completely resistant to sulfathiazol, penicillin and erythromycin. Moderate sensitivity is shown to streptomycin, and the susceptibility to dihydrostreptomycin is variable. Highly sensitive to aureomycin, chloramphenicol and terramycin.

Comments: The occurrence of pleuropneumonia-like organisms in the human genital tract was first demonstrated by Dienes and Edsall in 1937 (Proc. Soc. Exp. Biol. and Med., 36, 1937, 740; also see Dienes, *ibid.*, 44, 1940, 468). Six strains isolated by Dienes from 1939 to 1940 were later classified by Edward (*op. cit.*, 1954, 54) as type 2 (now *Mycoplasma hominis* Edward, type 2).

Source: Isolated from human male and female genital tract and anal canal; also recovered in pure cultures from the blood of a patient suffering from a puerperal septicemia and from the pus of a broncho-pleural fistula in another case (Stokes, Lancet, 1, 1955, 276).

Habitat: Frequently found as an inhabitant of the human genital and rectal mucosa. The etiological implications of this organism in non-gonococcal urethritis and other inflammatory conditions of the lower genital tract are still obscure.

13. **Mycoplasma salivarium** Edward, 1955. (Human type 4, Nicol and Edward, Brit. Jour. Vener. Dis., *29*, 1953, 148; also see Edward, Jour. Gen. Microbiol., *10*, 1954, 55; Edward, in Freundt, Internat. Bull. of Bact. Nomen. and Taxon., *5*, 1955, 73; see Edward, Internat. Bull. of Bact. Nomen. and Taxon., *5*, 1955, 90.)

sa.li.va′ri.um. L. adj. *salivarius* salivary, slimy; intended to mean of saliva.

Morphological characters not recorded. Gram-negative.

Horse-serum agar: A film and spots may or may not be produced.

Horse-blood agar: No hemolysis.

Rabbit-serum agar: Very good growth.

Semi-solid media: Smooth growth, best near the bottom.

Glucose is not attacked.

Growth is improved by the addition of thymonucleic acid upon primary isolation.

Methylene blue is slowly reduced.

Anaerobic on primary isolation.

Serologically distinct from the genital species.

Pathogenicity: Not tested.

Comments: Other strains isolated from the mouth and pharynx in humans by Smith and Morton (Science, *113*, 1951, 623), Morton et al. (Jour. Dent. Res., *30*, 1951, 415), Dienes and Madoff (Proc. Soc. Exp. Biol. and Med., *82*, 1953, 36) and by Freundt (Acta Path. et Microbiol. Scand., *34*, 1954, 127) appear to differ from *Mycoplasma salivarium* Edward in their growth and cultural properties. Additional comparative studies are needed before the relationships of these organisms can be ascertained.

Source: Isolated from human saliva.

14. **Mycoplasma fermentans** Edward, 1955. (G strains, Ruiter and Wentholt, Jour. Invest. Dermat., *18*, 1952, 322; also see Acta Dermat. Venereol., *33*, 1953, 123 and 130; human type 3, Nicol and Edward, Brit. Jour. Vener. Dis., *29*, 1953, 147; also see

Edward, Jour. Gen. Microbiol., *10*, 1954, 54 and 55; *Micromyces hominis*, group II, Freundt, Acta Path. et Microbiol. Scand., *34*, 1954, 143; also see Atti del VI Congresso Internazionale di Microbiologia, Roma, *1*, 1953, 138; Edward, in Freundt, Internat. Bull. of Bact. Nomen. and Taxon., *5*, 1955, 73; see Edward, Internat. Bull. of Bact. Nomen. and Taxon., *5*, 1955, 90.)

fer.men′tans. L. part.adj. *fermentans* fermenting.

Relatively stable mycelioid structure with filaments varying from 10 to 30 microns in length (Freundt, *op. cit.*, 1954, 143). Gram-negative.

Horse-serum agar: A film and spots are produced.

Horse-blood agar: No hemolysis.

Rabbit-serum agar: Good growth.

Semi-solid media: Smooth growth, preferably near the bottom.

Broth: Generalized opacity.

Acid from glucose, fructose, galactose, maltose, glycogen, dextrin and starch; no acid from mannose, xylose, sucrose, lactose, salicin, glycerol or mannitol.

Growth is usually improved by the addition of thymonucleic acid and by aerobic conditions at pH 6.0 to 6.6 and by anaerobic conditions at pH 7.0 to 8.0.

Reduction of methylene blue is rather rapid.

Anaerobic or microaerophilic; usually very poor growth under aerobic conditions.

Serologically distinct from *Mycoplasma hominis* Edward and *M. salivarium* Edward.

Pathogenicity: May or may not be pathogenic for mice; abscesses are sometimes produced when inoculations of early subcultures are made in the foot pad of mice.

Completely resistant to sulfathiazol, penicillin and erythromycin. Moderate sensitivity is shown to streptomycin, and the susceptibility to dihydrostreptomycin is variable. Highly sensitive to aureomycin, chloramphenicol and terramycin.

Source: Isolated from human male and female genital tract.

Habitat: Found not only in ulcerative genital lesions associated with fusiform bacilli and spirilla but also on the apparently normal genital mucosa.

15. **Mycoplasma laidlawii** (Sabin, 1941) Freundt, 1955. (Types A and B, Laidlaw and Elford, Proc. Roy. Soc. London, B, *120*, 1936, 292; *Sapromyces laidlawi* AB, Sabin, Bact. Rev., *5*, 1941, 59; Freundt, Internat. Bull. of Bact. Nomen. and Taxon., *5*, 1955, 73; also see Edward, Internat. Bull. of Bact. Nomen. and Taxon., *5*, 1955, 91.)

laid.law'i.i. M.L. gen.noun *laidlawii* of Laidlaw; named for P. Laidlaw, one of the bacteriologists who first isolated this species.

Relatively stable mycelioid structure with filaments of moderate length (10 to 30 microns) (Ørskov, Zent. f. Bakt., I Abt., Orig., *141*, 1938, 229; also see Acta Path. et Microbiol. Scand., *19*, 1942, 586; Freundt, unpublished observation). Elementary bodies, but no filaments, have been demonstrated in electron micrographs by Ruska and Poppe (Ztschr. f. Hyg., *127*, 1947, 201) and by Kandler and Kandler (Arch. f. Mikrobiol., *21*, 1954, 178 and 202). Gram-negative.

Serum is not required for growth.

Horse-serum agar: Neither film nor spots are produced.

Horse-blood agar: Alpha hemolysis.

Semi-solid media: Fluffy growth near the surface.

Broth: Strong opalescence.

Hydrogen sulfide is not produced.

Acid from glucose, fructose, maltose, starch, glycogen and dextrin; acid may or may not be produced from galactose. No acid from mannose, lactose, sucrose, xylose, salicin, glycerol, mannitol or dulcitol.

Nitrites not produced from nitrates.

Ammonia is not produced.

Methylene blue is rapidly reduced.

Sodium tellurite is slowly reduced.

Aerobic; poor growth under anaerobic conditions.

Optimum temperature, about 30°C. Growth between 22° and 37°C.

Laidlaw and Elford (*op. cit.*, 1936, 292) recognized three serological types by agglutination tests: A, B and C. A and C are quite distinct antigenically, and B is more closely related to A than to C.

Comments: Various strains, which are similar to the A and B strains of Laidlaw and Elford culturally, physiologically, serologically and with respect to their habitats, have been described in the literature, *viz.* Seiffert's Strains (Seiffert, Zent. f. Bakt., I Abt., Orig., *139*, 1937, 337; also see *ibid.*, *140*, 1937, 168; Klieneberger, Jour. Hyg., *40*, 1940, 204; and Kandler and Kandler, Zent. f. Bakt., II Abt., *108*, 1955, 383) and S Strains (Edward, Jour. Gen. Microbiol., *4*, 1950, 4). The C strains of Laidlaw and Elford are regarded by Sabin (*op. cit.*, 1941, 59) as belonging to a separate species, *Sapromyces laidlawi* C. The C strain has been lost and has not been compared culturally or physiologically by appropriate methods with the A and B strains for which reason it has not been included in *Mycoplasma laidlawii* Freundt.

Source: Isolated from sewage (Laidlaw and Elford). Seiffert obtained his strains from manure, humus and soil, and Edward secured his as a contaminant of cultures from the genital tract of cattle.

Habitat: Apparently frequently found as saprophytes in sewage, manure, humus and soil.

ADDENDUM TO CLASS II. SCHIZOMYCETES VON NAEGELI.

BACTERIA SYMBIOTIC OR PARASITIC IN PROTOZOA.

In studying various species of *Protozoa*, protozoologists have occasionally found them to be infected with organisms living either on the surface of the protozoan cells or more frequently intracellularly. Many of the intracellular microorganisms cause diseases that may destroy the host organisms.

These intracellular parasites of *Protozoa* are of the size of ordinary bacteria. Some have the morphology of cocci, and these have sometimes been placed in a special genus, *Caryococcus* Dangeard, near the genus *Micrococcus* Cohn, while one species has been placed in *Micrococcus*. In a similar way other species have been placed in *Cladothrix* Cohn (*Sphaerotilis* Kützing) or in *Myxococcus* Thaxter. Some spirally shaped cells have been assigned to a special genus placed near *Vibrio* and *Spirillum*. Still others of these bacteria form spores and have been placed in the special genus *Holospora* Haffkine. The spores appear to resemble the endospores found in the genus *Bacillus* Cohn.

Because the majority of these intracellular parasites are so highly specialized that they, like rickettsias and viruses, cannot be cultured outside of the cells that they parasitize, the descriptions that have been published of these parasities were arranged in an appendix to the order *Rickettsiales* in the sixth edition of the MANUAL (1948, p. 1121). However, these protozoan parasites have been described by those who have studied them as being related to quite a variety of genera of bacteria belonging in various orders of the class *Schizomycetes*. Furthermore, these organisms are not in any sense of the word intermediate in character between rickettsias and viruses, even though all are highly specialized intracellular parasites. For these reasons the parasites of protozoa are placed in this edition of the MANUAL in an Addendum to Class II, *Schizomycetes*.

While only about one dozen species of these bacteria have as yet been described and named, several additional species have been well described without having been named. Still other species are known to exist. No special student of the group has as yet attempted to place these interesting organisms in relation to recognized families and genera of bacteria more definitely than is indicated above. The organisms in question are, as yet, best known to protozoologists and are rarely mentioned in textbooks of bacteriology. Their existence suggests that other groups of invertebrate animals may suffer from similar bacterial diseases as yet unknown.—The Editors.

GENERA AND SPECIES OF PARASITES OF PROTOZOA.*

I. *Species placed in special genera:*

Genus A. **Caryococcus** *Dangeard, 1902.*

(Compt. rend. Acad. Sci., Paris, *134*, 1902, 1365.)

Ca.ry.o.coc′cus. Gr. noun *caryum* nut, kernel, nucleus; Gr. noun *coccus* berry, coccus; M.L. mas.n. *Caryococcus* nuclear coccus.

Spherical organisms parasitic in the nucleus of *Euglena*.

The type species is *Caryococcus hypertrophicus* Dangeard.

1. **Caryococcus hypertrophicus** Dangeard, 1902. (Compt. rend. Acad. Sci., Paris, *134*, 1902, 1365.)

hy.per.tro′phi.cus. Gr. pref. *hyper* over, more than; Gr. adj. *trophicus* nursing; M.L. adj. *hypertrophicus* overfed, causing hypertrophy.

Occurs in the nucleus as an agglomeration of close-set, spherical corpuscles. The nucleus increases considerably in volume, the chromatin is reduced to thin layers against the membrane, and the interior of the nucleus is divided into irregular compartments by chromatic trabeculae.

Parasitic in the nucleus of a flagellate (*Euglena deses*).

2. **Caryococcus cretus** Kirby, 1944. (Univ. Calif. Publ. Zool., *49*, 1944, 240.)

cre′tus. L. p.adj. *cretus* visible, discernible.

Spherules 1.0 to 1.5 microns or more in diameter. Appear clear in preparations with usually a chromatic, sharply defined, crescentic structure peripherally or interiorly situated, sometimes with two such bodies or several chromatic granules. Parasitic in nucleus. The parasitized nucleus is enlarged only moderately or not at all, and the chromatin is altered but not greatly diminished in amount.

Parasitic in the nucleus of a flagellate (*Trichonympha corbula*) from the intestine

---

* Prepared by Prof. Harold Kirby, Jr., University of California, Berkeley, California, October, 1946; revised by Prof. Bronislaw M. Honigberg, University of Massachusetts, Amherst, Massachusetts, March, 1955.

of a termite (*Procryptotermes sp.*) from Madagascar.

3. Caryococcus dilatator Kirby, 1944. (Univ. Calif. Publ. Zool., *49*, 1944, 238.) di.la.ta′tor. L. p.adj. *dilatus* dilate; M.L. noun *dilatator* the dilator.

Spherules 0.5 micron or less in diameter. Internally differentiated with a stainable granule or stainable region peripherally situated. Parasitic in nucleus and nucleolus. The nucleus becomes greatly enlarged, and the chromatin mostly or entirely disappears.

Parasitic in the nucleus of flagellates (*Trichonympha chattoni* and other species of *Trichonympha*) from the intestine of a termite (*Glyptotermes iridipennis*) from Australia; also found in other species of termites.

4. Caryococcus invadens Kirby, 1944. (Univ. Calif. Publ. Zool., *49*, 1944, 238.) in.va′dens. L. p.adj. *invadens* invading.

Spherules, 1.0 to 1.5 microns in diameter, sometimes arranged in pairs. Often internally differentiated with stainable central or peripheral granules or stained areas. Parasitic in the nucleolus and nucleus. The parasitized nucleolus becomes greatly enlarged and crossed by trabeculae, the nucleolus eventually being consumed; the nucleus becomes moderately enlarged, but the chromatin does not disappear.

Parasitic in the nucleus of a flagellate (*Trichonympha peplophora*) from the intestine of a termite (*Neotermes howa*) from Madagascar.

5. Caryococcus nucleophagus Kirby, 1944. (Univ. Calif. Publ. Zool., *49*, 1944, 236.) nu.cle.o′pha.gus. L. noun *nucleus* a small nut, a nucleus; Gr. v. *phagein* to eat; M.L. adj. *nucleophagus* nucleus-destroying.

Spherules with a diameter of about 0.5 micron, sometimes arranged in pairs, sometimes with a thicker, crescentic, stainable area of the periphery on one side. Parasitic within the nucleus, lying exteriorly or interiorly to the chromatin mass; the chromatin mass may be diminished in amount but does not disappear; the parasitized nucleus also is not appreciably enlarged.

Parasitic in the nucleus of a flagellate (*Trichonympha corbula*) from the intestines of termites (*Procryptotermes sp.*) from Madagascar and from three species of *Kalotermes* from Madagascar.

Genus B. **Drepanospira** *de Petschenko, 1911.*

(*Müllerina* de Petschenko (not validly published; rejected by author), Cent. f. Bakt., I Abt., Orig., *56*, 1910, 90; de Petschenko, Arch. f. Protistenk., *22*, 1911, 252; see Editorial Board, Internat. Bull. of Bact. Nomen. and Taxon., *2*, 1952, 9.)

Dre.pa.no′spi.ra. Gr. noun *drepane* a sickle; Gr. noun *spira* spiral; M.L. noun *Drepanospira* sickle spiral.

Cells incurved in two spiral turns that are not abrupt, one of the ends being pointed, the other a little rounded. No flagella; movement helicoid by means of all the body. No cell division. So-called endospores are formed. Regular spherical colonies are formed by individuals at certain stages of development.

The author regards this genus as belonging in the family *Spirillaceae* between *Spirosoma* (= *Spirillum*) and *Microspira* (= *Vibrio*).

The type species is *Drepanospira muelleri* de Petschenko.

1. Drepanospira muelleri de Petschenko, 1911. (*Müllerina paramecii* de Petschenko (name rejected by author), Cent. f. Bakt., I Abt., Orig., *56*, 1910, 90; *Drepanospira Mülleri* (sic) de Petschenko, Arch. f. Protistenk., *22*, 1911, 252; also see Kirby, in Calkins and Summers, Protozoa in Biological Research, 1941, 1036; and Bu-chanan, Internat. Bull. of Bact. Nomen. and Taxon., *2*, 1952, 9.)

mue′lle.ri. M.L. gen.noun *muelleri* of Müller; named for J. Müller, who studied ciliates and who directed attention to these parasites of *Paramecium*.

Develop from a group of curved rods in the cytoplasm to a large, ellipsoidal mass almost filling the body. Nuclear portion occupying part of the cell.

Parasitic in the cytoplasm of *Paramecium caudatum.*

Genus C. **Holospora** *Haffkine, 1890.*

(Ann. Inst. Past., *4*, 1890, 151.)

Ho.lo'spo.ra. Gr. adj. *holus* whole, complete; Gr. noun *sporus* seed; M.L. noun *spora* spore; M.L. fem.n. *Holospora* whole spore.

Parasities of the ciliate *Paramecium aurelia* (= *Paramecium caudatum?*). Develop spore-like cells.

The type species is *Holospora undulata* Haffkine.

1. **Holospora undulata** Haffkine, 1890. (Ann. Inst. Past., *4*, 1890, 151.)

un.du.la'ta. L. adj. *undulatus* undulated, with waves.

Gradually tapered at ends. Possesses 1.5, 2.0 or 2.5 spiral turns. Develops from a small, fusiform body which grows and divides transversely; brings about a great enlargement of the micronucleus, which becomes filled with the spirals (see *Drepanospira muelleri* de Petschenko).

Source: Found in the micronucleus of the ciliate *Paramecium aurelia* (= *P. caudatum?*).

2. **Holospora elegans** Haffkine, 1890. (Haffkine, Ann. Inst. Past., *4*, 1890, 154; also see Kirby, in Calkins and Summers, Protozoa in Biological Research, New York, 1941, 1035.)

e'le.gans. L. adj. *elegans* fine, elegant.

Vegetative stage fusiform; elongated, ellipsoidal, nucleus-like body in some.

Divides equatorially, budding at one end. Transformation into spores entails enlargement, clear space separating membrane at sides, spores pointed at ends.

Source: Found in the micronucleus of the ciliate *Paramecium aurelia* (= *P. caudatum?*).

3. **Holospora obtusa** Haffkine, 1890. (Haffkine, Ann. Inst. Past., *4*, 1890, 153; also see Fiveiskaja, Arch. f. Protistenk., *65*, 1929, 276.)

ob.tu'sa. L. adj. *obtusus* obtuse.

Spores not spiralled, and both ends are rounded. Reproduction by fission, also by formation of a bud at one of the extremities of the fusiform cell. Bodies 0.6 to 0.8 by 12.0 to 30.0 microns, with rounded ends; also occur as spindle-shaped bodies with pointed ends, 0.5 by 3.0 to 6.0 microns (Fiveiskaja, *loc. cit.*).

Source: Found in the macronucleus of the ciliate *Paramecium aurelia* (= *P. caudatum?*).

II. *Species placed in recognized genera of* **Schizomycetes:**

D. **Micrococcus batrachorum** Yakimov, 1930.

(*Micrococcus batrochorum* (sic) Yakimov, Arch. f. Protistenk., *72*, 1930, 137.)

ba.tra.cho'rum. M.L. noun *batrachorum* the specific epithet of the flagellate host, *Trichomonas batrachorum.*

Round organisms, 1.0 to 1.5 microns in diameter, generally grouped in aggregates of irregular form, but they may also occur individually.

Source: Found in the cytoplasm of the flagellate *Trichomonas batrachorum* from the tree toad (*Hyla arborea*). Also observed free in preparations of the intestinal contents of *Hyla*.

E. **Bacterium parapelomyxae** Keller, 1949.

(Ztschr. f. Naturforsch., *4b*, 1949, 296.)

pa.ra.pe.lo.my'xae. Gr. prefix *para* beside, near; M.L. noun *pelomyxae* specific epithet of *Myxococcus pelomyxae;* M.L. adj. *parapelomyxae* (*Myxococcus*) *pelomyxae*-like.

Morphologically almost indistinguishable from *Myxococcus pelomyxae*. On agar enriched with an infusion of a ground suspension of *Pelomyxa*, there are some growth differences between the two species.

Short rods, 0.6 to 0.8 by 0.8 to 1.0 micron, relatively uniform in shape and size. Motility uncertain. Non-differentially stained with fuchsin. Non-acid-fast. Gram-negative.

Gelatin: No liquefaction.

Agar colonies: Circular, slightly larger than those of *Myxococcus pelomyxae*, smooth, entire, shiny, moderately raised, butter-like consistency, colorless to yellowish, transparent.

Broth: Slight clouding, grayish white ring at surface, slight sediment, no odor.

Litmus milk: Unchanged.

Indole not produced.

Hydrogen sulfide not produced.

Acid from glucose, lactose, sucrose, xylose, salicin and mannitol. No acid from glycerol, inulin or dextrin.

Starch not hydrolyzed.

Nitrites produced from nitrates.

Source: Found in the cytoplasm of the rhizopod *Pelomyxa palustris* Greeff.

F. **Cladothrix pelomyxae** Veley, 1905.

(Veley, Jour. Linn. Soc., Zool., *29*, 1905, 375; also see Leiner, Arch. f. Protistenk.,
47, 1924, 282; Kirby, in Calkins and Summers, Protozoa in Biological
Research, New York, 1941, 1025; and Hollande, Bull. Biol.
France Belg., *79*, 1945, 49.)

pe.lo.my'xae. M.L. fem.n. *Pelomyxa* a genus of rhizopods; M.L. gen.noun *pelomyxae* of *Pelomyxa*.

Rods, 1.5 to 22.0 microns or more in length, divided into several to many sections by transverse partitions. Generally aggregated in proximity to the nuclei, which may be thickly invested by close-set organisms applied to the surface.

Source: Found in the cytoplasm of the rhizopod *Pelomyxa palustris* Greeff and probably also in other species of *Pelomyxa*.

G. **Myxococcus pelomyxae** Keller, 1949.

(Ztschr. f. Naturforsch., *4b*, 1949, 296.)

pe.lo.my'xae. M.L. fem.n. *Pelomyxa* a genus of rhizopods; M.L. gen.noun *pelomyxae* of *Pelomyxa*.

Short, ellipsoidal rods, about 1 by 2 microns, very uniform in shape and size. One end stains deeply with fuchsin, organisms thus stained appearing pyriform. Highly motile in young cultures, but no flagella are demonstrable by staining. Non-sporeforming. Non-acid-fast. Gram-negative.

Gelatin: No liquefaction.

Agar colonies: Circular, about 2 mm in diameter, smooth, entire, shiny, moderately raised, of very soft nearly mucoid consistency, colorless.

Broth: Slight clouding, white ring at surface, no sediment, no odor.

Litmus milk: Unchanged.

Indole not produced.

Hydrogen sulfide not produced.

Acid from glucose, xylose, mannitol and dulcitol. No acid from lactose, sucrose, glycerol, salicin, inulin or dextrin.

Starch not hydrolyzed.

Nitrites produced in slight amounts from nitrates.

No nitrogen fixation.

Suggestion of ability to digest cellulose.

Comment: According to Keller the large rods described by Veley et al. from the rhizopod *Pelomyxa palustris* represent fruiting bodies of *Myxococcus pelomyxae*. If this view were to be accepted, *M. pelomyxae* Keller would be identical with *Cladothrix pelomyxae* Veley.

Source: Found in the cytoplasm of the rhizopod *Pelomyxa palustris* Greeff.

CLASS III

MICROTATOBIOTES PHILIP

By

CORNELIUS B. PHILIP

Rocky Mountain Laboratory, U. S. Public Health Service, Hamilton, Montana

AND

Specialists whose names appear on the following pages in connection
with the sections prepared by them

CLASS III. MICROTATOBIOTES PHILIP, 1956.*

(Canad. Jour. Microbiol., *2*, 1956, 261.)

Mic.ro.ta.to.bi.o'tes. Gr. sup.adj. *microtatus* smallest; Gr. noun *biote* life; M.L. fem.pl.n. *Microtatobiotes* smallest living things.

Includes the smallest of the living things. All are manifested by a dependence on other living organisms for their growth and multiplication. Parasitism is axiomatic since there is no way to determine if there are free-living forms. Most of these organisms occur intracellularly; *Rickettsia quintana* Schmincke of trench fever is an example of extracellular growth in its host, the body louse. A few of the visible forms are known to occur intranuclearly. Characteristic, intracellular inclusion bodies are often associated with the smaller agents. Hosts are represented from the highest members of the plant and animal kingdoms to the lowliest of microbial life. Some species utilize both intermediate and definitive hosts for their propagation. The largest members are the rickettsia-like organisms which are often pleomorphic, including coccoid to filamentous forms, while others show morula-like clusters of elementary bodies occurring as one or up to twenty colonies in an infected cell. Some species show larger ellipsoidal granules with a fairly compact matrix of as much as 2 microns in diameter termed initial bodies from which, in most instances, the groups of smaller elementary bodies are believed to be derived though no life cycle is postulated (Coles, Ann. N. Y. Acad. Sci., *56*, 1953, 458). At least three of these larger species, visible under the light microscope, have phases which pass through coarse or medium filters, e.g., *Coxiella burnetii* Philip of Q fever.

The small members grade downward to filterable virus particles susceptible of measurement only by physico-chemical techniques and by special preparation under the electron microscope. Special staining procedures are required for forms visible under the light microscope and for studying characteristic pathologic reactions or associated inclusion bodies in the tissues of affected hosts. Special tissue-culture techniques have been developed for the more adequate investigation of many of the species.

Two orders are included in Class *Microtatobiotes*.

Key to the orders of class **Microtatobiotes.**

I. Individual organisms are not ultramicroscopic except perhaps in rare filterable phases and are usually more than 0.1 micron in diameter. Parasites of members of the animal kingdom.

Order I. *Rickettsiales*, p. 934.

II. Individual organisms are usually ultramicroscopic and filterable. Except for a few pox viruses of animals and a few plant viruses, the virus particles are less than 0.1 micron in diameter. Parasites of both the plant and animal kingdoms.

Order II. *Virales*, p. 985.

---

* Prepared and edited by Dr. Cornelius B. Philip, U. S. Public Health Service, Rocky Mountain Laboratory, Hamilton, Montana.

ORDER I. RICKETTSIALES BUCHANAN AND BUCHANAN, 1938, emend. GIESZCZKIEWICZ, 1939.

(Buchanan and Buchanan, Bacteriology, 4th ed., New York, 1938, 49; Gieszczykiewicz, Bull. Intern. Acad. Polon. Sci., Classe Math., B (1), 1939, 9–30.)

Ri.ckett.si.a'les. M.L. fem.pl.n. *Rickettsiaceae* type family of the order; *-ales* ending to denote an order; M.L. fem.pl.n. *Rickettsiales* the *Rickettsiaceae* order.

Small, rod-shaped, coccoid and often pleomorphic microorganisms occurring as elementary bodies which are usually intracellular but which may occasionally be facultatively or exclusively extracellular. May also develop larger "initial bodies" as intracellular, spherical or less regular inclusions. Intracytoplasmic forms may be diffuse, compacted into colonies or morulae and may be located in special situations. Usually non-filterable. Gram-negative. Cultivated outside the host only in living tissues, embryonated chicken eggs or rarely in media containing body fluids. Parasitic organisms almost always intimately associated with not only reticulo-endothelial and vascular endothelial cells or erythrocytes in vertebrates, but also often in invertebrates which may act as vectors. The intracellular parasites of *Protozoa* and other invertebrates are provisionally assigned here also. May cause diseases in man or other animals or both. Seldom kill the invertebrate hosts.

Key to the families of order **Rickettsiales.**

I. Parasites, intracellular or intimately associated with tissue cells other than erythrocytes or with certain organs in arthropods; rarely extracellular in arthropods.
   A. Frequently cause diseases of vertebrates. Transmitted by arthropod vectors.
   Family I. Rickettsiaceae, p. 934.
   B. Intracellular parasites found in tissues of vertebrates. Not known to be transmitted by arthropod vectors.
   Family II. Chlamydiaceae, p. 957.
II. Parasites, intracellular or facultatively extracellular; found characteristically in or on the erythrocytes of vertebrates, exceptionally in fixed-tissue cells.
   A. Small, rod-shaped, bacteria-like cells. At least one species, when cultured, may show a single, polar flagellum. Arthropod transmission established for some members of the family.
   Family III. Bartonellaceae, p. 968.
   B. Very small, virus-like particles occurring in the erythrocytes of vertebrates. Transmitted by arthropods.
   Family IV. Anaplasmataceae, p. 980.

FAMILY I. RICKETTSIACEAE PINKERTON, 1936.*

(Parasitology, *28*, 1936, 186.)

Ri.ckett.si.a'ce.ae. M.L. fem.n. *Rickettsia* type genus of the family; *-aceae* ending to denote a family; M.L. fem.pl.n. *Rickettsiaceae* the *Rickettsia* family.

* Revised by Dr. Cornelius B. Philip, Rocky Mountain Laboratory, Hamilton, Montana, January, 1954, from the original by Dr. Ida A. Bengtson, Sixth Edition of the MANUAL.

Small, rod-shaped, ellipsoidal, coccoid and diplococcus-shaped, often pleomorphic organisms which are often intimately associated with arthropod tissues, usually in an intracellular position. Gram-negative. The species pathogenic for vertebrates have not been cultivated to date in cell-free media. May be parasitic in man and other animals causing disease (typhus and related ills) that may be transmitted by invertebrate vectors (chiefly lice, fleas, ticks and mites). Information is still inadequate for the systematic assignment of many of the species which inhabit arthropod hosts and which were originally described in this family.

Key to the tribes of family Rickettsiaceae.

I. Adapted to existence in arthropods; vertebrate hosts include man; cells rod-shaped, ellipsoidal, coccoid and diplococcoid; rarely filamentous.

Tribe I. *Rickettsieae*, p. 935.

II. Only a few species adapted to invertebrate existence; pathogenic for certain mammals but not for man; cells spherical, occasionally pleomorphic.

Tribe II. *Ehrlichieae*, p. 948.

III. Adapted to existence in arthropods as symbiotes but not in vertebrates as highly pathogenic parasites; cells pleomorphic, coccoid to short or long and curved rods, or even filamentous.

Tribe III. *Wolbachieae*, p. 952.

TRIBE I. RICKETTSIEAE PHILIP, TRIB. NOV.

(*Rickettsiaceae* (sic) Philip, Ann. N. Y. Acad. Sci., *56*, 1953, 486; *Rickettsieae* Philip (*nomen nudum*), Canad. Jour. Microbiol., *2*, 1956, 262.)

Ri.ckett.si′e.ae. M.L. fem.n. *Rickettsia* type genus of the tribe; *-eae* ending to denote a tribe; M.L. fem.pl.n. *Rickettsieae* the *Rickettsia* tribe.

Small, pleomorphic, mostly intracellular organisms adapted to existence in arthropods and pathogenic for suitable vertebrate hosts.

Key to the genera of tribe Rickettsieae.

I. Non-filterable; produce typhus-like rash and usually *Proteus* X (Weil-Felix) agglutinins in man.

Genus I. *Rickettsia*, p. 935.

II. Filterable; produce neither rash nor Weil-Felix agglutinins in man.

Genus II. *Coxiella*, p. 947.

Genus I. Rickettsia da Rocha-Lima, 1916.

(Da Rocha-Lima, Berl. klin. Wochnschr., *53*, 1916, 567; *Dermacentroxenus* Wolbach, Jour. Med. Res., *41*, 1919–20, 87; *Rochalimaea* Macchiavello, Prim. Reunion Interamer. del Tifo, Mexico, 1947, 410; *Zinssera* Macchiavello, *ibid.*, 416.)

Ri.ckett′si.a. M.L. fem.n. *Rickettsia* named for H. T. Ricketts, one of the discoverers of the organisms bearing his name, who eventually lost his life while studying typhus infection in Mexico.

Small, often pleomorphic, rod-shaped to coccoid organisms which usually occur intracytoplasmically in lice, fleas, ticks and mites. Occasionally occur extracellularly in gut lumen. Non-filterable. Gram-negative. Have not been cultivated in cell-free media. Pathogenic species parasitic on man and other animals. Cause mild to severe typhus-like infections in appropriate vertebrate hosts of arthropod vectors; intracytoplasmic, occasionally intranuclear in tissues. Etiological agents of epidemic typhus, murine or endemic typhus, Rocky Mountain spotted fever, tsutsugamushi disease, rickettsialpox and other diseases. Many related organisms, described as symbiotes in arthropods not pathogenic for vertebrates, have been assigned here, but information is much less complete than for the pathogenic forms, and their congeneracy with the type species is uncertain. Phylogenetic relationships remain to be established. (Weyer (Acta Tropica, *11*, 1954, 194) has recently used comparative growth in human-body lice and meal-worms as a means of studying the relationships of strains of various rickettsias.)

The type species is *Rickettsia prowazekii* da Rocha-Lima.*

Key to the species of genus **Rickettsia**.

I. Grow in embryonated chicken eggs; exhibit intracellular parasitism; *Proteus* OX agglutinins are stimulated in human hosts.
  A. Intracytoplasmic only; transmitted by insects or trombiculid mites.
    1. Transmitted by insect vectors, but there is no transovarial transmission; OX_{19} agglutinins but no eschar produced in human hosts (Subgenus A, *Rickettsia*).
      a. Louse-borne; animal reservoir in man.
                1. *Rickettsia prowazekii.*
      aa. Chiefly flea-borne; animal reservoir in rodents.
                2. *Rickettsia typhi.*
    2. Transmitted by trombiculid-mite vectors; transovarial transmission; OXK agglutinins and often eschar and adenitis produced in human hosts (Subgenus B, *Zinssera*).
                3. *Rickettsia tsutsugamushi.*
  B. Intracytoplasmic and intranuclear; transmitted by ticks or small tick-like mites with transovarial transmission; OX_{19} agglutinins (Subgenus C, *Dermacentroxenus*).
    1. No eschar or adenitis produced in man; specific vaccine affords protection.
                4. *Rickettsia rickettsii.*
    2. Eschar and adenitis present; spotted-fever vaccine does not protect.
      a. Tick transmission demonstrated or presumed.
        b. High specific, homologous fixation of complement (So. Europe, Asia and Africa).
                5. *Rickettsia conorii.*
      bb. Complement fixation differs (Australia).
                6. *Rickettsia australis.*
      aa. Dermanyssid mite-borne (only in urban areas of Atlantic Coast, U. S. A.).†
                7. *Rickettsia akari.*
II. Does not grow in embryonated chicken eggs; extracellular growth in gut of body louse; no *Proteus* OX agglutinins, eschar or adenitis produced in human hosts (Subgenus D, *Rochalimaea*).
                8. *Rickettsia quintana.*

---

* The editors of the MANUAL follow Recommendation 27d of the International Bacteriological Code in regard to the endings used for the specific epithets. This calls for the use of the *ii* ending for epithets taken from the name of a man ending in a consonant (except names ending in *er*).

† OX_{19} Weil-Felix test only occasionally positive; transovarial passage of agent in mite vector has been demonstrated in experimental vector *Bdellonyssus bacoti* (Philip and Hughes, Amer. Jour. Trop. Med., *28*, 1948, 697) and in natural vector, *Allodermanyssus sanguineus* (Kiselov and Volchanetskaia, in Pavlovsky et al., Nat. Nidi Hum. Dis. and Regional Epidemiol. (Russian), 1955, 251).

Subgenus A. *Rickettsia* Philip, 1943.

(Amer. Jour. Hyg., *37*, 1943, 307.)

Ri.ckett'si.a. M.L. fem.n. *Rickettsia* named for H. T. Ricketts.

Organisms intracytoplasmic only; insect vectors, no transovarial transmission; OX_{19} agglutinins stimulated, but no eschar in human host.

The type species of the subgenus is *Rickettsia prowazekii* da Rocha-Lima.

1. **Rickettsia prowazekii** da Rocha-Lima, 1916. (Da Rocha-Lima, Berl. klin. Wochnschr., *53*, May 22, 1916, 567; *Rickettsia kairo* da Rocha-Lima, in Kolle and Wassermann, Handb. d. path. Mikroorg., Fischer, Jena, *8*, 1930, 1350; *Rickettsia exanthematotyphi* Kodama, Kitasato Arch. Exp. Med., *9*, 1932, 360; *Rickettsia prowazeki* var. *prowazeki* Pinkerton, Parasitology, *28*, 1936, 186; *Rickettsia prowazeki* subspecies *prowazeki* Philip, Amer. Jour. Hyg., *37*, 1943, 307.)

pro.wa.ze'ki.i. M.L. gen.noun *prowazekii* of Prowazek; named for S. von Prowazek, who lost his life studying typhus fever.

Minute, cocco-bacillary, sometimes ellipsoidal or long, rod-shaped cells which are occasionally filamentous. Often occur in pairs and occasionally in chains. In infected lice the minute coccoid and paired coccoid forms predominate over the short and long rods and over the filamentous forms, which are up to 40 microns in length.* Single elements from yolk sacs under the electron microscope average 0.5 by 1.1 microns with maxima of 0.3 to 0.7 by 0.5 to 2.0 microns. In resistant hosts, clumps resembling morulae have been reported in infected cells resembling those seen in some of the other genera. Within the same smear of infected mammalian cells, the organisms are quite uniform in size and morphology. Occur intracytoplasmically in vascular endothelial cells and in serosal cells. Non-motile. Characteristically colored purplish with Giemsa stain; the two individuals of a pair are connected by a zone of faintly blue-stained material. Colored blue with Castañeda stain and bright red against a blue background with Macchiavello stain. Gram-negative.

Cultivation: Growth occurs in plasma tissue cultures of mammalian cells, in the louse intestine, in modified Maitland media with and without agar and in chorio-allantoic membrane and yolk sac of chick embryo, the latter being currently the medium of choice. Mouse and rat lungs have yielded rich harvests following intranasal inoculation.

Optimum temperature, 32° C. in plasma tissue culture and 35° C. in chick embryo cells.

Resistance to chemical and physical agents: Readily inactivated by heat and chemical agents. Death occurs at 50° C. in 15 to 30 minutes; 0.5 per cent phenol and 0.1 per cent formalin also kill the organism.

Immunology: Immunity prolonged but may not be permanent in man. Indistinguishable from endemic (murine) typhus in cross-immunity tests in guinea pigs, but distinguishable from Rocky Mountain spotted fever and other rickettsial diseases in such tests though there is variable reciprocal or partial cross-immunity. Neutralizing antibodies are found in the serum of recovered guinea pigs and convalescent persons two to three weeks after defervescence. Recrudescence of infection ("Brill's disease") many years after an initial typhus episode without intervention of lice has recently been confirmed. Killed vaccines produced from infected lice, rat lungs and yolk sacs afford a high degree of protection against the disease. Hyperimmune antisera for therapeutic use have been produced in rabbits by injection with infected yolk-sac suspensions and in horses and donkeys with infected mouse-lung suspensions. Attenuated living strains have also been used successfully in human vaccination.

* Gönnert (Zent. f. Bakt., I Abt., Orig., *152*, 1947, 203) describes "atypische Ri. pr.-Formen" with exaggerated pleomorphism and so-called "R-Formen" in lice infected by injection.

Serology: Strains from various parts of the world are closely related as determined by complement fixation, are distinguishable from other rickettsiae by agglutination, complement fixation and precipitin tests, have a common antigenic factor (alkali-stable polysaccharide) with *Proteus* OX_{19} and have a soluble antigen in yolk culture.

Lethal effect: Heavily infected yolk-sac cultures injected intravenously or intra-peritoneally are fatal to white mice in a few hours. The toxin, in neutralization tests, has been shown to be specific and is distinguishable from murine typhus toxin.

Pathogenic for man, apes, monkeys, guinea pigs, cotton rats, gerbilles and the louse (*Pediculus humanus*). Inapparent infections occur in white mice, white rats and rabbits. A characteristic febrile reaction with no mortality and usually without scrotal swelling occurs in the guinea pig. Passage in guinea pigs is accomplished by transfer of blood or brain from infected animals; causes a febrile disease with exanthema and high mortality in man. Does not persist for extended periods in brains of white rats compared to endemic (murine) typhus. A characteristic skin reaction can be produced in recovered rabbits and man.

Source: Observed sparingly in the blood of typhus patients and abundantly in smears of epithelial cells of the intestinal tracts of lice fed on typhus patients.

Habitat: Found in the body louse (*Pediculus humanus* var. *humanus*), head louse (*P. humanus* var. *capitis*) and monkey louse (*Pedicinus longiceps*). The etiological agent of epidemic typhus (European typhus, classical typhus, typhus exanthematicus). Man is the probable animal reservoir.

2. Rickettsia typhi (Wolbach and Todd, 1920) Philip, 1943. (*Dermacentroxenus typhi* Wolbach and Todd (not Tood), Ann. Inst. Past., *34*, 1920, 158; minute intracellular bodies, Mooser, Jour. Inf. Dis., *43*, 1928, 261; *Rickettsia manchuriae* Kodama, Takahashi and Kono, Saikingaku-Zasshi (Jap.), No. 426, 427, Aug. and Sept., 1931; see Kodama, Kono and Takahashi bibliography, Kitasato Arch. Exp. Med., *9*, 1932, 95; *Rickettsia mooseri* Monteiro, Mem. Inst. Butantan, *6*, 1931, 97 (pub. July, 1932);

see Franco do Amaral and Monteiro, bibliography, Mem. Inst. Butantan, *7*, 1932, 367; *Rickettsia exanthematofebri* Kodama, Kitasato Arch. Exp. Med., *9*, 1932, 360; *Rickettsia muricola* Monteiro and Fonseca, Brasil Med., *46*, 1932, 1032; *Rickettsia murina* and *Rickettsia fletcheri* Megaw, Trans. Roy. Soc. Trop. Med. Hyg., *29*, 1935, 105; *Rickettsia prowazeki* var. *mooseri* Pinkerton, Parasitology, *28*, 1936, 185; *Rickettsia prowazeki* subsp. *typhi* Philip, Amer. Jour. Hyg., *37*, 1943, 304; *Rickettsia typhi* Philip, *loc. cit.*; not *Rickettsia typhi* Franco do Amaral and Monteiro, Rev. Sud. Amér. de Méd. et Chirug., *4*, 1933, 806; *Rickettsia murina mooseri* Veintemillas, Tratado sobre rickett-siasis, etc., Bolivia, 1944, 100.)

ty'phi. Gr. noun *typhus* cloud, hence stupor arising from fever; M.L. noun *typhus* fever, typhus; M.L. gen.noun *typhi* of typhus.

Resembles *Rickettsia prowazekii* morphologically and in staining properties but averages slightly smaller, 0.45 by 1.0 micron with individual variation of 0.35 to 0.6 by 0.7 to 1.3 microns, under the electron microscope. Non-motile. Gram-negative.

Giroud (1952) proposed the term "typhus murin tropical" for a virulent form in Equatorial Africa.

Cultivation: May be cultivated in plasma tissue culture of mammalian cells, in modified Maitland media with and without agar, in fleas and lice, in the peritoneal cavities of X-rayed rats, in the lungs of white mice and of white rats following intranasal inoculation, in the lungs of rabbits following intratracheal inoculation and in the chorio-allantoic membrane and the yolk sac of the chick embryo.

Optimum temperature, 35° C. in chick-embryo cells.

Immunology: Prolonged immunity in man and animals following infection. Complete cross immunity between epidemic and endemic typhus in guinea pigs recovered from infections with *Rickettsia prowazekii* and *R. typhi*. No cross immunity between endemic typhus and Rocky Mountain spotted fever, Q fever or tsutsugamushi disease in guinea pigs.

Serology: Distinguishable from the rickettsiae of spotted fever, Q fever and tsutsugamushi disease by complement fixation, agglutination and precipitin tests, less readily from *Rickettsia prowazekii* by these tests. Possesses a common antigenic factor with *Proteus* OX_{19} and a soluble antigen in yolk-sac cultures.

Lethal effect: Heavily infected yolk-sac cultures injected intravenously or intraperitoneally are fatal to white mice in a few hours. Toxin neutralization test in white mice is specific and distinct from that of epidemic typhus toxin.

Pathogenic for man, apes, monkeys, rabbits, guinea pigs, white rats, eastern cotton rat, white mice and gerbilles. Other susceptible animals include the woodchuck, house mouse, meadow mouse, white-footed mouse, old-field mouse, cotton mouse, golden mouse, wild rat (*Rattus norvegicus*), wood rat, rice rat, flying squirrel, gray squirrel, fox squirrel, gopher, cottontail rabbit, swamp rabbit, chipmunk, skunk, opossum and cat. Persists for at least a year in rat brains in contradistinction to *Rickettsia prowazekii* and members of the subgenus *Dermacentroxenus*. After intraperitoneal inoculation, a characteristic febrile reaction occurs in the guinea pig with scrotal swelling without necrosis. Passage in guinea pigs is accomplished by transfer of tunica and testicular washings or of blood from infected animals. Cause of a febrile disease with exanthema in man, producing low mortality.

Source: Observed by Wolbach and Todd (*op. cit.*, 1920, 158) in the endothelial cells of the capillaries, arterioles and veins in sections of skin from cases of Mexican typhus (tabardillo). Also described by Mooser in sections and smears of the proliferated tunica vaginalis of guinea pigs reacting to the virus of Mexican typhus.

Habitat: Found in infected rat fleas (*Xenopsylla cheopis, X. astia, Nosopsylla fasciatus*), infected chicken fleas (*Echidnophaga gallinacea*) found on wild rats, and the rat louse (*Polyplax spinulosus*). Will also grow in human lice. Wild rats and field mice act as the animal reservoir of infection. The etiological agent of endemic (murine) typhus which is transmitted to man by the rat flea.

Subgenus B. *Zinssera* Macchiavello, 1947.

(Macchiavello, Prim. Reunion Interamer. del Tifo, Mexico, 1947, 416; *Trombidoxenus* Zhdanov and Korenblit, Jour. Microbiol., Epidemiol. and Immunobiol. (Russian), No. 9, 1950, 42.)

Zins'se.ra. M.L. noun *Zinssera* named for Hans Zinsser, who studied rickettsial agents.

Organisms intracytoplasmic but not intranuclear. Transovarial transmission in trombiculid mite vectors, only the larvae of which are parasitic on vertebrates. Disease in man elicits OXK Weil-Felix serological reactions and is accompanied by adenitis and often by an eschar at point of mite bite.

The type species of the subgenus is *Rickettsia tsutsugamushi* (Hayashi) Ogata.

3. **Rickettsia tsutsugamushi** (Hayashi, 1920) Ogata, 1931.* (*Theileria tsutsugamushi* Hayashi, Jour. Parasit., *7*, 1920, 63; *Rickettsia orientalis* Nagayo, Tamiya, Mitamura and Sato, Jikken Igaku Zasshi, *14*, (May 20) 1930, 8 pp.; *Rickettsia tsutsugamushi* Ogata, Zent. f. Bakt., I Abt., *122*, 1931, 249; *Rickettsia akamushi* Kawamura and Imagawa, Zent. f. Bakt., I Abt., *122*, 1931, 258; *Rickettsia orientalis* var. *schüffneri* Franco do Amaral and Monteiro, Mem. Inst. Butantan, *7*, 1932, 360; *Rickettsia megawi* Franco do Amaral and Monteiro, *loc. cit.*; *Rickettsia megawai* var. *fletcheri* Franco do Amaral and Monteiro, *ibid.*, 361; *Rickettsia tsutsugamushi-orientalis* Kawamura, Nisshin Igaku (Modern Medicine), *23*, 1934, 909; *Rickettsia pseudotyphi* Vervoort, see Donatien and Lestoquard, Acta Conv. Tertii Trop. atque malariae morbis, pars I, 1938, 564; *Rickettsia sumatranus* (sic) Kouwenaar and Wolff, Proc. 6th Pacific Sci. Cong. (1939), *5*, 1942,

---

* The reasons for transferring Hayashi's species from the genus *Theileria* to *Rickettsia* and other questions of nomenclatorial priority in regard to this species are discussed in Manual, 6th ed., 1948, 1089 and 1090 (footnotes).

636; *Rickettsia* (*Rickettsia*) *orientalis* Philip, Amer. Jour. Hyg., *37*, 1943, 305; *Dermacentroxenus orientalis* Moshkovskiy, Uspekhi Souremennoi Biologii (Advances in Modern Biology), *19*, 1945, 13; *Rickettsia orientalis* var. *tropica* Hayakawa and Hokari, A comparative study of Japanese and tropical (scrub typhus) tsutsugamushi diseases (*R. orientalis* var. *tropica*), Tokyo, 1947, 35; *Zinssera orientalis* Macchiavello, Prim. Reunion Interamer. del Tifo, Mexico, 1947, 416; *Rickettsia* (*Zinssera*) *tsutsugamushi* Philip, Ann. N. Y. Acad. Sci., *56*, 1953, 487; *Trombidoxenus orientalis* Zhdanov and Korenblit, Jour. Microbiol., Epidemiol. and Immunobiol. (Russian), No. 9., 1950, 42; also see Zhdanov, Opredelitel Virusov Celovska i Zivotmych, Izd. Akad. Med. Nauk, U. S. S. R., Moskau, 1953, 54 and 160.)

tsu.tsu.ga.mu'shi. From two Japanese ideographs transliterated *tsutsuga* something small and dangerous, and *mushi* a creature now known to be a mite.

Small, pleomorphic bacterium-like microorganisms, usually wider and less sharply defined than the cells of *Rickettsia prowazekii*, *R. typhi*, *R. rickettsii* and *Coxiella burnetii*. Ellipsoidal or rod-shaped, often appearing as a diplococcus or as a short bacillus with bipolar staining resembling that of the plague bacillus. Diffusely distributed in the cytoplasm of the cell. 0.3 to 0.5 by 0.8 to 2.0 microns. Non-motile. Colored purplish with Giemsa's stain and red against a blue background with Macchiavello's stain. Stains well with azur III and methylene blue. Gram-negative.

Cultivation: Grows in plasma tissue culture of mammalian cells, on the chorioallantoic membrane and in the yolk sac of the chick embryo and in rabbit testes and in the endothelial cells overlying Descemet's membrane of the rabbit eye. The only species of *Rickettsia* known to separate in the interface during ether treatment after harvest of yolk sacs. Weyer (Acta Tropica, *11*, 1954, 194) has reported the unusual difficulty of growth in inoculated arthropods.

Resistance to chemical and physical agents: Readily inactivated by heat and chemical agents. Destroyed by 0.1 per cent formalin and 0.5 per cent phenol. Killed in 10 minutes at 50° C.

Immunology: Immunity conferred by infection, which is probably influenced by strain differences, appears less complete than that found in typhus and Rocky Mountain spotted fever. Strains from several different areas have been found to cross immunize in guinea pigs, but the true relationship of the disease occurring in different localities remains to be determined. Reciprocal cross immunity between mite strains and human strains has been demonstrated in rabbits, hamsters and mice.

Serology: Antigens from different strains vary in sensitivity when tested by complement fixation with immune sera. There are probably a number of different types on the basis of complement fixation with immune sera. Possesses a common antigenic factor with *Proteus* OXK.

Pathogenic for man, monkeys, gibbons, guinea pigs, hamsters, rats, voles, mice, gerbilles, rabbits (by intraocular injection) and chick embryo. There is a wide variation in the virulence of different strains for laboratory animals: infection with a few is established with difficulty while other strains may cause a high mortality. The white mouse is the laboratory animal of choice. Infection may persist in the brains of white rats for at least 98 days. A febrile reaction may occur in guinea pigs. Passage in guinea pigs and mice is accomplished by inoculation of peritoneal washings, spleen or blood from an infected animal, passage in rabbits by intraocular or intratesticular inoculation of blood, lymph node or organ emulsions of infected native animals. Ascites and enlarged spleen, often with a fibrinous deposit, are characteristic. A specific toxin, lethal for white mice, has been reported in the Gilliam strain. In man an eschar often develops at the site of the mite bite with accompanying adenopathy. A febrile reaction with exanthema occurs, and mortality is variable in different localities but remains about the same in a given focus. In rabbits, infection of Descemet's membrane follows intraocular injection of infected material.

Source: Observed by Hayashi in smears and sections of the lesion (eschar) at the site of the mite bite and in smears and sections of the adjacent lymph nodes from cases of the disease; also observed by Ogata (Zent. f. Bakt., I Abt., Orig., *163*, 1955, 150) as early as 1927 in preparations of infected rabbit testicles and by Nagayo et al. (*op. cit.*, 1930) in the endothelial cells overlying Descemet's membrane in rabbits inoculated intraocularly with infectious material.

Habitat: Found in trombiculid mites (particularly *Trombicula akamushi* and *T.* (or var.?) *deliensis*). Passes through the mite ova to the next generation. Only the larvae are parasitic on vertebrates. Reser-

voir animal hosts are probably wild rodents, including house and field rats, mice and voles, and probably some birds in which infection may be persistent. The etiological agent of tsutsugamushi disease and of scrub typhus (for numerous other designations of the disease, see Farner and Katsampes, U. S. Naval Med. Bull., *43*, 1944, 800). Many human cases have recently been discovered well south of the classic foci in Japan, and Sasa (Jap. Jour. Exp. Med., *24*, 1954, 335) discusses four epidemiologically distinct "types."

Subgenus C. *Dermacentroxenus* (Wolbach, 1919) Philip, 1943.

Wolbach, Jour. Med. Res., *41*, 1919–20, 87; subgenus *Dermacentroxenus* Philip, Amer. Jour. Hyg., *37*, 1943, 304; *Acaroxenus* Zhdanov and Korenblit, Jour. Microbiol., Epidemiol. and Immunobiol. (Russian), No. 9, 1950, 42; *Ixodoxenus* Zhdanov, Opredelitel Virusov Celovska i Zivotmych, Izd. Akad. Med. Nauk, U.S.S.R., Moskau, 1953, 51 and 155; *Gamasoxenus* Zhdanov, *ibid.*, 159; see Philip, Canad. Jour. Microbiol., *2*, 1956, 264.)

Der.ma.cen.tro′xe.nus. M.L. noun *Dermacentor* a genus of ticks; Gr. noun *xenus* host, guest; M.L. mas.n. *Dermacentroxenus* tick dweller.

Organisms capable of intranuclear parasitism. Produce a typhus-like disease. Transmitted by acarid vectors.

The type species of the subgenus is *Rickettsia rickettsii* (Wolbach) Brumpt.

4. Rickettsia rickettsii (Wolbach, 1919) Brumpt, 1922. (*Dermacentroxenus rickettsi* (sic) Wolbach, Jour. Med. Res., *41*, 1919–20, 87; *Rickettsia rickettsi* (sic) Brumpt, Précis de Parasitologie, 3rd ed., 1922, 757; *Rickettsia brasiliensis* Monteiro, Mem. Inst. Butantan, *6*, 1931, 3; *Rickettsia typhi* Franco do Amaral and Monteiro, Rev. Sud. Amér. de Méd. et Chirurg., *4*, 1933, 806; *Dermacentroxenus rickettsi* var. *brasiliensis* Pinkerton, Parasitology, *28*, 1936, 186; *Rickettsia (Dermacentroxenus) rickettsi* Philip, Amer. Jour. Hyg., *37*, 1943, 304; *Rickettsia colombiensis* Veintemillas, Tratado sobre rickettsiasis, etc., Bolivia, 1944, 102; *Ixodoxenus rickettsi* Zhdanov, Opredelitel Virusov Celovska i Zivotmych, Izd. Akad. Med. Nauk, U.S.S.R., Moskau, 1953, 51 and 155.)

ri.ckett′si.i. M.L. gen.noun *rickettsii* of Ricketts; named for Howard Taylor Ricketts, who first saw and described the organisms causing Rocky Mountain spotted fever.

Minute, paired organisms surrounded by a narrow clear zone or halo; often lanceolate, resembling in appearance a minute pair of pneumococci. Average 0.6 by 1.2 microns

under the electron microscope. Non-motile. In smears of mammalian tissues there occur, in addition to the lanceolate forms, slender rod-shaped forms stained blue with Giemsa stain, sometimes exhibiting polar granules stained purplish or reddish. There are also minute, pale blue-staining, rounded forms. In the tick there are three forms: (1) pale blue bacillary forms curved and club-shaped, (2) smaller, bluish rods with deeply staining chromatoid granules, and (3) more deeply staining, purplish, lanceolate forms. A very minute form may appear in tightly packed masses in the nuclei of the cells. Occurs in the cytoplasm and nucleus in all types of cells in the tick including sperm cells; also occurs in mammals in the vascular endothelium, in macrophages, in the serosal cells of the peritoneal cavity and in smooth-muscle cells of arteriolar walls. In yolk-sac cultures and in the Maitland media cultures, bacillary forms often occur in pairs. In single smears from infected yolk sacs, the cells are rather uniform in size and morphology and are definitely larger than those of *Rickettsia prowazekii* and *R. typhi*. They also grow more sparsely. Stain blue with the Castañeda stain and bright red against a blue background of tissue with the Macchiavello stain. Gram-negative.

Cultivation: May be cultivated in plasma tissue culture of mammalian cells, in Maitland media with and without agar, on the chorio-allantoic membrane, in the yolk sac of the chick embryo and in ticks. Growth and toxin production are enhanced in killed embryo continued in incubation 24 hours. Growth in intrarectally injected human-body lice destroys intestinal epithelium and may destroy these insects (Weyer, Acta Tropica, *11*, 1954, 193).

Optimum temperature, 32° C. in plasma tissue culture and 35° C. in chick embryo cells. Killed in 10 minutes at 50° C.

Resistance to chemical and physical agents: Readily inactivated by heat and chemical agents. Destroyed by 0.5 per cent phenol and 0.1 per cent formalin. Destroyed by ordinary desiccation in about 10 hours.

Immunology: Prolonged immunity in man and animals after recovery from infection. Killed vaccines produced from infected ticks and from infected yolk sacs afford considerable protection against the disease. Therapeutic antisera have been produced by the injection of rabbits with infected tick and yolk-sac suspensions. No cross immunity between spotted fever in guinea pigs recovered from infections with *Rickettsia rickettsii* and typhus in guinea pigs recovered from infections with *R. prowazekii* and *R. typhi*. Cross immunity between spotted fever in guinea pigs recovered from infections with *R. rickettsii* and boutonneuse fever in guinea pigs recovered from infections with *R. conorii*. Spotted-fever vaccine does not experimentally protect against the boutonneuse-fever group of infections in the Mediterranean and other Eastern Hemisphere areas.

Serology: Distinguishable from *Rickettsia prowazekii* and *R. typhi* by complement fixation and by agglutination with specific antigens. Because of confusing cross fixation, the complement-fixation test is inadequate to distinguish between agents of the subgenus *Dermacentroxenus*.

Pathogenic for man, monkeys and guinea pigs. Rabbits and white rats are moderately susceptible. Animals susceptible in varying degrees include species of ground squirrels, tree squirrels, chipmunks, cottontail rabbits, jack rabbits, snowshoe hares, marmots, sheep, dogs, wood rats, weasels, meadow mice and deer mice. In Brazil, the opossum, rabbit, dog and cavy have been found naturally infected, and the Brazilian plains dog, capybara, coati and certain bats are also susceptible. Does not persist in brains of rats and ground squirrels but has been recovered from node tissues of man convalescent one year (Parker et al., Jour. Immunol., *73*, 1954, 383).

A febrile reaction occurs in guinea pigs with typical scrotal lesions, involving petechial hemorrhages in the skin, which may become necrotic. Virulent strains kill 80 to 90 per cent of the animals, milder strains kill 20 to 25 per cent. Passage in guinea pigs is accomplished by transfer of blood, spleen or tunica from infected animals. A febrile reaction accompanied by exanthema occurs in man. Mortality is consistently high in some localities, low in others.

Comments: In 1906 Ricketts (Jour. Amer. Med. Assoc., *47*, 1906, 33) infected monkeys and guinea pigs with blood from patients suffering from Rocky Mountain spotted fever. Later in the same year it was demonstrated independently by Ricketts (*ibid.*, 358) and by King (U. S. Public Health Reports, *21*, 1906, 863) that the wood tick *Dermacentor andersoni* was the primary vector in the Rocky Mountain area. (See Howard Taylor Ricketts, 1870–1910, Chicago, Univ. of Chicago Press, 1911, 333.)

Source: Observed by Ricketts (Jour. Amer. Med. Assoc., *52*, 1909, 379) in the blood of guinea pigs and monkeys experimentally infected with Rocky Mountain spotted fever and in the salivary glands, alimentary sacs and ovaries of infected ticks as well as in their ova.

Habitat: Found in the infected wood tick (*Dermacentor andersoni*), the dog ticks (*D. variabilis* and *Rhipicephalus sanguineus*), the rabbit ticks (*Haemaphysalis leporis-palustris*, *D. parumapertus* and *Otobius lagophilus*) and in *Amblyomma brasiliense*, *A. cajennense*, *A. striatum*, *A. americanum* and *Ixodes dentatus*. A number of ticks belonging to the genera *Amblyomma, Dermacentor, Rhipicephalus, Ornithodoros* and *Haemaphysalis* have been experimentally infected. The agent is transmissible through tick ova. The etiological agent of Rocky Mountain spotted fever, São Paulo exanthematic typhus of Brazil, Tobia fever of Colombia and spotted fevers of Minas Gerais and Mexico, which are all transmitted to man by the bite of infected ticks. Gould and Miesse (Proc. Soc. Exp. Biol. and Med., *85*, 1954, 558) reported the first isolation in the U. S. A. of identified infection in a *Microtus* field mouse.

5. Rickettsia conorii Brumpt, 1932. (*Rickettsia conori* (sic) Brumpt, Compt. rend. Soc. Biol., Paris, *110*, 1932, 1199; *Rickettsia megawi* var. *pijperi* Franco do Amaral and Monteiro, Mem. Inst. Butantan, *7*, 1932, 361; *Rickettsia blanci* Caminopetros, 1er Cong. Internat. Hyg. Mediterr., Rapports et Compt. rend., *2*, 1932, 202; *Dermacentroxenus rickettsi* var. *pijperi* Mason and Alexander, Onderst. Jour. Vet. Sci. and Anim. Ind., *13*, 1939, 74; *Dermacentroxenus rickettsi* var. *conori* Mason and Alexander, *loc. cit.*; *Rickettsia* (*Dermacentroxenus*) *conori* Philip, Amer. Jour. Hyg., *37*, 1943, 307; *Dermacentroxenus conori* Steinhaus, Insect Microbiology, 1946, 339; *Dermacentroxenus pijperi* Macchiavello, Prim. Reunion Interamer. del Tifo, Mexico, 1947, 414; *Ixodoxenus conori* Zhdanov, Opredelitel Virusov Celovska i Zivotmych, Izd. Akad. Med. Nauk, U.S.S.R., Moskau, 1953, 52 and 157.)

co.no′ri.i. M.L. gen.noun *conorii* of Conor; named for A. Conor, the first to describe adequately boutonneuse fever.

Resembles *Rickettsia rickettsii*. In the tick, diplococcoid and diplobacillary forms predominate, though they are smaller and more coccoid when they occur in compact masses. In tissue cultures the organisms are lanceolate, diplococcoid and diplobacillary, occurring in the nuclei as well as in the cytoplasm of the cells. 0.3 to 0.4 by 1.0 to 1.75 microns. Non-motile. Stain purplish with Giemsa's stain, blue with Castañeda's stain and bright red with a blue background with Macchiavello's stain. Gram-negative.

Cultivation: May be cultivated in plasma tissue culture of mammalian cells, in modified Maitland media and in the yolk sacs of chick embryos. Weyer (Acta Tropica, *11*, 1954, 194) found differences in growth of Kenya and South African strains compared to a classic strain from the Mediterranean area.

Immunology: The disease is related immunologically to Rocky Mountain spotted fever with which it cross immunizes, but spotted-fever vaccine does not protect against the Mediterranean, Asiatic and South African strains of boutonneuse fever. Attempts to produce potent vaccines either from tick or culture sources have so far been ineffective.

Serology: Cross fixation occurs with *R. rickettsii* by complement-fixation test. Possesses a common antigenic factor with *Proteus* OX_{19} and OX_2 but not with OXK.

Pathogenic for man and guinea pigs. Also pathogenic in varying degrees for dogs, horses, spermophiles, monkeys, rabbits, gerbilles and white mice. Boutonneuse fever is a much less virulent infection for the guinea pig than is Rocky Mountain spotted fever. A temperature reaction, accompanied by scrotal swelling, occurs but there is no sloughing. There is practically no mortality. Passsage in guinea pigs is accomplished most effectively by transfer of testicular washings. In man there occur localized primary sores (taches noires) at the site of the tick bite and inflammatory reactions in the regional lymph nodes. A febrile reaction with exanthema occurs, and mortality is low.

Source: Observed by Caminopetros (Compt. rend. Soc. Biol., Paris, *110*, 1932, 344) in smears from the tunica vaginalis of guinea pigs inoculated with infected dog ticks (*Rhipicephalus sanguineus*).

Habitat: Found in the brown-dog tick (*Rhipicephalus sanguineus*) and also in the ticks *Amblyomma hebraeum, Haemaphysalis leachii, Rhipicephalus appendiculatus, R. evertsi* and *Boophilus decoloratus*. Transmissible through the ova of ticks to following generations. The probable animal reservoir is the dog in the Mediterranean area and, in addition, perhaps veld rodents in South Africa. The etiological agent of boutonneuse fever in man (also known as eruptive, Mediterranean or Marseilles fever and probably Indian tick typhus, Kenya typhus and South African tick-bite fever, though the identity of the latter with boutonneuse fever has been questioned).

6. **Rickettsia australis** Philip, 1950. (Agent of North Queensland tick typhus, Andrew, Bonnin and Williams, Med. Jour. Australia, 1946 (Aug. 24), 253; *Rickettsia (Dermacentroxenus) australis* Philip*, in Pullen, Communicable Diseases, Lea & Febiger Co., 1950, 786; *Ixodoxenus australis* Zhdanov, Opredelitel Virusov Celovska i Zivotmych, Izd. Akad. Med. Nauk, U.S. S.R., Moskau, 1953, 52 and 159.) aus.tra'lis. L. adj. *australis* southern.

Minute, ellipsoidal or coccoidal forms resembling *Rickettsia prowazekii* morphologically and in staining properties. Non-motile. Gram-negative.

Cultivation: In yolk sacs of developing chicken eggs, at 32° to 35° C., poor to moderate growth reveals cocco-bacillary, short bacillary and diplo-bacillary forms. As in other members of the subgenus *Dermacentroxenus*, richer growth is reported on Zinsser agar tissue culture, in which both intracytoplasmic and intranuclear parasitism is readily demonstrated.

Immunology: Duration of immunity is unknown in man in this recently discovered malady. Recovered guinea pigs remain solidly immune for at least 8 months and may show partial to complete immunity within 50 days to heterologous challenge with strains of *Rickettsia conorii* and *R. typhi* but no immunity to *R. conorii* 8 months or longer after recovery. No cross immunity was found with *R. tsutsugamushi* in white mice.

Serology: Convalescent sera of patients contained agglutinins for *Proteus* OX$_{19}$ or OX$_2$ but none for OXK. The sera failed to fix complement in the presence of rickettsial antigens of epidemic or murine typhus,

boutonneuse fever and American spotted fever, though homologous fixation was reported. Sera of recovered rabbits or guinea pigs have shown this agent to be a distinct member of the spotted-fever group in complement-fixation tests and to have a higher homologous than heterologous reaction in certain of these tests.

Pathogenic for man; infected guinea pigs develop fever and scrotal reactions. White mice do not usually show signs of infection. In contrast to *R. typhi*, *R. australis* does not persist in the brains of white rats, though male rats may develop scrotal reactions when injected with cultures.

Lethal effect: Intravenous injection of laboratory mice with cultures has not demonstrated the presence of a toxin, in this respect resembling *Rickettsia akari*.

Source: Observed by Andrew et al. (*op. cit.*, 1946, 253) in smears of peritoneal exudate of white mice injected with blood of two patients in North Queensland, Australia.

Habitat: Tick transmission has not been demonstrated but has been presumed by the finding of either larval or adult *Ixodes holocyclus* on a few patients. The occurrence of primary eschars on patients implicates a probable acarine vector, but *Dermacentor andersoni*, a natural vector of *Rickettsia rickettsii*, does not experimentally transmit *R. australis*. Complement-fixing antibodies have been found in four kinds of native Queensland marsupials and in one species of rat.

7. **Rickettsia akari** Huebner et al., 1946. (Huebner, Jellison and Pomerantz, U. S. Public Health Rep., *61*, 1946, 1682; *Rickettsia (Dermacentroxenus) akari* Philip and Hughes, Amer. Jour. Trop. Med., *28*, 1948, 705; *Acaroxenus varioleidis* (sic) Zhdanov and Korenblit, Jour. Microbiol., Epidemiol. and Immunobiol. (Russian), No. 9, 1950, 42; *Gamasoxenus muris* Zhdanov, Opredelitel

---

* Publishing date, June 16, 1950. By coincidence this name, including the same subgenus, was published by Zhdanov and Korenblit the same year (Jour. Microbiol., Epidemiol. and Immunobiol. (Russian), No. 9, 1950 (reprint states September), 42). This name had also been used by these authors in a report to a scientific conference (Ukranian Int. imeni Mechnikov, Khar'kov, October 11, 1949), although, according to Rule 11, it was not effectively published at that time so far as known.

Virusov Celovska i Zivotmych, Izd. Akad. Med. Nauk, U.S.S.R., Moskau, 1953, 52 and 159.)

a′ka.ri. Gr. neut.n. *akari* a mite.

Minute diplobacilli and bipolarly stained rods. Resemble typical rickettsiae morphologically with an average size, under the electron microscope, of 0.6 by 0.9 to 1.4 microns; very similar to *Rickettsia rickettsii* from yolk-sac cultures. Occur intracytoplasmically; have been seen intranuclearly in yolk-sac cells. Non-motile. Stain well by Macchiavello's method, the organisms appearing bright red against a blue background. Stain poorly with methylene blue. Gram-negative.

Cultivation: Grows in the yolk sac of the chick embryo and in intrarectally injected body lice. No growth on artificial culture media.

Immunology: Guinea pigs recovered from rickettsialpox of human origin are immune to infection with strains isolated from infected mites and from house mice. There is partial to complete experimental cross immunity with other members of the subgenus *Dermacentroxenus*.

Serology: Antigens prepared from infected yolk sacs are highly specific except for cross reactions with Rocky Mountain spotted fever group antigens. Sera from convalescent patients fixed complement with the homologous antigen and usually with Rocky Mountain spotted fever antigens though at a lower titer. A rising titer against *Proteus* OX$_{19}$ has been shown in some convalescent cases.

Pathogenic for man with initial erythematous focal lesion at the site of the mite bite and with adenopathy followed by fever and appearance of macular rash. No mortality. Experimental infections have been produced in white mice and guinea pigs by the inoculation of infected blood (irregularly), infected liver and spleen suspensions, infected brain, infected lymph nodes, tunica washings of infected animals and of infected yolk sacs. Guinea pigs show marked scrotal reactions. It has not been found pathogenic for monkeys, thus distinguishing it from *Rickettsia conorii*. It is also probably more pathogenic for white mice than is *R. conorii*.

Source: Isolated from the blood of a human case of rickettsialpox in New York City.

Habitat: Found in the tissues of human cases and of the mite *Allodermanyssus sanguineus* Hirst, an ectoparasite of rodents. House mice have also been found to be naturally infected. The etiological agent of human rickettsialpox (vesicular rickettsiosis). Known only in cities on the eastern seaboard of the U. S. A. and in unnamed urban centers of the U.S.S.R. (an original report is by Zhdanov, Korenblit, Lavruskin, Alexandrova and Kiselov, Vrachevnoye Delo (Physician's Work), No. 10, 1950; also see Zhdanov, Communicable Diseases of Humans. Medgiz, Moscow, 1955, 305–366 (*Gamasoxenus murinus*) and Zdrodovskiy and Golinevitch, Treatise on Rickettsia and Rickettsiosis, Medgiz, Moscow, 1956, 276–286 (*Dermacentroxenus murinus*)). As in the U. S. A., strains of infection were reported from patients, house mice (also gray rats, *R. norvegicus*) and the same mite vector, *A. sanguineus* (see Kiselov and Volchanetskaia, in Pavlovsky et al., Nat. Nidi Hum. Dis. and Regional Epidemiol. (Russian), 1955, 248–252).

Subgenus D. *Rochalimaea* Macchiavello, 1947.

(Subgenus *Rocha-Limae* (sic) Macchiavello, Prim. Reunion Interamer. del Tifo, Mexico, 1947, 410; *Welhynia* (sic) Zhdanov and Korenblit, Jour. Microbiol., Epidemiol. and Immunobiol. (Russian), No. 9, 1950, 42; *Wolhynia* Zhdanov, Opredelitel Virusov Celovska i Zivotmych, Izd. Akad. Med. Nauk, U.S.S.R., Moskau, 1953, 55 and 164.)

The subgeneric name *Rochalimaea* Macchiavello was validly published and was transferred to the genus *Rickettsia* (Philip, Canad. Jour. Microbiol., *2*, 1956, 265) even though it was originally proposed as a subgenus of *Burnetia* (=*Coxiella*) and wrongly associated thereby with *Coxiella burnetii* (Derrick) Philip.

Ro.cha.li.mae′a. M.L. fem.n. *Rochalimaea* named for H. da Rocha-Lima, who studied rickettsial agents in human-body lice.

Organisms exclusively extracellular in the gut of, and non-pathogenic for, the human-body louse, which acts as the vector of this agent of trench fever.

The type species of the subgenus is *Rickettsia quintana* Schmincke.

8. Rickettsia quintana Schmincke, 1917. (Schmincke, Münch. med. Wochnschr., *64*, 1917, 961; *Rickettsia pediculi* Munk and da Rocha-Lima, Münch. med. Wochnschr., *64*, 1917, 1423; *Rickettsia wolhynica* Jungmann and Kuczynski, Ztschr. f. klin. Med., *85*, 1918, 261; *Rickettsia weigli* Mosing, Arch. Inst. Past., Tunis, *25*, 1936, 380; *Burnetia* (*Rocha-Limae*) *wolhynica* Macchiavello, Prim. Reunion Interamer. del Tifo, Mexico, 1947, 410; *Burnetia* (*Rocha-Limae*) *weigli* Macchiavello, *loc. cit.*; *Wolhynia quintanae* (sic) Zhdanov and Korenblit, Jour Microbiol., Epidemiol. and Immunobiol. (Russian), No. 9, 1950, 42.)

quin.ta′na. M.L. adj. *quintanus* fifth; referring to five-day fever, one of the colloquial names of the fever caused by this species.

Coccoid or ellipsoidal organisms, often occurring in pairs. More plump and stain more deeply with Giemsa's stain than does *R. prowazekii*. 0.2 to 0.4 micron (da Rocha-Lima). In lice, appear as short rods, frequently occurring in pairs and often bipolarly stained. Occur extracellularly in the region of the epithelial lining of the lumen of the gut of the louse. Non-motile. Stain reddish violet with Giemsa's stain. Gram-negative.

Cultivation: Has not been cultivated in tissue culture, yolk sacs of chick embryos or any other cell-free medium (report of cultivation of *Rickettsia pediculi* and *R. rochalimae*, which are regarded as identical with this species, on cell-free media remains to be confirmed). Grows in body lice injected intrarectally or fed on patients, but unlike most other *Rickettsia spp.*, it was not found to grow in living meal-worm larvae (Weyer, Acta Tropica, *11*, 1954, 207).

Serology: Possesses no common antigenic factor with *Proteus* strains. No practical serological procedure has been developed, though louse guts and louse feces have been reported to provide antigens for agglutination tests. Laboratory diagnosis, therefore, additional to clinical and epidemiological data, is largely dependent for confirmation on the demonstration of extracellular rickettsiae in carefully selected louse stocks fed either during the human febrile episode or later.

Pathogenic for man, causing rash and recurrent fever. Blood of cases has been shown to be infectious on transfer to volunteers as long as 4, 5 and even 8 years following clinical recovery. Mooser and his colleagues, among others, have repeatedly infected lice fed during such periods of latency in apparently healthy persons. Man, therefore, is the obvious reservoir of the infection. Codeleoncini infected the baboon, and Mooser and Weyer found rhesus monkeys susceptible.

Immunology: Partial immunity is produced after an attack of the disease. The disease is characterized by relapses which may occur as long as 2 to 3 years after the initial attack.

Distinctive characters: Resists a temperature of 60° C. moist heat for 30 minutes or a dry heat of 80° C. for 20 minutes. Resists desiccation in sunlight for 4 months. Has been filtered under certain conditions but not when in plasma or serum. Present in filtrates of infected vaccine sediments and for long periods in the feces of infected lice. Intracutaneous injection of living organisms from lice produces skin lesions in the rabbit which can be inhibited by the use of convalescent serum.

Source: Observed in lice fed on trench-fever patients by Töpfer (Münch. med. Wochnschr., *61*, 1916, 1495).

Habitat: Found in the epithelial lining of the gut of the body louse (*Pediculus humanus* var. *humanus*) where the rickettsiae occur extracellularly; also found in *P. humanus* var. *capitis*. Not transmissible through the ova. The etiological agent of trench fever (Wolhynian fever, shin-bone fever, five-day fever).

Addendum: Two pathogenic agents of importance in the U. S. S. R. have come to attention since this section was prepared:

1) *Dermacentroxenus sibericus* Zdrodovskiy (Zhur. Mikrobiol., Epidemiol., Immunobiol., No. 10, 1949, 19; in Zhdanov and Korenblit, *ibid.*, 1950, 42, and later articles, *Dermacentroxenus* is reduced to a subgenus under *Rickettsia*), which is probably related to *R. conorii*, was proposed for the tick-borne agent of Siberian tick typhus; rickettsial relationships and an account of the former are most recently provided by Zdrodovskiy and Golinevitch (Treatise on Rickettsia and Rickettsiosis, Medgiz, Moscow, 1956, 82–168); 2) *Rickettsia pavlovskii* Korshunova (in Pavlovsky et al., Nat. Nidi Hum. Dis. and Regional Epidemiol., Medgiz, Moscow, 1955, 242) was more recently proposed for a disease agent carried by ticks, mites and fleas.

Genus II. **Coxiella** *Philip, (1943) 1948.*

(Subgenus *Coxiella* Philip, Amer. Jour. Hyg., *37*, 1943, 306; *Burnetia* Macchiavello, Prim. Reunion Interamer. del Tifo, Mexico, 1947, 408; subgenus *Dyera* Macchiavello, *loc. cit.*; see Philip, Ann. New York Acad. Sci., *56*, 1953, 490; *Coxiella* Philip, U. S. Public Health Rep., *63*, 1948 (January 9), 58 (incorrectly attributed to Bengson, in Manual, 6th ed., 1948 (January 26), 1092); *Cexiella* (sic) Zhdanov and Korenblit, Jour. Microbiol., Epidemiol. and Immunobiol. (Russian), No. 9, 1950, 42.)

Co.xi.el′la. M.L. fem.dim.ending *-ella*; M.L. fem.dim.n. *Coxiella* named for Herald R. Cox, who was a codiscoverer of the agent of Q fever in America.

Small, pleomorphic, rod-shaped or coccoid organisms occurring intracellularly in the cytoplasm of infected cells and possibly extracellularly in infected ticks. Filterable. Stain lightly with aniline dyes. Gram-negative. Have not been cultivated in cell-free media. Parasites of man and other animals. Includes the etiological agent of Q fever. Produces no typhus-like rash or Weil-Felix titer in man. Not dependent on arthropod transmission in the infectious cycle.

The type species is *Coxiella burnetii* (Derrick) Philip.

1. **Coxiella burnetii** (Derrick, 1939) Philip, (1943) 1948. (*Rickettsia burneti* (sic) Derrick, Med. Jour. Australia, *1*, 1939, 14; *Rickettsia diaporica* Cox, U. S. Pub. Health Rep., *54*, 1939, 1826; *Rickettsia burneti* var. *americana* Anonymous, Brit. Med. Jour., *2*, 1941, 588; *Rickettsia (Coxiella) burneti* (sic) Philip, Amer. Jour. Hyg., *37*, 1943, 306; *Burnetia (Dyera) burneti* Macchiavello, Prim. Reunion Interamer. del Tifo, Mexico, 1947, 409; *Burnetia (Dyera) burneti* var. *diaporica* Macchiavello, *loc. cit.*; *Coxiella burneti* (sic) Philip, U. S. Pub. Health Rep., *63*, 1948, 58; *Rickettsia burneti* var. *caprina* Caminopetros, Ann. Inst. Past., *77*, 1949, 750; *Cexiella* (sic) *diaporica* Zhdanov and Korenblit, Jour. Microbiol., Epidemiol. and Immunobiol. (Russian), No. 9, 1950, 42; *Rickettsia burneti* var. *henzerling* Kausche and Sheris, Ztschr. f. Hyg., *133*, 1951, 158.)

bur.ne′ti.i. M.L. gen.noun *burnetii* of Burnet; named for F. M. Burnet, who first studied the agent causing Q fever in Australia.

Small, bacterium-like, pleomorphic organisms varying in size from coccoid forms to well-marked rods. Occur as intracellular micro-colonies with diffuse or compact distribution of the organisms through the cytoplasm. Also seen extracellularly, where they appear as small, lanceolate rods, diplobacilli and occasionally segmented filamentous forms. Chains of 3 to 6 elements often seen. Quite uniform in size and morphology in infected yolk sacs and in mouse spleen with exceedingly minute forms in heavily infected material. Small lanceolate rods, 0.25 by 0.4 to 0.5 micron, bipolar forms 0.25 by 1.0 micron, diplobacilli 0.25 by 1.5 microns. Non-motile. Under the electron microscope, organisms from yolk-sac sources average 0.32 by 0.73 micron with closer-fitting envelopes over a more regular internal organization than that of *Rickettsia prowazekii*. With Giemsa's stain the cells appear reddish purple; with Macchiavello's stain, bright red against a blue background. Gram-negative.

Cultivation: May be cultivated in plasma

tissue cultures, in modified Maitland media, in the yolk sacs of chick embryos and by injection into meal worms and certain other arthropods.

Filterability: The infectious agent of Q fever readily passes through Berkefeld N filters, which are impermeable to ordinary bacteria, and W filters, which are impermeable to typhus fever and spotted fever rickettsiae.

Resistance to chemical and physical agents: Comparatively resistant to heat and to drying and chemical agents. Resists 60° C. for 1 hour. Survives in cell-free media at least 109 days without loss of titer. Resistant to 0.5 per cent formalin and 1.0 per cent phenol for 24 hours when tested in fertile eggs. Survives several years in dried tick feces.

There is complete cross immunity in guinea pigs between strains causing Q fever in various parts of the world; the guinea pigs remain solidly immune to attempted reinfection. A vaccine has been developed which protects cattle and probably laboratory personnel from infection.

Serology: American and Australian strains are identical by agglutination and agglutinin absorption. Strains from various countries are serologically related as shown by complement fixation. Q fever is distinguishable from other rickettsial diseases by complement-fixation tests. No common antigenic factor with any Proteus strain has been demonstrated.

Pathogenic for man, guinea pigs and white mice. The monkey, dog, white rat and rabbit are mildly susceptible. Certain bush animals in Australia, particularly the bandicoot, have been found naturally infected. Other rodents and marsupials are mildly susceptible. Natural infections occur among cattle, sheep and goats. A febrile reaction occurs in guinea pigs, but the mortality is low except with heavily infected yolk sac, which causes a high mortality. On subcutaneous or intradermal inoculation, a marked inflammatory thickening of the skin occurs at the site of inoculation. On autopsy, the spleen is enlarged from 2 to 12 times by weight and is engorged with blood. Passage in guinea pigs and mice is accomplished by transfer of infected blood, liver and spleen. A febrile reaction often accompanied by pneumonitis occurs in man, but mortality is nil in uncomplicated cases.

Source: First observed by Burnet and Freeman (Med. Jour. Australia, 2, 1937, 299) in stained smears from mice inoculated intraperitoneally with infectious material from Australian patients. Independently, organisms were also seen in preparations of guinea pigs injected with Dermacentor andersoni ticks from "Nine-Mile" area of Montana (U. S. Pub. Health Rep., 53, 1938, 2270).

Habitat: Isolated from at least 17 species of naturally infected ticks in North America, Australia, Africa, Europe and Asia Minor. Several other species of ticks have been shown experimentally to transmit the agent of Q fever. Transovarial survival occurs in Dermacentor andersoni and Haemaphysalis humerosa. The bandicoot (Isoodon macrourus) is probably the natural animal reservoir of the disease in Australia, and the gerbille has been reported in Africa with natural infection. Cows, sheep and goats have been shown to shed organisms in milk and placentas. The etiological agent of Q (for "query," not Queensland as surmised by some writers) fever in man.

TRIBE II. EHRLICHIEAE PHILIP, TRIB. NOV.

(Ehrlichieae Philip (nomen nudum), Ann. N. Y. Acad. Sci., 56, 1953, 486; also see Canad. Jour. Microbiol., 2, 1956, 262.)

Ehr.li.chi'e.ae. M.L. fem.n. Ehrlichia type genus of the tribe; -eae ending to denote a tribe; M.L. fem.pl.n. Ehrlichieae the Ehrlichia tribe.

Minute, rickettsia-like organisms pathogenic for certain vertebrate hosts, not including man. Adapted to existence in invertebrates, chiefly arthropods.

Key to the genera of tribe **Ehrlichieae.**

I. Transmitted by ticks.
    A. Transmitted transovarially; parasites of circulating monocytes of vertebrate hosts.
                         Genus III. *Ehrlichia,* p. 949.
    B. Not transmitted transovarially; parasites of endothelial cells of vertebrate hosts.
                         Genus IV. *Cowdria,* p. 950.
II. Transmitted by parasitic trematodes; pathogenic principally for canines.
                         Genus V. *Neorickettsia,* p. 951.

Genus III. **Ehrlichia** *Moshkovskiy, (1937) 1945.*

(Subgenus *Ehrlichia* Moshkovskiy, Compt. rend. Soc. Biol., Paris, *126*, 1937, 382; *Ehrlichia* Moshkovskiy, Uspekhi Souremennoi Biol. (U.S.S.R.), *19*, 1945, 10; *Nicollea* (in part) Macchiavello, Prim. Reunion Interamer. del Tifo, Mexico, 1947, 416; possibly *Donatienella* Rousselot, Bull. Soc. path. exot., *41*, 1948, 110.)

Ehr.li'chi.a. M.L. noun *Ehrlichia* named for Paul Ehrlich, a German bacteriologist.

Small, often pleomorphic, usually coccoid organisms occurring intracytoplasmically in the circulating monocytes of suitable mammalian hosts. Parasitic. The etiological agents of tick-borne diseases of dogs, cattle and sheep.

The type species is *Ehrlichia canis* (Donatien and Lestoquard) Moshkovskiy.

Key to the species of genus **Ehrlichia.**

I. Causes a serious and often fatal disease of dogs.
                         1. *Ehrlichia canis.*
II. Cause diseases of ruminants.
    A. Causes a non-fatal disease of cattle.
                         2. *Ehrlichia bovis.*
    B. Causes a rickettsia-like disease of sheep.
                         3. *Ehrlichia ovina.*

1. Ehrlichia canis (Donatien and Lestoquard, 1935) Moshkovskiy, (1937) 1945. (*Rickettsia canis* Donatien and Lestoquard, Bull. Soc. path. exot., *28*, 1935, 418; *Ehrlichia (Rickettsia) canis* Moshkovskiy, Compt. rend. Soc. Biol., Paris, *126*, 1937, 382; *Ehrlichia canis* Moshkovskiy, Uspekhi Souremennoi Biol. (U.S.S.R.), *19*, 1945, 18; *Nicollea canis* Macchiavello, Prim. Reunion Interamer. del Tifo, Mexico, 1947, 416; *Kurlovia (Ehrlichia) canis* Zhdanov, Opredelitel Virusov Celovska i Zivotmych, Izd. Akad. Med. Nauk, U.S.S.R., Moskau, 1953, 57 and 168.)

ca'nis. M.L. noun *canis* the dog.

Minute, coccoid, ellipsoidal or boat-shaped organisms, 0.2 to 0.3 micron in diameter, occurring intracytoplasmically in plaques or colonies in the circulating monocytes of infected dogs. Stain blue with Giemsa's stain.

Cultivation: Not reported.

Serology: Not reported.

Immunology: Not reported.

Pathogenicity: Reported as causing a serious and often fatal disease in dogs in North and East Africa. Injection of a monkey, *Maccacus innuus,* caused a febrile response with attendant rickettsiemia. The ordinary laboratory animals are not susceptible.

Comment: Regarded as the type species of the genus *Ehrlichia* by Moshkovskiy (*op. cit.,* 1945).

Source: Observed by Donatien and Lestoquard (*op. cit.,* 1935) in the cytoplasm of monocytes of dogs infected by tick bite in Algeria.

Habitat: Found in the common dog tick, *Rhipicephalus sanguineus,* all stages of which are reported to transmit the infection and in which transovarial passage has been observed.

2. Ehrlichia bovis (Donatien and Lestoquard, 1936) Moshkovskiy, 1945. (*Rickettsia* *bovis* Donatien and Lestoquard, Bull. Soc. path. exot., *29*, 1936, 1057; Moshkovskiy, Uspekhi Souremennoi Biol. (U.S.S.R.), *19*, 1945, 18; *Kurlovia (Ehrlichia) bovis* Zhdanov, Opredelitel Virusov Celovska i Zivotmych, Izd. Akad. Med. Nauk, U.S.S.R., Moskau, 1953, 57 and 169.)

bo′vis. L. noun *bos* the ox; M.L. gen.noun *bovis* of the ox.

Occurs in circular, elliptical and polygonal colonies, 1 to 6 or 11 microns in diameter, in the cytoplasm of circulating monocytes of infected cattle. The individual organisms are difficult to see in these masses and measurements are not given. Stain deep lavender or purple with Giemsa's stain.

Cultivation: Not reported.

Serology: Not reported.

Immunology: Circulating infection persists for at least a year (premunition) and is not transmissible to sheep. Susceptibility of small laboratory animals not stated.

Pathogenicity: No mortality in cattle, which are the only reported susceptible hosts. Defibrinated blood has remained infectious at laboratory temperatures for 26 hours. Infection transmissible by blood subinoculation as well as through the agency of ticks.

Source: Observed by Donatien and Lestoquard (*op. cit.*, 1936, 1057) in the monocytes of Moroccan cattle which were infected by adult ticks reared from immature stages imported on other cattle from Iran.

Habitat: Found in Iranian cattle ticks (*Hyalomma sp.*) in which at least transstadial transmission was demonstrated. The etiological agent of a non-fatal cattle disease in Iran. Further experimental and transovarial tick transmission not reported.

3. **Ehrlichia ovina** (Lestoquard and Donatien, 1936) Moshkovskiy, 1945. (*Rickettsia ovina* Lestoquard and Donatien, Bull. Soc. path. exot., *29*, 1936, 108; Moshkovskiy, Uspekhi Souremennoi Biol. (U.S.S.R.), *19*, 1945, 18; *Kurlovia (Ehrlichia) ovina* Zhdanov, Opredelitel Virusov Celovska i Zivotmych, Izd. Akad. Med. Nauk, U.S.S.R., Moskau, 1953, 57 and 169.)

o. vi′na. L. adj. *ovinus* pertaining to sheep.

The organisms occur in plaques or colonies, 2 to 8 microns in diameter, in the cytoplasm of monocytes of infected sheep. Stain a deep reddish with Giesma's stain.

Cultivation: Not reported.

Serology: Not reported.

Immunology: Not reported.

Pathogenicity: Causes mild infections with low mortality in sheep in Algeria and Turkey; transmissible by blood subinoculation.

Source: Observed by Lestoquard and Donatien (*op. cit.*, 1936, 108) in the circulating monocytes of sheep infected by injection of ticks.

Habitat: Found in the tick *Rhipicephalus bursa*, though feeding experiments have not been reported. The etiological agent of a rickettsiosis-like disease of sheep in the Mediterranean Basin.

Genus IV. Cowdria *Moshkovskiy, (1945) 1947.*

(Subgenus *Cowdria* Moshkovskiy, Uspekhi Souremennoi Biol., *19*, 1945, 18; *Cowdria* Moskovskiy, Science, *106*, 1947, 62 (incorrectly attributed to Bengston, in Manual, 6th ed., 1948, 1094); not *Cowdryia* Macchiavello, Prim. Reunion Intramer. del Tifo, Mexico, 1947, 417; *Nicollea* Macchiavello, *ibid.*, 415; *Kurlovia* Zhdanov, Opredelitel Virusov Celovska i Zivotmych, Izd. Akad. Med. Nauk, U.S.S.R., Moskau, 1953, 166; see Philip, Canad. Jour. Microbiol., *2*, 1956, 265.)

Cow′dri.a. M.L. noun *Cowdria* named for E. V. Cowdry, who first described the organism in heartwater diseases of three ruminants: sheep, goats and cattle.

Small, pleomorphic, spherical or ellipsoidal, occasionally rod-shaped organisms occurring intracellularly in ticks and characteristically localized in clusters inside vacuoles in the cytoplasm of vascular endothelial cells of host vertebrates. Gram-negative. Have not been cultivated in cell-free media. Not transovarially transmitted in tick vectors. The etiological agent of heartwater of cattle, sheep and goats.

The type species is *Cowdria ruminantium* (Cowdry) Moshkovskiy.

1. **Cowdria ruminantium** (Cowdry, 1925) Moshkovskiy, (1945) 1947. (*Rickettsia ruminantium* Cowdry, Jour. Exp. Med., *42*, 1925, 231; *Rickettsia* (*Cowdria*) *ruminantium* Moshkovskiy, Uspekhi Souremennoi Biol. (Russian) (Advances in Modern Biology), *19*, 1945, 18; *Cowdria ruminantium* Moshkovskiy, Science, *106*, 1947, 62; *Kurlovia* (*Cowdria*) *ruminantium* Zhdanov, Opredelitel Virusov Celovska i Zivotmych, Izd. Akad. Med. Nauk, U.S.S.R., Moskau, 1953, 56 and 166.)

ru.mi.nan'ti.um. M.L. neut.gen.pl.n. *ruminantium* of *Ruminantia*, formerly an ordinal name for cud-chewing mammals.

Differ morphologically from typical typhus-like rickettsiae, showing usually spherical and ellipsoidal forms, occasionally bacillary forms. Irregular pleomorphic forms occur. Grow in the cytoplasm but not in the nuclei of cells, sometimes in densely packed masses. Cocci measure 0.2 to 0.5 micron in diameter in the endothelial cells of animals and 0.2 to 0.3 micron in diameter in ticks. In ticks bacillary forms are 0.2 to 0.3 by 0.4 to 0.5 micron and pairs are 0.2 by 0.8 micron. Non-motile. Stain blue with Giemsa's stain; can also be stained by methylene blue and other basic aniline dyes. Gram-negative.

Cultivation: Not reported.

Immunology: Immunity incomplete after recovery from the infection. The organisms are found in the tissues long after recovery (premunition). There is some evidence of a variety of strains.

Pathogenic for goats, sheep and cattle. Transmissible to goats by inoculation of infected blood intrajugularly. The most characteristic lesion is the hydropericardium of infected animals. The only small animal shown to be susceptible is the ferret.

Source: Observed in the endothelial cells of renal glomeruli and in the endothelial cells of the cerebral cortex of animals suffering from heartwater; also observed in the tick *Amblyomma hebraeum*.

Habitat: Found in the bont tick (*A. hebraeum*) and also in *A. variegatum*, in which the infection has been shown to be transstadial but not transovarial. The etiological agent of heartwater in sheep, goats and cattle in South Africa.

Genus V. **Neorickettsia** *Philip et al., 1953.*

(Philip, Hadlow and Hughes, Riassunti delle Comunicazioni, VI Congresso Internaz. di Microbiol., Roma, *2*, 1953, 256; also see Exp. Parasitol., *3*, 1954, 336; and Atti del VI Congresso Internaz. di Microbiol., Roma (1953), *4*, 1955, 70.)

Ne.o.ri.ckett'si.a. Gr. prefix *neo-* new; M.L. fem.n. *Rickettsia* type genus of family *Rickettsiaceae*; M.L. fem.n. *Neorickettsia* the new *Rickettsia*.

Small, coccoid, sometimes pleomorphic (in the form of short rods, crescents and even rings), intracytoplasmic organisms which occur in the reticulo-endothelial cells of certain mammals and in tissues of at least mature fluke vectors. No intranuclear forms have been observed. Non-filterable. Non-motile. Not cultivable on cell-free media. The etiological agent of a helminth-borne disease of canines.

The type species is *Neorickettsia helminthoeca* Philip et al.

1. **Neorickettsia helminthoeca** Philip et al., 1953. (*Neorickettsia helmintheca* (sic) Philip, Hadlow and Hughes, Riassunti delle Comunicazioni, VI Congresso Internaz. di Microbiol., Roma, *2*, 1953, 256; also see Exp. Parasitol., *3*, 1954, 336; *Neorickettsia helminthēca* (sic) Philip, Hadlow and Hughes, Atti del VI Congresso Internaz. di Microbiol., Roma (1953), *4*, 1955, 70.)

hel.min'thoe.ca. Gr. noun *helmins, helminthis* worm; Gr. noun *oicus* house; M.L. adj. *helminthoecus* worm-dwelling.

Minute, coccoid and ellipsoidal forms to short rods and clubs, occasionally crescentic and even ring-like. Often form morula-like clusters either singly or in multiple colonies in the cytoplasm of reticuloendothelial cells of infected canines. The most common coccoid forms range from 0.3 to 0.4 micron in diameter. Non-filterable. Non-motile. In node imprint preparations, these organisms stain bluish with Giemsa's stain and faintly by Castañeda's method. Gram-negative.

Cultivation: Will not grow in ordinary bacteriological media or in embryonated chicken eggs. Has been grown in certain tissue-culture explants from infected dog-node tissues.

Immunology: Recovered dogs are solidly immune to reinfection, but mild febrile relapses may occur during which infection is recoverable from the blood. Guinea pigs injected with this agent are not cross-immunized against Rocky Mountain spotted fever, endemic typhus or Q fever. Natural resistance in dogs has not been observed, but dogs have been immunized by infectious materials of reduced virulence which have caused mild or inapparent infections.

Serology: Attempts to prepare a usable antigen from heavily infected dog nodes have not been successful, and no other source of antigen is yet available. Hyper-immunized dogs and rabbits have shown no common antigenic factor with strains of *Proteus vulgaris*.

Resistance to chemical and physical agents: Inactivated within a few hours in a saline suspension at room temperature. Dog nodes frozen at −20° C. have remained infectious for at least 158 days but survive more consistently at −70°C. Survival under lyophilization is short.

Antibiotic therapy: Symptoms in ill dogs quickly alleviated by oral administration of aureomycin or terramycin, as little as 250 mg in 15-pound beagles. Sulfonamids also effective in treatment.

Pathogenicity: Untreated dogs show upwards of 90 per cent mortality after feeding on infected fish or when injected with infected dog tissues and blood. Foxes and coyotes are also susceptible. Causes mild response in guinea pigs, hamsters and white mice; this response is retrogressive on passage and is not maintained. Raccoons and mink do not show clinical reactions to attempted experimental infections. Trout are not infected by injection of infected dog-node suspensions.

Source: First observed in node-imprint preparations of experimentally infected dogs by Cordy and Gorham (Amer. Jour. Path., *26*, 1950, 457).

Habitat: Found in the intestinal trematode *Nanophyetus salmincola* (Chapin), which probably acts as the natural reservoir of infection. The etiological agent of a salmon-poisoning disease of canines.

TRIBE III. WOLBACHIEAE PHILIP, 1955.

(Bact. Rev., *19*, 1955, 271.)

Wol.ba.chi'e.ae. M.L. fem.n. *Wolbachia* type genus of the tribe; -*eae* ending to denote a tribe; M.L. fem.pl.n. *Wolbachieae* the *Wolbachia* tribe.

Includes many species heretofore assigned to the genus *Rickettsia* which are rickettsia-like in growth and in morphological and staining properties and which are mostly intracellular symbiotes or parasites of various species of arthropods, sometimes occupying special tissues or mycetomes. Characterization has often been not so adequate as in the preceding forms that are pathogenic for vertebrates, and differentiation has been arbitrarily assigned chiefly on the basis of presumed host-specificity in arthropods, though differences in development and morphology are often noted.

At present three genera are recognized in the tribe *Wolbachieae*; however, future knowledge may show that a better and more satisfactory arrangement is possible.

Key to the genera of tribe **Wolbachieae.**

I. No known filterability; no reported association with intracellular crystalline inclusions.
   A. Symbiotic to highly pathogenic; no mycetomes produced in hosts.
          Genus VI. *Wolbachia*, p. 953.

B. Symbiotic to the point that special mycetomes are developed for harboring the organisms, which are not pathogenic, in the host.

Genus VII. *Symbiotes*, p. 956.

II. Filterable; cause blue disease of beetle larvae; associated with intracellular, crystalline inclusions; reportedly invade cell nuclei.

Genus VIII. *Rickettsiella*, p. 957.

Genus VI. **Wolbachia** Hertig, 1936.

(Parasitology, *28*, 1936, 472.)

Wol.ba'chi.a. M.L. fem.n. *Wolbachia* named for S. B. Wolbach, who described the rickettsial agent of Rocky Mountain spotted fever.

Microorganisms possessing the general characteristics of the rickettsiae and exhibiting not only minute, bacterium-like forms appearing with dark-field illumination as luminous rods and points but also enlarged forms within the body of which are contained one to several smaller individuals. Pleomorphism is characteristic, and it is usually found in organisms in an intracellular location; the few extracellular species, *e.g. Wolbachia melophagi*, may eventually be regarded as not belonging to this genus.

The type species is *Wolbachia pipientis* Hertig.

Key to the species of genus **Wolbachia.**

I. Found in insects.
  A. Found in mosquitoes.
    1. Found in the gonadal cells of mosquitoes, where degeneration occurs.
      1. *Wolbachia pipientis.*
    2. Found in the epithelial lining of the stomach of mosquitoes, where destruction of the hind gut occurs.
      2. *Wolbachia culicis.*
  B. Not found in mosquitoes.
    1. Found in fleas.
      3. *Wolbachia ctenocephali.*
      4. *Wolbachia pulex.*
    2. Found in lice.
      5. *Wolbachia trichodectae.*
      6. *Wolbachia linognathi.*
    3. Found in the sheep ked; grows on non-living media (glucose-blood-bouillon-agar).
      7. *Wolbachia melophagi.*
II. Found in arachnids.
  A. Found in the Rocky Mountain wood tick.
      8. *Wolbachia dermacentrophila.*
  B. Found in mites.
      9. *Wolbachia sericea.*

1. **Wolbachia pipientis** Hertig, 1936. (*Rickettsia* of *Culex pipiens*, Hertig and Wolbach, Jour. Med. Res., *44*, 1924, 329; Hertig, Parasitology, *28*, 1936, 453.)

pi.pi.en'tis. M.L. *pipiens* specific epithet of the host mosquito, *Culex pipiens*; M.L. gen.noun *pipientis* of *pipiens*.

Small, coccoid forms measure 0.25 to 0.5 micron in diameter, and the rods measure 0.25 to 0.5 by 0.5 to 1.3 microns. Paired and diplococcoid forms are also observed. Irregularity rather than symmetry is pronounced. The larger coccoid forms may measure up to 1.8 microns in diameter. Stain well with Giemsa's stain but poorly with aniline dyes.

Cultivation: Attempts to cultivate this organism in cell-free media have been unsuccessful; attempts in embryonated chicken eggs are unreported.

Comment: Hertig (*loc. cit.*) regarded this species as possibly related to *Rickettsia lectularia* Arkwright et al. Philip (Canad. Jour. Microbiol., *2*, 1956, 266), however, regards these two species as more logically placed in different genera.

Pathogenicity and source: This species is described in the role of a harmless parasite which causes some degeneration of parasitized gonad cells of the mosquito host, *Culex pipiens*; studied in mosquitoes of North America and China. It is passed through the eggs of the host to succeeding generations.

2. Wolbachia culicis (Brumpt, 1938) Philip, 1956. (*Rickettsia culicis* Brumpt, Ann. Parasitol. Hum. et Comp., *16*, 1938, 153; Philip, Canad. Jour. Microbiol., *2*, 1956, 267.)

cu.li′cis. M.L. noun *Culex* a genus of mosquitoes; M.L. gen. noun *culicis* of *Culex*.

Small, pleomorphic, intracellular organisms. Stained in sections with haemalum, and with erythrosine-orange and toluidine-blue. Gram-negative.

Cultivation: No attempts reported.

Pathogenicity and source: Found in the ↄithelial lining of the stomach of mosquitoes (*Culex fatigans*), where destruction of the cells of the hind gut occurs. Differentiation from *W. pipientis* Hertig is presumably on the basis of this pathogenicity, though it remains to be proved that this is not a strain difference. Brumpt postulated that parasitism of man might occur since the original mosquitoes had been fed on filaria-carrying persons.

3. Wolbachia ctenocephali (Sikora, 1918) Philip, 1956. (*Rickettsia ctenocephali* Sikora, Arch. f. Schiffs- u. Tropen-Hyg., *22*, 1918, 445; Philip, Canad. Jour. Microbiol., *2*, 1956, 267.)

cte.no.ce′pha.li. M.L. mas.n. *Ctenocephalus* (now *Ctenocephalides*) a genus of fleas; M.L. gen.noun *ctenocephali* of *Ctenocephalus*.

Organisms of two sizes were observed by Sikora, the larger resembling *Rickettsia pediculi* and the smaller, *Rickettsia melophagi*. Vary from minute cocci, 0.3 to 0.4 micron in diameter, to rather large, swollen, curved rods, 0.3 by 1.5 to 2.0 microns-

Stain reddish with Giemsa's stain. Bipolar staining observed in some rods. Gram-negative.

Cultivation: Not reported, though propagation in the coelomic fluid of the body louse is claimed.

Comment: Regarded by Macchiavello (Prim. Reunion Interamer. del Tifo, Mexico, 1947, 418) as a variety of his later described *Cowdryia pulex*.

Pathogenicity and source: Found on the surface of organs in the body cavity and in the coelomic fluid of cat fleas (presumably *Ctenocephalides felis*) where no particular damage was reported.

4. Wolbachia pulex (Macchiavello, 1947) Philip, 1956. (*Cowdryia pulex* Macchiavello, Prim. Reunion Interamer. del Tifo, Mexico, 1947, 418; Philip, Canad. Jour. Microbiol., *2*, 1956, 267.)

pu′lex. M.L. noun *Pulex* a genus of fleas.

Described as rickettsioid organisms and as typical rickettsias which, in fleas, can be confused with bacteria, especially those of the intestine. Macchiavello's stain serves to differentiate these organisms. Presumably stain red by Macchiavello's method.

Cultivation: Not attempted.

Pathogenicity and source: Non-pathogenic for the host fleas. Hundreds of inocula, consisting of batches of fleas, when injected into guinea pigs caused, in two instances, symptomatic responses. However, in neither case could this organism be related to the response nor could *Rickettsia typhi* be eliminated as a potential excitant.

5. Wolbachia trichodectae (Hindle, 1921) Philip, 1956. (*Rickettsia trichodectae* Hindle, Parasitology, *13*, 1921, 152; Philip, Canad. Jour. Microbiol., *2*, 1956, 267.)

tri.cho.dec′tae. M.L. fem.n. *Trichodectes* a genus of biting lice; M.L. gen.noun *trichodectae* of *Trichodectes*.

Rickettsia-like, extracellular, minute coccoid and rod-shaped organisms resembling *Wolbachia melophagi* in morphology, averaging 0.3 to 0.5 by 0.5 to 0.9 micron. Stain purple with Giemsa's stain.

Cultivation: Not reported.

Source: Found in 7 to 8 per cent of biting lice (*Trichodectes pilosus*) where it propagates in the lumen of the alimentary tract and passes out with the feces. This is the supposed means of transmission between lice. The original lice were taken from horses, but the latter are not presumed hosts of the organism as the lice do not suck the blood of their hosts.

6. Wolbachia linognathi (Hindle, 1921) Philip, 1956. (*Rickettsia linognathi* Hindle, Parasitology, *13*, 1921, 157; Philip, Canad. Jour. Microbiol., *2*, 1956, 267.)

li.nog.na'thi. M.L. noun *Linognathus* a genus of sucking lice; M.L. gen.noun *linognathi* of *Linognathus*.

Resembles *Wolbachia trichodectae* in appearance. Stain bluish with Giemsa's stain.

Cultivation: Not reported.

Source: Observed in two of 57 goat lice (*Linognathus stenopsis*), where it was found extracellularly in the lumen of the gut. Probably not pathogenic for the host, but also not adapted to the point of occurring in a high percentage of neighboring hosts.

7. Wolbachia melophagi (Nöller, 1917) Philip, 1956. (*Rickettsia melophagi* Nöller, Arch. f. Schiffs- u. Tropen-Hyg., *21*, 1917, 70; Philip, Canad. Jour. Microbiol., *2*, 1956, 267.)

me.lo'pha.gi. M.L. mas.n. *Melophagus* a genus of sheep keds (sometimes incorrectly called "ticks"); M.L. gen.noun *melophagi* of *Melophagus*.

Minute, rickettsia-like, extracellular, coccoid, ellipsoidal and, occasionaly, short rods occurring characteristically in pairs of fairly uniform size, 0.3 to 0.6 micron in diameter. In eggs of the wingless-fly host, the organisms are more rod-shaped with a tendency to pleomorphism. In cultures, the rods may measure up to 1.0 micron in length. Stain purple with Giemsa's stain and reddish with Macchiavello's stain. Gram-negative.

Cultivation: This is the only one of the rickettsia-like microorganisms that has been confirmed as cultivable on non-living media (glucose-blood-bouillon-agar). Also grows in embryonated chicken eggs.

Pathogenicity and source: Occurs as continuous or broken masses lining the intestinal epithelium; occurs extracellularly in the sheep ked ("sheep tick") (*Melophagus*

ovinus). Intracellular growth has been disputed and is not generally credited at present. Injury to the host has not been reported, and since this organism is almost universally present, including the larvae of the viviparous host, symbiosis is an advanced stage approaching the condition in *Symbiotes lectularius* without the development of mycetomes. Infection in ked-infested sheep is disputed, and cultivation from sheep's blood has been claimed. At least such an infection is low-grade or inapparent as far as symptoms are concerned. Laboratory animals, including vitamin-deficient guinea pigs, have failed to become infected by injection of cultures.

8. Wolbachia dermacentrophila (Steinhaus, 1942) Philip, 1956. (*Rickettsia dermacentrophila* Steinhaus, U. S. Public Health Rept., *57*, 1942, 1376; Philip, Canad. Jour. Microbiol., *2*, 1956, 267.)

der.ma.cen.tro'phi.la. M.L. noun *Dermacentor* a genus of ticks; Gr. adj. *philus* loving; M.L. adj. *dermacentrophilus Dermacentor*-loving.

Minute, rickettsia-like organisms, measuring 0.3 to 0.8 by 0.5 to 2.8 microns. May occur joined in short chains of two or three organisms or occasionally as filaments. On the average, larger in size than *Rickettsia rickettsii*. Stain reddish with Machiavello's stain and bluish with Giemsa's stain. Not acid-fast. Gram-negative.

Cultivation: Failed to grow on 14 ordinary cell-free, bacteriological media. Readily cultivated in embryonated chicken eggs, growing chiefly in yolk sacs and apparently in the embryonic fluids.

Pathogenicity and source: Found most abundantly in the epithelial cells of the intestinal diverticula of the Rocky Mountain wood tick (*Dermacentor andersoni*), but may also occur throughout the various tissues of the host. Extracellular occurrence is also possible. Observed in every stage of the tick host including the egg. Not lethal for the tick host. Attempts at infecting various laboratory animals susceptible to spotted fever failed; such animals were not immune to challenge with strains of tick-borne, rickettsial pathogens. Spotted-fever-immune sera showed agglutination in dilutions too low to be considered positive.

9. **Wolbachia sericea** (Giroud and Martin, 1946) Philip, 1956. (*Rickettsia sericea* Giroud and Martin, Bull. Soc. path. exot., *39*, 1946, 264; Philip, Canad. Jour. Microbiol., *2*, 1956, 267.)

se.ri'ce.a. M.L. adj. *sericeus* silken.

Minute, coccoid, diplococcoid and short rods up to 0.5 micron in length. Violet with Giemsa's stain and red with Macchiavello's stain. Bipolar staining may be observed.

Cultivation: Not reported.

Pathogenicity and source: Found both extracellularly and intracellularly in 19 of 241 mites examined (*Sericothrombium holosericeum*, a species which is not parasitic on vertebrates in any stage). No longer considered pathogenic for the host mites. No susceptibility was found in laboratory animals.

Genus VII. Symbiotes *Philip, 1956.*

(*Cowdryia* Macchiavello, Prim. Reunion Interamer. del Tifo, Mexico, 1947, 417; not *Cowdria* Moshkovskiy, Uspekhi Souremennoi Biol., *19*, 1945, 18; Philip, Canad. Jour. Microbiol., *2*, 1956, 267.)

Although *Cowdryia* Macchiavello (1947) antedates *Symbiotes* Philip (1956), the former generic name is an orthographic variant of an earlier generic name, *Cowdria* Moshkovskiy (1945), and is therefore an illegitimate homonym.

Sym.bi.o'tes. Gr. mas.n. *symbiotes* one who lives with a companion, a partner.

Rickettsia-like, pleomorphic organisms living chiefly intracellularly in arthropod tissues and approaching most nearly the true symbiotic or commensalistic relationship to their hosts; this is evidenced by the development in the host of special organs, or mycetomes, though no species of the *Rickettsiales* is yet known to be confined to such a location.

The type species is *Symbiotes lectularius* (Arkwright et al.) Philip.

1. **Symbiotes lectularius** (Arkwright et al., 1921) Philip, 1956. (*Rickettsia lectularia* Arkwright, Atkin and Bacot, Parasitology, *13*, 1921, 35; *Cowdryia lectularia* Macchiavello, Prim. Reunion Interamer. del Tifo, Mexico, 1947, 417; *Symbiotes lectularia* (sic) Philip, Canad. Jour. Microbiol., *2*, 1956, 267.)

lec.tu.la'ri.us. M.L. adj. *lectularius* the specific epithet of the common bedbug, *Cimex lectularius*.

Minute, pleomorphic, intracellular organisms, the typical form being coccoid or diplococcoid, 0.2 by 0.4 to 0.5 micron, staining deep purple with Giemsa's stain. Bacillary, lanceolate and thread forms, 0.25 to 0.3 by 3.0 to 8.0 microns, occur which stain more red than purple with Giemsa's stain. Granules were reported in the thread forms which were liberated during dark-field examination. Motility of some of the filamentous forms has been reported. The possibility that a true bacterium occurs in association has also been postulated.

Cultivation: Attempts to grow this organism on cell-free media have been unsuccessful. However, Steinhaus (Jour. Bact., *42*, 1941, 757) cultivated, from suitable host sources, a diphtheroid in semi-solid media and embryonated chicken eggs; the relationship of the diphtheroid to this species was uncertain.

Pathogenicity and source: Found especially in paired, special organs, the mycetomes, in the common bedbug (*Cimex lectularius*); also occurs in other tissues, the alimentary tract, ovaries, testes, Malpighian tubules and Berlese's organ. Transovarially transmitted between generations and so mutualistically adapted that it seems probable that every bedbug harbors the organism. The same, or a related organism, was observed in the swallow bedbug (*Cimex hirundinis*) and in "accessory lobes" (mycetomes?) in the tropical bedbug (*Cimex rotundatus*). The only effect on the host was reported as swellings in the Malpighian tubules due to masses of organisms in the cells, though destruction of such cells was not noted. No effects were produced by injection into laboratory animals and into two human volunteers.

Genus VIII. **Rickettsiella** *Philip, 1956.*

(*Coxiella* Dutky and Gooden, Jour. Bact., *63*, 1952, 749; not *Coxiella* Philip, Amer. Jour. Hyg., *37*, 1943, 306; Philip, Canad. Jour. Microbiol., *2*, 1956, 267.)

Ri.ckett.si.el'la. M.L. dim.ending -*ella*; M.L. fem.n. *Rickettsiella* named for H. T. Ricketts, one of the discoverers of the organisms bearing his name, who eventually lost his life while studying typhus infection in Mexico.

Minute, intracellular, rickettsia-like organisms which are pathogenic for certain insect larvae but which are not known to be pathogenic for any vertebrates. Filterable. Associated with microscopic, intracellular, crystalline inclusions and reported to infect cell nuclei (though this needs to be confirmed).

The type species is *Rickettsiella popilliae* (Dutky and Gooden) Philip.

1. **Rickettsiella popilliae** (Dutky and Gooden, 1952) Philip, 1956. (*Coxiella popilliae* Dutky and Gooden, Jour. Bact., *63*, 1952, 743; *Rickettsia melolonthae* Krieg, Ztschr. f. Naturforsch., *10b*, 1955, 35; Philip, Canad. Jour. Microbiol., *2*, 1956, 267.)

po.pil'li.ae. M.L. fem.n. *Popillia* a genus of beetles; M.L. gen.noun *popilliae* of *Popillia*.

Occurs intracellularly in the Japanese beetle (*Popillia japonica*), initially in the fat bodies of infected larvae, causing a bluish discoloration. Other tissues become infected as ruptured cells release the organisms into the hemolymph, and, preceding death, the infection eventually spreads to discolor the entire larva. Nuclei of infected cells are reported to be invaded, but no clear evidence of this has been illustrated or described. The organisms are fairly uniform, small, kidney-shaped rods, 0.2 by 0.6 micron under the electron microscope, with denser areas at the poles or outlined by a capsule-like structure. Pass 7-pound medium and 13-pound fine porosity Mandler filters. Capable of infecting healthy larvae by subinjection of hemolymph. Experimental infection has also been produced by contamination of soil in which healthy larvae were fed.

FAMILY II. CHLAMYDIACEAE RAKE, Fam. Nov.*

(*Chlamydozoaceae* Moshkovskiy, Uspekhi Souremennoi Biologii (Russian) (Advances in Modern Biology), *19*, 1945, 12.)

Chla.my.di.a'ce.ae. M.L. neut.n. *Chlamydia* type genus of the family; -*aceae* ending to denote a family; M.L. fem.pl.n. *Chlamydiaceae* the *Chlamydia* family.

Small, coccoid microorganisms with a characteristic developmental cycle. Stain with aniline dyes. Gram-negative. Have not been cultivated in cell-free media. Obligate, intracytoplasmic parasites or saprophytes. Found in various warm-blooded animals, where they are usually pathogenic.

Key to the genera of family **Chlamydiaceae.**

I. Non-cultivable in chicken embryonic tissues.
  A. Organisms coccoid; do not exhibit pleomorphism.

    Genus I. *Chlamydia*, p. 958.
  B. Organisms usually coccoid or ellipsoidal; exhibit marked pleomorphism.
    1. Pleomorphic forms small (200 millimicrons to 2 microns). Pathogenic.
      a. Occur intracytoplasmically as prominent colonies.

        Genus II. *Colesiota*, p. 959.

* Prepared by Prof. Geoffrey W. Rake, University of Pennsylvania, Philadelphia, Pennsylvania, December, 1955.

aa. Occur intracytoplasmically as scattered growth.

Genus III. *Ricolesia*, p. 959.

2. Pleomorphic forms large (2 microns). Apparently non-pathogenic; may be saprophytic.

Genus IV. *Colettsia*, p. 961.

II. Cultivable in chicken embryonic tissues.

Genus V. *Miyagawanella*, p. 961.

Genus I. **Chlamydia** *Rake, 1956.* *

(*Prowazekia* Coles, Ann. New York Acad. Sci., *56*, 1953, 461; not *Prowazekia* Hartmann and Chagas, Mem. Inst. Oswaldo Cruz, 1910, 89 (a protozoan genus).)

Chla.my'di.a. Gr. fem.n. *chlamys, chlamydis* a cloak; M.L. fem.dim.n. *Chlamydia* a small cloak.

Coccoid and spherical cells with a developmental cycle. Gram-negative. Occur intracytoplasmically. Non-cultivable in chicken embryonic tissues. Have not yet been cultivated in tissue culture. Susceptible to the action of sulfonamides and of antibiotics. Cause ophthalmic and urogenital diseases in man; transferable to other primates.

In the previous edition of the MANUAL (Manual, 6th ed., 1948, 1114), the generic name *Chlamydozoon* von Prowazek (incorrectly attributed in Manual (*loc. cit.*) to Halberstaedter and von Prowazek, Arb. a. d. kaiserl. Gesundheitsamte, *26*, 1907, 44) was used for this group of organisms. However, it has been shown (Buchanan, Internat. Bull. of Bact. Nomen. and Taxon., *5*, 1955, 121) that *Chlamydozoon* is not available as a generic name for these organisms because its type species, *Chlamydozoon bombycis* von Prowazek, was presumably a virus, not a member of the family *Chlamydiaceae*.

The type species is *Chlamydia trachomatis* (Busacca) Rake.

Key to the species of genus **Chlamydia.**

I. Causes trachoma in man.

1. *Chlamydia trachomatis.*

II. Causes inclusion conjunctivitis in man.

2. *Chlamydia oculogtenialis.*

1. **Chlamydia trachomatis** (Busacca, 1935) Rake, *comb. nov.* (*Rickettsia trachomae* (sic) Busacca, Arch. Ophthalm., *52*, 1935, 567; *Rickettsia trachomatis* Foley and Parrot, Compt. rend. Soc. Biol., Paris, *124*, 1937, 230; also see Arch. Inst. Past. d'Algerie, *15*, 1937, 339; *Chlamydozoon trachomatis* Moshkovskiy, Uspekhi Souremennoi Biologii, *19*, 1945, 12.)

tra.cho'ma.tis. Gr. noun *trachoma* roughness; M.L. noun *trachoma* trachoma; M.L. gen.noun *trachomatis* of trachoma.

Coccoid cells. Small cells 200 to 350 millimicrons in diameter are the elementary bodies. Initial bodies up to 800 millimicrons in diameter and plaques up to 10 microns are also found. All larger forms are encapsulated with a substance derived either from the cell or from the cytoplasm of the parasitized cells. The elementary body is the basic unit. Occurs in pairs or in clusters. Non-motile. Stains poorly with aniline dyes, blue or reddish blue with Giemsa's stain and red or blue, depending on the metabolic state, with Macchiavello's stain. The matrices of the plaques give a strong reaction for glycogen. Gram-negative.

Cultivation: Has never been cultivated.

Immunology: Possesses one or more antigens in common with or closely resembling one or more of those present in *Miyagawanella spp.* Produces, in low concentrations,

---

* The first appearance of the name *Chlamydia* in bacteriological literature (Jones, Rake and Stearns, Jour. Inf. Dis., *76*, 1945, 55) was as a *nomen nudum*, and as such the generic name *Chlamydia* Jones et al. has no standing.

antibodies which fix complement with anti-gen from *Miyagawanella lymphogranuloma-tosis*.

Pathogenic for man, apes and monkeys, affecting only the cornea and the conjunctiva, causing highly destructive lesions.

Antibiotic- and chemo-therapy: Susceptible to sulfonamides and to antibiotics.

Source: Found in the scrapings of either the cornea or the conjunctiva in cases of trachoma.

Habitat: The etiological agent of trachoma in man.

2. **Chlamydia oculogenitalis** (Moshkovskiy, 1945) Rake, *comb. nov.* (*Chlamydozoon oculogenitale* Moshkovskiy, Uspekhi Souremennoi Biologii, *19*, 1945, 12.)

o.cu.lo.ge.ni.ta'lis. L. noun *oculus* eye; L. adj. *genitalis* genital; M.L. adj. *oculo-genitalis* (apparently intended to mean) the ocular and genital (organism).

Resembles *Chlamydia trachomatis* morphologically and in staining reactions.

Cultivation: Has not been cultivated.

Immunology: Same as for *C. trachomatis*.

Pathogenic for man, baboons and monkeys. Causes an acute conjunctivitis and, in man, an inflammation of the lower urogenital tract.

Antibiotic- and chemo-therapy: Susceptible to sulfonamides and to antibiotics.

Source: Found in conjunctival exudates and in exudates from infected urethra or cervix. Also present in contaminated pools of water.

Habitat: The etiological agent of swimming-pool conjunctivitis (neonatal, or inclusion, conjunctivitis).

Genus II. Colesiota *Rake, 1948.*

(Rake, in Manual, 6th ed., 1948, 1119.)

Co.le.si.o'ta. M.L. dim.ending -*iota*; M.L. noun *Colesiota* named for Prof. J. D. W. A. Coles, the first to study these organisms.

Usually coccoid cells, but pleomorphism is marked. Gram-negative. Occur intracytoplasmically as colonies. Cause ophthalmic diseases in sheep.

The type species is *Colesiota conjunctivae* (Coles) Rake.

1. **Colesiota conjunctivae** (Coles, 1931) Rake, 1948. (*Rickettsia conjunctivae* Coles, 17th Rept. Dir. Vet. Serv. and Anim. Ind. Union So. Africa, 1931, 175; *Chlamydozoon conjunctivae* Moshkovskiy, Uspekhi Souremennoi Biologii, *19*, 1945, 19; Rake, in Manual, 6th ed., 1948, 1119; *Chlamydozoon pecoris* Zhdanov and Korenblit, Jour. Microbiol., Epidemiol. and Immunobiol. (Russian), No. 9, 1950, 43; *Rickettsia conjunctivae ovis* Coles, Ann. New York Acad. Sci., *56*, 1953, 460.)

con.junc.ti'vae. L. adj. *conjunctivus* connective; M.L. fem.n. *conjunctiva* the conjunctiva; M.L. gen.noun *conjunctivae* of the conjunctiva.

Pleomorphic cells with diameters ranging from 200 millimicrons to 2 microns. May be uniformly staining coccoid forms or bacillary, triangular, annular or horse-shoe in form. Do not occur in chains. Colony-like masses are frequent. Not encapsulated. Non-motile. Stain with ordinary aniline dyes but less intensely than do bacteria. Gram-negative.

Cultivation: Has not been cultivated.

Immunology: Unknown.

Tissue tropism: Affects only the conjunctiva and the cornea.

Pathogenic for sheep. Causes acute conjunctivitis and keratitis.

Habitat: Found in the scrapings of the cornea, the conjunctiva and in the discharges from affected eyes of sheep. The etiological agent of infectious, or specific, ophthalmia in sheep.

Genus III. Ricolesia *Rake, gen. nov.*

Ri.co.le'si.a. *Ri-* an arbitrarily formed prefix taken from *Rickettsia;* M.L. noun *Colesia* named for Prof. J. D. W. A. Coles, the first to study these organisms; M.L. fem.n. *Ricolesia* an arbitrarily formed generic name.

Usually coccoid cells, but pleomorphism is marked. Gram-negative. Occur intracytoplasmically as scattered growth. Cause ophthalmic diseases of warm-blooded animals. The type species is *Ricolesia pullorum* (Zhdanov and Korenblit) Rake.

Key to the species of genus **Ricolesia.**

I. Affects fowls, causing a form of ocular roup.

                             1. *Ricolesia conjunctivae.*

II. Do not affect fowls.

  A. Affect ruminants, causing infectious conjunctivitis.

    1. Affects cattle.

                           2. *Ricolesia bovis.*

    2. Affects goats.

                           3. *Ricolesia caprae.*

  B. Does not affect ruminants; affects swine, causing infectious conjunctivitis.

                           4. *Ricolesia lestoquardii.*

1. Ricolesia conjunctivae (Coles, 1940) Rake, *comb. nov.* (*Rickettsia conjunctivae galli* Coles, Onderstepoort Jour. Vet. Sci. and Anim. Ind., *14*, 1940, 474; *Colesiota conjunctivae-gallii* Rake, in Manual, 6th ed., 1948, 1120; *Chlamydozoon conjunctivae galli* Krassilnikov, Guide to the Bacteria and Actinomycetes, Izd. Akad. Nauk, U.S.S.R., Moskau, 1949, 735; *Chlamydozoon pullorum* Zhdanov and Korenblit, Jour. Microbiol., Epidemiol. and Immunobiol. (Russian), No. 9, 1950, 43.)

con.junc.ti'vae. L.adj. *conjunctivus* connective; M.L. fem.n. *conjunctiva* the conjunctiva; M.L. gen.noun *conjunctivae* of the conjunctiva.

Pleomorphic. There are many coccoid cells, measuring 200 millimicrons to 2 microns in diameter. Other cells are bacillary, triangular, annular or horse-shoe in form. Most stain uniformly. Purplish red or blue with Giemsa's stain. Gram-negative.

Cultivation: Has not been cultivated.

Immunology: Unknown.

Pathogenic for the domestic fowl. Causes an acute conjunctivitis and keratitis.

Tissue tropism: Affects only the conjunctiva and the cornea.

Habitat: The etiological agent of one form of ocular roup in fowls.

2. Ricolesia bovis Rake, *comb. nov.* (*Rickettsia conjunctivae bovis* Coles, South Afr. Vet. Med. Assoc., *7*, 1936, 223; *Chlamydozoon conjunctivae-bovis* Moshkovskiy, Uspekhi Souremennoi Biologii, *19*, 1945, 19.)

bo'vis. L. noun *bos* a cow; L. gen.noun *bovis* of a cow.

Pleomorphic. Resembles *Ricolesia conjunctivae* morphologically and in staining reactions.

Cultivation: Has not been cultivated.

Immunology: Unknown.

Pathogenic for cattle. Causes an acute conjunctivitis and keratitis.

Tissue tropism: Affects only the conjunctiva and the cornea.

Habitat: The etiological agent of infectious kerato-conjunctivitis in cattle.

3. Ricolesia caprae Rake, *comb. nov.* (*Rickettsia conjunctivae caprae* Coles, Ann. New York Acad. Sci., *56*, 1953, 460.)

ca'prae. L. noun *capra* a she-goat; L. gen.noun *caprae* of a she-goat.

Pleomorphic. Resembles *Ricolesia conjunctivae.*

Cultivation: Has not been cultivated.

Immunology: Unknown.

Pathogenic for goats. Causes acute conjunctivitis and keratitis.

Tissue tropism: Affects only the conjunctiva and the cornea.

Habitat: The etiological agent of infectious kerato-conjunctivitis in goats.

4. Ricolesia lestoquardii (Donatien and Gayot, 1942) Rake, *comb. nov.* (*Rickettsia lestoquardi* (sic) Donatien and Gayot, Bull. Soc. path. exot., *35*, 1942, 325; *Chlamydozoon lestoquardi* (sic) Krassilnikov, Guide to the Bacteria and Actinomycetes, Izd. Akad. Nauk, U.S.S.R., Moskau, 1949, 735; *Rickettsia conjunctivae suis* Coles, Ann. New York Acad. Sci., *56*, 1953, 460.)

le.sto.quar′di.i. M.L. gen.noun *lesto-quardii* of Lestoquard; named for F. Lesto-quard.

Pleomorphic. Resembles *Ricolesia con-junctivae* morphologically and in staining reactions.

Cultivation: Has not been cultivated.

Immunology: Unknown.

Pathogenic for swine. Causes acute con-junctivitis and keratitis.

Tissue tropism: Affects only the conjunc-tiva and the cornea.

Habitat: The etiological agent of infec-tious kerato-conjunctivitis in swine.

Genus IV. Colettsia *Rake, nom. nov.*

(Unnamed new genus, Coles, Ann. New York Acad. of Sci., *56*, 1953, 461, (89).)

Co.lett′si.a. *-ttsia* an arbitrarily formed suffix taken from *Rickettsia; Cole-* from Coles; named for Prof. J. D. W. A. Coles, the first to study these organisms; M.L. fem.n. *Colettsia* an arbitrarily formed generic name.

Large, pleomorphic cells occurring intracytoplasmically. Apparently non-pathogenic, but may be saprophytic. Found only in the conjunctival cells of goats, sheep and cattle.

The type species is *Colettsia pecoris* Rake.

1. Colettsia pecoris Rake, *nom. nov.* (See Coles, Ann. New York Acad. of Sci., *56*, 1953, 461, (8).)

pe′co.ris. L. noun *pecus* cattle (as a col-lective herd); L. gen.noun *pecoris* of cattle.

Pleomorphic cells. Larger than members of the genera *Colesiota* and *Ricolesia*. Usual form is ellipsoidal, 2 microns in diameter; the cells are often coccoid, but annular, horse-shoe and comma forms occur. Occur scattered in the cytoplasm. Gram-negative.

Cultivation: Has not been cultivated.

Immunology: Unknown.

Apparently non-pathogenic, but may be saprophytic.

Tissue tropism: Found in the conjunctiva.

Habitat: Found only in the cells of the conjunctiva of goats, sheep and cattle.

Genus V. Miyagawanella *Brumpt, 1938.*

(Brumpt, Ann. de Parasitol., *16*, 1938, 153; *Rickettsiaformis* Zhdanov and Korenblit, Jour. Microbiol., Epidemiol. and Immunobiol. (Russian), No. 9, 1950, 43; also see Zhdanov, Opredelitel Virusov Celovska i Zivotmych, Izd. Akad. Med. Nauk, U.S.S.R., Moskau, 1953, 175; see Philip, Canad. Jour. Microbiol., *2*, 1956, 265.)

Mi.ya.ga.wa.nel′la. M.L. fem.dim.ending *-ella;* M.L. fem.n. *Miyagawanella* named for Prof. Y. Miyagawa, a Japanese bacteriologist, the first (1935) to grow the type species of this genus in the chick embryo.

Coccoid cells with a developmental cycle. Occur intracytoplasmically. Gram-negative. Cultivable in chicken embryonic tissues in tissue culture. Susceptible to sulfonamides and antibiotics. Pathogenic, causing various diseases in warm-blooded animals.

The type species is *Miyagawanella lymphogranulomatosis* Brumpt.

Key to the species of genus Miyagawanella.

I. The etiological agent of lymphogranuloma venereum, lymphogranuloma inguinale, climatic bubo and esthiomène in man.

1. *Miyagawanella lymphogranulomatosis.*

II. The etiological agent of psittacosis (parrot fever).

2. *Miyagawanella psittaci.*

III. The etiological agent of ornithosis (Meyer).

3. *Miyagawanella ornithosis.*

IV. The etiological agent of one type of viral pneumonia.

4. *Miyagawanella pneumoniae.*

V. The etiological agent of mouse pneumonitis (Gönnert).
5. *Miyagawanella bronchopneumoniae.*
VI. The etiological agent of feline pneumonitis (Baker).
6. *Miyagawanella felis.*
VII. The etiological agent of Louisiana pneumonitis.
7. *Miyagawanella louisianae.*
VIII. The etiological agent called the Illinois virus; the cause of one type of viral pneumonia.
8. *Miyagawanella illinii.*
IX. The etiological agent of paralysis in opossums; opossum A virus (Roca-Garcia).
9. *Miyagawanella opossumi.*
X. The etiological agent of ovine abortion (Stamp, McEwen, Watt and Nisbet).
10. *Miyagawanella ovis.*
XI. An agent from the intestinal tract of calves (York and Baker).
11. *Miyagawanella bovis.*
XII. The etiological agent of sporadic bovine encephalomyelitis (McNutt).
12. *Miyagawanella pecoris.*

1. **Miyagawanella lymphogranulomatosis** Brumpt, 1938. (Brumpt, Ann. de
Parasitol., *16*, 1938, 155; *Ehrlichia lymphogranulomatosis* Moshkovskiy, Uspekhi
Souremennoi Biologii (Russian) (Advances
in Modern Biology), *19*, 1945; *Rickettsiaformis lymphogranulomatis* Zhdanov and Korenblit, Jour. Microbiol., Epidemiol. and
Immunobiol. (Russian), No. 9, 1950, 43
(type species (by subsequent designation,
Philip, Canad. Jour. Microbiol., *3*, 1956, 265)
of genus *Rickettsiaformis* Zhdanov and Korenblit, *op. cit.*, 1950, 43; *Chlamydozoon lymph-
ophilus* Ryzhkov, Voprosy Meditsinskoi
Virusologii (Problems of Med. Virology),
Akad. Med. Nauk, S.S.S.R., Moskau, *3*,
1950, 17.)

lym.pho.gran.u.lo.ma.to'sis. M.L.
fem.n. *lymphogranulomatosis* the disease
lymphogranulomatosis; M.L. gen.noun
lymphogranulomatosis of lymphogranulomatosis.

Coccoid cells 200 to 350 millimicrons in
diameter are the elementary bodies. Initial
bodies up to 1 micron and plaques up to 10
microns in diameter are also found. All
larger forms are encapsulated with a substance derived either from the agent or from
the cytoplasm of parasitized cells. The elementary body is the basic unit. Occur in
pairs or clusters. Non-motile. Stain with
aniline dyes. Stain purple with Giemsa's and
red or blue, depending on the metabolic
state, with Macchiavello's stain. The matrix of the plaque does not give the reaction
for glycogen. Gram-negative.

Filterability: Passes through Chamberland L_2 and L_3, Berkefeld V and N and
sometimes through Seitz EK filters.

Cultivation: Growth occurs in tissue cultures of mammalian cells, in mammalian
cells on agar and in the chorio-allantoic
membrane, and particularly in the yolk sac,
of the chicken embryo but not in the allantoic sac.

Optimum temperature, 37° C. in tissue
cultures and 35° C. in the chicken embryo.

Immunology: Possesses one or more antigens in common with or closely resembling
one or more of those present in the chlamydiae and in other miyagawanellae. Antisera
against any of the species in these two genera react with antigens from *Miyagawanella
lymphogranulomatosis* or the other miyagawanellae thus far tested. One common antigen has been isolated as a soluble fraction
distinct from the bodies of the agent.
Sharply distinguished from the other miyagawanellae by antitoxic neutralization of
the toxic factor or by neutralization of infections in mice with chicken antisera. Evidence exists that these two serological reactions are with distinct specific antigens.
Immunity in man or other animals is probably poor in the absence of continuing apparent or inapparent infection.

Toxic factor: High concentrations of this
agent in infected yolk sac or in yolk injected
intravenously or intraperitoneally are rapidly fatal to mice. Produces characteristic
lesions on the skin of normal guinea pigs.

Pathogenic for man, apes, monkeys, guinea pigs, cotton rats, hamsters, mice and chicken embryos. Inapparent infections may occur with the agent harbored in the organs. Causes local genital lesions, septicemia, lymphadenitis, meningitis, ophthalmitis and rarely pneumonitis in man.

Tissue tropism: In laboratory rodents, this species is infective by the intranasal (pneumonitis), the intracerebral (meningitis) and the intradermal routes.

Antibiotic- and chemo-therapy: Susceptible to the tetracycline antibiotics, to chloramphenicol, to relatively high concentrations of penicillin, to the sulfonamides and to some antimony compounds.

Source: Most commonly found in the genital secretions of infected individuals or in the draining lymph nodes. Also occasionally found in blood, spinal fluid and ocular secretions.

Habitat: The etiological agent of lymphogranuloma venereum, lymphogranuloma inguinale, climatic bubo, esthiomène and some forms of anorectal inflammation.

2. **Miyagawanella psittaci** (Lillie, 1930) Moshkovskiy, 1945. (*Rickettsia psittaci* Lillie, U. S. Public Health Repts., *45*, 1930, 773; *Microbacterium multiforme psittacosis* Levinthal,* 1st Cong. Internat. de Microbiol., *1*, 1930, 523; Moshkovskiy, Uspekhi Souremennoi Biologii (Russian) (Advances in Modern Biology), *19*, 1945, 12; *Ehrlichia psittaci* Moshkovskiy, *ibid.*, 19; *Rickettsiaformis psittacosis* Zhdanov and Korenblit, Jour. Microbiol., Epidemiol. and Immunobiol. (Russian), No. 9, 1950, 43; *Chlamydozoon psittaci* Ryzhkov, Voprosy Meditsinskoi Virusologii (Problems of Med. Virology), Akad. Med. Nauk, S.S.S.R., Moskau, *3*, 1950, 17.)

psit'ta.ci. Gr. noun *psittacus* a parrot; M.L. gen.noun *psittaci* of a parrot.

Coccoid cells resemble those of *Miyagawanella lymphogranulomatosis*.

Filterability: Partly filterable through Berkefeld N, Chamberland L and Q and Seitz EK filters.

Cultivation: Same as for *Miyagawanella*

lymphogranulomatosis, but growth occurs readily in the allantoic sac without adaptation.

Immunology: Same as for *M. lymphogranulomatosis*, but no soluble fraction has yet been demonstrated.

Toxic factor: High concentrations of this agent in infected yolk sac or in yolk injected intravenously or intraperitoneally are rapidly fatal to mice.

Pathogenic for most birds, for man, monkeys, guinea pigs, pocket gophers, hamsters, white rats, kangaroo rats, mice, rabbits and for chicken embryos. Inapparent infections may occur with the agent harbored in the organs. Causes a pneumonitis of varying severity with or without septicemia in man.

Tissue tropism: Causes a septicemia. In man this species shows predilection for the respiratory tract. In laboratory rodents, it is infective by the intranasal, the intraperitoneal (peritonitis and septicemia), the intracerebral and the intravenous routes.

Antibiotic- and chemo-therapy: Susceptible to broad-spectrum antibiotics and to relatively high concentrations of penicillin. Some strains are susceptible to sulfonamides.

Source: Found in the organs and nasal secretions of infected birds and, from the latter, spreads to plumage by preening and other methods. Plentiful in droppings or dust from infected cages. Relatively resistant under such conditions.

Habitat: The etiological agent of psittacosis (parrot fever) and also of some cases of atypical pneumonia.

3. **Miyagawanella ornithosis** Rake, 1948. (Rake, in Manual, 6th ed., 1948, 1117; *Rickettsiaformis ornithosis* Zhdanov and Korenblit, Jour. Microbiol., Epidemiol. and Immunobiol. (Russian), No. 9, 1950, 43; *Chlamydozoon columbi* Ryzhkov, Voprosy Meditsinskoi Virusologii (Problems of Med. Virology), Akad. Med. Nauk, S.S.S.R., Moskau, *3*, 1950, 17; *Chlamydozoon meningophilus* Ryzhkov, *loc. cit.*)

---

* Type species of genus *Microbacterium* Levinthal (*op. cit.*, 1930, 523), which is invalid as a generic name because it is a later homonym of *Microbacterium* Orla-Jensen, 1919 (see p. 600).

or.ni.tho′sis. Gr. noun *ornis, ornithis* a bird; Gr. suffix *-osis* ending to denote a disease of; M.L. gen.noun *ornithosis* a disease of birds, ornithosis.

Coccoid cells resemble those of *Miyagawanella lymphogranulomatosis.*

Cultivation: Same as for *Miyagawanella psittaci.*

Immunology: Possesses one or more antigens in common with or closely resembling one or more of those present in chlamydiae and in other miyagawanellae as shown by a cross reaction in complement-fixation tests. Sharply distinguished from other miyagawanellae by toxin-antitoxin neutralization or by neutralization of infection in mice with chicken antisera. The latter test, however, suggests that the agent of meningopneumonitis (Francis and Magill, Jour. Exp. Med., *68*, 1938, 147) is this species rather than something different. Immunity in man or other animals is probably poor except in the presence of continuing apparent or inapparent infections. Cross reactions suggest that *Miyagawanella ornithosis* may be more closely related to *M. lymphogranulomatosis* than is *M. psittaci.*

Toxic factor: Same as for *Miyagawanella psittaci.*

Pathogenic for birds (especially non-psittacine species), man, ferrets, guinea pigs, hamsters, white rats, kangaroo rats, mice, rabbits and for chicken embryos. Inapparent infections may occur. Causes a pneumonitis of varying severity with or without septicemia in man.

Tissue tropism: Causes a septicemia. In birds and man, shows a predilection for the lungs. In laboratory rodents, this species is infective by the intranasal, intracerebral, intravenous and, with relatively large inocula of most strains, by the intraperitoneal routes.

Antibiotic- and chemo-therapy: Susceptible to many antibiotics including relatively large doses of penicillin. Not susceptible to sulfonamides.

Source: Found in the organs and nasal secretions of finches, pheasants (including domestic chickens), other poultry, domesticated doves, fulmar petrels and other birds. Spreads from the secretions to plumage and droppings.

Habitat: The etiological agent of ornithosis and of meningopneumonitis (Francis and Magill, *loc. cit.*).

4. Miyagawanella pneumoniae Rake, 1948. (Rake, in Manual, 6th ed., 1948, 1118; *Ehrlichia pneumoniae* Krassilnikov, Guide to the Bacteria and Actinomycetes, Izd. Akad. Nauk, U.S.S.R., Moskau, 1949, 743; *Rickettsiaformis pneumoniae* Zhdanov and Korenblit, Jour. Microbiol., Epidemiol. and Immunobiol. (Russian), No. 9, 1950, 43; *Chlamydozoon hominis* Ryzhkov, Voprosy Meditsinskoi Virusologii (Prob. Med. Virol.), Akad. Med. Nauk, S.S.S.R., Moskau, *3*, 1950, 17.)

pneu.mo′ni.ae. Gr. noun *pneumonia* pneumonia; M.L. gen.noun *pneumoniae* of pneumonia.

Coccoid cells resemble those of *Miyagawanella lymphogranulomatosis* but are slightly smaller, measuring about 200 millimicrons in diameter.

Cultivation: Same as for *Miyagawanella psittaci.*

Immunology: Same as for *Miyagawanella psittaci.* Distinct from *Miyagawanella ornithosis* by the neutralization test with chicken antisera.

Pathogenic for birds, man, cotton rats, hamsters, white rats, kangaroo rats, mice and for chicken embryos. Causes a fatal pneumonitis in man.

Tissue tropism: Same as for *Miyagawanella ornithosis.*

Antibiotic- and chemo-therapy: Same as for *Miyagawanella ornithosis.*

Source: Found in the lungs of infected humans. Possibly originally of avian origin.

Habitat: The etiological agent of one type of viral pneumonia. The type strain is the so-called strain S-F (Eaton, Beck and Pearson, Jour. Exp., Med., *73*, 1941, 641).

5. Miyagawanella bronchopneumoniae Moshkovskiy, 1945. (Bronchopneumonie virus, Gonnert, Zent. f. Bakt., I Abt., Orig., *147*, 1941, 161; Moshkovskiy, Uspekhi Souremennoi Biologii, *19*, 1945, 19; *Ehrlichia bronchopneumoniae* Moshkovskiy, *loc. cit.; Cystidium bronchopneumoniae muris* Ruska, Poppe and Kausche, Ztschr. f. Hyg., *127*, 1947, 201; *Cystidium gonnertianum*

Ruska et al., *loc. cit.; Rickettsiaformis muris* Zhdanov and Korenblit, Jour. Microbiol., Epidemiol. and Immunobiol. (Russian), No. 9, 1950; *Chlamydozoon murinus* Ryzhkov, Voprosy Meditsinskoi Virusologii (Problems of Medical Virology), Akad. Med. Nauk, S.S.S.R., Moskau, *3*, 1950, 17.)

bron.cho.pneu.mo'ni.ae. Gr. noun *bronchus* trachea, bronchus; Gr. noun *pneumonia* pneumonia; M.L. noun *bronchopneumonia* bronchopneumonia; M.L. gen.noun *bronchopneumoniae* of bronchopneumonia.

Coccoid cells resemble those of *Miyagawanella pneumoniae*.

Cultivation: Same as for *Miyagawanella lymphogranulomatosis*. Does not grow in the allantoic cavity of the chick.

Immunology: Same as for *M. lymphogranulomatosis*, but no soluble antigen has been demonstrated.

Toxic factor: High concentrations of this agent in heavily infected yolk sacs and in yolk injected intravenously are very rapidly fatal to mice.

Pathogenic for mice, hamsters and ferrets. Produces a moderately severe pneumonitis.

Tissue tropism: Shows a predilection for the lungs. In mice, it is also infective by the intravenous route.

Antibiotic- and chemo-therapy: Susceptible to sulfonamides and to antibiotics.

Source: Found in the lungs of certain stocks of the laboratory mouse.

Habitat: The etiological agent of mouse pneumonitis.

6. **Miyagawanella felis** Rake, 1948. (Rake, in Manual, 6th ed., 1948, 1118; *Ehrlichia felis* Krassilnikov, Guide to the Bacteria and Actinomycetes, Izd. Akad. Nauk, U.S.S.R., Moskau, 1949, 743; *Rickettsiaformis felis* Zhdanov and Korenblit, Jour. Microbiol., Epidemiol. and Immunobiol. (Russian), No. 9, 1950, 43; *Chlamydozoon felis* Ryzhkov, Voprosy Meditsinskoi Virusologii (Prob. Med. Virol.), Akad. Med. Nauk, S.S.S.R., Moskau, *3*, 1950, 17; *Miyagawanella felinis* Sprockhoff, Deutsch. Tierarztl. Wochnschr., *23-24*, 1953, 256.)

fe'lis. L. noun *felis* the cat.

Coccoid cells resemble those of *Miyagawanella lymphogranulomatosis*.

Cultivation: Same as for *Miyagawanella psittaci*.

Immunology: Same as for *M. psittaci*, but nothing is known about inapparent infections in the natural host, the domestic cat.

Toxic factor: Infected yolk sac or other membranes and yolk or other fluids are rapidly fatal when injected intravenously into mice or chicken embryos or intraperitoneally into mice.

Pathogenic for cats, hamsters, mice and chicken embryos. Causes a fatal pneumonitis with acute conjunctivitis in cats.

Tissue tropism: Shows a predilection for the lungs and for the conjunctivae. In laboratory rodents this species is infective by the intranasal, intraperitoneal, intracerebral and intravenous routes.

Antibiotic- and chemo-therapy: Same as for *Miyagawanella ornithosis*.

Source: From the lungs of infected cats.

Habitat: The etiological agent of one form of cat nasal catarrh, influenza or distemper (Baker, Science, *96*, 1942, 475) and feline pneumonitis.

7. **Miyagawanella louisianae** Rake, 1948. (Rake, in Manual, 6th ed., 1948, 1118; *Ehrlichia lousianae* (sic) Krassilnikov, Guide to the Bacteria and Actinomycetes, Izd. Akad. Nauk, U.S.S.R., Moskau, 1949, 743.)

lou.i.si.a'nae. M.L. noun *Louisiana* the state Louisiana; M.L. gen.noun *louisianae* of Louisiana.

Coccoid cells resemble those of *Miyagawanella psittaci*.

Filterability: Passes through Berkefeld N and Mandler 6, 7 and 9 filters.

Cultivation: Grows in the yolk sac of the chicken embryo.

Immunology: Indistinguishable from other miyagawanellae by complement-fixation tests with yolk-sac antigens. Partly distinguished from *Miyagawanella psittaci* and *M. ornithosis* by active immunization in mice and guinea pigs.

Pathogenic for man, guinea pigs, cotton rats, mice and chicken embryos. Slightly pathogenic for white rats, golden hamsters and deer mice. Monkeys (*Macacus rhesus*), rabbits, muskrats and nutria are unaffected.

Causes a highly fatal pneumonitis and septicemia in man.

Tissue tropism: Causes a septicemia. In man this species shows predilection for the respiratory tract. In laboratory rodents it is infective by the intranasal, intraperitoneal, intracerebral, intramuscular and subcutaneous routes.

Antibiotic- and chemo-therapy: Same as for *Miyagawanella ornithosis*.

Source: From the sputa and organs of infected persons.

Habitat: The etiological agent of Louisiana pneumonitis (Olson and Larson, U. S. Pub. Health Repts., *59*, 1944, 1373); the so-called Borg strain.

8. **Miyagawanella illinii** Rake, 1948. (The Illinois virus, Zichis and Shaughnessy, Science, *102*, 1945, 301; Rake, in Manual, 6th ed., 1948, 1119; *Ehrlichia illinii* Krassilnikov, Guide to the Bacteria and Actinomycetes, Izd. Akad. Nauk, U.S.S.R., Moskau, 1949, 743.)

il.li′ni.i. Fr. noun *Illinois* a place name; M.L. gen.noun *illinii* (probably intended to mean) of Illinois.

Coccoid cells resemble those of *Miyagawanella lymphogranulomatosis*.

Filterability: Passes through Berkefeld N and W filters.

Cultivation: Grows in the yolk sac of the chicken embryo.

Immunology: Distinguished from other miyagawanellae by neutralization tests in mice with chicken antisera and partly from *Miyagawanella psittaci, M. ornithosis* and *M. pneumoniae* by active immunization in mice.

Pathogenic for man and for white mice. Causes a highly fatal pneumonitis in man.

Tissue tropism: Infective in mice by the intranasal, intraperitoneal, intracerebral and subcutaneous routes.

Source: From the lungs of infected persons.

Habitat: The etiological agent of a highly fatal pneumonitis in man.

9. **Miyagawanella opossumi** (Ryzhkov, 1950) Rake, *comb. nov.* (Opossum virus A, Roca-García, Jour. Inf. Dis., *85*, 1949, 275; *Chlamydozoon opossumi* Ryzhkov, Voprosy Meditsinskoi Virusologii (Prob. Med.

Virol.), Akad. Med. Nauk, S.S.S.R., Moskau, *3*, 1950, 17; *Rickettsiaformis opposum* (sic) Zhdanov, Opredelitel Virusov Celovska i Zivotmych, Izd. Akad. Med. Nauk, U.S.S.R., Moskau, 1953, 185.)

o.pos′su.mi. Am.Ind. noun *opossum* the opossum, a North and South American marsupial; M.L. gen.noun *opossumi* of the opossum.

Coccoid cells resemble those of *Miyagawanella lymphogranulomatosis*. Non-motile. Stain red-purple with Giemsa's or Wright's stain, and red with Macchiavello's and blue with Castañeda's stain. Gram-negative.

Filterability: Passes through a Berkefeld V but not an N or a Seitz filter.

Cultivation: Grows in tissue cultures of mouse or chicken cells and in the yolk sac of the chicken embryo.

Immunology: Contains a group complement-fixing antigen in common with the other miyagawanellae. Shows a serological relationship to *M. pneumoniae* by cross-protection tests.

Toxic factor: Same as for *M. lymphogranulomatosis*.

Pathogenic for South American opossums, producing a central-nervous-system disease and a paralysis of the hind quarters. Pathogenic for mice and chicken embryos. Not pathogenic for pigeons or guinea pigs.

Tissue tropism: Infects opossums in the laboratory by the intraperitoneal but not by the subcutaneous route. Infects mice by the intracerebral or the intranasal but not by the intraperitoneal route.

Chemotherapy: Not susceptible to sulfonamides.

Source: Isolated from an opossum (*Didelphys paraguayensis*) trapped in a district of the municipality of Cáqueza, State of Cundinamarca, Colombia.

Habitat: The etiological agent of paralysis in opossums.

10. **Miyagawanella ovis** (Zhdanov, 1953) Rake, *comb. nov.* (Minute organisms from enzootic abortion of ewes, Stamp, McEwen, Watt and Nisbet, Vet. Record, *62*, 1950, 251; Virus of ovine enzootic abortion, Stamp, Jour. Comp. Path. and Therap., *61*, 1951, 215; also see Monsur and Barwell, Brit. Jour. Exp. Path., *32*, 1951, 414; *Rickettsia-*

formis ovis Zhdanov, Opredelitel Virusov Celovska i Zivotmych, Izd. Akad. Med. Nauk, U.S.S.R., Moskau, 1953, 188.)

o'vis L. noun *ovis* a sheep.

Elementary bodies are coccoid bodies resembling those of *Miyagawanella lymphogranulomatosis*. Often occur in clusters. Found in cell cytoplasm and free. Stain red with Ziehl-Neelsen's stain. Also stain with Giemsa's, with Castañeda's and with Macchiavello's stains.

Filterability: Passes through a 0.4 micron gradacol membrane.

Cultivation: Grows in the yolk sac of the chicken embryo.

Viable after storage at −20° or −70° C.

Pathogenicity and tissue tropism: Pathogenic for sheep, causing abortion in the pregnant female. When injected into sheep subcutaneously, intravenously or intradermally, a febrile response is produced. No symptoms are produced when injected intranasally or into the prepuce or the conjunctiva. In the pregnant cow, produces abortion with elementary bodies found in the placenta. Produces no symptoms in calves injected intranasally. No disease is produced in male guinea pigs. In the pregnant female guinea pig after subcutaneous or intraperitoneal injection, but not after intracerebral injection, elementary bodies are found in the placenta. In mice and rats no disease is produced by subcutaneous, intraperitoneal or intracerebral inoculation. In mice, but not in rats, intranasal inoculation produces pneumonitis.

Habitat: The etiological agent of enzootic abortion in ewes. Elementary bodies are found in the placenta, fetal membranes and uterine discharges.

11. **Miyagawanella bovis** York and Baker, 1951. (York and Baker, Jour. Exp. Med., *93*, 1951, 587; *Rickettsiaformis bovis* Zhdanov, Opredelitel Virusov Celovska i Zivotmych, Izd. Akad. Med. Nauk, U.S.S.R., Moskau, 1953, 187.)

bo'vis. L. noun *bos* a cow; M.L. gen.noun *bovis* of a cow.

Coccoid cells. Stain red with Macchiavello's stain.

Filterability: Passes through both Berkefeld V and N filters.

Cultivation: Grows particularly well in the yolk sac of chicken embryos, less well in the allantoic cavity and even less well on the chorio-allantoic membrane.

Immunology: Contains the group antigen of the miyagawanellae, giving cross reactions in the neutralization test. A specific neutralization can be obtained with chicken sera, and the agent can be distinguished from *Miyagawanella felis*.

Toxic factor: Possesses a specific toxin as in *M. lymphogranulomatosis*.

Pathogenic for pigs, guinea pigs, mice, cats, rabbits and chicken embryos. Produces an infection but no disease in calves. Dogs are not susceptible.

Tissue tropism: Appears in the feces of calves after feeding. Mice are infected intranasally only after passage and are not infected by intraperitoneal or intracerebral routes. Guinea pigs are infected intraperitoneally with the production of fever and of peritonitis. Cats are infected either intranasally or by intracardiac injection with the production of fever but are not infected *per os*. Rabbits are infected intraperitoneally and pigs are infected intravenously with the production of fever.

Antibiotic- and chemo-therapy: Susceptible to aureomycin and penicillin but not to sulfonamides.

Habitat: Found in the feces of normal calves, where no obvious disease is produced.

12. **Miyagawanella pecoris** Rake, *nom. nov.* (Agent of infectious encephalomyelitis of cattle, McNutt, Vet. Med., *35*, 1940, 228; also see North Amer. Vet., *23*, 1942, 242.)

pe'co.ris. L. noun *pecus* cattle (as a collective herd); L. gen.noun *pecoris* of cattle.

Elementary bodies are coccoid bodies 375 millimicrons in diameter when coated with heavy metal. Staining reactions are similar to those of *Miyagawanella lymphogranulomatosis*.

Filterability: Passes through Berkefeld N or V filters and fritted glass filters.

Cultivation: Grows in the yolk sac of the chicken embryo.

Viable after storage at 24° C. for 227 days and at −60° or −70° C. for 18 months.

Immunology: Complement-fixing antibodies are produced in calves, monkeys and guinea pigs, showing cross-fixation with other miyagawanellae.

Pathogenicity and tissue tropism: Intracerebral injection in calves produces fever and encephalitis while intraperitoneal injection produces peritonitis and encephalitis. After subcutaneous injection a syndrome like the natural sporadic bovine encephalomyelitis is produced. Encephalitis is produced in monkeys after intracerebral or intraperitoneal inoculation. In rabbits there are no symptoms after intracerebral, intratesticular or corneal inocula-

tion. In cotton rats and guinea pigs, intracerebral inoculation produces encephalitis, and in guinea pigs, intraperitoneal inoculation produces peritonitis. In mice, only dubious results are produced by intracerebral, intranasal or intraperitoneal inoculation. In hamsters, intracerebral inoculation produces encephalitis.

Antibiotic therapy: Susceptible to the action of aureomycin and terramycin.

Habitat: The etiological agent of sporadic bovine encephalomyelitis. Elementary bodies are present in the exudate over the brain and in the peritoneum.

FAMILY III. BARTONELLACEAE GIESZCZYKIEWICZ, 1939.*

(Bull. Acad. Polon. Sci., Lettres, Classe Sci. Math. Nat., B (I), 1939, 9–27.)

Bar.to.nel.la'ce.ae. M.L. fem.n. *Bartonella* type genus of the family; *-aceae* ending to denote a family; M.L. fem.pl.n. *Bartonellaceae* the *Bartonella* family.

Rod-shaped, coccoid, ring- or disc-shaped, filamentous and beaded microorganisms, usually less than 3 microns in greatest dimension. Parasites of the erythrocytes in man and other vertebrates. Not acid-alcohol-fast. Stain lightly with many aniline dyes but distinctly with Giemsa's stain after methyl alcohol fixation; following this technique the *Bartonellaceae* are readily distinguished from the protozoa which also parasitize erythrocytes in that the former stain with no differentiation into nucleus and cytoplasm. Gram-negative. Cultivation *in vitro* on non-living media has been achieved in two genera. At least one species bears a single polar flagellum in culture. Arthropod transmission has been established in the majority of genera. Cause bartonellosis in man and haemobartonellosis, grahamellosis and eperythrozoönosis in lower animals.

Attempts at the familial classification of the genera *Haemobartonella*, *Eperythrozoon* and *Grahamella* are fundamentally unsatisfactory at present because of inadequate knowledge. Suggestions have been made that one or more of these genera be placed in families as varied as *Pseudomonadaceae* and *Actinomycetaceae*. Another proposal, almost the opposite, is that these organisms are not bacteria at all but belong to some ill-defined group related to the viruses. Finally, there has been some questioning of the validity of the generic distinctions themselves. Divergences of this magnitude reflect inadequacy of the basic data. Until such data are available, these genera are retained in *Bartonellaceae*, first, as a convenience for grouping microorganisms with common important features, and second, because these microorganisms cannot be better classified in any other family. Future information may suggest reclassification; this is clearly realized.

Other possibly related forms, e.g. *Aegyptianella* Carpano (Boll. d. Min. d. Agricultura egiziano, 1928) and *Cytoecetes* Tyzzer (Parasitol., *30*, 1938, 242), are not included here since it is even less evident that these microorganisms are bacteria.

Key to the genera of family **Bartonellaceae.**

I. Multiply on erythrocytes and within fixed-tissue cells. Usually possess a single, polar flagellum when cultivated in or on non-living media. Provoke a progressive anemia

---

* Revised by Dr. David Weinman, Department of Microbiology, Yale University, New Haven, Connecticut, September, 1955.

or a cutaneous eruption, usually both in succession, not both coincidentally. Found in man and *Phlebotomus spp.*

Genus I. *Bartonella*, p. 969.

II. Not known to multiply in fixed-tissue cells; parasitize erythrocytes and may multiply there. Flagella not demonstrated. Occur in mammals and possibly in other vertebrates, but not known from man.

    A. Usually parasitize less than 5 per cent of the total erythrocytes, rarely more. Relatively monomorphic in erythrocytes. Non-pathogenic or only slightly so. Affected little, if at all, by splenectomy. Cultivable on non-living media. Occur within the red blood cells; epi-erythrocytic forms are problematical.

Genus II. *Grahamella*, p. 971.

    B. Parasitized cells may constitute more than 90 per cent of the total erythrocytes at the peak of infection. Polymorphism is marked when in or on red blood cells. May or may not be pathogenic. Marked increase in numbers following splenectomy. Cultivation on non-living media not confirmed. Occur on the red blood cells; situation within red cells possible but not proved.

        1. Extremely polymorphic; however, rods of varying sizes almost invariably occur, often in chains. Habitat predominantly epi-erythrocytic. Usually pathogenic, provoking a progressive, sometimes fatal, anemia.

Genus III. *Haemobartonella*, p. 972.

        2. Fundamental morphological type is ring- or disc-shaped. Rods are one disc- or ring-diameter in length; composite rods are made of these units. Occur in great numbers in the blood plasma as well as on the erythrocytes. Usually non-pathogenic.

Genus IV. *Eperythrozoon*, p. 977.

Genus I. **Bartonella** *Strong, Tyzzer and Sellards, 1915.*

(*Bartonia* Strong, Tyzzer, Brues, Sellards and Gastiaburú, Jour. Amer. Med. Assoc.,
61, 1913, 1715; not *Bartonia* Mühlenberg, in Willdenow, Neue Schrift Ges. Nat.
Fr., Berlin, *3*, 1801, 444; not *Bartonia* Sims, Bot. Mag., 1804; not *Bartonia*
Crossman, Essais de Paléoconchologie Comparée, 4ᵉ Livr., Paris,
1901; Strong, Tyzzer and Sellards, Jour. Amer. Med. Assoc.,
64, 1915, 808; also see Tyzzer and Weinman, Amer. Jour.
Hyg., *30* (B), 1939, 143; and Weinman, Trans. Amer.
Philosoph. Soc., *33*, (N.S.), 1944, 246.)

Bar.to.nel′la. M.L. dim.ending -*ella*; M.L. fem.dim.n. *Bartonella* named for Dr. A. L. Barton, who described these organisms in 1909.

Microorganisms which multiply in fixed-tissue cells and on erythrocytes. On the red blood cells in stained films, the organisms appear as rounded or ellipsoidal forms or as slender, straight, curved or bent rods occurring either singly or in groups. Characteristically occur in chains of several segmenting organisms, sometimes swollen at one or both ends and frequently beaded (Strong et al., *op. cit.*, 1913, 1715), without a distinct differentiation of nucleus and cytoplasm. In the tissues they are situated within the cytoplasm of endothelial cells as isolated elements and are grouped in rounded masses. Possess independent motility. Reproduce by binary fission. May be cultivated by unlimited serial transfers on cell-free media. Occur spontaneously in man and in arthropod vectors. One species has been recognized, and it is known to be established only on the South American continent and perhaps in Central America. Human bartonellosis may be manifested clinically by one of the two syndromes constituting Carrión's disease (Oroya fever or Verruga Peruana) or by an asymptomatic infection.

The type species is *Bartonella bacilliformis* (Strong et al.) Strong et al.

1. **Bartonella bacilliformis** (Strong et al., 1913) Strong et al., 1915. (*Bartonia bacilliformis* Strong, Tyzzer, Brues, Sellards and Gastiaburú, Jour. Amer. Med. Assoc., *61*, 1913, 1715; Strong, Tyzzer and Sellards, Jour. Amer. Med. Assoc., *64*, 1915, 808; also see Tyzzer and Weinman, Amer. Jour. Hyg., *30* (B), 1939, 143; and Weinman, Trans. Amer. Philosoph. Soc., *33* (N.S.), 1944, 246.)

ba.cil.li.for′mis. L. dim.noun *bacillus* a small staff, rodlet; L. noun *forma* shape, form; M.L. adj. *bacilliformis* rodlet-shaped.

Small, polymorphic organisms which show their greatest morphological range in the blood of man where they appear as red-violet rods or coccoids situated on the red cells when stained with Giemsa's stain. Bacilliform bodies are the most typical, measuring 0.25 to 0.5 by 1.0 to 3.0 microns. Often curved; may show polar enlargement and granules at one or both ends. Rounded organisms measure about 0.75 micron in diameter, and a ring-like variety is sometimes abundant. On semi-solid media, a mixture of rods and granules appears. The organisms may occur singly or in large and small, irregular dense collections measuring up to 25 microns or more in length. Punctiform, spindle-shaped and ellipsoidal forms occur which vary in size from 0.2 to 0.5 by 0.3 to 3.0 microns. Motile in cultures. Electron microscope techniques applied to cultures show a definite cell membrane, undifferentiated protoplasm and a tuft of 1 to 10 polar flagella which are approximately 20 millimicrons in diameter and which have an average undulation phase of 0.95 micron (Peters and Wigand, Ztschr. f. Tropenmed. u. Parasit., *3*, 1952, 313; also see Bact. Rev., *19*, 1955, 150). Stain poorly or not at all with many aniline dyes but satisfactorily with Romanowsky's and Giemsa's stains. Not acid-fast. Gram-negative.

Gelatin: No liquefaction.

Cultivation: Grows in semi-solid agar with fresh rabbit serum and rabbit hemoglobin, in semi-solid agar with the blood of man, horse or rabbit with or without the addition of fresh tissue and certain carbohydrates, in other culture media containing blood, serum or plasma, in Huntoon's hormone agar at 20 per cent, in semi-solid gelatin media, in blood-glucose-cystine agar and in chorio-allantoic fluid and yolk sac of chick embryo.

No action on lead acetate.

No acid or gas from glucose, sucrose, galactose, maltose, fructose, xylose, lactose, mannose, mannitol, dulcitol, arabinose, raffinose, rhamnose, dextrin, inulin, salicin or amygdalin.

Obligately aerobic.

Grows at 28° and 37° C., with greater longevity at 28° C. Cultures viable after storage for five years at −70° C.

Immunology: Natural immunity to infection has not been demonstrated in susceptible species. Acquired immunity is apparent both during and after the disease. Bartonellae from different sources appear to provoke similar responses. Bartonellae from Oroya fever protect against infection with organisms obtained from verruga cases.

Serology: Immune sera fix complement; employing heterologous strains, no significant titer differences were found in quantitative tests. Immune rabbit sera have not agglutinated *Proteus* OX_{19}, OX_2 or OXK at titers above 1:20. Agglutination of suspensions of *Bartonella* by sera from recovered cases has been reported.

Pathogenicity: Three forms of the disease bartonellosis occur in man: the anemic (Oroya fever), the eruptive (Verruga Peruana) and, rarely, mixed types of both of these forms. Experimental Oroya fever has not been successfully produced in animals, except rarely in an atypical form in monkeys. Experimental Verruga Peruana has been produced in man and in a number of species of monkeys.

Antibiotic- and chemo-therapy: Not sensitive *in vivo* to neosalvarsan nor in general to other arsenical compounds; sensitive to penicillin, streptomycin and chloramphenicol. Inhibited *in vitro* by 0.1 microgram of oxytetracycline per cc of semi-solid rabbit-serum agar at pH 8.0.

Source: Isolated from blood and endothelial cells of lymph nodes, spleen and liver of human cases of Oroya fever; also found in blood and in eruptive elements in Verruga Peruana.

Habitat: Found in the blood and endothelial cells of infected man; probably also found in sand flies (*Phlebotomus verrucarum*).

Genus II. **Grahamella** *Brumpt, 1911.**

(*Grahamia* Tartakowsky, Trav. IXᵉ Cong. Int. Med. Vet., *4*, 1910, 242; not *Grahamia* Theobald, Colonial Office, Misc. Pub. No. 237, 1909; Brumpt, Bull. Soc. path. exot., *4*, 1911, 514.)

Gra.ha.mel'la. M.L. dim.ending *-ella*; M.L. fem.dim.n. *Grahamella* named for Dr. G. S. Graham-Smith, who discovered these organisms in the blood of moles.

Microorganisms occurring within the erythrocytes of lower mammals. Morphologically these organisms bear a resemblance to but are less polymorphic than the species in *Bartonella* and stain more deeply with Giemsa's stain than do the bartonellae. Neither motility nor flagella have been demonstrated. Not acid-fast. Gram-negative. Several species have been cultivated on non-living media. Growth is favored by the addition of hemoglobin. In cultures, the slight propensity to grow in unbranched filaments is variable; rods and coccoids with indistinct contours are commonly cemented together in dense masses. Aerobic. Parasitic. Splenectomy has little effect on the course of infection. Non-pathogenic. Not affected by arsenicals. The etiological agent of grahamellosis of rodents and of some other vertebrates.

The type species is *Grahamella talpae* Brumpt.

1. **Grahamella talpae** Brumpt, 1911. (Bull. Soc. path. exot., *4*, 1911, 514.)

tal'pae. M.L. fem.n. *Talpa* a genus of moles; M.L. gen.noun *talpae* of *Talpa*.

Long or short rods of irregular contour lying within the red blood cells, many with a marked curve, often near one of the extremities. One or both ends of the longer form is enlarged, giving a wedge- or club-shaped appearance. Some of the medium-sized forms are definitely dumbbell-shaped; small forms are nearly round. With Giemsa's stain, the protoplasm of the organism stains light blue with darker areas at the enlarged ends. Dark staining areas of the longer forms give the organism a banded appearance. Occasionally free in the plasma, but then usually occur in groups. Most of the infected corpuscles contain between 6 and 20 organisms, but relatively few erythrocytes are infected (rarely more than one per cent (Graham-Smith, Jour. Hyg., *5*, 1905, 453)).

Infectivity: Infective for moles.

Source and habitat: Found in moles.

2. **Grahamella peromysci** Tyzzer, 1942. (Proc. Amer. Philosoph. Soc., *85*, 1942, 363.)

pe.ro.mys'ci. M.L. mas.n. *Peromyscus* a genus of mice; M.L. gen.noun *peromysci* of *Peromyscus*.

Occurs as rather uniform rods, spaced within red blood cells, with no morphological features to distinguish it from other species. Non-motile.

Grows on non-living media containing blood at temperatures varying from 20° to 28° C. under aerobic conditions. Colonies rarely exceed 1.5 mm in diameter and are composed of rods as long as 1.5 microns, varying in thickness from 0.25 to 0.75 micron, and coccoids, 0.25 to 1.0 micron in diameter, occurring together in compact clumps. Older cultures may contain chains of rods and globoid bodies 12 microns or less in diameter. Organisms in cultures stain poorly with alkaline methylene blue solution (Loeffler's) but well with Giemsa's stain. Motility not reported.

Hemolysis: Not reported.

Infectivity: Blood or cultures infect the

---

* Revised by Dr. David Weinman, Department of Microbiology, Yale University, New Haven, Connecticut, September, 1955.

normal host, the deer mouse (*Peromyscus leucopus novaboracensis*), but not the white Swiss mouse. Monkeys (*Macaca mulatta*) are not infected by cultures.

Comment: Numerous species of *Grahamella* have been named according to their hosts, and there is no satisfactory evidence that they are different microorganisms.

Grahamella peromysci has been described here only in order to include information on the cultural characteristics of the genus *Grahamella*, and no opinion as to the validity of this species is expressed thereby.

Source and habitat: Occurs naturally in the deer mouse (*Peromyscus leucopus novaboracensis*).

Genus III. **Haemobartonella** *Tyzzer and Weinman, 1939.**

(Amer. Jour. Hyg., *30* (B), 1939, 141.)

Hae.mo.bar.to.nel'la. Gr. noun *haema* blood; M.L. fem.dim.n. *Bartonella* type genus of the family *Bartonellaceae;* M.L. fem.dim.n. *Haemobartonella* the blood(-inhabiting) *Bartonella*.

Parasites of the red blood cells. There is no demonstrable multiplication in tissues, and cutaneous eruptions are not produced. Typically rod-shaped or coccoid organisms which show no differentiation into nucleus and cytoplasm. The morphological range may vary with the type of host employed. Stain well with Romanowsky-type stains and poorly with many other aniline dyes. Not acid-alcohol-fast. Gram-negative. Not cultivated indefinitely in cell-free media. Distributed over the surface of the erythrocytes and possibly sometimes within them. Rarely produce disease in animals without splenectomy. The experimental host range is restricted: an organism infective for one species of rodent may commonly infect other rodents but not primates. Markedly influenced by arsenotherapy but, so far as is known, do not respond to penicillin. Occur naturally as parasites of vertebrates. Transmitted by arthropods. Geographical distribution of the best-studied species is similar to that of the vertebrate host and may be world wide.

The type species is *Haemobartonella muris* (Mayer) Tyzzer and Weinman.

Key to the species of genus **Haemobartonella.†**

I. Found in rodents.
  A. Found in the albino rat.
            1. *Haemobartonella muris.*
  B. Found in the vole.
            2. *Haemobartonella microti.*
  C. Found in the guinea pig.
            3. *Haemobartonella tyzzeri.*
  D. Found in the deer mouse.
            4. *Haemobartonella peromysci.*
  E. Found in squirrels.
            5. *Haemobartonella sciuri.*
II. Not found in rodents.
  A. Found in herbivorous animals.
    1. Found in the cow.
            6. *Haemobartonella bovis.*

---

* Revised by Dr. David Weinman, Department of Microbiology, Yale University, New Haven, Connecticut, September, 1955.

† The species in this genus are not yet well defined. For convenience they have been arranged here according to their usual hosts even though it may be evident from their descriptions that other criteria are used and are sometimes essential for establishing their individuality. In all probability the organisms listed here are distinct species, although it may eventually be shown that this arrangement does not represent their true relationships.

2. Found in the buffalo.

7. *Haemobartonella sturmanii.*

B. Not found in herbivorous animals.

1. Found in carnivorous animals (dogs).

8. *Haemobartonella canis.*

2. Found in insectivorous animals (shrews).

9. *Haemobartonella blarinae.*

1. **Haemobartonella muris** (Mayer, 1921) Tyzzer and Weinman, 1939. (*Bartonella muris* Mayer, Arch. f. Schiffs. u. Tropen-Hyg., *25*, 1921, 151; *Bartonella muris ratti* Regendanz and Kikuth, Compt. rend. Soc. Biol., Paris, *98*, 1928, 1578; Tyzzer and Weinman, Amer. Jour. Hyg., *30* (B), 1939, 143.)

mu'ris. L. noun *mus* the mouse; L. gen. noun *muris* of the mouse.

Slender rods with rounded ends, frequently showing granules or swellings at either one or both extremities and dumbbell, coccoid or diplococcoid forms. Occur singly, in pairs or in short chains of 3 or 4 elements and, when abundant, in parallel groupings. The rods measure 0.1 by 0.7 to 1.3 microns, sometimes as much as half the length of a red blood cell, and the coccoids measure 0.1 to 0.2 micron in diameter. Electron photographs of blood preparations, utilizing enlargements of 7000 × or more, show the rods to be composed of monomorphic, rounded discs 0.3 to 0.5 micron in diameter; no cell membrane is evident, and the protoplasm appears structureless. No flagella were demonstrated (Wigand and Peters, Ztschr. f. Tropenmed. u. Parasit., *2*, 1950, 206; also see *ibid.*, *3*, 1952, 437). These organisms have been reported as occurring on and in erythrocytes and in depressions of the surfaces of the red blood cells as well as in the plasma. There is lack of agreement among investigators regarding the ability to see and to determine the motility of these organisms in the fresh state. Various authors report (1) Brownian movement, (2) slow and sinuous motion in the red cell, or (3) rapid motion. Preferred stains are those of the Romanowsky type. With Giemsa's stain, various investigators report (1) an intense red coloration, (2) a bluish tinge with distinct pink shading, or (3) blue with purple granules. With Wright's stain, the organisms stain bluish with reddish granules at the ends. With Schilling's methylene blue-eosin stain, the organisms stain a bright red color and the erythrocytes stain blue. Stain faintly with Manson's stain, pyronin-methyl green and fuchsin. Gram-negative.

Cultivated with difficulty. Divergent results have been published. Growth has been reported on various media (blood agar, agar with 2 per cent defibrinated rat blood, horse blood agar, N. N. N., Blutrösplatte of Wethmar, hormone agar with blood of rabbit, horse or man, ascitic fluid agar, chocolate agar, semi-solid rabbit serum agar, semi-solid rabbit blood agar, Noguchi-Wenyon medium, defibrinated rat blood, glucose broth, Tarozzi broth, peptone water), but usually growth was scant or could not be continued by transfer to the same medium, or the organism isolated was either non-infectious or the possibility of latent infections in the recipient animal was not excluded. Best results are apparently obtained with semi-solid rabbit- or rat-serum agar and semi-solid rabbit-blood agar. No conclusive results have been reported in tissue culture; with the chick embryo, the reports are either contradictory or divergent.

Filterability: Non-filterable with either the Seitz or the Berkefeld N filter.

Immunology: No authentic case of true natural immunity in rats has been established. Acquired immunity occurs in (1) the latently infected rat, (2) the infected rat after splenectomy and recovery from the disease, the period of resistance corresponding to the duration of latency, (3) the non-splenectomized, non-carrier rat following infection, and (4) animals other than the rat following infection.

Serology: No precipitins, thrombocytobarin, isoagglutinins or cold hemolysins have been reported in the sera of anemic rats. Contradictory results have been obtained in the Weil-Felix reaction utilizing

Proteus OX$_{19}$, OXK and sera from rats recovered from haemobartonellosis.

Pathogenicity: Infected blood, liver suspension, defibrinated laked blood, washed
red blood cells, plasma and hemoglobinuric
urine may produce infection by the subcutaneous, intravenous, intraperitoneal or
intracardiac routes. Slight, transient or no
haemobartonellosis then occurs in adult,
non-splenectomized, haemobartonella-free,
albino rats; in adult, non-splenectomized,
albino rats of carrier stock; or finally in
adult, splenectomized rats previously infected, during a period lasting 15 weeks to
8 months after infection. Typical haemobartonellosis occurs in adult, splenectomized,
haemobartonella-free, albino rats and in
young, non-splenectomized, haemobartonella-free, albino rats weighing 20 to 30
grams at 3 weeks. Latent infections regularly become patent following splenectomy
and may follow coincident infections with
other microorganisms, chemotherapy, injections of polonium nitrate or of "anti-rat-
spleen" serum. Variable results have been
obtained by different investigators with
wild mice, guinea pigs, rabbits, hamsters,
pigeons and monkeys ("*Macacus rhesus*"
and *Macacus sp.*). Known to be infectious
for wild rats, albino mice, rabbits and for
two Palestinian rodents (*Spalax typhlops*
and *Meriones tristrami*). Negative results
have been reported in dogs, kittens, cats,
sheep and various birds. Causes a definite
and characteristic anemia without cutaneous eruption.

Antibiotic- and chemo-therapy: Penicillin
is ineffective; there is true sterilization of
latent or recognized infection with organic
arsenical compounds; chlortetracycline (aureomycin) and oxytetracycline (terramycin)
are active.

Source: Found in the blood of infected
albino rats.

Habitat: Found in ectoparasites such as
the rat louse (*Polyplax spinulosus*), the flea
(*Xenopsylla cheopis*) and possibly the bedbug (*Cimex lectularius*). Also found para-
sitizing the erythrocytes of susceptible
animals. World wide distribution.

2. **Haemobartonella microti** Tyzzer
and Weinman, 1939. (Tyzzer and Weinman,

Amer. Jour. Hyg., *30* (B), 1939, 143; also see
Weinman, Trans. Amer. Philosoph. Soc.,
33 (N.S.), 1944, 312.)

mi.cro′ ti. M.L. mas.n. *Microtus* a genus
of voles; M.L. gen.noun *microti* of *Microtus*.

In infected animals the morphology resembles that of *Haemobartonella canis*, the
organisms occurring as rods, coccoids,
filaments, club forms, ring forms and granular masses. In addition to these forms there
occur in Giemsa-stained blood films ellipsoids and diamond- or flame-shaped small
forms as well as coarse, segmented or unsegmented filaments up to 5 microns in
length. The filaments may contain one or
more rings or may be composed in part or
entirely of diamond-shaped, coccoid or
ovoid elements, sometimes arranged in
parallel rows. Rods often show intense
bipolar staining. Coccoid forms, usually
scattered, may occur as aggregates or
clumps on the red blood cell, apparently
embedded in a faint blue matrix. A pale
blue, veil-like substance may cover nearly
half of one surface of the red blood cell
and show, at its border, typical red-
violet-stained rods or filaments in the
Giemsa-stained specimens. A bow-shaped
arrangement of elements is characteristic.
Morphology varies markedly with the kind
of host employed. Organisms lie on the surfaces of the red blood cells. In cultures,
organisms are more uniform in morphology.
Individual organisms are fine rods, 0.3 by
1.0 to 2.0 microns, sometimes occurring in
chains and often in clumps. Small, round
forms measuring 0.5 micron in diameter
and occasionally round, disc-like structures
occur.

Cultivation: Growth in Noguchi's semi-
solid serum agar two weeks after inoculation
with citrated or heparinized blood and incubated at 23° C. appears as white, rounded
masses measuring up to about 1 mm in the
upper 15 mm of the tube. In tissue culture
the organism grows in small, rounded, compact masses within the cytoplasm of infected cells. Indefinite maintenance of the
strains isolated on artificial media has not
been possible.

Pathogenicity: Splenectomized white
mice and splenectomized laboratory-reared
voles are readily susceptible to infection.

Neither marked anemia nor any mortality occurs in heavily infected animals. Splenectomized dogs, white rats and deer mice are not susceptible.

Source and habitat: Occurs in the blood of the vole (*Microtus pennsylvanicus pennsylvanicus*). The natural mode of transmission has not been determined, though ticks and mites are suspected.

3. Haemobartonella tyzzeri (Weinman and Pinkerton, 1938) Weinman, 1944.

(*Bartonella tyzzeri* Weinman and Pinkerton, Ann. Trop. Med., *32*, 1938, 217; Weinman, Trans. Amer. Philosoph. Soc., *33* (N.S.), 1944, 314.)

tyz′ze.ri. M.L. gen.noun *tyzzeri* of Tyzzer; named for Dr. E. E. Tyzzer, protistologist and investigator of this group of microorganisms.

Single or composite rods measuring about 0.25 by 1.4 to 4.0 microns. Short rods averaging 0.2 to 0.3 by 0.8 micron as well as round forms with diameters of 0.2 to 0.3 micron also occur. Occasional granular swellings and enlarged poles occur. Stain intensely red-violet with Giemsa's or with May-Grünwald-Giemsa's solutions. Gram-negative.

Cultivation: Initial cultures on Noguchi's semi-solid serum agar are obtained irregularly. When incubated at 28°C., colonies appear as isolated, white spheres about 1 mm in diameter in the upper 8-mm border of the medium. The clumps are composed of rods and granules with larger round structures or discs occurring occasionally. Also cultivated on the Zinsser, Wei and Fitzpatrick modification of the Maitland medium. Prolonged maintenance on semi-solid media has not been obtained.

Pathogenicity: Splenectomized, haemobartonella-free guinea pigs may be infected by blood or by cultures injected subcutaneously or intraperitoneally. Splenectomized, *Haemobartonella muris*-free rats are not susceptible when inoculated with infected guinea-pig blood. Monkeys (*Macacus rhesus*) are also not susceptible to inoculations of infected blood, tissue and cultures. Infection of the guinea pig is subclinical in its manifestations.

No definite anemia accompanies infection.

Comment: Since 1944, at which time this species was classified as belonging to the genus *Haemobartonella*, knowledge has accrued which suggests a restudy to determine whether this species might more properly be placed in the genus *Grahamella*.

Source and habitat: Found in the blood of the Peruvian guinea pig (*Cavia porcellus*); also encountered in the blood of native guinea pigs in Colombia. Observed in latently infected animals only after splenectomy. The natural mode of transmission is unknown, although the flea may be a possible vector.

4. Haemobartonella peromysci Tyzzer, 1942. (Proc. Amer. Philosoph. Soc., *85*, 1942, 377.)

pe.ro.mys′ci. M.L. mas.n. *Peromyscus* a genus of mice; M. L. gen.noun *peromysci* of *Peromyscus*.

Occurs as delicate, filamentous forms (which may be branched) on red blood cells. These filaments may become beaded and may give rise to a number of coccoids and rods from which ring forms may develop. Stains by Giemsa's method, but the staining process must be intense in order to demonstrate the organism.

Pathogenicity: Infection transmissible to splenectomized white rats (irregularly), white mice (frequently) and voles, producing a more or less severe illness with anemia.

Habitat: Found in the blood of deer mice (*Peromyscus leucopus novaboracensis*).

5. Haemobartonella sciuri Tyzzer, 1942. (Proc. Amer. Philosoph. Soc., *85*, 1942, 385.)

sci.u′ri. M.L. mas.n. *Sciurus* a genus of squirrels; M.L. gen.noun *sciuri* of *Sciurus*.

Very polymorphic. Occurs as minute rods and filaments which are either continuous or segmented. The rods and filaments vary in thickness, some being very uneven and some very coarse. Beaded chains may develop from the thickened forms. The bead-like elements stain a dull reddish at the periphery with Giemsa's stain, while the remainder is very faintly stained in contrast to the intensely staining basophilic rods and filaments. Some of the rounded forms have the appearance of large, thick rings. Beads and rings may arise from slender, deeply staining rods, simulating very closely spores within bacilli, though no germination of filaments from them has been observed.

Slightly pathogenic for the gray squirrel; non-pathogenic for normal white mice.

Habitat: Found in the blood of gray squirrels (*Sciurus carolinensis leucotis*).

6. **Haemobartonella bovis** (Donatien and Lestoquard, 1934) Weinman, 1944. (*Bartonella bovis* Donatien and Lestoquard, Bull. Soc. path. exot., *27*, 1934, 652; *Bartonella sergenti* Adler and Ellenbogen, Jour. Comp. Path. and Therap., *47*, 1934, 221; (?) *Bartonella bovis* Rodriguez, Rev. del Inst. Llorente, *13*, 1935, 5; abst. in Bull. Inst. Past., *34*, 1936, 1033; *Haemobartonella sergenti* Weinman, Trans. Amer. Philosoph. Soc., *33* (N.S.), 1944, 290; Weinman, *ibid.*, 308.)

bo'vis. L. noun *bos* the ox; L. gen.noun *bovis* of the ox.

Rods, coccobacilli and cocci, occur singly, in pairs or in short chains or groups of 10 or more elements. The rods measure 1.2 to 2.0 microns in length and are very slender. The coccobacilli occur singly or in pairs measuring 0.3 by 0.6 to 0.8 micron, and the diameters of the cocci are about 0.3 micron. May occupy a central or marginal position on the red blood cell, the number on a cell varying from 1 to 20. Not more than 20 per cent of the red blood cells are parasitized. Using the Romanowsky stain, the organisms stain similarly to the chromatin of *Piroplasma spp.*

Source and habitat: Recovered from the blood of bulls in Algeria and from a non-splenectomized calf in Palestine.

7. **Haemobartonella sturmanii** (Grinberg, 1939) Weinman, 1944. (*Bartonella sturmani* (sic) Grinberg, Ann. Trop. Med. and Parasitol., *33*, 1939, 33; Weinman, Trans. Amer. Philosoph. Soc., *33* (N.S.), 1944, 313.)

stur.ma'ni.i. M.L. gen.noun *sturmanii* of Sturman; named for Dr. M. Sturman.

Similar to *Haemobartonella bovis* and to *H. canis* morphologically and in staining properties. Occurs as rods and as coccobacillary and coccoid forms, varying in length from 0.5 to 1.5 microns. The number of organisms per infected red blood cell varies from 1 to 15; they occur individually, scattered irregularly in clumps or sometimes in chains stretching across the cell. At the height of the infection, more than 90 per cent of the cells are infected.

Pathogenicity: Causes a temperature rise in buffaloes and slight anemia after direct blood inoculation. Splenectomized rabbits, hamsters and calves inoculated with blood from infected buffaloes remained free of the organism.

Source and habitat: From the blood of buffaloes in Palestine.

8. **Haemobartonella canis** (Kikuth, 1928) Tyzzer and Weinman, 1939. (*Bartonella canis* Kikuth, Klin. Wochnschr., *7²*, 1928, 1729; Tyzzer and Weinman, Amer. Jour. Hyg., *30* (B), 1939, 151.)

ca'nis. L. noun *canis* the dog.

One of the most polymorphic of the haemobartonellae, occurring as thin rods, straight or slightly curved, dumbbell-shaped organisms, dots, coccoids or rings. Chains of rods, of coccoids or of rings also occur; these consist of only one type of these forms or a mixture of types. The chains may be straight, curved, branched or annular. Variable in size. Round forms vary from 0.2 or 0.5 micron to the limit of visibility. Single rods measure 0.2 by 1.0 to 5.0 microns, while the composite forms vary from 1.0 to 4.0 microns or more. Considered to be non-motile by most investigators. With Giemsa's stain, the organisms are red-violet, usually intensely so. Methylene blue used as a vital stain colors the organisms distinctly. Not acid-fast. Gram-negative.

Cultivation has not been demonstrated in semi-solid rabbit-serum agar medium, in media containing serum of splenectomized dogs, in N. N. N., in Noguchi's medium for leptospires, in blood broth nor in Chatton's medium covered with vaseline for *Trichomastix*.

Filterability: Results are equivocal.

Immunology: The outstanding phenomena resemble those found in the rat infected with *Haemobartonella muris*.

Pathogenicity: Anemia follows splenectomy in infected dogs, otherwise infection usually remains asymptomatic. Negative results in splenectomized, haemobartonella-free guinea pigs, rats, rabbits and monkeys (*Cercopithecus sabaeus*). No infection or anemia in unoperated mice, white rats, young rabbits, young dogs or young guinea pigs. By serial passage, the splenectomized cat has been found to carry the infection.

Arsenical therapy: Complete sterilization obtained with neoarsphenamine.

Source: Found in the blood of infected splenectomized dogs.

Habitat: Found in dog fleas (*Ctenocephalides sp.*) and in the erythrocytes of infected animals. Wide-spread distribution, the infection occurring spontaneously in Europe, India, North and South Africa and in North and South America.

9. **Haemobartonella blarinae** Tyzzer, 1942. (Proc. Amer. Philosoph. Soc., *85*, 1942, 382.)

bla.ri'nae. M.L. fem.n. *Blarina* a genus of shrews; M.L. gen.noun *blarinae* of *Blarina*.

Extremely polymorphic with delicate rods and coccus-like forms, often occurring in chains which also contain larger elements which have a deeply stained, bead-like granule. In the early stages of infection, the microorganisms may occur as thick bands or filaments stretching over the red blood cells, usually with a bead or granule. The bands take a bluish tint with Giemsa's stain, while the more delicate forms stain a slate-violet. The bead is distinctly reddish. In the fully developed infection, rods and filaments predominate over rounded forms. The organisms may be scattered on the surfaces of the red blood cells or may form a dense cap which is intensely stained. Threads may be found radiating from a central portion, and reddish-stained material with ill-defined contours may occur at the ends of the branches of the threads.

Pathogenic for the short-tailed shrew but not for deer mice or white mice. Causes anemia in the shrew.

Habitat: Found in the blood of the short-tailed shrew (*Blarina brevicauda*).

Genus IV. **Eperythrozoon** *Schilling, 1928.*[*]

(Schilling, Klin. Wochnschr., *7*[2], 1928, 1854; *Gyromorpha* Dinger, Nederl. tijdschr. geneesk., *72*, 1928, 5903.)

Ep.e.ryth.ro.zo'on. Gr. prefix *epi-* on; Gr. adj. *erythrus* red; Gr. noun *zoum* or *zoon* living thing, animal; M.L. neut.n. *Eperythrozoon* (presumably intended to mean) animals on red (blood cells).

Microorganisms found in blood plasma and on erythrocytes. Stain well with Romanow-sky-type dyes, then appearing as rings, coccoids or short rods, 1 to 2 microns in greatest dimension, and staining bluish or pinkish violet; show no differentiation of nucleus and cytoplasm with this technique. Not acid-alcohol-fast. Gram-negative. Not cultivated in cell-free media. Splenectomy activates latent infection. Arthropod transmission has been established for one species (Weinman, Trans. Amer. Philosoph. Soc., *33* (N.S.), 1944, 321).

The organisms in this genus have been considered as belonging to the *Protozoa* by Neitz, Alexander and du Toit (Onderstepoort Jour. Vet. Sci., *3*, 1934, 268) and to the bacteria by Mesnil (Bull. Soc. path. exot., *22*, 1929, 531) and by Tyzzer (in Weinman, *op. cit.*, 1944, 244). The evidence at hand favors the inclusion of this group among those organisms which are not clearly protozoan in nature but which appear to be closely related to the bacteria.

The type species is *Eperythrozoon coccoides* Schilling.

Key to the species of genus **Eperythrozoon.**[†]

I. Found in rodents.
  A. Found in the albino mouse.

1. *Eperythrozoon coccoides.*

---

[*] Revised by Dr. David Weinman, Department of Microbiology, Yale University, New Haven, Connecticut, September, 1955.

[†] For convenience this key has been arranged on the basis of host relationships; it is not intended to signify that this is the only, or the most important, or even a valid criterion for the determination of species. The full descriptions of the species should be consulted.

B. Found in the deer mouse.

　　　　　　　　　2. *Eperythrozoon varians.*

C. Found in the vole and in the dwarf mouse.

　　　　　　　　　3. *Eperythrozoon dispar.*

II. Not found in rodents.

　A. Found in herbivorous animals.

　　1. Found in cattle.

　　　　　　　　　4. *Eperythrozoon wenyonii.*

　　2. Found in sheep.

　　　　　　　　　5. *Eperythrozoon ovis.*

　B. Found in omnivorous animals (swine).

　　1. Large, non-filterable and often pathogenic organisms.

　　　　　　　　　6. *Eperythrozoon suis.*

　　2. Small, filterable and usually non-pathogenic organisms.

　　　　　　　　　7. *Eperythrozoon parvum.*

1. **Eperythrozoon coccoides** Schilling, 1928. (Schilling, Klin. Wochnschr., *7²*, 1928, 1854; *Gyromorpha musculi* Dinger, Nederl. tijdschr. geneesk., *72*, 1928, 5905.)

coc.co.i′des. Gr. noun *coccus* a berry; M.L. noun *coccus* a coccus; Gr. noun *eidus* shape; M.L. adj. *coccoides* coccus-shaped.

In stained blood films these organisms appear as rings, coccoids and rods, the majority as rings of regular outline with clear centers. The proportion of forms appearing as rings varies with the technique employed; if desiccation is prevented, rings occur in minimal numbers (Wigand and Peters, Ztschr. f. Tropenmed. u. Parasitol., *3*, 1952, 461). Measure 0.5 to 1.4 microns in greatest dimension. No limiting membrane and no differentiated internal structure observed with the electron microscope. Occur in plasma and on red blood cells. Suggested methods of multiplication are binary fission, budding and development of small coccoidal to annular forms. Stain pale red or reddish blue with either the Giemsa or the May-Grünwald-Giemsa technique. Gram-negative.

Filterability: Reported to pass collodion membranes of an average pore size of 0.36 micron (Niven et al., Lancet, *263*, 1952, 1061).

Has not been cultivated.

Immunology: The immunological state in animals is that of the premunition type. Latent infection in mice is made manifest by splenectomy.

Pathogenicity: Infects white mice, rabbits, white rats, wild mice and hamsters

(*Cricetus auratus*); usually maximal in young animals or in splenectomized adults. Reported to cause fatal mouse hepatitis when associated with another etiological agent (a virus), otherwise moderate to no anemic changes reported. Virus titers are increased one hundred fold in combined infections (Niven et al., *loc. cit.*).

Antibiotic- and chemo-therapy: Neoarsphenamine very effective; chlortetracycline (aureomycin) and oxytetracycline (terramycin) active; sulphonamides and sulphones show little to no activity.

Source: Recovered from the blood of splenectomized white mice.

Habitat: Found in the blood of infected mammals; also found in the mouse louse (*Polyplax serrata*) and probably in other arthropods.

2. **Eperythrozoon varians** Tyzzer, 1942. (Proc. Amer. Philosoph. Soc., *85*, 1942, 387.)

va′ri.ans. L. part.adj. *varians* varying.

Occurs as rings, as coccoids of varying sizes and occasionally as very minute, bacillary forms. Many of the bacilliform elements show an unstained, lens-like swelling, indicating the formation of a ring within the substance of the rod. At the height of the infection, most of the organisms are found in the plasma. Stain intensely whenever in contact with a red cell.

Infectivity: Infective for the gray-backed deer mouse (causing anemia) and for the splenectomized common deer mouse. Not infective for splenectomized white mice.

Source and habitat: Found in the blood of the gray-backed deer mouse (*Peromyscus maniculatus gracilis*).

3. Eperythrozoon dispar Bruynoghe and Vassiliadis, 1929. (Ann. de Parasitol., *7*, 1929, 353.)

dis'par. L. adj. *dispar* unlike.

Resembles *Eperythrozoon coccoides* in staining, in distribution on the erythrocytes and also in appearance, except that circular discs with solid staining centers may greatly outnumber the ring forms. Found on the red blood cells and in the plasma. Size range similar to that of *Eperythrozoon coccoides*; there are also some larger ring forms.

Has not been cultivated.

Immunology: Infection is followed by premunition, and latent infection is made manifest by splenectomy. Splenectomized rabbits premunized against *E. coccoides* do not react to inoculation with *E. dispar*; if the latter is injected first, the rabbits do not react to *E. coccoides*.

Infectivity: Infective for the European vole (*Arvicola (Microtus) arvalis*), the American vole (*Microtus pennsylvanicus pennsylvanicus*), the dwarf mouse (*Mus minutus*), the rabbit and *Mus acomys*. Not infective for albino rats or albino mice.

Source: Recovered from the blood of infected animals.

4. Eperythrozoon wenyonii Adler and Ellenbogen, 1934. (Jour. Comp. Path. and Therap., *47*, 1934 (Sept. 3), 220.)

wen.yo'ni.i. M.L. gen.noun *wenyonii* of Wenyon; named for Dr. C. M. Wenyon, who studied these organisms.

Morphologically similar to *Eperythrozoon coccoides*. Coccoid and often vesicular, staining pale red with Giemsa's stain and varying from 0.2 to 1.5 microns in diameter. Multiplication seems to be by budding, by fission and by filamentous growths from the ring forms. Up to 50 or 60 organisms are found on one red blood cell. These are arranged in irregular chains or in tightly packed groups.

Cultivation: Not reported.

Immunology: The organism creates a state of premunition; latent infection is made manifest by splenectomy.

Pathogenicity: Cattle are susceptible, but sheep are not infected either before or after splenectomy; a splenectomized pig proved non-susceptible.

Source: Recovered from the blood of infected cattle.

Habitat: Found in the blood of infected cattle; arthropod transmission has not been proved.

5. Eperythrozoon ovis Neitz et al., 1934. (Neitz, Alexander and du Toit, Address, Biological Society, Pretoria, Mar. 15, 1934; from Neitz, Onderstepoort Jour. Vet. Sci. and Anim. Ind., *9*, 1937, 9.)

o'vis. L. noun *ovis* a sheep.

Delicate rings approximately 0.5 to 1.0 micron in diameter, though occasionally larger. In addition there are triangular forms with rounded angles as well as ovoid, comma, rod, dumbbell and tennis-racket forms. Found supra-cellularly on the erythrocytes, but often free. Colored pale purple to pinkish purple with Giemsa's stain. Suggested mode of multiplication is by budding.

Has not been cultivated.

Immunology: The immunological state in sheep appears to be that of the premunition type.

Pathogenicity: Sheep, antelopes and probably goats and splenectomized calves are susceptible. Dogs, rabbits and guinea pigs are refractory, and a splenectomized pig was not infected. The distinctive feature of *Eperythrozoon ovis* is its ability to provoke illness in normal animals without resorting to splenectomy.

Source: Found in the blood of infected sheep in South Africa and in the United States.

Habitat: Occurs in the blood of infected animals. No ectoparasites found on sheep were naturally infected, but an arthropod is suspected as a vector.

6. Eperythrozoon suis Splitter, 1950. (Science, *111*, 1950, 513.)

su'is. L. noun *sus, suis* a pig.

Rods, rings, coccoids and various budding forms have been reported, a ring form averaging 0.8 to 1.0 micron in diameter being the most common. Larger ring and discoid types up to 2.5 microns also occur. This is perhaps the largest species in the genus.

Cultivation has not been successful.

Immunology: Latent infection made manifest by splenectomy; under field conditions, animals with spleen sicken and present massive infections.

Pathogenicity: Implicated in "icteroanemia" of swine, heavy infection and disease being provoked without splenectomy. Has not infected one or more of: lamb, calf and the following splenectomized animals: white mouse, deer mouse (*Peromyscus maniculatus*), rats, guinea pigs and rabbits.

Chemotherapy: Neoarsphenamine, at doses of 15 milligrams per kilogram of pig, is effective in controlling the infection.

Source: Occurs in the blood of swine in the United States and perhaps in the Belgian Congo.

7. **Eperythrozoon parvum** Splitter, 1950. (Science, *111*, 1950, 513.)

par'vum. L. adj. *parvus* small.

One of the smallest of the eperythrozoa. Disc or coccus forms measuring less than 0.5 micron in diameter predominate and are mixed with occasional ring forms 0.5 to 0.8 micron in diameter. Filterable through Seitz EK and Berkefeld W filters and by this means can be separated from *E. suis*, which does not pass these filters.

Differentiation from *E. suis* is based on size, on morphological differences and on the failure of either species to cross-immunize against the other. Resembles *E. dispar* in appearance, and the two have not been proved to be distinct.

Rarely pathogenic. Has not infected one or more of: calf, lamb, splenectomized white mouse and splenectomized *Peromyscus maniculatus*.

Chemotherapy: Relatively resistant to neoarsphenamine *in vivo*, frequently resisting doses of 45 milligrams per kilogram of hog.

Source: Found in the blood of swine in the United States.

FAMILY IV. ANAPLASMATACEAE PHILIP, Fam. Nov.*

(*Anaplasmidae* Lestoquard, Les piroplasmoses du mouton et de la chèvre. Inst. Past. d'Algerie, 1926; also see Yakimov, Handbook of Protozoology, Moscow, 1931; and Neitz, Alexander and du Toit, Onderstepoort Jour. Vet. Sci. and Anim. Ind., *3*, 1934, 263.)

A.na.plas.ma.ta'ce.ae. Gr. neut.n. *Anaplasma* type genus of the family; -*aceae* ending to denote a family; M.L. fem.pl.n. *Anaplasmataceae* the *Anaplasma* family.

Organisms which parasitize red blood cells. There is no demonstrable multiplication in other tissues. In blood smears fixed with May-Grünwald and stained with Giemsa's stain, these organisms appear in the erythrocytes as spherical chromatic granules which stain a deep reddish violet color. Show no differentiation into nucleus and cytoplasm. Occur naturally as parasites of ruminants. Transmitted by arthropods. Situated at or near the margin and/or at or near the center of the red blood cells. The position within the erythrocyte and/or host differences serve as bases for differentiating species. Attempts at cultivation in a variety of media have failed. Produce disease in non-splenectomized and in splenectomized ruminants. The natural and experimental host range is fairly wide, these organisms occurring in members of the families *Bovidae* and *Camelidae*. Influenced by aureomycin and terramycin. Widely distributed throughout the world.

There is a single genus.

---

* Arranged by Dr. Cornelius B. Philip, Rocky Mountain Laboratory, Hamilton, Montana, March, 1956; see Canad. Jour. Microbiol., *2*, 1956, 269.

Genus I. **Anaplasma** *Theiler, 1910.**

(Rept. Govt. Vet. Bact. for 1908–09, Dept. Agr., Transvaal, 1910, 7–64; also see Transvaal Med. Jour., *5*, (January) 1910, 110; Bull. Soc. path. exot., *3*, (March 9) 1910, 135; and Trans. Roy. Soc. So. Africa, *2*, (October 27) 1910, 69.)

A.na.plas'ma. Gr. prefix *an-* without; Gr. noun *plasma* anything formed or molded; M.L. neut.n. *Anaplasma* a thing without form.

Description same as for the family.

The type species is *Anaplasma marginale* Theiler.

Key to the species of genus **Anaplasma**.

I. Cause infections in cattle.
    A. The etiological agent of malignant anaplasmosis of cattle.
                1. *Anaplasma marginale.*
    B. The etiological agent of benign anaplasmosis of cattle.
                2. *Anaplasma centrale.*
II. Causes anaplasmosis of sheep and goats.
                3. *Anaplasma ovis.*

1. Anaplasma marginale Theiler, 1910. (Theiler, Rept. Govt. Vet. Bact. for 1908–09, Dept. Agr., Transvaal, 1910, 7; *Anaplasma theileri* Cardamatis, 1911; *Anaplasma argentinum* Lignières, Cent. f. Bakt., I Abt., Orig., *74*, 1914, 133; also see 10ᵉ Congres intern. de Méd. Vet., Londres, 1914; *Anaplasma rossicum* Yakimov and Beliawine, Cent. f. Bakt., I Abt., Orig., *103*, 1927, 419.)

mar.gi.na'le. L. noun *margo, marginis* edge, margin; M.L. adj. *marginalis* marginal.

In blood smears fixed with May-Grünwald and stained with Giemsa's stain, this organism appears in the erythrocytes as one or more chromatic granules which stain a deep purple color. Varies in size from 0.3 to 0.8 micron, averaging about 0.5 to 0.6 micron. Usually round or elliptical in shape, although irregular forms are not uncommon. About 90 per cent of the bodies are situated at or near the margin of the erythrocytes, while 10 per cent are situated at or near the centers of the host cells. DeRobertis and Epstein (Proc. Soc. Exp. Biol. and Med., *77*, 1951, 254) have studied the structure of this organism with the electron microscope: the typical organism occurring at the margin of the erythrocyte appears to be constituted of a central, undivided mass and of peripheral elementary bodies, 170 to 220 millimicrons in diameter, of high electron density; in some cases the whole mass of the organism is divided into submicroscopic bodies. Usually occurs singly in the red blood cells, but double forms are not uncommon. Rarely three, four, five and even six organisms may be seen in one red blood cell. A halo may sometimes be seen surrounding the organism. During the height of the reaction, as many as 50 per cent or more of the erythrocytes may be parasitized. Responsible for a variable degree of anemia and icterus. When anemic changes progress, the number of infected erythrocytes decreases to a point where they cannot be demonstrated microscopically. This phenomenon should be remembered by workers engaged in chemotherapeutic studies, and the disappearance of organisms following the administration of drugs should not, without due consideration, be attributed to the action of the drug. Recovery is usually followed by the asymptomatic reappearance of the organisms in relatively small numbers for a period varying from 10 to 60 days, sometimes even longer. It is generally assumed that in the mammalian host multiplication of these organisms takes place by simple binary fission. Lotze and

---

* Prepared by Dr. W. O. Neitz, Department of Agriculture, Division of Veterinary Services, Onderstepoort, Union of South Africa, December, 1954.

Yiengst (Amer. Jour. Vet. Res., *3*, 1942, 312) state that each organism undergoes growth which is then followed by multiple fission resulting in the formation of eight small spherical bodies. Studies on the life cycle of this organism in arthropods are limited. Regendanz (Zent. f. Bakt., I Abt., Orig., *137*, 1933, 214) claims to have demonstrated granules varying from 0.1 to 0.4 microns in diameter in the salivary glands of known-infected *Dermacentor andersoni* and *Dermacentor variabilis* adult ticks.

Cultivated on Bass medium. Continued to grow through two generations, but growth could not be detected after the third passage. No growth in a wide variety of bacteriological and tissue-culture media, in chick embryo or in sealed collodion bags containing infective blood which had been placed in the peritoneal cavity of a rabbit.

Non-filterable with Berkefeld filter (du Toit, Rept. Direct. Vet. Educ. Res., Union So. Africa, Pt. I, 1928, 157). Filterable with a three-pound Mandler filter (Foot, No. Amer. Vet., *35*, 1954, 19).

Immunology: No authentic case of true natural immunity in cattle has been established. Calves under one year of age show a milder reaction than do older animals. Acquired immunity occurs in (1) the latently infected ox, (2) the infected ox after splenectomy and recovery from the disease, (3) the non-splenectomized, non-carrier ox following infection, and (4) animals other than the ox following infection. Carrier state usually persists for periods longer than 12 years. Autosterilization in both non-splenectomized and splenectomized cattle is of relatively rare occurrence. A partial cross immunity exists between this organism and *A. centrale*.

Serology: Complement fixation has been reported with sera of carrier cattle. About 90 per cent of the serum samples drawn from known carriers gave positive results while 10 per cent gave discordant reactions. Antibodies were detected in the sera of artificially infected animals before the organism was microscopically demonstrable.

Pathogenicity: Infected blood, washed red blood cells and organ suspensions produce infection by the subcutaneous, intra-muscular and intravenous routes. Infectious for cattle, zebu, water buffalo (*Babalus babalis*), bison (*Bison bison*), African antelopes (white-tailed gnu (*Connochaetes gnou*), blesbuck (*Damaliscus pygargus albifrons*) and duiker (*Sylvicapra grimmia*)), American deer (southern black-tailed deer and Rocky Mountain mule deer (*Odocoileus spp.*)), elk and camel (*Camelus bactrianus*). Sheep and goats develop a submicroscopic infection. The African buffalo (*Syncerus caffer*) is refractory. Rabbits, guinea pigs, white rats, gray rats, white mice, field mice, dogs, cats, ferrets and chickens are all refractory to bovine anaplasmosis. Mortality has been recorded in cattle, zebu, water buffalo and camel.

Antibiotic therapy: True sterilization of latent or recognized infection occurs with massive repeated doses of aureomycin and terramycin.

Source: Observed by Theiler (*op. cit.*, 1910, 7) in the blood of infected cattle.

Habitat: Found in arthropods such as *Argas persicus, Boophilus annulatus, B. australis, B. calcaratus, B. decoloratus, B. microplus, Dermacentor albipictus, D. andersoni, D. occidentalus, D. variabilis, Haemaphysalis cinnabarina punctata, Hyalomma excavatum, Ixodes ricinus, I. scapularis, Rhipicephalus bursa, R. sanguineus* and *R. simus*. Also found in the erythrocytes of susceptible animals. World wide distribution.

2. **Anaplasma centrale** Theiler, 1911. (1st Rept. Dir. Vet. Res., Union So. Africa, 1911, 7.)

cen.tra′le. L. adj. *centralis* central.

In blood smears fixed with May-Grünwald and stained with Giemsa, the organisms appear in erythrocytes as irregularly spherical, chromatic granules which stain a deep purple color. Vary in diameter from 0.4 to 0.95, averaging 0.65, micron. Resembles *A. marginale* very closely but differs from it by its slightly greater size and by its usually central position in the erythrocyte. Approximately 88 per cent of the organisms are situated at or near the center and 12 per cent at or near the margin of the host cell. Usually occurs singly in the red blood cells, but double forms are not uncommon. Rarely three or four organisms may be seen in the same red blood cell. During the height of the reaction, as many as 15 per cent or more of the erythrocytes may be parasitized. Responsible for anemia and icterus. When anemic changes progress, the number of infected erythrocytes decreases to a point where they cannot be demonstrated microscopically. Recovery is usually followed by the reappearance of the organisms in relatively small numbers for a period of from 10 to 30 days and sometimes even longer. The life cycle of *A. centrale* is in all probability the same as that of *A. marginale*. No attempts have yet been made to study the life cycle of *A. centrale* in the arthropod vector.

Cultivation: No attempts have been made.

Filterability: No information available.

Immunology: No authentic case of true natural immunity in cattle has been established. Acquired immunity occurs in (1) the latently infected ox, (2) the infected ox after splenectomy and recovery from disease, the period of resistance corresponding to the duration of latency, (3) the nonsplenectomized, non-carrier ox following infection, and (4) animals other than the ox following infection. Recovered animals remain carriers for periods of up to 20 years. A partial cross immunity exists between this organism and *A. marginale*. *A. centrale* has been employed on the African continent and in Palestine as an immunizing agent against *A. marginale*. Approximately 350,000 doses of *A. centrale* vaccine (infective citrated blood) are issued annually to farmers in South Africa. No cases of autosterilization have been observed.

Serology: No work attempted.

Pathogenicity: Infected blood and organ suspensions produce infection by the subcutaneous, intramuscular and intravenous routes. *A. centrale* is infectious for cattle. The African antelope, the blesbuck (*Damaliscus pygargus albifrons*), develops a submicroscopic infection.

Antibiotic therapy: No information available. Aureomycin and terramycin may possibly be as effective for *A. centrale* as for *A. marginale*.

Source: Observed in the blood of infected cattle.

Habitat: Found in the arthropods *Boophilus decoloratus* and *Haemaphysalis cinnabarina punctata*; also found in the erythrocytes of cattle. Found in Africa, Roumania and Palestine.

3. **Anaplasma ovis** Lestoquard, 1924. (Bull. Soc. path. exot., *17*, 1924, 784.)

o'vis. L. noun *ovis* the sheep.

In blood smears fixed with May-Grünwald and stained with Giemsa, the organisms appear in the red blood cells as irregularly spherical, chromatic granules which stain a deep purple color. Vary from 0.4 to 0.8, averaging 0.5, micron in diameter. Resembles *A. marginale* very closely but differs from the latter by its pathogenicity and by its position in the erythrocytes. Approximately 65 per cent of the organisms are situated at or near the margin and 35 per cent at or near the center of the erythrocyte. Occurs singly in the red blood cells, but double forms are not uncommon. Rarely three or four organisms may be seen in the same cell. During the height of the reaction, as many as 5 per cent or more of the erythrocytes may be parasitized. Responsible for anemia and icterus. When anemic changes progress, the number of infected erythrocytes decreases to a point where they cannot be demonstrated microscopically. Recovery is usually followed by the reappearance of the organisms in relatively small numbers for a period from 10 to 30 days and sometimes even longer. The life cycle is in all probability the same as that of *A. marginale*. No attempts have yet been made to study the life cycle of this organism in the arthropod vector.

Cultivation: No attempts have yet been made.

Filterability: No information available.

Immunology: No authentic case of true natural immunity in sheep or goats has been established. Acquired immunity occurs in (1) latently infected sheep and goats, (2) the infected sheep and goat after splenectomy and recovery from the disease, the period of resistance corresponding to the duration of latency, (3) the non-splenectomized, non-carrier sheep and goat following infection, and (4) animals other than the sheep and goat following infection. Recovered animals remain carriers for periods of up to four years; the end point has not been determined.

Serology: No work has been attempted.

Pathogenicity: Infected blood and organ suspensions produce infection by the subcutaneous, intramuscular and intravenous routes. Infectious for sheep, goats and the African antelope, the blesbuck (*Damaliscus pygargus albifrons*). The eland (*Taurotragus oryx oryx*) develops a submicroscopic infection. Cattle are refractory. No cases of autosterilization have been observed.

Antibiotic therapy: No tests conducted. Aureomycin and terramycin may possibly be as effective for *A. ovis* as for *A. marginale*.

Source: Observed in the blood of infected sheep and goats.

Habitat: Found in arthropods such as *Rhipicephalus bursa, Dermacentor silvarum* and *Ornithodoros lahorensis*; also found in the erythrocytes of sheep and goats. Found in Africa, Southern Europe and Asia.

ORDER II. VIRALES BREED, MURRAY AND HITCHENS, 1944.*

(Jour. Bact., 47, 1944, 421.)

Viruses are etiological agents of disease, typically of small size and capable of passing filters that retain bacteria, increasing only in the presence of living cells, giving rise to new strains by mutation. A considerable number of plant viruses have not been proved filterable, it is nevertheless customary to include these viruses with those known to be filterable because of similarities in other attributes and in the diseases induced. Some not known to be filterable are inoculable only by special techniques, as by grafting or by the use of insect vectors, and suitable methods for testing their filterability have not been developed; moreover, it is not certain that so simple a criterion as size measured in terms of filterability will prove to be an adequate indicator of the limits of the natural group. Viruses cause diseases of bacteria, plants and animals.

Our incomplete knowledge of the entities known as viruses has made their classification, and consequently their nomenclature, a difficult matter. It is difficult to describe viruses adequately because of their small size and because they are not cultivable. Electron microscopy has enabled a determination of the size and morphology of some of the viruses. Likewise, serological methods have been developed which are proving to be useful in distinguishing between different species and types of viruses, but in many cases these methods have not been applied.

The usual characteristic that permits recognition of viruses is their capacity to produce specific diseases. As indicated in the previous edition of the MANUAL (6th ed., 1948, 1127), three constituent groups of viruses have come to be recognized, and to some extent named and classified, through the largely separate efforts of bacteriologists, animal pathologists and plant pathologists. Taxonomic overlapping of the three groups, viruses affecting bacteria, viruses having human and other animal hosts and viruses invading higher plants, can hardly be justified as yet by available evidence. Nevertheless, it has been shown that a single virus may multiply within, and cause morphological changes in, both a plant host and an insect vector (Littau and Maramorosch, Virology, 2, 1956, 128). This seems to dispose of the thought that adaptation to one environment necessarily precludes the utilization of other sources for the materials needed for growth and multiplication.

Because of the difficulties involved in preparing adequate descriptions of species of viruses, many investigators have felt it undesirable to use binomials according to the Linnean system and therefore have proposed numbering or lettering systems for species and subspecies of viruses (see Johnson, Wis. Agr. Exp. Sta. Res. Bull. 76, 1927; Proc. Sixth Internat. Bot. Cong. (Amsterdam), 2, 1935, 193; and Smith, Textb. of Plant Virus Dis., Philadelphia, 1937, 615 pp). These systems have made it difficult for persons other than

* Prepared by the Editorial Board, March, 1956, from a tentative outline by Dr. Robert S. Breed, January, 1956. Reviewed by Dr. C. H. Andrewes, Medical Research Council, National Institute for Medical Research, London, England, Dr. F. O. Holmes, The Rockefeller Institute for Medical Research, New York, N. Y., and Dr. E. A. Steinhaus, Agricultural Experiment Station, University of California, Berkeley, California, March, 1956.

specialists to recognize the viruses under discussion, thus prompting some workers to suggest standardizing the numbering or lettering systems.

Other investigators have felt that if a classification were drawn up according to the Linnean system and that if the procedures outlined in Codes of Nomenclature were followed, a binomial nomenclature could be developed for viruses. Such a system was first presented for the plant viruses by Holmes (Handbook of Phytopathogenic Viruses, Burgess Publishing Co., Minneapolis, 1939, 221 pp). This was followed by the more complete classification given in the last edition of the MANUAL (6th ed., 1948, 1125).

At the 5th International Congress of Microbiology, held at Rio de Janeiro in August, 1950, the consensus of opinion seemed to be that an acceptable system of classification could be achieved by giving primary consideration to the viruses that are best known and that can be most adequately described. Specialists were asked to prepare classifications for several groups of viruses, and the results of this plan were reported in 1953 by Andrewes (Annals N. Y. Acad. Sci., *56*, 1953, 428).

So-called "non-Linnean" names for a number of groups of viruses were presented in 1954 (Andrewes, Nature, *173*, 1954, 620). Among these were binomial names applying to the viruses of the smallpox, herpes simplex, poliomyelitis and influenza groups as well as names applicable to some viruses causing diseases in insects.

Substantial revisions of virus taxonomy and nomenclature in the human and other animal virus field have been published also in Russia by Zhdanov (Opredelitel' Virusov Cheloveka i Zhivotnych, Izd. Akad. Med. Nauk, U.S.S.R., Moskau, 1953, 348 pp) and in Canada by van Rooyen (Canadian Jour. Microbiology, *1*, 1954, 227). Revisions of the classification of viruses causing diseases in insects were published in 1949 and 1953 by Steinhaus (Bact. Rev., *13*, 1949, 203; Annals N. Y. Acad. Sci., *56*, 1953, 517) and in 1953 by Bergold (Annals N. Y. Acad. Sci., *56*, 1953, 495).

For the present it seems feasible to continue with the custom, tacitly accepted in the past, of classifying bacteriophages separately as one sub-group, viruses causing diseases in higher plants as a second sub-group and those causing diseases in man and other animals as a third sub-group. It should be recognized that this may prove to be only a temporary arrangement, necessary because we have little or no evidence to warrant taxonomic overlapping of the three groups and useful while we await critical investigations and possible development of a substitute plan capable of displaying natural relationships to better advantage. It is further possible that there may be discoveries of common physical properties which would aid in formulating an interlocking classification, for which at present we lack any substantial basis. It is interesting to note that Ryzhkov (Mikrobiologiia, *21*, 1952, 458) has attempted to outline such a classification; confirmation of the ideas underlying this attempt at a unified classification must be sought in the future.

The rapid expansion of the field, by the frequent discovery of new viruses and the development of new methods for their recognition and characterization, together with some uncertainties evidenced by virologists, makes it seem inappropriate to include a formal classification of *Virales* in this edition of the MANUAL. The need for an accepted nomenclature and classification has now made itself felt, and it is expected that recognition of this will be reflected in the next report of the Committee of the I.A.M.S.

A KEY FOR THE

DETERMINATION OF THE

GENERIC POSITION OF ORGANISMS

LISTED IN THE MANUAL

By

V. B. D. SKERMAN

Department of Bacteriology, University of Queensland, Brisbane, Australia

INTRODUCTION

The following key has been designed to enable the user to determine whether any isolated organism bears any resemblance to an organism described in the MANUAL. Although the key terminates in most cases at a genus, it has been formulated on individual species descriptions. Every effort has been made to see that if the description of any species within the MANUAL is applied to the key, the description will lead to the genus into which the species has been placed in the MANUAL. Keys provided by the various contributors should be followed in deciding which species within the genus most closely agrees with the isolate. It is quite possible, owing to the limited description of many species, that the new isolate will be described more extensively and may fit into more than one species. It is unlikely, but not impossible, that it may fit into more than one genus.

No attempt has been made to fit the key to any *system* of classification. While it may undoubtedly act as a guide to the proper classification of an undescribed organism, it is designed solely for the purpose of identification of described species. The user must judge for himself whether an isolate is identical with a described species and, if not, determine its taxonomic position.

Characters were chosen solely for their suitability for purposes of differentiation and for the ease with which they could be determined. The sequence in which they have been employed was determined in part by common usage, in part by necessity through lack of other information and in part by design to encourage comparison of apparently closely related organisms and to enforce the use of some tests quite commonly ignored.

Where variation in any character has been well established, due allowance

987

has been made for it. The sequence of tests employed has largely eliminated the necessity to treat an organism as positive or negative with respect to a character for which the information was not given. In the few instances where this device has been employed, the species involved has been cited in the key, and the assumption made has been noted or the species has been traced through the key as far as the information permitted, a note having been made to this effect at the appropriate point.

Cowan's assertion (Canad. Jour. Microbiol., *2*, 1956, 212–219) that the previous *system* broke down because of the use of the "positive or negative" approach, while apparently theoretically correct, was, in fact, not so. Such a device obviously could not have been used where genera with single species were involved. However, with the larger genera it proved to be valid where it was employed simply because the genera already had species, adequately described, which were either positive or negative with respect to the character, and the genera therefore appeared at two or more places in the key. The use of the "positive or negative" approach merely placed the poorly described species in one or the other of these categories.

In the present key, pathogenicity to animals has not been used as a sole differentiating character. It has been coupled with other tests in the separation of these genera. The plant pathogens and the *Rhizobia* have been separated on the basis of pathogenicity and nodule formation respectively. They have, in addition, been treated as organisms isolated from the soil, have been traced through the key as far as described characters would permit and have been cited at the appropriate points. Species of *Pseudomonas* producing water-soluble pigments have been separated on this characteristic. They were, however, also checked through the key as though not pigmented. With few exceptions those adequately described terminated at points where non-pigmented pseudomonads were located; the few which did not have been individually cited. Of fifteen species for which no sugar reactions were cited, thirteen terminated at *Pseudomonas* when the possible "positive or negative" combinations for glucose and lactose were applied. The others were non-motile and have been cited in the key.

The description of the genus *Paracolobactrum* as presented in the MANUAL contains too little information to be of use in the key. Reference was made to the original paper of Stuart, Wheeler, Rustigian and Zimmerman (Jour. Bact., *45*, 1943, 101–119), and the strain descriptions used. While these strains do not appear as such in the MANUAL, the value of such strain specifications over generalizations for the species should be apparent.

The recommendations regarding designations of groups in the *Enterobacteriaceae* published by the Enterobacteriaceae Subcommittee of the Nomenclature Committee of the International Association of Microbiologists (Internat. Bull. Bact. Nomen. and Taxon., *4*, 1954, 1–94) are also indicated in the key by the insertion of the generic name followed by "Rome, 1953".

The primary division on the basis of cell width is purely arbitrary. A great deal of latitude has been allowed in respect to this character. Cells with widths between 1.7 and 2.3 microns appear in both sections of the key. While every endeavor has been made to avoid inaccuracies in the key, some are inevitable. In order to avoid any repetition of these, users are requested to supply the author with a detailed statement of these as they are encountered. The author would also welcome reprints of any papers relating to subjects of taxonomic interest.

A COMPREHENSIVE KEY TO THE
GENERA OF THE MANUAL

Use of the key

First, determine the characters of the organism and then consult the key, *always* commencing from the beginning. The key poses a series of questions which can be answered in the affirmative or negative. Numbers on the right hand side of the key indicate the next number on the left to be consulted. The sequence should be followed until the right hand number is replaced by a generic name. Keys to the particular genus in the MANUAL should then be consulted for species identification.

1. Organisms green, blue-green or yellowish green, brown or red, containing chlorophyll "a" either in well-defined chloroplasts or in the cytoplasm.........**Algae**   *p. 30*
   Organisms colorless; if pigmented, green pigments do not have the characteristics of chlorophyll "a"...**2**
2. Diameter or width of cells exceeds 2.0 microns; proceed to.......Section A   *p. 991*
   Diameter or width does not exceed 2.0 microns; proceed to.......Section B   *p. 996*
   Note: (1) In assessing diameter or width, measurement must be made of the cells themselves and not of any capsular structures or sheaths which may surround them. In Section A some cells have widths up to 100 microns and are clearly visible to the naked eye.

   (2) To avoid confusion the following terms have the following meanings throughout the key:

   Trichome: A uniseriate multicellular organism in which the multicellular character is clearly visible without staining after removal of any cell inclusions, such as sulfur. The term includes all gliding, non-flagellated organisms regardless of whether they are obviously multicellular, with all cells excepting terminal ones of uniform size and with square ends, or apparently unicellular organisms in chains.

   The term includes also the obviously multicellular peritrichously flagellated organisms in which division of the trichome normally results in separation of obviously multicellular elements. The latter may, however, separate into single discoid elements which grow out into multicellular forms.

   The term does not include the peritrichously flagellated cells which form chains in which the individual cells do not appear multicellular without special staining procedures.

   The presence or absence of a sheath should not be taken into consideration.

   Chain of cells: Organisms which characteristically divide in one plane only and remain attached to each other by a continuity of the cell wall. The individual cells do not appear multicellular without special staining. They are either non-motile or, if motile, possess flagella. The presence or absence of a sheath should not be taken into consideration.

   Filament: An elongated rod which shows no evidence of multicellularity without special staining.

SECTION A

versely and longitudinally towards the tip to produce large numbers of coccoid elements; attached by means of a holdfast 12

Width of the sheath uniform or variable; division of cells in a transverse direction only 13

12. Cells within the basal portion of the sheath longer than wide; when growing in iron-bearing waters, the sheath becomes heavily impregnated with iron
Crenothrix   *p. 272*

Cells within the basal portion of the sheath much wider than long; sheaths remain colorless in iron-bearing waters . . . .**Phragmidiothrix**   *p. 273*

13. Cells within the base of the sheath 2 by 10 microns with rounded ends; divide transversely near the tip to produce spherical non-motile cells which are extruded either singly or in chains. The sheath becomes heavily impregnated with iron or manganese, becoming wide at the base and tapering towards the tip; attached by a holdfast; false branching is common . . . .**Clonothrix**   *p. 274*

Spirally wound to straight chains up to 250 microns long; sheaths heavily encrusted with iron . . . .**Leptothrix**   *p. 264*

Note: The single species may be a *Sphaerotilus.*

Not as above 14

14. Chains of cells enclosed in a sheath of uniform width; attached by means of a conspicuous holdfast; free cells motile by means of subpolar flagella
Sphaerotilus   *p. 263*

Note: Species of *Sphaerotilus* have been shown to precipitate iron in the sheath, in which state they strongly resemble species of *Leptothrix.* The author has shown that *S. natans* will also deposit sulfur internally, though the possible relationship to *Thiothrix* is uncertain.

Not as above; if motile, not flagellated 15

15. Sulfur deposited internally when grown in water containing hydrogen sulfide 16

Sulfur not deposited internally 17

16. Several trichomes within a common sheath . . . .**Thioploca**   *p. 841*

A single trichome within each sheath; usually attached by a holdfast
Thiothrix   *p. 842*

17. Colorless trichomes, attached at the base, tapering from the base to the tip; most characteristically arranged in rosettes but may occur singly. Constriction of the outer wall near the tips produces a beaded appearance. Single cells are abstricted and may exhibit a gliding motility on a solid surface. The trichomes themselves are immobile . . . .**Leucothrix**   *p. 850*

Note: Although Harold and Stanier state that no sheath is visible, the description of *Pontothrix,* which they consider identical, cites a prominent sheath.

Colorless trichomes up to 500 microns in length; each cell contains one or more gas vacuoles which gleam reddish or bluish in transmitted light; enclosed in a thin transparent sheath; occur singly . . . .**Pelonema**   *p. 271*

Note: Peloploca, which has a similar cellular morphology, although described as "no sheath evident," and which occurs in bundles, should be compared carefully with *Pelonema.*

18. Spiral cells 19

Not as above 23

19. Cells contain bacteriochlorophyll and carotenoid pigments; cell masses various shades of red or purple 20

Not as above 21

20. Oxidize hydrogen sulfide, depositing sulfur internally . . . .**Thiospirillum**   *p. 46*

Do not oxidize hydrogen sulfide . . . .**Rhodospirillum**   *p. 58*

21. Rigid cells 6 to 50 microns long; actively motile by means of polar flagella; deposit sulfur internally when growing in waters containing hydrogen sulfide

                                                          Thiospira *p. 82*

    Flexible cells; not flagellated; do not deposit sulfur internally....................22

22. Large, spiral cells, with tapered ends, up to 100 microns long; protoplast wound spirally around a well defined axial filament; no cross striations; motile by means of a flexuous movement..**Spirochaeta** *p. 893*

    Spiral cells with a round cross section and blunt ends; up to 60 microns long; cells have a ridge or crista composed of numerous fibrils running along one side of the spiral; cross striations distinct; found in the intestinal tract of molluscs

                                                    Cristispira *p. 895*

23. Stalked cells; aquatic in habit...24

    Cells not borne on stalks...25

24. Cells rod-shaped; 2 by 6 to 12 microns; single cells attached terminally and at right angles to branches of a lobose, dichotomously branched stalk; form globular bush-like or plate-like growths on the surface of waters.............**Nevskia** *p. 216*

    Cells pear-shaped to spherical; multiply by budding; cells attached by a long slender stalk to a holdfast, several stalks frequently arising from one holdfast. (This organism has so far been found only in lake waters where temperature does not exceed 23°C.)..**Blastocaulis** *p. 279*

    Cells pear-shaped; borne on a very short stalk; cells grow attached to each other in a cauliflower-like mass and reproduce by longitudinal division and budding. Colonies break up at intervals, and liberated cells start new colonies. Cells and methods of reproduction resemble those found in *Chaemosiphon*, a blue-green alga; discovered in the body cavity of a fresh-water crustacean...............**Pasteuria** *p. 279*

25. Endospores produced...26

    No endospores produced..27

26. Spherical cells in cubical packets............................**Sarcina** *p. 467*

    Rod-shaped cells...**Clostridium** *p. 634*

27. Cells contain bacteriochlorophyll and carotenoid pigments; cell masses are various shades of red and purple; proceed to........................Section J *p. 1031*

    Not as above...28

28. Iron deposited on the cells or in capsules......................................29

    Note: In the absence of further information, these organisms are identified on their iron-depositing characteristics. Most iron organisms studied in pure culture metabolize the organic compound which forms the iron chelate, and the liberated iron chelates with some cell component. Citrate-utilizing organisms will, for example, release iron from ferric ammonium citrate. Accumulation of the iron in or on the cell may depend only on the nature of the cell substance. Pure-culture studies may place these organisms in more commonly recognized genera. Many more organisms, if tested, may fall into the following genera. They should also be treated as non-iron-depositing cells and should be followed through the key.

    Not as above...32

29. Iron deposited as a torus, a solid ring partially or completely around the cell in one area only giving the cells the appearance of open or closed links of a chain.......30

    Iron deposited uniformly over the cells or capsules............................31

30. Cells completely surrounded by a torus....................**Naumanniella** *p. 223*

    Cells only partially enclosed, appearing like a horseshoe. Flagella of unequal length borne at the open end....................................**Ochrobium** *p. 225*

    Note: The type of flagellation suggests that this may be an alga.

31. Spherical cells 1 to 2 microns in diameter, 2 to 60 or more cells occurring in a primary
    capsule 10 to 20 microns wide; secondary capsules unite to form a mucilaginous
    colony; iron or manganese compounds are stored in the secondary capsules.
    Siderocapsa   *p. 218*
    Cells coccoid to ovoid, 4.8 to 5.0 by 6.5 microns, forming short chains embedded in a
    thin mucilaginous layer; iron compounds stored in the surface membrane of the cells
    Sideronema   *p. 220*
    Cells rod-shaped, 2.5 by 6 to 15 microns, straight or slightly bent; not encapsulated;
    iron or manganese stored on the surface or in the membrane of the cell
    Siderobacter   *p. 226*
32. Strict intracellular parasites occurring in the cytoplasm of conjunctival cells in cattle,
    goats and sheep. Elliptical, coccoid, rod-shaped and comma-shaped cells occur
    Colettsia   *p. 961*
    (See MANUAL keys for the class **Microtatobiotes**)........................*p. 933*
    Spherical cells produced in macroscopic fruiting bodies on decaying vegetable material
    or in culture; fruiting bodies sessile or nearly so. The cocci germinate to produce
    rod-shaped cells which glide on a solid surface; not flagellated
    Myxococcus   *p. 883*
    Or...**Chondrococcus**   *p. 886*
    (See MANUAL keys for the order **Myxobacterales**)........................*p. 858*
    Pleomorphic cultures consisting of large and small cocci and small rod-shaped cells
    which are motile by means of a single polar flagellum; strongly halophilic, requiring
    20 to 30 per cent salt for optimum growth; Gram-negative **Halobacterium**
    (*H. cutirubrum*)   *p. 207*
    Not as above..33
33. Cells spherical to ovoid, varying from spheres 5 microns in diameter to large cylindrical
    organisms 35 to 100 microns long; sulfur deposited internally when growing in the
    present of hydrogen sulfide. In one of the two recorded species, large crystals of cal-
    cium carbonate fill the cells; motile with a slow jerky rotating action when in con-
    tact with solid surfaces.............................**Achromatium**   *p. 852*
    Cells spherical to ovoid, 5 to 20 microns in diameter, with the cytoplasm compressed in
    one end of the cell; sulfur deposited in the cytoplasmic layer; exhibits an extremely
    rapid darting motion in free solution suggestive of flagella, which have never been
    demonstrated; found in waters containing hydrogen sulfide, forming a tenacious
    web-like growth in a zone of critical hydrogen sulfide-oxygen concentration
    Thiovulum   *p. 81*
    Not as above..34
34. Cocci varying in diameter from 0.5 to 4.0 microns; grow in a mineral salts bicarbonate
    medium with formate as the only known source of available carbon, fermenting it to
    methane, CO_2 and possibly hydrogen; pH range, 7.4 to 9.2
    Methanococcus   *p. 473*
    (*M. vannielii*)
    Not as above..35
35. Spherical cells...36
    Rods, curved or straight..43
36. Arranged in cubical packets.............................**Sarcina**   *p. 467*
    Not as above..37
37. Motile by means of peritrichous flagella.................................38
    Non-motile..40
38. Gram-positive; cells occur in irregular clusters..............**Micrococcus**   *p. 455*
    (*M. cryophilus*)
    Gram-negative...39

39. Cells coccoid only at pH 7.0 on peptone yeast extract acetate agar; develop into multicellular rods with peritrichous flagella under other conditions; do not fix atmospheric nitrogen..**Caryophanon** *p. 831*
   Cells grow in nitrogen-free mineral salts media, fixing atmospheric nitrogen

   Azotobacter *p. 283*

40. Aerobic..**41**
   Anaerobic..**42**

41. Gram-positive; cells occur in irregular clusters..............**Micrococcus** *p. 455*
   Gram-negative; fix atmospheric nitrogen. The coccoid form is only part of a cycle of morphological forms, the initial stage of which is a large rod

   Azotobacter *p. 283*

42. Large cocci, 3 to 4 microns wide, sometimes bearing rod-shaped protuberances on opposite sides and at an obtuse angle to one another—a pleomorphic stage of a rod-shaped cell 0.8 by 2.4 to 10 microns; produce copious gas from peptone

   Sphaerophorus *p. 441*
   (*S. ridiculosis*)

   Spherical cells; pleomorphic, ranging in diameter from 0.7 to 2.5 microns; occurring in pairs, short chains and in irregular groups; dependent on glycine for growth in organic media. Glycine is decomposed to CO_2 , NH_3 and acetic acid

   Peptococcus *p. 474*
   (*P. glycinophilus*)

43. Large, cylindrical, pear-shaped or slightly curved rods 3 to 14 microns wide; actively motile by means of single polar flagella; contain large spherules of calcium carbonate and may also contain sulfur.............................**Macromonas** *p. 80*
   Not as above..**44**

44. Curved rods..**45**
   Straight rods...**46**

45. Curved rods with a bunch of flagella inserted laterally in the concave part of the cell; anaerobic; recorded from the cecum of the guinea pig, the buccal cavity of man and the rumen of the herbivora...........................**Selenomonas** *p. 258*
   Curved rods with polar flagella; 1.7 to 2.4 by 6.6 to 14.0 microns; contain small globules of sulfur in the center of the cell and a single large volutin granule at each end

   Thiospira *p. 82*

46. Cells 1.4 to 2.0 by 4.0 to 5.0 microns; motile by means of polar flagella; anaerobic to microaerophilic; ferments glucose, producing ethyl alcohol, carbon dioxide and lactic acid..**Zymomonas** *p. 199*
   Motile by means of peritrichous flagella; grow in a nitrogen-free mineral salts medium, fixing atmospheric nitrogen.............................**Azotobacter** *p. 283*

SECTION B

Note: Criteria for the separation of the small colorless protozoan forms from bacteria are very limited. Cells in which the chromatinic material is clearly organized into chromosomes which divide and separate during mitosis are probably protozoa. Robinow (Bacteriol. Rev., *20*, 1956, 207–242) states that he "knows of no other protists, besides the blue-green algae, with nuclei resembling the chromatin bodies of bacteria though it is probable that they exist". The reader is referred to this review for a detailed statement on the position.

It is suggested that all microbial forms which come under this Section be followed through the key. This practice may assist materially in clarifying the situation.

1. Ultra-microscopic and filterable forms; strict intracellular parasites of animals and plants not cultivable on artificial media but transferable by contact or by arthropod vectors..**Virales**   *p. 985*

2. Strict parasites occurring within tissue cells of animal hosts or on or in erythrocytes. With few exceptions, which have been treated under Section H, they cannot be or have not been cultivated in artificial media. Some can be cultivated in chick embryos or in tissue cultures. In the tissues or blood stream they occur *either* as spherical elementary bodies and initial bodies from 0.2 to 2.0 microns in diameter or slightly larger (usually 0.20 to 0.35 micron), singly or in aggregations in plaques several microns in diameter *or* as bacillary, triangular, ring-shaped horseshoe-shaped and other pleomorphic forms. Bacillary forms may be as long as 3 microns. Stain with Giemsa's or Macchiavello's stain without differentiation into cytoplasmic and nuclear structures, a condition which would be suggestive of protozoa. See MANUAL keys for the class **Microtatobiotes**...*p. 933*

3. Small, spherical bodies, 150 to 300 millimicrons in diameter, which germinate to produce filaments approximately 0.2 micron wide and from 2 to 50 microns long, sparcely or richly branching. At a later stage of growth small endomycelial corpuscles develop in the filaments by a process of successive condensation and constriction. As a result the homogeneous filaments are retransformed into chains of close-set spherical bodies which are released by fragmentation; highly resistant to penicillin and sulfathiazole; colonies on agar have a dense granulated central area which penetrates into the agar and which is surrounded by a translucent flat peripheral zone or consist of a pearly film containing numerous spots due to calcium or magnesium soaps; do not ferment lactose, sucrose, mannitol or dulcitol......................**Mycoplasma**   *p. 914*

    Note: L-phase colonies of some bacteria bear a strong resemblance to the colonies of *Mycoplasma*. They are generally more opaque, more heavily marked on the surface, tend to revert to the normal bacillary form in penicillin-free semi-solid media, are more difficult to subculture, do not require cholesterol for growth and ferment the same carbohydrates as the parent organism.

4. Spiral cells; proceed to..Section C   *p. 998*

    This section does not include: (a) all forms like *Vitreoscilla*, which, through their great length and extreme flexibility, are apt to coil in one plane in watch-spring fashion; (b) spiral cells of the streptomyces type which arise from branching Gram-positive filaments; and (c) chains of vibrios. The latter do not possess the true helical twist of the spiral organisms.

5. Spherical to ovoid cells which reproduce by production of a tubular outgrowth, 0.2 to 0.3 micron wide, from the cell on the end of which a daughter cell is formed. The tubular outgrowths may be simple or branched. Daughter cells are initially spherical but are later ovoid to rod-shaped; colorless or contain photosynthetic pigments.

Colorless cells, ovoid, 0.5 by 1.0 micron when mature; motile by means of a single polar flagellum; daughter cells may break loose from the tubular outgrowth and form tubes of their own while still actively motile. .**Hyphomicrobium**   *p. 277*

Cell masses salmon-pink to a deep orange-red; cells ovoid, 1.2 by 2.8 microns; non-motile; contain photosynthetic pigments; grow only under anaerobic conditions when exposed to light.....................**Rhodomicrobium**   *p. 277*

6. Spherical cells which reproduce by binary fission or by budding. Well-defined stalks are secreted by some species, the budding form of reproduction being confined to the stalked types; proceed to................................Section D   *p. 1000*

7. Vegetative cells, rod-shaped; Gram-negative; microcysts produced in macroscopically visible fruiting bodies or occur loosely among elongated S-shaped, twisted or straight flexible Gram-negative rods; germinate to produce rod-shaped cells which are motile only by a creeping action on solid surfaces. These rods may contract to form spherical microcysts or may combine in groups to form fruiting bodies in which the spherical or rod-shaped microcysts are formed. See MANUAL keys for the order **Myxobacterales**...*p. 858*

8. Rod-shaped cells, 0.5 to 1.5 by 2 to 5 microns, which grow in colonies on the surface of water containing sulfide and which deposit sulfur either inside or outside the cells. One species forms bladder-like gelatinous colonies with the bacteria embedded in the surface...**Thiobacterium**   *p. 79*

Note: This very ill-defined group is separated here because of a complete lack of information of other properties. It is suggested that any such forms, if found, should be keyed out in the section on rods to determine their possible taxonomic relationship. The presence of the sulfur around the cells in such a location may not be significant.

9. Rod-shaped and filamentous forms reproducing by binary fission, by fragmentation of the mycelium, by the production of endospores or conidia or by the production of microcysts; proceed to......................................Section E   *p. 1003*

SECTION C

preparations; flexible rods in the living state; motile by means of a creeping action on solid surfaces....................................possibly **Cytophaga** *p. 858*

(See Manual keys for the order **Myxobacterales**)........................*p. 858*

Not as above; cells actively motile in free solution.............................**9**

9. Cells relatively rigid; motile by means of polar flagella...........................10

Cells flexible; motile by means of a helicoid flexing action.......................12

10. Cells oxidize hydrogen sulfide, depositing sulfur as small globules in the center of the cell with volutin granules towards the ends..................**Thiospira** *p. 82*

Not as above...11

11. Cells consisting of a single complete spiral twist; rather sharply angulated; cells 1.5 to 2.0 microns wide at the center and tapering towards both ends. In the center of the cell is an ovoid to rounded body almost as wide as the cell and clearly visible without staining. It stains deeply with neutral red in killed cells and with Heidenhain's iron-haematoxylin or Giemsa's stain in fixed cells and is considered to be a nucleus; motile by means of polar flagella; when attached to an object at one end, cells are capable of contraction to a more angulated spiral.................**Paraspirillum** *p. 257*

Note: The author has seen in pond waters several cells very similar morphologically to these cells except that the central body appeared pale green and may be a chloroplast.

Not as above; spirals quite rigid; movement in liquids of a definite helical type

Spirillum *p. 253*

Note: Several species of vibrios are described as forming spiral chains (*V. sputigenus*, *V. jejuni*, *V. coli*, *V. indicus*, *V. luminosus*, *V. marinopraesens*). If a vibrio is curved only along one axis, formation of a true spiral is not possible. Cells forming a true spiral when in chains must have the basic helical twist in the axis of the individual cells and should be classified as *Spirillum*.

12. Cells 20 to 300 microns long and 0.25 to 2.0 microns wide (generally 0.25 to 0.5 micron) with the protoplast wound around a well-defined axial filament; cells very flexible and actively motile; flagella absent; fresh- and salt-water forms

Spirochaeta *p. 893*

Spiral cells, 0.5 to 3.0 microns wide and 10 to 100 microns long, with a spiral amplitude of 6 to 8 microns; flexible cells characterized by a thin membrane or crista on one side of the body which extends the entire length of the cell; cross striations in stained cells are distinct; actively motile without flagella; recorded from the crystalline style sac in the alimentary canal of molluscs........................**Cristispira** *p. 895*

Spiral cells, 0.5 to 1.2 microns wide and 60 to 80 microns long, with a spiral amplitude of 4 to 25 microns; cross striations in stained cells distinct; no axial filament or crista; actively motile but not flagellated; found in oysters and also free living

Saprospira *p. 894*

Not as above...13

13. Not readily stained; stain with Giemsa's stain or by silver impregnation methods; visible unstained under darkground but rarely by ordinary light microscopy......14

Cells stain readily; Gram-negative; cells rarely more than 1 micron wide; spirals frequently irregular and of variable amplitude...................**Borrelia** *p. 897*

14. Aerobic; cells 0.1 to 0.2 micron thick; wound in a very fine coil and hooked at one or both ends; can be cultivated *in vitro* in semi-solid rabbit plasma media

Leptospira *p. 907*

Anaerobic; very fine coiled cells of uniform amplitude; may be pointed at both ends but not hooked..**Treponema** *p. 904*

SECTION D

Organisms contain photosynthetic pigments alone or with carotenoid pigments. Cells in masses appear green to greenish yellow or red to purple. These organisms will grow in certain media under anaerobic conditions only when exposed to light. Certain species are also capable of aerobic growth in the dark..........................29

Not as above..2

2. Single cells borne on the end of elongated stalks; aquatic forms.....................3

   Cells not borne on stalks...4

3. Stalks band-shaped and twisted into a flat spiral; dumb-bell shaped in cross section; composed entirely of or impregnated with ferric hydroxide; dissolves completely in dilute mineral acids; a single cell is borne at the end of each stalk

   Gallionella   *p. 214*

   Stalks long and slender; attached to some solid object by means of a holdfast; cells spherical to pear-shaped; reproduce by budding, the daughter cells subsequently secreting individual stalks..............................**Blastocaulis**   *p. 279*

4. Cells or their capsules impregnated with iron or manganese.........................5

   Note: In the absence of further information, these organisms are identified on their iron-depositing characteristics. Most iron organisms studied in pure culture metabolize the organic compound which forms the iron chelate, and the liberated iron chelates with some cell component. Citrate-utilizing organisms will, for example, release iron from ferric ammonium citrate. Accumulation of the iron in or on the cell may depend only on the nature of the cell substance. Pure-culture studies may place these organisms in more commonly recognized genera. Many more organisms, if tested, may fall into the following genera. They should also be treated as non-iron-depositing cells and should be followed through the key.

   Not as above...7

5. Not encapsulated..**Siderococcus**   *p. 225*

   Cells encapsulated..6

6. Groups of cocci arranged in pairs in a common capsule....**Siderosphaera**   *p. 220*

   Cocci occur singly or in unordered groups in a common capsule

   Siderocapsa   *p. 218*

7. Cells coccal only as a stage in a definite life cycle *or* as a pleomorphic phase of rod-shaped bacteria..8

   Cells coccal at all stages of growth..15

8. Cells have a definite cyclic form of development; spherical cells germinate at one or more points to produce rod-shaped cells which elongate and divide. At the point of division, growth of the cells continues at an angle to the original axis. When the side branch is equal in size to the parent cell, division occurs at the angle. This process is repeated during the growth of the colony. *In older colonies, the rods transform entirely into a mass of cocci.* Rods are most frequently Gram-negative with Gram-positive granules; cocci are frequently Gram-positive; soil inhabitants.

   Arthrobacter   *p. 605*

   Note: The emphasis lies on the final transformation into cocci. Some authorities may consider that limited true branching may occur. If this is admitted, the dividing line between *Arthrobacter* and *Nocardia* becomes very slim. The author's observations of *Arthrobacter globiforme* fit the above statement, and it is suggested that these criteria be adopted, true branching forms which later disintegrate being assigned to *Nocardia*.

   Not as above...9

9. Gram-positive..10
   Gram-negative...11
10. Organisms occur as cocci under anaerobic conditions in neutral media; in media becoming acid, they assume a diphtheroid form; extremely pleomorphic under aerobic conditions; *produce propionic acid from lactic acid*....**Propionibacterium**   *p. 569*
    Not as above...possibly **Mycococcus**   *p. 707*
    Note: The description of *Mycococcus* has a strong resemblance to that of *Arthrobacter* in the earlier literature, and the two generic names may be synonyms. *Micrococcus cinnabareus* and *M. rhodochrous* are included here.
11. Anaerobic; non-motile; Gram-negative; principally rod-shaped cells exhibiting a coccoid phase; recorded from genital and alimentary tracts of man and other animals
    Sphaerophorus   *p. 441*
    Aerobic...12
12. Obligate halophiles requiring 16 to 30 per cent salt for growth; not luminescent
    Halobacterium   *p. 207*
    Not obligate halophiles...13
13. Parasites attacking erythrocytes and endothelial cells of man; extremely pleomorphic within the host; straight and curved rods, ring forms and cocci occur; grow in semisolid rabbit serum agar mainly as rods and cocci; polar flagella
    Bartonella   *p. 969*
    Note: This genus is selected as an example only of a large group of intracellular parasites which are pleomorphic and have coccal stages. Only an odd species has been cultivated. For other species, see the MANUAL keys for the class
    Microtatobiotes...   *p. 933*
    Animal parasites; non-motile; produce tularemia or tularemia-like infections in rodents..**Pasteurella**   *p. 395*
    Not as above...14
14. Bioluminescent when grown on fish agar or meat infusion agar containing 3 per cent salt
    Photobacterium   *p. 193*
    Organisms not fitting into any of the above groups are probably pleomorphic forms of rod-shaped cells; proceed to.............................Section E   *p. 1003*
15. Organisms parasitic within the cytoplasm or nucleus of flagellated protozoa.........16
    Not as above...17
16. Parasitic on the nucleus or nucleolus......................**Caryococcus**   *p. 927*
    Parasitic in the cytoplasm of *Trichomonas batrachorum*......**Micrococcus**   *p. 929*
    (*M. batrachorum*)
17. Strict autotrophs; will not grow on organic media; oxidize ammonia to nitrite or nitrite to nitrate...18
    Heterotrophic..19
18. Oxidize ammonia to nitrite; non-motile; not encapsulated....**Nitrosococcus**   *p. 69*
    Other than above; proceed to.............................Section G   *p. 1008*
19. Obligate anaerobes..20
    Aerobic or microaerophilic...23
20. Gram-variable; cells occur singly or in masses; ferment acetate vigorously with the production of methane; discovered in mud............**Methanococcus**   *p. 473*
    Not as above...21
21. Gram-positive..22
    Gram-negative; arranged in pairs and clusters; diameter of cells varies between species from 0.3 to 2.0 microns...................................**Veillonella**   *p. 485*
22. Organisms arranged in pairs or chains only.........**Peptostreptococcus**   *p. 533*
    Organisms arranged in cubical packets........................**Sarcina**   *p. 467*

Organisms arranged singly, in pairs and in irregular clusters; rarely in chains

Peptococcus   *p. 474*

Note: Peptococcus constellatus may belong to *Peptostreptococcus*.

23. Gram-negative, kidney-shaped to hemispherical cells occurring basically in pairs with the flat sides adjacent; animal parasites...................**Neisseria**   *p. 480*

Note: Micrococcus morrhuae and *M. roseus* are described as Gram-negative occurring singly and in pairs.

Not as above...24

24. Organisms arranged in cubical packets...........................**Sarcina**   *p. 467*

Organisms from liquids are arranged singly, in pairs or as tetrads and occasionally in short chains; tetrads common in acid media; produce at least 0.5 to 0.7 per cent acid in yeast-extract-glucose-tryptose-phosphate broth, lowering the pH below 4.0; *lactic acid produced is optically inactive*; found in fermented liquids and foods

Pediococcus   *p. 529*

Not as above...25

25. Organisms arranged in pairs only or in chains of varying lengths when growing in liquid media...26

Organisms arranged singly, in pairs and in clusters in liquid media; occasional species are motile...28

26. Organisms produce gas in Eldredge tubes when growing in yeast-extract-glucose-tryptose-phosphate broth; *lactic acid produced is levo-rotatory*; frequently produce a copious slime (dextran) in sucrose broth...................**Leuconostoc**   *p. 531*

Not as above; *lactic acid produced is dextro-rotatory*...............................27

27. Parasitic; cells usually in pairs, particularly in pathological material, where they are encapsulated; chains are common in culture media; bile-soluble; found in the respiratory tract of man.......................................**Diplococcus**   *p. 507*

Other than above; parasitic or saprophytic.................**Streptococcus**   *p. 508*

28. Cells occur predominantly as tetrads and are encapsulated in body fluids; occur as tetrads and in irregular masses in cultures.......................**Gaffkya**   *p. 466*

Not as above...**Micrococcus**   *p. 455*

Staphylococcus   *p. 464*

Note: Placed in the genus *Staphylococcus* are two species, *Staphylococcus aureus* and *Staphylococcus epidermidis*. Reference should be made to the species descriptions for separation from the other micrococci.

29. Cell masses are green or yellowish green; probably contain chlorobium chlorophyll and not bacteriochlorophyll...30

Cell masses red or purple; proceed to...........................Section J   *p. 1031*

30. Spherical to ovoid cells occurring in chains and forming flat sheets in which the chains are parallel. Oxidize hydrogen sulfide but do not store sulfur inside the cells

Pelodictyon   *p. 63*

Spherical cells united in loose trellis-like aggregates. Sulfur is deposited internally

Clathrochloris   *p. 64*

SECTION E

(See note on *Leptothrix* and *Thiothrix* (*vide supra* 7 and 10).)

Trichomes..**12**

12. Trichomes attached; free cells formed by abstriction from the terminal portion are motile by a gliding action on a solid surface....................**Leucothrix** *p. 850*

 Note: Although Harold and Stanier claim that *Leucothrix* does not form a sheath, they consider it to be identical with *Pontothrix*, which was originally recorded as a sheathed organism.

 Not as above; if motile, whole trichomes move; cells within the trichomes each contain one or more pseudovacuoles which give a reddish gleam in transmitted light.....**13**

13. Trichomes occur singly..**Pelonema** *p. 271*

 Trichomes occur in bundles......................................**Peloploca** *p. 270*

 Note: Peloploca is described as "sheath not demonstrated." It is included here on the possibility that it is sheathed and because of the morphological similarity to *Pelonema*.

14. Trichomes 6 to 20 microns long; motile by means of peritrichous flagella; rigid, multicellular, bacillary forms in which the stained cells are differentiated into a series of light and dark bands; end cells rounded; commonly form chains up to 200 microns long. Individual cells in a trichome may separate as discoid elements and may grow out into filaments; common in peat and cow dung.........**Caryophanon** *p. 831*

 General morphology similar to that found in *Caryophanon*, but individual trichomes are shorter and usually composed of 4 cells or 4 cell-pairs; trichomes are chain-forming but *non-motile*; recorded from the oral cavity of man and domestic animals

 Simonsiella *p. 833*

 Not as above...**15**

15. Long trichomes attached by a globular holdfast to the intestinal walls of some insects and millipeds; a single endospore may be produced in any or all cells of the trichome, and if so, it usually lies in an oblique position............**Arthromitus** *p. 835*

 Trichomes 1.5 to 22.0 microns long; found in the cytoplasm of the rhizopod *Pelomyxa palustris*, generally aggregated close to the nucleus.........**Cladothrix** *p. 930*

 Not as above...**16**

16. Entire trichomes unattached and actively motile by a gliding action on a solid surface; no flagella...**17**

 Trichomes attached or free; non-motile; abstricted cells may be motile with a gliding action on solid surfaces...**19**

 Note: References have been made in the literature to the multicellular nature of many small cells previously regarded as unicellular. They are mostly cells not more than 6 microns long and will be found by other characteristics to belong to genera located in Section F *et seq.*

17. Organisms oxidize hydrogen sulfide, depositing sulfur inside the cell

 Beggiatoa *p. 838*

 Not as above...**18**

18. Trichomes composed of cells which are not clearly articulated at the junctions; complete trichomes very flexible............................**Vitreoscilla** *p. 845*

 Trichomes composed of rod-like elements with little individual flexibility; bending occurs freely at the junctions............................**Bactoscilla** *p. 848*

19. Colorless trichomes; attached; cells are abstricted from the terminal position and are motile by a gliding action on a solid surface. Sulfur is not deposited internally

 Leucothrix *p. 850*

 Colorless trichomes; arranged in bundles; non-motile; each cell in the trichome contains one or more gas vacuoles which gleam reddish in transmitted light

 Peloploca *p. 270*

 Cells deposit sulfur internally............................**Thiothrix** *p. 842*

 Note: Thiothrix is inserted here although classical descriptions of the genus indicate a sheath.

SECTION F

1. Pear-shaped cells; 1.0 to 2.0 by 4.0 to 5.0 microns; non-motile; grow attached to each other or to solid surfaces by a holdfast secreted from the narrow end; sessile; multiply by longitudinal fission and by budding at the free end.........**Pasteuria** *p. 279*
   Not as above..2
2. Curved or straight rods which produce a well-differentiated stalk by which they *may* attach to a surface; a single cell occurs at the end of each stalk except during the process of multiplication..3
   Not as above..6
3. Cells curved; stalk produced as a continuation of the cell wall parallel to the long axis of the cell; reproduction by transverse fission of the cell from the free end, the daughter cell developing a single polar flagellum, then breaking away and producing a stalk from the end of the cell at which the flagellum is located
   Caulobacter *p. 213*
   Not as above; cells produce a stalk at right angles to the main axis of the cell.......4
4. Large rods, 2.0 by 6.0 to 12.0 microns, borne on the ends of lobose, dichotomously branched stalks composed of gum, forming a gummy colony which floats on water; may become attached.....................................**Nevskia** *p. 216*
   Not as above; stalks composed of or impregnated with ferric hydroxide; dissolve completely in hydrochloric acid; cells curved with the stalk secreted from the concave side; reported only from iron-bearing waters....................................5
5. Stalks ribbon-like and usually twisted; cells located terminally
   Gallionella *p. 214*
   Stalks horn-shaped; not twisted; round in cross section......**Siderophacus** *p. 216*
6. Obligate autotrophes which oxidize ferrous to ferric iron at low pH in mineral synthetic media; Gram-negative rods...7
   Not as above..8
7. Thiosulfate is oxidized...................................**Thiobacillus** *p. 83*
   (*T. ferrooxidans*)
   Thiosulfate is not oxidized.............................**Ferrobacillus** *p. 227*
   (*F. ferrooxidans*)
8. Organisms which store oxides of manganese or iron either in the cell membrane, in the cell wall or in the surrounding capsules; found in water and mud................9
   Note: In the absence of further information, these organisms are identified on the basis of their iron-depositing characteristics. Most iron organisms studied in pure culture metabolize the organic compound which forms the iron chelate, and the liberated iron then chelates with some cell component. Citrate-utilizing organisms will, for example, release iron from ferric ammonium citrate. Accumulation of the iron in or on the cell may depend only on the nature of the cell substance. Pure-culture studies may place these organisms in more commonly recognized genera. They should also be treated as non-iron-depositing cells and should be followed through the key.
   Not as above..13
9. Cells encapsulated or embedded in mucus or surrounded by a torus of iron.........10
   Not as above; iron or manganese stored in cell membrane or cell wall
   Siderobacter *p. 226*
10. Encapsulated cells occurring singly or in short chains, each capsule being completely surrounded by a ring (torus) heavily impregnated with iron or manganese giving the general appearance of links in a chain....................**Naumanniella** *p. 223*
    Not as above..11
11. Cells surrounded by a ring (torus) which is open at one end; cells motile by means of two unequal polar flagella...............................**Ochrobium** *p. 225*

Note: The unequal length of the flagella suggests that this may be an algal or protozoan cell.

Not as above..12

12. Rods arranged at random in zoogloea; encrusted with iron....**Sideromonas**   *p. 222*
    (Including *Siderocapsa major*)

    Cells arranged in pairs or chains in capsules.............**Ferribacterium**   *p. 221*

13. Cells *in mass* appear green to greenish yellow; contain a photosynthetic pigment which is not bacteriochlorophyll or chlorophyll "a" but which may be chlorobium chlorophyll; individual cells usually colorless; grow anaerobically when exposed to light, oxidizing sulfide to sulfur, which is deposited outside the cell; no growth aerobically 14

    Not as above..18

14. Cells found adherent to the surface of other organisms, apparently living in symbiosis with them..15
    Note: The taxonomic significance of these groups is doubtful, but until they are isolated from the supposed symbiont and studied separately, they must be treated in this fashion.

    Cells free-living..17

15. Green cells attached to the surface of a protozoan.......**Chlorobacterium**   *p. 65*

    Green cells attached to bacteria.....................................16

16. Aggregates small, barrel-shaped, actively motile, consisting of a central, polar-flagellate, rod-shaped cell covered with the green organisms; green cells 0.5 to 1.0 by 1.0 to 2.5 microns, usually 8 to 16 surrounding the central cell; aggregates measure 2.5 to 5.0 by 7 to 12 microns.....................**Chlorochromatium**   *p. 65*

    Aggregates large, long and cylindrical; non-motile; consist of green cells, 0.5 to 1.0 by 2.0 to 4.0 microns, lying on the surface of a slime capsule which covers the inner cylindrical cell. They are themselves covered by a layer of slime. Aggregates measure 7.0 to 8.0 microns wide by up to 50 microns long...........**Cylindrogloea**   *p. 66*

17. Encapsulated cells forming characteristic aggregates consisting of net-like structures, irregular three-dimensional masses or two-dimensional masses in which cells lie in parallel strands...**Pelodictyon**   *p. 63*

    Cells may produce slime but usually remain dispersed; in young healthy cultures, small ovoid rods, 0.7 to 0.9 by 1.5 microns, forming chains; at pH 7.5 to 8.0, involution forms such as cork-screw type rods and cocci are characteristic....**Chlorobium**   *p. 62*

18. Cell masses are various shades of red or purple................................19

    Not as above..20

19. Cells contain bacteriochlorophyll and carotenoid pigments; capable of growth anaerobically when exposed to light; proceed to....................Section J   *p. 1031*

    Not as above..20

20. Cells motile only by a gliding movement on solid surfaces or along each other; single cells non-motile when free in solution. Motility can be observed at the glass-water interface on a slide or on the surface of agar plates where cells move singly or in groups, frequently leaving a trail of slime behind. Cells are flexible, the extent of the flexibility being dependent on length and turgidity (see note below)...........21

    Note: This subdivision is represented by two main groups: In one the cells are usually less than 10 microns long, frequently only 2.0 to 5.0 microns; Gram-negative; in wet preparations fixed with osmic acid, they may appear as blunt-ended rods; in stained preparations subjected to heat fixation, they are frequently curved, S-shaped, bent or spirilliform. In the other, the cells are usually longer than 10 microns and may form articulated chains.

        There are, however, much shorter representatives of this subdivision which, because of their shortness, are more rigid and resemble ordinary bacteria in many respects except for their gliding movement and lack of flagella. Species of both groups so far described have been found in fresh and salt water, soil and decomposing organic matter, especially dung.

Not as above; cells non-motile or motile, when free in solution, by means of flagella; proceed to...Section G   p. *1008*

21. Cells which, on rabbit dung or bacterial cell agar or other suitable media, produce spherical or rod-shaped microcysts either lying free among the rods or borne in macroscopically visible fruiting bodies formed by transformation of whole or part of the population of rod-shaped cells; cells rarely more than 10 microns long; proceed to

MANUAL keys for the order **Myxobacterales**   *p. 858*

Not as above...22

22. Rod-shaped cells forming articulated chains..................**Bactoscilla**   *p. 848*

Not as above...23

23. Filaments from 12 to 100 microns or more in length, highly flexible and actively motile by gliding motion; cells may bend and wave but do not rotate

Microscilla   *p. 849*

Not as above...24

24. Cells usually less than 12 microns long. Two groups are possibly represented here: If the colonies are pigmented yellow, pink, green, orange or black, they probably belong to the genus..**Cytophaga**   *p. 858*

If they are white and albuminous, they may belong to Soriano's genus

Flexibacter   *p. 858*

SECTION G

1. Organisms will not grow on meat extract or other complex organic media; strict autotrophs which use carbon dioxide as the sole source of carbon and which obtain their energy from the oxidation of carbon monoxide or other inorganic substances......2
   Note: The genus *Methanomonas* has to be considered here. The information in the MANUAL does not indicate whether the organism is a strict or facultative autotroph. For this reason any polar flagellate terminating at the genus *Pseudomonas* should be checked for its ability to grow by autotrophically oxidizing methane. (See also note on *Carboxydomonas*.)
   Not as above...6
2. Organisms oxidize ammonia to nitrite...3
   Organisms oxidize nitrite to nitrate..5
   Organisms oxidize inorganic sulfur compounds...............**Thiobacillus**   *p. 83*
   Organisms oxidize ferrous iron............................**Ferrobacillus**   *p. 227*
   Organisms oxidize carbon monoxide...................**Carboxydomonas**   *p. 77*
   Note: It is reasonably certain that *Carboxydomonas* is also heterotrophic and may be identical with *Hydrogenomonas*.
3. Cells encapsulated; form zoogloeae...4
   Cells not encapsulated.................................**Nitrosomonas**   *p. 68*
4. Zoogloeae encysted.......................................**Nitrosocystis**   *p. 70*
   Zoogloeae not encysted..................................**Nitrosogloea**   *p. 71*
5. Zoogloeae formed ....**Nitrocystis**   *p. 73*
   Zoogloeae not formed ....**Nitrobacter**   *p. 72*
6. Gram-positive...7
   Gram-negative; proceed to.............................Section H   *p. 1015*
7. Aerobic...8
   Anaerobic..35
8. Endospores formed..**Bacillus**   *p. 613*
   Note: Five species of *Clostridium* (89 to 93) are described as aerotolerant. Their growth under aerobic conditions is very restricted.
   No endospores produced...9
9. Organisms show distinct branching in young cultures.........................10
   Organisms do not branch...19
   Note: No provision appears to be made for organisms which, under optimal growth conditions, produce long *unbranched* filaments which, like *Nocardia*, eventually disintegrate into a series of short rods. The MANUAL descriptions of *Nocardia globerula* and *N. rubropertincta* suggest such forms. The author has observed others in rabbit dung media. It would seem better to assign such forms to a new genus in order to retain the branching character in *Nocardia*.
10. True branching mycelium produced in young cultures...........................11
    Branching very rudimentary, limited to simple branching of isolated rods, no mycelium formed...16
11. Long, branching filaments which show little or no tendency to fragment completely into short bacillary and coccal elements..12
    Organisms produce a well-defined mycelium in the early stages of development and then completely fragment into short bacillary elements. When aerial mycelium is produced it also fragments into rods and coccal elements but does not produce differentiated conidia. Fragmentation of the mycelium may commence within a few hours or may be delayed for several days.....................**Nocardia**   *p. 713*
    Note: (1) Cultures of *Actinoplanes*, when cultured on certain media, fail to produce sporangia and resemble *Nocardia*.

(2) *Actinomyces*, generally regarded as anaerobic, is considered by some to be microaerophilic. Organisms growing poorly aerobically but better anaerobically should be compared carefully with the *Actinomyces spp.*

12. Organisms which grow over or within submerged plant tissues and on certain laboratory media, producing conidia within sporangia borne on aerial hyphae..........13

   Not as above..14

13. Mycelium penetrates the submerged plant tissue; conidia, 1.0 to 1.5 microns in diameter, produced in coils or irregularly within the sporangia; conidia globose to slightly angular; sporangia, 8.4 to 22.0 microns in diameter, borne on long aerial hyphae; conidia *motile;* germinate to produce a branched mycelium

   Actinoplanes *p. 826*

   Mycelium grows over the surface of submerged plant tissue; conidia spherical, 1.8 to 2.0 microns in diameter, produced in coils within the sporangia; sporangia 7 to 19 microns in diameter produced apically or on branches of aerial hyphae; conidia *non-motile* and forcibly ejected from a protuberance formed from the sporangium wall when the sporangia are immersed in water......**Streptosporangium** *p. 828*

14. Chains of conidia produced from the ends of aerial hyphae....**Streptomyces** *p. 744*

   Note: (1) Cultures of *Actinoplanes* or *Streptosporangium* on some laboratory media are morphologically similar to *Streptomyces.*

   (2) Certain species of *Nocardia* in which fragmentation is delayed may produce thickened aerial hyphae which abstrict cells from the tip, proceeding towards the base and finally involving the whole mycelium. Early stages in this change may be confused with *Streptomyces*, e.g., *N. fordii* and *N. paraffinae.*

   Conidia produced singly on the tips of short side branches; branches may occur singly or in clusters giving the appearance of bunches of grapes.......................15

   Mycelium persistent with no production of conidia. These forms should be regarded in the same sense as the *Mycelia sterilia* of the *Fungi* until something more definite is known of possible fruiting structures.

15. Do not grow between 50° and 60°C......................**Micromonospora** *p. 822*

   Growth occurs between 50° and 60°C.; aerial mycelium produced

   Thermoactinomyces *p. 824*

16. Acid-fast...**Mycobacterium** *p. 695*

   Non-acid-fast..17

17. Rudimentary branching rods only under aerobic conditions or in acid media anaerobically; produce chains of cocci or short rods in neutral media under anaerobic conditions; *propionic acid produced from lactic acid*......**Propionibacterium** *p. 569*

   Cells have a definite cyclic development; spherical cells germinate at one or more points to produce rod-shaped cells which elongate and divide. At the point of division, growth of the cells continues at an angle to the original axis. When side branches are equal in size to the parent cell, division occurs at the angle. This process is repeated during the growth of the colony. *In older colonies the rods transform entirely into a mass of cocci.* Rods are most frequently Gram-negative with Gram-positive granules; the coccal forms are frequently Gram-positive. Recorded mainly from soils

   Arthrobacter *p. 605*

   Note: The emphasis lies on the final transformation into cocci. Some authorities may consider that limited true branching may occur. If this is admitted, the dividing line between *Arthrobacter* and *Nocardia* becomes very slim. The author's observations of *Arthrobacter globiforme* fit the above statement, and it is suggested that these criteria be adopted, true branching forms which later disintegrate being assigned to *Nocardia.*

   Organisms produce both coccoid and rod-shaped forms, the latter frequently branching. Coccoid resting cells are produced which may germinate at one or more points. The coccoid forms generally predominate..............**Mycococcus** *p. 707*

Note: The descriptions given for species in this genus are like early descriptions given for *Arthrobacter* and in some instances could fit *Nocardia.*

Not as above...**18**

18. Organisms disintegrate filter paper in 0.5 per cent peptone water; produce clearing on precipitated cellulose agar plates; motile (except *C. flavigena*)

            Cellulomonas *p. 601*

Not as above.................................possibly **Corynebacterium** *p. 579*

19. Motile at 37° or at 25°C...**20**

 Non-motile...**27**

20. Organisms pathogenic to warm-blooded animals causing monocytosis; catalase-positive; acid produced from glucose, salicin and aesculin........**Listeria** *p. 597*

 Not as above...**21**

21. Pathogenic to plants...**22**

 Not pathogenic to plants..**24**

22. Yellow colonies; polar flagella................possibly **Corynebacterium** *p. 579*

       (*C. flaccumfaciens* or *C. tritici*)

 ....Or....**Xanthomonas** *p. 152*

       (*X. proteamaculans* or *X. conjac*)

 Yellow colonies; peritrichous flagella............................**Erwinia** *p. 349*

       (*E. citrimaculans*)

 Colonies not yellow..**23**

23. Flagella polar....................................**Corynebacterium** *p. 579*

     (*C. poinsettiae* or *C. hypertrophicans*)

 ....Or....**Pseudomonas** *p. 89*

       (*P. polygoni*)

 Flagella peritrichous...**Erwinia** *p. 349*

       (*E. carnegieana*)

 Note: Erwinia species are generally regarded as Gram-negative. Gram-variable species are recorded.

24. Organisms disintegrate filter paper in 0.5 per cent peptone water; produce clearing on precipitated cellulose agar plates......................**Cellulomonas** *p. 601*

 Not as above...**25**

25. No acid from carbohydrates......................................**26**

 Acid from carbohydrates............................**Brevibacterium** *p. 490*

   (Including *Flavobacterium suaveolens* and *F. marinum*)

26. Organisms occur in long chains; colonies colorless and spreading....**Kurthia** *p. 503*

 Organisms arranged singly; colonies yellow..............**Brevibacterium** *p. 490*

       (*B. sulfureum*)

27. Acid-fast....................................**Mycobacterium** *p. 695*

 Not acid-fast...**28**

28. Organisms 0.2 to 0.4 by 0.5 to 2.5 microns; long filaments common in rough colonies; occur singly and also in chains; pinpoint transparent colonies on agar in 24 hours at 37°C., extending on further incubation to 1.5 mm; acid only produced from glucose and lactose and some other carbohydrates but not from aesculin; final pH in glucose broth, about 6.0; hydrogen sulfide is produced; causes swine erysipelas, human erysipeloid, mouse septicemia and infections in sheep, birds and fish

         Erysipelothrix *p. 599*

 Not as above...**29**

29. Rods 0.4 to 0.7 by 1 to 3 microns; show granular staining with methylene blue; arranged in angular fashion similar to the corynebacteria; only 2 species recorded, both of which produce acid from glucose, fructose and mannose; catalase-positive; resist heating to 72°C. for 15 minutes; normally found in dairy products and equipment

         Microbacterium *p. 600*

 Not as above...**30**

30. Organisms grow on agar under aerobic conditions only if heavy inocula are used; slightly pleomorphic, including branched forms; *propionic acid is produced from glucose and also from lactic acid;* catalase-positive.... **Propionibacterium** *p. 569*

    (*P. arabinosum*)

    Not as above..31

31. Small spindle-shaped cells usually occurring in long intertwined chains in liquid media; microaerophilic; ferments glucose with the production of ethyl alcohol with small amounts of CO_2 and acetic acid and possibly lactic and formic acids; acid and gas in glucose in 3 to 5 days............................**Zymobacterium** *p. 577*

    Not as above..32

32. Colonies usually 1 mm or less in diameter, colorless, little or no growth on media devoid of carbohydrates; rods frequently arranged in chains, grow in glucose broth, producing a pH much below 6.0; acid produced from lactose by all species except *L. delbrueckii* and *L. brevis*............................**Lactobacillus** *p. 543*

    Not as above..33

33. Lactose fermented; cells pleomorphic; arranged in palisades and chinese-letter forms; frequently bar-shaped, beaded and clubbed..........**Corynebacterium** *p. 579*

    Lactose not fermented...34

34. Organisms occur singly, in pairs or in short chains; not pleomorphic

    Brevibacterium *p. 490*

    (See also *B. healii*)

    Organisms normally found in palisade or chinese-letter forms, pleomorphic; barred, beaded and club-shaped forms common...............**Corynebacterium** *p. 579*

    Note: Criteria for separation of these two genera are inadequate.

35. Organisms produce a true branching mycelium which later disintegrates into simple rods, cocci and rods with remnants of branches............**Actinomyces** *p. 742*

    Organisms do not branch or, if branching occurs, it is limited to bifurcations and branching of isolated rods; no true mycelium formed...........................36

36. Endospores produced..37

    No endospores produced..38

37. Organisms reduce CO_2 to CH_4 while oxidizing secondary alcohols to ketones and primary alcohols to acids.................................**Methanobacterium** *p. 250*

    (*M. omelianskii*)

    Not as above...**Clostridium** *p. 634*

38. Cells motile; gas produced from peptone in the absence of carbohydrates

    Cillobacterium *p. 566*

    Note: Glucose and other carbohydrates are fermented by all species; butyric acid is frequently among the byproducts.

    Cells non-motile..39

39. Visible gas produced in culture media either in the presence or absence of carbohydrates
....40

    Note: In the ensuing section of the key, from 40 to 44 inclusive, the statement "acid from" infers "acid" or "acid and gas," since it is not clear whether gas produced in the presence of carbohydrate arises from the fermentation of the sugar or action on the peptone.

    Visible gas in culture media either in the presence or absence of carbohydrates; glucose fermentation not recorded; pathogenic to guinea pigs; rods occur singly, in pairs, in V-formation, in short chains and in clumps.

    See *Eubacterium niosii* and *Eubacterium quintum*

    No visible gas produced in culture media in the presence or absence of carbohydrates
....45

40. Acid produced from glucose, lactose and fructose...........................41

    Acid produced from glucose and fructose but not from lactose...................42

Acid produced from glucose and lactose but not from fructose.....................**43**
Acid produced from glucose but not from lactose or fructose......................**44**

41. Large rods with rounded ends occurring as short swollen and long curved forms; bifurcation common; acid produced also from maltose, galactose and sucrose; strict anaerobes...**Catenabacterium**   *p. 560*
   (*C. filamentosum*)

   Slender rods sometimes undulating and filamentous; form acute V- and Y-shaped angles giving an appearance of false branching; acid also from galactose and trehalose; strict anaerobes..............................**Ramibacterium**   *p. 563*
   (*R. pseudoramosum*)

   Microaerophilic, pleomorphic organisms occurring as chains of cocci in acid media anaerobically and as rods with branching forms aerobically; aerobic growth very poor; propionic acid produced from lactic acid; limited gas from carbohydrates but none from peptone...............................**Propionibacterium**   *p. 569*

   Small, spindle-shaped cells usually occurring in long intertwined chains in liquid media; ferments glucose with the production of ethyl alcohol and small amounts of CO_2 and acetic acid and possibly lactic and formic acids; *no butyric or propionic acid produced*; acid and gas in glucose in 3 to 5 days
   Zymobacterium (*Z. oroticum*)   *p. 577*

   Rods occurring singly, in pairs or in short or long chains; strict anaerobes
   Eubacterium   *p. 552*
   (See also *Lactobacillus brevis*.)

42. Organisms occur in long chains; acid from glucose, fructose, maltose, sucrose, galactose, xylose and arabinose; propionic acid produced among the byproducts; strict anaerobes...**Catenabacterium**   *p. 560*
   (*C. contortum*)

   Organisms arranged in chains and in acute V- and Y-shaped forms suggestive of false branches; gelatin not liquefied; nitrites not produced from nitrates; no acid from maltose; butyric acid is produced; strictly anaerobic....**Ramibacterium**   *p. 563*
   (*R. dentium* and *R. alactolyticum*)

   Microaerophilic pleomorphic organisms occurring as chains of cocci in acid media anaerobically and as rods with branching forms aerobically; aerobic growth very poor; *propionic acid produced from lactic acid;* limited gas from carbohydrates but none from peptone...............................**Propionibacterium**   *p. 569*

   Other than above; organisms occur singly or in short chains; acid from maltose; butyric acid is produced by one species; strict anaerobes....**Eubacterium**   *p. 552*
   (*E. foedans*, *E. quartum*, *E. limosum;* see also *Lactobacillus brevis*.)

43. Organisms occur in short or long chains with zig-zag arrangement and acute V and Y forms suggestive of false branching; propionic acid produced by one species
   Ramibacterium   *p. 563*
   (*R. ramosum* and *R. ramosoides*)

   Organisms occur singly or in a long, sinuous chain of cells....**Eubacterium**   *p. 552*
   (*E. rectale*)

   Note: There is a strong resemblance between the descriptions of *Ramibacterium ramosoides* and *Eubacterium rectale*.

44. Organisms occur in short chains and as long pleomorphic filaments; acid produced from glucose, maltose, sucrose, galactose and glycerol; hydrogen sulfide is produced; gelatin is liquefied; butyric acid is produced.........**Catenabacterium**   *p. 560*
   (*C. helminthoides*)

   Organisms arranged singly; butyric acid, acetic acid and CO_2 produced from glucose, maltose and lactic acid.............................**Butyribacterium**   *p. 577*
   (*B. rettgeri*)

Organisms arranged singly; amines, ammonia and nitrogen produced

Eubacterium   *p. 552*

(*E. obstii*)

Organisms arranged predominantly in Y-shaped forms suggestive of false branching; acid from glucose and galactose; gelatin not liquefied.... **Ramibacterium**   *p. 563*

(*R. pleuriticum*) (See also *Corynebacterium diphtheroides.*)

45. No acid from carbohydrates...............................**Eubacterium**   *p. 552*

Acid from carbohydrates..46

46. Acid from glucose, lactose and fructose....................................49

Acid from glucose and lactose but not from fructose....**Catenabacterium**   *p. 560*

(*C. lottii*) (See also *Lactobacillus caucasicus.*)

Acid from glucose and fructose but not from lactose...........................47

Acid from glucose but not from lactose or fructose...........................53

47. Organisms pathogenic to mice and rabbits; cause urinary-tract infection in horses, cattle, sheep and dogs; propionic acid not produced from lactic acid; strictly anaerobic.....................................**Corynebacterium**   *p. 579*

(*C. renale*)

Not as above...48

48. Organisms found mainly in fermenting foods; *propionic acid produced from lactic acid;* microaerophilic to anaerobic......................**Propionibacterium**   *p. 569*

No propionic acid produced from lactic acid; microaerophilic to anaerobic

Lactobacillus   *p. 542*

49. Butyric acid produced...50

Propionic acid produced...51

No propionic or butyric acid produced......................................52

50. Organisms occurring in very long chains..............**Catenabacterium**   *p. 560*

(*C. catenaforme*)

Organisms occurring singly, in pairs and in clumps........**Eubacterium**   *p. 552*

(*E. parvum*) (See also *Corynebacterium avidum.*)

51. Strictly anaerobic....................................**Eubacterium**   *p. 552*

(*E. disciformans*)

Microaerophilic to anaerobic; *propionic acid produced from lactic acid;* catalase-positive.......................................**Propionibacterium**   *p. 569*

52. Long rods, 0.3 by 8.0 microns, with tapered, rounded or swollen ends; often occurring in short or long chains..........................**Catenabacterium**   *p. 560*

(*C. leptotrichoides*)

Slender rods, 0.5 to 0.7 by 2 to 8 microns, occurring in short or long chains; bifurcations common; produce lactic and volatile acids from glucose; microaerophilic to anaerobic

Lactobacillus   *p. 542*

Rods 1.0 by 3.0 microns; produced in short or long chains; acetic and lactic acids produced from glucose....................................**Eubacterium**   *p. 552*

Note: E. crispatum has a similar sugar-fermentation range to that of *Lactobacillus bifidus*, but acetic acid appears to predominate.

53. Propionic acid produced..55

Butyric acid produced from lactic acid; acid from glucose and maltose

Butyribacterium   *p. 577*

(*B. rettgeri*)

No propionic or butyric acid produced......................................54

54. Organisms arranged in short to very long chains........**Catenabacterium**   *p. 560*

(*C. nigrum*)

Organisms occurring singly and in groups arranged in a palisade or Chinese-letter fashion......................................**Corynebacterium**   *p. 579*

(*C. granulosum* and *C. parvum*)

55. Catalase-positive; *propionic acid produced from lactic acid*

Propionibacterium   *p. 569*

Catalase-positive; propionic acid produced from glucose but not from lactic acid

Corynebacterium   *p. 579*

(*C. acnes*)

SECTION H

tract; will grow in selected synthetic media using pneumococcal capsular poly-
saccharide as the sole source of carbon........**Saccharobacterium**
Note: This genus is recorded in the sixth but not in the seventh edition of the
MANUAL.
Not as above...10

10. Colonies with a purple pigment......................**Chromobacterium**   *p. 292*
Note: Chromobacterium marismortui has a bluish-brown pigment; see also
Pseudomonas iodinum and *Pseudomonas beijerinckii.*
Colonies red at 37° or 25°C., sometimes with a red, soluble pigment..............11
Other than above..17

11. Red color due to prodigiosin; motile by means of peritrichous flagella or non-motile
Serratia   *p. 359*
Red color not due to prodigiosin...12

12. Obligate halophiles requiring 20 to 30 per cent salt for growth; highly pleomorphic
Halobacterium   *p. 207*
Not obligately halophilic..13

13. Organisms metabolize alkylamines; non-motile or motile by means of polar flagella
Protaminobacter   *p. 200*
Not as above...14

14. Motile by means of polar flagella; straight or curved rods......................15
Motile by means of peritrichous flagella.....................................16

15. Straight rods...**Pseudomonas**   *p. 89*
(P. melophthora)
Curved rods..**Vibrio**   *p. 229*
(V. extorquens and *V. hyphalus)*

16. Methyl-red positive; Voges-Proskauer negative..............**Escherichia**   *p. 335*
(E. aurescens)
Methyl-red negative; Voges-Proskauer positive; pathogenic on rhubarb
Erwinia   *p. 349*
(E. rhapontica)

17. Organisms produce a water-soluble, blue, green or yellow pigment...............18
Not as above...19

18. Agar hydrolyzed; alginic acid decomposed..............**Alginomonas**   *p. 202*
(A. fucicola) (See also *Pseudomonas gelatica* and *Vibrio fuscus.*)
Agar not hydrolyzed.................................**Pseudomonas**   *p. 89*

19. Plant pathogens...20
Not pathogenic or known to be pathogenic to plants..........................24

20. Organisms produce hyperplastic diseases such as galls and hairy root
Agrobacterium   *p. 288*
Not as above...21

21. Colonies yellow...22
Colonies not yellow...23

22. Flagella polar...**Xanthomonas**   *p. 152*
(See also *Bacterium tardicrescens, Bacterium albilineans, Pseudomonas trifolii,
Pseudomonas panicimiliacei, Pseudomonas radiciperda* and *Pseudomonas levistici.*)
Flagella peritrichous...**Erwinia**   *p. 349*
Note: The following yellow-pigmented pathogenic organisms are either non-
motile or motility has not been recorded: *Bacterium stewartii, Xanthomonas
clerodendri, Xanthomonas sesbaniae* and *Corynebacterium agropyri.*

23. Flagella polar...**Pseudomonas**   *p. 89*
(See also *Xanthomonas panici, X. proteamaculans, X. manihotis, X. rubrisubalbi-
cans, X. cannae, X. zingiberi* and *X. translucens.*)
Flagella peritrichous...**Erwinia**   *p. 349*

24. Curved and irregular cells; may branch in young cultures; capable of using phenolic compounds as the sole source of carbon; gas, presumably nitrogen, produced in 0.1 per cent nitrate broth but no nitrites are produced; no acid from carbohydrates
Mycoplana *p. 204*
Not as above........ 25

25. Curved rods, very small, about 1.0 micron in length, which, during growth, produce closed rings, 2.0 to 3.0 microns in diameter, which later change to two horseshoe-shaped halves fastened together without any evidence of divisional lines. These divide into separate rods which reproduce the cycle; encapsulated; grow well in 0.5 per cent peptone water.......................**Microcyclus** *p. 253*
Not as above........ 26

26. Curved or S-shaped rods, 0.1 to 0.2 by 6 to 8 microns or longer; very poor growth on peptone agar;
or
short straight rods 0.5 by 1 to 2 microns; good growth on peptone agar; on inorganic thiosulfate agar, small watery colonies produced which turn white from the deposition of sulfur; grow autotrophically, oxidizing thiosulfate to sulfur and sulfate
Thiobacillus *p. 83*
Not as above........ 27

27. Curved cells, 1 by 5 to 10 microns, which form chains which may twist around each other to form coiled, non-septate, non-motile colorless bundles; enclosed in a spherical, solid gelatinous mass from 10 to 17 microns in diameter; found floating on water containing decomposing plant material.................**Myconostoc** *p. 260*
Not as above........ 28

28. Curved organisms which grow on precipitated-cellulose mineral-salts agar producing a clearing of the medium around the colonies; also grow in 0.5 per cent peptone water in which a strip of filter paper is half immersed, weakening the filter paper sufficiently for the fibers to separate on slight agitation or reducing it to a pulpy mass; organisms are arranged in palisade fashion similar to the corynebacteria
Cellulomonas *p. 601*
(See also *Vibrio agarliquefaciens* and *V. fuscus*.)
Not as above........ 29

29. Curved organisms which grow on a filter-paper mineral-salts medium oxidizing the cellulose to oxycellulose................29........ 30
Not as above........ 31

30. Sickle-shaped; cells no longer than 2.0 microns; stain more intensely at the center than at the ends; no growth on a mineral salts agar containing starch; green, cream or brownish on filter paper.............................**Cellfalcicula** *p. 252*
Curved cells 1.5 to 5.0 microns in length, with rounded ends; grow moderately well on mineral salts agar containing starch; cream, brown or no pigment on filter paper
Cellvibrio *p. 250*

31. Curved rods which transform completely into coccoid forms during growth of the colony. Rods elongate and divide. At the point of division the rods grow out at an angle to the original axis and divide again at the angle when the cell has doubled its length. This process continues until a colony is formed. *Ultimately the rods transform completely into cocci*............................**Arthrobacter** *p. 605*
Note: The emphasis lies on the final transformation into cocci. Some authorities may consider that limited true branching may occur. If this is admitted, the dividing line between *Arthrobacter* and *Nocardia* becomes very slim. The author's observations of *Arthrobacter globiforme* fit the above statement, and it is suggested that these criteria be adopted, true branching forms which later disintegrate being assigned to *Nocardia*.
Not as above........ 32

32. Curved rods; motile by means of polar flagella...................................33
    Straight rods...34
33. Oxidize hydrogen sulfide, depositing sulfur inside the cell.......**Thiospira**   *p. 82*
    Note: If *Thiospira* should prove to be anaerobic, this insertion would be invalid.
    Do not deposit sulfur inside the cell...........................**Vibrio**   *p. 229*
    Note: Spencer states that species of *Photobacterium* are also curved.
34. Acid produced from lactose within 40 days......................................35
    No acid produced from lactose...71
35. Agar is digested..36
    Agar is not digested; organisms parasitic on the cytoplasm of the rhizopod *Pelomyxa palustris*...................................*Bacterium* parapelomyxae*   *p. 929*
    Not as above..38
36. Yellow colonies...37
37. Polar flagella..**Pseudomonas**   *p. 89*
    (Including *P. segnis* and *P. lacunogenes*, placed in the appendix to *Xanthomonas*)
    Motile by means of peritrichous flagella or non-motile....**Agarbacterium**   *p. 322*
38. Motile at 37° or at 20°C..39
    Non-motile...59
    Motility not recorded (See *Xanthomonas clerodendri* and *X. sesbaniae*.)
39. Acid and gas from glucose..40
    Acid only from glucose...52
40. Gelatin liquefied..41
    Gelatin not liquefied..46
41. Flagella polar; colorless colonies; litmus milk acid, coagulated and slowly digested; 2–3–butylene-glycol produced from glucose; cause a fatal septicemia in fish and frogs
    Aeromonas   *p. 189*
    Flagella polar; colorless colonies; not as above.............**Pseudomonas**   *p. 89*
    Flagella polar; yellow colonies.................possibly **Xanthomonas**   *p. 152*
    (*X. hemmiana*)
    Flagella peritrichous; colonies colorless...42
42. Protopectinase produced...**Erwinia**   *p. 349*
    Protopectinase is not produced...43
43. Lactose fermented in 2 days...44
    Lactose fermentation delayed.......................**Paracolobactrum**   *p. 346*
    (*P. arizonae* and *P. aerogenoides* strains 4611, 1721 and 19111; see also *Erwinia chrysanthemi* and Arizona Group, Rome, 1953.)
44. Methyl-red positive; Voges-Proskauer positive or negative.......................45
    Methyl-red negative; Voges-Proskauer positive...............**Aerobacter**   *p. 341*
45. No gas produced from lactose within 2 days...........**Paracolobactrum**   *p. 346*
    (*P. intermedium* strains 8011, 13311, 11411)
    Gas produced from lactose within 2 days..................**Escherichia**   *p. 335*
    (*E. freundii*) (See also Arizona Group, Rome, 1953.)
    Note: Erwinia carnegieana and *Erwinia atroseptica* may terminate here.
46. Flagella polar; litmus milk unchanged; starch hydrolyzed; hydrogen sulfide produced; wide range of sugars fermented; organisms will grow in a nitrogen-free medium fixing atmospheric nitrogen....................**Azotomonas**   *p. 198*

---

* Not recognized in the MANUAL.

Flagella polar; acid only in lactose; indole-negative; luminescent on a variety of media at pH 8.0....................................**Photobacterium** *p. 193*

Note: The polar flagellated plant pathogens *Pseudomonas petasitis* (colorless) and *Xanthomonas conjac* (yellow pigmented), if it is lactose-positive, may terminate here.

Not as above: flagella peritrichous...47

47. Alginate fermented with the production of acid and gas; hydrogen sulfide produced; methyl-red positive; Voges-Proskauer weak; citrate utilized; nitrite produced from nitrate......................................**Alginobacter** *p. 348*

Not as above..48

48. Methyl-red positive; Voges-Proskauer negative...............................49

Methyl-red negative; Voges-Proskauer positive................................51

Note: Erwinia nimipressuralis and *E. dissolvens* should be compared with genera terminating between numbers 49 to 51 inclusive.

49. Lactose fermented within 2 days...50

Lactose fermentation delayed........................**Paracolobactrum** *p. 346*

P. coliforme strains 28221, 5511, 6611, 2611, 31611, 111, 15411, 1811, 33811 and 4361.

P. intermedium strains 14011, 12611 and 1421.

Bethesda and Ballerup Groups, Rome, 1953, for gas-producing strains with slow lactose fermentation.

50. Acid and gas from lactose...............................**Escherichia** *p. 335*

(*Escherichia*, Rome, 1953, for motile strains)

Acid only from lactose.............................**Paracolobactrum** *p. 346*

(*P. intermedium* strains 14011 and 12611)

51. Lactose fermented in 2 days...............................**Aerobacter** *p. 341*

Lactose fermentation delayed......................**Paracolobactrum** *p. 346*

(*P. aerogenoides* strains 721, 37711 and 37211)

52. Organisms cause a glanders-like infection (melioidosis) in rats, guinea pigs, rabbits and man; colonies on agar small, circular, slightly raised, thick, opaque and cream-colored with an irregular margin; litmus milk slowly coagulated; blood serum slowly liquefied; optimum temperature, 37°C..................**Pseudomonas** *p. 89*

(*P. pseudomallei*)

Organisms which produce granular conjunctivitis in monkeys and apes and which are believed to be a cause of trachoma in man; optimum temperature, between 28° and 30° C. with motility only at low temperatures; colonies on blood agar small, circular, grayish and translucent, becoming sticky and mucoid

Noguchia *p. 421*

Not as above..53

53. Organisms grow in 0.5 per cent peptone water containing a filter paper strip, weakening the latter sufficiently to cause disintegration on slight agitation or reducing it to a pulp; produce clearings around colonies on precipitated cellulose agar plates; cells commonly arranged in angular fashion like corynebacteria

Cellulomonas *p. 601*

(See also *Pseudomonas arguta, P. tralucida* and also *P. ephemerocyanea* if the latter produces no pigment.)

Not as above..54

54. Colonies yellow..55

Colonies not yellow..57

55. Flagella polar.....................................**Xanthomonas** *p. 152*

(See also *Pseudomonas perlurida, P. subcreta, P. cepacia* and also *P. radiciperda* and *Bacterium tardicrescens* should the latter two be lactose fermenters.)

Flagella peritrichous..56

56. Marine organisms; nitrites not produced from nitrates; starch hydrolyzed

                                                Flavobacterium   *p. 309*

Not as above..possibly **Erwinia**   *p. 349*

    Note: Erwinia ananas, E. mangiferae, E. vitivora and *E. milletiae* terminate here.

57. Organisms found in the cytoplasm of the rhizopod *Pelomyxa*

                                    Bacterium* *parapelomyxae*   *p. 929*

    Note: This entry is valid only if the organism is motile.

Not as above..**58**

58. Flagella polar...**Pseudomonas**   *p. 89*

Flagella peritrichous.............................**Paracolobactrum**   *p. 346*

    (Anaerogenic strains)

    Note: (1) From published data the following organisms, if isolated from the soil, may terminate here: *Agrobacterium rhizogenes, Erwinia amylovora, E. aroideae, Rhizobium leguminosarum, R. trifolii* and *R. phaseoli.*

    In addition the following may also be listed if they prove to be lactose fermenters: *Achromobacter delicatulum, A. superficiale, Agrobacterium tumefaciens, Rhizobium meliloti* and *Erwinia salicis.*

      (2) Non-gas-producing strains of Ballerup and Bethesda Groups, Rome, 1953, which ferment lactose slowly.

59. Acid and gas from glucose...**60**

Acid only from glucose...**64**

60. Bioluminescent...................................**Photobacterium**   *p. 193*

Not as above...**61**

61. Methyl-red positive; Voges-Proskauer negative.................................**62**

Methyl-red negative; Voges-Proskauer positive.................................**63**

62. Lactose fermented in 2 days.............................**Escherichia**   *p. 335*

    (*Escherichia,* Rome, 1953, for non-motile strains)

Lactose fermentation delayed.......................**Paracolobactrum**   *p. 346*

    (*P. coliforme* strains 311, 17611 and 16911)

63. Encapsulated organisms; pathogenic, causing infections in man and animals, principally of the respiratory tract...........................**Klebsiella**   *p. 344*

Not as above...**Aerobacter**   *p. 341*

    (*Klebsiella* (*Klebsiella-Aerogenes*) Group, Rome, 1953)

64. Small, ovoid coccobacilli causing pneumonia in sheep and cattle

                                  Pasteurella   *p. 395*

Organisms which produce mucoid to cartilaginous colonies adherent to the medium; grow on meat infusion agar; colonies usually 1 mm in diameter in 24 hours but may enlarge on further incubation to 3 to 6 mm; produce a granulated growth on the walls of the tube in liquid media; occur in necrotic lesions as granules resembling actinomycotic granules in cases of actinobacillosis of cattle and joint ill of foals or in complicating actinomycotic infections. One species may be a commensal in the alimentary canal of solipeds.............................**Actinobacillus**   *p. 414*

Not as above..**65**

65. Fastidious organisms; do not grow on meat infusion agar in the absence of X-factor on primary isolation under aerobic conditions but may be trained to grow without it; colonies on blood agar 0.5 mm in diameter but may be much larger on Levinthal agar; coccobacillary, arranged singly, in short chains or in clumps

                                Haemophilus   *p. 406*

Species represented here cause bronchopneumonia of sheep (*H. ovis*), respiratory infection in mice (*H. influenzae-murium*) and endocarditis (*H. aphrophilus*).

Fastidious organisms; require blood or ascitic fluid; highly pleomorphic; rod-shaped

---

*Not recognized in the MANUAL.

or filamentous; may reach 100 to 150 microns in length; homogeneous in young cultures but become granulated, beaded and swollen in old cultures and tend to fragment into rods and cocci; large spherical swellings packed with granules common; cholesterol globules appear among the growth; only rods and short filaments appear in pathological material; non-branching; non-acid fast; colonies on ascitic agar 1 to 2.5 mm in 3 days, circular, low convex, colorless; L-phase variants are common; highly virulent for mice causing polyarthritis. Causes rat-bite or Haverhill fever in man..**Streptobacillus** *p. 451*
(*S. moniliformis*)

Not as above: grow well on media without blood or serum.....................66

66. Colonies colorless...67
Colonies yellow..70

67. Organisms grow in 0.5 per cent peptone containing filter paper, causing the latter to disintegrate; gelatin liquefied; nitrite produced from nitrate; starch hydrolyzed
Cellulomonas *p. 601*

Not as above..68

68. Lactose fermented in two days..69
Lactose fermentation delayed; enteric pathogens..............**Shigella** *p. 384*
(*Shigella* Group, Rome, 1953, slow lactose-fermenters)

69. Encapsulated cells; pathogenic...............................**Klebsiella** *p. 344*
Not as above.......................................**Achromobacter** *p. 300*

70. Curved rods which transform completely into coccoid forms during growth of the colony. Rods elongate and divide. At the point of division the rods grow out at an angle to the original axis and divide again at the angle when the cell has doubled its length. This process continues until a colony is formed. *Ultimately the rods transform completely into cocci*...............................**Arthrobacter** *p. 605*
Note: The emphasis lies on the final transformation into cocci. Some authorities may consider that limited true branching may occur. If this is admitted the dividing line between *Arthrobacter* and *Nocardia* becomes very slim. The author's observations of *Arthrobacter globiforme* fit the above statement, and it is suggested that these criteria be adopted, true branching forms which later disintegrate being assigned to *Nocardia*.

Not as above; starch hydrolyzed.......................**Flavobacterium** *p. 309*
In addition to the above, the following species, two of them plant pathogens, terminate at this point: *Pseudomonas iridescens*, *Corynebacterium agropyri* and *Bacterium stewartii*.

71. Non-motile...72
Motile..103

72. Acid and gas from glucose..73
Acid but no gas from glucose...77
No acid or gas from glucose..85

73. Only a small amount of gas from glucose; causes dysentery in man; agglutinated by polyvalent antiserum to *Shigella flexneri*.....................**Shigella** *p. 384*
(Newcastle strain)
Organisms which cause bacillary white diarrhoea of chickens; agglutinated with *Salmonella* group D "O" antiserum.........................**Salmonella** *p. 368*
(*S. pullorum*)

Not as above..74

74. Bioluminescent on 3 per cent salt agar, especially with a fish base; pleomorphic and branching rods on asparagine-sugar media; 2-3-butylene-glycol produced
Photobacterium *p. 193*

Not bioluminescent...75

75. Gelatin liquefied; nitrites produced from nitrates; methyl-red negative; Voges-Pros-

kauer negative; starch hydrolyzed; pathogenic to the fish *Salmonidae*

Aeromonas   *p. 189*

Not as above: Voges-Proskauer positive 76

76. Organisms encapsulated; cause respiratory and other infections in man

Klebsiella   *p. 344*

Not as above . . . .**Paracolobactrum**   *p. 346*

(*P. aerogenoides* strains 32011 and 32811)

77. Obligate halophiles requiring 20 to 30 per cent salt for growth; pleomorphic; yellow colonies . . . . **Halobacterium**   *p. 207*

Not as above 78

78. Organisms will not grow on meat infusion agar without the addition of blood or ascitic fluid or X and V factors or other enrichments 79

Not as above 80

79. Pleomorphic coccobacillary organisms; grow well on blood agar producing colonies up to 4 mm in diameter on prolonged incubation; hydrogen sulfide produced from cystine media; slight acid from glucose, fructose and mannose and possibly from other sugars. Pathogenic, producing tularemia or tularemia-like infections in laboratory animals . . . .**Pasteurella**   *p. 395*

Organisms usually 0.2 to 0.5 micron wide and 0.5 to 2.0 microns long but frequently produce long filaments; do not grow on nutrient agar or on MacConkey's lactose bile salt agar; grow on nutrient agar with the addition of X factor or V factor or both or with the addition of diphosphothiamine or adenosine triphosphate; colonies on suitable media rarely more than 1 mm in diameter after 2 days incubation; nitrites produced from nitrates; various species have been reported as responsible for or associated with viruses in:

   (i) Purulent meningitis and conjunctivitis in man (*H. influenzae*)

  (ii) Sub-acute endocarditis (*H. hemolyticus*)

 (iii) Acute and sub-acute conjunctivitis in man (*H. aegyptius*)

 (iv) Soft chancre (*H. ducreyi*)

  (v) Vesicular eruptions in the genitals of cattle (*H. citreus*)

 (vi) Ulcers of trout (*H. piscium*)

(vii) Commonly present in the respiratory tract of man (various species) and preputial secretions of dogs (*H. haemoglobinophilus*)

(viii) Pharyngitis (*H. parahaemolyticus*)

 (ix) Non-pathogenic (*H. parainfluenzae*)

  (x) Fowl coryza (*H. gallinarum*)

 (xi) Swine influenza (*H. suis*)

(xii) Respiratory tract of ferrets (*H. putoriorum*) . . . .**Haemophilus**   *p. 406*

Note: This is the main entry for the genus *Haemophilus*. Owing to variable biochemical characteristics, other entries occur in other parts of the key.

Fastidious organisms; require blood or ascitic fluid; highly pleomorphic; rod-shaped or filamentous; may reach 100 to 150 microns in length; homogeneous in young cultures but become granulated, beaded and swollen in old cultures and tend to fragment into rods and cocci; large spherical swellings packed with granules common; cholesterol globules appear among the growth; only rods and short filaments appear in pathological material; non-branching; non-acid fast; colonies on ascitic agar 1 to 2.5 mm in 3 days; circular, low convex, colorless. L-phase variants are common. Highly virulent for mice causing polyarthritis; causes rat-bite or Haverhill fever in man . . . .**Streptobacillus**   *p. 451*

(*S. moniliformis*)

80. Slender rods; 1.0 to 3.0 microns long and often arranged in angular fashion; pleomorphic; produce smooth, entire, butyrous, translucent, grayish yellow colonies 0.5 to 1.0 mm in diameter in 2 days at 37°C. on meat infusion agar; may increase

slightly in size on further incubation; light brown on potato; Straus reaction produced in guinea pigs; strict parasites causing glanders in man and animals

Actinobacillus *p. 414*
(*A. mallei*)

Small ovoid coccobacilli arranged singly and in pairs or in small bundles; sometimes pleomorphic; frequently exhibit bipolar staining; colonies on meat infusion agar 0.1 to 1.0 mm in diameter in 24 hours at 37° C.; may increase in size up to 4 to 6 mm in 5 days at 37° C. A slight thin layer or no growth on potato; organisms cause plague in man and rodents or hemorrhagic septicemia in various other animals and in birds . . . .**Pasteurella** *p. 395*

Organisms cause actinobacillosis in man and other animals and may also be found in actinomycotic lesions; colonies on agar small, circular, bluish gray, translucent, with a smooth surface and an entire edge, up to 1.5 mm in diameter in 24 hours at 37° C. but increase considerably in size on further incubation; on alkaline potato a slight glistening grayish yellow growth is produced . . . . . .**Actinobacillus** *p. 414*

Not as above **81**

81. Curved rods which transform completely into coccoid forms during growth of the colony. Rods elongate and divide. At the point of division the rods grow out at an angle to the original axis and divide again at the angle when the cell has doubled its length. This process continues until a colony is formed. *Ultimately the rods transform completely into cocci.* Colonies yellow or colorless . . . .**Arthrobacter** *p. 605*
Note: The emphasis lies on the final transformation into cocci. Some authorities may consider that limited true branching may occur. If this is admitted the dividing line between *Arthrobacter* and *Nocardia* becomes very slim. The author's observations of *Arthrobacter globiforme* fit the above statement, and it is suggested that these criteria be adopted, true branching forms which later disintegrate being assigned to *Nocardia*.

Not as above **82**

82. Colonies yellow . . . .**Flavobacterium** *p. 309*
Colonies colorless **83**

83. Enteric pathogens of man; agglutinate with *Shigella* antisera . . . . . .**Shigella** *p. 384*
(*Shigella* Group, Rome, 1953; non-lactose-fermenters)
Organisms pathogenic to birds; agglutinate with *Salmonella* Group D "O" antiserum

Salmonella *p. 368*
(*S. gallinarum*)

Not as above **84**

84. Organisms cause disintegration of filter paper in 0.5 per cent peptone water

Cellulomonas *p. 601*

Not as above . . . .**Achromobacter** *p. 300*

85. Soil organisms; curved rods which transform completely into coccoid forms during growth of the colony. Rods elongate and divide. At the point of division the rods grow out at an angle to the original axis and divide again at the angle when the cell has doubled its length. This process continues until a colony is formed; *ultimately the rods transform completely into cocci*; colonies yellow or colorless

Arthrobacter *p. 605*

Note: The emphasis lies on the final transformation into cocci. Some authorities may consider that limited true branching may occur. If this is admitted the dividing line between *Arthrobacter* and *Nocardia* becomes very slim. The author's observations of *Arthrobacter globiforme* fit the above statement, and it is suggested that these criteria be adopted, true branching forms which later disintegrate being assigned to *Nocardia*.

Not as above **86**

86. Agar digested..**Agarbacterium**   *p. 322*
    Agar not digested...87
87. Colonies yellow..88
    Colonies not yellow..92
88. Organisms will grow in a mineral salts medium using CO_2 as a source of carbon and
    oxidizing hydrogen.............................**Hydrogenomonas**   *p. 75*
    Organisms grow in a mineral salts medium using alkylamines as the sole source of
    carbon and nitrogen.............................**Protaminobacter**   *p. 200*
    Not as above...89
89. Obligate halophiles requiring 20 to 30 per cent salt for growth
                                                Halobacterium   *p. 207*
    Not as above...90
90. Litmus milk acid or unchanged.......................**Flavobacterium**   *p. 309*
    Litmus milk alkaline...91
91. Nitrites produced from nitrates....................**Flavobacterium**   *p. 309*
                        (*F. lutescens* and *F. fucatum*)
    Nitrites not produced from nitrates.....................**Alcaligenes**   *p. 297*
                        (*A. marshallii*)
92. Loeffler's inspissated serum liquefied...........................93
    Not as above...94
93. Recorded from septicemia in ducks.......................**Pasteurella**   *p. 395*
    Cause acute ophthalmia (pink eye) of cattle; angular conjunctivitis in man, monkeys
    and apes and recorded as a possible cause of trachoma in man
                                                Moraxella   *p. 419*
94. Organisms recorded from an enzootic of chronic pneumonia in calves; thin Gram-
    negative rods arranged in groups in tissues and as coccoid and bacillary forms in
    culture; in the condensation water of blood serum, produce mulberry-like flakes up
    to 1 mm in diameter consisting of cells arranged in chains, the latter encased in a
    non-stainable material which usually is swollen at the tip
                                                Actinobacillus   *p. 414*
                        (*A. actinoides*)
    Not as above...95
95. Slender rods; 1.0 to 3.0 microns long, often arranged in angular fashion; pleomorphic;
    produce smooth, entire, butyrous, translucent, grayish yellow colonies 0.5 to 1.0
    mm in diameter in 2 days at 37° C. on meat infusion agar; may increase slightly in
    size on further incubation; *cafe au lait*-colored on potato; Straus reaction produced
    in guinea pigs; strict parasite causing glanders in man and other animals
                                                Actinobacillus   *p. 414*
                        (*A. mallei*)
    Not as above...96
96. Organisms cause brucellosis in man and other animals; often cause abortion in ani-
    mals; good growth on liver extract agar or tryptose phosphate agar; increased CO_2
    tension necessary for isolation of one species; litmus milk alkaline
                                                Brucella   *p. 404*
    Not as above...97
97. Organisms causing whooping cough in man, principally in children. One species
    (*B. pertussis*) will not grow on primary isolation on meat extract agar but does not
    require X or V factor; the other species (*B. parapertussis*) grows profusely on meat
    extract agar. Both species grow well on Bordet-Gengou medium producing smooth,
    raised, entire, pearly, glistening colonies in 48 to 72 hours at 37° C.; nitrites not
    produced from nitrates; inspissated serum not liquefied. Following intraperitoneal
    injection into mice, death occurs in 2 to 4 days. Autopsy shows extensive hyperemia
    of the peritoneal wall, infiltration of glands and the presence of an extremely mucoid

exudate in the peritoneal cavity; hemorrhagic necrosis occurs following intradermal inoculation of the rabbit; agglutinated by antisera to *Bordetella pertussis*

Bordetella *p. 402*

Not as above..**98**

98. Organisms usually 0.2 to 0.5 micron wide and 0.5 to 2.0 microns long but frequently produce long filaments; do not grow on nutrient agar without the addition of X factor or V factor or both or the addition of diphosphothiamine or adenosinetriphosphate; colonies on suitable media rarely more than 1 mm in diameter after 2 days' incubation; various species have been reported as responsible for or associated with viruses in:

  (i) Purulent meningitis and conjunctivitis in man (*H. influenzae*)

  (ii) Sub-acute endocarditis (*H. haemolyticus*)

  (iii) Acute and sub-acute conjunctivitis in man (*H. aegyptius*)

  (iv) Soft chancre (*H. ducreyi*)

  (v) Vesicular eruptions in the genitals of cattle (*H. citreus*)

  (vi) Ulcers of trout (*H. piscium*)

  (vii) The respiratory tract of man (various species) and preputial secretions of dogs (*H. haemoglobinophilus*)

  (viii) Pharyngitis (*H. parahaemolyticus*)

  (ix) Non-pathogenic (*H. parainfluenzae*)

  (x) Fowl coryza (*H. gallinarum*)

  (xi) Swine influenza (*H. suis*)

  (xii) Respiratory tract of ferrets (*H. putoriorum*)

Of the above, *H. ducreyi* and *H. putoriorum* are the ones most likely to terminate here. The others may do so owing to variation in biochemical reactions

Haemophilus *p. 406*

Not as above..**99**

99. Organisms grow in a mineral salts medium with an alkylamine as the sole source of carbon and nitrogen..............................**Protaminobacter** *p. 200*

Not as above..**100**

100. Organisms found growing in waters among decomposing plant tissue; coccobacillary forms embedded in a gelatinous matrix which usually forms in long finger-like processes in which the cells are well isolated from each other; produce a zoogloeal mass and cartilaginous colonies in culture.....................**Zoogloea** *p. 206*

Not as above..**101**

101. Litmus milk alkaline...**102**

Litmus milk acid or unchanged........................**Achromobacter** *p. 300*

102. Colonies on nutrient agar colorless; up to 1 mm in diameter in 5 days at 28° C.; grow autotrophically, oxidizing sodium thiosulfate to sodium sulfate and sulfuric acid

Thiobacillus *p. 83*

Note: This entry applies to *T. novellus* if it produces no acid from carbohydrates.

Not as above..**Alcaligenes** *p. 297*

103. Acid and gas from glucose..**104**

Acid but no gas from glucose.....................................**109**

No acid or gas from glucose.......................................**120**

104. Colonies yellow; flagella polar........................**Xanthomonas** *p. 152*

  (*X. plantaginis* and *X. conjac* (if lactose-negative) terminate here.)

Colonies not yellow..**105**

105. Organisms produce a luminescent growth on agar containing 2.8 to 3.0 per cent salt; usually no luminescence on media with the usual 0.5 per cent salt

Photobacterium *p. 193*

Not as above..**106**

106. Flagella polar; gelatin liquefied; some species are pathogenic to fish, frogs and snakes while others are saprophytic.............................**Aeromonas** *p. 189*
    (See also *Pseudomonas polygoni* and *P. colurnae* (if lactose is not fermented).)
    Flagella peritrichous...107

107. Gelatin liquefied *or* indole produced *or* both; organisms may show a marked spreading growth on solidified agar with a film of moisture on the surface....**Proteus** *p. 364*
    (See also *Paracolobactrum coliforme* strains 4361 and 33811 and Providence Group, Rome, 1953, for aerogenic strains.)
    Note: Proteus spp. are probably also urease-positive. The character is not mentioned in MANUAL descriptions.
    Gelatin is not liquefied and indole is not produced; colonies do not spread on solidified agar..108

108. Voges-Proskauer positive.............................**Paracolobactrum** *p. 346*
    (*P. aerogenoides* strains 32011, 37711, 35611, 37211, 37511 and 32821)
    Voges-Proskauer negative...................................**Salmonella** *p. 368*
    (*Salmonella* Group, Rome, 1953)
    (See also *Paracolobactrum intermedium* strains 12611 and 1421 and non-lactose-fermenting strains of the Bethesda-Ballerup Group, Rome, 1953.)

109. Colonies yellow..110
    Colonies not yellow..113

110. Bioluminescent on media containing 3 per cent salt......**Photobacterium** *p. 193*
    Not as above...111

111. Chitin is hydrolyzed.......................................**Beneckea** *p. 328*
    Not as above...112

112. Flagella polar...**Xanthomonas** *p. 152*
    (See *Pseudomonas xantha* and *P. pictorum* and also *P. trifolii*, *P. radiciperda* and *Bacterium tardicrescens* if they produce no acid from lactose.)
    Flagella peritrichous....................................**Flavobacterium** *p. 309*
    Note: The following plant pathogens also terminate at this point: *Erwinia cassavae*, *E. citrimaculans* and *Agrobacterium gypsophilae*.

113. Animal parasites; colonies mucoid; isolated from the eye of the Rhesus monkey
                                     Noguchia *p. 421*
    Small translucent colonies; mucoid, small slender rods in smooth colonies; ovoid rods with bipolar staining in rough colonies; motile at 37° C.; organisms cause meliodiosis in man and other animals..........................**Pseudomonas** *p. 89*
                                 (*P. pseudomallei*)
    Note: This insertion covers strains which have lost their ability to produce acid from lactose.
    Small umbonate colonies, translucent with a dull finely granular "beaten copper" surface, entire, butyrous; organisms cause pseudotuberculosis in rodents
                                 Pasteurella *p. 395*
    Organisms found in the cytoplasm of the rhizopod *Pelomyxa palustris*
                                 Myxococcus *p. 930*
                                 (*M. pelomyxae*)
    Not as above...114

114. Organisms cause typhoid fever in man; agglutinated by *Salmonella* group D "O" antiserum when not in the "Vi" phase; flagella peritrichous
                                 Salmonella *p. 368*
                                 (*S. typhosa*)
    Not as above...115

115. Agar is digested...**Agarbacterium** *p. 322*
    Agar is not digested...116

116. Chitin is hydrolyzed..**Beneckea** *p. 328*
Chitin not hydrolyzed...117
117. Bioluminescent on media containing 3 per cent salt; may not be luminescent on 0.5
per cent salt.......................................**Photobacterium** *p. 193*
Not as above...118
118. Flagella polar...**Pseudomonas** *p. 89*
(See also *Xanthomonas manihotis, X. proteamaculans* and *Rhizobium meliloti* (if
lactose negative).)
Flagella peritrichous..119
119. Cause hyperplastic diseases of plants....................**Agrobacterium** *p. 288*
(*A. rubi, A. tumefaciens* (if lactose negative) and *A. pseudotsugae*)
Cause wilts or necrotic diseases of plants......................**Erwinia** *p. 349*
(*E. amylovora, E. tracheiphila* and *E. salicis* (if lactose negative))
Not as above.......................................**Achromobacter** *p. 300*
Note: Some anaerogenic paracolons terminate here (strains 33111, 29911 and
8911). See also anaerogenic strains of the Providence Group, Rome, 1953.
120. Curved rods which transform completely into coccoid forms during growth of the colony. Rods elongate and divide. At the point of division the rods grow out at an angle
to the original axis and divide again at the angle when the cell has doubled its length.
This process continues until a colony is formed. *Ultimately the rods transform completely into cocci.*.....................................**Arthrobacter** *p. 605*
Note: The emphasis lies on the final transformation into cocci. Some authorities may consider that limited true branching may occur. If this is admitted
the dividing line between *Arthrobacter* and *Nocardia* becomes very slim. The
author's observations of *Arthrobacter globiforme* fit the above statement, and
it is suggested that these criteria be adopted, true branching forms which
later disintegrate being assigned to *Nocardia.*
Organisms which will grow in a mineral salts medium using phenol as the sole source
of carbon; reduce nitrates with the liberation of gas, presumably nitrogen
Mycoplana *p. 204*
Not as above...121
121. Colonies yellow..122
Colonies not yellow...126
122. Agar hydrolyzed.......................................**Agarbacterium** *p. 322*
Agar not hydrolyzed..123
123. Organisms grow in a mineral salts base using CO₂ as the sole source of carbon and
oxidizing hydrogen.................................**Hydrogenomonas** *p. 75*
Not as above...124
124. Flagella polar...**Xanthomonas** *p. 152*
(See also *Pseudomonas lasia, P. cerevisiae, P. caudata, P. levistici, P. ochracea*
and *P. panicimiliacei.*)
Flagella peritrichous...125
125. Litmus milk strongly alkaline...........................**Alcaligenes** *p. 297*
(See also *Flavobacterium harrisonii.*)
Litmus milk acid or unchanged.......................**Flavobacterium** *p. 309*
126. Pleomorphic rods; do not grow on meat infusion agar; grow well in semisolid media
containing horse, rabbit or human blood or other complex substances; rods and
coccoid forms predominate in culture; flagella polar; pathogenic to man; multiply
on erythrocytes and in fixed-tissue cells; transmitted through the sandfly *Phlebotomus verrucarum*.......................................**Bartonella** *p. 969*
Colonies mucoid, small, circular and translucent; organisms cause conjunctival folliculosis in rabbits.......................................**Noguchia** *p. 421*

Small, smooth, raised, entire, pearly colonies on meat infusion agar; medium discolored; litmus milk alkaline in 1 to 2 days; cause bronchopneumonia in rodents and sometimes associated with canine distemper..........**Bordetella** *p. 402*

Not as above..127

127. Agar digested...128

Agar not digested...129

128. Alginates are metabolized; flagella polar.................**Alginomonas** *p. 202*

(See also *Pseudomonas gelatica*.)

Alginate metabolism not recorded; flagella peritrichous....**Agarbacterium** *p. 322*

129. Obligate halophiles, requiring 20 to 30 per cent salt for growth

Halobacterium *p. 207*

Not as above..130

130. Alginates metabolized; flagella polar....................**Alginomonas** *p. 202*

Not as above..131

131. Organisms found growing in water among decomposing plant tissue; produce a characteristic lobed gelatinous zoogloea in which the cells are well isolated from each other; produce cartilaginous colonies on agar.................**Zoogloea** *p. 206*

Cells actively motile, by means of polar flagella; deposit sulfur internally when growing in the presence of hydrogen sulfide...................**Thiospira** *p. 82*

Note: It is doubtful whether this genus should appear under aerobic organisms.

Not as above..132

132. Flagella polar...133

Flagella peritrichous...135

133. Organisms will grow in a mineral salts medium using CO_2 as the sole source of carbon and will oxidize hydrogen.....................**Hydrogenomonas** *p. 75*

Rods 0.5 by 1 to 2 microns; gelatin liquefied; nitrites and gas produced from nitrates; starch hydrolyzed; lipolytic; will grow autotrophically, oxidizing thiosulfate to sulfate and tetrathionate with an increase in pH. Sulfur is not precipitated

Thiobacillus *p. 83*

Not as above..134

134. Organisms cause disintegration of filter paper when growing in 0.5 per cent peptone water..**Cellulomonas** *p. 601*

(See also *Pseudomonas mira*.)

Not as above....................................**Pseudomonas** *p. 89*

(See also *Agrobacterium stellulatum*, *A. radiobacter*, *Xanthomonas panici*, *X. rubrisubalbicans*, *X. cannae*, *X. zingiberi* and *Rhizobium japonicum*.)

135. Litmus milk alkaline..**Alcaligenes** *p. 297*

(See also *Agrobacterium radiobacter* and *Rhizobium spp*.)

Litmus milk acid or unchanged........................**Achromobacter** *p. 300*

SECTION I

No gas produced in peptone; pleomorphic forms not uncommon

                                        Bacteroides   *p. 424*

                          (See also *Sphaerophorus gulosus.*)

10. Halophilic, requiring more than 4 per cent salt for growth; gas produced from peptone

                                          Bacteroides   *p. 424*

                          (*B. halosmophilus*)

Not halophilic...11

11. Very pleomorphic; gas produced from peptone............**Sphaerophorus**   *p. 441*

    (*S. necrogenes* and *S. necrophorus* and possibly *S. varius* and *S. bullosus*)

Bifurcated cells; gas production from peptone doubtful.......**Bacteroides**   *p. 424*

                          (*B. furcosus*)

12. Acid produced from lactose...13

No acid produced from lactose..16

13. Motile..**Bacteroides**   *p. 424*

                          (*B. variegatus*)

Non-motile...14

14. Non-pleomorphic, *fusiform* cells growing poorly on plain agar (?)

                                      Fusobacterium   *p. 436*

Not as above...15

15. Gelatin liquefied; very pleomorphic on ordinary or blood agar

                                  Sphaerophorus   *p. 441*

                          (*S. glycolyticus*)

and...**Bacteroides**   *p. 424*

                          (*B. uncatus*)

Gelatin liquefied; not pleomorphic.........................**Bacteroides**   *p. 424*

    (*Bacteroides exiguus, B. uniformis, B. tumidus* and some strains of *B. distasonis*)

Gelatin not liquefied......................................**Bacteroides**   *p. 424*

16. Motile; fusiform rods; pleomorphic......................**Fusobacterium**   *p. 436*

                          (*F. praeacutum*)

Non-motile...17

17. Very small rods capable of passing through a Chamberland L$_2$ filter; acid produced from glucose, sucrose and mannitol; recorded from the respiratory tract of man

                                      Dialister   *p. 440*

Not as above...18

18. Organisms dependent on serum or ascitic fluid for growth; pleomorphic

                                  Sphaerophorus   *p. 441*

                       (*S. floccosus* and *S. abscedens*)

Not as above...19

19. Slender, pointed rods...................................**Fusobacterium**   *p. 436*

                     (*F. polymorphum* and *F. vescum*)

Rods with rounded ends.....................................**Bacteroides**   *p. 424*

    (*B. cylindroides, B. capillosus, B. fragilis, B. perfoetans, B. uncatus* and *B. succinogenes*)

20. Acid from fructose.....................................**Sphaerophorus**   *p. 441*

                            (*S. siccus*)

Not as above...21

21. Organisms require serum or ascitic fluid for growth; pleomorphic

                                  Sphaerophorus   *p. 441*

                       (*S. caviae*)

Not as above; not pleomorphic............................**Bacteroides**   *p. 424*

    (*B. putidus, B. putredinus* and *B. coagulans*)

SECTION J

1. Cells occur singly; motile by means of polar flagella; may be encapsulated and may form zoogloeae but if so, do not oxidize hydrogen sulfide and do not deposit sulfur internally 2

   Cells occur singly, in pairs or in short chains; non-motile; individual cells encapsulated and usually contain two pseudovacuoles per cell which makes them buoyant and which may give them a polygonal appearance; sulfur is deposited internally

   Cells occur in well-defined aggregates. When growing in the presence of hydrogen sulfide, sulfur is deposited internally 4

2. Hydrogen sulfide is not oxidized. Sulfur is not deposited internally

   Hydrogen sulfide is oxidized, and globular sulfur is deposited internally 3

3. Cells of uneven width and length; often swollen, spindle-shaped and filamentous

   Cells of uniform width; spherical to cylindrical, the latter sometimes slightly curved

   Note: Single cells of *Thiothece*, *Thiocystis* and *Lamprocystis* resemble *Chromatium* very closely. Also cells of *Thiospirillum violaceum* are indistinguishable from curved cylindrical forms of *Chromatium*.

4. Cells occur in cubical packets ....

   Cells in young colonies appear as flat sheets in which cells are arranged in parallel rows embedded in a capsular material. In an unfavorable position or environment, irregular clumping of cells may occur ....

   Other than above 5

5. Individual cells or cell masses embedded in conspicuous capsules or zoogloea 6

   Individual cells or cell masses apparently devoid of capsular material although cells within the mass may be clearly separated in space 7

6. Cells spherical, occurring in large numbers well separated in a conspicuous common slime capsule. In dry conditions the capsular material forms a double contoured membrane around the cells. On moistening, the mass slowly swells and bursts. As the liberated cells divide they form a flat, spreading colony in which the cells are no more than three layers deep but are separated from each other by capsular material

   Cells spherical and encapsulated. In the early stages of growth of the colony, cells form in tetrads* resembling those of *Thiocystis*. Further division of the cells gives rise to a compact opaque mass of cocci embedded in a large slime capsule. This is followed by formation of arched fragments similar in appearance to sections of a hollow sphere, the fragments being arranged as if on the surface of a sphere within the capsule. Continued growth of the arched fragments results in their edges touching but not coalescing. Infolding of the arched pieces takes place, finally almost filling the internal cavity and producing a network resembling a sponge. The enveloping capsule eventually ruptures, liberating fragments of the zoogloeal network which reorganize into small groups interlinked by single cocci. Under unfavorable conditions the cocci are vacuolated, and sulfur is confined to the peripheral cytoplasm. Free cells are motile (*cf. Chromatium*). The total transformation occurs in 40 days

---

* Winogradsky considered that cells which form tetrads divide in *three* directions, the result being a four-pointed group rather than a flat group of four.

Cells spherical to cylindrical. Develop in small clusters, the compact clusters of 4 to 20 cells being widely separated in an almost spherical and seemingly cartilagenous capsule, the outer layer of which is neither sharply differentiated nor obviously deliquescent. As each cluster proliferates, it eventually separates into a number of smaller clusters *within the zoogloea*. Single cells are rare. At some stage individual clusters leave the mass as a result of either swelling and dispersion of the whole mass or a softening of the mass at one or more points. After separation, the cluster becomes motile. The process of separation of clusters occupies 3 weeks. Generation time is approximately two days...**Thiocystis**   *p. 42*

Cells spherical to cylindrical; heavily encapsulated, the capsules remaining attached to form zoogloeae. The individual capsules are very thick. Following division the cells become separated in space by the developing capsules and are eventually arranged at an obtuse angle to each other. Swarming is preceded by a softening of the capsule and an irregular rearrangement of the cells. Individual cells separate by a slow rotatory action and once free are actively motile (*cf. Chromatium*). Cells are pale gray. Sulfur granules are small and confined to the peripheral layer of cytoplasm

Thiothece   *p. 42*

7. Cells spindle-shaped; 1.5 to 1.7 by 2.5 to 5.0 microns. Cell families may consist of a long irregular body made up of cells 2 to 3 layers thick arranged in parallel fashion. When separated from other cell masses the cells rearrange to form an open pyramidal network in which the cells meet only at their tips. Colonies may be several hundred microns across and resemble *Hydrodictyon* of the blue-green algae. Small cell groups detached from the mass are motile; compact masses form under unfavorable conditions. Individual cells contain an elongated vacuole and are pale in color; sulfur is confined to the peripheral cytoplasm.....................**Thiodictyon**   *p. 41*

Cells compressed into a compact mass; colored rose-red; surrounded by a capsule composed of an inner, poorly refracting layer and an outer, strongly refracting layer. Placed in a favorable environment, the cyst cracks and the cell mass slowly creeps out (1 to 2 days). The empty cyst remains unchanged for some time. The group of cells does not disperse but grows in an irregularly contoured mass. Whole families are motile. Most cells are spherical. Division occurs only in one direction. Cells may be compressed or may be freely separated in the non-encysted state. There are rarely more than two to four within a group in the colony. They are continually changing position and proximity in the colony. Internal colonial movement can occur without much lateral movement. Coordinated lateral movement is amoeboid. Single cells occasionally become isolated from the mass and then are drawn back. Masses ultimately may separate into smaller groups. No capsular material can be discerned in the families. Families can be penetrated by small motile bacteria with ease. Winogradsky considered that the connection was via plasma threads, but he was unable to demonstrate them. He considered the dense compact masses to occur in the presence of O_2 and the open structure in the presence of hydrogen sulfide

Amoebobacter   *p. 44*

Shapeless, thick aggregates of small spherical vividly colored cells; non-motile; do not form hollow spherical structures. The extremely smooth surface of the colony suggests a limiting capsular material, but no obvious capsule is visible. Eventually growth, in the form of threads and flaps, appears on the surface, and cells become separated

Thiopolycoccus   *p. 45*

INDEX OF SCIENTIFIC NAMES

Key to the various fonts used in this index:

Nomenclature

CAPITALS:

ROMAN	accepted* names of taxa higher than genera
ITALICS	unaccepted names of taxa higher than genera

Lower Case:

Roman	specific epithets and generic names (the latter in parentheses) of accepted combinations of accepted species names
Italics	unaccepted names of genera
	accepted generic names *when used in unaccepted combinations* (in species and subspecies names)
	specific epithets of unaccepted species names
Boldface	accepted names of genera

Pagination

Roman	indicates page reference to the name of an unaccepted taxon or to the incidental mention of the name of an accepted taxon
Boldface	indicates page reference to the name of an accepted taxon

---

* NOTE: As used here, the term "accepted" has two implications: (1) taxonomically it means that the taxon under consideration is *included* in the classification scheme of BERGEY'S MANUAL *and* is *described* therein and (2) nomenclaturally it means that the name used in the MANUAL for the taxon was deemed by the editor in chief, Dr. Breed, on the basis of facts then at hand, to be the *correct* name.

INDEX OF SCIENTIFIC NAMES

1035

delbrueckii (Lactobacillus), 543
delesseriae (Agarbacterium), 325, 328
delesseria (Bacterium), 323, 328
delicatulus (Achromobacter), 300, 303
delicatulus (Bacillus), 302
delmarvae (Achromobacter), 301, 308
delmarvae (Acinetobacter), 308
delphinii (Bacillus), 123
delphinii (Pseudomonas), 94, 98, 123
delplata (Salmonella ser.), **381**
denitrificans II (Bacillus), 115
denitrificans fluorescens (Bacillus), 116
denitrificans (Micrococcus), 456, 463
denitrificans (Pseudomonas), 93, 116
denitrificans (Sulfomonas), 86
denitrificans (Thiobacillus), 83, 86
dentium (Fusiformis), 437
dentium (Ramibacterium), 563, 565
denver (Salmonella ser.), **377**
deprimata (Cytophaga), 859, **861**
derby (Salmonella ser.), **376**
dermacentrophila (Rickettsia), 955
dermacentrophila (Wolbachia), 953, **955**
Dermacentroxenus, 935, 936, 941, 942
  conori, 943
  orientalis, 940
  pijperi, 943
  rickettsi, 941
  rickettsi var. *brasiliensis*, 941
  rickettsi var. *conori*, 943
  rickettsi var. *pijperi*, 943
  sibericus, 947
  typhi, 938
desaiana (Phytomonas), 129
desaiana (Pseudomonas), 94, 96, 129
desmodii (Xanthomonas), 153, 155, 161
desmodiigangeticii (Xanthomonas), 153, 155, **162**
desmodii-gangeticii (Xanthomonas), 162
desmolytica (Pseudomonas), 92, 114
destillationis (Bacterium), 434
destillationis (Bacteroides), 425, **434**
destillationis (Ristella), 434
Desulfovibrio, 228, **248,** 1029
  aestuarii, **249**
  desulfuricans, **248,** 249, 1029
  rubentschikii, **249**
desulfuricans (Desulfovibrio), **248,** 249
desulfuricans (Spirillum), 248
desulfuricans (Sporovibrio), 248
deversoir (Salmonella ser.), **383**
devorans (Bacillus), 320
devorans (Flavobacterium), 311, **320**
dextranicum (Leuconostoc), 531, **532**
dextranicus (Lactococcus), 532
Dialister, 424, **440,** 1029, 1030
  granuliformans, **441**
  pneumosintes, 440, **441**
diaporica (Cexiella), 947
diaporica (Rickettsia), 947
diaphthirus (Bacillus), 669
diastaticus (Actinomyces), 767
diastaticus (Streptomyces), 747, **767,** 770
diastatochromogenes (Actinomyces), 773
diastatochromogenes (Streptomyces), 747, **773**

dichotoma (Cladothrix), 264
dichotomus (Sphaerotilus), **264**
Dicrobactrum, 360
Didymohelix ferruginea, 215
dieffenbachiae (Phytomonas), 162
dieffenbachiae (Xanthomonas), 153, 162
difficile (Clostridium), 635, **645**
difficilis (Bacillus), 645
diffluens (Cytophaga), 859, **862**
diffusum (Flavobacterium), 310, 317
diffusus (Bacillus), 317
dilatator (Caryococcus), **928**
djasiman (Leptospira ser.), 909, 911
dimorpha (Mycoplana), 204, **205**
diphteroides (Corynebacterium), 597
diphtheriae (Bacillus), 581
diphtheriae (Corynebacterium), 579, **581,** 596
diphtheriae *type* gravis (Corynebacterium), 582
diphtheriae *type* intermedius (Corynebacterium), 582
diphtheriae *type* mitis (Corynebacterium), 582
diphtheriae vitulorum (Bacillus), 443
diphtheroides (Corynebacterium), 581, **597**
Diplobacillus liquefaciens, 420
  moraxaxenfeld, 420
Diplococcus, 506, 507, **1002**
  constellatus, 474, 477
  glycinophilus, 475, 478
  intracellularis, 482
  intracellularis meningitidis, 482
  magnus anaerobius, 539
  morbillorum, 540
  orbiculus, 489
  paleopneumoniae, 540
  pharyngis siccus, 483
  plagarumbelli, 540
  pneumoniae, 507, **508**
  reniformis, 489
  rubeolae, 540
  siccus, 484
dipodilli (Borrelia), 898, **903**
dipodilli (Spirochaeta), 903
disciformans (Bacillus), 559
disciformans (Eubacterium), 553, 559
disciformis (Angiococcus), **889**
disciformis (Myxococcus), 889
discoides (Neisseria), 488
discoides (Veillonella), 486, **488**
discophora (Leptothrix), 265, **266**
discophora (Megalothrix), 266
discophorus (Sphaerotilus), 846
dispar (Bacillus), 390
dispar (Eperythrozoon), 978, **979,** 980
dispar (Shigella), 384, **390**
dissolvens (Clostridium), 641, **688**
dissolvens (Erwinia), 350, **354**
dissolvens (Pseudomonas), 354
distasonis (Bacteroides), 425, **433**
distasonis (Ristella), 433
djasiman (Leptospira ser.), **909,** 911
Donatienella, 949
donna (Salmonella ser.), **383**
Donovania granulomatis, 418